Proceedings of the

1993 American Control Conference

The Westin St. Francis Hotel, San Francisco, California
June 2-4, 1993

Sponsoring Organization

The American Automatic Control Council

U.S. National Member Organization of the

International Federation of Automatic Control (IFAC)

MEMBER ORGANIZATIONS

American Institute of Aeronautics and Astronautics
American Institute of Chemical Engineers
Association of Iron and Steel Engineers
American Society of Mechanical Engineers
Institute of Electrical and Electronic Engineers
Instrument Society of America
Society of Computer Simulation

The 1993 ACC is held in cooperation with *IFAC*

Volume 1 of 3

Cover photo courtesy of the San Francisco Convention and Visitors Bureau, by Kerrick James.

American Automatic Control Council
c/o Department of EECS
Northwestern University
2145 Sheridan Road
Evanston IL 60208-3118
(708) 491-3641

These conference proceedings will be distributed through the

IEEE Service Center
445 Hoes Lane
PO Box 1331
Piscataway NJ, 08855-1331
(908) 981-0060 or (800) 678-4333

IEEE Catalog number 93CH3225-0

Library of Congress number 92-54779

ISBN	0-7803-0860-3	(Softbound)
ISBN	0-7803-0861-1	(Casebound)
ISBN	0-7803-0862-X	(Microfiche)

FOREWORD

Welcome to the 1993 American Control Conference (ACC) -- the annual meeting sponsored by the American Automatic Control Council (AACC) in cooperation with the International Federation of Automatic Control (IFAC). This is the thirteenth ACC, which in 1982 succeeded the Joint Automatic Control Conference. This year ACC is held in beautiful San Francisco, the future site of the 1996 IFAC Congress.

The ACC maintains its vitality as a control and automation conference catering to theory and applications in wide areas of control with 741 technical papers. The process of paper selection and assembling the Program was expertly handled by the Program Committee chaired by Prof. Bruce Krogh of Carnegie-Mellon University, with co-chairs Steve Yurkovich of Ohio State University and Jeff Kantor of the University of Notre Dame. I would like to thank them for their dedication and tireless effort at putting the Program together with the help of an excellent Program Committee and the assistance of the AACC member societies' representatives and review chairs.

Continuing with the tradition started last year there are three distinguished speakers who will deliver plenary lectures and there will be no luncheon speaker. Dr. John F. Cassidy, Jr., Vice President, United Technologies Corporation, will present Wednesday morning lecture on "Control Technology and the 21st Century". Our Thursday morning speaker is Prof. Stephen Boyd of Stanford University, the 1992 Eckman Award recipient, who will speak on "Control Systems Analysis and Synthesis via Linear Matrix Inequalities". On Friday morning the plenary speaker is Prof. Sanjoy Mitter, director of the Laboratory for Information and Decision Systems at MIT, who will present a lecture on "Perception, Cognition, and Situated Actions".

This year the ACC is preceded by seven tutorial workshops expertly organized by Dr. Michael Masten of Texas Instruments. The two-day workshops are on Intelligent Control, Behavior Design and Analysis using State-charts, Numerical Methods for Control System Design (with Emphasis on State-Space Models), and Real-Time Applications in Control Using Digital Signal Processors. One-day workshops cover Automated System Identification & Control with Applications, Nonlinear and Adaptive Control, and Petri Net Modeling, Control & Performance Analysis for Manufacturing Systems. Our thanks to Mike and the workshop organizers and speakers for such an exciting set of workshops.

The ACC continues to attract a number of exhibits from book publishers, software companies, and hardware control laboratory experiments. The exhibits will be displayed in the California room. Dr. Ching-Fang Lin of the American GNC Corp. deserves our thanks for coordination of the exhibits.

The highlight of the ACC is the Awards Luncheon during which the 1993 AACC Awards are presented. The biographies of this year recipients are shown on the following pages.

The success of the ACC is impossible without the dedicated work of the members of the Operating Committee who handle all the minute details that ensure the smooth operation of the Conference. In particular, I would like to thank Prof. Bonnie Heck of Georgia Tech for handling the publicity, Prof. Michael Peshkin of Northwestern University for taking care of the publication of the Program and the Proceedings, and Prof. Joe Chow for holding the purse strings. Special thanks are due to the tireless work of the Registration Chair, Prof. Tony Healey of the Naval Postgraduate School and Local Arrangements Chair Prof. Dave Auslander of the University of California at Berkeley. The minute details involved in these last two tasks leave no room for error and must be accomplished in real-time. Dave was responsible for the four special social events that we hope you enjoyed on Wednesday and Thursday evening. I am grateful to Dale Seborg, the 1992 ACC General Chair for the many helpful comments and suggestions.

Finally, the ACC owes its success to you the authors, session chairs, and attendees. On behalf of the Operating and Program Committees I would like to thank you for participating in this ACC and welcome you to enjoy the Conference.

Abraham H. Haddad, 1993 ACC General Chair

ACC'93 OPERATING COMMITTEE

General Chair
Abraham H. Haddad
EE/CS, Northwestern University
Evanston, IL 60208-3118
(708) 491-3641 / FAX -4455
ahaddad@eecs.nwu.edu

Publicity Chair
Bonnie S. Heck
EE, Georgia Inst. of Technology
Atlanta, GA 30332-0250
(404) 894-3145 / FAX 853-9171
bheck@ee.gatech.edu

Program Chair
Bruce H. Krogh
ECE, Carnegie Mellon University
Pittsburgh, PA 15213
(412) 268-2472 / FAX -3890
krogh@ece.cmu.edu

Workshop Chair
Michael K. Masten
Texas Instruments
2309 Northcrest
Plano, TX 75075
(214) 462-3433 / FAX -3126
m.masten@ieee.org

Finance Chair
Joe H. Chow
ECSE, Rensselaer Polytechnic Inst.
Troy, NY 12180-3590
(518) 276-6374 / FAX -6261
chowj@ecse.rpi.edu

Exhibits Chair
Ching-Fang Lin
President, American GNC Corp.
9131 Mason Avenue
Chatsworth, CA 91311
(818) 407-0092 / FAX -0093
American_GNC@cup.portal.com

Local Arrangements Chair
David M. Auslander
ME, UC Berkeley
Berkeley, CA 94720
(510) 642-4930 / FAX same
dma@euler.berkeley.edu

Vice-Chair, Invited Sessions
Stephen Yurkovich
EE, Ohio State University
2015 Neil Avenue
Columbus, OH 43210-1272
(614) 292-2586 / FAX -7596
s.yurkovich@ieee.org

Registration Chair
Anthony J. Healey
Dept. of Mechanical Eng.
Naval Postgraduate School
Monterey, CA 93943
(408) 656-3462 / FAX -2238
healey@lex.me.nps.navy.mil

Vice-Chair, Contributed Sessions
Jeffrey C. Kantor
Chem. Eng, Univ. of Notre Dame
Notre Dame, IN 46556
(219) 239-5797 / FAX 631-8366
Jeffrey.C.Kantor.1@nd.edu

Publications Chair
Michael A. Peshkin
ME, Northwestern University
Evanston, IL 60208
(708) 491-4630 / FAX -3915
peshkin@nwu.edu

Society Review Chairs
R.K. Yedavalli (AIAA)
A. Cinar (AIChE)
C. Kelly (AISE)
M. Tomizuka (ASME)
M. Polis (IEEE)
C. Batur (ISA)
M. Zohdy (SCS)

ACC'93 PROGRAM COMMITTEE

E. Barbieri	J. Bentsman	R. Bishop	M. Bodson	C. Cassandras
R. Colgren	J. Freudenberg	B. Heck	J. Kantor	G. Huang
G. Ianculescu	H. Javid	H. Kazerooni	C. Kelly	G. King
J. Krause	B. Krogh	D. Minto	C. Nett	K. Passino
R. Rhinehart	R. Stengel	J. Winkelman	S. Yurkovich	E. Yaz
E. Zafiriou	M. Zohdy			

Awards of the
American Automatic Control Council

1993

The Richard E. Bellman Control Heritage Award

Awarded to **Eliahu I. Jury** in recognition of his pioneering and extensive contributions to the theory of digital control and digital signal processing over space and time; and in particular, of his development of the modified Z-transformation, the Jury stability test, and the theory and application of matrix inners.

Eliahu I. Jury was born in Baghdad, Iraq, in 1923. He received his degree in Electrical Engineering in 1947 from the Israel Institute of Technology in Haifa, where he was Goldberg Scholar. He received his M.S. degree with distinction from Harvard in 1949 and in 1953 his Sc.D. from Columbia University, where he was Higgins Fellow. In 1954, he joined the Department of Electrical Engineering and Computer Science of the University of California at Berkeley and was promoted to full professor in 1964. he joined the University of Miami in 1981 as Research Professor of Electrical and Computer Engineering.

Professor Jury has authored over two hundred research papers and three books: *Sample-Data Control, The Z-transform,* and *Inners and Stability*. His books have been translated into Russian, French, Polish and Japanese. He is the recipient of many national and international honors and awards, including the 1986 Oldenburger Medal from the American Society of Mechanical Engineers, as well as the 1986 Educational Award from the Institute of Electrical and Electronic Engineers, of which he is a Fellow. In 1982 he was awarded an Honorary Doctor of Science by the faculty of the Swiss Federal Institute of Technology in Zurich.

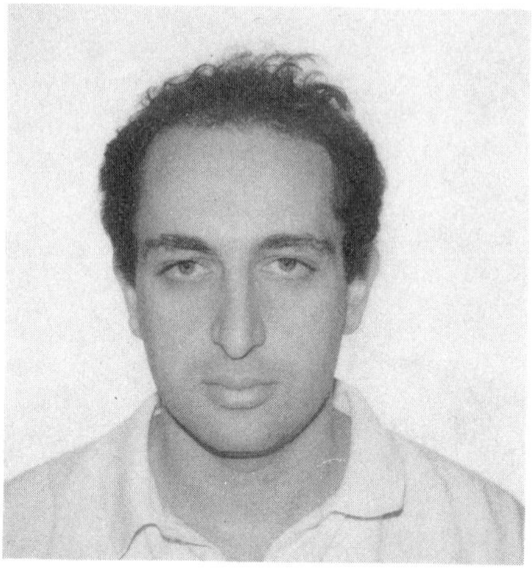

The Donald P. Eckman Award

Awarded to **Munther A. Dahleh**, for contributions to the development of L_1-Optimal Control Theory.

Munther Dahleh was born in 1962. He received his B.S. degree from Texas A&M University in 1983, and his Ph.D. degree in 1987 from Rice University, Houston Texas both in Electrical Engineering. In 1987 he joined the Department of Electrical Engineering and Computer Science at the Massachusetts Institute of Technology where he is now a Finmeccanica Associate Professor with the . In the spring of 1993 he was a visiting Professor of Electrical Engineering at the California Institute of Technology. He has held consulting positions with C.S. Draper Laboratory and NASA since 1988, and FIAT Research Center since 1991.

Dr. Dahleh was the recipient of the Ralph Budd Award in 1987 for the best thesis at Rice University, the George Axelby Outstanding Paper Award (paper co-authored with J.B. Pearson) in 1987, an NSF Presidential Young Investigator Award in 1991, and the Finmeccanica Career Development Chair in 1992.

He is currently serving as an Associate Editor for the Systems and Control Letters. He is the author (with Ignacio Diaz-Bobillo) of the book *Control of Uncertain Systems: A Linear Programming Approach* to be published by Prentice-Hall.

Dr. Dahleh`s interests include robust control and identification, application of mathematical programming in synthesizing multivariable controllers, and the analysis and design of hybrid systems.

The AACC Education Award

Awarded to **Dale E. Seborg** for excellence in classroom teaching, training of undergraduate and graduate students in process control, and the development of educational materials including a leading undergraduate textbook.

Dale E. Seborg is a Professor of Chemical Engineering at the University of California, Santa Barbara. He received his B.S. degree from the University of Wisconsin and his Ph.D. degree from Princeton University. Before joining UCSB in 1977, he taught at the University of Alberta for nine years. He served as the department chairman at UCSB for three years.

Dr. Seborg has published over 130 articles on process control and related topics. He is the co-author of an award winning 1989 textbook, *Process Dynamics and Control*, with Professor Mellichamp (UCSB) and Professor Edgar (U. Texas). He is also a co-author of *Multivariable Computer Control - A Case Study* and co-editor of *Chemical Process Control 2*. Dr. Seborg has received two awards: the Joint Automatic Control Conference Best Paper Award and the Technical Achievement Award from the AIChE Southern California Section. He is an active industrial consultant and has served as a director of three organizations: the American Automatic Control Council, the AIChE Computing and Systems Technology Division, and the ASEE ChE Division. Dr. Seborg has also served on the editorial boards of two journals: the IEEE Transactions on Automatic Control, and Adaptive Control and Signal Processing. He was the general chairman for the 1992 American Control Conference.

The O. Hugo Schuck Best Paper Award

Awarded to **Kameshwar Poolla, Pramod Khargonekar, Ashok Tikku, James Krause** and **Krishan Nagpal**, for their paper "A Time-Domain Approach to Model Validation" presented at the 1992 American Control Conference.

Kameshwar Poolla received the B. Tech. from the Indian Institute of Technology, Bombay in 1980 and the Ph.D. degree from the University of Florida in 1984, both in Electrical Engineering. he has taught at the University of Illinois, Urbana and held visiting positions at the Massachusetts Institute of Technology, McGill University and Honeywell SRC. He was a recipient of the NSF Presidential Young Investigator Award in 1988. He is currently an Associate Professor in Mechanical Engineering at the University of California, Berkeley. His research interests include robust control, system identification, and computation.

Pramod Khargonekar received his education at the Indian Institute of Technology, Bombay and the University of Florida. After working at the University of Florida and the University of Minnesota, he joined The University of Michigan where he is a Professor of Electrical Engineering and Computer Science. He is a recipient of the AACC's Donald Eckman Award and the NSF Presidential Young Investigator Award, and is a Fellow of IEEE. He is a co-recipient (with Professors Doyle, Francis, and Glover) of the 1991 IEEE W.R.G. Baker Prize Award and the 1990 George Axelby Best Paper Award. His current research interests include robust control, H_2, H_∞, and H_2/H_∞ optimal control, sampled-data systems, robust and H_∞ identification, robust adaptive control, time-varying systems, and industrial applications of control theory.

Ashok Tikku received the B.S. and M.S. degrees from the University of Illinois at Urbana in 1989 and 1991. He is currently a Ph.D. student at the University of California at Berkeley. His research interests include system identification and robust multivariable control.

James Krause received the B.S. degree from Marquette University in 1981, the S.M. degree from the Massachusetts Institute of Technology in 1983, and the Ph.D. degree from the University of Minnesota in 1987, all in the field of electrical engineering. Since 1983, he has conducted research in the theory and application of control and estimation, fault tolerant avionics, and embedded software at the Honeywell Systems and Research Center in Minneapolis, Minnesota, where is currently Section Chief of Guidance and Control.

Krishan M. Nagpal received the B.Tech. in Chemical Engineering from the Indian Institute of Technology, Kanpur in 1982. He received his graduate education in West Virginia University from 1982 to 1987. He has held visiting appointments at the Universities of Minnesota, Michigan, and Illinois. His professional interests include learning a few things about systems and control.

Proceedings Table of Contents

'W' sessions (WA1, WA2, etc.) may be found in volume 1, 'T' in volume 2, and 'F' in volume 3
'x' indicates that no manuscript was received.
An alphabetical index to all volumes by authors' and coauthors' surnames may be found at the end of each volume.

Wednesday Midday

WM1 - Georgian
Mixed H_2/H_∞ Control

Chairs B. Tongue — Univ. of California - Berkeley
H Ozbay — Ohio State University

WM2 - Colonial
Robust Stability II

Chairs M. Steinbuch — Philips Research Laboratories
S. K. Ahmed — Univ. of Massachusetts

WM3 - Elizabethan A
Performance in Adaptive Control

Chairs P.J. Antsaklis — University of Notre Dame
P. A. Ioannou — Univ. of Southern California

WM4 - Elizabethan B
Control of Automotive Systems

Chairs J.K. Hedrick — University of California
R. Isermann — Technical Univ. of Darmstadt

WM12 – Olympic South
Control Functional Differential Equations (Invited)

WM13 – Olympic North
Control of Nonlinear Flexible Pointing Systems I (Invited)

WM14 – Kent
Control and Design of Unmanned Underwater Vehicles (Invited)

Wednesday Afternoon

WP1 – Georgian
H_∞ Control

WP2 – Colonial
Robust Control

WP3 – Elizabethan A
Nonlinear and Adaptive Control of Electromechanical Systems (Invited)

WP4 – Elizabethan B
Automotive Systems: Engine Control and Diagnosis (Invited)

Organizer G. Rizzoni — Ohio State University
Chairs G. Rizzoni — Ohio State University
R. Rajamani — University of California, Berkeley

WP5 – Elizabethan C
Robot Control I

Chairs P.H. Meckl — Purdue University
G.F. Franklin — Stanford University

WP6 – Elizabethan D
Fuzzy Control I

WP7 – Borgia
Predictive Control II

WP8 – Yorkshire
Nonlinear Control Theory I

Wednesday Evening 17:30-19:00

NSF Session on Control Programs
Colonial Room

Chairs: Elbert Marsh — NSF
Kishan Baheti — NSF

Thursday Morning

Plenary session II
Grand Ballroom

Chairs B. Krogh — Carnegie-Mellon University
A. Haddad — Northwestern University

TA1 – Georgian
H_∞ for Discrete/Sampled Data Systems

Chairs R.E. Skelton — Purdue University
M.A. Rotea — Purdue University

TA2 – Colonial
Positive Real Robust Control

Chairs D.M. Dawson — Clemson University
S. Jayasuriya — Texas A&M University

TM9 – Oxford
Discrete Manufacturing Systems

TM10 – Victorian
Identification III

TM11 – Essex
Numerical Methods and Computation in Control (Invited)

13:00-14:30 - Grand Ballroom
Awards luncheon

Thursday Afternoon

TP1 – Georgian
Numerical Algorithms in Robust Control

TP2 – Colonial
Quantitative Feedback Theory

TP3 – Elizabethan A
Applications of Adaptive and Optimal Control Theory (Invited)

TP4 – Elizabethan B
Automotive Systems: Active Suspension and Driver Interaction (Invited)

Organizer G. Rizzoni — Ohio State University
Chairs G. Rizzoni — Ohio State University
B. Powell — Ford Scientific Research

TP5 – Elizabethan C
Robot Control II

Chairs S.M. Shahruz — Berkeley Eng Research Institute
Z. S. Tumeh — United Parcel Service

TP9 – Oxford
Control of Manufacturing Processes (Invited)

TP10 – Victorian
Identification IV

FM10 – Victorian
Estimation and Control of Discrete Time Systems

FM11 – Essex
Numerical Methods

FM12 – Olympic South
Optimal Control III

FP2 – Colonial
Robust Performance

FP3 – Elizabethan A
Adaptive Nonlinear Control of Mechanical Systems (Invited)

FP8 – Yorkshire
Nonlinear Control Theory II

FP9 – Oxford
Modeling and Control of Microelectronics Manufacturing (Invited)

Proceedings of the
American Control Conference
San Francisco, California • June 1993

Attenuation of Structurally Generated Interior Noise Through Active Control

X. H. Yang J. van Niekerk K. S. Parwani A. Packard B. Tongue

Department of Mechanical Engineering
University of California, Berkeley
Berkeley, CA 94720
correspondence to pack@erg.berkeley.edu
510.642.6152
510.643.7959

Abstract

Active feedback control was used to modify the acoustic/structural dynamics in a reverberant acoustic enclosure. The physical system was modeled as a single-input, multi-output system and an $\mathcal{H}_\infty$ design approach was used to obtain a robust controller. Experimentally obtained results exhibited a significant reduction in the dominant acoustic modes. Furthermore, the controller was seen to be effective in achieving noise reductions in the region of space surrounding the sensor, thus indicating that localization of the noise reduction was not a limiting factor in the design.

1 Introduction

The objective of this experimental investigation was to assess the effectiveness of single-input multi-output $\mathcal{H}_\infty$ control techniques in reducing the interior noise level in a reverberant enclosure. For the case under consideration, the noise was generated by direct structural excitation of the enclosure. Many researchers are pursuing **active noise cancellation** of acoustic disturbances, using a feedforward signal based on measured data which is highly correlated with the disturbance source. In this work, we assume that a measurement signal highly correlated with the disturbance source is NOT available. By using an active feedback law, the acoustic/structural dynamics governing the enclosure are altered. Thus the effect of **external disturbances** on the microphone error signal is modified. Undesirable dynamic properties of the enclosure, such as large resonances at certain frequencies, can be significantly modified using a suitable feedback law.

The main drawback of feedback is that the actual closed-loop system may be unstable even though the feedback controller performs acceptably on the mathematical model, due to the differences between the actual enclosure dynamics and the mathematical model on which the controller design is based. A **robust control design methodology** is implemented that takes these potential differences into account and optimizes the performance criterion in either a **worst-case** or **average-case** manner.

The experimental acoustic enclosure consisted of a rectangular box of dimension $1.0\times0.75\times0.45$ (all dimensions in meters, m). The walls of the box were constructed of plywood, and were braced every 0.15 m, in order to ensure structural rigidity. The most flexible structural element of the box was the top, a 3.5 mm thick steel plate. Because the top is flexible, the enclosure provides a coupled structural/acoustic environment. An electro-dynamic shaker was connected to the flexible top through a stinger, ensuring the transmission of the axial forces while precluding the lateral forces or moments. Excitation of the interior acoustic field was obtained by this direct structural excitation of the flexible top. No direct sensing of the structural vibration was used in this study.

A B&K microphone provided the measurement of the interior acoustical signal, while two JBL bookshelf loudspeakers provided the interior acoustic control. Figures 1 through 3 show the schematic diagram of the experimental setup.

The control approach employed in this study contained several distinct steps: system identification using open-loop experiments; model reduction using balanced realizations; uncertainty modeling to account for unmodeled dynamics and sensor noise, performance objective characterization as a weighted $\mathcal{H}_\infty$ norm criterion, robust control design, and implementation. This process was not a single pass procedure; iteration between the control design, performance objectives and uncertainty estimation was required.

2 System Identification and Model Reduction

Using commercially available signal processing equipment, (in this case a GenRad dynamical analyzer, Model 2515) a non-parametric frequency response model of the 3-input, 1-output system was experimentally identified. By **system**, we mean the open-loop 3-input, 1-output system, with the following features:

1. All inputs, d, u_1, and u_2, are voltage. The disturbance voltage input d, was amplified and then drove the shaker, which in turn caused the vibration of the flexible top. The control action was implemented by loudspeakers, which in turn were driven by the signals from a discrete form controller written in the Digital Signal Processing board. The voltage inputs to control speakers were sampled at a rate of 4000 Hz, zero-order held, and filtered by the internal circuitry of the Spectrum Signal Processing/Texas Instruments DSP electronics.

2. The enclosure's acoustic and structural properties govern how the actions of shaker and loudspeakers affect the error microphone signal. Due to the reflection of sound from the rigid walls as well as the reflective top cover, and a relatively low degree internal damping, the enclosure was reverberant.

3. The output of the system, $y(s)$, is the analog voltage from the B&K microphone preamplifier, which is driven directly by the microphone.

The overall system is modeled as a linear, time-invariant, continuous-time system, which can be modeled by the transfer function

$$y(s) = G_d(s)d(s) + G_u(s)u(s)$$

Denote $G_d(s), G_u(s)$ and $u(s)$ as

$$\begin{aligned} G_d(s) &= G_1(s) \\ G_u(s) &= [\, G_2(s)\ G_3(s) \,] \\ u(s) &= \begin{bmatrix} u_1(s) \\ u_2(s) \end{bmatrix} \end{aligned}$$

Then $y(s)$ can be expressed as

$$y(s) = G_1(s)d(s) + G_2(s)u_1(s) + G_3(s)u_2(s)$$

The transfer functions G_1,G_2 and G_3 are identified by off-line nonparametric identification, followed by least squares curve fitting. First, the dynamic response of the true system in the range of 25 Hz up to 225 Hz is obtained experimentally at N = 1,000 different frequencies,

$$\left.\begin{array}{ll} G_{1,k}^{\text{true}}, & \text{at } \omega_k \\ G_{2,k}^{\text{true}}, & \text{at } \omega_k \\ G_{3,k}^{\text{true}}, & \text{at } \omega_k \end{array}\right\} \qquad k = 1, 2, \ldots, N$$

Using an iterative procedure, rational transfer functions $\hat{G}_1(s)$, $\hat{G}_2(s)$, and $\hat{G}_3(s)$ that fit the true data are calculated. Each step of the iterative procedure requires solving a least squares problem. The order of the three curve fits are 28, 14 and 14 respectively.

Next, a three-input, one-output plant model is constructed as shown below

$$\hat{G}_p(s) = \left[\hat{G}_d(s)\ \hat{G}_u(s)\right]$$

This plant model captures the dynamic behavior between the shaker's voltage input and the microphone output, and the dynamic behavior between the speakers voltage input and the output of the same microphone. The order of $\hat{G}_p(s)$ is 56, much higher than $\hat{G}_i(s)$, i=1, 2, 3. In order to eliminate the duplicated modes in $\hat{G}_p(s)$, a balanced realization of $\hat{G}_p(s)$ is computed, and the states in this realization corresponding to small Hankel singular values are truncated, [3], [4]. After the balanced truncation, the order of the 3-input, 1-output system, denoted as $G_p(s)$, is 34. The frequency response of $G_p(s)$ is plotted against the experimental data in Figure 4 through Figure 6.

Due to the lower order approximation of the mathematical model, some model inaccuracy is unavoidable. The dynamics in frequency range higher than 225 Hz are not modeled, so there is a significant difference between the actual plant model and the mathematical model beyond the 225 Hz range. These modeling errors will be treated as unmodeled dynamics in Section 3.

The simple model $G_p(s)$ has several advantages over $\hat{G}_p(s)$. In the controller design stage, significant computational savings are realized by using lower-order plant models. More importantly, the order of the controller will be reduced, when working with a low-order plant model. Most popular optimal control strategies ($\mathcal{H}_2, \mathcal{H}_\infty$, LQG) yield controllers with state dimension equal to that of the open-loop plant. The low order of controller has an important impact, since controller order is the primary limitation on the sampling time for real-time implementation.

3 Uncertainty Description

Due to the complex nature of the actual physical system, and the practical limitations of control implementation, the mathematical model obtained either theoretically or experimentally cannot exactly predict the real system's dynamical behavior. The difference between the model and reality can be attributed to the following sources: unmodeled dynamics, parametric uncertainty and parametric inaccuracy, and exogenous disturbance signals affecting the measured output of the physical system.

The identification experiments described in Section 2 yield frequency response data over a bounded frequency interval. However, the curve fitting technique gives a rational function in s, defined for all values of s. Certainly, this rational **model** has no relation to the real system's behavior at high frequency. Therefore the mathematical model obtained from fitting the experimental data will most likely be quite inaccurate outside the frequency range of the experiment (in fact, the identification experiments give information about the frequency response only at a finite number of frequencies; bounds on the potential interpolation errors are available [5], though in this study we do not consider these errors). In particular, the acoustical and structural dynamics of higher order modes have been neglected in the low order mathematical model. Also, a linear, time-invariant model does not predict any nonlinear and/or time-varying dynamical properties that the real physical system may possess. All these factors, if not properly included in the controller design, will have a serious impact on the effect of control. Any design methodology based on optimization **must** respect the discrepancies between the physical and theoretical model.

We account for the differences between the mathematical model and the real physical system by the use of an **additive uncertainty** plant model. Denote $G_i(s)$ as the **nominal** plant model, or mathematical model. Ideally, the error and measurement signal are generated via

$$y = e = G_1 d + G_2 u_1 + G_3 u_2$$

A feedback controller measures y and produces control u, so the control loop is fed back around the dynamical system modeled by G_2 and G_3. For closed-loop system stability and performance we need to consider the effects of uncertainty on this feedback control loop. An additive uncertainty model is one technique that can be used to quantify the amount of uncertainty. This model is simple enough so that robust control design methodologies which account for the uncertainty are available. A block diagram illustrating the additive uncertainty structure is shown in Figure 7.

Given the nominal model G_u, as well as the weighting function $W_a(s)$, the additive model set, $\mathcal{A}(G_u, W_a)$ is defined as

$$\{ \; G_u(s) + W_a(s) \cdot \Delta(s) \; : \; \Delta(s) \text{ stable}, \; \|\Delta(j\omega)\|_\infty \le 1 \; \}$$

Under this definition, $W_a(s)$ is the additive uncertainty weight, which specifies the amount of uncertainty in the model, as a function of frequency. It is chosen by the engineer and reflects engineering judgement on the quality of the nominal model. The uncertainty weighting function $W_a(s)$ is stable and minimum phase, and should have a small amplitude in the frequency range where the plant model $G_u(s)$ is most accurate and a large amplitude where $G_u(s)$ does not accurately represent the true physical system. Δ is an unknown, bounded transfer function, parameterizing all the possible differences between the nominal model and the actual dynamical behavior of the physical system. It represents uncertainties such as unmodeled dynamics and parameter inaccuracy.

An arbitrary element in the model set $\mathcal{A}(G_u, W_a)$ is denoted as $\tilde{G}_u(s)$. This represents a potential plant that might be encountered in a real control implementation. The model set $\mathcal{A}(G_u, W_a)$ contains the linear, time-invariant system whose frequency response is equal to the measured frequency response from the identification experiment. A robust controller design is based on the **entire set** rather than just the nominal model G_u.
In our problem, the specific uncertainty weight is chosen in the following way:

1. The structure of $\Delta(j\omega)$ is chosen as

   $$\Delta(j\omega) = [\; \Delta_1(j\omega) \;, \; \Delta_2(j\omega) \;]$$

   where the $\Delta_i(j\omega)$ are scalar functions of frequency.

2. $W_a(s)$ is chosen to be a 2 by 2 diagonal matrix, i.e.

   $$W_a(s) = \begin{bmatrix} W_1(s) & 0 \\ 0 & W_2(s) \end{bmatrix}$$

3. In the frequency range from 100 to 200 Hz, where we wish to achieve noise reduction, $W_a(s)$ is chosen so that

   $$\begin{aligned} \left|\hat{W}_1(j\omega)\right| &\ge \left|G_2(j\omega) - G_2^{\text{true}}(j\omega)\right| \\ \left|\hat{W}_2(j\omega)\right| &\ge \left|G_3(j\omega) - G_3^{\text{true}}(j\omega)\right| \end{aligned}$$

   i.e., the magnitude of additive uncertainty, $\left|\hat{W}_i(j\omega)\right|$ should be at least as large as the magnitude of the difference between the frequency response from the experimental data and from the reduced-order model of the plant, $G_u(s)$, for each control channel. However such a component-by-component coverage does not guarantee that

   $$\|\Delta(j\omega)\|_\infty \le 1$$

4. To ensure the above inequality, we let

   $$W_a(s) = \lambda \hat{W}_a(s)$$

   where λ is

   $$\begin{aligned} \lambda &= \max_\omega \left\{ \bar{\sigma} \left\{ \left[G_u^{\text{true}}(j\omega) - G_u(j\omega)\right] W_a^{-1}(j\omega) \right\}\right\} \\ &= \left\| \left[G_u^{\text{true}} - G_u\right] W_a^{-1} \right\|_\infty \end{aligned}$$

5. Outside of the 100 - 200 Hz frequency range, the amplitude of $W_a(s)$ chosen to be large, in order to account for the unmodeled dynamics.

Figure 8 shows the frequency response of each control channel, i.e. $|G_i(j\omega)|$, as well as the corresponding modeling error, i.e.

$$\left|G_i(j\omega) - G_i^{\text{true}}(j\omega)\right| \qquad i = 2, 3$$

The frequency response of $W_a(s)$ is shown in Figure 9. The $W_a(j\omega)$ versus the modeling error in the interested frequency range is also shown in Figure 10. The uncertainty in the plant model is approaching to 100% in the high frequeny range. The nominal open-loop gain of the feedback system at these frequencies will necessarily be small so that stability is guaranteed even in the face of perturbations.

4 Performance Objectives

In our approach, the performance objective is to reduce the effect that the disturbance d has on the error e. We measure this effect quantitatively using a weighted $\mathcal{H}_\infty$ norm. The equations describing the closed-loop system are

$$\begin{aligned} e &= G_d d + G_u u \\ y &= e \\ u &= K y \end{aligned} \qquad (1)$$

where G_d is the transfer function from disturbance d to measurement microphone e, G_u is the transfer function from control u to e, and K is the controller, i.e.

$$K(s) = \begin{bmatrix} K_1(s) \\ K_2(s) \end{bmatrix}$$

Solving for e gives,

$$e = \frac{G_d}{1 - G_u K} d = T_{de} d$$

where

$$T_{de} := \frac{G_d}{1 - G_u K}$$

In order to achieve the desired properties for the closed-loop frequency response, we will require, as a **performance objective**, that $|T_{de}(j\omega)| < b(\omega)$, for some prescribed objective function $b(\omega)$. If $W_p(s)$ is chosen stable and minimum phase, with

$$|W_p(j\omega)| = \frac{1}{b(\omega)}$$

then the performance objective is characterized as

$$\max_\omega \|W_p(j\omega) T_{de}(j\omega)\| =: \|W_p T_{de}\|_\infty < 1 \qquad (2)$$

The weighted $\mathcal{H}_\infty$ norm objective in (2) is a convenient mathematical specification of frequency-dependent shaping objectives. This norm is easy to compute, and optimization of closed-loop, weighted $\mathcal{H}_\infty$ norms is mathematically solvable [2].

Figure 11 shows the performance weighting function used in our acoustic experiment as well as the open-loop disturbance-to-error frequency response. The function b chosen in our design ensures that the closed-loop will achieve 12 dB, 24 dB, and 13 dB reductions in the regions around the enclosure's acoustic modes at 110 Hz, 169 Hz, and 194 Hz, respectively, and allow a few dB degradation in other frequency ranges if all design requirements are met.

In addition to potential instability problems, feedback can also amplify the noise introduced during the sensing process. This limits the feedback gain at frequencies where the sensor noise is dominant. To account for this performance limitation, we introduce a sensor noise weighting function, $W_n(s)$, which penalizes the closed-loop transfer function

$$\frac{G_u K}{1 - G_u K}$$

in the frequency range for which sensor noise is likely.

We combine the above performance objectives into a single, robust control design task: find a controller K so that for every $\tilde{G}_u \in \mathcal{A}(G_u, W_a)$, the closed-loop system is stable and

$$\max_{\omega} \left(\left| \frac{G_d}{1 - \tilde{G}_u K} W_p \right|^2 + \left| \frac{\tilde{G}_u K}{1 - \tilde{G}_u K} W_n \right|^2 \right)^{\frac{1}{2}} < 1$$

Note that the objective involves a performance criterion that should be achieved for every plant model $\tilde{G}_u \in \mathcal{A}(G_u W_a)$. This type of objective is called a **robust performance** objective, and is exactly addressed by the structured singular value theory, μ [1].

In terms of the additive uncertainty model, and the sensor noise and disturbance rejection objectives, the overall closed-loop structure is represented by the block diagram shown in Figure 12.

In the block diagram, G_d and G_u represent the nominal, low order models of the acoustic/structural behavior. Recall that the weighting functions W_p, W_a and W_n are specified by the designer and reflect the performance objectives, as well as uncertainty assumptions about the process. The transfer function $\Delta(j\omega)$ represents the unknown model uncertainties.

In this methodology it is convienient to group all the known functions into one block, called IC, and isolate the controller K and perturbation $\Delta(j\omega)$, so that the closed-loop structure can be drawn as in Figure 13.

The controller K is designed to minimize the structured singular value of the unperturbed transfer function from (w, d, n) to (z, e). This minimization is achieved using scaled $\mathcal{H}_\infty$ design techniques ([1], and references therein). This involves iteratively searching over the space of stabilizing controllers (an $\mathcal{H}_\infty$ optimal control problem) and a scaling function $\hat{d}(s)$ (convex optimization to find the optimal d at each frequency, and then nonlinear optimization to find a rational approximation).

5 Simulation, Implementation and Experimental Results

The structured singular value design was carried out using the μ **Analysis and Synthesis Toolbox** in conjunction with MATLAB and a stable, 44th order controller that provides acceptable robust performance characteristics was obtained. Implementation required attention to two factors. First, the sampling rate must be high as compared to the bandwidth of the controller. Using a factor of 20, we concluded that a sampling rate of 4000 Hz., would be acceptable. Second, one must consider the computation time needed for the 44th order controller. Our algorithms allowed an implementation at approximately 7KHz, well above the chosen rate of 4000 Hz. Hence, the controller was implemented on Texas TMS320C30 digital signal processor without further order reduction. Figure 11 shows the frequency response of the closed-loop system. Note that the three resonant peaks of the enclosure are suppressed in the closed-loop system.

Figure 14 shows that the computer simulation of closed loop response is very close to the experimental data of the closed loop response with the designed controller. Figure 15 shows that the resonace peaks at 110 Hz, 169 Hz, and 194 Hz are suppressed by 12, 24, and 13 dB respectively. Figure 16 shows that the closed loop response very closely follows our performance objective.

6 Sensitivity of the Measurement Location

The noise attenuation in the neighborhood of the measurement (feedback) microphone position was also investigated. With the measurement microphone held in a fixed position, additional microphones were placed at different measurement positions, as shown in Figure 12. The distance between successive microphones was 70 mm i.e., about 10% of the width of the enclosure. The original controller was used in these experiments, feeding back the unchanged measurement variable y. Thus the outputs of e_1, e_2, ... e_8 illustrate the range of the noise reduction. A schematic diagram of the 8 measurement positions is shown in Figure 17

Figure 18 and 19 show the T_{d,e_i} of the closed-loop versus open-loop frequency response, both obtained from the experimental data. Here, T_{d,e_i} represents the frequency response from the disturbance to the additional error microphones. The results show that the resonance peaks at 110 Hz and 169 Hz were reduced in all 8 positions. The least amount of reduction in each case is more than 6 dB and 10 dB respectively. It can be seen that attenuation of disturbances in the closed-loop response was achieved not just at the error microphone position, but also in the local region surrounding it. However the noise is increased around the 250 Hz range, especially for the positions 4 through 7.

7 Conclusions

It has been shown that single-input multi-output $\mathcal{H}_\infty$ control techniques can be used effectively to provide a significant overall reduction of interior acoustic noise for a reverberant enclosure. Large reductions of the most prominent peaks in the response spectra were obtained at the cost of small increases at less important frequencies. An attractive feature of the methodology is that unmodeled elements of the real system are explicity addressed in the controller design. As more information is made available with regard to unmodeled dynamics, sensor noise levels, etc., the controller can be progressively upgraded, leading to increased levels of sound reduction. The control was shown to be effective, not just at the specific location of the error microphone, but for a significant spatial region surrounding this sensor.

8 Acknowledgements

The authors would like to thank the Mazda Motor Corporation for their financial support of this project. A. Packard also thanks the National Science Foundation for their support, grant CTS-9057420.

References

[1] G. Balas, J. Doyle, K. Glover, A. Packard, and R. Smith, *μ-Analysis and Synthesis Toolbox*, MUSYN and The Mathworks, 1991.

[2] J. Doyle, K. Glover, P. Khargonekar, and B. Francis, "State Space Solutions to $\mathcal{H}_2$ and $\mathcal{H}_\infty$ Control Problems," *IEEE Trans. Auto. Control*, vol. 34, no. 8, pp. 831-847, August, 1989.

[3] D. Enns, "Model reduction for control system design," PhD dissertation, Stanford University, June, 1984

[4] K. Glover, "All optimal Hankel-norm approximations of linear multivariable systems and their $\mathcal{L}_\infty$ error bounds," *International Journal of Control*, vol. 39, pp. 1115-1193, 1984.

[5] A. J. Helmicki, C. A. Jacobson, and C. N. Nett, "Control-oriented system identification: a worst-case/deterministic approach in $\mathcal{H}_\infty$, " to appear in the *IEEE Transactions on Automatic Control.*

[6] G.A. Latham and B.D.O. Anderson "Frequency-weighted optimal Hankel norm approximation of state transfer functions," *Systems and control Letters*, vol. 5, pp. 229-236, 1985.

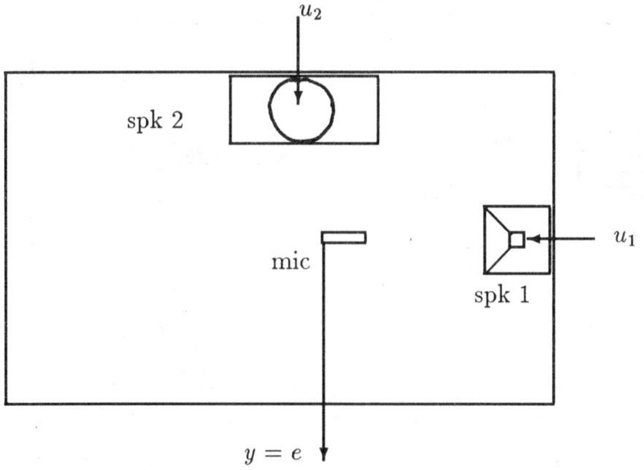

Figure 1: Top View of inside Enclosure

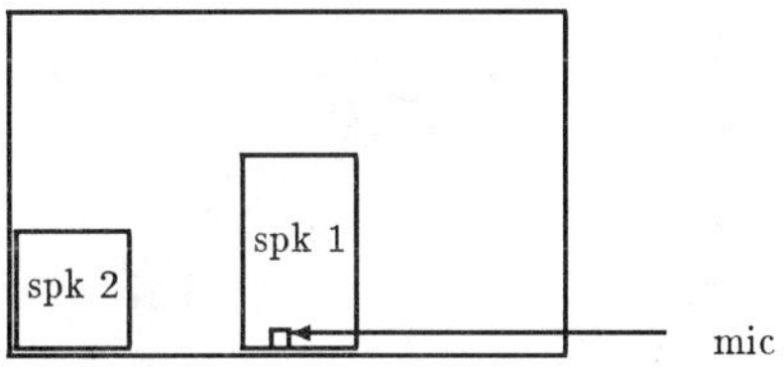

Figure 2: Side View of inside Enclosure

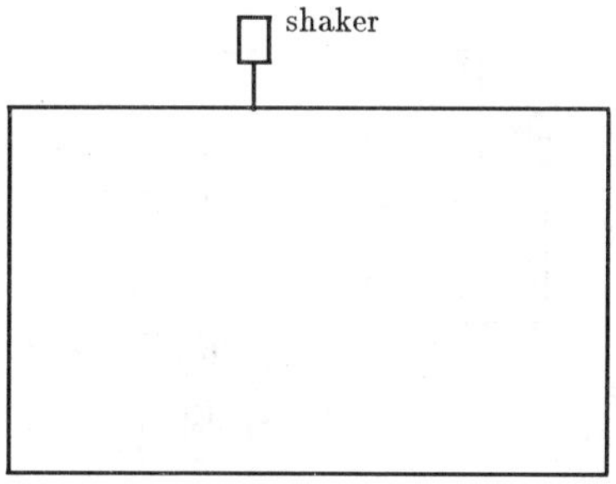

Figure 3: Side View of outside Enclosure

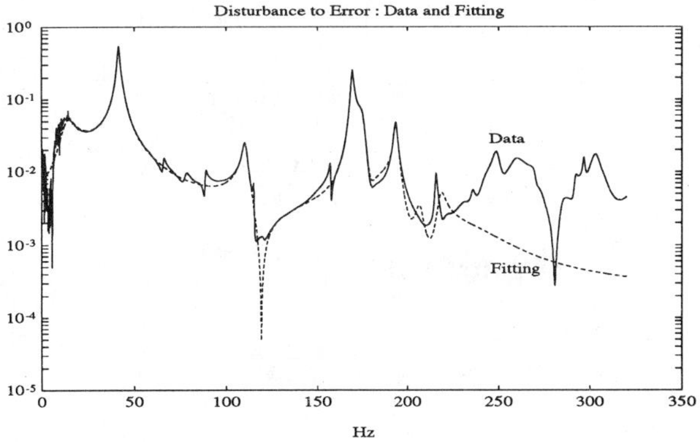

Figure 4: Disturbance to Error : Experimental Data versus System Model

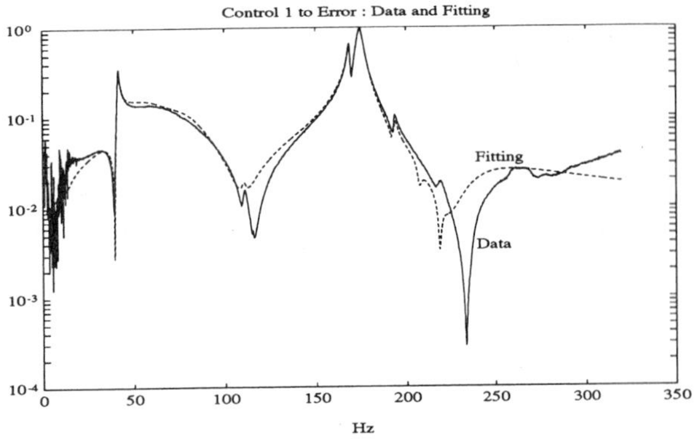

Figure 5: Control 1 to Error : Experimental Data versus System Model

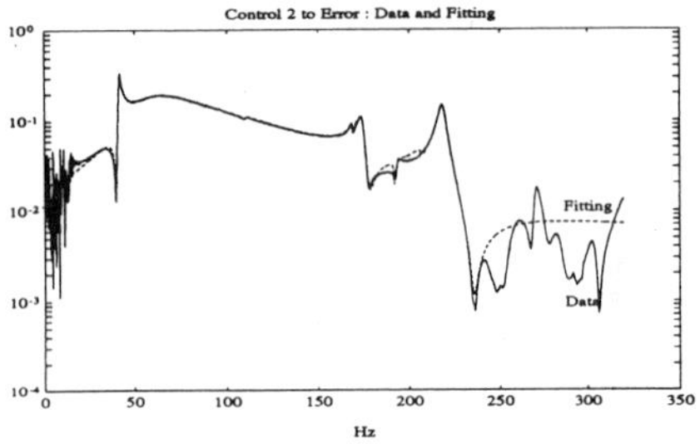

Figure 6: Control 2 to Error : Experimental Data versus System Model

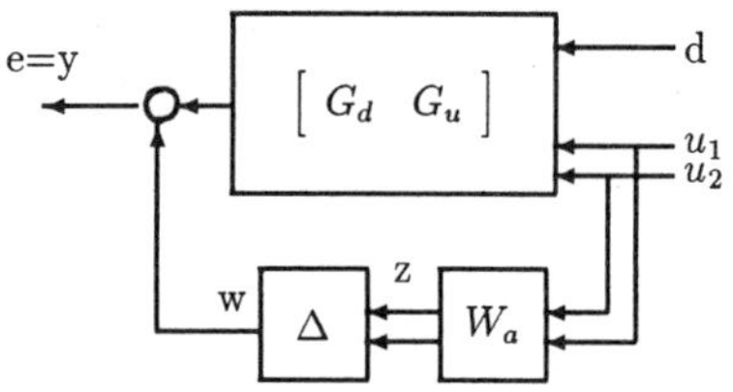

Figure 7: Additive Uncertainty Model for Control-to-Microphone Channel

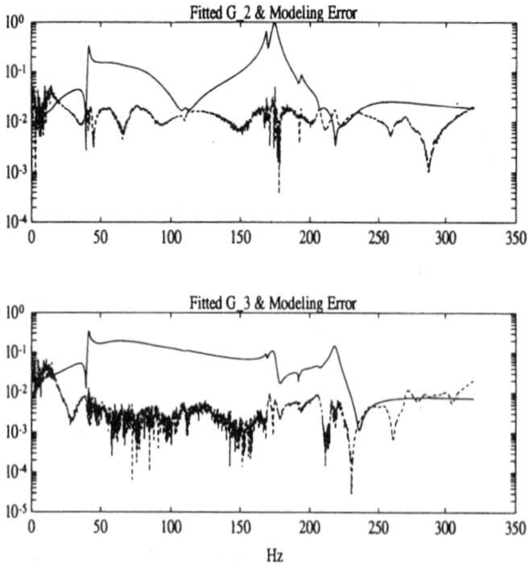

Figure 8: System Model of G_u and the Modeling Error

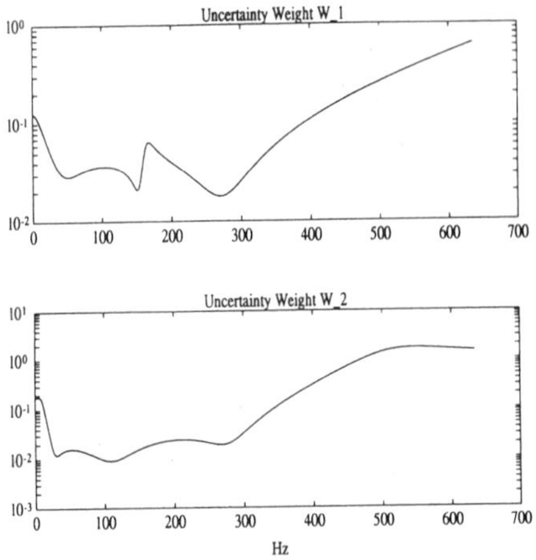

Figure 9: Additive Uncertainty Weighting Function

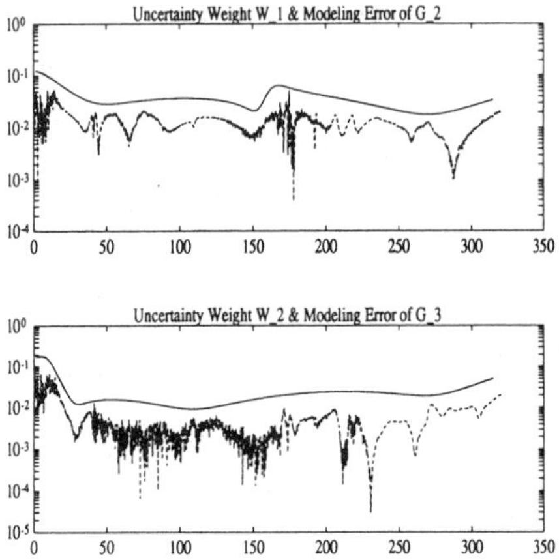

Figure 10: Uncertainty Weights versus Modeling Error of Each Control Channel

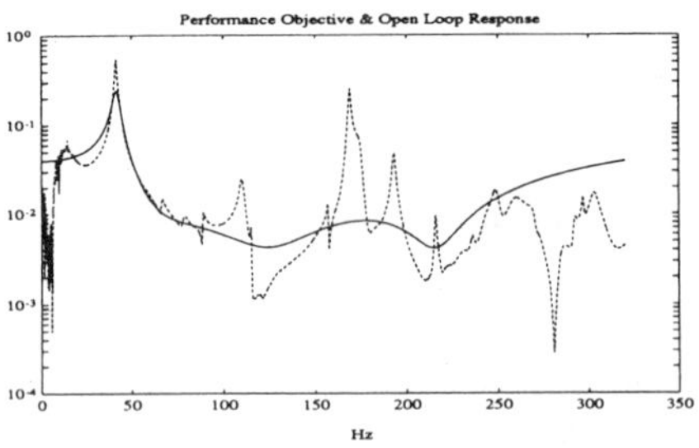

Figure 11: Open Loop Response and Performance Objective

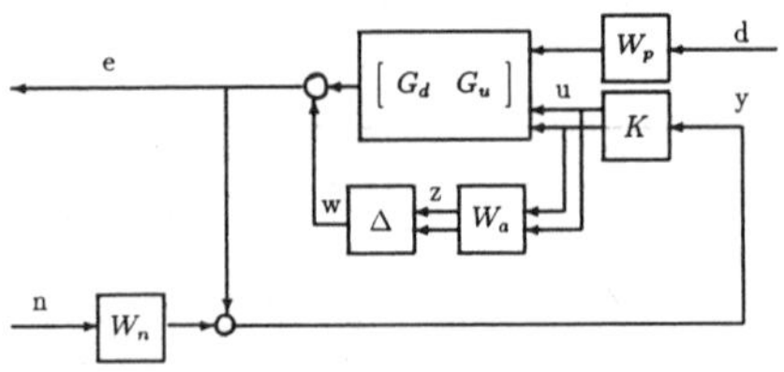

Figure 12: Closed-Loop Interconnection Diagram

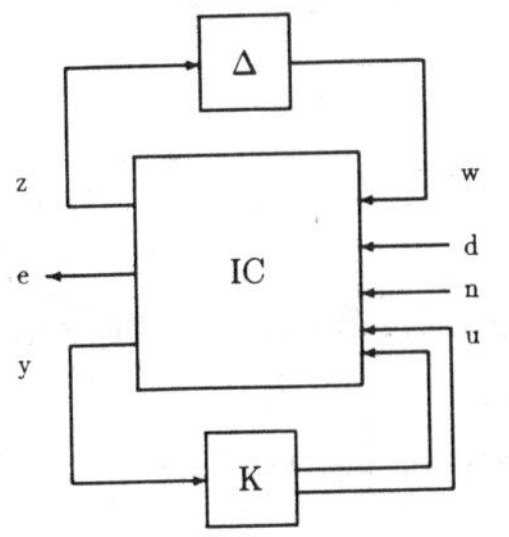

Figure 13: Generalized Closed-Loop Interconnection

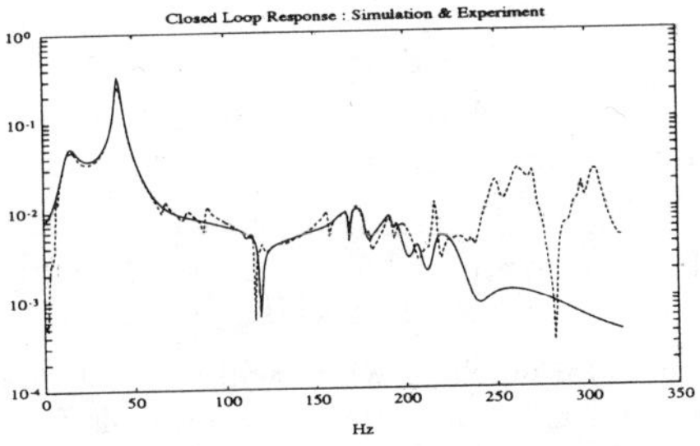

Figure 14: Computer Simulation and Experiment

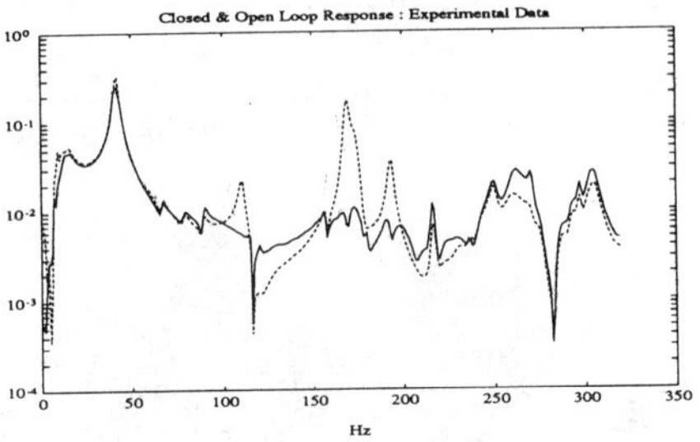

Figure 15: Closed Loop and Open Loop Response : Experimental Data

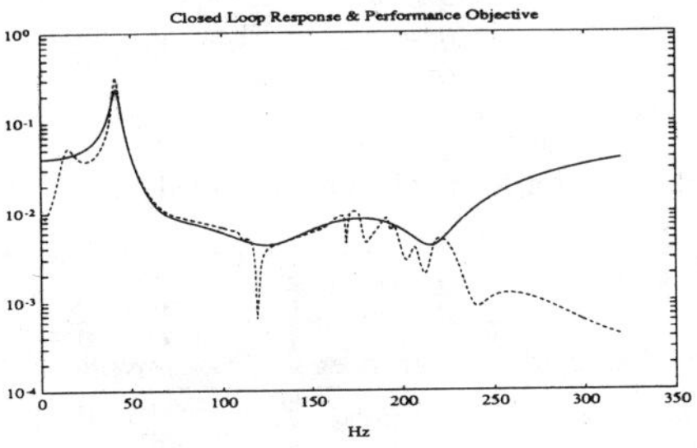

Figure 16: Closed Loop Response versus Performance Goal

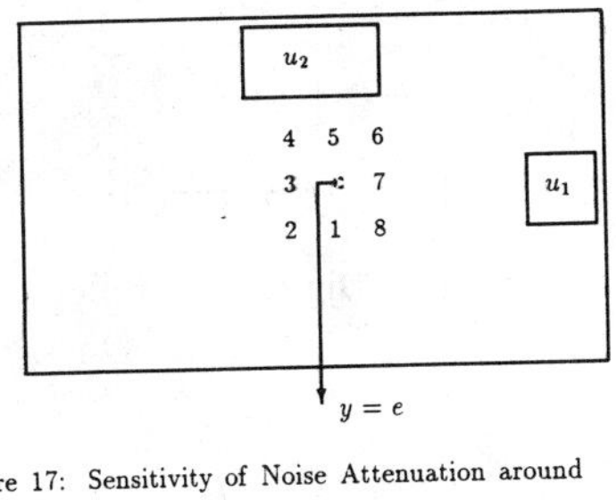

Figure 17: Sensitivity of Noise Attenuation around Nominal Position

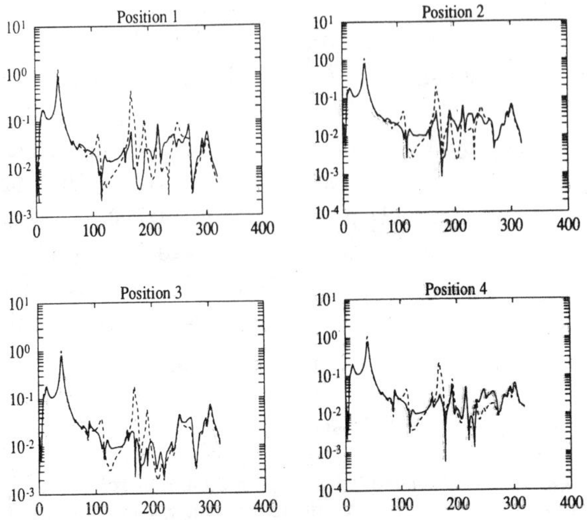

Figure 18: Sensitivity Measurement : Positions 1 - 4

Solid Line : Closed-Loop
Broken Line : Open-Loop

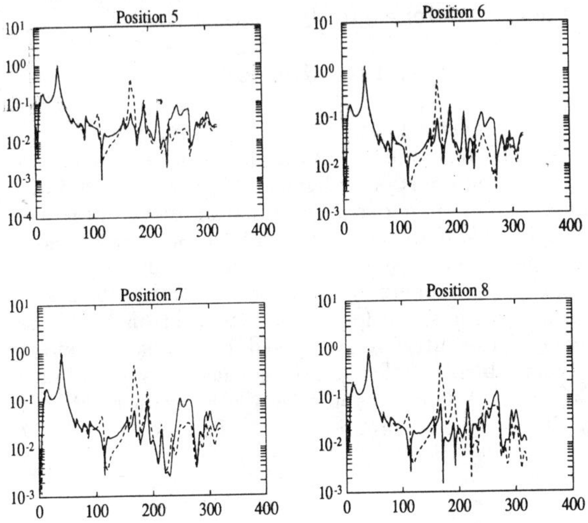

Figure 19: Sensitivity Measurement : Positions 5 - 8

Solid Line : Closed-Loop
Broken Line : Open-Loop

Proceedings of the
American Control Conference
San Francisco, California • June 1993

Experiments on the Loop Shaping Based H_∞ Control of a Magnetic Bearing

Masayuki Fujita†, Kazuhiro Hatake‡, Fumio Matsumura‡ and Kenko Uchida§

†School of Information Science, Japan Advanced Institute of Science and Technology, Hokuriku
Tatsunokuchi, Ishikawa 923-12, Japan, e-mail:fujita@jaist-east.ac.jp
‡Department of Electrical and Computer Engineering, Kanazawa University
2-40-20 Kodatsuno, Kanazawa 920, Japan
§Department of Electrical Engineering, Waseda University
3-4-1 Okubo, Shinjuku, Tokyo 169, Japan

Abstract

This paper is concerned with H_∞ robust control design of a magnetic bearing. We design a control system using the 'Loop Shaping Design Procedure (LSDP)'. After the introduction of our experimental machine and digital controller, a mathematical model of the magnetic bearing is shown. Then, H_∞ controllers are designed based on the LSDP so as to reject the disturbances caused by unbalance on the rotor asymptotically. Finally, with experimental results, we show that the synchronous vibratory response of the rotor is greatly reduced.

1. Introduction

By using magnetic bearings, a rotor is supported contactless. The technique of contactless support for rotors becomes more important in light and heavy industrial applications. This paper is a continuation of the previous research [1], where we have considered stability robustness against the uncertainty caused by gyroscopic effect.

In this paper, among many serious control problems in magnetic bearings, we focus our attention on both the problem of the interference caused by gyroscopic effect and the problem of the vibration caused by unbalance on the rotor. A Loop Shaping Design Procedure (LSDP) using H_∞ synthesis, proposed by McFarlane and Glover [5], is adopted for robust control design. In particular, H_∞ controllers are designed so as to achieve asymptotic disturbance rejection.

Table 1: Parameters of experimental machine

Parameter	Value
Mass of the Rotor : m	$1.39e1$ [kg]
Moment of Inertia about X : J_x	$1.348e-2$ [kg m^2]
Moment of Inertia about Y : J_y	$2.326e-1$ [kg m^2]
Distance between Center of Mass and Left Electromagnet : l_l	$1.30e-1$ [m]
Distance between Center of Mass and Right Electromagnet : l_r	$1.30e-1$ [m]
Distance between Center of Mass and Motor : l_m	0 [m]
Steady Attractive Force : $F_{l1,r1}$	$9.09e1$ [N]
Steady Attractive Force : $F_{l2\sim l4,r2\sim r4}$	$2.20e1$ [N]
Steady Current : $I_{l1,r1}$	$6.3e-1$ [A]
Steady Current : $I_{l2\sim l4,r2\sim r4}$	$3.1e-1$ [A]
Steady Gap : W	$5.5e-4$ [m]
Resistance : R	$1.07e1$ [Ω]
Inductance : L	$2.85e-1$ [H]

2. Experimental Machine and Digital Controller

The experimental machine which will be used throughout the paper is a 4-axis controlled horizontal shaft magnetic bearing with symmetric structure. An outline of the setup is depicted in Fig. 1. Physical parameters of this experimental machine are shown in Table 1. As depicted in Fig. 2, a digital signal processor(DSP)-based controller is used for real-time control of the experimental machine. The controllers to be implemented are designed by using MATLAB with μ-Analysis and Synthesis Toolbox on the SUN SPARCstation 2.

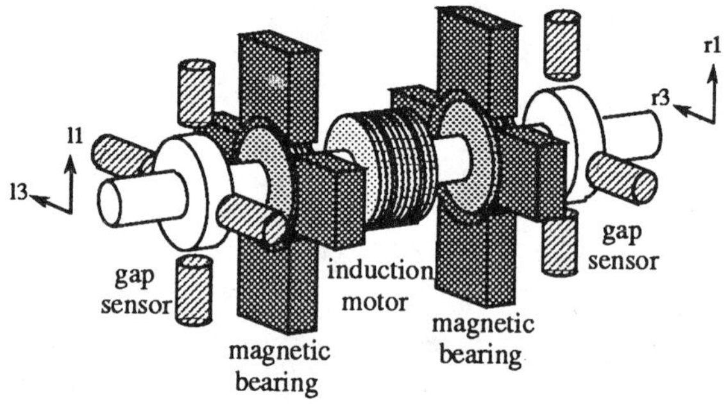

Fig. 1. Diagram of experimental machine

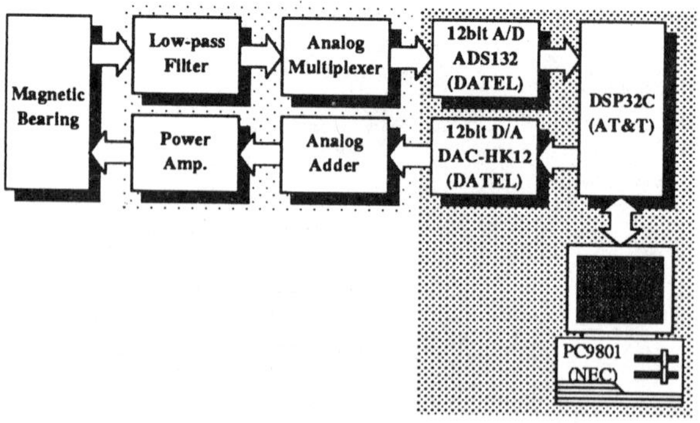

Fig. 2. Digital controller

3. Modeling of Magnetic Bearing

A mathematical model of a magnetic bearing has been derived in [3] is given by

$$\begin{bmatrix} \dot{x}_v \\ \dot{x}_h \end{bmatrix} = \begin{bmatrix} A_v & pA_{vh} \\ -pA_{vh} & A_h \end{bmatrix} \begin{bmatrix} x_v \\ x_h \end{bmatrix} + \begin{bmatrix} B_v & 0 \\ 0 & B_h \end{bmatrix} \begin{bmatrix} u_v \\ u_h \end{bmatrix} \quad (1)$$

$$\begin{bmatrix} y_v \\ y_h \end{bmatrix} = \begin{bmatrix} C_v & 0 \\ 0 & C_h \end{bmatrix} \begin{bmatrix} x_v \\ x_h \end{bmatrix} \quad (2)$$

where the subscripts 'v' and 'h' in the vectors and the matrices stand for the vertical motion and the horizontal motion of the magnetic bearing, respectively. In addition, the subscript 'vh' stands for the interference term between the vertical motion and the horizontal motion, and p denotes the rotational speed of the rotor.

Each vector in (1) and (2) is defined as

$$x_v = [\, g_{l1} \quad g_{r1} \quad \dot{g}_{l1} \quad \dot{g}_{r1} \quad i_{l1} \quad i_{r1} \,]^T \quad (3)$$

$$x_h = [\, g_{l3} \quad g_{r3} \quad \dot{g}_{l3} \quad \dot{g}_{r3} \quad i_{l3} \quad i_{r3} \,]^T \quad (4)$$

$$u_v = [\, e_{l1} \quad e_{r1} \,]^T \quad (5)$$

$$u_h = [\, e_{l3} \quad e_{r3} \,]^T \quad (6)$$

where

g_j : deviations from the steady gap lengths between the electromagnets and the rotor

i_j : deviations from the steady currents of the electromagnets

e_j : deviations from the steady voltages of the electromagnets

$j = l1, r1, l3, r3$.

The subscripts 'l' and 'r' denote the left-hand side and the right-hand side of the magnetic bearing respectively, and the subscripts '1' and '3' denote one of the vertical directions and one the horizontal directions of the rotor respectively.

Each matrix in (1) and (2) is as follows.

$$A_v = \begin{bmatrix} 0 & 0 & 1 & 0 & 0 & 0 \\ 0 & 0 & 0 & 1 & 0 & 0 \\ 5.937e4 & -2.933e2 & 0 & 0 & -6.225e1 & 3.076e{-1} \\ -2.933e2 & 5.937e4 & 0 & 0 & 3.076e{-1} & -6.225e1 \\ 0 & 0 & 0 & 0 & -3.754e1 & 0 \\ 0 & 0 & 0 & 0 & 0 & -3.754e1 \end{bmatrix}$$

$$A_h = \begin{bmatrix} 0 & 0 & 1 & 0 & 0 & 0 \\ 0 & 0 & 0 & 1 & 0 & 0 \\ 2.314e4 & -1.143e2 & 0 & 0 & -4.105e1 & 2.028e{-1} \\ -1.143e2 & 2.314e4 & 0 & 0 & 2.028e{-1} & -4.105e1 \\ 0 & 0 & 0 & 0 & -3.754e1 & 0 \\ 0 & 0 & 0 & 0 & 0 & -3.754e1 \end{bmatrix}$$

$$A_{vh} = \begin{bmatrix} 0 & 0 & 0 & 0 & 0 & 0 \\ 0 & 0 & 0 & 0 & 0 & 0 \\ 0 & 0 & -3.034e{-3} & 3.034e{-3} & 0 & 0 \\ 0 & 0 & 3.034e{-3} & -3.034e{-3} & 0 & 0 \\ 0 & 0 & 0 & 0 & 0 & 0 \\ 0 & 0 & 0 & 0 & 0 & 0 \end{bmatrix}$$

$$B_v = B_h = \begin{bmatrix} 0 & 0 \\ 0 & 0 \\ 0 & 0 \\ 0 & 0 \\ 3.509 & 0 \\ 0 & 3.509 \end{bmatrix}$$

$$C_v = C_h = \begin{bmatrix} 1 & 0 & 0 & 0 & 0 & 0 \\ 0 & 1 & 0 & 0 & 0 & 0 \end{bmatrix}$$

4. Loop Shaping Design Procedure

In this section, we introduce the 'Loop Shaping Design Procedure (LSDP)' [5]. Let $(N,\ M)$ represent a normalized left coprime factorization of a plant G. Let these coprime factors be assumed to have uncertainties Δ_N, Δ_M, and let G_Δ represent the plant with these uncertainties.

$$\begin{aligned} G_\Delta &= M_\Delta^{-1} N_\Delta \\ &= (M + \Delta_M)^{-1}(N + \Delta_N) \end{aligned} \quad (7)$$

where N_Δ and M_Δ represent a left coprime factorization of G_Δ, and

$$\Delta = \{[\Delta_N,\ \Delta_M] \in RH_\infty; \|[\Delta_N,\ \Delta_M]\|_\infty < \varepsilon\}. \quad (8)$$

G_Δ can be written in a form of an Upper Linear Fractional Transformation (ULFT) as follows.

$$\begin{aligned} G_\Delta &= F_U(P,\ \Delta) \\ &= P_{22} + P_{21}\Delta(I - P_{11}\Delta)^{-1}P_{12} \end{aligned} \quad (9)$$

where

$$P = \begin{bmatrix} P_{11} & P_{12} \\ P_{21} & P_{22} \end{bmatrix} = \begin{bmatrix} 0 & I \\ M^{-1} & G \\ M^{-1} & G \end{bmatrix}. \quad (10)$$

The robust stabilizability problem for the uncertain plant (7) can be treated as the following H_∞ control problem:

$$\left\| \begin{bmatrix} K \\ I \end{bmatrix} (I - GK)^{-1} M^{-1} \right\|_\infty \le \varepsilon^{-1}. \quad (11)$$

It is known that the solution of this problem and the largest number of ε ($= \varepsilon_{max}$) can be obtained by solving two Riccati equations without iterative procedure. All controllers K satisfying (11) are given by

$$K = (L_{11}\Phi + L_{12})(L_{21}\Phi + L_{22})^{-1} \quad (12)$$

$$\Phi \in RH_\infty \text{with } \|\Phi\|_\infty \le 1. \quad (13)$$

For the calculation of L_{ij} $(i, j = 1, 2)$ and ε_{max}, see [5]. A particular controller corresponding to $\Phi = 0$ is the central controller. McFarlane and Glover proposed the LSDP consisting of the following three steps:

Step 1 Loop Shaping

Selecting shaping functions W_1 and W_2, the singular values of the nominal plant G are shaped to have a desired open loop shape. Let G_s represent this shaped plant

$$G_s = W_2 G W_1. \quad (14)$$

W_1 and W_2 should be selected such that G_s has no hidden unstable modes.

Step 2 Robust Stabilization

The maximum stability margin $\varepsilon_{\max}$ is calculated. If $\varepsilon_{\max} << 1$, return to step 1 and W_1 and W_2 are reselected. Otherwise, ε is appropriately selected as $\varepsilon \le \varepsilon_{\max}$, and an H_∞ controller K_∞ is synthesized for G_s such as (12) .

Step 3 Final Controller

The final controller K can be obtained by the combination of W_1, W_2 and K_∞

$$K = W_1 K_\infty W_2. \quad (15)$$

The maximum stability margin $\varepsilon_{\max}$ indicates the magnitude of the allowable maximum perturbation of the shaped plant G_s. In this procedure, $\varepsilon_{\max}$ is treated as a design indicator rather than a maximum stability margin of G_s.

5. Controller Design

In this section, the feedback controllers are designed with the LSDP. Firstly, we should consider the linear design model G. It is noted that the stabilizing controller is required by all means when the rotor is at rest (that is, the rotational speed $p = 0$). If $p = 0$ in (1), there is no coupling between the vertical motion and the horizontal motion. In this case, the plant model can be separated into the vertical plant G_v and the horizontal plant G_h, respectively.

(v) Vertical plant : $G_v(s) = C_v(sI - A_v)^{-1}B_v$

(h) Horizontal plant : $G_h(s) = C_h(sI - A_h)^{-1}B_h$

With these, we adopt

$$G = \begin{bmatrix} G_v & 0 \\ 0 & G_h \end{bmatrix} \tag{16}$$

as the linear design model in the sequel.

Then, two controllers will be separately designed for the vertical plant G_v and for the horizontal plant G_h, respectively. The final controller, denoted by K_{LSDP}, for the entire plant G will be constructed with the combination of these controllers.

$$K_{LSDP} = \begin{bmatrix} K_v & 0 \\ 0 & K_h \end{bmatrix} \tag{17}$$

where K_v denotes the controller for the vertical plant, and K_h denotes the controller for the horizontal plant.

Recall that the dynamics of magnetic bearings change when the rotational speed varies. The interference terms in (1) are called gyroscopic effect. It is widely known that the gyroscopic effect causes a serious problem. Hence, each controller K_v, K_h must be designed so as to stabilize the entire closed loop system robustly against changes in the rotational speed of the rotor [1].

Moreover, if there exists residual unbalance on the rotor, a shaft vibration is arisen when the rotor rotates. In practical applications, better positioning accuracy is required at a regular rotational speed. The effects caused by unbalance can be modeled as sinusoidal disturbances [4]. Therefore, each controller K_v, K_h should be further designed so as to reject the sinusoidal disturbances asymptotically at the regular rotational speed. In the following, we will design two LSDP-based robust controllers achieving asymptotic disturbance rejection.

Design 1 : Shaping Function Method

In the shaping function method, we choose the shaping functions not only to give desired open-loop properties [1], but to have oscillators which correspond to the internal model of the sinusoidal disturbances. The shaping functions and the design parameters are selected as follows.

(v) Design for vertical motion

$$\begin{aligned} W_{1v}(s) &= \frac{1300(1+s/(2\pi\cdot 5))(1+s/(2\pi\cdot 35))}{(1+s/(2\pi\cdot 0.01))(1+s/(2\pi\cdot 700))} \\ &\quad \times \frac{(1+s/(2\pi\cdot 50))}{(1+s/(2\pi\cdot 1200))}\begin{bmatrix} 1 & 0 \\ 0 & 1 \end{bmatrix} \end{aligned} \tag{18}$$

$$W_{2v}(s) = 10000\left(1 + \frac{10s}{s^2+\omega_0^2}\right)\begin{bmatrix} 1 & 0 \\ 0 & 1 \end{bmatrix} \tag{19}$$

$$\varepsilon_{\max v} = 0.19926 \tag{20}$$

$$\varepsilon_v^{-1} = \gamma_v = 5.25 \tag{21}$$

(h) Design for horizontal motion

$$\begin{aligned} W_{1h}(s) &= \frac{1100(1+s/(2\pi\cdot 5))(1+s/(2\pi\cdot 25))}{(1+s/(2\pi\cdot 0.01))(1+s/(2\pi\cdot 700))} \\ &\quad \times \frac{(1+s/(2\pi\cdot 40))}{(1+s/(2\pi\cdot 1200))}\begin{bmatrix} 1 & 0 \\ 0 & 1 \end{bmatrix} \end{aligned} \tag{22}$$

$$W_{2h}(s) = 10000\left(1 + \frac{10s}{s^2+\omega_0^2}\right)\begin{bmatrix} 1 & 0 \\ 0 & 1 \end{bmatrix} \tag{23}$$

$$\varepsilon_{\max h} = 0.27276 \tag{24}$$

$$\varepsilon_h^{-1} = \gamma_h = 3.75 \tag{25}$$

As in (19) and (23), the shaping functions have the imaginary poles at $\pm j\omega_0$. Here ω_0 denotes the angular velocity of the regular rotational speed of the rotor and, in this study, we set

$$\omega_0 = 40\pi \quad \text{(1200 rpm)}. \tag{26}$$

When we obtain the shaped plant, a model reduction technique has been employed. The procedure of the model reduction is 'The Nominal Plant Model Reduction Procedure' as shown in [5, Procedure 5.5]. The order of the shaped plant has been reduced from 16 states to 12 states using the Balanced Truncation Approximation in each case. Hence, by this model reduction procedure, the final controller has 44 states.

Let this designed controller be denoted by K_1. The singular values of the shaped plant G_s and of the open loop transfer function GK_1 are shown in Fig. 3 . Fig. 4 shows the singular values of the sensitivity function with K_1. The sensitivity approaches zero at the frequency ω_0.

Design 2 : Free Parameter Method

The LSDP controller has been parametrized with the free parameter Φ as shown in (12) and (13) . By choosing an adequate Φ, we can get a controller containing oscillators. Equation (12) can be converted to a Lower Linear Fractional Transformation (LLFT) form as

$$K = F_L(K_a, \Phi) := K_{11} + K_{12}\Phi(I - K_{22}\Phi)^{-1}K_{21} \tag{27}$$

$$K_a := \begin{bmatrix} K_{11} & K_{12} \\ K_{21} & K_{22} \end{bmatrix} \tag{28}$$

If it is possible to choose Φ such that

$$\Phi(\pm j\omega_0) = K_{22}(\pm j\omega_0)^{-1} \tag{29}$$

we can get the controller with the imaginary poles at $\pm j\omega_0$. From the so-called internal model principle, this guarantees asymptotic disturbance rejection [6].

In this design, the shaping functions W_{1v} and W_{1h} are the same as (18) and (22) , respectively. W_{2v} and W_{2h} are chosen as

$$W_{2v}(s) = W_{2h}(s) = 10000\begin{bmatrix} 1 & 0 \\ 0 & 1 \end{bmatrix} \tag{30}$$

The maximum stability margins $\varepsilon_{\max v}$ and $\varepsilon_{\max h}$ are calculated as follows.

$$\varepsilon_{\max v} = 0.19944 \tag{31}$$

$$\varepsilon_{\max h} = 0.27432 \tag{32}$$

We choose $\gamma_v = 5.25$ and $\gamma_h = 3.75$, which are the same as (21) and (25)

In order to satisfy the constraints (29) , the free parameter Φ is selected as

$$\Phi = C_u(sI - A_u)^{-1}B_u + D_u \tag{33}$$

where

$$A_u = \begin{bmatrix} -aI & 0 \\ 0 & -bI \end{bmatrix}, \quad B_u = \begin{bmatrix} I \\ I \end{bmatrix}$$

$$C_u = [\,C_{u1} \quad C_{u2}\,], \qquad D_u = 0$$

$$C_{u1} = \frac{(a^2+\omega_0^2)}{\omega_0(a-b)}\{\omega_0 \mathrm{Re}(K_{22}^{-1}(j\omega_0)) + b\mathrm{Im}(K_{22}^{-1}(j\omega_0))\}$$

$$C_{u2} = \frac{(b^2+\omega_0^2)}{\omega_0(b-a)}\{\omega_0 \mathrm{Re}(K_{22}^{-1}(j\omega_0)) + a\mathrm{Im}(K_{22}^{-1}(j\omega_0))\}$$

with

$$\omega_0 = 40\pi \tag{34}$$

$$a = 1500 \tag{35}$$

$$b = 10. \tag{36}$$

The same model reduction technique is used for the shaped plant. The order has been reduced from 12 states to 8 states in each case. The final controller has 36 states.

Let this designed controller be denoted by K_2. The singular values of the shaped plant G_s and of the open loop transfer function GK_2 are shown in Fig. 5 . Fig. 6 shows the singular values of the sensitivity function with K_2. Again, the sensitivity approaches zero at the frequency ω_0. In order to compare the characteristic of the designed controllers K_1 and K_2 to the controller without oscillators, the plots with the controller K_0 [1] are shown in from Fig. 3 to 6 by dash-dotted lines.

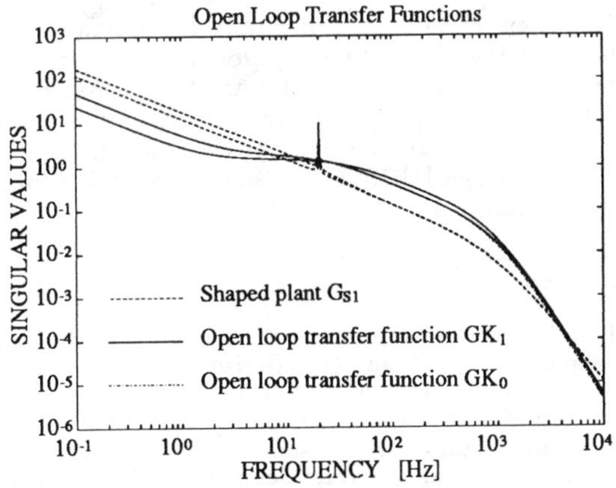

Fig. 3. Open loop transfer functions with K_1

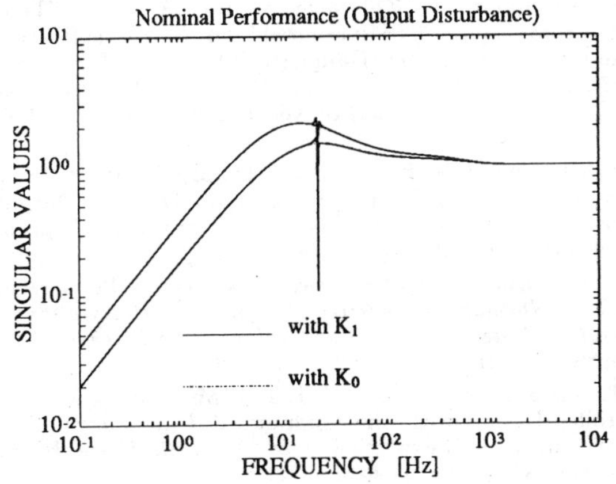

Fig. 4. $\sigma((I - GK_1)^{-1})$

6. Experimental Results

We have made experiments using the experimental machine shown in Section 2. The designed continuous-time controllers K_0, K_1 and K_2 are discretized via the well known Tustin transform at the sampling rate of 184 μs, 323 μs and 252 μs, respectively.

The rotor has been suspended stably by using any controller K_0, K_1 or K_2. To ascertain the effectiveness of unbalance control, we rotate the rotor by the induction motor at $p = 1200$ rpm which is the regular rotational speed in this study. Throughout the experiments, by adding a small weight to the rotor so as to increase the residual unbalance, we strengthen the synchronous response of the rotor. We have measured the displacement of the rotor for a period of 0.5 s. In the following figures, (a) shows the result of the left side and (b) is one of the right side. Each vertical axis g_{l1} or g_{r1} shows the displacement of the rotor on the vertical direction, and each horizontal axis g_{l3} or g_{r3} shows the displacement on the horizontal direction. Hence, these figures are the time history of the shaft on the cross plane at the arranged place of the electromagnets.

In Fig. 7 , the results with the controller K_0 are shown. Similarly, the results with the controllers K_1 and K_2 are shown in Fig. 8 and Fig. 9 , respectively. From Fig. 7 , it can be seen that the displacements of the rotor show the synchronous vibratory response due to the unbalance. However, in Fig. 8 , the orbits are significantly reduced by using the controller K_1. We can also see, from Fig. 9 , that the controller K_2 reduces the orbits greatly. Therefore, with the designed controllers K_1 and K_2, the vibration caused by unbalance on the rotor can be eliminated.

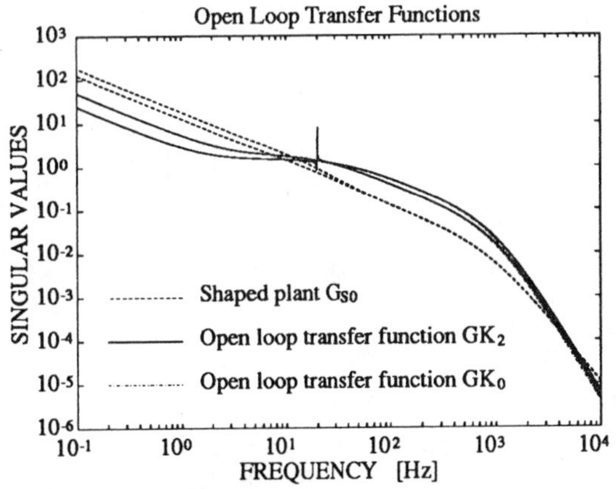

Fig. 5. Open loop transfer functions with K_2

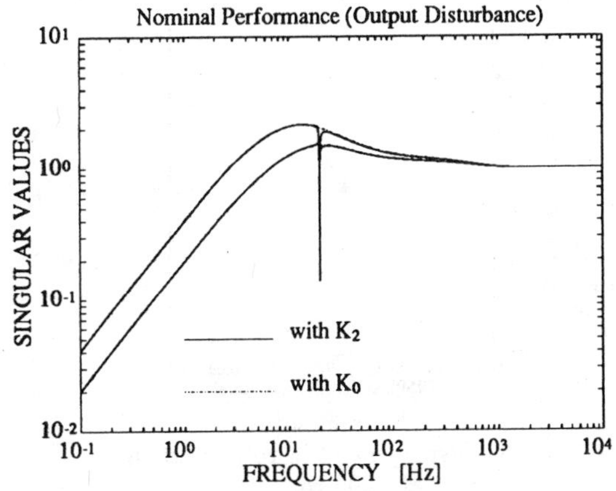

Fig. 6. $\sigma((I - GK_2)^{-1})$

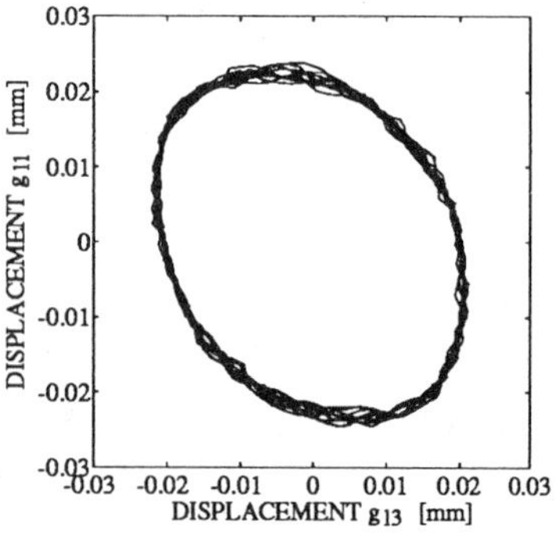

(a) left side

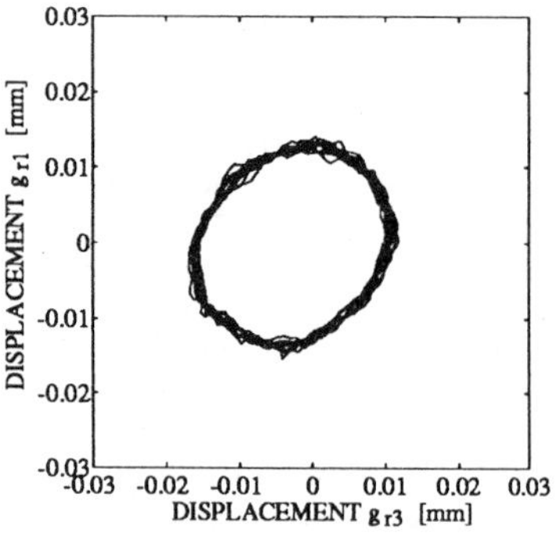

(b) right side

Fig. 7. Displacement of rotor with K_0 at 1200 rpm

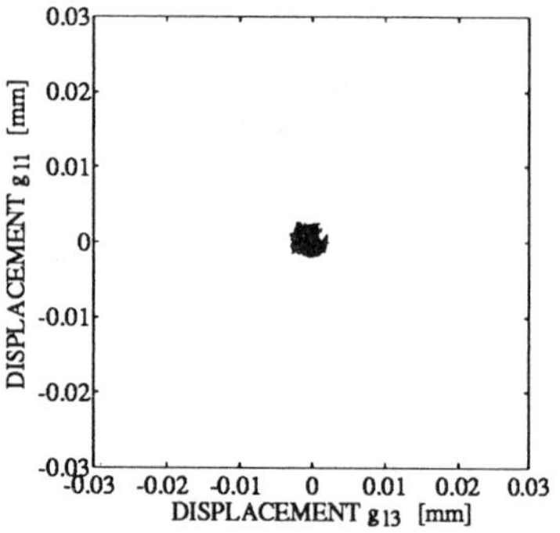

(a) left side

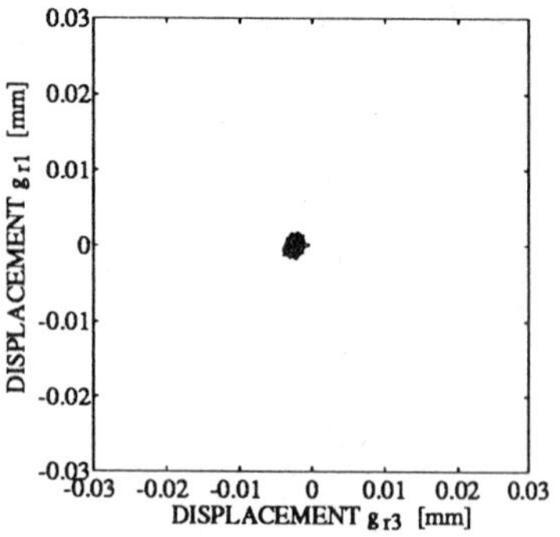

(b) right side

Fig. 8. Displacement of rotor with K_1 at 1200 rpm

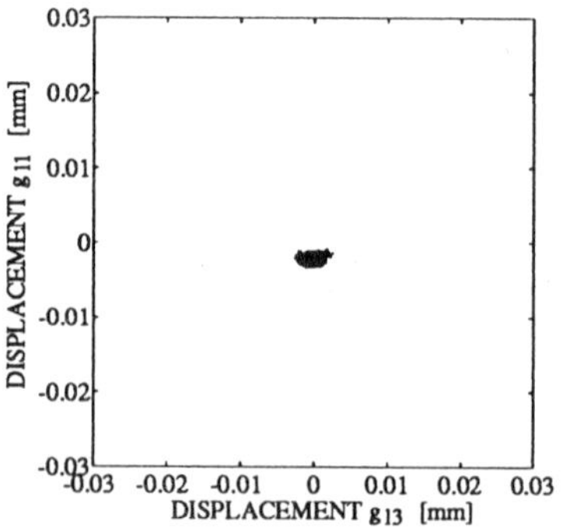

(a) left side

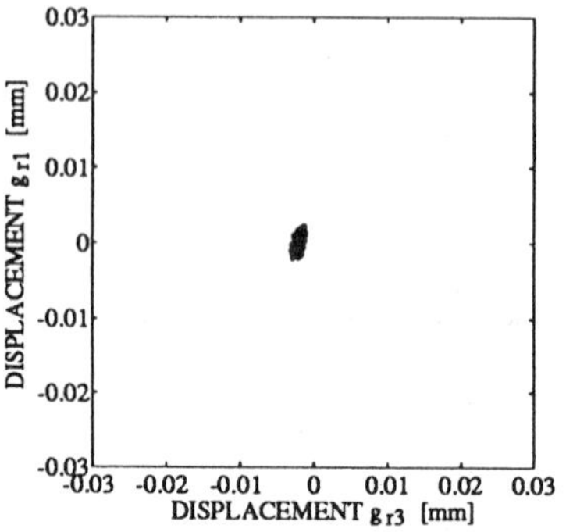

(b) right side

Fig. 9. Displacement of rotor with K_2 at 1200 rpm

7. Conclusions

In this paper, we have experimentally demonstrated the availability of the 'Loop Shaping Design Procedure' for the disturbance rejection control. As the controller design method, the shaping function method and the free parameter method have been proposed. In [2], a comparison between the LSDP design and the μ-design for a magnetic bearing is reported

References

[1] M. Fujita, K. Hatake, and F. Matsumura, "Loop Shaping Based H^∞ Robust Control of a Horizontal Shaft Magnetic Bearing," *Proc. 31st SICE Annual Conference*, pp. 941–944, Kumamoto, Japan, 1992.

[2] M. Fujita, K. Hatake, F. Matsumura, and K. Uchida, "An Experimental Evaluation and Comparison of H_∞/μ Control for a Magnetic Bearing," to be presented at the *12th IFAC World Congress*, Sydney, Australia, 1993.

[3] F. Matsumura, H. Kobayashi, and Y. Akiyama, "Fundamental Equation of Horizontal Shaft Magnetic Bearing and its Control System Design (in Japanese)," *Trans. IEE of Japan*, vol. 101-C, no. 6, pp. 137–144, 1981; also *Electrical Engineering in Japan*, vol. 101, no. 3, pp. 123–130, 1981.

[4] F. Matsumura, M. Fujita, and K. Hatake, "Output Regulation in Magnetic Bearing Systems by a Dynamic Output Feedback Controller (in Japanese)," *Trans. IEE of Japan*, vol. 112-C, no. 10, pp. 977–983, 1992.

[5] D. McFarlane and K. Glover, *Robust Controller Design Using Normalized Coprime Factor Plant Descriptions* , *Lecture Notes in Control and Information Sciences*, 138, Springer-Verlag, 1990.

[6] T. Sugie, M. Fujita, and S. Hara, "Multiobjective Controller Design with the Guaranteed H_∞ Control Performance," to be presented at the *12th IFAC World Congress*, Sydney, Australia, 1993.

Proceedings of the
American Control Conference
San Francisco, California • June 1993

Active Feedback Controller Design for a Thin Airfoil

Hitay Özbay and *Glen R. Bachmann*
Department of Electrical Engineering
The Ohio State University
2015 Neil Avenue
Columbus, OH 43210

Abstract

In this paper we study the problem of active feedback controller design for a thin airfoil, whose mathematical model is derived from classical Theodorsen's formulation. A finite dimensional controller stabilizing the original infinite dimensional model is obtained using H^∞ control techniques. We also consider the gust alleviation problem, and show that it can be formulated as a disturbance attenuation problem in the mixed H^2/H^∞ control framework. We use existing results on H^∞ and mixed H^2/H^∞ control to illustrate our approach with a numerical example.

1 Introduction

In this paper we consider the problem of active feedback controller design for a thin airfoil in unsteady aerodynamics. The mathematical model we adopt for this system is obtained from Theodorsen's formulation. Using the H^∞ control theory we derive a finite dimensional feedback controller stabilizing this infinite dimensional model. Then, we study the gust alleviation problem and show that it can be seen as a disturbance attenuation problem, which can be solved using the mixed H^2/H^∞ control methods.

In general, mathematical models for airfoils in unsteady aerodynamics are linear time invariant infinite dimensional systems. The basic difficulty in such systems is to compute the aerodynamic loads due to unsteady flow. The simplest models (in the frequency domain) for the unsteady aerodynamics contain Theodorsen's function as the infinite dimensional part. Because of the interaction between the structure and the flow, flutter (dynamic instability) occurs at a certain flow speed. Therefore, it is important to design active feedback controllers stabilizing the airfoil. Gust can be seen as a perturbation in the flow, and its effect on the airfoil can be modeled as an external disturbance. In our feedback controller design, besides closed loop stability, we would like to reduce the effect of this external disturbance on the system response.

There are several techniques for designing feedback controllers directly from the infinite dimensional airfoil model see e.g. [2]. In this method the controller itself is infinite dimensional, and hence one has to approximate it in order to obtain an implementable finite dimensional controller. Another method is to approximate the infinite dimensional part of the system and design a finite dimensional controller from the finite dimensional approximate model.

Most of the work found in the literature, on active flutter suppression, for the Theodorsen's model of a thin airfoil, uses the second method. In other words, Theodorsen's function (or the system model generating aeroelastic loads) is approximated first, and a controller designed (based on several different control techniques) from this finite dimensional model, see e.g. [12] [15] [14] and references therein. However, to our knowledge, *robustness of these controllers to approximations of Theodorsen's function* has not been studied, in the flutter suppression and gust alleviation context. One has to make sure that the finite dimensional controller designed from the approximate model, behaves as desired for the original infinite dimensional model which contains Theodorsen's function. This problem will be studied in the paper, and a procedure to obtain an appropriate controller will be given. The basic idea here is to use H^∞ and mixed H^2/H^∞ control techniques. The H^∞ part of this problem is to guarantee closed loop stability in the presence of unmodeled dynamics. The H^2 part of it deals with the issue of minimizing the energy of the system response due to gust.

The paper is organized as follows. In the next section we define the mathematical model to be considered for an airfoil in unsteady flow. In Section 3 we present an H^∞ control approach to flutter suppression in the presence of unmodeled aerodynamics. Section 4 contains a discussion on how to model the gust, and how to put the gust alleviation problem in the framework of the mixed H^2/H^∞ control problem. We present a numerical example in Section 5. Concluding remarks are made in the last section.

2 A mathematical model for the airfoil

We consider the following mathematical model (see e.g. [2], [3]), for the thin airfoil shown in Figure 1,

$$M_s\ddot{z}(t) + B_s\dot{z}(t) + K_s z(t) = \frac{1}{m_s}F(t) + Gu(t), \tag{1}$$

where $z(t) = [h(t), \alpha(t), \beta(t)]^T$, and $u(t)$ represents the control input (torque applied at the flap). The scalar m_s denotes the mass of the structure, and the matrices M_s, B_s, K_s and G can be computed in terms of the physical parameters of the structure.

In this paper we consider the indicial problem (see e.g. [2], and [5]), i.e. we assume that $z(t) = 0$ for $t \leq 0$. The aeroelastic loads are represented by $F(t)$ which can be expressed as

$$F(t) = M_a\ddot{z}(t) + B_a\dot{z}(t) + K_a z(t) + F_c(t) \tag{2}$$

where $F_c(t)$ is the "circulatory" part of $F(t)$. The matrices M_a, B_a and K_a can be computed in terms of the parameters of the structure, and the air flow, see e.g. [3], [8], [14], [17], [18].

According to Theodorsen's formulation, $F_c(t)$ can be expressed in the frequency domain as (cf. [17] pp. 395–396, or [14] pp. 26–28)

$$\widehat{F}_c(s) = T(s)(b_1c_1 + sb_1c_2)\widehat{z}(s) \tag{3}$$

where s is the Laplace transform variable, $\widehat{\ }$ represents the Laplace transformed version of a time signal, $T(j\omega)$ is the Theodorsen's function, and b_1, c_1, c_2 are known constant vectors (3×1, 1×3 and 1×3 respectively), see [16] and [18] for the exact values of these vectors and Theodorsen's function. The vectors b_1, c_1 and c_2 depend on the properties of the structure and the flow. Let

$$y(t) := c_1 z(t) + c_2\dot{z}(t)$$

be the measured output of the system. Then, taking the Laplace transforms of (1) and (2), and then using (3) we obtain a transfer function from u to y, denoted by $P(s)$:

$$\frac{\widehat{y}(s)}{\widehat{u}(s)} = P(s) = \frac{C_o(sI - A)^{-1}B_o}{1 - C_o(sI - A)^{-1}B_1\ T(s)} \tag{4}$$

where $C(s)$ is the Theodorsen's function, and

$$A = \begin{bmatrix} 0_{3\times 3} & I_{3\times 3} \\ (M_s - \frac{M_a}{m_s})^{-1}(\frac{K_a}{m_s} - K_s) & (M_s - \frac{M_a}{m_s})^{-1}(\frac{B_a}{m_s} - B_s) \end{bmatrix}$$

$$C_o = [c_1 \quad c_2]\,, \quad B_1 = \begin{bmatrix} 0_{3\times 1} \\ (M_s - \frac{M_a}{m_s})^{-1}b_1 \end{bmatrix}\,, \quad B_o = \begin{bmatrix} 0_{3\times 1} \\ (M_s - \frac{M_a}{m_s})^{-1}G \end{bmatrix}$$

Note that the plant can be seen as a feedback system whose feedback path consists of the aerodynamics represented by Theodorsen's function, as shown in Figure 2.

In practice $T(s)$, which represents an infinite dimensional system, is approximated by a low order rational function, say $T_a(s)$. This leads to a finite dimensional approximate model for the plant to be controlled

$$P_f(s) = \frac{C_o(sI - A)^{-1}B_o}{1 - C_o(sI - A)^{-1}B_1\ T_a(s)}.$$

In [16] approximation of T by a second order rational function T_a has been discussed in detail, and the L^∞ error bounds (i.e. $\|T - T_a\|_\infty = \sup_\omega |T(j\omega) - T_a(j\omega)|$) in several approximation methods have been compared. In the next section we design a feedback controller for $P_f(s)$, which is guaranteed to stabilize both $P_f(s)$ and $P(s)$. The main tools used are the H^∞ control techniques.

3 Stabilization by a finite dimensional controller

Let us consider the thin airfoil model obtained above. When flutter occurs the plant $P(s)$ is unstable, and we would like to design a feedback controller stabilizing the closed loop system, shown in Figure 3. In our design we will consider a stable finite dimensional T_a (see e.g. [16] for the exact numerical values of the coefficients of T_a). This will give us an approximate plant model P_f. A robustly stabilizing finite dimensional controller $K_f(s)$ will be obtained from P_f, and it will be shown that under a certain condition, this controller stabilizes the original infinite dimensional airfoil model, with a certain robustness level.

Consider the finite dimensional approximate plant

$$P_f(s) = \frac{C_o(sI - A)^{-1}B_o}{1 - C_o(sI - A)^{-1}B_1\ T_a(s)}.$$

We can find rational transfer functions $N_1, N_2, M \in H^\infty$ such that

$$C_o(sI - A)^{-1}B_o = \frac{N_o(s)}{M(s)} \quad \text{and} \quad C_o(sI - A)^{-1}B_1 = \frac{N_1(s)}{M(s)}.$$

Therefore, we can express P and P_f in the form

$$P_f(s) = \frac{N_o(s)}{M(s) - N_1(s)T_a(s)} \qquad P(s) = \frac{N_o(s)}{M(s) - N_1(s)T(s)}.$$

Thus, P and P_f differ in their denominator, in the sense that

$$P(s) = \frac{N_p(s)}{M_p(s)} \quad \text{and} \quad P_f(s) = \frac{N_p(s)}{M_f(s)}$$

where $N_p(s) = N_o(s)$, $M_p(s) = M(s) - N_1(s)T(s)$, $M_f(s) = M_p(s) + \Delta_M(s)$, and $\Delta_M(s) = N_1(s)(T(s) - T_a(s))$. Let ϵ_a be an upper bound of the L^∞ approximation error for Theodorsen's function, i.e. $\|T - T_a\|_\infty < \epsilon_a$. In [16] it was shown that a second order rational function T_a, (see Section 5 for the precise definition of $T_a(s)$) gives an error bound $\epsilon_a = 0.012$.

Lemma 1: A controller K_f stabilizing P_f and achieving an H^∞ performance level

$$\gamma(K_f) = \|N_1 M_f^{-1}(1 + P_f K_f)^{-1}\|_\infty \tag{5}$$

stabilizes the infinite dimensional plant P if

$$\epsilon_a \gamma(K_f) \le 1\,. \tag{6}$$

Proof: A controller K_f stabilizes the closed loop system with the plant P if and only if $S = (1 + PK_f)^{-1}$, PS, $K_f S \in H^\infty$, [9]. Since K_f stabilizes P_f, it has to be in the form $K_f = \frac{X + M_f Q}{Y - N_p Q}$ for some $X, Y, Q \in H^\infty$, such that $N_p X + M_f Y = 1$, see e.g. [9], [11]. Then, the sensitivity function of the feedback system with controller K_f and the actual plant P is of the form

$$S = \frac{1}{1 + PK_f} = \frac{(M_f + \Delta_M)(Y - N_p Q)}{1 + \Delta_M(Y - N_p Q)}.$$

From this expression we get

$$\begin{aligned} K_f S &= \frac{(M_f + \Delta_M)(X + M_f Q)}{1 + \Delta_M(Y - N_p Q)} \\ PS &= \frac{N_p(Y - N_p Q)}{1 + \Delta_M(Y - N_p Q)}. \end{aligned}$$

Hence, $S, K_f S, PS \in H^\infty$ if, (see e.g. [7], [9])

$$\|\, \Delta_M(Y - N_p Q)\, \|_\infty < 1. \tag{7}$$

Since $|\Delta_M(j\omega)| < \epsilon_a |N_1(j\omega)|$, the inequality (7) holds if

$$\epsilon_a \,\|\, N_1(Y - N_p Q)\, \|_\infty \le 1$$

On the other hand, it is easy to see that

$$N_1(Y - N_p Q) = N_1 M_f^{-1}(1 + P_f K_f)^{-1} = \gamma(K_f). \qquad \square$$

The controller K_f^{opt}, which minimizes $\gamma(K_f)$ over all controllers stabilizing P_f, has the best chance of satisfying (6). That is, if we define

$$\gamma_{opt} := \inf_{K_f \ stabilizing \ P_f} \gamma(K_f) =: \gamma(K_f^{opt}),$$

then the controller K_f^{opt} stabilizes P_f, and all plants of the form P, whose approximation error ($\epsilon_a = \|T - T_a\|_\infty$) satisfies

$$\epsilon_a \le \gamma_{opt}^{-1}.$$

4 Gust alleviation problem

In this section we would like to outline a mixed H^2/H^∞ control approach to the gust alleviation problem. We can model the gust as a disturbance in the flow. Therefore, gust enters the mathematical model in the computation of aerodynamic loads. Following [2] we can think that $F(t)$ is perturbed by a term $n_g(t)$ which is the output of a filtered white noise, i.e.

$$n_g(t) = \int_0^t W_g(t - \tau)w(\tau)d\tau,$$

where w is white Gaussian with unit spectral density, and $\widehat{W}_g(s)$ is a 3×1 filter shaping the spectral density of the gust. The term $n_g(t)$ modifies the equation (1) governing the airfoil motion in such a way that we now have

$$\widehat{y}(s) = P(s)\widehat{u}(s) + \frac{C_o(sI - A)^{-1}A_1\widehat{W}_g(s)}{1 - C_o(sI - A)^{-1}B_1 T(s)}\ \widehat{w}(s)$$

where $A_1 = \frac{1}{m_s}\begin{bmatrix} 0_{3\times 3} \\ (M_s - \frac{M_a}{m_s})^{-1} \end{bmatrix}$. We would like to "minimize" the effect of the gust on the system output, i.e. the output energy is to be minimized when the system is excited by the gust. The feedback controller generates the command signal: $\widehat{u}(s) = -K_f(s)\widehat{y}(s)$. Therefore, we want to minimize the energy of $z_{reg} := y$ over all controllers K_f stabilizing the closed loop system. That is we want to minimize

$$\gamma_2(K_f) := \|(1 + PK_f)^{-1} \frac{C_o(sI - A)^{-1}A_1\widehat{W}_g(s)}{1 - C_o(sI - A)^{-1}B_1T(s)}\|_2 = \|z_{reg}\|_2 \quad (8)$$

while keeping the closed loop system stable. It can be shown that the feedback system is equivalent to the system shown in Figure 4, where $\Delta_T(s) = T(s) - T_a(s)$.

Now consider the closed loop system shown in Figure 5, where the outer loop containing Δ_T in Figure 4 has been ignored. In this system the output to be regulated is denoted by z_1, and the command signal is represented by u_1. After some algebraic manipulations, it can be shown that

$$\|z_{reg}\|_2 \leq \frac{1}{1 - \epsilon_a\|\frac{C_o(sI-A)^{-1}B_1}{1+C_o(sI-A)^{-1}B_oK_f(s)-C_o(sI-A)^{-1}B_1T_a(s)}\|_\infty}\|z_1\|_2. \quad (9)$$

Note that

$$\left\|\frac{C_o(sI - A)^{-1}B_1}{1 + C_o(sI - A)^{-1}B_oK_f(s) - C_o(sI - A)^{-1}B_1T_a(s)}\right\|_\infty = \gamma(K_f).$$

Hence, we conclude that if $\epsilon_a\ \gamma(K_f) \ll 1$, then $\|z_{reg}\|_2 \approx \|z_1\|_2$.

Let us now modify the system shown in Figure 5, by adding two more external inputs: measurement noise n (white, uncorrolated with w) and input disturbance v (deterministic, whose energy is bounded), see Figure 6, where $W_n(s)$ is a weighting function for n. It is easy to see that

$$\epsilon_a\ \gamma(K_f) = \|S_{z_1 \leftarrow v}\|_\infty,$$

where $S_{z_1\leftarrow v}$ denotes the transfer function from v to z_1. Let us now define

$$\gamma_2' := \|S_{\begin{bmatrix} z_1 \\ ru_1 \end{bmatrix} \leftarrow \begin{bmatrix} w \\ n \end{bmatrix}}\|_2$$

and

$$\gamma_\infty' := \|S_{\begin{bmatrix} z_1 \\ ru_1 \end{bmatrix} \leftarrow v}\|_\infty$$

for some $0 < r \ll 1$.

Lemma 2: A finite dimensional controller K_f stabilizing the finite dimensional feedback system shown in Figure 6 stabilizes the original infinite dimensional plant P, if $\gamma_\infty' < 1$. Furthermore, this controller guarantees that

$$\|z_{reg}\|_2 \leq \frac{\gamma_2'}{1 - \gamma_\infty'} =: \gamma_{z_{reg}}, \quad (10)$$

i.e. the energy of gust response is bounded by $\gamma_{z_{reg}}$.

Proof. From Lemma 1 we have that K_f stabilizes P if $\epsilon_a\gamma(K_f) < 1$. But, $\epsilon_a\gamma(K_f) \leq \gamma_\infty'$. Hence K_f stabilizes P if $\gamma_\infty' < 1$. On the other hand, by (9) we know that

$$\|z_{reg}\|_2 \leq \frac{1}{1 - \gamma_\infty'}\|z_1\|_2.$$

It is also easy to see that $\|z_1\|_2 \leq \gamma_2'$. □

Note that as $r \to 0$, and $W_n \to 0$ we have $\gamma_2' \to \|z_1\|_2$.

In summary, for robust stability and gust alleviation we want to design a controller K_f so that $\gamma_\infty' < 1$, and $\gamma_{z_{reg}}$ is minimized. It is obvious that $\gamma_\infty' \geq \epsilon_a\gamma_{opt}$. Intuitively speaking if we try to make γ_∞' small (i.e. close to $\epsilon_a\gamma_{opt}$) then the resulting γ_2' can be very large. In this case even though $\frac{1}{1-\gamma_\infty'}$ is small $\gamma_{z_{reg}}$ can be large. Converesely, if we try to minimize γ_2', then γ_∞' can be close to 1, and again $\gamma_{z_{reg}}$ can be large. Therefore, the optimal (i.e. smallest) value of $\gamma_{z_{reg}}$ corresponds to a γ_∞' value which is between $\epsilon_a\gamma_{opt}$ and 1.

The problem defined above can be solved using an iterative method by computing a mixed H^2/H^∞ controller at each step. The procedure is described below:

1. Choose a number γ slightly larger than $\epsilon_a\gamma_{opt}$.
2. Minimize γ_2' subject to the condition that $\gamma_\infty' < \gamma$.
3. Find the controller corresponding to minimal γ_2' computed in 2.
4. Calculate the actual $\gamma_{z_{reg}}$ for this controller.
5. Go to Step 1, increase γ, and repeat the procedure until $\gamma = 1$.
6. Plot $\gamma_{z_{reg}}$ versus γ; the minimal value of $\gamma_{z_{reg}}$ is the optimal performance.

An important point to remark here is that Step 2 of the above procedure requires minimization of γ_2', under the condition $\gamma_\infty' < \gamma$. This is a *true mixed H^2/H^∞ optimization* problem, for which there is no simple solution. A solution to the modified version of this problem, which minimizes an upper bound of γ_2', is available, see [4] [10] [13] [19], and references therein. Recall that originally we wanted to minimize $\|z_{reg}\|_2$, but it was difficult to do so and we introduced γ_2', which gives an *upper bound* for $\|z_{reg}\|_2$. In the numerical example below, instead of minimizing γ_2', in Step 2 we minimize an upper bound of γ_2' (see [4], [10], [19] for the precise definition of this upper bound, and a discussion on how conservative this bound is) and obtain a controller, from this modified mixed H^2/H^∞ control problem. Then, in Step 4 we can compute the actual γ_2' and γ_∞' corresponding to this controller. This requires computation of the 2-norm and ∞-norm of finite dimensional transfer functions, which can be done easily, see e.g. [6], [9], [11], and references therein for details.

5 Numerical example

We choose following numerical values for the parameters of the thin airfoil shown in Figure 1: (these numerical values were taken from page 18, example 1 of [18]; for more details on the physical significance of these parameters see [18], or [17])

a	$= -0.400$	units of b ,	$\omega_\alpha =$	100.0	rad/sec
b	$= 1.000$	feet ,	$\omega_\beta =$	90.0	rad/sec
c	$= 0.500$	units of b ,	$\omega_h =$	60.0	rad/sec
x_α	$= 0.200$	units of b ,	$r_\alpha =$	0.500	units of b
x_β	$= \frac{1}{80}$	units of b ,	$r_\beta =$	$\sqrt{\frac{1}{160}}$	units of b
ζ_β	$= 0.007$				
ρ	$= 0.031830989$				
V	$= 200.0$	feet/sec			
m_s	$= 1.000$	slugs			

From these parameters, we can compute the system matrices A, B_0, B_1, C_0 based on the equations given in [16]. Then, we need an approximation of $T(s)$, i.e. we need a rational function $T_a(s)$ and an error bound ϵ_a, to obtain a finite dimensional plant model $P_f(s)$. Note that Theodorsen's function is a function of reduced frequency $s = \frac{b}{V}(j\omega)$. In this case, when $b = 1.000$ feet and $V = 200$ feet/sec, we can define, [16],

$$T_a(s) = \frac{(18.6 \times 1.000 \times s/200 + 1)(2.06 \times 1.000 \times s/200 + 1)}{(21.98 \times 1.000 \times s/200 + 1)(3.44 \times 1.000 \times s/200 + 1)}.$$

It was shown that, [16], for this particular choice of T_a we have $\epsilon_a = 0.012$.

Using the above second order stable T_a, we can now obtain our approximate plant as

$$P_f(s) = K\left(\frac{\prod_{i=1}^{7}(s-z_i)}{\prod_{j=1}^{8}(s-p_i)}\right) \qquad \text{where,}$$

$K = 1352.1$

$z_1 = -711.80$	$p_1 = -74.86 + 80.28i$
$z_2 = -58.14$	$p_2 = -74.86 - 80.28i$
$z_3 = -28.67$	$p_3 = -36.28$
$z_4 = -9.10$	$p_4 = -22.40 + 106.81i$
$z_5 = 28.70$	$p_5 = -22.40 - 106.81i$
$z_6 = 0.32 + 68.08i$	$p_6 = -7.96$
$z_7 = 0.32 - 68.08i$	$p_7 = 17.84 + 89.45i$
	$p_8 = 17.84 - 89.45i$

Note that the plant is non-minimum phase and unstable. For this numerical example, γ_{opt} defined in (8) can be computed as, see e.g. [1],

$$\gamma_{opt} = 2.7590.$$

Let us now consider the gust alleviation problem with

$$\widehat{W}_g(s) = \begin{bmatrix}1\\1\\1\end{bmatrix}\frac{20}{s+20}, \qquad W_n(s) = \frac{0.02\,s}{s+0.01}$$

and $r = 0.001$. We follow the procedure described in Section 4. In Step 2 of our procedure, we apply the results of [4] [10] [19] to minimize *an upper bound* of γ_2', subject to $\gamma_\infty' < \gamma$, for each fixed γ. A plot of $\gamma_{z_{reg}}$ versus γ is given in Figure 7 for $1 > \gamma > \epsilon_a\gamma_{opt} = 0.035$. We see that the minimum occurs at $\gamma = 0.056$, and for this value of γ we find that $\gamma_\infty' = 0.0544$, $\gamma_2' = 0.4892$ and $\gamma_{z_{reg}} = 0.5174$. The controller which corresponds to these numbers is given by:

$$K_f(s) = K\left(\frac{\prod_{i=1}^{9}(1-s/z_i)}{\prod_{j=1}^{10}(1-s/p_j)}\right) \qquad \text{where}$$

$K = -0.1249$

$z_1 = -208.4 + 1.32j$	$p_1 = -1352318$
$z_2 = -208.4 - 1.32j$	$p_2 = -711.8$
$z_3 = -8.90 + 72.28j$	$p_3 = -146.3$
$z_4 = -8.90 - 72.28j$	$p_4 = 1.77 + 68.12j$
$z_5 = -71.47$	$p_5 = 1.77 - 68.12j$
$z_6 = -32.61$	$p_6 = -58.14$
$z_7 = -17.62$	$p_7 = -28.67$
$z_8 = -7.82$	$p_8 = -20.00$
$z_9 = -0.01$	$p_9 = -9.10$
	$p_{10} = -0.0108$

This controller guarantees that the closed loop system, with finite dimensional controller K_f and the infinite dimensional plant P, is stable because

$$\epsilon_a\gamma(K_f) = \|S_{z_1\leftarrow v}\|_\infty < \gamma_\infty' = 0.0544 \ll 1.$$

Moreover, it gives a performance bound:

$$\|S_{z_{reg}\leftarrow w}\|_2 < \gamma_{z_{reg}} = 0.5174.$$

A plot of $|S_{z_1\leftarrow w}(j\omega)|$ versus ω is shown in Figure 7. This figure shows that the closed loop system passes only the low frequency (less than 10^3 rad/sec) content of the disturbance w with an amplification less than 0.07 (i.e. the attenuation level is greater than $\frac{1}{0.07} \approx 23$ dB).

6 Concluding remarks

In this paper we have considered a thin airfoil model, which is infinite dimensional. We have shown that a finite dimensional controller stabilizing this system can be obtained by solving a one block H^∞ control problem. A sufficient condition for such a controller K_f to stabilize the plant P is $\gamma(K_f) \le 1/\epsilon_a$, where $\gamma(K_f)$ depends only on the finite dimensional plant P_f, and ϵ_a is the L^∞ error in the approximation of Theodorsen's function. In Section 5 we have shown a numerical example illustrating this approach.

The gust alleviation problem is formulated in the framework of the mixed H^2/H^∞ control problem, where the plant to be controlled is finite dimensional. It can be seen from the discussion of Section 4 that the original gust alleviation problem becomes the same as the mixed H^2/H^∞ control problem defined in the paper if $W_n \to 0$, $r \to 0$ and $\epsilon_a\gamma(K_f) \to 0$. Although W_n and r can be made arbitrarily small, we need $W_n \ne 0$ and $r \ne 0$, in order to have a well-posed mixed H^2/H^∞ problem. In Section 5 we have used certain results on mixed H^2/H^∞ control (e.g. [4], [10], [19]) to give a numerical example for the gust alleviation procedure outlined in Section 4.

References

[1] G. R. Bachmann, *Robust Control Design Techniques for the Active Control of an Aeroelastic System*, M.S. thesis, The Ohio State University, Autumn 1992.

[2] A. V. Balakrishnan, "Active control of airfoils in unsteady aerodynamics," *Applied Math. and Optimization*, **4** (1978), pp. 171–195.

[3] A. V. Balakrishnan and J. W. Edwards, "Calculation of the transient motion of elastic airfoils forced by control surface motion and gusts," NASA Technical Memorandum 81351, August 1980.

[4] D. S. Bernstein and W. M. Haddad, "LGQ control with an H_∞ performance bound: a Riccati equation approach," *IEEE Transactions on Automatic Control*, **34** (1989), pp. 293–305.

[5] R. L. Bisplinghoff, H. Ashley and R. Halfman, *Aeroelasticity*, Addison-Wesley, Cambridge, 1955.

[6] Bruinsma, N.A. and M. Steinbuch, "A fast algorithm to compute the H^∞-norm of a transfer function matrix", *Systems and Control Letters*, **14** pp. 287-293.

[7] M. J. Chen and C. A. Desoer, "Necessary and sufficient condition for robust stability of linear distributed feedback systems," *Int. J. Control*, **35** (1982), pp. 255–267.

[8] E. H. Dowell, H. C. Curtiss Jr., R. H. Scanlan, and F. Sisto, *A Modern Course in Aeroelasticity*, Kluwer Academic Publishers, Dordrecht, 1989.

[9] J. C. Doyle, B. A. Francis and A. R. Tannenbaum, *Feedback Control Theory*, Macmillan New York, 1992.

[10] J. C. Doyle, K. Zhou, and B. Bodenheimer,"Optimal Control with Mixed H_2 and H^∞ Performance Objectives," Proc. of the American Control Conference, Pittsburgh PA, June 1989, pp. 2065-2070.

[11] B. A. Francis, *A Course in H_∞ Control Theory*, Springer-Verlag, New York, 1987.

[12] G. L. Ghiringhelli, M. Lanz and P. Mantegazza, "Active flutter suppression for a wing model," *AIAA Journal of Aircraft*, **27** (1990), pp. 334–341.

[13] P. P. Khargonekar and M. A. Rotea, "Mixed H_2/H_∞ control: a convex optimization approach," *IEEE Transactions on Automatic Control*, **36** (1991), pp. 824–837.

[14] R. L. Moore, *Aeroservoelastic Stability Analysis of an Airplane with a Control Augmentation System*, PhD dissertation, The Ohio State University, 1978.

[15] V. Mukhopadhyay, "Flutter suppression digital control law design and testing for the AFW tunnel model," NASA Workshop on Distributed Parameter Modeling and Control of Flexible Aerospace Systems, Williamsburg VA, 1992.

[16] H. Özbay and G. R. Bachmann, "Robust control design techniques for active flutter suppression," NASA Workshop on Distributed Parameter Modeling and Control of Flexible Aerospace Systems, Williamsburg VA, 1992.

[17] R. H. Scanlan and R. Rosenbaum, *Introduction to the Study of Aircraft Vibration and Flutter*, Macmillan, New York, 1951.

[18] T. Theodorsen, "General Theory of Aerodynamic Instability and the Mechanism of Flutter," *National Advisory Committee for Aeronautics Report* **496**(1935).

[19] H-H. Yeh, S. S. Banda, B-C. Chang, "Necessary and sufficient conditions for mixed H_2 and H_∞ optimal control," Proc. of the 29th Conference on Decision and Control, Honolulu Hawaii, December 1990, pp. 1013–1017.

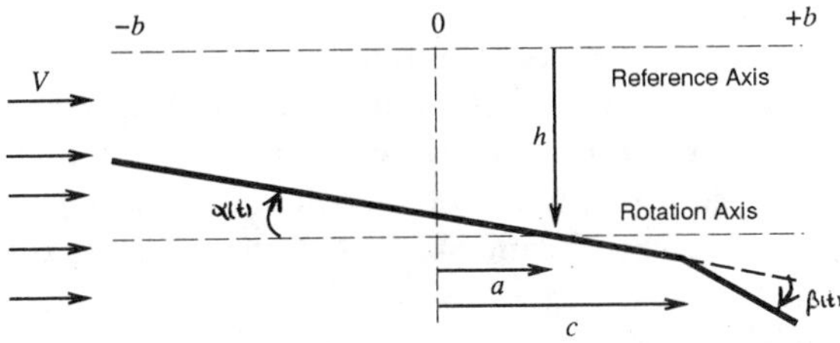

Figure 1: Thin airfoil

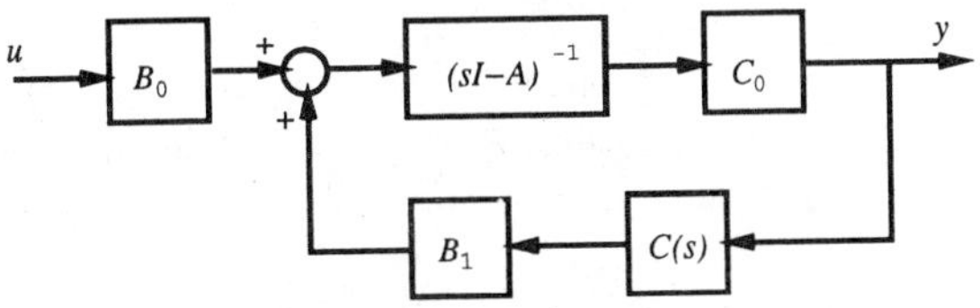

Figure 2: Structure of the plant

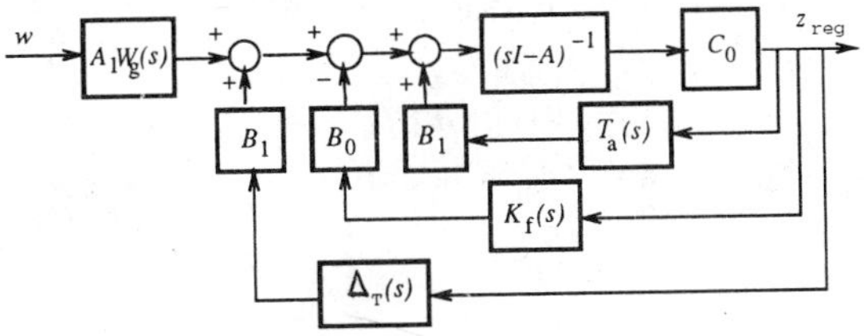

Figure 3: Feedback system

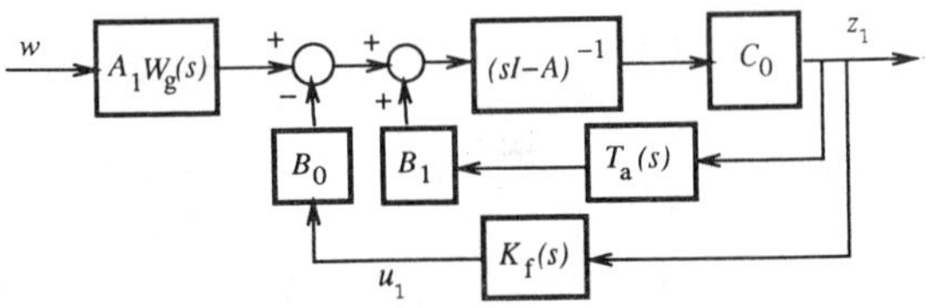

Figure 4: Modified feedback system: Δ_T ignored

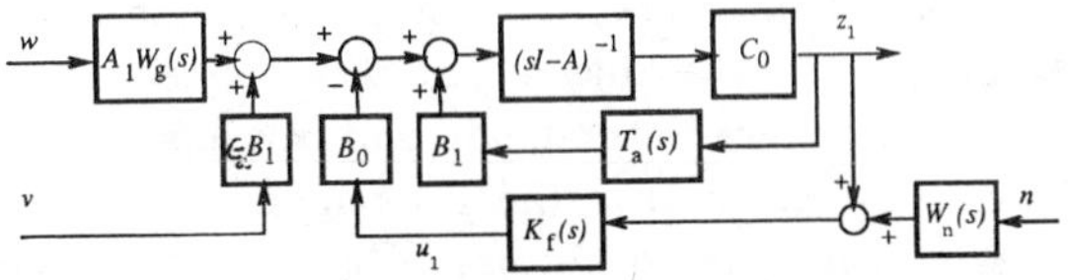

Figure 5: Modified feedback systemwith v and n

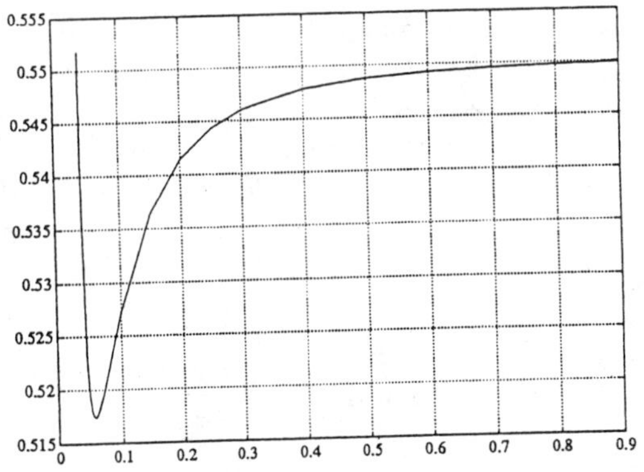

Figure 6: $\gamma_{z_{reg}}$ versus γ

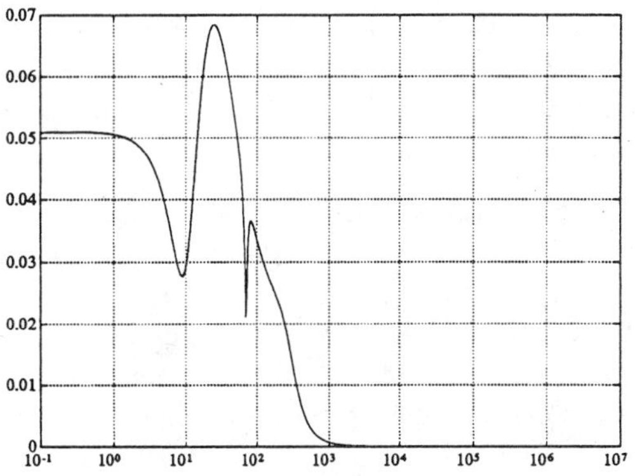

Figure 7: Magnitude Plot of $|S_{z_1 \leftarrow w}(j\omega)|$

WA1 - 10:15

Proceedings of th
American Control Conferenc
San Francisco, California • June 199

SERVO DESIGN FOR A LASER 3D MEASUREMENT SYSTEM

Jia-Yush Yen
Associate Professor

Chao-Si Jeng
Graduate Student

Department of Mechanical Engineering,
National Taiwan University, Taipei, Taiwan, R.O.C.

Abstract

The servo design of a laser 3-D measurement system is discussed in this paper. The laser 3-D measurement system uses two sets of tracking mirrors to reflect laser beams loward a retro reflector attached to the measurement object. The servo system checks the offset of the reflected beam and corrects the mirror orientations so that the laser lights will always follow the measurement point. By applying inverse kinematics to the mirro rotation angles, one can then calculate the position of the target point. The system is a highly nonlinear system. Usual servo design specifications do not apply. In this paper, we derived the relationship between the tracking angle rotations and the measured beam offsets. By including this relationship in our model the H_∞ optimization technique can by applied for controller synthesis. All the design specifications are then directly implemented. Experiments are performed to verify the results.

1 Introduction

This paper addresses the servo technology for the laser three-dimensional (3-D) measurement systems. The laser 3-D measurement system is mainly used for the direct non-contact measurement of the end point position of robot manipulators. Since the measurement is direct from the target point, it is used for off-line system calibration as well as for real time position measurement. As the use of the robot manipulators becomes popular in the manufacturing industry, the 3-D measurement system also becomes an interesting topic for research and development.

The design of the 3-D laser tracking measurement system can be divided into single station [7,10] and multi-station method [6]. The single station approach uses a laser interferometer for distance detection, and the multi-station approach utilizes kinematic relationship for calculating the distance. The same servo mechanism is used in both systems, except one servo system is required for each station. Therefore, the same servo problems are attacked in both approaches. In this paper, the servo design of a two station laser tracking system is discussed. In the two station laser tracking measurement system, two laser beams are directed toward the the measurement point by bouncing them off two sets of rotating mirrors. By examining the rotation angles of these mirrors, the 3-D position of the point can be calculated from the geometric relationship among the stations and the measurement point. In order to track a moving target, the servo systems have to aim the laser beams toward the point and keep the tracking error at a minimum level at all time. Traditional approach take the sensor signal from the reflected laser light as feedback information and use a P-I-D algorithm for the controller design [2]. This approach will work for target points moving at low speeds; however, it is cautioned that the tracking mirror is used merely to reflect the laser beams, which means the laser beam offset may not reflect the required angular error directly. The system thus becomes nonlinear, and the specifications for the servo design can only be examined by a trial and error method. In addition, the ratio between the measured beam offset and the required angular movement changes with the distance from the target point to the tracking mirrors. Without compensation for the nonlinearity, the controller will only work for some unpredicted range around the measurement system. In this paper, the relationship between the measured beam offset and the desired mirror motion are derived. It is shown that the servo system becomes a linear system when this relationship is included. All the modern controller design technique can now be applied. In the paper, the H_∞ optimization technique is used for the controller design of the servo motor driver. Experimental results show that the performance has improved from only tracking slow motion targets to tracking a point moving with a 2 to $4Hz$ oscillation.

In this paper, we will skip the well known kinematic relationship and describe only the servo design of the

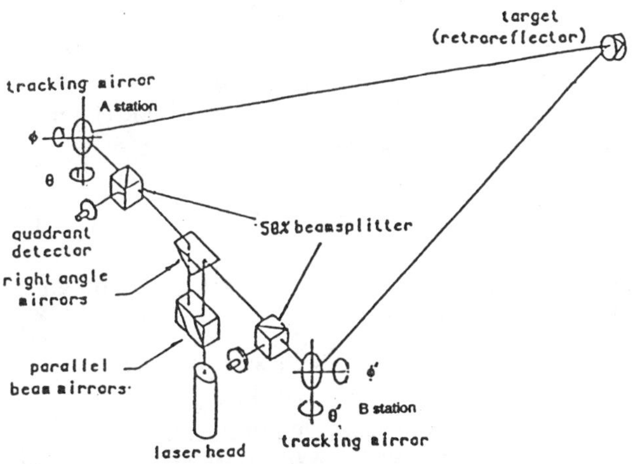

Figure 1: 3-D laser tracking measurement system

system.

2 System Descriptions

In this section, the physical configuration of the system will be described. As shown in Fig.1, the two station 3-D laser tracking measurement system uses two sets of tracking lasers to locate the position of the target point. A $1mw$ He-Ne laser with $5mm$ beam waist is used for the laser source. Since the quadrature sensor might not maintain linear output if the brightened area is too small, the wide beam waist helps to maintain sensor linearity. The laser beam from the source is sent through a beam divider to obtain two parallel and equal intensity laser beams which are $32.61mm$ apart. These beam are then passed through a $25.4mm$ 50% beam splitter and then directed toward the target point by bouncing them off two sets of tracking mirrors. A retro reflector is attached to the target point so that the laser beams can be reflected along paths parallel to the incoming beams back to the tracking mirrors. These reflected beams will now be reflected from the 50% beam splitter and into the quadrature sensor for signal feedback. By examining the offset between the incoming beam and the reflected beam, the orientation of the tracking mirror can be adjusted. For each tracking mirror, there are two sets of servo motors to drive it in the horizontal and vertical direction so that it will face any desired orientation in the space. The laser lights basically impose no loading on the motor. Therefore, very small torques are required to drive the mirrors. Nevertheless, large ratio harmonic drives are still desired so that high accuracy targeting can be achieved.

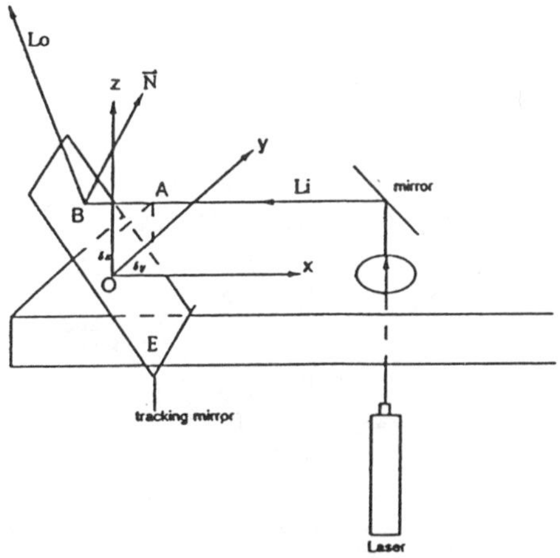

Figure 2: Coordinate systems for the reflecting mirrors

3 Sensor Relationship

The quadrature sensor senses the position of the reflected laser beam on the sensor plate. i.e. the distance of the illuminated spot from the center. The correction of the offset is based on the following rules: Referring to Fig.1, when the reflected beam falls in the first quadrature, then the horizon motor should turn right and the vertical motor should also turn right. The situations for the rest of the quadratures are similar. Notice that the offset measured by the quadrature sensor may not be the same as the actual offset between the tracking beam and reflected beam.

The bold face characters will represent vector quantities. The simple geometry yields the relationship between the measured beam offset and the required rotation angle. The $X - Y - Z$ coordinate vectors will be denoted by a hat above. Upper case characters represent straight lines in space, and calligraphic characters will be used to represent planes. Referring to Fig.2, let the positive X axis be pointing toward the direction of the normal of the tr acking mirror with the mirror facing the direction toward which the incident laser from the source coincides with the reflected laser. Let the Z axis be pointing upward, and let the Y axis be defined by the right hand rule. Since the laser beams travel at light speed, only static relationship needs to be considered. Two assumptions are made for the derivation:

1. The rotation axes for the horizontal and vertical driving motor intercept with each other orthogonally. (This is a practical assumption since the assembly tolerance demand the distance to be smaller than $\pm 0.01mm$.) The intercepting point is then defined to be the origin of the $X - Y - Z$ coordinate.

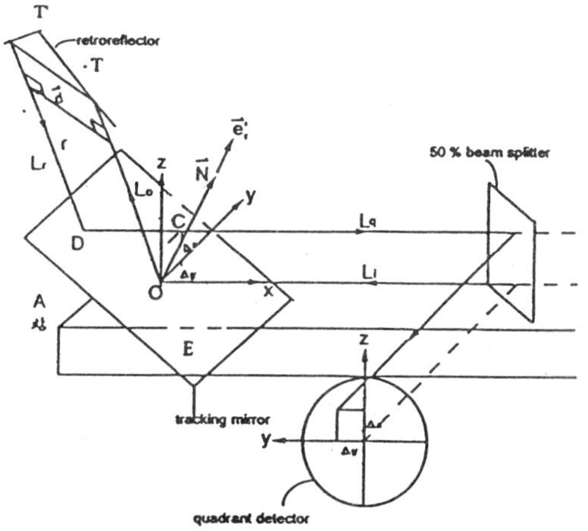

Figure 3: Relationship between $\mathbf{d}$ and Δy, Δz

2. Referring to Fig.2, the reflecting surface of the tracking mirror passes through the intercepting point of the vertical and horizontal rotation axes of the mirror (the origin of the coordinate system).

Consider the station A in Fig.1. Let the incident beam be L_i and the reflected beam be L_o. The symbol $\mathbf{L}_i$ denotes the direction vector of the incident beam, and $\mathbf{L}_o$ denotes the direction vector of the reflected beam. The rotation angle of the in the vertical direction will be denoted by ϕ, and the rotation angle in the horizontal direction will be denoted by θ. The unit normal vector become $\mathbf{e}_n$ $= [\cos\phi\cos\phi \;\; \cos\phi\sin\theta \;\; \sin\phi]$. Suppose the incident light intercept with the $Y-Z$ plant at $(0, \delta y, \delta z)$. Let $\mathcal{F}$ be the plane defined by L_i and L_o. Let $\mathbf{d}$ be the offset between the tracking and the reflected laser beams, and let L_i' and L_o' be the reflected light for the retro reflector and then from the mirror, respectively. Take the direction of the incoming laser as $\mathbf{L}_i = -\hat{i}$. From Fig.3 and some geometry yields the unit vector along L_o, $\mathbf{e}_r$, and the unit vector perpendicular to $\mathbf{e}_n$ in $\mathcal{F}$, $\mathbf{e}_t$

$$\mathbf{e}_r = [1 - 2\cos^2\theta\cos^2\phi \quad -2\cos\theta\cos^2\phi\sin\theta \tag{1}$$

$$-2\cos\theta\sin\phi\cos\phi],$$

$$\mathbf{e}_b = [0 \quad \frac{\sin\phi}{M} \quad \frac{-\cos\phi\sin\theta}{M}], \tag{2}$$

$$\mathbf{e}_t = \frac{1}{M}[\sin^2\phi + \sin^2\theta\cos^2\phi \tag{3}$$

$$-\sin\theta\cos\theta\cos^2\phi \quad -\cos\theta\sin\phi\cos\phi].$$

where $M = \sqrt{\sin^2\phi + \cos^2\phi\sin^2\theta}$. The relation between the plane $\mathcal{F}$, the incoming beam offset $\mathbf{d}_i$, and the outgoing beam offset $\mathbf{d}_o$ can be derived as

$$\mathbf{d}_i \cdot \mathbf{e}_n = \mathbf{d}_o \cdot \mathbf{e}_n, \;\; \mathbf{d}_i \cdot \mathbf{e}_t = -\mathbf{d}_o \cdot \mathbf{e}_t, \;\; \mathbf{d}_i \cdot \mathbf{e}_b = \mathbf{d}_o \cdot \mathbf{e}_b. \tag{4}$$

In our setup the sensor plat is in the $X-Y$ plane. The measurement on the sensor will be $\mathbf{d}_m = [\Delta x \;\; \Delta y \;\; 0]$.

This measurement comes from the 50% beam splitter. Thus, for the beam splitter, $\theta = 0$ and $\phi = 45°$. From (4), the plane normal component of the offset can be obtained by $d_o^\theta = \mathbf{d}_o \cdot \mathbf{e}_\theta$.

$$d_o^\theta = \frac{1}{M}(\Delta y \sin\phi - \Delta z \sin\theta\cos\phi). \tag{5}$$

The vertical component of the offset can be obtained by $d_o^\phi d = \mathbf{d}_o \cdot \mathbf{e}_\phi$.

$$d_o^\phi = \Delta y \sin\theta\sin 2\phi - \Delta z\cos 2\phi. \tag{6}$$

The desired motor rotation angle can now be calculated. Notice that these offsets are usually double the amount of the desired correction. Assuming these errors are small. We have

$$\Delta\phi \approx \tan\Delta\phi = \frac{|\, d_o^\phi \,|}{2r} \tag{7}$$

$$= \frac{\Delta y}{2r}\sin\theta\sin 2\phi - \frac{\Delta z}{2r}\cos 2\phi.$$

$$\Delta\theta \approx \tan\Delta\theta = \frac{|\, d_o^\theta \,|}{2r} \tag{8}$$

$$= \frac{\Delta y}{2rM}\sin\phi - \frac{\Delta z}{2rM}\sin\theta\cos\phi.$$

4 Servo System Design and Implementation

Since the mirror is mounted symmetrically on the horizontal motor, the orientation of the mirror does not change the inertia loading on both motors. In addition, the tracking mirrors are used to reflected the laser light to the target retro reflector. There is no interference between the two mirror.

System Identification

The motor system transfer functions are each experimentally identified. The vertical motors are identified with the horizontal motor mounted and with zero input. As discussed before, the position of the horizontal motor does not change the vertical motor inertia. In order to guarantee persistent excitation, a white noise signal is generated in the computer by the MATLAB white noise function and this signal is used as the input u_d to the motor driver. The Box-Jenkins model is used for the identification. Notice that the servo motor from the input voltage signal to its output angular position is a 3rd order system. A 5th order transfer function is used for the noise model. Due to space limitation the identification results will not be shown.

Controller Design

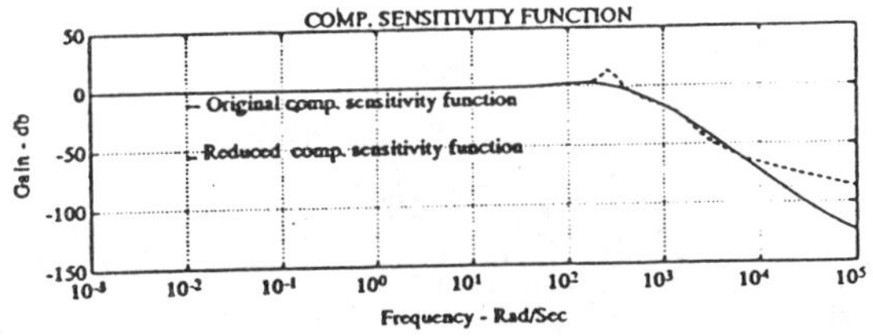

Figure 4: Vertical motor servo closed-loop response

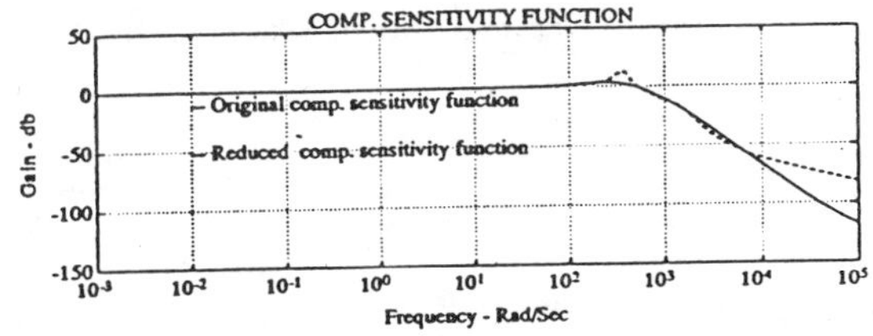

Figure 5: Horizontal motor servo closed-loop response

The popular H_∞ optimization technique is employed. The performance weighting is choosen to guarantee $15Hz$ bandwidth and the robustness weighting is choosen to prevent the resonance above $150Hz$ to be excited. Model reduction is performed on the results to obtained a 3rd order controller. Fig.4 shows the resulted closed- loop response for the vertical motor. The controller design for the horizontal motor is shown in Fig.5. The same specifications are applied for both horizontal and vertical motors since the target may move in both directions with equal probability.

5 Controller Implementation

The experimental setup is as shown in Fig.1. The servo system is implemented with a 80188 PGA board and a DC servo motor driver board both designed by Prof. P.J.Tang in National Chau-Tung University, Taiwan. A PC-386 is used for monitoring the system performance and for programming the 80188 CPU. The controller code is first written in the combination of the C-language and the in-line assembly.

Figs.6-9 show the experiment tracking result. The input signal is generated by hand holding the retro reflector and moving it in mid-air. The straight lines at the end of the plots show the situations when the laser tracking system can no longer track the retro reflector. It is observed that the worst case control can achieve $3Hz$ bandwidth. The system performance is also limited on the minimum laser intensity required by the quadrature sensor to be able to make out the beam offset. Better tracking is observed with station B because the laser divider has an uneven division between the two beams and the B station receives higher light intensity.

6 Conclusions

The 3-D laser tracking measurement system finds its application mostly in the robotic end point measurements; however, there are many circumstances such as precision machining, contour check, etc. where dimensional measurement technology will be greatly appreciated. The high performance tracking will soon become important as the application of the system gets its popularity.

In this paper, the Servo design of the 3-D laser tracking measurement system was conducted. The relationship between the quadrature sensor measurement and the required mirror rotation was derived. It was shown that the desired rotation angles of the tracking mirrors depend both on the orientation and the distance of the target point. With the inclusion of this relationship, a linear system model can be obtained. All the well known linear control technique can then be applied. In this paper the popular H_∞ optimization was used for the controller design. It was shown that the frequency domain specifications could be introduced with the linear system model. The experimental tracking performance was also compared with the simulation.

7 Acknowledgments

Thanks to Prof. Pei-Chung Tang in the National Chau-Tung University for making the controller board and the motor driver board available to this experiment. Thanks to Prof. Kwang-Chao Fang for providing with the laser and the calibration equipment and also for his instruction in precision measurement.

References

[1] An,C.H., Atkeson,C.G., Griffiths,J.D., and Hollerbach,J.M., 1987, "Experimental evalution of feedfroward and computer torque control," *Proc. IEEE Int. Conf. on Robotics and Automation*, Raleigh, NC, Mar.31-Apr.3, pp.165-168.

[2] Chen,M.Z., 1989, "Path control of an intelligent robot manipulator," *NSF report No. NSF 78-0422-E002-04*, Taiwan, R.O.C.

[3] Franklin,G.F. Powell,J.D., Workman,M.L., 1990, **Digital Control of Dynamic Systems**, 2nd ed, Addison-Wesley publishing Co.

[4] Gilby,J. and Parker,G., 1982, "Laser tracking system to measure robot arm performance," *Sensor Review*, Oct.

[5] Kasahara,H. and Narita,S., 1985, "Parallel processing of robot-arm control computation on a multimicroprocessor system," *IEEE J. Robotics, Automat.*, Vol.RA-1, June, pp.104-113.

[6] Lau,K.L., Hayness,L., and Hocken,R., 1985, "Robot performance measurements using automatic laser tracking techniques," *Robotics & Computer-Integrated Manufacturing*, pp.227-236.

[7] Lau,K., Hocken,R.J., and Haight,W., 1985, "An automatic laser tracking interferometer system for robot metorlogy," *NBS Report.*

[8] Lee,C.G.S. and Chung,M.J., 1984, "An adaprive control strategy for mechanical manupulators," *IEEE Trans. Automat. Contr.*, Vol.AC-19, pp.837-840.

[9] Lee,C.G.S. and Chang,P.L., 1987, "Efficient parallel algorithms for robot forward dynamic computation," *Proc. IEEE Int. Conf. on Robotics and Automation*, Raleigh, NC, Mar.31-Apr.3, pp.654-659.

[10] LEICA Co., 1990, **SMART 310 introduction menu.**

[11] Ljung,L. and Soderstrom,T., 1987, **Theory and practice of recursive identification**, The MIT Press.

[12] Lhote,F., Kauffmann,J., Andre,P., and Taillard,J., 1983, **Robot components and systems**, Anchor Brendon Ltd, Tiptree, Essex.

[13] Miller III,W.T., Hewes,R.P., Glanz,F.H., and Kraft,III,L.G., 1990, "Real-time dynamic control of an industrial manipulator using a neural-network-based learning controller," *IEEE Trans. on Robotics and Automat.*, Vol.6, No.1, Feb. pp.1-9.

[14] Neuman,C.P. and Tourassia,V.D., 1987, "Robust discrete nonlinear feedback control for robotic manipulators," *J. Robotic Syst.*, Vol.4, Feb., pp.115-143.

[15] Wang,Y. and Butner,S.E., 1987, "A new architucture for robot controls," *Proc. IEEE Int. Conf. on Robotics and Automat.*, Raleigh, NC., Mar.31-Apr.3, pp.664-670.

[16] Whitney,D.E., et al, 1984, "Industrial robot calibration method and results," *Proc. Computer in Engineering*, Vol.I, pp.92-100.

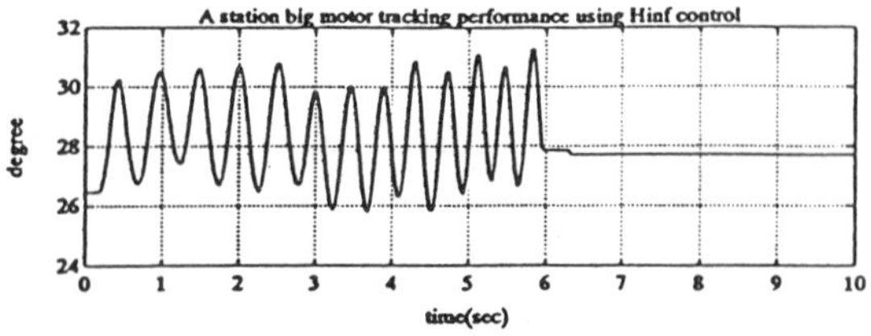

Figure 6: A station vertical motor tracking H_∞ controller

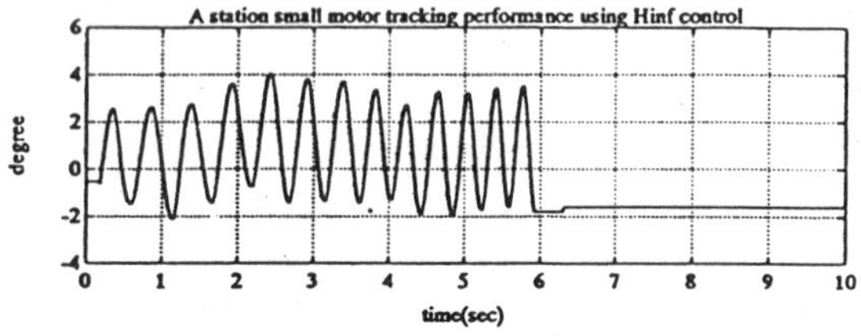

Figure 7: A station horizontal motor tracking H_∞ controller

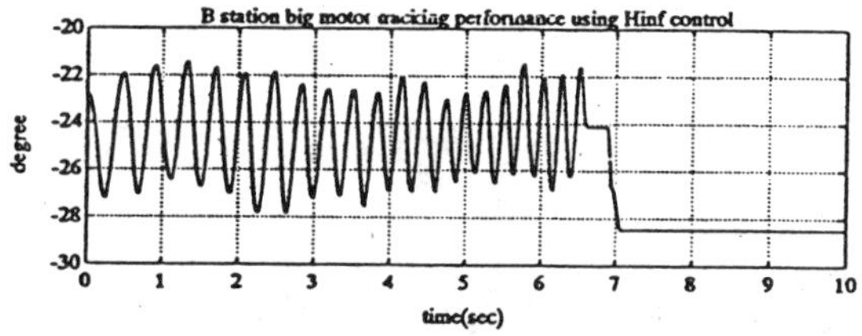

Figure 8: B station vertical motor tracking H_∞ controller

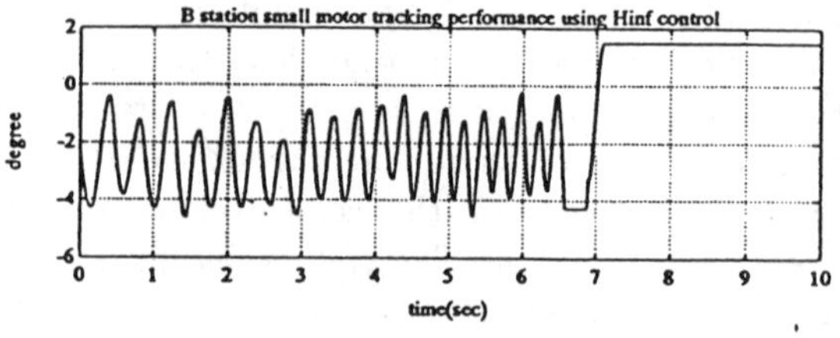

Figure 9: B station Horizontal motor tracking H_∞ controller

Proceedings of the
American Control Conference
San Francisco, California • June 1993

Stability of polynomial families with multiaffine coefficient perturbations

Jacob Kogan
Department of Mathematics and Statistics
University of Maryland, Baltimore County Campus
Baltimore, MD 21228, USA

1. Introduction

In many control applications one is confronted with the following problem: "Given a region Ω in the complex plane, and a family of polynomials $\mathcal{P}$ determine whether or not all the roots of the polynomials are located in Ω." Important examples of the regions Ω are the left half plane, and the unit disc. The famous Kharitonov theorem [K] provides an elegant solution for the problem when the region Ω is the left half plane, and $\mathcal{P}$ contains polynomials whose coefficients are allowed to vary independently in specified intervals.

Numerous results concerning efficient tests for Ω stability of polynomials whose coefficients depend affinely on physical parameters have been derived in recent years. An extraction of a testing subset $\mathcal{P}' \subset \mathcal{P}$, so that the Ω stability of $\mathcal{P}'$ would imply the Ω stability of the whole family $\mathcal{P}$ has been an important objective of the research. The famous Edge Theorem [BHL] is the best known general result concerning this problem.

A number of results concerning technical conditions that lead to the "easily testable" criteria have been reported recently by Polyak [P], Anderson, Kraus, Mansour, Dasgupta [AKMD], and Tsing, Tits [TT]. The goal of this note is to provide robust stability conditions under "minimal assumptions"–our criterion is less conservative, and the results presented in this note are implied by those given in [P], [AKMD], and [TT].

The outline of the paper is as follows. In Section 2 we introduce the basic notations, and state the problem. In Section 3 we consider the image of a box under a multiaffine mapping, and introduce principal vertices of the box. A simple robust stability criterion completes the section. In Section 4 we recall and compare results reported in [P], [AKMD], and [TT].

2. Notations and the problem

In this paper we consider a polynomial family

$$\mathcal{P} = \{a_0(\mathbf{x})+a_1(\mathbf{x})s+\ldots+a_{n-1}(\mathbf{x})s^{n-1}+s^n,\ \mathbf{x}\in \mathbf{B}^m \subseteq R^m\}, \quad (2.1)$$

where $a_i(\mathbf{x})$, $i = 0, 1, \ldots, n-1$ are multiaffine mappings from R^m to R, and $\mathbf{B}^m$ is an m dimensional box, i.e.,

$$\mathbf{B}^m = \{\mathbf{x} : \mathbf{x} \in R^m,\ \underline{x}_i \le x_i \le \overline{x}_i,\ |\underline{x}_i - \overline{x}_i| = \Delta_i > 0,\ i = 1, \ldots, m\}.$$

The set of vertices of the box $\mathbf{B}^m$ is denoted by $\mathbf{V}^m$.

Let an open subset of the complex plane Ω be given. We shall say that the polynomial $\mathbf{p}(s, \mathbf{x})$ is Ω stable if all the roots of the polynomial are located in Ω. The family $\mathcal{P}$ is Ω stable if all the polynomials in $\mathcal{P}$ are Ω stable. Consider a parameterization $\delta : I_\Omega \to \partial\Omega$ of the boundary of Ω (i.e., when, for example, Ω is the open left half plane, then $I_\Omega = (-\infty, \infty)$, and $\delta(w) = jw$; when Ω is the open unit disc, then $I_\Omega = [0, 2\pi)$, and $\delta(w) = e^{jw}$). If for some $\mathbf{x}^0 \in \mathbf{B}^m$ the polynomial $\mathbf{p}(s, \mathbf{x}^0)$ is Ω stable, and for $\mathbf{x}^1 \in \mathbf{B}^m$ the polynomial $\mathbf{p}(s, \mathbf{x}^1)$ has a root outside of Ω, than a simple continuity argument shows the existence of $0 \le \lambda < 1$ so that at least one root of the polynomial $\mathbf{p}(s, \lambda\mathbf{x}^0 + (1-\lambda)\mathbf{x}^1)$ belongs to the boundary $\partial\Omega$ of the domain Ω, i.e.,

$$\text{there exists } w \in I_\Omega \text{ such that } \mathbf{p}(\delta(w), \lambda\mathbf{x}^0 + (1-\lambda)\mathbf{x}^1) = 0. \quad (2.2)$$

Relation (2.2) and the convexity of $\mathbf{B}^m$ yield a basic tool of robustness analysis:

Theorem 2.1. (Zero exclusion criterion, see e.g., [FD].) Let $\mathcal{P}_w = \{\mathbf{p}(\delta(w), \mathbf{x}),\ \mathbf{x} \in \mathbf{B}^m\}$. Suppose that $\mathbf{p}(s, \mathbf{x}^0)$ is Ω stable. The polynomial family $\mathcal{P}$ is Ω stable if and only if

$$\forall w \in I_\Omega \text{ one has } 0 \notin \mathcal{P}_w. \quad (2.3)$$

If, in addition, it is known that $0 \notin \mathcal{P}_{w_0}$ for at least one $w_0 \in I_\Omega$, then (2.3) can be relaxed as follows.

Theorem 2.2. Suppose that $\mathbf{p}(s, \mathbf{x}^0)$ is Ω stable, and there exists $w_0 \in I_\Omega$ such that $0 \notin \mathcal{P}_{w_0}$. The polynomial family $\mathcal{P}$ is Ω stable if and only if

$$\forall w \in I_\Omega \text{ one has } 0 \notin \partial\mathcal{P}_w. \quad (2.4)$$

It is of interest to know when the sets $\partial\mathcal{P}_w$ can be easily described, and simple methods can be devised to determine if they contain the origin. If assumptions of Theorem 2.2 hold, and $\mathcal{P}_{w_0}$ is a convex set, then the stability can only be lost if for some $w \in I_\Omega$ the *outer* boundary of the value set $\mathcal{P}_w$ contains the origin (see e.g., [AKMD]). In the next section we provide simple conditions under which the outer boundary of the value set is a boundary of a polygon.

3. Principal vertices and robust stability

In this section we consider a multiaffine function $f : R^m \to C$, i.e., for each real t one has

$$f(\mathbf{x} + t\mathbf{e}^i) = f(\mathbf{x}) + t\frac{\partial f}{\partial x_i}(\mathbf{x}),\ i = 1, \ldots, m, \quad (3.1)$$

where $\{\mathbf{e}^1, \ldots, \mathbf{e}^m\}$ is the standard orthonormal basis in R^m. We provide conditions under which the set $f(\mathbf{B}^m)$ contains the boundary of its convex hall.

Definition 3.1. Two vertices $\mathbf{v} \ne \mathbf{w}$ are neighboring vertices if there exists an index k so that $v_k \ne w_k$, and $v_i = w_i$, $i \ne k$.

Definition 3.2. A vertex $\mathbf{v}$ is a principal vertex of the box if there exists a half plane that contains all the complex numbers

$$f(\mathbf{w}) - f(\mathbf{v}),\ \mathbf{w} \in \mathbf{V}^m \quad (3.2)$$

Due to the Mapping Theorem [ZD] one has $\operatorname{conv} f(\mathbf{B}^m) = \operatorname{conv} f(\mathbf{V}^m)$. According to Definition 3.2 images of principal vertices belong to the boundary of $\operatorname{conv} f(\mathbf{B}^m)$.

Lemma 3.1. Suppose that $\mathbf{x}$ belongs to the interior of $\mathbf{B}^m$, i.e.,

$$\mathbf{x} = \sum_{i=1}^{2^m} \alpha_i \mathbf{v}^i, \qquad \sum_{i=1}^{2^m} \alpha_i = 1,\ \alpha_i > 0,\ i = 1, \ldots, 2^m.$$

Then

$$f(\mathbf{x}) = \sum_{i=1}^{2^m} \beta_i f(\mathbf{v}^i), \qquad \sum_{i=1}^{2^m} \beta_i = 1,\ \beta_i > 0,\ i = 1, \ldots, 2^m.$$

Proof. For $m = 1$ the proof is obvious. For $m \ge 2$ the proof follows from induction arguments (see, for example, [AKMS], or [TT]).

Lemma 3.2. If the boundary of the convex polygon $\operatorname{conv} f(\mathbf{V}^m)$ belongs to the image of the box $\mathbf{B}^m$, then $\partial \operatorname{conv} f(\mathbf{V}^m)$ is covered by images of edges of $\mathbf{B}^m$.

Proof. Let z be an element of an edge, say $[z_1, z_2]$, of the polygon $\partial \operatorname{conv} f(\mathbf{V}^m)$. There exists $\mathbf{x} \in \mathbf{B}^m$ so that $z = f(\mathbf{x})$. If there exists a vertex $\mathbf{v}$ with $z = f(\mathbf{v})$, then the proof is completed. Otherwise, let $\mathbf{B}^k$ be the minimal face of $\mathbf{B}^m$, that contains $\mathbf{x}$. Let $\mathbf{V}^k = \left\{\mathbf{v}^1, \ldots, \mathbf{v}^{2^k}\right\}$ be the set of the vertices of $\mathbf{B}^k$. Then, due to Lemma 3.1

$$f(\mathbf{x}) = \sum_{i=1}^{2^k} \beta_i f(\mathbf{v}^i), \qquad \sum_{i=1}^{2^k} \beta_i = 1,\ \beta_i > 0,\ i = 1, \ldots, 2^k.$$

The last relation implies $f(\mathbf{v}) \in [z_1, z_2]$ for each $\mathbf{v} \in \mathbf{V}^k$. The set of vertices $\mathbf{V}^k$ is made up of two nonempty subsets

$$\mathbf{V}^k_l = \{\mathbf{v} : f(\mathbf{v}) \in [z_1, z)\},\ \mathbf{V}^k_r = \{\mathbf{v} : f(\mathbf{v}) \in (z, z_2]\}.$$

Since both sets are nonempty there exist $\mathbf{v}_l \in \mathbf{V}_l^k$, and $\mathbf{v}_r \in \mathbf{V}_r^k$ so that $[\mathbf{v}_l, \mathbf{v}_r]$ is an edge of $\mathbf{B}^m$. The image of this edge covers z.

Next we present conditions that should be met when the outer boundary of $f(\mathbf{B}^m)$ coincides with the boundary of the convex polygon conv$f(\mathbf{V}^m)$.

Theorem 3.1 If the boundary of conv$f(\mathbf{V}^m)$ belongs to $f(\mathbf{B}^m)$, then there exists a finite set of pairs of principal vertices $\{\mathbf{v}_p^i, \mathbf{w}_p^i\}_{i=1}^k$ such that:

1. $\mathbf{v}_p^i$, and $\mathbf{w}_p^i$ are neighboring vertices.
2. $f(\mathbf{v}_p^i)$, and $f(\mathbf{w}_p^i)$ belong to the same edge of conv$f(\mathbf{V}^m)$.
3. $f(\mathbf{v}_p^i) \neq f(\mathbf{w}_p^i)$.
4. The segments $[f(\mathbf{v}_p^i), f(\mathbf{w}_p^i)]$, $i = 1, \ldots k$ cover the boundary of conv$f(\mathbf{V}^m)$.

Proof. When $f(\mathbf{B}^m)$ is a single point the proof is trivial. Otherwise we construct two closed sets ∂_1, and ∂_2 such that

$$\partial_1 \bigcup \partial_2 = \partial \text{conv} f(\mathbf{V}^m), \text{ and } \partial_1 \bigcap \partial_2 = \emptyset.$$

Let $z \in \partial$conv$f(\mathbf{V}^m)$. Due to Lemma 3.2 there exists an edge of the box covering z. If there exists a pair of neighboring vertices $\mathbf{v}$, $\mathbf{w}$, such that $z \in [f(\mathbf{v}), f(\mathbf{w})]$, $f(\mathbf{v}) \neq f(\mathbf{w})$, and $[f(\mathbf{v}), f(\mathbf{w})]$ belongs to an edge of conv$f(\mathbf{V}^m)$, then $z \in \partial_1$, otherwise $z \in \partial_2$. Then ∂_1 is a union of a finite set of intervals, and ∂_2 is a union of a finite set of points. Due to connectedness of ∂conv$f(\mathbf{V}^m)$ either $\partial_1 = \emptyset$, or $\partial_2 = \emptyset$. Since the boundary of a polygon can not be covered by a finite set of points $\partial_2 = \emptyset$, and $\partial_1 = \partial$conv$f(\mathbf{V}^m)$.

Theorem 3.1 provides necessary conditions for ∂conv$f(\mathbf{V}^m) \subseteq f(\mathbf{B}^m)$. The sufficiency of these conditions is obvious (see condition 4 above). A combination of Theorem 2.2 and Theorem 3.1 generate the robust stability conditions given next.

Theorem 3.2 Suppose that:
1. $\mathbf{p}(s, \mathbf{x}^0)$ is Ω stable.
2. There exists $w_0 \in I_\Omega$ such that $0 \notin$ conv$\mathcal{P}_{w_0}$.
3. $\forall w \in I_\Omega$ the conditions of Theorem 3.1 are satisfied for $f(\mathbf{x}) = \mathbf{p}(\delta(w), \mathbf{x})$.
4. $\forall w \in I_\Omega$ the origin does not belong to the conv$f(\mathbf{V}^m)$.
Then the polynomial family $\mathcal{P}$ is Ω stable.

Remark 3.1 If the boundary of the stability domain contains at least one real point, the corresponding value set is an interval in the real line. So, for example, in the two important cases of Hurwitz and Schur stability the verification of the second condition is trivial.

4. Image of a box under multiaffine transformation

The Mapping Theorem [ZD] implies $f(\mathbf{B}^m) \subseteq$ conv$f(\mathbf{V}^m)$. In what follows we provide conditions under which $f(\mathbf{B}^m) =$ conv$f(\mathbf{V}^m)$.

Definition 4.1. Let z_1 and z_2 be complex numbers, and $z_1 \neq 0$. We say that $z_1 \prec z_2$ if $0 < \text{Im } \frac{z_2}{z_1}$. **Definition 4.2.** Let $\mathbf{X}$ be a subset of R^m. A multiaffine function f is a $\mathcal{O}_\mathbf{X}$ (orientation preserving in $\mathbf{X}$) function if $\forall \mathbf{x} \in \mathbf{X}$, and for each integer k one has

$$\frac{\partial f}{\partial x_k}(\mathbf{x}) \prec \frac{\partial f}{\partial x_{k+i}}(\mathbf{x}), \quad i = 1, \ldots, m-1, \qquad (4.1)$$

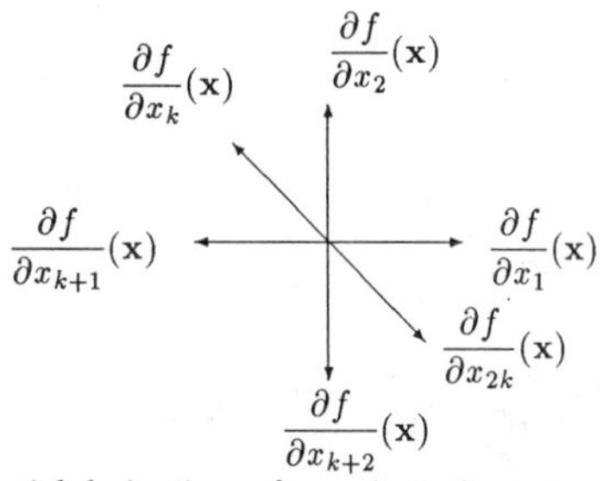

Partial derivatives of an orientation preserving function f

Here $\frac{\partial f}{\partial x_{k+2m}}(\mathbf{x}) = \frac{\partial f}{\partial x_k}(\mathbf{x})$, and $\frac{\partial f}{\partial x_{m+i}}(\mathbf{x}) = -\frac{\partial f}{\partial x_i}(\mathbf{x})$.

Theorem 4.1. (B.T. Polyak [P]). Let f be a multiaffine $\mathcal{O}_{\mathbf{B}^m}$-function. Then

- The $2m$ vertices

Name	Vertex
$\mathbf{v}_p^1$	$(\underline{x}_1, \underline{x}_2, \ldots, \underline{x}_{m-1}, \underline{x}_m)$
$\mathbf{v}_p^2$	$(\overline{x}_1, \underline{x}_2, \ldots, \underline{x}_{m-1}, \underline{x}_m)$
...	...
$\mathbf{v}_p^m$	$(\overline{x}_1, \overline{x}_2, \ldots, \overline{x}_{m-1}, \underline{x}_m)$
$\mathbf{v}_p^{m+1}$	$(\overline{x}_1, \overline{x}_2, \ldots, \overline{x}_{m-1}, \overline{x}_m)$
$\mathbf{v}_p^{m+2}$	$(\underline{x}_1, \overline{x}_2, \ldots, \overline{x}_{m-1}, \overline{x}_m)$
...	...
$\mathbf{v}_p^{2m}$	$(\underline{x}_1, \underline{x}_2, \ldots, \underline{x}_{m-1}, \overline{x}_m)$

are the principal vertices of the box $\mathbf{B}^m$.

- $f(\mathbf{B}^m)$ is a convex polygon conv $\{f(\mathbf{v}_p^1), \ldots, f(\mathbf{v}_p^{2m})\}$ whose consecutive vertices are $f(\mathbf{v}_p^1), \ldots, f(\mathbf{v}_p^{2m})$.

Assumptions of Theorem 4.1 can be relaxed as follows:

Theorem 4.2. (Anderson, Kraus, Mansour, Dasgupta [AKMD]). Let f be a multiaffine $\mathcal{O}_{\mathbf{V}^m}$-function. Then the conclusions of Theorem 4.1 hold.

The following two conditions hold for a multiaffine $\mathcal{O}_{\mathbf{V}^m}$-function f.

Condition 4.1 Each vertex of conv $f(\mathbf{V}^m)$ is the image of a unique vertex of $\mathbf{B}^m$, and no other vertex of $\mathbf{B}^m$ has its image on an edge of conv $f(\mathbf{V}^m)$.

Condition 4.2 The edges of conv $f(\mathbf{V}^m)$ are mapped from edges of $\mathbf{B}^m$.

Results of [AKMD] show that Condition 4.2 alone does not guarantees the convexity of $f(\mathbf{B}^m)$. When, in addition, Condition 4.1 is also satisfied the following result holds (see Tsing and Tits [TT]):

Theorem 4.3 Let f be a multiaffine function that satisfies Conditions 4.1 and 4.2. Then

$$f(\mathbf{B}^m) = \text{conv} f(\mathbf{V}^m).$$

Finally we note, that the following chain of implications holds:

Theorem 4.1 $\Rightarrow$ Theorem 4.2 $\Rightarrow$ Theorem 4.3 $\Rightarrow$ Theorem 3.1.

4. References

[AKMD] Anderson B.D.O., Kraus F., Mansour M., Dasgupta S., Easily testable sufficient conditions for the robust stability of systems with multilinear parameter dependence, preprint, 1991.

[BHH] Bartlett A.C., Hollot C.V., Huang L., Root locations of an entire polytope of polynomials: It suffices to check the edges. Math. Contr., Signals Syst., Vol. 1, pp. 61-71, 1988.

[FD] Frazer R.A., Duncan W.J., On the criteria for stability for small motions. Proceedings of the Royal Society A, Vol. 124, pp. 642-654, 1929.

[K] Kharitonov V.L., Asymptotic stability of an equilibrium position of a family of systems of linear differential equations. Differential Equations, Vol. 14, pp. 1483-1485, 1979.

[P] Polyak B.T., Robustness analysis: small multilinear perturbations can be treated as linear ones. Preprint, The Weizmann Institute of Science, 1992.

[TT] Tsing N.-K., Tits A., When is a multiaffine image of a cube a polygon? Techical Research Report 92-52, Systems Research Center, University of Maryland.

[ZD] Zadeh L., Desoer C.A., Linear System Theory. McGraw Hill, NY, 1963.

Proceedings of the
American Control Conference
San Francisco, California • June 1993

COMPARISON OF THE WHOLE BENIFITS IN A MIMO CONTROL SYSTEM WITH LARGE PARAMETER VARIATIONS

Bor-Chyun Wang† *and* Chun-Kao Lee*

† Dept. of Control Eng., National Chiao-Tung Univ.,Hsinchu,
Chung-Shan Institute of Science and Technologe,Lung-Tan,TAIWAN,ROC.
* Dept. of Power Mechanical Eng., National Tsing-Hua Univ.,Hsinchu,TAIWAN,ROC.

Abstract

The quantitative feedback technique (QFT) is successful in synthesis of control system with large parameter variations. Several QFT design methods are developed with different advantages. In this paper, the **whole benifits** of QFT which is according to both the design cost (the complexity of designing procedure) and the bandwidth cost (how much overdesign in bandwidth causing the noise amplification) are discussed. For a MISO (multiple-input single output) single loop system,the ICQFT (improved conventional QFT) possesses best bandwidth cost, but its design cost is too high. On the other hand, the EDA (equivalent disturbance attenuation) method can simplify the design complexity, but the resulted bandwidth is too conservative. For a MIMO (multiple-inut multiple-output) system, a $n \times n$ system can be decomposed to n^2 MISO system with n different loops, by using the Schauder's fixed point theory. Each single loop can be designing by a suitable method, so a combination of various methods to n loops may be a wiser choice. The **whole benifits** concept can, in this paper, not only evaluate the design result, but also provide the designer a good judgement of choosing QFT method.

1.Introduction

In practical world, uncertainty and noise always exist. The QFT methods can cope the bounded uncertainty and noise by designing feedback loops with tolerable system response. MIMO system is investigated in this paper. Four QFT methods are considered here, the CQFT [1] method was called old method in liternature; the ICQFT [2] method was called improved method; the EDA method [3] and AEDA (alternative-EDA) [4] are using the disturbance attenuation concept to convert the uncertainty to an equivalent extral disturbance and design the feedback loops. The formal three methods are directly using the Schauder's fixed point theory to transfer the $n \times n$ MIMO system to n^2 MISO system with n different loops, then designing the single loop system. In the last (AEDA) method, the uncertainty is first converted to an equivalent extral disturbance and then transfer the $n \times n$ MIMO system to n^2 MISO system with n different loops.

2.Statement of the problem

For a high uncertain mxm plant $\underline{P} \in \wp = \{ p_1, p_2, \cdots \}$ where $p_i, i = 1, 2, ..m$ are known or at least bounded.

Design a two degree of freedom feedback system to satisfy a set of specified input-output time domain specifications $\{t_{ij}\}$. Suppose the inverse matrix of $\underline{P}$ is exist,

$$\underline{P}^{-1} = [p^*_{ij}] \tag{1}$$

Applying the fixed point theory, this mxm MIMO system can be translated to an equivalent m^2 single-loop systems by using a $\underline{Q}$ matrix,

$$\underline{Q} = [q_{ij}] = [1/p^*_{ij}] \tag{2}$$

The details are shown in [1].

3.Numerical example

For a 2x2 system,

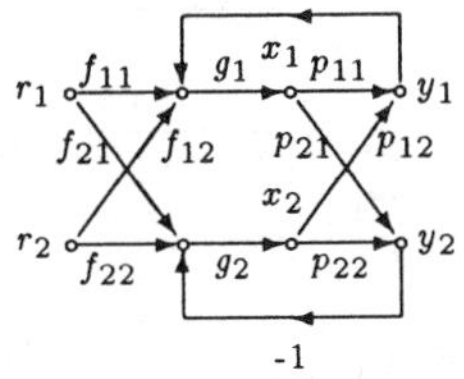

Fig.1. A 2x2 uncertained MIMO plant

$$p_{ij} = \frac{k_{ij}}{s}, \tag{3}$$

$5 \le k_{11} \le 10$, $0.5 \le k_{12} \le 1$, $1 \le k_{21} \le 2$, $0.6 \le k_{22} \le 2$,
The frequency domain specification of $t_{11}; t_{22}$, which is translated

from time domain, is shown in [4]. And $|t_{12}|;|t_{21}| \leq 0.1$ for all frequency. The disturbance rejection constraint for each loops are $\leq$ 3db.

Notation

$g_i^{(CQFT)}$: g_i is designed by (CQFT) method; (i=1,2; ●●)

$g_i^{(EDA)}$: g_i is designed by (EDA) method; (i=1,2; ××)

$g_i^{(AEDA)}$: g_i is designed by (AEDA) method; (i=1,2; oo)

$g_i^{(ICQFT)CQFT}$: g_i is designed by (ICQFT) method while g_j is designed by (CQFT) method; (i=1,j=2,★★); (i=2,j=1, ..)

$g_i^{(ICQFT)EDA}$: g_i is designed by (ICQFT) method while g_j is designed by (EDA) method; (i=1,j=2, -.-.); (i=2,j=1, - -)

$g_i^{(ICQFT)AEDA}$: g_i is designed by (ICQFT) method while g_j is designed by (AEDA) method; (i=1,j=2, + +); (i=2,j=1,–)

RESULTS

Design sequency : loop 1 $\longrightarrow$ loop 2 :

CQFT $\longrightarrow$ ICQFT

$$g_1^{(CQFT)} = \frac{7.5 \times 210^2 \times (s+13)(s+42)(s+90)}{(s+6)(s+32)(s+72)(s^2+210S+210^2)} \tag{4}$$

$$f_{11}^{(CQFT)} = \frac{20 \times 40}{(s+40)(s^2+12s+20)} \tag{5}$$

$$g_2^{(ICQFT)CQFT} = \frac{20 \times 130^2 \times (s+12)(s+34)(s+72)}{(s+6)(s+30)(s+59)(s^2+130S+130^2)} \tag{6}$$

AEDA $\longrightarrow$ ICQFT

$$g_1^{(AEDA)} = \frac{9 \times 220^2 \times (s+20)(s+58)(s+90)}{(s+8)(s+42)(s+82)(s^2+220S+220^2)} \tag{7}$$

$$f_{11}^{(AEDA)} = \frac{16 \times 30}{(s+30)(s^2+10s+16)} \tag{8}$$

$$g_2^{(ICQFT)AEDA} = \frac{13 \times 120^2 \times (s+11)(s+36)(s+68)}{(s+6)(s+26)(s+54)(s^2+120S+120^2)} \tag{9}$$

EDA $\longrightarrow$ ICQFT

$$g_1^{(EDA)} = \frac{15 \times 500^2 \times (s+50)(s+14)(s+220)}{(s+15)(s+100)(s+200)(s^2+400S+500^2)} \tag{10}$$

$$f_{11}^{(EDA)} = \frac{12 \times 15}{(s+15)(s^2+8s+12)} \tag{11}$$

$$g_2^{(ICQFT)EDA} = \frac{7 \times 110^2 \times (s+12)(s+31)(s+60)}{(s+6)(s+22)(s+47)(s^2+110S+110^2)} \tag{12}$$

Design sequency : loop 2 $\longrightarrow$ loop 1 :

CQFT $\longrightarrow$ ICQFT

$$g_2^{(CQFT)} = \frac{30 \times 160_2 \times (s+12)(s+40)(s+90)}{(s+4)(s+30)(s+70)(s^2+160S+160^2)} \tag{13}$$

$$f_{22}^{(CQFT)} = \frac{20 \times 40}{(s+40)(s^2+12s+20)} \tag{14}$$

$$g_1^{(ICQFT)CQFT} = \frac{5.5 \times 200_2 \times (s+12)(s+40)(s+90)}{(s+6)(s+30)(s+70)(s^2+200S+200^2)} \tag{15}$$

AEDA $\longrightarrow$ ICQFT

$$g_2^{(AEDA)} = \frac{40 \times 300_2 \times (s+20)(s+70)(s+120)}{(s+10)(s+42)(s+100)(s^2+300S+300^2)} \tag{16}$$

$$f_{22}^{(AEDA)} = \frac{16 \times 30}{(s+30)(s^2+10s+16)} \tag{17}$$

$$g_1^{(ICQFT)AEDA} = \frac{4.5 \times 180_2 \times (s+18)(s+45)(s+65)}{(s+6)(s+35)(s+56)(s^2+180S+180^2)} \tag{18}$$

EDA $\longrightarrow$ ICQFT

$$g_2^{(EDA)} = \frac{66 \times 360_2 \times (s+30)(s+100)(s+180)}{(s+10)(s+70)(s+160)(s^2+300S+360^2)} \tag{19}$$

$$f_{22}^{(EDA)} = \frac{12 \times 15}{(s+15)(s^2+8s+12)} \tag{20}$$

$$g_1^{(ICQFT)EDA} = \frac{3.5 \times 160_2 \times (s+16)(s+43)(s+62)}{(s+6)(s+32)(s+54)(s^2+160S+160^2)} \tag{21}$$

4.The whole benifits

From Fig.1, the noise response

$$\frac{X_1}{N_1} = \frac{g_1}{1+g_1p_{11}+g_2p_{22}}; \frac{X_2}{N_2} = \frac{g_2}{1+g_1p_{11}+g_2p_{22}} \tag{22}$$

It is reasonable to trade the noise as a white noise with constant magnitude spectrum and only valuable at the high frequency (hf) range. Since the loop gain, $L_i = g_ip_{ii}$; i=1,2, is negligible compare to 1 at *hf* range, so,

$$\frac{X_1}{N_1} = g_1 \simeq \frac{L_1}{p_{11}}; \frac{X_2}{N_2} = g_2 \simeq \frac{L_2}{p_{22}} \tag{23}$$

The response of noises at the input point of plant are : $X_1 = N_1g_1$ $X_2 = N_2g_2$ It is reasonable to evaluate the *whole benifits (WB)* by the summation of noise responses at each individual plants, $WB = X_1 + X_2 = N_1g_1 + N_2g_2$ under the simpler design procedures. Let $N_1 = \alpha_1 N$, $N_2 = \alpha_2 N$, the normorized WB can be expressed as,

$$WB_N = \frac{WB}{N} = \alpha_1 g_1 + \alpha_2 g_2 \tag{24}$$

Five noise conditions are considered,

1. $\alpha_1 = \alpha_2 = 1$, the WB_N is shown in Fig.2 .a.
2. $\alpha_1 = 10, \alpha_2 = 1$, the WB_N is shown in [4].
3. $\alpha_1 = 100, \alpha_2 = 1$, the WB_N is shown in Fig.2.b.
4. $\alpha_1 = 1, \alpha_2 = 10$, the WB_N is shown in [4].
5. $\alpha_1 = 1, \alpha_2 = 100$, the WB_N is shown in [4].

5.Conclusions

The results of Fig.2 indicate that, when $N_1 \ll N_2$, g_2 should be designed by g_2(ICQFT)EDA; similary, when $N_2 \ll N_1$, g_2 should be designed by g_1(ICQFT)EDA. The reason is that : the cost of feedback by using (ICQFT)EDA is the best. This gives the designer a good judgement to choose methods of QFT.

6.Reference

1. IJC,Vol.30,No.1,pp.81-106,UK,1979.
2. IJC,Vol.36,No.6,pp.977-988,UK,1982.
3. C-TAT,Vol.6,No.2,pp.257-271,JAPAN,1990.
4. M.S.Thesis,C.K.Lee,NCH Univ.,Taiwan,ROC.1992.

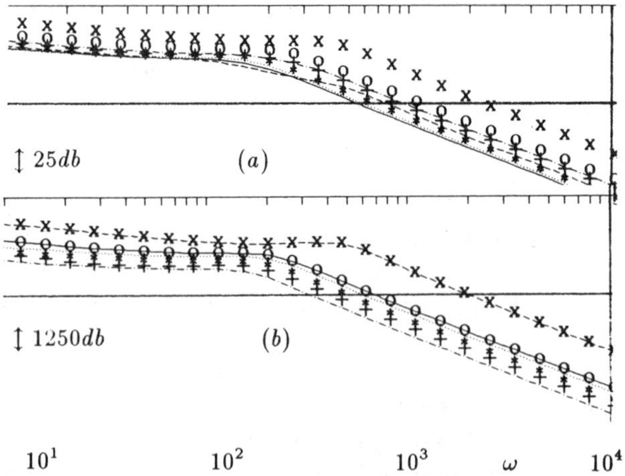

Fig.2. The feedback effect of EDA, CQFT and AEDA. Magnitude ofWB_N in db.

Proceedings of the
American Control Conference
San Francisco, California • June 1993

ROBUST STABILITY ANALYSIS FOR PERTURBED LARGE-SCALE DISCRETE SYSTEMS

Pin-Lin Liu
Department of Electrical Engineering,
Chien Kao Junior College of Technology,
Changhua 500, Taiwan, R.O.C..

Te-Jen Su
Department of Electronic Engineering,
National Kaohsiung Institute of Technology
415, Chien-Kung Rd. Kaohsiung, Taiwan

Jyh-Horng Chou
Department of Mechanical Engineering,
National Yunlin Institute of Technology,
Touliu, Yunlin 640, Taiwan, R.O.C..

Abstract

The sufficient stability criterion for perturbed large-scale discrete systems is presented. The explicit bound on linear perturbations with highly structured information is obtained. An example is given to illustrate the application of the presented result.

1. Introduction

The stability of linear discrete-time systems has been widely studied in the literature [3,4,5,7]. Chou [3] has proposed a new approach for the stability analysis of discrete interval systems. Kolla et al. [4] have reported robust stability bounds on time-varying perturbations for state-space models of linear discrete-time systems. Rachid [7] has shown a sufficient condition for the stability of linear discrete systems under structured perturbation.

The sufficient stability criterion for perturbed large-scale discrete systems is presented. The explicit bounds on linear perturbations with highly structured information is obtained. An example is given to illustrate the application of the presented result.

This technical note is organized as follows. In section 2, a robust stability analysis for large-scale discrete systems is presented. The robust stability criterion is derived for perturbed large-scale discrete systems in section 3. As an application, an example is illustrated in section 4, and a conclusion is given in section 5.

2. Stability analysis

Let $r[M]$ denote the spectral radius of the matrix M. $|M|_m$ denotes the modulus matrix of M, and I is the identity matrix. For two any matrices $M=[m_{ij}]$ and $T=[t_{ij}]$, $M\leqq T$ denotes $m_{ij}\leqq t_{ij}$, for all i and j.

Lemma 1A [2]

The zero state of $x(k+1)=Mx(k)$ is asymptotically stable if and only if all the eigenvalues of M have magnitudes less than one.

Lemma 1A can be rewritten in another form as:

Lemma 1B

The zero state of $x(k+1)=Mx(k)$ is asymptotically stable if and only if

$$|\det(zI-M)|>0, \text{ for } |z|\geqq 1.$$

Lemma 2 [6]

For any nxn matrices R, T, and V, if $|R|_m\leqq V$, then

(a) $r[R]\leqq r[\,|R|_m]\leqq r[V]$.

(b) $r[RT]\leqq r[\,|R|_m|T|_m]\leqq r[V|T|_m]$.

(c) $r[R+T]\leqq r[\,|R+T|_m]$
$\leqq r[\,|R|_m+|T|_m]$
$\leqq r[V+|T|_m]$

Lemma 3 [3]

If $G(z)$ is a pulse transfer function matrix, then

$$|G(z)|_m\leqq \sum_{k=0}^{\infty} |G(K)|_m$$

$$\equiv H(G(K)) \quad \text{for } |z|\geqq 1,$$

where $G(K)$ is the pulse-response sequence matrix of the multivable system $G(z)$.

Lemma 4 [1]

For an $n\times n$ matrix R, if $r[R]<1$, $|\det(I\pm R)|>0$.

3. Robust stability analysis for perturbed large-scale discrete systems

Consider a perturbed large-scale discrete system S composed of N linear interconnected subsystems S_i (i=1,2,...N). Each subsystem S_i is described by

$$x_i(k+1)=[A_{ii}+\Delta A_{ii}]x_i(k)+w_i(k)+\Delta w_i, \tag{1a}$$

$$w_i(k)=\sum_{j=1,j\neq i}^{N} A_{ij}x_j(k), \tag{1b}$$

$$\Delta w_i(k)=\sum_{j=1,j\neq i}^{N} \Delta A_{ij}x_j(k), \tag{1c}$$

i=1,2,...N.
j=1,2,...N.

where, for the ith subsystem, $x_i(k)$ is the n_i-dimensional state vector; $w_i(k)$ is n_i-dimension vector and interaction with the other subsystems; A_{ii} and A_{ij} are constant matricies with appropriate dimensions; ΔA_{ii} and ΔA_{ij} are $n_i\times n_i$ dimensional structured perturbation matrices, and $\Delta w_i(k)$ contains the uncertainties in the interactions between the ith subsystem and the other subsystems.

Aggregating N of (1), the overall systems are formulated by

$$x_p(k+1)=A_p x_p(k)+A_q x_p(k)+E_p x_p(k), \tag{2}$$

where

$$x_p(k)=[x_1(k) \quad x_2(k) .... \quad x_N(k)]^T,$$

$$A_p=\mathrm{diag}[A_{11}, A_{22}, ..., A_{NN}],$$

$$A_q=\begin{bmatrix} 0 & A_{12} & \cdots & A_{1N} \\ A_{21} & 0 & \cdots & A_{2N} \\ . & 0 & \cdots & . \\ . & & \cdots & . \\ . & & & \\ A_{N1} & A_{N2} & \cdots & 0 \end{bmatrix},$$

$$E_q=\begin{bmatrix} \Delta A_{11} & \Delta A_{12} & \cdots & \Delta A_{1N} \\ \Delta A_{21} & . & . & \Delta A_{2N} \\ . & . & . & . \\ . & . & . & . \\ . & & & \\ \Delta A_{N1} & \Delta A_{N2} & \cdots & \Delta A_{NN} \end{bmatrix},$$

where $x_p(k)$ is the n-dimensional state vector, A_p, A_q are constant matrices with appropriate dimensions; E_p is an n×n perturbation matrix. The perturbations in the various elements of the system matrix are idependent of each other. In a practical situation. the perturbation matrix is not know exactly and only the magnitude of the deviation that can be expected in the entries of A_p and A_q may be know. In this case of highly structured perturbation, the matrix E_p satisfies $|E_p|_m \leqq qU$, where q is a positive real number and U is a non-negative matrix representing highly structured information for perturbation on the entries of A_p and A_p.

The following theorem will give a sufficient conditioin for ensuring the stability of the uncertain system (2).

Theorem

The large-scale discrete system (2) is asymptotically stable, if A_p is an asymptotically stable matrix, and if the following inequality is satisfied

$$r[H(G(K))(|A_q|+qU)] < 1 \qquad (3)$$

where H(G(K)) has been defined in Lemma 3, and G(K) is the pulse-response sequence matrix of the $G(z)=(zI-A_p)^{-1}$.

Proof

Using the identity

$$\det[RT]=\det[R]\det[T]$$

for any two nxn matrices R and T, we have

$$\det[zI-(A_p+A_q+E_p)]$$
$$=\det[I-(zI-A_p)^{-1}(A_q+E_p)]\det[zI-A_p]. \qquad (4)$$

Since A_p is an asymptotically stable matrix, then using Lemma 1B it is obvious that

$$\det[zI-A_p]>0, \qquad \text{for } |z|\geqq 1. \qquad (5)$$

If (3) is satisfied, by Lemmas 2 and 3, we have

$$\begin{aligned} r[(zI-A_p)^{-1}(A_q+E_p)] &= r[G(z)(A_q+E_p)] \\ &\leqq r[|G(z)|_m(|A_q|+qU)] \\ &\leqq r[H(G(K))(|A_q|+qU)] \\ &< 1, \quad \text{for } |z|\geqq 1. \end{aligned} \qquad (6)$$

Using (4)-(6) and applying Lemma 4, we have

$$|\det[zI-(A_p+A_q+E_p)|$$
$$=|\det[I-(zI-A_p)^{-1}(A_q+E_p)]|\;|\det(zI-A_p)|$$
$$>0, \quad \text{for } |z|\geqq 1.$$

Therefore, by Lemma 1B, the time-delay system (2) is asymptotically stable.

Remark 1

From the sufficient condition (3), we can know how much perturbation a nominally stable system $x_p(k+1)=A_px_p(k)$ can tolerate such that the system (2) is still asymptotically stable.

Remark 2

H(G(K)) can be evaluated from the pulse response of the stable transfer function matrix $G(z)=(zI-A_p)^{-1}$. That is, H(G(K)) can be evaluated by using $G(0)=0$, and $G(K)=A_p^{k-1}$ (for k=1,2,3,...), therefore, the sufficient condition (3) is computationally simple to use.

4. Example

Consider a discrete-time large-scale perturbed system

$$x_i(k+1)=[A_{ii}+\Delta A_{ii}]x_i(k)+w_i(k)+\Delta w_i,$$

$$w_i(k)=\sum_{j=1,j\neq i}^{2} A_{ij}x_j(k),$$

$$\Delta w_i=\sum_{j=1,j\neq i}^{2} \Delta A_{ij}x_j(k),$$

where

$$A_{11}=A_{22}=\begin{bmatrix} 0 & 1 \\ -0.5 & -1 \end{bmatrix}, \quad A_{12}=A_{21}=\begin{bmatrix} 0 & 1 \\ 0 & 1 \end{bmatrix},$$

the highly structured perturbation

$$|\Delta A_{ii}| \leqq \begin{bmatrix} 0.1 & 0 \\ 0 & 0.1 \end{bmatrix}, \quad |\Delta A_{ij}| \leqq \begin{bmatrix} 0 & 0.1 \\ 0.1 & 0 \end{bmatrix},$$

From theorem we can obtain H(G(k))=

$$\begin{bmatrix} 2.67 & 3.33 & 0 & 0 \\ 1.67 & 3.33 & 0 & 0 \\ 0 & 0 & 2.67 & 3.33 \\ 0 & 0 & 1.67 & 3.33 \end{bmatrix},$$

we empoly the sufficient condition (3), we have q=0.62.

5. Conclusion

In this paper, we have proposed a sufficient condition for the linear discrte-time large-scale perturbed systems. The explicit bound on inear perturbations with highly structured information are obtained. The test for stability using our criterion can be carried out rather simply.

References

01. Chen, K.H., Robust analysis and design of Multiloop control systems, Ph. D. dissertation, National Tsing-Hua University, Taiwain, R.O.C. 1989.
02. Chen, C. T., Linear System Theory and Design. New York: Pond Woods, Stony Brook, 1984.
03. Chou, J. H., "New Approach for the Stability Analysis of Discrete Interval Systems," Control Theorey and Advanced Technology, vol. 7, no. 1, pp. 147-152, 1991.
04. Kolla, S. R., R. K. Yedavalli and J. B. Farison, "Robust Stability Bounds on Time-Varying Perturbations for State-Space Models of Linear Discrete-Time Systems," Int. J. Control, vol, 50, no. 1, pp. 151-159, 1989.
05. Ogata, K., Discrete-Time Control Systems, prentice-hall, 1987.
06. Ortega, J. M., and W. C. Rheinboldt, Inerative Soluation of Non-Linear Equation in Several Variables, New York: Academic press, 1970.
07. Rachid, A. "Robust of Discrete Systems under Structured Uncertainties," Int. J. Control, vol, 50, pp. 1563-1566, 1989.

Proceedings of the
American Control Conference
San Francisco, California • June 1993

Uncertainties With Bounded Rates of Variation

Anders Rantzer[1]
Institute for Mathematics and its Applications
University of Minnesota
514 Vincent Hall
206 Church Street S.E.
Minneapolis, Minnesota 55455

Abstract

This paper treats stability robustness for linear systems with uncertain time-varying parameters, exploiting "bandwidth constraints" on the parameters.

1. Introduction

It is well known that conservatism of small gain criteria for stability for linear systems with structured uncertainty can be reduced by scaling (see e.g. [4]). Frequency dependent scalings are used for time-invariant uncertainty, while constant scalings are used when the uncertainty is supposed to be time-varying. In this paper, we have shown that the gap between the two extrema can be bridged by exploiting "bandwidth constraints" on the uncertainty.

We consider the system

$$\begin{cases} \dot{x}(t) = Ax(t) + Bu(t) \\ y(t) = Cx(t) + Du(t) \\ u(t) = \Delta(t)y(t), \end{cases} \qquad (1)$$

where $\Delta = \mathrm{diag}\{\delta_1, \ldots, \delta_n\} \in L^\infty(\mathbf{R}, \mathbf{R}^n)$ is uncertain, but $\|\delta_i\|_\infty < 1$ and the rate of time-variation is restricted in a certain sense.

In the sixties and seventies there were several papers devoted to this problem with derivative bounds on a scalar Δ. See [2] and references therein. The basic idea was to relax the circle criterion using multipliers. Recently these results were generalized by [5], e.g. allowing block structure in $\Delta(t)$. Typical for stability criteria based on bounds on $d\Delta/dt$ is that they are stated in terms of transfer function values off the imaginary axis.

In this paper, we shall introduce a new type of bound on the variations in Δ, restricting the support of the Fourier transform $\widehat{\Delta}$, (which is defined in the sense of a temperate distribution when $\Delta \in L^\infty$). Slow time-variations in Δ are then modelled as a small bandwidth ($\widehat{\Delta}$ has support in a small interval).

It is worth noting that if $\Delta \in L^\infty$ and $\widehat{\Delta}$ has compact support, then there is an entire function on $\mathbf{C}$ that equals Δ a.e. on the real axis, (see e.g. [3]). Furthermore, the entire function satisfies

$$\sup_t |\Delta'(t)| \leq a \sup_t |\Delta(t)| \quad \text{(Bernstein's inequality)},$$

so there is a correspondence between bandwith constraints and derivative constraints. For proof of this and other properties of entire functions, see [1].

We have the following main result, which gives sufficient conditions for stability of such systems.

2. Main Result

Let $\mathbf{H}_\infty$ be the space of functions on $\mathbf{C}$ that are analytic and bounded in the open right half plane. We use the notation $\mathbf{RH}_\infty$ to restrict to real rational functions. The set of $m \times n$ matrices with elements in $\mathbf{H}_\infty$ ($\mathbf{RH}_\infty$) will be denoted $\mathbf{H}_\infty^{m\times n}$ ($\mathbf{RH}_\infty^{m\times n}$). We use $\bar{\sigma}$ to denote the largest singular value of a matrix.

Theorem 1 *Given*

$$\begin{aligned} G(s) &= C(sI - A)^{-1}B + D \in \mathbf{RH}_\infty^{N\times N} \\ \Delta(t) &= \mathrm{diag}\{\delta_1(t)I_{n_1}, \ldots, \delta_m(t)I_{n_m}\} \in L^\infty(\mathbf{R}, \mathbf{R}^{N\times N}) \end{aligned}$$

with $\|\delta_i\|_\infty < 1$ *and* $\mathrm{supp}\, \widehat{\delta}_i \subset [-a_i, a_i] \subset [-\infty, \infty]$, *if there exists a* $D = \mathrm{diag}\{D_1, \ldots, D_m\}$ *with* $D_i \in \mathbf{RH}_\infty^{n_i\times n_i}$ *such that*

$$\begin{cases} \sup_{\omega\in[0,\infty]} \bar{\sigma}\left(D(j\omega)G(j\omega)D(j\omega + ja)^{-1}\right) < 1 \\ \frac{\partial}{\partial\omega}\left[D(j\omega)^* D(j\omega)\right] \leq 0 \text{ for } \omega \in [0, +\infty), \end{cases}$$

where $D(j\omega + ja)$ *is short for* $\mathrm{diag}\{D_1(j\omega + ja_1), \ldots, D_n(j\omega + ja_n)\}$, *then (1) is well posed and asymptotically stable.*

[1]This work was supported by the Swedish Natural Science Research Council.

Remark If the condition is satisfied with $a_i = \infty$, $i = 1, \dots, m$, we have $\|D(0)G(j\omega)D(0)^{-1}\|_\infty < 1$, so the test can be restricted to constant scalings. On the other hand, with $a_1 = \cdots = a_m = 0$ we can choose $D(j\omega)$ independently for each frequency, then multiply with a scalar function to satisfy the growth condition. Again our test reduces to the classical one.

Several generalizations of Theorem 1 as well as connections to other results had to be excluded from this short paper but will be presented elsewhere.

3. Proof of the main result

The proof will be based on the following lemma.

Lemma 2 *Suppose* $g(t) = \delta(t)f(t)$ *where* $f \in L^2(\mathbf{R}, \mathbf{R}^n)$, $\delta \in L^\infty(\mathbf{R}, \mathbf{R})$, $\|\delta\|_\infty < 1$, *and* $\operatorname{supp} \widehat{\delta} \subset [-a, a] \subset [-\infty, \infty]$. *Then for any decreasing matrix function* $0 \le X(\omega) = X(\omega)^* \in \mathbf{R}^{n \times n}$, $\omega \in [0, \infty)$, *we have*

$$\int_0^\infty \widehat{g}(j\omega)^* X(\omega+a)\widehat{g}(j\omega)d\omega \le \int_0^\infty \widehat{f}(j\omega)^* X(\omega)\widehat{f}(j\omega)d\omega.$$

Proof. For $\nu > 0$, let $f_{\nu+a} \in L^2(\mathbf{R}, \mathbf{R}^n)$ have a Fourier transform that satisfies $\widehat{f}_{\nu+a}(j\omega) = \widehat{f}(j\omega)$ for $|w| \le \nu + a$ and $\widehat{f}_{\nu+a}(j\omega) = 0$ elsewhere. Then for any $Y = Y^* \ge 0$, we have

$$\begin{aligned}
&\int_0^\nu \widehat{g}(j\omega)^* Y \widehat{g}(j\omega)d\omega \\
&= \int_0^\nu (\widehat{\delta} * \widehat{f})^* Y (\widehat{\delta} * \widehat{f})d\omega \\
&= \int_0^\nu (\widehat{\delta} * \widehat{f}_{\nu+a})^* Y (\widehat{\delta} * \widehat{f}_{\nu+a})d\omega \\
&\le \frac{1}{2}\int_{-\infty}^\infty (\delta(t)f_{\nu+a}(t))^T Y \delta(t) f_{\nu+a}(t))dt \\
&\le \frac{1}{2}\int_{-\infty}^\infty f_{\nu+a}(t)^T Y f_{\nu+a}(t)dt \\
&= \int_0^{\nu+a} \widehat{f}(j\omega)^* Y \widehat{f}(j\omega)d\omega,
\end{aligned}$$

Let $X_{k,\varepsilon} = X(k\varepsilon + a) - X((k+1)\varepsilon + a)$ for $\varepsilon > 0$ and positive integers k and put $X_\infty = \lim_{\omega \to \infty} X(\omega)$. Then

$$\begin{aligned}
&\int_0^\infty \widehat{g}(j\omega)^* X(\omega + a + \varepsilon)\widehat{g}(j\omega)d\omega \\
&\le \int_0^\infty \widehat{g}^* X_\infty \widehat{g} d\omega + \sum_{k=1}^\infty \int_0^{k\varepsilon} \widehat{g}(j\omega)^* X_{k,\varepsilon} \widehat{g}(j\omega)d\omega \\
&\le \int_0^\infty \widehat{f}^* X_\infty \widehat{f} d\omega + \sum_{k=1}^\infty \int_0^{k\varepsilon+a} \widehat{f}(j\omega)^* X_{k,\varepsilon} \widehat{f}(j\omega)d\omega \\
&\le \int_0^\infty \widehat{f}(j\omega)^* X(\omega)\widehat{f}(j\omega)d\omega
\end{aligned}$$

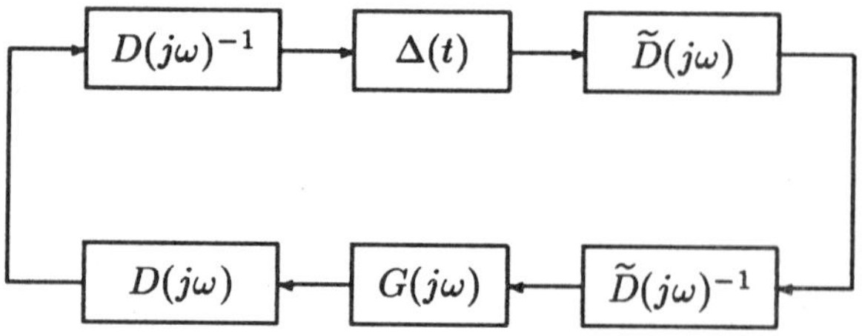

Figure 1: Uncertainty loop with scalings

for arbitrarily small ε. This proves the lemma. □

Proof of Theorem 1. By spectral factorization, one can find a $\widetilde{D} = \operatorname{diag}\{\widetilde{D}_1, \dots, \widetilde{D}_m\}$ with $\widetilde{D}_i \in \mathbf{H}_\infty^{n_i \times n_i}$ and $\widetilde{D}_i(j\omega)^* \widetilde{D}_i(j\omega) = D_i(j\omega + ja_i)^* D_i(j\omega + ja_i)$ for $i = 1, \dots, m$ and $\omega \in [0, \infty)$. Application of Lemma 2 with $X(\omega) = D_i(j\omega)^* D_i(j\omega)$ and $a = a_i$ for $i = 1, \dots, n$ shows that the map $\widetilde{D}\Delta D^{-1}$ is contractive on $L^2(\mathbf{R}, \mathbf{R}^N)$. The assumption $\sup_{\omega \in [0,\infty]} \bar{\sigma}\left(D(j\omega)G(j\omega)D(j\omega + ja)^{-1}\right) < 1$ implies that $DG\widetilde{D}^{-1}$ is strictly contractive, so we have stability by the small gain theorem (Figure 1). □

4. Acknowledgemnts

The author would like to thank B. Bernhardsson, J.C. Doyle, P.P. Khargonekar, L. Qiu, A. Megretskii and J.C. Willems for criticism and useful comments on this work.

References

[1] R.P. Boas, *Entire functions*, Academic Press, 1954.

[2] M.K. Sundareshan and M.A.L. Thathachar, *L_2-stability of linear time-varying systems—conditions involving noncasual multipliers*, IEEE Transaction on Automatic Control **17** (1972), no. 4, 504–510.

[3] W.F. Donoghue, Jr., Distributions and Fourier Transforms, 148, Academic Press, 1969, p. 148.

[4] M.K.H. Fan, A.L. Tits, and J.C. Doyle, *Robustness in presence of mixed parametric uncertainty and unmodeled dynamics*, IEEE Transations on Automatic Control **AC-36** (1991), no. 1, 25–38.

[5] A. Megretskii, *Frequency-domain criteria of robust stability for slowly time-varying systems*, Tech. Report EE9280, The University of Newcastle, Australia, 1992, Submitted to IEEE TAC.

Proceedings of the
American Control Conference
San Francisco, California • June 1993

Learning to Coordinate Control Policies of Hybrid Systems

M.D. Lemmon *, J. Stiver, P.J. Antsaklis
Dept. of Electrical Eng.
University of Notre Dame
Notre Dame, IN 46556

Abstract

Hybrid control systems consist of a discrete event system (DES) supervising the behaviour of a continuous state system (CSS) through the issuance of logical control directives. This paper derives sufficient conditions on the DES/CSS interface which guarantee the existence of a supervisor which transitions the plant through an arbitrary sequence of commanded events. It is further demonstrated that this interface can be learned using an inductive inference protocol which converges after a finite number of updates.

1 Introduction

Hybrid systems consist of a continuous-state system (CSS) interfaced to a discrete event system (DES). The resulting system can be seen as consisting of 3 distinct layers. The lowest layer is the continuous-state system or **plant**. The highest layer is a discrete event system or **supervisor**. The middle layer is an interface which facilitates communication between the supervisor and plant. The interface therefore behaves as a 2-way communication port which admits a natural decomposition into two subsystems, one for each communication direction. The subsystem handling control event transformations is called the **actuator**. The subsystem transforming plant states into plant symbols is called the **generator**.

This paper discusses a class of hybrid system in which the interface generator and actuator consist of memoryless mappings [Stiver 1992] [Antsaklis 1993]. The following sections establish sufficient conditions on the interface which guarantee the existence of a supervisor which drives the plant through a connected sequence of events. These conditions provide the basis for an inductive inference protocol which can be used by the system to "learn" the appropriate actuator.

The remainder of this paper is organized as follows. Section 2 discusses the hybrid system under study. Section 3 states the "supervisability" conditions. Section 4 shows how these conditions lead to an inductive inference protocol for automatically learning how to "supervise" the system. Section 5 illustrates the proposed framework for a simple example. Section 6 summarizes the results.

*The partial financial support of the National Science Foundation (IRI91-09298) is gratefully acknowledged

2 Hybrid Systems

The system to be controlled, called the plant, is modeled as a time-invariant continuous-time system. This part of the hybrid control system contains the entire continous-time portion of the system, possibly including a continuous-time controller. Mathematically, the plant is represented by the equations

$$\dot{\mathbf{x}} = f(\mathbf{x}, \mathbf{r}) \quad (1)$$

$$\mathbf{z} = g(\mathbf{x}) \quad (2)$$

where $\mathbf{x} \in \Re^n$, $\mathbf{r} \in \Re^m$, and $\mathbf{z} \in \Re^p$ are the state, control, and observation vectors, respectively. $f : \Re^n \times \Re^m \to \Re^n$ and $g : \Re^n \to \Re^p$ are functions.

For the purposes of this work we assume that $\mathbf{z} = \mathbf{x}$ and we assume that the plant is linear in the controls so that

$$\dot{\mathbf{x}} = \sum_{i=1}^{m} r_i f_i(\mathbf{x}) \quad (3)$$

The vector $\mathbf{r} = (r_1, \ldots, r_m)' \in \Re^m$ can be interpreted as "coordinating" a set of control policies represented by the set of m vector fields, $f_i(\mathbf{x})$.

The supervisor is a discrete event system which is modeled as a deterministic automaton. This automaton can be specified by a quintuple, $\{\tilde{S}, \tilde{Z}, \tilde{R}, \delta, \phi\}$, where $\tilde{S}$ is the (possibly infinite) set of states, $\tilde{Z}$ is the set of plant symbols, $\tilde{R}$ is the set of controller symbols, $\delta : \tilde{S} \times \tilde{Z} \to \tilde{S}$ is the state transition function, and $\phi : \tilde{S} \to \tilde{R}$ is the output function. The symbols in set $\tilde{R}$ are called controller symbols because they are generated by the controller. Likewise, the symbols in set $\tilde{Z}$ are called plant symbols and are generated by the occurrence of events in the plant. The action of the controller can be described by the equations

$$\tilde{s}[n] = \delta(\tilde{s}[n-1], \tilde{z}[n]) \quad (4)$$

$$\tilde{r}[n] = \phi(\tilde{s}[n]) \quad (5)$$

where $\tilde{s}[n] \in S, \tilde{z}[n] \in \tilde{Z}$, and $\tilde{r}[n] \in \tilde{R}$. The index n is analogous to a time index in that it specifies the order of the symbols in a sequence. The input and output signals associated with the controller are asynchronous sequences of symbols, rather than continuous-time signals. Notice that there is no delay in the controller. The state transition, from $\tilde{s}[n-1]$ to $\tilde{s}[n]$, and the controller symbol, $\tilde{r}[n]$, occur immediately when the plant symbol $\tilde{z}[n]$ occurs.

The controller and plant cannot communicate directly in a hybrid control system because each utilizes a different type of signal. Thus an interface is required which can convert continuous- time signals to sequences of symbols and vice versa. The interface consists of two memoryless maps, a and g. The first map, called the actuating function or actuator, $a : \tilde{R} \rightarrow \Re^m$, converts a sequence of controller symbols to a piecewise constant plant input as follows

$$\mathbf{r} = a(\tilde{r}) = \left(\begin{array}{ccc} a_1(\tilde{r}) & \cdots & a_m(\tilde{r}) \end{array} \right)' \tag{6}$$

The plant input, $\mathbf{r} \in \Re^{\mathbf{m}}$, can only take on certain constant values, where each value is associated with a particular controller symbol. Thus the plant input is a piecewise constant signal which may change only when a controller symbol occurs. The second map, the plant symbol generating function or generator, $g : \Re^n \rightarrow \tilde{Z}$, is a function which maps the state space of the plant to the set of plant symbols as follows

$$\tilde{z} = g(\mathbf{x}) \tag{7}$$

The plant symbol generating function, g, is designed based on an open covering of the state space of the plant. Consider a collection of p open subsets in $\Re^n$ which form an open cover for the plant state space. Let this collection be represented as

$$C = \{ \begin{array}{ccc} c_1 & \ldots & c_p \end{array} \} \tag{8}$$

The collection consists of open subsets, each subset is called a covering event. Let the ith covering event, c_i, be associated with a unique covering symbol, $\tilde{c}_i$. The "alphabet" of covering symbols can therefore be represented as

$$\tilde{C} = \{ \begin{array}{ccc} \tilde{c}_1 & \ldots & \tilde{c}_p \end{array} \} \tag{9}$$

These covering symbols are used to define the plant symbols as follows

$$\tilde{z} = g(\mathbf{x}) = \{ \tilde{c}_i : \mathbf{x} \in c_i \} \tag{10}$$

As shown in Equation 10, a plant symbol is a collection of covering symbols which defines a region in the state space. It is convenient to treat this collection as a symbol. A plant symbol is generated only when a new event first occurs. The overall effect is that the state space of the plant is partitioned into a number of regions and each is associated with a unique plant symbol which is generated whenever the state enters that region.

The use of open covers to describe the state space is motivated by several things. The generator, g, must take subsets of states onto a "unique" plant symbol. The representation should be "well posed" in the sense that small changes of state or system structure do not result in discontinuous variations in the state's symbolic representation. The well-posedness constraints suggests that events should be open subsets of the state space. The representation must also be complete, meaning every state must be contained within a plant event. These conditions suggest that g should realize an open covering of the state space.

In this paper, the covering events are assumed to have a special form. This form is motivated by the modest computational complexity associated with the evaluation of linear forms. The specific covering events assumed are denoted as

$$C = \{ \begin{array}{ccccccc} c_1 & c_1^+ & c_1^- & \cdots & c_p & c_p^+ & c_p^- \end{array} \} \tag{11}$$

where each event is defined by the following open sets in $\Re^n$.

$$\begin{aligned} c_i &= \{ \mathbf{x} \in \Re^n : \mathbf{s}_i'\mathbf{x} > \alpha_i \} && (12) \\ c_i^+ &= \{ \mathbf{x} \in \Re^n : \mathbf{s}_i'\mathbf{x} > \alpha_i + \beta_i + \delta \} && (13) \\ c_i^- &= \{ \mathbf{x} \in \Re^n : \mathbf{s}_i'\mathbf{x} > \alpha_i + \beta_i - \delta \} && (14) \end{aligned}$$

where $\mathbf{s}_i \in \Re^n$ and $\alpha_i, \beta_i, \delta > 0$. Associated with the events c_i, $c_i^{\pm}$ are the covering symbols, $\tilde{c}_i$, $\tilde{c}_i^{\pm}$.

3 Supervisability

In many applications, it is required to drive the plant through a well defined sequence of events. A plant for which this can be done will be said to be "supervisable". This section derives sufficient conditions for a system to be supervisable.

Definition 1 *Let C be the plant's event covering with associated alphabet $\tilde{C}$. Let the jth command event be any set, u_j, formed by the intersection of q covering events as shown below $u_j = \bigcap_{i=1}^{q} c_{j_i}$ where j_i is an integer between 1 and p and $c_{j_i} \in C$.*

The preceding definition implies that the jth command event is associated with a set of integers $j_1, \ldots, j_q$ indexing the covering events comprising u_j. This set of integers will be called the index set, I_j, of the command event u_j.

Definition 2 *Let C be the covering events with associated alphabet $\tilde{C}$. Two command events, u_1 and u_2 are said to be connected if and only if their index sets, I_1 and I_2, satisfy the relation, $I_1 \subset I_2$ or $I_2 \subset I_1$.*

Theorem 1 *Consider a hybrid system with event covering C and covering alphabet $\tilde{C}$. Consider the covering events*

$$\begin{aligned} c^+ &= \{ \mathbf{x} \in \Re^n : \mathbf{s}'\mathbf{x} - \alpha - \beta - \delta \} && (15) \\ c^- &= \{ \mathbf{x} \in \Re^n : \mathbf{s}'\mathbf{x} - \alpha - \beta + \delta \} && (16) \end{aligned}$$

If the functional, $V(\mathbf{x}) = (\mathbf{s}'\mathbf{x} - \alpha - \beta)^2$, is a Lyapunov functional for the system

$$\dot{\mathbf{x}} = \begin{cases} \sum_{j=1}^{m} a_j(\tilde{c}^+) f_i(\mathbf{x}) & \text{if } \mathbf{x} \in c^+ \\ \sum_{j=1}^{m} a_j(\tilde{c}^-) f_i(\mathbf{x}) & \text{if } \mathbf{x} \in c^- \end{cases} \quad (17)$$

then if $\mathbf{x} \in (c^+ \cup c^-)$ at $t = 0$, there exists a time $T > 0$ such that for all $t > T$, $\mathbf{x} \notin (c^+ \cup c^-)$.

Proof: By assumption, $V(\mathbf{x})$, is a Lyapunov functional so that by theorem 8 of [Utkin 1977] it can be inferred that the complement of $c^+ \cup c^-$ is an attracting invariant set. •

The significance of the preceding theorem is that it suggests a form for the actuator and supervisor which "blocks" the system state out of the event $c^+ \cup c^-$. The following theorem indicates how the "blocking" conditions allow for the system to supervise transitions between two connected events.

Theorem 2 *Consider a hybrid system with event covering C and alphabet $\tilde{C}$. Let u_1 and u_2 be 2 connected command events with index sets I_1 and I_2, respectively. Let the functionals, $V_i(\mathbf{x}) = (\mathbf{s}_i'\mathbf{x} - \alpha_i - \beta_i)^2$, be Lyapunov functionals for the system*

$$\dot{\mathbf{x}} = \begin{cases} \sum_{j=1}^{m} a_j(\tilde{c}_i^+) f_i(\mathbf{x}) & \text{if } \mathbf{x} \in c_i^+ \\ \sum_{j=1}^{m} a_j(\tilde{c}_i^-) f_i(\mathbf{x}) & \text{if } \mathbf{x} \in c_i^- \end{cases} \quad (18)$$

for all $i \in I_1 \cup I_2$. There exists a supervisor which transitions the plant state from u_1 to u_2.

Proof: Since u_1 and u_2 are connected, then either $I_1 \subset I_2$ or $I_2 \subset I_1$. In the first case, $\mathbf{x}$ is already an element of u_2 so that only the second case need be considered.

In the second case, the inclusion of I_1 in I_2 implies that $u_2 \subset u_1$. Let $\tilde{z}$ be the plant symbol issued by the generator (i.e., $\tilde{z} = g(\mathbf{x})$) when $\mathbf{x} \in u_1$. Define the supervisor so that it maps $\tilde{z}$ onto the covering symbol, $\tilde{c}_i^{\pm}$, within the collection $\tilde{z}$ which has the largest index i.

If the control symbol issued by the supervisor is $\tilde{c}_i^{\pm}$ then by theorem 1, the plant state will eventually be taken out of the set $c_i^+ \cup c_i^-$. After leaving this set, the subsequent plant symbol issued by the generator will not contain either $\tilde{c}_i^+$ or $\tilde{c}_i^-$. The supervisor then issues a new control symbol, $\tilde{c}_j^+$, which forces the removal of $\tilde{c}_j^+$ and $\tilde{c}_j^-$ from the plant symbol $\tilde{z}$ issued by the generator. Furthermore, the ith positive and negative covering symbols cannot be put back into $\tilde{z}$ since this would automatically result in the issuance of a control symbol which takes these symbols out of $\tilde{z}$. Consequently, the proposed supervisor will successively drive the plant state out of all covering sets $c_i^{\pm}$ which have indices in I_2. This then means that the plant state must eventually lie in u_2. •

Note that the event covering will also define a finite partition of the state space. Let V denote a collection of such "partitioning" events, $v \in V$. The following theorem provides conditions for the existence of a supervisor which transitions the plant between any 2 partition events.

Theorem 3 *Let v_0 and v_f be any two parititon events of V. If the assumptions of theorem 2 hold for $i = 1, \ldots, p$, then there exists a supervisor which transitions the plant state from v_0 to v_f.*

Proof: v_0 and v_f can be contained within a closed connected set, M, which has a finite open cover contained within C. Event v_0 and v_f can also be defined by subcollections, $\tilde{z}_0$ and $\tilde{z}_f$, of covering symbols issued by the generator. Let I_0 and I_f be the corresponding index sets.

If $I_0 \cap I_f$ is not empty, then it is trivial to construct a sequence of command events. This is accomplished by enlarging the collection, $\tilde{z}_0$, with elements from $\tilde{z}_f$ and then removing those symbols of $\tilde{z}_0$ which are not in $\tilde{z}_f$. If $I_0 \cap I_f$ is empty, then the fact that M has a connected open subcover implies that an event can be found which does connect these two events. In this case, the preceding procedure is followed again to construct a sequence of connected command events containing v_0 and v_f.

Once the sequence of command events is constructed, then theorem 2 implies the existence of a supervisor which transitions the plant state between any 2 connected events in the sequence thereby yielding the supervisability between v_0 and v_f asserted in the theorem. •

4 Learning to Coordinate by Example

The preceding section showed that the plant can be sequenced through a collection of connected events provided control vectors $\mathbf{r}_i$ ($i = 1, \ldots, p$) can be specified which stabilize the system with regard to the Lypunov functionals, $V_i(\mathbf{x}) = (\mathbf{s}_i'\mathbf{x} - \alpha_i - \beta_i)^2$. This condition implies that for all $\mathbf{x}$,

$$(\mathbf{s}_i'\mathbf{x} - \alpha_i - \beta_i)(\mathbf{s}_i'\dot{\mathbf{x}}) < 0 \quad (19)$$

Without loss of generality assume that $\mathbf{s}_i'\mathbf{x} - \alpha_i - \beta_i > 0$. In light of the supervisor constructed in the proof of theorem 2, this implies that the control symbol to be issued will be $\tilde{c}_i^+$. Using this fact in equation 19 as well as the assumed plant model yields

$$\begin{pmatrix} \mathbf{s}_i' f_1(\mathbf{x}) & \cdots & \mathbf{s}_i' f_m(\mathbf{x}) \end{pmatrix} \begin{pmatrix} r_1 \\ \cdots \\ r_m \end{pmatrix} < 0 \quad (20)$$

where $r_j = a_j(\tilde{c}_i^+)$ for $j = 1, \ldots, m$ and $a_j : \tilde{R} \rightarrow \Re$ are the components of the actuator mapping.

Equation 20 forms a set of linear inequalities. The problem is to define the actuator mappings, a, which map control symbols, $\tilde{c}_i^{\pm} \in \tilde{C}$, onto control vectors,$\mathbf{r}_i^{\pm} \in \Re^m$ so that the inequalities of equation 20 are satisfied for all i. The solution to this problem is a search procedure for a feasible point for the inequality system. Numerical algorithms for doing such searches are well known. One particularly appealing approach is the central-cut ellipsoid method [Shor 1977]. The advantage of this approach is that it has well understood convergence properties.

The search for the feasible point of inequality system 20 can be easily framed in terms of an inductive inference procedure. Inductive inference is a machine learning algorithm which has found extensive applications in the learning of Boolean functions by example [Angluin 1983] and the proof of polynomial time-complexity for certain linear programming algorithms [Khachiyan 1979]. The ability to reframe the search as an inductive inference protocol immediately suggests that the search can be viewed as a "learning" procedure. This means that the use of such protocols will provide a method by which the hybrid system can learn a set of coordinating control vectors $\mathbf{r}$ by simply observing the plant's behaviour. In other words, for a given set of covering events, these ideas imply that the system can automatically learn those controls which insure that the given events yield a "supervisable" hybrid control system.

The specific inductive protocol proposed in this paper consists of four fundamental components.

1. **Hypothesis:** Form an initial hypothesis. Let $\tilde{R}$ be consist of symbols $\{\tilde{c}_i^{\pm}\}$. Specify an acutator mapping $a : \tilde{R} \rightarrow \Re^m$ such that $a(\tilde{c}_i^{\pm}) = \mathbf{r}_i^{\pm}$ for all $i = 1, \ldots, p$. The hypothesis is that the actuator mapping satisfies the Lyapunov inequalities implied by equation 20.

2. **Experiment:** The information needed to evaluate inequality system 20 is contained in $\mathbf{s}_i' f_j(\mathbf{x})$ for all $i = 1, \ldots, p$. This requires that the individual influence of each control policy, $f_j(\mathbf{x})$, must be measured or estimated. The "experiment" consists of the hybrid system's measurment of these quantities.

3. **Oracle Query:** The information gathered by the experiment is tested to see if it is consistent with the hypothesis. This test is simply the evaluation of inequality 20. The oracle is then a Boolean functional which declares TRUE if the current data satisfies the inequalities and declares FALSE if the current data does not satisfy (i.e. is inconsistent) with the inequalities.

4. **Update Algorithm:** If the oracle detects no inconsistency, then nothing is done. If, however, the oracle detects an inconsistency between the currently collected data and the hypothesis, then that implies the hypothesis is incorrect. The direct application of the central-cut ellipsoid method [Shor 1977] allows the computation of a new hypothesis (actuator mapping) which is consistent with the current and all prior data collected by the experiment.

More details on the use of this algorithm can be found in [Lemmon 1992].

Remark 1: The preceding algorithm makes extensive use of the so-called ellipsoid algorithm. The value of using the ellipsoid updating method is that it can be easily shown to converge after a finite number of updates. If it is known that the supervising control vectors $\mathbf{r}_i^{\pm}$ associated with control symbol $\tilde{c}_i^{\pm}$ lie within an m-dimensional ellipsoid of volume v, then the learning protocol can be shown [Lemmon 1992] to find the desired control vector after no more than $2m \ln v^{-1}$ updates.

Remark 2: The finite time bound determined in remark 1 will also imply polynomial time complexity. Using the fact that the volume of an m-dimensional unit sphere is bounded below by m^{-m}, it can be shown that the bound cited in remark 1 will scale as $m^2 \ln m \approx m^{2.5}$.

5 Example

The hybrid system framework introduced in this paper can be illustrated by a simple example. The event collection, C, for a hypothetical second order system is shown in figure 1.

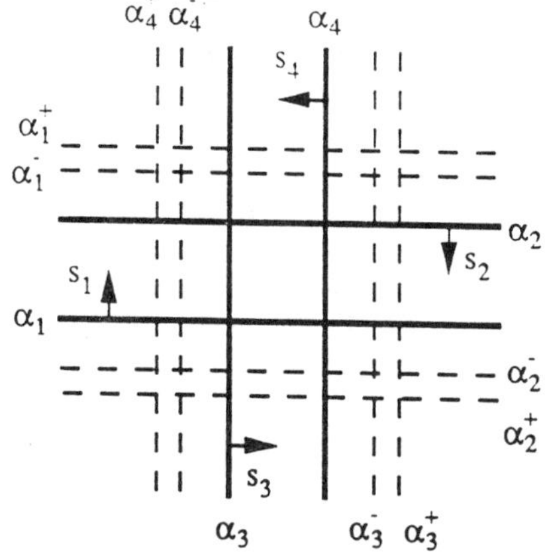

Figure 1: Event Covering for Example

The illustrated event covering consists of twelve events,

$$c_1 \quad c_1^+ \quad c_1^- \quad \cdots \quad c_4 \quad c_4^+ \quad c_4^- \tag{21}$$

where the plant events are characterized by 2-dimensional vectors $\mathbf{s}_i$ and real parameters, α_i, β_i, and δ, for $i = 1, \ldots, 4$.

This section shows how the proposed supervisor transitions the plant from partition event $v_0 = c_1 \cap c_4$ to partition event $v_f = c_2 \cap c_3$. In order to accomplish this task, we must first determine a connected sequence of command events for the initial and final partition events. In this example the command sequence of events will be

$$c_1 \cap c_4 \quad c_4 \quad c_4 \cap c_2 \quad c_2 \quad c_2 \cap c_3 \tag{22}$$

Assume that the plant starts at the location marked "A" in figure 2. In this case, the first symbol issued by the generator will be

$$\tilde{z}_A = \{\ \tilde{c}_1 \quad \tilde{c}_1^+ \quad \tilde{c}_2^- \quad \tilde{c}_3^- \quad \tilde{c}_4 \quad \tilde{c}_4^+\ \} \qquad (23)$$

The positive and negative index sets will be $I_A = \{1,2,3,4\}$. The first commanded event is $c_1 \cap c_4$ with index set $\{1,4\}$. Therefore the control symbol issued by the supervisor will be $\tilde{c}_4^+$. This control symbol will drive the plant state out of c_4^+ and c_4^- so that the plant state, $\mathbf{x}$, is constrained to the shaded boundary layer marked as "B" in figure 2.

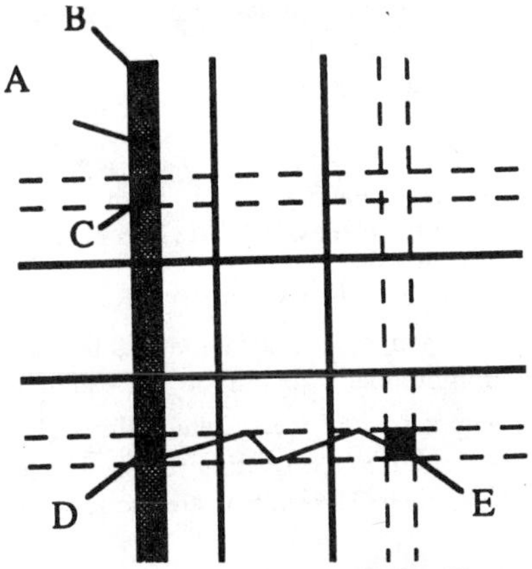

Figure 2: Event Trajectory for Example

With the plant state confined to the boundary layer marked "B", then the generator issues a different event of the form

$$\tilde{z}_B = \{\ \tilde{c}_1 \quad \tilde{c}_1^+ \quad \tilde{c}_2^- \quad \tilde{c}_3^- \quad \tilde{c}_4 \quad \} \qquad (24)$$

The positive and negative index sets will be $I_B^+ = \{1,2,3\}$. The command event is still $c_1 \cap c_4$ so that the control symbol issued by the supervisor will be $\tilde{c}_1^+$. This control symbol drives the plant state out of c_1^+ and c_1^- so that the plant state, $\mathbf{x}$, is constrained to the shaded region marked as "C" in figure 2.

Note that the collection of control symbols generated by the supervisor will now be the empty set. This control symbol signals that the supervisor should use the next command event to supervise the plant. The next command event is c_4. Which will once again yield the empty set as the control symbol. The following command event, $c_4 \cap c_2$ must therefore be used. This results in the control symbol $\tilde{c}_2^-$ being issued by the supervisor. The resulting action is to drive the plant state into region "D" of figure 2. Once the plant enters region "D", then the final command events c_2 and $c_2 \cap c_3$ can be used by the supervisor in the same way. This leads to the issuance of control symbols which drive the plant along another boundary layer connecting events "D" and "E" as shown in figure 2. Event "E" is, of course, the final desired state of the system.

6 Summary

This paper builds upon prior work [Stiver 1992] in which the interface between a CSS plant and DES supervisor was consisted of two memoryless mappings between continuous and logical variables. The current work modifies that earlier work in that the generator realizes a finite open cover for the plant's state space which is formed by a family of linear halfspaces. This paper has two principal results concerning this family of hybrid systems. The first result establishes sufficient conditions for the plant to be supervised through a sequence of "command" events. The second result shows that an interface satisfying these supervisability conditions can be learned using an inductive inference protocol after a finite number of updates.

References

[Angluin 1983] D. Angluin, C.H. Smith, *Computing Surveys*, 15(3):237-269, September 1983.

[Antsaklis 1993] P.J. Antsaklis, M.D. Lemmon, and J.A. Stiver, *Hybrid System Modeling and Event Identification*, Technical Report of the Group for Intedisciplinary Studies of Intelligent Systems, ISIS-93-002, Department of Electrical and Computer Engineering, University of Notre Dame, Notre Dame, IN, January 1993.

[Groetschel 1988] Groetshel, Lovasz, and Schrijver (1988), *Geometric Algorithms and Combinatorial Optimization*, Springer-Verlag, 1988.

[Khachiyan 1979] L.G. Khachiyan (1979), *Soviet Mathematics Doklady*, 20:191-194, 1979.

[Lemmon 1992] M.D. Lemmon, "Ellispoidal Methods for the Estimation of Sliding Mode Domains of Variable Structure Systems", *Procedings of 1992 Conference on Information Sciences and Systems*, Dept. of Electrical Eng., Princeton University, Princeton, New Jersey, pg 1018-1023.

[Shor 1977] N.Z. Shor (1977), *Cybernetics*, 13:94-96, 1977.

[Stiver 1992] J.A. Stiver, P.J. Antsaklis, "Modeling and Analysis of Hybrid Control Systems", *Proc. 31st Conference on Decision and Control*, 1992.

[Utkin 1977] V.I. Utkin (1977), *IEEE Transactions on Automatic Control*, Vol. AC-22:212-222.

Proceedings of the
American Control Conference
San Francisco, California • June 1993

Robustness and Convergence of P-type Learning Control

Samer S. Saab, William G. Vogt, Marlin H. Mickle
Department of Electrical Engineering
University of Pittsburgh, Pittsburgh, Pennsylvania 15261

Abstract

The robustness and convergence of P-type learning control algorithms for a class of time-varying, nonlinear systems to state disturbances, measurement noise at the output, and reinitialization errors at each iteration is studied extensively. We present the uniform boundedness of the system states with respect to the existence of errors of initialization, measurement noises and fluctuations of system dynamics. Furthermore, the system output converges uniformly to the desired one whenever all disturbances tend to zero. Moreover, implication of our results to robot manipulator, and linear systems are presented.

1. Introduction

"Learning", which is one of the most essential characteristics of human beings, can be adopted in engineering systems. In general, the input for a trial execution of the trajectory is a function of the previous input and the resulting trajectory errors. Since learning control algorithms are iterative schemes, the robustness of such algorithms is critical in the presence of disturbances, measurement noise and perturbed errors of initialization. Recently there have been a number of efforts toward the robustness of learning algorithms. Arimoto et al [2] dealt with time-invariant mechanical systems and demonstrated robustness to initial state error and differentiable state disturbances, with the initial trajectory in a small neighborhood. Bondi et al [4] proved the uniform boundedness of trajectories throughout the repetition of training in a local sense under the assumption that the given initial trajectory lies close to the desired one, again for time-invariant mechanical systems. Heinzinger et al [5] has studied the robustness problem for the nonlinear system given in [3] for a class of PID-type learning control. Arimoto in his recent work [7-9] has proved robustness of P-type learning controls based on the passitivity analysis of robot dynamics. Hac [6] examined the properties of the P-type and D-type learning algorithms for linear time-invariant systems in the presence of measurement noise. However, none of the papers have studied the robustness of P-type learning algorithms with respect to the simultaneous existence of disturbances, reinitialization errors and measurement noise for nonlinear systems, and not even for linear time-invariant systems. Learning algorithms require measurements of the output, e.g., angular velocity of the joints in robotic systems. As is known, measured velocity signals are contaminated by noise. Differentiation generally amplifies the noise while integration tends to smooth it. Thus, P-type learning control algorithms are considered more desirable than D-type algorithms. Since the proofs of robustness and convergence of the P-type learning algorithms are crucial in a mathematical sense as was mentioned in [7], but also elusive, this paper is devoted to developing some sufficient conditions which will assure these proporties while at the same time being broader applicable to some systems which do not satisfy positivity conditions often involved [6,10]. In this paper we consider the class of nonlinear, time-varying systems described by the following state space equations:

$$\dot{x}(t) = f(x(t),t) + B(x(t),t)u(t)$$
$$y(t) = Cx(t)$$

This is significant because we can apply our results to a plant with a feedback controller attached. The form of the learning algorithm operates on the error of the previous output error in a memoryless linear fashion:

$$u_{k+1}(t) = (1-\alpha)u_k(t) + \alpha u_0(t) + \phi e_k(t)$$

where $0 \leq \alpha < 1$ and ϕ is a gain matrix, the subscript k denotes the iteration number of operation, for example, $e_k(t)$ is the value of the output error of the system at time t, $0 \leq t \leq T$, at the kth operation, and α is a forgetting factor, which was first introduced in [5]. Such algorithms are called the P-type learning algorithms.

The inclusion of this more general form represents the main contribution of this paper.

In section 2 we state the problem formally and study the robustness of the P-type learning algorithms. Section 3 presents the convergence properties of the algorithms. Section 4 examines the implications to robot manipulator and linear time-varying systems of our conditions and we show that the results of our implication to linear time-varying systems are broader than the linear time invariant systems studied in [6,10]. Finally, in section 5 we give a conclusion.

2. Robustness

In this section we present the global robustness of P-type learning algorithms for a class of nonlinear systems.

Consider the time varying nonlinear systems with linear input action described by the state space equations:

$$\dot{x}_k(t) = f(x_k(t),t) + B(x_k(t),t)u_k(t) + \eta_k(t)$$
$$y_k(t) = Cx_k(t) + \xi_k(t) \tag{1}$$

where $x_k(t)$ and $\eta_k(t) \in \Re^n$, $u_k(t)$, $y_k(t)$ and $\xi_k(t) \in \Re^p$. The functions $f: \Re^n \times [0,T] \rightarrow \Re^n$ is piecewise continuous in t and $B: \Re^n \times [0,T] \rightarrow \Re^p$ is differentiable in t and x. Consider inputs $u_k:[0,T] \rightarrow \Re^p$ to be piecewise continuous in t, and the the desired trajectory $x_d(t)$ to be differentiable in t.

We denote by the inner product $\forall\, t \in [0,T]$

$$<x\,,y> = \int_0^t e^{-\lambda\tau} x^T(\tau)y(\tau)d\tau \quad where\ \lambda > 0.$$

Notations to be used for simplification:

$f_k \equiv f(x_k(t),t)$, $f_d \equiv f(x_d(t),t)$, $B_k \equiv B(x_k(t),t)$, $B_d \equiv B(x_d(t),t)$, $\Delta u_k \equiv u_k(t) - u_d(t)$, $r_k \equiv x_k(t) - x_d(t)$

Assumptions

(A1) The disturbance η_k is such that $\| \eta_k(t) \| \leq b_\eta$, and the measurement noise of the output $\xi_k(t)$ is such that $\| \xi_k(t) \| \le b_\xi$ $\forall$ t $\in$ [0,T] and for all k.

(A2) The input coupling matrix B has a full column rank, and $C^T B^+$ is symmetric positive semi-definite, where $B^+ = (B^T B)^{-1} B^T$ $\forall$ t $\in$ [0,T] and for all k.

(A3) The initial setting is satisfied within an admissible deviation level, i.e. $\| x_d(0) - x_k(0) \| \le b_{x0}$ $\forall$ k.

(A4) The functions f(. , .) and B(. , .) are uniformly globally Lipschitz in x on [0,T], i.e. $\exists$ a positive constant L_h such that $\forall$ t $\in$ [0,T]

$$\| h(x_1,t) - h(x_2,t) \| \le L_h \| x_1(t) - x_2(t) \|$$

(A5) The desired trajectory $y_d(t)$ is differentiable on [0,T].

(A6) For λ large enough, there exists a positive constant c_f such that the following inequality is satisfied $\forall$ k

$$< f_k - f_d - c_f r_k , B_k^{+T} C r_k > \le \varepsilon_1$$

$\forall$ t $\in$ [0,T], where ε_1 is any constant.

(A1) restricts the disturbances which require random and deterministic disturbances to be bounded, although they may be discontinuous such as stiction. (A3) and (A4) are not unreasonable for physical systems. (A6) is an important restriction on the system, but some validations of this assumption are given in section 4. (A2) requires that the number of inputs to be equal to the number of outputs and it can be satisfied if the input coupling matrix B is related to the output coupling matrix C as follows: $B^T = PC$, where P is a positive definite matrix and $CC^T P^T$ is symmetric.

Consider the update law given by

$$u_{k+1}(t) = (1 - \alpha) u_k(t) + \alpha u_0(t) + \phi e_k(t) \qquad (2)$$

where $0 \le \alpha < 1$ and the error $e_k(t) = y_d(t) - y_k(t)$, ϕ is a constant gain matrix, symmetric and positive definite.

Remark: $M < N \Leftrightarrow (N - M)$ is positive definite.

Theorem1:

Suppose the system of (1) satisfies assumptions (A1)-(A6). If α is chosen to satisfy $(1 - \alpha)(I + 2b_\xi \sqrt{\phi}) < I$, then the learning operator given by (2) will generate a sequence of inputs $u_k(t)$, t$\in$ [0,T], such that the error between $u_k(t)$ and $u_d(t)$, $x_k(t)$ and $x_d(t)$, $\dot{x}_k(t)$ and $\dot{x}_d(t)$, and the error between $y_k(t)$ and $y_d(t)$ are all bounded $\forall$ k and $\forall$ t$\in$ [0,T].

The proof of Theorem 1 is given in detail in either [1] or [11].

3. Convergence

In this section the convergence properties of the P-type learning algorithm are presented. The same assumptions are employed as in Theorem 1 except for (A6), with an additional one relating the input coupling matrix B to the output coupling matrix C as follows: $B_k^T = P_k C$, where P_k is a positive definite matrix and $CC^T P_k^T$ is symmetric.

(A6') In addition to (A6), for λ large enough, there exists a positive constant c_P such that the following inequality is satisfied $\forall$ k and $\forall$ t $\in$ [0,T]

$$\| I - (P_k^T)^{-1} P_d^T \| \le c_P \| C(x_k(t) - x_d(t)) \|$$

Note that if $B_k = B_d$ for all k, then (A6) and (A6') will be the same.

Theorem 2:

Suppose the system of (1) satisfies (A1)-(A5),(A6'), and assume that $B_k^T = P_k C$, where P_k is a positive definite matrix and $CC^T P_k^T$ is symmetric, $\forall$ k on [0,T], then the learning operator given by (2) will generate a sequence of inputs $u_k(t)$, t $\in$ [0,T], such that the error converges to zero uniformly, i.e. $\| e_k \| = \| y_d - y_k \| \to 0$ as $k \to \infty$ and whenever α, b_{x0}, b_ξ, and b_η tend to zero.

The proof of Theorem 2 is given in detail in [11].

In the following we give a substitute assumption to (A6').

(A6'') For λ large enough, $\exists$ $c_f > 0$, such that the following inequality is satisfied $\forall$ k on [0,T]

$$< f_k - f_d + (B_k - B_d) u_d - c_f r_k , B_k^{+T} C r_k > \le \varepsilon_1$$

where ε_1 is any constant which tends to zero as all disturbances tend to zero.

Again, if $B_k = B_d$ for all k, then (A6) and (A6'') will coincide.

Theorem 3:

Suppose the system of (1) satisfies (A1)-(A5),(A6''), and assume that $B_k^T = P_k C$, where P_k is a positive definite matrix and $CC^T P_k^T$ is symmetric $\forall$ k on [0,T], then the learning operator given by (2) will generate a sequence of inputs $u_k(t)$, t $\in$ [0,T], such that the error converges to zero uniformly, i.e. $\| e_k \| = \| y_d - y_k \| \to 0$ as $k \to \infty$ and whenever α, b_{x0}, b_ξ, and b_η tend to zero.

The proof of Theorem 3 is given in detail in [11].

4. Implications

In this section we apply the P-type learning algorithm to the dynamics of a class of connected arms robot manipulator and linear systems and examine the implications of our results.

Robot Manipulator: If $q \in \Re^p$ is the vector of joint angles of such a robot manipulator, then we have the dynamics as

$$(H_0 + H(q))\ddot{q} + (B_0 + \dot{H}(q))\dot{q} - \frac{\partial K}{\partial q} + g(q) = u \qquad (3)$$

where H_0 is a positive diagonal matrix representing inertial terms of internal load distribution of actuators, H is an inertia matrix which is symmetric and positive definite and each entry of H is constant or a trigonometric function in q. B_0 is a positive definite matrix representing damping factors and coefficients of electro-motive forces, $K = \dot{q}^T(H_0 + H(q))\dot{q}/2$ is the kinetic energy, g(q) a vector of gravity terms, and u is a vector of input torques generated at actuators.

If a PD feedback is used as an inner loop in the actuator servos which is described by

$$u = v + A(q_d - q) - B_1 \dot{q} \qquad (4)$$

where q_d is a given reference position input and v is an external feedforward input, and A is a symmetric positive definite matrix, then it can be shown [11] that all the assumptions in this paper for robustness and convergence are satisfied. Numerical applications to two-link robot arm is given in [1].

Linear Systems: Consider the time varying linear systems described by

$$\dot{x}_k(t) = A(t) x_k(t) + B(t) u_k(t) + \eta_k(t)$$
$$y_k(t) = C x_k(t) + \xi_k(t) \qquad (5)$$

Where $x_k(t) \in \Re^n$, $u_k(t)$ and $y_k \in \Re^p$, $\eta_k(t) \in \Re^n$, and $\xi_k(t) \in \Re^p$. $B:[0,T] \to \Re^p$ is differentiable in t. Consider inputs $u_k:[0,T] \to \Re^p$ to be piecewise continuous in t. To apply our results we need to check that assumptions (A1)-(A6) are satisfied. We assume (A1),(A3) and (A5) and check for (A2),(A4) and (A6). (A4) is satisfied since the system is linear. Thus the assumptions on (5) are as follows:

(($A2$) $\Leftrightarrow$) B has a full column rank and C^TB^+ is symmetric positive definite.
(($A6$) $\Leftrightarrow$) C^TB^+A is symmetric. Since for c_f large enough we have $M \equiv c_fI - A$ is positive definite, and whenever C^TB^+A is symmetric, C^TB^+M is symmetric, using proposition 1 we have C^TB^+M positive semi-definite, this implies that for c_f large enough, we have

$$\int_0^t e^{-\lambda\tau}(x_k - x_d)^T C^T B^+ (A - c_f I)(x_k - x_d) d\tau \leq 0$$

Employing theorem 1 and using the two assumptions above, we have the learning control given in (2) is robust. Since $B_k = B_d$ $\forall$ k, (A6), (A6') and (A6'') will coincide. Therefore, to achieve convergence employing theorem 2 or 3, it is sufficient to have $B^T = PC$ where P is positive definite and CC^TP^T is symmetric.
To show our contribution, we compare the results of our implication to linear time-varying systems to the linear time invariant systems studied by Hac [6] (and Arimoto [10] where it was shown the convergence of the P-type learning algorithms for linear time invariant and strictly positive systems in absence of all disturbances). Recall that the system must be time invariant and strictly positive, i.e. for any input u(t), and $\eta = 0$, $t \in [0,T]$ and zero initial conditions, the following inequality is satisfied

$$\int_0^T u^T(t)y(t)dt \geq \alpha \int_0^T u^T(t)u(t)dt \qquad (6)$$

with a constant $\alpha > 0$. Note that such inequality requires that the number of inputs to be equal to the number of outputs. Moreover, the disturbance vector $\eta_k(t)$ is T-periodic which is unrealistic, for example, friction is not T-periodic. Furthermore, the reinitialization error is equal to zero for all k, i.e. $x_k(0) = x_0$ $\forall$ k. On the other hand, our sufficient conditions on the system are as follows: B has a full column rank, $B^T = PC$ where $P > 0$, CC^TP^T is symmetric, and C^TB^+A is symmetric which are not very restrictive and easy to check. Moreover, the uniform boundedness of the system states was with respect to *the existence of errors of initialization, measurement noises and fluctuations of system dynamics.*
In the following, we give a simple example of a linear time invariant system which satisfies our sufficient conditions, where the system is *not* strictly positive.

$$y(t) = ay(t) + u(t)$$
$$\text{where } u(t) = \sin(t) \qquad t \in [0,T]$$

Using (63), we have A = a, B = C = 1 which implies that our sufficient conditions for robustness and convergence are satisfied. Note that for zero initial conditions,

$$\int_0^T u(t)y(t)dt = \frac{1}{a^2+1}\left[\frac{e^{aT}}{a^2+1}(a\sin(T) - \cos(T)) - \frac{\sin^2(T)}{2} - \frac{aT}{2} + \frac{a\sin(2T)}{4} + \frac{1}{a^2+1}\right]$$

The equality above is strictly negative for $T = 1.5\pi$ and $a \geq 0.2$, *or* for a=.1 and $T \in [4.8,7.6] \cup$ (other ranges of T), which shows that such systems can not be strictly positive since the right hand term of (6) is always nonnegative. From this example we may conclude that our conditions can be applied to a class of systems where the condition given by Hac [6] and Arimoto [10] fails.

5. Conclusion

The robustness and convergence of P-type learning control algorithms for a class of time-varying, nonlinear systems subject to state disturbances, measurement noise, and reinitialization errors at each iteration was presented. Furthermore, it was shown that the system output converges uniformly to the desired one whenever all disturbances tend to zero. Moreover, implication of our results to robot manipulator, and linear systems were presented. Finally, it was shown that the implication for linear systems are broader than all the results appearing in the literature, in particular, for time-varying systems subject to not only measurement errors, but also to state disturbances and reinitialization errors.

References

[1] S. S. Saab, "Learning Control Convergence and Robustness," Ph.D. dissertation, *University of Pittsburgh*, Pittsburgh, 1992.
[2] S. Arimoto, S. Kawamura, and F. Miyazaki, "Convergence, Stability, and Robustness of Learning Control Schemes for Robot Manipulators," *Int. Sym. on Robot Manipulators: Modeling, Control and Education Albuquerque, NM,* 1986.
[3] J. Hauser, "Learning Control for a Class of Nonlinear Systems," *Proceedings of the 26th Conference on Decision and Controol, Los Angeles,CA.*, 1987 ", pp. 859-860.
[4] P. Bondi, G. Casalino, and L. Gambardella, "On the Iterative Learning Control Theory for Robotic Manipulators," *IEEE Journal of Robotics and Automation*, 1988", pp. 14-22.
[5] G. Heinzinger, D. Fenwick, B. Paden, and F. Miyaziki, "Robust Learning Control," *Proceedings of the 28th Conference on Decision and Control Tampa,Florida,* 1989, pp. 436-440.
[6] Aleksander Hac, "Learning Control in the Presence of Measurement Noise," *American Control Conference,* 1990, pp. 2846-2851.
[7] S. Arimoto, "Learning Control Theory for Robotic Motion," *Int. Journal of Adaptive Control and Signal Proceedings,* 1990, pp. 544-564.
[8] S. Arimoto, T. Naniwa, and H. Suzuki, "Robustness of P-type Learning Control with a Forgetting Factor for Robotic Motions," *Proceedings of the 29th Conference on Decesion and control Honolulu, Hawaii,* 1990, pp. 2640-2645.
[9] S. Arimoto, T. Naniwa, and H. Suzuki, "Selective Learning with a Forgetting Factor for Robotic Motion," *IEEE Int. Conf. on Robotics and Automation Sacramento, CA,* 1991, pp. 728-733.
[10] S. Arimoto, S. kawamura, F. Miyazaki, and S. Tamaki, "Learning Control Theory for Dynamical Systems," *Proceedings of 24th Conference on Decision and Control Ft. Lauderdale FL.*, 1985, pp. 1375-1380.
[11] S. S. Saab, W. G. Vogt, and M. H. Mickle, "Theory of P-type Learning Control with Implication for the Robot Manipulator," *IEEE Int. Conf. on Robotics and Automation Atlanta, GA,* May 1993.

Proceedings of the
American Control Conference
San Francisco, California • June 1993

Intelligent Control via Learning Methods

B.S. Zhang and J.R. Leigh

Industrial Control Centre
University of Westminster, London W1M 8JS, U.K

1. Introduction

Many important industrial processes cannot be well described mathematically and therefore conventional control methods often fail or are inadequate. Interest arises in using ideas from artificial intelligence (AI) in control as AI has generated useful ideas and techniques that may be used to make better control systems, forming an area that can be roughly designated *intelligent control*. There is however no agreed scientific meaning for the term intelligent control. As we understand more about human intelligence, our concept on intelligence changes. We may consider that intelligent control relates to human thinking or learning ability. It consists of a collection of different approaches including expert control, neural networks, learning, genetic algorithms, qualitative simulation and fuzzy control.

The purpose of this paper is to describe some of our research activities in intelligent control, based on various learning methods including time-sequence learning methods, state learning control and trainable pattern classifiers. The ideas of these learning control methods are illustrated and their features and natures are compared.

2. Learning and Learning Control

Learning can be defined as any deliberate or directed change in the knowledge structure of a system that allows it to perform better on later repetitions of some given type of task. Learning is essential to intelligent control systems since a controller cannot be designed to explicitly anticipate all possible situations, but must be capable of effective self-modification. Learning may be achieved by given examples or through performance feedback.

Terms like *adaptive*, *self-tuning* and *self-organizing* have all been used to describe systems which have some learning abilities. Usually, *adaptive* and *self-tuning* are used in adaptive control involving a mathematical model to describe the desired performance or to describe the process to be identified. Adaptive systems by their very nature are non-linear, however, most of the theories of such systems are deeply rooted in linear systems theory. This implies that the range of uncertainties cannot be very large. *Self-organizing* has been used to describe some internal structure changing capability of systems. In neural networks, it means the modification of many processing elements at once. In fuzzy control, it means the self-adjustment of fuzzy control rules.

In learning control systems, the learned information is considered as an experience of the controller, and it will be used to improve the quality of the controller whenever similar control situations recur. Three methods which we have used for different applications are addressed here.

The idea of time-sequence learning control was first proposed by Uchiyama, and more formally presented by Arimoto [1]. It was proposed for robot motion control to obtain a desired motion by repeating trials in the same way that human beings learn a desired motion pattern through training.

The idea of state learning control methods resulted from the concept of self-organizing fuzzy logic control [6]. It was more formally proposed in [7] with some theoretical investigations. In state learning control, the control law is viewed as a set of control rules modified by a learning procedure according to system performance feedback.

The basic idea of learning control by trainable pattern classifier is due to Rosenblatt, who proposed and used a trainable threshold logic unit as the learning element of a system called α perceptron, with an attempt to parallel the functioning of the human brain.

3. Learning Control Methods

To simplify the description, consider the system

$$\dot{\mathbf{x}} = \mathbf{f}(\mathbf{x}) + \mathbf{g}(\mathbf{x})u, \qquad y = h(\mathbf{x}) \tag{1}$$

where the state $\mathbf{x} \in \mathbb{R}^n$, the input $u \in \mathbb{R}$, the output $y \in \mathbb{R}$, the vector functions $\mathbf{f}(\mathbf{x})$ and $\mathbf{g}(\mathbf{x})$ may be unknown.

Time sequence learning control

The control signal for Eq. (1) generated by the time sequence learning control method is as a time sequence

$$u = u(t) \tag{2}$$

The learning algorithm is

$$u^{k+1}(t) = u^k(t) + \Gamma(e^k(t)) \tag{3}$$

where $u^k(t)$ is the input at the kth iteration, $e^k(t)$ denotes the error between a desired output $y_d(t)$ and the actual output $y^k(t)$ as the response to $u^k(t)$, and $\Gamma(e^k(t))$ is a function which produces modification to the control sequence.

The learning control is so achieved that for each repetition, the input, u^k, is stored, along with the resulting system output, y^k. The learning controller then evaluates the error and computes a new input, u^{k+1} which is stored for use in the next repetition. The task in the time sequence learning control is to specify the algorithm for generating the next input, given the current input and output, so that convergence to the desired output (in the sense of some norm) is attained. Ideally, the convergence property of the learning control algorithm would require a minimal knowledge of the system parameters and would be independent of the desired response, y_d.

The features of this method are that:

- a prespecified desired trajectory $y_d(t)$ is given,
- the learned control signals are stored as a time sequence $u^k(t)$ for the kth repetition,
- this sequence $u^k(t)$, is used for repeated task, $y_d(t)$, $0 < t < T$, T is the period,
- it must start with same initial conditions each time,
- $u^k(t)$ can be precisely stored (at sampling points),
- it is open loop control in nature for each repetition.

The open loop nature and the restriction on initial condition limit the usefulness of the method. We modified this method by putting a predictive feature to learn the best control pattern for a fed batch fermentation process.

State learning control

The control signal in Eq. (1) by the state learning control method is as a rule based state feedback

$$u = \mathcal{U}(\mathbf{x}) \tag{4}$$

The learning algorithm is

$$\mathcal{U}^{k+1}(\mathbf{x}) = \mathcal{U}^{k}(\mathbf{x}) + \delta\mathcal{U}(\mathbf{x}) \quad (5)$$

where $\mathcal{U}^k(\mathbf{x})$ is the control action when the kth time the state $\mathbf{x}$ appears. $\mathcal{U}^{k+1}(\mathbf{x})$ is the future control action for the same state $\mathbf{x}$ to recur. $\delta\mathcal{U}(\mathbf{x})$ denotes the control action modification value derived according to the actual performance and the desired performance of the system based on the idea of rule modification [6] [7]. Combined with the concept of sliding mode, this learning control method was proposed and theoretically investigated [7].

The features of the state learning control are that:

- it is unnecessary to have a prespecified desired trajectory,
- the learned control signals are stored according to system state instead of time,
- it is unnecessary to have a repeated task,
- the system state for storage needs to be quantized,
- the method is a feedback control strategy.

This method has been applied to various processes with unknown dynamics, linear or nonlinear, open loop stable or unstable, such as inverted pendulum problems.

Learning control by trainable pattern classifier

A learning controller can be realised by a trainable pattern classifier whose weights are trained so that an optimal control law may be gradually established for the various classes of control situations and the admissible control actions. To do this, the state space is transformed into a pattern space and the state variables are encoded into pattern vectors. The outputs of the classifier can be the control actions or their classes. The weights of the classifier are trained by a given training set (a finite number of control situations with known optimal control actions). The training pattern vectors are fed to the classifier sequentially several times to train the weights until all the training pattern vectors can be correctly classified.

The output of an optimal controller is usually a continuously function except for time optimal control. Therefore we can use a linear summation of the outputs of discriminants as the classifier output, instead of directly using a maximum selector. Generally the control law is nonlinear. However, a linear classifier can be used as a piecewise linear approximation provided that there is no cross product term. To achieve this, first, each element x_i of the state $\mathbf{x}$ is transformed into a finite number of d_i levels encoded by a set of linearly independent vector X_i of dimension d_i, associated with a d_i dimensional weight vector W_i. A nonlinear control law may then be approximated by

$$u = \Sigma_{i=1}^{n} W_i^T X_i = W^T X \quad (6)$$

where $W^T = [W_1^T, W_2^T, \cdots, W_n^T]$ is the total weight vector and $X^T = [X_1^T, X_2^T, \cdots, X_n^T]$ is the total pattern vector. The weight vector can be modified by adding/subtracting a vector in the direction of the training pattern vector for which the classification by the classifier is incorrect, i.e,

$$W^{k+1} = W^k \pm \alpha X \quad (7)$$

The features of this method are that:

- a linear classifier may be used to approximate the nonlinear control law,
- a training set with known answer is usually needed,
- it usually stops learning when the training process is terminated,
- it forms a closed loop controller.

Using the ideas of performance feedback it can also achieve on-line learning feedback control. We have used the pattern classification method as a tool to learn the most appropriate input patterns of a fed-batch fermentation process using a set of data from an industrial plant.

4. Some Remarks and Conclusion

Three learning control methods which we have used in the design of intelligent control systems are described in this paper. Many other techniques for learning which can be used in control, however, are not discussed. The idea of a time-sequence iterative learning control scheme is to apply a simple algorithm repetitively to an unknown plant until a perfect tracking is achieved. The state learning controller can be viewed as a rule based controller with learning capability based on the ideas in self-organizing fuzzy logic control. Learning control by trainable pattern classifier is adapted from the theory of pattern recognition.

The common feature of these learning control methods is that the control quality of an unknown process is improved by memorizing past experience. The basic difference is the way they store the control experience. In time sequence learning control the past experience is stored as a time sequence. In state learning control it is usually stored as fuzzy rules in terms of situations and actions. While in the trainable pattern classifier method the experience is stored by a weight vector.

One restriction with the time sequence learning control is the requirement that the initial conditions for each repetition should be the same. In state learning control the process state needs to be quantized and this decreases precision. Increasing the number of the quantization levels can increase precision but reduces the speed of learning and increases the size of memory. We used fuzzy sets to solve this problem because of their interpolative nature. Quantization of state variables is also needed in the trainable pattern classifier, which makes a linear classifier capable of storing nonlinear functions. A linear classifier can approximate a nonlinear control law to an arbitrary degree of accuracy by increasing the number of quantization levels, but for a linear classifier this is true only when there is no cross product term in the control law.

The time sequence learning control method is suitable for processes that are repetitive in nature and operate on a fixed interval. The method is open loop control in nature for each repetition. The learning can be achieved off-line. The state learning control is a form of feedback control which can learn any nonlinearities if the system fits into certain forms [7]. The learning is usually achieved on-line. The trainable pattern classifier resembles the state learning controller in that both the features (to the pattern classifier) and the input situations (to the state learning controller) are formed from the state of the system. It can learn from open-loop control trajectories and form a closed loop controller. The learning is usually achieved off-line by providing a training set. It can also realize on-line learning by using performance feedback.

References

[1] Arimoto S, Kawamura S and Miyasaki F, "Bettering operation of robots by learning", *J. Robotic Syst.*, vol.1, 123-140, 1984

[2] Åström K.J, "Intelligent control", *Proc. ECC'91*, 2328-2339, 1991

[3] Fu, K.S, "Learning control systems— review and outlook", *IEEE Trans. Automatic Control*, AC-15 (2), 210-221, 1970

[4] Miller W.T, Sutton R.S and Werbos P.J (eds), *Neural Networks for Control*, A Bradford Book, 1990

[5] Nilsson N.J, *Learning Machines*, McGraw-Hill Book Company, 1965

[6] Procyk T.J and Mamdani E.H, "A linguistic self-organizing process controller", *Automatica*, 15, 15-30, 1979

[7] Zhang B.S and Edmunds J.M, "A state learning controller", *Proc. 1992 ACC*, 3057-3061, 1992.

Proceedings of the
American Control Conference
San Francisco, California • June 1993

On-line Learning of Linear Systems *

S.E. Posner, S.R. Kulkarni
posner@ee.princeton.edu, kulkarni@ee.princeton.edu
Department of Electrical Engineering
Princeton University, Princeton, NJ 08544

Abstract

We consider the problem of learning/identification of a linear system by sampling its frequency response. A cumulative prediction error type criterion is used to describe the learnability of classes of (continuous- or discrete-time) linear systems which may have discontinuous frequency responses but of bounded variation. Upper and lower bounds are obtained for three input frequency sampling schemes: worst-case, random, and worst-case with small noise on the input frequency. Bounds are also obtained for the random sampling scheme with ℓ_1 noise or i.i.d. noise corrupting the frequency response samples.

1. Introduction

The focus of recent work on system identification has been on the worst-case minimization of the norm between a system and its approximation based on some algorithm. One scheme is to observe the output of a noisy system until time n and construct a system approximation based on that data using some algorithm. Results in [7] indicate that the ℓ_1 norm between a discrete-time linear system and its approximation goes to zero asymptotically. Another approach for analysis of continuous-time linear systems is to obtain samples of the frequency response and to construct an approximation that converges to the true system in $\mathcal{H}_\infty$ [2, 6, 4, 5].

We propose an alternate setup for the learning of linear systems, namely minimizing the cumulative error of prediction. Given a continuous- (or discrete-) time linear time-invariant system we can obtain frequency response samples $\hat{g}(j\omega)$ by observing the output subject to sinusoidal excitation. This reduces the system identification problem to a general function learning problem. While other frameworks indicate that identification of certain classes is possible asympototically, they do not give an indication of the magnitude of the errors occurring at all times. An interesting measure used by the computational learning community [3] is the sum of absolute errors. A cumulative error type criterion reveals much about the complexity of the function under study. Growth of the cumulative error provides a refined measure of the complexity of identifying a linear system. If the growth is "slow" then nontrivial learning is taking place. The work in the PAC learning community [1] has a different perspective on function learning and does not imply our results.

*This work was supported in part by the National Science Foundation under grant IRI-9209577 and by the U.S. Army Research Office under grant DAAL03-92-G-0320.

Our scheme works for both continuous- and discrete-time systems. We proceed with a study of continuous-time systems; the results carry over readily to discrete-time systems. Our approach is to obtain samples of the frequency-response of the system and to predict other values based on those samples previously seen. The prediction is based on the simple "nearest-neighbor" algorithm. As might be expected, it will be shown that smoothness conditions are key to ensuring the cumulative error to have modest growth rate. Results from [3] show that the cumulative error is finite for various classes of differentiable functions. Here we prove a number of statements about functions with discontinuities but of bounded variation. We consider both worst-case sampling and random sampling, and we introduce a new mixed setting which combines worst-case and random sampling and is interpreted as noise on the input frequency. In this paper we present such a framework for systems with both noiseless and noisy outputs.

2. Problem Formulation

Given a continuous-time linear time-invariant system with impulse response $g(t)$ and associated Fourier transform $\hat{g}(j\omega)$, we consider noisy frequency response samples $\{\hat{g}(j\omega_i) + d_i\}$. The noise sequence $\{d_i\}$ is either identically zero (noiseless), a sequence in ℓ_1, or i.i.d. zero mean finite variance noise. An algorithm $\phi = \{\phi_n\}$ computes an estimate of $\hat{g}(j\omega_n)$— call it $\phi_n(j\omega_n)$— based on the pairs $\{\omega_i, \hat{g}(j\omega_i)\}_{i=1}^{n-1}$. We then define the prediction error $e_n := |\hat{g}(j\omega_n) - \phi_n(j\omega_n)|$. We define our problem on a compact set $I \subset \mathbb{R}$, i.e., $\sigma := \{\omega_i\}_{i=1}^{n} \subset I$ is a sequence of frequencies in the interval under consideration. Define T as the length of I. We assume that $\hat{g}$ restricted to I belongs to a function class $\mathcal{M}$. The cumulative error of on-line learning by algorithm ϕ of a function $\hat{g}$ given samples σ is defined as $\sum_{i=2}^{n} e_i$.

We consider systems belonging to the following set:

$$\mathcal{M}_{BV} = \{\hat{f} : \|\hat{f}\|_{BV} \leq V\}$$

where $BV[I]$ is the Banach space of functions of bounded variation over the bounded interval I, and $V \in \mathbb{R}_+$. We present results for three sampling schemes: worst-case, random, and a new intermediate mixed sampling scheme. Worst-case sampling is where an adversary can choose input frequencies, random sampling is where input frequencies are drawn i.i.d. from a fixed probability distribution, and mixed sampling is where an adversary chooses input frequencies but the actual frequency sample is drawn uniformly from a small δ neighborhood about the adversary-chosen point. The interpretation of mixed sampling is of worst-case sampling with a limitation on the power of the adversary.

3. Results

Kimber and Long [3] considered function classes consisting of piecewise twice differentiable functions on bounded intervals with smoothness constraints on their first derivatives over that interval. We extend their work to the class $\mathcal{M}_{BV}$ which contains nonsmooth functions. Thus, we allow for systems with discontinuous frequency responses, e.g., a rectangle.

We present our results in the form of the following theorems. The first two theorems are a presentation of results for noiseless outputs, i.e., the learner sees noiseless frequency response samples $\{\hat{g}(j\omega_i)\}$. These results reflect the complexity of a given function class and sampling scheme.

Theorem 1 (Noiseless Output/Upper Bounds) *There exists algorithms such that for any $\hat{g} \in \mathcal{M}_{BV}$,*

- *Worst-Case*— $\sup_{\{\omega_i\}_{i=1}^n} \sum_{k=2}^n e_k = Vn$
- *Random*— $E\sum_{k=2}^n e_k \leq 13V\log^2 n$
- *Mixed*— $\sup_{\{\omega_i\}_{i=1}^n} \sum_{k=2}^n e_k \leq 8V\sqrt{n}(\frac{T}{\delta} + 13\log n)$

Theorem 2 (Noiseless Output/Lower Bounds) *For any algorithm there exists a $\hat{g} \in \mathcal{M}_{BV}$ and a sequence $\{\omega_i\}_{i=1}^n$ such that*

- *Worst-Case*— $\sum_{k=2}^n e_k \geq Vn$
- *Random*— $E\sum_{k=2}^n e_k \geq \frac{V}{2}\log\frac{n}{2}$
- *Mixed*— $\sum_{k=2}^n e_k \geq O(\frac{T}{\delta} + \log n)$

This shows that an arbitrary limitation in the power of an adversary drastically reduces the growth rate. The next two theorems contain bounds for the random sampling case with either ℓ_1 noise (in a ball of radius δ) or i.i.d. (zero mean, finite variance σ^2) noise corrupting the output.

Theorem 3 (Noisy Output/Upper Bounds) *There exists algorithms such that for any $\hat{g} \in \mathcal{M}_{BV}$,*

- *ℓ_1 noise*— $E\sum_{k=2}^n e_k \leq 13(V+\delta)\log^2 n$
- *i.i.d. noise*— $E\sum_{k=2}^n e_k \leq 3(V+\sigma)n^{\frac{2}{3}}$

Theorem 4 (Noisy Output/Lower Bounds) *For any algorithm there exists a $\hat{g} \in \mathcal{M}_{BV}$ and a sequence $\{\omega_i\}_{i=1}^n$ such that*

- *ℓ_1 noise*— $E\sum_{k=2}^n e_k \geq \frac{V}{2}\log\frac{n}{2}$
- *i.i.d. Gaussian noise*—$E\sum_{k=2}^n e_k \geq \frac{3\sigma}{2}(\sqrt{n} - \sqrt{2})$

Hence the cumulative error growth is the same amid ℓ_1 noise but increases with i.i.d. noise with an arbitrarily small variance.

4. Connections to other Identification Schemes

We now discuss the connection between our work and that of traditional uniform identification frameworks [7, 6, 2]. While our criterion is certainly stronger than others, a statement about the closeness of our approximating system can still be made. The following statement is that in the probabilistic setup we have that the system approximation ϕ_n, based on the nearest neighbor algorithm at the nth step, will a.s. converge to the system in $\mathcal{L}_1$.

Proposition 1 *If $\sigma = \{\omega_i\}$ is i.i.d. uniform on $[0,1]$, then for any $\hat{f} \in \mathcal{M}_{BV}$ we have*

$$\|\hat{f} - \phi_n\|_{\mathcal{L}_1} \to 0 \qquad a.s.$$

This is in fact a corollary of Theorem 1 and the proof is straightforward. Certainly in a deterministic worst-case setting no such statement can be made as the adversary can focus on one section of the domain. However, consider an adversary who can choose points σ maliciously but must maintain that $T_\sigma(n) \overset{n\to\infty}{\longrightarrow} 0$, where $T_\sigma(n)$ is the length of the largest unsampled subinterval after n steps. That is, if we consider worst-case sampling that covers the whole interval densely, we have the following result.

Proposition 2 *If $T_\sigma(n) \overset{n\to\infty}{\longrightarrow} 0$, then for any $\hat{f} \in \mathcal{M}_{BV}$ we have*

$$\|\hat{f} - \phi_n\|_{\mathcal{L}_1} \overset{n\to\infty}{\longrightarrow} 0$$

References

[1] Haussler, D. "Decision Theoretic Generalizations of the PAC Model for Neural Net and Other Learning Applications," Information and Computation, vol. 100, pp. 78-150, 1992.

[2] Helmicki, A.J., C.A. Jacobson, and C.N. Nett. "Control Oriented System Identification: A Worst-Case/Deterministic Approach in $\mathcal{H}_\infty$", IEEE Trans. Automat. Contr., vol. AC-36, pp. 1163-1176, Oct. 1991.

[3] Kimber, D. and P.M. Long. "The Learning Complexity of Smooth Functions of a Single Variable," Proc. of 5th Workshop on Computational Learning Theory, COLT, 1992.

[4] Makila, P.M. "Approximation and identification of continuous-time systems," Int. J. Control, vol. 52, no. 3, 669-687, 1990.

[5] Makila, P.M. and J.R. Partington. "Robust approximation and identification in $\mathcal{H}_\infty$," Proceedings of the 1991 ACC.

[6] Partington, J.R. "Worst-case identification in Banach spaces," Syst. Contr. Lett., vol. 18, pp. 423-428, 1992.

[7] Tse, D.N.C., M.A. Dahleh, and J.N. Tsitsiklis. "Optimal Asymptotic Identification Under Bounded Disturbances," to appear Trans. Automat. Contr.

Proceedings of the
American Control Conference
San Francisco, California • June 1993

An Optimal Mid-Course Guidance Law For Fixed-Interval Propulsive Maneuvers*

Mohammad-Ali Massoumnia
Integrated Systems Inc., 3260 Jay Street, Santa Clara, CA 95054

Abstract

In this paper we develop an optimal mid-course strategy for guiding an interceptor. We assume that the target is outside of the sensible atmosphere and is not maneuvering throughout the engagement, and the thrust vector controlled interceptor has a fixed maneuvering time which ends well before the actual intercept. We will later extend the optimal solution to a family of guidance laws that guarantee perfect intercept for the fixed-interval maneuvering problems.

1 Introduction

In this paper we concentrate on the problem of guiding a missile to intercept a non-maneuvering target moving at high velocities outside the atmosphere. The important distinguishing constraint that we impose on this problem is that the thrust vector controlled interceptor has a fixed maneuvering time which ends well before the actual intercept. Therefore, there is a period of time before the intercept that the missile is not maneuvering at all and is coasting ballistically toward the target.

This scenario is representative of a midcourse strategy during which the missile is guided so as to assure a proper collision course to the target before the depletion of the propulsive subsystem which provides the missile maneuvering capability. Following propulsion depletion, the missile coasts ballistically to the target intercept region where a small kinetic energy kill vehicle (KKV) is released to achieve target impact with minimum steering effort.

Here, we ignore the kill vehicle and concentrate our effort on developing the guidance law for the propelled stage that delivers the KKV to its intercept region.

2 Optimal Guidance Law

Assuming the intercept takes place outside of any appreciable atmosphere and the target is not maneuvering, the equations of motion of the missile and the target in an appropriate inertial frame can be described as follows:

$$\dot{\underline{v}}_M = \underline{a}_M + \underline{g}_M, \quad \dot{\underline{r}}_M = \underline{v}_M \tag{1}$$

$$\dot{\underline{v}}_T = \underline{g}_T, \quad \dot{\underline{r}}_T = \underline{v}_T \tag{2}$$

where $\underline{r}_M$ and $\underline{r}_T$ denote the position of the missile and the target and $\underline{v}_M$ and $\underline{v}_T$ denote the respective velocities. Also, $\underline{a}_M$ represents the thrust acceleration of the missile. The two position dependent terms $\underline{g}_M$ and $\underline{g}_T$ respectively denote the gravitational acceleration of the missile and the target. Moreover, we assume the position difference between the target and the missile is small enough so the gravitational acceleration terms are approximately equal, $\underline{g}_M \approx \underline{g}_T$. By subtracting (1) from (2), the relative equations of motion in terms of the relative position $\underline{r} = \underline{r}_T - \underline{r}_M$ and relative velocity $\underline{v} = \underline{v}_T - \underline{v}_M$ are as follows:

$$\dot{\underline{v}}(t) = -\underline{a}_M(t), \; \dot{\underline{r}}(t) = \underline{v}(t) \tag{3}$$

Note that the direction of $\underline{r}$ is along the line of sight (LOS) from the missile to the target.

Our objective is to compute the missile acceleration $\underline{a}_M$ at the present time t as a function of present relative position $\underline{r}(t)$ and relative velocity $\underline{v}(t)$ so a minimum effort intercept occurs at time T which is after the missile burn out time t_f ($t_f \leq T$). To solve this problem, we compute $\underline{a}_M(t)$ by minimizing the following objective function

$$J = \frac{\gamma}{2}\underline{r}^T(T)\underline{r}(T) + \frac{1}{2}\int_t^{t_f} \underline{a}_M^T(\tau)\underline{a}_M(\tau)d\tau \tag{4}$$

with the weighting $\gamma \geq 0$. Note that the first term in the right hand side of (4) is the weighted miss distance squared and by choosing very large values for γ, we can guarantee that $\underline{r}(T)$ takes small values and an intercept at time T actually occurs.

Assuming the thrust acceleration of the missile is zero during the time period from t_f to T, we have

$$\underline{r}(T) = \underline{r}(t_f) + \underline{v}(t_f)(T - t_f) \tag{5}$$

Next we substitute (5) in (4) and solve the resulting optimal control problem using standard procedures given in [2]. The optimal acceleration command $\underline{a}_{MO}$ will have the form of state feedback

$$\underline{a}_{MO}(t) = \frac{t_g}{1/\gamma + t_b(t_g^2 - t_g t_b + t_b^2/3)}[\underline{r}(t) + t_g\underline{v}(t)] \tag{6}$$

where $t_b = t_f - t$ denotes the time to missile burn out, and $t_g = T - t = \delta + t_b$ denotes the time to go until intercept. Note that if we let $\gamma \to \infty$ in (6) and set $t_g = t_b$ ($T = t_f$) which then allows maneuvering the missile until the intercept point, the usual proportional navigation guidance law with the navigation constant of 3 (c.f. [4]) will be obtained.

3 Analysis of the Solution

In this section we completely analyze the properties of the guidance law given in (6) for the case $\gamma \to \infty$. Specifically,

*This work was sponsored by The Strategic Defense Initiative Organization (SDIO) under ANSER subcontract 92-ISIC-009-7-DSD3 (prime contract DSD3-0501-ISIC)

we shall show in this case that the term inside the bracket shrinks in such a rate that the acceleration command $\underline{a}_{MO}$ always remains finite and well behaved inspite of the fact that the coefficient outside the bracket in (6) goes to infinity as t_b approaches zero.

For this we solve the differential equation governing $\underline{r}(t)$. Let $1/\gamma = 0$ in (6) and substitute the resulting $\underline{a}_{MO}$ for $\underline{a}_M$ in (3). The resulting vector differential equation is time varying and has a regular singular point (c.f. [1]) at $t = t_f$. It can be shown that the solution has the following form

$$\underline{r}(t) = \underline{p}_1(t_b^3 + 3\delta t_b^2) + \underline{p}_2(t_b + \delta), \quad t \le t_f \tag{7}$$

where $\underline{p}_1$ and $\underline{p}_2$ are the constant vectors determined from the initial conditions. Let us take the time origin ($t = 0$) as the beginning of the engagement and denote the relative position and velocity at this reference time by $\underline{r}_0$ and $\underline{v}_0$ respectively. Then $\underline{p}_1$ and $\underline{p}_2$ in terms of $\underline{r}_0$ and $\underline{v}_0$ are as follows:

$$\underline{p}_1 = \frac{-1}{2(T^3 - \delta^3)}\underline{m}_0 \tag{8}$$

$$\underline{p}_2 = \frac{3(T^2 - \delta^2)}{2(T^3 - \delta^3)}\underline{m}_0 - \underline{v}_0 \tag{9}$$

where $\underline{m}_0 = \underline{r}_0 + T\underline{v}_0$ denotes the zero-effort-miss vector (c.f. [4]) at time $t = 0$. Differentiating (7) twice and substituting for $\underline{p}_1$ from (8), we have

$$\underline{a}_{MO}(t) = -\ddot{\underline{r}}(t) = \frac{3t_g}{T^3 - \delta^3}\underline{m}_0, \quad 0 \le t \le t_f \tag{10}$$

Therefore, the magnitude of $\underline{a}_{MO}$ is always finite and has its maximum at $t = 0$, and this magnitude decreases linearly after that until $t = t_f$. Note that $\underline{a}_{MO}$ is zero for $t > t_f$ and the magnitude of $\underline{a}_{MO}$ has a discontinuity at $t = t_f$ (which is the burn out time). Also the maximum magnitude of $\underline{a}_{MO}$ which occurs at $t = 0$ is proportional to the magnitude of the zero effort miss vector at this time.

Moreover, explicit computation shows that $\underline{r}(t_f) = \delta\underline{p}_2$ and $\underline{v}(t_f) = -\underline{p}_2$ so the relative velocity is colinear with the relative position at $t = t_f$ (i.e., $\underline{r}(t_f) \times \underline{v}(t_f) = \underline{0}$) and these two vectors will remain colinear thereafter since the relative velocity is constant after t_f. In other words, this guidance law drives the line of sight rate exactly to zero at $t = t_f$ (although the commanded acceleration is nonzero at this time) and this line of sight rate remains zero thereafter and a perfect intercept at $t = T$ will occur since $\underline{r}(T) = \underline{r}(t_f) + \delta\underline{v}(t_f) = \underline{0}$.

Motivated by the similarities between the proposed guidance law and the PN guidance law for the case $N = 3$, it may be conjectured whether it is possible to generalize the optimal guidance law given in (6) to a more general form that guarantees a perfect intercept although not necessarily minimizing any particularly useful objective function. As a matter of fact it can be shown that for the following guidance law

$$\underline{a}_{MN}(t) = \frac{N t_g^{N-2}}{t_g^N - \delta^N}\left[\underline{r}(t) + t_g\underline{v}(t)\right] \tag{11}$$

we have

$$\underline{r}(t_f) = \frac{NT^{N-1}\delta - N\delta^N}{(N-1)(T^N - \delta^N)}\underline{m}_0 - \delta\underline{v}_0 \tag{12}$$

$$\underline{v}(t_f) = \frac{N\delta^{N-1} - NT^{N-1}}{(N-1)(T^N - \delta^N)}\underline{m}_0 + \underline{v}_0 \tag{13}$$

Hence the relative position and velocity are colinear at $t = t_f$ and $\underline{r}(t_f) + \delta\underline{v}(t_f) = \underline{0}$ so an intercept at $t = T$ will occur.

Substituting (11) in (3) and solving the resulting differential equation, it can be shown that the acceleration $\underline{a}_{MN}(t)$ will have the following form

$$\underline{a}_{MN}(t) = \frac{N t_g^{N-2}}{T^N - \delta^N}\underline{m}_0, \quad 0 \le t \le t_f \tag{14}$$

with $\underline{a}_{MN}(t)$ assumed zero for $t > t_f$. Referring to this relation, if $N > 2$ then the magnitude of the commanded acceleration is monotonically decreasing during the period $0 \le t \le t_f$. The astonishing fact is that the guidance law given in (11) achieves a perfect intercept for any given initial conditions $\underline{r}_0$ and $\underline{v}_0$ and for all non-zero values of N if $\delta > 0$. However, the maximum acceleration command is large if $N < 2$ and δ is small compared to T.

4 Actual Implementation

Actual implementation of the guidance law given in (6) for the three dimensional case requires a few minor modifications as we shall indicate shortly. First, note that for computing $\underline{a}_{MO}$ we need to measure (or estimate) the relative position and velocity. We assume this information is provided by a combination of external target tracking, missile self-navigation (or tracking), and state estimation.

Moreover, we require estimates for time to go until intercept t_g and time to missile burn out t_b. If the burning period of the rocket motor t_f is known accurately and the maneuvering starts right after the motor ignition, then t_b can be computed using its definition $t_b = t_f - t$ where t denotes the present time.

Another approach to estimating t_b is based on using the known total impulse (ΔV) of the missile. For this we integrate the actual thrust acceleration of the missile and use it in the following relation:

$$t_b = \frac{\Delta V - \int_0^t a_M(\tau)d\tau}{a_T(t)} \tag{15}$$

Here, a_M denotes the magnitude of the thrust acceleration vector of the missile $\underline{a}_M$ (which we assume is measured). Note that (15) is an exact estimate if a_M is constant from current time to burnout. Otherwise this is an approximation whose accuracy improves as we get closer and closer to the burnout. Simulation results indicate that this approximation is quite adequate for our purpose. If necessary, we can even use a weighted average of $t_f - t$ (assuming t_f is known with reasonable accuracy) and t_b given in (15). Moreover, special care should be taken to make sure that the computed t_b is always positive and within reasonable bounds.

Also note that we have used $\underline{a}_M$ to denote the missile thrust acceleration vector which is different from the optimal acceleration command $\underline{a}_{MO}$ computed using (6). The difference is because we may be forced to command a nonzero acceleration along the LOS, since we may not have any control on the magnitude of the missile acceleration. We will clarify this point shortly.

For computing the time to go t_g, let us denote the length of the vector $\underline{r}$ by r (which is the same as the missile-target distance). Then, an estimate for t_g is obtained using

$$t_g = -\frac{r}{\dot{r}} \tag{16}$$

Note that the term $\dot{r}$ in (16) is computed using

$$\dot{r} = \frac{1}{r}\underline{v}^T\underline{r} \tag{17}$$

Also there is an important property that deserves some attention. If we compute t_g using relation (16), then the zero-effort-miss vector appearing inside the bracket in (6) is perpendicular to the LOS. Therefore, in this case the computed acceleration command $\underline{a}_{MO}(t)$ is perpendicular to the LOS.

The estimate given in (16) is exact if $\dot{r}$ is constant, but this is not the case in our problem. However, the accuracy improves as we get closer and closer to the time of missile burn out. A better estimate for t_g can be obtained by using the value of $\ddot{r}$. It is simple to show that if $\ddot{r}$ is constant during the burn period, an exact relation for t_g is as follows:

$$t_g = \frac{t_b^2\ddot{r}(t)/2 - r(t)}{t_b\ddot{r}(t) + \dot{r}(t)} \tag{18}$$

Even if $\ddot{r}$ is not constant, this relation leads to a good approximation of t_g. For small values of t_b or $\ddot{r}$, (18) and (16) are almost identical. To use (18), we need to compute $\ddot{r}$. For this we use the following identity

$$\ddot{r} = \frac{1}{r}\dot{\underline{v}}^T\underline{r} + \frac{1}{r}(v^2 - \dot{r}^2) \tag{19}$$

Noting $\dot{\underline{v}} = -\underline{a}_M$, the first term in the right hand side of (19) is the negative of the component of the thrust acceleration vector along the line of sight.

Extensive simulations indicate that for best performance, *t_g appearing inside the bracket in (6) should be computed using (16) and t_g apprearing in the coefficient outside the bracket should be computed using (18).*

In computing t_g and t_b, a check is made to see whether the computed t_g is larger than the computed t_b (i.e., the intercept actually occurs after burn out). If this is not the case, we assign the value of t_g to t_b.

Another important practical constraint is that usually there is no control on the magnitude of the thrust vector, and the only means of control is the direction of this vector. The function of the guidance law is to generate the desired direction of the thrust vector, and the autopilot rotates the missile so its thrust vector (approximately the missile axial direction) is aligned with this commanded direction.

We will compute the direction of the desired thrust vector in such a way that if the missile thrust is aligned with this vector, the component of missile acceleration perpendicular to LOS is equal to $\underline{a}_{MO}$ computed from (6). For this, we first check to make sure that the magnitude of acceleration command computed using (6) is within the maneuvering capability of the missile. This is done by checking the validity of the following inequality

$$a_{MO} \leq \alpha a_M \tag{20}$$

where α is a design factor close to one (usually 0.9) and a_M is the magnitude of the thrust acceleration of the missile. If (20) does not hold, we scale $\underline{a}_{MO}$ as follows:

$$\underline{a}_{MO}^{new} = \frac{\alpha a_M}{a_{MO}}\underline{a}_{MO} \tag{21}$$

Note that the value of α can be used as a design parameter to limit the attitude maneuver of the missile whenever necessary. From now on we assume that the acceleration command vector is scaled properly so its magnitude is within the achievable bounds and the same symbol $\underline{a}_{MO}$ is used to denote $\underline{a}_{MO}^{new}$.

Now let the component of the thrust acceleration vector $\underline{a}_T$ along the line of sight from the missile to the target be denoted by β. We want to compute β in such a way that the magnitude of $\underline{a}_M$ is equal to the instantaneous measured acceleration of the missile a_M. For this write

$$\underline{a}_M = \underline{a}_{MO} + \frac{\beta}{r}\underline{r} \tag{22}$$

Now take the dot product of (22) by itself and assuming $\underline{a}_{MO}$ is perpendicular to the LOS we have

$$a_M^2 = a_{MO}^2 + \beta^2 \tag{23}$$

Solving (23) for β we have

$$\beta = \sqrt{a_M^2 - a_{MO}^2} \tag{24}$$

Note that the term under the square root is positive because of the constraint we imposed on the magnitude of a_{MO}. We also only use the positive solution of β in (23) because otherwise the component of the missile thrust acceleration along the LOS will decrease the closing velocity.

Finally, we substitute the computed β in (22) and command the direction of the resulting $\underline{a}_M$ to the attitude autopilot of the missile.

5 Conclusion

We implemented the guidance law given in (6) in SystemBuild [3] environment using both simple point-mass flat-earth and six-degree-of-freedom rotating-earth models. Simulation results indicate that the guidance law repeatedly delivers the KKV well within the intercept region in the presence of measurement noise, computational delays, and autopilot lag. Moreover, the magnitude of the normal acceleration profile closely exhibits the behavior predicted in (10). Note that the magnitude of $\underline{a}_M$ at the time of burn out t_f is an important parameter that effects the overall accuracy. By increasing the value of N in the generalized guidance law given in (11), this magnitude is reduced and the guidance law becomes less sensitive to the errors in estimating t_b; however, this leads to a higher initial acceleration which may result in saturation.

References

[1] W.E. Boyce and R.C. Diprima, *Elementary Differential Equations and Boundary Value Problems*, Wiley, 1986

[2] A.E. Bryson and Y.C. Ho, *Applied Optimal Control*, Hemisphere Publishing Corp., 1975

[3] SystemBuild simulation software package, *Integrated Systems Inc.*, 3260 Jay St., Santa Clara, CA 95054

[4] P. Zarchan, *Tactical and Strategic Missile Guidance*, Volume 124, Progress in Aeronautics and Astronautics, published by AIAA, 1990

Proceedings of the
American Control Conference
San Francisco, California • June 1993

On Attitude Stabilization of Symmetric Spacecraft with Two Control Torques

Panagiotis Tsiotras and James M. Longuski

School of Aeronautics and Astronautics
Purdue University
West Lafayette, IN 47907-1282

Abstract

It is a well-known fact in the literature of spacecraft stabilization, that a symmetric spacecraft with two control torques supplied by gas jet actuators is not controllable, if the two control torques are along axes that span the two-dimensional plane which is orthogonal to the axis of symmetry. However, feedback control laws can be derived for a restricted problem corresponding to attitude stabilization about the symmetry axis. The final orientation angle about this axis is undetermined. The purpose of this paper is to present a new methodology for constructing feedback control laws for this restricted problem, based on a new formulation for the kinematics.

1 Introduction

The problem of attitude stabilization of a rigid body has received a lot of attention recently [1, 2, 3, 4, 5, 6, 7]. One of the earliest works on the subject is due to Mortensen [1], where he considered global asymptotic stabilization of the complete attitude motion using three independent gas jet actuators. A complete mathematical description of the problem however, was first given by Crouch [3], where he provided necessary and sufficient conditions for controllability of a rigid body in case of one, two, or three independent acting torques. The results of [3] can be summarized as follows. For *three* independent control torques the system is completely controllable, although for the case of momentum wheel actuators a certain minimum control effort is required. A necessary and sufficient condition for complete controllability of a *symmetric* rigid body with control torques supplied by *two* pairs of *gas jet* actuators, about axes spanning a two dimensional plane, is that the axis orthogonal to this plane must not be a principal axis of symmetry of the spacecraft. For the general case, the system is generically controllable, unless the inertia matrix is a multiple of the identity matrix and certain algebraic criteria also hold. These criteria impose certain conditions on the relative magnitude of the principal inertias, as in the case of stability considerations. For such a system, it is further shown that controllability is equivalent to local controllability at any equilibrium. When a spacecraft is controlled by less than three independent *momentum wheel* actuators, the system is not controllable, or even accessible at any equilibrium.

Many results are available in the literature for the case of three independent controls. For example [2, 4, 5] derive linear and nonlinear feedback stabilizing control laws for the attitude regulation of rigid spacecraft. On the contrary, the problem of attitude stabilization with less than three independent control torques has been only recently dealt with [6, 7]. In [6] it is shown that a rigid spacecraft controlled by two pairs (couples) of gas jet actuators cannot be asymptotically stabilized to an equilibrium using a continuously differentiable, i.e. $\mathcal{C}^1$, feedback control law. In [7] the problem of attitude stabilization of a symmetric spacecraft is treated, using control torques supplied by two pairs of gas jet actuators about axes spanning a two dimensional plane orthogonal to the axis of symmetry. The complete dynamics of the spacecraft system fail to be controllable or even accessible in these cases thus, the methodologies of [3] and [6] are not applicable. However, the spacecraft dynamics is strongly accessible and small time locally controllable in a restricted sense, namely when the spin rate remains zero. It is shown that the restricted (non-spinning spacecraft) dynamics cannot be asymptotically stabilized using *smooth* $\mathcal{C}^1$ feedback. A *nonsmooth* control strategy is developed for the restricted spacecraft dynamics which achieves an arbitrary reorientation of the spacecraft. This nonsmooth control law is based on previous results on stabilization of nonholonomic mechanical systems [8, 9].

In this paper the problem of attitude stabilization of a rigid body (spacecraft) is revisited. Specifically, we consider the attitude stabilization of an axially symmetric spacecraft using two control torques by a pair of gas jets about axes spanning a two-dimensional plane orthogonal to the axis of symmetry. Without loss of generality we can assume that the torques are acting along the principal axes. This problem is of particular theoretical and practical interest because, under these assumptions, as mentioned earlier, the system dynamics is not controllable or even accessible. Using a new formulation of the kinematic equations derived in [10], we derive asymptotically stabilizing feedback controls for the restricted problem of a non-spinning spacecraft. The results can be naturally extended to the case of non-zero spin rate, and in this case lead to spin axis stabilization, i.e., to a revolute motion about the axis of symmetry. This is of prime practical importance, since spin stabilization is often utilized during deployment and station-keeping of modern satellites in orbit.

2 System Dynamics and Kinematics

Euler's Equations of Motion

Let $\omega_1, \omega_2, \omega_3$ denote the angular velocity components along a body-fixed reference frame located at the center of mass, and aligned along the principal axes of a rotating rigid body. Then Euler's equations of motion describe the dynamics of the motion and, for a symmetric body ($I_1 = I_2$) subject to two control torques along principal axes, take the form

$$\dot{\omega}_1 = a_1\omega_2\omega_3 + u_1 \quad (1a)$$

$$\dot{\omega}_2 = a_2\omega_3\omega_1 + u_2 \quad (1b)$$

$$\dot{\omega}_3 = 0 \quad (1c)$$

where $a_1 \triangleq (I_2 - I_3)/I_1$, $a_2 \triangleq (I_3 - I_1)/I_2$, $u_1 \triangleq M_1/I_1$ and $u_2 \triangleq M_2/I_2$. Here M_1, M_2 are the acting torques and I_1, I_2, I_3 denote the principal moments of inertia. Introducing the complex variables $\omega \triangleq \omega_1 + i\omega_2$ and

$u \triangleq u_1 + i\,u_2$, one rewrites (1a-1b) in the compact form

$$\dot{\omega} = -ia_1\omega_{30}\omega + u \tag{2}$$

where $\omega_{30} = \omega_3(0)$. A complete formulation of the attitude problem requires the description of the kinematics, in addition to the dynamics introduced here. In contrast to the dynamics formalism, there is more than one way to describe the kinematics of a rotating body.

Kinematics

The kinematic equations relate the components of the angular velocity vector with the rates of a set of parameters, that describe the relative orientation of two reference frames (commonly the inertial and the body-fixed frames). Any two reference frames are related by a rotation matrix R. The set of all such matrices form what is commonly known as the (three-dimensional) rotation group, consisting of all matrices which are orthogonal and have determinant $+1$, denoted by $SO(3)$. Henceforth, we will refer to $SO(3)$ simply as the rotation group. In fact, $SO(3)$ is more than a group, but carries an inherent smooth manifold structure, and thus, forms a (continuous) Lie group. The attitude history of the moving reference frame with respect to the constant (inertial) reference frame can therefore be described by a curve traced by the corresponding rotation $R(t) \in SO(3)$, with $SO(3)$ taken with its manifold structure. The differential equation satisfied while $R(t)$ is moving along this trajectory is given by

$$\dot{R}(t) = S(\omega_1, \omega_2, \omega_3)R(t) \tag{3}$$

where $S(\omega_1, \omega_2, \omega_3)$ is the skew-symmetric matrix

$$S(\omega_1, \omega_2, \omega_3) \triangleq \begin{bmatrix} 0 & \omega_3 & -\omega_2 \\ -\omega_3 & 0 & \omega_1 \\ \omega_2 & -\omega_1 & 0 \end{bmatrix}$$

There is more than one way to parametrize the rotation group, i.e., to specify a set of parameters such that every element R in $SO(3)$ is uniquely and unambiguously determined [11]. The commonly used three-dimensional parametrization of the rotation group leads to the familiar Eulerian angle formulation of the kinematical equations. Introducing, for example, the three-dimensional parametrization of $SO(3)$, based on a 3-2-1 Eulerian angle sequence [12], one has that the rotation matrix $R = R(\psi, \theta, \phi)$ is given by

$$R = \begin{bmatrix} c\psi c\theta & s\psi c\theta & -s\theta \\ -s\psi c\phi + c\psi s\theta s\phi & c\psi c\phi + s\psi s\theta s\phi & c\theta s\phi \\ s\psi s\phi + c\psi s\theta c\phi & -c\psi s\phi + s\psi s\theta c\phi & c\theta c\phi \end{bmatrix} \tag{4}$$

where c and s denote cos and sin, respectively. The associated kinematic equations are

$$\dot{\phi} = \omega_1 + (\omega_2 \sin\phi + \omega_3 \cos\phi)\tan\theta \tag{5a}$$

$$\dot{\theta} = \omega_2 \cos\phi - \omega_3 \sin\phi \tag{5b}$$

$$\dot{\psi} = (\omega_2 \sin\phi + \omega_3 \cos\phi)\sec\theta \tag{5c}$$

Using this parametrization of $SO(3)$, the orientation of the local body-fixed reference frame with respect to the inertial reference frame is found by first rotating the body about its 3-axis through an angle ψ, then rotating about its 2-axis by an angle θ and finally rotating about its 1-axis by an angle ϕ. Equations (5) exhibit a singularity at $\theta = \pm\pi/2$. For this reason one must restrict the subsequent discussion to $-\pi < \phi \leq \pi$, $-\pi/2 < \theta < \pi/2$ and $-\pi < \psi \leq \pi$. Let $\mathcal{M}$ denote the submanifold of $T^3 \triangleq S^1 \times S^1 \times S^1$ determined by the previous inequalities, where S^1 represents the usual mathematical notation for the unit circle. That is, let $\mathcal{M} = \{(\phi, \theta, \psi) \in T^3 : -\pi < \phi \leq \pi, -\pi/2 < \theta < \pi/2, -\pi < \psi \leq \pi\}$. On this submanifold, ϕ and θ determine the orientation of the local body-fixed 3-axis (the symmetry axis) with respect to the inertial 3-axis, and ψ determines the relative rotation about this axis [12]. Throughout the following discussion we will assume that the system trajectories are confined on $\mathcal{M}$.

3 Alternative Formulation of the Kinematics

Next we present a reformulation of the kinematics that will simplify the consequent analysis significantly. This new formulation is based on an idea by Darboux [13], and was initially applied to the problem of attitude dynamics in [10], although it appears that Leimanis [14] was aware of this possibility. From (3) one sees that this matrix differential equation involves nine parameters (the direction cosines of the corresponding frames), however because of the constraint $RR^t = I$ imposed on the elements of $SO(3)$, there are actually only *three* free parameters involved in the system of equations (3). These three parameters can be chosen as the direction cosines of one of the body-axes with respect to the inertial axes. Let $[a, b, c]^t$ denote any column vector of the matrix representation of R having entries r_{ij}, for $i, j = 1, 2, 3$. That is, $[a, b, c]^t = [r_{1j}, r_{2j}, r_{3j}]^t$, for some $j = 1, 2, 3$. Clearly,

$$\begin{bmatrix} \dot{a} \\ \dot{b} \\ \dot{c} \end{bmatrix} = \begin{bmatrix} 0 & \omega_3 & -\omega_2 \\ -\omega_3 & 0 & \omega_1 \\ \omega_2 & -\omega_1 & 0 \end{bmatrix} \begin{bmatrix} a \\ b \\ c \end{bmatrix} \tag{6}$$

Note that these three parameters do not provide another three-dimensional parametrization of the rotation group. (Check, for example, that the transformation $(\phi, \theta, \psi) \leftrightarrow (a, b, c)$ is singular.) Because of the constraint $a^2 + b^2 + c^2 = 1$ we can eliminate one of the three parameters a, b, c, to get a system of *two* first order differential equations. The most natural and elegant way to reduce the third order system (6) to a second order system is by the use of *stereographic projection* [15]. That is, if we let a, b, and c represent coordinates on the unit sphere $S^2 = \{(x_1, x_2, x_3) \in \mathbf{R}^3 : x_1^2 + x_2^2 + x_3^2 = 1\}$, then, for $(a, b, c) \in S^2$, the stereographic projection $\sigma : S^2 \to \mathbf{C}$ defined by

$$w = \sigma(a, b, c) \triangleq \frac{b - ia}{1 + c} = \frac{1 - c}{b + ia}$$

induces the following differential equation for the complex quantity w

$$\dot{w} + i\,\omega_3 w = \frac{\omega}{2} + \frac{\bar{\omega}}{2}w^2 \tag{7}$$

where $\omega = \omega_1 + i\,\omega_2$ and the bar denotes complex conjugate. Equation (7) is a scalar Riccati equation with time-varying coefficients. The real and imaginary parts of $w = w_1 + i\,w_2$ satisfy the differential equations

$$\dot{w}_1 = \omega_3 w_2 + \omega_2 w_1 w_2 + \frac{\omega_1}{2}(1 + w_1^2 - w_2^2)$$

$$\dot{w}_2 = -\omega_3 w_1 + \omega_1 w_1 w_2 + \frac{\omega_2}{2}(1 + w_2^2 - w_1^2)$$

The stereographic projection σ establishes a one-to-one correspondence between the unit sphere S^2 and the complex plane $\mathbf{C}$. It can be easily verified that the inverse map $\sigma^{-1} : \mathbf{C} \to S^2$, $w \mapsto (a, b, c)$ is given by

$$a = \frac{i(w - \bar{w})}{|w|^2 + 1}, \quad b = \frac{w + \bar{w}}{|w|^2 + 1}, \quad c = -\frac{|w|^2 - 1}{|w|^2 + 1}$$

and can be used to find a, b, c once w is known. Here $|\cdot|$ denotes the absolute value of a complex number, i.e., $z\bar{z} = |z|^2$, $z \in \mathbf{C}$.

In order to establish the relationship between w and the particular Eulerian angle set used, notice that we can in principle identify $[a, b, c]^t$ with any column vector of the rotation matrix R, where R can be expressed in terms of any of the parametrizations of $SO(3)$. This gives a great deal of flexibility in the analysis and design of control laws for attitude stabilization. For the three-dimensional 3-2-1 Eulerian angle parametrization, the matrix $R = R(\psi, \theta, \phi)$ is given by (4). Any other parametrization is equally valid, however. Identifying, for example, $[a, b, c]^t$ with the third column of R one establishes a one-to-one correspondence between w and (θ, ϕ) from

$$w = \frac{\sin\phi\cos\theta + i\sin\theta}{1 + \cos\phi\cos\theta}$$

or in terms of real and imaginary parts of w,

$$w_1 = \frac{\sin\phi\cos\theta}{1+\cos\phi\cos\theta}, \qquad w_2 = \frac{\sin\theta}{1+\cos\phi\cos\theta} \tag{8}$$

As can easily be checked, the determinant of the Jacobian of the transformation (8) is $\cos\theta/(1+\cos\phi\cos\theta)^2$. Zeros occur for $\theta = \pm\pi/2$. Moreover, $1 + \cos\phi\cos\theta \neq 0$ as long as $\theta \neq \pm\pi/2$. Thus, the proposed transformation does not introduce any additional singularities, than the original ones due to the intrinsic singularity of the particular Eulerian angle formulation. In fact, (8) establishes a smooth change of coordinates (i.e., a diffeomorphism) between the (w_1, w_2) and (ϕ, θ).

Although not necessary at this point, for completeness we also give the counterpart of the differential equation (5c) for ψ in the (ω, w) space:

$$\dot{\psi} = \frac{i}{2}(\omega - \bar{\omega})\frac{(w+\bar{w})(1+|w|^2)}{(1+w^2)(1+\bar{w}^2)}$$

4 Control Strategy

It is clear from equation (1c) that for a symmetric body, no control can affect the value of the component of the angular velocity ω_3 along the symmetry axis. In fact, the value of ω_3 remains constant for all times. Clearly, as already mentioned, this system is not controllable. Therefore, if the initial condition $\omega_3(0)$ is not zero, no control can drive the system to the origin ($\omega_1 = \omega_2 = \omega_3 = \phi = \theta = \psi = 0$). Of course, if $\omega_3(0) \neq 0$ then it is meaningless to require $\psi = 0$, but we may require a control law such that $\omega_1 = \omega_2 = \phi = \theta = 0$. This last control corresponds to spin axis stabilization for a spinning (symmetric) spacecraft and is of important practical interest. From equations (8) notice that $w = 0$ implies that $\sin\theta = 0$ and $\sin\phi = 0$, therefore $w = 0$ implies $\theta = 0$ and $\phi = 0$ on $\mathcal{M}$. We have therefore that $w = 0$ (with the previous identification of the third column of the rotation matrix) implies that the body-fixed 3-axis (the symmetry axis), is aligned with the inertial 3-axis (for the 3-2-1 set). However, we have no *a priori* information about the relative rotation of the body about its symmetry axis. That is, stabilization is achieved about a submanifold $\psi = const.$ of $\mathcal{M}$. On this submanifold, the angle ψ can have any value.

Zero Spin-Rate Case

We now turn our attention to the problem of zero spin rate, i.e., assume ***a priori*** that $\omega_3(0) = 0$. Following the terminology of [7] we refer to this problem as the *restricted* stabilization problem. For $\omega_3 \equiv 0$ the restricted spacecraft dynamics are given by the equations

$$\dot{\omega}_1 = u_1 \tag{9a}$$
$$\dot{\omega}_2 = u_2 \tag{9b}$$

$$\dot{\phi} = \omega_1 + \omega_2 \sin\phi\tan\theta \tag{10a}$$
$$\dot{\theta} = \omega_2\cos\phi \tag{10b}$$
$$\dot{\psi} = \omega_2 \sin\phi\sec\theta \tag{10c}$$

In this section we present a methodology to construct feedback control laws for the system of equations (9) and (10a-10b), which depends on the alternative formulation of the kinematic equations presented in section 3. Asymptotic stability of the closed-loop system is easily demonstrated by Lyapunov's direct method. Recalling that ψ is an ignorable variable for the system (10), in the subsequent analysis we tacitly discard the equation for ψ. The problem of also stabilizing $\psi = 0$ is more difficult. In fact, in [7] it was shown that any stabilizing feedback control law of the complete restricted system, i.e., for $(\omega_1, \omega_2, \phi, \theta, \psi)$, must be necessarily ***nonsmooth***. In the same paper a methodology based on the theory of control of nonholonomic systems [8, 9] was used to construct such nonsmooth stabilizing control laws. The stabilization of the complete system (9)-(10) will be the subject of a forthcoming paper [16].

Introducing the complex control variable $u = u_1 + i\,u_2$ equations (9) and the kinematic equation (7) simplify to

$$\dot{\omega} = u \tag{11a}$$
$$\dot{w} = \frac{\omega}{2} + \frac{\bar{\omega}}{2}w^2 \tag{11b}$$

where $(\omega, w) \in \mathbf{C}\times\mathbf{C}$. This system of differential equations is in one-to-one correspondence with the system of equations (9)-(10a-10b). The system (11) falls within the more general class of nonlinear systems of the form

$$\dot{y} = u \tag{12a}$$
$$\dot{x} = f(x, y) \tag{12b}$$

where $f : \mathbf{R}^n \times \mathbf{R}^m \to \mathbf{R}^n$ is smooth, with $f(0,0) = 0$. System (12) is a system in cascade form and it is a well-known result [17] that for systems of this form, if the subsystem $\dot{x} = f(x,y)$ is smoothly stabilizable (regarding y as a control-like variable), then the extended system (12) is also smoothly stabilizable. In other words, if in (12) the subsystem (12b) is smoothly stabilizable, then adding an integrator does not change this property. We will use this result in order to derive asymptotically stabilizing control laws for the system (11). We have the following theorems concerning asymptotic stabilization of the system (11).

Theorem 4.1 *The choice of the linear feedback control*

$$\omega = -\kappa w \tag{13}$$

where $\kappa > 0$, globally asymptotically stabilizes (11b).

Proof. With this choice of feedback, the closed-loop system becomes

$$\dot{w} = -\frac{\kappa}{2}(1+|w|^2)w \tag{14}$$

The positive definite function $V : \mathbf{C} \to \mathbf{R}$ defined by $V(w) = w\bar{w} = |w|^2$ is a Lyapunov function for (14). Indeed, differentiating along trajectories of (14) one obtains

$$\begin{aligned}\dot{V}(w) &= \dot{w}\bar{w} + w\dot{\bar{w}} \\ &= -\frac{\kappa}{2}(1+|w|^2)w\bar{w} - \frac{\kappa}{2}(1+|w|^2)\bar{w}w \\ &= -\kappa(1+|w|^2)|w|^2 \leq 0\end{aligned}$$

Since $\dot{V}(w) = 0$ if and only if $w = 0$, the closed-loop system (14) is asymptotically stable. Global asymptotic stability follows from the facts that these statements hold for all $w \in \mathbf{C}$ and V is radially unbounded, i.e., $V(w) \to \infty$, for $|w| \to \infty$. Notice that since $\dot{V} \leq -\kappa V$ one, in fact, guarantees *exponential stability* for the system (14) with rate of decay $\kappa/2$. ■

Theorem 4.2 *The choice of the feedback control law*

$$u = -\frac{\kappa}{2}(\omega + \bar{\omega}w^2) - \alpha(\omega + \kappa w) \tag{15}$$

with $\kappa > 0$ and $\alpha > 0$, globally asymptotically stabilizes system (11).

Proof. With this choice of feedback, the closed-loop system becomes

$$\dot{\omega} = -\frac{\kappa}{2}(\omega + \bar{\omega}w^2) - \alpha(\omega + \kappa w) \tag{16a}$$

$$\dot{w} = \frac{\omega}{2} + \frac{\bar{\omega}}{2}w^2 \tag{16b}$$

The set $\mathcal{E} = \{(\omega, w) \in \mathbf{C}\times\mathbf{C} : \omega + \kappa w = 0\}$ is a positively invariant set and a global asymptotic attractor for (16). To see this, let $z \triangleq \omega + \kappa w$. Then the system equations become

$$\dot{z} = -\alpha z \tag{17a}$$

$$\dot{w} = -\frac{\kappa}{2}w + \frac{z}{2} - \frac{\kappa}{2}w|w|^2 + \frac{\bar{z}}{2}w^2 \tag{17b}$$

La Salle's theorem guarantees the global asymptotic stability of (16), if the trajectories of (16), or equivalently of (17) remain bounded [18]. To this end, let V be the positive definite function of Theorem 4.1, i.e., let $V(w) = |w|^2$. We will show that V is nonincreasing outside a bounded set that contains the origin; in particular, we claim that $\dot{V}(w) \leq 0$ on the set $\mathcal{D} = \{w \in \mathbf{C} : |w| \geq |z(0)|/\kappa\}$. This will imply boundedness of solutions of w, hence of (17). Differentiating along trajectories of (17b) one obtains

$$\begin{aligned}\dot{V}(w) &= -\kappa|w|^2 - \kappa|w|^4 + \frac{z}{2}\bar{w}(1+|w|^2) + \frac{\bar{z}}{2}w(1+|w|^2)\\ &= -\kappa|w|^2 - \kappa|w|^4 + Re(z\bar{w})(1+|w|^2)\\ &\leq -\kappa|w|^2 - \kappa|w|^4 + |z||\bar{w}|(1+|w|^2)\end{aligned}$$

where $Re(.)$ denotes the real part of a complex number and where we made use of the fact that $Re(z) \leq |z|$ for all $z \in \mathbf{C}$. From (17a) one has that $z(t) = z(0)e^{-\alpha t}$ and in particular $|z(t)| \leq |z(0)|$. Thus,

$$\begin{aligned}\dot{V}(w) &\leq -\kappa|w|^2 - \kappa|w|^4 + |z(0)||\bar{w}|(1+|w|^2)\\ &= -(1+|w|^2)|w|(\kappa|w| - |z(0)|)\end{aligned}$$

For $|w| \geq |z(0)|/\kappa$ one has $\dot{V}(w) \leq 0$ as claimed. This completes the proof. ■

The previous control law is not the only choice of stabilizing feedback for the system (11). In fact, one has the following

Theorem 4.3 *The choice of the feedback control law*

$$u = -\frac{\kappa}{2}(\omega + \bar{\omega}w^2) - \alpha(\omega + \kappa w) - w(1+|w|^2) \tag{18}$$

with $\kappa > 0$ and $\alpha > 0$, globally asymptotically stabilizes system (11).

Proof. With this choice of feedback, the closed-loop system becomes

$$\dot{\omega} = -\frac{\kappa}{2}(\omega + \bar{\omega}w^2) - \alpha(\omega + \kappa w) - w(1+|w|^2) \tag{19a}$$

$$\dot{w} = \frac{\omega}{2} + \frac{\bar{\omega}}{2}w^2 \tag{19b}$$

Indeed, the positive definite function $V : \mathbf{C}\times\mathbf{C} \to \mathbf{R}$ defined by $V(\omega, w) = |w|^2 + |\omega + \kappa w|^2/2$ is a Lyapunov function for the system (19). Differentiating along trajectories of the system (19), one can show that

$$\dot{V}(\omega, w) = -\alpha|\omega + \kappa w|^2 - \kappa|w|^2(1+|w|^2) \leq 0$$

Since $\dot{V}(\omega, w) = 0$ if and only if $w = 0$ and $\omega = 0$, the system (19) is asymptotically stable. Global asymptotic stability follows from the facts that the previous statements hold for all $(\omega, w) \in \mathbf{C}\times\mathbf{C}$ and V is radially unbounded, i.e., $V(\omega, w) \to \infty$, for $||(\omega, w)|| \to \infty$. In fact, since $\dot{V} \leq -\beta V$, where $\beta = \min\{2\alpha, \kappa\}$ the system (19) is *globally exponentially stable* with rate of decay $\beta/2$. ■

Non-zero Spin-Rate Case

We mention in passing that, surprisingly enough, the stabilizing control laws given above, can also be used to achieve stabilization about the symmetry axis, even when the spin rate ω_3 is *not* zero. In such a case the final state is a pure revolute motion about the symmetry axis. Using (2) and (7) the attitude equations for a symmetric body, with $\omega_3(0) \neq 0$, can be written as

$$\dot{\omega} = -i\, a_1\omega_{30}\omega + u \tag{20a}$$

$$\dot{w} = -i\,\omega_{30}w + \frac{\omega}{2} + \frac{\bar{\omega}}{2}w^2 \tag{20b}$$

Notice first that with the control (13) the subsystem (20b) is (locally) asymptotically stable; for its linearization has eigenvalue $-\kappa/2 - i\omega_{30}$ ($\kappa > 0$). In fact, one can easily verify the following two Theorems.

Theorem 4.4 *The choice of the feedback control law*

$$\omega = -\kappa w \tag{21}$$

with $\kappa > 0$ globally asymptotically stabilizes (20b).

Proof. Use the Lyapunov function of Theorem 4.1. In fact, with this Lyapunov function one can show *global exponential* stability of (20b) with rate of decay $\kappa/2$. ■

Theorem 4.5 *The choice of the feedback control law*

$$u = i\, a_1\omega_{30}\omega + \kappa(i\omega_{30}w - \frac{\omega}{2} - \frac{\bar{\omega}}{2}w^2) - \alpha(\omega + \kappa w) \tag{22}$$

with $\kappa > 0$ and $\alpha > 0$, globally asymptotically stabilizes system (20).

The proof of Theorem 4.5 traces the steps of the proof of the Theorem 4.2, and will not be repeated here.

5 Numerical Example

We illustrate the previous ideas with a numerical example. The control law given in Theorem 4.2 is used to stabilize the system of equations (11) about the origin. The initial conditions are given by $\omega_1(0) = 0.75$ *rad/sec*, $\omega_2(0) = -0.5$ *rad/sec*, $\omega_3(0) = 0$, $\phi(0) = 2.5$ *rad*, $\theta(0) = 0.5$ *rad* and $\psi(0) = 0.25$ *rad*. The results with control law (15) and $\kappa = \alpha = 1$ are shown in Figs. 1-2.

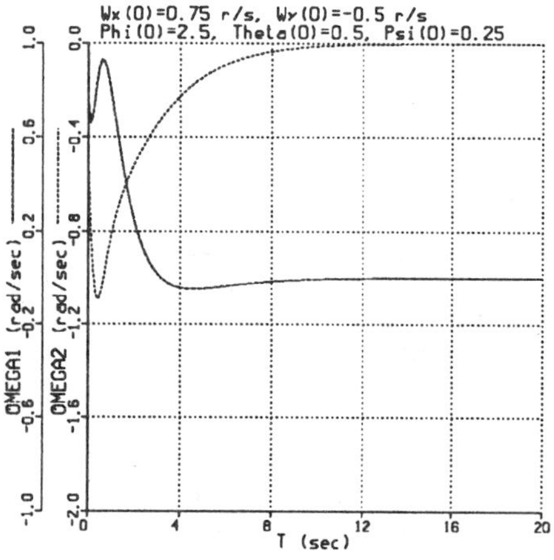

Figure 1: Angular velocities ω_1 and ω_2.

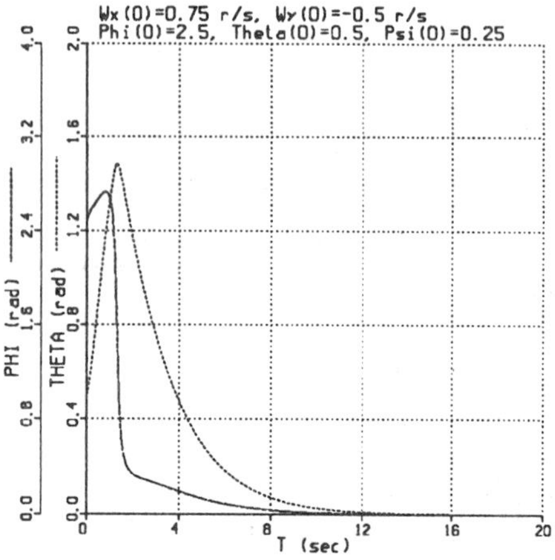

Figure 2: Eulerian angles ϕ and θ.

6 Conclusions

The problem of stabilization of a symmetric spacecraft with two gas jet actuators aligned about the principal axes of equal moments of inertia is investigated. Using a new formulation for the kinematic equations, asymptotically stabilizing controls have been derived for the restricted problem of spin axis stabilization. The asymptotic stability of the closed-loop system is proved by construction of appropriate Lyapunov functions. The stabilizing control laws derived are especially simple and elegant. Moreover, they do not depend on the particular choice of the Eulerian angle set, used to describe the attitude orientation in the inertial space. This provides a great deal of freedom in the analysis and design of attitude control laws.

Acknowledgements

The authors would like to thank Professor M. Corless for fruitful discussions during the preparation of this work. This research has been supported by the National Science Foundation under Grant No. MSS-9114388.

References

[1] R.E. Mortensen, "A globally stable linear attitude regulator," *Int. J. of Cont.*, Vol. 8, No. 3, pp. 297-302, 1968.

[2] L.A. D'Amario, and G.S. Stubbs, "A new single-rotation-axis autopilot for rapid spacecraft attitude maneuvers," *J. of Guid. Cont., and Dyn.*, Vol.2, No. 4, pp. 339-346, 1979.

[3] P. E. Crouch, "Spacecraft attitude control and stabilization: Applications of geometric control theory to rigid body models," *IEEE Tran. on Aut. Cont.*, Vol. AC-29, No. 4, April, pp. 321-331, 1984.

[4] S.V. Salehi, and E.P. Ryan, "A non-linear feedback attitude regulator," *Int. J. of Cont.*, Vol. 41, No. 1, pp. 281-287, 1985.

[5] B. Wie, H. Weiss, and A., Arapostathis, "Quaternion feedback regulator for spacecraft eigenaxis rotation," *J. of Guid. Cont., and Dyn.*, Vol. 12, No. 3, pp. 375-380, 1989.

[6] C.I. Byrnes, and A. Isidori, "On the attitude stabilization of a rigid spacecraft," *Automatica*, Vol. 27, No. 1, 1991, pp. 87-95, 1991.

[7] H. Krishnan, H. McClamroch, and M. Reyhanoglu, "On the attitude stabilization of a rigid spacecraft using two control torques," *Proc. ACC*, Chicago, Illinois, June 26-29, pp. 1990-1995, 1992.

[8] A.M. Bloch, N.H. McClamroch, and M. Reyhanoglu, "Controllability and stabilizability properties of a nonholonomic control system," *Proc., 29th IEEE CDC*, Honolulu, Hawaii, pp. 1312-1314, 1990.

[9] A.M. Bloch, and N.H. McClamroch, "Control of mechanical systems with classical nonholonomic constraints," *Proc., 28th IEEE CDC*, Tampa, Florida, pp. 201-205, 1989.

[10] P. Tsiotras and J.M. Longuski, "On the large angle problem in rigid body attitude dynamics," IAF Paper 92-0034, *43rd Cong., Int. Astr. Fed.*, Washington, DC, Aug. 28- Sept. 6, 1992.

[11] J. Stuelpnagel, "On the parametrization of the three-dimensional rotation group," *SIAM Rev.*, Vol. 6, No. 4, pp. 422-430, 1964.

[12] T.R. Kane, P.W. Likins and P.A. Levinson, *Spacecraft Dynamics*, McGraw-Hill Inc., New York, 1983.

[13] G. Darboux, *Lecons sur la théorie générale des surfaces*, Vol. 1, Gauthier-Villars, Paris, 1887.

[14] E. Leimanis, *The General Problem of the Motion of Coupled Rigid Bodies About a Fixed Point*, Springer-Verlag, New York, 1965.

[15] J.B. Conway, *Functions of One Complex Variable*, Springer Verlag, New York, 1978.

[16] P. Tsiotras, M. Corless, and J.M. Longuski, "Invariant manifold techniques for attitude control of spacecraft," (to appear).

[17] D. Aeyels, "Remarks on the stabilizability of nonlinear systems by smooth feedback," *Perspectives in Control Theory: Proc. of the Sielpia Conference, Sielpia, Poland, Sept. 19-24, 1988*, (B. Jakubczyk, K. Malanowski and W. Respondek, Eds.), Birkhäuser, Boston, pp. 1-11, 1990.

[18] P. Seibert, and R. Suarez, "Global stabilization of nonlinear cascade systems," *Sys. & Cont. Let.*, Vol. 14, pp. 347-352, 1990.

Proceedings of the
American Control Conference
San Francisco, California • June 1993

Vertical Guidance in Turbulence using Optimal Dynamic Interpolation With Application to a Lockheed L1011-100

Charles R. Tolle *
Department of Electrical Engineering
Utah State University
Rocky Mountain NASA Space Grant Consortium
324A SER Building
Logan, UT 84322-4436

Armando A. Rodriguez †
Department of Electrical Engineering
Arizona State University
Center for Systems Science and Engineering
Tempe, AZ 85287-5706

Abstract

The motivation for the work is aircraft guidance in a time controlled air traffic management system (ATM). This paper discusses two forms of optimal dynamic interpolation guidance (ODIG) and the effects of turbulence on its performance. The first form of ODIG is based on a cost functional that penalizes acceleration. The second form of ODIG penalizes both acceleration and velocity excursion. Both have been applied to the L1011-100 vertical guidance problem in the presence of turbulence (the Dryden turbulence model was used). A flight management system's (FMS) vertical flight plan is used to obtain waypoints which serve as inputs to the ODIG algorithm. The algorithm produces reference commands which are issued to a certified FAA L1011-100 model and an autopilot. The resulting dynamic behavior is compared to the results obtained from reference commands produced by an L1011-like commercial aircraft's flight management system model (FMSM) under the same turbulence.

1 Introduction

This paper is a continuation of ODIG papers[17]-[18]. It has been shown that the emerging next generation air traffic management system (ATM) will involve some time based spacing control methods instead of the current distance based spacing[1]-[3]. The new ATM system will also take advantage of the fast developing required time of arrival (RTA) algorithms[4]-[6] and some 4D guidance algorithms, yet to be determined, such as ODIG and multiple waypoint RTA, to reduce holding patterns and increase landing rates at major airports. Each of these efforts are being made in part to eliminate the long landing queues which pilots today experience at major airports. These long queues can be attributed in part to the limitations in the Instrumentation Landing Systems (ILS's) currently in use[18].

FMS systems in use today only supply simple curve trajectory options such as constant arcs, straight legs, and preflight-climb-cruise adjustable RTA waypoints (once you have reached the top of decent, you can't change your RTA fix.) There have been a number of methods proposed as solutions in the last ten years for more complicated curved approach paths and control schemes[10]-[14]. However, most of these aren't time based algorithms. For this reason, ODIG is the approach which we shall address in this paper.

Dynamic interpolation obtains the accelerations for an object needed to pass through a set of predetermined points, known as waypoints, with the added constraints of the initial and final velocities. The optimal solution can be found by minimizing a cost functional in each axis independently (if the controls for each axis are decoupled)[8]. In the case of a transport aircraft, the longitudinal and latitudinal aerodynamics are clearly decoupled. It has been shown that for this type of aircraft, a set of pseudocontrols can fully decouple the three axis controls[15],[8]. Therefore, the full 3D optimization problem can be solved by three separate axis optimization problems to obtain the 4D path targets. In this paper, we will address the vertical guidance optimal problem. This problem is concerned with the vertical and forward motion of the aircraft. It is not concerned with the lateral motion (roll and yaw). Therefore, we assume that the vertical guidance problem we are solving is 2D + time problem (this is without loss of generality). We will use the z-x plane for our 2D vertical guidance simulation problem. It should be noted that the z axis reflects aircraft altitude, while the x axis reflects the aircraft distance to destination. In the true 3D + time guidance problem, the x axis would be resolved into the spacial x-y plane, with the z axis remaining unchanged.

We have discussed the tradeoffs between the two forms of ODIG in a previous paper[18]. Therefore, the next step in studying ODIG is to look at the effects of turbulence on the algorithm. To do this, we will use the Dryden Turbulence Model (DTM) described in the FAA TSO-C117 document. The results of the added turbulence to the L1011-100 nonlinear simulation under ODIG control were further compared with the controls obtained from an L011-100 like aircraft FMS model (FMSM). The results of both simulations are given at the end of the paper.

---

*Utah State University Rocky Mt. NASA Space Grant Consortium Fellow; Research has been supported by Rocky Mt. NASA Space Grant Consortium and Honeywell CFSG.

†Assistant Professor; Research has been supported by ASU FGIA Award DWR-B717

2 L1011-100, Autopilot, and Dryden Models

The simulations performed in this experiment were made by using a modified FAA certified six degree of freedom L1011-100 model, valid up to 20,000 feet. For the vertical guidance problem, we are only interested in the following four states[16]:

$$x^T = [u \quad w \quad \theta \quad \dot{\theta}]$$

The vertical control for an L1011-100 is obtained through the use of the column, while the distance to destination control is obtained through the throttle. On most conventional aircraft, the column is used to move the elevator; however, on the L1011 the column also moves the stabilizer. The movement of the stabilizer and elevator produce the necessary pitching moments required to produce vertical control. Likewise, the throttle changes the engine pressure ratio (EPR), which can change the thrust and in turn speed up or slow down the aircraft, thus enabling the control of the distance to destination. Therefore our controls are:

$$\hat{u}_z = Column$$

$$\hat{u}_x = Throttle$$

The column commands are produced through the use of an L1011 simulated autopilot. Theta commands are issued to the autopilot which converts these commands into the column commands. Then the simulation produces the equivalent elevator and stabilizer movements. Furthermore, speed targets are issued to an auto-throttle which converts these targets into a throttle position and then an EPR command.

The Dryden Turbulence Model generates turbulent wind in each axis by passing a zero mean, unit variance, Gaussian white noises signal through the following filters:

$$Turb_u(s) = \sigma_u \sqrt{\frac{\tau_u}{\pi}} \left(\frac{1}{1 + \tau_u s} \right)$$

$$Turb_w(s) = \sigma_w \sqrt{\frac{\tau_w}{2\pi}} \left(\frac{1 + \sqrt{3}\,\tau_w s}{(1 + \tau_w s)(1 + \tau_w s)} \right)$$

where

σ_u and σ_w are the RMS intensities,

τ_u and τ_w are scaling factors based on altitude and true airspeed.

Note, we aren't interested in wind in the y axis for this simulation (roll and yaw). As σ is enlarged the strength of the turbulence is increased. Once $Turb_u(t)$ and $Turb_w(t)$ have been calculated they are added to the simulated aircraft velocity vectors, thus simulating a turbulent wind. Note, the turbulent wind is stored so that both the FMSM and ODIG algorithms can be compared using the same turbulence wind pattern.

3 Dynamic Interpolation

The development of the ODIG shown in this segment is given for the cubic spline solution[9]. The quadratic development can be found in reference [8]. The controls of the linearized system that we are interested in are given as a set of pseudo control equations in [15]. However, in the vertical guidance problem we are interested in the z and x axis equations:

$$\dddot{z}(t) = U_z(t) \quad ; t_o \le t \le t_N$$

$$\dddot{x}(t) = U_x(t) \quad ; t_o \le t \le t_N$$

It should be noted that these pseudocontrols are nonlinear functions of the aircraft dynamics (e.g. thrust, drag, angle of attack, and flight path angle). We chose M^{th} monomial splines to represent these pseudocontrols:

$$U_z(t) = \sum_{j=0}^{M} g_{z,i}(j) \frac{(t - t_{i-1})^j}{j!} \quad ; t_{i-1} \le t \le t_i, \; ; 1 \le i \le N$$

$$U_x(t) = \sum_{j=0}^{M} g_{x,i}(j) \frac{(t - t_{i-1})^j}{j!} \quad ; t_{i-1} \le t \le t_i, \; ; 1 \le i \le N$$

From this point on, the optimization formulation will be for the z axis only. However, the x axis equations can be obtained by substituting x for z in this derivation. Continuing on with the monomial construction, the z axis ODIG problem can be stated as one of the following problems:

Minimum acceleration (MA):

$$\min_{M^{th} \text{ order splines}} \int_{t_o}^{t_N} \|\ddot{z}(t)\|^2 dt$$

Minimum acceleration and velocity deviation (MAV):

$$\min_{M^{th} \text{ order splines}} \int_{t_o}^{t_N} [\alpha\|\ddot{z}(t)\|^2 + \beta\|\dot{z}(t) - \dot{z}_{desired}\|^2] dt$$

with the added waypoint constraints:

Position constraints:

$$z(t_i) = z_i \quad ; t_o \le t \le t_N$$

Velocity constraints:

$$\dot{z}(t_o) = \dot{z}_o$$

$$\dot{z}(t_N) = \dot{z}_N$$

C^2 constraints:

$$\dot{z}(t) \quad continuous \quad over \quad t_o \le t \le t_N$$

$$\ddot{z}(t) \quad continuous \quad over \quad t_o \le t \le t_N$$

$$\dddot{z}(t) \quad continuous \quad over \quad t_o \le t \le t_N$$

In the case of quadratic splines being used instead of cubic splines, the C^2 constraint is replaced by a C^1 constraint (once continuously differentiable). Each of these problems can be translated into the following cost functionals:

Minimum acceleration (MA):

$$J_{acc} = \frac{1}{2} \int_{t_o}^{t_N} (\ddot{z}(t))^2 dt$$

Minimum acceleration and velocity deviation (MAV):

$$J_{vel} = \frac{1}{2} \int_{t_o}^{t_N} [\alpha(\ddot{z}(t))^2 + \beta(\dot{z}(t) - \dot{z}_{constant})^2] dt$$

Once the initial cost functional (with respect to the spline coefficients J_{acc} or J_{vel}) is chosen, the augmented cost functional, J_{aug}, can be expressed as:

$$J_{aug} = J_{choice} + \sum_{i=1}^{N} C_i$$

Where the constraint functionals are:

$$C_i = [P_{i,1}[\sum_{j=1}^{i} \delta_i D_j G_j + B_j G_j - z_{i-1} + z_i + \delta_i \dot{y}_o]$$

$$+P_{i,2}[E_i G_i - e_1 G_{i+1}] + P_{i,3}[\dot{E}_i G_i - e_2 G_{i+1}]]$$

where $1 \leq i < N$

$$C_i = [P_{i,1}[\sum_{j=1}^{i} \delta_i D_j G_j + B_j G_j - z_{i-1} + z_i + \delta_i \dot{y}_o]$$

$$+P_{i,2}[e_1 G_1] + P_{i,3}[\sum_{j=1}^{i} D_j G_j - \dot{y}_o + \dot{y}_N]]$$

where $i = N$.

Through the use of Variational Calculus[8] it has been shown that our (M+1)N coefficients

$$G_i^T = [\ g_o \quad g_1 \quad \dots \quad g_M\ ]$$

can be found by solving the linear equation:

$$V\hat{x} = V \begin{bmatrix} G_1 \\ : \\ G_N \\ \dots \\ P \end{bmatrix} = \begin{bmatrix} K \\ \dots \\ W \end{bmatrix} = R$$

A detailed description of this equation is given in [18].

4 Nonlinear Simulation Results for an L1011-100

The first step in using dynamic interpolation in the vertical guidance problem is to decide on a desired path. In this case, we decided to use the path created by an actual FMS of a L1011-like aircraft (weight = 367,000 lbs.) The results shown at the end of this paper were produced around the following path definition:

Z axis:

$$z_0 = 1824(ft) \qquad t_0 = 0(sec)$$
$$z_1 = 1138(ft) \qquad t_1 = 50(sec)$$
$$z_2 = 655(ft) \qquad t_2 = 100(sec)$$
$$z_3 = 91(ft) \qquad t_3 = 160(sec)$$

X axis:

$$x_0 = 0.00(Nm) \qquad t_0 = 0(sec)$$
$$x_1 = 2.90(Nm) \qquad t_1 = 50(sec)$$
$$x_2 = 5.46(Nm) \qquad t_2 = 100(sec)$$
$$x_3 = 8.50(Nm) \qquad t_3 = 160(sec)$$

This path was then flown within our nonlinear simulation of the L1011-100 with the FMSM "on path" reference commands. The dynamics for the FMSM simulated flight are shown in figures 1 and 2 along with the dynamics of the two different types of ODIG flown (both figures include the turbulence wind effects). The next step in solving the vertical ODIG problem, is to choose the initial and final axis velocities.

Z axis:

$$\dot{z}_0 = -1.13(ft/sec)$$
$$\dot{z}_3 = -9.28(ft/sec)$$

X axis:

$$\dot{x}_0 = 405.8(ft/sec)$$
$$\dot{x}_3 = 305.6(ft/sec)$$

These velocities were chosen from the results obtained from the L1011-100 FMSM flight simulation without turbulence. Once the FMS simulation was completed, we had all the information needed to apply ODIG to the path. From the solution of the $V\hat{x} = R$ equation for the z and x axes, we obtained the optimal acceleration splines for the desired trajectory. The accelerations were then converted to L1011-100 autopilot theta commands (using the FMS outer loop theta controller) and throttle commands using the following equations:

$$\theta_{cmd}(t) = FMS\left(Altitude, w, \int_{t_o}^{t} \ddot{z}(s)ds, \int_{t_o}^{t}\int_{t_o}^{s} \ddot{z}(q)dqds\right)$$

$$CAS_{cmd}(t) = f\left(u, distance\ to\ dest., \int_{t_o}^{t} \ddot{x}(s)ds, \int_{t_o}^{t}\int_{t_o}^{s} \ddot{x}(q)dqds\right)$$

The choice of these commands force the autopilot and auto-throttle into a vertical speed hold mode and speed on throttle mode, respectively. These modes will then steer the plane down the desired path as long as we do not saturate the column or throttle controls and our updated target commands change slowly enough so that the autopilot and auto-throttle can track the inputs (without interference with each other). Two forms of ODIG with turbulence are presented here: one, the MA method (minimum energy) which is shown in figure 1; and two, the MAV method (minimum energy with minimum velocity excursion tradeoff of $\alpha = 1$ and $\beta = 1$) in figure 2. The major differences between MA and MAV that can be seen in the plots presented are: first, MAV captures the FMSM path about one nautical mile sooner than MA does (note, MA captures the FMSM's path about half of a nautical mile sooner without turbulence[18]); second, the vertical velocity excursion in MA damps out faster then MAV (to the FMSM vertical velocity value for the last segment), this is a change from the non-turbulence case[18]; and third, the MA column movement is smoother then MAV, this also is a reversal from the non-turbulence case[18]. These effects become more pronounced as the balance of α and β is changed in favor of the velocity. Have we lost the advantage of MAV when turbulence is encountered? As β is increased in the MAV ODIG algorithm the area under the acceleration curve will increase. This in turn will cause the velocity to change more rapidly. Therefore, when turbulence is encountered, a larger velocity error is created and the longer damping time is the result. The increased damping time in MAV will also cause the column movement to increase proportionally. As long as the magnitude of the turbulence is low, the increased velocity errors will not over shadow the MAV's advantages. It should be noted that the turbulence shown in figures 1 and 2 is quick strong (in places it approaches a small-short lived wind shear – +1 => -1 => 0 in 3 seconds.) Finally, when the ODIG controls are compared to the FMSM's controls, we see that turbulence has a strong effect on the ODIG method. This is to be excepted, because the ODIG velocity targets are always changing slowly (in general) along the entire path. However, with FMSM, its target velocity is constant along each segment. Therefore, the effects of the zero mean turbulence on the velocity errors balance out, producing smoother controls. In the ODIG cases presented here, the control perturbations generated by the velocity error were the same order magnitude as the FMSM's controls during an initial segment captures. Therefore, ODIG's controls, though somewhat degraded, are still within the acceptable limits.

5 Summary and Directions for Future Research

In this portion of the project we were interested in testing the robustness of the MA and MAV ODIG algorithm given a wind turbulence perturbation. The results were then compared to those shown above for the FMSM. Even though the FMSM controls seem more robust during turbulence then ODIG, ODIG's controls were still acceptable. However, as the lateral dynamics are added to the problem the effects of turbulence on the controls may need to be re-evaluated. There is an ongoing effort to add the lateral portion of the control problem to this simulation. Furthermore, the addition of speed and acceleration limits to the ODIG method must also be addressed before it can be implemented in the next generation FMS and flight Control Computers (FCC). A new project involving a neural network to choose the waypoint time constraints is being considered to address these flight plan and performance constraints. Finally, further considerations for the MAV cost functional need to be explored within lateral guidance problem.

Figure 1: L1011-100 dynamics for FMSM and minimum acceleration interpolation cubic spline guidance using an FMSM outer loop controller (Weight = 367,000 lbs.)

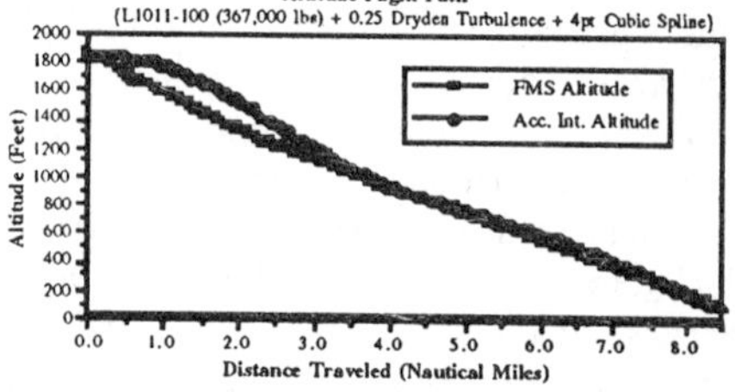

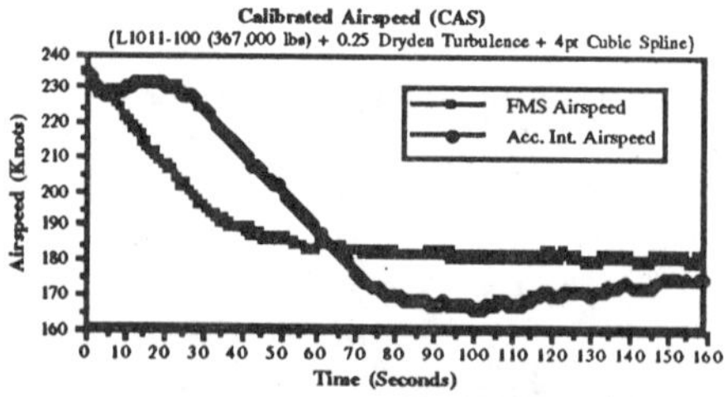

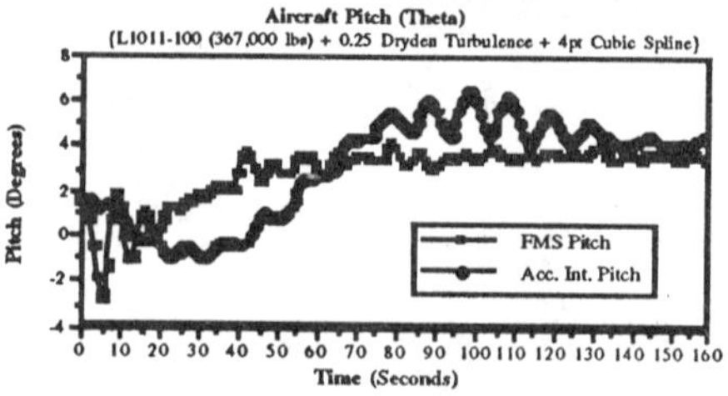

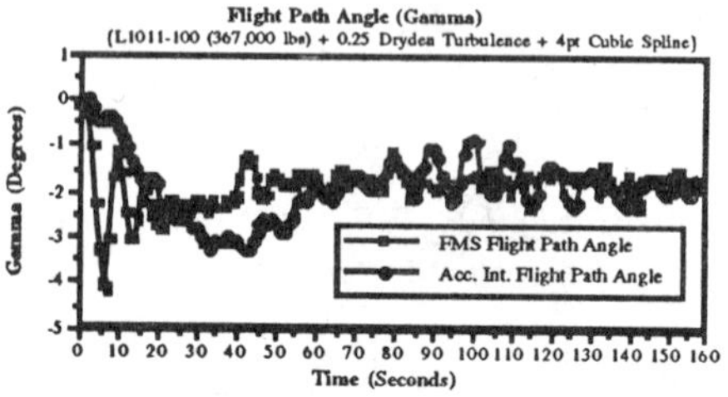

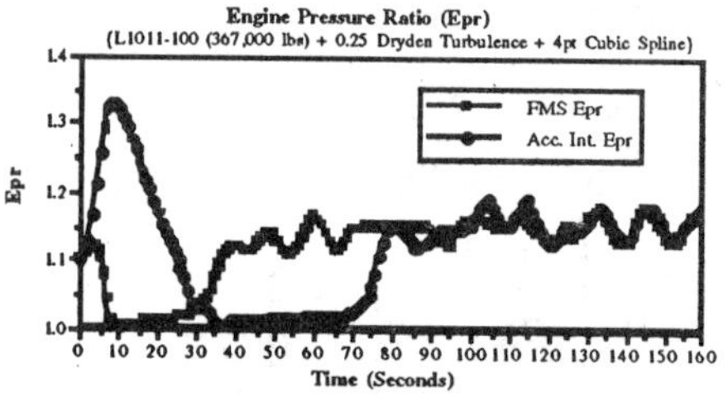

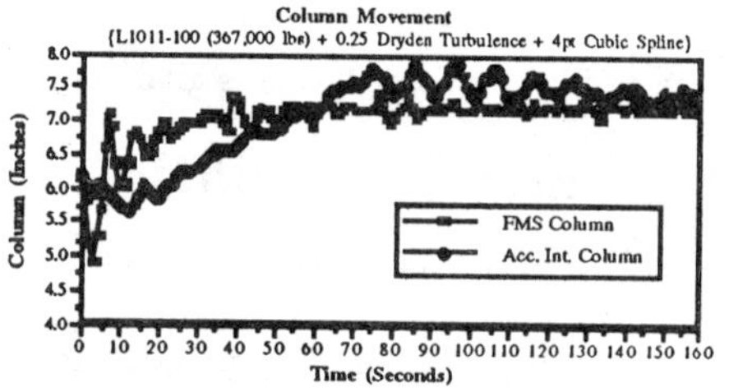

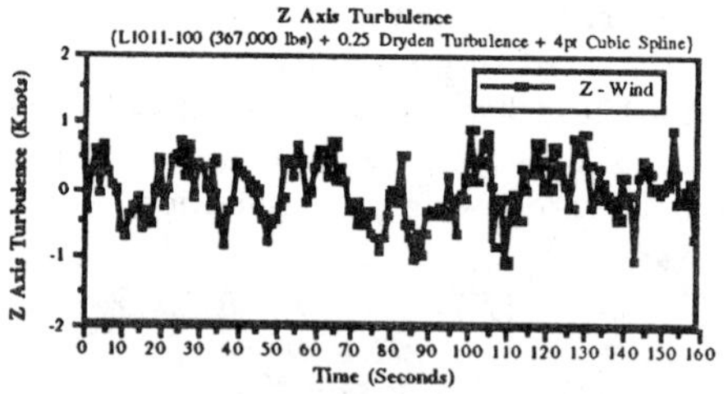

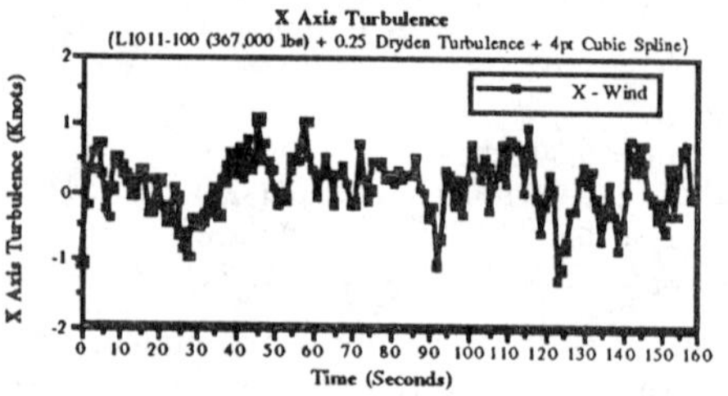

Figure 2: L1011-100 dynamics for FMSM and minimum acceleration and velocity ($\alpha = 1, \beta = 1$) interpolation cubic spline guidance using an FMSM outer loop controller (Weight = 367,000 lbs.)

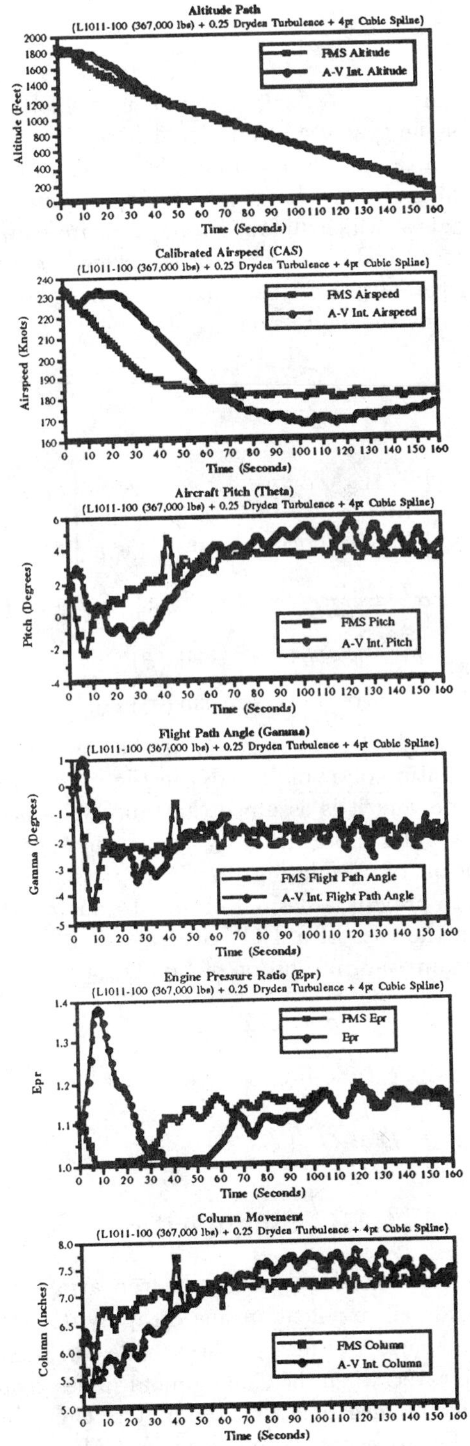

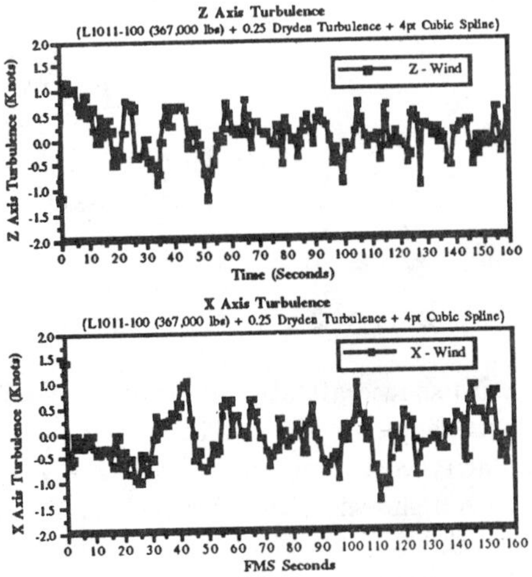

Acknowledgements

We would like to thank Dave Burdon for his help and support throughout the course of the ongoing research and his concern for new FMS technology. Furthermore, we would like to thank Dr. Joseph Jackson for his interest and help in the continuation of his PhD. work. Also, we would like to thank a number of the members of the FMS group at Honeywell CFSG that added to this project with their knowledge and support.

References

[1] David H. Williams, and Steven M. Green "Airborne Four-Dimensional Flight Management in Time-Based Air Traffic Control Environment," NASA Technical Memorandum 4249, 1991.

[2] Boeing Commercial Airplane Group "ATM Compatible FMF System Concept - Draft," Boeing Commercial Airplane Group, 1992.

[3] J.L. Groce, K.H. Izumi, C.H. Markham, R.W. Schwab, and J.A. Taylor "An Investigation of TNAV-Equipped Aircraft in Simulated En Route Metering Environment," NASA CR-178031, 1986.

[4] J.W. Burrows "Fuel-Optimum 4-D Aircraft Trajectories with Fixed Arrival Times," Journal of Guidance, Control, Vol 6, No. 1, 1983, pp. 14-19.

[5] Michael K. DeJonge "Required Time Of Arrival (RTA) Control System," United States Patent 5,121,325, June 9, 1992.

[6] S.P. Liden "Optimum 4-D Guidance For Long Flights," AIAA/IEEE 11th Digital Avionics Systems Conference, Seattle WA., Oct. 1992.

[7] Thomas J. Davis, Heinz Erzberger, and Steven M. Green "Design and Evaluation of an Air Traffic Control Final Approach Spacing Tool," Journal of Guidance, Control, and Dynamics, Vol 14, No. 4, 1991, pp. 848-854.

[8] J. W. Jackson "Dynamic Interpolation and Application to Flight Control," PhD. thesis, Arizona State University, 1991, pp.34-122.

[9] J. W. Jackson and Peter Crouch "Dynamic Interpolation and Application to Flight Control," Journal of Guidance, Control, and Dynamics, Vol 14, No. 4, 1991, pp. 814-822.

[10] Robert L. Schultz "Three-Dimensional Trajectory Optimization for Aircraft," Journal of Guidance, Control, and Dynamics, Vol 13, No. 6, 1990, pp. 936-943.

[11] Vincent Yen and Mark L. Nagurka "Fourier-Based Optimal Control Approach for Structural Systems," Journal of Guidance, Control, and Dynamics, Vol 13, No. 2, 1990, pp. 265-276.

[12] H. Erzberger, and J.D. McLean "Fuel-Conservative Guidance Systems for Power-Lift Aircraft," Journal of Guidance, Control, and Dynamics, Vol 4, No. 3, 1981, pp. 253-261.

[13] H. Erzberger, and H.Lee "Constrained Optimum Trajectories with Specified Range," Journal of Guidance, Control, and Dynamics, Vol 3, No. 1, 1980, pp. 78-85.

[14] H. Erzberger, J.D. McLean, and J.F. Barman, "Fixed-Range Optimal Trajectories for Short Haul Aircraft," NASA TND-8115, Dec. 1975.

[15] P.K.A. Menon, "Short-Range Nonlinear Feedback Strategies for Aircraft Pursuit-Evasion," Journal of Guidance, Control, and Dynamics, Vol 12, No. 1, 1989, pp. 27-32.

[16] Robert Nelson, "Flight Stability and Automatic Control," McGraw-Hill, Inc., 1989, pp. 112-148.

[17] C.R. Tolle, and A.A. Rodriguez, "Vertical Guidance for a Lockheed L1011-100 Using Dynamic Interpolation", Proceedings of the American Conference on Control, 1992.

[18] C.R. Tolle, and A.A. Rodriguez, "Aircraft Trajectory Optimization With Application to a Lockheed L1011-100", Proceedings of the 31st IEEE Conference on Decision and Control, 1992.

Proceedings of the
American Control Conference
San Francisco, California • June 1993

CMG Singularity Avoidance in Attitude Control of a Flexible Spacecraft

Raymond H. Kraft

Boeing Defense & Space Group
Seattle, Washington

Abstract

This paper deals with spacecraft attitude control using an array of 4, single-axis CMGs. This paper investigates a singularity cost function involving a p norm ($p = 20$ has been shown to be effective). This approach highly weights the CMG closest to singularity, while avoiding the problems encountered with infinity norms and the resulting chatter that occurs when several CMGs have close to equal proximity to a singularity. Cost function sensitivities are calculated analytically to improve performance. Performance is evaluated using a realistic, flexible-body simulation of the ASTREX, space-based mirror.

1. Introduction

Control Moment Gyros (CMGs) are an attractive means of producing relatively large control torques for spacecraft. Single-axis CMGs, in particular, have significant advantages in torque capability over momentum wheels due to the large torque amplification factor from gimbal input torques to CMG output torques.

They do, however, have certain caveats — one in particular being the presence of singular CMG array configurations. When such singularities are encountered, the CMG array is unable to produce output torques in a particular direction; mathematically, the mapping from gimbal angle rates to output torques becomes singular.

This paper deals with spacecraft attitude control using an array of 4, single-axis CMGs. Having 4 CMGs with which to control 3 degrees of freedom in attitude provides one level of redundancy. It also provides a means of avoiding singularities. By forming a cost function that is a measure of singularity proximity, this extra degree of redundancy can be utilized to minimize the cost function, and thereby avoid singular configurations.

2. Governing Equations

A single-axis CMG consists of spinning rotor, an outer gimbal ring, and a gimbal torque motor. The CMG, in turn, is attached to a rotating vehicle. In the case of the spacecraft considered here, four such CMGs are arranged in a tetrahedron configuration. The gimbal angles are designated σ_1, σ_2, σ_3, and σ_4, and the angle at which all four gimbal axes are skewed off the vertical is designated β, or the skew angle.

The torque output of the CMG array may be approximated by the expression

$$\boldsymbol{C}\dot{\boldsymbol{\sigma}} = \boldsymbol{T} \tag{1}$$

where

$$\boldsymbol{C} = h_0 \begin{bmatrix} s_1 & -c_2 c_\beta & -s_3 & c_4 c_\beta \\ -c_1 c_\beta & -s_2 & c_3 c_\beta & s_4 \\ c_1 s_\beta & c_2 s_\beta & c_3 s_\beta & c_4 s_\beta \end{bmatrix}, \tag{2}$$

$$\dot{\boldsymbol{\sigma}}^T = \begin{bmatrix} \dot{\sigma}_1 & \dot{\sigma}_2 & \dot{\sigma}_3 & \dot{\sigma}_4 \end{bmatrix}, \tag{3}$$

$$\begin{aligned} c_\beta &\triangleq \cos(\beta) \quad s_\beta \triangleq \sin(\beta) \\ c_i &\triangleq \cos(\sigma_i) \quad s_i \triangleq \sin(\sigma_i) \end{aligned} \tag{4}$$

for $i = 1, 2, 3, 4$. The quantity h_0 is the central angular momentum of a single CMG in the gimbal reference frame, and it is assumed that all CMGs have the same angular momentum h_0. Equation (1) provides a means of calculating the CMG gimbal rates necessary to provide a desired output torque on the vehicle. In the case of a 4 CMG array, $\boldsymbol{C} \in \mathcal{R}^{3\times 4}$. The minimum 2-norm solution of Eq.(1) for $\dot{\boldsymbol{\sigma}}$ is

$$\dot{\boldsymbol{\sigma}} = \boldsymbol{D}\boldsymbol{T}, \tag{5}$$

where $\boldsymbol{D}$ is the pseudo-inverse of $\boldsymbol{C}$ given by

$$\boldsymbol{D} = \boldsymbol{C}^T \left(\boldsymbol{C}\boldsymbol{C}^T\right)^{-1} \tag{6}$$

3. CMG Singularities

Under most circumstances, a tetrahedron array of 4 CMGs affords an excellent means of applying relatively large control torques to the vehicle for 3-axis control. However, when the CMG gimbal angles given by $\boldsymbol{\sigma}$ become aligned such that the matrix $\boldsymbol{C}\boldsymbol{C}^T$ indicated in Eq.(6) becomes singular, the CMG array can no longer provide the desired output torque.

Naturally it is desirable to avoid such configurations. The single degree of redundancy provided by having 4 CMGs allows one to accomplish this. The location of the CMG singularities can easily be found by solving the equation

$$\boldsymbol{T} \cdot \boldsymbol{n} = 0 \tag{7}$$

where $\boldsymbol{n}$ represents a direction in $\mathcal{R}^3$ and is defined by

$$\boldsymbol{n} = n_1 \boldsymbol{v}_1 + n_2 \boldsymbol{v}_2 + n_3 \boldsymbol{v}_3 \tag{8}$$

The solution to Eq.(7) is

$$\sigma_1 = \tan^{-1}\left(\frac{c_\beta n_2 - s_\beta n_3}{n_1}\right) + m_1 \pi \tag{9}$$

$$\sigma_2 = \tan^{-1}\left(\frac{-c_\beta n_1 + s_\beta n_3}{n_2}\right) + m_2 \pi \tag{10}$$

$$\sigma_3 = \tan^{-1}\left(\frac{c_\beta n_2 + s_\beta n_3}{n_1}\right) + m_3 \pi \tag{11}$$

$$\sigma_4 = \tan^{-1}\left(\frac{-c_\beta n_1 - s_\beta n_3}{n_2}\right) + m_4 \pi \tag{12}$$

with $m_i = 0, 1$ for $i = 1, 2, 3, 4$. By letting m_i take on values of 0 and 1 in Eqs.(9)–(12), one can obtain the 16 singular gimbal configurations corresponding to a particular torque output direction.

4. Singularity Avoidance

The basic concept behind most CMG singularity avoidance algorithms is to first calculate the gimbal rates necessary to provide the desired CMG output torques, and to then augment these torque producing gimbal rates with non-torque-producing gimbal rates in order to avoid singularities.

Gimbal rate vectors in the null-space of $\boldsymbol{C}$ produce no output torque. It is easy to verify that vectors in the null space of $\boldsymbol{C}$ can be expressed as

$$\boldsymbol{V}_n = (\boldsymbol{I} - \boldsymbol{D}\boldsymbol{C})\, \boldsymbol{v}_a \tag{13}$$

where $\boldsymbol{v}_a$ is an arbitrary vector. Thus, if $\dot{\boldsymbol{\sigma}}_n$ is a gimbal rate vector in the null-space direction $\boldsymbol{V}_n$, and $\dot{\boldsymbol{\sigma}}_t$ is the torque-producing gimbal rate found from Eq.(5), the total commanded gimbal rate is

$$\dot{\boldsymbol{\sigma}} = \dot{\boldsymbol{\sigma}}_t + \dot{\boldsymbol{\sigma}}_n. \tag{14}$$

One method for avoiding singularities is based upon calculating the exact, instantaneous location of the singular gimbal angle set corresponding to the saturation singularity, and steering the gimbal angles towards it [1].

Another method of singularity avoidance based on a gradient-type algorithm, attempts to minimize the maximum row norm of the pseudo-inverse matrix $\boldsymbol{D}$ [2]. This scheme effectively attempts to move the CMG that is closest to singularity, in a direction that reduces the maximum row norm. Define J_i to be the 2-norm squared of the ith row of $\boldsymbol{D}$. This algorithm then attempts to find the set of gimbal angles that satisfy

$$\boldsymbol{\sigma}_{\text{opt}} = \min_{\sigma} \max_{i} J_i. \tag{15}$$

Essentially, this approach minimizes the ∞-norm of J_i. A difficulty with this algorithm is that it frequently causes chattering in the gimbal rate commands. Initially, a particular CMG is identified as the one nearest singularity, and gimbal rate commands are generated to move it away from singularity. Eventually, however, two or more CMGs become nearly equally close to singularity. In this situation, what benefits one CMG may hurt the others, and the optimization process will begin to oscillate between helping the various CMGs. In such instances, it would be more appropriate to concentrate on the collective proximity to singularity of the entire CMG cluster, than on the proximity to singularity of any one CMG.

The singularity avoidance method proposed in this paper is based upon minimizing the p-norm of J_i rather than the ∞-norm. As will be shown, optimization of the p-norm produces smooth gimbal rate commands, and avoids the problem of chattering between several gimbals that are equally close to singularities. The cost function to be minimized for this algorithm is

$$J_T = \sum_{i=1}^{4} J_i^p. \tag{16}$$

Taking the derivative of J_T with respect to the gimbal angles, the elements of the gradient of J_T are

$$(\nabla J_T)_j \triangleq \frac{\partial J_T}{\partial \sigma_j} = p \sum_{i=1}^{4} J_i^{p-1} \frac{\partial J_i}{\partial \sigma_j} \tag{17}$$

for $j = 1, 2, 3, 4$. It is a relatively simple matter to obtain analytic expressions for this cost function gradient. Based on this gradient approach, the singularity avoidance gimbal rate vector elements are calculated according to

$$\dot{\sigma}_{\text{sa}_j} = -k_{\text{gd}} \frac{\sum_{i=1}^{4} J_i^{p-1} \frac{\partial J_i}{\partial \sigma_j}}{\sum_{i=1}^{4} J_i^{p-1}} \tag{18}$$

where k_{gd} is the gradient descent gain. Equation (18) may also be interpreted as a weighted average of the cost function sensitivities. For a given gimbal, the commanded gimbal rate is calculated from the average cost function sensitivity for that CMG, weighted by the cost function value associated with each of the gimbals.

Finally, to obtain the total commanded gimbal rate, $\dot{\boldsymbol{\sigma}}_{\text{sa}}$ must be combined with the torque producing gimbal rates $\dot{\boldsymbol{\sigma}}_t$. This is done by projecting the

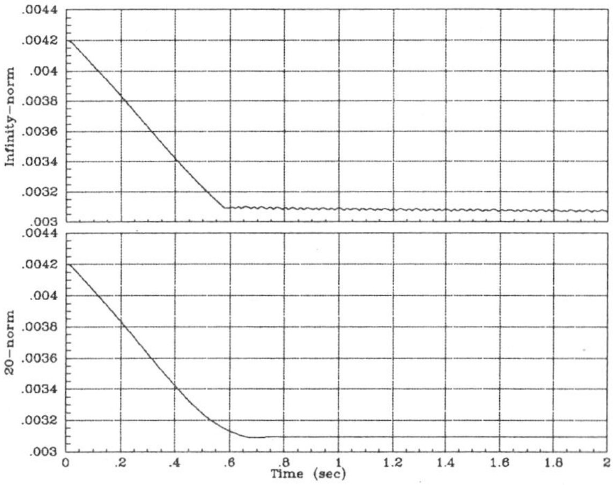

Figure 1: Pseudo-Inverse Infinity-Norm Time History

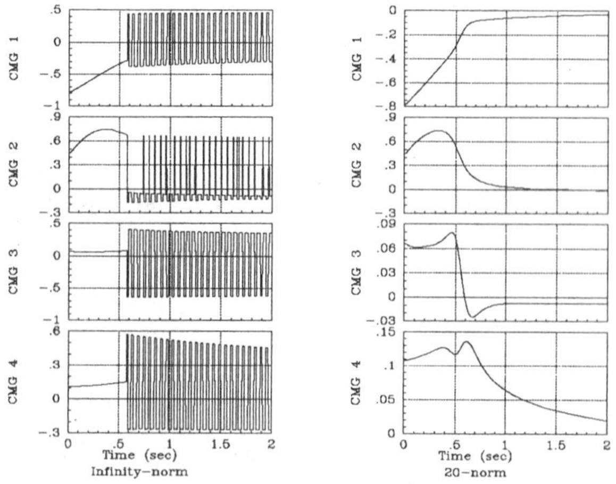

Figure 2: Gimbal Angle Time History

singularity avoidance gimbal rates on the null-space direction, and adding the result to the torque producing gimbal rates. The commanded gimbal rate in the null-space is

$$\dot{\boldsymbol{\sigma}}_n = (\dot{\boldsymbol{\sigma}}_{\text{sa}} \cdot \boldsymbol{V}_n)\, \boldsymbol{V}_n. \tag{19}$$

The total commanded gimbal rate is then given by Eq.(14).

5. Simulation Results

The performance of the ∞-norm and p-norm algorithms was evaluated using a non-linear, flexible-body simulation of an experimental test article known as ASTREX (Advanced Space Structures Technology Research Experiment). Shown in Fig. 1 is the time history of the ∞-norm for both an ∞-norm and a p-norm optimization. The gimbal angles in both cases were initialized to angles in the vicinity of a singularity, and the controller was instructed to move the gimbals away from singularities. In this particular case, the controller was also instructed to ignore constraints on null-space motion for singularity avoidance. Notice that the ∞-norm algorithm arrives at a minimum value quickest, however, it also exhibits oscillatory behavior not seen in the p-norm algorithm.

Figure 2 shows the cause of the oscillatory behavior in the ∞-norm algorithm. Depicted are the gimbal rate commands for each of the CMGs using the two algorithms (units are in radians per second). Note that at roughly $t = 0.6$ seconds, the ∞-norm algorithm arrives at the situation where more than one CMG is equally close to singularity, and a very undesirable command time history begins. The p-norm algorithm, on the other hand, maintains a smooth command profile. Similar benefits in command smoothness have also been shown during slew commands where null-space motion was enforced.

6. Conclusions

This paper proposes a gradient-based, CMG singularity, avoidance algorithm that optimizes a cost function based on a p-norm. The cost function minimized by the avoidance algorithm is given by the p-norm of the 2-norms of the rows of the pseudo-inverse matrix. For p large, this has the desirable property of identifying the CMG most in need of rescue from a singularity, while shifting emphasis to the health of the entire CMG cluster when several CMGs come equally close to singularity. Also, this switching of CMG emphasis via minimization of the p-norm is a smooth process, and does not require complicated, discrete switching logic. A value of $p = 20$ has been demonstrated to provide these desirable properties.

References

[1] D.E. Cornick. Singularity avoidance control laws for single gimbal control moment gyros. In *AIAA Guidance and Control Conference*, pages 20–33, Boulder, CO, August 1979. Martin Marietta Corporation.

[2] R.D. Hefner and C.H. McKenzie. A technique for maximizing the torque capability of control momenent gyro systems. In *Astrodynamics 1983; Proceedings of the Conference*, pages 905–920, San Diego, CA, August 1983. The Aerospace Corporation.

Proceedings of the
American Control Conference
San Francisco, California • June 1993

A Suboptimal Robot Path Planning Scheme for Loosely Constrained Trajectories

Dan Simon *
TRW, SB2-1062
PO Box 1310
San Bernardino, CA 92402

Can Isik
Syracuse University
Dept. of Electrical Engineering
Syracuse, NY 13244

Abstract

Approximation of a desired robot path can be accomplished by interpolating a curve through a sequence of joint-space knots. A smooth interpolated trajectory can be realized by using trigonometric splines (TSs). But sometimes the joint trajectory is not required to exactly pass through the given knots. The knots may rather be centers of tolerances *near* which the trajectory is required to pass. In this paper, we optimize TSs through a given set of knots subject to user-specified knot tolerances. The contribution of this paper is the straightforward way in which intermediate constraints (i.e. knot angles) are incorporated into the parameter optimization problem. Another contribution is the exploitation of the decoupled nature of TSs to reduce the computational expense of the problem. The additional freedom of varying the knot angles results in a lower objective function and a higher computational expense, compared to the case where the knot angles are constrained to exact values. The specific objective functions considered are minimum jerk and minimum energy. In the minimum jerk case, the optimization problem reduces to a quadratic programming problem. Simulation results for a two-link manipulator are presented to support the results of this paper.

I. Introduction

The industrial robot is a highly nonlinear, coupled multivariable system with nonlinear constraints. For this reason, robot control algorithms are often divided into two stages: *path planning* and *path tracking*. A conceptually simple approach to the path planning problem is to generate a joint-space trajectory based on interpolation of a sequence of desired joint angles. This approach ignores most of the dynamics of the robot, so the resultant trajectories do not take full advantage of the robot's capabilities. But the trajectories are typically computationally inexpensive, making this approach a popular method [1]. In this approach, a number of knot points are chosen along the desired Cartesian path. The number of knots chosen is a tradeoff between exactness and computational expense. The Cartesian knots are then mapped into joint knots using inverse kinematics. Finally, an analytic interpolating curve is fit to the joint knots. This curve provides the path tracker with joint angles and derivatives at the controller rate.

A recent development [2, 3] is the use of trigonometric polynomials to efficiently generate joint trajectories with little overshoot but continuous velocity, acceleration, and jerk. Trigonometric polynomials have the characteristic that if they are appropriately normalized in time, they are very smooth [4]. That is, the magnitude of the derivatives are relatively low, and the overshoot is relatively small. If piecewise continuous trigonometric polynomials are joined together, the computational expense is low [5], and each polynomial is of low order, preventing oscillations between knots. These piecewise continuous trigonometric polynomials are called *trigonometric splines*, hereafter referred to as TSs.

In this paper, we show how a TS which is required to pas *near* a given set of joint knots can be optimized. The objective functions which are used are minimum jerk and minimum energy. In the minimum jerk case, the problem reduces to a quadratic programming problem with linear constraints. The maximum error at the knots is specified by the user. The unique contribution of this paper is the straightforward way in which the intermediate knot angle constraints are incorporated into the optimization problem. In addition, the decoupled nature of TSs can be taken advantage of to reduce the computational expense of the problem.

II. Trigonometric Splines

In this section, the TSs used in this paper will be defined, and their application to robot path planning will be summarized. See [2, 3] for details.

A desired Cartesian trajectory can be discretized into $(n+1)$ Cartesian goal points at times $t_0 < t_1 < \ldots < t_n$. Then inverse kinematics can be performed at each of these goal points, resulting in a set of $(n+1)$ joint space goal points y_i for each joint. Then n fourth-order trigonometric polynomials $y_i(t)$ can be generated. Fourth-order polynomials are used so that the first three derivatives at each endpoint can be constrained. This allows the user to join the polynomials together so as to have a joint-space path with continuous derivatives up to the third order. The TS segment $y_i(t)$ $(i = 1, \ldots, n)$ is defined *only* on the time interval $[t_{i-1}, t_i]$. The time interval of each segment can be normalized to a *fixed* t_{i-1} and t_i. In this paper, it will be assumed that $t_{i-1} = 0$ and $t_i = \pi/4$, $(i = 1, \ldots, n)$. These values give computational stability and smoothness of motion [4]. Then each TS segment can be written as

$$y_i(t) = a_{i,0} + \sum_{k=1}^{3}(a_{i,k}\cos kt + b_{i,k}\sin kt) + a_{i,4}\cos 4t \qquad t \in [0, \pi/4]. \tag{1}$$

These n trigonometric polynomials are joined together to form a TS. The eight constraints used to determine the coefficients of $y_i(t)$ are

$$\begin{aligned} y_i(t_{i-1}) &= y_{i-1} &&\equiv y(t_{i-1}) \\ y_i(t_i) &= y_i &&\equiv y(t_i) \\ y_i^{(r)}(t_{i-1}) &= y_{i-1}^{(r)} &&\equiv y^{(r)}(t_{i-1}) \quad (r = 1,2,3) \\ y_i^{(r)}(t_i) &= y_i^{(r)} &&\equiv y^{(r)}(t_i) \quad (r = 1,2,3). \end{aligned} \tag{2}$$

The first two constraints of (2) are given by the inverse kinematics solution of the Cartesian trajectory. There are several

*This work was performed while the author was with Syracuse University.

different ways to specify the last six constraints of (2). One way is that the user may desire certain joint derivatives at the knots. Another possibility is that these constraints could be determined to minimize some objective function (see Section III). Yet another possibility is that these constraints could be chosen using some simple, heuristic method [5].

Equations (1) and (2) are used to determine the coefficients of the spline segments $y_i(t)$. The multiplication of an 8×8 matrix A_i^{-1} by an eight-element vector gives the eight coefficients of $y_i(t)$ as follows.

$$\left[\begin{array}{ccc} a_{i,0} & \cdots & a_{i,4} \end{array}\right]^T = A_i^{-1} \left[\begin{array}{ccc} y_{i-1} & \cdots & y_i''' \end{array}\right]^T. \quad (3)$$

See [2, 3] for the numerical value of A_i and the existence theorem which guarantees the invertibility of A_i. Since the segment $y_i(t)$ is defined on $t \in [0, \pi/4]$ for all i, the time-scaled TS $y(t)$ is given by

$$y(t + (i-1)\pi/4) = y_i(t), \quad t \in [0, \pi/4], \quad (i = 1, \ldots, n). \quad (4)$$

The function $y(t)$ is a TS which satisfies the desired interpolation conditions, and which has length $n\pi/4$ seconds. The unscaled spline $\theta(t)$ given by

$$\theta(t) = y(n\pi t/4T) \qquad t \in [0, T] \quad (5)$$

stretches the trajectory from its normalized length $n\pi/4$ to a desired length T.

III. Optimization

The user of the trajectory formulation algorithm described in the previous section is free to choose the first three trajectory derivatives at each knot. The knot derivatives can be chosen to minimize some objective function. Since $\vec{\theta}(t)$ is a time-scaled and time-shifted version of $\vec{y}(t)$ (5) where $\vec{y}(t)$ is the P-vector of normalized TSs, and $\vec{y}(t)$ is composed of the n spline segments $\vec{y}_i(t)$ (4), a general objective function can be written in the form

$$J = g[\sum_{k=1}^{n} \vec{y}_k(t)] \quad (6)$$

where $g(\cdot)$ is a general nonlinear function, $\vec{y}_k(t)$ is a P-vector of TS segments, and P is the number of joints that the robot has. The minimization of this general objective function becomes a parameter optimization problem, since $\vec{y}(t)$ is a function of the $3P(n-1)$ free knot derivatives, where $(n-1)$ is the number of interior knots of each joint trajectory.

If J is known to have only one minimum, then (6) is minimized when

$$\begin{array}{l} \dfrac{\partial}{\partial y_{i,j}^{(r)}} g[\sum_{k=1}^{n} \vec{y}_k(t)] = 0, \quad (i = 1, \ldots, n-1), \\ (r = 1, 2, 3), \quad (j = 1, \ldots, P) \end{array} \quad (7)$$

where $y_{i,j}^{(r)}$ is the r-th derivative of the i-th normalized spline segment of the j-th joint of the robot. Since $\vec{y}_k(t)$ is a function of $y_{i,j}^{(r)}$ only for $k \in \{i, i+1\}$ (1,3), we can write (7) as

$$\frac{\partial}{\partial y_{i,j}^{(r)}} g[\vec{y}_i(t) + \vec{y}_{i+1}(t)] = 0. \quad (8)$$

Further simplification from this point depends on the form of (6).

So the optimal control problem is simplified by reducing its dimension, thereby converting it to a parameter optimization problem. This general approach to optimal control is similar to that taken by others [6]–[8]. But their formulations are applicable only for constraints at the initial and final time, and do not allow for constraints at specific times in between. In other words, as applied to the robot path planning problem, their approaches are valid only for path planning between an initial point and a final point, and do not allow for intermediate knots. Two specific examples of optimization (minimum jerk and minimum energy) are considered in the following sections.

A. Minimum Jerk Trajectory

Suppose that the user desires to minimize the jerk of each joint throughout its trajectory. Kyriakopoulos and Saridis [9] report that the joint position errors of the path tracker increase with the magnitude of joint jerk. Also, Flanagan and Ostry [10] present evidence that the human brain plans arm movements so as to minimize a function of joint jerk. So minimizing some function of joint jerk would seem to be desirable, resulting in a coordinated motion which could be accurately followed by the robot path tracker. The objective function could then be written as

$$J = \int_0^T [\theta'''(t)]^2 dt = \int_0^{n\pi/4} [y'''(t)]^2 dt \quad (9)$$

where the second equality follows from (4) and (5). In order to minimize (9), we want to set each of the partial derivatives with respect to the $(n-1)$ normalized interior knot derivatives equal to zero. So (9) will be minimized when

$$\begin{array}{l} \dfrac{\partial}{\partial y_i^{(r)}} \left\{ \displaystyle\int_0^{n\pi/4} [y'''(t)]^2 dt \right\} = 0 \\ (i = 1, \ldots, n-1), \quad (r = 1, 2, 3). \end{array} \quad (10)$$

Recall that $y(t)$ is composed of the functions $y_i(t)$ $(i = 1, \ldots, n)$, each of which is an analytic function of the eight parameters $(y_j^{(r)})$, $(j = i-1, i)$, $(r = 0, 1, 2, 3)$. So the differentiation and integration of (9) can be performed analytically to obtain the $(n-1)$ matrix equations

$$D_1 \begin{pmatrix} y_{i-1} \\ y_i \\ y_{i+1} \end{pmatrix} + D_2 Y_{i-1}^{(r)} + D_3 Y_i^{(r)} + D_4 Y_{i+1}^{(r)} = 0 \quad (11)$$

where we assume that the derivatives of the trajectory are constrained at the endpoints, the D_k are 3×3 matrices, and the $Y_i^{(r)}$ vectors are defined by

$$Y_i^{(r)} \equiv (\begin{array}{ccc} y_i' & y_i'' & y_i''' \end{array})^T. \quad (12)$$

Then (11) can be written as the single matrix equation

$$\Delta \begin{pmatrix} Y_1^{(r)} \\ \vdots \\ Y_{n-1}^{(r)} \end{pmatrix} = C \quad (13)$$

where the block tridiagonal matrix Δ has constant blocks with known numerical entries on its diagonal, upper diagonal, and lower diagonal, and the vector C is a constant with known numerical entries [2, 3]. It can be shown that Δ is always nonsingular. This property follows from the fact that (9) is always greater than zero unless all of the knot derivatives are zero.

B. Minimum Energy Trajectory

Recall that the P-element torque vector of a P-joint robot can be given as

$$\mathcal{T}(\vec{\theta}) = M(\vec{\theta})\vec{\theta}\,'' + S(\vec{\theta}, \vec{\theta}\,') \tag{14}$$

where M is the $P \times P$ mass matrix, and S is a vector of centrifugal, Coriolis, and gravity terms. Suppose the user wants to choose the interior knot derivatives of the TS for each joint so as to achieve a minimum energy trajectory. Then the objective function could be written as

$$J = \int_0^T \mathcal{T}^T(\vec{\theta}) R \mathcal{T}(\vec{\theta}) d\tau \tag{15}$$

where R is a $P \times P$ positive-definite weighting matrix. Using the fact (5) that $\vec{\theta}(\tau) = \vec{y}(n\pi\tau/4T)$, the torque vector $\mathcal{T}$ can be written as a function of the normalized joint trajectory $\vec{y}(t)$, and the objective function of (15) can be rewritten as

$$J = \frac{4T}{n\pi} \int_0^{n\pi/4} \mathcal{T}_y^T R \mathcal{T}_y dt \tag{16}$$

where $\mathcal{T}_y$ is given by

$$\mathcal{T}_y = M(\vec{y})(n\pi/4T)^2 \vec{y}\,'' + S(\vec{y}, (n\pi/4T)\vec{y}\,'). \tag{17}$$

Since $\vec{y}$ is formed by joining together the individual $\vec{y}_i$ components, each of which is defined only on the time interval $t \in [0, \pi/4]$ (4), we obtain

$$J = \frac{4T}{n\pi} \int_0^{\pi/4} \sum_{i=1}^{n} \mathcal{T}_{yi}^T R \mathcal{T}_{yi} dt \equiv \sum_{i=1}^{n} J_i \tag{18}$$

where $\mathcal{T}_{yi}$ is the normalized torque vector which is applied during the i-th spline segment. That is, $\mathcal{T}_{yi}$ is equal to (17) when $\vec{y}$ is replaced by $\vec{y}_i$.

So J is completely determined by the $3P(n-1)$ free parameters $\vec{y}_i^{(r)}$, $(r = 1, 2, 3)$, $(i = 1, \ldots, n-1)$. The optimal control problem of (15) has thus been converted into a parameter optimization problem. Note that the objective function could also be minimized with respect to T (the actual path length) using some parameter optimization scheme.

A significant computational savings in the solution of (18) can be realized by taking advantage of the fact that $\mathcal{T}_{yj}$ is an explicit function of $\vec{y}_i^{(r)}$ only for $j \in \{i, i+1\}$ (due to the decoupling of the spline segments). Therefore (18) can be solved as

$$\min_{\vec{y}_i^{(r)}} (J_i + J_{i+1}) \qquad (i = 1, \ldots, n-1) \tag{19}$$

where J_i is defined in (18). So the $3P(n-1)$-dimensional minimization problem of (18) has been converted into $(n-1)$ separate minimization problems, each of dimension $3P$. Of course, (19) is a highly nonlinear function of the parameters $\vec{y}_i^{(r)}$ and must be solved using some numerical method.

C. Optimization With Nonzero Knot Tolerances

The user may not really require the robot trajectory to pass exactly through the knots. The knots may be more like "centers of tolerance" *near* which the robot is required to pass. The TSs discussed earlier in this paper, and most algebraic splines, are planned so as to exactly pass through the given knots. The remainder of this section discusses the use of TSs when the robot is not required to pass exactly through the given knots. This additional freedom is used to improve the performance of the robot trajectory with respect to the objective functions discussed earlier in this section: minimum jerk and minimum energy.

C.1. Minimum Jerk Trajectory with Nonzero Knot Tolerances

As before, we desire to minimize the integral of the square of the jerk of the joint trajectory

$$\int_0^T [\theta'''(t)]^2 dt = \int_0^{n\pi/4} [y'''(t)]^2 dt = \sum_{i=1}^{n} \int_0^{\pi/4} [y_i'''(t)]^2 dt \tag{20}$$

where $y_i(t)$ is the i-th normalized TS segment. As described in Subsection A, $y_i'''(t)$ is a linear function of the eight parameters $y_j^{(r)}$, $(j = i-1, i)$, $(r = 0, 1, 2, 3)$. Therefore

$$\int_0^{\pi/4} [y_i'''(t)]^2 dt = \frac{1}{2} x_i^T \hat{Q} x_i \tag{21}$$

where x_i^T is given by

$$x_i^T = (\ y_{i-1} \quad y_{i-1}' \cdots y_i'''\ ) \tag{22}$$

and $\hat{Q}$ is an 8×8 symmetric positive semidefinite matrix. Now we partition the vectors x_i and the matrix $\hat{Q}$ as

$$x_i = (\ \phi_{i-1}^T \quad \phi_i^T\ )^T \tag{23}$$

$$\hat{Q} = \begin{pmatrix} \hat{Q}_{11} & \hat{Q}_{12} \\ \hat{Q}_{12}^T & \hat{Q}_{22} \end{pmatrix} \tag{24}$$

where each submatrix in $\hat{Q}$ is a 4×4 matrix. Further matrix manipulations [4, 14] eventually yield

$$\min \int_0^T [\theta'''(t)]^2 dt = \min_x (\frac{1}{2} x^T Q x - b^T x) \tag{25}$$

where the $4(n-1) \times 4(n-1)$ block tridiagonal matrix Q is given by

$$Q = \begin{pmatrix} \hat{Q}_{11} + \hat{Q}_{22} & \hat{Q}_{12} & \cdots & 0 \\ \hat{Q}_{12}^T & \hat{Q}_{11} + \hat{Q}_{22} & \cdots & 0 \\ \vdots & \ddots & \ddots & \vdots \\ 0 & \cdots & \hat{Q}_{11} + \hat{Q}_{22} & \hat{Q}_{12} \\ 0 & \cdots & \hat{Q}_{12}^T & \hat{Q}_{11} + \hat{Q}_{22} \end{pmatrix} \tag{26}$$

and the $4(n-1)$-vectors b and x are given by

$$x^T = (\ \phi_1^T \ \ \ldots \ \ \phi_{n-1}^T\ ). \tag{27}$$

$$b^T = -(\ \phi_0^T \hat{Q}_{12} \ \ 0 \ \ \ldots \ \ 0 \ \ \phi_n^T \hat{Q}_{12}^T\ ) \tag{28}$$

The $\hat{Q}$ matrices of (24) and following are given numerically in [4].

Now the user may not require the TS to pass exactly through the given interior knots. The user may rather specify a desired tolerance for each knot. This increases the domain of the optimization problem, and thus results in a lower objective function value and a larger computational effort. The knot tolerances result in the following inequality constraints being associated with the minimization problem of (20).

$$|y_i - y_{ci}| \le y_{toli} \qquad (i = 1, \ldots, n-1) \tag{29}$$

where y_i is the angle of the TS at knot i, y_{ci} is the desired knot angle (the center of tolerance), and y_{toli} is the allowable joint angle error at knot i. These constraints can be written as

$$Ax \le c \tag{30}$$

where A is the $2(n-1) \times 4(n-1)$ matrix

$$A = \text{diag}(\ A_s \ \cdots \ A_s\ ) \quad (31)$$

$$\text{and } A_s = \begin{pmatrix} -1 & 0 & 0 & 0 \\ 1 & 0 & 0 & 0 \end{pmatrix}. \quad (32)$$

The vector x is the $4(n-1)$-vector given in (27), and c is the $2(n-1)$-vector given by

$$c^T = [\ (y_{tol1} - y_{c1}) \ \ (y_{tol1} + y_{c1}) \ \ (y_{tol2} - y_{c2}) \ \cdots \\ (y_{tol(n-1)} + y_{c(n-1)})]. \quad (33)$$

So by combining (25) and (30), the minimum jerk problem with nonzero knot tolerances can be written as

$$\min_x(\frac{1}{2}x^T Qx - b^T x) \text{ subject to } Ax \leq c. \quad (34)$$

Matrix Q can be shown to be positive definite by similar reasoning as used for the matrix in (13).

So the problem has been reduced to a quadratic programming problem with linear constraints. This type of problem can be solved by several different methods, among which is Hildreth's Algorithm [12, 13]. Note that trajectory derivative inequality constraints at the knots can easily be incorporated into this problem by a straightforward modification of matrix A in (30).

C.2. Minimum Energy Trajectory with Nonzero Knot Tolerances

Now suppose we desire to find a minimum energy TS through a given sequence of knots, but with a specified allowable knot tolerance (29) given by

$$|\vec{y}_i - \vec{y}_{ci}| \leq \vec{y}_{toli} \qquad (i = 1, \ldots, n-1). \quad (35)$$

Each vector in (35) has P elements, with P being the number of joints of the robot. The vector inequality in (35) is taken component by component.

In principle, the energy objective function could be augmented with a penalty function [13] corresponding to (35). Unfortunately, when the objective function is highly nonlinear, the penalty function approach may result in an augmented objective function with many hills and valleys. So a local minimum of might be significantly larger than other nearby minima. This indeed turns out to be the case for the minimum energy TS problem with nonzero knot tolerances. So rather than using a penalty function method, the following method, which makes use of the physical significance of the constraints of (35), is proposed.

$$\min_{\vec{y}_i}\left[\min_{\vec{y}_i^{(r)}} \int_0^{\pi/4} (T_i^T R T_i + T_{i+1}^T R T_{i+1}) d\tau\right], \quad (36) \\ (i = 1, \ldots, n-1), \qquad (r = 1, 2, 3).$$

This method is a set of $(n-1)$ minimizations (the outer minimization) over P-dimensional domains ($\vec{y}_i$). The function which each of these $(n-1)$ minimizations minimizes is itself the solution to a minimization problem (the inner minimization) over $3P$-dimensional domains ($\vec{y}_i^{(r)}$).

The above algorithm recognizes the increased number of hills and valleys in the objective function due to the increased number of free parameters (i.e. the knot angles). The algorithm also recognizes that the optimum knot derivatives $\vec{y}_i^{(r)}$ are functions of the knot angles $\vec{y}_i$.

IV. Simulation Results

In this section, simulation results will be presented to support the work done in the previous section. The robot manipulator which is considered is a two-link robot which is described in Craig [1, Section 6.7]. The robot operates in the vertical plane, and each link's mass ($m_1 = 4.6$ kg and $m_2 = 2.3$ kg) is concentrated at its distal end. Each link is 0.5 meters in length. The torque (in Newton-meters) due to viscous friction for each joint is assumed to be five times the joint velocity (in radians/second).

Seven Cartesian knots are specified. The TS is required to pass through (or near in the case of nonzero knot tolerances) these seven knots. The seven knots are given in Table I, along with the corresponding joint angles at the knots (obtained by inverse kinematics). There is currently no other literature which discusses optimum robot path planning through a given set of knots. So these knots were chosen somewhat arbitrarily to represent what might be a typical task for an industrial robot. The length of the path was fixed at 30 seconds. In this section five different types of TSs are computed: nominal splines (no optimization), minimum jerk splines, minimum energy splines, minimum jerk splines with nonzero (four degree) knot tolerances, and minimum energy splines with nonzero (four degree) knot tolerances.

Knot Number	Cartesian Knots (meters) x	y	Joint Angles 1	2
1	$\sqrt{2}/2$	0	45	-90
2	$\sqrt{2}/2$	$\sqrt{2}/4$	64	-76
3	$\sqrt{2}/4$	$\sqrt{2}/2$	101	-76
4	0	1	90	0
5	$-\sqrt{2}/4$	$\sqrt{2}/2$	79	76
6	$-\sqrt{2}/2$	$\sqrt{2}/4$	116	76
7	$-\sqrt{2}/2$	0	135	90

Table I: Seven Cartesian and Joint Space Knots

Hildreth's algorithm was used for the minimum jerk trajectory with nonzero knot tolerances. Since Hildreth's algorithm is iterative in nature, it could theoretically take an infinite number of iterations before convergence is achieved. Therefore, some error y_e in the solution is allowed. Once Hildreth's algorithm achieves a solution with knot errors within $\pm(y_{toli} + y_e)$, the algorithm is considered to have converged. The allowable error y_e was chosen to be 0.1 degrees. So the actual allowable knot tolerances were 4.1 degrees, while the parameters y_{toli} were fixed at four degrees.

For the minimum energy trajectories, Powell's method of nonlinear parameter optimization was implemented on a DEC Vax 8820. Powell's method was used to perform $(n-1)$ separate $3P$-dimensional minimization problems, as indicated in (19). The number of knots is $(n+1)$, and the number of joints is P (two for the manipulator considered in this section). The weighting matrix R of (15) was taken to be the identity matrix. The algorithm was considered to have converged when the objective function decreased by less than 0.5 percent. The additional minimization with respect to the knot angles (for the case of minimum energy with nonzero knot tolerances) was considered to have converged when the knot angle under consideration changed by less than 0.5 degrees.

The resulting trajectories are shown in [4, 14]. A compari-

	Type of Trigonometric Spline				
		Minimum Jerk		Minimum Energy	
	Nominal	Zero Knot Tolerance	Nonzero Knot Tolerance	Zero Knot Tolerance	Nonzero Knot Tolerance
Joint 1 Jerk	1.453	0.2229	0.1741	1.608	2.355
Joint 2 Jerk	2.351	0.8190	0.4028	2.342	1.278
Energy	27341	3674	3021	557	507
Computational Effort	760 flops	767 flops	2.7 sec	55 sec	390 sec

Table II: Objective Functions and VAX 8820 Computational Effort for Trigonometric Splines

son of the various objective functions is given in Table II. The numbers in Table II are radians^2/second^5 for the jerk objective function, and (Newton-meter)^2·seconds for the energy objective function. Note from Table II the sizeable improvement in the energy objective function when optimization is used. Even the minimum jerk splines improve the energy consumption by a factor of five or six when compared to the nominal splines. This indicates that the minimization of jerk is a big step towards the minimization of energy. In contrast, the use of minimum energy splines does not result in any improvement of the jerk objective function when compared to the nominal splines.

Table II shows that the introduction of nonzero knot tolerances results in a decrease of the objective function under consideration. This is as expected. The optimization algorithm is given more free parameters, and this results in better performance.

Table II also shows the computational effort which was required for each spline. The nominal spline and minimum jerk splines have closed-form solutions, and so their computation effort can be measured in *flops* (floating point operations). The other splines in Table II require iterative solutions, and so their computational effort is measured in CPU time on a Vax 8820 computer. It has been shown that the computational effort increases linearly with the number of knots [5].

V. Conclusion

It has been shown that the use of trigonometric splines for robot path planning is amenable to path optimization subject to user-specified knot tolerances. The knots may be chosen to avoid obstacles. So the robot path may not need to path exactly through the knots, but rather *near* the knots. This possibility makes optimization subject to user specified knot tolerances a desirable feature of a path planning method. The objective function under consideration can decrease significantly if the knot tolerances are used wisely. The optimization procedures presented in this paper are iterative, and thus cannot be performed in real time. But if the objective function is minimum jerk subject to knot tolerances, then the optimization problem reduces to a quadratic programming problem with linear constraints. This is a well known problem, and there are several ways of solving it.

If the objective function includes the dynamics of the robot, then the optimization problem must be solved using an iterative method due to the nonlinearity of robot dynamics. But the decoupled nature of TS segments means that the optimization problem can be split into many smaller subproblems (one for each knot). This decreases the computational effort by a significant amount. The simulation results of this paper indicate that the minimization of an energy objective function can result in a decrease of energy by a factor of 25 or more. This would result in less wear and tear on the robot, and lower power requirements. Both of these results would be attractive to robot users.

References

[1] J. Craig, *Introduction to Robotics*. Reading, MA: Addison-Wesley, 1989.

[2] D. Simon and C. Isik, "Optimal Trigonometric Robot Joint Trajectories," *Robotica*, 9:379-386, Oct. 1991.

[3] D. Simon and C. Isik, "A Trigonometric Trajectory Generator for Robotic Arms," *International Journal of Control*, in print.

[4] D. Simon, "A Unified Approach to Robot Path Planning Using Trigonometric Splines," Ph.D. Dissertation, Syracuse University, Department of Electrical Engineering, Syracuse, NY, Aug. 1991.

[5] D. Simon and C. Isik, "Computational Complexity and Path Error Analyses of Trigonometric Joint Trajectories," *International Journal of Robotics and Automation*, in print.

[6] C. Neuman and A. Sen, "A Suboptimal Control Algorithm for Constrained Problems Using Cubic Splines," *Automatica*, 9:601-613, 1973.

[7] J. Vlassenbroeck and R. Van Dooren, "A Chebyshev Technique for Solving Nonlinear Optimal Control Problems," *IEEE Transactions on Automatic Control*, AC-33:333-340, April 1988.

[8] V. Yen and M. Nagurka, "Fourier-Based Optimal Control Approach for Structural Systems," *Journal of Guidance, Control, and Dynamics*, 13:265-276, March 1990.

[9] K. Kyriakopoulos and G. Saridis, "Minimum Jerk Path Generation," *IEEE International Conference on Robotics and Automation*, 1:364-369, 1988.

[10] J. Flanagan and D. Ostry, "Trajectories of Human Multi-Joint Arm Movements: Evidence of Joint Level Planning," in *Experimental Robotics I, The First International Symposium*, ed. by V. Hayward and O. Khatib, New York: Springer-Verlag, 1990.

[11] W. Press, B. Flannery, S. Teukolsky, and W. Vetterling, "Numerical Recipes," New York: Cambridge University Press, 1986.

[12] C. Hildreth, "A Quadratic Programming Procedure," *Naval Research Logistics Quarterly*, 4:79-85, 1957.

[13] D. Luenberger, "Optimization by Vector Space Methods," New York: Wiley, 1968.

[14] D. Simon and C. Isik, "Suboptimal Robot Joint Interpolation Within User-Specified Knot Tolerances," *Journal of Robotic Systems*, submitted for review.

Proceedings of the
American Control Conference
San Francisco, California • June 1993

PATH-TRACKING FOR A CARLIKE MOBILE ROBOT

DeSantis, R.M.,

Génie Electrique et Genie Informatique
Ecole Polytechnique de Montréal

Abstract

Path tracking for a carlike mobile robot is considered by assuming a motion that is planar and exempt from sideslippage, by taking into account both the dynamic and the kinematic properties of the vehicle, and by adopting a modified notion of path tracking. It is shown that a controller capable of tracking an assigned path may be computed by means of a memoryless function of the lateral, heading, and velocity tracking-offsets. If these offsets are kept small, the path is a straight line or a circular arc and the assigned tracking velocity is constant, then the controller may be given a simple, linear, time invariant and decoupled PID structure.

1. The Vehicle's Dynamic Model

In discussing the dynamics of the carlike mobile robot, we will use the following notations:

(x, y): position of the center of mass of the vehicle (c.o.m.) with respect to a fixed frame;
(v_u, v_w): velocity of the c.o.m. expressed in vehicle's frame coordinates;
θ: orientation (heading) of the vehicle;
Ω: angular velocity (yaw rate);
F_p,: propulsion control;
F_{u1}, F_{u2}: longitudinal forces exerted on the vehicle by the front (1) and the rear tires (2);
F_{w1}, F_{w2}: lateral forces exerted by the front (1) and the rear tires (2);
a (b): distance between the c.o.m and the front (rear) axle;
M: mass of the vehicle;
J: yaw moment of inertia relative to c.o.m.

Proposition 1 [El.1]. If: the vehicle's motion is planar, the vehicle's properties enjoy a full symmetry with respect to its longitudinal axis, the contact between tires and surface of motion is point-wise, and the steering angle is small, then: the dynamic model of a carlike robot is given by

$$\dot{v}_u = v_w\Omega + \frac{F_{u1}\cos\delta}{M} - \frac{F_{w1}\sin\delta}{M} + \frac{F_p}{M} + \frac{F_{u2}}{M} \tag{1}$$

$$\dot{v}_w = - v_u\Omega + \frac{F_{u1}\sin\delta}{M} + \frac{F_{w1}\cos\delta}{M} + \frac{F_{w2}}{M} \tag{2}$$

$$\dot{\Omega} = \frac{F_{u1}a\sin\delta}{J} + \frac{F_{w1}a\cos\delta}{J} - \frac{F_{w2}b}{J} \tag{3}$$

$$\dot{x} = \cos\theta v_u - \sin\theta v_w \tag{4}$$

$$\dot{y} = \sin\theta v_u + \cos\theta v_w \tag{5}$$

$$\dot{\theta} = \Omega. \tag{6}$$

The vehicle's model is completed by adding to (1-6) the dynamics of the angle between the longitudinal axis of the vehicle and the longitudinal axis of the front wheels (**steering angle**). This dynamics will be described by

$$\dot{\delta} = F_s, \tag{7}$$

where δ is the steering angle, and F_s is the steering control.

The vectors **q**:=[x y θ], **t**:=[v_u v_w Ω], $\mathbf{a}_t$:=[$\dot{v}_u$ $\dot{v}_w$ $\dot{\Omega}$] are, respectively, referred to as the vehicle's **configuration**, **twist** and **acceleration**. The vector X:= [x y θ v_u v_w Ω δ] is referred to as the **state** of the vehicle.

2. Non-holonomic Constraints.

The assumption of an absence of sideslippage in the motion of the wheels, creates an interdependence among the forward, the lateral, and the angular velocities of the vehicle (non-holonomic constraints).

Proposition 2 [Al.1, La.1, Sa.1]. In the absence of a sideslippage, the lateral and angular velocities of the vehicle are a well-defined function of the vehicle's forward velocity and of its steering angle. In particular, one has

$$At = 0, \tag{8}$$

where t is the twist of the vehicle, and

$$A := \begin{bmatrix} -\frac{b\tan\delta}{L} & 1 & 0 \\ -\frac{\tan\delta}{L} & 0 & 1 \end{bmatrix} \tag{9}$$

with L:= a+b.

An additional consequence of the absence of a side-slippage is that the lateral forces exerted by the tires become a well-defined function of the longitudinal forces and of the propulsion and steering forces.

Proposition 3. In the absence of a sideslippage, the lateral forces exerted by the tires on the vehicle are given by

$$F_w = G_1 + G_2F_u + G_3F_p + G_4F_s, \quad (10)$$

where

$$F_w := [F_{w1}\ F_{w2}]' \quad (11)$$

$$F_u := [F_{u1}\ F_{u2}]' \quad (12)$$

$$G_1 := -[AG_w]^{-1}AG_0 \quad (13)$$

$$G_2 := -[AG_w]^{-1}AG_u \quad (14)$$

$$G_3 := -[AG_w]^{-1}AG_p \quad (15)$$

$$G_4 := [AG_w]^{-1}G_s \quad (16)$$

$$G_0 := [v_w\Omega\ \ -v_u\Omega\ \ 0]' \quad (17)$$

and

$$G_w := \begin{bmatrix} -\dfrac{\sin\delta}{M} & 0 \\ \dfrac{\cos\delta}{M} & \dfrac{1}{M} \\ \dfrac{a\cos\delta}{J} & -\dfrac{b}{J} \end{bmatrix} \quad (18)$$

$$G_u := \begin{bmatrix} -\dfrac{\sin\delta}{M} & 0 \\ \dfrac{\sin\delta}{M} & 0 \\ \dfrac{a\sin\delta}{J} & 0 \end{bmatrix} \quad (19)$$

$$G_p := [\dfrac{1}{M}\quad 0\quad 0]' \quad (20)$$

$$G_s := [-\dfrac{bv_u}{L\cos^2\delta}\quad -\dfrac{v_u}{L\cos^2\delta}\quad]'. \quad (21)$$

As a result of Propositions 1, 2 and 3, the vehicle's dynamic model may be simplified as follows.

Proposition 4. In the absence of a sideslippage, the dynamic model of the vehicle described by (1-7) is equivalent to

$$\dot{v}_u = g_0 + g_uF_u + g_pF_p + g_sF_s \quad (22)$$

$$v_w = \frac{bv_u\tan\delta}{L} \quad (23)$$

$$\Omega = \frac{v_u\tan\delta}{L} \quad (24)$$

$$\dot{\delta} = F_s \quad (25)$$

$$\dot{x} = \cos\theta v_u - \sin\theta v_w \quad (26)$$

$$\dot{y} = \sin\theta v_u + \cos\theta v_w \quad (27)$$

$$\dot{\theta} = \Omega, \quad (28)$$

where

$$g_0 := [1\ 0\ 0]\{G_0 + G_wG_1\} \quad (29)$$

$$g_u := [1\ 0\ 0]\{G_u + G_wG_2\} \quad (30)$$

$$g_p := [1\ 0\ 0]\{G_p + G_wG_3\} \quad (31)$$

$$g_s := [1\ 0\ 0]G_wG_4 \quad (32)$$

and G_0, G_1, G_2, G_3, G_4, G_u, G_p, G_s are as in (13-21).

3. The Path Tracking Problem

A path-tracking assignment is the combination of a path and of a profile of linear and angular velocities and accelerations with which this path has to be followed. A path [La.1, ch.9] is described by a set of continuous functions,

$$q_p(s) := [x_p(s)\ \ y_p(s)\ \ \theta_p(s)],$$

where $s\in[0, \infty)$ is a parameter defining a point of the path, and $q_p(s)$ is the value of the configuration that the vehicle is required to have at the point of the path defined by s.

Similarly, a velocity and acceleration profile along a path is described by a set of continuous functions

$$t_p(s) := [v_{up}(s)\ \ v_{wp}(s)\ \ \Omega_p(s)],$$

$$a_p(s) := [a_{up}(s)\ \ a_{wp}(s)\ \ a_{\theta p}(s)], \qquad s\in[0, \infty),$$

where $t_p(s)$ and $a_p(s)$ represent the twist and the acceleration which should characterize the motion of the vehicle at point s.

A path tracking assignment is admissable if there exists a smooth function s(t), $t\in[0, \infty)$, such that, using the notations

$x_p(t) := x_p(s(t))$; $y_p(t) := y_p(s(t))$;

$\theta_p(t) := \theta_p(s(t))$;

$v_{up}(t) := v_{up}(s(t))$; $v_{wp}(t) := v_{wp}(s(t))$;

$\Omega_p(t) := \Omega_p(s(t))$;

$a_{up}(t) := a_{up}(s(t))$; $a_{wp}(t) := a_{wp}(s(t))$;

$a_{\theta p}(t) := a_{\theta p}(s(t))$,

one has

$$v_{up}(t) := \dot{x}_p(t)\cos\theta_p(t) + \dot{y}_p(t)\sin\theta_p(t)$$

$$v_{wp}(t) := -\dot{x}_p(t)\sin\theta_p(t) + \dot{y}_p(t)\cos\theta_p(t)$$

$$\Omega_p(t) := \dot{\theta}_p(t)$$

and

$$a_{up}(t) = \dot{v}_{up}(t);\ a_{wp}(t) = \dot{v}_{wp}(t);\ a_{\theta p}(t) = \dot{\Omega}_p(t)$$

For both technical and physical reasons, the function $X_p(s) := [q_p(s)\ t_p(s)]$ is required to be continuous not only with respect to s, but also with respect to its projection on the work space. More specifically, $[q_p(s)\ t_p(s)]$ must be such that, given any $\epsilon>0$, there exists a $\mu(\epsilon)>0$ with the property that, for any $s_1\ s_2 \in [0, \infty)$ one has

$$|[q_p(s_1)\ t_p(s_1)] - [q_p(s_2)\ t_p(s_2)]| < \epsilon,$$

providedthat

$$|(x_p(s_1), y_p(s_1)) - (x_p(s_2), y_p(s_2))| < \mu(\epsilon), \qquad (33)$$

where

$$[q_p(s_i)\ t_p(s_i)] :=$$

$$[x_p(s_i)\ y_p(s_i)\ \theta_p(s_i)\ v_{up}(s_i)\ v_{wp}(s_i)\ \Omega_p(s_i)],$$

$$i = 1,2. \qquad (34)$$

Given an admissable path-tracking assignment, path-tracking is the problem of generating the propulsion and the steering forces required for the vehicle to follow the assigned path with the specified velocity. More formally, (F_p, F_s) must be selected so that

$$\lim_{t\to\infty} X(t) = X_p(s), \qquad (35)$$

for some $s \in [0, \infty)$.

Given a state of the vehicle,

$$X := [x\ y\ \theta\ v_u\ v_w\ \Omega\ \delta], \qquad (36)$$

the vehicle's desired state in correspondence to a path-tracking assignment is defined by

$$X_d := [q_d\ t_d\ \delta_d] \qquad (37)$$

$$q_d := [x_d\ y_d\ \theta_d] \qquad (38)$$

$$t_d := [v_{ud}\ v_{wd}\ \Omega_d], \qquad (39)$$

$$\delta_d := \tan^{-1} \frac{\Omega_d L}{v_{ud}} \qquad (40)$$

where

$$[x_d\ y_d\ \theta_d] := [x_p(s')\ y_p(s')\ \theta_p(s')], \qquad (41)$$

and

$$[v_{ud}\ v_{wd}\ \Omega_d] := [v_{up}(s')\ v_{wp}(s')\ \Omega_p(s')]. \qquad (42)$$

The value of $s' \in [0, \infty)$ in (40, 41) is selected so that $(x_p(s'), y_p(s'))$ is the point of the path (in work space) closest to (x, y). More specifically, s' is such that

$$(x-x_p(s'))^2+(y-y_p(s'))^2<(x-x_p(s))^2+(y-y_p(s))^2$$

for each $s \neq s'$, $s \in [0, \infty)$. (43)

Proposition 5. Path-tracking is equivalent to the problem of generating the propulsion and steering forces required to have

$$\lim_{t\to\infty} X(t) = X_d(t) \qquad (44)$$

where $X(t)$ is the state of the vehicle at time t, and $X_d(t)$ is the desired state associated with $X(t)$.

4. The Path Tracking Controller

The accuracy with which the vehicle's motion complies with the path assignment is described by means of the notions of velocity (v_{os}), heading (θ_{os}), lateral (L_{os}), and steer (δ_{os}) offsets. These offsets are defined by the following equations

$$v_{os}(t) := v_u(t) - v_{ud}(t) \qquad (45)$$

$$\theta_{os}(t) := \theta(t) - \theta_d(t) \qquad (46)$$

$$L_{os}(t) := -\{x(t)-x_d(t)\}\sin\theta_d(t) + \{y(t))-y_d(t)\}\cos\theta_d(t) \qquad (47)$$

$$\delta_{os}(t) := \delta(t) - \delta_d(t), \qquad (48)$$

While the physical interpretation of v_{os}, θ_{os}, and δ_{os} is rather obvious, it may be helpful to note that the lateral offset, L_{os}, represents the (signed) distance between the position of the center of mass of the vehicle and the projection of the path in work-space.

Proposition 6. The dynamics of the path-tracking offsets is described by

$$\dot{v}_{os} = u_1(t) \qquad (49)$$

$$\dot{\theta}_{o-s} = \frac{(v_{ud}+v_{os})\tan(\delta_d+\delta_{o-s})}{L} - \frac{v_{ud}\tan\delta_d}{L} \qquad (50)$$

$$\dot{L}_{os} = (v_{ud}+v_{os})\sin\theta_{os} + \frac{b}{L}\tan(\delta_d+\delta_{os})(v_{ud}+v_{os})\cos\theta_{os} - \frac{b}{L}v_{ud}\tan\delta_d \qquad (51)$$

$$\dot{\delta}_{os} = u_2(t), \qquad (52)$$

where

$$u_1 := -\dot{v}_{ud} + g_0 + g_u F_u + g_p F_p + g_s F_s, \qquad (53)$$

$$u_2 := -\dot{\delta}_d + F_s, \qquad (54)$$

and g_0, g_u, g_p, g_s are as in (28, 31).

Proposition 7. Path-tracking is equivalent to the problem of generating the propulsion and steering forces required to have

$$\lim_{t \to \infty} [v_{os}(t)\ \theta_{os}(t)\ L_{bs}(t)] = 0 \qquad (55)$$

By combining Propositions 6 and 7, it becomes clear that the problem of path tracking may be viewed as equivalent to the following stabilization problem.

Proposition 8. Path tracking is equivalent to the problem of stabilizing the dynamic system

$$\dot{v}_{os} = u_1(t) \qquad (56)$$

$$\dot{\theta}_{os} = \frac{(v_{ud}+v_{os})\tan(\delta_d+\delta_{os})}{L} - \frac{v_{ud}\tan\delta_d}{L} \qquad (57)$$

$$\dot{L}_{bs} = (v_{ud}+v_{os})\sin\theta_{os} + \frac{b}{L}\tan(\delta_d+\delta_{os})(v_{ud}+v_{os})\cos\theta_{os} - \frac{b}{L}v_{ud}\tan\delta_d \qquad (58)$$

$$\dot{\delta}_{os} = u_2(t). \qquad (59)$$

Using Proposition 8, path-tracking may be now studied by bringing to bear well-known control systems' theory results [Ch.1, Ka.2].

Proposition 9. A path tracking controller exists. Its action may be computed in terms of the path- tracking assignment and of the heading, lateral and velocity offsets.

Proposition 10. If the path tracking offsets are kept sufficiently small, then path-tracking is equivalent to the stabilization of the linear system

$$\dot{x} = Ax + Bu, \qquad (60)$$

where

$$B' := \begin{bmatrix} 1 & 0 & 0 & 0 \\ 0 & 0 & 0 & 1 \end{bmatrix} \qquad (61)$$

and

$$A := \begin{bmatrix} 0 & 0 & 0 & 0 \\ \frac{\tan\delta_d}{L} & 0 & 0 & \frac{v_{ud}}{L\cos^2\delta_d} \\ \frac{b\tan\delta_d}{L} & v_{ud} & 0 & \frac{bv_{ud}}{L\cos^2\delta_d} \\ 0 & 0 & 0 & 0 \end{bmatrix}. \qquad (62)$$

From proposition 10, it follows that if the path in work space is a straight line or a circular arc, and if the required forward velocity is constant, then the linearized model of the vehicle is time invariant. Under these conditions, the path tracking controller may be designed by applying classical techniques such as PID compensation, pole placement, and linear state feedback [Ka.1]. Among the various solutions opened up by this possibility, a particularly attractive one is represented by a partly decentralized controller. This controller consists of a steering component which generates F_s as a function of $\theta_{os}(t)$, $L_{bs}(t)$ and $\delta_{os}(t)$), and of a propulsion component which provides F_p as a function of F_s and $v_{os}(t)$. These components may be designed so that the dynamics of the speed offset is decoupled from the dynamics of the vehicle's lateral, heading and steering offsets, and vice-versa.

Proposition 11. Under the hypotheses that: the assigned path in the workspace be a straight line or a circular arc; the desired tracking velocity is constant; the path-tracking offsets are kept sufficiently small,
Then: path-tracking may be ensured by the combination of two time-invariant controllers: first, a position/ orientation controller providing the steering action

$$F_s(t) = -\{K_{s1}\theta_{os}(t) + K_{s2}L_{bs}(t) + K_{s3}\delta_{os}(t)\}, \qquad (63)$$

where K_{si}, i=1,2,3, are constant gains; second, a speed controller providing the propulsion

$$F_p(t) = F_{p1}(t) + F_{p2}(t), \qquad (64)$$

where

$$F_{p1} = g_p^{-1}\{\dot{v}_{ud} - g_0 - g_{u1}F_{u1} - g_{u2}F_{u2} + g_pF_p - g_sF_s\} \qquad (65)$$

and

$$F_{p2} = -g_p^{-1}\{K_{p1}v_{os} + K_{p2}\int v_{os}\,dt\} \qquad (66)$$

wher K_{pi}, i=1,2, are constant gains.

Proposition 12. The controller described by (63-66) has the following properties:

a) the dynamics of v_{os} is described by

$$\ddot{v}_{os} - (p_{11}+p_{12})\dot{v}_{os} + p_{11}p_{12}v_{os} = 0, \qquad (67)$$

where

$$K_{p1} = -(p_{11}+p_{12}), \qquad K_{p2} = p_{11}p_{12}, \qquad (68)$$

and p_{11}, p_{12} are the poles characterizing the dynamics of v_{os};

b) constant gains $K_s := [K_{s1}\ K_{s2}\ K_{s3}]$ may be chosen so as to stabilize the matrix

$$A - BK_s, \qquad (69)$$

where

$$B := [0\ 0\ 1]' \qquad (70)$$

and

$$A := \begin{bmatrix} 0 & 0 & \frac{v_{ud}}{L\cos^2\delta_d} \\ 0 & 0 & 0 \\ v_{ud} & 0 & \frac{bv_{ud}}{L\cos^2\delta_d} \end{bmatrix}. \quad (71)$$

It is to be noted that while (66) clearly represents a speed controller with a PI (proportional + integral) feedback action, (63) may also be interpreted as representing a position/orientation controller with a PID (proportional + integral + derivative) feedback. Indeed, for small offsets, using (48, 40) one has

$$\delta_{os}(t) \approx \frac{L(\Omega - \Omega_d)}{v_{ud}} = \frac{L}{v_{ud}} \dot{\theta}_{os}(t) \quad (72)$$

and, using (51),

$$\dot{L}_{os} \approx v_{ud}\theta_{os} + \theta_{os} \quad (73)$$

It follows that the gains K_{s1}, K_{s2}, and K_{s3} may be computed or tuned by adopting both classical and modern PID technology [De.1, De.2].

Closure

The assumption of a motion exempt from sideslippage and a modified interpretation of path tracking, allow a fruitful discussion of questions of existence, of structure and of design of path-tracking controllers for a carlike mobile robot. In particular, they lead to useful characterizations of the vehicle's kinematic properties (Proposition 2), as well as of the vehicle's dynamic properties (Propositions 3 and 4). They also allow to establish the equivalence of various characterizations of path tracking (Propositions 5, 6 and 7).

This equivalence, in turn, leads to the establishment of an equivalence between the problem of path tracking and the problem of stabilizing an appropriate dynamic system (Proposition 8). This latter equivalence makes it possible to state conditions under which a controller capable of tracking a planned path exists (Proposition 9). It also makes it possible to show that such a controller may be designed by bringing to bear linear, albeit time variant, techniques (Proposition 10). Furthermore, if the assigned path is a straight line or a circular arc then, under the condition of a constant tracking velocity, the controller may be implemented using a simple, linear and decoupled structure (Proposition 11). The gains of this structure may be determined using classical time invariant techniques (Proposition 12).

Simulated experiments suggest that these conclusions are reasonably robust with respect to a relaxation of the main hypothesis which has been used to attain them, namely that the motion is exempt from sideslippage.

References

[Al.1] Alexander, J.C., Maddocks, J.H., On the Maneuvering of Vehicles, **Siam J. Applied Math**, Vol 48, n.1, Feb. 1988.

[Bo.1] Borenstein, J., Koren, Y., Motion Control Analysis of a Mobile Robot, **Journal of Dynamic Systems Measurement and Control**, Trans ASME, Vol. 109, June 1987.

[Ch.1] Chen, C.-T., **Linear System Theory and Design**, HRW 1987.

[Co.1] Cox, I., J., Wilfong, G. T., (Editors), **Autonomous Robot Vehicles**, Springer-Verlag 1990.

[Da.1] D'Andrea-Novel, B., Bastin, G., Campion, G., Dynamic Feedback Linearization of Nonholonomic Wheeled Mobile Robots, **Proceedings of the 1992 International Conference on Robotics and Automation**, Nice, France, May 1992.

[De.1] DeSantis, R.M., Hurteau, R., Veicoli Autonomi: Controllo del Movimento con Tecnica Sliding Mode, **Automazione e Strumentazione**, Vol.3, March 1990, pp. 137-150.

[De.2] DeSantis, R.M., An Adaptive PI/Sliding-Mode Controller for a Speed Drive, **Journal of Dynamic Systems Measurement and Control**, Trans ASME, Vol. 111, Sept 1989, pp. 409-415.

[Fe.1] Fenton, R.E., On the Steering of Automated Vehicles: Theory and experiments, **IEEE Trans on AC**, Vol AC-21, No.3, June 1976

[Gi.1] Giralt, G., **Les Robots Mobiles Autonomes**, LAAS, Toulouse, TR. No. 87308, 1988.

[He.1] Hemami, A., Mehrabi, M.G., Cheng, R.M.H., A Synthesis of an Optimal Control Law for Path Tracking in Mobile Robots, **Automatica**, Vol.8, N.2, pp. 383 - 387, 1992.

[La.1] Latombe, J.C., **Robot Motion Planning**, Kluwer 1991.

[Ka.1] Kanayama, Y., Kimura, Y., Miyazaki, F., Noguchi, T., A Stable Tracking Control Method for an Autonomous Mobile Robot, **Proc. International Conference on Robotics and Automation**, Cincinnati, Ohio, 1990, p.384-389.

[Ka.2] Khalil, H. K., **Nonlinear Systems**, MacMillan 1992.

[Ke.1] Kehtarnavaz, N., Griswold, N.C., Lee, J.S., Visual Control of an Autonomous Vehicle (BART): The Vehicle-Following Problem, **IEEE Trans on Vehicular Technology**, Vol. 40, No.3, Aug 1991.

[Sa.1] Saha, S.K., Angeles, Kinematics and Dynamics of a Threewheeled 2-DOF AGV, **1989 IEEE, International Conference on Robotics and Automation**, Scottsdale, Arizona 1989.

[Sh.1] Shladover, S.E., @ Co. (13 co-authors), Automatic Vehicle Control Developments **in the** Path Program, **IEEE Trans on Vehicular Technology**, Vol. 40, No.1, Feb 1991.

[Sh.2] Shin,D.H., Singh, S., Lee, J.J., Explicit Path-Tracking by Autonomous Vehicles, **Robotica**, Vol. 16, pp. 537-554, 1992.

Proceedings of the
American Control Conference
San Francisco, California • June 1993

Improved Tracking Control for Robots Using Neural Networks

Gang Feng

Dept. of Systems and Control, School of Electrical Engineering
University of New South Wales, Kensington, NSW 2033, Australia

Abstract

The tracking control of robots in joint space is studied in this paper. A new control algorithm is proposed based on the well known computed torque method and a feedforward compensating controller. The function of the feedforward controller, which is realized using an RBF neural network, is to provide high tracking accuracy of robot path following performance. It is demonstrated through simulations that the proposed scheme could achieve much better tracking performance.

1. Introduction

Conventional fixed gain linear feedback controllers are prevalent in current commercial robot systems, however, their performance is limited in controlling robot motions. Usually the high tracking performance can not be expected for such controllers. As such, numerous nonlinear robot control schemes have been studied during the past decade. One of them is the well known computed torque method [1-2], which uses a dynamic model of the robot to calculate the joint drive torques for the specified trajectory. While computed torque methods are capable of providing excellent results if the complete dynamics is known, they actually result in no better performance than that of the conventional fixed gain controllers due to the fact that no perfect dynamic model could be obtained for all the robots but the most simple one in practice. It is understood that both the conventional linear feedback controller and the computed torque method could provide reasonable robot control results, but fail to provide the high tracking performance in most cases.

Considerable work has been reported concerning the application of adaptive control techniques to the robot control problems [3-5]. Such controllers can accommodate varying environments and are not sensitive to modelling error.

Several studies have also reported on the application of learning control techniques to robot controller for improving the performance in trajectory following tasks over successive attempts at following the same trajectory [6-8].

Recently, increasing attention has been paid to the use of artificial neural networks in robot control [9-11]. The basic theme of most studies is to use the neural network to learn the characteristics of the robot system, rather than to have to specify explicit robot system models. Previous use of neural networks to improve robot path following performance has concentrated on replacing either the entire control system or the feedforward controller and/or prefilter with neural networks. Such research work was based on the desire to obtain the benefits of model-based control without *a priori* knowledge of system dynamics, or the computational burden of classical dynamic equations. However, in many cases, the approximate dynamic model of the robot manipulators can be found *a priori* indeed. Actually, the feasibility of model-based control has been demonstrated [12-14]. Therefore, *a priori* knowledge of robot dynamic model should be appropriately used rather than be totally discarded.

In this paper, a new robot tracking control scheme is proposed. This scheme takes advantage of simplicity of the computed torque methods, and incorporates a feedforward compensating controller as an add-on device to achieve high tracking performance. The feedforward compensating controller is independent of the original model-based controller, and therefore it does not affect the design of the original control system. The add-on controller is based on an RBF neural network, which is trained off-line or on-line to identify the robot modelling error.

The rest of this paper is organized as follows. In section 2 and section 3, the problem is formulated and the RBF neural network is reviewed respectively. The new robot tracking control is presented in section 4. Simulation results are provided in Section 5.

2. Problem formulation

A standard method for driving the dynamics equations of mechanical system is via the so called Euler-Lagrange equations. Using this method, the equations of motion of an n-link rigid robot can be expressed as the form

$$D(q)\ddot{q} + C(q,\dot{q})\,\dot{q} + G(q) = \tau + d \qquad (1)$$

where $D(q)$ is an $n\times n$ inertia matrix, which is a positive definite matrix. $C(q,\dot{q})$ is an $n\times n$ matrix containing the centrifugal and coriolis terms. $G(q)$ is an $n\times 1$ vector containing gravitational forces and torques. q is generalized joint coordinates, τ is joint drive torques (and/or forces) and d is external disturbances.

According to the computed torque method, the robot controller should be chosen as

$$\tau = D(q)(\ddot{q}_d - k_v\,\dot{e} - k_p\, e) + C(q,\dot{q})\,\dot{q} + G(q) \qquad (2)$$

where,

$$e = q - q_d\,, \quad \dot{e} = \dot{q} - \dot{q}_d\,,$$

and q_d, $\dot{q}_d$, and $\ddot{q}_d$ are the desired joint position, velocity and acceleration respectively. k_v and k_p are constant design matrices to specify the desired transient performance of the closed loop system.

When the external disturbances are absent, the closed loop system can be expressed as

$$\ddot{e} + k_v \dot{e} + k_p e = 0 \qquad (3)$$

Therefore, the robot tracking can be achieved with its transient performance specified by eqn.(3).

However, the perfect robot model can be hardly obtained and the external disturbances are always present in practice. Usually only the nominal model of the robot could be obtained. It is supposed that the nominal model of the robots are denoted by $D_0(q)$, $C_0(q,\dot{q})$, and $G_0(q)$. Therefore, if the nominal model is used for the design of the computed torque controller, i.e.

$$\tau = D_0(q)(\ddot{q}_d - k_v \dot{e} - k_p e) + C_0(q,\dot{q})\dot{q} + G_0(q) \quad (4)$$

we have

$$D(q)\ddot{q} + C(q,\dot{q})\dot{q} + G(q) =$$

$$D_0(q)(\ddot{q}_d - k_v \dot{e} - k_p e) + C_0(q,\dot{q})\dot{q} + G_0(q) + d \quad (5)$$

Denoting $\Delta D = D_0 - D$, $\Delta C = C_0 - C$, $\Delta G = G_0 - G$, we can obtain the following closed loop equations:

$$\ddot{e} + k_v \dot{e} + k_p e = D_0^{-1}(\Delta D\ddot{q} + \Delta C\,\dot{q} + \Delta G + d) \quad (6)$$

It can be clearly seen that imperfect modelling of the robots will lead to degradation of the robot tracking performance. In some cases, the robot system could become unstable. However in this paper, we just consider those cases that the closed loop system based on the nominal robot model is stable, but has degradated tracking performance. Our objective is to design a compensating controller to improve the robot tracking performance.

Let $x = (e\ \dot{e})^T$, $f = D_0^{-1}(\Delta D\ddot{q} + \Delta C\,\dot{q} + \Delta G + d)$, then we can have the following state space equation expression:

$$\dot{x} = A\,x + B\,f \qquad (7)$$

where,

$$A = \begin{pmatrix} 0 & I \\ -k_p & -k_v \end{pmatrix}, \quad B = \begin{pmatrix} 0 \\ I \end{pmatrix}.$$

It can be easily verified that the f is a nonlinear function of state variable x. Therefore, it will be denoted as f(x). If the nonlinear function f(x) were known *a priori*, then a modified computed torque controller

$$\tau = D_0(q)(\ddot{q}_d - k_v \dot{e} - k_p e) + C_0(q,\dot{q})\dot{q} + G_0(q) - D_0(q)\,f \quad (8)$$

would lead to the closed loop system expressed as in eqn.(3), i.e., the known modelling uncertainties could be well compensated. Unfortunately, the non-linear function f(x) is unknown *a priori* in practice. Therefore the above modified controller could not be implemented. However, this controller suggests indeed that a well estimated function $\hat{f}(x)$ of the non-linear function f(x) could be used to improve the robot tracking performance.

Due to their great approximation capability, artificial neural networks will be used to identify this non-linear function in this paper. For this we make the following assumption.

Assumption 1:

The closed loop robot system, whose controller is designed based on the nominal robot model, is globally stable, and the tracking error vector x belongs to a compact set X.

Remark 1:

Our concentration in this paper is focused on the improvement of the robot tracking. The closed loop robot system is therefore supposed to be globally stable. It can be easily seen that the tracking error x will fall inside a compact region $B(x) = \{x, \|x\| \le R\}$, which is a ball with large enough radius R.

In the next section, we first review the Radial Basis Function neural networks.

3. RBF neural networks

Improved learning algorithm, coupled with advances in microelectronics, has stimulated considerable renewed interests in neural networks across a spectrum of research areas. Multilayer neural networks with sigmoidal nonlinearities and radial basis function neural networks with Gaussian activation functions are most popular two types of artificial neural network architectures. In this paper, we are going to take RBF neural networks as example to explore using neural networks for adaptive identification of unknown nonlinear functions.

RBF neural networks were first invented by Broomhead and Lowe in 1988 [15]. Since then several applications and a number of theoretical results have been obtained for such neural networks [16-17]. Recently, RBF neural networks have also been used in adaptive control of nonlinear dynamic systems [18]. RBF networks are feedforward networks. They form mappings from an input vector x to an output vector y. An RBF neural network, with m_r inputs, n_r outputs and n^* hidden or kernal units, can be characterized by

$$\phi_i = g(\|x - c_i\|^2/\sigma_i^2) \quad i = 1, 2, ..., n^*$$

$$y = W\phi(x)$$

where $x \in R^{m_r}$ is the input, $\phi = [\phi_1, \phi_2, ..., \phi_{n^*}]^T \in R^{n^*}$ is the output of the hidden layer, $y \in R^{n_r}$ is the output of the network; $W \in R^{n_r \times n^*}$ is the weight matrix, while $c_i \in R^{m_r}$, and $\sigma_i > 0$ are the center and width of the ith kernal unit respectively. Usually the Euclidean norm $\|\cdot\|$ is employed. The continuous function $g: [0,\infty) \to R$ is the activation function which is often chosen to be the Gaussian function $g(\alpha) = \exp(-\alpha^2)$. It can be seen that each kernal node in the RBF network computes an output that depends on a radially symmetric function, and usually the strongest output is obtained when the input is near the centroid of the node.

In the above configuration, the weights of the network, the center and width of the each kernal units are the adjustable parameters. However, in order to obtain mathematical tractability in some applications, the centers and/or widths of the network could be fixed.

For our case, it is essential to choose c_i, σ_i *a priori* according to some preliminary training or an *ad hoc* procedure and to keep these values fixed during the learning phase. Then, it can be observed that the nonlinear function g(·) appears linearly with respect to the network weights, which are now only adjustable parameters in this configuration. As will be seen later, this configuration will greatly simplify our analysis for the system with use of neural networks.

It has recently been shown that under mild assumptions, RBF neural networks are capable of universal approximations, i.e. approximation of any continuous function over a compact set to any degree of accuracy [19-20]. This thus provides us with an approach to approximating the nonlinear function f(·) with an RBF neural network with output $\hat{f}(\cdot)$ in our context. Based on the reported results, the following assumptions on the RBF neural networks are in order.

Assumption 2:

(i) Given a positive constant ε_0 and a continuous function f: $C \rightarrow R$, where $C \subset R^{m_r}$ is a compact set, there exists a weight vector $\theta = \theta^*$ such that the output $\hat{f}(x, \theta)$ of the neural network architecture with n^* nodes satisfies

$$\max_{x \in C} |\hat{f}(x, \theta^*) - f(x)| \leq \varepsilon_0.$$

where n^* may depend on precision parameter ε_0 and the function f.

(ii) The output $\hat{f}(x, \theta)$ of the neural network architecture is continuous with respect to its arguments for all finite (x,θ).

In next section, the RBF neural network will be used to represent the unknown nonlinear function described in section 2, and then an adaptive scheme will be developed to identify that function based on the tracking error equations. Moreover, a new robot tracking control scheme is developed which incorporates the nominal computed torque controller and an add-on compensating controller.

4. New control scheme

Following the above results, the unknown nonlinear function f(x) are parameterized by a static RBF neural network with output $\hat{f}(x, \theta)$, where $\theta \in R^{n^*}$ is the adjustable weights, and n^* denotes the number of weights in the neural network approximation. Then the eqn.(7) can be rewritten as

$$\dot{x} = A\,x + B\,\hat{f}(x(k),\theta^*) + B\,[f(x) - \hat{f}(x(k),\theta^*)] \qquad (9)$$

where θ^* denotes the optimal weight values in the approximation for x belonging to a compact set $C \subset R^{2n}$. In general, the "optimal" weight θ^* in eqn.(9) could take arbitrarily large values. However, in order to avoid any numerical problems that may arise due to too large weights and to prevent the weights from drifting to infinity which is a phenomenon that may occur with standard adaptive laws, we are only concerned with weights that belong to a large compact set B(M), where M is a design constant, and $B(M) := \{\theta: \|\theta\| \leq M\}$ denotes a ball of radius M. In the design of adaptive law, we also restrict the estimate of θ^* to the compact set B(M) through the use of a projection approach. In this way, the optimal weight θ^* is defined as the element in B(M) that minimizes the function $|f(x) - \hat{f}(x,\theta)|$ for $x \in C$, i.e.

$$\theta^* := \arg \min_{\theta \in B(M)} \{ \sup_{x \in C} |f(x) - \hat{f}(x,\theta)|\} \qquad (10)$$

Now eqn.(9) can be expressed as

$$\dot{x} = A\,x + B\,\hat{f}(x,\theta^*) + \eta \qquad (11)$$

where η denotes the modelling error due to the use of the neural network,

$$\eta := B[\,f(x) - \hat{f}(x,\theta^*)] \qquad (12)$$

The modelling error η is bounded by a finite constant η_0, where

$$\eta_0 := \sup_{t \geq 0} |\,B\,[f(x) - \hat{f}(x,\theta^*)]\,| \qquad (13)$$

According to the properties of the RBF neural networks, the function $\hat{f}(\cdot)$ can be expressed in the form

$$\hat{f}(x,\theta^*) = \theta^{*T}\,\phi(x) \qquad (14)$$

where θ^* is $1 \times n^*$ vector representing the optimal weight values subject to the constraints $\|\theta^*\| \leq M$, the vector field $\phi(x) \in R^{n^*}$, which is refereed to regressor, is Gaussian type of functions defined element-wise as

$$\phi_i(x) = \exp(-\frac{|x-c_i|^2}{\sigma_i^2}) \qquad i = 1, 2, .., n^*.$$

For the sake of tractable analysis, the c_i and σ_i are chosen *a priori* and kept fixed. The local training techniques presented in [16] could be used for appropriately choosing the centers and widths of the RBF neural network. In such case, the only adjustable parameters θ appear linearly with respect to the known nonlinearity $\phi(x)$.

Now, eqn.(11) can be rewritten as

$$\dot{x} = A\,x + B\,\theta^{*T}\,\phi(x) + \eta \qquad (15)$$

We define our identification model as follows:

$$\dot{\hat{x}} = A\,\hat{x} + B\,\theta^T\,\phi(x) \qquad (16)$$

where θ is the parameters to be estimated.

Let $\varepsilon := \hat{x} - x$, then we can have the identification error model as:

$$\dot{\varepsilon} = A\,\varepsilon + B\,\tilde{\theta}^T\,\phi(x) - \eta \qquad (17)$$

where

$$\tilde{\theta} = \hat{\theta} - \theta^* \qquad (18)$$

Based on the Lyapunov type function, we can develop the following network parameter update law with projection.

$$\dot{\hat{\theta}} = -\gamma\,\phi\varepsilon^T PB + c_0\,\gamma\,\frac{\varepsilon^T PB\hat{\theta}^T\phi}{M^2}\,\hat{\theta}, \qquad (19)$$

$$c_0 = \begin{cases} 1 & \text{if } \|\hat{\theta}\| = M \text{ and } \varepsilon^T PB\hat{\theta}^T\phi < 0 \\ 0, & \text{otherwise} \end{cases}$$

It can be easily verified that if the initial parameters are chosen to be inside the ball, i.e., $\|\hat{\theta}(0)\| := \{tr[\hat{\theta}(0)^T\hat{\theta}(0)]\}^{1/2} \le M$, then we have $\|\hat{\theta}(t)\| \le M$ for all $t \ge 0$. Using this projection algorithm, we can have the following convergence results.

Lemma 1:

If the parameter update law (19) is used for identification of the nonlinear function f(x), the following properties is guaranteed:

(i) If $\eta_0 = 0$, then we have $\varepsilon(t)$, $\dot{\hat{\theta}}(t) \in l_2$; $\hat{\theta}(t)$, $\phi(x) \in l_\infty$. And $\varepsilon(t)$, $\dot{\hat{\theta}}(t) \to 0$.

(ii) If $\sup_{t \ge 0} |\eta(t)| \le \eta_0 \ne 0$, then we have $\varepsilon(t)$, $\hat{\theta}(t)$, $\phi(x) \in l_\infty$, and when t approaches infinity,

$|\varepsilon(t)| \le 2\beta\eta_0$. $\beta = \dfrac{\lambda_{max}(P)}{\lambda_{min}(Q)}$, where $\lambda_{max}(P)$ and $\lambda_{min}(Q)$ denote the maximum and minimum singular values of the matrices P and Q respectively.

Proof is omitted.

According to the above lemma, the identification error of the closed loop robot characteristic will converge to zero or fall inside a residue ball when time approaches infinity. Then it can be expected that the unknown nonlinear function f(x), which represents modelling error, could be well approximated by its estimate $\hat{f}(x)$. Therefore, the estimated $\hat{f}(x)$ could be used to compensate the system modelling error. That is, a new robot tracking control law can be developed such that the control torque consists of the original computed torque signal and a compensating signal,

$$\tau = \tau_1 + \tau_2$$

where

$$\tau_1 = D_0(q)(\ddot{q}_d - k_v\,\dot{e} - k_p\,e) + C_0(q,\dot{q})\,\dot{q} + G_0(q)$$

$$\tau_2 = -D_0\hat{f}$$

Then we can have the closed loop system expressed as

$$\ddot{e} + k_v\,\dot{e} + k_p\,e = f - \hat{f} \qquad (20)$$

It can be easily seen that if $\hat{f}$ approaches f, then the closed loop robot system will be asymptotically characterized by the error equation (3), which is the result of the computed torque methods for perfect modelling. If $\hat{f}$ is a reasonable approximate of f, it can also be expected that the tracking error could be reduced. Actually, in order to improve the transient performance of the system, the compensating signal will be switched into the system only when the identification error converges to some prespecified limit. The improved robot tracking performance for the new control law has been demonstrated through extensive simulations. Some results are reported in the next section.

5. An Example of simulation

In this section, a simulation study is conducted to demonstrate the performance of our algorithm. A simple two degrees of freedom manipulator was used in the simulation [4].

The desired joint trajectory is described by the following equations

$$q_{d1} = 1 + 0.2\sin(\pi t)$$
$$q_{d2} = 1 - 0.2\cos(\pi t)$$

Using ordinary computed torque control method the following simulation result has been obtained.

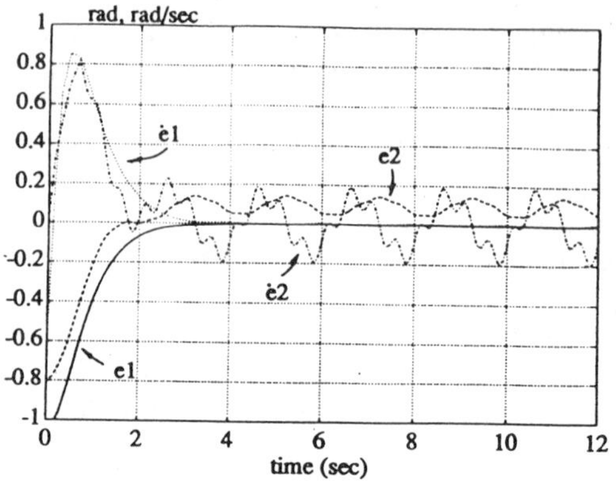

Tracking errors and their derivatives

Fig.1 Computed torque control

It can be observed that due to the modelling error and the external disturbance, the computed torque method leads to the stable robot system, But the joint tracking errors are quite significant, especially for the second joint.

It can also be seen that the tracking error x belongs to a compact set of four-dimension with center at origin and each side length 0.4. Therefore, we will constrain our attention on that compact set when designing the RBF neural network compensator. The centers of the RBF neural network are chosen as the mesh nodes in the set with mesh step 0.1 for each side and therefore $n^* = 625$, the widths of the network are chosen as 1, M = 10 and $\gamma_1 = 10$. And the initial conditions for the robot and initial weight values are all set to zero. Then, we have the following results, where the compensator is added to the robot system at t = 6 sec.

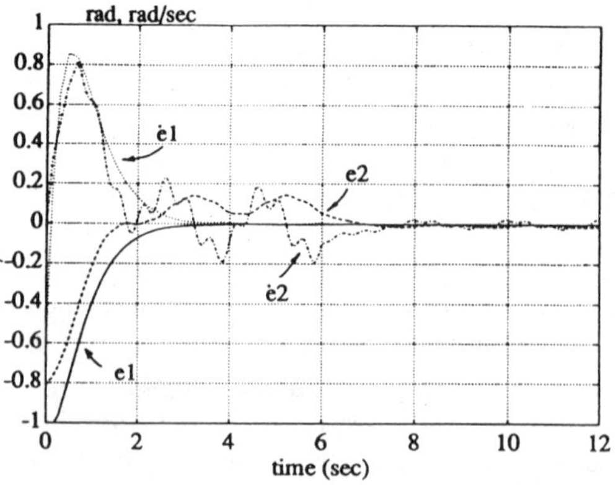

Tracking errors and their derivatives

Fig.2 New robot control with RBF neural network

It is clearly observed from the above figure that the error function f(x) is effectively approximated by its identification $\hat{f}(x)$ through the RBF neural network and the tracking error of robot in joint space is greatly improved.

6. Conclusions

A new robot tracking control scheme is developed in this paper. The proposed scheme consists of a well known computed torque controller, which is based on the known nominal robot dynamics model, and a feedforward compensating controller, which is based on an RBF neural network. The compensating controller works like an add-on device to improve the robot tracking performance. The simulation results have demonstrated the efficiency of the proposed scheme. The obtained results are quite promising and suggest that further study in this respect could be rewarding.

References

[1] J.Y.S. Luh, M.W. Walker and R.P. Paul, "Resolved-acceleration control of mechanical manipulators", *IEEE Trans. Automat. Contr.*, vol.AC-25, pp.468-474, 1980.

[2] C.H. An, C.G. Atkeson, J.D. Griffiths, and J.M. Hollerbach, "Experimental evaluation of feedforward and computer torque control", *Proc. IEEE Int. Conf. Robotics and Automation*, Raleigh, NC, pp.185-168, 1987.

[3] J.-J.E. Slotine and W. Li, "On the adaptive control of robot manipulators", *Int. J. of Robotics Research*, vol.6, no.3, pp.49-59, 1987.

[4] J.J. Craig, P. Hsu, and S.S. Sastry, "Adaptive control of mechanical manipulators", *Proc. IEEE Int.Conf. on Robotics and Automation.* (San Francisco, CA, 1986).

[5] R.H. Middleton and G.C. Goodwin, "Adaptive computed torque control for rigid-link manopilators", *Proc. 25th Conf. on Decision and Control* (Athens, Greece, 1986), pp.68-73.

[6] S. Arimoto, S. Kawamura and F. Miyazaki, "Bettering operation of robots by learning", *J. Robotics Systems*, vol.1, pp.123-140, 1984.

[7] C.G. Atkeson and J. McIntyre, "Robot trajectory learning through practice", *Proc. IEEE Int. Conf. Robotics and Automation*, San Francisco, CA, pp.1737-1742, 1986.

[8] M. Togai and O. Yamano, "Learning control and its optomality: Analysis and its application to controlling industrial robots", *Proc. IEEE Int. Conf. Robotics and Automation*, San Francisco, CA, pp.248-253, 1986.

[9] T.W. Miller, R.P. Hewes, F.H. Galnz and L.G. Kraft, "Real time dynamic control of an industrial manipulator using a neural network based learning controller", *IEEE Trans. Robot. Automat.*, vol.RA-6, no.1, pp.1-9, 1990.

[10] S.Y. Kung and J.N. Hwang, "Neural netwiork architectures for robotic applications", *IEEE Trans. Robot. Automat.*, vol.RA-5, pp.641-657, 1989.

[11] M. Kuperstein and J. Wang, "Neural controller for adaptive movements with unforeseen payloads", *IEEE Trans. Neural Network*, vol.1, pp.137-142, 1990.

[12] P.K. Khosla and T. Kanade, "Experimental evaluation of non-linear feedback and feedforward control schemes for manipulators", *Int. J. Robot. Res.*, vol.7, pp.18-28, 1988.

[13] P.K. Khosla and T. Kanade, "Real-time implementation and evaluation of computed-torque scheme", *IEEE Trans. Robot. Automat.*, vol.RA-5, pp.245-253, 1989.

[14] M.B. Leahy, Jr., D.E. Bossert and P.V. Whalen, "Robust model-based control: An experimental case study", *Proc. IEEE Conf. Robot. Automat.*, pp.1982-1987, 1990.

[15] D.S. Broomhead and D. Lowe, "Multivariable functional interpolation and adaptive networks", *Complex Systems*, vol.2, pp.321-355, 1988.

[16] J. Moody and C.J. Darken, "Fast learning in networks of locally-tuned processing units", *Neural Computation* , vol.1, pp.281-294, 1989.

[17] S. Renals and R. Rohwer, "Phoneme classification experiments using radial basis functions", *Proc. Int. Joint. Conf. on Neural Networks* , vol.1, pp.461-467, 1989.

[18] R.M. Sanner and J.J.E. Slotine, "Gaussian networks for direct adaptive control", *Proc. American Control Conf.*, pp.2153-2159, 1991.

[19] E.J. Hartman, J.D. Keeler and J.M. Kowalski, "Layered neural networks with gaussian hidden units as universal approximations", *Neural Computation* , vol.2, pp. 210-215, 1990.

[20] J. Park and I.W. Sandberg, "Universal approximation using radial-basis-function networks", *Neural Computation*, vol.3, pp.246-257, 1990.

Proceedings of the
American Control Conference
San Francisco, California • June 1993

USING PATTERN RECOGNITION IN CONTROLLER ADAPTATION AND PERFORMANCE EVALUATION

Ralph F. Hinde, Jr. and Douglas J. Cooper†
Department of Chemical Engineering
University of Connecticut, U-222
Storrs, CT 06269-3222

ABSTRACT

This work presents pattern recognition-based methods for controller adaptation and performance evaluation. These methods comprise a passive model-based adaptive control algorithm that is simple to use, easy to understand, stable, and fairly robust in a wide variety of applications. Controller adaptation in this work uses excitation diagnostics to initiate batch-wise regression of a process model to dynamic closed-loop process data. The process model is then employed in model-based controller tuning relations to update the controller's character. Controller performance evaluation is used to determine appropriate adjustments to the tuning relations such that an accurate process model will produce desired controller performance. These adaptive techniques are implemented using vector quantizing neural networks as efficient pattern recognition tools.

The adaptive algorithm is presented in a structure that allows for the implementation of these advanced techniques without requiring the replacement of an existing feedback controller. This is demonstrated using a simulated nonlinear third order process and an IMC tuned PI controller with Smith Predictor.

INTRODUCTION

The manner in which a controller is performing may be determined by observing the recent history of either the controller error or the process output after a sustained set point step change. Patterns in these histories reveal the degree of effort the controller is exerting. If a controller is too aggressive, the set point response pattern will be marked by an excessive overshoot and slow damping. Similarly, a sluggish controller will produce a response pattern that is overdamped with no overshoot.

A pattern-based approach to performance feedback for controller adaptation was first proposed by Bristol [1]. This unique approach determines appropriate updates to the parameters of a PID controller based on measures of the controller performance. The measures used are features of the set point response pattern such as overshoot and damping ratio. The difference between observed features and operator specified desired features is used to tune a PID controller in a manner reminiscent of Ziegler and Nichols [2]. Other researchers have explored the use of feature-based pattern recognition in adaptive process control including the development of a commercial product, the Foxboro EXACT [3-6].

Whereas these methods have been proven to be successful, they have two limitations. The first limitation is that the algorithms are designed to update only PID controllers. An algorithm that can adapt several different types of feedback controllers would be more widely applicable. The second limitation is that robust feature extraction requires a cumbersome rule base.

Extracting features from the set point response pattern involves locating the local maxima and minima within that response pattern. This becomes very difficult as process nonidealities arise. Nonidealities such as significant measurement noise and nonstationarity mask the location of the maxima and minima, corrupting the estimates of the features. The rule base grows and becomes cumbersome as the effects of these nonidealities are identified and accounted for [7,8]. A simpler and more efficient method of pattern recognition would prove to be beneficial.

Recently, artificial neural networks (ANNs) have been found to be efficient tools for pattern recognition and classification [9-11]. Seeing the potential for such tools, researchers have employed ANNs in pattern-based adaptive process control strategies. These include controller performance feedback driven adaptive pole placement and a pattern based approach to open-loop PID controller tuning [12,13].

The authors have explored the use of ANNs for performance feedback model-based adaptive control. By adapting a process model rather than a specific controller, the algorithm is widely applicable to any one of a number of model-based controllers. Through this work, ANNs have been found to be less sensitive to nonidealities than feature-based pattern recognition methods. This is due to the manner in which ANNs consider the entire pattern and not just features of that pattern [8,14].

Unfortunately, performance feedback model-based adaptation has been found to contain a drawback when performed alone. Model accuracy is often sacrificed when a process model is updated based solely on the controller performance. For example, if the value of the IMC closed loop time constant, τ_c, should no longer provide desired controller performance given an accurate process model, adaptation will adjust one or more model parameters to account for the error in τ_c. The accuracy of other model-based algorithms, such as Smith Prediction of the controller error, is then compromised. This may lead to a reduction of controller performance rather than an improvement.

What is required is an adaptive algorithm that keeps an accurate model for wide applicability and insures that the model produces desired performance. This work fulfills that requirement by extending the use of ANN-based pattern recognition for controller adaptation and performance evaluation. Two ANNs are used in a unique approach to excitation diagnostics for closed-loop passive process identification and model-based controller design. A third ANN is used in performance feedback diagnostics for adaptation of model-based controller tuning relations. Both methods employ the ART2-A vector quantizing neural network (VQN) architecture of Carpenter *et al.* for the pattern recognition task [15]. These adaptive strategies are presented in a framework that allows for their application to an existing feedback controller without calling for the replacement of that controller.

This new adaptive algorithm is shown in Figure 1 being implemented with an existing feedback controller. When on-line,

† Author to whom correspondence should be addressed

the adaptive algorithm first uses a performance diagnostics VQN to perform pattern recognition on set point step change response patterns to determine if adaptation is necessary. If the observed performance is not desired, the excitation diagnostic VQNs monitor process data and determine when sufficient dynamics exist for regression of a process model [16].

Once model parameters have converged, a second model-based controller is designed. The second controller is then put on-line in a manner which overrides the effort of the existing controller without replacing it. Excitation diagnostics are then continually performed leading to further updates of the process model. Likewise, performance diagnostics continue to monitor controller performance and adjust the controller design algorithms so that accurate model parameters will produce desired controller performance.

A simulated third order nonlinear process is employed in a demonstration of this work. IMC tuned PI controllers with Smith Predictor are used as both the existing and second controllers.

ADAPTIVE PI CONTROL

The velocity form of the PI algorithm computes the incremental control action, $\Delta u(t)$, at sample number t as:

$$\Delta u(t) = K_c\left[e(t) - e(t-1) + e(t)\Delta t/\tau_i\right] \qquad (1)$$

where K_c is the controller gain and τ_i is the reset time [17,18]. Here, a Smith predictor calculates the controller error, e(t), as the difference between the set point, $y_{sp}(t)$, and the value of the process output, y(t), predicted one dead time into the future [19].

A first order plus dead time (FOPDT) model is used for the prediction. The difference form of the FOPDT model is:

$$y'(t) = y'(t-1) + \exp(-\Delta t/\tau_p)\Delta y'(t-1) + Kp\left[(1 - \exp(-\Delta t/\tau_p)\right]\Delta u(t-k) \qquad (2)$$

where y'(t) is the predicted process output, K_p is the steady state gain, τ_p is the dominant time constant and k is one plus the integer number of sample times, Δt, in one dead time, t_d. The prediction is obtained by performing k iterations on Equation (2).

The PI tuning relations employed are derived from the internal model control (IMC) architecture [20]. Having compensated for the dead time, the process gain and time constant from the FOPDT model are combined with a first order filter to obtain the IMC tuning relations:

$$K_c = \frac{\tau_p}{\tau_c K_p} \qquad \tau_i = \tau_p \qquad (3)$$

where τ_c, the one IMC tuning knob, is the desired closed loop time constant. This algorithm is made adaptive by updating K_p, τ_p, t_d and τ_c in Equations (2) and (3).

To implement this model based controller, K_p, τ_p and t_d must be specified at start-up. These parameters are typically based on the regression of data collected from a single open loop step test made in the start-up operating regime. The sample time, Δt, is set equal to $0.04\tau_p$. The parameter τ_c is set to a value that produces desired controller performance which in this work is a quick response with very little overshoot.

The closed loop time constant is defined in this work as:

$$\tau_c = \gamma\tau_p \qquad (4)$$

where γ is initially equal to 0.50 and is later adjusted through performance feedback. The closed loop time constant is also allowed to change as adaptation changes the value of τ_p.

PATTERN RECOGNITION

Pattern-based adaptation in this work involves the extension of previous pattern recognition methods to performance feedback diagnostics and process excitation diagnostics [8,16]. ART2-A VQNs are employed for the pattern recognition task [15]. What follows is a summary of VQN pattern recognition and the ART2-A architecture. A further discussion of the ART2-A VQN as applied to this work may be found in [16].

VQNs take incoming patterns and assign them to specific discrete classes. As shown in Figure 2, this is done by comparing the incoming pattern to a library of exemplar patterns where each exemplar pattern represents a specific pattern class. A matching score between each exemplar pattern and the incoming pattern is developed in the comparison. Matching scores give a measure of how closely the incoming pattern resembles their associated exemplar patterns. The exemplar pattern with the largest matching score is the one that is most similar to the incoming pattern.

For the ART2-A VQN, classification does not end with identification of the exemplar pattern with the largest matching score. If the incoming pattern is unlike any exemplar pattern in the library, the largest matching score will be low representing a weak match. Therefore, a vigilance test is used to make sure that the best match is a good match. The vigilance test simply checks to see if the largest matching score is above some minimum value called the vigilance parameter. If it is, then the vigilance test is passed and the incoming pattern is recognized as belonging to the class represented by that exemplar pattern.

Before the VQN can recognize and classify incoming patterns, the library of exemplar patterns must be developed through training. Training involves introducing the VQN to numerous patterns that cover the breadth and depth of the patterns the network needs to classify. The VQN forms its exemplar patterns by clustering similar training patterns together.

In training, the first pattern introduced to the network becomes the first exemplar pattern. The second training pattern is compared to the existing exemplar pattern. If the vigilance test is passed, the two patterns are clustered to form a new first exemplar pattern. If the vigilance test is failed, then the second training pattern becomes the second exemplar pattern. Training continues in this manner until no new exemplar patterns are formed or until room for new exemplar patterns is no longer available. Obviously, the value of the vigilance parameter is key to exemplar pattern formation.

Performance Feedback Diagnostics

Performance feedback diagnostics serve two purposes in the adaptive algorithm. They first decide whether or not controller performance is desired. They then determine an appropriate action that will maintain or obtain desired performance. This is accomplished by performing VQN pattern recognition on the recent history of the controller error after sustained set point step changes.

The VQN first classifies the incoming set point response pattern as belonging to a class displaying a certain degree of controller performance. Each controller performance class has associated with it a corrective action that will restore or retain desired performance. In past work, performance-based corrective actions were made to the process model [8]. Again, when an adaptive or corrective action is made to the process model, model accuracy is often compromised in an effort to improve performance. Therefore, an alternative corrective action is necessary.

Model-based control algorithms such as IMC and DMC typically have one or more adjustable parameters that the practitioner may use to obtain desired controller performance given an accurate process model. In the IMC PI tuning relations, this parameter is the closed loop time constant. In DMC, the parameter is the input suppression factor [21]. This work employs an IMC tuned PI controller with Smith Predictor so corrective action is taken on the closed loop time constant, τ_c.

The performance feedback diagnostic VQN is, therefore, trained on set point response patterns that have been developed by adjusting γ used in the determination of τ_c in Equation (4) from its correct value. An IMC tuned PI controller with Smith Predictor is implemented on a simulated linear second order process. The value of γ is then mismatched from that value that produces desired controller performance (0.5 in this work). A set point step change is made and the resulting response pattern and associated γ mismatch are sent to the VQN for training.

During training, the VQN not only clusters similar training patterns, but it clusters their associated γ mismatches as well. In this way, when an incoming response pattern is classified as being similar to a certain exemplar pattern, the γ mismatch associated with that exemplar pattern is known. In order to restore desired controller performance, the correct adaptive action to take is to make the inverse mismatch to the present value of γ.

In this work, γ mismatches of one third to three times 0.5 are used to train the network. In order to achieve a library of manageable size, the vigilance parameter is set to 0.9998 which results in 80 exemplar patterns. Training patterns consist of 50 samples where controller sample time is equal to $0.10\tau_p$.

When performance feedback diagnostics are on-line, response pattern collection begins whenever there is a set point change. As mentioned previously, the controller sample time for implementation is $0.04\tau_p$. Response patterns must then be collected in a manner such that 50 samples cover the time span of five times the present estimate of the dominant process time constant. If the set point changes during pattern collection then collection is aborted until the next set point change. This avoids collecting patterns from non-sustained set point step changes that the network has not been trained to recognize.

Process Excitation Diagnostics

With performance feedback diagnostics insuring that an accurate process model provides desired performance, what remains to be determined is a way to maintain process model accuracy. The most reliable approach is to periodically regress a model to closed-loop process data. However, successful closed-loop identification requires that the process data be dynamic and that information contained in the process data not be masked by measurement noise [22].

Pattern-based approaches to determining a controller's behavior have been extended to determining process behavior. This has lead to the development of a process excitation diagnostic methodology [16]. Rather than classify long term response patterns intermittently as in performance feedback diagnostics, excitation diagnostics employ two VQNs working in tandem to continually observe short term (one time constant's duration) patterns in both process variables. The objective is to find many short term dynamic trends in both process variables to signify that a global process dynamic event is occurring that may be used in process identification.

Each VQN is trained to recognize generic dynamic patterns in its respective process variable. The training patterns are generated by randomly adjusting the set point of the controller of choice (IMC tuned PI control with Smith Predictor in this work) implemented on a simulated second order process. Using a vigilance parameter of 0.9200 results in 400 exemplar patterns in the process input VQN and 100 exemplar patterns in the process output VQN. Two separate VQNs are required because process input history patterns reflect the nature of the controller whereas process output history patterns reflect the nature of the process. The need for more exemplar patterns in the process input VQN results from the fact that the process input is freely manipulated by the controller while the process output responds according to the slower dynamics of the process.

Unlike performance diagnostics, excitation diagnostics do not require the identification of the exemplar pattern that is most like the incoming history pattern. Instead, only the result of the vigilance test needs to be known. Through past work employing VQNs as pattern recognition tools the authors have noticed that the matching score not only provides a measure of resemblance, but may also be used to indirectly determine the signal-to-noise ratio of the data within the incoming history pattern [8,16]. The larger the noise component in the data, the lower the matching score will be. Therefore, if the vigilance test is passed, then the process variable history pattern is declared to be both dynamic and relatively free from noise. The results of the vigilance tests from both VQNs are sent to a decision maker.

The decision maker is a simple rule base system that receives dynamic classifications from the VQNs and determines both when the process model should be updated and which data should be used. The decision maker looks for relatively simultaneous multiple dynamic trend classifications from both VQN's. This is done by keeping a running sum of the results of the vigilance tests from each VQN. A passed test is assigned +1 and a failed test is assigned −1. The minimum sum is zero.

A process variable dynamic state is defined when that variable's running sum is incremented up to a trigger value. This trigger value is set equal to five which represents one dominant time constant's duration of dynamics since the VQNs are activated every five samples. A dynamic flag for that process variable is then set to one and its running sum is reset to zero.

When both process variable dynamic flags are equal to one within one dominant time constant's duration of each other, sufficient dynamics for process model updating have been found and the modeling algorithm is activated. In this work, the modeling algorithm is a batchwise regression minimizing a sum of squared errors.

Data for the model regression are collected from the present back to the last steady state. A steady state is declared when either both process variable running sums are simultaneously equal to zero for a trigger value's duration or when one running sum is equal to zero for one estimated response time as long as the process input is not saturated. To help insure proper characterization and converged process model parameters, an additional model regression is performed just prior to the first steady state after a dynamic event.

Using these rules, a set point response event, for example, may be modeled three or four times during its duration. Each modeling instance will contain more information than the last until a new steady state is found.

Once the dynamic data have been modeled, the new model parameters must be tested for accuracy and convergence before they are implemented. Spurious results from the modeling algorithm may produce poor control. Such is often the case at the first modeling instance of a dynamic event where there is minimal information available in the data. Poor control may also result from model parameters produced by data that are dominated by the dynamics of an unmeasured process disturbance.

The first step in determining the validity of the data is to consider the new estimate of the process gain. Vogel and Edgar note that the value of the new estimate of K_p provides an indication of the validity of the new model parameters [23]. If the new estimate of K_p does not fall within a reasonable range of the previous estimate, than the new model is assumed false or corrupted and is discarded. This is first determined by checking if the sign of the gain has changed. If the new estimate has the opposite sign of the old previously implemented estimate then the model is determined to be invalid. Next, if the new estimate of K_p is approximately 20 times larger or smaller than the present estimate then the new estimate is considered invalid and the new model is rejected.

If the new model is not rejected, then it is valid and each parameter is checked for convergence. Convergence is determined separately as each new model parameter estimate is compared to its associated present valid estimate. Each model parameter whose estimate is determined to be converged is then implemented in the internal controller model.

In order to avoid over-adapting the overall algorithm, adjustments to γ suggested by the performance diagnostics are not implemented if excitation diagnostics have lead to significant model parameter changes during the set point response event.

ADAPTIVE CONTROL DEMONSTRATION

A simulated nonideal process is used to demonstrate the adaptive algorithm. The process consists of three FOPDT difference equations in series making the overall process character third order. The gains and time constants of the FOPDT difference equations are all initially equal to 1.00 and the overall true dead time is equal to $12\Delta t$.

The process is made nonideal through the addition of measurement noise, process nonlinearity and model order mismatch. Measurement noise is simulated by adding random error with a standard deviation of 0.10 to the process output. Process nonlinearity is introduced by making the overall process gain a nonlinear function of the process input as:

$$K_p = (20.0)^{[(u(t)/50.0) - 1.0]} \quad (5)$$

At the beginning of the demonstration, both the process input and output equal 50.0. The use of a FOPDT model as the controller's internal model in controlling this third order process introduces the nonideality of model order mismatch. Model order mismatch also exists in that the training patterns for the performance diagnostic VQN were made using a simulated second order process and not a third order process.

A batchwise regression of a FOPDT model to an open-loop step test made in the start-up operating regime produces model parameter estimates of $K_p = 1.00$, $\tau_p = 2.70$ and $t_d = 2.42$. The existing controller is an IMC tuned PI controller with Smith Predictor that is designed using the model parameter estimates and $\gamma = 0.50$. The parameters of the existing controller are then fixed and not allowed to change throughout the demonstration. Again, the sample time, Δt, equals $0.04\tau_p$.

Figure 3 shows the result of implementing the adaptive algorithm on this demonstration process. The adaptive algorithm is activated at the beginning of the demonstration and the performance feedback diagnostic VQN begins to look for set point step change response patterns to evaluate. The set point is stepped from 50.0 to 52.5 at sample 500 and the performance feedback diagnostic VQN begins collecting the response pattern. A complete response pattern is diagnosed at sample 625. As the existing controller is properly tuned for this operating regime, desired performance is found to exist and no adaptation is made.

At sample 1000, the set point is stepped from 52.5 to 60. The process input is increased during the response to this set point change. This results in the process gain increasing to approximately 1.6 which produces a very aggressive response marked by large overshoot and slow damping. The displayed performance is correctly diagnosed by the performance diagnostic VQN as being aggressive at sample 1125. This leads to the activation of the excitation diagnostic VQNs. At sample 1335, the first steady state is found allowing dynamic event identification to begin. Note that no model has been identified yet so the existing controller is still in command.

At sample 1500, the set point is stepped from 60.0 up to 62.5 and the performance diagnostic VQN begins collecting a new response pattern. At that time, the excitation diagnostic VQNs begin to identify the presence of significant process excitation within both process variables. This leads to a total of three modeling instances during the set point response event. The second modeling instance at sample 1590 produces converged estimates of all three model parameters. At that time, the second controller is designed as an IMC tuned PI controller with Smith Predictor and put on-line so as to override the effort of the existing controller. Initially, $\tau_c = 0.50$.

Since the second controller did not take command until halfway through this set point response event, the response pattern appears very aggressive. The performance diagnostic VQN accordingly recommends a large adjustment to γ. However, since the estimate of K_p significantly changed during the set point response, the adjustment to γ that is suggested is not implemented so as not to over-adapt the second controller.

The response to the fourth set point step change made at sample 2000 is diagnosed as being only slightly sluggish. As a result, only a small adjustment to γ is suggested. Four modeling instances are identified and acted upon by the excitation diagnostic VQNs during this response, but no significant changes are made in the model parameters. Since the small degree of sluggishness is not found to be accounted for by model parameter error, the suggested adjustment to γ is made.

Desired performance identical to that displayed at the first set point step change is found to exist at the last set point step change made at sample 2500. Since no significant change is made in either the model parameters or the closed loop time constant, it is concluded that the adaptive algorithm has successfully updated both the process model and the tuning relations regaining desired performance.

ACKNOWLEDGEMENT

Acknowledgement is gratefully made to the National Science Foundation through Grant CTS-9008596, Connecticut Innovations Inc. through an Elias Howe grant, the University of Connecticut Precision Manufacturing Center, and Larry Megan.

LITERATURE CITED

[1] Bristol E.H., "Pattern Recognition: An Alternative to Parameter Identification in Adaptive Control," *Automatica*, **13**, 197 (1977).

[2] Ziegler, J.B. and N.B. Nichols, "Optimum Settings for Automatic Controllers," *Trans. ASME*, **64**, 759 (1942).

[3] Litt, J., "An Expert System to Perform On-Line Controller Tuning," *IEE Control Systems*, **11**, 3 (1991).

[4] Litt, J., "An Expert System for Adaptive PID Tuning Based on Pattern Recognition Techniques," *Proc. 1986 Conf. on Instr. & Control Systems*, Secaucus, NJ (1986).

[5] Chia, T.L., J.R. Parrish and J.V. Shutty, "Multi-Level Expert Adaptive Control Software," *Proc. 1987 ACC*, Minneapolis, MN, 677 (1987).

[6] Kraus, T.W., and T.J. Myron, "Self-Tuning PID Controller Uses Pattern Recognition Approach," *Control Engng.*, **31**, 106 (1984).

[7] Cooper, D.J., R.J. Hinde, Jr. and L. Megan, "Pattern-Based Adaptive Process Control," *Computers Chem. Engng.*, **14**, 12, 1339 (1990).

[8] Hinde, R.F., Jr. and D.J. Cooper, "Adaptive Process Control Using Pattern-Based Performance Feedback," *J Proc. Cont.*, **1**, 228 (1991).

[9] Jau, J.Y., Y. Fainman and S.H. Lee, "Comparison of Artificial Neural Networks with Pattern Recognition and Image Processing," *Appl. Opt.*, **28**, 302 (1989).

[10] Pao, Y.H., *Adaptive Pattern Recognition and Neural Networks*, Addison-Wesley, New York, NY (1989).

[11] Wong, A.J., "Recognition of General Patterns Using Neural Networks," *Biol. Cybern.*, **58**, 361 (1988).

[12] Kumar, S.S., and A. Guez, "ART Based Adaptive Pole Placement for Neurocontrollers," *Neural Networks*, **4**, 3 (1991).

[13] Swiniarski, R.W., "Novel Neural Network Based Self-Tuning PID Controller Which Uses Pattern Recognition Technique," *Proc. 1990 ACC*, San Diego, CA, 3023 (1990).

[14] Megan, L. and D.J. Cooper, "Neural Network Based Adaptive Control Via Temporal Pattern Recognition," *Can. J Chem. Eng.*, **70**, 1208 (1992).

[15] Carpenter, G.A., S. Grossberg and D.B. Rosen, "ART2-A: An Adaptive Resonance Algorithm for Rapid Category Learning and Recognition," *Neural Networks*, **4**, 4, 493 (1991).

[16] Hinde, R.F., Jr. and D.J. Cooper, "A Neural Network for Closed-Loop Process Excitation Diagnostics and Adaptive Process Control," *AIChE Annual Meeting*, Miami Beach, FL (1992).

[17] Seborg, D.E., T.F. Edgar, and D.A. Mellichamp, *Process Dynamics and Control*, Wiley, New York, NY (1989).

[18] Smith, C.A., and A.B. Corripio, *Principles and Practice of Automatic Process Control*, Wiley, New York, NY (1985).

[19] Smith, O.J.M., "Close Control of Loops with Dead Time," *Chem. Engng. Progress*, **53**, 5 (1957).

[20] Rivera, D.E., M. Morari, and S. Skogestad, "Internal Model Control. 4. PID Controller Design," *Ind. Eng. Chem. Process Des. Dev.*, **25**, 252 (1986).

[21] Cutler, C.R. and B.L. Ramaker, "Dynamic Matrix Control – A Computer Control Algorithm," *AIChE Annual Meeting*, Houston, TX (1979).

[22] Gustavsson, I., L. Ljung and T. Söderström, "Identification of Processes in Closed Loop – Identifiability and Accuracy Aspects – Survey Paper," *Automatica*, **13**, 59 (1977).

[23] Vogel, E.F. and T.F. Edgar, "Application of an Adaptive Pole-Zero Placement Controller to Chemical Processes With Variable Dead Time," *Proc. 1982 ACC*, Alington, VA 536 (1982).

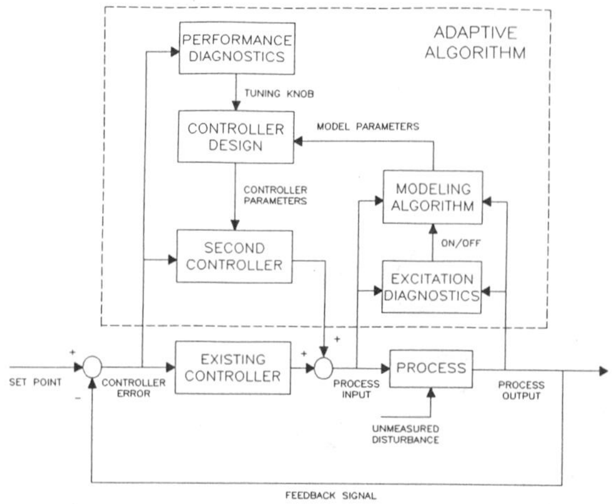

Figure 1 – Adaptive algorithm with feedback controller

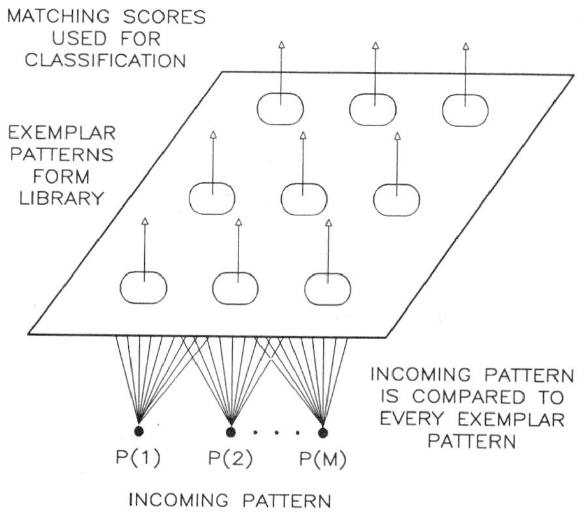

Figure 2 – Vector quantizing neural network architecture

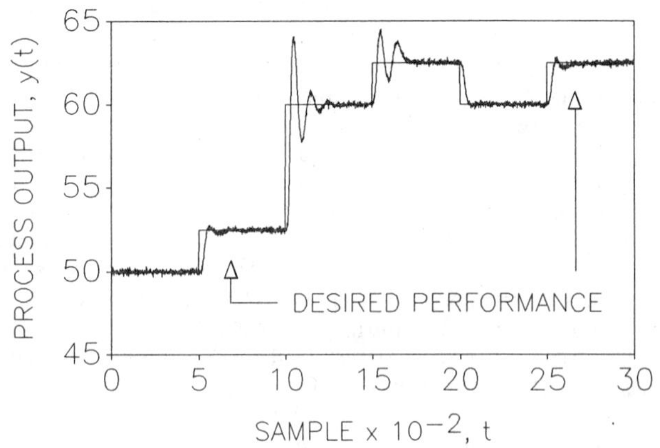

Figure 3 – Adaptive control demonstration

Proceedings of the
American Control Conference
San Francisco, California • June 1993

A NEW NEURAL NETWORK CONTROL ARCHITECTURE FOR A CLASS OF NONLINEAR DYNAMIC SYSTEMS

Shao-Liang Chang, Graduate Student
Satish S. Nair, Assistant Professor
Computer Controlled Systems Laboratory
Department of Mechanical and Aerospace Engineering
University of Missouri - Columbia
Columbia, MO 65211

ABSTRACT

Neural network control strategies are considered for a class of nonlinear time varying systems. Neural networks have been shown to be viable alternatives to present day controllers for nonlinear systems. This paper reports a novel neural network architecture for the control of a class of nonlinear systems. This architecture incorporates both feedforward and feedback components using multiple networks. Implementation in simulation shows that the architecture is capable of modeling and 'learning' the nonlinear system characteristics more efficiently with very good control characteristics when compared with two other designs even for varying operating points.

1. INTRODUCTION

Control design for nonlinear time varying systems is typically performed on a case by case basis since there are no universally applicable tools at the present time. Conventional control strategies to deal with nonlinear systems are based on well established results in linear systems theory. For example, a proportional integral derivative (PID) controller can be designed to handle many of the industrial control problems by linearizing the system at specific operating points and employing the classical techniques of linear systems analysis and synthesis. But for most of the cases, this technique is not valid, especially for systems with significant nonlinearities and stochastic disturbances which cannot be approximated by linear equations. Besides, if the operating conditions change, the performance will not always be satisfactory, and, in some cases, instability may result. Neural network algorithms have recently emerged as viable alternatives with potential for applications where conventional control performance is unsatisfactory. Neural networks possess the potential for quantifying complex mapping characteristics, for learning, and optimization [1].

Two common types of back propagation algorithms are referred to as static and dynamic schemes. The term 'static' refers to the back propagation algorithm which does not take the plant dynamics into account i.e. the partial derivative of the output with respect to input is equal to one. The dynamic back propagation method, on the other hand, estimates the partial derivative by using the neural network identification model [2]. This identifier model which must approximate the plant "sufficiently" accurately, is obtained prior to control implementation.

A new neural network architecture is proposed in this paper for a class of nonlinear dynamic systems. The proposed architecture consists of both feedforward and feedback components and for the class of systems considered, it adapts very well to changing operating conditions. The example case system modeled is nonlinear with time dependent coefficients. For constant operating speeds the system is periodically time-varying as discussed in the following section. The load consisting of a four bar linkage which has geometrical nonlinearities, is driven by a DC motor. Few studies pertaining to such complex systems have been reported in the literature.

2. DESCRIPTION OF THE SYSTEM

The example case system considered is shown schematically in Figure 1. A four bar linkage system which is driven by a permanent magnet DC motor through a flexible coupling can be described by the following set of nonlinear dynamic differential equations [3, 7]:

$$L_m \frac{di_m(t)}{dt} + R_m i_m(t) + K_b \dot{\theta}_m(t) = E_a(t) \tag{1}$$

$$J_m \ddot{\theta}_m(t) + B_m \dot{\theta}_m(t) + T_{cm} = K_t i_m(t) - K(\theta_m(t) - \theta_2(t)) \tag{2}$$

$$\begin{aligned} &CA2(\theta_2(t), l_i, m_i)\ddot{\theta}_2(t) + CO2(\theta_2(t), l_i, m_i)\dot{\theta}_2{}^2(t) \\ &\quad + CT2(\theta_2(t), l_i, m_i) = K(\theta_m(t) - \theta_2(t)) - B_l\dot{\theta}_2(t) \\ &\quad - T_d - F(\theta_2(t), \dot{\theta}_2(t)) \end{aligned} \tag{3}$$

The subscript l and m refers to the load and the DC motor respectively. The nominal parameters for the DC motor and the links are given in Table 1. For the linkage, θ_i, l_i and m_i are the angular position, length and mass of link i, respectively. Angular position θ is measured from the horizontal for each link. $I_{c.g.i}$ is inertial moment for the ith link about its center of gravity, and z_i is its distance from the joint. θ_2 represents the angular position of link 2 and $F(\cdot)$ represents unmodeled dynamics of the system. The coefficient terms CA2, CO2 and CT2 are spatially periodic in θ_2 and represent the effective inertia terms, the centrifugal and Coriolis terms, and the gravity terms, respectively. The dependence part $(\cdot)$ is dropped in subsequent developments, for convenience. Assuming that the coupling stiffness is high and the angular position of the motor shaft is equal to the angular position of link 2 in this case (i.e., stiff coupling, K large), the overall system dynamic equation can be written as:

$$\begin{aligned} T(t) = &(CA2 + J_m)\ddot{\theta}_2(t) + CO2\dot{\theta}_2^2(t) + (B_m + B_l)\dot{\theta}_2(t) \\ &+ CT2 + T_{cm} + T_d + F(\theta_2(t), \dot{\theta}_2(t)) \end{aligned} \tag{4}$$

or $T(t) = \overline{CA2}\ddot{\theta}_2(t) + \overline{CO2}\dot{\theta}_2^2(t) + \overline{CT2} + \overline{F}(\theta_2(t), \dot{\theta}_2(t))$ (5)

where T represents the torque applied to the motor, $\overline{F}(\theta_2(t), \dot{\theta}_2(t))$ includes friction, disturbances, and unmodeled dynamics. Unmodeled dynamics include out-of-plane movement of the linkage, wobbling, etc. It is noted that the four bar linkage is assumed to be moving in the vertical plane and only Coulomb friction is considered. Substituting the parameter values (Table 1) for an experimental setup available in our laboratory, significant variation is seen in the coefficients with θ_2. For instance, there is approximately

100 % variation in CA2 with θ_2 in the range [0, 2π] rad. Similar variations are seen for the coefficients CO2 and CT2 also. To further illustrate the time-varying nature of the system, the open loop response for a constant torque input of 0.5 N-m shows that the velocity of link 2 varies from 10.5 to 16.8 rad/sec. i.e. a variation of 23% about the average speed. An important characteristic of this system is its periodicity. At a constant speed, the four bar linkage mechanism is a periodically time-varying system, which is a special case of a generally defined time-varying system. In general, if θ_2 is periodic in the time domain, CA2, CO2, CT2 terms are also periodic since they are only functions of θ_2. From a control point of view, this feature is very useful since it provides repeated "patterns" to a learning controller.

3. NEURAL CONTROLLER DESIGNS

Three kinds of NN controller design techniques will be presented in this section for controlling the speed of link 2, $\dot{\theta}_2$. The first one is the proposed NN controller, with a novel feedforward plus feedback architecture. The others, a single feedback NN controller and a feedback error learning controller respectively, are implemented for comparison with the proposed controller structure. The simulation studies use the system model described in the previous section with the parameter values of an experimental setup available in our control laboratory. The structure and characteristics of these controller designs are discussed below.

3.1 Proposed NN Controller

The proposed NN control architecture is illustrated in Fig. 2. The basic concept behind this technique is that several neural networks are used to learn the dynamic characteristics of the system including the inertial terms, the centrifugal and Coriolis terms, the gravity terms, the friction terms, and even the unmodeled dynamics. Friction is assumed to be of the form $\overline{F}(\theta_2(t),\dot{\theta}_2(t)) = F_1(\theta_2(t))+F_2(\theta_2(t))\dot{\theta}_2(t)$. Then, specifically, the net N_1 is structured to learn the term $\overline{CO2}$, N_2 to learn F_2, N_3 to learn $\overline{CT2}$ and F_1, while net N_4 learns $\overline{CA2}$. The error signal is the difference between the desired set point and the output of the actual system. This signal is used to update the parameters of all networks by employing the dynamic back propagation scheme which provides a better estimate of the gradient as compared to static schemes. Strictly speaking, this is a type of computed-torque technique except that all the system parameters are not available to the designer. Since the coefficients are functions of θ_2, only the known desired position θ_{2d} is required as input to the nets N_1-N_3. Consequently, the generalization capability of the networks will not be restricted by a particular training set point and, therefore, makes this control structure invariant for different speed requirements. It is noted that the periodic characteristic of the system is useful for rapid training of the neural network controller, as opposed to a general time varying characteristic.

An identification model which emulates the dynamic behavior of the plant is necessary for this design and plays an important role in the update of the controller parameters. This update is achieved by obtaining a better estimate of the gradient in the gradient descent technique using the trained identifier. It is noted that NN identifier is trained in a series-parallel mode before being used for control. The parameters of the identifier were continuously updated to follow the dynamics of the plant in the reported research since this was found to increase accuracy. For digital control design, the plant is assumed to be described by the discrete-time neural network model given below:

$$\hat{\dot{\theta}}_2(k+1)=N_m[\theta_2(k),\dot{\theta}_2(k),\dot{\theta}_2(k-1),\dot{\theta}_2(k-2),\dot{\theta}_2(k-3),T(k),T(k-1)] \quad (6)$$

where N_m represents identification network with five inputs, and the torque T(k) is modeled as given in Eqn.(7).

$$T(k)=N_1[\theta_{2d}(k)]\dot{\theta}^2_{2d}(k)+N_2[\theta_{2d}(k)]\dot{\theta}_{2d}(k)+N_3[\theta_{2d}(k)]+N_4[e(k),\theta_2(k)] \quad (7)$$

Since the dynamic characteristics are spatially periodic with the angular position of link 2, as mentioned earlier, θ_2 was also chosen as the input to the identification model. The error function to be minimized in this case is: $J=\left[\dot{\theta}_{2d}(k+1)-\dot{\theta}_2(k+1)\right]^2/2$. By employing the gradient descent method, the change of weights for the ith network follows the rule, $w(k+1)=w(k)-\eta\frac{\partial J}{\partial w(k)}$, in this case,

$$\frac{\partial J}{\partial w(k)}=-e(k+1)\left[\frac{\partial N_m[\cdot]}{\partial\dot{\theta}_2(k)}\frac{\partial\dot{\theta}_2(k)}{\partial w(k)}+\cdots+\frac{\partial N_m[\cdot]}{\partial\dot{\theta}_2(k-3)}\frac{\partial\dot{\theta}_2(k-3)}{\partial w(k)}+\frac{\partial N_m[\cdot]}{\partial T(k)}\frac{\partial T(k)}{\partial w(k)}+\frac{\partial N_m[\cdot]}{\partial T(k-1)}\frac{\partial T(k-1)}{\partial w(k)}\right] \quad (8)$$

These derivative terms are obtained using standard back propagation. These functional derivatives of output with respect to inputs can be obtained in a matrix/vector form as shown below [1]:

$$\left[\frac{\partial N_m[.]}{\partial\dot{\theta}_2(k-3)}\cdots\frac{\partial N_m[.]}{\partial\dot{\theta}_2(k)}\frac{\partial N_m[.]}{\partial T(k-1)}\frac{\partial N_m[.]}{\partial T(k)}\frac{\partial N_m[.]}{\partial\theta_2(k)}\right]^T = W_1^T\{F'[W_2^T F'(W_3^T\delta)]\} \quad (9)$$

where, $F'(x)=(1-x^2)/2$. If the output neuron is a linear element, as used in this case, then $\delta=1$. If the output neuron is a nonlinear element, then

$$\delta=F'(W_3 Z) \quad (10)$$

Also, referring to Eqn.(7),

$$\frac{\partial T(k)}{\partial w^i(k)}=\frac{\partial N_1[\cdot]}{\partial w^i(k)}\dot{\theta}^2_{2d}(k)+\frac{\partial N_2[\cdot]}{\partial w^i(k)}\dot{\theta}_{2d}(k)+\frac{\partial N_3[\cdot]}{\partial w^i(k)}+\frac{\partial N_4[\cdot]}{\partial w^i(k)} \quad (11)$$

Some of the derivative terms in the Eqn.(11) will be neglected depending on the network to be updated. For example, to update N1, the term $\frac{\partial T(k+1)}{\partial w^1(k)}=\frac{\partial N_1[.]}{\partial w^1(k)}\dot{\theta}^2_{2d}(k)$ will be used in the learning algorithm, and so on. Fig. 3 shows the sensitivity network considering network N_1. Details of the calculation of the partial derivatives can be found in Appendix.

3.2 Feedback Error Learning Controller

For comparison purposes, a feedback error learning method, proposed by [4] for robots, is also considered. The structure of the feedback error learning method differs from the proposed design (Fig. 2) in three important respects. Firstly, a "well behaved" conventional feedback controller is used instead of N_4. Secondly, the authors in [4] do not have additional terms multiplying the outputs of N_1 and N_2. Finally, another important difference is the fact that the feedback error learning method uses a static update scheme instead of the dynamic one. The feedback torque is used as the error signal in the update scheme for all the networks. Formally speaking, the feedback error learning method may be seen as a kind of critic design, in which a preprogrammed feedback controller acts as a non adaptive critic. Naturally, the performance of this kind of technique depends on how good the feedback controller is. The feedback gains K_I and K_p used in this research were K_p = 30.0 N-m-sec/rad and K_I = 30.0 N-m/rad. These gains were obtained by employing the Ziegler-Nichols method which is a rule of thumb to determine the PID gains based on experiments.

4. RESULTS AND DISCUSSION

The neural network control architecture with the back propagation algorithm is a viable alternative to existing conventional controllers. This is particularly so when the nonlinearities are significant with additional parametric uncertainty. Although adaptive control methods are suitable for some specific classes of nonlinear systems, the prior information needed is quite prohibitive [5]. To investigate the characteristics of neural control algorithms for complex systems, the NN designs discussed in the previous section are implemented in simulation for the example case system. Identification, which is essential for implementing the control strategies, is considered first. Subsequently, the control design results are discussed for simulations. The performance of the proposed design is investigated at several speed set points. Comparisons are then made with other NN designs and conventional strategies including PID, computed torque, computed torque with learning, and MRAC.

4.1 Identification

Most dynamic systems can be described in the discrete time form given below using ARMA model approximations as x(k+1) = f[x(k), x(k-1), ..., x(k-n+1); u(k), u(k-1), ..., u(k-m+1)] where x(k) and u(k) are the system output and input, respectively. If a series-parallel model is used as an identifier, then it can be described as

$$\hat{x}(k+1) = N[x(k), x(k-1), \ldots, x(k-n+1); \quad u(k), u(k-1), \ldots, u(k-m+1)] \qquad (12)$$

where the output of the neural network N depends on the output of the plant and its past values. The partial derivative of e(k+1) with respect to w_{ij} becomes

$$\frac{\partial e(k+1)}{\partial w_{ij}} = \frac{N[x(k), \cdots, x(k-n+1); u(k), \cdots, u(k-n+1)]}{\partial w_{ij}} \qquad (13)$$

This derivative can be estimated using standard back propagation techniques. It should be noted that if a parallel identification model is used instead, the calculations are complex requiring use of dynamic back propagation techniques [2]. Generally speaking, the advantages of a series-parallel model include the following: (1) for a BIBO (bounded input bounded output) stable plant, all the signals used in the identification procedure are bounded; (2) since no feedback loop exists in the model, the static back propagation method can be implemented in a straightforward manner [6]. A series-parallel model is used for the simulation studies reported.

A reference input T(t) = 0.3sin(2πt) + 0.2sin(7πt) N-m was first arbitrarily selected for the simulation. After training for 500 seconds, with a 10^4 Hz update rate for the network parameters, another sine-wave function T(t) = 0.2sin(2πt) + 0.2sin(6πt) + 0.1 N-m was used to test the performance of the identifier. The result was not satisfactory, with errors of up to 100%. A randomly generated torque T(t) ∈ [-0.5, 0.5] N-m changing at a rate of 2 Hz was then used as the reference input for the same procedure. An improved performance resulted with errors limited to 3%. This is to be expected since the random input is "richer" in frequencies leading to an increased generalization capability for the identification model.

4.2 Control

After successful training, the identification model is used in the control algorithm. It is noted that the parameters of the identifier are continuously updated to follow the dynamics of the system in the simulation. For each run, the controlled system was simulated for 100 seconds. The desired speed set point was 100 rpm (10.47 rad/sec) and the update rate for the neural network parameters was 10^4 Hz. Each neural controller had a different learning rate (Table 2) arrived at by a trial-and-error procedure. A computed torque control technique is implemented for comparison with the NN controllers. Since voltage to the motor is the primary input in the model, the desired torque values are converted to the desired voltage values, to include the motor dynamics : $T = K_t i_m$ and $E_a = L_m di_m(t)/dt + R_m i_m(t) + K_b \dot{\theta}_m(t)$. Table 2 also lists the steady state errors for all NN controllers at the (trained) set point of 100 rpm (10.47 rad/sec). The neural controller using the dynamic update scheme is similar to the one reported in a related publication. Table 3 shows the performance of the controllers under different speed set points, with the learning rate η set to zero.

Proposed NN Control vs. Computed Torque Control

Both the proposed NN controller and the single feedback dynamic NN controller performed well, as seen from Figures 4 and 5. It is interesting to note that the proposed architecture does converge and exhibit very good control performance. For the computed torque control strategy, a complete knowledge of the system parameters is necessary. In contrast, all the system parameters are assumed unknown in the proposed NN control method. This might be very helpful in practical applications where unmodeled dynamics are significant and robustness problems arise. It is also noted that the proposed NN controller uses a single neural network in place of the PI control used by the computed torque technique. The need for selecting K_p and K_I for the PI control part then no longer exists. Furthermore, it is found that, in industrial applications, the computation of the joint torques is very inefficient. As a result, real-time closed-loop digital control is difficult in this case. However, with the proposed NN controller, once it is well trained, the tedious computation procedures could be avoided and, consequently, the design technique for such kinds of nonlinear systems becomes more easier and robust.

Proposed NN Control vs. Feedback Error Learning Control

It is noted that the feedback error learning method performed well for the 100 rpm set point case but behaved poorly as the set point changed. The main reason might be that the PI controller used in the four bar linkage system is no longer optimal. More specifically, when comparing with the computed torque or proposed NN controller, the feedback PI controller used in this method does not take into account the inertial terms in Eqn.(4) or (5) precisely. On the other hand, the proposed NN controller was able to control the plant at different speed set points (Table 3) due to its adaptive feedback control component. The proposed neural network controller has the advantage that, compared to the other neural network controller designs studied, there is no need for an additional cumbersome training to adjust to set point variations. When the desired velocity is varying, this controller structure is still expected to perform well since the desired velocity is not involved in the training process of the neural networks in the first place. For the other neural network controller designs, the training procedure should ensure that the model is "accurate enough", which can be a complex and time consuming process.

4.3 Comparison with Conventional Schemes

Several conventional control techniques are considered for comparison with neural network techniques. These include PID, computed torque, computed torque with learning, and MRAC strategies. Some of these are reported here for the sake of completion but only the computed torque technique result is shown in Table 2.

For the PI controller, at steady state (no significant change observed for 5 consecutive periods), the velocity fluctuates between 9.6 to 11.2 rad/sec (8.5% error). The computed torque scheme results in a variation between 9.9 to 11.1 rad/sec (6 % error). This is to be expected because the parameters are not known exactly. If learning is added to this computed torque scheme, an improvement is seen. However, a steady state error of approximately 5.5 % still exists because this method only works if the unmodeled part is repeatable. Using the MRAC scheme, the velocity fluctuates between 10.31 and 10.47 rad/sec in simulation at steady state (after approximately 12 sec). One reason for this is the fact that a constant velocity cannot be achieved with zero reference acceleration.

Neural network control design requires very little knowledge about the system dynamics. In contrast, all conventional techniques, including the simple PID designs, require apriori knowledge about the system. This is clearly exemplified by the MRAC design requirements which are prohibitive. Another important distinction is that the conventional control designs derive heavily from linear systems theory while neural network designs are fundamentally structured for nonlinear systems. This fact is illustrated clearly in this study by the comparisons and it is shown that NN controllers are viable alternatives.

5. SUMMARY AND CONCLUSIONS

Neural network algorithms have been formulated and successfully implemented for the velocity control of a typical electromechanical system which belongs to a class of systems with nonlinear, dynamics of a periodically time-varying type. The fundamental differences of such NN structures for control as compared to conventional schemes have been illustrated both analytically and using simulations, and the viability of NN controllers has been demonstrated. The comparative study reveals the lack of flexibility of conventional controllers and the prohibitive amount of prior information needed for control design for such systems. In contrast to this, NN controllers can model nonlinearities better, require less system information, and possess the inherent capability of learning.

A new neural control strategy is proposed and found to perform better than the standard static and dynamic neural controllers for the complex system considered. It should be noted that the theoretical issues of convergence and stability are not well understood for neural algorithms at present. This proposed architecture has the following salient characteristics: a complete knowledge of the system parameters is not necessary for control design. The neural networks can learn the system dynamics on-line from the sensor information, which makes the design technique more robust; the proposed architecture avoids the use of a reference model because of difficulties in choosing such models for systems in which the effects of coupling forces are significant in system dynamics and a linear second order reference model is not adequate; the performance of the controller will not be restricted to a particular training pattern. After adequate training, this controller structure is suitable for any set point without additional learning. On-going research focuses on the effect of time-varying desired trajectories, network update rates, etc., and extending the research to other time-varying systems. A separate paper [7] considers experimental implementation and real-time control issues as well as comparisons with other neural controllers.

6. ACKNOWLEDGMENT

This work was partially supported by the National Center for Supercomputing Applications (NCSA) under grant number CEE920013N and utilized the computer system CRAY Y-MP4/464 at the NCSA, University of Illinois at Urbana-Champaign.

7. REFERENCES

[1] D. Rumelhart, G. Hinton, and R. Williams, *Parallel Distributed Processing : Explorations in the Microstructure of Cognition*, Cambridge, MA ; MIT Press, 1986.

[2] K. S. Narendra and K. Parthasarathy, "Identification and Control of Dynamical Systems Using Neural Networks," *IEEE Transactions on Neural Networks*, vol. 1, pp. 4-27, March 1990 and "Gradient Methods for Optimization of Dynamical Systems Containing Neural Networks," *IEEE Transactions on Neural Networks*, vol. 2, pp. 252-262, March 1991.

[3] S. L. Chang, "A Novel Neural Network Control Architecture for a Class of Periodically Time-varying Nonlinear Systems," *MS thesis*, University of Missouri-Columbia, August 1992.

[4] M. Kawato, Y. Uno, M. Lsobe, and R. Suzuki, "Hierarchical neural network model of voluntary movement with application to robotics," *IEEE Control Systems Magazine*, pp. 8-16, April 1988.

[5] S. Outangoun and S. S. Nair, "Neural Network Controller Designs, Implementations, and Comparisons for Time-varying Dynamic Systems," *Modelling and Scientific Computing, International Journal*, Special Issue on Neural Networks for Identification and Control of Dynamic Systems, Pergamon Press, (accepted for publication).

[6] F. C. Chen, "Back-propagation and neural network for nonlinear self-tuning adaptive control," in *Proc. IEEE Int. Symp. Intelligent Control* (Albany, NY), pp. 274-279, Sept. 25- 26, 1989.

[7] S. I. Mistry, S. L. Chang and S. S. Nair, "Experimental Implementation of Neural Control Architectures for a Class of Nonlinear Dynamic Systems," *American Control Conference*, 1993, (accepted for publication).

APPENDIX

Calculation of partial derivatives for the proposed controller architecture

Referring to Figure 2

$$\mathbf{VI} = \mathbf{W1}\cdot T + \mathbf{W2}\cdot\dot{\theta}_2 + \mathbf{P}$$

$$\mathbf{VC} = \mathbf{W3}\cdot(\dot{\theta}_{2d} - \dot{\theta}_2) + \mathbf{P'}$$

$$\mathbf{W1} = (0, z^{-1}, 1, 0, 0, 0, 0)^T$$

$$\mathbf{W2} = (0, 0, 0, z^{-1}, z^{-2}, z^{-3}, z^{-4})^T$$

$$\mathbf{W3} = (0, 0, 0, z^{-1}, z^{-2}, z^{-3})^T$$

$$\mathbf{P} = (\theta_2, 0, 0, 0, 0, 0, 0)^T$$

$$\mathbf{P'} = (\theta_2(k), \theta_2(k-1), \theta_2(k-2), 0, 0, 0)^T$$

The partial derivatives are calculated according to the following equations:

$$\frac{\partial\hat{\dot{\theta}}_2}{\partial w_{ij}} = \frac{\partial NI[\mathbf{VI}]}{\partial \mathbf{VI}}\frac{\partial \mathbf{VI}}{\partial w_{ij}}; \quad \frac{\partial \mathbf{VI}}{\partial w_{ij}} = \mathbf{W2}\frac{\partial\hat{\dot{\theta}}_2}{\partial w_{ij}} + \mathbf{W1}\frac{\partial T}{\partial w_{ij}}$$

$$\frac{\partial T}{\partial w_{ij}} = \frac{\partial N1[\theta_{2d}]}{\partial w_{ij}}\dot{\theta}_{2d}^2 + \frac{\partial N2[\theta_{2d}]}{\partial w_{ij}}\dot{\theta}_{2d} + \frac{\partial N3[\theta_{2d}]}{\partial w_{ij}} + \frac{\partial N4[VC]}{\partial w_{ij}}$$

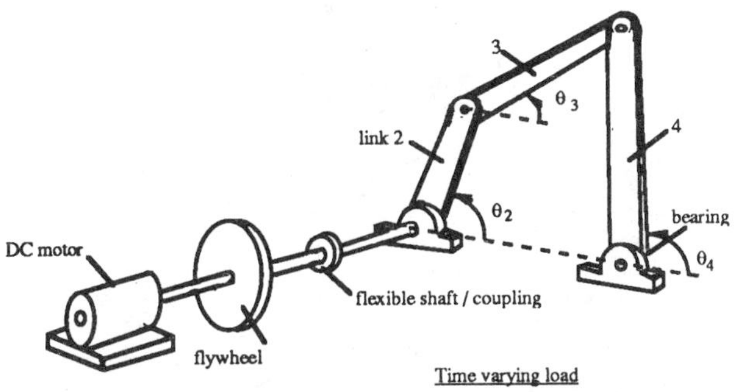

Fig. 1. Schematic of the experimental example case system

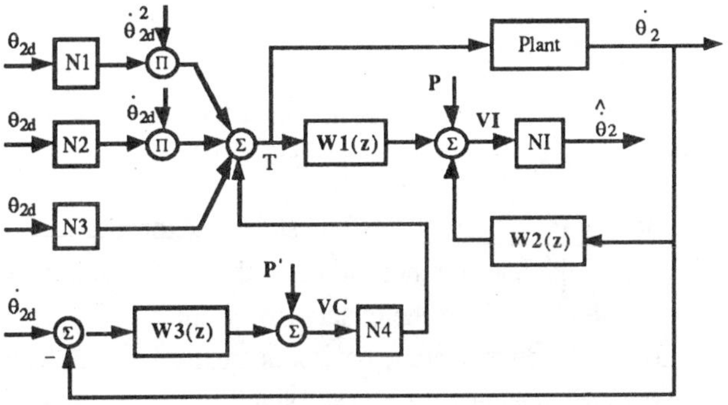

Fig. 2. Structure of the Proposed NN Controller

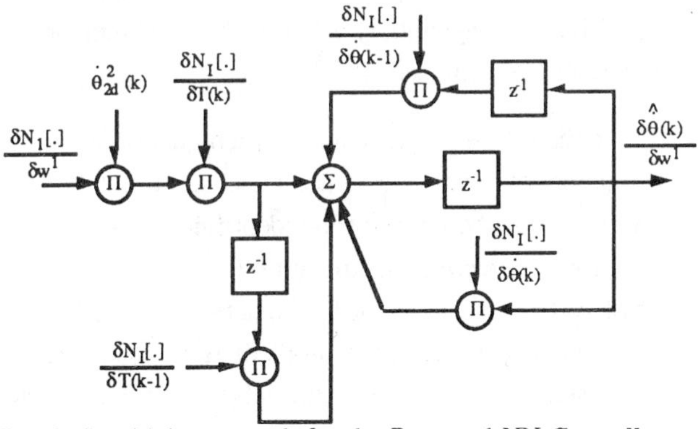

Fig. 3. Sensitivity network for the Proposed NN Controller architecture.

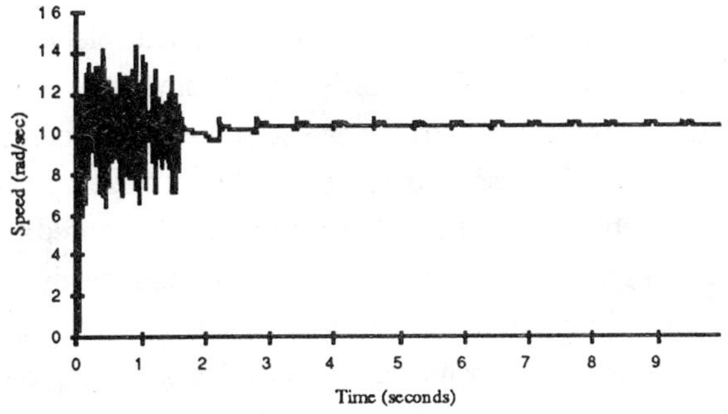

Fig. 4. Velocity response with the Proposed NN Controller

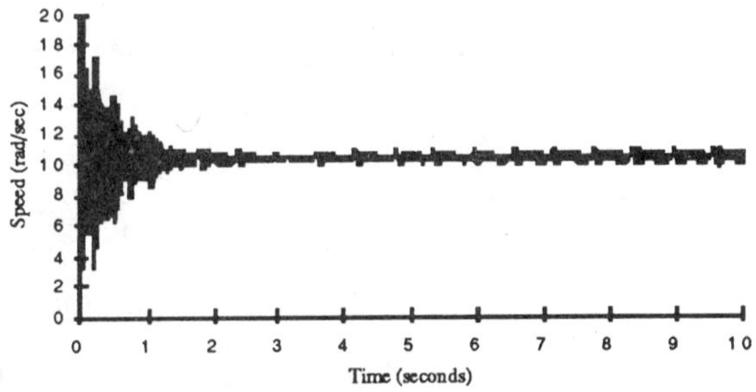

Fig. 5 Velocity response using the Single Feedback Dynamic NN Controller

Table 1. System parameters for the example case

(a) DC motor

Parameter	Symbol	Value
Torque constant	K_t	0.41 N-m/amp
Voltage constant	K_b	0.41 Volt-sec/rad
Armature resistance	R_m	1.9 Ohm
Armature inductance	L_m	4.18 E -3 Henry
Viscous damping	B_m	2.08 E -4 N-m-sec/rad
Armature moment of inertia	J_m	1.10 E -3 Kg-m^2

(b) Four bar linkage

	Link 1	Link 2	Link 3	Link 4
Mass (Kg)	-	0.147	0.277	0.277
Mass moment of inertia (Kg-mm)	-	278.82	1686.97	1686.97
Length (mm)	190.5	61.0	215.0	215.0

Table 2. Steady state errors and Learning rates for the NN controller designs

Controller (ω_d = 10.47 rad/sec)	velocity error / Learning rate (rad/sec)	Maximum error (% absolute)
Proposed NN	10.3 - 10.6 / 1.0 E-3	1.6
Feedback error learning	10.0 - 10.9 / 2.0 E-1	4.5
NN using dynamic BP	10.0 - 10.6 / 2.0 E-2	4.5
NN using static BP	9.8 - 11.1 / 2.0 E-2	6.3
Computed torque	10.2 - 10.7 / -	2.6

Table 3. Maximum steady state errors for different speed set points with $\eta = 0$

(steady state error % absolute)

	Speed set point (rpm)					
Controller	50	100	200	500	1000	1500
Proposed NN	2.8	1.6	3.0	10.4	19.3	20.1
Feedback Error Learning	98.8	4.5	38.0	31.6	23.2	25.3
NN using Dynamic BP	82.5	4.5	33.1	27.9	27.4	27.6
NN using Static BP	89.5	8.2	37.8	32.4	32.3	35.7

Proceedings of the
American Control Conference
San Francisco, California • June 1993

A FEEDBACK SCHEME FOR IMPROVING DYNAMIC RESPONSE OF NEURO-CONTROLLERS

K. P. Venugopal*# S. M. Smith*

* Advanced Marine Systems Group
Department of Ocean Engineering
\# Department of Electrical Engineering
Florida Atlantic University, Boca Raton, FL 33431

Abstract

A neural network controller designed solely to realize maximum acceptable steady state error may have unsatisfactory transient response such as excessive overshoot and large rise time. Conversely, a controller designed to realize very good transient response may have unacceptable steady state characteristic. In this paper we investigate the effectiveness of adding velocity reference feedback for simultaneously improving the transient and steady state response of a neural network controller. Using the direct control scheme on the nonlinear dynamics of an underwater vehicle, we show that specific improvements in overshoot, rise time and settling time could be achieved with this method. The control scheme and results are discussed in detail.

1. Introduction

The application of neural network techniques for the learning control of linear as well as nonlinear systems is an intensive area of research. A number of studies are done[1][2][9][10][11] on such techniques; often many of them on practical problems[6][7][8]. From a control system point of view, neural networks represent nonlinear mapping between the inputs and outputs[1]. Learning in feedforward networks correspond to static mapping, and that in recurrent networks correspond to dynamic mapping. The mapping capabilities of these networks are well studied[3] and show that a network having at least two hidden layers (of neurons) can approximate any nonlinearity. Also, static neural networks with dynamical components are able to approximate very large classes of dynamical systems[1][3]. These properties are sufficient to make them strong candidates for many of the identification and control applications, especially the tracking control, were the objective is to minimize the error between the desired and actual trajectories of the system.

In most of the studied cases, the static backpropagation[4] is used as the learning algorithm, with on-line adaptation of the weights. Since the exact error gradient information is not obtained when static networks are used with dynamical systems, the performance and stability of such networks may not be satisfactory[1]. Recent extensions on backpropagation such as the recurrent backpropagation[9] and dynamic backpropagation[1] address this problem but are computationally intensive.

For the identification and control of a higher order system, the number of layers and neurons needed in each layer for a network may be large for the identification and control. Also, for an effective identification (or control), the number of system states needed by the network could be large. One way to approach this problem is to feed back the delayed states as the inputs to the network. Still, the system performance may not be of the desired level since the network has no information about the desired value of these states.

Hence, a neural network controller designed solely based on the desired response of the dynamics may not be the best one in terms of the transient and steady state responses. It may have an excessive overshoot and larger rise time. Alternatively, a controller designed to get the desired transient response may not achieve the desired steady state characteristics. In this paper we investigate the effectiveness of using a velocity reference feedback for improving the dynamic response of the neural network controllers. In addition to a reference signal for the error used in the normal schemes we introduce an additional reference signal for the change in error. Using the direct control scheme, on a nonlinear model of an underwater vehicle, we show that specific improvements in overshoot, rise time and settling time can be achieved with this method. The control scheme, the analysis and simulation results are presented in detail, in the following sections.

2. Control Scheme

Consider a nonlinear, time varying dynamical system represented by the set of nonlinear differential equations,

$$\dot{x} = f(x, u, t),\ y = h(x, t),\ u = g(x, t), \tag{1}$$

where x denotes the state vector, y the system output and u the input. Then $\dot{x} = f[x, g(x, t), t]$ represents the closed loop system dynamics. The objective of an on-line learning controller is to adaptively generate the appropriate signal $g(x,t)$ such that the error between the desired output $y_d(t)$ and the actual output $y(t)$, $(y_d(t) - y(t))$ is driven to zero in a satisfactory manner.

There are two basic schemes for learning control using neural networks viz., direct and indirect control[1]. The system to be controlled need not be known in both of these methods. In the indirect control scheme, the system dynamics are identified at one instant and the identified dynamics are used as the controller at the next instant of time. On the other hand, in the direct control scheme, the input to the dynamics is used both for identification and control simultaneously. In this case, the identification stage is, rather, implicit. In the studies presented in this paper, the direct control scheme is used. The error backpropagation algorithm[4] is used as the learning algorithm for the neural network. The algorithm used in this paper is given below in a summarized form:

The output value net_i of neuron i in a given layer of the NN controller is found by the weighted sum of the outputs of the neurons in the previous layer, i. e.

$$net_i = \sum_j w_{ij} out_j + \theta_i \tag{2}$$

where w_{ij} is the interconnection strength from neuron j of the lower layer to the neuron i, out_j is the output of neuron j, and θ_i represents the bias term for neuron i.

A nonlinear sigmoidal transformation, $f(\ )$ applied to net_i results in,

$$out_i = f(net_i) = \frac{1 - exp\ (-\ net_i)}{1 + exp\ (-\ net_i)} \tag{3}$$

The performance function to be optimized by the network is taken as the squared error at the output of the system, of the form;

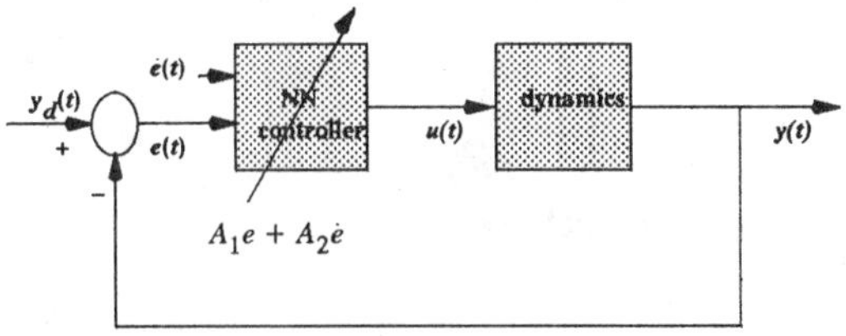

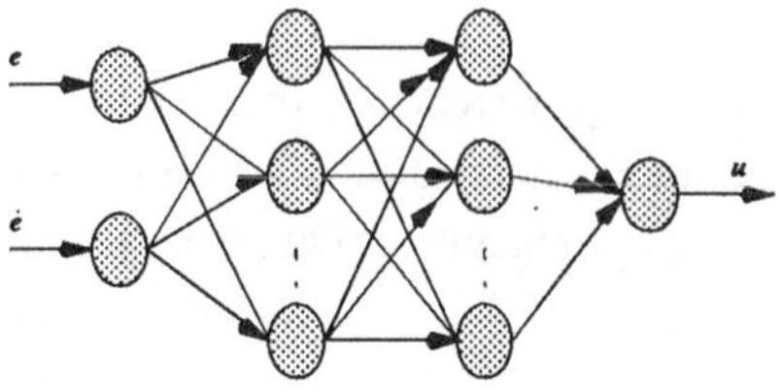

Fig. 1. (a). Controller architecture using neural network.
(b). The neural network architecture. The bias term θ_i is implemented as an additional neuron of fixed input of value 1.0 (not shown in Fig.)

$$E = \frac{1}{2} A_1 e_i^2 + \frac{1}{2} A_2 \dot{e}_i^2 \tag{4}$$

where e_i and $\dot{e}_i$ are the error and change in error given in Eqns.(5), (6). A_1 and A_2 are constant scaling factors for e_i and $\dot{e}_i$ respectively and are chosen empirically so that the contributions from both the errors are approximately equal. Expressing the errors as a function of time,

$$e_i(t) = y_d(t) - y(t) \tag{5}$$

$$\dot{e}(t) = e(t-1) - e(t-2) \tag{6}$$

The error at the output of the network could be generated by multiplying the system error by the inverse of the instantaneous differential gain of the dynamics[2]. The network interconnection strengths are updated at each instant in time using the following sets of equations,

$$w_{ij}(t+1) = w_{ij}(t) + \Delta w_{ij}(t+1) \tag{7}$$

where,

$$\Delta w_{ij}(t+1) = \eta \delta_i out_j \tag{8}$$

is the change in weight w_{ij} at instant $(t+1)$, out_j corresponds to the output of jth neuron, and η is the learning coefficient of the network. The error signal δ_i is defined by,

$$\delta_i = \frac{1}{2} J_a^{-1}(A_1 e_i + A_2 \dot{e}_i)(1 - out_i^2) \quad (9)$$

for the output layer

and $$\delta_j = \frac{1}{2}(1 - out_j^2) \sum_i \delta_i w_{ij} \quad (10)$$

for any other layer

In Eqn. (9) J_a^{-1} denotes the approximate inverse of the instantaneous inverse differential gain of the dynamics, estimated from the change in input u and output y, over two instants of time.

The network weights are first initialized to random values and the updating is done at each instant in time, according to the above set of equations. The error e_i is kept zero for the first iteration and $\dot{e}_i$ is kept zero for the first two iterations.

3. Simulation Results

We applied the proposed scheme on the nonlinear dynamics model of an underwater vehicle. The vehicle pitch is controlled by a 'stern plane' and the objective of the neural network controller is to give a correct deflection angle to the 'stern plane' actuator to maintain the vehicle at the commanded pitch. The vehicle is assumed to be travelling at a fixed speed. The vehicle dynamics for the above relationship represented by the following nonlinear expression[5].

$$\sum M_M = I_y \dot{q} + (I_x - I_y)rp - (\dot{p} + qr)I_{xy} + (p^2 - r^2)I_{xz} + (qp - \dot{r})I_{yz} + m[z_G(\dot{u} - vr + wq) - x_G(\dot{w} - uq + vp)] \quad (11)$$

where $\sum M_M$ corresponds to the summation of all the moments with respect to the y axis, which is a nonlinear function involving the 'stern plane' deflection δs; u,v and w are the linear velocities along the three co-ordinate axis and p, q, and r are the angular velocities. 'I' stands for the moment of inertia, with the subscripts indicating whether planar or axial and m, the mass of the vehicle. The normal operating range of the vehicle pitch is +20 deg. to -20 deg.

The response of the vehicle for a commanded pitch of 10 deg. is shown in Fig. 2. The neural network controller is of size 2x20x10x1, having two hidden layers of 20 and 10 neurons each. For a learning rate of 0.003, the rise time for the system is about 42 sec. with an overshoot of 70%. The time taken by the network to settle to the commanded pitch is more than 200 sec. The learning rate determines the time constant of the systems and is the most important parameter affecting the transient response. For example, the rise time

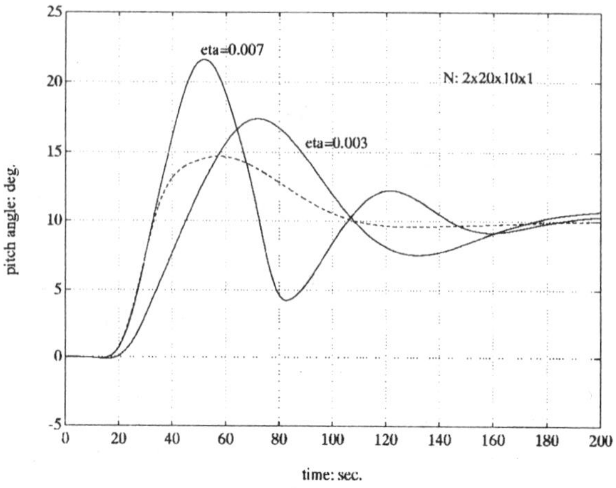

Fig. 2. System response for a commanded pitch of 10 deg. Dotted lines represent the response with velocity reference.

can be improved by making the network learn faster (by increasing the learning rate). For a learning rate of 0.007, the rise time is smaller than that for 0.003 but the overshoot is more than 100%. Obviously, the response is more oscillatory and settling time is more than 200 sec.

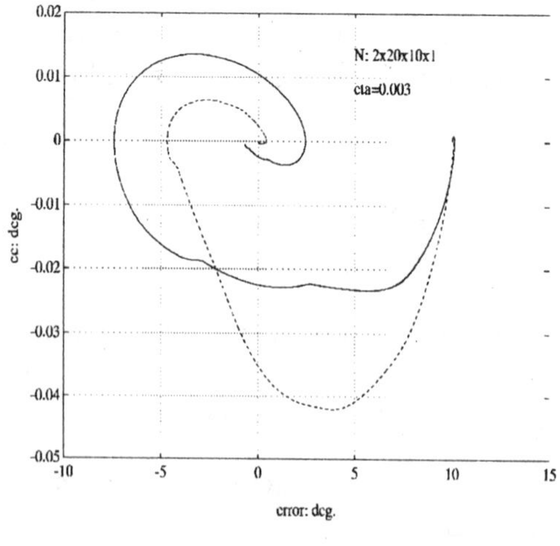

Fig. 3. System trajectory, with and with out velocity reference Dotted lines represent the response with velocity reference.

Representing the system trajectory in a state space form (Fig. 3), it could be seen that the larger rise time is due to the fact that the initial control input by the network is not accelerating fast enough. Also the network is not able to decelerate the control input at the switching point e=0, for a lesser overshoot. This is clearly because of the lack of information presented to the network. Simulation studies showed that an increase in number of layers or number of interconnections does not improve the system performance. Adding a reference signal (Fig. 4) for the second input signal to the network, $\dot{e}_i$, forces the system trajectory to track in a better way. The reference signal helps the network to drive the system faster in the initial region region of the state space trajectory (+ve e, -ve $\dot{e}$), and decelerate faster in the (-ve $\dot{e}$, -ve e) region. The corresponding response of the system is shown in Fig.4. The system rise time is improved to 27 sec. and the overshoot is reduced to 42%. Also the settling time of the system is about 150 sec. which is much less than with the scheme without the velocity reference feedback. The control signals generated by the neural network for the three cases referred in Fig. 2, is shown in Fig. 5. It could be seen that with the velocity reference scheme, the network is able to generate a control signal which results in reduced rise time, overshoot and settling time.

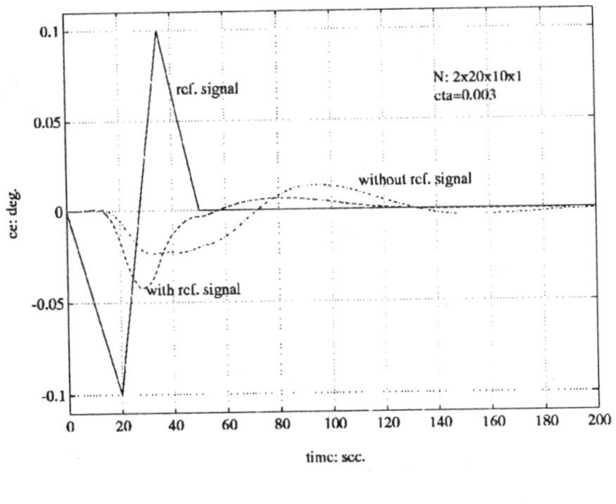

Fig. 4. The velocity reference signal and its effect on the change in error $\dot{e}$

4. Conclusion

A neural network controller trained solely on the desired response of the system may not have the desired dynamic responses. The control system which has good transient response may not have the desired steady state response. Conversely, a system with good steady state response may not have acceptable transient response. We presented a velocity reference feedback scheme for the neural network controllers that simultaneously improve the transient and steady state response of the system. Through simulation studies, we showed that the approach gives specific improvements in the dynamic response. At present, the reference signal is determined by observing the system trajectory. For an arbitrary command signal, generating the velocity reference may not be easy. One approach to this problem may be to adapt the shape of the reference signal, on-line, using the error and change in error signals.

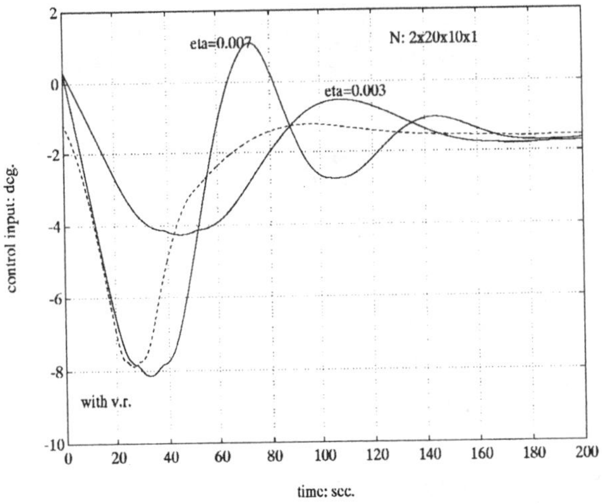

Fig. 5. The control signals generated by the neural network

5. References

[1] K. S. Narendra, and K. Parthasarathy, "Identification and control of dynamical systems using neural networks", *IEEE Transactions on Neural Networks*, vol 1, March '90, pp 4-27.

[2] V. C. Chen and Y. H. Pao, "Learning control using neural networks," *Proc. IEEE Intl. Conf. on Robotics and Automation*, vol. 3, 1989, pp. 1448-1153.

[3] K. Hornik, M. Stinchcombe, and H. White, "Multilayer feedforward networks are universal approximators," *Neural networks*, vol. 2, 1989, pp. 359-366.

[4] D. E. Rumelhart, G. E. Hinton, and R. J. Williams., "Learning internal representations by error propagation", in *Parallel Distributed Processing, vol 1: Foundations*, MIT Press, 1986.

[5] J. Feldman, "DTNSRDC revised standard submarine

equations of motion," David W. Taylor Naval Ship Research and Development Center, *Technical Report: no. SPD-0393-09*, 1979.

[6] K. P. Venugopal, R. Sudhakar and A. S. Pandya, "On-line learning control of autonomous underwater vehicles using feedforward neural networks," *IEEE J. Ocean. Eng.*, vol. 17, no. 4, 1992, pp. 308–320.

[7] R. M. Sanner and D. L. Akin, "Neuromorphic pitch attitude regulation of an underwater tele-robot," *IEEE Control Systems Mag.*, April 1990, pp. 62–67.

[8] W. T. Miller, R. P. Hewes, F. H. Glanz and G. Kraft, "Real-time dynamic control of an industrial manipulator using a neural network based learning controller," *IEEE Tran. Robotics and Automation*, vol. 6, no. 1, 1990, pp. 1–9.

[9] W. T. Miller, R. S. Sutton and P. J. Werbos (Eds.), *Neural networks for control*, MIT Press, Cambridge, MA, 1991.

[10] R. M. Sanner and J. J. E. Slotine, "Direct adaptive control using Gaussian networks," Nonlinear Syatems Labs., *Tech. Report: NSL-910303*, 1991.

[11] Polycarpou, M. M., and Ioannou, P. A. 1991. Identification and control of nonlinear systems using neural network models: design and stability analysis. *TR 91-09-01*. Univ. of Southern California. Dept. of Elec. Eng.-Systems, 1991.

Proceedings of the
American Control Conference
San Francisco, California • June 1993

State Feedback Stabilization of Nonlinear Systems via the Neural Network Approach

Bo Ling *and* **Fathi M.A. Salam**
Circuits and Systems & Artificial Neural Nets Laboratory
Department of Electrical Engineering
Michigan State University
East Lansing, MI 48824

Abstract - **We consider the state feedback stabilization of autonomous nonlinear systems described by $dx/dt = Ax + Bu - f(x)$, where $f(x)$ is a memoryless nonlinearity and does not necessarily satisfy the sector conditions. Classical results can not be used to infer stability of the closed loop system. By using neural network techniques, however, we find a state feedback gain matrix that ensures the asymptotic stability for any specified equilibrium.**

I. INTRODUCTION

Feedback stabilization of nonlinear systems has been a major topic in control theory. Many techniques have been proposed to stabilize certain nonlinear systems. Papers ([1]-[6]) represent a broad spectrum of approaches ranging from Lyapunov theory, Hopf bifurcation theory, and general state/output feedback theories. The Circle criterion and the Popov criterion ([7], [8]) are widely used to render certain nonlinear systems stable. In addition to some other conditions like Hurwitz and strictly positive real, both criteria require the nonlinearity in the system to satisfy the sector conditions ([7], [8]).

Many nonlinear physical systems can be represented as a linear dynamic system with a nonlinear element in the feedback loop ([7], [8]). In this paper, we consider autonomous nonlinear systems of the form:

$$dx/dt = Ax + Bu - f(x) \tag{1.1}$$

where $f(x)$ is a memoryless nonlinearity and does not necessarily satisfy the sector conditions ([7], [8]). Classical results ([7]-[10]) can not be used to stabilize this kind of nonlinear systems.

The Hopfield neural network [11] is a special nonlinear dynamical system. By properly choosing weights, it renders any set of given state vectors equilibria of the system. In [12], we proposed an analytical learning algorithm to find weights given a set of patterns. In this paper, we extend our method to state feedback stabilization of (1.1) with the memoryless nonlinear function f. Instead of finding weights, however, we solve for a state feedback gain matrix to achieve asymptotic stability at a specific equilibrium of the closed loop system.

This paper is organized as follows: in section II, we formulate the state feedback problem; in section III, the formulation of the Hopfield neural network is sketched; our state feedback stabilization approach is introduced in section IV; and in section V, the stability property is considered; in section VI, we deal with how to find gain matrices; finally, in section VII, a numerical example is given as an illustration.

II. FORMULATION OF THE STATE FEEDBACK STABILIZATION

Consider the autonomous nonlinear system

$$\begin{aligned} dx/dt &= Ax + Bu - f(x) \\ y &= Cx \end{aligned} \tag{2.1}$$

where $x \in R^n$, $y \in R^p$, $u \in R^q$, (A, B) is controllable, (A, C) is observable. The matrix A is not necessarily Hurwitz. The nonlinear function $f(x)$ is decentralized in the sense that $f(x) = [f_1(x_1), ..., f_n(x_n)]^T$ with f_i: $R \to R$, $i = 1, ..., n$. Moreover, f is assumed to be a C^1-function on an open subset of R^n. Thus, for each initial condition $x(0)$, the solution of (2.1) uniquely exists for $t \geq 0$ [16].

Define the state feedback as follows:

$$u = -Kx + K_R r \tag{2.2}$$

where $K \in R^{q \times n}$, $K_R \in R^{q \times m}$, and the reference input, r, is fixed. By substituting (2.2) into (2.1), we obtain:

$$dx/dt = A_c x + B_c r - f(x) \tag{2.3}$$

where $A_c = A - BK$ and $B_c = BK_R$.

Define

$$g(x) = A_c x + B_c r - f(x) \tag{2.4}$$

Let x^0 be an equilibrium of (2.3), i.e., $g(x^0) = 0$. Then

$$D_x g(x^0) = A_c - D_x f(x^0) \tag{2.5}$$

where, since f is decentralized, $D_x f(x^0) = \mathrm{diag}(f_1'(x_1^0), ..., f_n'(x_n^0))$ and f_i' is the derivative with respect to x_i. It is known x^0 is asymptotically stable if $D_x g(x^0) < 0$.

III. FEEDBACK NEURAL NETWORK

In this section, we overview the Hopfield continuous time neural network and its related properties. The details could be found in some recent literature ([13] - [15]). The mathematical model for the Hopfield continuous-time neural network is

$$\begin{aligned} c_i \frac{du_i}{dt} &= \sum_{j=1}^{N} w_{ij} v_j + I_i - \frac{1}{r_i} u_i \\ v_i &= s_i(u_i) \end{aligned} \tag{3.1}$$

for $i = 1, 2, ..., N$, where $c_i, r_i > 0$, $u_i \in R$ and $v_i \in (-\Delta, \Delta)$ with $0 < \Delta \in R$. s_i: $R \to (-\Delta, \Delta)$ is a monotone increasing C^1-function with $s_i(0) = 0$, $s_i(x) = \Delta$ (or $-\Delta$) if and only if $x \to \infty$ (or $-\infty$). N denotes the number of neurons in the network (2.1). Without loss of generality, we set $I_i = 0$ for all i.

In compact matrix form, (3.1) can be written as

$$\begin{aligned} C\frac{du}{dt} &= Wv - R^{-1}u \\ v &= s(u) \end{aligned} \tag{3.2}$$

where $u = [u_1, ..., u_N]^T \in R^N$, $v = [v_1, ..., v_N]^T \in R^N$, $C = \mathrm{diag}(c_1, ..., c_N) \in R^{N \times N}$, $R = \mathrm{diag}(r_1, ..., r_N) \in R^{N \times N}$, and $s(u) = [s_1(u_1), ..., s_N(u_N)]^T \in R^N$, and T denotes the transpose of a matrix.

The Hopfield energy function is given as follows ([11]):

This work is supported in part by ONR Grant N00014-92-J-1441 and the Michigan Research Excellent Fund (REF).

$$E(v) = -\frac{1}{2}\sum_{i=1}^{N}\sum_{j=1}^{N} w_{ij}v_iv_j + \sum_{i=1}^{N}\frac{1}{r_i}\int_0^{v_i} s_i^{-1}(x)\,dx \tag{3.3}$$

From a dynamic system point of view, the Hopfield network is a special non-linear dynamic system. We thus can apply well-known tools in non-linear system analysis (such as the Lyapunov method) to analyze the dynamic behavior of the Hopfield network. Many interesting properties about the Hopfield network have been described recently ([13]-[15]). Here, we summarize some of them as follows:

(1) For the energy function defined in (3.3), for all $v \in (-\Delta, \Delta)^N$, $dE(v)/dt \leq 0$, and $dE(v)/dt = 0$ if and only if v is an equilibrium point of (3.2).

(2) For any $v \in (-\Delta, \Delta)^N$, there exists a unique solution of (3.2) for $t \geq 0$.

(3) Isolated local minima of $E(v)$ are asymptotically stable equilibria of (3.2).

(4) There are only finite number of equilibrium points of (3.2).

(5) Let v^0 be an equilibrium point of (3.2). v^0 is a local minimum of the function $E(v)$ if and only if the Jacobian matrix $J_{\nabla E}(v^0)$ is positive definite.

(6) Let v^0 be an equilibrium point of (3.2). v^0 is isolated if $\det(J_{\nabla E}(v^0)) \neq 0$.

(7) If v^0 is an equilibrium of (3.2), then so is $(-v^0)$ with the same stability property.

(8) No limit cycle exits.

(9) All solutions are bounded.

IV. Controlling the Equilibrium

Let $0 \neq x^d \in R^n$ be a desired point. Our objective is to find A_c such that x^d is an equilibrium of system (2.3). Notice that there is a difference between (3.2) and (2.3). In (3.2), nonlinear functions are required to be monotone increasing C^1-functions; in (2.3), f is required only to be a C^1-function, not necessarily monotone increasing.

Suppose x^d is an equilibrium of (2.3). Then x^d satisfies $A_c x^d = f(x^d) - B_c r$. Denote $b = f(x^d) - B_c r$. Mathematically, A_c can be any real matrix in R^{n5n}. In order to form the Hopfield-type energy function, A_c is required to be symmetric. Thus, among n^2 elements of A_c, there are only $n(n+1)/2$ unknowns. Denote this number by N_A. By proper algebraic operations, the matrix equation $A_c x^d = b$ can be rewritten as:

$$Xz = b \tag{4.1}$$

where

$$X = \left[\begin{array}{c|c|c|c|c} x_1^d \;\cdots\; x_n^d & 0 & & & \\ \hline x_1^d I_{n-1} & \begin{array}{c|c} x_2^d & \cdots \; x_n^d \\ \hline 0 & x_2^d I_{n-2} \end{array} & \cdots & 0 & \\ \hline 0 & & & & x_n^d \end{array}\right]$$

$$z = [z_1, \ldots, z_{NA}]^T$$

with

$$z_i = \begin{cases} a^c_{1,i} & 1 \leq i \leq n \\ a^c_{2,i-n+1} & n+1 \leq i \leq 2n-1 \\ \vdots & \vdots \\ a^c_{n,n} & i = N_A \end{cases}$$

The following lemma can be shown by the special structure of X:

Lemma 4.1: Let X be defined in (4.1). Rank(X) = n if $x_i^d \neq 0$ for $i = 1, \ldots, n$.

Suppose $x_i^d \neq 0$ for $i = 1, \ldots, n$. Since rank(X) = n, $b \in R(X)$ (range of X). Thus, $Xz = b$ is consistent which leads to the following theorem:

Theorem 4.2: Let X be defined in (4.1). Then solutions of (4.1) exist if $x_i^d \neq 0$ for $i = 1, \ldots, n$.

Remark: Theorem 4.2 implies that it is always possible to find a matrix A_c such that any non-zero point in R^n can be made as equilibrium of (2.3). This is an important property.

The general solution of $Xz = b$ is given by $z = X^+b + N(X)$ where $z = X^+b$ is the minimum-norm solution, $N(X)$ represents the null space of X. Once z is solved, the matrix A_c, which is symmetric, can be easily reconstructed as

$$A_c = \begin{bmatrix} z_1 & z_2 & \cdots & z_{n-1} & z_n \\ z_2 & z_{n+1} & \cdots & z_{2n-2} & z_{2n-1} \\ \hline z_n & z_{2n-1} & \cdots & z_{NA-1} & z_{NA} \end{bmatrix} \tag{4.2}$$

This matrix A_c will make x^d an equilibrium of (2.3).

V. Stability Analysis

Suppose x^d is a desired state vector. In the previous section, we are able to determine a matrix A_c such that x^d is made into an equilibrium of (2.1). In this section, we will consider how to find A_c such that x^d is asymptotically stable.

Let X, z and b be defined as in (4.1). The desired state vector x^d is an equilibrium of (2.3) if and only if $Xz = b$, where $b = f(x^d) - B_c r$. It is well-known that x^d is asymptotically stable if and only if the Jacobian matrix of (2.3), $A_c - D_x f(x^d)$, is negative definite, where $D_x f(x^d) = \mathrm{diag}(f_1'(x_1^d), \ldots, f_n'(x_n^d))$. And consequently, x^d is asymptotically stable if

$$f_i'(x_i^d) > \sum_{j=1}^{n} |a_{ij}^c| \tag{5.1}$$

for $i = 1, \ldots, n$, which requires $f_i'(x_i^d)$ to be positive and satisfy (5.1). Let $f'(x^d) = [f_1'(x_1^d), \ldots, f_n'(x_n^d)]^T$. Our first assumption is as follows:

Assumption 1: There exists $\varepsilon > 0$ such that $f'(x^d) > \varepsilon$, i.e., $f_i'(x_i^d) > \varepsilon$ for $i = 1, \ldots$, n.

Define

$$\Theta = \left[\begin{array}{ccc|ccc|c} 1 & \cdots & 1 & & 0 & & \\ \hline & & & 1 & \cdots & 1 & \\ \cline{4-6} & I_{n-1} & & & & & 0 \\ & & & 0 & I_{n-2} & & \\ 0 & & & & & & 1 \end{array}\right] \qquad (5.2)$$

which has the same structure as X in (4.1). Thus, rank(Θ) = n. Define $\varphi = \Theta^{+} f'(x^d)$.

Assumption 2: There exists $0 < \delta \in R$ such that $\varphi_i > \delta > 0$, for $i = 1, ..., N_A$.

Theorem 5.1: Let x^d be a desired state vector. Let X, z be defined as in (4.1), $b = f(x^d) - B_c r$, and $\varphi = \Theta^{+} f'(x^d)$. Then x^d is an asymptotically stable equilibrium of (2.3) if

$$Xz = b \qquad (5.3)$$
$$0 < z < \varphi$$

has solutions.

Proof: Suppose (5.3) has a solution. Since $Xz = b$, x^d is an equilibrium of (2.1). $z > 0$ implies all elements of A_c are positive. And $z < \varphi$ is equivalent to $\Theta z < f'(x^d)$ which implies $A_c - D_x f(x^d) < 0$ since $a^c_{ij} > 0$ for all i, j. Thus, x^d is also asymptotically stable. This completes our proof.

Note: Assumption 1 is needed since $\Theta z > 0$. In Theorem 5.1, b is determined by B_c and r which are parameters in our state feedback formulation.

Theorem 5.2: Let x^d be a desired state vector. Let X, z be defined as in (4.1), $b = f(x^d) - B_c r$, and $\varphi = \Theta^{+} f'(x^d)$. Then (5.3) has a solution if Assumption 2 is satisfied.

Proof: Suppose Assumption 2 is true. Then there exists $\varepsilon \geq \delta$ such that $\varepsilon < \min\{\varphi_i, i = 1, ..., N_A\}$. Let $z = \varphi - \varepsilon$. It follows that $z > 0$. Define $b = Xz$. Therefore, z satisfies $Xz = b$ and $0 < z < \varphi$. This completes our proof.

Remark: In general, the solution of (5.3) is not unique. The proof of theorem 5.2 also suggests how to actually find the solution of (5.3). The existence of the vector b will be the topic of the next section.

VI. Finding the State Feedback Gain Matrix

Suppose that a matrix A_c is found such that x^d becomes as an equilibrium of (2.3). By definition of A_c, the state feedback gain matrix K satisfies:

$$BK = A - A_c \qquad (6.1)$$

where A, A_c and B are all constant; $A, A_c \in R^{n \times n}$ and $B \in R^{n \times q}$.

Partition $K = [k_1, ..., k_n]$, $A - A_c = [a_1, ..., a_n]$. Then (6.1) is equivalent to $Bk_i = a_i$ for $i = 1, ..., n$. It is known that the equation $Bk_i = a_i$ has solutions if and only if $a_i \in R(B)$ (the range of B). In case that $q \geq n$ and rank(B) = n, the minimum-norm solution of $Bk_i = a_i$ can be formulated by $k_i = B^{+} a_i$ for $i = 1, ..., n$. Thus, the minimum-norm solution K of (6.1) is given by $K = B^{+}(A - A_c)$ where $B^{+} = B^T(BB^T)^{-1}$. If $q < n$ and rank(B) = q, the minimum-norm solution K of (6.1) is still $B^{+}(A - A_c)$, but with $B^{+} = (B^T B)^{-1} B^T$.

Now, consider the existence of a vector b in (5.3). Recall that $b = f(x^d) - B_c r = f(x^d) - BK_R r$, where $K_R \in R^{q \times m}$, $r \in R^{m \times 1}$. Let $b' = f(x^d) - b$, $K_R r = y$ which is an unknown vector. Then, $BK_R r = f(x^d) - b$ is equivalent to $By = b'$ which has solutions if and only if $b' \in R(B)$ (the range of B). Thus, in case that $q \geq n$ and rank(B) = n, the minimum-norm solution of $By = b'$ can be solved by $y = B^{+} b'$. If $q < n$ and rank(B) = q, the minimum-norm solution of $By = b'$ is still $B^{+} b'$ where $B^{+} = (B^T B)^{-1} B^T$. It is observed that we can always find K_R and r such that $K_R r = y$ since the number of unknowns is greater than the number of knowns. Therefore, the vector b in (5.3) can be arbitrarily assigned.

VII. Example

Consider the following nonlinear system:

$$\begin{bmatrix} x_1' \\ x_2' \end{bmatrix} = \begin{bmatrix} 1 & -2 \\ 3 & 2 \end{bmatrix} \begin{bmatrix} x_1 \\ x_2 \end{bmatrix} + \begin{bmatrix} 1 & 1 & 0 \\ 1 & 0 & 1 \end{bmatrix} \begin{bmatrix} u_1 \\ u_2 \\ u_3 \end{bmatrix} - \begin{bmatrix} \sin^2 3x_1 + 0.5 \\ 1.5\sin^2 2x_2 \end{bmatrix}$$

$$y = \begin{bmatrix} 1 & 0 \end{bmatrix} \begin{bmatrix} x_1 \\ x_2 \end{bmatrix}$$

It can be easily checked that (A, B) is controllable, (A, C) is observable. Let $x^d = [0.26, 0.39]^T$ be a desired point. Define the state feedback as $u = -Kx + K_R r$. The closed loop system is given as

$$\begin{bmatrix} x_1' \\ x_2' \end{bmatrix} = A_c \begin{bmatrix} x_1 \\ x_2 \end{bmatrix} + B_c r - \begin{bmatrix} \sin^2 3x_1 + 0.5 \\ 1.5\sin^2 2x_2 \end{bmatrix}$$

$$y = \begin{bmatrix} 1 & 0 \end{bmatrix} \begin{bmatrix} x_1 \\ x_2 \end{bmatrix}$$

It is easy to verify that $d(\sin^2 3x_1 + 0.5)/dx_1 = 3$ at $x_1 = 0.26$, and $d(1.5\sin^2 2x_2)/dx_2 = 3$ at $x_2 = 0.39$. Thus, $f'(x^d) = [3, 3]^T > 0$ which implies Assumption 1 is satisfied. The matrix Θ and X are constructed as follows:

$$\Theta = \begin{bmatrix} 1 & 1 & 0 \\ 0 & 1 & 1 \end{bmatrix} \qquad X = \begin{bmatrix} 0.26 & 0.39 & 0 \\ 0 & 0.26 & 0.39 \end{bmatrix}$$

It is easy to verify that $\varphi = \Theta^{+} f'(x^d) = [1, 2, 1]^T$ which indicates Assumption 2 is satisfied. Let $\varepsilon = 0.5$. Define $z = \varphi - \varepsilon = [0.5, 1.5, 0.5]^T$. Thus, the matrix A_c is constructed as:

$$A_c = \begin{bmatrix} 0.5 & 1.5 \\ 1.5 & 0.5 \end{bmatrix}$$

Since rank(B) = 2, the state feedback matrix K can be solved by $K = B^{+}(A - A_c)$:

$$K = \begin{bmatrix} 0.6667 & -0.6667 \\ -0.1667 & -2.8333 \\ 0.8333 & 2.1667 \end{bmatrix}$$

Define $b = Xz = [0.7150, 0.5850]^T$. Since $f(x^d) = [0.9946, 0.4946]^T$, $b' = f(x^d) - b = [0.2796, -0.0904]^T$. Thus, $K_R r = B^{+} b' = [0.0631, 0.2165, -0.1535]^T$. For simplicity, let $r = [1, 1, 1]^T$. K_R can be chosen as

$$K_R = \begin{bmatrix} 0.0631 & 0 & 0 \\ 0 & 0.2165 & 0 \\ 0 & 0 & -0.1535 \end{bmatrix}$$

Therefore, the state feedback is

$$u = -\begin{bmatrix} 0.6667 & -0.6667 \\ -0.1667 & -2.8333 \\ 0.8333 & 2.1667 \end{bmatrix} x + \begin{bmatrix} 0.0631 & 0 & 0 \\ 0 & 0.2165 & 0 \\ 0 & 0 & -0.1535 \end{bmatrix} \begin{bmatrix} 1 \\ 1 \\ 1 \end{bmatrix}$$

and the closed loop system is

$$\begin{bmatrix} x_1' \\ x_2' \end{bmatrix} = \begin{bmatrix} 0.5 & 1.5 \\ 1.5 & 0.5 \end{bmatrix} \begin{bmatrix} x_1 \\ x_2 \end{bmatrix}$$

$$+ \begin{bmatrix} 0.0631 & 0.2165 & 0 \\ 0.0631 & 0 & -0.1535 \end{bmatrix} \begin{bmatrix} 1 \\ 1 \\ 1 \end{bmatrix} - \begin{bmatrix} \sin^2 3x_1 + 0.5 \\ 1.5 \sin^2 2x_2 \end{bmatrix}$$

The phase portrait near $x^d = [0.26, 0.39]^T$ is shown in Fig. 1, from which we know x^d is indeed asymptotically stable. The energy surface is plotted in Fig. 2. Fig. 3 shows the same energy surface from a different viewing point. It can be seen that x^d is a local minimum of the energy function which confirms our theoretical results. Thus, we have successfully made the given point, $x^d = [0.26, 0.39]^T$, an asymptotically stable equilibrium.

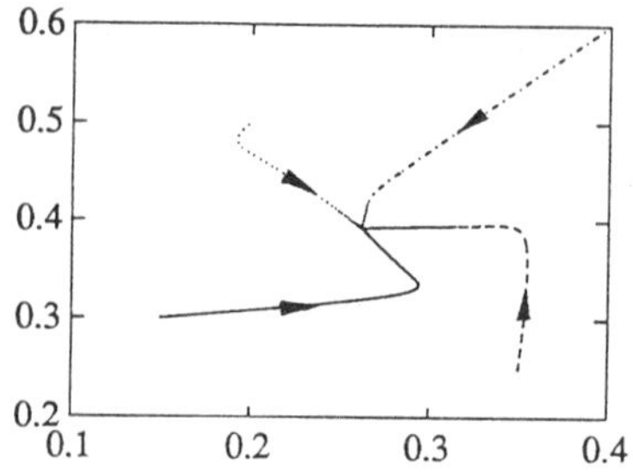

Fig. 1: The phase portrait round $x^0=[0.26, 0.39]^T$. It is observed that x^0 is asymptotically stable.

VIII. CONCLUSION

In this paper, we consider state feedback stabilization of one type of a general autonomous nonlinear system with relaxed nonlinear decentralized functions. As we pointed out, classical results can not be used to achieve stability of the closed loop system. We successfully apply the neural network technique to find a state feedback gain matrix such that the closed loop system is asymptotically stable at a specified point. Computer simulation results have substantiated our approach. Since the gain matrix is not unique for a fixed equilibrium, it is possible to find a gain matrix to achieve a better system performance.

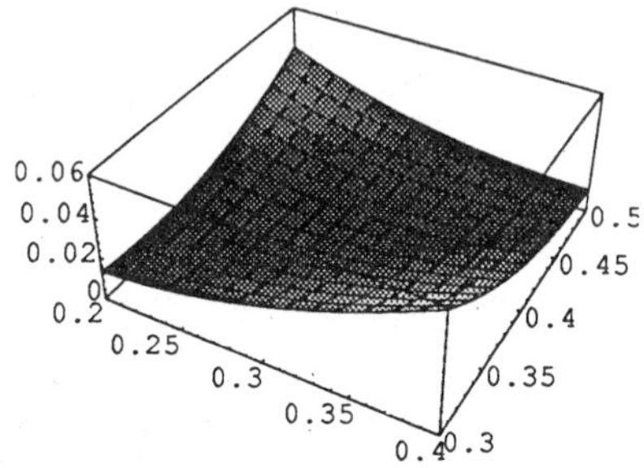

Fig. 2: The energy surface round $x^0=[0.26, 0.39]^T$.

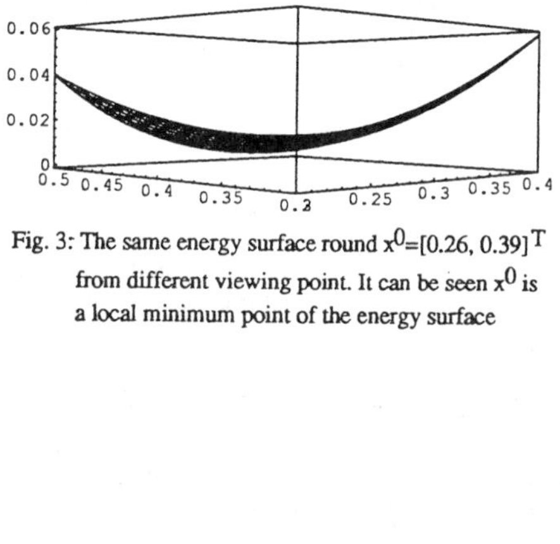

Fig. 3: The same energy surface round $x^0=[0.26, 0.39]^T$ from different viewing point. It can be seen x^0 is a local minimum point of the energy surface

REFERENCES

[1] Eyad H. Abed, "Local bifurcation control", pp. 225-241 in *Dynamic Systems Approaches to Nonlinear Problems in Systems and Circuits*, ed. Fathi M.A. Salam, Mark L. Levi, SIAM, Philadelphia 1988.

[2] Dirk Aeyels, "Stabilization of a class of nonlinear systems by a smooth feedback control", *Systems & Control Letters* 5 (1985), pp. 289-294.

[3] Eyad H. Abed, "A simple proof of stability on the center manifold for Hopf bifurcation", *SIAM Review*, Vol. 30, No. 3, Sep. 1988, pp. 487-491.

[4] R.W. Brockett, "Asymptotic stability and feedback stabilization", pp. 181-191 in *Differential Geometric Control Theory*, ed. R.W. Brockett, R.S. Millman and H.J. Sussmann, Birkhauser, Boston (1983).

[5] J. Tsinias, N. Kalouptsidis, "Output feedback stabilization", *IEEE Trans. Automat. Contr.*, Vol. 35, pp. 951-954, Aug. 1990.

[6] S.H. Zak, "On the stabilization and observation of nonlinear/uncertain dynamic systems", *IEEE Trans. Automat. Contr.*, Vol. 35, No. 5, May 1990.

[7] Hassan K. Khalil, *Nonlinear Systems*, Macmillan Publishing Company, 1992.

[8] M. Vidyasagar, *Nonlinear Systems Analysis*, Prentice-Hall, 1978.

[9] Solomon Lefschetz, *Differential Equation: Geometric Theory* (2nd edition), Interscience Publishers, 1963.

[10] J.M. Ortega, W.C. Rheinboldt, *Iterative Solution of Nonlinear Equations in Several Variables*, Academic Press, 1970.

[11] J.J. Hopfield, "Neurons with graded response have collective computational properties like those of two-state neurons", in *Proc. Natl. Acad. Sci. U.S.A.*, vol. 81, pp. 3088-3092, 1984.

[12] Bo Ling, Fathi M.A. Salam, "A cellular network formed of Hopfield networks", *Proc. of the 35th Midwest Symposium on Circuits and Systems*, Washington, D.C., Aug. 9-12, 1992.

[13] Fathi M.A. Salam, Y. Wang, M. Choi, "On the analysis of dynamic feedback neural nets", *IEEE Trans. on Circuits Syst.*, Vol. 38, No. 2, Feb. 1991.

[14] J.H. Li, A.N. Michel, W. Porod, "Qualitative analysis and synthesis of a class of neural networks", *IEEE Trans. on Circuits Syst.*, Vol. 35, No. 8, Aug. 1988.

[15] A,N, Michel, J.A. Farrell, W. Porod, "Qualitative analysis of neural networks", *IEEE Trans. on Circuits Syst.*, Vol. 36, No. 2, Feb. 1989.

[16] M.W. Hirsch, S. Smale, *Differential Equations, Dynamical Systems, and Linear Algebra*, Academic Press, 1974.

Proceedings of the
American Control Conference
San Francisco, California • June 1993

A Method for Verifying Measurements and Models of Linear and Nonlinear Systems

FEEI WANG*
Hewlett-Packard Laboratories
1501 Page Mill Road, M/S 2U
Palo Alto, CA 94304
Phone: (415) 857-7807

DANIEL ABRAMOVITCH
Hewlett-Packard Laboratories
1501 Page Mill Road, M/S 2U
Palo Alto, CA 94304
Phone: (415) 857-3806

GENE FRANKLIN
Information Systems Laboratory
Stanford University
Stanford, CA 94305
Phone: (415) 723-4837

Abstract— **A method has been developed to help verify system models and measurements and identify system nonlinearities. This method involves measuring the response of physical systems with a swept sine measurement device, such as the HP3562(3)A Control Systems Analyzer (CSA)[1], and simulating system models with a dynamic system simulation tool, such as SIMULINK, using swept sine input. The input-output time sequences obtained from the simulations are analyzed in a similar fashion as done by the CSA to enable more accurate comparisons. A parallelism between swept sine measurements and describing functions is exploited to allow this method to be used in identifying nonlinear systems. Using the measured and simulated frequency response functions as a guide the designer can iteratively improve the model of the system and verify the correctness of the measurements.**

I. Introduction

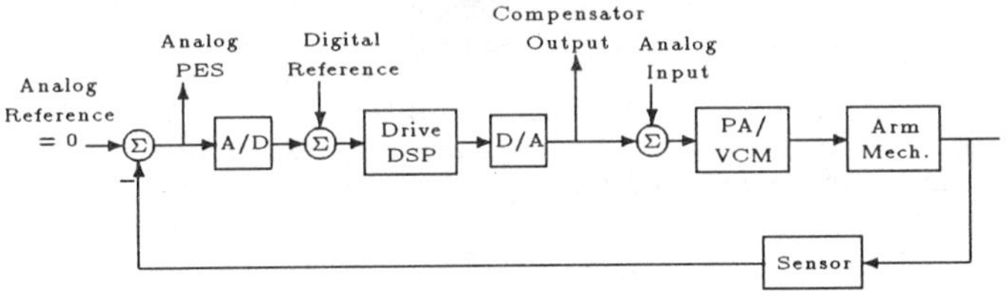

Figure 1: Typical Disk Drive Measurement Block Diagram

A typical disk drive block diagram is shown in Figure 1. This is a good metaphor for what will follow as it contains all elements of a typical SISO digital control loop. The plant consists of the portion from the input to the power amplifier to the output of the sensor. The compensator is typically a DSP chip sandwiched between an A/D and a D/A converter. The system contains both electrical and mechanical parts and the sensor (in this case the magnetic head passing over magnetic domains on the disk) can be nonlinear at either end of its range. The A/D and D/A converters typically have between 8 and 12 bit quantizers in them and their voltage range is limited, resulting in the possibility of both input and output saturation. The sample rates are high enough to require a DSP chip, yet costs must be pushed down because this is a mass production product (as opposed to a fighter aircraft). Furthermore, the packages are small enough to make test points hard to come by. Finally, the sensors can only be kept in their linear region by having the drive in some nominal feedback control loop. Not only does this create a chicken and egg type scenario for the designer, but one also must deal with trying to extract open-loop plant information from closed-loop measurements.

This is also a good metaphor[2] for yet another attempt at bridging the gap between academic and industrial control problems. In particular, this paper will deal with a new identification methodology that came about because the authors were trying to get consistent agreement between a parametric system model[3] and measurements made in the lab on physical hardware[4].

In a textbook control problem one starts with a parametric model where some features of the problem *i.e.*, some parameters may not be known. In addition there may be a nonlinearity of known character and certain noise properties are assumed. The objective from this point is to design a controller to give "good" performance along some metric. The problem discussed here starts earlier in the process. Here, the starting point is a set of electrical and mechanical parts that are accompanied by some nominal parametric models. These are used to create a nominal controller. From this point the system can be measured and an improved controller can be generated. This process is iterated until either the system meets its performance requirements or time and cost constraints dictate that the system has met its time and cost requirements.

It is important to note that in the latter problem, the measurements are not necessarily (or even often) the parametric, time-domain measurements so prevalent in the on line identification literature [1, 2, 3]. More often, nonparametric frequency domain methods are used to obtain a frequency response function (FRF) from a given system input to a given system output [4, 5, 6]. Often, control design is done strictly in the frequency domain without reducing the measurement to a parametric model [7, 8, 9]. However, in order to use the sophisticated control algorithms and CAD programs now available, or in order to deal with multivariable problems in a graceful way, a parametric model is essential. This can be obtained by curve fitting a transfer function to the frequency response function [10, 11, 12, 13, 14]. This process itself is imperfect and is one of the main difficulties in obtaining decent parametric models of industrial control problems [15, 16].

While there is considerable parallelism between time and frequency domain methods [17, 1], the latter do have some great advantages that make them hard to ignore:

- Measurements can be made on both analog and digital systems.

*Feei Wang is a Ph.D. candidate at the Information Systems Lab and is doing joint research at HP Labs under Hewlett-Packard's SEED program.

[1] The HP3562A is an instrument designed for making analog measurements of dynamic systems and is known as a Dynamic Signal Analyzer (DSA). The HP3563A has logic analysis features added in, which allows it to do direct digital measurements and analysis of digital control systems as well. It contains a superset of the features found in the DSA, and is referred to as a Control Systems Analyzer (CSA). For this paper, only the DSA functionality was used.

[2] Or in the words of John Cleese, "Idiom".

[3] implemented in SIMULINK.

[4] in this case a HP 3562A.

- Measurements can be made without modifying the existing nominal controller. Making a physical measurement is not much more difficult than connecting a digital oscilloscope to the system.

- Issues of persistent excitation show themselves in different ways. For FFT based measurements, the system input is "white noise" (which is about as exciting as a signal gets). The noise spectrum is often shaped to emphasize or deemphasize some frequency bands. In this case, regions in the frequency domain where the excitation is poor are easy to spot due to the "fuzzy looking" frequency response plot and values of the coherence function [6] far below 1.

  For swept sine measurements, the system is both stimulated and measured at a single frequency providing extremely high signal to noise ratios. Much of the "fuzziness" of FFT based measurements disappears and the coherence functions are closer to 1. Since at any individual frequency only a magnitude and phase are being estimated, a single sine wave at that frequency provides enough excitation.

⋆ Parallels between swept sine measurements and describing functions (which will be shown) allow the designer to characterize the system including nonlinearities [4].

II. Background

II.A The Modeling Problem

A typical modeling process is shown in Figure 2. As stated

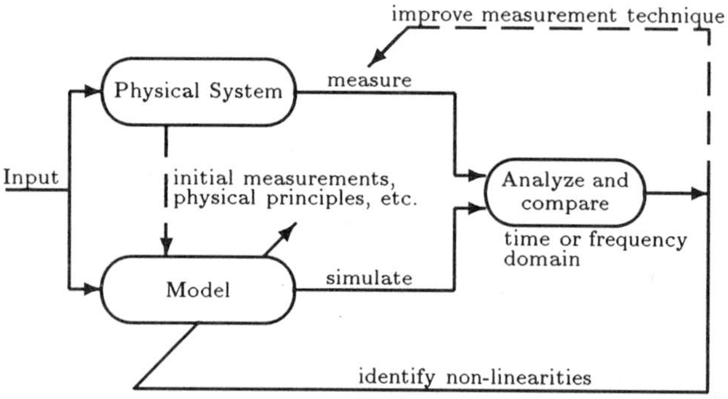

Figure 2: Block Diagram of System Modeling Procedure

earlier, this is an iterative process. While it is well known that this iteration is used to improve the system model, the system model can also be used to determine and correct flaws in the measurement procedure. The initial model is typically obtained from physical principles, component level measurements, or manufacturers' specifications. The model can take many forms, but its validity is based on how well it predicts the measurements of the physical system. Typical measurements are made in both the time and frequency domains. In comparing measured and simulated data it is important to:

- Give both the model and the physical system the same external inputs. This may mean recording the inputs given to the physical system and using these to generate the model's external inputs. This ensures that both the model and the physical system see all the nonidealities of the physical systems input.

- Take the characteristics of the physical measurement into account in the model. Just as any model is imperfect, so is any measurement scheme. It is important to account for sampling and timing issues of both the system and the measurement device (particularly in a system with a digital compensator) as well as coupling and quantization issues of the measurement device.

A useful newcomer to the modeling field is scaled 913SIMULINK from the MathWorks [18] which, like System Build from ISI and Model-C from SCT, allows for a block diagram based model and simulation of a dynamic system. An extremely important feature of this is that one can start with an idealized, linear, textbook model and add in nonideal features to make the model more closely approximate the lab setup. One can also tap into signals which may or may not be accessible on the physical plant. Furthermore, simulations can be run in "continuous-time", which will in most cases be more accurate than discrete-time simulations, and both "analog" and digital data can be readily obtained[5]. Of course, this could all be done with a FORTRAN or C program, but the intuitive ease of a graphical user interface makes this much simpler in the block diagram based tools.

An advantage SIMULINK has over other similar tools is that SIMULINK (and its base program MATLAB) can be run efficiently on a PC. This is especially convenient when one wishes to interface to other applications or instruments. For example, it is potentially possible to set up a system such that SIMULINK is used to simulate a digital compensator, and that control design can be directly downloaded to a PC based DSP system [19]. Also, a vast pool of very useful routines such as FFT already exist in Matlab, making the analysis procedure a little easier.

II.B Measurements of Dynamic Systems

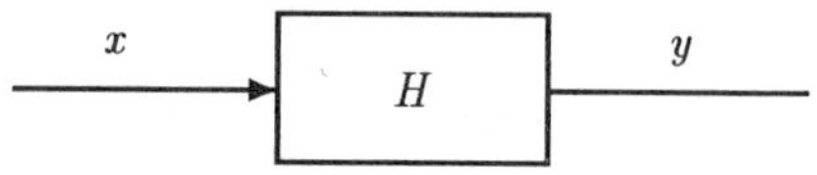

Figure 3: Open-Loop ID of a SISO System

As stated earlier, in industry much of the system measurement and identification that is done is in the frequency domain. A brief review follows. In Figure 3 the frequency response function of H is unknown. The user has access to both the injected input x and the output y. If the system is linear then x and y are related by the frequency response function, $H(f)$, which can be obtained from:

$$H(f) = \frac{Y(f)}{X(f)}, \quad \text{or} \tag{1}$$

$$H(f) = \frac{G_{yx}(f)}{G_{xx}(f)}, \tag{2}$$

where $X(f)$ and $Y(f)$ are the Fourier Transforms of $x(t)$ and $y(t)$ (DFT if x and y are discrete), and $G_{yx}(f)$ and $G_{xx}(f)$ are the one-sided cross and auto spectral density functions given by

$$\begin{aligned} G_{yx}(f) &= \begin{cases} 2E\{Y(f)X^*(f)\}, & f \geq 0 \\ 0 & f < 0 \end{cases} \quad \text{and} \\ G_{xx}(f) &= \begin{cases} 2E\{X(f)X^*(f)\}, & f \geq 0 \\ 0 & f < 0. \end{cases} \end{aligned} \tag{3}$$

Almost always the latter relation, Equation 2, is used because it produces an unbiased estimate of the true frequency response [1, 9].

Swept sine measurements stimulate the system at one frequency, f_0, at a time, producing

$$H(f_0) = \frac{G_{yx}(f_0)}{G_{xx}(f_0)}. \tag{4}$$

This allows for high signal to noise ratios, as narrow band filters can be used around f_0. In actuality, $G_{xx}(f_0)$ exists only

[5] "Continuous-time" and "analog" refer to the analog system ODE being solved numerically to high precision.

in the limit, so $H(f_0)$ is computed using Fourier series theory. The selected frequency is "swept" upwards or downwards in either a linear or logarithmic progression. Because only one frequency at a time is measured, this mode allows for some other tricks to improve the SNR, such as automatically scaling the input level to maximize the linear range of the signal. This feature must not be used when trying to characterize nonlinearities.

In general the input and the output can be any two accessible signals tapped off of the system. Often the input is chosen to be the same as the source, in which case the measurement procedure is called a two-wire measurement, as opposed to a three-wire measurement. There are advantages and disadvantages associated with either choice, but they will not be discussed in this paper.

III. Algorithm

The algorithm discussed in this paper closely follows the swept sine mode of the HP3562(3)A dynamic systems analyzer. Note that the method is not limited to this one instrument, but whichever instrument is chosen must be precisely mimicked in the simulation.

III.A Theory

A brief review of swept sine measurements follows. More detail can be found in [20].

The objective is to obtain a gain and phase relation from some input signal $x(t)$ to some output signal $y(t)$. Assuming that both signals are periodic, we can expand them into Fourier series:

$$x(t) = \sum_{n=-\infty}^{\infty} c_n e^{j\omega n t} \tag{5}$$

$$y(t) = \sum_{n=-\infty}^{\infty} d_n e^{j\omega n t}, \tag{6}$$

where c_n and d_n are complex Fourier coefficients. The first components are

$$c_1 = \frac{1}{T}\int_0^T x(t)e^{-j\omega t}dt, \quad \text{and} \tag{7}$$

$$d_1 = \frac{1}{T}\int_0^T y(t)e^{-j\omega t}dt. \tag{8}$$

The frequency response function from $x(t)$ to $y(t)$ is then d_1/c_1, the ratio of the first harmonics.

In practice, the integration in computing c_1 (and d_1) takes place over multiple periods. This allows for more samples of $x(t)$ and therefore better resolution of c_1. The process of computing c_1 can be summarized in Figure 4.

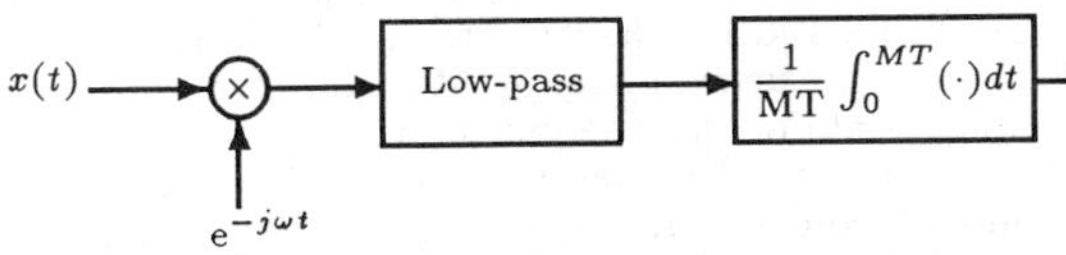

Figure 4: Theoretical Computation of First Harmonic

Note that after the signal $x(t)$ is mixed with $e^{-j\omega t}$, its fundamental component is at DC. Thus a low-pass filter is employeed. Theoretically, this low-pass operation is not needed, based on the assumption that the signals are sinusoidal. However, actual signals will be contaminated by non-periodic noise which will not integrate to zero, causing the resulting Fourier coefficients to be biased. Thus, the signals need to be passed through a low-pass filter before the integration operation.

Figure 4 cannot be implemented as shown because integration cannot be done exactly. What can be done however, is to first sample the signals, then perform a polynomial fit to the sampled data so that an approximation to the integration operation can be obtained. To more closely mimic the HP3562(3)A, the integration is approximated using a fifth-order composite quadrature formula, implemented as an FIR filter. As FIR filters are used to do both low-pass and integration, the two can be combined via convolution. The integration must be taken over an integral multiple of the signal period to properly compute the Fourier components. The process can be summarized in Figure 5 below.

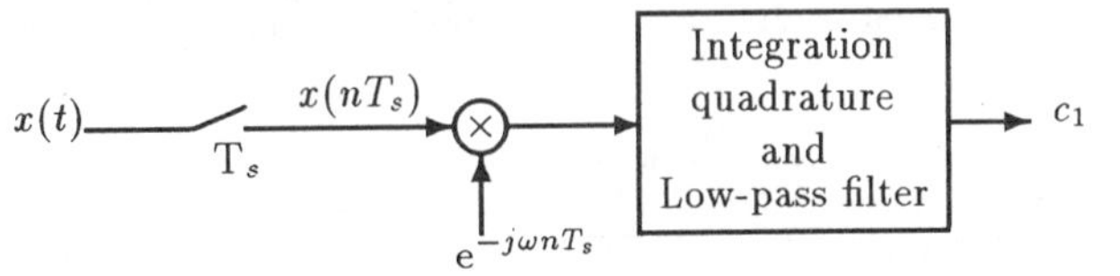

Figure 5: Implementation of Computation of First Harmonic

Much effort was made in assuring that the algorithms used in the analysis of simulated data are the same as thosed used in the HP3562(3)A. This is done to make sure that the characteristics, including the flaws, of the measurement process are taken into account in the model.

III.B Parallels Between Swept Sine and Describing Functions

One of the methods of analyzing nonlinear systems is the *describing function* method[6]. The notion here is that many nonlinear systems can be effectively analyzed by considering the effect of a sinusoidal input on the system and examining the first Fourier component. The equations used to compute a describing function of a nonlinear system are precisely Equations 5–8. In other words, for a fixed amplitude input sinusoid *the swept sine measurement of a nonlinear system measures the describing function of that system.*

The connection between describing functions and swept sine measurements has two important consequences:

- The frequency response function generated by a swept sine measurement degrades gracefully from a transfer function measurement to a describing function measurement as the system moves from linear behavior to nonlinear behavior.
- The nonlinear elements can be characterized by *simulating* a swept sine measurement in some modeling environment. In other words, one can propose a linear system model, based on either physical models or empirical measurements, and generate a swept sine frequency response function. From here nonlinear elements can be added to the model and the swept sine "measurement" can be repeated. This process is repeated until the discrepancy between the frequency response function measured in the lab and the one generated on the computer is reduced to the designer's satisfaction.

It is important to note that this method will not generate a parametric describing function. Instead it will generate exactly what we can measure with a swept sine measurement: the frequency response function of the nonlinear system. Unlike the frequency response function of a linear system, this is not independent of amplitude. In fact, generating a family of these frequency response functions can help to characterize the effect of an amplitude dependent nonlinearity.

This is a departure from previous uses of describing function analysis. In previous work describing function analysis

[6]There are many forms of describing functions. In this paper only the sinusoidal-input describing function is considered.

has largely been limited to isolated nonlinearities. Its main use was in predicting limit cycles and aiding the analysis and design of controllers for systems with some known or assumed nonlinearities. In order to use describing functions for this purpose, an assumption has been made that the higher harmonics caused by the effect of the sinusoid passing through the nonlinearity were sufficiently attenuated by the system to not have been of great importance [8].

There is some reference to using a swept sine measurement to identify nonlinearities in [21]. This is limited to nonlinearities that can be directly stimulated with a sinusoidal input and for which the output can be directly measured. Another reference to swept sine measurements of nonlinear systems is in [4]. However, there is no discussion of how to use such a measurement to determine the character of the system nonlinearity.

As used in this paper, only the first harmonic is computed at a specific frequency in the measurement from both the experiment and the model. Because this work is more concerned with matching these describing function measurements than in getting an analytical result, the assumption that the higher harmonics are attenuated is not necessary. Furthermore, since the measurement process is precisely mimicked in the model, there is no need to assume that the nonlinearity must be measured on its own. Thus, this method expands the concept of describing functions from isolated nonlinearities to overall systems. Its main use is to help identifiy nonlinearities in the system.

III.C MATLAB/SIMULINK *Implementation*

First a system model is constructed in SIMULINK using various blocks already provided. A MATLAB routine is then written to mimic the CSA. An equivalent block diagram is shown in Figure 6.

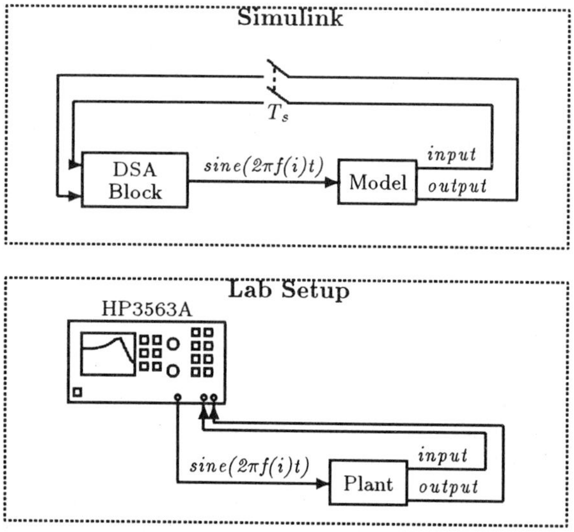

Figure 6: Simulation Implementation, Compared to Physical Setup

The MATLAB script routine performs the following:

1. Specify the frequencies to be swept. Initialize frequency and iteration counters.

2. Call a Matlab simulation routine such as rk45 (Runge-Kutta fifth-order method) to simulate the system model for a specified duration, long enough so that enough sample points can be gathered.

3. Process collected data sequences as described in [20].

4. If not done with specified number of iterations, increment iteration counter and go back to step 2. Otherwise go on.

5. If not done with all frequencies, increment frequency counter and go back to step 2. Otherwise done.

IV. Example

The swept sine algorithm is applied to a disk drive system with block diagram as shown in Figures 7–8. Note in 8 that the deadzone and preload[7] nonlinearities can be switched on or off at will.

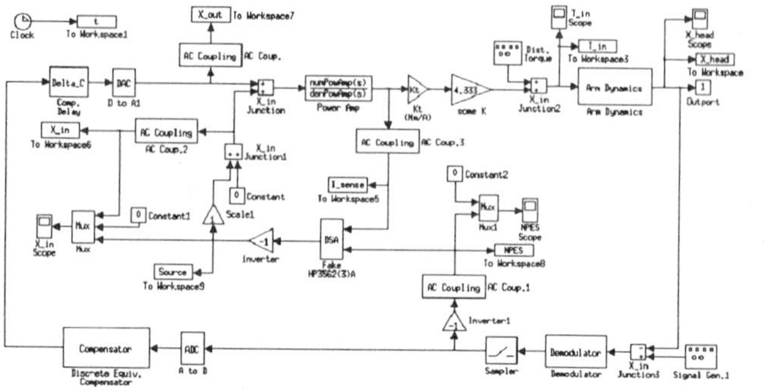

Figure 7: Disk Drive Simulation Block Diagram

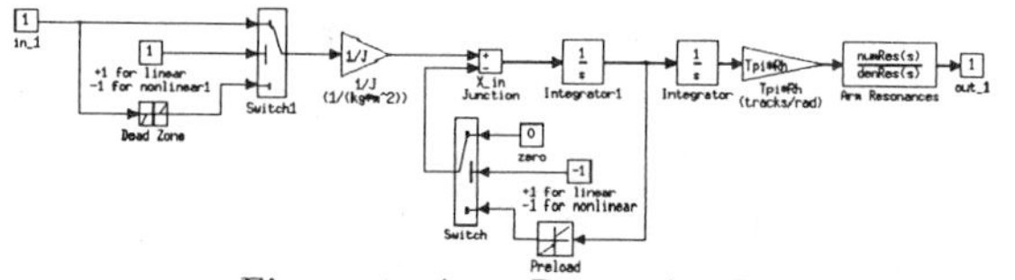

Figure 8: Arm Dynamics Block

The simulated frequency response with neither nonlinearity switched on is shown in Figure 9. The actual measured response is also plotted for comparison. Typical models for disk drive actuators have the actuator mechanics behaving as a double integrator at low frequencies. However, in this case the measured response at low frequencies at low frequencies indicate some nonlinear behavior, since the system gain tapered off and the phase rose towards zero as the frequency dropped off.

The system in Figure 7 was then simulated with the the preload switched on (in this example the dead zone is not used). The simulation results are shown in Figure 10. The magnitude plots now match nearly perfectly, and the discrepancy in the phase plots has been significantly reduced.

V. Conclusions

The above method shows considerable promise for both verifying parametric system models against non-parametric laboratory measurements and for characterizing nonlinear behaviour observed in those measurements. As it is an iterative process, with the designer supplying the candidate nonlinear elements, it does not excuse the designer from a general knowledge of nonlinear models and describing functions. Moreover, it provides an empirical tool for verifying the designer's guesses about what is actually going on in the system. That being done, the control design problem can be worked on with a much improved confidence in the system model. While the usage in this paper has been limited to the HP3562(3)A and the SIMULINK program, this method is applicable to other measurement and simulation tools. The key is to closely mimic the

[7] Preload is a velocity-dependent friction with both viscous and Coulomb components.

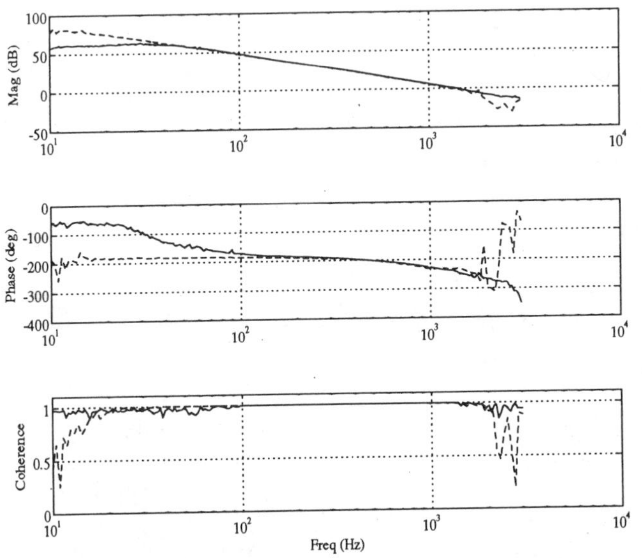

Figure 9: Simulated vs. Measured Swept Sine Frequency Response of Linear Disk Drive. Solid line: simulated, dashed line: measured.

measurement process, complete with its flaws, in the modeling process.

VI. Acknowledgements

The authors would like to thank Doug Wagner of Hewlett-Packard's Lake Stevens Instruments Division for his assistance in understanding the inner workings of the HP 3562A and 3563A. The authors would also like to thank the MathWorks for giving them early access to SIMULINK, which has proven quite useful.

References

[1] L. Ljung, *System Identification: Theory for the User.* Prentice-Hall Information and System Sciences Series, Englewood Cliffs, New Jersey 07632: Prentice-Hall, 1987.

[2] L. Ljung and T. Söderström, *Theory and Practice of Recursive Identification.* MIT Press Series in Signal Processing, Optimization, and Control, Cambridge, Mass 02142: MIT Press, 1983.

[3] G. C. Goodwin and K. S. Sin, *Adaptive Filtering Prediction and Control.* Information and Systems Science Series, Englewood Cliffs, N.J. 07632: Prentice-Hall, 1984.

[4] Hewlett-Packard, *Control System Development Using Dynamic Signal Analyzers: Application Note 243-2*, 1984.

[5] Hewlett-Packard, *HP 3563A Control Systems Analyzer*, 1990.

[6] J. S. Bendat and A. G. Piersol, *Random Data: Analysis and Measurement Procedures.* New York, NY: John Wiley & Sons, second ed., 1986.

[7] G. F. Franklin, J. D. Powell, and A. Emami-Naeini, *Feedback Control of Dynamic Systems.* Menlo Park, California: Addison-Wesley, second ed., 1991.

[8] K. Ogata, *Modern Control Engineering.* Prentice-Hall Instrumentation and Controls Series, Englewood Cliffs, New Jersey: Prentice-Hall, 1970.

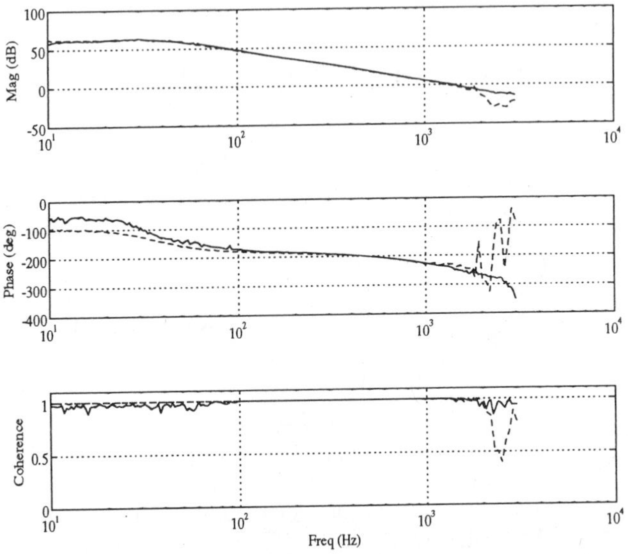

Figure 10: Simulated vs. Measured Swept Sine Frequency Response of Disk Drive with Preload. Solid line: simulated, dashed line: measured.

[9] G. F. Franklin, J. D. Powell, and M. L. Workman, *Digital Control of Dynamic Systems.* Menlo Park, California: Addison-Wesley, second ed., 1990.

[10] E. Levy, "Complex-curve fitting," *IRE Transactions on Automatic Control*, vol. AC-4, pp. 37–43, 1959.

[11] J. L. Adcock, "Curve fitter for pole-zero analysis," *Hewlett-Packard Journal*, vol. 38, pp. 33–37, January 1987.

[12] Hewlett-Packard, *Curve Fitting in the HP 3562A*, product note hp 3562a-3 ed., 1989.

[13] Hewlett-Packard, *z-Domain Curve Fitting in the HP 3563A Analyzer*, hp 3563a-1 product note ed., 1989.

[14] R. L. Dailey and M. S. Lukich, "MIMO transfer function curve fitting using chebyshev polynomials." Presented at the SIAM 35th Anniversary Meeting, Denver, CO, October 1987.

[15] H. Vold and A. Melø, "Pase errors in complex mode structural modification," *Sound and Vibration*, vol. 26, pp. 32–34, June 1992.

[16] M. D. Sidman, F. E. DeAngelis, and G. C. Verghese, "Parametric system identification on logarithmic frequency response data," *IEEE Transactions on Automatic Control*, vol. 36, pp. 1065–1070, September 1991.

[17] L. Ljung and K. Glover, "Frequency domain versus time domain methods in system identification," *International Federation of Automatic Control*, vol. 17, no. 1, pp. 71–86, 1981.

[18] The MathWorks, Inc., Sherborn, MA, *SIMULINK: A Program for Simulating Dynamic Systems*, 1992.

[19] D. Y. Abramovitch, "The Banshee Multivariable Workstation: A tool for disk drive research," in *Proceedings of the 1992 ASME Winter Meeting*, ASME, November 1992.

[20] R. C. Blackham, J. A. Vasil, E. S. Atkinson, and R. W. Potter, "Measurement modes and digital demodulation for a low-frequency analyzer," *Hewlett-Packard Journal*, vol. 38, pp. 17–25, January 1987.

[21] J.-J. E. Slotine and W. Li, *Applied Nonlinear Control.* Englewood Cliffs, New Jersey: Prentice-Hall, first ed., 1991.

Proceedings of the American Control Conference San Francisco, California • June 1993

A NEW INTERPRETATION OF THE FAULT DETECTION FILTER: THE OPTIMAL DETECTION FILTER

Jaehong Park
Department of Electrical Engineering and Computer Science
The University of Michigan

Giorgio Rizzoni
Department of Mechanical Engineering
The Ohio State University

Abstract: This paper presents the formulation of the optimal detection filter problem, for optimization with respect to process and measurement noises. The necessary conditions for the existence of the optimal detection filter are obtained, and a numerical solution technique is shown to be feasible by virtue of the uniqueness of the detection filter gains.

Key words: fault detection, eigenstructure assignment, optimal detection filter, detection filter, model-based diagnostics.

1 Introduction

One of the recognized shortfalls of the fault detection filter approach has been its lack of robustness with respect to noise and disturbances. The objective of this papern is to show how the design freedom in the detection filter can be exploited in order to provide improved noise rejection properties of the detection filter by optimally placing the eigenvalues and eigenvectors.

Jones [2] first proposed to exploit the freedom left after satisfying the directionality constraints of the detection filter to reduce the effects of process and measurement noise. He developed an algorithm for optimizing n eigenvalues (but not the eigenvectors), for the restrictive case in which the number of faults equals the number of measurements, and the system is mutually detectable.

Recently Attar [9] has proposed a formulation for the optimal detection filter. He obtains two different results based on the choice of the cost function. Attar's approach involves optimization procedures consisting of minimizing the squared output error residual in one case, and of iteratively adjusting the eigenvalues until a certain cost function is brought close to zero. Unfortunately, his problem formulation is not well-suited to deriving any formal proof of optimality, and therefore there is no guarantee that the detection filter thus obtained is in fact optimal.

Recently a closed-form expression of the fault detection filter has been developed [5], [7]. In this paper we extend the detection filter formulation to include noise models, resulting in the formulation of an optimal detection filter. Optimality is achieved here by using the freedom left to assign the eigenvalues to minimize the effect of noises on the fault detection filter. The optimal detection filter in this paper is intended, therefore, as a detection filter which satisfies the conventional directionality condition and which has optimally placed eigenvalues and eigenvectors so that the effect of process and measurement noise is minimized. Alternatively, the optimal detection filter may be regarded as an optimal observer with the additional constraint of directionality of the output error residual in the event of a fault.

In Section 2.1 the optimal detection filter problem is formulated as a constrained optimization problem; the advantage in using the formulation of [5], [7] is that the constraints are explicitly included in the equation for the detection filter. In Section 2.2, the necessary conditions are given for the solution of the problem formulated in Section 2.1.

The covariance equation thus obtained is then solved to determined the detection gains. The covariance equation is fairly complicated. An analytical solution for this equation cannot be found, but a method is developed to numerically solve for the optimal detection gains. Also, it can be simplified when the direction of output error residual and the variance for the observation noise satisfy certain conditions. In Section 2.4, a simple numerical example is given.

2 Optimal Fault Detection Filter

2.1 Formulation of the Problem

Given matrices $A \in R^{n\times n}$, $B \in R^{n\times r}$, $C \in R^{m\times n}$, $D_i \in R^{\nu\times m}$, $V_\nu \in R^{n\times\nu}$, $W(t) \in R^{n\times n}$, and a fault event vector $f_i \in R^n$, and white noises $w(t)$, $v(t)$, we want to find the two matrices, $D_j \in R^{\nu\times m}$ and $D_k \in R^{n\times m}$ which minimize

$$\lim_{t\to\infty} E\{e^T(t)e(t)\}$$

where

$$e(t) = x(t) - \hat{x}(t) \tag{2.1}$$

$$\begin{aligned}\dot{x}(t) &= Ax(t) + Bu(t) + w(t) && (2.2)\\ y(t) &= Cx(t) + v(t) && (2.3)\\ \dot{\hat{x}}(t) &= A\hat{x}(t) + Bu(t) + D_i(y(t) - \hat{y}(t)) \\ &\quad + V_\nu D_j(t)(y(t) - \hat{y}(t)) \\ &\quad + D_k(t)(I - (Cf_i)(Cf_i)^+)(y(t) - \hat{y}(t)) && (2.4)\\ \hat{y}(t) &= C\hat{x}(t) && (2.5)\end{aligned}$$

and $(Cf_i)^+$ is given as

$$(Cf_i)^+ = (Cf_i)^T Cf_i)^{-1}(Cf_i)^T.$$

The matrices A_i, D_i, and V_ν are defined as follows:

$$\begin{aligned}D_i &= (Af_i)(Cf_i)^+\\ A_i &= A - D_iC\\ V_\nu &= [v_1, v_2, \cdots v_\nu]\end{aligned}$$

where $v_1, v_2, \cdots v_\nu$ are eigenvectors of A_i such that

$$Cf_i = \alpha_i C v_i, \quad i = 1, 2, \cdots \nu$$

and α_i is a scalar. Also a scalar ν is defined as the detection order of f_i. Equations (2.4) and (2.5) are proven to be a closed-form expression for the detection filter [5], [7].

2.2 Necessary Conditions

Let us define P as the error covariance as follows:

$$P(t) = E\{e(t)e^T(t)\}$$

and let

$$C_p = (I - (Cf_i)(Cf_i)^+).$$

Then, by assuming uncorrelated process and measurement noise, $w(t)$, and $v(t)$, i.e.,:

$$\begin{aligned}E\{w(t)w^T(\tau)\} &= Q\delta(t-\tau)\\ E\{v(t)v^T(\tau)\} &= R\delta(t-\tau)\\ E\{w(t)v^T(\tau)\} &= 0\\ E\{e(t)\} &= 0\end{aligned}$$

The differential equation for $P(t)$ obtained after some algebra is as follows:

$$\begin{aligned}\dot{P} &= [A - (D_iC + V_\nu D_jC + D_kC_pC)]P\\ &+ P[A - (D_iC + V_\nu D_jC + D_kC_pC)]^T + Q \quad (2.6)\\ &+ (D_i + V_\nu D_j + D_kC_p)R(D_i + V_\nu D_j + D_kC_p)^T.\end{aligned}$$

The mean square error in the estimate can be expressed as:

$$E\{e^T(t)e(t)\} = trace\{P(t)\}$$

The necessary conditions for this problem are obtained by minimizing $trace\{P\}$ with respect to the two variables D_j, D_k

$$\frac{\partial}{\partial D_j}E\{e^T(t)e(t)\} = \frac{\partial}{\partial D_j}trace\{P\} = 0 \quad (2.7)$$

$$\frac{\partial}{\partial D_k}E\{e^T(t)e(t)\} = \frac{\partial}{\partial D_k}trace\{P\} = 0. \quad (2.8)$$

Differentiating both sides with respect to time and interchanging $\frac{d}{dt}$ with $\frac{\partial}{\partial D_\cdot}$ gives [1]:

$$\frac{d}{dt}[\frac{\partial}{\partial D_j}trace\{P\}] = \frac{\partial}{\partial D_j}trace\{\dot{P}\} = 0 \quad (2.9)$$

$$\frac{d}{dt}[\frac{\partial}{\partial D_k}trace\{P\}] = \frac{\partial}{\partial D_k}trace\{\dot{P}\} = 0 \quad (2.10)$$

or

$$V^T D_i R - V_\nu^T PC^T + V_\nu^T V_\nu D_j R + V_\nu^T D_k C_p R = 0 \quad (2.11)$$

$$D_i RC_p - PC^T C_p^T + V_\nu D_j RC_p^T + D_k C_p RC_p^T = 0 \quad (2.12)$$

At steady state, $\dot{P} = 0$, and we obtain the following from (2.6):

$$\begin{aligned}0 &= [A - (D_iC + V_\nu D_jC + D_kC_pC)]P\\ &+ P[A - (D_iC + V_\nu D_jC + D_kC_pC)]^T + Q \quad (2.13)\\ &+ (D_i + V_\nu D_j + D_kC_p)R(D_i + V_\nu D_j + D_kC_p)^T\end{aligned}$$

Equations (2.11) to (2.13) constitute the necessary conditions for the optimal detection gain. In the remaining part of this section the three equations are combined to obtain close- form expressions for D_j, D_k. These D_j, D_k will be substituted into (2.13) to obtain an equation for P.

In equations (2.11) and (2.12), the matrices R, $V_\nu^T V_\nu$ are non-singular but the matrix C_pRC_p is singular. Therefore in order to obtain a closed-form expression, we need to investigate the general inverse of the singular matrix C_pRC_p, where $C_p = (I - (Cf_i)(Cf_i)^+)$. Let the columns of an orthogonal matrix H be the eigenvectors of C_pRC_p. Then C_pRC_p can be written as

$$C_pRC_p = H\begin{bmatrix}0 & 0\\ 0 & \Lambda_{C_pRC_p}\end{bmatrix}H^T \quad (2.14)$$

where $\Lambda_{C_pRC_p}$ is a $(m-1)\times(m-1)$ diagonal matrix. Define an $m \times m$ matrix $(C_pRC_p)^{++}$ as

$$(C_pRC_p)^{++} = H\begin{bmatrix}0 & 0\\ 0 & \Lambda^{-1}_{C_pRC_p}\end{bmatrix}H^T \quad (2.15)$$

Then the matrix has the following properties:

$$\begin{aligned}(C_pRC_p)^{++}(C_pRC_p) &= (C_pRC_p)(C_pRC_p)^{++} = C_p\\ (C_pRC_p)^{++}C_p &= C_p(C_pRC_p)^{++} = (C_pRC_p)^{++}\\ ((C_pRC_p)^{++})^T &= (C_pRC_p)^{++}\end{aligned}$$

Also, the matrix C_p has the following properties:

$$C_pC_p = C_p \quad (2.16)$$

$$C_p^T = C_p \quad (2.17)$$

The Lemma below provides a general solution of a linear equation:

[1] This is possible because P, as can be seen from (2.6), is a smooth function.

Lemma 2.1: Consider three matrices X, A, and B which are of appropriate dimension. The necessary and sufficient condition for $XA = B$ to have a solution (i.e., the condition that B be in the row-space of A) is

$$BA^{++}A = B, \tag{2.18}$$

and the general solution is given as

$$X = BA^{++} + Z(I - AA^{++}) \tag{2.19}$$

where Z is arbitrary.

Proof: For a proof, see [10]. □

Equation (2.12) satisfies (2.18). Therefore, D_k can be obtained by utilizing the lemma (after substituting (2.11) into (2.12)) to eliminate D_j:

$$\begin{aligned} D_k = PC^T C_p(C_pRC_p)^{++} - D_iR(C_pRC_p)^{++} \\ +Z(I - (C_pRC_p)(C_pRC_p)^{++}). \end{aligned} \tag{2.20}$$

But D_k always appears in the the form of D_kC_P, i.e.,

$$Z(I - (C_pRC_p)(C_pRC_p)^{++})C_p = 0$$

Therefore, D_k can be written as

$$D_k = PC^T(C_pRC_p)^{++} - D_iR(C_pRC_p)^{++} \tag{2.21}$$

D_j is obtained from (2.11) as

$$\begin{aligned} D_j &= (V_\nu^TV_\nu)^{-1}V_\nu^TPC^TR^{-1} - (V_\nu^TV_\nu)^{-1}V_\nu^TD_i \\ &\quad -(V_\nu^TV_\nu)^{-1}V_\nu^TPC^T(C_pRC_p)^{++} \end{aligned} \tag{2.22}$$

P is the solution of the following equation which is obtained by substituting (2.21) and (2.22) into (2.13), and by utilizing the previously mentioned properties of the matrices.

$$\begin{aligned}
0 &= PC^T(C_pRC_p)^{++}CPV_\nu(V_\nu^TV_\nu)^{-1}V_\nu^T \\
&+ V_\nu(V_\nu^TV_\nu)^{-1}V_\nu^TPC^T(C_pRC_p)^{++}CP \\
&- V_\nu(V_\nu^TV_\nu)^{-1}V_\nu^TPC^TR^{-1}CP \\
&- PC^TR^{-1}CPV_\nu(V_\nu^TV_\nu)^{-1}V_\nu^T \\
&- PC^T(C_pRC_p)^{++}CP \\
&+ V_\nu(V_\nu^TV_\nu)^{-1}V_\nu^TPC^TR^{-1}CPV_\nu(V_\nu^TV_\nu)^{-1}V_\nu^T \\
&- V_\nu(V_\nu^TV_\nu)^{-1}V_\nu^TPC^T(C_pRC_p)^{++}CPV_\nu(V_\nu^TV_\nu)^{-1}V_\nu^T \\
&+ AP + PA^T - D_iCP - PC^TD_i^T \\
&+ V_\nu(V_\nu^TV_\nu)^{-1}V_\nu^TD_iCP + PC^TD_i^TV_\nu(V_\nu^TV_\nu)^{-1}V_\nu^T \\
&- PC^T(C_pRC_p)^{++}RD_i^TV_\nu(V_\nu^TV_\nu)^{-1}V_\nu^T \\
&- V_\nu(V_\nu^TV_\nu)^{-1}V_\nu^TD_iR(C_pRC_p)^{++}CP \\
&+ PC^T(C_pRC_p)^{++}RD_i^T + D_iR(C_pRC_p)^{++}CP \\
&- D_iR(C_pRC_p)^{++}CPV_\nu(V_\nu^TV_\nu)^{-1}V_\nu^T \\
&- V_\nu(V_\nu^TV_\nu)^{-1}V_\nu^TPC^T(C_pRC_p)^{++}RD_i^T \\
&- V_\nu(V_\nu^TV_\nu)^{-1}V_\nu^TPC^TD_iV_\nu(V_\nu^TV_\nu)^{-1}V_\nu^T \\
&- V_\nu(V_\nu^TV_\nu)^{-1}V_\nu^TD_iCPV_\nu(V_\nu^TV_\nu)^{-1}V_\nu^T \\
&+ V_\nu(V_\nu^TV_\nu)^{-1}V_\nu^TPC^T(C_pRC_p)^{++}RD_i^TV_\nu(V_\nu^TV_\nu)^{-1}V_\nu^T \\
&+ V_\nu(V_\nu^TV_\nu)^{-1}V_\nu^TD_iR(C_pRC_p)^{++}CPV_\nu(V_\nu^TV_\nu)^{-1}V_\nu^T \\
&+ D_iCPV_\nu(V_\nu^TV_\nu)^{-1}V_\nu^T + V_\nu(V_\nu^TV_\nu)^{-1}V_\nu^TPC^TD_i^T \\
&- D_iRD_i^TV_\nu(V_\nu^TV_\nu)^{-1}V_\nu^T - V_\nu(V_\nu^TV_\nu)^{-1}V_\nu^TD_iRD_i^T \\
&+ D_iR(C_pRC_p)^{++}RD_i^TV_\nu(V_\nu^TV_\nu)^{-1}V_\nu^T \\
&+ D_iR(C_pRC_p)^{++}RD_i^T \\
&+ D_iRD_i^T - D_iR(C_pRC_p)^{++}RD_i^T \\
&+ V_\nu(V_\nu^TV_\nu)^{-1}V_\nu^TD_iRD_i^TV_\nu(V_\nu^TV_\nu)^{-1}V_\nu^T \\
&- V_\nu(V_\nu^TV_\nu)^{-1}V_\nu^TD_iR(C_pRC_p)^{++}RD_i^TV_\nu(V_\nu^TV_\nu)^{-1}V_\nu^T
\end{aligned} \tag{2.23}$$

P is obtained from (2.23), then D_j and D_k are obtained, by substituting that P into (2.21) and (2.22). Also, the mean square error is given by

$$E\{e^T(t)e(t)\}|_{t\to\infty} = trace\{P\}$$

2.3 Numerical Solution of the Covariance Equation

The equation (2.23) for the error covariance matrix P is virtually intractable from a practical stand point. This complexity is caused by the fact that there are two variables D_j and D_k, as well as constraints imposed by V_ν and C_p. In this section, an algorithm is proposed to numerically compute the gain matrices, D_j and D_k, which minimize the mean square estimation error by eliminating one of the variables.

Because of the detection equivalent faults, the practical dimension of the detection space is one or two [5], [6]. Since one- or two-dimensional space is small enough to search, we can first assign one (or two) eigenvalues to the detection space, (thus fixing D_j,) and then find an optimal gain D_k for the completion space[2]. Then we can select the detection space (and the associated eigenvalues) that minimizes the overall mean square estimation error. By assuming the detection gain D_j is given (since for given eigenvalues, D_j is fixed) the constraint V_ν can also be eliminated. Therefore, now D_k alone is to be considered.

By rearranging Equation (2.6), we obtain

$$\begin{aligned} \dot{P} &= [(A - D_{ij}C) - D_kC_pC]P \\ &\quad +P[(A - D_{ij}C) - D_kC_pC]^T + Q \\ &\quad +D_{ij}RD_{ij} + (D_{ij}RC_p)D_k^T \\ &\quad +D_k(C_pRD_{ij}^T) + D_kC_pRC_pD_k^T. \end{aligned}$$

where D_{ij} is defined as:

$$D_{ij} = D_i + V_\nu D_j. \tag{2.24}$$

This equation has the same form as the optimal observer problem with correlated state excitation and observation noise. The term corresponds to the observation noise, C_pRC_p is singular since C_p equals $(I-(Cf)(Cf)^+)$. Therefore, we can view our problem as a singular optimal observer problem with correlated state excitation and observation noise where the system matrix is $(A-D_iC-V_\nu D_jC)$,

[2] Since the detection space can be described as a single-output system, there always exist an unique gain matrix D_j given the eigenvalues [5], [7].

the output matrix is C, the state noise covariance matrix is $Q + D_{ij}RD_{ij}^T$, the singular observation noise covariance matrix is C_pRC_p (not R), and the state and observation correlated variance matrix is $D_{ij}RC_p$ (not $D_{ij}R$).

2.3.1 Numerical Solution for the Special Case $C_pR = RC_p$

In this section, the singular optimal observer problem in the previous section will be converted into a *non-singular* optimal observer problem under the following condition:

$$C_pR = RC_p \tag{2.25}$$

The condition is not overly restrictive, especially when the fault is observed through only a few sensors. And it is always satisfied when the fault is observed through only one sensor. (That is, if the output error residual contains only one non-zero element, e.g., the output error residual is in the direction of $[0 \;\; 0 \;\; 1]^T$.)

By rearranging Equation (2.6) with the condition (2.25) the problem of finding the optimal gain matrix D_k (for the completion space) can be viewed as a nonsingular optimal observer problem with correlated state excitation and observation noises. For the problem, It is well known [8] that the optimal observer for the steady state is achieved by choosing the gain matrix D_k of the observer as

$$D_k = (\tilde{P}\tilde{C}^T - \tilde{S})R^{-1} \tag{2.26}$$

where $\tilde{P}$ is the solution of the matrix Riccati equation

$$\begin{array}{c}[\tilde{A} - \tilde{S}\tilde{R}^{-1}\tilde{C}]\tilde{P} + \tilde{P}[\tilde{A} - \tilde{S}\tilde{R}^{-1}\tilde{C}]^T \\ +\tilde{Q} - \tilde{S}\tilde{R}^{-1}\tilde{S}^T - \tilde{P}\tilde{C}^T\tilde{R}^{-1}\tilde{C}\tilde{P} = 0\end{array} \tag{2.27}$$

and $\tilde{A}$, $\tilde{C}$, $\tilde{Q}$, $\tilde{R}$, $\tilde{S}$ are

$$\tilde{A} = (A - D_{ij}C) \tag{2.28}$$
$$\tilde{C} = C_pC \tag{2.29}$$
$$\tilde{Q} = Q + D_{ij}RD_{ij}^T \tag{2.30}$$
$$\tilde{R} = R \tag{2.31}$$
$$\tilde{S} = D_{ij}RC_p \tag{2.32}$$

2.4 Examples

In this subsection, a 3×3 system matrix and a fault event vector with one-dimensional detection space are considered. This example is that used by Beard [1] and White [3]. The optimization method given in Section 2.3.1 is illustrated after verifying the condition (2.25). Then the solutions obtained by the method are checked by Equations (2.11) to (2.13) to see if they satisfy the original necessary conditions.

Consider the problem given in Section 2.1. The system matrices, $A \in R^{3\times3}$, output matrix, $C \in R^{2\times2}$, fault event vector, $f_i \in R^3$, and the variance, Q, R, for noises $w(t)$, $v(t)$ are given as follows:

$$A = \begin{bmatrix} 0. & 3. & 4. \\ 1. & 2. & 3. \\ 0. & 2. & 5. \end{bmatrix}$$

$$C = \begin{bmatrix} 0. & 1. & 0. \\ 0. & 0. & 1. \end{bmatrix}$$

$$f_i = \begin{bmatrix} 1.000 \\ -0.500 \\ 0.500 \end{bmatrix}$$

$$Q = \begin{bmatrix} 0.01 & 0.00 & 0.00 \\ 0.00 & 0.02 & 0.00 \\ 0.00 & 0.00 & 0.03 \end{bmatrix}$$

$$R = \begin{bmatrix} 0.0001 & 0.0000 \\ 0.0000 & 0.0001 \end{bmatrix}$$

$B \in R^{3\times r}$ can be arbitrary. The detection order ν can be easily found as $\nu = 1$.

The procedure to find the optimal detection gain is as follows:

1. Check if the condition for Lemma 2.1 is satisfied:

   $$RCf_i = 0.0001 \times \begin{bmatrix} -0.500 \\ 0.500 \end{bmatrix} = 0.0001 \times Cf_i$$

   Cf_i is R invariant so the condition is satisfied. Therefore we can use the method in Section 2.3.1.

2. Assume an eigenvalue λ_1 and obtain D_j (or D_{ij}) which assigns λ_1 as the eigenvalue for the detection space.

   $$\begin{aligned} D_{ij} &= D_i + V_\nu D_j \\ &= Af(Cf_i)^+ - V_\nu\lambda_1(Cf_i)^+ \end{aligned}$$

3. Given D_{ij}, find D_k by solving (2.26)-(2.32).

4. Go to step 2 by assuming another λ_1 until a λ_1 is found that yields a minimal $trace\{\tilde{P}\}$.
   The results for the example are summarized in Figure 1. The x axis is the value of λ_1 and the y axis is $\lim_{t\to\infty} E\{e^T(t)e(t)\} = trace\{\tilde{P}\}$.

5. Obtain D_k, D_{ij}, and the optimal gain D_o.
   the eigenvalue for the detection space, λ_1, the gain matrix, D_{ij} and D_k, and the error covariance matrix, P, are found after some iteration:

$$\lambda_1 = -0.9$$

$$D_{ij} = \begin{bmatrix} -1.4000 & 1.4000 \\ -1.0500 & 1.0500 \\ -1.9500 & 1.9500 \end{bmatrix}$$

$$D_k = \begin{bmatrix} 23.0597 & 23.0597 \\ 25.4284 & 25.4284 \\ 0.3522 & 0.3522 \end{bmatrix}$$

$$P = \begin{bmatrix} 0.0325 & 0.0200 & -0.0154 \\ 0.0200 & 0.0224 & -0.0173 \\ -0.0154 & -0.0173 & 0.0174 \end{bmatrix}$$

$$trace\{P\} = 0.072$$

The optimal detection gain is: as

$$\begin{aligned} D_o &= D_{ij} + D_kC_p \\ &= \begin{bmatrix} 21.6597 & 24.4597 \\ 24.3784 & 26.4784 \\ -1.5978 & 2.3022 \end{bmatrix} \end{aligned}$$

Figure 1: Eigenvalue of detection space, λ_1 vs. $\lim_{t\to\infty} E\{e^T(t)e(t)\}$

Now, we check the results obtained with Equations (2.11) to (2.13) to see if they satisfy the original necessary conditions. The left hand sides of Equation (2.11) with the above values are:

$$1.0^{-3} \times \begin{bmatrix} -0.5966 & 0.5966 \end{bmatrix} \tag{2.33}$$

It should be noted that as we get more accurate optimal eigenvalues, the value in (2.33) becomes smaller. When we consider the fact that the eigenvalues in the detection space are approximated only to one decimal point, 0.0005 can be regarded as near zero. The left-hand sides of Equation (2.12) with the above values are:

$$1.0^{-15} \times \begin{bmatrix} -0.2429 & -0.2429 \\ -0.3469 & -0.3469 \\ 0.3469 & 0.3469 \end{bmatrix}$$

The left-hand sides of Equation (2.13) with the above values are:

$$1.0^{-13} \times \begin{bmatrix} 0.1861 & 0.2078 & -0.0022 \\ 0.1851 & 0.2059 & 0.0036 \\ 0.1187 & 0.1298 & 0.0003 \end{bmatrix}$$

This results shows that the results satisfy the original necessary conditions.

3 CONCLUSION

In this paper, using the closed-form expression of the fault detection filter developed in [5], [7], the optimal detection filter problem is formulated for optimization with respect to process and measurement noises. The necessary conditions for the existence of the optimal detection filter are obtained, and a numerical solution technique is shown to be feasible by virtue of the uniqueness of the detection filter gains.

References

[1] R. V. Beard, "Failure Accommodation in Linear Systems through Self-reorganization," Man-Vehicle Lab., Mass. Inst. Technol. Cambridge, MA, Rep. MVT-71-1, Feb. 1971.

[2] H.L. Jones, "Failure Detection in Linear Systems", Ph.D. Thesis, MIT, Sep. 1973.

[3] J. E. White and J. L. Speyer, "Detection Filter Design: Spectral Theory and Algorithms," *IEEE transaction on Automatic Control*, vol. AC-32, no. 7, pp.593-603, July 1987

[4] J. Park, G. Rizzoni, W. B. Ribbens, "On the Representation of Sensor Faults in Detection Filters", Submitted to Automatica.

[5] J. Park, "A Unified Theory of Fault Detection and Isolation in Dynamic Systems", Ph.D. Thesis, The University of Michigan, June 1991.

[6] J. Park, G. Rizzoni, "An Eigenstructure Assignment Algorithm for the Design of Fault Detection Filters", Submitted to *IEEE transaction on Automatic Control.*

[7] J. Park, G. Rizzoni, "A Closed-Form Expression of the Fault Detection Filter", Submitted to *International Journal of Control.*

[8] R. Kalman, "A New Approach to Linear Filtering and Prediction Problems," *Trans. ASME*, vol. 82, pp. 35-45, 1960

[9] S. Attar, Analysis and Design of Detection Filters within Closed-Loop Systems, PhD. Dissertation, University of Texas, Austin, 1987

[10] R. Penrose, "A Generalized Inverse for Matrices," Proc. Camb. Phil. Soc., 62, 673-7.

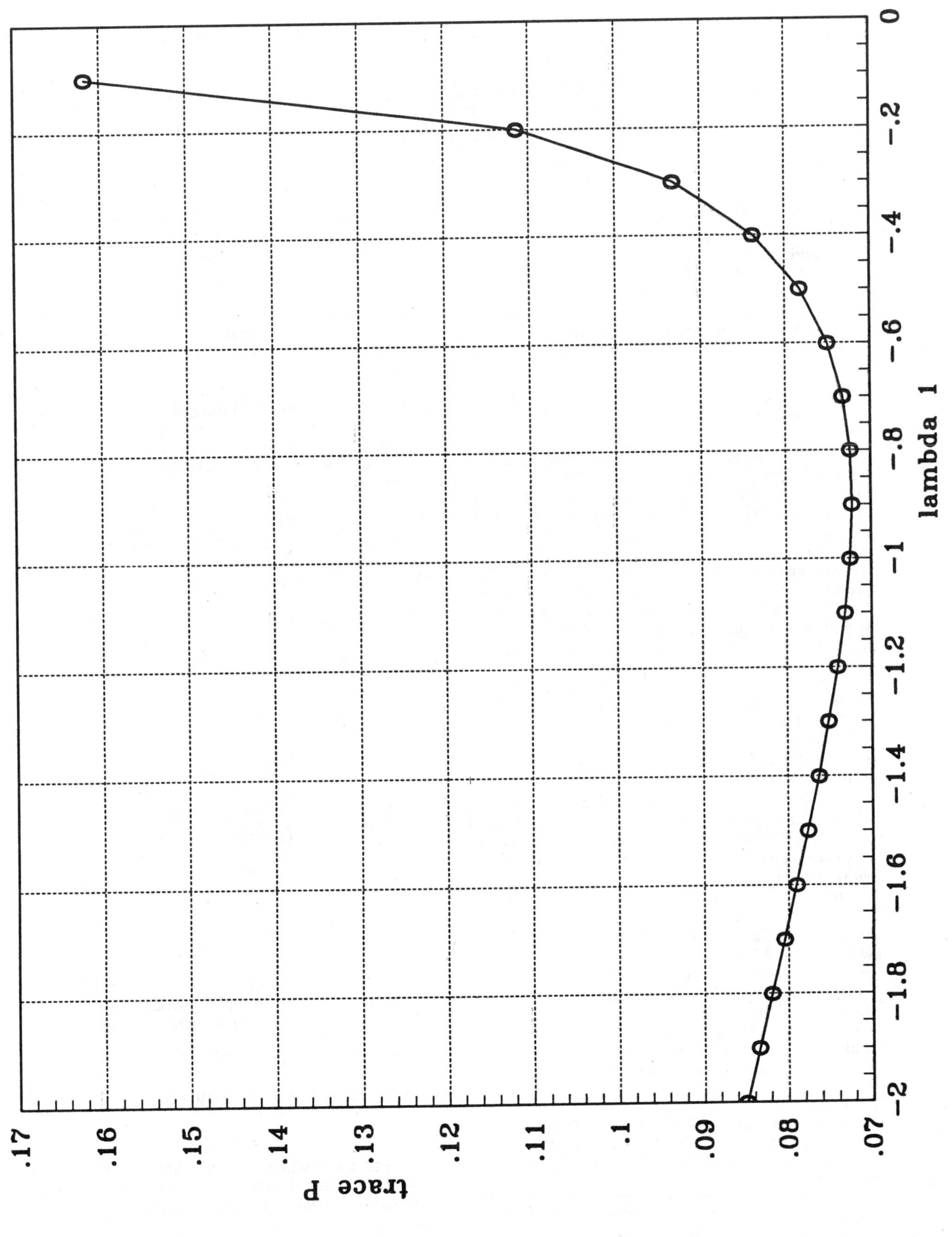

trace P
lambda 1
.17
.16
.15
.14
.13
.12
.11
.1
.09
.08
.07
−2
−1.8
−1.6
−1.4
−1.2
−1
−.8
−.6
−.4
−.2
0

Proceedings of the
American Control Conference
San Francisco, California • June 1993

Recursive Methods for Model Validation *

Fen Wu, Andy Packard, and Kameshwar Poolla†
Department of Mechanical Engineering
University of California, Berkeley, CA 94720

Abstract

We consider a class of time-domain model validation problems as treated in [6]. As shown in that paper, these model validation problems reduce to an associated *extension problem*. In this paper we offer recursive algorithms for the solution of these extension problems. These algorithms can be employed, via the reduction in [6], for on-line model validation.

1 Introduction

Imagine that we are given a prior *uncertainty model* for a physical plant. This could consist of a nominal plant model together with bounds on the unmodeled dynamics, initial condition uncertainty, and measurement noise. Having conducted experiments on the physical plant, we also have available *time-domain* input-output data over a finite horizon. The problem we wish to address is that of determining whether or not the input-output data record is consistent with the uncertainty model of the plant. In other words, the problem is to decide whether the observed data could have been produced by the model for some choice of unmodeled dynamics, initial condition, and measurement noise satisfying the given bounds. This is called the *model validation problem.*

Model validation problems have been previously addressed in some studies. The book by Ljung [1] contains a discussion of model validation in the traditional identification setting. The papers by Smith and Doyle [7, 8] address model validation problems in *frequency domain* with structured uncertainty. they show that the resulting problem can be converted into a μ problem (see also [5]).

More recently, a general class of time-domain model validation problems were considered in [6]. In that paper it is shown that these model validation problems reduce to certain *extension* problems in which we are given some *partial* input-output data and wish to know the minimum norm causal operator that could produce this data. More precisely, these extension problems are of the following form:

> Given sequences $u = \{u_0, u_1, \cdots, u_{\ell-1}\}$ and $y = \{y_0, y_1, \cdots, y_{\ell-1}\}$. When does there exist a stable, causal operator Δ with $\|\Delta\| \leq 1$ and such that
>
> $$\Delta(u_0, \cdots, u_{\ell-1}, *, \cdots) = (y_0, \cdots, y_{\ell-1}, *, \cdots)?$$

In this paper we offer recursive algorithms for the solution of these extension problems for linear time-invariant and for linear time-varying operators Δ. The utility of these recursive schemes is in the context of *on line* model validation via the reduction of a large class of model validation problems to extension problems as in [6]. The interested reader may consult [6] for the details of this reduction. Related research on algorithms for interpolation problems may be found in [9].

The remainder of this paper is organized as follows. In Section 2 we establish notation and present two results from [6] that we shall require subsequently. Next, in Section 3, we describe our recursive algorithms for model validation. Finally, in Section 4 we offer conclusions and discuss open research directions.

All proofs are omitted from this preliminary manuscript.

2 Preliminaries

For a matrix $M \in \mathbf{R}^{p\times m}$ we denote its largest singular value by $\bar{\sigma}(M)$. For a vector sequence $u = \{u_0, u_1, \cdots, u_{\ell-1} \in \mathbf{R}^m\}$, let $U_\ell \in \mathbf{R}^{m\ell\times\ell}$ denote the associated block Toeplitz matrix defined as

$$U_\ell = \begin{bmatrix} u_0 & 0 & 0 & \cdots & 0 \\ u_1 & u_0 & 0 & \cdots & 0 \\ \vdots & \vdots & \vdots & \cdots & \vdots \\ u_{\ell-1} & u_{\ell-2} & u_{\ell-3} & \cdots & u_0 \end{bmatrix}$$

Let ℓ_2^m be the Hilbert space of one-sided square-summable sequences equipped with the usual norm. Define the *k-step truncation operator* π_k by

$$\pi_k : \ell_2^m \to \ell_2^m : (u_0, \cdots) \to (u_0, \cdots u_{k-1}, 0, \cdots)$$

In this paper we treat stable, linear, causal operators

$$\Delta : \ell_2 \to \ell_2$$

Througout this paper we shall assume that these operators are relaxed prior to application of the input. The induced 2−norm of such an operator Δ is defined as

$$\|\Delta\|_{i2} = \sup_{u\neq 0} \frac{\|\Delta u\|_2}{\|u\|_2}$$

*Supported by the National Science Foundation under Grant ECS 89-57461, and by gifts from Rockwell International.

† Tel.: (510)642-4642, Email: wufen@erg.berkeley.edu, pack@erg.berkeley.edu, poolla@jagger.berkeley.edu

We now present two results form [6] that we shall require subsequently. The first of these is an extension theorem for linear *time-invariant* operators.

Theorem 2.1
Given sequences $u = \{u_0, u_1, \cdots, u_{\ell-1} \in \mathbf{R}^m\}$ *and* $y = \{y_0, y_1, \cdots, y_{\ell-1} \in \mathbf{R}^p\}$, *there exists a stable, causal, linear and time-invariant operator* Δ *with* $\|\Delta\|_{i2} \leq \gamma$ *and such that*

$$\Delta(u_0, \cdots, u_{\ell-1}, *, \cdots) = (y_0, \cdots, y_{\ell-1}, *, \cdots)$$

iff

$$Y_\ell' Y_\ell \leq \gamma^2 U_\ell' U_\ell$$

where Y_ℓ *and* U_ℓ *are associated block Toeplitz matrices formed by the sequences* u *and* y *respectively.*

We now state an extension theorem for linear *time-varying* operators:

Theorem 2.2
Given sequences $u = \{u_0, u_1, \cdots, u_{\ell-1} \in \mathbf{R}^m\}$ *and* $y = \{y_0, y_1, \cdots, y_{\ell-1} \in \mathbf{R}^p\}$, *there exists a stable, causal, linear and time-varying operator* Δ *with* $\|\Delta\|_{i2} \leq \gamma$ *and such that*

$$\Delta(u_0, \cdots, u_{\ell-1}, *, \cdots) = (y_0, \cdots, y_{\ell-1}, *, \cdots)$$

iff

$$\|\pi_k y\|_2 \leq \gamma \|\pi_k u\|_2 \qquad for \quad k = 0, \cdots, \ell - 1$$

3 Recursive Algorithms

In this section, we offer recursive algorithms for extension problems with linear time-invariant operators and with linear time-varying operators. As indicated in Section 1, these algorithms may be used for on-line model validation for a class of uncertainty models. Throughout we assume (without loss of generality) that $u_0 \neq 0$ and that $\gamma = 1$.

3.1 Linear Time-invariant operators

In this section, we limit our attention to *single-input single-output* stable, causal, linear time invariant operators.

The problem we consider is as follows. We are given the input- output data record $u_i, y_i : i = 0, \cdots, k-1$. We shall call the data record *admissible* if there exists an operator Δ with $\|\Delta\|_{i2} \leq 1$ that could have produced the given data record. We wish to determine recusively whether or not the given data record is admissible.

To this end, observe that from this data record we can *uniquely* deduce $h_0, \cdots, h_{k-1}$ where $\{h_0, h_1, \cdots\}$ is the impulse response of Δ. It is straightforward to verify from Theorem (2.1) that the data record is admissible iff

$$X_k = I - H_k' H_k \geq 0$$

where H_k is the lower Toeplitz matrix formed from $h_0, \cdots, h_{k-1}$. We can exploit the Toeplitz structure of H_k to arrive at the following algorithm for testing the positivity of X_k.

---

0. Initialize: $k = 0$, $v_0 = s_0 = t_0 = [\,]$, $\beta_0 = \frac{y_0}{u_0}$, $p_0 = 1 - \beta_0^2$

1. Test for Positivity: If $|\beta_k| > 1$ exit : *model is invalidated.*

2. Compute new Markov parameter:

$$h_{k+1} = \frac{1}{u_0}\left[y_{k+1} - \sum_{i=0}^{k} h_i u_{k+1-i}\right]$$

3. Update variables:

$$\begin{aligned}
\beta_{k+1} &= \frac{h_{k+1} + v_k' s_k}{p_k} \\
v_{k+1} &= \begin{bmatrix} v_k \\ h_{k+1} \end{bmatrix} \\
t_{k+1} &= \begin{bmatrix} t_k \\ 0 \end{bmatrix} + \beta_{k+1} \begin{bmatrix} s_k \\ 1 \end{bmatrix} \\
s_{k+1} &= \begin{bmatrix} 0 \\ s_k \end{bmatrix} + \beta_{k+1} \begin{bmatrix} h_0 \\ t_k \end{bmatrix} \\
p_{k+1} &= \left(1 - \beta_{k+1}^2\right) p_k
\end{aligned}$$

4. Increment k and return to Step 1.

Remark 3.3 The above scheme is related to the Levinson recursion algorithm (see [4]). The variables β_k play a role analogous to the Schur reflection coefficients.

As is well-known (see for example [3]), the set of admissable h_{k+1} such that $X_{k+2} \geq 0$ form a disc in the complex plane. This disc is centered at $-v_k' s_k$ and has radius p_k. There are available expressions for the center and radius of this disc. However, these expressions are not well-suited for recursion.

Remark 3.4 The above recursive algorithm requires $4k + O(1)$ flops at the $k-$th step of the recursion. Thus, at the end of the $k-$th step we used $2k^2 + O(k)$ flops for checking the positivity of the k by k symmetric matrix $(I - H_k' H_k)$. In contrast, positivity checking via the QR algorithm will require approximately k^3 flops (see [2]). The difference, of course, is because we exploit the Toeplitz structure of H_k in our algorithm.

We intend to conduct a backward sensitivity analysis of the recursive scheme presented above.

Remark 3.5 The above scheme treats *single-input single-output* operators Δ. Given the first k Markov parameter (matrices) of a multivariable operator Δ, set of admissable h_{k+1} such that $X_{k+2} \geq 0$ form a disc

$$\left\{C_k + L_k^{-1}\phi R_k^{-1} : \ \bar{\sigma}[\phi] \leq 1\right\}$$

Here C_k is the center of the disc, while $L_k > 0$ and $R_k > 0$ are the left and right radii of the disc. Again there are available expressions for C_k, L_k, R_k from which one could probably obtain a recursive positivity check.

A substantially more serious problem is the following. In the multivariable case we cannot *uniquely* deduce the Markov parameters $h_0, \cdots, h_{k-1}$ from the input-output data record. We are therefore compelled to work directly with the input-output data and employ the positivity test $U_\ell' U_\ell - Y_\ell' Y_\ell \geq 0$ as in Theorem (2.1). This test is not as readily amenable to recursion.

3.2 Linear Time-varying operators

The situation here is straightforward, even in the multivariable case. Using Theorem (2.2) we can immediately get the following simple, recursive scheme for the associated extension problem:

---

0. Initialize: $k = 0, \ p_0 = \|u_0\|_2^2 - \|y_0\|_2^2$
1. Test for Positivity: If $p_k < 0$ exit : *model is invalidated.*
2. Update the variables:

$$p_{k+1} = p_k + \|u_{k+1}\|_2^2 - \|y_{k+1}\|_2^2$$

3. Increment k and return to Step 1.

---

4 Conclusions

In this paper, we have developed recursive methods for certain extension problems. These methods can be used for on-line model validation for a class of uncertainty models.

We can also consider model validation problems (and the associated extension problems) for linear systems with the induced ∞−norm. For time-varying systems a recursive algorithm is immediate. However, for time- invariant systems, the associated extension problem reduces to linear programming and we feel that a recursive technique is unlikely to exist.

The challenge is to develop recursive methods for model validation of uncertainty models that accomodate some combination of the following factors: slow time-variation, uncertainty in initial conditions, and measurement noise. This is essential in order to develop a methodology for practical model validation.

References

[1] L. Ljung, *System Identification;Theory for the User*, Prentice-Hall, Englewood Cliffs, New Jersey, 1987.

[2] G. H. Golub, C. F. Van Loan, *Matrix Computations*, Johns Hopkins University Press, Baltimore, 1989.

[3] M. G. Krein and A. A. Nudelman, *The Markov Moment Problem and Extremal Problems*, AMS, Providence, 1977.

[4] N. Levinson, "The Wiener RMS Error Criterion in Filter Design and Prediction," *J. Math. Phys.*, vol. 25, pp.261-278, 1947.

[5] A. Packard, J. Doyle, "The Complex Structured Singular Value," 1992.

[6] K. Poolla, P. P. Khargonekar, A. Tikku, J. Krause and K. M. Nagpal, "A Time-Domain Approach to Model Validation," *Proc. of the 1992 Amer. Contr. Conf.*, Chicago, ILL, pp.313-317, 1992.

[7] R. Smith, Ph. D. Dissertation, Caltech, 1990.

[8] R. Smith and J. C. Doyle, "Towards a methodology for robust parameter identification," *Proc. of the 1990 Amer. Contr. Conf.*, San Diego, CA, pp.2394-2399, 1990.

[9] A. H. Sayed, T. Constantinescu and T. Kailath, "Lattice Structures for Time-invariant Interpolation problems," *Proc. of 1992 Contr. Dec. Conf.*, 1992.

Proceedings of the
American Control Conference
San Francisco, California • June 1993

Fault Diagnosis in an Oil Production Plant Prototype Using a Diagnostic Model Processor

Alexandre C. Dias, Amit Bhaya*and Eugenius Kaszkurewicz

Dept. of Elect. Eng. and Parallel Computing Center
Federal University of Rio de Janeiro
COPPE/UFRJ - P.O. Box 68504
21945-970 Rio de Janeiro, RJ - Brazil
E-mail: NA.BHAYA@NA-NET.ORNL.GOV

Abstract

This paper describes an implementation of the Diagnostic Model Processor methodology for fault analysis of a gas-oil separation stage derived from the design of a real oil production plant in an offshore platform. The theory of the method is reviewed and two examples of the diagnostic system's performance are given. One of the examples exposes some problems of the method when applied to a process with few sensors. Some suggestions for improvements are considered, specially with respect to the multiple fault identification problem. The prototype system studied was supplied with data from a simulator and was operated off-line.

1. Introduction

One of the major problems in the process of separation of petroleum extracted in oilrigs is to maintain production within an acceptable range. In view of this, it is necessary that any failure that occurs during the operation be identified and corrected as fast as possible, in order to keep the process in the normal steady state. This is an important motivation for the study and implementation of diagnostic systems that assist operators of such plants.

The aim of this paper is to describe the application of the Diagnostic Model Processor methodology, as presented in [4], to a prototype oil separation process, with the goal of achieving reliability and speed in fault diagnosis. Furthermore, whenever possible, the diagnostic system attempts to arrange the search for faults in order of priority.

Diagnostic systems can, broadly speaking, be classified according to the following features:

a) The form of knowledge representation: knowledge about the system can be rule-based or model-based. In the first case, there is some difficulty in eliciting knowledge from the expert, because it is usually hard for an expert to codify his knowledge in the form of rules. In addition, a rule-based implementation requires an inference engine [1]. In the second case, it is necessary to have process models available, and this is not always possible;

b) Type of knowledge: the knowledge about the system may only represent a direct relation between observed symptoms and causes –this is referred to as shallow knowledge– or may consider cause-effect relations among the process elements (deep-knowledge);

c) The form of data representation: process data can be used qualitatively, increasing the speed with which the conclusions are reached, but losing more precise numerical information. On the other hand, the data can be dealt with quantitatively: this furnishes more detailed process information with a correspondingly higher computational cost.

According to this classification, the Diagnostic Model Processor methodology uses a model-based system with deep-knowledge and quantitative analysis. This kind of diagnostic system is applicable to the oil separation process, which has sensors allowing quantitative measures of several variables and for which mathematical models are available for some components [2].

2. Description of the Oil Separation Process

The fluid pumped up from the seabed consists of a mixture of natural gas, oil (petroleum), water and solid impurities such as sand. The objective of the separation process is to extract natural gas and petroleum, reasonably free of impurities, from the mixture.

The prototype plant is composed of an oil separation stage which, in turn, has two stages of passage through in separator vessels, as shown in figure 1. The gas is separated out, also in two steps, by heating of the petroleum. The following process variables are controlled: petroleum temperature, level and pressure in the two vessels and the outflow from the second vessel. All controllers are proportional-integral (PI), except the temperature controller which is PID.

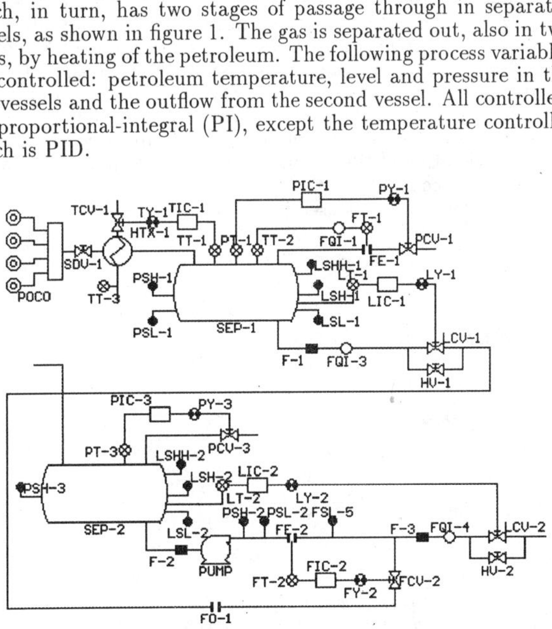

Figure 1 - The Oil Separation Process

In brief, the process works as follows: after passing through the normally open shutdown valve SDV-1, the petroleum extracted is heated by hot water in the heat-exchanger HTX-1. It then goes to the vessel SEP-1, where the initial separation between oil and gas is performed. The gas is exported through the pipe leaving the top of SEP-1 while the oil goes to the second separator vessel, SEP-2. The entering petroleum temperature is controlled indirectly by the valve TCV-1 that regulates the hot water flow. The gas pressure and the oil level are controlled, respectively, by the openings of

---

*Corresponding author. This research was partially supported by research grants from CNPq, the Brazilian National Council for Scientific and Technological Research.

the valves PCV-1 and LCV-1. The final separation between the oil and the gas is carried out in SEP-2. Gas pressure (PCV-3) and oil level (LCV-2) are controlled. Flow control maintains a minimum oil flow through the pump. If this flow is too low, the valve FCV-2 opens, allowing oil recirculation.

All the controllers, sensors and integrators are connected to a process data acquisition network, which provides the diagnostic system with the following data:

- Output, input and error signals of the controllers
- Parameters and states of the controllers
- Output signals of the sensors
- Output signals and states of the integrators
- Pump state (on or off)

3. The Diagnostic Model Processor Methodology

In this section, we follow [4] closely and give a rapid review of the Diagnostic Model Processor (DMP) methodology. It is based on observation of the behavior of a set of so-called residual equations extracted from the process. These equations should evaluate to zero at any instant in which the system is in normal operation and steady state.

When the value of an equation becomes different from zero, the existence of a problem in the process is indicated, because the system has left the normal state. To avoid wrong conclusions about the violation of the equations, a tolerance value is associated with each equation. This tolerance allows the operator to distinguish between small variations on the residuals (caused by measurement noise or modeling errors) and larger variations, presumably caused by faults.

A set of assumptions that, whenever satisfied, guarantees zero values of the residuals is also needed. Thus, if the sensitivity of each residual to each assumption is known, it is possible to draw some conclusions about the possibility of violation of an assumption, by analysis of the non-zero residuals. If there are many non-zero residuals with non-zero sensitivity to a certain assumption, the violation of this assumption is likely to have been caused by the fault occurring in the system.

The basic equations used in the methodology are of the type:

$$e_j = c_j(A, D) \tag{1}$$

where

- A : assumptions $(a_1, a_2, ..., a_i, ...)$
- D : system data
- e_j : j-*th* residual equation

$$sf_j = sgn(e_j)\frac{|e_j/\tau_j|^n}{1+|e_j/\tau_j|^n} \tag{2}$$

where

- $sgn(x) = \begin{cases} -1 & x<0 \\ 0 & x=0 \\ 1 & x>0 \end{cases}$
- τ_j : tolerance
- sf_j : violation level that indicates the degree to which the equation c_j is satisfied (0: perfectly satisfied; -1,$+1$: severely violated low and high, respectively)

$$S_{ij} = \frac{1}{\tau_j}\frac{\partial c_j}{\partial a_i} \tag{3}$$

where it is assumed that some consistent meaning can be attached to the symbols $\frac{\partial c_j}{\partial a_i}$ and

- S_{ij} : sensitivity of c_j with respect to assumption a_i

$$P_i = \frac{\sum_{j=1}^{N}(S_{ij}\ sf_j)}{\sum_{j=1}^{N}|S_{ij}|} \tag{4}$$

where

- P_i : likelihood of violation of the assumption a_i

It should be observed that P_i is not a probability, because it has a sign and yields only comparative information on the chances of a fault to be the cause of the situation observed in the system. So, P_i is treated as a "likelihood".

Moreover, it is possible to create new equations from the initial set, so that they become independent of a given fault. This is useful because if the new residual is zero, while the others are non-zero, the likelihood of violation of the assumptions associated to this residual is reduced, as can be deduced from the formulas above. The creation of new equations can be done as follows:

$$e_{jk;i} = e_j - \frac{\partial c_j/\partial a_i}{\partial c_k/\partial a_i}\, e_k \tag{5}$$

$$\tau_{jk;i} = \tau_j + \left|\frac{\partial c_j/\partial a_i}{\partial c_k/\partial a_i}\right|\, \tau_k \tag{6}$$

$$\frac{\partial c_{jk;i}}{\partial a_l} = \frac{\partial c_j}{\partial a_l} - \frac{\partial c_j/\partial a_i}{\partial c_k/\partial a_i}\frac{\partial c_k}{\partial a_l} \tag{7}$$

where

- $c_{jk;i}$: equation created from the equations c_j and c_k and independent of the assumption a_i

Assuming that it is possible to evaluate a quantitative variation in the assumption a_i, this variation will cause a change in the value of $c_j(\cdot)$, represented by the residual e_j, as follows:

$$\Delta a_i \quad \longrightarrow \quad e_j$$

Calculating the first order partial derivatives, we have the following approximation:

$$\Delta a_i \quad \rightarrow \quad e_j = \frac{\partial c_j}{\partial a_i}\,\Delta a_i \quad \Rightarrow \quad \Delta a_i = \frac{e_j}{\partial c_j/\partial a_i}$$

In case equations $c_j(\cdot)$ and $c_k(\cdot)$ are dependent on a_i :

$$e_j = \frac{\partial c_j}{\partial a_i}\,\Delta a_i,\ e_k = \frac{\partial c_k}{\partial a_i}\,\Delta a_i \quad \Rightarrow \quad e_j = \frac{\partial c_j/\partial a_i}{\partial c_k/\partial a_i}\, e_k$$

Thus,

$$\frac{\partial c_{jk;i}(\cdot)}{\partial a_l} = \frac{\partial c_j(\cdot)}{\partial a_l} - \frac{\partial c_j/\partial a_i}{\partial c_k/\partial a_i}\frac{\partial c_k(\cdot)}{\partial a_l}$$

is independent of a_i, since any variation of e_j caused by a variation of a_i will be compensated by the variation of e_k, multiplied by a scale factor and subtracted from e_j.

This result can also be formalized using the implicit function theorem.

The method also yields a priori estimate of the likelihood of multiple faults when only a single fault actually occurs. This is done using the comparison matrix [4] (analogous to a correlation matrix), calculated as:

$$C_{ik} = \sum_{j=1}^{N}\frac{(sig_{kj}\ sig_{ij})}{max\{sig_i\}} \tag{8}$$

where

- $sig_{ij} = \frac{S_{ij}}{\sum_{j=1}^{N} |S_{ij}|}$, the significance of the model equation c_j to the diagnosis of the fault a_i

- C_{ik} : Likelihood of diagnosing violation of a_k when the assumption truly violated is a_i

In order for the violation of a_i to be diagnosed exactly, without multiple diagnoses, it is necessary that the i-*th* row of (C_{ij}) has all elements practically zero, except C_{ii}, which is equal to +1. In other words, a diagonally dominant matrix C is associated to a good fault separation, and a diagonal matrix C reflects the ideal situation of totally decoupled faults.

4. The DMP applied to a Prototype Gas-Oil Separation Process

As can be observed in figure 1, there are sensors to measure level and pressure in the vessels (LT-1, PT-1, LT-2 and PT-3), oil and hot water temperature (TT-1 and TT-3), oil outflow from the vessels (FQI-3 and FT-2) and oil exportation flow (FQI-4). This relatively small number of measurements does not allow the use of several model and balance equations, such as balance in the first vessel (gas and oil inflow are not measured). Thus, simpler equations are used (steady-state equations). These equations evaluate to zero when the system is in steady-state. However, the use of these equations requires the knowledge of the steady state values of several process variables, such as the output signals and controller states.

The equations used were:

$$
\begin{aligned}
e_1 &= 3600\frac{dV_{oSEP-1}}{dt} + Q_{FQI-3} - Qin_{exp} \\
e_2 &= Q_{FQI-3} + Q_{ADIT} + 3600\frac{dV_{oSEP-2}}{dt} - Q_{FQI-4} \\
e_3 &= Q_{FQI-3} + Q_{ADIT} - Q_{FQI-4} \\
e_4 &= SP_{LIC-1} - SP_{LIC-1_{exp}} \\
e_5 &= Y_{LIC-1} - Y_{LIC-1_{calc}} \\
e_6 &= Y_{LIC-1} - Y_{LIC-1_{exp}} \\
e_7 &= SP_{PIC-1} - SP_{PIC-1_{exp}} \\
e_8 &= Y_{PIC-1} - Y_{PIC-1_{calc}} \\
e_9 &= Y_{PIC-1} - Y_{PIC-1_{exp}} \\
e_{10} &= SP_{TIC-1} - SP_{TIC-1_{exp}} \\
e_{11} &= Y_{TIC-1} - Y_{TIC-1_{calc}} \\
e_{12} &= Y_{TIC-1} - Y_{TIC-1_{exp}} \\
e_{13} &= SP_{LIC-2} - SP_{LIC-2_{exp}} \\
e_{14} &= Y_{LIC-2} - Y_{LIC-2_{calc}} \\
e_{15} &= Y_{LIC-2} - Y_{LIC-2_{exp}} \\
e_{16} &= SP_{PIC-3} - SP_{PIC-3_{exp}} \\
e_{17} &= Y_{PIC-3} - Y_{PIC-3_{calc}} \\
e_{18} &= Y_{PIC-3} - Y_{PIC-3_{exp}} \\
e_{19} &= SP_{FIC-2} - SP_{FIC-2_{exp}} \\
e_{20} &= Y_{FIC-2} - Y_{FIC-2_{calc}} \\
e_{21} &= Y_{FIC-2} - Y_{FIC-2_{exp}} \\
e_{22} &= Q_{FQI-3} - Q_{LCV-1} \\
e_{23} &= Q_{FQI-1} - Q_{PCV-1} \\
e_{24} &= L_{LT-1} - L_{LT-1_{exp}} \\
e_{25} &= P_{PT-1} - P_{PT-1_{exp}} \\
e_{26} &= T_{TT-1} - T_{TT-1_{exp}} \\
e_{27} &= L_{LT-2} - L_{LT-2_{exp}} \\
e_{28} &= P_{PT-3} - P_{PT-3_{exp}} \\
e_{29} &= T_{TT-3} - T_{TT-3_{exp}} \\
e_{30} &= Q_{FQI-3} - Q_{FQI-3_{exp}} \\
e_{31} &= Q_{FQI-4} - Q_{FQI-4_{exp}} \\
e_{32} &= Q_{FE-2} - Q_{FQI-4_{exp}} \\
e_{33} &= Q_{FE-2} - Q_{FQI-4} \\
e_{34} &= \frac{dL_{LT-1}}{dt} \\
e_{35} &= \frac{dP_{PT-1}}{dt} \\
e_{36} &= \frac{dT_{TT-1}}{dt} \\
e_{37} &= \frac{dL_{LT-2}}{dt} \\
e_{38} &= \frac{dT_{TT-3}}{dt}
\end{aligned}
$$

where:

- V_{oSEP-1}, V_{oSEP-2} : oil volume in the vessels, calculated from the oil level in the vessel and its geometric model

- Qin_{exp} : expected oil inflow to the oil well

- Q_{ADIT} : additional oil inflow to the second vessel

- $SP_{LIC-1_{exp}}$, $SP_{PIC-1_{exp}}$, $SP_{TIC-1_{exp}}$, $SP_{LIC-2_{exp}}$, $SP_{PIC-3_{exp}}$, $SP_{FIC-2_{exp}}$: expected values of the controller set-points

- $Y_{LIC-1_{calc}}$, $Y_{PIC-1_{calc}}$, $Y_{TIC-1_{calc}}$, $Y_{LIC-2_{calc}}$, $Y_{PIC-3_{calc}}$, $Y_{FIC-2_{calc}}$: calculated values of the controller output signals using discrete models

- $Y_{LIC-1_{exp}}$, $Y_{PIC-1_{exp}}$, $Y_{TIC-1_{exp}}$, $Y_{LIC-2_{exp}}$, $Y_{PIC-3_{exp}}$, $Y_{FIC-2_{exp}}$: expected values of the controller output signals in steady state

- Q_{LCV-1}, Q_{PCV-1} : flow in the valves calculated using the controller signal (from LIC-1 and PIC-1) and dynamic models of the valves

- $L_{LT-1_{exp}}$, $P_{PT-1_{exp}}$, $T_{TT-1_{exp}}$, $L_{LT-2_{exp}}$, $P_{PT-3_{exp}}$, $T_{TT-3_{exp}}$, $Q_{FQI-3_{exp}}$, $Q_{FQI-4_{exp}}$: expected values of the sensor output signals in steady state

- Q_{FE-2} : flow in FE-2 calculated using the FE-2 dynamic model

The assumptions were defined as follows:

$a_1 \ldots a_6$: There is no bias in the output signals of LIC-1, PIC-1, TIC-1, LIC-2, PIC-3 and FIC-2

$a_7 \ldots a_{12}$: The set-points of LIC-1, PIC-1, TIC-1, LIC-2, PIC-3 and FIC-2 are correctly calibrated

a_{13},a_{14} : There is no oil leak in SEP-1 and SEP-2

$a_{15} \ldots a_{20}$: There is no loss of air supply to the pneumatic mechanism of LCV-1, PCV-1, TCV-1, LCV-2, PCV-3 and FCV-2

$a_{21} \ldots a_{26}$: The shafts of LCV-1, PCV-1, TCV-1, LCV-2, PCV-3 and FCV-2 are not stuck

$a_{27} \ldots a_{29}$: The F-1, F-2 and F-3 filters are not partially obstructed

$a_{30} \ldots a_{32}$: The F-1, F-2 and F-3 filters are not totally obstructed

a_{33} : The pump is not cavitating

a_{34} : The pump is not off

a_{35},a_{36} : There is no gas leak in SEP-1 and SEP-2

a_{37},a_{38} : The by-pass valves HV-1 and HV-2 are not open

a_{39} : There is no water to oil leak in HTX-1

a_{40} : There is no incrustation in the tubes of HTX-1

a_{41} : The assumed value of the heat exchange coefficient of HTX-1 is correct

a_{42} : There is no variation of oil production in the oil well

a_{43} : There is no variation of gas production in the oil well

a_{44} : The hot water pressure has not changed

a_{45} : The hot water temperature has not changed

$a_{46} \dots a_{51}$: There is no bias in the output signals of LT-1, PT-1, TT-1, LT-2, PT-3 and TT-3

Obviously, the faults to be diagnosed correspond to the negation of one or more of the assumptions above.

While determining the sensitivity of the equations to these assumptions, some problems were detected with respect to the effects of non-linearities and qualitative faults. As an example, suppose that the LCV-1 valve shaft is stuck. The sensitivity of e_{30} to this assumption (a_{21}) cannot be evaluated using (3) because the fault "The shaft of LCV-1 is stuck" cannot be modeled quantitatively, since the shaft may be stuck in an arbitrary position. Another relevant example is incorrect calibration of the FIC-2 set-point. Since the controller is used to guarantee a minimal outflow from SEP-2, it usually operates in a saturated state. Thus, in order to have recirculation so that e_{33} evaluates to a non zero value, it is necessary that the outflow of SEP-2 fall to a value lower than some minimal value. Thus, the sensitivity of e_{33} to a_{12} is non-zero only if $Q_{FE-2} < Q_{FE-2_{min}}$, implying the existence of a non-linearity.

In case of an equation c_j that is not "differentiable" with respect to an assumption, the following heuristic procedure was adopted: the effects of the fault in the 38 equations implemented were simulated. For the equations violated (residuals close to +1 or −1), sensitivity values +1 or −1 are assigned, depending on the residual signals. This is followed by a tuning of the values in accordance with the results of validation tests of the diagnostic system.

Two examples of system diagnoses are presented below, using the rule that faults with $P_i > 0.5$ are the more likely ones.

Diagnosis for the fault "Bias in the input signal of PIC-1"

This is an example where the system is able to diagnose the fault exactly. The likelihood of the fault quickly increases to a positive value close to +1, while the other fault likelihoods are very small, as can be seen in figure 2.

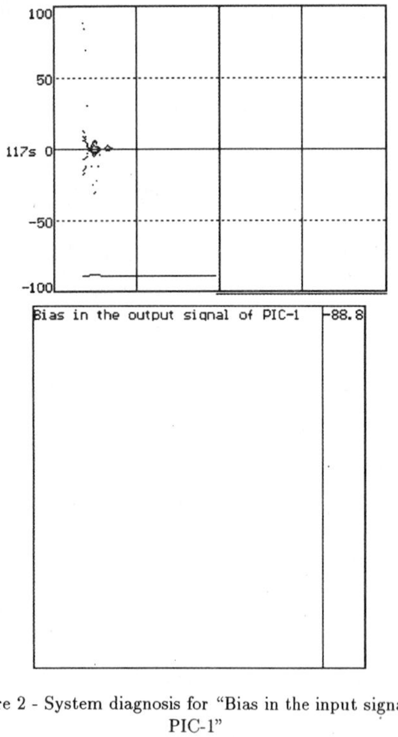

Figure 2 - System diagnosis for "Bias in the input signal of PIC-1"

Diagnosis for the fault "Loss of air supply to the pneumatic mechanism of LCV-2"

In this case, the system is unable to identify exactly which fault occurs in the process. This is caused by an insufficient number of sensors as shown in figure 3, that allow only a reduced number of equations to be used in the diagnosis. However, all the faults diagnosed by the system might actually be occurring in the process, given the perturbations observed. Due to the loss of air to the pneumatic mechanism of LCV-2, this valve is ramped closed. This causes a fall of oil outflow from SEP-2, which sets off the opening of the FCV-2 recirculation valve. This oil recirculation causes, in turn, an increase of the oil level in SEP-2. All these consequences can be generated, to a greater or lesser degree, by the faults that the diagnostic system calculates as having high likelihoods. In the cases of the pump turning off and partial obstruction of F-3, the consequences are the same, given the analysis allowed by the sensors. In the case of loss of air supply to FCV-2, this valve will be ramped open, allowing oil recirculation. In the case of an water to oil leak in HTX-1, there will be a change in the steady-state value of the measurement of FQI-4 (e_{31}). The same will happen in the case of the set-point of LIC-2 are not correctly calibrated or in the case of variation of oil production.

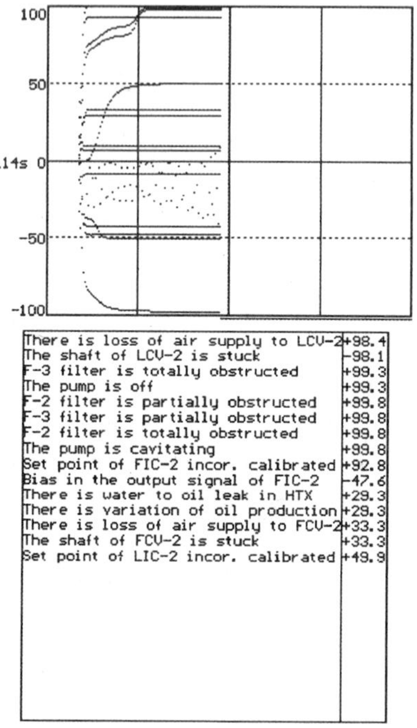

Figure 3 - System diagnosis for "Loss of air supply to the pneumatic mechanism of LCV-2"

5. Discussion and Concluding Remarks

The performance of the Diagnostic Model Processor methodology is adversely affected mainly by an insufficient number of sensors in the prototype process studied. This lack of sensors prevents the use of several component models (as in the case of valves for which it is necessary to know the values of the inlet and outlet pressures to be able to evaluate the flow) that form the base of the set of equations cited in [4] and also prevents the use of redundancy equations [5]. In fact, as can be observed from the equations $e_1 \dots e_{33}$, it is only possible to carry out the oil mass balance in the second vessel and to use the mathematical models of the valves LCV-1 and PCV-1 and of the controllers.

To get around this problem, simpler equations, called steady-state equations, are set up to indicate whether the process is operating in steady-state or not. However, this modification requires the knowledge of the state variables of the process in steady-state and also assumes that the process is kept in a fixed operating point, i.e. the process always receives and refines the same quantity of gas and oil (which is not true in most cases). In case of a big change in the process operating point, it may become necessary to tune the diagnostic system for the new steady-state.

Another limitation of the method is the necessity of a dynamic simulator that yields simulated values for the sensor and system variables, so that it is possible to evaluate the sensitivities that cannot be calculated mathematically and to help in the validation of the diagnostic system. The simulator is useful because it is usually impossible to provoke all possible faults in the process, just in order to observe the results and evaluate sensitivities. An alternative that would reduce simulator use would be to use log-files that contain available system data for observed operating modes of the system (normal and faulted modes).

In some cases, the system produces multiple diagnoses when only one fault occurs (this is the case in example 2: loss of air supply to the pneumatic mechanism of LCV-2). However, all the faults identified can, in greater or lesser degree, cause the observed state of the process. Moreover, the value of P_i for the true fault is very high indicating that the system manages to identify this fault (in example 2 it is equal, in modulus, to the value of P_i of the faults "filter F-3 partially obstructed" and "Pump off", because these faults can not be distinguished from the true fault due to the lack of sensors), correctly ordering the fault search by the operator in order of priority.

Two options to minimize the problem of multiple diagnoses are being studied. The first is the insertion of rules in the diagnostic process. These rules are activated whenever it is necessary to decide between diagnoses, and make use of experience and/or heuristics. A good example is the fault "variation (reduction) of oil production from the oil well", that is diagnosed to have the same likelihood as a negative oil leak in the first vessel. Since it is impossible to have a negative leak, this ambiguity can be resolved by a rule. Another alternative is the creation of new residual equations -this idea was mentioned in [3]. As an example, consider a case in which, at a given instant,

$$(S_{ij}) = \begin{bmatrix} 1 & 1 & 1 \\ 1 & 1 & 0 \end{bmatrix}, \; sf_1 = sf_2 = sf_3 = 1 \quad \Rightarrow \quad P_1 = P_2 = 1$$

The situation above shows that, although the assumption a_2 cannot cause the violation of e_3 (since $S_{13} = 0$), it has the same likelihood as a_1 which can cause the violation of the three equations. To create a difference between P_1 and P_2, we can include the new equation:

$$sf_4 = sf_1 \; sf_2 \; (1 - |sf_3|), \quad (S_{ij}) = \begin{bmatrix} 1 & 1 & 1 & 0 \\ 1 & 1 & 0 & 1 \end{bmatrix}$$

This equation (using sf_1, sf_2 and sf_3 instead of e_1, e_2 and e_3 to normalize the result) emulates the logic equation $sf_4 = sf_1 \wedge sf_2 \wedge \overline{sf_3}$, indicating that P_2 will have a high value only if e_1 and e_2 are violated and e_3 is not. With this new equation, P_1=1 and P_2=0.67, which reflects the actual situation better.

It is clear that the two faults can occur simultaneously and thus P_1= P_2=1 could be the best diagnosis. However, the use of the new equation, with the right adjustment of S_{24}, does not exclude the possibility of occurrence of a second fault, but only furnishes an order of priority for the search.

References

[1] Chester, D., Lamb, D. and Dhurjati, P., "Rule-Based Computer Alarm Analysis in Chemical Process Plants", *Annual Micro-Delcon*, March, pp.22-29, 1984.

[2] Giozza, W. F., "Simulation of Gas-Oil Separator Behavior under Flow Condition", Master's Thesis, University of Tulsa, Oklahoma, 1983.

[3] Petti, T. F. and Dhurjati, P. S., "Object-Based Automated Fault Diagnosis", *Chem. Eng. Comm.*, vol. 102, pp.107-126, 1991.

[4] Petti, T. F., Klein, J. and Dhurjati, P. S., "Diagnostic Model Processor: Using Deep Knowledge for Process Fault Diagnosis", *AIChE J.*, vol. 36, No. 4, pp.565-575, 1990.

[5] Surgenor, B. W. and Jofriet, P. J., "Thermal Fault Analysis and the Diagnostic Model Processor", *IFAC Symposium On-Line Fault Detection and Supervision in the Chemical Process Industries*, Newark, Delaware, USA, April, pp.20-25, 1992.

Proceedings of the
American Control Conference
San Francisco, California • June 1993

LIMITS ON ACHIEVABLE ROBUSTNESS AGAINST COPRIME FACTOR UNCERTAINTY

Laurie Christian
MS NP-2L
P.O. Box 800
Princeton, NJ 08543
lchristi@astro.ge.com

Jim Freudenberg
EECS Department
University of Michigan
Ann Arbor MI 48109-2122
jfr@eecs.umich.edu
(313) 763-0586

ABSTRACT

We consider the problem of robustness optimization against normalized coprime factor uncertainty in single-input, single-output systems. We show that loop shapes known from classical analysis to be inconsistent with closed-loop robust stability will tend to have poor optimal robustness. Such loop shapes include those with a high crossover frequency relative to a nonminimum phase zero, a low crossover frequency relative to an unstable pole, or a rapid rolloff rate near gain crossover. Our results consist of a set of lower bounds on the optimal cost of the robustness optimization problem, each lower bound being appropriate to one of these three problematic loop shapes. The lower bounds are derived using the Poisson integral, and display the qualitative relationship between the loopshape and the level of optimal robustness.

1. INTRODUCTION

In recent years, the problem of optimizing robustness in closed-loop systems against additive perturbations to the plant coprime factors has received much attention. Vidyasagar and Kimura [ViK86] have shown that finding a robustly stabilizing controller for the above problem reduces to solving an H_∞ optimization problem. Glover and McFarlane [GlM89] linked the H_∞ optimization problem to the Nehari extension problem and, by using the normalized coprime factorization of the plant, derived a state-space solution that avoids the iterative methods usually required for H_∞ controller synthesis. These authors introduce a design methodology in [MFG90] that blends classical and multivariable loop shaping and robust optimization techniques. Georgiou and Smith [GeS90] show that optimizing robustness for normalized coprime factor uncertainty is equivalent to optimizing robustness in the gap metric.

Our work is motivated by the design methodology introduced by McFarlane and Glover [MFG90]. Their design procedure combines loop shaping techniques from classical control with H_∞ synthesis to optimize robustness against coprime factor uncertainty. Briefly, the design procedure consists of two stages; we summarize for a single input, single output plant. First, the Bode magnitude plot of the nominal plant is modified by a compensator to achieve a loop shape that reflects the desired design goals; usually, high gain at low frequencies for small sensitivity and low gain at high frequencies for small complementary sensitivity. This step is performed without regard to the plant phase, and hence to nominal stability and gain/phase margins. We will call the result of this step the *desired* loop shape. Second, an H_∞ optimal controller is synthesized for the shaped plant to achieve stabilization and to optimize robustness against coprime factor uncertainty. We will call the result of this step the *achieved* loop shape. In general, the achieved loop shape may deviate significantly from the desired loop shape. McFarlane and Glover [MFG90, pp.106-118] interpret the optimal cost of the H_∞ synthesis problem as an indicator of the compatibility of the desired loop shape with closed-loop stability requirements. They show that the discrepancy between the achieved and desired loop shapes at a given frequency is determined by the controller gain at that frequency. The controller gain, in turn, is bounded as a function of the optimal cost. If the optimal cost is small, then the achieved loop shape will be close to the desired loop shape. If the optimal cost is large, then the achieved loop shape will deviate from the desired loop shape. Since a large optimal cost corresponds to a small stability margin, the authors interpret the deterioration in the desired loop shape, and thus the value of the optimal cost, as an indication of the compatibility of the loop shape with robust closed-loop stability.

In this paper, we study the relation between the value of the optimal cost and the compatibility of the desired loop shape with closed-loop stability. Restricting our attention to single-input, single-output systems allows us to study this problem using classical analysis techniques. From classical results, we know that certain loop shapes are incompatible with satisfactory closed-loop properties. These include loops with

(i) a high crossover frequency relative to the location of a nonminimum phase zero,

(ii) a low crossover frequency relative to the location of an unstable pole,

(iii) a rapid rolloff rate near gain crossover frequency.

To explore the dependence between the optimal cost and the desired loop shape, we will derive, for a given desired loop shape, three lower bounds on the optimal cost. If any of these lower bounds is large, then the desired loop shape is inconsistent with closed-loop robust stability requirements. Hence, as observed in [MFG90], the achieved loop shape will deviate significantly from the desired loopshape. These bounds are useful in identifying the reasons why the desired loop shape is incompatible with closed-loop stability, and give insight into tradeoffs between conflicting design goals.

We emphasize that the utility of our bounds lies in the proof they provide that certain loopshapes are incompatible with closed loop robust stability, and for the qualitative insight they provide into the nature of the incompatibility. By way of contrast, our bounds are more difficult to evaluate than the optimal cost itself; however, the optimal cost does not display the qualitative information contained in the bounds.

2. LOOP SHAPING DESIGN PROCEDURE

We consider a single input, single output (SISO) finite dimensional, linear, time-invariant plant . Denote the transfer function of the plant by G(s), and let [A,B,C,D] be a minimal realization of G(s). Let K(s) denote the compensator transfer function. Define the sensitivity function, $S(s) := (1+G(s)K(s))^{-1}$ and the complementary sensitivity function, $T(s) := G(s)K(s)(1+G(s)K(s))^{-1}$.

We will consider a normalized coprime factorization of the plant [MFG90], $G(s) = M(s)^{-1}N(s)$, where N(s), M(s) $\in H_\infty$ are coprime and satisfy the normalization condition $|N(j\omega)|^2 + |M(j\omega)|^2 = 1$. Suppose that the coprime factors of the true plant are perturbed versions of those of the nominal plant: $G_\Delta(s) = (M(s) + \Delta_M(s))^{-1}(N(s) + \Delta_N(s))$, where the uncertainty matrix $\Delta(s) := [\ \Delta_N(s)\ \ \Delta_M(s)\ ]$ satisfies $\Delta(s) \in RH_\infty$ and $\|\Delta\|_\infty < \varepsilon$ [MFG90, pp 29, 51]. The robustness optimization problem we consider is to design a stabilizing controller K(s) that maximizes the amount of coprime factor uncertainty the nominal sytem can tolerate without going unstable. As explained in [MFG90, p.52], this optimization problem is equivalent to that of minimizing the H_∞ norm of the mixed sensitivity function

$$S_{mixed}(s) := \begin{bmatrix} K(1+GK)^{-1}M^{-1} \\ (1+GK)^{-1}M^{-1} \end{bmatrix} = \begin{bmatrix} KSM^{-1} \\ SM^{-1} \end{bmatrix} \quad (2.1)$$

Lemma 2.1[MFG90]: The system $G_\Delta = (M + \Delta_M)^{-1}(N + \Delta_N)$ is stabilized by the controller K for all $\|\Delta\|_\infty < \varepsilon$ if and only if (1) K stabilizes G , and (2) $\gamma := \| S_{mixed} \|_\infty < 1/\varepsilon$. Moreover, the maximum level of uncertainty that can be tolerated is given by $\varepsilon_{max} = 1/\gamma_{opt}$, where

$$\gamma_{opt} = \inf_{K\ stab} \| S_{mixed} \|_\infty \quad (2.2)$$

The value of γ_{opt} can be calculated explicitly as follows:

Lemma 2.2 [MFG90, pp.54-55, 63]

Let G = [A,B,C,D]. Then $\gamma_{opt} = \sqrt{1+\lambda_{max}(ZX)}$, where X and Z are the unique positive definite solutions to certain generalized algebraized Riccati equations. ###

Note that γ_{opt} is bounded below by one. For later reference, we note that γ_{opt} is invariant under a constant 180° change in the phase of G(s).

Lemma 2.3:

Consider G := [A,B,C,D]. Then $\gamma_{opt}(G) = \gamma_{opt}(-G)$. ###

We now describe the loop shaping design procedure of [MFG90] in the special case of a SISO system.

The Loop Shaping Design Procedure [MFG90 p106]

1) Loop Shaping - Use a precompensator, W, to shape the gain of the nominal plant to obtain a desired open loopshape. Combine the nominal plant, G, and the compensator, W, to form the shaped plant, G_S, where $G_S := WG$ and has no hidden unstable modes.

2) Robust Stabilization - Calculate ε_{max}. If $\varepsilon_{max} << 1$, then return to 1) and redefine W. Otherwise, select $\varepsilon \le \varepsilon_{max}$ and use H_∞ synthesis to generate a feedback controller, K_∞, which robustly stabilizes the normalized coprime factorization of G_S against coprime factor uncertainty satisfying $\|\Delta\|_\infty < \varepsilon$.

3) Controller Design - The final feedback controller, K, is constructed by combining the H_∞ controller, K_∞, and the shaping function, W, yielding $K=WK_\infty$.

Note that the role of the weighting functions used in the usual H_∞ synthesis procedure is taken by the precompensator used to shape the plant magnitude to achieve the desired loopshape. Typically, the desired loopshape will have high gain at low frequencies to achieve small sensitivity, and low gain at high frequencies to achieve small complementary sensitivity. *Throughout the rest of the paper we shall assume without loss of generality that W = 1.* Results for the case of a nonidentity weighting follow immediately by replacing G with G_S in the relevant formulas.

For this design procedure to be effective, one must have an understanding of the relation between the desired loopshape and the resulting value of γ_{opt}. Such understanding will be useful in obtaining a desired loopshape that will yield a reasonable value of γ_{opt}, either *a priori*, or via successive iteration. It is clear from the discussion in [MFG90] that desired loopshapes having the one of the characteristics (i)-(iii) listed in Section 1 should tend to yield a large value of γ_{opt}. However, no proof of this statement is presented. It is our goal to present such a proof for each of (i)-(iii).

To derive our bou nds, we shall utilize the Poisson integral.

Lemma 2.4 (Poisson Integral) [DFT92,p.92], [FrL88, p.37]:

Let f(s) be analytic in the closed right-half plane. Then under mild restrictions

$$f(s) = \frac{1}{\pi}\int_{-\infty}^{\infty} f(j\omega)\frac{x}{x^2+(y-\omega)^2}d\omega \quad (2.3)$$

###

We will factor a nonminimum phase, unstable system into a minimum phase, stable portion and two Blaschke products, defined below.

Definition 2.5 [DFT92, p94-95], [FrL88 p32-36]:

Consider a rational transfer function G(s) with poles and zeros in the open right half plane $\{z_i\ ,\ i = 1, ..., N_z\}$ and $\{p_j\ ,\ j = 1, ..., N_p\}$. Define the Blaschke products of nonminimum phase zeros

$$B_z(s) := \prod_{i=1}^{N_z} \frac{z_i-s}{z_i+s} \quad (2.4)$$

and unstable poles

$$B_p(s) := \prod_{j=1}^{N_p} \frac{p_j-s}{p_j+s} \quad (2.5)$$

Then

$$G(s) = G_0(s)B_z(s)B_p^{-1}(s), \quad (2.6)$$

where $G_0(s)$ has no poles or zeros in the ORHP. ###

For later reference, note that each Blaschke product is allpass of unit magnitude, and thus can be viewed as contributing additional phase lag (for a zero) or phase lead (for a pole) without changing the gain of G(s).

3. NONMINIMUM PHASE PLANTS

A standard feedback problem requires disturbance rejection over a low frequency range. This requirement is stated as an upper bound on sensitivity at low frequencies. Equivalently, open loop gain should satisfy a lower bound over this frequency range. It is known that nonminimum phase plants pose a potential difficulty in robustly achieving such a design specification. Specifically, a loop shape achieving small sensitivity (large open loop gain) throughout a low frequency range can be obtained only at the expense of large sensitivity at other frequencies. Since large sensitivity corresponds to the Nyquist plot being close to the critical point, the stability margin of the resulting feedback system will be small. Hence, good feedback properties are obtained at low frequencies at the expense of poor properties at higher frequencies. The location of the nonminimum phase plant zeros relative to the region of small sensitivity plays a crucial role in this tradeoff. Specifically, when the region of small sensitivity extends into the frequency range where the zero contributes significant phase lag, the peak in sensitivity will be larger than when the zero is located outside this region [FrL88, pp.31-44].

Since the design tradeoff just described is inherent in linear time invariant feedback systems, it must manifest itself in the design procedure of [MFG90]. Indeed, an example of a nonminimum phase plant is presented in [MFG90] wherein the authors show that the size of the optimal cost grows as the open loop crossover frequency is increased relative to the location of the zero. We shall now derive a lower bound on γ_{opt} illustrating the relation between the desired loopshape, the nonminimum phase zero location, and the value of the optimal cost.

Theorem 3.1:

Let G(s) be a scalar rational transfer function. Suppose that G(s) has a zero,z, in the open right half plane. Then

$$\gamma_{opt} \geq \gamma_{lower\ bound} ,$$

where

$$\log(\gamma_{lower\ bound}) :=$$

$$\frac{1}{2\pi}\int_0^{\infty}\log(1+|G(j\omega)|^2)W(z,\omega)d\omega - \log|B_p(z)| \qquad (3.1)$$

For real z=x, $W(z,\omega) = \frac{2x}{x^2+\omega^2}$ and for complex z=x+jy, $W(z,\omega) = \frac{x}{x^2+(y-\omega)^2} + \frac{x}{x^2+(y+\omega)^2}$

###

For a given loop shape $|G(j\omega)|$, the lower bound (3.1) may be evaluated directly via numerical integration. It is also instructive to consider an estimate for the bound.

Corollary 3.2:

Let G(s) be a scalar rational transfer function, with a zero, z, in the open right half plane. Suppose that

$$|G(j\omega)| \geq \alpha > 1 \quad , \forall\ \omega \leq \omega_1 .$$

Then

$$\gamma_{opt} \geq (1+\alpha^2)^{W(z,\Omega)/2\pi}\, |B_p^{-1}(z)| , \qquad (3.2)$$

where $\Omega := [0,\omega_1]$, $W(z,\Omega) := \int_0^{\omega_1} W(z,\omega)d\omega$.

###

Theorem 3.1 and Corollary 3.2 show that the lower bound on $\log(\gamma_{opt})$ will be large (1) if G(s) has an unstable pole near a nonminimum phase zero, or (2) if $|G(j\omega)|$ is large over a frequency range that is wide relative to the location of the nonminimum phase zero. Let us elaborate upon the latter condition. In [FrL88], it is shown that for real z = x, $W(z,\Omega) = -\angle\frac{x-j\omega_1}{x+j\omega_1}$, the negative of the phase lag contributed by the term due to the zero in the factorization of the plant (2.6). It follows that γ_{opt} will be large if the region of high gain extends to frequencies at which the zero contributes significant additional phase lag. A similar interpretation holds for complex zeros.

In [MFG90, pp.108-109] an example of a nonminimum phase plant is used to illustrate that the optimal cost increases as the region of large gain extends to high frequency relative to the nonminimum phase zero.We use this example to compare the results of our bound and the value of the optimal cost.

Example 3.3:

Let $G(s) = \frac{k(-1+s)}{s(s+2)}$, where k varies from 0.1 to 20 to vary the the open loop gain crossover frequency. Applying Lemma 2.2 and Theorem 3.1, we calculate γ_{opt} and $\gamma_{lower\ bound}$ for various values of k. The first term in (3.1) was evaluated via numerical integration. Table 3.1 shows that as the crossover frequency increases both γ_{opt} and the lower bound $\gamma_{lower\ bound}$ become large. These results are consistent with those of [MFG90].

TABLE 3.1:
EFFECT OF VARYING k ON γ_{opt} AND $\gamma_{lower\ bound}$

k	ω_0 (rad/sec)	γ_{opt}	$\gamma_{lower\ bound}$
0.1	0.05	1.4676	1.0486
1.0	0.55	1.9850	1.5446
5.0	4.5	4.5945	4.0697
20.0	20.0	14.627	13.9785

Alternately, it is instructive to fix the crossover frequency and vary the location of the zero.

Example 3.4:

Let $G(s) = \frac{30}{s(s+.2)}\frac{(z-s)}{(z+s)}$, where z varies from .01 to 100.Applying Lemma 2.2 and Theorem 3.1, we calculate γ_{opt} and $\gamma_{lower\ bound}$ for different values of z. Figure 3.1 shows that γ_{opt} and $\gamma_{lower\ bound}$ both become large as the zero decreases relative to the open-loop gain crossover frequency of 5 rad/sec .

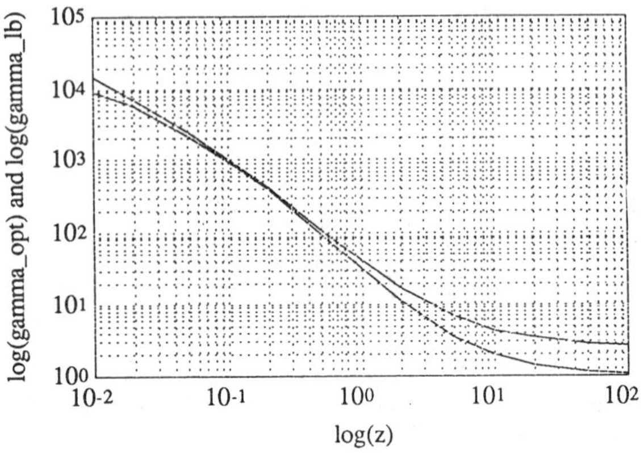

FIGURE 3.1: γ_{opt} and $\gamma_{lower\ bound}$ vs zero location

The results of this section describe show that the well-known design limitations and tradeoffs due to nonminimum phase zeros manifest themselves in the loop shaping design procedure of [MFG90].

4. UNSTABLE PLANTS

When a system to be controlled is open loop unstable, classical design rules indicate that the loop gain should be shaped so that gain crossover frequency is at least as large as the radius of the unstable poles (cf [LoF91]). Since realistic feedback problems also include bandwidth constraints, this fact may lead to design conflicts. Specifically, when complementary sensitivity (and thus open loop gain) is required to be small at frequencies that are relatively low with relation to the radius of the unstable poles, then there is necessarily a large peak in complementary sensitivity at lower frequencies. Mathematically, this phenomenon is dual to the tradeoff associated with nonminimum phase zeros described in Section 3. We shall now derive a lower bound on γ_{opt} showing that if the gain of the desired loop shape is too low with respect to the pole location, then the value of the optimal cost will be large.

Theorem 4.1:

Let G(s) be a scalar rational transfer function. Suppose that G(s) has a pole, p, in the open right half plane. Then

$$\gamma_{opt} \geq \gamma_{lower\ bound}$$

where

$$\log(\gamma_{lower\ bound}) =$$

$$\frac{1}{2\pi}\int_0^{\infty}\log\left(1+\frac{1}{|G(j\omega)|^2}\right)W(p,\omega)d\omega - \log|B_z(p)| \qquad (4.1)$$

For real p=x, $W(p,\omega) = \frac{2x}{x^2+\omega^2}$ and for complex p=x+jy, $W(p,\omega) = \frac{x}{x^2+(y-w)^2} + \frac{x}{x^2+(y+w)^2}$

###

Corollary 4.2:

Let G(s) be a scalar rational transfer function with a pole, p, in the open right half plane. Suppose that

$$|G(j\omega)| \le \beta < 1 \quad , \forall\ \omega \ge \omega_2$$

Then,

$$\gamma_{opt} \ge (1+\frac{1}{\beta^2})^{W(p,\Omega^c)/2\pi}\, |B_z^{-1}(p)|$$

where $\Omega^c := [\omega_2,\infty)$ and $W(p,\Omega^c) := \int_{\omega_2}^{\infty} W(p,\omega)d\omega$.

###

Theorem 4.2 shows that γ_{opt} will be large (1) if G(s) has a nonminimum phase zero near the unstable pole, or (2) if $|G(j\omega)|$ is small above a frequency that is relatively low with respect to the location of the pole. Let us elaborate upon the latter condition. For real z = x, $W(p,\Omega^c) = \pi - \angle\frac{x+j\omega_2}{x-j\omega_2}$, or π minus the additional phase lead contributed by the pole in the plant factorization (2.6). It follows that γ_{opt} will be large if low gain is imposed at a frequency for which the additional phase lead contributed by the pole is not significant. This phenomenon is plausible because additional lead is needed to obtain the proper number of encirclements of the critical point needed for closed loop stability.

5. RAPID RATE OF ROLLOFF AT GAIN CROSSOVER

In Section 3 we saw that achieving a loop shaping goal of high gain over a wide low frequency range for a nonminimum phase plant may be inconsistent with robust closed loop stability. In Section 4 we saw a similar result for the problem of achieving a bandwidth constraint for an unstable plant. In each case, the existence of the limitation is due to the presence of a plant singularity that cannot be removed without violating internal stability. The analysis in each case was performed rather easily using the Poisson integral. The next design limitation we discuss is more subtle, and, as we shall see, requires more work to analyze.

Suppose that we desire high gain to achieve small sensitivity over a low frequency range, and low gain to achieve small complementary sensitivity over a high frequency range. Satisfying both these goals will require the loop transfer function to roll off at a certain rate near gain crossover frequency. The Bode gain-phase relation (cf [FrL88],[DFT92]) states that, for a stable minimum phase rational function, a 20N db/decade rate of gain decrease near crossover frequency will result in -90N° phase lag at crossover. Hence if the rate of gain decrease is too rapid, the Nyquist plot will either violate the encirclement count needed for closed loop stability, or will have a poor phase margin. Hence, there is a design tradeoff between achieving high gain at low frequencies and low gain at high frequencies. This tradeoff is dictated by the need to achieve closed loop stability as well as reasonable feedback properties at intermediate frequencies. The tradeoff will become worse as the width of the intermediate frequency range narrows. An alternate means of analyzing this tradeoff is via the Bode sensitivity integral (cf [FrL88],[DFT92]).

The design limitations just described must manifest themselves in the loop shaping design procedure. We now show that if the shaped plant has either a poor phase margin or Nyquist encirclements inconsistent with closed-loop stability (both of which can occur due to excessively rapid rolloff near gain crossover), then the optimal cost will be large.

Theorem 5.1:

Let G(s) be a rational function with no poles or zeros in the open right-half plane, and suppose that G(0) > 0. Then, for all x real and positive,

$$\gamma_{opt} \ge \gamma_{lower\ bound}(x)$$

with

$$\log(\gamma_{lower\ bound}(x))$$

$$= \frac{1}{\pi}\int_0^{\infty} \log\frac{\sqrt{1+|G(j\omega)|^2}}{|1+G(j\omega)|}\, W(x,\omega)d\omega - \log|B'_p(x)| \qquad (5.1)$$

where

(1) $B'_p(s)$ is the Blaschke product containing the unstable poles (if any) of $(1+G(s))^{-1}$

and

(2) $W(x,\omega) = \frac{2x}{x^2+\omega^2}$.

Furthermore, any poles of $(1+G(s))^{-1}$ in the open right half plane must be complex. ###

Theorem 5.1 shows that γ_{opt} will tend to be large (1) if the Nyquist plot of $G(j\omega)$ is inconsistent with closed loop stability, so that the second term in (5.1) is large, or (2) if $G(j\omega)$ has a poor phase margin, so that the first term in (5.1) is large. (Note that since $(1+G(s))^{-1}$ can have no poles that are real and positive, the second term in (5.1) is finite.)

Theorem 5.1 is valid for any x real and positive. To evaluate a bound on γ_{opt}, we must choose a specific value of x. To yield a meaningful bound, x should be chosen so that at least one of the two terms on the right hand side of (5.1) will tend to be maximized. Consider the first term. If $G(j\omega)$ has a small phase margin, then the integrand will be large near gain crossover frequency, which we shall denote ω_c. It is easy to verify that $W(x,\omega_c)$, the value of the weighting function at this frequency, is maximized over x by setting $x = \omega_c$. Alternately, if 1/(1+G(s)) is unstable, the second term in (5.1) may be emphasized by setting x equal to the radius of an unstable pole pair (recall our assumptions imply that 1/(1+G(s)) can have no real unstable poles). Often the radius of the unstable poles will be approximately equal to the gain crossover frequency. In the following example, we calculate $\gamma_{lower\ bound}$ by setting $x = \omega_c$. The first term in (5.1) was evaluated via numerical integration.

Example 5.2: Let $G(s) = \frac{1}{s^k}$, where k varies from 1 to 5. Using Lemma 2.2 and Theorem 5.1, we can calculate γ_{opt} and $\gamma_{lower\ bound}$ for various values of k. The results are shown in Table 5.1. As k increases, the roll-off rate increases, and γ_{opt} and $\gamma_{lower\ bound}$ both become large.

TABLE 5.1:
EFFECT OF VARYING k ON γ_{opt} and $\gamma_{lower\ bound}$

k	γ_{opt}	$\gamma_{lower\ bound}$
1	1.4142	1.0000
2	2.6131	1.6968
3	5.9136	3.0001
4	15.290	5.3202
5	42.349	9.4662

Although the lower bound does not approximate γ_{opt} as closely as those in Sections 3 and 4, it does indicate the trend of γ_{opt} and thus demonstrates the inherent problems in specifying a loop shape that requires rapid roll-off near crossover.

We now present a generalization of Theorem 5.1 to systems that have poles and/or zeros in the open right half plane.

Theorem 5.3:
Let G(s) be a rational function. Consider x real and positive. Then

$$\gamma_{opt} \geq \gamma_{lower\ bound}(x)$$

with

$$\log(\gamma_{lower\ bound}(x)) =$$

$$\frac{1}{\pi}\int_0^\infty \log\frac{\sqrt{1+|G(j\omega)|^2}}{|1+G_x(j\omega)|}W(x,\omega)d\omega - \log|B'_p(x)| \quad , \qquad (5.2)$$

where

(1) $G_x(s) := \begin{cases} G(s) \text{ if } G(x) \geq 0 \\ -G(s) \text{ if } G(x) < 0 \end{cases}$,

(2) $B'_p(s)$ is the Blaschke product containing the unstable poles (if any) of $(1+G_x(s))^{-1}$,

and

(3) $W(x,\omega) = \dfrac{2x}{x^2+\omega^2}$.

Furthermore, $(1+G_x(s))^{-1}$ has no pole at s = x. ###

Theorem 5.3 can be applied to find a lower bound on the optimal cost for plants with poles or zeros in the open right half plane. Even though additional limitations due to such poles and zeros do not appear explicitly in (5.2), they may appear indirectly because such poles and zeros will make it less likely that $(1+G_x(s))^{-1}$ is stable.

REFERENCES

[DFT92] Doyle,J.C., B.A.Francis,and A.R.Tannenbaum, *Feedback Control Theory*, Macmillan, New York,1992

[FrL88] Freudenberg, J. S. and D. P. Looze, *Frequency Domain Properties of Scalar and Multivariable Feedback Systems*, vol. 104 in Lecture Notes in Control and Information Sciences, Springer-Verlag, New York, 1988

[GeS90] Georgiou, T. T. and M. C. Smith, Optimal Robustness in the Gap Metric, *IEEE Trans. Automat. Control* 35 (1990), 673-685

[GlM89] Glover, K. and D. C. McFarlane, Robust Stabilization of Normalized Coprime Factor Plant Descriptions with H_∞-Bounded Uncertainty, *IEEE Trans. Automat. Control* 34 (1989), 821-830

[LoF91] Looze, D. P. and J. S. Freudenberg, Limitations of Feedback Properties Imposed by Open-Loop Right Half Plane Poles, *IEEE Trans. Automat. Control* 36 (1991).

[MFG90] McFarlane, D. C. and K. Glover, *Robust Controller Design Using Normalized Coprime Factor Plant Descriptions*, vol. 138 in Lecture Notes in Control and Information Sciences, Springer- Verlag, New York,1990

[ViK86] Vidyasagar,M. and H.Kimura, Robust Controllers for Uncertain Linear Multivariable Systems, *Automatica* 22 (1986), 85-94

Proceedings of the
American Control Conference
San Francisco, California • June 1993

Robust Control of Nonlinear Uncertain Systems Under Generalized Matching Conditions

Zhihua Qu
Department of Electrical and Computer Engineering
University of Central Florida
Orlando, FL 32826, U.S.A.

Abstract:

This paper consider the problem of stabilizing nonlinear uncertain systems. First, we define for nonlinear uncertain systems the generalized matching conditions which encompass a larger class of uncertain systems than the existing matching conditions. Then, a systematic procedure of robust control design is developed for the class of systems satisfying the generalized matching conditions. The procedure is recursive and straightforward, and makes the stability results be easily established. The proposed control is a continuous and bounded function of the system state and requires only nonlinear bounding functions on the size of uncertainties. Global stability in terms of either asymptotic, exponential, or uniform ultimate bounded stability is guaranteed under the proposed control. Extension to tracking problem is shown to be trivial.

1 Introduction

The problem of designing a nonlinear state feedback control that renders a certain type of global stability for a nonlinear system containing uncertainties has been the subject of considerable research over the last decade. We brief synopsis of the primary results. Gutman(1979) developed a discontinuous min-max control which asymptotically stabilizes nonlinear uncertain systems under the matching conditions. Corless and Leitmann(1981) introduced a class of continuous state feedback control guaranteeing uniform ultimate boundedness under the same matching conditions. Several results on robustness analysis in the absence of the matching conditions have been proposed, for example, Barmish and Leitmann(1982), Chen(1987), Chen and Leitmann(1987), Qu and Dorsey(1991). These results on coping with the mismatched uncertainties are basically built on the stability margin of the stabilized nominal systems. For example, if the nominal system can be stabilized with arbitrarily large convergence rate, it has been shown that the uncertain system with arbitrarily large unmatched uncertainties can be stabilized(Qu and Dorsey, 1991). Although these results present some progress in loosening the matching conditions, applications of these results require an explicit expression of the nominal system, therefore, neither can robust control design be done in a systematic manner nor can a conclusive stability result be reached.

It should be noted that, for a linear uncertain system not satisfying the standard matching conditions, robust control may still be designed to guarantee global stability. Such a result was proposed by Thorp and Barmish(1981) in which a design procedure of robust control was given under the so-called generalized matching conditions defined only for linear uncertain systems. The proposed design procedure is based on finding positive definite solutions of a sequence of Lyapunov matrix equations for all uncertainties bounded by constant. For nonlinear uncertain systems in which the uncertainties are bounded by functions of the state and time, this design procedure merely guarantees local stability only if the size of uncertainties is under certain threshold. Recently, progress has been made to get rid of the threshold on the size of nonlinear uncertainties. As example, for a nonlinear uncertain system described by two equations in the form of Lagrange-Euler formulation, a robust control always guaranteeing *local* stability in the presence of arbitrarily large unmatched uncertainties was obtained by a judicious choice of nonlinear Lyapunov function(Qu, 1992b). The main idea in Qu(1992b) is to find a Lyapunov function for the specific system so that its nominal system will have arbitrarily large convergence rate with respect to not arbitrary uncertainty but only the possible uncertainties in Lagrange-Euler formulation. This approach is partially based on the concept of stability margin of nominal system, and consequently the stability result is inherently local. These two results motivate that, in order to achieve global stability for nonlinear uncertain systems not satisfying matching conditions, a new design procedure which is not based on stability margin must be originated.

This paper introduces generalized matching conditions (GMCs) for nonlinear uncertain systems which broaden the standard matching conditions (SMCs) and the existing generalized matching conditions for linear uncertain systems. Under the generalized matching conditions, a new design procedure of robust control is proposed. This design procedure together with the generalized matching conditions significantly extend the class of nonlinear uncertain systems for which robust controllers can be systematically designed. Each step of the systematic design procedure interlaces a translational change of coordinates with a choice of Lyapunov function and the construction of a fictitious robust control law. The resulting fictitious robust control laws constitute a recursive mapping which generates the actual robust controller at the end of the design procedure. An important feature of this design scheme is that, in the process of coordinate transformations, uncertainties satisfying GMCs become uncertainties satisfying SMCs with respect to fictitious control variables. In fact, although no coordinate transformation was employed, the same idea was implicitly embedded in the design procedure proposed by Thorp and Barmish(1981).

The conceptual simplicity of the proposed design procedure allows the designer to choose Lyapunov function freely and makes the stability proof be a straightforward Lyapunov argument. From an application point of view, the most important advantages of the robust control scheme presented in this paper are its wide applicability and conclusive stability results. The newly defined generalized matching conditions specify one of the largest classes of nonlinear uncertain systems for which a robust control can be systematically designed (Other classes will be summarized in the conclusion). The resulting robust control guarantees global stability in terms of either asymptotic, exponential, or uniform ultimate bounded stability.

The presentation is organized into five sections. In section two we introduce the generalized matching conditions for nonlinear uncertain systems. Under the generalized matching conditions, the design procedure is presented in section three. In sections four and five, different kinds of global stability of the overall system under the designed control are investigated. Finally, a simple example is introduced in section six to illustrate the design procedure.

2 Problem Formulation

We shall consider a class of nonlinear uncertain systems to be described by the following nonlinear differential equations:

$$\dot{x}_1 = f_1(x_1,t) + \Delta f_1(x_1,\eta_1,t) + g_1(x_1,x_2,\eta_1,t) \tag{1}$$

$$\dot{x}_i = f_i(x_1,\cdots,x_i,t) + \Delta f_i(x_1,\cdots,x_i,\eta_i,t) + g_i(x_1,\cdots,x_i,x_{i+1},\eta_i,t)$$
$$i = 2,\cdots,m-1, \tag{2}$$

$$\dot{x}_m = f_m(x_1,\cdots,x_m,t) + \Delta f_m(x_1,\cdots,x_m,\eta_m,t) + g_m(x_1,\cdots,x_m,u,\eta_m,t). \tag{3}$$

where $x = [\ x_1^T \ \cdots \ x_m^T\ ]^T$ is the state vector of the system, the state vector x is decomposed into state subvectors $x_i \in \mathbf{R}^{n_i}$, $i = 1,\cdots,m$. The vector $u \in \mathbf{R}^{n_{m+1}}$ denotes the control inputs into the systems. The variables η_i, $i = 1,\cdots,m$, represent the uncertain time-varying parameters, and their domain is a prescribed compact set of $\mathbf{R}^{p_i}$.

We assume that the sum of the functions $f_i + \Delta f_i + g_i$ be Caratheodory, and that the uncertain variables η_i be Lebesgue measurable. Furthermore,

$$g_i(x_1,\cdots,x_i,0,\eta_i,t) = 0 \quad \forall (x_1,\cdots,x_i,\eta_i,t)\ \forall i \in \{1,\cdots m\}.$$

It is well known that the system (1) to (3) has global existence of continuous solutions under any control which is continuous with respect to time and the states.

The class of uncertain systems given by (1) to (3) is a special case of general uncertain systems described by

$$\dot{x} = F(x,t) + \Delta F(x,\eta,t) + G(x,u,\eta,t). \tag{4}$$

A system whose dynamics is described by (4) usually contains significant uncertainties. To stabilize such an uncertain system, one often uses the so-called deterministic design approach. The technique involves two steps. First, find a deterministically bounding functions for the uncertainties. Second, based on the bounding functions, a stabilizing control is designed using Lyapunov's direct method. The resulting control, if exists, is then called robust control. Up to now, there are no general results on robust control for systems given by (4). The only complete solution available on robust control is for the systems satisfying the matching conditions(Corless and Leitmann, 1981). The objective of this paper is to develop robust control for systems not satisfying the matching conditions. More specifically, we will develop robust control for the class of uncertain systems specified by (1) to (3). The general result to be developed is due to the special structure of these systems. Such a structural property is more general than the matching conditions and is then called *the generalized matching conditions* whose formal definition is listed below.

Definition: A system described by (4) is said to satisfy *the generalized matching conditions* if the following conditions are satisfied.

C.1 The system can be decomposed into the subsystems described by (1) to (3). Moreover, the dimensions of the decomposition satisfy the following inequality.

$$n_1 \le n_2 \le \cdots \le n_m \le n_{m+1}.$$

C.2 For the functions g_i, $i = 1,\cdots,m$, there exist known continuous, positive definite functions α_i and non-negative functions φ_i such that $\forall (x_1,\cdots,x_i,x_{i+1},\eta_i,t)$

$$\alpha_i(\|S_{(i+1)i}(x_{i+1})\|)(1+\varphi_i(x_1,\cdots,x_i,x_{i+1},t))$$
$$\le S^T_{(i+1)i}(x_{i+1})g_i(x_1,\cdots,x_i,S^{-1}_{(i+1)i}(S_{(i+1)i}(x_{i+1})),\eta_i,t),$$

and $\forall (x_1,\cdots,x_m,u,\eta_m,t)$

$$\alpha_m(\|S_{(m+1)m}(u)\|)(1+\varphi_m(x_1,\cdots,x_m,u,t))$$
$$\le S^T_{(m+1)m}(u)g_m(x_1,\cdots,x_m,S^{-1}_{(m+1)m}(S_{(m+1)m}(u)),\eta_m,t),$$

where $S_{(i+1)i}(\cdot) : \mathbf{R}^{n_{i+1}} \to \mathbf{R}^{n_i}$, $i \doteq 1,\cdots,m$, are the selection functions which select n_i elements from the elements of an $n_{i+1} \times 1$ vector to form an $n_i \times 1$ vector. The inverse function of $S_{(i+1)i}(x_{i+1})$, $S^{-1}_{(i+1)i}(\cdot) : \mathbf{R}^{n_i} \to \mathbf{R}^{n_{i+1}}$, is defined to form a vector of dimension n_{i+1} in the way such that the resulting vector consists of the same elements of x_{i+1}, which are selected by the selection function $S_{(i+1)i}$, and zero anywhere else.

C.3 For the functions α_i, there exist known, continuous and positive definite functions ϕ_i such that the following inequality holds for every $i = 1,\cdots,m$.

$$\alpha_i(q_1\phi_i(q_2)) \ge q_1 q_2 \phi_i(q_2), \quad \forall\ 2 \ge q_1 \ge 1,\ q_2 \ge 0.$$

Moreover, the first-order derivative of $q^l\phi_i(q)$ with respect to q is well defined for some $l \ge 0$.

C.4 For an arbitrarily given $x^d_{i+1} = x^d_{i+1}(x_1,\cdots,x_i,t)$, there exist known continuous, non-negative functions ψ_i such that

$$\|g_i(x_1,\cdots,x_i,x_{i+1},\eta_i,t) - g_i(x_1,\cdots,x_i,x^d_{i+1},\eta_i,t)\| \le \|x_{i+1} - x^d_{i+1}\|\psi_i(x_1,\cdots,x_i,x_{i+1},t)$$

holds for all $(x_1,\cdots,x_i,x_{i+1},\eta_i,t)$ and for all $i \in \{1,\cdots,m-1\}$.

Remark 1: It is easy to verify that the proposed generalized matching conditions for nonlinear uncertain systems include as a special case the existing generalized matching conditions for linear uncertain systems (Thorp and Barmish, 1981). However, in contrast to a linear control law used in Thorp and Barmish(1981), the control in this paper is chosen to be nonlinear. Therefore, if the uncertain system is linear, it is preferable to use the control proposed by Thorp and Barmish(1981). □

Remark 2: A nonlinear uncertain system is said to satisfy the matching conditions (Corless and Leitmann, 1981) if

$$\dot{x} = F(x,t) + B(x,t)\Delta F'(x,\eta,t) + B(x,t)G'(x,u,\eta,t),$$

where $B(x,t) \in \mathbf{R}^{N\times M}$, normally with $N > M$, can be assumed without loss of any generality to be of full rank for all (x,t). Thus, there exist square and non-singular matrices $T_1(x,t)$ and $T_2(x,t)$ such that

$$T_1(x,t)B(x,t)T_2^{-1}(x,t) = \begin{bmatrix} 0 \\ I_{M\times M} \end{bmatrix} \triangleq B^*,$$

where $\triangleq$ denotes the operation of making a new definition. Let us define the transformation

$$y = \int T_1(x,t)dx, \quad \text{or} \quad \frac{\partial y}{\partial x} = T_1(x,t),$$

where $\int$ denotes indefinite integral with respect to the given variable. In the region on which the above transformation is one-to-one and onto, the system equation can be rewritten as

$$\dot{y} = T_1(x,t)F(x,t) - \int \frac{\partial}{\partial t}T_1(x,t)dx + B^*T_2(x,t)\Delta F'(x,\eta,t) + B^*T_2(x,t)G'(x,u,\eta,t),$$

which is in the form of (1) to (3). Therefore, the generalized matching conditions include the matching conditions as special cases. □

Remark 3: As an example, consider $n_{i+1} = 3$ and $n_i = 2$. If $S_{(i+1)i}\left(\begin{bmatrix} 1 & 2 & 3 \end{bmatrix}^T\right) = \begin{bmatrix} 1 & 3 \end{bmatrix}^T$, then $S^{-1}_{(i+1)i}\left(S_{(i+1)i}\left(\begin{bmatrix} 1 & 2 & 3 \end{bmatrix}^T\right)\right) = \begin{bmatrix} 1 & 0 & 3 \end{bmatrix}^T$. Also as an example, if $\alpha_i(q) = q^b$ with $b > 1$, then $\phi_i(q_2) = q_2^{\frac{1}{b-1}}$. □

The main contribution of this paper is to define the generalized matching conditions for nonlinear uncertain systems and to develop systematic procedure of designing robust control for any systems satisfying the generalized matching conditions.

Before pursuing detailed stability analysis, we shall first investigate the property of the following system. The discussion is essential for the subsequent analysis.

$$\dot{x}_i = f_i(x_1, \cdots, x_i, t) + \Delta f_i(x_1, \cdots, x_i, \eta_i, t) + g_i(x_1, \cdots, x_i, x_{i+1}, \eta_i, t). \tag{5}$$

Considering the above system, we can make the following assumptions without loss of any generality.

A.1 The uncertainties are bounded in their Euclidean norm by known continuous functions of the states and time, namely

$$\|\Delta f_i(x_1, \cdots, x_i, \eta_i, t)\| \leq \rho_i(x_1, \cdots, x_i, t).$$

Moreover, under the condition that $x_j > 0$ for $1 \leq j \leq i$, these bounding functions ρ_i are differentiable up to order $m - i$ with respect to their arguments.

A.2 The function $f_i(x_1, \cdots, x_i, t)$ can be arbitrarily chosen. Therefore, the nominal subsystem $\dot{x}_i = f_i(x_1, \cdots, x_i, t)$ can be assumed to be globally asymptotically stable. As a consequence, there exist a C^1 Lyapunov function $V_i(\cdot) : \mathbf{R}^{n_i} \times \mathbf{R} \to \mathbf{R}^+$, positive definite functions γ_{ij}, $j = 1, 2, 3$, and non-negative function γ_{i4} such that

$$\lim_{r \to \infty} \gamma_{i1}(r) = \infty, \quad \lim_{r \to \infty} \gamma_{i2}(r) = \infty, \quad \gamma_{i1}(\|x_i\|) \leq V_i(x_i, t) \leq \gamma_{i2}(\|x_i\|),$$

$$\frac{\partial V_i(x_i, t)}{\partial t} + \nabla^T_{x_i} V_i(x_i, t) f_i(x_1, \cdots, x_i, t) \leq -\gamma_{i3}(\|x_i\|) - \gamma_{i4}(x_1, \cdots, x_i, t).$$

The assumption A.2 comes from the fact that system (5) can be rewritten into the following form for any given $f'_i(x_1, \cdots, x_i, t)$

$$\dot{x}_i = f'_i(x_1, \cdots, x_i, t) + \Delta f'_i(x_1, \cdots, x_i, \eta_i, t) + g_i(x_1, \cdots, x_i, x_{i+1}, \eta_i, t),$$

where $\Delta f'_i(x_1, \cdots, x_i, \eta_i, t) = f_i(x_1, \cdots, x_i, t) - f'_i(x_1, \cdots, x_i, t) + \Delta f_i(x_1, \cdots, x_i, \eta_i, t)$. The above system has the same expression as system (5). The bounding function for $\Delta f'_i(x_1, \cdots, x_i, \eta_i, t)$ can be easily found. In the subsequent discussion, making a specific choice of $f_i(x_1, \cdots, x_i, t)$ (or specific choices of $V_i(\cdot)$ and γ_{ij}) implies that the system equation has been rewritten into a specific form as shown above.

3 Robust Control Design

We now design robust control for systems of form (1) to (3) under the generalized matching conditions. The proposed robust control design procedure is recursive. The design procedure interlaces, at each step, a change of coordinates with the construction of a fictitious robust control law. The fictitious robust control laws generated at every step constitute a recursive mapping which results in the actual robust control after the procedure is completed. Not only is the design procedure systematic and conceptually simple, but also the stability proof is a straightforward application of Lyapunov's direct method.

The new robust control for the systems described by (1) to (3) is designed step-by-step as follows.

Step 0: Choose the *fictitious robust controls* v_i, $i = 1, 2, \cdots, m$, to be

$$v_i = -\theta_i(z_1, x_1, \cdots, z_i, x_i, t)\phi_i(\rho'_i(z_1, x_1, \cdots, z_i, x_i, t)), \tag{6}$$

where $\epsilon > 0, \beta \geq 0$ are constants, z_i, $V_i(z_i, t)$, and $\rho'_i(z_1, x_1, \cdots, z_i, x_i, t)$, $i = 1, \cdots, m$, will be defined in the later steps, $\mu_i(z_1, x_1, \cdots, z_i, x_i, t) \triangleq \nabla_{z_i} V_i(z_i, t)\rho'_i(z_1, x_1, \cdots, z_i, x_i, t)$, and

$$\theta_i(z_1, x_1, \cdots, z_i, x_i, t) \triangleq \frac{\|\mu_i(z_1, x_1, \cdots, z_i, x_i, t)\|^2 + \epsilon^2 e^{-2\beta t}}{\|\mu_i(z_1, x_1, \cdots, z_i, x_i, t)\|^3 + \epsilon^3 e^{-3\beta t}} \mu_i(z_1, x_1, \cdots, z_i, x_i, t).$$

It is worth noting that the fictitious controls are continuous. If $\beta = 0$, the functions θ_i have continuous first-order partial derivatives with respect to μ_i; if $\beta \neq 0$, these partial derivatives are guaranteed to exist and to be continuous at any finite time instant. Furthermore,

$$\|\theta_i(z_1, x_1, \cdots, z_i, x_i, t)\| \leq 2 \quad \forall (z_1, x_1, \cdots, z_i, x_i, t),$$

$$\|\theta_i(z_1, x_1, \cdots, z_i, x_i, t)\| \geq 1 \quad \text{if } \|\mu_i(z_1, x_1, \cdots, z_i, x_i, t)\| \geq \epsilon e^{-\beta t}.$$

Remark 4: It will be shown in the subsequent discussion that continuous bounding functions on the first-order partial derivatives of v_i will be needed in order to generate v_{i+1}. The fictitious controls v_i are functions of bounding functions ρ'_i which are usually in terms of Euclidean norm. Since Euclidean norm of a vector, say $\|y\|$, is not differentiable with respect to the elements in y, differentiability of v_i appears to be a technical problem. Fortunately, there are at least two ways to guarantee the existence of first-order partial derivatives of v_i, as summarized below:

(i) Although $\|y\|$ is not differentiable, $\|y\|^a$ is for any $a > 1$. Thus, to guarantee existence of partial derivatives, we need only choose the controls v_i such that v_i does not contain Euclidean norms of first-order. This can be done as follows. First, using triangular inequality, rewrite $\rho'_i(y)$ into the form of either $\|y\| \cdot \rho''_i(y)$ or $c + \|y\|^2 \rho''_i(y)$ for some constant c and some positive definite function $\rho''_i(y)$. Then, choose the controls v_i as that in (6) except

$$\theta_i(z_1, x_1, \cdots, z_i, x_i, t) \triangleq \frac{\|\mu_i(z_1, x_1, \cdots, z_i, x_i, t)\|^2 + \epsilon^2 e^{-2\beta t}}{\|\mu_i(z_1, x_1, \cdots, z_i, x_i, t)\|^{\tau_i+3} + \epsilon^{\tau_i+3} e^{-(3+\tau_i)\beta t}} \|\mu_i\|^{\tau_i} \mu_i,$$

where $\tau_i \geq 0$ is chosen such that $\|\mu_i\|^{\tau_i} \mu_i \phi_i$ becomes a function of $\rho'_i(y)$ of higher-order. It is easy to verify that the subsequent discussion holds for all $\tau_i \geq 0$.

(ii) One can rewrite bounding functions in terms of some user-defined norms. As examples, letting $\|y\|_c \triangleq \sqrt{\|y\|^2 + c}$ for some constant $c > 0$, we can guarantee existence of partial derivatives. Although this approach is much simpler than the first one, the trade-off is that not asymptotic stability but only stability of globally uniform and ultimate boundedness can be achieved. □

Remark 5: The condition C.3 in the generalized matching conditions can be modified to include the following cases.

C.3′ For some functions α_i, $i \in \{1, \cdots, m\}$, there exist known positive definite functions ϕ_i such that the following inequality holds.

$$\alpha_i(q_1 \phi_i(q_2)) \geq q_1 q_2 \phi_i(q_2), \quad \forall \ 1 \geq q_1 \geq 0, \ q_2 \geq 0.$$

As an example, if $\alpha_i(q) = q^b$ with $b < 1$, then $\phi_i(q_2) = 1/q_2^{\frac{1}{1-b}}$. It follows from (6) that the variable for ϕ_i is a bounding function which can always be chosen to be greater than zero. Therefore, the functions ϕ_i are well defined. In these cases, the corresponding fictitious controls v_i are those given in (6) but

$$\theta_i(z_1, x_1, \cdots, z_i, x_i, t) \triangleq \frac{\|\mu_i(z_1, x_1, \cdots, z_i, x_i, t)\|^2}{\|\mu_i(z_1, x_1, \cdots, z_i, x_i, t)\|^3 + \epsilon^3 e^{-3\beta t}} \mu_i(z_1, x_1, \cdots, z_i, x_i, t),$$

which yields $0 \leq \|\theta_i(z_1, x_1, \cdots, z_i, x_i, t)\| \leq 1$. □

Let the *fictitious desired trajectories* for x_{i+1} and the selection functions be chosen such that

$$S_{(i+1)i}(x^d_{i+1}) = v_i, \quad x^d_{i+1} = S^{-1}_{(i+1)i}(S_{(i+1)i}(x^d_{i+1})), \quad i = 1, \cdots, m-1.$$

The actual robust control is chosen to be $S_{(m+1)m}(u) = v_m$ and $u = S^{-1}_{(m+1)m}(S_{(m+1)m}(u))$.

Step 1: Consider a state vector defined by $z_1 = x_1$. It then follows from (1) that

$$\dot{z}_1 = f_1(z_1, t) + \Delta f_1(z_1, \eta_1, t) + g_1(z_1, x_2, \eta_1, t). \tag{7}$$

It follows from Assumption A.1 that the uncertainties $\Delta f_1(z_1, \eta_1, t)$ is bounded as

$$\|\Delta f_1(z_1, \eta_1, t)\| \leq \rho_1(z_1, t) \triangleq \rho'_1(z_1, t).$$

It follows from Assumption A.2 that the nominal system $\dot{z}_1 = f_1(z_1, t)$ is globally asymptotically stable. That is, there exists a Lyapunov function $V_1(z_1, t)$ such that

$$\gamma_{11}(\|z_1\|) \leq V_1(z_1, t) \leq \gamma_{12}(\|z_1\|)$$

$$\frac{\partial V_1(z_1, t)}{\partial t} + \nabla^T_{z_1} V_1(z_1, t) f_1(z_1, t) \leq -\gamma_{13}(\|z_1\|).$$

Taking time derivative of the Lyapunov function along the trajectory of system (7) yields

$$\begin{aligned}
\dot{V}_1(z_1, t) &= \frac{\partial V_1(z_1, t)}{\partial t} + \nabla^T_{z_1} V_1(z_1, t)[f_1(z_1, t) + \Delta f_1(z_1, \eta_1, t)] + \nabla^T_{z_1} V_1(z_1, t) g_1(z_1, x_2, \eta_1, t) \\
&\leq -\gamma_{13}(\|z_1\|) + \nabla^T_{z_1} V_1(z_1, t)\Delta f_1(z_1, \eta_1, t) + \nabla^T_{z_1} V_1(z_1, t) g_1(z_1, x_2, \eta_1, t) \\
&\leq -\gamma_{13}(\|z_1\|) + \| \nabla^T_{z_1} V_1(z_1, t)\| \|\Delta f_1(z_1, \eta_1, t)\| + \nabla^T_{z_1} V_1(z_1, t) g_1(z_1, x^d_2, \eta_1, t) \\
&\quad + \nabla^T_{z_1} V_1(z_1, t)[g_1(z_1, x_2, \eta_1, t) - g_1(z_1, x^d_2, \eta_1, t)] \\
&\leq -\gamma_{13}(\|z_1\|) + \|\mu_1(z_1, t)\| + \nabla^T_{z_1} V_1(z_1, t) g_1(z_1, x^d_2, \eta_1, t) \\
&\quad + \| \nabla^T_{z_1} V_1(z_1, t)\| \|x_2 - x^d_2\| \psi_1(z_1, x_2, t)
\end{aligned}$$

where the last step comes from Condition C.4. It follows from Conditions C.2 and C.3 that, if $\|\mu_1(z_1, t)\| \leq \epsilon e^{-\beta t}$, $\nabla^T_{z_1} V_1(z_1, t) g_1(z_1, x^d_2, \eta_1, t) \leq 0$, and that, if $\|\mu_1(z_1, t)\| > \epsilon e^{-\beta t}$,

$$\begin{aligned}
\nabla^T_{z_1} V_1(z_1, t) g_1(z_1, x^d_2, \eta_1, t) &= -\frac{\|\mu_1(x_1, t)\|}{\|\theta_1(x_1, t)\| \phi_1(\rho'_1(x_1, t)) \rho'_1(x_1, t)} \times S_{21}(x^d_2) g_1(z_1, x^d_2, \eta_1, t) \\
&\leq -\frac{\|\mu_1(x_1, t)\|}{\|\theta_1(x_1, t)\| \phi_1(\rho'_1(x_1, t)) \rho'_1(x_1, t)} \alpha_1(\|v_1\|)(1 + \varphi_1(z_1, x^d_2, t)) \\
&\leq -\frac{\|\mu_1(x_1, t)\|}{\|\theta_1(x_1, t)\| \phi_1(\rho'_1(x_1, t)) \rho'_1(x_1, t)} \alpha_1(\|\theta_1(x_1, t)\| \phi_1(\rho'_1(x_1, t))) \\
&\leq -\|\mu_1(x_1, t)\|.
\end{aligned}$$

Therefore, we have that $\forall (z_1, t)$

$$\dot{V}_1(z_1, t) \leq -\gamma_{13}(\|z_1\|) + \epsilon e^{-\beta t} + \| \nabla^T_{z_1} V_1(z_1, t)\| \|x_2 - x^d_2\| \psi_1(z_1, x_2, t). \tag{8}$$

The objective in every step is to choose the bounding function ρ'_i and the Lyapunov function V_i, to justify the choice of x^d_{i+1}, and to derive the expression for $\dot{V}_i$. That is, the design procedure not only chooses the controls but also consists of necessary derivation for stability analysis.

Step i ($2 \leq i \leq m-1$): Let $z_i = x_i - x^d_i$ where x^d_i has been defined in terms of the previous definitions for z_1 up to z_{i-1}. Using the definition of z_i, we can express systems (2) as

$$\begin{aligned}
\dot{z}_i &= f_i(x_1, \cdots, x_i, t) + \Delta f_i(x_1, \cdots, x_i, \eta_i, t) - \dot{x}^d_i + g_i(x_1, \cdots, x_i, x_{i+1}, \eta_i, t) \\
&\triangleq f'_i(z_1, x_1, \cdots, z_i, x_i, t) + \Delta f'_i(z_1, x_1, \cdots, z_i, x_i, \eta_i, t) + g_i(x_1, \cdots, x_i, x_{i+1}, \eta_i, t),
\end{aligned} \tag{9}$$

where $\Delta f'_i(z_1, x_1, \cdots, z_i, x_i, \eta_i, t) \triangleq \Delta f_i(x_1, \cdots, x_i, \eta_i, t) - \dot{x}^d_i + f_i(x_1, \cdots, x_i, t) - f'_i(z_1, x_1, \cdots, z_i, x_i, t)$. It follows from Assumption A.2 that the nominal system $\dot{z}_i = f'_i(z_1, x_1, \cdots, z_i, x_i, t)$ is globally asymptotically stable. That is, there exists a Lyapunov function $V_i(z_i, t)$ such that

$$\gamma_{i1}(\|z_i\|) \leq V_i(z_i, t) \leq \gamma_{i2}(\|z_i\|)$$

$$\frac{\partial V_i(z_i, t)}{\partial t} + \nabla^T_{z_i} V_i(z_i, t) f'_i(z_1, x_1, \cdots, z_i, x_i, t) \leq -\gamma_{i3}(\|z_i\|) - \gamma_{i4}(z_1, x_1, \cdots, z_i, x_i, t).$$

Furthermore, it follows from Assumption A.2 that $f'_i(z_1, x_1, \cdots, z_i, x_i, t)$ can be arbitrarily chosen such that

$$\gamma_{i4}(z_1, x_1, \cdots, z_i, x_i, t) \geq \| \nabla^T_{z_{i-1}} V_{i-1}(z_{i-1}, t)\| \|z_i\| \psi_{i-1}(z_1, x_1, \cdots, z_{i-1}, x_{i-1}, x_i, t). \tag{10}$$

An pair of obvious choices for $f'_i(z_1, x_1, \cdots, z_i, x_i, t)$ and the corresponding V_i, which guarantees inequality (10), is $V_i(z_i, t) = \frac{1}{2} z_i^T z_i$ and

$$f'_i(z_1, x_1, \cdots, z_i, x_i, t) = -z_i - \text{sgn}(z_i) \| \nabla^T_{z_{i-1}} V_{i-1}(z_{i-1}, t)\| \psi_{i-1}(z_1, x_1, \cdots, z_{i-1}, x_{i-1}, x_i, t),$$

where $\text{sgn}(\cdot)$ is a natural extension of a usual scalar sign function to the vector case. The choice of $f'_i(\cdot)$ is not unique. It is worth emphasizing that, no matter whether the choice of $f'_i(\cdot)$ is continuous, the right-hand side of (9) is always continuous. That is, existence of continuous solution for both x_i and z_i is guaranteed under continuous control u and is not coupled to continuity of $f'_i(\cdot)$. Also, continuity of controls v_i can be guaranteed by choosing continuous bounding functions for $\|f'_i(\cdot)\|$.

After making proper choice of $f'_i(z_1, x_1, \cdots, z_i, x_i, t)$, we can bound the uncertainty term $\Delta f'_i(z_1, x_1, \cdots, z_i, x_i, \eta_i, t)$ as follows.

$$\begin{aligned}
&\|\Delta f'_i(z_1, x_1, \cdots, z_i, x_i, \eta_i, t)\| \\
&= \|\Delta f_i(x_1, \cdots, x_i, \eta_i, t) - \dot{x}^d_i + f_i(x_1, \cdots, x_i, t) - f'_i(z_1, x_1, \cdots, z_i, x_i, t)\| \\
&\leq \|\Delta f_i(x_1, \cdots, x_i, \eta_i, t)\| + \|\dot{x}^d_i\| + \|f_i(x_1, \cdots, x_i, t)\| + \|f'_i(z_1, x_1, \cdots, z_i, x_i, t)\| \\
&\leq \rho_i(x_1, \cdots, x_i, t) + \|\dot{x}^d_i\| + \|f_i(x_1, \cdots, x_i, t)\| + \|f'_i(z_1, x_1, \cdots, z_i, x_i, t)\| \\
&\leq \rho'_i(z_1, x_1, \cdots, z_i, x_i, t),
\end{aligned}$$

for some *known* function $\rho'_i(z_1, x_1, \cdots, z_i, x_i, t)$. It is worth noting that $f_i(x_1, \cdots, x_i, t)$ and $f'_i(z_1, x_1, \cdots, z_i, x_i, t)$ are known functions and therefore can be easily bounded. Thus, we need find a bounding function for $\|\dot{x}^d_i\|$ in terms of x_1 up to x_i and z_1 up to z_i in order to find the bounding function $\rho'_i(z_1, x_1, \cdots, z_i, x_i, t)$. First, note that $\|x^d_i\| = \|S_{(i+1)i}(v_{i-1})\| = \|v_{i-1}\|$. It then follows from (6) that

$$\begin{aligned}
\|\dot{x}_i^d\| &= \|\dot{v}_{i-1}\| \\
&= \left\| \frac{\partial v_{i-1}}{\partial t} + \sum_{k=1}^{i-1} \frac{\partial v_{i-1}}{\partial z_k} \dot{z}_k + \sum_{k=1}^{i-1} \frac{\partial v_{i-1}}{\partial x_k} \dot{x}_k \right\| \\
&\leq \left\| \frac{\partial v_{i-1}}{\partial t} \right\| + \sum_{k=1}^{i-1} \left\| \frac{\partial v_{i-1}}{\partial z_k} \right\| \|\dot{z}_k\| + \sum_{k=1}^{i-1} \left\| \frac{\partial v_{i-1}}{\partial x_k} \right\| \|\dot{x}_k\|,
\end{aligned}$$

in which every term can be bounded using the results in the previous steps, namely, the definitions for v_{i-1} and the differential equations for $\dot{x}_k$ and $\dot{z}_k$. Once the bounding function $\rho_i'(z_1, x_1, \cdots, z_i, x_i, t)$ is determined, the fictitious control v_i (that is, x_i^d) is well defined. Taking time derivative of the Lyapunov function along the trajectory of system (9) yields

$$\begin{aligned}
\dot{V}_i(z_i,t) &= \frac{\partial V_i(z_i,t)}{\partial t} + \nabla_{z_i}^T V_i(z_i,t)[f_i'(z_1,x_1,\cdots,z_i,x_i,t) + \Delta f_i'(z_1,x_1,\cdots,z_i,x_i,\eta_i,t)] \\
&\quad + \nabla_{z_i}^T V_i(z_i,t) g_i(x_1,\cdots,x_i,x_{i+1},\eta_i,t) \\
&\leq -\gamma_{i3}(\|z_i\|) - \gamma_{i4}(z_1,x_1,\cdots,z_i,x_i,t) + \nabla_{z_i}^T V_i(z_i,t)\Delta f_i'(z_1,x_1,\cdots,z_i,x_i,\eta_i,t) \\
&\quad + \nabla_{z_i}^T V_i(z_i,t) g_i(x_1,\cdots,x_i,x_{i+1},\eta_i,t) \\
&\leq -\gamma_{i3}(\|z_i\|) - \gamma_{i4}(z_1,x_1,\cdots,z_i,x_i,t) + \|\nabla_{z_i}^T V_i(z_i,t)\| \\
&\quad \times \|\Delta f_i'(z_1,x_1,\cdots,z_i,x_i,\eta_i,t)\| + \nabla_{z_i}^T V_i(z_i,t) g_i(x_1,\cdots,x_i,x_{i+1}^d,\eta_i,t) \\
&\quad + \nabla_{z_i}^T V_i(z_i,t)[g_i(x_1,\cdots,x_i,x_{i+1},\eta_i,t) - g_i(x_1,\cdots,x_i,x_{i+1}^d,\eta_i,t)] \\
&\leq -\gamma_{i3}(\|z_i\|) - \gamma_{i4}(z_1,x_1,\cdots,z_i,x_i,t) + \|\mu_i(z_1,x_1,\cdots,z_i,x_i,t)\| \\
&\quad + \nabla_{z_i}^T V_i(z_i,t) g_i(x_1,\cdots,x_i,x_{i+1}^d,\eta_i,t) \\
&\quad + \|\nabla_{z_i}^T V_i(z_i,t)\|\|x_{i+1} - x_{i+1}^d\|\|\psi_i(z_1,x_1,\cdots,z_i,x_i,x_{i+1},t),
\end{aligned}$$

where the last step comes from Condition C.4. It follows from Conditions C.2 and C.3 that, if $\|\mu_i(z_1,x_1,\cdots,z_i,x_i,t)\| \leq \epsilon e^{-\beta t}$, $\nabla_{z_i}^T V_i(z_i,t) g_i(x_1,\cdots,x_i,x_{i+1}^d,\eta_i,t) \leq 0$, and that, if $\|\mu_i(z_1,x_1,\cdots,z_i,x_i,t)\| > \epsilon e^{-\beta t}$,

$$\begin{aligned}
&\nabla_{z_i}^T V_i(z_i,t) g_i(x_1,\cdots,x_i,x_{i+1}^d,\eta_i,t) \\
&= -\frac{\|\mu_i(z_1,x_1,\cdots,z_i,x_i,t)\|}{\theta_i(z_1,x_1,\cdots,z_i,x_i,t)\|\phi_i(\rho_i'(z_1,x_1,\cdots,z_i,x_i,t))\rho_i'(z_1,x_1,\cdots,z_i,x_i,t)} \\
&\quad \times S_{(i+1)i}(x_{i+1}^d) g_i(x_1,\cdots,x_i,x_{i+1}^d,\eta_i,t) \\
&\leq -\frac{\|\mu_i(z_1,x_1,\cdots,z_i,x_i,t)\|}{\theta_i(z_1,x_1,\cdots,z_i,x_i,t)\|\phi_i(\rho_i'(z_1,x_1,\cdots,z_i,x_i,t))\rho_i'(z_1,x_1,\cdots,z_i,x_i,t)} \\
&\quad \times \alpha_i(\|v_i\|)(1+\psi_i(z_1,x_1,\cdots,z_i,x_i,x_{i+1}^d,t) \\
&\leq -\frac{\|\mu_i(z_1,x_1,\cdots,z_i,x_i,t)\|}{\theta_i(z_1,x_1,\cdots,z_i,x_i,t)\|\phi_i(\rho_i'(z_1,x_1,\cdots,z_i,x_i,t))\rho_i'(z_1,x_1,\cdots,z_i,x_i,t)} \\
&\quad \times \alpha_i(\|\theta_i(z_1,x_1,\cdots,z_i,x_i,t)\|\phi_i(z_1,x_1,\cdots,z_i,x_i,t)) \\
&\leq -\|\mu_i(z_1,x_1,\cdots,z_i,x_i,t)\|.
\end{aligned}$$

Therefore, we have that $\forall (z_1,x_1,\cdots,z_i,x_i,t)$

$$\begin{aligned}
\dot{V}_i(z_i,t) &\leq -\gamma_{i3}(\|z_i\|) - \gamma_{i4}(z_1,x_1,\cdots,z_i,x_i,t) + \epsilon e^{-\beta t} \\
&\quad + \|\nabla_{z_i}^T V_i(z_i,t)\|\|x_{i+1} - x_{i+1}^d\|\|\psi_i(z_1,x_1,\cdots,z_i,x_i,x_{i+1},t). \qquad (11)
\end{aligned}$$

Step m: Let $z_m = x_m - x_m^d$ where x_m^d has been defined in terms of the previous definitions for z_1 up to z_{m-1}. Using the definition of z_m, we can express systems (3) as

$$\dot{z}_m = f_m'(z_1,x_1,\cdots,z_m,x_m,t) + \Delta f_m'(z_1,x_1,\cdots,z_m,x_m,\eta_m,t) + g_m(x_1,\cdots,x_m,x_{i+1},\eta_m,t), \qquad (12)$$

where $\Delta f_m'(z_1,x_1,\cdots,z_m,x_m,\eta_m,t) \triangleq \Delta f_m(x_1,\cdots,x_m,\eta_m,t) - \dot{x}_m^d + f_m(x_1,\cdots,x_m,t) - f_m'(z_1,x_1,\cdots,z_m,x_m,t)$.

The procedure of choosing the function $f_m'(z_1,x_1,\cdots,z_m,x_m,t)$ and its corresponding Lyapunov function $V_m(z_m,t)$ is exactly the same as that in Step i ($2 \leq i < m$). That is, choose $f_m'(z_1,x_1,\cdots,z_m,x_m,t)$ and $V_m(z_m,t)$ such that

$$\gamma_{m1}(\|z_m\|) \leq V_m(z_m,t) \leq \gamma_{m2}(\|z_m\|)$$

$$\frac{\partial V_m(z_m,t)}{\partial t} + \nabla_{z_m}^T V_m(z_m,t) f_m'(z_1,x_1,\cdots,z_m,x_m,t) \leq -\gamma_{m3}(\|z_m\|) - \gamma_{m4}(z_1,x_1,\cdots,z_m,x_m,t),$$

and

$$\gamma_{m4}(z_1,x_1,\cdots,z_m,x_m,t) \geq \|\nabla_{z_{m-1}}^T V_{m-1}(z_{m-1},t)\|\|z_m\|\psi_{m-1}(z_1,x_1,\cdots,z_{m-1},x_{m-1},x_m,t). \qquad (13)$$

After the function $f_m'(z_1,x_1,\cdots,z_m,x_m,t)$ is determined, we can find a bounding function $\rho_m'(z_1,x_1,\cdots,z_m,x_m,t)$ for $\Delta f_m'(z_1,x_1,\cdots,z_m,x_m,\eta_m,t)$ in a similar fashion as that in Step i ($2 \leq i < m$). This bounding function is used to construct the *actual* robust control u (namely, v_m) as defined in Step 0. Having the robust control u, we can take time derivative of the Lyapunov function along the trajectory of system (12) under the control u. That is,

$$\begin{aligned}
\dot{V}_m(z_m,t) &= \frac{\partial V_m(z_m,t)}{\partial t} + \nabla_{z_m}^T V_m(z_m,t)[f_m'(z_1,x_1,\cdots,z_m,x_m,t) \\
&\quad + \Delta f_m'(z_1,x_1,\cdots,z_m,x_m,\eta_m,t)] + \nabla_{z_m}^T V_m(z_m,t) g_m(x_1,\cdots,x_m,u,\eta_m,t) \\
&\leq -\gamma_{m3}(\|z_m\|) - \gamma_{m4}(z_1,x_1,\cdots,z_m,x_m,t) + \|\mu_m(z_1,x_1,\cdots,z_m,x_m,t)\| \\
&\quad + \nabla_{z_m}^T V_m(z_m,t) g_m(x_1,\cdots,x_m,u,\eta_m,t).
\end{aligned}$$

It follows from Condition C.2 that, if $\|\mu_m(z_1,x_1,\cdots,z_m,x_m,t)\| \leq \epsilon e^{-\beta t}$,

$$\nabla_{z_m}^T V_m(z_m,t) g_m(x_1,\cdots,x_m,u,\eta_m,t) \leq 0,$$

and that, if $\|\mu_m(z_1,x_1,\cdots,z_m,x_m,t)\| > \epsilon e^{-\beta t}$,

$$\begin{aligned}
&\nabla_{z_m}^T V_m(z_m,t) g_m(x_1,\cdots,x_m,u,\eta_m,t) \\
&= -\frac{\|\mu_m(z_1,x_1,\cdots,z_m,x_m,t)\|}{\theta_m(z_1,x_1,\cdots,z_m,x_m,t)\|\phi_m(\rho_m'(z_1,x_1,\cdots,z_m,x_m,t))\rho_m'(z_1,x_1,\cdots,z_m,x_m,t)} \\
&\quad \times S_{(m+1)m}(u) g_m(x_1,\cdots,x_m,u,\eta_m,t) \\
&\leq -\frac{\|\mu_m(z_1,x_1,\cdots,z_m,x_m,t)\|}{\theta_m(z_1,x_1,\cdots,z_m,x_m,t)\|\phi_m(\rho_m'(z_1,x_1,\cdots,z_m,x_m,t))\rho_m'(z_1,x_1,\cdots,z_m,x_m,t)} \\
&\quad \times \alpha_m(\|v_m\|)(1+\psi_m(z_1,x_1,\cdots,z_m,x_m,u,t) \\
&\leq -\frac{\|\mu_m(z_1,x_1,\cdots,z_m,x_m,t)\|}{\theta_m(z_1,x_1,\cdots,z_m,x_m,t)\|\phi_m(\rho_m'(z_1,x_1,\cdots,z_m,x_m,t))\rho_m'(z_1,x_1,\cdots,z_m,x_m,t)} \\
&\quad \times \alpha_m(\|\theta_m(z_1,x_1,\cdots,z_m,x_m,t)\|\phi_m(z_1,x_1,\cdots,z_m,x_m,t)) \\
&\leq -\|\mu_m(z_1,x_1,\cdots,z_m,x_m,t)\|.
\end{aligned}$$

Therefore, we have that $\forall (z_1,x_1,\cdots,z_m,x_m,t)$

$$\dot{V}_m(z_m,t) \leq -\gamma_{m3}(\|z_m\|) - \gamma_{m4}(z_1,x_1,\cdots,z_m,x_m,t) + \epsilon e^{-\beta t}. \qquad (14)$$

The above design procedure consists of a set of translational coordinate transformations. The transformation is one-to-one, onto, and continuous since the fictitious and actual controls v_i, $i = 1,\cdots,m$, are continuous. The design procedure also generates important properties on the time derivatives of individual Lyapunov functions, which will be used to establish stability in the next two sections.

4 Global Stability

We now state the first result on global stability of the system consisting of equations (7), (9), and (12).

Theorem 1: *Suppose that the robust control $u = v_m$ is chosen following the design procedure in section three. Then, under the control u with $\beta = 0$, the system consisting of equations (7), (9), and (12) is globally uniformly ultimately bounded, namely, there exist $d_i' \geq 0$ such that $\forall i$*

$$\lim_{t\to\infty} \sup_{\tau \geq t} \|z_i(\tau)\| = d_i' < \infty.$$

Proof: Consider the Lyapunov function $V(z_1,\cdots,z_m,t) = \sum_{i=1}^m V_i(z_i,t)$ where $V_i(z_i,t)$ are the individual Lyapunov functions defined in section three. It follows from (8), (11), and (14) that

$$\begin{aligned}
\dot{V}(z_1,\cdots,z_m,t) &= \sum_{i=1}^m \dot{V}_i(z_i,t) = \sum_{i=1}^m \left[\frac{\partial V_i(z_i,t)}{\partial t} + \nabla_{z_i}^T V_i(z_i,t)\dot{z}_i\right] \\
&\leq -\gamma_{13}(\|z_1\|) + \|\nabla_{z_1}^T V_1(z_1,t)\|\|z_2\|\psi_1(z_1,x_2,t) + \epsilon e^{-\beta t} + \sum_{i=2}^{m-1}[-\gamma_{i3}(\|z_i\|) \\
&\quad -\gamma_{i4}(z_1,x_1,\cdots,z_i,x_i,t) + \epsilon e^{-\beta t} + \|\nabla_{z_i}^T V_i(z_i,t)\|\|x_{i+1} - x_{i+1}^d\| \\
&\quad \times \psi_i(z_1,x_1,\cdots,z_i,x_i,x_{i+1},t)] - \gamma_{m3}(\|z_m\|) - \gamma_{m4}(z_1,x_1,\cdots,z_m,x_m,t) + \epsilon e^{-\beta t} \\
&= -\sum_{i=1}^m \gamma_{i3}(\|z_i\|) + m\epsilon e^{-\beta t} - \sum_{i=2}^m [\gamma_{i4}(z_1,x_1,\cdots,z_i,x_i,t) \\
&\quad -\|\nabla_{z_{i-1}}^T V_{i-1}(z_{i-1},t)\|\|z_i\|\psi_i(z_1,x_1,\cdots,z_{i-1},x_{i-1},x_i,t)] \\
&\leq -\sum_{i=1}^m \gamma_{i3}(\|z_i\|) + m\epsilon e^{-\beta t}, \qquad (15)
\end{aligned}$$

where the last step comes from inequalities (10) and (13).

It follows from the discussion in section two that, under the continuous control u, the solutions x_i are continuous, and therefore so are the solutions z_i, $i = 1,\cdots,m$. Noting that $\beta = 0$ in (15), we have

$$\dot{V}(z_1,\cdots,z_m,t) \leq -\sum_{i=1}^m \gamma_{i3}(\|z_i\|) + m\epsilon.$$

Since ϵ is a constant chosen by the designer, it follows from the theorem in Corless and Leitmann(1981) that the system is uniformly ultimately bounded. The bounds d_i' can be determined using the theorem after finding expressions for γ_{ij}. □

Remark 6: Beside conceptual simplicity of the procedure, another important feature of the robust control design procedure is that the nominal systems and corresponding individual Lyapunov functions can be freely picked by designer in every design step. This feature makes the design procedure attractive even for known nonlinear systems. The reason is that, for a known nonlinear system of high dimension, one usually has difficulty in finding a proper Lyapunov function to design a regular control (in contrast to robust control). If a nonlinear system is described by (1) to (3) with $\eta_i = 0$ for all i, one can easily find a stabilizing control following the proposed design procedure. □

The above stability analysis is for the system in terms of the states z_i. The following theorem shows the stability of original system states x_i.

Theorem 2: *Suppose that the robust control $u = v_m$ is chosen following the design procedure in section three. Then, under the control u with $\beta = 0$, the system consisting of equations (1), (2), and (3) is globally uniformly ultimately bounded as*

$$\lim_{t\to\infty} \sup_{\tau \geq t} \|x_i(\tau)\| = d_i < \infty,$$

if $\forall i \in \{2,\cdots,m\}$,

$$d_i' + 2 \lim_{\epsilon\to 0} \lim_{t\to\infty} \sup_{\tau \geq t} \sup_{\substack{x_j \in B_j(0,d_j+\epsilon) \\ z_j \in B_j(0,d_j'\epsilon) \\ 1 \leq j < i}} \phi_{i-1}(\rho_{i-1}'(z_1,x_1,\cdots,z_{i-1},x_{i-1},\tau))\,|_{\beta=0} \triangleq d_i < \infty \qquad (16)$$

with $d_1 = d_1'$, where $B_j(a_1,a_2)$ represents an n_j-dimensional ball of radius a_2 centered at a_1.

Proof: It follows from Theorem 1 and the definitions for z_i that

$$\lim_{t\to\infty} \sup_{\tau \geq t} \|z_1(\tau)\| = d_1' \quad \Longrightarrow \quad \lim_{t\to\infty} \sup_{\tau \geq t} \|x_1(\tau)\| = d_1',$$

$$\lim_{t\to\infty} \sup_{\tau \geq t} \|z_i(\tau)\| = d_i' \quad \Longrightarrow \quad \lim_{t\to\infty} \sup_{\tau \geq t} \|x_i(\tau) - x_i^d(\tau)\| = d_i', \quad i = 2,\cdots,m.$$

For $i \geq 2$, it follows from the definition of x_i^d that

$$\begin{aligned}
\|x_i\| &= \|x_i - x_i^d + x_i^d\| \\
&\leq \|x_i - x_i^d\| + \|x_i^d\| \\
&= \|z_i\| + \|v_{i-1}\| \\
&\leq \|z_i\| + \|\theta_{i-1}(z_1,x_1,\cdots,z_{i-1},x_{i-1},t)\|\phi_{i-1}(\rho_{i-1}'(z_1,x_1,\cdots,z_{i-1},x_{i-1},t)) \\
&\leq \|z_i\| + 2\phi_{i-1}(\rho_{i-1}'(z_1,x_1,\cdots,z_{i-1},x_{i-1},t)), \qquad (17)
\end{aligned}$$

which holds for all $(z_1,x_1,\cdots,z_i,x_i,t)$.

The following discussion is based on induction. It is obvious that $\|x_1\|$ is uniformly ultimately bounded by $B_1(0,d_1)$ with $d_1 = d_1'$. It can be assumed without loss of any generality that x_j, $1 \leq j < i$, be uniformly ultimately bounded by $B_j(0,d_j)$. Therefore, for any $\epsilon > 0$, there exists $t_0 > 0$ such that $x_j \in B_j(0,d_j+\epsilon)$ and $z_j \in B_j(0,\epsilon)$ for all $1 \leq j < i$. It then follows from (17) that $t \geq t_0$

$$\begin{aligned}
\|x_i(t)\| &\leq d_i' + \epsilon + 2\phi_{i-1}(\rho_{i-1}'(z_1,x_1,\cdots,z_{i-1},x_{i-1},t)) \\
&\leq d_i' + \epsilon + 2 \sup_{\substack{x_j \in B_j(0,d_j+\epsilon) \\ z_j \in B_j(0,d_j'+\epsilon) \\ 1 \leq j < i}} \phi_{i-1}(\rho_{i-1}'(z_1,x_1,\cdots,z_{i-1},x_{i-1},t)).
\end{aligned}$$

Taking the upper limit as $t \to \infty$ yields

$$\lim_{t\to\infty} \sup_{\tau \geq t} ||x_i(\tau)|| \leq d_i' + \varepsilon + 2 \lim_{t\to\infty} \sup_{\tau\geq t} \sup_{\substack{x_j \in B_j(0, d_j+\varepsilon) \\ z_j \in B_j(0, d_j' + \varepsilon) \\ 1 \leq j < i}} \phi_{i-1}(\rho_{i-1}'(z_1, x_1, \cdots, z_{i-1}, x_{i-1}, \tau)).$$

Note that ε and t_0 are arbitrary and that $\varepsilon \to 0$ if $t_0 \to \infty$. Therefore, we have

$$\lim_{t\to\infty} \sup_{\tau\geq t} ||x_i(\tau)|| \leq d_i.$$

□

Remark 7: The system consisting of equations (1), (2), and (3) is internally unstable if there exists $i \in \{2, \cdots, m\}$ such that, for some finite $d > 0$,

$$\lim_{t\to\infty} \sup_{\tau\geq t} \sup_{x_j, z_j \in B_j(0,d), 1 \leq j < i} \phi_{i-1}(\rho_{i-1}'(z_1, x_1, \cdots, z_{i-1}, x_{i-1}, \tau)) \mid_{\beta=0} = \infty.$$

It is stressed that the possibility of internal instability is dictated by the form of the nonlinear system, and is not due to the robust control. Even when there is no uncertainty, the system still have internal instability. For example, assume that equation (1) be given by

$$\dot{x}_1 = -x_1 + f_1(t) + x_2,$$

where $\lim_{t\to\infty} f(t) = \infty$. Then, such a system can not be stabilized under any bounded control. Therefore, the requirement (16) is a necessary and sufficient condition for internal stability. Moreover, the requirement guarantees that the designed robust control always stays bounded since $||v_i|| \leq 2\phi_i(\rho_i'(z_1, x_1, \cdots, z_i, x_i, t))$ for all $i \in \{1, \cdots, m\}$. □

Remark 8: The above study gives solutions to the regulation problem of nonlinear system (1), (2), and (3). An extension to the track problem is straightforward by making a minor change in the first step of the design procedure: Define the state variable z_1 to be $z_1 = x^* - x_1$ where x^* represents the desired trajectory for the state variable x_1 of the system. This type of partial state tracking is common in many control applications, for instance, end-point tracking of flexible-joint robots, control of power generators, etc. Due to the structure of the system, it is not possible to make all the state of the system track an arbitrarily given trajectory. Due to the presence of uncertainties, it is also impossible to predict what class of desired trajectories are achievable. Thus, tracking in terms of x_1 is the only tracking problem that is well defined. As long as the desired trajectory x^* and their time derivatives are bounded by constants for all time, the stability analysis will be exactly the same, and the resulting control will be bounded. □

Remark 9: It is worth noting that a system of form (1), (2) and (3) can be viewed as one consisted of cascaded nonlinear uncertain subsystems if

$$f_i(x_1, \cdots, x_i, t) = f_i(x_i, t), \qquad \Delta f_i(x_1, \cdots, x_i, \eta_i, t) = \Delta f_i(x_i, \eta_i, t),$$

$$g_i(x_1, \cdots, x_i, x_{i+1}, \eta_i, t) = g_i(x_i, x_{i+1}, \eta_i, t).$$

Therefore, the generalized matching conditions include series connection of nonlinear systems as a special cases. As a result, the proposed design technique can be used to construct smooth robust controls for cascaded, nonlinear uncertain dynamical systems in which every subsystem satisfy the generalized matching conditions. □

5 Further Study on Stability

The following lemma will facilitate the subsequent discussion.

Lemma 1: (Barbalat Lemma (Slotine and Li, 1991)) *Let $g(\cdot)$ be a scalar, uniformly continuous function. If*

$$\lim_{t\to\infty} \int_{t_0}^{t} g(\tau) d\tau < +\infty,$$

then, $\lim_{t\to\infty} g(t) = 0$.

We now state a result on global asymptotic stability of the system consisting of equations (7), (9), and (12).

Theorem 3: *Suppose that the robust control $u = v_m$ is chosen following the design procedure in section three. Then, under the control u with $\beta > 0$, the system consisting of equations (7), (9), and (12) is globally asymptotically stable.*

Proof: Consider the same Lyapunov function as that in Theorem 1. It follows from (15) that

$$\dot{V}(z_1, \cdots, z_m, t) \leq -\sum_{i=1}^{m} \gamma_{i3}(||z_i||) + m\epsilon e^{-\beta t}.$$

Taking finite integration from t_0 to t ($t \geq t_0$) on both sides of the above inequality yields

$$V(z_1(t), \cdots, z_m(t), t) - V(z_1(t_0), \cdots, z_m(t_0), t_0) \leq -\sum_{i=1}^{m} \int_{t_0}^{t} \gamma_{i3}(||z_i(\tau)||) d\tau + m \int_{t_0}^{t} \epsilon e^{-\beta\tau} d\tau.$$

Thus, we have

$$\begin{aligned} V(z_1(t), \cdots, z_m(t), t) &+ \sum_{i=1}^{m} \int_{t_0}^{t} \gamma_{i3}(||z_i(\tau)||) d\tau \\ &\leq V(z_1(t_0), \cdots, z_m(t_0), t_0) + \frac{m\epsilon}{\beta}(e^{-\beta t_0} - e^{-\beta t}) \\ &\leq V(z_1(t_0), \cdots, z_m(t_0), t_0) + \frac{m\epsilon}{\beta} e^{-\beta t_0} \triangleq C_{t_0} < \infty, \end{aligned}$$

where C_{t_0} is a finite constant, or

$$\begin{aligned} V(z_1(t), \cdots, z_m(t), t) &\leq C_{t_0} \quad \forall\, t \geq t_0, \\ \int_{t_0}^{t} \gamma_{i3}(||z_i(\tau)||) d\tau &\leq C_{t_0} \quad \forall\, t \geq t_0, \ \forall\, i \in \{1, \cdots, m\}. \end{aligned} \tag{18}$$

Taking the limit as time approaches infinity in (18) yields

$$\int_{t_0}^{\infty} \gamma_{i3}(||z_i(\tau)||) d\tau \leq C_{t_0} < \infty \quad \forall\, i \in \{1, \cdots, m\}.$$

It follows from the discussion in section two that, under the continuous control u, the solutions x_i are continuous, and therefore so are the solutions z_i, $i = 1, \cdots, m$. It follows from Theorem 1 that $\dot{z}_i$ is bounded, and consequently z_i is uniformly continuous. It follows from Lemma 1 that

$$\lim_{t\to\infty} ||z_i(t)|| = 0 \quad \forall\, i \in \{1, \cdots, m\}.$$

□

Recall that the design procedure gives us the freedom of choosing specific nominal systems and corresponding Lyapunov functions. This feature can be used to achieve better stability performance. For example, if $V_i(z_i, t) = 0.5||z_i||^2$ and $\gamma_{i3} = ||z_i||^2$, one can use the following theorem to show global and exponential stability for system described by (7), (9), and (12).

Lemma 2:(Qu and Dawson, 1991) *Let V be a Lyapunov function candidate for any given continuous time system with the following properties:*

$$\begin{aligned} &(1) \quad \lambda_1||y||^{\delta_1} \leq V(y,t) \leq \lambda_2||y||^{\delta_2} \quad \forall (y,t) \in \mathbf{R}^N \times \mathbf{R} \\ &(2) \quad \dot{V}(y,t) \leq -\lambda_3||y||^{\delta_2} + \epsilon e^{-\beta t} \quad \forall (y,t) \in \mathbf{R}^N \times \mathbf{R}, \end{aligned}$$

where $N, \delta_1, \delta_2, \lambda_1, \lambda_2, \lambda_3, \beta > 0$ are constants. Then, the states of the system, $||y||$, exponentially converge to the origin in the large. Furthermore, if $\lambda_3 > \lambda_2\beta$, then

$$||y|| \leq C(y_{t_0}, \epsilon) e^{-\frac{\beta}{\delta_1} t},$$

where $C(\cdot)$ is a constant depending on the initial conditions.

Based on the above stability results for the states z_i, the following theorem shows the stability of original system states x_i. Its proof can be proceeded in a similar fashion as Theorem 2 and therefore is omitted for briefness.

Theorem 4: *Suppose that the robust control $u = v_m$ is chosen following the design procedure in section three. Then, under the control u with $\beta > 0$, the system consisting of equations (1), (2), and (3) satisfy the following stability properties.*

1. *The state x_1 always asymptotically or exponentially converges to zero in the large.*
2. *Suppose that the following inequality holds $\forall i \in \{2, \cdots, m\}$*

$$\lim_{\epsilon\to 0} \lim_{t\to\infty} \sup_{\tau\geq t} \sup_{\substack{x_j \in B_j(0, d_j + \epsilon) \\ z_j \in B_j(0,\epsilon) \\ 1 \leq j < i}} \phi_{i-1}(\rho_{i-1}'(z_1, x_1, \cdots, z_{i-1}, x_{i-1}, \tau)) \mid_{\beta>0} \triangleq \frac{1}{2} d_i < \infty \tag{19}$$

where $d_1 = 0$. Then, the state x_i, $i = 2, \cdots, m$, are asymptotically or exponentially converge to zero in the large if $d_i = 0$, or globally uniformly ultimately bounded by $B_i(0, d_i)$ if $d_i > 0$.

Remark 10: Similar to the discussion in Remark 7, the condition (19) does not hold if the system is internally unstable. But, unlike condition (16), condition (19) is not sufficient to conclude internal instability. The reason is the following. The bounding function ρ_i' depends on the bounds of the first-order partial derivatives of v_{i-1} with respect to its variables. Some of these partial derivatives will in turn depend on the first-order partial derivatives of θ_i with respect to μ_i. As we discussed in section three, the partial derivative $\frac{\partial\theta_i}{\partial\mu_i}$ with $\beta > 0$ exists at any finite time instant but may approach infinity as time increases to infinity. In the case that the partial derivative does not exist in the limit, condition (19) is not valid. It is not difficult to show using Lemma 2 and Theorem 4 that the sufficient conditions guaranteeing the requirement (19) are:

1. Choose the Lyapunov functions V_i and corresponding γ_{3i} to be quadratic.
2. The bounding functions ρ_i have the property that $\forall i \in \{1, \cdots, m-1\}$ and $\forall t$

$$\lim_{r\to 0} \frac{1}{r^2} \rho_i(x_1, \cdots, \dot{x}_i, t) \phi_i(\rho_i(x_1, \cdots, x_i, t)) \mid_{\substack{x_j = r\mathbf{1}_j \\ j \leq i}} < \infty,$$

where $\mathbf{1}_j$ denotes an $n_j \times 1$ vector whose elements are all constant 1.

□

6 Example

As an illustration of the proposed design technique we introduce a simple nonlinear uncertain system which violates the existing matching conditions. As the result of lacking the matching conditions, there has been no robust control available to stabilize the system.

Example: Consider the nonlinear system

$$\begin{aligned} \dot{x}_1 &= \Delta f_1(x_1, \eta_1, t) + \eta_0 x_2 \\ \dot{x}_2 &= \Delta f_2(x_1, x_2, \eta_2, t) + u \end{aligned} \tag{20}$$

where $x_1, x_2, u \in \mathbf{R}$, η_0, η_1, and η_2 are uncertain, time-varying parameters which domains are in prescribed compact sets of $\mathbf{R}$. Furthermore, suppose that

$$1 \leq \eta_0 \leq 2, \quad |\Delta f_1(x_1, \eta_1, t)| \leq \xi + |x_1| + x_1^2, \quad |\Delta f_2(x_1, x_2, \eta_2, t)| \leq 1 + x_1^2 + x_2^2,$$

where $\xi \geq 0$ is a known constant. This system is already in the forms of (1), (2), and (3). It is easy to see that $\alpha_1(q) = \alpha_2(q) = q^2$, $\phi_1(q_2) = \phi_2(q_2) = q_2$, $\psi_1(x_1, x_2, t) = 2$. Therefore, the system satisfies the generalized matching conditions.

The design procedure of section three, applied to (20), is as follows:

Step 0: Choose the fictitious robust controls v_i, $i = 1, 2$, to be

$$v_i = -\theta_i(z_1, x_1, \cdots, z_i, x_i, t)\rho_i'(z_1, x_1, \cdots, z_i, x_i, t),$$

where $\epsilon, \gamma > 0$ are constants, z_i and $\rho_i'(z_1, x_1, \cdots, z_i, x_i, t)$, $i = 1, 2$, will be defined in the later steps, and

$$\mu_i(z_1, x_1, \cdots, z_i, x_i, t) = \nabla_{z_i} V_i(z_i, t)\rho_i'(z_1, x_1, \cdots, z_i, x_i, t),$$

$$\theta_i(z_1, x_1, \cdots, z_i, x_i, t) = \frac{\mu_i^2(z_1, x_1, \cdots, z_i, x_i, t) + \epsilon^2 e^{-2\beta t}}{|\mu_i(z_1, x_1, \cdots, z_i, x_i, t)|^3 + \epsilon^3 e^{-3\beta t}} \mu_i(z_1, x_1, \cdots, z_i, x_i, t).$$

Step 1: Define $z_1 = x_1$. It then follows from (20) that

$$\begin{aligned} \dot{z}_1 &= -z_1 + \Delta f_1(z_1, \eta_1, t) + z_1 + \eta_0 x_2 \\ &\triangleq -z_1 + \Delta f_1'(z_1, \eta_1, t) + \eta_0 x_2. \end{aligned}$$

The newly defined nominal system $\dot{z}_1 = -z_1$ is stable. Thus, the Lyapunov function can then be chosen to be $V_1(z_1, t) = \frac{1}{2} z_1^2$ which yields $\nabla_{z_1} V_1(z_1, t) = z_1$. It follows from Assumption A.1 that the *total* uncertainties $\Delta f_1'(z_1, \eta_1, t)$ is bounded as $||\Delta f_1'(z_1, \eta_1, t)|| \leq ||\Delta f_1(z_1, \eta_1, t)|| + ||z_1|| \leq \xi + x_1^2 + 2|z_1|$. To guarantee that the resulting v_1 is differentiable, we shall choose the bounding function $\rho_1'(z_1)$ as suggested in Remark 4. That is,

$$\rho_1'(z_1) \triangleq \begin{cases} \xi + \xi' + (1 + \frac{1}{\xi'})z_1^2 & \text{if } \xi \neq 0 \\ |z_1|(2 + |z_1|) & \text{if } \xi = 0 \end{cases},$$

where $\xi' > 0$ is an arbitrary constant. It is easy to verify that $||\Delta f_1'(z_1, \eta_1, t)|| \leq \rho_1'(z_1)$.

Hence, the fictitious robust control is given by

$$v_1 = -\frac{\mu_1^2(z_1, t) + \epsilon^2 e^{-2\beta t}}{|\mu_1(z_1, t)|^3 + \epsilon^3 e^{-3\beta t}} \mu_1(z_1, t)\rho_1'(z_1), \qquad \mu_1(z_1, t) = z_1\rho_1'(z_1), \tag{21}$$

under which the time derivative of the Lyapunov function V_1 satisfies

$$\dot{V}_1(z_1) \leq -z_1^2 + 2|z_1||x_2 - v_1| + \epsilon e^{-\beta t}.$$

Step 2: Define $z_2 = x_2 - v_1$. It then follows from (20) that

$$\begin{aligned} \dot{z}_2 &= -z_2 - 2|z_1|\text{sgn}(z_2) + \Delta f_2(x_1, x_2, \eta_2, t) + 2|z_1|\text{sgn}(z_2) + z_2 - \dot{v}_1 + u \\ &\triangleq -z_2 - 2|z_1|\text{sgn}(z_2) + \Delta f_2'(z_1, x_1, z_2, x_2, \eta_2, t) + u. \end{aligned}$$

The newly defined nominal system $\dot{z}_2 = -z_2 - 2|z_1|\text{sgn}(z_2)$ is stable. Thus, the Lyapunov function can then be chosen to be $V_2(z_2, t) = \frac{1}{2}z_2^2$ which yields $\nabla_{z_2} V_2(z_2, t) = z_2$. It follows from Assumption A.1 that the *total* uncertainties $\Delta f_2'(z_1, x_1, z_2, x_2, \eta_2, t)$ is bounded as

$$\begin{aligned} \|\Delta f_2'(z_1, x_1, z_2, x_2, \eta_2, t)\| &\leq \|\Delta f_2(x_1, x_2, \eta_2, t)\| + 2|z_1| + |z_2| + |\dot{v}_1| \\ &\leq 1 + x_1^2 + x_2^2 + 2|z_1| + |z_2| + |\dot{v}_1| \\ &\leq \rho_2'(z_1, x_1, z_2, x_2, t), \end{aligned}$$

where $\rho_2'(z_1, x_1, z_2, x_2, t)$ is to be defined. To determine a bounding function for $\dot{v}_1$, we shall first find its partial derivatives. Rewriting (21) into

$$v_1 = -\frac{z_1^2 \varrho_1(z_1) + \epsilon^2 e^{-2\beta t}}{|z_1|^3 \varrho_1^{\frac{3}{2}}(z_1) + \epsilon^3 e^{-3\beta t}} z_1 \varrho_1(z_1), \qquad \varrho_1(z_1) = [\rho_1'(z_1)]^2,$$

we have

$$\dot{v}_1 = \frac{\partial v_1}{\partial t} + \frac{\partial v_1}{\partial z_1}\dot{x}_1 + \frac{\partial v_1}{\partial \varrho_1}\frac{\partial \varrho_1}{\partial z_1}\dot{x}_1,$$

where the partial derivatives are well defined and given by

$$\frac{\partial v_1}{\partial t} = \left\{ \frac{2\epsilon^2 e^{-2\beta t}}{|z_1|^3 \varrho_1^{\frac{3}{2}}(z_1) + \epsilon^3 e^{-3\beta t}} - \frac{z_1^2 \varrho_1(z_1) + \epsilon^2 e^{-2\beta t}}{[|z_1|^3 \varrho_1^{\frac{3}{2}}(z_1) + \epsilon^3 e^{-3\beta t}]^2} 3\epsilon^3 e^{-3\beta t} \right\} \beta z_1 \varrho_1(z_1),$$

$$\frac{\partial v_1}{\partial z_1} = \left\{ -\frac{3z_1^2 \varrho_1^2(z_1) + \epsilon^2 e^{-2\beta t}\varrho_1(z_1)}{|z_1|^3 \varrho_1^{\frac{3}{2}}(z_1) + \epsilon^3 e^{-3\beta t}} + \frac{z_1^2 \varrho_1(z_1) + \epsilon^2 e^{-2\beta t}}{[|z_1|^3 \varrho_1^{\frac{3}{2}}(z_1) + \epsilon^3 e^{-3\beta t}]^2} 3|z_1|^3 \varrho_1^{\frac{5}{2}}(z_1) \right\},$$

$$\frac{\partial v_1}{\partial \varrho_1} = \left\{ -\frac{2z_1^3 \varrho_1(z_1) + z_1 \epsilon^2 e^{-2\beta t}}{|z_1|^3 \varrho_1^{\frac{3}{2}}(z_1) + \epsilon^3 e^{-3\beta t}} + \frac{z_1^2 \varrho_1(z_1) + \epsilon^2 e^{-2\beta t}}{[|z_1|^3 \varrho_1^{\frac{3}{2}}(z_1) + \epsilon^3 e^{-3\beta t}]^2} \frac{3}{2} z_1^4 \varrho_1^{\frac{3}{2}}(z_1) \right\},$$

$$\frac{\partial \varrho_1}{\partial z_1} = \begin{cases} 4z_1 + 12z_1|z_1| + 4z_1^3 & \text{if } \xi = 0 \\ 4(1 + \frac{1}{\xi'})[\xi + \xi' + (1 + \frac{1}{\xi'})z_1^2]z_1 & \text{if } \xi \neq 0 \end{cases}.$$

It then follows that

$$\left|\frac{\partial v_1}{\partial t}\right| \leq 8\beta\rho_1'(z_1), \qquad \left|\frac{\partial v_1}{\partial z_1}\right| \leq 6\frac{\mu_1^2(z_1, t) + \epsilon^2 e^{-2\beta t}}{|\mu_1(z_1, t)|^3 + \epsilon^3 e^{-3\beta t}}[\rho_1'(z_1)]^2,$$

$$\left|\frac{\partial v_1}{\partial \varrho_1}\right| \leq \frac{7}{2}\frac{\mu_1^2(z_1, t) + \epsilon^2 e^{-2\beta t}}{|\mu_1(z_1, t)|^3 + \epsilon^3 e^{-3\beta t}}|z_1|, \qquad \left|\frac{\partial \varrho_1}{\partial z_1}\right| \leq (8\xi + 8)|z_1| + 12z_1^2 + 16|z_1|^3.$$

Thus, we can choose that

$$\begin{aligned} \rho_2'(z_1, x_1, z_2, x_2, t) &= 1 + x_1^2 + x_2^2 + 2|z_1| + |z_2| + 8\beta\rho_1'(z_1) \\ &\quad + 6\frac{\mu_1^2(z_1, t) + \epsilon^2 e^{-2\beta t}}{|\mu_1(z_1, t)|^3 + \epsilon^3 e^{-3\beta t}}[\rho_1'(z_1)]^2(2|x_2| + \rho_1'(z_1)) \\ &\quad + \frac{7}{2}\frac{\mu_1^2(z_1, t) + \epsilon^2 e^{-2\beta t}}{|\mu_1(z_1, t)|^3 + \epsilon^3 e^{-3\beta t}}|z_1| \\ &\quad \times[(8\xi + 8)|z_1| + 12z_1^2 + 16|z_1|^3](2|x_2| + \rho_1'(z_1)). \end{aligned}$$

Hence, the actual robust control is given by

$$u = v_2 = -\frac{\mu_2^2(z_1, x_1, z_2, x_2, t) + \epsilon^2 e^{-2\beta t}}{|\mu_2(z_1, x_1, z_2, x_2, t)|^3 + \epsilon^3 e^{-3\beta t}} \mu_2(z_1, x_1, z_2, x_2, t)\rho_2'(z_1, x_1, z_2, x_2, t),$$

$$\mu_2(z_1, x_1, z_2, x_2, t) = z_2\rho_2'(z_1, x_1, z_2, x_2, t),$$

under which the time derivative of the Lyapunov function V_2 satisfies

$$\dot{V}_2(z_2) \leq -z_2^2 - 2|z_1||z_2| + \epsilon e^{-\beta t}.$$

The global stability of system (20) under the resulting robust control is guaranteed by Theorems in sections four and five. As discussed in Theorems 2 and 4, the choice of the parameter β in the control depends on the value ξ. If $\xi = 0$, we can choose $\beta > 0$ which makes the states x converge to zero exponentially. If $\xi > 0$, it is safe to choose $\beta = 0$ which renders uniform ultimate bounded stability for the states x. Moreover, the uniform ultimate bounded stability can be made to approach asymptotic stability by choosing smaller ϵ.

Conclusion

The objective of this paper is to develop robust control for nonlinear uncertain systems not satisfying the standard matching conditions (SMCs) in Corless and Leitmann(1981). To this end, the generalized matching conditions (GMCs) for nonlinear uncertain systems have been defined. It has been shown that the GMCs include as special cases the standard matching conditions (Corless and Leitmann, 1981) as well as the existing generalized matching conditions for linear uncertain systems(Thorp and Barmish, 1981). Under the newly defined generalized matching conditions, a systematic design procedure is proposed to construct robust controls. The resulting robust control guarantees global stability, either asymptotic stability, exponential stability, or uniformly ultimately bounded stability. The design procedure is shown to be conceptually simple and applicable to one of the largest classes of nonlinear uncertain systems for which robust control can be systematically designed.

We conclude our discussion by pointing out that several classes of uncertain systems violating the GMCs have been shown to be globally stabilizable. For example, stabilizability of linear uncertain systems not satisfying GMCs was investigated by Wei(1990); robust control was proposed in Qu(1992a) to globally stabilize a class of nonlinear uncertain systems with equivalently matched uncertainties (the equivalently matched uncertainties are not overlapped in general with those satisfying GMCs). Future research should be directed to merge these results together and to specify eventually the class of all stabilizable uncertain systems, linear and nonlinear. This paper presents a step of progress toward the ultimate objective.

Reference

Barmish, B.R., M.J.Corless and G.Leitmann(1983). A new class of stabilizing controllers for uncertain dynamical systems. *SIAM J. Contr. Optimiz.*, **21**, pp.246-255.

Barmish, B.R., and G.Leitmann(1982). On ultimate boundedness control of uncertain systems in the absence of matching assumptions. *IEEE Transaction on Automat. Contr.*, **27**, pp.153-158.

Chen, Y.H.(1987). On the robustness of mismatched uncertain dynamical systems. *J. of Dynamic Systems, Measurement, and Control*, **109**, pp29-35.

Chen, Y.H.(1987). Deterministic control for a new class of uncertain dynamical systems. *IEEE Trans. Automat. Contr.*, **32**, pp.73-74.

Chen, Y.H.(1988). Design of robust controllers for uncertain dynamical systems. *IEEE Trans. Automat. Contr.*, **33**, pp.487-491.

Chen, Y.H., and G.Leitmann(1987). Robustness of uncertain systems in the absence of matching assumptions. *Int. J. Control*, **45**, pp.1527-1542.

Corless, M.J. and G.Leitmann(1981). Continuous state feedback guaranteeing uniform ultimate boundedness for uncertain dynamic systems. *IEEE Trans. AC*, **26**, pp.1139-1144.

Gutman, S.(1979). Uncertain dynamical systems — A lyapunov min-max approach. *IEEE Trans. Automat. Contr.*, **24**, pp.437-443.

Hale, J.K.(1980) *Ordinary Differential Equations*, Robert E. Krieger Publishing Co., Inc.

Qu, Z.(1992a). Global stabilization of nonlinear systems with a class of unmatched uncertainties. *Systems & Control Letters*, **18**, pp.217-222.

Qu, Z.(1992b). Robust control of a class of nonlinear uncertain systems. *IEEE Transactions on Automatic Control*, **37**, pp.1437-1442.

Qu, Z. and D.M.Dawson(1991). Continuous feedback control guaranteeing exponential stability for uncertain dynamical systems. *The 30th IEEE CDC*, Brighton, U.K., pp.2636-2638.

Qu, Z., and J.F.Dorsey(1991). Robust control of generalized dynamic systems without matching conditions. *J. of Dyn. Syst., Meas., And Contr.*, **113**, pp.582-589.

Schmitendorf, W.E., and B.R. Barmish(1987). Guaranteed asymptotic output stability for systems with constant disturbance. *J. of Dynamic Systems, Measurement, and Control*, **109**, pp.186-189.

Slotine, J.J., and W. Li(1991). *Applied Nonlinear Control*, Englewood Cliffs, Prentice-Hall, Inc.

Thorp, J.S., and B.R. Barmish(1981). On guaranteed stability of uncertain linear systems via linear control. *J. of Optimization Theory and Applications*, **35**, pp.559-579.

Vidyasagar, M.(1978). *Nonlinear Systems Analysis*, Englewood Cliffs, Prentice-Hall, Inc.

Wei, K.(1990). Quadratic stabilizability of linear systems with structural independent time-varying uncertainties. *IEEE Trans. Automat. Contr.*, **35**, pp.268-277.

This work is supported in part by U.S. National Science Foundation under grant MSS-9110034.

WA8 - 10:15

Proceedings of the
American Control Conference
San Francisco, California • June 1993

A NEW MATCHING CONDITION FOR ROBUST CONTROL DESIGN

Y.H. Chen
The George W. Woodruff School of Mechanical Engineering
Georgia Institute of Technology
Atlanta, GA 30332-0405

Abstract

We study the control design problem for uncertain nonlinear systems. A new matching condition is presented. The main idea is to configure the possible route through which the uncertainty may affect the stability. Compared with the previous case, the current matching condition prescribes the route nonlinearly while the early matching condition is a special case of the linear description. The advantage is demonstrated. As an example, the number of required independent controls drops from three to one in a rotational rigid-body problem by using the new matching condition.

1. Introduction

We consider the control problem for nonlinear systems with (possibly fast) time-varying uncertainty. In the past, the design has been mainly based on a structural condition on the system, namely, the matching condition (Corless and Leitmann 1981, Barmish *et al.* 1983). The control law can be synthesized constructively if the matching condition is satisfied. However, the condition may be restrictive in certain instance and the dynamic system under consideration may fall out of the domain. Naturally, numerous past work has been devoted to this subject. There have been mainly two approaches used to tackle this issue.

First, one studies the robustness of the controlled system against the mismatched uncertainty. The idea is to first decompose the uncertainty into two categories, namely, the matched and mismatched. The control is first designed as if there was no mismatched uncertainty. Then a passive stability analysis is made as the mismatched uncertainty is reintroduced. The framework is first introduced by Barmish and Leitmann (1982) for linear systems and followed by Chen and Leitmann (1987) for nonlinear systems.

Second, one intends to reconfigure the structural condition so as to incorporate either a larger or a different class of uncertainty. There has been numerous work in this domain for *linear systems.* Petersen and Hollot (1986) and Schmitendorf (1987) adopted the Riccati approach. Barmish (1985) introduced a necessary and sufficient structural condition under which the robust control design is feasible. Finally, Gu *et al.* (1991) and Chen and Chen (1991) established a two-level optimization setting for the search of the control. It was proven to be necessary and sufficient that the setting can indeed search for the global extreme solution.

The current work mainly falls into the second approach. The emphasis is however on *nonlinear systems.* We introduce a new matching condition which renders the previous one a special case. The main idea is to configure the route under which the uncertainty may affect the system's stability. This is then to be covered by the robust control. Once this route is identified, the control magnitude can be tuned to compensate the uncertainty in the worst case sense. The new matching condition describes the route in a nonlinear way. The previous one, judging from this aspect, is simply a special case of the linear description (this means the previous case is not equivalent to the linear case). Illustrative examples, which include the rotational rigid body system and the chaotic Lorenz system, are used to demonstrate the design procedure. The numbers of independent controls in these examples drop by using the new matching condition.

2. Uncertain System and New Matching Condition

Consider the following uncertain system

$$\begin{aligned}\dot{x}(t) =& f(x(t),t) + \Delta f(x(t),\sigma(t),t)\\ &+ [B(x(t),t) + \Delta B(x(x),\sigma(t),t)]u(t),\end{aligned} \tag{2.1}$$

where $t \in \mathbf{R}$, $x(t) \in \mathbf{R}^n$ is the state, $u(t) \in \mathbf{R}^m$ is the control, and $\sigma(t) \in \mathbf{R}^q$ is the uncertain parameter. The matrices, resp. vectors $f(x,\sigma,t)$, $\Delta f(x,\sigma,t)$, $B(x,\sigma,t)$, and $\Delta B(x,\sigma,t)$ are of appropriate dimensions. The functions $f(\cdot)$, $\Delta f(\cdot)$, $B(\cdot)$, and $\Delta B(\cdot)$, known or unknown, are continuous. We note that most of the continuity assumptions in this paper can in fact be relaxed to be either Caratheodory or strong Caratheodory. This is however not be to discussed for simplicity. The following assumptions are proposed for the robust control design.

Assumption 1. The function $\sigma : \mathbf{R} \to \Sigma \subset \mathbf{R}^q$ is Lebesgue measurable with Σ prescribed and compact.

Assumption 2. $f(0,t) = 0\ \forall t \in \mathbf{R}$. Furthermore, there exist a C^1 function $v : \mathbf{R}^n \times \mathbf{R} \to \mathbf{R}_+$ and **KR**-functions $\gamma_i : \mathbf{R}_+ \to \mathbf{R}_+$, $i = 1,2,3$, such that for all $(x,t) \in \mathbf{R}^n \times \mathbf{R}$,

$$\gamma_1(\|x\|) \le v(x,t) \le \gamma_2(\|x\|), \tag{2.2}$$

$$\dot{v}(x,t) = \frac{\partial v(x,t)}{\partial t} + \nabla_x^T v(x,t) f(x,t) \le -\gamma_3(\|x\|). \tag{2.3}$$

This assumption asserts that there exists a Lyapunov function $v(\cdot)$ which guarantees that $x = 0$ is a global uniformly asymptotically stable equilibrium point of the uncontrolled nominal system

$$\dot{x}(t) = f(x(t),t). \tag{2.4}$$

In practice, if the uncontrolled nominal system does not possess such a Lyapunov function, all one needs to do is to stabilize the nominal system first via a control, say, $q(x,t)$. The uncertain system then reads

$$\begin{aligned}\dot{x} =& [f(x,t) + B(x,t)q(x,t)] + [\Delta f(x,\sigma,t) + \Delta B(x,\sigma,t)q(x,t)]\\ &+ [B(x,t) + \Delta B(x,\sigma,t)]u(t).\end{aligned} \tag{2.5}$$

This is in fact equivalent to (2.1). Hence in a sense this assumption is equivalent to that (f,B) is stabilizable.

Assumption 3. There exist a function $E : \mathbf{R}^n \times \Sigma \times \mathbf{R} \to \mathbf{R}^{m\times m}$ and a constant $\rho_E > -1$ such that for all $(x,t) \in \mathbf{R}^n \times \mathbf{R}$,

$$\Delta B(x,\sigma,t) = B(x,t)E(x,\sigma,t), \tag{2.6}$$

$$\min_{\sigma\in\Sigma} \frac{1}{2}\lambda_{\min}[E(x,\sigma,t) + E^T(x,\sigma,t)] \ge \rho_E. \tag{2.7}$$

Assumption 4. Let $\alpha(x,t) := B^T(x,t)\nabla_x v(x,t)$. (i) There exist continuous functions $\rho_i : \mathbf{R}_+ \times \mathbf{R}^n \times \mathbf{R} \to \mathbf{R}_+$, $i = 1,2,\cdots,s$, such that for all (x,t),

$$\max_{\sigma\in\Sigma} \nabla_x^T v(x,t)\Delta f(x,\sigma,t) \le \sum_{i=1}^{s} \rho_i(\|\alpha\|,x,t). \tag{2.8}$$

(ii) For each i, $\rho_i(0,x,t) = 0\ \forall (x,t)$.

(iii) For any $\epsilon_i > 0$, there exists a unique continuous function $\kappa_i : \mathbf{R}^n \times \mathbf{R} \to \mathbf{R}_+$ such that

$$\rho_i(\kappa_i(\epsilon_i, x, t), x, t) = \epsilon_i. \tag{2.9}$$

Let $\pi_i(\epsilon_i, \alpha, x, t) := \alpha(x,t)[\kappa_i(\epsilon_i, x, t)]^{-2}$. The function $\pi_i(\epsilon_i, \cdot)$ is defined and continuous in $\mathbf{R}^m \times \mathbf{R}^n \times \mathbf{R}$.

The function $\rho_i(\cdot)$ stands for the worst possible effect of uncertainty in stability analysis (shown later in Theorem 1). Part (i) assures this effect of uncertainty is upper bounded by functions which are only dependent on, besides (x,t), $\|\alpha\|$. This enables the designer to configure the needed control magnitude to compensate the worst possible case uncertainty through a feasible strategy which "enters" the system through α. It will be seen more clearly in the proof of the theorem in the next section. Part (ii) assures the uncertainty can not jeopardize the stability when there is no control action available, i.e., $\alpha = 0$.

3. Comparison with the Early Matching Condition

In the early work such as Barmish *et al.* (1983) and Corless and Leitmann (1981), one requires the existence of a continuous function $e : \mathbf{R}^n \times \Sigma \times \mathbf{R} \to \mathbf{R}^m$ such that for all $(x, \sigma, t) \in \mathbf{R}^n \times \Sigma \times \mathbf{R}$,

$$\Delta f(x, \sigma, t) = B(x,t)e(x, \sigma, t). \tag{3.1}$$

Furthermore, there is a known continuous function $\tilde{\rho} : \mathbf{R}^n \times \mathbf{R} \to \mathbf{R}_+$ which bounds $e(\cdot)$:

$$\max_{\sigma \in \Sigma} \|e(x, \sigma, t)\| \le \tilde{\rho}(x,t), \forall (x,t). \tag{3.2}$$

The structural condition (3.1) is often recognized by the society as the matching condition (see, for example, Gavel, D.T., and Siljak, D.D., 1989, Kanellakopoulos *et al.* 1990). The configuration is both generic and practical. For each (x, σ, t), $e(x, \sigma, t)$ is in the range space of $B(x,t)$. Loosely speaking, this means the uncertainty can be "reached" by the control. Note that this can always be met by using sufficient number of controls, an extreme case of which may be $m = n$. The condition includes a large class of uncertain systems, examples of which may include mechanical manipulators, vehicle systems, building structures, etc. (see Corless and Leitmann 1990 for a complete survey). A practical interpretation of (3.1), which is in fact one of its major motivation but has been rarely mentioned, is closely relevant to the characteristics of mechanical systems: Given a multi-body mechanical system, the matching condition can be viewed as the need for an actuator in each mode. For example, consider a spring-mass-damper system with uncertain variations in the spring constant, mass, and damping coefficient. If there is an actuator, it can be shown easily that all the variations are within the "reach" of the actuator and the uncertainty is hence "matched."

Certainly, one the other hand, the condition (3.1) is ***sufficient***, but not necessary, to assure that the uncertainty is within the reach by the control. In light of this, the current structural condition, as shown in Assumption 4, intends to explore a less stringent configuration of the uncertainty. The major motivations are as follows. First, if it is possible for some state variable, which can be easily manipulated by the control, to reach the uncertainty, then one might not always need to insist on a direct capture of such uncertainty through the control. Second, the way to reach the uncertainty does not always need to be linear which was implied by (3.1, 2). In a sense, these motivations are the basis for the new matching condition. They can be further elaborated as the following.

Based on (3.1, 2), one has

$$\max_{\sigma \in \Sigma} \nabla_x^T v(x,t) \Delta f(x, \sigma, t) \le \|\alpha\| \tilde{\rho}(x,t) =: \rho(\|\alpha\|, x, t). \tag{3.3}$$

Comparing with (2.8), the early matching condition (3.1) is a special case of Assumption 4 with ρ_i linear in $\|\alpha\|$ and $s = 1$. Assumption 4 (ii) and (iii) are both met with $\kappa_1 = \epsilon_1 / \tilde{\rho}(x,t)$. We stress that (3.1, 2) are only the sufficient but not necessary condition for the ρ in (3.3) to be linear in $\|\alpha\|$. In other words, the early matching condition is a special case of the linear case of the current new matching condition.

4. Robust Control Design

We now propose the robust control based on the new matching condition. Let

$$\hat{\rho}_i(\|\alpha\|, x, t) := \rho_i(\|\alpha\|, x, t)(1 + \rho_E)^{-1}. \tag{4.1}$$

Note that $\hat{\rho}_i(0, x, t) = 0$ based on Assumption 4(ii). For any given $\epsilon_i > 0$, $i = 1, 2, \cdots, s$, the control is given by

$$u(t) = \sum_{i=1}^{s} p_i(\alpha(x(t), t), x(t), t), \tag{4.2}$$

where

$$p_i(\alpha, x, t) = \begin{cases} -\dfrac{\alpha \hat{\rho}_i(\|\alpha\|, x, t)}{\|\alpha\|^2}, & \text{if } \hat{\rho}_i(\|\alpha\|, x, t) > \epsilon_i, \\ -\dfrac{\alpha \hat{\rho}_i(\|\alpha\|, x, t)}{\kappa_i^2}, & \text{if } \hat{\rho}_i(\|\alpha\|, x, t) \le \epsilon_i. \end{cases} \tag{4.3}$$

Note that $p_i(\cdot)$ are continuous.

In the special case that $\hat{\rho}_i(\|\alpha\|, x, t) = \|\alpha\|_i^r \tilde{\rho}_i(x,t)$, $r_i > 0$ (not necessarily an integer), the robust control (4.3) takes the form (note that $\kappa_i = \epsilon_i^{1/r_i} \tilde{\rho}_i^{-1/r_i}$)

$$p_i(\alpha, x, t) = \begin{cases} -\dfrac{\alpha \hat{\rho}_i(\|\alpha\|, x, t)}{\|\alpha\|^2}, & \text{if } \hat{\rho}_i(\|\alpha\|, x, t) > \epsilon_i, \\ -\dfrac{\alpha \tilde{\rho}^{\frac{2}{r_i}} \hat{\rho}_i(\|\alpha\|, x, t)}{\epsilon_i^{\frac{2}{r_i}}}, & \text{if } \hat{\rho}_i(\|\alpha\|, x, t) \le \epsilon_i. \end{cases} \tag{4.4}$$

The work in Corless and Leitmann (1981) corresponds to $r = 1$ and $s = 1$. In this special case, the present control is in the same form as the previous case for $\hat{\rho}_1 > \epsilon_1$. As $\hat{\rho}_1 \le \epsilon_1$, the present control is $-(\alpha \|\alpha\| \tilde{\rho}_1^2 / \epsilon_1^2) \tilde{\rho}_1$ and the early control is $-(\alpha \tilde{\rho}_1 / \epsilon_1) \tilde{\rho}_1$. For given (x,t), the current control magnitude is always no greater than Corless and Leitmann (1981) since as $\hat{\rho}_1 \le \epsilon_1$, $\|\alpha\|^2 \tilde{\rho}_1^2 / \epsilon_1^2 \le \|\alpha\| \tilde{\rho}_1 / \epsilon_1$. In particular, $\|\alpha\|^2 \tilde{\rho}_1^2 / \epsilon_1^2 < \|\alpha\| \tilde{\rho}_1 / \epsilon_1$ as $0 < \hat{\rho}_1 < \epsilon_1$.

Theorem 1. Subject to Assumptions 1-4, the uncertain system (2.1) under the control (4.2) is practically stable (the definition of practical stability can be found in Chen and Leitmann 1987).

Proof. For the stability analysis of the controlled uncertain system, consider the Lyapunov function candidate $v(x,t)$ in Assumption 2. For any admissible $\sigma(\cdot)$, the time derivative of v along the solution of the controlled uncertain system is given by

$$\begin{aligned} \dot{v}(x,t) \le & \frac{\partial v(x,t)}{\partial t} + \nabla_x^T v(x,t)[f(x,t) + \Delta f(x,t)] \\ & + \nabla_x^T v(x,t) B(x,t)[I + E(x, \sigma, t)] \sum_{i=1}^{s} p_i(\alpha, x, t). \end{aligned} \tag{4.5}$$

Note that the control (4.3) implies $p_i(\alpha, x, t) = -\alpha h_i(\|\alpha\|, x, t)$ where $h_i(\|\alpha\|, x, t) \ge 0$ is defined in an obvious way. Using (2.3), (2.7), and (2.8), one can show that

$$
\begin{aligned}
\dot{v}(x,t) \leq & -\gamma_3(\|x\|) + \sum_i [\rho_i - \alpha^T \alpha h_i - \frac{1}{2}\alpha^T(E+E^T)\alpha h_i] \\
\leq & -\gamma_3(\|x\|) + \sum_i [\rho_i - \|\alpha\|^2 h_i - \|\alpha\|^2 \rho_E h_i].
\end{aligned} \tag{4.6}
$$

As $\hat{\rho}_i > \epsilon_i$,

$$
\begin{aligned}
&\rho_i - \|\alpha\|^2 h_i - \|\alpha\|^2 \rho_E h_i \\
=&\rho_i - \hat{\rho}_i - \rho_E \hat{\rho}_i \\
=&\rho_i - \hat{\rho}_i(1+\rho_E) \\
=&0.
\end{aligned} \tag{4.7}
$$

As $\hat{\rho}_i \leq \epsilon_i$ (note that $\hat{\rho}_i \geq 0$),

$$
\begin{aligned}
&\rho_i - \|\alpha\|^2 h_i - \|\alpha\|^2 \rho_E h_i \\
=&\rho_i - \|\alpha\|^2 \kappa_i^{-2} \hat{\rho}_i - \|\alpha\|^2 \kappa_i^{-2} \rho_E \hat{\rho}_i \\
=&\rho_i - \|\alpha\|^2 \kappa_i^{-2} \hat{\rho}_i (1+\rho_E) \\
\leq&\hat{\rho}_i(1+\rho_E) \\
\leq&\epsilon_i(1+\rho_E).
\end{aligned} \tag{4.8}
$$

Thus the Lyapunov derivative is in-the-worst-case upper bounded by

$$
\dot{v}(x,t) \leq -\gamma_3(\|x\|) + (1+\rho_E)\sum_{i=1}^{s} \epsilon_i. \tag{4.9}
$$

The rest of the proof follows directly from the standard argument in Corless and Leitmann (1981). The uniform boundedness ball is with radius

$$
d(r) = \begin{cases} (\gamma_1^{-1} \circ \gamma_2)(R), & \text{if } r \leq R, \\ (\gamma_1^{-1} \circ \gamma_2)(r), & \text{if } r > R, \end{cases} \tag{4.10}
$$

where

$$
R = \gamma_3^{-1}(\bar{\epsilon}), \qquad \bar{\epsilon} = (1+\rho_E)\sum_{i=1}^{s} \epsilon_i. \tag{4.11}
$$

The uniform ultimate boundedness ball is with radius $\bar{d}$ such that $\bar{d} > (\gamma_1^{-1} \circ \gamma_2)(R)$ and the maximum amount of time it takes to enter this ball (and remains there thereafter) is

$$
T(\bar{d}, r) = \begin{cases} 0 & \text{if } r \leq (\gamma_2^{-1} \circ \gamma_1)(\bar{d}), \\ \dfrac{\gamma_2(r) - (\gamma_1 \circ \gamma_2^{-1} \circ \gamma_1)(\bar{d})}{(\gamma_3 \circ \gamma_2^{-1} \circ \gamma_1)(\bar{d})} & \text{otherwise.} \end{cases} \tag{4.12}
$$

The uniform stability ball is with radius $\delta(\bar{d}) = R$. *Q.E.D.*

5. Mismatched Uncertainty and Nonlinear Input Matrix

We now address the mismatched uncertainty, namely, the uncertainty that does not meet Assumptions 3 and 4. The framework proposed in Chen and Leitmann (1987) is readily adopted in this case.

Choose $\Delta f_m(x,\sigma,t)$, $\Delta \tilde{f}(x,\sigma,t)$, $\Delta B_m(x,\sigma,t)$, and $\Delta \tilde{B}(x,\sigma,t)$ such that for all $(x,\sigma,t) \in \mathbf{R}^n \times \Sigma \times \mathbf{R}$,

$$
\Delta f(x,\sigma,t) = \Delta f_m(x,\sigma,t) + \Delta \tilde{f}(x,\sigma,t), \tag{5.1.1}
$$

$$
\Delta B(x,\sigma,t) = \Delta B_m(x,\sigma,t) + \Delta \tilde{B}(x,\sigma,t). \tag{5.1.2}
$$

Assumption 5. (i) Assumptions 3 and 4 are met by replacing $\Delta f(x,\sigma,t)$ and $\Delta B(x,\sigma,t)$ with $\Delta f_m(x,\sigma,t)$ and $\Delta B_m(x,\sigma,t)$.

(ii) There exists a function $\gamma_4 : \mathbf{R}_+ \to \mathbf{R}$ such that for the $v(x,t)$ in Assumption 2,

$$
\begin{aligned}
&\max_{\sigma\in\Sigma} \nabla_x^T v(x,t) \left[\Delta \tilde{f}(x,\sigma,t) + \Delta \tilde{B}(x,\sigma,t) \sum_{i=1}^{s} p_i(\alpha(x,t),x,t)\right] \\
&\leq \gamma_4(\|x\|)
\end{aligned} \tag{5.2}
$$

for all (x,t). Furthermore, there are positive constants s_1 and s_2 (possibly infinite) such that $s_2 > (\gamma_1^{-1} \circ \gamma_2)(s_1)$ and $\gamma_3(\|x\|) - \gamma(\|x\|)$ is non-negative, strictly increasing for $\|x\| \in [s_1, s_2)$.

The uncertainty $\Delta f(x,\sigma,t)$ and $\Delta B(x,\sigma,t)$ are decomposed into two parts in (5.1). Only one part, namely, the *matched* part, needs to fit in the framework of Assumptions 3 and 4.

Lemma 1. Subject to Assumptions 1,2 and 5, the uncertain system under the control (4.2) is practically stable. If $s_2 = \infty$, then the practical stability is global. If $s_2 < \infty$, then it is local.

Proof. The proof follows closely to that of Chen and Leitmann (1987) and is omitted here for simplicity. *Q.E.D.*

The system's input part $[B(x,t) + \Delta B(x,\sigma,t)]u$ in (2.1) can also be extended to be the nonlinear type $B(x,t)g(x,u,\sigma,t)$ where

$$
u^T g(x,u,\sigma,t) \geq -\beta_1(x,\sigma,t)\|u\| + \beta_2(x,\sigma,t)\|u\|^2, \tag{5.3}
$$

$\beta_{1,2} : \mathbf{R}^n \times \Sigma \times \mathbf{R} \to \mathbf{R}_+$. This renders the present consideration a special case. Detailed discussions are shown in Corless and Leitmann (1990). The robust control design introduced here is applicable. Only a slight modification is needed. This can be easily figured out by combining both work and is omitted here for simplicity.

6. Illustrative Examples

Example 1. Consider the uncertain system

$$
\begin{aligned}
\dot{x}_1(t) =& -x_1(t) + \sigma_1(t)|x_2(t)|^{1/2}, \\
\dot{x}_2(t) =& -x_1(t) - 2x_2(t) + (1+\sigma_2(t))u(t) \\
&+ |x_2(t)|^{1/2} e(x_1(t), x_2(t), \sigma_1(t), t),
\end{aligned} \tag{6.1}
$$

where $\sigma = [\sigma_1 \; \sigma_2]^T$ is the uncertain parameter which is bounded by

$$
\underline{\sigma}_1 \leq \sigma_1(t) \leq \bar{\sigma}_1, \underline{\sigma}_2 \leq \sigma_2(t) \leq \bar{\sigma}_2, \qquad \underline{\sigma}_2 > -1. \tag{6.2}
$$

Furthermore, the function $e(\cdot)$, which is unknown, is bounded by a known continuous scalar function $\rho(\cdot)$:

$$
\max_{\sigma_1} |e(x_1,x_2,\sigma_1,t)| \leq \tilde{\rho}(x_1,x_2,t). \tag{6.3}
$$

The uncertainty $\sigma_1|x_2|^{1/2}$ is considered mismatched in Barmish *et al.* (1983) and Corless and Leitmann (1981). The system is in the form of (2.1) by choosing

$$
f(x,t) = \begin{bmatrix} -x_1 \\ -2x_2 \end{bmatrix}, \Delta f(x,\sigma,t) = \begin{bmatrix} \sigma_1|x_2|^{1/2} \\ -x_1 + |x_2|^{1/2} e(x_1,x_2,\sigma_1,t) \end{bmatrix}, \tag{6.4}
$$

$$
B(x,t) = \begin{bmatrix} 0 \\ 1 \end{bmatrix}, \Delta B(x,t) = \begin{bmatrix} 0 \\ \sigma_2 \end{bmatrix}. \tag{6.5}
$$

For the control design, we choose the Lyapunov function $v(\cdot)$ to be

$$
v(x) = \frac{1}{2}(x_1^2 + x_2^2) \tag{6.6}
$$

and therefore $\alpha = x_2$. Assumption 2 is met by taking $\gamma_1(\|x\|) = \gamma_2(\|x\|) = \frac{1}{2}\|x\|^2$, $\gamma_3(\|x\|) = \|x\|^2$. Assumption 3 is met with $E(x,\sigma,t) = \sigma_2$, $\rho_E = \underline{\sigma}_2$. Assumption 4 is met since

$$
\begin{aligned}
&\max_{\sigma} \nabla_x^T v(x) \Delta f(x,\sigma,t) \\
&\leq \max_{\sigma_1} |\sigma_1||x_1||\alpha|^{1/2} + |\alpha||x_1| + |\alpha|^{3/2}\tilde{\rho}(x_1,x_2,t) \\
&=: \rho_1(\|\alpha\|,x,t) + \rho_2(\|\alpha\|,x,t) + \rho_3(\|\alpha\|,x,t).
\end{aligned} \tag{6.7}
$$

Obviously, $\rho_i(0,x,t) = 0$, $i = 1,2,3$. The robust control (4.3) is given by the following (with $s = 3$):

$$p_1 = \begin{cases} -\frac{\alpha}{|\alpha|^2}\rho_1(1+\underline{\sigma}_2)^{-1}, \text{if } \rho_1(1+\underline{\sigma}_2)^{-1} > \epsilon_1, \\ -\frac{\alpha\left(\max_{\sigma_1}|\sigma_1||x_1|\right)^4}{\epsilon_1^4}\rho_1(1+\underline{\sigma}_2)^{-1}, \text{if } \rho_1(1+\underline{\sigma}_2)^{-1} \le \epsilon_1, \end{cases} \quad (6.8.1)$$

$$p_2 = \begin{cases} -\frac{\alpha}{|\alpha|^2}\rho_2(1+\underline{\sigma}_2)^{-1}, & \text{if } \rho_2(1+\underline{\sigma}_2)^{-1} > \epsilon_2, \\ -\frac{\alpha|x_1|^2}{\epsilon_2^2}\rho_2(1+\underline{\sigma}_2)^{-1}, & \text{if } \rho_2(1+\underline{\sigma}_2)^{-1} \le \epsilon_2, \end{cases} \quad (6.8.2)$$

$$p_3 = \begin{cases} -\frac{\alpha}{|\alpha|^2}\rho_3(1+\underline{\sigma}_2)^{-1}, & \text{if } \rho_3(1+\underline{\sigma}_2)^{-1} > \epsilon_3, \\ -\frac{\alpha\tilde{\rho}^{4/3}}{\epsilon_3^{4/3}}\rho_2(1+\underline{\sigma}_2)^{-1}, & \text{if } \rho_3(1+\underline{\sigma}_2)^{-1} \le \epsilon_3. \end{cases} \quad (6.8.3)$$

Note that if one uses the matching condition and control design in Corless and Leitmann (1981), then the system is considered mismatched. The robustness study in Chen and Leitmann (1987) is still applicable to such case. However, the guaranteed system performance is then degraded since the size of the ultimate boundedness ball increases. With the current setting, the ultimate boundedness ball can be made arbitrary small.

Example 2. Consider the rotational motion of a rigid body with one point fixed in an inertial space, which is governed by (Goldstein 1980)

$$I\dot{\omega} + \omega \times I\omega = M, \quad (6.9)$$

where I is the 3×3 inertia matrix about a body-fixed coordinate system whose origin is the fixed point, $\omega = [\omega_x \ \omega_y \ \omega_z]^T$ is the angular velocity of the body, M is the external 3×1 moment vector. The coordinate axes are chosen to be the principal axes of the body and hence $I = \mathrm{diag}\{I_x, I_y, I_z\}$. Suppose that the first mode is under an active control and the bearings of the second and third axes are under viscous friction. Then the system can be represented by

$$\begin{aligned} I_x\dot{\omega}_x &= -(I_z - I_y)\omega_y\omega_z + u, \\ I_y\dot{\omega}_y &= -(I_x - I_z)\omega_x\omega_z - l_y\omega_y, \\ I_z\dot{\omega}_z &= -(I_y - I_x)\omega_y\omega_x - l_z\omega_z, \end{aligned} \quad (6.10)$$

where u is the external active control, $l_{y,z} > 0$ are the viscous friction coefficients. Consider the situation that the payloads of the three axes vary due to different operating conditions and the prediction is difficult. We then treated the following as time-varying uncertain parameters:

$$\underline{I}_i \le I_i(t) \le \bar{I}_i, i = x, y, z, \quad (6.11)$$

where $\underline{I}_i$ and $\bar{I}_i$ are the known constant bounds. Certainly, we expect $I_i(t) > 0$ for all t. This in turn implies $\underline{I}_i > 0$. Note that no particular order on the magnitude of I_x, I_y, and I_z is imposed. We further decompose $I_x(t) = I_x^o + \Delta I_x(t)$ where I_x^o is the nominal portion, $\Delta I_x(t)$ is the uncertain portion and is bounded by $\Delta\underline{I}_x \le \Delta I_x(t) \le \Delta\bar{I}_x$. Assume, without lose of generality, that $I_x^o > 0$. The viscous friction coefficients are also uncertain and vary with time:

$$0 < \underline{l}_k \le l_k(t) \le \bar{l}_k, k = y, z. \quad (6.12)$$

The system (6.10) can also be represented by

$$\dot{\omega}_x = -\left(\frac{I_z(t) - I_y(t)}{I_x(t)}\right)\omega_y\omega_z + \frac{1}{I_x(t)}u =: \xi_1(t)\omega_y\omega_z + \frac{1}{I_x(t)}u,$$

$$\dot{\omega}_y = -\left(\frac{I_x(t) - I_z(t)}{I_y(t)}\right)\omega_x\omega_z - \frac{l_y(t)}{I_y(t)}\omega_y =: \xi_2(t)\omega_x\omega_z - \eta_1(t)\omega_y,$$

$$\dot{\omega}_z = -\left(\frac{I_y(t) - I_x(t)}{I_z(t)}\right)\omega_x\omega_y - \frac{l_z(t)}{I_z(t)}\omega_z =: \xi_3(t)\omega_x\omega_y - \eta_2(t)\omega_z. \quad (6.13)$$

The newly defined parameters $\xi_j(t)$, $j = 1, 2, 3$, are bounded:

$$\underline{\xi}_j \le \xi_j(t) \le \bar{\xi}_j, \quad (6.14)$$

where the bounds can be easily determined based on $\underline{I}_i$ and $\bar{I}_i$. For example, $\bar{\xi}_1 = (\bar{I}_y - \underline{I}_z)/\underline{I}_x$ if $\bar{I}_y \ge \underline{I}_z$; $\bar{\xi}_1 = (\bar{I}_y - \underline{I}_z)/\bar{I}_x$ if $\bar{I}_y < \underline{I}_z$. The parameters η_k, $k = 1, 2$, are bounded by

$$0 < \underline{\eta}_k \le \eta_k(t) \le \bar{\eta}_k. \quad (6.15)$$

Here the > 0 sign is determined by the fact that $l_k(t), I_k(t) > 0$ for all t. The robust control (4.3) is given by the following (with $s = 2$):

$$p_1 = \begin{cases} -\frac{\alpha}{|\alpha|^2}\rho_1(1+\rho_E)^{-1}, \text{if } \rho_1(1+\rho_E)^{-1} > \epsilon_1, \\ -\frac{\alpha|\omega_y|^2|\omega_z|^2(\bar{\xi}_x + \bar{\xi}_y + \bar{\xi}_z)^2 I_x^{o2}}{\epsilon_1^2}\rho_1(1+\rho_E)^{-1}, \\ \text{if } \rho_1(1+\rho_E)^{-1} \le \epsilon_1, \end{cases} \quad (6.16.1)$$

$$p_2 = \begin{cases} -\frac{\alpha}{|\alpha|^2}\rho_2(1+\rho_E)^{-1}, & \text{if } \rho_2(1+\rho_E)^{-1} > \epsilon_2, \\ -\frac{\alpha I_x^o}{\epsilon_2}\rho_2(1+\rho_E)^{-1}, & \text{if } \rho_2(1+\rho_E)^{-1} \le \epsilon_2. \end{cases} \quad (6.16.2)$$

If the setting in Corless and Leitmann (1981) is used, then one will need three independent controls to ensure the matching condition.

Example 3. The problem of controlling chaotic systems has attracted a large amount of attention and interest during the recent past. For a reference, see, for instance, Ott *et al.* (1990) and its bibliographies. However, so far, there has been no work that can address the uncertainty issue.

Consider the following Lorenz system under control:

$$\begin{aligned} \dot{x} &= \eta(y - x), \\ \dot{y} &= rx - y - xz + u, \\ \dot{z} &= xy - bz. \end{aligned} \quad (6.17)$$

In Lorenz (1963), x is proportional to the intensity of convective motion, y is proportional to the temperature difference between the ascending and descending currents, z is proportional to the distortion of the vertical temperature profile from being linear, η and r are proportional to the Prantle and Rayleigh numbers, respectively, and b is proportional to some proportions of the region under consideration. In the natural convection setting of Ehrhard and Muller (1990), u corresponds to the tilt angle of the loop from the vertical. The control problem is to drive the state (x, y, z) to either one of the three equilibrium positions of the uncontrolled system: $(\pm[b(r-1)]^{1/2}, \pm[b(r-1)]^{1/2}, r-1)$ (unstable), $(0, 0, 0)$ (stable). Assume $r > 1$ for otherwise only one equilibrium position $(0, 0, 0)$ exists and is a trivial case. Here we only consider the control for one unstable equilibrium position for simplicity. Define the new state variables $x_1 = x - [b(r-1)]^{1/2}$, $x_2 = y - [b(r-1)]^{1/2}$, $x_3 = z - (r-1)$. The system (6.17) can be transformed to

$$\begin{aligned} \dot{x}_1 &= \eta(x_2 - x_1), \\ \dot{x}_2 &= x_1 - x_2 - x_1x_3 - \beta x_3 + u, \\ \dot{x}_3 &= x_1x_2 - bx_3 + \beta(x_1 + x_2). \end{aligned} \quad (6.18)$$

where $\beta = [b(r-1)]^{1/2}$. In practice, since the Prantle and Rayleigh numbers are dependent on viscosity, they may vary due to temperature change. We treat both as time-varying uncertain parameters:

$$\eta(t) = \eta_0 + \Delta\eta(t), \qquad 0 < \underline{\eta} \le \eta(t) \le \bar{\eta}, |\Delta\eta(t)| \le \Delta\bar{\eta}, \forall t, \tag{6.19}$$

$$r(t) = r_0 + \Delta r(t), \qquad \underline{r} \le r(t) \le \bar{r}, \Delta\underline{r} \le \Delta r(t) \le \Delta\bar{r}, \forall t, \tag{6.20}$$

where η_0 and r_0 are the nominal parameters, $\Delta\eta(t)$ and $\Delta r(t)$ are the uncertain portions. The bounds of the uncertain parameters are characterized in two ways. They are either in terms of the uncertain parameter itself (such as $\eta(t)$) or its uncertain portion (such as $\Delta\eta(t)$). Consequently, we can decompose β as follows:

$$\beta(t) = \beta_0 + \Delta\beta(t), \qquad \beta_0 = [b(r_0 - 1)]^{1/2}. \tag{6.21}$$

Furthermore, the bounds are given: $\underline{\beta} \le \beta(t) \le \bar{\beta}$ and $|\Delta\beta(t)| \le \Delta\bar{\beta}$. The control law is proposed in a slightly different setting as (4.2). We first choose the nominal control law

$$u = -k_1x_1 - k_2x_2 + \left(1 - \frac{k_1 - 1}{\eta_0 p_1}\right) x_1x_3 + \beta_0 \left(1 - \frac{k_1 - 1}{\eta_0 p_1}\right) x_3, \tag{6.22}$$

where k_1, k_2, and p_1 are design parameters such that

$$k_1 > 1,\ k_2 > -1,\ p_1 > \frac{\beta_0^2}{4b\eta_0}. \tag{6.23}$$

The controlled nominal system is given by

$$\begin{aligned} \dot{x}_1 &= \eta_0(x_2 - x_1), \\ \dot{x}_2 &= (1 - k_1)x_1 - (1 + k_2)x_2 - \beta_0 \left(\frac{k_1 - 1}{\eta_0 p_1}\right) x_3 - \frac{k_1 - 1}{\eta_0 p_1} x_1x_3, \\ \dot{x}_3 &= x_1x_2 - bx_3 + \beta_0(x_1 + x_2). \end{aligned} \tag{6.24}$$

Take the following Lyapunov function candidate

$$v(x) = \frac{1}{2}\left(p_1x_1^2 + \frac{\eta_0 p_1}{k_1 - 1}x_2^2 + x_3^2\right). \tag{6.25}$$

Its derivative along the solution of the controlled nominal system is given by

$$\begin{aligned} \dot{v}(x) &= -p_1\eta_0x_1^2 - \frac{\eta_0 p_1}{k_1 - 1}(1 + k_2)x_2^2 - bx_3^2 + \beta_0x_1x_3 \\ &= -\begin{bmatrix} x_1 & x_3 \end{bmatrix} \begin{bmatrix} p_1\eta_0 & -\frac{1}{2}\beta_0 \\ -\frac{1}{2}\beta_0 & b \end{bmatrix} \begin{bmatrix} x_1 \\ x_3 \end{bmatrix} - \frac{\eta_0 p_1}{k_1 - 1}(1 + k_2)x_2^2. \end{aligned} \tag{6.26}$$

The robust control is chosen to be of the form (4.3) with $s = 2$,

$$\alpha = \frac{\eta_0 p_1}{k_1 - 1}x_2, \rho_E = 0, \rho_1 = \frac{k_1 - 1}{\eta_0}\Delta\bar{\eta}|\alpha||x_1|,$$

$$\rho_2 = \Delta\bar{\beta}|x_3||\alpha|, \rho_3 = \frac{k_1 - 1}{\eta_0 p_1}|\alpha||x_3|\Delta\bar{\beta}.$$

Furthermore, we modify the choice of p_1:

$$p_1 > \frac{\bar{\beta}^2}{4b\underline{\eta}}. \tag{6.27}$$

The robust control (4.3) is given by the following (with $s = 3$):

$$p_1 = \begin{cases} -\dfrac{\alpha}{|\alpha|^2}\rho_1, & \text{if } \rho_1 > \epsilon_1, \\ -\dfrac{\alpha}{\epsilon_1^2}\left(\dfrac{k_1 - 1}{\eta_o}\Delta\bar{\eta}|x_1|\right)^2 \rho_1, & \text{if } \rho_1 \le \epsilon_1, \end{cases} \tag{6.28.1}$$

$$p_2 = \begin{cases} -\dfrac{\alpha}{|\alpha|^2}\rho_2, & \text{if } \rho_2 > \epsilon_2, \\ -\dfrac{\alpha}{\epsilon_2^2}\left(\Delta\bar{\beta}|x_3|\right)^2 \rho_2, & \text{if } \rho_2 \le \epsilon_2, \end{cases} \tag{6.28.2}$$

Schmitendorf, W.E., 1988, "Designing stabilizing controllers for uncertain systems using the Riccati equation approach," *IEEE Transactions on Automatic Control*, Vol. 33, pp. 376-379.

$$p_3 = \begin{cases} -\dfrac{\alpha}{|\alpha|^2}\rho_3, & \text{if } \rho_3 > \epsilon_3, \\ -\dfrac{\alpha}{\epsilon_3^2}\left(\dfrac{k_1 - 1}{\eta_o p_1}\Delta\bar{\beta}|x_3|\right)^2 \rho_1, & \text{if } \rho_3 \le \epsilon_3. \end{cases} \tag{6.28.3}$$

The time derivative of the Lyapunov function along the solution of the controlled uncertain system is in-the-worst-case upper bounded by

$$\begin{aligned} \dot{v}(x) &\le -\begin{bmatrix} |x_1| & |x_3| \end{bmatrix} \Psi \begin{bmatrix} |x_1| \\ |x_3| \end{bmatrix} - \frac{\eta_0 p_1}{k_1 - 1}(1 + k_2)x_2^2 + \epsilon_1 + \epsilon_2 \\ &\le -\underline{\lambda}\|x\|^2 + \epsilon_1 + \epsilon_2, \end{aligned} \tag{6.29}$$

where

$$\Psi = \begin{bmatrix} p_1\underline{\eta} & -\frac{1}{2}\bar{\beta} \\ -\frac{1}{2}\bar{\beta} & b \end{bmatrix}, \tag{6.30}$$

$$\underline{\lambda} = \min\{\lambda_{\min}(\Psi), \frac{\eta_0 p_1}{k_1 - 1}(1 + k_2)\}. \tag{6.31}$$

Note that p_1 in (6.27) assures $\lambda_{\min}(\Psi) > 0$.

References

Barmish, B.R., 1985, "Necessary and sufficient conditions for quadratic stabilizability of an uncertain system", *Journal of Optimization Theory and Applications*, Vol. 46, pp. 399-408.

Barmish, B.R., Corless, M., and Leitmann, 1983, "A new class of stabilizing controllers for uncertain dynamical systems," *SIAM Journal of Control and Optimization*, Vol. 21, pp. 246-255.

Barmish, B.R., and Leitmann, G., 1982, "On ultimate boundedness control of uncertain systems in the absence of matching conditions", *IEEE Transactions on Automatic Control*, Vol. 27, pp. 153-157.

Chen, Y.H. and J.S. Chen, 1991, "Robust Control of Uncertain Systems with Time-Varying Uncertainty -An Optimization Setting", *Mechanics and Control*, J.M. Skowronski, H. Flasher, and R.S. Guttalu (eds.), pp. 97-114, Springer-Verlag, New York.

Chen, Y.H., and Leitmann, G., 1987, "Robustness of uncertain systems in the absence of matching assumptions", *International Journal of Control*, Vol. 45, pp. 1527-1542.

Corless, M.J. and Leitmann, G., 1981, "Continuous state feedback guaranteeing uniform ultimate boundedness for uncertain dynamic systems," *IEEE Transactions on Automatic Control*, Vol. 26, pp. 1139-1144.

Corless, M., and Leitmann, G., 1990, "Deterministic control of uncertain systems: a Lyapunov theory approach," *Variable Structure Control Systems*, A. Zinober (ed.), IEE Control Engineering Series 40, Peter Peregrinus Ltd., London.

P. Ehrhard and U. Muller, 1990, "Dynamic behavior of natural convection in a single-phase loop," *Journal of Fluid Mechanics*, Vol. 217, pp. 487-518.

Gavel, D.T., and Siljak, D.D., 1989, "Decentralized adaptive control: structural conditions for stability", *IEEE Transactions on Automatic Control*, Vol. 129, pp. 413-426.

Goldstein, H., 1980, *Classical Mechanics*, Second Edition, Addison-Wesley, Reading.

Gu, K., Chen, Y.H., Zhody, M.A., and Loh, N.K., 1991, "Quadratic stabilizability of uncertain systems: a two level optimization setup", *Automatica*, Vol. 27, pp. 161-165.

Kanellakopoulos, I., Kokotovic, P.V., and Middleton, R.H., 1990, "Observer-based adaptive control of nonlinear systems under matching conditions", *Proceedings of the 1990 American Control Conference*, San Diego, pp. 549-555.

Lorenz, E.N., 1963, "Deterministic nonperiodic flow," *Journal of The Atmospheric Sciences*, Vol. 20, pp. 130-141.

Ott, E., Grebogi, C., and Yorke, J.A., 1990, "Controlling chaos," *Physical Review Letters*, Vol. 64, pp. 1196-1199.

Petersen, I.R. and Hollot, C.V., 1986, "A Riccati equation approach to the stabilization of uncertain linear systems," *Automatica*, Vol. 22, pp. 397-411.

Proceedings of the American Control Conference San Francisco, California • June 1993

Optimal, Low-sensitivity, Feedback Controllers for Interconnected Discrete-Time Systems

Rajab Challoo, Jose Perez
Jian Zhou, and R.A. McLauchlan*
EE/CS Department, Campus Box 192
*ME/IE Department, Campus Box 191
Texas A&I University, Kingsville, Texas 78363

ABSTRACT

A large-scale, interconnected, discrete-time system is considered. The system consists of an uncontrolled main subsystem which communicates directly with N local subsystems, all of which have inputs. There is no direct communication from one local subsystem to another. Futhermore, it is assumed that there are uncertain parameters involved in all the subsystems. The treated problem is to design state feedback controllers for all the sub-systems by minimizing a performance index while reducing trajectory sensitivities with respect to the uncertain parameters of the subsystems.

INTRODUCTION

The decentralized control problem has been studied extensively in recent years. It has been found that a single controller for the entire system is not only impractical, but, in the majority of cases, unrealistic. Therefore, considerable effort has been applied to the design of local controllers. The design of controllers insensitive to parameter variations has also been the focus of much research. In this note, necessary conditions for optimality are derived for the minimization of local performance criteria which take trajectory sensitivities into account [1]. The gains are constrained to be nondynamic. For this, it was necessary to assume that there are no decentralized fixed modes present [2].

PROBLEM FORMULATION

Consider a large-scale system represented by the following discrete-time dynamics:

$$x_1(k+1) = A_{11}(\mu_1)x_1(k) + A_{1j}(\mu_j)x_j(k) + \sum_{I_2} A_{1i}(\mu_i)x_i(k) \tag{1a}$$

$$x_i(k+1) = A_{i1}(\mu_1)x_1(k) + A_{ii}(\mu_i)x_i(k) + B_i u_i(k) \qquad \text{for } i \in I_1 , \tag{1b}$$

where $x_i(k) \in R^{ni}$, $i \in I$, are the state vectors and $u_i(k) \in R^{mi}$, $i \in I_1$, are the input vectors. The state matrices $A(\mu_i)$ and input matrices B_i are time-invariant and of dimensions $n_i \times n_i$ and $m_i \times n_i$, respectively. The sets I, I_1, I_2 are defined as follows. $I=\{1, 2, \ldots j, \ldots, N+1\}$, $I_1=I/\{1\}$, and $I_2=I/\{1_j\}$.

The inputs for the interconnected subsystems are given by

$$u_i(k) = G_{i1}x_2(k) + G_{ii}x_2(k) \qquad \text{for } i \in I_1 , \tag{2}$$

where G_{i1} are constant matrices which are selected to minimize the cost functionals

$$J_i = \sum_{k=0}^{\infty} [x_1^T(k)Q_1x_1(k) + x_i^T(k)Q_ix_i(k) + u_i^T(k)R_iu_i(k) + \sigma_1^T(k)S_1\sigma_1(k) + \sigma_i^T(k)S_i\sigma_i(k)] \qquad \text{for } i \in I_1 \tag{3}$$

while reducing trajectory sensitivities along a nominal μ_{i0}. The matrices Q and R are positive semidefinite and positive definite, respectively. And, the state sensitivity functions, $\sigma_i(k) \in R^{ni}$, are defined by

$$\sigma_i(k) = \frac{\partial x_i(k,\mu_i)}{\partial \mu_i}\Big|_{\mu_i = \mu_{i0}} \qquad \text{for } i \in I . \tag{4}$$

Substituting (2) into (1), taking the partial derivatives with respect to μ_i evaluated at μ_{i0}, and employing definition (4), the following augmented system is formed.

$$x_1(k+1) = A_{11}x_1(k) + A_{1j}x_j(k) + \sum_{I_2} A_{1j}x_i(k) \tag{5a}$$

$$x_i(k+1) = F_{i1}x_1(k) + F_{ii}x_i(k) \tag{5b}$$

$$\sigma_1(k+1) = A_{\mu 1}x_1(k) + A_{11}\sigma_1(k) \tag{5c}$$

$$\sigma_i(k+1) = A_{\mu i}x_i(k) + F_{ii}\sigma_i(k) , \qquad \text{for } i \in I_1 \tag{5d}$$

where

$$F_{i1} = A_{i1} + B_iG_{i1} \tag{6a}$$

$$F_{ii} = A_{ii} + B_iG_{ii} \tag{6b}$$

$$A_{\mu i} = \frac{\partial A_{ii}(\mu_i)}{\partial \mu_i}\Big|_{\mu_i = \mu_{i0}} \tag{6c}$$

For convenience, the argument μ_i has been omitted. In the sequel, this shall be common practice. We shall now focus our attention on the minimization of the jth performance index. Since the jth local subsystem does not have any information about the other subsystems, it is possible to ignore the interconnections, $\Sigma A_{1i}x_i(k)$. Thus the system reduces to

$$x_i(k+1) = A_{11}x_1(k) + A_{1j}x_j(k) \tag{7a}$$

$$x_j(k+1) = F_{j1}x_1(k) + F_{jj}x_j(k) \tag{7b}$$

$$\sigma_1(k+1) = A_{\mu 1}x_1(k) + A_{11}\sigma_1(k) \tag{7c}$$

$$\sigma_j(k+1) = A_{\mu j}x_j(k) + F_{jj}\sigma_j(k) . \tag{7d}$$

or written more compactly,

$$\hat{x}_i(k+1) = F_j\hat{x}(k) \tag{8a}$$

$$\hat{\sigma}(k+1) = A_\mu \hat{x}(k) + F_0\hat{\sigma}(k) , \tag{8b}$$

where $\hat{x}(k) = [x_1^T(k), x_j^T(k)]^T$, $\hat{\sigma}(k) = [\sigma_1^T(k), \sigma_j^T(k)]^T$, and

$$F_j = \begin{bmatrix} A_{11} & A_{1j} \\ F_{j1} & F_{jj} \end{bmatrix}, \; A_\mu = \text{block diag.}[A_{11}, A_{jj}], \; F_0 = \text{block diag.}[A_{11}, A_{jj}].$$

Substituting (2) into (3), for i=j, the performance index may be written as

$$J_i = \sum_{k=0}^{\infty} [x_1^T(k)Q_{11}x_1(k) + 2x_i^T(k)Q_{1j}x_j(k) + x_j^T(k)Q_{jj}x_j(k) + \sigma_1^T(k)S_1\sigma_1(k) + \sigma_j^T(k)S_j\sigma_j(k)], \tag{9}$$

where

$$Q_{11} = Q_1 + G_{j1}^TR_jG_{j1} \tag{10a}$$

$$Q_{1j} = G_{j1}^TR_jG_{jj} \tag{10b}$$

$$Q_{jj} = Q_j + G_{jj}^TR_jG_{jj} . \tag{10c}$$

Equation (9) may be written more compactly as

$$J_j = \sum_{k=0}^{\infty} [\hat{x}^T(k)\hat{Q}\hat{x}(k) + \hat{\sigma}^T(k)S\hat{\sigma}(k)] , \tag{11}$$

where

$$\hat{Q} = \begin{bmatrix} Q_{11} & Q_{1j} \\ Q_{1j}^T & Q_{jj} \end{bmatrix}, \text{ and } S = \text{block diag.}[S_1, S_j] .$$

It is required that all eigenvalues of $A_j + \hat{B}_jG_j$ be inside the unit circle, and the triple $(A_j, \hat{B}_j, Q)$ be completely controllable and observable. Here, we define

$$A_j = \begin{bmatrix} A_{11} & A_{1j} \\ A_{j1} & A_{jj} \end{bmatrix}, \; \hat{B}_j^T = [0, B_j^T], \; Q = \text{block diag.}[Q_1, Q_j] \text{ and, } G_j = [G_{j1}, G_{jj}] .$$

DERIVATION OF NECESSARY CONDITIONS

Form the Hamiltonian functional

$$H_j = \hat{x}^T(k)\hat{Q}\hat{x}(k) + \hat{\sigma}^T(k)S\hat{\sigma}(k) + \lambda_x^T(k+1)F_j\hat{x}(k) + \lambda_\sigma^T(k+1)A_\mu\hat{x}(k) + \lambda_\sigma^T(k+1)F_0\hat{\sigma}(k) , \tag{12}$$

in which, $\lambda_x^T(k) = [\lambda_{x1}^T(k), \lambda_{xj}^T(k)]$, $\lambda_\sigma^T(k) = [\lambda_{\sigma 1}^T(k), \lambda_{\sigma j}^T(k)]$ are the costate vectors defined by

$$\lambda_x(k) = K_1(k)\hat{x}(k) + K_2(k)\hat{\sigma}(k) \tag{13a}$$

$$\lambda_\sigma(k) = K_3(k)\hat{x}(k) + K_4(k)\hat{\sigma}(k)\ . \qquad (13b)$$

Matrices $K_1(k)$ and $K_4(k)$ are symmetric, and $K_2(k) = K_3^T(k)$. They are defined by

$$K_1(k) = \begin{bmatrix} K_{11} & K_{12} \\ K_{21} & K_{22} \end{bmatrix},\ K_2(k) = \begin{bmatrix} K_{13} & K_{14} \\ K_{23} & K_{24} \end{bmatrix},\ K_4(k) = \begin{bmatrix} K_{33} & K_{34} \\ K_{43} & K_{44} \end{bmatrix},$$

in which all entries are functions of k.
Substituting (13) and (8) into (12), and rearranging terms allows the Hamiltonian to be expressed as

$$H_j = \hat{x}^T(k)[Q+F_j^TK_1^T(k+1)F_j+A_\mu^TK_2^T(k+1)F_j+F_j^TK_3^T(k+1)A_\mu+A_\mu^TK_4^T(k+1)A_\mu]\hat{x}(k)$$

$$+\hat{x}^T(k)[F_j^TK_1^T(k+1)F_1+F_j^TK_1^T(k+1)F_1]\hat{\sigma}(k)+\hat{\sigma}(k)[F_j^TK_1^T(k+1)F_1+F_j^TK_1^T(k+1)F_1]\hat{x}(k)$$

$$+\hat{\sigma}(k)F_j^TK_1^T(k+1)F_1\hat{\sigma}(k)\ . \qquad (14)$$

Applying the minimum principle, and substituting (13) in the result gives

$$K_1(k)\hat{x}(k)+K_2(k)\hat{\sigma}(k) = \frac{\partial H_j}{\partial \hat{x}} = [2Q+2F_j^TK_1^T(k+1)F_j+2A_\mu^TK_2^T(k+1)F_j+$$

$$2F_j^TK_3^T(k+1)A_\mu+2A_\mu^TK_4^T(k+1)A_\mu]\hat{x}(k)+[F_j^TK_3^T(k+1)F_0+2A_\mu^TK_4^T(k+1)F_0]\hat{\sigma}(k) \qquad (15a)$$

$$K_3(k)\hat{x}(k)+K_4(k)\hat{\sigma}(k) = \frac{\partial H_j}{\partial \hat{x}} = [2F_0^TK_2^T(k+1)F_j+2F_0^TK_4^T(k+1)A]\hat{x}(k)$$

$$+[2S+2F_0^TK_4^T(k+1)F_0]\hat{\sigma}(k)\ . \qquad (15b)$$

Equations (15a) and (15b) hold for any $\hat{x}$ and $\hat{\sigma}$. Furthermore, in the steady state, the arguments k and k+1 can be dropped. Therefore, we can write

$$K_1 = 2Q+2F_j^TK_1F_j+2A_\mu^TK_2^TF_j+2F_j^TK_3^TA_\mu+2A_\mu^TK_4A_\mu \qquad (16a)$$

$$K_2 = 2F_j^TK_2F_0+2A_\mu^TK_4F_0 \qquad (16b)$$

$$K_4 = 2S+2F_0^TK_4F_0\ . \qquad (16c)$$

Equations (16) are all of the Lyapunov form and can be solved in the sequence (16a), (16b), and (16c). To show the dependence of H_j on G_j explicitly, the Hamiltonian is rewritten in the form

$$H_j = tr[(Q+G_j^TR_jG_j)\hat{x}^T(k)+(A_j+\hat{B}_jG_j)^TK_1^T(A_j+\hat{B}_jG_j)\hat{x}^T(k)+A_\mu^TK_2^T(A_j+\hat{B}_jG_j)\hat{x}^T(k)$$

$$+(A_0+\hat{B}_jG_j)^TK_2^T(A_j+\hat{B}_jG_j)\hat{x}(k)\hat{\sigma}^T(k)+(A_j+\hat{B}_jG_j)^TK_3^TA_\mu\hat{\sigma}(k)\hat{x}^T(k)$$

$$+A_\mu^TK_4A_\mu\hat{x}(k)\hat{x}^T(k)+(A_0+\hat{B}_jG_j)^TK_jA_\mu\hat{x}(k)\hat{\sigma}^T(k)+(A_j+\hat{B}_jG_j)^TK_3^T(A_0-\hat{B}_jG_j)\hat{\sigma}(k)\hat{x}^T(k)$$

$$+A_\mu^TK_4(A_0+\hat{B}_jG_j)\hat{\sigma}^T(k)\hat{x}^T(k)+(A_0+\hat{B}_jG_j)^TK_4(A_0+\hat{B}_jG_j)\hat{\sigma}(k)\hat{\sigma}^T(k)\ , \qquad (17)$$

where A_0=block diag.$[A_{11},\ A_{jj}]$.
Taking the expected value of the partial derivative of H_j with respect to G_j [3] yeilds the necessary condition for minimization

$$O = (R_j+B_jK_1B_j)G_jM_1+B_jK_3B_jG_jM_2+B_jK_2B_jG_jM_2+B_jK_4B_jG_jM_4+\hat{B}_j^TK_1A_jM_1$$

$$+\hat{B}_j^TK_2A_\mu M_1+\hat{B}_j^TK_2^TA_0M_2+\hat{B}_j^TK_2^TA_jM_2^T+\hat{B}_j^TK_4A_\mu M_2^T+\hat{B}_j^TK_4A_0M_4\ , \qquad (18)$$

in which

$$M_1 = E\left\{\sum_{k=0}^{\infty}\hat{x}(k)\hat{x}^T(k)\right\},\quad M_2 = E\left\{\sum_{k=0}^{\infty}\hat{\sigma}(k)\hat{x}^T(k)\right\},\quad \text{and } M_4 = E\left\{\sum_{k=0}^{\infty}\hat{\sigma}(k)\hat{\sigma}^T(k)\right\}.$$

Define

$$\hat{F} = \begin{bmatrix} F_j & 0 \\ A_\mu & F_0 \end{bmatrix},\quad M = \begin{bmatrix} M_1 & M_2 \\ M_2^T & M_4 \end{bmatrix},\quad \Omega = \begin{bmatrix} \Omega_1 & 0 \\ 0 & 0 \end{bmatrix}.$$

where

$$\Omega_1 = E\{x(0)x^T(0)\}\ .$$

M is the solution of the Lyponov equation

$$M = \hat{F}M\hat{F}^T+\Omega$$

COMPUTATION PROCEDURE

Step 1. Select a stabilizing matrix G_j.
Step 2. Solve for K_1,K_2,K_3, and K_4 form equations (16).
Step 3. Solve equation (19) for M, and M_1,M_2,and M_4.
Step 4. Find the new G_j. If convergence has been achieved within an acceptable error margin, stop. If not, update G_j and go to step 2.

CONCLUSIONS

The problem of state feedback controller design with low trajectory sensitivity to small parameter variations is considered for large-scale interconnected discrete-time systems. The necessary considerations for optimality for sensitivity augmented performance criteria are derived. An iterative algorithm is proposed for the determination of the state feedback gains.

REFERENCES

[1] J.B. CRUZ and M.E. SAWAN, "Low-sensitivity Optimal Feedback Control for Linear Discrete-Time Systems", IEEE Trans. Automat. Contr., vol AC-24, pp. 119-122, Feb. 1979.

[2] B.D.O. ANDERSON and J.B. MOORE, "Decentralized Control Using Time-Varying Feedback", Control and Dynamics, Advances in Theory and Applications, vol 22, pp. 85-115, 1985.

[3] W.S. LEVINE and M. ATHANS, "On the Determination of the Optimal Constant Output Feedback Gains for Multivariable Systems", IEEE Trans. Automat. Contr. vol AC-15, pp. 44-48, Feb. 1970.

Proceedings of the
American Control Conference
San Francisco, California • June 1993

ROBUSTNESS OF SAMPLED-DATA CONTROL TO UNMODELED HIGH-FRENQUENCY DYNAMICS

Joseph H. Dinh and Mahmoud E. Sawan

Department of Electrical Engineering
The Wichita State University
Wichita, Kansas 67208

Abstract

Robustness of sampled-data control designs to unmodeled high-frequency dynamics is studied using singular perturbation theory. When a plant is preceded by a zero-order holder, a direct transmission term of the reduced-order model should be modeled as a delay element in order to ensure robustness.

1. Introduction

Robustness of feedback control designs to unmodeled high-frequency dynamics has been using singular perturbation theory. Consider the system:

$$\begin{aligned} \dot{x}(t) &= A_{11}x(t) + A_{12}z(t) + B_1u(t) \\ \alpha\dot{z}(t) &= A_{21}x(t) + A_{22}z(t) + B_2u(t) \\ y(t) &= C_1x(t) + C_2z(t) \end{aligned} \quad (1)$$

where $x(t)\in R^n, z(t)\in R^m, u(t)\in R^p, y(t)\in R^q$, and A_{22} is Hurwitz matrix, and α is a small positive scalar. The reduced-order slow model of the system (1) is :

$$\begin{aligned} \dot{x}_s(t) &= A_ox_s(t) + B_ou_s(t) \\ y_s(t) &= C_ox_s(t) + D_ou_s(t) \end{aligned} \quad (2)$$

where $A_o = A_{11}-A_{12}A_{22}^{-1}A_{21}$, $B_o = B_1-A_{12}A_{22}^{-1}B_2$

$C_o = C_1-C_2A_{22}^{-1}A_{21}$, $D_o = -C_2A_{22}^{-1}B_2$

A stabilizing compensator is designed based on the slow model. Robustness of the control design can be examined by applying the compensator to the full model and analyzing the behavior of the closed-loop system as $\alpha \to 0$. A strictly proper stabilizing compensator for the reduced-order slow submodel is both the necessary and sufficient condition for closed-loop stability of the full model for sufficiently small α.

2. Problem Statement

Consider the closed-loop system with G(s) is the Laplace transfer function of the system (1) which is preceded by a zero-order holder ZOH. We assume that the slow model (2) is stabilizable and detectable. It is required to design a compensator C(z), where z denotes z-transform, such that the closed-loop system is asymptotically stable for sufficiently small α.

A typical approach to design a sampled-data control system is as follow:

The discretization of model (2) is

$$\begin{aligned} x_s(n+1) &= A_dx_s(n) + B_du_s(n) \\ y_s(n) &= C_ox_s(n) + D_ou_s(n) \quad (3) \\ G_s(z) &= C_o[zI-A_d]^{-1}B_d + D_o \quad (4) \end{aligned}$$

where $A_d = \exp(A_oT)$, $B_d = \int_0^T \exp(A_ot)B_o dt$

$G_s(z)$ is the z-transfer function of system (3) and the sampling period T is chosen such that the state-space realization (3) is stabilizable and detectable. The compensator is designed to stabilize $G_s(z)$.

Because sampling and ZOH act as a low-pass filter the compensator C(z) will not destabilize the full system provided that α is sufficiently small.

To ensure robustness, the direct transmission term D_o of (4) should be replaced by $z^{-1}D_o$. In actual closed-loop system, the ZOH acts on the full system, which means that the discretization takes place for α not equal to zero. Thus we should discretize the full system before setting α equal to 0. To discretize the full system (1), we decouple it into slow and fast subsystem. Assume that after decoupling the system (1), we have:

$$\begin{aligned} \dot{x}_s(t) &= A_1x_s(t) + B_1u(t) \\ \alpha\dot{z}_f(t) &= A_2z_f(t) + B_2u(t) \\ y(t) &= C_1x_s(t) + C_2z_f(t) \end{aligned} \quad (5)$$

where $A_i, B_i, C_i; i=1,2$ are analytic at $\alpha=0$, and $A_2(0)$ is HUrwitz. The discretization of (5) results in:

$$\begin{aligned} x_s(n+1) &= Q_s(\alpha)x_s(n)+P_s(\alpha)u(n) \\ z_f(n+1) &= Q_f(\alpha)z_f(n)+P_f(\alpha)u(n) \\ y(n) &= C_1(\alpha)x_s(n)+C_2(\alpha)z_f(n) \end{aligned} \quad (6)$$

where $Q_s(\alpha)=\exp[A_1(\alpha)T]$, $Q_f(\alpha)=\exp[A_2(\alpha)T/\alpha]$

$P_s(\alpha)= \int_0^T D_1(\alpha)dt$, $P_f(\alpha)=(1/\alpha)\int_0^T D_2(\alpha)B_2(\alpha)dt$,

with $D_1(\alpha)=\exp[A_1(\alpha)t]B_1(\alpha)$, $D_2(\alpha)=\exp[A_2(\alpha)t]$

For sufficiently small α, we have:

$$\begin{aligned} Q_s(\alpha) &= Q_s(0) + 0(\alpha) \\ P_s(\alpha) &= P_s(0) + 0(\alpha) \\ Q_f(\alpha) &= 0(\alpha) \\ P_f(\alpha) &= -A_2^{-1}(0)B_2(0) + 0(\alpha) \end{aligned} \quad (7)$$

and the system (6) becomes:

$$\begin{aligned} x_s(n+1) &= Q_s(0)x_s(n)+P_s(0)u(n) \\ z_f(n+1) &= -A^{-1}(0)B_2(0)u(n) \\ y(n) &= C_1(0)x_s(n)+C_2(0)z_f(n) \end{aligned} \quad (8)$$

The reduced-order system (5) has the transfer function:

$$G_o(s)=C_1(0)[sI-A_1(0)]^{-1}B_1(0) -C_2(0)A_2^{-1}(0)B_2(0) \quad (9)$$

The transfer function of system (8), with $z_f(n)=-A_2^{-1}(0)B_2(0)u(n-1)$, is:

$$G_*(z)=C_1(0)[zI-Q_s(0)]^{-1}P_s(0) -z^{-1}C_2(0)A_2^{-1}(0)B_2(0) \quad (10)$$

From (9) and (10), we can conclude that the direct transmission term of the reduced-order model should be modeled as a delay element.

3. Main Rerult

Consider the transfer function:

$$G_*(z) = C_o[zI - A_d]^{-1}B_d + z^{-1}D_o$$

where A_d, B_d, C_o, D_o are given in (3) and (4)

Theorem: Any feedback compensator C(z) that stabilizes $G_*(z)$ is robust to unmodeled high-frequency dynamics of (2), i.e., the closed-loop system is stable for sufficiently small α.

4. Example

Consider the two-time scale transfer function

$$G(s,\alpha) = 2/(s-1) + 1/(\alpha s+1)$$

The corresponding model is:

$$\dot{x}(t) = x(t)+2u(t)$$

$$\alpha z(t) = -z(t)+u(t) \qquad (11)$$

$$y(t) = x(t)+z(t)$$

The transfer function of the reduced model is

$$G(s,0) = 2/(s-1) + 1$$

Let T=0.1 sec., the discretization of G(s,0) in (4) is:

$$G_o(z) = 0.21034/(z-1.1052)+1 \qquad (12)$$

Choose $C(z) = 2.4448/(z-2.057)$.

The zeros of $1+C(z)G_o(z)$ are $0.433 \pm j0.25$, inside the unit disk. The discretization $G(z,\alpha)$ of the full system (11) is

$$G(z,\alpha) = \frac{0.21034}{z-1.1052} + \frac{1-\exp(-0.1/\alpha)}{z-\exp(-0.1/\alpha)} \qquad (13)$$

The zeros of $1+C(z)G(z,\alpha)$ approach to 0.7958, and $1.2575 \pm j1.3468$ as α comes to 0. Hence the closed-loop system is unstable for sufficiently small α.

NOw, if we replace the direct transmission term 1 of (12) by z^{-1} to have

$$G_*(z) = 0.21034/(z-1.1052)+z^{-1}$$

and choose $C(z) = 3.575z/(z-4.200)$

The zeros of $1+C(z)G_*(z)$ are at $0.489 \pm j0.672$ inside the unit disk. Moreover, the zeros of $1+C(z)G(z,\alpha)$ approach to $0.489 \pm j0.672$ as α comes to zero. Hence, the closed-loop system is stable for sufficiently small α.

The above example shows that if we replace the direct transmission term of the reduced-order model by a delay element, and the compensator C(z) is designed based on the new transfer function will stabilize the closed-loop system for sufficiently small α.

Notes:

1) If the full system is not strictly proper, a design based on $G_*(z)$ may destabilize the closed-loop system.

2) It is obvious that when the reduced- order model (2) is strictly proper, $G_*(z)$ coincides with the conventional model $G_o(z)$.

5. Conclusion

The sampled-data control will be robust to unmodeled high-frequency dynamics for sufficiently small α. This paper shows that the direct transmission term should be modeled as a delay element to insure robustness.

6. Appendix

The closed-loop system has the figure as follow:

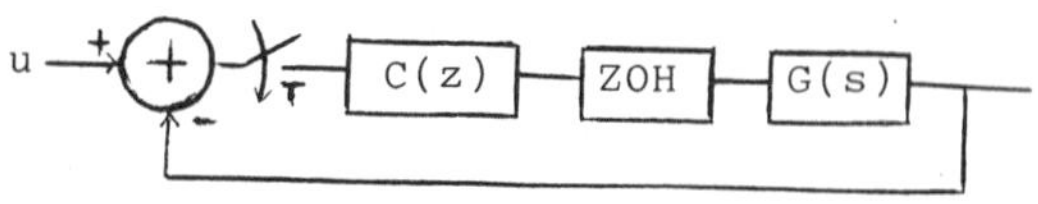

7. References

[1] H.K.KHALIL, "On the robustness of output feedback control methods to modeling errors IEEE Trans.Automat.Contr., vol.44, AC-26, pp. 524-526, Apr.1981.

[2] J.O'REILLEY, "Robustness of linear feedback control systems to unmodeled high-frequency dynamics." Int.J.Contr., vol.44, pp.1077-1088, Oct.1986.

[3] P.V.KOKOTOVIC, R.E.O'MALLEY, Jr., and P.SANNUTI, "Singular perturbation and order reduction in control theory-An Overview." Automatica, vol.12, pp.123-132, 1976.

[4] M.T.TRAN and M.E.SAWAN, "Reduced order discrete-time models." Int.J.SystemsSCI., vol. 14, No7, pp.745-752, 1983.

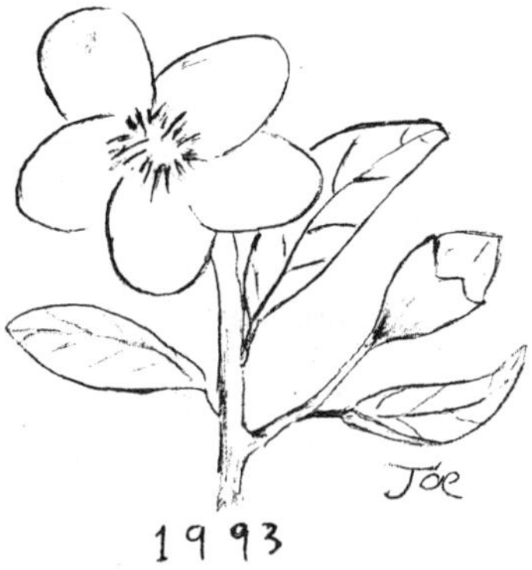

Proceedings of the
American Control Conference
San Francisco, California • June 1993

A FAMILY OF DYNAMIC CONTROLLERS WITH LOOP TRANSFER RECOVERY

M. TADJINE*, M. M'SAAD* and L. DUGARD*

Laboratoire d'Automatique de Grenoble, URA CNRS 228
B.P. 46 E.N.S.I.E.G,
38402 - SAINT-MARTIN-D'HERES, FRANCE

* The authors are also with the GDR CNRS "AUTOMATIQUE"

Abstract.

This paper presents a family of controllers with asymptotic loop transfer recovery capability for both the plant input and output nodes. It is shown that the availabble loop transfer recovery regulators belong to this family. The involved controllers are particularly motivated by their better degree of recovery with respect to the well known LQG controller. The delta operator formulation is used to treat the discrete as well as the continuous time systems in a unified framework while ensuring an appropriate numerical robustness [1].

1. INTRODUCTION.

A fundamental problem concerning the linear quadratic gaussian (LQG) controller is that the attractive robustness properties of either the linear quadratic (LQ) regulator or the Kalman filter (KF) are lost. The loop transfer recovery (LTR) may be viewed as a simple loop shaping procedure which allows to preserve the robustness properties of the LQ control or the KF when designing a LQG control. The LTR was pioneered by Doyle and Stein [2] and subsequently investigated by several researchers (see for istance [3] to [7] and references therein).

Most of the LTR litterature is concerned with the observer based control design. This leads to the following natural question: what are the advantages, with respect to the observer based control design, if one uses any stabilizing controller for performing LTR? Such an issue has been recently addressed in [6] where a new continuous time compensator structure with a better degree of recovery is proposed. This approach has been pursued for the discrete time case in [7] uisng the delta operator formulation that has been recently rehabilited in [1]. Of particular importance, it was shown that the discrete time compensator tends to its underlying continuous time compensator as the sampling period goes to zero. In this paper, we show that the available LTR regulators belong to a same family of controllers with asymptotic LTR capability. More specifically, this family is parametrized by a tuning parameter α whose value allows to select any controller structure. The delta operator formulation is mainly adopted to treat the discrete as well as the continuous time systems in a unified framework.

The paper is organized as follows. In section 2, the LTR control design problem is reformulated using the delta operator formulation for both the plant input and output nodes. The available LTR controllers are briefly presented in section 3, and their properties are emphasized. Section 4 presents the family of controllers with asymptotic LTR capability for both the plant input and output cases. Some concluding remarks end the paper.

2. THE GENERAL LTR PROBLEM.

2.1 Notation.

We will consider linear time-invariant systems with m inputs and m outputs, modelled by the following discrete time state representation

$$\delta x(t) = Ax(t)+Bu(t) \text{ and } y(t) = Cx(t) \qquad (1)$$

where $x(t) \in \mathcal{R}^n$ denotes the state vector, $u(t) \in \mathcal{R}^m$ and $y(t) \in \mathcal{R}^m$ are the plant input and output respectively, and δ is the delta operator which is fully investigated in [1]. The system (1) can be also described by the transfer function

$$G(\gamma)=C\Phi(\gamma)B \in \mathcal{R}(\gamma)^{m\times m} \text{ with } \Phi(\gamma)=(\gamma I-A)^{-1} \quad (2)$$

where γ denotes the delta transform operator and $\mathcal{R}(\gamma)^{a\times b}$ denotes the set of (a,b) rational matrices in γ. It is well known that the model $G(\gamma)$ does not give a complete description of a real plant as there exists always model uncertainties as parameter variations, unmodelled dynamics and nonlinearities. A commonly used description of the plant model uncertainties is the so called unstructured multiplicative perturbations at the plant input or plant output. The real (but unkown) transfer functions for the plant input and plant output nodes cases are respectively given by

$$G_r(\gamma)=G(\gamma)\,[I+\Delta(\gamma)] \text{ and } G_r(\gamma) = [\,I + \Delta(\gamma)\,]G(\gamma)$$

where $\Delta(\gamma)$ is an arbitrary stable transfer function matrix which can be loosely interpreted as actuator uncertainties for the plant input case or sensor uncertainties for the plant output case. Consider the control scheme of figure 1 where $R(\gamma)$ is a rational controller and $u(\gamma)$ and $y(\gamma)$ denote the input and output delta transforms, respectively. For MIMO systems, it is important to test the robustness margins at both the plant input and the plant output that are respectively indicated by the nodes x and xx in figure 1. Indeed the stability margins may be excellent at one point and critical at the other. These stability margins are nothing but the margins of the open loop transfer function at the plant input ($R(\gamma)G(\gamma)$) or at the plant output ($G(\gamma)R(\gamma)$). Throughout the paper, we will assume that

A1. The system is stabilizable and detectable.

A2. The system is inversely stable.

The assumption A1 is standard, while the assumptions A2 define the class of plants for which the LTR problem is addressed.

2.2 Loop Transfer Recovery.

The LTR design procedure is performed in three steps. Firstly, one formulate the design specifications at either the plant input or output nodes, namely the required robust stability and performance. Secondly, one determines a target loop satisfying the design specifications at the specified node. The LTR is performed at the last step which consists in recovering the target loop over the desired bandwidth. The stucture of the target loop depends on the point where the design specifications are formulated. At the plant input node, the target loop is nothing but the LQ control loop as shown in figure 2. The feedback gain is given by

$$K_c = [\,\Lambda + TB^TPB]^{-1}B^TP(\,I + TA)$$

with

$$0 = Q+ A^TP +PA +TA^TPA - K_c^T[\,\Lambda + TB^TPB]\,K_c$$

where Q and Λ are the LQ contol wheighting matrices. Notice that the open loop transfer function obtained by breaking the state feedback loop at the input point of the plant is given by

$$L(\gamma) = K_c\Phi(\gamma)\,B \qquad (3)$$

When the design specifications are formulated at the output node, the structure of the target loop is shown in figure 3. It is simply defined by the KF gain matrix K_p given by

$$K_p = (I + TA)PC^T[\,\Gamma + TCPC^T]^{-1}$$

with

$$0 = \Omega+ PA^T +AP +TAPA^T- K_p[\,\Gamma + TCPC^T]\,K_p^T$$

where Ω and Γ denote the process and measurement noise spectral densities. Notice that the open loop transfer function obtained by breaking the filter loop at the output node of the plant is given by

$$F(\gamma) = C\Phi(\gamma)K_p \qquad (4)$$

3. THE LQG/LTR CONTROLLERS.

The structure of the LQG controller is shown in figure 4 where the gains K_c and K_p are the only free design parameters, and K_f denotes the filter observer gain whis is commonly determined from the observer gain through the relation $K_p = (I+TA)K_f$. The controller transfer function is given by

$$R_f(\gamma) = (1+T\gamma)K_c[\gamma I -(I-TK_fC)(A -BK_c)+K_fC]^{-1}K_f \quad (5)$$

In the time domain, the controller $R_f(\gamma)$ is defined by

$$\delta z(t) = A\, z(t) + Bu(t) + K_p(y(t)-Cz(t))$$
$$z_f(t) = z(t)+TK_f(y(t)-Cz(t)) \text{ and } u(t) = -K_c\, z_f(t)$$

The matrices K_c and K_p are computed in a special way. The state feedback gain K_c (resp. the observer gain K_p when the design specifications are reflected at the ouput node) is fixed to be that found in the target feedback loop. The observer gain K_p (resp. the state feedback gain K_c when the design specifications are reflected at the output node) is designed with the spectral densities $\Omega = BB^T$ and $\Gamma = \rho I$ for $\rho \to 0$ (resp. with the wheighting matrices $Q = C^TC$ and $\Lambda = \rho I$ for $\rho \to 0$). This leads to the following result

$$\lim_{\rho\to 0} [R_f(\gamma)G(\gamma)] = L(\gamma) \qquad (\text{resp. } \lim_{\rho\to 0} [G(\gamma)R_f(\gamma)] = F(\gamma)\,)$$

Hence, the loop transfer function matrix $R_f(\gamma)G(\gamma)$ (resp. $G(\gamma)R_f(\gamma)$) of the system we are going to build approximate the loop transfer function matrix $L(\gamma)$ (resp. $F(\gamma)$) when $R_f(\gamma)$ is designed according to the LTR methodology as shown in [7]. The LQG controller may be drawn as illustrated in figure 5 for the plant input case (resp. in figure 6 for the plant output case). The corresponding matrices $M(\gamma)$ and $N(\gamma)$ are given by

$$M(\gamma) = K_c(I+TA)^{-1}[\gamma I-A+K_pC]^{-1}(I+TA-TK_pC)B$$

$$\text{(resp. } M(\gamma) = C[I+T(A-BK_c)][\gamma I-A+BK_c]^{-1}K_f\text{) (6)}$$

$$N(\gamma) = (1+T\gamma)K_c(I+TA)^{-1}(\gamma I-A+K_pC)^{-1}K_p$$

$$\text{(resp. } N(\gamma) =(1+T\gamma)K_c[\gamma I-A+BK_c]^{-1}K_f\text{)} \quad (7)$$

Furthermore, the mismatch between the LQ open loop transfer function $L(\gamma)$ (resp. the KF loop $F(\gamma)$) and the corresponding LQG open loop transfer function $R_f(\gamma)G(\gamma)$ (resp. $G(\gamma)R_f(\gamma)$) is shown to be given by

$$E(\gamma)=M(\gamma)(I+M(\gamma))^{-1}(I+K_c\Phi(\gamma)B)$$

$$\text{(resp. } E(\gamma) = (I+C\Phi(\gamma)K_p)\ (I+M(\gamma)\ )^{-1}M(\gamma)\text{)} \quad (8)$$

where the transfer matrix $M(\gamma)$ is given by equation (6). This means that the link between the control signal u(t) and the observer (resp. between the observation error and the observer output) vanishes as $\rho \to 0$. Such an observation was adopted to derive a new discrete time LTR compensator as shown in figure 7 (resp. in figure 8). The resulting compensator may be given the following form

$$\delta z(t)=Az(t)+K_p(y(t)-Cz(t)) \text{ (resp. } \delta z(t)=Az(t)+Bu(t)+K_py(t))$$

$$z_f(t)=z(t)+TK_f(y(t)-Cz(t)) \text{ (resp. } z_f(t)=z(t)+TK_fy(t)\text{)}$$

$$u(t) = -K_c\ z_f(t)$$

Except for the absence of the mentionned link, the new compensator is exactly the same as the standard LQG controller. In particular, the compensator transfer function and the the corresponding recovery error are respectively given by

$$R_n(\gamma) = (1+T\gamma)K_c[\gamma I-(I-TK_fC)A+K_fC]^{-1}K_f$$

$$\text{(resp. } R_n(\gamma) = (1+T\gamma)K_c[\gamma I-A+BK_c]^{-1}K_f\text{)} \quad (9)$$

$$E_n(\gamma) = L(\gamma) - R_n(\gamma)G(\gamma) = M(\gamma)$$

$$\text{(resp. } E_n(\gamma) = F(\gamma) - G(\gamma)R_n(\gamma) = M(\gamma)\text{)}$$

This clearly show that provided $\sigma_{min}\{L(\gamma)\}>1$ (resp. $\sigma_{min}\{F(\gamma)\}>1$), one has $\sigma_{max}\{E_n(\gamma)\} < \sigma_{max}\{E(\gamma)\}$. This means that the compensator (9) outperforms the LQG controller from recovery point of view. However, we have to prove that the underlying control system is asymptotically stable, i.e. there exists a real number ρ_1 such that the closed loop is stable for all $\rho < \rho_1$. This is a fundamental problem since for low value of ρ the measurement noise is directly injected at the output (resp. the input noise is directly injected at the input) as shown in [7].

4. CONTROL WITH LTR CAPABILITY.

In this section we will show that there exists a family of controllers that achieve better degree of LTR than the LQG controller at the plant input and at the plant output.

4.1 The plant input case.

Consider the following dynamic controller family

$$\delta z(t) = A_\alpha z(t) + Bu(t) + K_{p\alpha}(y(t)-Cz(t))$$

$$z_f(t) = z(t) + TK_f\ (y(t)-Cz(t)) \quad (10)$$

$$u(t) = -K_c\ z_f(t)$$

where $A_\alpha=A+\alpha BK_c$, $K_{p\alpha}=(I+TA_\alpha)K_f$ and $0 \leq \alpha \leq 1$. The only unknown parameters are K_f and α. The underlying scheme is depicted in figure 9 and the controller transfer function is given by :

$$R_\alpha(\gamma)=(1+T\gamma)K_c[\gamma I-(I-TK_fC)(A_\alpha-BK_c)+K_fC]^{-1}K_f \quad (11)$$

It is worth noticing that the LQG controller corresponds to $\alpha=0$ while the compensator (9) corresponds to $\alpha=1$. For each value of α in the set]0, 1[a new controller structure may be founded. The recovery properties of this familly of controllers are given by the following result.

Theorem 1: Consider the family of controllers (11) in closed loop with system (1) depicted in figure 9 and let the matrix given by equation (6), the following properties hold

P1. The error between the LQ open loop transfer function $L(\gamma)$ and the open loop transfer function of the proposed controllers, $R_\alpha(\gamma)\ G(\gamma)$, is given by

$$E_\alpha(\gamma) = L(\gamma - R_\alpha(\gamma)G(\gamma)$$

$$= M(\gamma)(I+(1-\alpha)M(\gamma)\ )^{-1}(I\ +(1-\alpha)K_c\Phi(\gamma)B)$$

P2. If $\sigma_{min}\ \{L(\gamma)\} > 1$ then one has

$$\sigma_{max}\ \{E_n(\gamma)\} < \sigma_{max}\{E_\alpha(\gamma)\} < \sigma_{max}\{E(\gamma)\}$$

P3. $R_\alpha(\gamma) \to K_c(sI-A_\alpha+BK_c+K_pC)^{-1}K_p$ as T goes to zero.

P4. The closed loop system is asymptotically stable for any real number α satisfying $0 \leq \alpha \leq 1$ provided that the observer gain K_p is determined to meet the LTR property. ΔΔΔ.

Proof : see [8]; extended version of the paper.

Notice that both properties of the LQG controller (α=0) and of the compensator (9) (α=1) are included in the above result. Otherwise, the discrete-time compensator $R_\alpha(\gamma)$ tends to its continuous time counterpart as the sampling period tends to zero. That is, the involved family of compensators covers both continuous and discrete time cases. Of fundamental interest, the asymptotic stability of the proposed controller family has been proven as the separation theorem is no longer valid.

4.2 The plant output case.

If we are interested in the output performance and robustness at the output node, then the family of controllers can be derived by direct analogy to the plant input case. The corresponding controller scheme is depicted in figure 10

$$\begin{aligned} \delta z(t) &= A_\alpha z(t) + Bu(t) + K_p(y(t)-Cz(t)) \\ z_f(t) &= (I + T\alpha K_f)z(t) + TK_f(y(t)-Cz(t)) \qquad (12) \\ u(t) &= - K_c\, z_f(t) \end{aligned}$$

with $A_\alpha = A+\alpha K_p C$. The underlaying controller transfer function is given by

$$R_\alpha(\gamma)=(1+T\gamma)K_c[\gamma I- (I-(1-\alpha)TK_fC)(A- BK_c) + (1-\alpha)K_fC]^{-1}K_f$$

and the main properties of the dual LTR controllers family are summarized in the following result.

Theorem 2: Consider the controller family (12) in closed loop with (1), one has the following properties

P 1. The recovery error may be written as

$$\begin{aligned} E_\alpha(\gamma) &= F(\gamma)-G(\gamma)R_\alpha(\gamma) \\ &= (I+(1-\alpha)C\Phi(\gamma)K_p)\,(I+(1-\alpha)M(\gamma))^{-1}M(\gamma) \end{aligned}$$

P 2. If $\sigma_{min}\{F(\gamma)\}>1$ then

$$\sigma_{max}\{E_n(\gamma)\} < \sigma_{max}\{E_\alpha(\gamma)\} < \sigma_{max}\{E(\gamma)\}.$$

P 3. $R_\alpha(\gamma) \dashrightarrow R_\alpha(s) = K_c[sI -A+BK_c+ (1-\alpha)K_fC]^{-1}K_p$ as T goes to zero.

P4. The closed loop system is asymptotically stable for any real number α satisfying $0 \le \alpha \le 1$ provided that the feedback gain K_c is determined so that the LTR at the plant output is asymptotically achieved. **ΔΔΔ.**

See [8] for the proof. As in the case of plant input node, the proposed family asymptotically achieves the LTR and is better than the LQG controller from a recovery point of vue. Furthermore the involved discrete time results converge to their continuous time counterparts when the sampling period goes to zero.

5. CONCLUSION.

A new family of controllers that asymptotically achieve the LTR either at the input or at the output of the plant has been proposed in this paper, using the delta operator formulation. Of particular importance, we have shown that all the discrete time results smoothly converge to their continuous time counterpart as the sampling period tends to zero. The bonus of the proposed controllers, namely their better degree of recovery with respect to the standard LQG controller has been theoretically emphasized.

REFERENCES

[1] Middelton, R. H., and Goodwin, G. C., 1990, Digital control and estimation : a unified approch (Englewood Cliffs, NJ : Prentice-Hall).

[2] Doyle, J. C., and Stein, G., 1979, Robustness with observers. I.E.E.E Transactions on Automatic Control, 2 4, 607-611.

[3] Stein, G., and Athans, M., 1987, The LQG/LTR procedure for multivariable feedback control design.I.E.E.E Transactions on Automatic Control, 3 2, 105-114.

[4] Maciejowki, J. M., 1985, Asymptotic recovery for discrete time systems. I.E.E.E Transactions on Automatic Control, 3 0, 602-605.

[5] Sogaard-Andersen, P., 1989, Loop transfer recovery an eigenstructure interpretation. Control Theory and Advanced Technology, 5, 351-365.

[6] Chen, B. M., Saberi, A., and Sannuti, P., 1991, A new stable compensator for exact and approximate loop transfer recovery. Automatica, 2 7, 257-289.

[7] Tadjine, M., M'saad, M., and, Dugard, L., 1992, An overview on the LQG/LTR using the delta operator . Proc of 31 st IEEE CDC, Tucson, AZ, USA.

[8] Tadjine, M., M'saad, M., and, Dugard, L., 1992, A family of dynamics controller with loop transfer recovery. Internal Report, LAG 92-227.

FIGURES

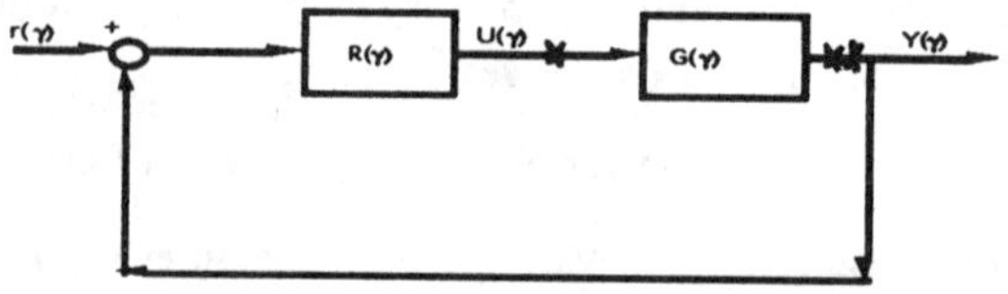

Figure 1. Input and Output nodes.

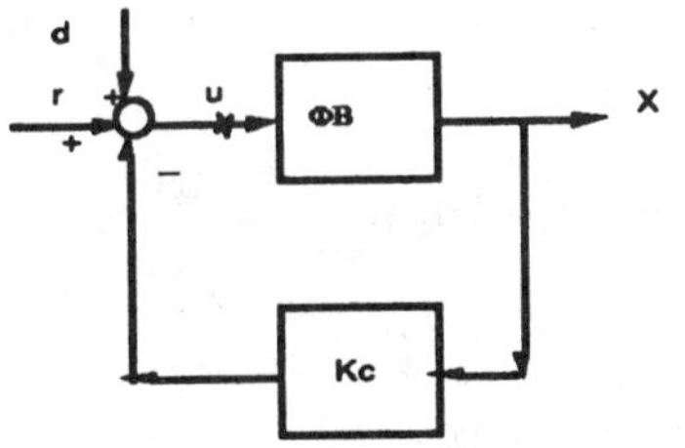

Figure 2. Full state feedback control.

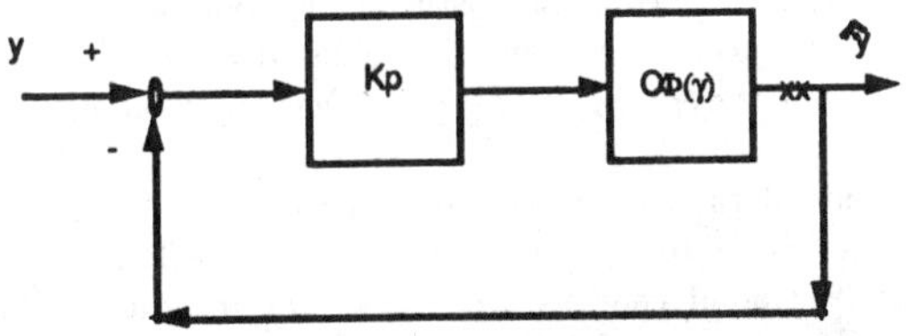

Figure 3. Kalman filter loop.

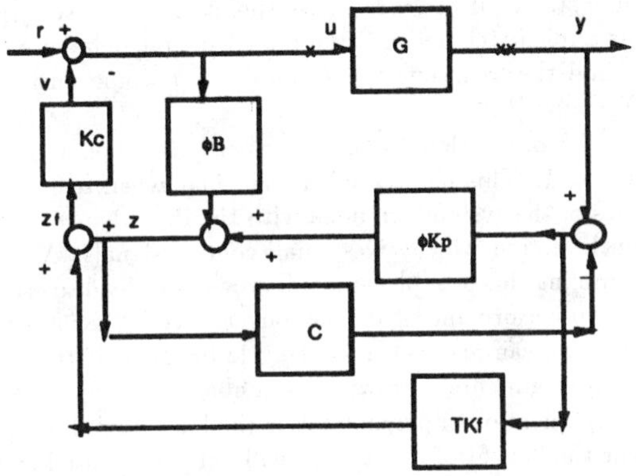

Figure 4. Observer based state feedback control.

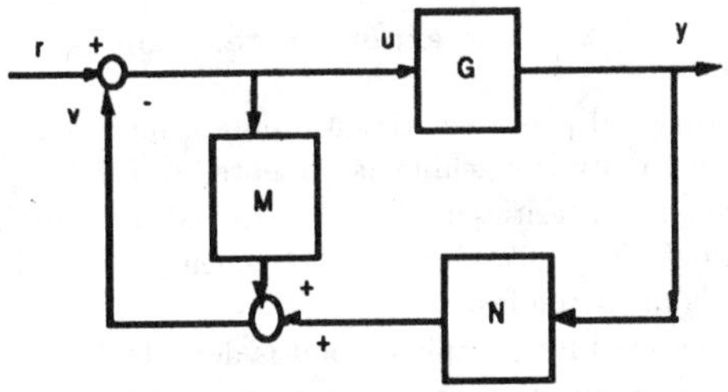

Figure 5 . General feedback control structure.

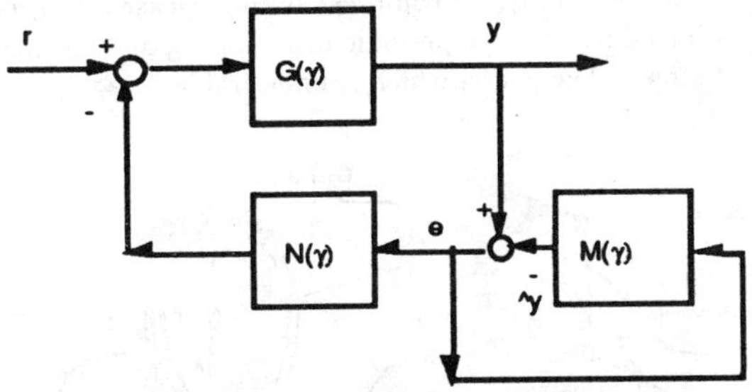

Figure 6. Dual recovery form.

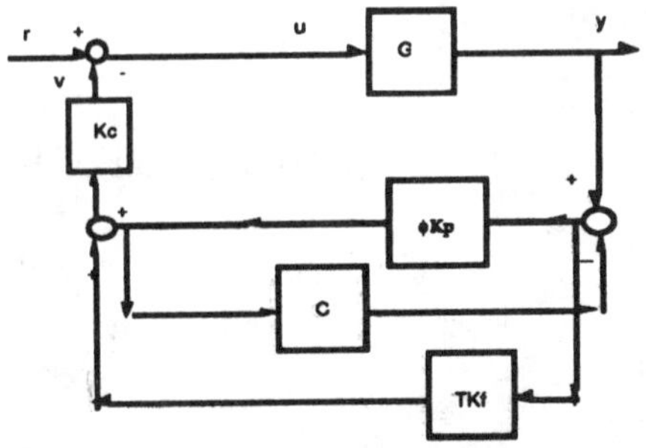

Figure 7. Compensator structure with LTR at the input.

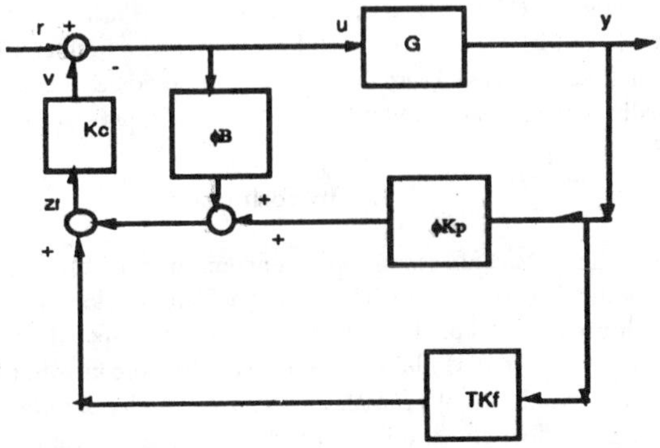

Figure 8.Compensator structure with LTR at the output.

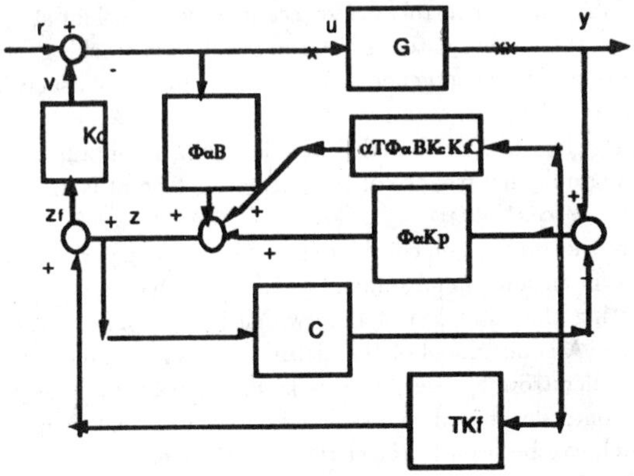

Figure 9. Controllers with plant input LTR capability.

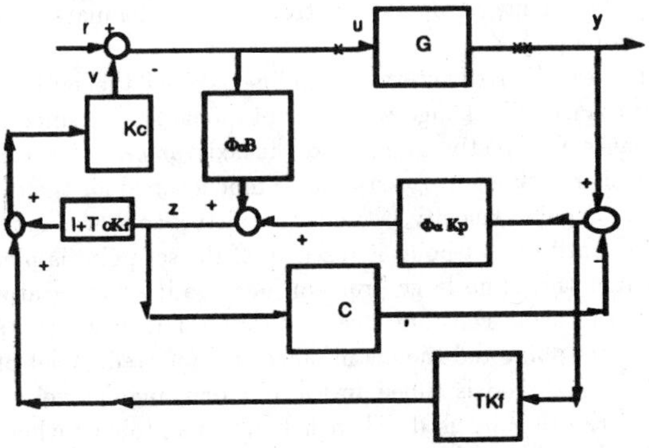

Figure 10. Controllers with plant output LTR capability.

Proceedings of the
American Control Conference
San Francisco, California • June 1993

Application of Repetitive Control to a Peristaltic Pump

Gunnar Hillerström Jan Sternby

Division of Automatic Control, Luleå University of Technology
S-951 87 Luleå, SWEDEN

Abstract

In many machinery there are rotating axis, which sometimes give problems with mechanically coupled disturbances from e.g. imperfect roundness or loads. These disturbance can be modeled as a nonlinear feedback, and treated under the framework of repetitive control.

1. Introduction

Periodic disturbances are often encountered in process control. Periodic disturbances rejection can basically be done in two ways. Both use a model of the disturbance; in the closed controller loop as in the Internal Model Principle(IMP) based controller by Francis and Wonham [5] or with an external model outside the loop trying to affect the stability of the closed loop system as little as possible, Tomizuka *et.al.*[10].

Control of a rotating axis, where the disturbance is coupled to the angle but not affecting its rotation, has been described for e.g. hard disc-drives control [3] and eccentricity control for strip rolling mills [4]. Closely related is also the problem of tracking a periodic set-point e.g. when generating a non-circular cross section using a lathe [11].

The class of IMP based controllers which contain a model of the periodic disturbance or the periodic set-point is known as the *repetitive controller*.

For the application considered in this paper, a peristaltic pump, there is an additional difficulty: the disturbance is significantly affecting the rotational speed, which in turn affects the disturbance. A good model of the disturbance is a nonlinear feedback, see Hillerström[6]. Despite this fact we here show how a repetitive controller, based on a separation of the disturbance and plant model, can be used to reject the disturbance.

The discrete time repetitive polynomial controller used, can be found in [9]. Controller polynomials are in this paper obtained by pole-placement, as found in Åström and Wittenmark [2; 1], and Walgama [12].

If 'normal' *fixed* interval sampling is used the period of the disturbance will change with the rotational speed, since the disturbance is directly coupled to the axis *angle.* If a repetitive controller with a static disturbance model tuned for the set-point of the angular velocity is used, the disturbance will not fit the model until the set-point is reached. If the set-point is piece-wise constant this is no large problem, because if an integrator is included to avoid constant steady state error it drives the process to the set-point and the disturbance gets rejected. A set of static disturbance models tuned to the different angular velocity set-points can then be used. There is however a problem when trying to track a time varying set-point because then the disturbance model must be altered. It is not straight forward to derive how to change the model and the controller parameters while keeping good performance and stability.

This technique also gives a slow convergence rate. A better technique is to sample with *varying* sampling interval at fixed angle positions of the axis, using a rotating pulse encoder. This gives fast convergence and set-point tracking is done without any problem. More important the disturbance model will then always fit the disturbance, because even if the disturbance is not periodic in real time it is periodic in the axis angle. A static disturbance model can be used.

This controller must however be robust to varying discrete time process model due to the varying sampling rate. This is no problem if the set-point changes are small. The internal model provides infinite closed loop gain for the modeled frequencies, and the controller removes the disturbance as long as the closed loop system is stable. If however the set-point change is so large that there is a mismatch between the modeled time delay used in the design and the 'real' one the system may become unstable, see e.g. Walgama [12].

The poles of the closed loop system are placed on a circle with radius $\alpha < 1$. This has the advantage that when α is near one, the poles of the system extended with the disturbance model are not much altered which gives small control signals. With 'normal' sampling this pole placement however may lead to oscillating closed loop performance and slow convergence. When altering the set-point, we can also get a limit cycle behavior if the limits of the control signal are narrow, see Rönnbäck *et.al.*[8].

The argument of all polynomials is the backward shift operator q^{-1}. For the benefit of clarity this will not be repeated explicitly everywhere.

2. The experimental plant

The experimental plant a peristaltic pump, intended for blood-pumping in a dialysis machine, is presented in Fig. 1.

There are nonlinearities in the plant originating from the rubber transmissions. This introduces high frequency oscillations if the controller is made too fast.

The pump used for pumping blood is described in more detail in Fig. 2. The construction is chosen not to destroy the blood cells. The rollers are pushing the fluid around.

Every lap the tube must be compressed and released by each roller. This introduces a large periodic disturbance, and the axis may almost stop at low paces, which is undesirable.

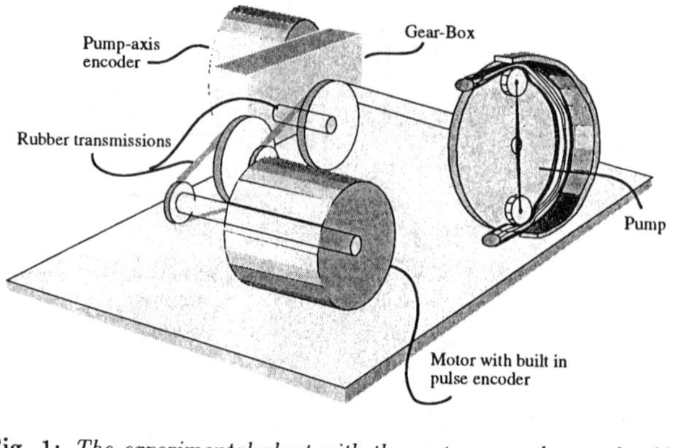

Fig. 1: *The experimental plant with the motor, encoders and rubber transmissions*

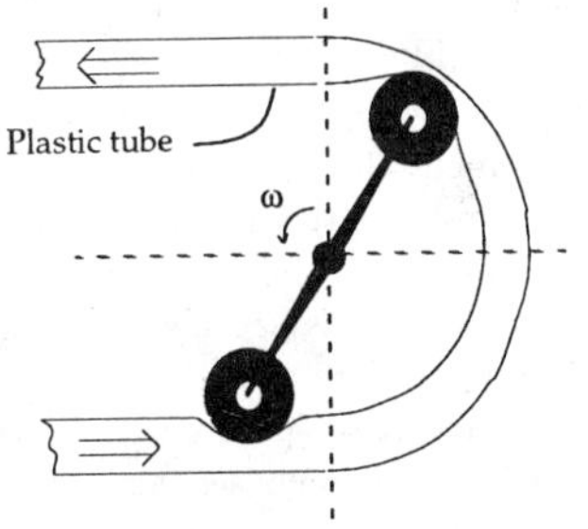

Fig. 2: *Illustration of the blood pump*

3. Model of the pump

The first order differential equations below describes the pump fairly well, θ is the axis angle and ω is the angular velocity.

$$\begin{aligned} \dot{\omega}(t) &= -\frac{1}{\tau}\omega(t) + \frac{k}{\tau}u(t-\tau_d) + \frac{k}{\tau}v(t) \\ \dot{\theta}(t) &= \omega(t) \end{aligned} \tag{1}$$

The disturbance v is coupled to the axis angle by some periodic function $g(\cdot)$, and thus a good model is $v(t) = g(\theta(t))$. This is obviously a nonlinear feed back. The problem with this process model is that $g(\cdot)$ is large and *unknown*, and controller design can not be done using linear theory. A different approach is tried. If the controller performs well the disturbance will asymptotically be periodic. The *approximation* that $v(t)$ is periodic and that the plant can be described by a linear model is used.

It is hard to get a good linear model because not only is the compression of the plastic tube a nonlinear source of disturbance but also the transmission from the motor to the pump device are made of rather elastic rubber. The straightforward method of setting up a system of differential equations is difficult to apply.

The model used for the plant is a linear first order with time delay d. The reason for choosing this model is that it is simple and might do for the purpose of designing the controller.

$$G_{pump} = \frac{B(q^{-1})q^{-d}}{A(q^{-1})} = \frac{bq^{-1}}{1+aq^{-1}}q^{-d} \tag{2}$$

The parameters are obtained by an identification experiment.

4. Disturbance model

The periodic disturbance v_k is assumed to have the discrete period p

$$v_{k-p} = v_k \Rightarrow (1-q^{-p})v_k = 0$$

Thus a discrete time model of a dynamic system that could have generated the disturbance is $1/H_p$ where $H_p = (1-q^{-p})$.

The frequency response of the filter H_p is of notch type and is shown in Fig. 4($\alpha = 0$). The zeros of H_p are equally spaced on the unit circle.

The pump has two equal rollers mounted on the pump axis. This gives that the dominating disturbance power is concentrated to even numbered harmonics of the fundamental frequency, the rotational speed. This makes it interesting to study a lower order disturbance model that only models the harmonics that are present in the disturbance. The set of indices of modeled frequencies is denoted by $\mathcal{K}$. A reduced disturbance model which is a product of M second order polynomials, each modeling one frequency is

$$\begin{aligned} H_m &= (1-q^{-1})\prod_{k\in\mathcal{K}} H_k \\ H_k &= \left(1 - 2q^{-1}\cos\left(\frac{2\pi kh}{T_0}\right) + q^{-2}\right) \\ \mathcal{K} &\subset \{l \in Z^+ | l \le \frac{p}{2}\} \end{aligned} \tag{3}$$

where $f_0 = 1/T_0$ is the fundamental frequency of the disturbance and Z^+ the set of positive integers.

The values of k together with the sampling frequency $f_s = 1/h$ and the fundamental frequency determines which frequencies that are modeled. The integrator corresponding to $k = 0$ in H_k, is introduced separately in H_m.

H_m is then of lower order than the pth order H_p, whenever p is odd. If p is even and all $M = p/2$ frequencies are modeled, there will be a double pole at the Nyquist frequency $k = p/2$ and thus H_m of order $p+1$. In all other cases H_m has only some of the notches of the complete model H_p.

H(whenever H is used the claim holds for both H_p and H_m) is close to zero for the frequencies near the fundamental and harmonics of the modeled disturbance. If H is placed in the denominator of the controller, the closed loop gain for these frequencies becomes large. This means that the effect of v_k will be removed from the output y_k.

5. Repetitive controller

The error tracking polynomial controller, see Fig. 3, will be used. The closed loop transfer functions are,

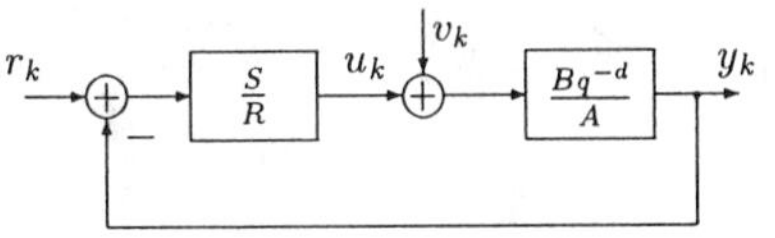

Fig. 3: *Polynomial error tracking controller*

$$H_r = \frac{Bq^{-d}S}{AR + Bq^{-d}S} \tag{4}$$

$$H_v = \frac{Bq^{-d}R}{AR + Bq^{-d}S} \tag{5}$$

from r_k and v_k to y_k respectively.

The internal model principle gives that the disturbance model H should be included in the controller as,

$$\frac{S}{R} = \frac{S}{R'H} \tag{6}$$

with some S and R' which make the total system stable. This can be seen as designing a controller for the system with the dynamics of the process and the disturbance model.

The poles of the transfer functions are, as always, the same, and can be placed at the zeros of A_m using the Diophantine identity* (7).

$$AHR' + Bq^{-d}S = A_m \tag{7}$$

The solution exists provided that B and AH are coprime. Here $B = b$ and this is thus always true.

If the total system is stable, the transfer function H_v between the disturbance and the output of the controlled system is also stable. Since H_v contains a factor H this gives,†

*Diophantus of Alexandria wrote a book in the third century A.D. about the problem of finding integer solutions to $ar + bs = c$ where $\{a, b, c\}$ are given integers.

†This is the key point of the internal model principle

$$y_k = H'_v H v_k + H_r r_k \rightarrow H_r r_k \tag{8}$$

and the convergence towards the *undisturbed* response is determined by the closed loop poles and the zeros of H_v. This means that if the disturbance fits the model H, complete disturbance rejection is achieved. The periodicity is then required to be exactly known. This can however in this case be achieved by measuring synchronously with the disturbance.

Solving (7) and assigning the desired closed loop poles, $A_m = H(\alpha q^{-1})A'_m$; $0.9 \leq \alpha < 1.0$ with equations (4,5) gives

$$\begin{aligned} y_k &= \frac{Bq^{-d}S}{H(\alpha q^{-1})A'_m} r_k + \frac{Bq^{-d}R'H(q^{-1})}{A'_m H(\alpha q^{-1})} v_k \\ &= \frac{Bq^{-d}S}{A_m} r_k + \frac{Bq^{-d}R'}{A'_m} H_\alpha v_k \end{aligned}$$

The disturbance is filtered through H_α given by

$$H_{p\alpha}(q^{-1}) \triangleq \frac{H_p(q^{-1})}{H_p(\alpha q^{-1})} \tag{9}$$

or

$$H_{m\alpha}(q^{-1}) \triangleq \frac{H_m(q^{-1})}{H_m(\alpha q^{-1})} \tag{10}$$

for the full and lower order model respectively.

The frequencies are rejected through a 'comb' filter as shown in Fig. 4. The highest α value gives the sharpest notches, and most equal magnification of all other components. IMP based pole location with 'comb' filtering can be used both with H_p and H_m models with different number of notches.

With this pole placement the poles of the closed loop system are moved very little compared to the open loop. This approach is robust to plant model errors and gives small control signals. For a discussion of these aspects see also [2] chapter 10. The disadvantage is that the poles are placed oscillative, which might lead to bad tracking of varying set-points with 'normal' sampling.

This robust pole placement is chosen also to prevent resaturation if control signal saturation occurs, see Rönnbäck *et.al.*[8]. The problem is that the system contains weakly dampened modes. If these modes are excited, the system might never stop oscillating.

Choosing the model The reduced model H_m gives a smaller polynomial design equation while the disturbance is band-limited and concentrated to even numbered harmonics. It is not necessary to model all $p/2$ harmonics. To avoid numerical errors, and thereby a non-rejecting disturbance model, it is however important to implement the disturbance model with care. The models for different harmonics H_k are implemented separately in a block-diagonal form. An implementation of the H_m polynomial in e.g. a controller form, can imply bad disturbance rejection and even unstable closed loop system.

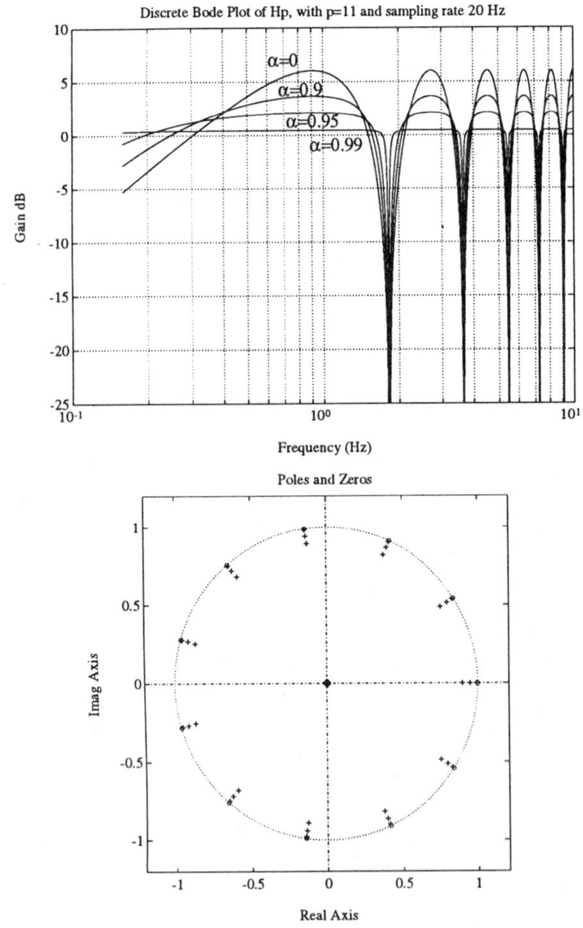

Fig. 4: *The 'comb' filter, Pole('+') and Zero('o') location of $H_{p\alpha}$ for α = 0, 0.99, 0.95 and 0.90, α near one gives sharper notches. Sampling frequency is 20 Hz and p = 11.*

6. Experimental results

The dynamics of the plant are sufficiently fast, and its modes preserved by choosing $A'_m = A$. This reduces the control signal magnitude and simplifies the solution of (7).

The model H_m used contains $M = 9$ harmonics of the periodic disturbance with $\mathcal{K}=\{1...6,8,10,12\}$.

The pump axis encoder shown in Fig. 1 is used with a frequency to voltage (F/V) converter. The 4th order Butterworth anti-aliasing filter and F/V-converter introduces some time delay, and the identification experiment gives $d = 3$ together with $a = 0.644$ and $b = 0.374$ at 20 Hz sampling rate ($p = 40$ for the 'synchronous' sampling). The Diophantine identity is solved with $deg\{S\} = 19$; $deg\{R'\} = 3$.

Two sampling techniques are compared.

'Normal' sampling Zero order hold [2] sampling with a fixed time interval h is used to get the angular velocity $y(t)$ at times kh, $y_k = y(kh)$.

'Synchronous' sampling The sampling is done by counting P pulses from the encoder that divides the total number of pulses per lap P_L, i.e. $P_L \ mod \ P = 0$.

To assure that no pulses are lost during the synchronous sampling, it is done using interrupt. Two timers on a LabMaster[‡] card are used. The first one is loaded by the number P and then counted down by the sensor output. When the counter reaches zero an interrupt is generated to initiate a new sampling.

6.1 'Normal' sampling

The convergence of the closed loop system, shown in Fig. 5, is slower than expected from the pole location ($\alpha = 0.97$). The disturbance model does not fit the actual disturbance until it reaches the set-point. This slows down the convergence. How the controller handles a large step disturbance at $t = 30$s is also shown in Fig. 5. As the controller drives the system back to the set point,

[‡]A AD/DA card with digital counters from Tecmar, Inc.

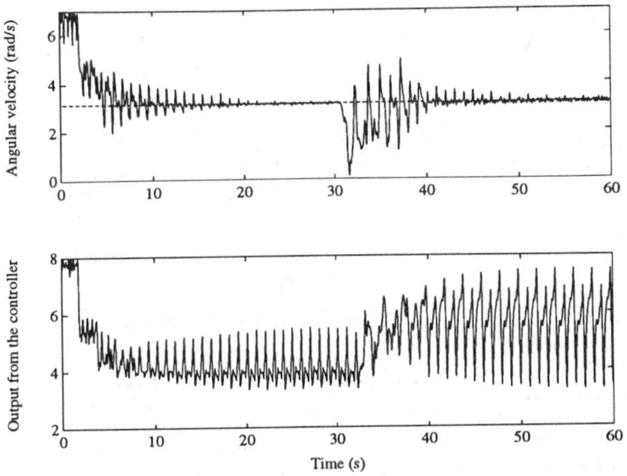

Fig. 5: *Controller performance with* $\alpha = 0.97$

the periodic disturbance gets rejected once again. The control voltage grows and becomes about twice as large as without the step disturbance. Note also that the step is so large that the pump initially stops completely.

From the control signal at the step disturbance we see the problem with 'normal' sampling. The internal disturbance model in the controller gets destroyed when the angular velocity and thereby the disturbance changes. The controller then has to build this up again almost from scratch.

The disturbance is generated by simply folding the plastic tube so that almost no water can be pumped around. The pressure in the tube rises and the pump is much harder to drive. In fact the only way to compensate is trough leakage back through the pump. This experiment is not so good for the pump, but illustrates how well the controller works. Remaining disturbance as stated in appendix A, is in stationarity 0.3%.

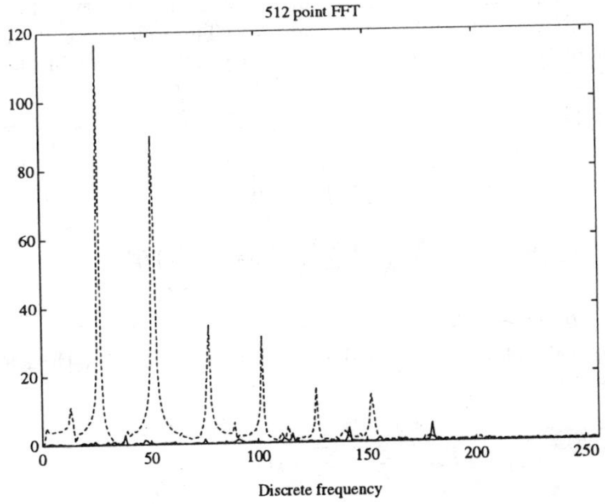

Fig. 6: *Controller performance with* $\alpha = 0.97$

A power spectrum of the stationary disturbance level with and without controller is shown in Fig. 6. A constant reference value serves as an input to the plant for the reference spectrum. This gives us a hint about how much of the fundamental frequency and harmonics of the disturbance that are left. Notice that the largest peak is about 5 units compared to over 100 for the uncontrolled plant.

The largest peak of the uncontrolled spectrum is located at two times the fundamental frequency of the pump axis rotation. This is due to the fact that there are *two* rollers mounted on the pump axis.

It is worth mentioning here that it takes some tuning to reach a good working controller mostly due to inaccuracy in the F/V-conversion. In this work the FFT plots are good help to see the location of the rejected frequencies and to tune the fundamental frequency of the model accordingly.

6.2 'Synchronous' sampling

Convergence to the set-point, shown in Fig. 7, is about twice as fast as with 'normal' sampling. Remaining disturbance after four laps is 2%.

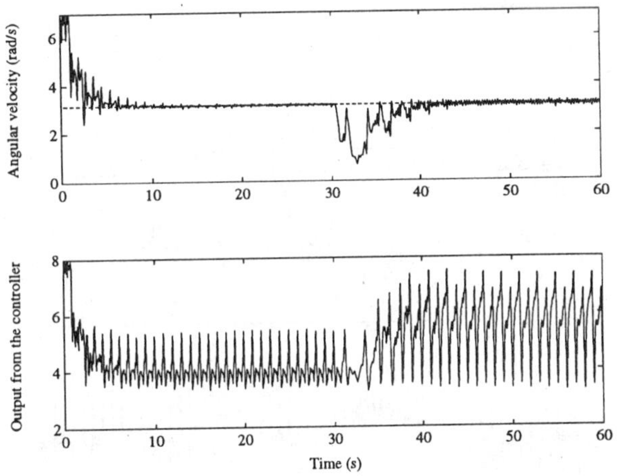

Fig. 7: *The same controller with synchronous sampling,* $\alpha = 0.97$

The robustness of the controller is tested as before, see Fig. 7. The step disturbance is rejected faster than before, due to that the model of the disturbance fits the actual disturbance better than in the previous case. This is despite the fact that sampling is done *slower* than for the 'normal' sampling during this time of reduced angular velocity.

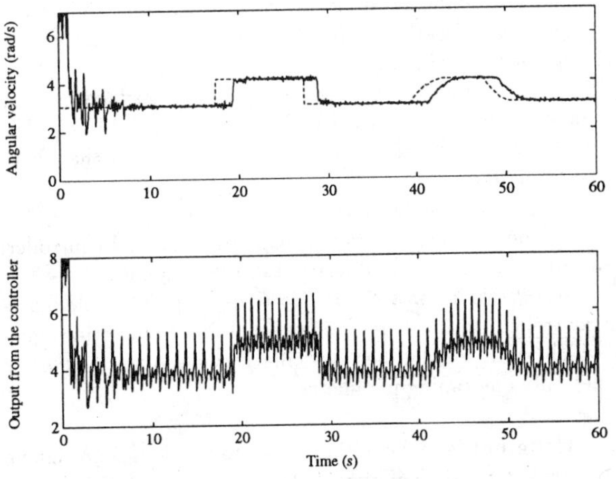

Fig. 8: *Tracking with the error controller,* $\alpha = 0.9$

With asynchronous sampling there was a problem with tracking a varying set point, due to the included disturbance model. The phase of the controller model does not match the 'real' frequencies after a step change in the set point. The synchronous sampling makes the internal states of the controller always match the disturbance and thus the problems become smaller. How the controller performs tracking with a faster pole placement $\alpha = 0.9$ is shown in Fig. 8.

The step response is fast but with a lag due to the large controller polynomials and the use of an error tracking controller. To get rid of the lag we can in this case introduce feed forward of the set-point, with a gain equal to the inverse static gain.

$$u = \frac{S}{R} e_k + \frac{A(1)}{B(1)} r_k$$

Fig. 9 shows the tracking performance. There is only one small transient appearing exactly one period or 2s after a step in the set-point is applied. However for less drastic set-point changes fast tracking is achieved.

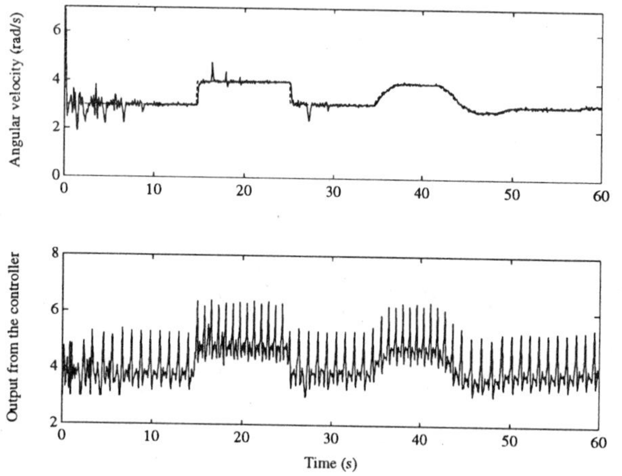

Fig. 9: *Tracking with the error controller extended with feed forward of the set-point,* $\alpha = 0.9$

7. Conclusions

Disturbances affecting rotating devices can, despite temporary non-periodicity in real time, be rejected using periodic disturbance rejection techniques.

If it is possible, much is to be gained by sampling synchronously with the disturbance instead of with a fixed time interval. The disturbance model fits the actual disturbance better than with 'normal' sampling.

Then it is also possible to achieve high accuracy tracking of a varying set point using the error tracking polynomial controller, completed with a simple feed forward of the set-point.

The error tracking controller is easy to develop. The pole placement controller just involves the solution of the Diophantine equation which, with the dampened oscillative pole placement used, includes only one tuning parameter α.

Acknowledgments The authors wish to thank K.S. Walgama and the reviewers for their comments.

References

[1] K.J. Åström and B. Wittenmark. Self-tuning controllers based on pole-zero placement. *IEE Proceedings-D*, 127(3):120–130, 1980.

[2] K.J. Åström and B. Wittenmark. *Computer controlled system.* Prentice-Hall, 1984.

[3] Kok Kia Chew and Masayoshi Tomizuka. Steady-state and stochastic performance of a modified discrete-time prototype repetitive controller. *ASME Journal of Dynamic Systems, Measurement, and Control*, 33(7):659–668, 1988.

[4] W.J. Edwards and P.J. Thomas. Roll eccentricity control for strip rolling mills. 10th *World Congress on Automatic Control*, 1987.

[5] B.A. Francis and W.M. Wonham. The internal model principle of control theory. *Automatica*, 12(5):457–465, 1976.

[6] G. Hillerström. Rejection of periodic disturbances. Licentiate thesis 1992:21L, Luleå University of Technology, October 1992.

[7] Alan V. Oppenheim, Alan S. Willsky, and Ian T. Young. *Signals and Systems.* Prentice-Hall, 1983.

[8] S. Rönnbäck, G. Hillerström, and J. Sternby. Periodic disturbance rejection and setpoint tracking with application to a peristaltic pump. *To appear at European Control Conference*, 1993.

[9] Masayoshi Tomizuka, Kok-Kia Chew, and Tsu-Chin Tsao. Discrete-time domain analysis and synthesis of repetitive controllers. *American Control Conference*, pages 860–866, 1988.

[10] Masayoshi Tomizuka, Kok-Kia Chew, and Wei-Chi Yang. Disturbance rejection through an external model. *ASME Journal of Dynamic Systems, Measurement, and Control*, 112:559–564, 1990.

[11] Tsu-Chin Tsao and Masayoshi Tomizuka. Adaptive and repetitive digital control algorithms for noncircular machining. *American Control Conference*, pages 115–120, 1988.

[12] K.S. Walgama. On the control of systems with input saturation or periodic disturbances. Doctoral Thesis 1991:093D, Luleå University of Technology, 1991.

A Controller performance evaluation

This section defines the comparison technique used for all controllers.

The idea is to measure how much disturbance energy is left by using an N-point FFT of a signal $x(t)$. The measure should be invariant to different sampling frequencies and number of points in the FFT.

The power equations for the signal $x(t)$ are

$$P_{cont} \triangleq \frac{1}{b-a}\int_a^b |x(t)|^2 dt \approx$$

$$P_{samp} = \frac{1}{Nh} h \sum_{k=0}^{N} |x_k|^2 = \frac{1}{N}\sum_{k=0}^{N} |x_k|^2$$

for $a = 0$ and $b = Nh$.

Parsevals relation [7] gives the disturbance power from the FFT, X_k.

$$P_{cont} \approx P_{samp} = \frac{1}{N}\sum_{k=0}^{N} |x_k|^2 = \frac{1}{N^2}\sum_{k=0}^{N} |X_k|^2$$

Remaining disturbance power is thus obtained from the sum of squares of the FFT spectra, normalized by the number of points used squared.

The value of the disturbance power for the pump run without any controller is used as a reference. The power in the controlled systems output are then divided by this reference, to get the fraction of the disturbance remaining in the output.

Proceedings of the
American Control Conference
San Francisco, California • June 1993

Sample Complexity for Worst-Case System Identification Problems *

Ashok Tikku‡ and Kameshwar Poolla†

Abstract

In this paper we treat a general worst-case system identification problem. This problem is worst-case with respect to *both* noise and system modelling uncertainty. We consider this problem under various *a priori* information structures. We determine bounds on the minimum duration identification experiment that must be run in order to identify the plant to within a specified guaranteed worst-case error bound. Our results are algorithm independent. We show that this minimum duration is prohibitively long. Based on our results we conclude that worst-case (with respect to *noise*) system identification requires unrealistic amounts of experimental data.

1 Introduction

There has recently been considerable research in the area of *control-oriented* system identification. See for example [3], [4], [5], [8], [9], [10] and the references cited therein. The broad objective of this research is to develop identification methodologies that deliver models appropriate for feedback control design. This research is motivated by the desire to synthesize system identification with existing robust control design methodologies.

A particular focus of control-oriented system identification is the general problem of *worst-case* system identification. Several different formulations of this paper are treated in the literature. For instance, frequency-domain approaches may be found in [3], [4], [5] and time-domain approaches may be found in [1], [8], [12], [13], [14], [17].

In this paper we focus on a particular time-domain worst-case system identification problem as developed in [17]. Here, it is assumed that the plant is *a priori* known to be some member of the *model set* $\mathcal{F}$. Two paradigms for the model set treated extensively in the literature are

$$\mathcal{F}_1 = \{h \in \ell_1 : |h_k| = 0,\ k \geq N\}$$

and

$$\mathcal{F}_2 = \left\{h \in \ell_1 : |h_k| \leq M\rho^k\right\}$$

The model set $\mathcal{F}_1$ arises from considering plants that are *a priori* known to have finite impulse response while the model set $\mathcal{F}_2$ describes plants that are *a priori* known to have overshoot bounded by M and to have all poles within a disk of radius ρ.

For the purposes of identifying the plant model, we may apply certain inputs to the plant and we are provided with noisy measurements of the corresponding output. Typically it is assumed that the magnitude of the admissible inputs is bounded by 1, and that the magnitude of the possible noises is bounded by δ. Thus δ represents the (input) signal-to-noise strength in these identification problems.

The problem of *worst-case system* identification is that of determining a suitable model for the plant based on the input-output data so that the *worst-case* (with respect to both noise and plant model uncertainty) identification error (in the ℓ_1 norm) is minimized. For a general class of model sets $\mathcal{F}$, it is shown in [17] that, regardless of the identification algorithm employed, this worst-case error can be no better than 2δ (within a factor of 2, see equation (3.7)). Moreover, it is possible to asymptotically identify the plant to the *optimal* guaranteed accuracy of 2δ (within a factor of 2) by using a particular input sequence u^* (a Galois sequence). The sequence u^* is chosen to be "sufficiently rich" in that it has significant spectral content at all frequencies.

In this paper we address the following question. How long an identification experiment must we conduct in order to identify the plant to within a guaranteed (suboptimal) accuracy of $2\delta + 2\epsilon$? We show that for the model set $\mathcal{F}_1$ it is necessary to conduct an experiment of duration $\mathcal{O}(exp(N/(1+\delta\epsilon)^2))$. For the model set $\mathcal{F}_2$ we show that it is necessary to conduct an experiment of duration $\mathcal{O}(poly(M\rho/\epsilon))$ where the degree of the bounding polynomial is $1/\log_2(1/\rho)$. As $\rho \to 1^-$, i.e. the poles of the plant could approach the unit circle, the order of this polynomial becomes large. In either event, one has to conduct a prohibitively long identification experiment.

Based on our results we draw the conclusion that this formulation of worst-case (with respect to *both* noise and plant model uncertainty) system identification problem requires unrealistically long input-output experimentation for good identification. This is because in this problem formulation, we are attempting to *ensure* good identification error against all possible noise sample paths, however improbable.

*Supported in part by the National Science Foundation under Grant ECS 89-57461, and by gifts from Rockwell International.

† Department of Mechanical Engineering, University of California, Berkeley, CA 94720, Tel. (510) 642-4642, Email: poolla@jagger.berkeley.edu

‡ Department of Electrical Engineering, University of California, Berkeley, CA 94720, Tel. (510) 642-6152, Email: tikku@jagger.berkeley.edu

While plant modelling uncertainty can be malicious, noise is generally neutral. Simply put, this problem formulation is overly pessimistic.

We would like to draw attention to the fact that the time-complexity of other worst-case system identification problems such as the frequency-domain problems treated in [4] and [5] have reasonable time complexity.

In light of the above discussion, we contend that a more reasonable problem formulation is that of worst-case with respect to modelling uncertainty and average-case with respect to noise system identification. Indeed, as suggested in [18], for many problems in information-based complexity the average-case complexity is provably polynomial.

Finally, we should like to remark that in order to prove our results we employ techniques from coding theory and from probability theory (see for example [11]). The connections between system identification and coding theory are particularly interesting. We may regard the (unknown) plant impulse response as the message to be decoded, the input sequence as a collection of codewords, and the measured output as a collection of (noisy) linear parity checks between the message and the codewords.

The remainder of this paper is organized as follows. In Section 2 we establish notation and state some results that we make use of subsequently. In Section 3 we describe the particular worst-case system identification problem that we address. Section 4 contains our principal contributions.

All proofs are omitted. The interested reader is referred to [15]. An extended version of this paper has been submitted under separate cover to the *IEEE Trans. on Auto. Control.*

We would like to thank Kevin Buescher for many useful discussions and for introducing us to large deviation bounds.

2 Preliminaries

In this section we establish notation and state some results that will be used in subsequent sections.

For a real number α, let $N = \lfloor \alpha \rfloor$ denote the greatest integer $N \leq \alpha$.

The inner product of two vectors $x, y \in \mathbf{R}^N$ is written as $\langle x, y \rangle$. For a set of vectors $\Omega \in \mathbf{R}^N$, $co(\Omega)$ denotes the *convex hull* of Ω.

Let ℓ_1 denote the Banach space of absolutely summable one-sided sequences of real numbers equipped with the usual norm. For a convex set $S \in \ell_1$, define its *diameter* and its *radius* respectively by

$$diam\ S = \sup_{g \in S} \sup_{f \in S} \|f - g\|_1$$

$$rad\ S = \inf_{g \in S} \sup_{f \in S} \|f - g\|_1$$

It is straightforward to establish that

$$diam\ S \geq rad\ S \geq \frac{1}{2} diam\ S$$

Let ℓ_∞ denote the Banach space of bounded one-sided sequences of real numbers equipped with the usual norm. Define the *L-step truncation operator* π_L with action

$$\pi_L : \ell_\infty \rightarrow \ell_\infty : (u_0, u_1, \cdots) \rightarrow (u_0, \cdots, u_{L-1}, 0, 0, \cdots)$$

and let $\tilde{\pi}_L = I - \pi_L$. Let H be any causal, stable, linear time-invariant system. As is standard, we may regard H as a bounded convolution operator

$$H : \ell_\infty \rightarrow \ell_\infty$$

We shall represent the operator H by its impulse response $h \in \ell_1$ and we denote the action of H on the input sequence u by $y = h * u$.

Finally, we shall require the following version of the Hoeffding bound (see [6]). Let $Y_i, i = 1, \cdots, N$ be independent random variables with $0 \leq Y_i \leq 1$. Consider the random variable $S = \sum_{i=0}^{N} Y_i$. Then, for $0 \leq t \leq 1 - E[S/N]$,

$$Prob\ \{S \geq E[S] + Nt\} \leq e^{-2Nt^2} \tag{2.1}$$

Here $E[\cdot]$ denotes the expectation operator. While the standard Chernoff bound (see [2]) is tighter, the Hoeffding bound is often more useful in providing closed form expressions.

3 Problem Formulation

In this section, we formulate a certain *worst-case* system identification problem that shall be the focus of this paper. This identification problem is worst-case with respect to *both* modelling uncertainty and noise, and is treated in Tse *et al.* [17].

We shall be exclusively concerned with the problem of identification of *linear time-invariant, stable, single-input single-output discrete-time* plants. We shall also assume that the plant to be identified is relaxed prior to the application of inputs, i.e. the initial conditions on the plant are zero.

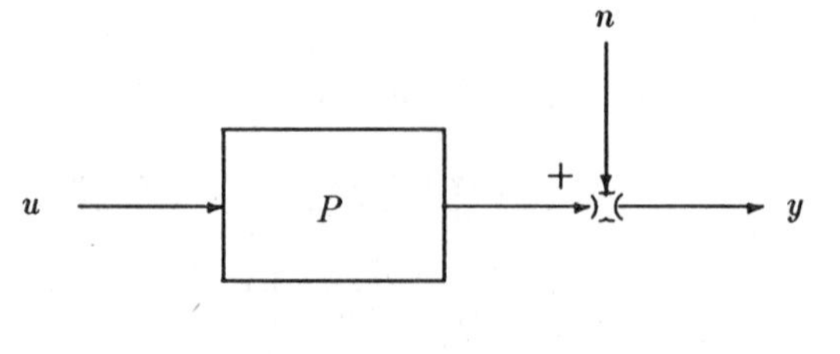

The situation we consider is illustrated above. The true plant h_{true} is known to lie in the *model set* $\mathcal{F}$.

This set captures any *a priori* information we may have regarding model uncertainty in our system. In this paper, we will consider model sets of the form

$$\mathcal{F} = \{h \in \ell_1 : |h_k| \leq g_k\} \tag{3.1}$$

where the sequence $g = (g_0, g_1, \cdots) \in \ell_1$ is assumed to be monotone non-increasing. Of particular interest are the following two instances of this model set:

$$\mathcal{F}_1 = \{h \in \ell_1 : \ |h_k| = 0, \ k \geq N\} \tag{3.2}$$

and

$$\mathcal{F}_2 = \left\{h \in \ell_1 : |h_k| \leq M\rho^k\right\} \tag{3.3}$$

The model set $\mathcal{F}_1$ arises from considering plants that are *a priori* known to have finite impulse response while the model set $\mathcal{F}_2$ describes plants that are *a priori* known to have all poles within a disk of radius ρ and to have overshoot bounded by M.

In order to identify the plant, we shall conduct an input-output experiment. Obvious practical considerations dictate that this experiment be of finite duration, say L. The experiment proceeds as follows. We apply an input sequence

$$u = (u_0, u_1, \cdots, u_{L-1}, *, *, \cdots)$$

to the physical system and observe the first L samples of the resulting noisy output

$$\begin{aligned} y &= (y_0, y_1, \cdots, y_{L-1}, *, *, \cdots) \\ &= h_{true} * u + n \end{aligned}$$

The admissible inputs we may apply are to be drawn from the *input set* $\mathcal{U}$ which we take to be

$$\mathcal{U} = \{u \in \ell_\infty : |u_k| \leq 1\}$$

This input set arises from the reasonable consideration that we can only apply bounded inputs to the system for reasons of safety or physical limitations. Without loss of generality, we assume the admissible inputs are bounded by 1.

We hypothesize that the measurement noise n that corrupts our observations y lies in the *noise set* $\mathcal{N}$. Thus, the noise set captures any prior information we may have regarding the signal uncertainty in our system. In this paper, we consider the noise set

$$\mathcal{N} = \{n \in \ell_\infty : |n_k| \leq \delta\},$$

Thus, δ effectively represents the *noise-to-(input) signal* ratio in our identification experiments.

For each input sequence

$$u = (u_0, u_1, \cdots, u_{L-1}, *, *, \cdots)$$

define the *output set* $\mathcal{Y}(u)$ as

$$\mathcal{Y}(u) = \{y = h * u + n : \ \ h \in \mathcal{F}, \ n \in \mathcal{N}\}$$

Thus $\mathcal{Y}(u)$ defines the set of possible observations resulting from the application of the input sequence u that are consistent with the prior model set and the prior noise set.

An *identification algorithm* $\mathcal{A}$ is a mapping

$$\mathcal{A} : \mathbf{R}^L \times \mathbf{R}^L \rightarrow \ell_1 : (\pi_L u, \pi_L y) \rightarrow \hat{h}$$

Equivalently, $\mathcal{A}$ processes the input-output data record $(\pi_L u, \pi_L y)$ (together with the prior model information $\mathcal{F}$ and the prior signal information $\mathcal{N}$) and produces an estimate

$$\hat{h} = \mathcal{A}(\pi_L u, \pi_L y) \in \ell_1$$

of the true physical plant h_{true}. In the terminology of [5] the algorithm $\mathcal{A}$ is *tuned* to the prior information.

We now introduce the following definition.

Definition 3.4 *Given an L sample input-output data record $\{\pi_L u, \pi_L y\}$, define the* consistent set *$S(u, y, L)$ as*

$$S(u, y, L) = \{h \in \mathcal{F} : \exists n \in \mathcal{N} : \pi_L y = \pi_L (h * u + n)\}.$$

The set $S(u, y, L)$ contains all plant models that could have produced the given input-output data record, or equivalently, all models that are consistent with both the input-output data record and the prior information. Therefore we cannot distinguish between models in the consistent set. In other words, based on the input-output data record and the prior information, the true plant h_{true} could be any member of this set.

Next, suppose that on application of the input u we observe the particular output y. Consider an identification algorithm $\mathcal{A}$. In light of the above discussion, the worst-case identification error $e(\mathcal{A}, u, y, L)$ of the algorithm $\mathcal{A}$ on the input-output data record $(\pi_L u, \pi_L y)$ is

$$e(\mathcal{A}, u, y, L) = \sup_{h_{true} \in S(u,y,L)} \|\mathcal{A}(\pi_L u, \pi_L y) - h_{true}\|$$

For the best possible identification algorithm, the identification error is

$$\begin{aligned} e_{opt}(u, y, L) &= \inf_{\mathcal{A}} e(\mathcal{A}, u, y, L) \\ &= rad \ S(u, y, L) \end{aligned}$$

Definition 3.5 *The* worst-case identification error *for the input u for an L sample experiment is*

$$\begin{aligned} E_{opt}(u, L) &= \sup_{y \in \mathcal{Y}(u)} e_{opt}(u, y, L) \\ &= \sup_{n \in \mathcal{N}} \sup_{h \in \mathcal{F}} \ rad \ S(u, h * u + n, L) \end{aligned}$$

Equivalently, $E_{opt}(u, L)$ defines the best (over all identification algorithms) worst-case (with respect to *both* noise and system modelling uncertainty) identification error (in the ℓ_1 topology).

We now introduce the following key notion.

Definition 3.6 *The* identification error *of the input u for an L sample experiment is*

$$J(u, L) = \sup_{n\in\mathcal{N}} \sup_{h\in\mathcal{F}} \quad diam \ S(u, h * u + n, L)$$

It then readily follows that

$$J(u, L) \geq E_{opt}(u, L) \geq \frac{1}{2} J(u, L) \qquad (3.7)$$

Therefore $J(u, L)$ represents the best (over all algorithms) worst-case error identification error *within a factor of two.* Following Kalman [7], we shall suppress the identification algorithm itself and focus on the quantity $J(u, L)$ as a measure of the performance of the input $\pi_L u$ for the purpose of worst-case system identification with respect to *both* the model set $\mathcal{F}$ and the noise set $\mathcal{N}$.

The following definition plays a central role in the remainder of this paper.

Definition 3.8 *The* optimal identification error *for an L sample identification experiment is*

$$J_{opt}(L) = \inf_{u\in\mathcal{U}} J(u, L)$$

We shall say that the model set $\mathcal{F}$ (or loosely, the plant) is *identifiable to within a guaranteed accuracy of* α if $J_{opt} \leq \alpha$.

Remark 3.9 Suppose we establish that

$$b < J_{opt}(L) \leq B$$

The implication of these inequalities is that the model set $\mathcal{F}$ (or loosely, the plant) is identifiable to within a guaranteed accuracy of B using some admissible L sample input sequence. Also, it is impossible to identify the plant to within a guaranteed accuracy of b using any L sample input.

In the remainder of the paper we shall be concerned with the following question:

> Given the model set $\mathcal{F}$ and the noise set $\mathcal{N}$, what is the minimum duration experiment we must run in order to identify the plant to within a guaranteed accuracy of α ? In other words, determine
>
> $$L_{min}(\alpha) = \{\min L : \ J_{opt}(L) \leq \alpha\}$$

Since computing this minimum duration $L_{min}(\alpha)$ exactly is quite difficult, we shall be content to provide good upper and lower bounds for $L_{min}(\alpha)$.

4 Main Results

In this section we present our principal results on the time complexity of system identification.

4.1 The General Case

We begin by considering the general model set

$$\mathcal{F} = \{h \in \ell_1 : |h_k| \leq g_k\}$$

where $g_0 > \delta$ and the sequence $g = (g_0, g_1, \cdots) \in \ell_1$ is assumed to be monotone non-increasing. We shall derive upper and lower bounds on $J_{opt}(L)$ for $\mathcal{F}$.

Theorem 4.1 *Consider the model set $\mathcal{F}$ above and define $N = \lfloor \log_2 L \rfloor$. Then*

$$2\delta + 2\min\left(g_{N+1}, \frac{\delta}{N+1}\right) < J_{opt}(L) \leq 2\delta + 4\sum_{k=N}^{\infty} g_k \qquad (4.2)$$

Remark 4.3 Since the bounding sequence $g \in \ell_1$ it follows that for N (or equivalently, L) large enough,

$$J_{opt}(L) > 2\delta + 2g_{N+1}$$

Remark 4.4 Theorem 4.1 implies that

$$\lim_{L\to\infty} J_{opt}(L) = 2\delta$$

i.e. the model set $\mathcal{F}$ is asymptotically identifiable to within a guaranteed accuracy of no better than 2δ. This was first established in [17]. In [17] it is shown that by using an infinite duration input sequence (a Galois sequence) it is possible to identify $\mathcal{F}$ to within a guaranteed accuracy of 2δ. The expression above that makes explicit the dependence of $J_{opt}(L)$ on L is however new.

4.2 The Finite-impulse Response Case

We now treat the model set

$$\mathcal{F}_1 = \{h \in \ell_1 : \ h_k = 0 \ , \ k \geq N\}$$

We can establish the following central result.

Theorem 4.5 *Consider the model set $\mathcal{F}_1$ above. In order to identify the plant to within a guaranteed accuracy of $2\delta(1+\epsilon)$ we must run an experiment of at least L_{min} samples where*

$$\frac{1}{2} e^{\left(\frac{N}{2(1+\epsilon)^2}\right)} \leq L_{min} \leq N + 2^{N+1-\frac{\epsilon}{2}}$$

Remark 4.6 The above result tells is that guaranteed identification to within $2\delta(1+\epsilon)$ requires $\mathcal{O}(exp(N/(1+\delta\epsilon)^2))$ time. For example, consider the problem of identifying $N = 100$ impulse response coefficients. Suppose we have an input signal to measurement noise ratio of δ and assume a sampling time of 50 *msec*. In order to identify the plant to within a guaranteed accuracy of 4δ we must conduct an experiment lasting more than 1.86 hours. This is a prohibitively long time to identify a 5 second impulse response.

4.3 The $M-\rho$ Model Set

We consider here the model set

$$\mathcal{F}_2 = \{h \in \ell_1 : |h_k| \leq M\rho^k\}$$

We shall make the reasonable assumption $M > \delta$, i.e. the prior plant model uncertainty is not insignificant.

Our first result is

Theorem 4.7 *Consider the model set $\mathcal{F}_2$ above. In order to identify the plant to within a guaranteed accuracy of $(2\delta + 2\epsilon)$ we must run an experiment of at least L_{min} samples where*

$$b \leq L_{min} \leq B \tag{4.8}$$

Here,

$$b = = \min\left(2^{\frac{1}{\epsilon}-1}, \left(\frac{M\rho}{\epsilon}\right)^{\frac{1}{\log_2\frac{1}{\rho}}}\right)$$

$$B = = \left(\frac{2M}{\epsilon\rho(1-\rho)}\right)^{\frac{1}{\log_2\frac{1}{\rho}}}$$

Remark 4.9 For small ϵ, equation (4.8) reduces to

$$\left(\frac{M\rho}{\epsilon}\right)^{\frac{1}{\log_2\frac{1}{\rho}}} \leq L_{min} \leq \left(\frac{2M}{\epsilon\rho(1-\rho)}\right)^{\frac{1}{\log_2\frac{1}{\rho}}}$$

Therefore, in order to identify the plant within a guaranteed accuracy of $(2\delta + 2\epsilon)$ it is necessary to conduct an experiment of duration $\mathcal{O}(poly(M\rho/\epsilon))$ where the degree of the bounding polynomial is $1/\log_2(1/\rho)$. As $\rho \to 1^-$, i.e. the poles of the plant could approach the unit circle, the order of this polynomial becomes large. This is consistent with our intuition that it takes longer to identify a lightly damped plant. For a modest $\rho = 0.95$ we have the $L_{min} \geq (M/\epsilon)^{13.5}$ which, while not exponential, becomes unreasonable rapidly.

References

[1] J. Chen, C. N. Nett, and M. K. H. Fan, "Worst-Case System Identification in H_∞: Validation of Apriori Information, Essentially Optimal Algorithms, and Error Bounds," to appear in the *Proc. of the 1992 Amer. Contr. Conf.*, Chicago.

[2] H. Chernoff, "A Measure of asymptotic efficiency for test of a hypothesis based on the sums of observation," in *Annals of Math. and Statistics*, vol. 23 pp. 493–507, 1952.

[3] G. C. Goodwin, B. Ninnes, and M. E. Salgado, "Quantification of uncertainty in estimation," *Proc. of the 1990 Amer. Contr. Conf.*, San Diego, CA, 2400-2405, 1990.

[4] G. Gu and P. P. Khargonekar, "Linear and nonlinear algorithms for identification in $\mathcal{H}_\infty$ with error bounds," to appear in *IEEE Trans. Automat. Control.* An abridged version is in *Proc. 1991 American Control Conference*, pp. 64-69.

[5] A. J. Helmicki, C. A. Jacobson, and C. N. Nett, "Control-oriented system identification: a worst-case/deterministic approach in $\mathcal{H}_\infty$, " to appear in the *IEEE Transactions on Automatic Control.*

[6] W. Hoeffding, "Probability inequalities for sums of bounded random variables," in *Amer. Stat. Assoc. Journal*, pp. 13–30, March 1963

[7] R E Kalman, "The problem of prejudice in scientific modeling," Recent Advances in Communication and Control Theory, eds. R. E. Kalman et al., Optimization Software Inc., pp. 448-461, 1987.

[8] R. L. Kosut, M. Lau and S. Boyd, "Identification of systems with parametric and nonparametric uncertainty," *Proc. of the 1990 Amer. Contr. Conf.*, 2412-2417, San Diego, CA, 1990.

[9] L. Ljung, *System Identification, Theory for the User*, Prentice-Hall, Inc., Englewood Cliffs, New Jersey, 1987.

[10] L. Ljung and Z-D Yuan, "Asymptotic properties of black-box identification of transfer functions," *IEEE Trans. Automat. Contr.*, vol. 30, 514-530, June 1985.

[11] F. J. MacWilliams and N. J. A. Sloane, *The Theory of Error-correcting Codes*, Vols. 1 & 2, North-Holland Press, New York, 1977.

[12] P. M. Mäkilä " Robust identificaton and Galois sequences," Technical Report 91-1, Process Control Laboratory, Swed. Univ. of Abo, Jan. 1991.

[13] P. M. Mäkilä and J. R. Partington, " Robust approximation and identification in $\mathcal{H}_\infty$," *Proceedings of the 1991 American Control Conference*, pp. 70-76.

[14] J. R. Partington, "Robust identification in $\mathcal{H}_\infty$," *J. Math. Anal. and Appl.*, to appear.

[15] K. Poolla and A. Tikku, "On the Time Complexity of Worst-Case SYstem Identification," submitted to the *IEEE Trans. Auto. Control*, 1992.

[16] R.T. Rockafellar, *Convex Analysis*, Princeton University Press, Princeton, New Jersey, 1970.

[17] D. N. C. Tse, M. A. Dahleh, and J. N. Tsitsiklis, "Optimal Asymptotic Identification under Bounded Disturbances", Preprint, LIDS, MIT, Cambridge, MA. An abridged version is in *Proc. 1991 American Control Conference*, pp. 1786-1787.

[18] J. F. Traub, G. Wasilkowski, and H. Wazniakowski, *Information- based Complexity*, Academic Press, New York, 1980.

Proceedings of the
American Control Conference
San Francisco, California • June 1993

Observer-Based Parameter Identifiers for Nonlinear Systems with Parameter Dependencies

Shahab Sheikholeslam *
Measurex Corporation
One Results Way Mail Stop 5244
Cupertino, CA 95014

Abstract We consider the class of nonlinear dynamical systems whose dynamics depends *linearly* on the unknown parameter vector. After reviewing a standard observer-based identifier for estimating the unknown parameters, we propose a family of new identifiers which exploit the a priori known parameter dependencies. Then, we establish that, under mild assumptions on the dynamical system, a) the proposed identifiers are stable, and b) the weighted norm of state-parameter errors using the proposed identifiers are less than the corresponding errors using the standard identifier, for a length of time after $t = 0$. The main contribution of this paper is that it introduces a family of observer-based identifiers which exhibit better transient performance than the standard identifier.

1 Introduction

The subject of adaptive identification and control has been studied extensively in the literature. (For the basic theory refer to [8], [5],[11], [9].) Adaptive parameter identifiers studied in the literature fall into two classes: a) identification algorithms which use the input-output relations to continuously estimate the unknown parameters (see [8], [5]), and b) *model reference identification* algorithms [11, p.50], [9], [7] which use an observer to continuously estimate the unknown parameters. The algorithms in class b) are useful for adaptive control. The identifiers in this paper belong to class b).

In most engineering applications, the unknown parameters in the system equations are *known* functions of the physical parameters of the model. In many such cases, the unknown parameters are *known* functions of a *strictly proper* subset of all the unknown parameters. Our approach in designing new parameter identifiers for a class of nonlinear systems is to exploit such parameter dependencies while maintaining the stability of the identifier. Intuitively, an identifier which exploits the a priori known parameter dependencies should yield smaller errors than a similar identifier which does not make use of such dependencies. In [3] and [1], the authors propose identification algorithms, in class a), which make use of parameter dependencies. The main contribution of this paper is that it introduces a family of identifiers, in class b), which exhibit better transient performance than a standard identifier. The method of proof used to show the superior transient performance can be used to prove that the parameter errors, resulting from using the identifier in [3] in class a), are smaller than the corresponding errors using a standard least- squares identification algorithm.

Recently, some authors have studied the problem of robust adaptive control of *linear time-invariant* systems [6], [4]. As pointed out in [6], one of the main limitations to the theory is the lack of a more convenient quantification of the transient performance. We believe that the results presented in this paper are preliminary attempts at such a quantification.

The paper is organized as follows: in section 2, we propose a new observer-based identifier for a class of nonlinear dynamical systems and state theorems regarding its stability and transient performance; to compare the transient performance of the proposed identifier with that of the standard identifier, in section 3, we show simulation results for adaptive identification of the longitudinal dynamics of a vehicle; in section 4, we outline the main results and provide future directions for research.

2 Parameter Identifiers

Throughout this paper, we use $|\cdot|$ to denote the Euclidean norm of a vector and $||\cdot||$ to denote the induced norm of a matrix.

2.1 Background

Consider the nonlinear time-invariant dynamical system

$$\begin{aligned} \dot{x} &= W^T(x,u)\theta^* \\ x(0) &= x_0 \end{aligned} \tag{1}$$

where $x \in R^n$ denotes the state of the system, $u \in R^m$ denotes the control input to the system, $\theta^* \in R^p$ is a *constant* vector of unknown parameters, and $W(\cdot,\cdot)$ is a $p \times n$ matrix of piecewise continuous functions. W^T denotes the transpose of the matrix W.

Parameter structure In (1), components of the unknown parameter vector θ^* are *known* functions of the physical parameters (e.g., engine time-lag (τ) and drag coefficient (K_d) in the vehicle dynamics (10) with θ^* defined in (13)). Previous papers [13], [15], [16], [2] have proposed observer-based identifiers, for (1), which do not exploit these parameter dependencies.

Identifier Structure (not using parameter dependencies) [13], [15], [16], [10]

Let $A \in R^{n\times n}$ be a Hurwitz matrix and $Q \in R^{n\times n}$ be a given symmetric, positive definite matrix; let $P \in R^{n\times n}$ denote the unique symmetric positive-definite solution of the Lyapunov equation

$$A^TP + PA = -Q; \tag{2}$$

for the dynamical system in (1) the identifier is chosen to be

$$\dot{\hat{x}}^u = A(\hat{x}^u - x) + W^T(x,u)\hat{\theta}^u \tag{3}$$

*Author supported by PATH Project under Grant number RTA-74H221

$$\dot{\hat{\theta}}^u = -W(x,u)P(\hat{x}^u - x) \quad (4)$$
$$\hat{x}^u(0) = \hat{x}_0 \quad (5)$$
$$\hat{\theta}^u(0) = \hat{\theta}_0. \quad (6)$$

The superscript 'u' in $\hat{x}^u$, $\hat{\theta}^u$ indicates that the Lyapunov function, used to prove the stability of the above identifier, is *unconstrained* with respect to parameter dependencies in (1). (See (9) below.)

A 1 [Boundedness of the Regressor] We assume that $W : R^n \times R^m \to R^{p\times n}$ is bounded. ■

Stability of the Identifier Define the state error and the parameter error by

$$e^u := \hat{x}^u - x \quad (7)$$
$$\phi^u := \hat{\theta}^u - \theta^*. \quad (8)$$

Theorem 1 [Stability of identifier (3)-(4)] Consider the dynamical system (1) with the identifier (3)- (4). Let A 1 hold, then $e^u \in L_2 \bigcap L_\infty$, $\dot{e}^u \in L_\infty$, and $\phi^u \in L_\infty$. ■

Proof (Theorem 1) See [16, (and references therein)], [11, sec.2.4].

The proof of Theorem 1 uses a standard *unconstrained* Lyapunov function candidate

$$V^u(e^u, \phi^u) := \frac{1}{2}e^{uT}Pe^u + \frac{1}{2}\phi^{uT}\phi^u. \quad (9)$$

2.2 New Identifier

In many engineering applications, the components of the unknown parameter vector θ^* are *known* functions of the physical parameters. In such instances, components of $\theta^* \in R^p$ are *known* functions of a *strictly* proper subset of θ_i^* for $i = 1, 2, \ldots, p$. (θ_i^* denotes the i-th component of θ^*.) This is illustrated in the following example.

Example Consider the following nonlinear differential equation representing the longitudinal dynamics of a vehicle [14], [12]

$$\dddot{x} = -2\frac{K_d}{m}\dot{x}\ddot{x} - \frac{1}{\tau}\left[\ddot{x} + \frac{K_d}{m}\dot{x}^2 + \frac{d_m}{m}\right] + \frac{u}{m\tau} \quad (10)$$

where x is the position of the vehicle's center of mass with respect to a fixed reference point O on the road; K_d denotes the vehicle's aerodynamic drag coefficient; m denotes the mass of the vehicle; τ denotes the vehicle's engine time-constant; d_m denotes the mechanical drag of the vehicle; and u denotes the throttle-command input to the vehicle's engine.

Equation (10) can be put into the form

$$\dddot{x} = w^T(\dot{x}, \ddot{x}, u)\theta^* \quad (11)$$

where

$$w(\dot{x}, \ddot{x}, u) := \left[-\frac{2}{m}\dot{x}\ddot{x}, -\ddot{x} - \frac{d_m}{m} + \frac{u}{m}, -\frac{\dot{x}^2}{m}\right]^T \quad (12)$$

and

$$\theta^* := \left[K_d, \frac{1}{\tau}, \frac{K_d}{\tau}\right]^T. \quad (13)$$

For the vehicle dynamics (11), $\theta_3^* = \theta_1^*\theta_2^*$.

Our approach in designing a new parameter identifier for (1) is to exploit such parameter dependencies while maintaining the stability of the identifier. Intuitively, an identifier which exploits the a priori known parameter dependencies should yield smaller errors than a similar identifier which does not make use of such dependencies.

Parameter dependencies

Definition [Parameter constraint set] Consider the dynamical system (1) with $\theta^* \in R^p$. The parameter constraint set is an N-dimensional C^2 submanifold of R^p parameterized by $\theta_1^*, \ldots, \theta_N^*$. Hence, the *parameter constraint manifold* is described by

$$\mathcal{C}(\{\gamma_i\ , N+1 \le i \le p\}) := \{\theta | \theta_i = \gamma_i(\theta_1, \ldots, \theta_N)\ , N+1 \le i \le p\} \quad (14)$$

where for $i = N+1, \ldots, p$, $\gamma_i : R^N \to R$ is a known C^2 map (i.e., γ_i is at least twice continuously differentiable).

Comments

(a) Note that $\theta^* \in \mathcal{C}(\{\gamma_i, i = N+1, \ldots, p\})$. Any $\theta \notin \mathcal{C}(\{\gamma_i, i = N+1, \ldots, p\})$ is inconsistent with the a priori parameter dependencies. Following [3], we add a penalty term to the Lyapunov function candidate (9) to take into account these parameter dependencies. (See (23) below.)

(b) *Penalty Function* Consider the parameter constraint set in (14). We define a penalty function $\tilde{P} : R^p \to R$ with

$$\tilde{P}(\hat{\theta}) := \frac{1}{2}\sum_{i=N+1}^{p} \lambda_i[\hat{\theta}_i - \gamma_i(\hat{\theta}_1, \ldots, \hat{\theta}_N)]^2 \quad (15)$$

where $\lambda_i > 0$ for all $i = N+1, \ldots, p$.

For the vehicle dynamics (11), the parameter constraint set is $\mathcal{C}(\{\gamma_3\}) = \{\theta \in R^3 | \theta_3 = \gamma_3(\theta_1, \theta_2) := \theta_1\theta_2\}$. The penalty function (15) with respect to the parameter constraint set $\mathcal{C}(\{\gamma_3\})$ is

$$\tilde{P}(\hat{\theta}) = \frac{1}{2}\lambda_3[\hat{\theta}_3 - \hat{\theta}_1\hat{\theta}_2]^2 \quad (16)$$

where $\lambda_3 > 0$.

Identifier Structure (using parameter dependencies) Let $A \in R^{n\times n}$, $Q \in R^{n\times n}$, and $P \in R^{n\times n}$ be the same matrices used in (2) and (3)-(4). Let $\tilde{P}$ be the penalty function in (15) for the parameter constraint set in (14).

The new identifier for the dynamical system (1) is

$$\dot{\hat{x}}^c = A(\hat{x}^c - x) + W^T(x,u)[\hat{\theta}^c + D\tilde{P}(\hat{\theta}^c)] \quad (17)$$
$$\dot{\hat{\theta}}^c = -W(x,u)P(\hat{x}^c - x) \quad (18)$$
$$\hat{x}^c(0) = \hat{x}_0 \quad (19)$$
$$\hat{\theta}^c(0) = \hat{\theta}_0 \quad (20)$$

where $D\tilde{P}(\cdot)$ denotes the differential of the penalty function.

We have used the superscript 'c' in $\hat{x}^c$, $\hat{\theta}^c$ to indicate that the Lyapunov function candidate, used to prove the stability of the above identifier, is *constrained* with respect to parameter dependencies in (1). (See (23) below.)

A 2 [Existence and Uniqueness] Throughout this paper, we assume that the solutions of the differential equations (17)-(18) with initial conditions (19)- (20) exist and are unique on $[0, \infty)$. ■

Stability of the Identifier Denote

$$e^c := \hat{x}^c - x \quad (21)$$
$$\phi^c := \hat{\theta}^c - \theta^*. \quad (22)$$

Theorem 2 [Stability of Identifier (17)-(18)] Consider the dynamical system (1) with the identifier (17)- (18). Let e^c, ϕ^c denote the identifier's state-error and parameter-error vectors, respectively. (See (21), (22).) Suppose A 1 [Boundedness of the Regressor] and A 2 [Existence and Uniqueness] hold, then $e^c \in L_2 \bigcap L_\infty$, $\dot{e}^c \in L_\infty$, and $\phi^c \in L_\infty$. ■

Comments

(**a**) Proof of Theorem 2 uses a Lyapunov function candidate of the form

$$V^c(e^c, \phi^c) := \frac{1}{2}e^{cT}Pe^c + \frac{1}{2}\phi^{cT}\phi^c + \tilde{P}(\phi^c + \theta^*). \quad (23)$$

Comparing (9) with (23), we note that the penalty term $\tilde{P}(\phi^c + \theta^*)$ is the new addition to the standard Lyapunov function candidate. The design of the new identifier (17)- (18) is motivated by using the Lyapunov function candidate (23).

(**b**) In [3, equation (2.14)], the authors propose a similar Lyapunov function for improving the robustness of a least-squares type identification algorithm. The main differences between the identification algorithms presented in [3] and the observer-based identifier in (17)-(18) are: a) the identifier in (17)- (18) belongs to the so-called *model reference identification* family of algorithms [11, p.50]. The algorithms in this family are useful for adaptive control. The identification algorithms in [3] use the input-output relations to estimate the unknown parameters; b) the dynamical systems in [3] are SISO, *linear*, time-invariant, whereas, we consider MIMO, *nonlinear*, time-invariant dynamical systems (see (1)); and c) in [3], the parameters are *multilinear* functions of the unknowns (i.e., the γ_i's, see (14), are multilinear functions); whereas, we allow more general parameter dependencies in the definition of the parameter constraint set (14).

Transient Performance We now compare the transient performance of the new identifier (17)-(18) with that of the standard identifier (3)-(4). In Theorem 3, we show that, for a period of time after $t = 0$, norm of the error vector using the identifier (17)-(18) is less than the corresponding norm using the standard identifier (3)-(4).

Consider the dynamical system represented by (1) with the parameter constraint set (14). Let $t \mapsto \hat{\theta}^u(t) := (\hat{\theta}^u_1(t), \ldots, \hat{\theta}^u_N(t), \hat{\theta}^u_{N+1}(t), \ldots, \hat{\theta}^u_p(t))^T \in R^p$ denote the solution of (4) with initial condition $\hat{\theta}^u(0)$.

A 3 [Deviation from constraint set] We assume that there exists a $j \in \{N+1, \ldots, p\}$ such that

$$\frac{d}{dt}\left[\hat{\theta}^u_j(0) - \gamma_j(\hat{\theta}^u_1(0), \ldots, \hat{\theta}^u_N(0))\right]|_{(4)} \neq 0. \ \blacksquare \quad (24)$$

Remark Intuitively, A 3 indicates that the direction of the velocity vector of the parameter estimates at $t = 0$, using the update law (4), lies outside the tangent space of the parameter constraint set (14) at $\hat{\theta}^u(0)$. Hence, after $t = 0$, the parameter estimates may not lie on the parameter contraint set (14).

Theorem 3 [Transient Performance] Consider the dynamical system represented by (1). Let the proposed identifier (17)-(18) and the standard identifier (3)-(4) have the same initial conditions (5)-(6). Suppose the parameter estimates initially lie on the parameter constraint set (14). Suppose A 1 [Boundedness of the Regressor], A 2 [Existence and Uniqueness], and A 3 [Deviation from Constraint Set] hold. Let $e^u : R_+ \to R^n$, $\phi^u : R_+ \to R^p$ be defined as in (7), (8), respectively. Let $e^c : R_+ \to R^n$, $\phi^c : R_+ \to R^p$ be defined as in (21), (22), respectively. Under these conditions, there exists an $\bar{\epsilon} > 0$ such that for all $\epsilon \in [0, \bar{\epsilon})$,

$$e^{cT}(\epsilon)Pe^c(\epsilon) + \phi^{cT}(\epsilon)\phi^c(\epsilon) \leq e^{uT}(\epsilon)Pe^u(\epsilon) + \phi^{uT}(\epsilon)\phi^u(\epsilon). \ \blacksquare \quad (25)$$

Comments

(**a**) Theorem 3 is the main result of this paper. It shows that initially the proposed identifier (17)-(18) results in smaller state and parameter errors than the standard identifier (3)-(4). In [3], the authors present simulation results to verify the improvement in the overall robustness characteristics of their proposed identifiers; they do not prove that their identifiers result in smaller parameter errors.

(**b**) Theorem 3 does not make any assertions comparing the magnitude of the parameter errors between the two identifiers. Using the same steps in the proof of Theorem 3 for the least-squares type identification algorithm in [3, equation (2.18)], one can show that:

there exists an $\bar{\epsilon} > 0$ such that for all $\epsilon \in [0, \bar{\epsilon})$,

$$\phi^{cT}(\epsilon)\phi^c(\epsilon) \leq \phi^{uT}(\epsilon)\phi^u(\epsilon). \quad (26)$$

Whether (26) remains valid for the identifier (17)- (18) remains an open question.

(**c**) In general the largest value of $\bar{\epsilon}$, for which (25) holds, depends on the choice of the penalty function $\tilde{P}(\cdot)$, the exogenous input vector u, and the dynamics of the system.

(**d**) At the present time, there are no systematic procedures for selecting the values of λ_i in (15). Intuitively, the choice of λ_i's reflects a trade-off between the weighted norm of the identifier's state-parameter error vectors and the deviation of the parameter estimates from the parameter constraint set.

(**e**) The proof of Theorem 3 is based on three observations: i) the first three terms in the Taylor expansion of $V^c(e^c(\epsilon), \phi^c(\epsilon)) - V^u(e^u(\epsilon), \phi^u(\epsilon))$, about $t = 0$, are zero; hence, $V^c(e^c(\epsilon), \phi^c(\epsilon)) - V^u(e^u(\epsilon), \phi^u(\epsilon))$ is $O(\epsilon^3)$; ii) the Taylor expansion of the penalty term $\tilde{P}(\phi^c(\epsilon) + \theta^*)$, about $t = 0$, is at least as large as $\frac{\epsilon^2}{2}c + O(\epsilon^3)$, for some constant $c > 0$; and iii) $V^c(e^c(\epsilon), \phi^c(\epsilon)) = V^u(e^c(\epsilon), \phi^c(\epsilon)) + \tilde{P}(\phi^c(\epsilon) + \theta^*)$. (See (9) and (23).)

3 Simulation

To compare the transient performance of the proposed identifier (17)- (18) with that of the standard identifier (3)-(4), we ran simulations using the nonlinear differential equation (10) representing the longitudinal dynamics of a vehicle. Equation (10) can be put into the form (11) with $w(\cdot, \cdot, \cdot)$ and θ^* defined in (12), (13), respectively.

The standard identifier for (11) is

$$\begin{aligned} \frac{d}{dt}\hat{\dot{x}}^u &= -\sigma_x(\hat{\dot{x}}^u - \dot{x}) + w^T(\dot{x}, \ddot{x}, u)\hat{\theta}^u && (27)\\ \frac{d}{dt}\hat{\theta}^u &= -\sigma_\theta w(\dot{x}, \ddot{x}, u)(\hat{\dot{x}}^u - \dot{x}) && (28)\\ \hat{\dot{x}}^u(0) &= \hat{\dot{x}}_0 && (29)\\ \hat{\theta}^u(0) &= \hat{\theta}_0 && (30) \end{aligned}$$

where $\hat{\dot{x}}^u \in R$, $\hat{\theta}^u \in R^3$, $\sigma_x > 0$, and $\sigma_\theta > 0$.

Using the penalty term $\tilde{P}(\cdot)$ in (16), the proposed identifier for (11) is

$$\begin{aligned} \frac{d}{dt}\hat{\dot{x}}^c &= -\sigma_x(\hat{\dot{x}}^c - \dot{x}) + w^T(\dot{x}, \ddot{x}, u)[\hat{\theta}^c + D\tilde{P}(\hat{\theta}^c)] && (31)\\ \frac{d}{dt}\hat{\theta}^c &= -\sigma_\theta w(\dot{x}, \ddot{x}, u)(\hat{\dot{x}}^c - \dot{x}) && (32)\\ \hat{\dot{x}}^c(0) &= \hat{\dot{x}}_0 && (33)\\ \hat{\theta}^c(0) &= \hat{\theta}_0 && (34) \end{aligned}$$

where $\hat{\dot{x}}^c \in R$ and $\hat{\theta}^c \in R^3$.

Vehicle Parameters In all the simulations conducted, the vehicle parameters were as follows: $m = 1136\ kg$, $d_m = 150.74\ N$, $K_d = 0.396\ kg/m$, and $\tau = 0.18\ s$.

Identifier Parameters We chose $\sigma_x = 1$ and $\sigma_\theta = 2$. For the proposed identifier (31)-(32), $\lambda_3 = 2$ was used for the penalty term $\tilde{P}(\hat{\theta})$ in (16). The initial state and parameter estimates were $\hat{x}_0 = 1$, $\hat{\theta}_0 = [0.44, 5, 2.2]^T$, respectively.
Simulation Set up Initially, the vehicle was traveling at a constant speed of 17.9 m/s (i.e., $\dot{x}(0) = 17.9\ m/s$, $\ddot{x}(0) = 0\ m/s^2$, $\dddot{x}\ (0) = 0\ m/s^3$). Starting at time $t = 1\ s$, the throttle-command input increased linearly, from its initial steady-state value of 381 N, at a rate of 1136 N/s until it reached its final value of 1517 N at $t = 2\ s$.
Simulation Results Figure 1 shows the state and the parameter errors for the standard identifier (27)-(28) and the proposed identifier (31)-(32). Note that the magnitude of the parameter errors using the proposed identifier (31)-(32) are smaller than the corresponding errors using the standard identifier (27)-(28), for a length of time after $t = 0\ s$. Also note that in either case the parameter errors do not converge to zero.

Figure 2 shows the weighted norm of the state-parameter error vectors for the standard identifier (27)-(28) (i.e., $t \mapsto V^u(e^u(t), \phi^u(t))$) and the proposed identifier (31)-(32) (i.e., $t \mapsto V^u(e^c(t), \phi^c(t))$). Note that, for all $t \in [0, 10]$, $V^u(e^c(t), \phi^c(t)) \leq V^u(e^u(t), \phi^u(t))$. (i.e., we can let $\tilde{\epsilon} = 10$ in the statement of Theorem 3 [Transient Performance]).

These simulation results show that the proposed identifier (31)-(32) has better transient performance than the standard one (27)-(28). Thus, we expect that using the parameter estimates from the identifier (31)-(32) together with a certainty- equivalence control law will result in superior closed-loop adaptive-control performance of a vehicle's longitudinal dynamics. Simulations of indirect adaptive control laws for a platoon of vehicles support this conclusion.

4 Conclusion

We have proposed a family of observer-based identifiers for a class of nonlinear dynamical systems which use the a priori known parameter dependencies. Under mild assumptions on the dynamical system, we have shown that a) the proposed identifiers are stable (see Theorem 2), and b) the weighted norm of state-parameter errors using the new identifier are less than the corresponding errors using the standard identifier, for a length of time after $t = 0$ (see Theorem 3).

There remain a number of open questions:
a) How can we select the coefficients λ_i, for $i = N+1, \ldots, p$, in the definition of the penalty function $\tilde{P}(\cdot)$ (see 15) so as to attain the "best" transient performance?
b) Is the proposed identifier more robust with respect to parameter variations and exogenous measurement noise?
c) Can we design stable identifiers which have the least number of states? (e.g., the update law only updates the basic parameters; other parameter estimates are then computed using estimates of the basic parameters.)

We believe that satisfactory answers to the above questions will lead to systematic strategies for designing robust, nonlinear, adaptive control laws.

Acknowledgement
The author would like to thank Professor Charles A. Desoer for his useful suggestions.

References

[1] G. Bastin, R.R. Bitmead, G. Campion, and M. Gevers. Identification of Linearly Overparameterized Nonlinear Systems. In *Proceedings of the Conference on Decision and Control*, pages 618–623, 1989.

[2] G. Bastin and M.R. Gevers. Stable Adaptive Observers for Nonlinear Time-Varying Systems. *IEEE Transactions on Automatic Control*, AC-33(7):650–658, July 1988.

[3] S. Dasgupta, B.D.O. Anderson, and R.J. Kaye. Identification of Physical Parameters in Structured Systems. *Automatica*, 24(2):217-225, March 1988.

[4] F. Giri, M. M' Saad, L. Dugard, and J.M. Dion. Robust Adaptive Regulation with Minimal Prior Knowledge. *IEEE Transactions on Automatic Control*, AC-37(3):305–315, March 1992.

[5] G.C. Goodwin and K.S. Sin. *Adaptive Filtering Prediction and Control.* Prentice-Hall, Englewood Cliffs, New Jersey, 1984.

[6] J.M. Krause, P.P. Khargonekar, and G. Stein. Robust Adaptive Control: Stability and Asymptotic Performance. *IEEE Transactions on Automatic Control*, AC-37(3):316–331, March 1992.

[7] G. Kreisselmeier. Adaptive Observers with Exponential Rate of Convergence. *IEEE Transactions on Automatic Control*, AC-22:2-8, 1977.

[8] L. Ljung. *System Identification: theory for the user.* Prentice-Hall, Englewood Cliffs, New Jersey, 1987.

[9] K.S. Narendra and A.M. Annaswamy. *Stable Adaptive Systems.* Prentice-Hall, Englewood Cliffs, New Jersey, 1989.

[10] J. Pomet and L. Praly. Indirect Adaptive Nonlinear Control. In *Proceedings of the Conference on Decision and Control*, pages 2414–2415, 1988.

[11] S.S. Sastry and M. Bodson. *Adaptive Control: Stability, Convergence, and Robustness.* Prentice Hall, 1st. edition, 1989.

[12] S. Sheikholeslam and C.A. Desoer. Longitudinal Control of a Platoon of Vehicles. In *Proceedings of the American Control Conference*, volume 1, pages 291–297, May 1990.

[13] S. Sheikholeslam and C.A. Desoer. Design of Decentralized Adaptive Controllers for a Class of Interconnected Nonlinear Dynamical Systems. In *Proceedings of the Conference on Decision and Control*, pages 284–288, 1992.

[14] S. Sheikholeslam and C.A. Desoer. A System-Level Study of the Longitudinal Control of a Platoon of Vehicles. *ASME Journal on Dynamic Systems, Measurement and Control*, 114(2):286–292, June 1992.

[15] S. Sheikholeslam and C.A. Desoer. Indirect Adaptive Control of a Class of Interconnected Nonlinear Dynamical Systems. March 1993. to appear in International Journal of Control, PATH technical memorandum 91-1.

[16] A. Teel, R. Kadiyala, P. Kokotovic, and S.S. Sastry. Indirect Techniques for Adaptive Input-Output Linearization of Nonlinear Systems. *International Journal of Control*, 53:193–222, 1991.

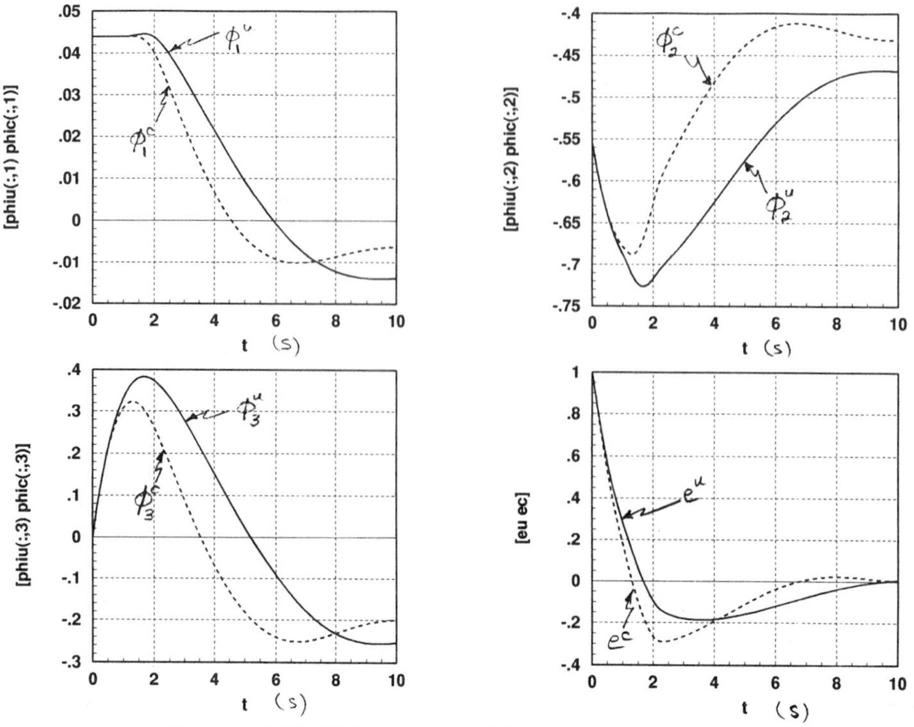

Figure 1: $\phi_i^u(t)$, $\phi_i^c(t)$ $(i = 1, 2, 3)$, $e^u(t)$, and $e^c(t)$ vs. t.

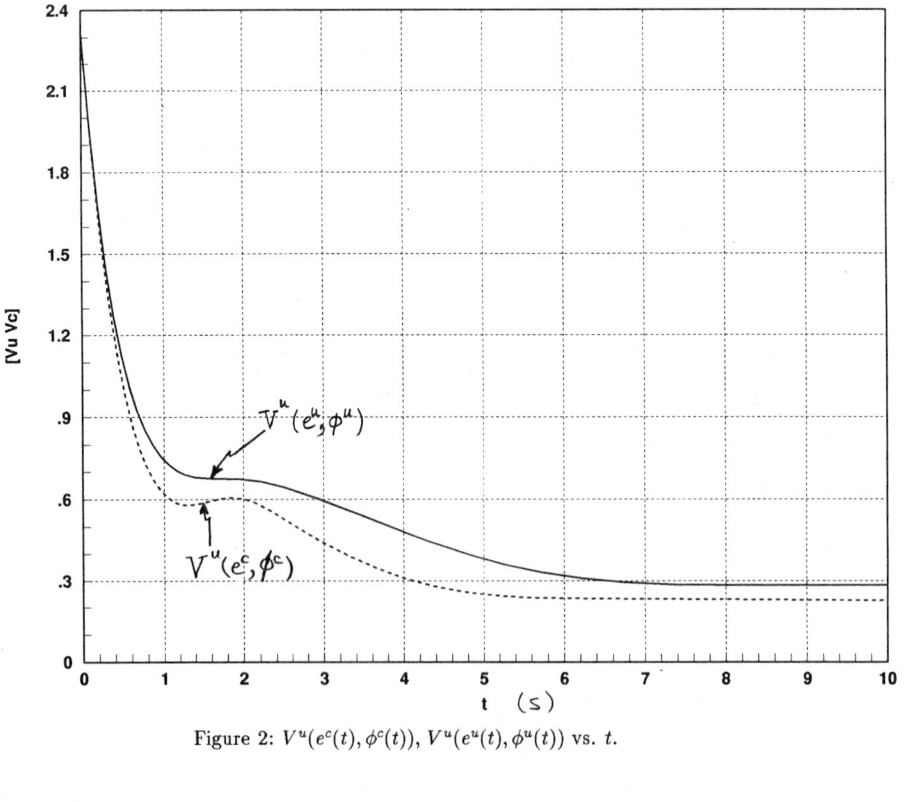

Figure 2: $V^u(e^c(t), \phi^c(t))$, $V^u(e^u(t), \phi^u(t))$ vs. t.

Proceedings of the
American Control Conference
San Francisco, California • June 1993

Digital Identification of A Continuous Time System and Some Related Problems

Er-Wei Bai

Dept. of Electrical and Computer Engineering
University of Iowa, Iowa City, IA 52242

Abstract

A scheme is presented in the paper for digital identification of a continuous time system. The identifier proposed operates on the sampled input output data, but generates an estimate of the unknown continuous time system directly. Convergence analysis of the identifier is given in the paper. Also discussed in the paper are some related problems. In particular, convergence of the identifier requires the persistent excitation condition on some signals in the identification loop and that condition is reduced to the controllability and observability of the sampled system of the unknown continuous time system. A result is derived in the paper concerning the controllability and observability of sampling an unknown continuous time system.

1 Problem formulation

With the dramatic developments in microelectronics, digital computers are being used increasingly as tools for analysis and design of control systems. Most physical systems are continuous time in nature, but digital computers deal with data digitally. Thus the control objective is to design a digital controller for the continuous time system. There are several ways to do that. The first one is to design a controller in continuous time and then discretize it. The advantage is that analog design is natural and one could expect recovery of the performance as the sampling frequency increases. The disadvantage is that the sampling frequency is not designable by control engineers in many industrial settings. The second approach is to model the continuous system by a discrete time equation and then do discrete time controller designs. The disadvantage is that intersample behavior has been ignored. Moreover, the sampling frequency has to be selected a priori. Note that either the first or the second approach is only a matter of "translating" the earlier analog designs into design of a digital controller for the continuous time system. It has been recently realized that digital controller design for a continuous time system actually presents an opportunity to employ elaborate control laws that might be ruled out in traditional control designs. The idea is to design a digital controller for the continuous time system directly [4], treating the controlled system as a sampled data system operating in continuous time. In other words, the design of a digital controller is based on the continuous time model directly.

This new design approach brings an old identification topic to a new life, i.e. if the continuous time system is unknown can we design an identifier which operates on sampled input output data only to generate a continuous time model (estimate) for the unknown continuous time system because of the use of digital computer. We refer this problem to as the digital identification of a continuous time system. Traditionally, on line identification for an unknown continuous time system can be roughly divided into two categories: continuous time identification and discrete time identification. In continuous time identification, all the input and output measurement data are assumed to be available for all time t and the parameter update law is in the differential equation form. Obviously, this approach does not work for digital identification of a continuous time system. In discrete time identification, the input output data are collected only at sampling instants and the parameter update law is based on the difference equation which seems to be suitable for use of digital computer. However, the model obtained by this approach is discrete. One way is to convert the identified discrete time model to an equivalent continuous time system. Unfortunately, the conversion of discrete time model to the continuous time model may not exist. Even it does exist, the solution may not be unique [1]. In this regard, a method was proposed [7] which assumes complete knowledge about the input output signals between sampling instants. This knowledge is then used to relate the coefficients of the continuous time model. If this knowledge is available to us prior to identification, then the obtained continuous time model is correct. On the other hand, if there is no such knowledge about input output signals between sampling instants, it is impossible to obtain the correct continuous time model from the discrete time model. A various approximation methods were proposed in [6] that determine the continuous time model for a given discrete time model so that the responses of these correspond closely at the sampling instants. The key point is the availability of knowledge about input output signals between sampling instants which is unlikely true in practice because of the use of digital computer. Thus just like design of a digital controller for the continuous time system, a preferred way for digital identification of a continuous time system is to design an identifier which operates on sampled input output data, but generates a continuous time model directly. Hopefully such an identifier will work for all reasonable sampling frequencies, not just for very high sampling frequencies.

In this paper, a scheme for digital identification of a continuous time system is proposed. The scheme is based on a well known discrete time gradient estimation law plus an adjustable filter. It is shown that if the coefficients of the filter are chosen appropriately, then the discrete time parameter estimate converges to that of the true but unknown continuous time system, independent of the sampling frequency and the behavior of input output signals between sampling instants. An algorithm for updating these coefficients is presented in the paper along with its convergence analysis. In addition, the paper discusses some related problems of digital identification of a continuous time system. In particular, convergence of the identifier requires the persistent excitation condition on some signals in the identification loop and that condition is reduced to the controllability and observability of the sampled system of the unknown continuous time system. A result is derived in the paper concerning the controllability and observability of sampling an unknown continuous time system. Also discussed in the paper is the effect of sampling on the sufficient richness condition. Suppose a continuous time signal is sufficiently rich, then a condition on the sampling rate is obtained which guarantees sufficient richness of the sampled signal. It is shown that fast sampling is not necessary as far as the sufficient richness is concerned.

2 Identification scheme and convergence analysis

Let

This work was supported in part by NSF ECS-9011359

$$g(s)=\frac{n(s)}{d(s)}=\frac{\beta_1 s^{n-1}+\cdots+\beta_n}{s^n+\alpha_1 s^{n-1}+\cdots+\alpha_n} \tag{2.1}$$

denote the continuous time plant which is to be identified. It is assumed that $g(s)$ is stable and the order n is known, but not the coefficients α_i's and β_j's. Consider a typical continuous time equation error type identifier [5] as shown in Fig. 2.1, where $\frac{1}{\lambda(s)}(s^{n-1},s^{n-2},...,1)^T$ is the filter with $\lambda(s)=s^n+\lambda_1 s^{n-1}+...+\lambda_n$ a Hurwitz polynomial. We identify each $\lambda(s)$ by its coefficient vector $\lambda=(\lambda_1,\lambda_2,\ldots,\lambda_n)^T$.

Let $v_1(t)$ and $v_2(t)$ denote the outputs of the filter $\frac{1}{\lambda(s)}(s^{n-1},s^{n-2},...,1)^T$ with inputs $u(t)$ and $y(t)$ respectively, and let

$$\theta_{1*}=(\beta_1,\beta_2,...,\beta_n)^T,\quad \theta_{2*}=(\lambda_1-\alpha_1,\ldots,\lambda_n-\lambda_n)\ \text{and}\ \theta_*=\begin{bmatrix}\theta_{1*}\\ \theta_{2*}\end{bmatrix} \tag{2.2}$$

then it was shown [5] that the output $y(t)$ of $g(s)$ can be written as $y(t)=\theta^T_*\cdot W(t)$, with $W(t)=(v_1(t),v_2(t))^T$ upto an exponentially decaying term due to initial conditions. θ_* is unknown, let $\theta(t)$ be its estimate. Define the parameter estimate law

$$\dot\theta(t)=-W(t)(y_i(t)-y(t)) \tag{2.3}$$

where $y_i(t)=\theta^T(t)W(t)$. It is a well known result [5] that $\theta(t)$ converges to θ_* globally and exponentially, provided $W(t)$ is persistently exciting. From θ_*, we can find β_i's and α_j's easily

$$(\beta_1,...,\beta_n)^T=\theta_{1*},\quad (\alpha_1,...,\alpha_n)^T=(\lambda_1,\ldots,\lambda_n)^T-\theta_{2*} \tag{2.4}$$

Now because of use of digital computers, we do not have values of $u(t)$ and $y(t)$ for all t. Instead, only $u(k)$ (=$u(kT)$) and $y(k)$ (=$y(kT)$) are available to us. Also the filter $\frac{1}{\lambda(s)}(s^{n-1},s^{n-2},...,1)^T$ has to be implemented digitally plus that inputs to the filters are $u(k)$ and $y(k)$ instead of $u(t)$ and $y(t)$. Let

$$\dot x=Ax+br,\ \ with\ A=\begin{bmatrix}0&1&0\\0&0&0\\ \cdot&\cdot&\cdot\\ &&1\\-\lambda_n&-\lambda_{n-1}&-\lambda_1\end{bmatrix},\quad b=\begin{bmatrix}0\\0\\ \cdot\\ \cdot\\1\end{bmatrix}$$

be the continuous time controllable canonical realization of the filter. When input to the filter is a piecewise constant $u(k)$ or $y(k)$, the output $v_{1d}(k)$ (=$v_{1d}(kT)$) and $v_{2d}(k)$ (=$v_{2d}(kT)$) can be obtained exactly through the equations

$$v_{1d}(k+1)=e^{AT}v_{1d}(k)+\int_0^T e^{Ah}dh\,b\,u(k) \tag{2.5a}$$

$$v_{2d}(k+1)=e^{AT}v_{2d}(k)+\int_0^T e^{Ah}dh\,b\,y(k),\quad W_d(k)=\begin{bmatrix}v_{1d}(k)\\ v_{2d}(k)\end{bmatrix} \tag{2.5b}$$

where T is the sampling interval. Our goal is to identify the continuous time model $g(s)$ on line in terms of α_i's and β_j's from the sampled date $\{u(k)\}$, $\{y(k)\}$ and $\{W_d(k)\}$ recursively. Now consider the identifier using sampled data $\{u(k)\}$ and $\{y(k)\}$ only. Let $\theta(k)$ indicate the estimate of θ_* at time k, we define the parameter update law using the sampled data only

$$\theta(k)=\theta(k-1)+\frac{W_d(k)}{1+W^T{}_d(k)W_d(k)}(y(k)-\theta^T(k-1)W_d(k)) \tag{2.6}$$

This algorithm may be considered as a digital implementation of equation (2.3) by approximating $\dot\theta(t)$ by $\frac{\theta(k+1)-\theta(k)}{T}$ and replacing the fixed step size T by a variable size $\frac{1}{1+W^T{}_d(k)W_d(k)}$. It can be expected that $\theta(k)$ converges to a neighborhood of θ_* if the sampling interval T is small and $W_d(k)$ is persistently exciting. However it is not clear how good (how bad) the algorithm (2.6) is when the sampling interval T is not necessarily very small.

To this end, we have the following results which basically say that the algorithm defined in (2.6) is a variant of the optimal one given sampled date $\{u(k)\}$ and $\{y(k)\}$ only.

Theorem 2.1: Given sequences $\{u(k)\}$, $\{y(k)\}$ and $\{W_d(k)\}$, let $J(\theta(k-1))=\frac{1}{2}(y(k)-\theta^T(k-1)W_d(k))^2$ and define $\theta(k)=\theta(k-1)-a(k)\frac{\partial J(\theta(k-1))}{\partial\theta(k-1)}$ with $a(k)=\underset{a}{argmin}\,q(k,a(k))=\underset{a}{argmin}(y(k)-\theta^T(k)W_d(k))^2$. Then the above optimization problem results in the following algorithm

$$\theta(k)=\theta(k-1)+\frac{W_d(k)}{W^T{}_d(k)W_d(k)}(y(k)-\theta^T(k-1)W_d(k)) \tag{2.7}$$

Remark: Algorithm (2.7) is in fact the optimal gradient algorithm for given sampled data. By comparing (2.6) with (2.7), we see that the algorithm (2.6) is a variant of the optimal gradient method by adding 1 to the denominator to avoid division by zero. In principle any small constant can be used for this purpose.

Having concluded that the algorithm (2.6) is essentially an optimal gradient one, we have not answered the questions: Does (2.6) converge? If it does, does it converge to θ_*? For this purpose, let us construct an artificial signal $W_c(k)=(v_{1d}(k),v_{2c}(k))^T$, where $v_{1d}(k)$ is the output at time kT of the filter (2.5) when input is u(k) and $v_{2c}(k)$ would be the output of the filter $\frac{1}{\lambda(s)}(s^{n-1},s^{n-2},\ldots,1^T$ at time kT if input were $y(t)$. Note that $v_{1d}(k)$ is the same as in (2.5) and $v_{2c}(k)$ is an artificial one. By using the notation of $W_c(k)$, the output $y(t)$ at time kT can be represented by $y(k)=W^T{}_c(k)\theta_*$ upto an exponentially decaying term. Thus we can rewrite the algorithm (2.6) as

$$\theta(k)=\theta(k-1)+\frac{W_d(k)}{1+W^T{}_d(k)W_d(k)}(W^T{}_c(k)\theta_*-\theta^T(k-1)W_d(k)) \tag{2.8}$$

Let $\tilde\theta(k)=\theta(k)-\theta_*$ be the estimation error, it follows that

$$\tilde\theta(k)=(I-\frac{W_d(k)W^T{}_d(k)}{1+W^T{}_d(k)W_d(k)})\tilde\theta(k-1)$$
$$+\frac{W_d(k)}{1+W^T{}_d(k)W_d(k)}(v_{2c}(k)-v_{2d}(k))^T\theta_{2*} \tag{2.9}$$

where $v_{2d}(k)$ is in (2.5) and θ_{2*} in (2.2).

The homogeneous part of the equation (2.9) is exponentially stable if $W_d(k)$ is persistently exciting. Thus $\tilde\theta(k)$ is bounded if $u(k)$ is bounded. The error $\tilde\theta(k)$ does not however converge to zero as $k\to\infty$ due to the second term. This is different from that of continuous time case (2.3), where the parameter estimate always converges to θ_* as long as $W(t)$ is persistently exciting. From equation (2.9), it can be seen that the error $\tilde\theta(k)$ would converge to zero if $(v_{2c}(k)-v_{2d}(k))^T\theta_{2*}$ is zero or converges to zero. This is the case when the sampling interval $T\to 0$, simply because $v_{2c}(k)-v_{2d}(k)\to 0$ for all k as $T\to 0$. But this requires fast sampling which may not be practical in many situations. It is our goal to find an alternative way to make the second term of (2.9) zero independent of the sampling interval T so that $\tilde\theta(k)\to 0$ as $k\to\infty$. It is obvious from equation (2.9) that an alternative way is to make $\theta_2*=0$. Note that $\theta_{2*}=(\lambda_1-\alpha_1,\ldots,\lambda_n-\alpha_1)^T$ which depends on the coefficients of the denominator of $g(s)$ as well as the filter coefficients $(\lambda_1,...,\lambda_n)$ chosen by designers. When $\lambda(s)$ is chosen to be $d(s)=s^n+\alpha_1 s^{n-1}+...+\alpha_n$, then $\theta_{2*}=(\lambda_1-\alpha_1,\ldots,\lambda_n-\alpha_n)=0$ and consequently $\tilde\theta(k)\to 0$ as $k\to\infty$. This property is independent of the sampling interval T as long as $W_d(k)$ is persistently exciting. Recall that in continuous time case, the role of the filter is to avoid derivative of signal and convergence result is independent of the choice of the filter. For any given Hurwitz polynomial $\lambda(s)$, the parameter estimate converges to θ_*. It is however a different scenario for digital identification of continuous time system, where different choice of filter $\lambda(s)$ results in different estimate $\theta(k)$, because of the second term in equation (2.9). When $\lambda(s)$ is chosen to be $d(s)$, then the second term of (2.9) is zero and accordingly $\theta(k) \to \theta_*$.

The problem is that $g(s)$ is unknown and so is $d(s)$. This lead us to the following question: can we find a recursive algorithm for the filter coefficient vector $\lambda(l)=(\lambda_1(l),\lambda_2(l),\ldots,\lambda_n(l))^T$ such that based on $\lambda(l)$ and other information, a new vector $\lambda(l+1)$ can be generated and hopefully $\lambda(l)=(\lambda_1(l),\ldots,\lambda_n(l)) \to (\alpha_1,\ldots,\alpha_n)$ as $l \to \infty$. Observe that for a given $\lambda(l)=(\lambda_1(l),\ldots,\lambda_n(l))$ there is a corresponding $\theta_{2*}=(\lambda_1(l)-\alpha_1,\ldots,\lambda_n(l)-\alpha_n)^T$. Let $\theta(k)$ be the parameter estimate and define $\lim_{k\to\infty}\theta(k) = \begin{bmatrix}\theta_{1d}\\ \theta_{2d}\end{bmatrix} \left(= \begin{bmatrix}\theta_{1d}(\lambda(l))\\ \theta_{2d}(\lambda(l))\end{bmatrix}\right)$ (where $\theta_{1d}(\lambda(l))$ and $\theta_{2d}(\lambda(l))$ indicate the dependence of θ_{1d} and θ_{2d} on $\lambda(l)$.) Then $\theta_{2d}=\theta_{2*}=0$ if $\lambda_1(l)=\alpha_1,\ldots,\lambda_n(l)=\alpha_n$ and $\theta_{2d}\neq 0$ if $\lambda(l)\neq(\alpha_1,\cdots,\alpha_n)^T$. Thus $\|\theta_{2d}(\lambda(l))\|$ is an indication of how close between $\lambda(l)$ and $(\alpha_1,\ldots,\alpha_n)^T$. In the following we will present a recursive algorithm which based on the current value of the filter coefficient $\lambda(l)$ and the size of θ_{2d} produces a new filter coefficient $\lambda(l+1)$ so that $\lambda(l) \to (\alpha_1,\ldots,\alpha_n)^T$ as $l \to \infty$ and accordingly $\theta(k) \to \theta_*$.

Algorithm

Init: Choose $\lambda(0)=(\lambda_1(0),\ldots,\lambda_n(0))^T$ such that $\lambda(s)=s^n+\lambda_1(0)s^{n-1}+\ldots+\lambda_n(0)$ is Hurwitz.

Step1:For each step l, apply equation (2.9) to compute $\theta_{2d}(\lambda(l))$ and

$$p^l_{ij} = \frac{\theta_{2d,i}(\lambda(l)+he_j) - \theta_{2d,i}(\lambda(l))}{h} \qquad i,j=1,2,\ldots,n$$

where $\theta_{2d,i}$ is the ith element of θ_{2d}, e_j is the jth unit vector in R^n and h>0 is a scalar. Let

$$P(l) = \begin{bmatrix} p^l_{11} & p^l_{1n} \\ \cdot & \cdot \\ p^l_{n1} & p^l_{nn}\end{bmatrix}$$

Step2:Define

$$\lambda(l+1) = \lambda(l) - P^{-1}(l)\theta_{2d}(\lambda(l))$$

Step3:If $\|\theta_{2d}(\lambda(l))\| \le$ some prescribed error bound then stop. Otherwise go to step 1.

Theorem 2.2: Consider the identifier described in (2.6) and the above algorithm. Assume

(1) There exists a $\rho>0$ such that such that $\theta_{2d}(\lambda)$ is continuously differentiable in a neighborhood $N(\rho)$ of $\alpha=(\alpha_1,\ldots,\alpha_n)^T$, where $N(\rho)=\{x\in R^n \mid \|x-\alpha\|\le\rho\}$

(2) The Jacobian matrix $J=\dfrac{\partial\theta_{2d}(\lambda)}{\partial\lambda}$ is Lipschitz with Lipschitz constant r in $N(\rho)$ and the inverse of the Jacobian matrix $J^{-1}(\lambda)$ exists and bounded $\|J^{-1}(\alpha)\|_{l_\infty} \le \beta$ for some $\beta > 0$.

(3) $W_d(k)$ is persistently exciting [2].

Then there exist some $\varepsilon, \eta > 0$ such that the sequence of filter coefficient $\lambda(l)$ generated by the algorithm is always Hurwitz and converges to $(\alpha_1,\ldots,\alpha_n)^T$ exponentially for all $0 < h < \varepsilon$ and $\lambda(0) \in N(\eta)$.

Remarks:

(1) Theorem 2.2 guarantees that not just $\lambda(l)\to\alpha$, but also the filter $\lambda(l)$ is Hurwitz at each step. This is important, since for on line identification it is necessary to have a stable filter at each step.

(2) At every iteration, theoretically $\theta_{2d}(\lambda(l))=\lim_{k\to\infty}\theta_{2d}(k)$. In practice, $\theta_{2d}(k)$ can be considered as an estimate of θ_{2d} for large enough k.

(3) The results of theorem is independent of the sampling interval T.

To illustrate the above algorithm, we consider the following example. Let the unknown continuous time system be $g(s)=\dfrac{2}{s+4}$ and input $u(t)=2\sin(t)$. Consider the identification scheme (2.6) and the above algorithm with initial filter $1/(s+2)$, i.e. $\lambda(0)=2$. Table below shows the values of $\lambda(l)$ and the corresponding plant estimate $\hat{g}(s)$ for $l=1,2,3$ and for different sampling intervals $T=0.1(sec)$ and $T=1(sec)$.

	T=0.1			T=1		
l	$\lambda(l)$	θ_{2d}	$\hat{g}(s)$	$\lambda(l)$	θ_{2d}	$\hat{g}(s)$
0	2	-1.64	$\frac{1.818}{s+3.63}$	2	-0.27	$\frac{1.14}{s+2.27}$
1	3.986	-0.01	$\frac{1.997}{s+3.996}$	3.24	-0.07	$\frac{1.655}{s+3.31}$
2	3.999	-0.0007	$\frac{1.9998}{s+3.99969}$	3.884	-0.01	$\frac{1.94669}{s+3.893517}$
3	3.9987	-0.00007	$\frac{1.99997}{s+3.99994}$	4.013	0.0005	$\frac{2.006}{s+4.0125}$

From table above, we see that a much better estimate $\hat{g}(s)$ could be obtained by updating the filter parameter $\lambda(l)$ on line. In fact when $T=0.1$, the first iteration gives $\hat{g}(s)=\dfrac{1.997}{s+3.996}$ which is very close to the true plant 2/(s+4). When $T=1$, the second iteration gives $\hat{g}(s)=\dfrac{1.95}{s+3.95}$ that is also very close to the true one while the initial estimate $\dfrac{1.14}{s+2.27}$ is far away from the true plant.

An algorithm was presented above to update $\lambda(l)$ on line so that a better estimate could be obtained, provided that $W_d(k)$ is persistently exciting. We now establish the conditions such that $W_d(k)$ is persistently exciting.

Let (A_g,b_g,c_g) be a nth order realization of the sampled system of $g(s)$ for a given sampling interval T. Together with the filter equation (2.5), we have the relationship from input $u(k)$ to the regressor $W_d(k)$ for a given T

$$\begin{bmatrix} v_{1d}(k+1)\\ v_{2d}(k+1)\\ x_d(k+1)\end{bmatrix} = \begin{bmatrix} e^{AT} & 0 & 0\\ 0 & e^{AT} & bc_g\\ 0 & 0 & A_g\end{bmatrix}\begin{bmatrix} v_{1d}(k)\\ v_{2d}(k)\\ x_d(k)\end{bmatrix} + \begin{bmatrix} \int_0^T e^{Ah}dhb\\ 0\\ b_g\end{bmatrix} u(k)$$

$$W_d(k) = (I,0)\begin{bmatrix} v_{1d}(k)\\ v_{2d}(k)\\ x_d(k)\end{bmatrix} \qquad (2.10)$$

In light of [2], we have the following results.

Theorem 2.3: $W_d(k)$ is persistently exciting if the system described by (2.10) is output controllable and $u(k)$ is sufficiently rich of order 2n [2].

Remarks:

(1) The stability of $g(s)$ is not required to establish persistent excitation. However, if $g(s)$ is stable, the conditions in the theorem are necessary and sufficient.

(2) Note that the system (2.10) is 3n-dimensional, but sufficient richness of order 2n of input (k) guarantees the persistent excitation condition of $W_d(k)$.

(3) If the sampled system of $g(s)$ is completely controllable and observable, then (A_g,b_g,c_g) is a minimal realization.

We now study when the system (2.10) is output controllable. To this end, we have

Lemma 2.4: The system (2.10) is output controllable if and only if $(e^{AT}, \int_0^T e^{Ah}dhb)$ is completely controllable and (A_g,b_g,c_g) is completely controllable and observable.

Thus the output controllability is achieved if the sampled system (2.5) of the filter is controllable and the sampled system (A_g,b_g,c_g) of the plant $g(s)$ is controllable and observable. For a given sampling interval T, we can easily check the controllability of the sampled system (2.5) of the filter. However it is not easy to check the controllability and/or observability of (A_g,b_g,c_g) of $g(s)$ for a given T, simply because $g(s)$ is unknown. Now the question is how to check the controllability and observability of (A_g,b_g,c_g) for a given T and an unknown $g(s)$ or given an unknown $g(s)$ with some prior information can we find all $T>0$ so that with such T the resultant sampled system is controllable and observable. This is the topic of the next section.

3 Controllability and observability of the sampled system with an unknown $g(s)$

We start with this section with a well known result [1].

Theorem: 3.1: If a scalar continuous time system is completely controllable and observable, then its sampled system is completely controllable and observable if and only if $Im(\lambda_i - \lambda_j) \neq \frac{2\pi}{n}$, $n=\pm1,\pm2,\cdots$ whenever $Re(\lambda_i - \lambda_j)=0$, where T is the sampling interval and $\lambda_i's$ are the eigenvalues of the continuous time system.

From theorem, we see that controllability and observability of the sampled system depend on the eigenvalues (or poles) of the continuous time system as well as the sampling interval. The purpose of this section is that: Given $g(s)=\frac{\beta_1 s^{n-1}+...+\beta_n}{s^n+\alpha_1 s^{n-1}+...+\alpha_n}=\frac{n(s)}{d(s)}$ and a sampling interval T, assuming that $\beta_i's$ and $\alpha_k's$ are unknown, but it is known that the coefficients of the denominator $\alpha=(\alpha_1,...,\alpha_n)\in\Omega\subset R^n$ for some known compact set $\Omega\subset R^n$, is the resulting sampled system completely controllable and observable for every $g(s)$ with $\alpha\in\Omega$.

Before proposing a solution to the above problem, we need several definitions. Let $d(s)=s^n+\alpha_1 s^{n-1}+...+\alpha_n$ then

Definition 3.1: Let $Q\subset\Omega\subset R^n$, then $R(Q)\subset C$ is the root space of $Q\subset\Omega$ with respect to d(s). More precisely,

$$R(Q)=\{\lambda\in C \mid d(\lambda)=0, \text{ for some } \alpha\in Q\subset\Omega\} \quad (3.1)$$

Definition 3.2: The sampling interval $T>0$ is said to be admissible with respective to Ω, if for every continuous time system $g(s)=\frac{n(s)}{d(s)}$ such that $d(s)=s^n+\alpha_1 s^{n-1}+...+\alpha_n$ with $\alpha=(\alpha_1,\ldots,\alpha_n)^T\in\Omega$, together with T, the sampled system is completely controllable and observable. Otherwise, T is said to be non-admissible.

For arbitrary shape of Ω, it is hard in general to find all admissible T. Note however that if T is small ($0<T\to0$), then T is admissible from the compactness of Ω and theorem 3.1. Therefore we discuss the following two problems

(P1) Find $T_0>0$, such that every $T\in(0,T_0)$ is admissible and T_0 is non-admissible.

(P2) Find all admissible $T>0$.

T_0 is the minimum positive number which is non-admissible and every T in the interval $(0,T_0)$ is admissible for a given $\Omega\subset R^n$. The importance of T_0 is that (1) P1 is much easy to solve than P2. (2) In practice, the sampling interval is small, although not necessarily extremely small. For a given problem, if T_0 has reasonable size and can be determined, then the solution of P2 is practically not required, because all $T\in(0,T_0)$ are admissible.

Now define $\lambda_\Omega=\max_{\lambda\in R(\Omega)} Im(\lambda)$. Since $R(\Omega)$ is compact, there exists some point which achieves the maximum, i.e. there is

$$\lambda_0\in R(\Omega) \quad s.t. \quad Im(\lambda_0)=\lambda_\Omega$$

Theorem 3.2: Given $g(s)=\frac{n(s)}{d(s)}$. Suppose $d(s)=s^n+\alpha_1 s^{n-1}+...+\alpha_n$ with $\alpha=(\alpha_1,\ldots,\alpha_n 0^T\in\Omega\subset R_n$ for some Ω. Then (1) $T_0=\frac{\pi}{\lambda_\Omega}$. (2) In the root space $R(\Omega)$, if there exists a curve connecting λ_0 to the real axis, then $0<T$ is admissible if and only if $T\in(0,T_0)=(0,\frac{\pi}{\lambda_\Omega})$.

Remark: The first part of theorem gives the exactly values of T_0. The second part states that T is admissible if and only if $T\in(0,T_0)$, if λ_0 can be connected to the real axis by some curve. This is certainly true when all roots of $d(s)=s^n+\alpha_1 s^{n-1}+...+\alpha_n$ are real at some point $\alpha=(\alpha_1,\ldots,\alpha_n)^T\in\Omega$.

Now the question that remains is how to calculate λ_Ω for a given $\Omega\subset R^n$. We first consider a simple case. Let $\Omega\subset R^n$ be a polytope, i.e. the convex hull of a finite number of points. More precisely

$$\Omega=\{\alpha \mid \alpha=M(r_1,\ldots,r_m)^T+q,\ r_i\in[\underline{r_i},\overline{r_i}]\}$$

for some n-dimensional constant vector q and some nxm constant matrix M. Exposed edge of Ω is defined as a one-dimensional set of form of $\Omega\cap H$, where H is a nontrivial supporting hyperplane of Ω. The union of all the exposed edges are denoted by $E\in\Omega$. Let $\lambda_E=\max_{\lambda\in R(E)} Im(\lambda)$. Then in light of [3], we have

Lemma 3.3: $\lambda_\Omega=\lambda_E$ and consequently $T_0=\frac{\pi}{\lambda_\Omega}=\frac{\pi}{\lambda_E}$

Remarks:

(1) The importance of lemma is that in determining λ_Ω, we need to calculate every point in Ω which is n-dimensional while calculation of λ_E is one-dimensional and thus can be carried out easily.

(2) It is natural to ask is lemma 3.3 tight in the sense that can we check only corner points of Ω to find λ_Ω? The following example shows that this is impossible and consequently lemma 3.3 is tight.

Example 3.1: Let $d(s)=s^3+\alpha_1 s^2+10s+2$, with $\alpha_1\in[21,31]$.

When $\alpha_1=21$, $d(s)$ has roots at -20.52 and $-0.2413\pm0.1981j$. When $\alpha_1=31$, $d(s)$ has roots at -30.68 and $-0.1619\pm0.1974j$. When $\alpha_1=26$, $d(s)$ has roots at When $\alpha_1=21$, $d(s)$ has roots at -25.61 and $-0.1931\pm0.2014j$. Clearly, λ_Ω is not achieved at the corner points $\alpha_1=21$ or 31.

If Ω is not a polytope and is arbitrarily shaped, it is very hard to determine $T_0=\frac{\pi}{\lambda_\Omega}$ if it is possible. This leads us to the following question: Given an arbitrarily shaped $\Omega\subset R^n$, does there exist an efficient way to find some $T_1\le T_0$? The motivation is that if T_0 is hard to find while T_1 is easy to obtain, then as long as T_1 is close to T_0 or T_1 has a reasonable size, then the knowledge of T_1 is enough for practical purpose of choosing sampling interval T since every $T\in(0,T_1)\subset(0,T_0)$ is admissible with respective to Ω. To this end, we have

Theorem 3.4: Let $g(s)=\frac{n(s)}{d(s)}$. Suppose $d(s)=s^n+\alpha_1 s^{n-1}+...+\alpha_n$ with $\alpha=(\alpha_1,\ldots,\alpha_n)^T\in\Omega\subset R^n$. Define

$$c=\max_{\alpha\in\Omega}\{|\alpha_n|,1,1+|\alpha_2|,\ldots,1+|\alpha_{n-1}|\}$$

Then $0<T_1=\frac{\pi}{c}\le T_0=\frac{\pi}{\lambda_\Omega}$ and accordingly every $T\in(0,T_1)$ is admissible.

To illustrate the effectiveness of theorem 3.4, consider $g(s)=\frac{n(s)}{d(s)}$ where $d(s)=s^5+\alpha_1 s^4+...+\alpha_1$. α is unknown, but is assumed to lie in the ellipsoid $\Omega\subset R^5$

$$\Omega=\{\alpha\in R^5 \mid \frac{\alpha^2{}_1}{100^2}+\frac{\alpha^2{}_2}{3^2}+\frac{\alpha^2{}_3}{1}+\frac{\alpha^2{}_4}{2^2}+\frac{\alpha^2{}_5}{4^2}=1\}$$

Then $c=\max\{|\alpha_5|,1,1+|\alpha_2|,1+|\alpha_3|,1+|\alpha_4|\}=4$, and $T_1=\frac{\pi}{4}=0.785$. Hence for any $g(s)$ such that $\alpha\in\Omega$ and any $T\in(0,0.758)$, the resulting sampled system is completely controllable and observable.

4 Effects of sampling on the sufficient richness condition

An algorithm was presented in section 2 which provides an estimate of unknown continuous time system $g(s)$ from sampled input output data {u(k) and {y(k)}. If the regressor $W_d(k)$ is persistently exciting, then the estimate converges to the true continuous time system $g(s)$ independent of the sampling interval T. Also the persistent excitation condition of $W_d(k)$ is reduced to that of controllability and observability of the sampled system (A_g, b_g, c_g) of $g(s)$ and the sufficient richness condition on input u(k). The problem of controllability and observability of (A_g, b_g, c_g) has been discussed in section 3. In this section, we like to find conditions on u(k) such that u(k) is sufficiently rich of order 2n [2]. This topic has been intensively studied before if u(k) is a discrete time signal. What we are interested here is the following question: It is quite often in digital control/identification of a continuous time system that u(k) is a sampling of some continuous time function u(t). Suppose u(t) is sufficiently rich, is u(k) sufficiently rich of order 2n for a given sampling interval T.

In light of the sampling theorem, it is easy to image that if the sampling interval T is small enough, the sufficient richness of u(k) is guaranteed. In fact, this is true. More precisely, let u(t) be a wide sense stationary signal and its power spectral density $S_u(\omega)$ is limited to the band $[0, \omega_u]$, then sufficient richness of order 2n of u(t) implies that of u(k) if the sampling interval $T \le \frac{\pi}{\omega_u}$. The problem with this is that it is only a sufficient condition. Therefore, if u(t) has some high frequency component, the sampling interval T has to be chosen very small which may not be practical. But in fact, since it is only a sufficient condition, it is possible for some $T > \frac{\pi}{\omega_u}$, the sampled signal u(k) is still sufficiently rich of order 2n. We would not study this problem for arbitrary signal u(t) in this section, instead we concentrate on a special signal $u(t) = \sum_{l=1}^{m} \gamma_l \sin(\omega_l t + \theta_l)$. The motivation is that once we can solve the problem for the above signal, then the results could be essentially extended to any periodical signal by Fourier series method. In this regard, we have

Theorem 4.1: Let $u(t) = \sum_{l=1}^{m} \gamma_l \sin(\omega_l t + \theta_l)$ and $u(k) = (u(kT)) = \sum_{l=1}^{m} \gamma_l \sin(\omega_l kT + \theta_l)$, where $\gamma_l \neq 0$ and $\omega_i \neq \omega_j$. Then $u(k)$ is sufficiently rich of order 2n [2] if $m \ge n$ and

$$\frac{\omega_i \pm \omega_j}{2} T \neq n\pi, \quad n = \pm 1, \pm 2, \ldots \quad i,j = 1,2,\ldots,m$$

Theorem 4.1 tells us that as far as the sufficient richness of u(k) is concerned, fact sampling of u(t) is not necessary. Consider a signal $u(t) = \sin(2t) + \sin t(200t)$. If the sampling frequency is chosen to be at least as twice fast as the highest frequency of u(t), then the sampling interval would be in the range $(0, \frac{\pi}{200}) = (0, 0.0157)$. But from theorem 4.1, we know that any sampling interval $T \neq \frac{n\pi}{200}, \frac{n\pi}{101}, \frac{n\pi}{2}, \frac{n\pi}{99}$ results in a sampled signal u(k) which is sufficiently rich of order 2n=4. The sampling interval does not have to be very small, as far as the sufficient richness of $u(k)$ is concerned.

5 Conclusion

The work of this paper is motivated by recently advancements in the design of digital controller for a continuous time system. If the system unknown, an on line identification scheme is presented in the paper which operates on the sampled input output data only to generate an continuous time estimate. The advantage of the scheme is that it is independent of the sampling interval T and does not depend on the knowledge of input output signals between sampling instants. Therefore it works for slow sampling and does not require prior knowledge about the input output signals. Also the conditions on the sampling rate for the controllability and observability of the sampled system of an unknown continuous time system are derived. This topic is itself an interesting one which has applications not only in digital identification of an continuous time system but also in various analysis and design of sampled systems.

6 References

(1) K.J. Astrom and B. Wittenmark "COMPUTER CONTROLLED SYSTEMS: THEORY AND DESIGN" Prentice-Hall, Englewood Cliffs, N.Y. 1984

(2) E.W. Bai and S.S. Sastry "Persistency of excitation, sufficient richness and parameter convergence in discrete time adaptive control" Syst. & Contr. Lett. Vol.6 (1985) pp153-163

(3) A. Bartlett, C. Hollot and L. Huang "Root locations of an entire polytope of polynomials:it suffices to check the edges" Math. of Contr., Signal and Syst. Vol.1 (1988) pp61-71

(4) T. Chen and B.A. Francis "H_2 Optimal sampled data control " IEEE Trans. on AC, Vol. 36 (1991) pp387-397

(5) G. Kreisselmeier "Adaptive observer with exponential rate of convergence" IEEE Trans. on AC, Vol. 22 (1977) pp2-8

(6) N.K. Sinha "Estimation of transfer function of continuous system from sampled data" Proc. IEE Vol. 119 (1972) pp612-614

(7) F.W. Smith "System Laplace transform estimation from sampled data" IEEE Trans. on AC, Vol.13 (1968) pp37-44

(8) M. Vidyasagar "NONLINEAR SYSTEMS ANALYSIS" Prentice-Hall, Englewood Cliffs, N.Y. 1978

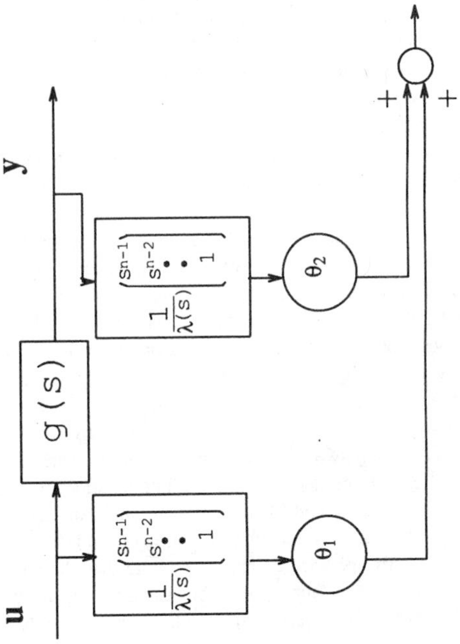

Fig. 2.1

Proceedings of the
American Control Conference
San Francisco, California • June 1993

Robust System Identification with Noisy Time/Frequency Response Experimental Data : Projection Operator and Linear Algorithms

Er-Wei Bai and Sundar Raman

Dept. of Electrical and Computer Engineering
University of Iowa, Iowa City, IA 52242

Abstract

In this paper we consider the problem of robust system identification with noisy time or frequency response measurement data. It is shown here that any linear identification algorithm which is convergent in the noise free case can be made robustly convergent in the presence of noise by incorporating a simple projection operator into the algorithm. Specific algorithms using this projection operator along with corrupted frequency/time response data are analyzed in detail. The computational simplicity and faster rate of convergence distinguish this approach from other existing robustly convergent non linear identification techniques.

1 Introduction

This paper is concerned with the problem of robust system identification with noisy experimental data. The purpose of system identification for robust control design is to determine a nominal model for the unknown system in some optimal sense along with an explicit worst case bound on the mismatch between this nominal model and the true but unknown system. This is motivated by worst case robust control designs, where an explicit bound on the model uncertainty is required.

There are a few feasible ways to tackle this problem. One is the traditional stochastic approach. There exist a large body of work in literature along this line [9]. By assuming some properties of the disturbance, many results can be derived. The other one is the deterministic approach, called the worst case identification. In this approach, the disturbance is assumed to be bounded by some known levels and is otherwise unknown. The bound given by the stochastic approach is usually soft while that given by the deterministic approach is hard but usually conservative. This paper follows the deterministic approach.

An original framework of the deterministic approach was formulated by Helmicki, Jacobson and Nett [6,7] and studied by many other researchers. In this formulation, the experimental data is assumed to be noisy measurements of the actual system frequency response. Algorithms have been devised that interpolate noisy data such that a worst case error bound can be derived and certain convergence results hold. It was shown that most linear algorithms are convergent in the absence of noise, but divergent in the presence of noise, no matter how small the noise is. It was thus conjectured [4,6] that there may not exist any linear algorithm which is robustly convergent in the presence of noise in an H_∞ sense. This conjecture was in fact proved by Partington in [11]. To this end, many two stage nonlinear algorithms were proposed, for example, Helmicki et al [7] used spline interpolation followed by Nehari approximation. Gu and Khargonekar [4,5] used the Cesaro sum followed by Nehari approximation and Partington [11] adopted the Jackson trigonometric polynomial approach. Note that although these two stage nonlinear algorithms solve the robustness problem, the price to be paid is increased computational complexity and possibly slower convergence rate. There are other approaches to this problem, for instance see Bai et al [1,2], Goodwin et al [3], Kosut et al [8], Zang, Bitmead and Gevers [12].

This work was supported in part by NSF ECS-9011359

This leads us to the following question: is it possible to combine the linear algorithms with some prior information so that the resulting algorithm is robust to noisy measurement data, computationally inexpensive and also exponentially convergent ? The answer to this question is provided in this paper. Roughly speaking, let $H(z)=\sum_{i=0}^{\infty}h(i)z^{-i}$ denote the unknown system such that $|h(i)|\leq M\rho^i$ for some $\infty>M>0$ and $0\leq\rho<1$. Then by incorporating a projection operator using the prior information of ρ and M, any linear algorithm can be made robustly convergent in the presence of noise, provided it is convergent in the absence of noise.

It should be pointed out here that use of prior information on ρ and M is not a limitation at all. For obtaining the nominal model a two stage nonlinear algorithm could be used. However, to determine the uncertainty bound, which is equally essential, information on ρ and M must be known. Therefore, the algorithm presented in this paper requires essentially the same amount of prior information as any two stage nonlinear algorithm does as far as worst case robust control design is concerned, but with substantially reduced computational complexity and possibly faster convergence rate.

In fact, the algorithms presented here are robust with respect to ρ,M. More precisely, even if the exact values of ρ,M are unknown and only their estimates, $\hat{\rho},\hat{M}$ respectively, are available, it will still be shown that the error between the identified model and the actual system is bounded and goes to zero as $\hat{M}\rightarrow M$ and $\hat{\rho}\rightarrow\rho$.

We also extend the results of the identification algorithms using noisy frequency response data to those using noisy time response measurements. It is shown that almost all results established for the former case carry over to the latter, especially the robustness properties of linear algorithms. In the interest of brevity all proofs have been ommitted.

2 Problem formulation

The class of systems under consideration consists of the stable SISO time invariant discrete time systems described by the convolution $y=h*u$ where u and y are the system input and output respectively and the corresponding system transfer function $H(z)$ is defined by $H(z)=\sum_{i=0}^{\infty}h(i)z^{-i}$. Let S be the collection of all exponentially stable transfer functions. Note that in our setup, stability corresponds to having no poles outside the unit circle. Let $B_{\rho,M}$ denote a subset of S

$$B_{\rho,M}=\{H(z)=\sum_{i=0}^{\infty}h(i)z^{-i}\ \Big|\ |h(i)|\leq M\rho^i, 0<M<\infty, 0\leq\rho<1\} \quad (2.1)$$

It is assumed that the true, but unknown and to be identified transfer function $H(z)\in B_{\rho,M}$ for some ρ and M. For each $H(z)\in B_{\rho,M}$, the norm of $H(z)$ is assumed to be the standard infinite norm, $\|H(\cdot)\|_\infty=\operatorname{ess\,sup}_{\omega\in[0,2\pi)}|H(e^{j\omega})|$. We will study two types of algorithms : one using noisy frequency response data to determine $H(z)$ and the other using noisy time response data. For a given number N, let

$$E^N(H,\eta)=\{H(e^{j\frac{2\pi k}{N}})+\eta_k;\ |\eta_k|\le\varepsilon,\ k=0,1,2,...,N-1\} \quad (2.2a)$$

represent the noisy frequency response data from some experimental measurements. $H(e^{j\frac{2\pi k}{N}})$ represents the true but unknown frequency response of the system at the frequencies $e^{j\frac{2\pi k}{N}}$, $k=0,1,2,...,N-1$ and η_k summarizes the effect of noise. It is assumed that the noise η_k is unknown, but that $|\eta_k|$ is uniformly bounded by some known constant $\varepsilon\ge 0$, i.e. $|\eta_k|\le\varepsilon$ for all N and k. In the perfect case, when $\eta_k\equiv 0$, we denote the data by $E^N(H,0)=\{H(e^{j\frac{2\pi k}{N}});\ k=0,1,2,...,N-1\}$.

If on the other hand an identification algorithm which maps the time response data to an estimate of $H(z)$ is used, then the noisy data is given by

$$E^N(H,\eta)=\{y(k)+\eta(k);\ |\eta_k|\le\varepsilon,\ k=0,1,2,...,N-1\} \quad (2.2b)$$

where $y(k)+\eta(k)$ is the corrupted output of $H(z)$ for some known input $\{r(k)\}$, $y(k)$ is the true unknown output and $\eta(k)$ denotes the bounded additive noise.

An identification algorithm A can be regarded as a sequence $\{A_N\}$ of mappings from the data $E^N(H,\eta)$ into an approximation $\hat{H}_N(z)$ of $H(z)$, i.e. $A_N(E^N(H,\eta))(z)=\hat{H}_N(z)=\sum_{i=0}^{n(N)} a^N(i)z^{-i}$, where $n(N)$, the order of the approximation, is a monotonically nondecreasing sequence of positive integers, and the $a^N(i)$'s are real numbers. The robust system identification problem can now be formulated as follows.

Given : An unknown $H(z)\in B_{\rho,M}$, the estimates $\hat{\rho}$ (<1), $\hat{M}$ on the bounds of ρ,M respectively and a finite number N of possibly corrupt frequency response data $E^N(H,\eta)$.

Find : An algorithm $A=\{A_N\}$ which maps $E^N(H,\eta)$ into the identified model.

$$A_N(E^N(H,\eta))(z)=\hat{H}_N(z)=\sum_{i=0}^{n(N)} a^N(i)z^{-i}$$

in such a way that for any $H(z)\in B_{\rho,M}$, and for all $|\eta_k|\le\varepsilon$, the following three conditions are satisfied.

(1) The identified model corresponding to $H(z)$, i.e. $\hat{H}_N(z)=\sum_{i=0}^{n(N)} a^N(i)z^{-i}$ is uniformly exponentially stable in N, in the sense that $|a^N(i)|\le M_1\hat{\rho}^i$, for all $N,i>0$ and for some constant $0<M_1<\infty$.

(2) If the estimates $\hat{\rho}$(<1) and $\hat{M}$ are true upper bounds on ρ M respectively i.e. $H(z)\in B_{\rho,M}\subset B_{\hat{\rho},\hat{M}}$ or equivalently $\rho\le\hat{\rho}<1$ and $M\le\hat{M}<\infty$, then $\|H(z)-\hat{H}_N(z)\|_\infty\le o(\frac{1}{N})+O(\varepsilon)$, where $o(\frac{1}{N})$ is bounded and $o(\frac{1}{N})\to 0$ as $N\to\infty$. $O(\varepsilon)$ is bounded if ε is bounded and $O(\varepsilon)\to 0$ as $\varepsilon\to 0$.

(3) If however $\hat{\rho}$ and/or $\hat{M}$ are underestimates of ρ,M respectively, i.e $0<\hat{\rho}<\rho$ and/or $0<\hat{M}<M$, then $\|H(z)-\hat{H}_N(z)\|_\infty\le o(\frac{1}{N})+O(\varepsilon)+O_1(\rho,\hat{\rho},M,\hat{M})$, where $o(\frac{1}{N})$ and $O(\varepsilon)$ are as defined above, and $O_1(\rho,\hat{\rho},M,\hat{M})$ is bounded and

$$O_1(\rho,\hat{\rho},M,\hat{M})=\begin{cases} O_1(\rho,\hat{\rho},\hat{M},\hat{M})\to 0,\ as\ \hat{\rho}\to\rho, & \text{if } \hat{\rho}<\rho\ \&\ \hat{M}\ge M \\ O_1(\hat{\rho},\hat{\rho},M,\hat{M})\to 0,\ as\ \hat{M}\to M, & \text{if } \hat{\rho}\ge\rho\ \&\ \hat{M}<M \\ O_1(\rho,\hat{\rho},M,\hat{M})\to 0,\ as\ \hat{\rho}\to\rho, \hat{M}\to M & \text{if } \hat{\rho}<\rho\ \&\ \hat{M}<M \end{cases}$$

If an algorithm $A=\{A_N\}$ satisfies the above three conditions, then A is said to be robustly convergent in the presence of noise with respect to the given estimates $\hat{\rho}$ and $\hat{M}$. Clearly, if $A=\{A_N\}$ is robustly convergent in the presence of noise, then $\lim_{N\to\infty,\ \varepsilon\to 0}\|H(z)-\hat{H}_N(z)\|_\infty=0$.

Definition 2.1:

An algorithm $A=\{A_N\}$ is said to be convergent in the absence of noise if (1) $A_N(E^N(H,0))=\hat{H}_N(z)=\sum_{i=0}^{n(N)} a^N(i)z^{-i}$ is uniformly stable in N as defined before. (2) $\|H(z)-\hat{H}_N(z)\|_\infty\le o(\frac{1}{N})\to 0\ as\ N\to\infty$

Note that convergence of A in the absence of noise is independent of the prior information on ρ,M. Now consider a sequence of transfer functions $\{G_N(z)\}$, with each $G_N(z)$, for a fixed N, being given by

$$G_N(z)=\sum_{i=-l(N)}^{n(N)} g^N(i)z^{-i} \quad (2.3)$$

where $l(N)$ and $n(N)$ are sequences of monotonically nondecreasing positive integers such that $n(N)\to\infty, l(N)\to\infty\ as\ N\to\infty$. Note that

(1) $G_N(z)$ is not necessarily stable.

(2) $G_N(z)$ is not necessarily causal.

(3) $\|H(z)-G_N(z)\|_\infty$ could be unbounded.

Assume however, that, $g^N(i)$ satisfies the following two assumptions.

(A1) For $i\ge 0$, $g^N(i)$ can be decomposed into two parts $g^N(i)=g_H^N(i)+g_\eta^N(i)$, and there exists constants $M_2<\infty$ and $M_3<\infty$ such that

$$|g_\eta^N(i)|\le M_2\varepsilon,\ |g_H^N(i)|\le M_3\rho^i \text{ for all } N,\ i\ge 0 \text{ and } 0\le\rho<1 \quad (2.4)$$

where $0\le\rho<1$ is as defined in (2.1).

(A2) The sequence $g_H^N(i)$, $i\ge 0$ converges to $H(z)$ in the sense that

$$\|H(z)-\sum_{i=0}^{n(N)} g_H^N(i)z^{-i}\|_\infty\le o(\frac{1}{N})\to 0\quad as\ N\to\infty \quad (2.5)$$

The sequence $\{G_N(z)\}$ could be any sequence of identified models obtained by an identification scheme along with a given data set $E^N(H,\eta)$. Typical examples include almost every linear identification algorithm, for instance, the Lagrange interpolation identification algorithm, one or two sided Cesaro sum method, the Fourier series method, the impulse response method, etc. We will show that any algorithm $A=\{A_N\}$, which results in a sequence $\{G_N(z)\}$ as described above, when combined with a projection operator will produce a robustly convergent algorithm in the face of noisy measurement data.

We now define the projection operator P_{ρ,M_3}. Let $G_N(z)=\sum_{i=-l(N)}^{n(N)} g^N(i)z^{-i}$ be as defined in (2.3)-(2.5). Define

$$P_{\rho,M_3}G_N(z)=\sum_{i=-l(N)}^{n(N)} P_{\rho,M_3}(g^N(i))z^{-i}=\sum_{i=0}^{n(N)}\hat{h}^N(i)z^{-i}$$

$$\hat{h}^N(i)=P_{\rho,M_3}(g^N(i))=\begin{cases} 0 & \text{if } i<0 \\ g^N(i) & \text{if } i\ge 0\ \&\ |g^N(i)|\le M_3\rho^i \\ M_3\rho^i & \text{if } i\ge 0\ \&\ g^N(i)\ge M_3\rho^i \\ -M_3\rho^i & \text{if } i\ge 0\ \&\ g^N(i)\le -M_3\rho^i \end{cases}$$

Letting $\hat{H}_N(z)=P_{\rho,M_3}G_N(z)$, we have the following key technical lemma.

Lemma 2.1:

Let $G_N(z)$ and $\hat{H}_N(z)=P_{\rho,M_3}G_N(z)=\sum_{i=0}^{n(N)}\hat{h}^N(i)z^{-i}$ be as defined above. Then

(1) $\hat{H}_N(z)$ is causal and uniformly stable in N, in the sense

$$|\hat{h}^N(i)|\le M_3\rho^i \quad \text{for all } N \text{ and } i=0,1,2,...,n(N) \quad (2.6)$$

(2) $$\|H(z)-\hat{H}_N(z)\|\le o(\frac{1}{N})+\varepsilon(c_1+c_2\log\varepsilon) \quad (2.7)$$

for some constants c_1,c_2 which are independent of N and $o(\frac{1}{N})\to 0\ as\ N\to\infty$.

Remarks :

(1) Lemma 2.1 is an essential step to establish the results of the following sections. Basically, it says that even though an

identification algorithm may not be robustly convergent in the presence of noise, if it contains two sub-sequences $g_H^N(i)$ and $g_\eta^N(i)$, one of which is convergent and the other bounded, then by projection, this algorithm becomes robustly convergent in the presence of noise. Notice that this lemma is independent of the source of the data and applies equally well to algorithms using either noisy frequency response data or noisy time response data.

(2) Let $A=\{A_N\}$ be any convergent algorithm in the absence of noise, but not a robustly convergent algorithm in the presence of noise. Then $\sum_{i=0}^{n(N)} g_H^N(i)z^{-i}$ may be considered as the approximation of $H(z)$ in noise free case by the algorithm A and $\sum_{i=-l(N)}^{-1} g^N(i)+\sum_{i=0}^{n(N)} g_\eta^N(i)$ may be considered as the perturbation due to noise. By the lemma, as long as the coefficients of the perturbation term $|g_\eta^N(i)|, i\geq 0$ are bounded then $P_{\rho,M},A=\{P_{\rho,M},A_N\}$ is a robustly convergent identification algorithm.

In reality, in order to apply the projection operator $P_{\rho,M}$, the constants ρ and M_3 must be known a priori. If the bounds on ρ, M and consequently M_3 are unknown, but only their estimates $\hat{\rho},\hat{M}_3$ are available, then there are four possible cases. (i) $1>\hat{\rho}\geq\rho,\ \infty>\hat{M}_3\geq M_3$ (ii) $1>\hat{\rho}\geq\rho,\ \hat{M}_3<M_3$ (iii) $0<\hat{\rho}<\rho,\ \infty>\hat{M}_3\geq M_3$ (iv) $0<\hat{\rho}<\rho,\ \hat{M}_3<M_3$. For case (i) we have $M_3\rho^i\leq\hat{M}_3\hat{\rho}^i$ and hence the results of lemma 2.1 remain unchanged with ρ and M_3 replaced by $\hat{\rho}$ and $\hat{M}_3$. For case (ii) $\hat{M}_3\rho^i\leq M_3\hat{\rho}^i$ and for case (iii) $M_3\hat{\rho}^i\leq\hat{M}_3\rho^i$. It follows that these two scenarios can be included in case (iv) where both ρ, M are underestimated. For the last three cases, we have the following lemma, similar to lemma 2.1.

Lemma 2.2:

Let $G_N(z)$ be as defined in lemma 2.1 and $\hat{H}_N(z)=P_{\hat{\rho},\hat{M}},G_N(z)=\sum_{i=0}^{n(N)}\hat{h}^N(i)z^{-i}$ with $\hat{M}_3<M_3$ and/or $\hat{\rho}<\rho$. Then

(1) $\hat{H}_N(z)$ is causal and uniformly stable in N, in the sense

$$|\hat{h}^N(i)|\leq\hat{M}_3\hat{\rho}^i \qquad \text{for all } N \text{ and } i=0,1,2,\ldots,n(N) \qquad (2.8)$$

(2) $$\|H(z)-\hat{H}_N(z)\|\leq o(\frac{1}{N})+\varepsilon(c_1+c_2\log\varepsilon)+O_1(\rho,\hat{\rho},M_3,\hat{M}_3) \qquad (2.9)$$

$$O_1(\rho,\hat{\rho},M_3,\hat{M}_3)=\begin{cases}2(\frac{\hat{M}_3}{1-\rho}-\frac{\hat{M}_3}{1-\hat{\rho}}) & \text{if } \hat{\rho}<\rho \ \&\ \hat{M}_3\geq M_3\\ 2(\frac{M_3}{1-\hat{\rho}}-\frac{\hat{M}_3}{1-\hat{\rho}}) & \text{if } 1>\hat{\rho}\geq\rho \ \&\ \hat{M}_3<M_3\\ 2(\frac{M_3}{1-\rho}-\frac{\hat{M}_3}{1-\hat{\rho}}) & \text{if } \hat{\rho}<\rho \ \&\ \hat{M}_3<M_3\end{cases} \qquad (2.10)$$

and $o(\frac{1}{N})$, c_1, c_2 are as given in lemma 2.1.

3 Linear algorithms with projection operator

In this section, we will apply lemmas 2.1 and 2.2 to linear algorithms using noisy frequency response data. We will discuss the Lagrange interpolation method.

Definition 3.1 :

Let $A=\{A_N\}$ be an identification algorithm. Then $A_N(E^N(H,\eta))(z)=\sum_{i=0}^{n(N)}a^N(i)z^{-i}$ is said to be linear and bounded in data, if it is linear and $|a^N(i)|\leq M_4 sup|E^N(H,\eta)|$, for some constant $\infty>M_4>0$ and for all N.

Theorem 3.1:

Let $A=\{A_N\}$ be an identification algorithm which maps noisy frequency response data (2.2) into the identified model. Assume it is linear and bounded in data. Moreover suppose A is convergent in the absence of noise, i.e.

$$\|A_N(E^N(H,0))-H(z)\|_\infty=\|\hat{H}_N(z)-H(z)\|_\infty\leq o(\frac{1}{N})\to 0 \ \ as\ N\to\infty$$

and $|a^N(i)|\leq M_5\rho^i$, $|\Delta a^N(i)|\leq M_6 sup|E^N(0,\eta)|\leq M_6\varepsilon$. for some constants $\infty>M_5,M_6>0$. Then $P_{\hat{\rho},\hat{M}_5}A=\{P_{\hat{\rho},\hat{M}_5}A_N\}$ is robustly convergent in the presence of noise, where $\hat{\rho}$ and $\hat{M}_5$ are the estimates of ρ and M_5 respectively.

Theorem 3.1 tells us that every linear identification algorithm bounded in data and convergent in the absence of noise can be made robustly convergent in the presence of noise by a simple projection.

Having obtained the results for general linear algorithms we now analyze the Lagrange interpolation method. Let $H(z)=\sum_{i=0}^{\infty}h(i)z^{-i}\in B_{\rho,M}$ be the unknown transfer function. For a given number N and noisy data $E^N(H,\eta)$, define the polynomial

$$L_N(E^N(H,\eta))(z)=\sum_{i=0}^{N-1}\alpha(i)z^{-i} \qquad (3.1)$$

such that $L_N(E^N(H,\eta))(e^{j\frac{2\pi k}{N}})=H(e^{j\frac{2\pi k}{N}})+\eta_k$, $k=0,1,2,\ldots,N-1$. $L_N(z)$ is the Nth order Lagrange interpolation of $H(z)$. The computation of the coefficients $\alpha(m)$ in (3.1) is equivalent to solving the linear equations determined by the equations (3.1) above.

$$\alpha(m)=\frac{1}{N}\sum_{k=0}^{N-1}H(e^{j\frac{2\pi k}{N}})e^{j\frac{2\pi mk}{N}}+\frac{1}{N}\sum_{k=0}^{N-1}\eta_k e^{j\frac{2\pi mk}{N}}$$

$$=\alpha_0(m)+\Delta\alpha(m) \qquad m=0,1,2,\ldots,N-1$$

where $\alpha_0(m)$ is the exact Lagrange coefficient and $\Delta\alpha(m)$ indicates the contribution due to noise. It is also easily verified that

$$\|H(z)-\sum_{m=0}^{N-1}\alpha_0(m)z^{-m}\|_\infty\leq M_8\rho^N \ \text{ and } \ |\Delta\alpha(m)|\leq\varepsilon \qquad (3.2)$$

where $M_8=\frac{2M}{(1-\rho)^2}$. It follows then that the Lagrange interpolation method is linear, bounded in data and convergent in the absence of noise. Consequently from theorem 3.1, we have

Theorem 3.2:

Let $L=\{L_N\}$ denote the identification algorithm of Lagrange method with M_8 as defined in (3.2). Then $P_{\hat{\rho},\hat{M}},L=\{P_{\hat{\rho},\hat{M}},L_N\}$ is a robustly convergent algorithm in the presence of noise with $\hat{\rho}$ (<1) and $\hat{M}_7$ denoting the estimates on the bounds of ρ and $M_7=\frac{M}{1-\rho}$ respectively. The error bound is given by

$$\|H(z)-P_{\hat{\rho},\hat{M}},L_N(E^N(H,\eta))(z)\|_\infty$$
$$\leq M_8\rho^N+\varepsilon(c_1+c_2\log\varepsilon)+O_1(\rho,\hat{\rho},M_7,\hat{M}_7)$$

where $O_1(\rho,\hat{\rho},M_7,\hat{M}_7),c_1,c_2$ are as defined in (2.10) and lemma 2.1.

The Lagrange method thus has an attractive exponential convergence rate which most two stage non-linear algorithms do not possess.

4 System identification using noisy time response data

It is assumed that

(A3) $H(z)=\sum_{i=0}^{\infty}h(i)z^{-i}$ is the unknown stable transfer function as described in equation (2.1). i.e. there exists some constants $0<M<\infty$ and $0\leq\rho<1$ such that

$$|h(i)|\leq M\rho^i \qquad for\ all\ i \qquad (4.1)$$

(A4) $\eta(k)$ denotes the noise at time k. $\eta(k)$ is unknown but bounded by some known constant $\varepsilon>0$.

$$|\eta(k)|\leq\varepsilon \qquad for\ all\ k \qquad (4.2)$$

$E^N(H,\eta)$ indicates the corrupted output measurement for $k=0,1,2,\ldots,N-1$ and for a given input sequence $\{r(k)\}_0^{N-1}$.

$$E^N(H,\eta) = \{y(k)+\eta(k) \mid k=0,1,2,...,N-1\} \quad (4.3)$$

Our goal here is to find a robustly convergent algorithm $A=\{A_N\}$ which, in the presence of noise, maps the time response data $E^N(H,\eta)$ into the model $A_N(E^N(H,\eta))(z) = \hat{H}_N(z) = \sum_{i=0}^{n(N)} a^N(i)z^{-i}$ such that (2.6) and (2.7) are satisfied. Similar to theorem 3.1, we have

Theorem 4.1

Let $A=\{A_N\}$ be an algorithm which maps noisy time response data $E^N(H,\eta)$ into the model, $\hat{H}_N(z) = \sum_{i=0}^{n(N)} a^N(i)z^{-i}$. Suppose $A=\{A_N\}$ is linear and bounded in data as defined in definition 3.1. Then the convergence of $A=\{A_N\}$ in the absence of noise implies the robust convergence of $P_{\rho,M}A = \{P_{\rho,M}A_N\}$, in presence of noise with ρ, M as defined in (4.1) and $P_{\rho,M}$ denotes the corresponding operator.

Although theorem 4.1 is very general and can be applied to a very large class of linear algorithms, we will concentrate on one particular linear method : the impulse response method to illustrate the technique. The idea is to determine the estimate $\hat{h}^N(i)$ of the impulse response $h(i)$ from $\{r(k)\}_0^{N-1}$ and $E^N(H,\eta)$ and consequently form the identified model $\hat{H}_N = \sum_{i=0}^{n(N)} \hat{h}^N(i)z^{-i}$

The impulse response method does not always have a solution for the purpose of system identification, even in the absence of noise. Observe that when $r(k)=0$, then $y(k)=0$ and consequently no algorithm can produce an estimate $\hat{h}^N(i)$. Thus, the first non trivial objective in this section is to establish conditions on $r(k)$ so that the solution to the identification problem exists.

Assume that the system $H(z)$ as shown in Fig. 4.1 is initially at rest. This assumption is not a restriction and can be relaxed. For a given known sequence $\{r(k)\}_0^{N-1}$ and unknown $\{\eta(k)\}_0^{N-1}$, let

$$R_N = \begin{bmatrix} r(0) & 0 & \cdots & 0 \\ r(1) & r(0) & \cdots & \cdot \\ \cdot & \cdot & \cdots & \cdot \\ \cdot & \cdot & \cdots & \cdot \\ \cdot & \cdot & \cdots & \cdot \\ r(N-1) & r(N-2) & \cdots & r(0) \end{bmatrix} \qquad Q_N = \begin{bmatrix} q(0) \\ q(1) \\ \cdot \\ \cdot \\ q(N-1) \end{bmatrix} \quad (4.4)$$

$$\Psi_N = (\eta(0)\eta(1)....\eta(N-1))^T \text{ and } Y_N = (y(0)y(1)\cdots y(N-1))^T \quad (4.5)$$

where Y_N denotes the actual but unknown output of $H(z)$. Notice however that the corrupted output value $Y_N+\Psi_N$ is available.

$$R_N\,(h(0),h(1),\ldots,h(N-1))^T = Y_N$$

The estimate Q_N of $(h(0),h(1),\ldots,h(N-1))^T$ is therefore given by

$$Q_N = R_N^{-1}(Y_N+\Psi_N) = R_N^{-1}Y_N + R_N^{-1}\Psi_N$$
$$= (h(0),h(1),\ldots,h(N-1))^T + R_N^{-1}\Psi_N \quad (4.6)$$

provided R_N^{-1} exists. In order to apply theorem 4.1, it is necessary to find conditions on R_N such that R_N is invertible and $\|R_N^{-1}\Psi_N\|_\infty$ is bounded. The $\eta(k)$'s being arbitrary

$$\sup_{|\eta(k)|\le\varepsilon} \|R_N^{-1}\Psi_N\|_\infty = \|R_N^{-1}\|_\infty\,\varepsilon$$

where $\|R_N^{-1}\|_\infty$ is the standard ∞ norm of a matrix. To this end, the following is a well known fact.

Lemma 4.2

R_N^{-1} exists and $\|R_N^{-1}\|_\infty$ is bounded if and only if for some $\alpha>0$

$$\|R_N X\|_\infty \ge \alpha \quad (4.7)$$

for every $X \in R^N$ with $\|X\|_\infty = 1$. Moreover if (4.7) holds, then $\|R_N^{-1}\|_\infty \le \frac{1}{\alpha}$.

Lemma 4.3

For a given N and a bounded sequence $\{r(k)\}_0^{N-1}$, let R_N be defined in (4.4). Then $\|R_N^{-1}\|_\infty \le \frac{1}{\alpha}$ if and only if $r(0)\neq 0$.

Remarks :

(1) In the problem setup, we try to find $h(0),\ldots,h(N-1)$ from the input $\{r(k)\}_0^{N-1}$ and data $E^N(H,\eta)$. If we modify the problem as follows : Given $\{r(k)\}_0^{N-1}$ and $E^N(H,\eta)$, determine $h(0), h(1),\ldots,h(i)$ for some $0\le i\le N-1$. Then, the if and only if condition of lemma 4.3 becomes that there exists some $r(l)$, $0\le l\le N-1-i$ such that $r(l)\neq 0$.

(2) For a given N, an if and only if condition is established to guarantee that R_N^{-1} is invertible and bounded. However, the bound $\|R_N^{-1}\|_\infty \le \frac{1}{\alpha}$ may be not only a function of input $\{r(k)\}_0^{N-1}$ alone, but also a function of N. Hence, to guarantee uniform convergence of (4.4), an uniform upper bound, independent of N is required.

(3) For a fixed N, calculation of the estimate $q(i)$ of the impulse response $h(i)$ in (4.6) involves the inversion of R_N. For large $N$and$N\to\infty$ this method is not efficient. A recursive method to calculate $q(i)$ would be more useful.

Let $\{r(k)\}_0^{N-1}$ denote a bounded input sequence and $R(z)=\sum_{i=0}^{\infty} r(i)z^{-i}$ be its z transform. Consider the system $R^{-1}(z)$ with input $E^N(H,\eta) = \{y(k)+\eta(k)\}$ and output $Q(z)$ as shown in Fig. 4.2. Then

$$Q(z) = R^{-1}(z)(Y(z)+\Psi(z)) = H(z) + R^{-1}(z)\Psi(z) \quad (4.8)$$

where $\Psi(z) = \sum_{i=0}^{\infty}\eta(i)z^{-i}$, $Q(z)=\sum_{i=0}^{\infty} q(i)z^{-i}$. Define

$$R^{-1}(z)\Psi(z) = \Delta Q(z) = \sum_{i=0}^{\infty}\Delta q(i)z^{-i} \quad (4.9)$$

It follows that

$$q(i) = h(i) + \Delta q(i) \quad (4.10)$$

Remarks :

(1) Equation (4.10) is an alternative to equation (4.6) and because $Q(z)$ is the output of $R^{-1}(z)$, calculation of $q(i)$ in (4.10) is recursive and in turn more efficient than that in (4.6).

(2) To make the system $R^{-1}(z)$ physically realizable, $R^{-1}(z)$ has to be causal, i.e. if $R^{-1}(z) = \sum_{i=-\infty}^{\infty} r'(i)z^{-i}$, then $r'(i)=0, i<0$. Note that $R(z)$ is the z transform of some causal sequence $\{r(k)\}$, therefore there exists some integer $l\ge 0$ such that $z^{-l}R^{-1}(z)$ is causal. In this case at the Nth step, the output of $z^{-l}R^{-1}(z)$ with input $\{y(k)+\eta(k)\}$ gives $\{0,0,...,0,q(0),\ldots,q(N-1-l)\}$ instead of the sequence $\{q(0),q(1),...,q(N-1)\}$. As far as the convergence property of the identification algorithm is concerned, this really does not change any thing. For simplicity, we restrict the discussion to the case where $R^{-1}(z)$ is assumed to be causal. The extension to non causal $R^{-1}(z)$ is straightforward.

(3) In order to apply theorem (4.1), there is still one question to be answered, i.e. when is $|\Delta q(i)|$ bounded ? This can be easily guaranteed by assuming the stability of $R^{-1}(z)$. If $R^{-1}(z)$ is stable and causal, then $c = \|R^{-1}(z)\|_1 = \sum_{i=0}^{\infty}|r'(i)|$ is bounded and in turn

$$\sup_i |\Delta q(i)| \le \|R^{-1}(z)\|_1 \sup_k |\eta(k)| \le c\varepsilon \quad (4.11)$$

(4) From Fig. 4.2, we see that in applying the impulse response method, the input $\{r(k)\}$ to the system need not necessarily be an impulse. It can be any signal as long as $R^{-1}(z)$ is stable.

We now formally define the identified model using the impulse response method as

$$I_N(E^N(H,\eta))(z) = \sum_{i=0}^{N-1} q(i)z^{-i} \tag{4.12}$$

where $q(i)$ is as defined in (4.9)-(4.11).

Theorem 4.4

Let $I = \{I_N\}$ be the identification algorithm of impulse response method. Suppose $R^{-1}(z)$ is stable. Then $P_{\hat{\rho},\hat{M}} I = \{P_{\hat{\rho},\hat{M}} I_N\}$ is robustly convergent in the presence of noise with $\hat{\rho}$ and $\hat{M}$ denoting the estimates on the bounds of ρ and M respectively. The error bound is given by

$$\|H(z) - P_{\hat{\rho},\hat{M}} I_N(E^N(H,\eta))(z)\|_\infty$$

$$\leq \frac{M}{1-\rho}\rho^N + \varepsilon(c_1 + c_2 \log\varepsilon) + O_1(\rho,\hat{\rho},M,\hat{M}) \tag{4.13}$$

where $$O_1(\rho,\hat{\rho},M,\hat{M}) = \begin{cases} 0 & \text{if } \hat{\rho} \geq \rho \ \& \ \hat{M} \geq M \\ 2(\frac{\hat{M}}{1-\rho} - \frac{\hat{M}}{1-\hat{\rho}}) & \text{if } \hat{\rho} < \rho \ \& \ \hat{M} \geq M \\ 2(\frac{M}{1-\hat{\rho}} - \frac{\hat{M}}{1-\hat{\rho}}) & \text{if } \hat{\rho} \geq \rho \ \& \ \hat{M} < M \\ 2(\frac{M}{1-\rho} - \frac{\hat{M}}{1-\hat{\rho}}) & \text{if } \hat{\rho} < \rho \ \& \ \hat{M} < M \end{cases}$$

and c_1, c_2 are as defined in (2.21) or (2.22) with $M_2 = c = \|R^{-1}(z)\|_1 = \sum_{i=0}^{\infty} |r'(i)|, M_3 = \hat{M}$.

Typical examples of input sequences $\{r(k)\}$ which have a stable inverse $R^{-1}(z)$ are impulse function $\delta(k)$ and the step function with corresponding $R^{-1}(z) = 1$ and $R^{-1}(z) = 1 - z^{-1}$ respectively. The following problem is interesting : for a given bound on the magnitude of the input $r(k)$, say $\sup_k |r(k)| = M_r$, what is the maximum reduction on the effect of noise in terms of M_r. Equivalently, what is the minimum value of $c = \|R^{-1}(z)\|_1$ which can be achieved subject to the constraint that $\sup_k |r(k)| = M_r > 0$. In this regard, we have

Theorem 4.5

Let $\{r(k)\}$ be a bounded sequence such that $R^{-1}(z)$ exists, and is stable and causal. Suppose $\sup_k |r(k)| = M_r$. Then

$$\|R^{-1}(z)\|_1 = c \geq \frac{1}{M_r} \tag{4.14}$$

5 Concluding Remarks

This paper has shown that any system identification algorithm which is linear and convergent in the absence of noise could be made robustly convergent in presence of noise by incorporating a simple projection operator. The significance of this approach lies in its computational simplicity and speed of convergence as against existing nonlinear algorithms.

6 References

(1) E.W. Bai, "Adaptive quantification of model uncertainties by rational approximation," *IEEE Trans. Automat. Control*, vol. AC-36, pp. 441-453, 1991.

(2) E.W. Bai and S. Raman, "On line H_2 , H_∞ and pointwise uncertainty bound quantification in identification of restricted complexity models" Proc. of CDC 1992 (to appear)

(3) G.C. Goodwin and M.E. Salgado, "A stochastic embedding approach for quantifying uncertainty in the estimation of restricted complexity model," *Int. J. Adapt. Control Signal Process*, vol. 3, pp. 333-356, 1989.

(4) G. Gu and P.P. Khargonekar, "Linear and nonlinear algorithms for identification in H_∞ with error bounds," *Proc. Amer. Control Conf.*, pp. 64-69, 1991.

(5) G. Gu and P.P. Khargonekar, "A class of algorithms for system identification in H_∞," *Automatica*, vol. 28, pp. 299-312, 1991.

(6) A.J. Helmicki, C.A. Jacobson and C.N. Nett, "Identification in H_∞: Linear Algorithms," *Proc. Amer. Control Conf.*, pp. 2418-2423, 1990.

(7) A.J. Helmicki, C.A. Jacobson and C.N. Nett, "Control oriented system identification: A worst case/deterministic approach in H_∞," *IEEE Trans. Automat. Control*, vol. AC-36, pp. 1163-1176, 1991.

(8) R.L. Kosut, M. Lau and S. Boyd, "Parameter set estimation of systems with uncertain nonparametric dynamics and disturbances," *IEEE Trans. on AC* July 1992

(9) L. Ljung, *System identification: Theory for the user*, Englewood Cliffs, NJ, Prentice-Hall, 1987.

(10) P.M. Makila and J.R. Partington, "Robust approximation and identification in H_∞," *Proc Amer. Control Conf.*, pp. 70-76, 1991.

(11) J.R. Partington, "Robust identification in H_∞," *J. Math Anal. & Appl.*, (to appear).

(12) Zang, Z, Bitmead, R. and Gevers, M. "Disturbance rejection: on line refinement of controllers by closed loop modeling" Proc. of ACC 1992

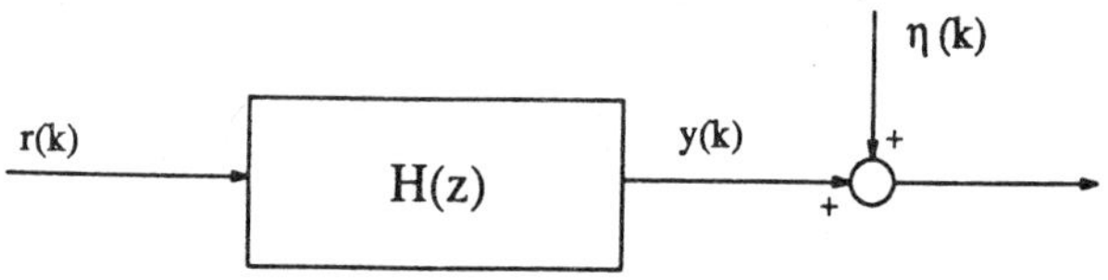

Figure 4.1 **Identification using time response data.**

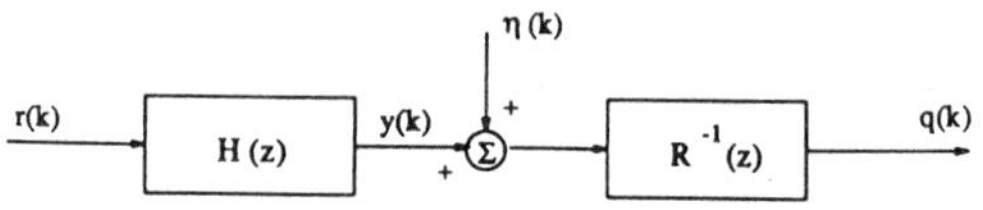

Figure 4.2 **Recursive method**

Proceedings of the
American Control Conference
San Francisco, California • June 1993

DISTRIBUTED DETECTION WITH MEMORY

Wei Chang*, Chris Rorres** and Moshe Kam*

*Department of Electrical and Computer Engineering

** Department of Mathematics and Computer Science

Drexel University, Philadelphia, PA 19104

Abstract

A binary distributed detection system comprises a bank of local decision makers (LDMs) and a central information processor (the data fusion center, DFC). All LDMs survey a common volume for a binary $\{H_0, H_1\}$ phenomenon. Each LDM forms a binary decision: it either accepts H_1 ("target-present") or H_0 ("target-absent"). The LDM is fully characterized by its performance probabilities (probability of false alarm and probability of detection). The decisions are transmitted to the DFC through noiseless communication channels. The DFC then optimally combines the local decisions to obtain a global decision ("target-present" or "target-absent") which minimizes a Bayesian objective function. The main difference between the present study and previous ones is that, along with the local decisions, the DFC in our architecture remembers and uses its most recent decision in synthesizing each new decision. We show that this feature endows our architecture with a detection performance that is generally much better than that of a memoryless DFC system. Moreover, when operating in a stationary environment, our architecture converges to a steady-state decision in finite time with probability one, and its detection performance during convergence and in steady state is strictly determined.

I. *Introduction*

Both parallel and serial decentralized distributed detection systems have been studied extensively since the early 1980's because of their applications in multi-sensor decision systems ([1]-[13], [15]). Common optimal criteria used in analyzing the overall system performance are the Bayes risk and Neyman-Pearson (N-P) criterion. Most studies involving parallel architecture assume memoryless local decision makers (LDMs) and a memoryless data fusion center (DFC). It is, however, possible for components in the system to remember and use past decisions for synthesis of new decisions with potentially significant performance advantages. In the present paper, the DFC is given a 1-bit memory through which its past output is used. The structure of the system is shown in Fig. 1. The n LDMs survey a common phenomenon and use a local performance index to determine whether or not a target is in sight. At each time instant t (t = 0, 1, ...), the ith LDM obtains new measurementsand makes a binary decision $u_i^{(t)}$, where $u_i^{(t)}$ = -1 means that hypothesis H_0 (target-absent) is accepted and $u_i^{(t)}$ = 1 means that hypothesis H_1 (target-present) is accepted. The local decisions are transmitted over noiseless communication channels to the DFC, and combined with the DFC's most recent global decision $u_g^{(t-1)}$ to form a new global binary decision $u_g^{(t)}$ at time t. Again, $u_g^{(t)}$ = -1 means "accept H_0" and $u_g^{(t)}$ = 1 means "accept H_1".

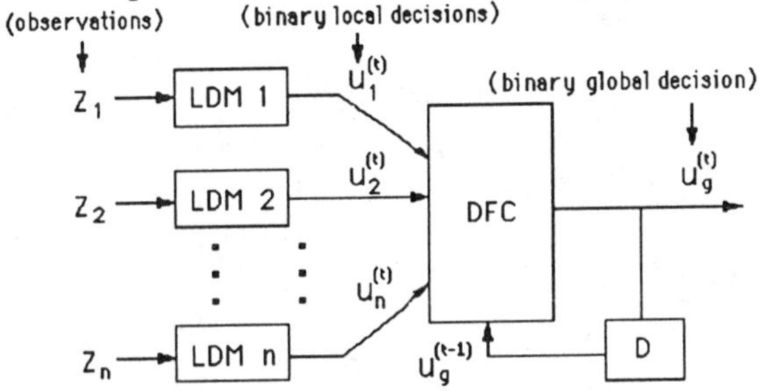

Fig. 1: The structure of the distributed detection system with feedback at the DFC

The global decision is made optimally by minimizing a Bayes risk of the form

$$\beta(P_{fg}^{(t)}, P_{dg}^{(t)}) = C_{00}P_0(1-P_{fg}^{(t)}) + C_{10}P_0P_{fg}^{(t)} + C_{01}P_1(1-P_{dg}^{(t)}) + C_{11}P_1P_{dg}^{(t)}, \quad (1)$$

where C_{ij} is the cost of accepting H_i when H_j is true (i, j = 0, 1), P_j is the a priori probability of hypothesis H_j (j = 0, 1), and $P_{fg}^{(t)} = P_r\{u_g^{(t)} = 1|H_0\}$ and $P_{dg}^{(t)} = P_r\{u_g^{(t)} = 1|H_1\}$ are the global probabilities of false alarm and detection, respectively, at time instant t. In the sequel use $C_{00} = C_{11} = 0$ and $C_{01} = C_{10} = 1$, so that the Bayes risk is the global probability of error (GPE). As we shall show, the performance of the 1-bit memory DFC improves uniformly until the DFC converges to a decision and needs no more samples from the (stationary) LDMs [(1)].

---

(1) The problem described by Fig. 1 can be cast as a serial detection problem. In a binary serial-detection architecture each decision maker (say the ith) obtains a set of observations y_i from the "environment", and a binary decision u from the previous decision maker, the $(i-1)^{th}$. On this basis it creates its own decision, $u_g^{(i)}$. One can assume that a time t we have

---

Acknowledgement: This study was supported by the National Science Foundation through grant ECS9057587.

To analyze the performance of this distributed detection system with memory, we make the following assumptions:

(i) Every decision made by a LDM is conditionally statistically independent of all other decisions under hypothesis H_j ($j = 0, 1$).

(ii) All LDMs are fixed with the same known time-invariant probabilities of false alarm $P_{fi} = P_f = P_r\{u_i^{(t)} = 1|H_0\}$ and detection $P_{di} = P_d = P_r\{u_i^{(t)} = 1|H_1\}$ for $i = 1, 2, ..., n$(2). We also assume that $0 < P_f < P_d < 1$.

Given P_f, P_d, $\{u_i^{(t)}\}_{i=1}^n$ and $u_g^{(t-1)}$ where $\{u_i^{(t)}\}_{i=1}^n$ and $u_g^{(t-1)}$ are conditionally statistically independent, we can obtain $u_g^{(t)}$, the global optimal decision at time t by using a generalization of the well-known Chair-Varshney fusion rule for distributed detection architectures with fixed LDMs ([1]). Our generalized fusion rule is expressed as

$$u_g^{(t)}=\mathbf{sgn}\left\{a\sum_{i=1}^{n} u_i^{(t)}+ a_g^{(t-1)} u_g^{(t-1)} - \left(2\log\tau + b + b_g^{(t-1)}\right)\right\}, \tag{2}$$

where $\mathbf{sgn}\{\bullet\}$ is the algebraic sign function:

$$\mathbf{sgn}\{x\} = \begin{cases} 1, & x \geq 0 \\ -1, & x < 0 \end{cases}, \quad a = \log\left[\frac{P_d\,(1 - P_f)}{P_f\,(1 - P_d)}\right],$$

$$b = n\log\left[\frac{P_f\,(1 - P_f)}{P_d\,(1 - P_d)}\right], \quad a_g^{(t-1)} = \log\left[\frac{P_{dg}^{(t-1)}\left(1 - P_{fg}^{(t-1)}\right)}{P_{fg}^{(t-1)}\left(1 - P_{dg}^{(t-1)}\right)}\right],$$

$$b_g^{(t-1)} = \log\left[\frac{P_{fg}^{(t-1)}\left(1 - P_{fg}^{(t-1)}\right)}{P_{dg}^{(t-1)}\left(1 - P_{dg}^{(t-1)}\right)}\right],$$ and $\tau = P_0/P_1$ (the decision threshold of the global detector).

In section II, we prove that when the system operates in a stationary environment, the DFC converges to a decision with probability one. Convergence is shown to be equivalent to having the global probability of false alarm and global probability of detection enter a certain polygon (the "stopping set") in the P_{fg}-P_{dg} plane. Once the probabilities ($P_{fg}^{(t)}$, $P_{dg}^{(t)}$) have entered this region, the DFC "freezes" and no further observations need be collected.

Knowing the boundaries of the stopping set allows the calculation of an upper bound on the global Bayes risk (Eq. (20)) that the system will achieve at convergence.

---

built a serial architecture of t decision makers in tandem; denoting them k=1,2,...,t, the kth decision maker obtains $y_k = \{u_i^{(k)}\}_{i=1}^n$ as inputs. Here $u_i^{(k)}$ is the output at time k of an auxiliary binary local decision maker which makes decisions about the hypothesis. In this formulation, results from [5],[6],[8],[9] and [15] become applicable.

(2) Otherwise, an upper bound on the global Bayes risk of the actual system can be obtained using our methods by setting $P_f = \max_i\{P_{fi}\}$ and $P_d = \min_i\{P_{di}\}$. The DFC fusion rule can be easily generalized for non-identical LDMs.

Additional examples and proofs are available in [2].

II. Performance Characteristics of a 1-bit Memory Data-Fusion Rule

Using the optimal fusion rule (2), the global probability of false alarm $P_{fg}^{(t)}$ and the global probability of detection $P_{dg}^{(t)}$ at time t = 1, 2, ... can be expressed in terms of their initial values ($P_{fg}^{(0)}$, $P_{dg}^{(0)}$) through the following iterative scheme:

$$P_{fg}^{(t)} = \mathbf{F}\left(P_{fg}^{(t-1)}, P_{dg}^{(t-1)}\right), \tag{3a}$$

$$P_{dg}^{(t)} = \mathbf{D}\left(P_{fg}^{(t-1)}, P_{dg}^{(t-1)}\right), \tag{3b}$$

where

$$\mathbf{F}(x, y) = \sum_{i=0}^{n} \binom{n}{i} P_f^i (1 - P_f)^{n-i}\left[(1 - x)\mathbf{U}_{-1}(\gamma_i(x,y)) + x\mathbf{U}_{-1}(\delta_i(x,y))\right] \tag{4a}$$

$$\mathbf{D}(x,y) = \sum_{i=0}^{n} \binom{n}{i} P_d^i (1 - P_d)^{n-i}\left[(1 - y)\mathbf{U}_{-1}(\gamma_i(x,y)) + y\mathbf{U}_{-1}(\delta_i(x,y))\right] \tag{4b}$$

and

$$\gamma_i(x, y)=P_d^i(1 - P_d)^{n-i}(1 - y) - \tau\, P_f^i\,(1 - P_f)^{n-i}(1 - x), \tag{5a}$$

$$\delta_i(x, y) = P_d^i(1 - P_d)^{n-i}y - \tau\, P_f^i\,(1 - P_f)^{n-i}x. \tag{5b}$$

Here, $\mathbf{U}_{-1}(\bullet)$ is the unit step function defined by

$$\mathbf{U}_{-1}(x) = \begin{cases} 1, & x \geq 0 \\ 0, & x < 0 \end{cases}.$$

These equations are based on the definitions

$$P_{fg}^{(t)} = P_r\{u_g^{(t)} = 1|H_0\} = \mathbf{E}[P_r\{u_g^{(t)} = 1|H_0, u_1^{(t)}, u_2^{(t)}, ..., u_n^{(t)}, u_g^{(t-1)}\}], \tag{6a}$$

$$P_{dg}^{(t)} = P_r\{u_g^{(t)} = 1|H_1\} = \mathbf{E}[P_r\{u_g^{(t)} = 1|H_1, u_1^{(t)}, u_2^{(t)}, ..., u_n^{(t)}, u_g^{(t-1)}\}], \tag{6b}$$

where $\mathbf{E}[\bullet]$ is an expectation function evaluated over all local decisions and the previous global decision.

The geometric interpretation of the above iterative scheme is as follows: Let S be the closed unit square S in the xy-plane:

$$S = \{(x, y)|\ 0 \leq x \leq 1, 0 \leq y \leq 1\}. \tag{7}$$

Then the mapping $(x, y) \rightarrow (\mathbf{F}(x, y), \mathbf{D}(x, y))$ maps S into itself (Lemma 1 in the appendix). For each i = 0, 1, ..., n, the equation $\gamma_i(x, y) = 0$ is the line $(1-y) = s_i(1-x)$ through the point (1, 1) with slope s_i given by

$$s_i = \tau\left(\frac{P_f}{P_d}\right)^i\left(\frac{1 - P_f}{1 - P_d}\right)^{n-i}. \tag{8}$$

Because of our assumption that $0 < P_f < P_d < 1$, we have

$$0 < s_n < s_{n-1} < ... < s_1 < s_0 < \infty. \tag{9}$$

Similarly, the equation $\delta_i(x, y) = 0$ is the line $y = s_i x$ through the point (0, 0). These n+1 pairs of parallel lines partition the unit square into 3- or 4-sided convex polygons (Fig. 2). In each polygon, $\mathbf{F}(x, y)$ is a linear function of x alone and $\mathbf{D}(x, y)$ is a linear function of y alone. Both functions change discontinuously as (x, y) moves from one polygon to another.

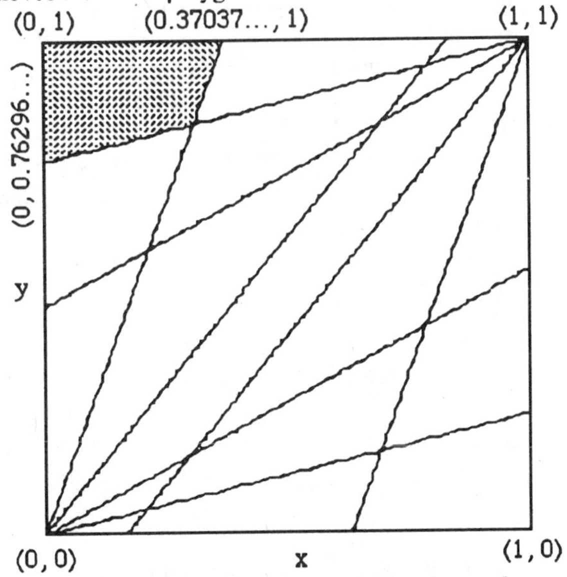

Fig. 2: The unit square S and its partition into polygons by the lines $\gamma_i(x, y) = 0$ and $\delta_i(x, y) = 0$ for i = 0, 1, ..., n. Here $n = 3$, $P_f = 0.4$, $P_d = 0.6$, and $\tau = 0.8$. The shaded region is the stopping set $\Re_S$ defined in Eq. (10).

Among the polygons that partition S, the following is of particular interest:

$$\Re_S = \{(x, y) \in S \mid \gamma_i(x, y) < 0,\ \delta_i(x, y) \geq 0\}. \qquad (10)$$

This is the polygon that always contains the point (0, 1) (the shaded polygon in Fig. 2). In this polygon we have $\mathbf{F}(x, y) = x$ and $\mathbf{D}(x, y) = y$ (Lemma 2 in [2]). We shall consequently call this polygon the *stopping set* because if an iterate $(P_{fg}^{(s)}, P_{dg}^{(s)})$ ever enters it, then $(P_{fg}^{(t)}, P_{dg}^{(t)}) = (P_{fg}^{(s)}, P_{dg}^{(s)})$ for all $t \geq s$, and so the iterates stop changing. In addition, the decisions of the DFC do not change from that time on; that is, $u_g^{(t)} = u_g^{(s)}$ for all $t \geq s$, regardless of the values of the local decisions $u_i^{(t)}$ for i = 1, 2, ..., n and $t \geq s$.

Next, suppose we choose the initial operating point $(P_{fg}^{(0)}, P_{dg}^{(0)})$ as $\left(\frac{1}{2}, \frac{1}{2}\right)$. Then from (2) we have $a_g^{(0)} = b_g^{(0)} = 0$ and so we need not know $u_g^{(0)}$ to compute $u_g^{(1)}$. In fact, the first iterate $(P_{fg}^{(1)}, P_{dg}^{(1)})$ coincides with the unchanging operating point of a memoryless system and the first global decision $u_g^{(1)}$ is the one of a memoryless system (see [4], Eqs. (6)).

We shall denote this particular point by $(P_{fg}^{(M)}, P_{dg}^{(M)})$. (In fact, all points in the polygon containing $\left(\frac{1}{2}, \frac{1}{2}\right)$ are mapped onto $(P_{fg}^{(M)}, P_{dg}^{(M)})$). This memoryless operating point is the reasonable initial point to begin with, and so for all the examples we shall assume that $(P_{fg}^{(0)}, P_{dg}^{(0)}) = \left(\frac{1}{2}, \frac{1}{2}\right)$. For certain extreme values of the system parameters, $(P_{fg}^{(M)}, P_{dg}^{(M)})$ and the stopping set are as follows:

Constant target-present decision case: If $\tau \leq \left(\frac{1-P_d}{1-P_f}\right)^n$, then from (8) and (9) we have $0 < s_n < \cdots < s_0 \leq 1$. The stopping set reduces to a triangular region, and the fusion rule (2) always returns a target-present decision ($u_g^{(t)} = 1$ for t = 1, 2, ...) regardless of the inputs from the local detectors.

Constant target-absent decision case: If $\tau > \left(\frac{P_d}{P_f}\right)^n$, then from (8) and (9) we have $1 < s_n < \cdots < s_0 < \infty$. The stopping set reduces to a triangular region the fusion rule (2) always returns a target-absent decision ($u_g^{(t)} = -1$ for t = 1, 2, ...) regardless of the inputs from the local detectors.

For both of the above cases, our 1-bit memory accomplishes nothing. We shall consequently make the following assumption to exclude these extreme cases (we also collect some of our previous assumptions as items 1-3):

ASSUMPTION 1. The system parameters P_f, P_d, τ, and n satisfy

1. $n \geq 1$; 2. $\tau > 0$; 3. $0 < P_f < P_d < 1$;

$$4.\ \left(\frac{1-P_d}{1-P_f}\right)^n < \tau \leq \left(\frac{P_d}{P_f}\right)^n. \qquad (11)$$

Under Assumption 1, there must exist an integer k ($1 \leq k \leq n$) such that $0 < s_n \cdots < s_k \leq 1 < s_{k-1} < \cdots < s_0 < \infty$. From (4), the memoryless initial point is then given by

$$P_{fg}^{(M)} = \sum_{i=k}^{n} \binom{n}{i} P_f^i (1 - P_f)^{n-i}, \qquad (12a)$$

$$P_{dg}^{(M)} = \sum_{i=k}^{n} \binom{n}{i} P_d^i (1 - P_d)^{n-i}. \qquad (12b)$$

As is shown in Lemma 4 in [2], this point lies in the interior of S and $(P_{fg}^{(M)}, P_{dg}^{(M)}) \notin \Re_S$.

The stopping set under Assumption 1 is a 4-sided polygon, as illustrated in Fig. 2, with a vertex lying in the interior of S, which we shall denote by (P_{fg}^*, P_{dg}^*). This vertex is at the intersection of the lines $(1-y) = s_n(1-x)$ and $y = s_0 x$ and has coordinates

$$P_{fg}^* = \frac{P_d^n(1-P_d)^n - \tau\, P_f^n(1-P_d)^n}{\tau\left[P_d^n(1-P_f)^n - P_f^n(1-P_d)^n\right]}, \qquad (13a)$$

$$P_{dg}^* = \frac{P_d^n(1-P_f)^n - \tau\, P_f^n(1-P_f)^n}{P_d^n(1-P_f)^n - P_f^n(1-P_d)^n}. \qquad (13b)$$

Notice that (P_{fg}^*, P_{dg}^*) does not belong to $\Re_S$.

We next return to the global probability of error (GPE), which we had previously defined at the point (x, y) as

$$\beta(x, y) = P_0 x + P_1(1 - y) = \frac{\tau x + (1-y)}{1+\tau}. \quad (14)$$

We define the change in the GPE from one iteration to the next as

$$\Delta\beta(x, y) = \beta(\mathbf{F}(x, y), \mathbf{D}(x, y)) - \beta(x, y). \quad (15)$$

We obviously have that $\Delta\beta(x, y) = 0$ if $(x, y) \in \Re_S$, since $(\mathbf{F}(x, y), \mathbf{D}(x, y)) = (x, y)$ in $\Re_S$. In addition, from Lemma 6 in [2], we have that $\Delta\beta(x, y) < 0$ outside of the closure of $\Re_S$. Consequently, if an iterate $(P_{fg}^{(t)}, P_{dg}^{(t)})$ lies outside of the closure of $\Re_S$, then the GPE of the next iterate, $(P_{fg}^{(t+1)}, P_{dg}^{(t+1)})$, is strictly less than the GPE of $(P_{fg}^{(t)}, P_{dg}^{(t)})$. The GPE can thus serve as a Lyapunov function for the dynamical system from which we can prove the following theorem:

THEOREM 1. Under Assumption 1, for any given initial point $(P_{fg}^{(0)}, P_{dg}^{(0)})$ in the unit square, the iterates $(P_{fg}^{(t)}, P_{dg}^{(t)})$, $t = 1, 2, \ldots$, behave according to one of the following three cases:

1. (The *stopping-time* case): There exists an integer t_S (the *stopping time*) such that $(P_{fg}^{(t)}, P_{dg}^{(t)}) \in \Re_S$ for all $t \geq t_S$;
2. (The *fixed-point* case): $(P_{fg}^{(t)}, P_{dg}^{(t)}) \notin \Re_S$ for any t and $(P_{fg}^{(t)}, P_{dg}^{(t)}) \to (P_{fg}^{*}, P_{dg}^{(*)})$ as $t \to \infty$. This case arises if and only if $n > 1$ and

$$\tau = \left[\frac{P_d(1-P_d)}{P_f(1-P_f)}\right]^n \left[\frac{P_f^n + (1-P_f)^n}{P_d^n + (1-P_d)^n}\right]; \quad (16)$$

3. (The *2-cycle* case): $(P_{fg}^{(t)}, P_{dg}^{(t)}) \notin \Re_S$ for any t and the iterates $(P_{fg}^{(t)}, P_{dg}^{(t)})$ alternately approach the two distinct points

$$\left(\frac{P_f^n[1-(1-P_f)^n]}{P_f^n + (1-P_f)^n - P_f^n(1-P_f)^n}, \frac{P_d^n[1-(1-P_d)^n]}{P_d^n + (1-P_d)^n - P_d^n(1-P_d)^n}\right) \quad (17)$$

and

$$\left(\frac{P_f^n}{P_f^n + (1-P_f)^n - P_f^n(1-P_f)^n}, \frac{P_d^n}{P_d^n + (1-P_d)^n - P_d^n(1-P_d)^n}\right) \quad (18)$$

on the boundary of $\Re_S$ as $t \to \infty$. This case arises if and only if

$$\tau = \left[\frac{P_d(1-P_d)}{P_f(1-P_f)}\right]^n \left[\frac{P_f^n + (1-P_f)^n - P_f^n(1-P_f)^n}{P_d^n + (1-P_d)^n - P_d^n(1-P_d)^n}\right]. \quad (19)$$

Case 1 in the above theorem is the generic case in that cases 2 and 3 require that the system parameters P_f, P_d, τ, and n satisfy Eq. (16) and/or (19). In addition, the limit points in cases 2 and 3 lie on the boundary of the stopping set $\Re_S$. Consequently, once the iterates have gotten sufficiently close to the limit points, then numerical error will perturb a future iterate into the stopping set with probability one. All of this is to say that cases 2 and 3 are mainly of theoretical interest and that, in practice, the iterates will enter the stopping set in finite time with probability one.

As was previously mentioned, the limiting point (P_{fg}^{*}, P_{dg}^{*}) in case 2 does not belong to the stopping set. It can also be verified that it is not a fixed point of the mapping. Rather, it can be described as a *potential* fixed point that certain sequences of iterates approach, but never reach. The same holds true for the 2-cycle case. It can be shown that one of the two limiting points in case 3 (the one in (18)) belongs to $\Re_S$ and the other does not, and both points have the same GPE. The two limiting points do not constitute a true 2-cycle of the mapping, but rather a potential 2-cycle. This situation can arise only because the mapping is not continuous.

Notice that if $P_f + P_d = 1$, then the exceptional value of τ for both the fixed-point case and the 2-cycle case is 1. Conversely, the fixed-point and 2-cycle cases can coexist only if $P_f + P_d = 1$ and $\tau = 1$. All three cases in Theorem 1 will then occur for various choices of the initial point $(P_{fg}^{(0)}, P_{dg}^{(0)})$. Each of the three cases has its own basin (the set of $(P_{fg}^{(0)}, P_{dg}^{(0)})$ leading to that case) and the three basins meet at the vertex (P_{fg}^{*}, P_{dg}^{*}) of the stopping set.

The slope τ of the level curves of the linear function $\beta(x, y)$ lies between the slopes of the two lines whose intersection determines (P_{fg}^{*}, P_{dg}^{*}); that is, $s_n < \tau < s_0$ (see Eq. (8)). By familiar linear-programming arguments, it follows that $\beta(x, y)$ is maximized within the closure of the convex polygon $\Re_S$ at the vertex (P_{fg}^{*}, P_{dg}^{*}). This maximum value is given by

$$\beta(P_{fg}^{*}, P_{dg}^{*}) = \frac{P_d^n(1-P_d)^n - (1+\tau)P_f^n(1-P_d)^n + \tau P_f^n(1-P_f)^n}{(1+\tau)\left[P_d^n(1-P_f)^n - P_f^n(1-P_d)^n\right]}. \quad (20)$$

This value serves as a convenient upper bound for the limiting value of the GPE of the iterates as $t \to \infty$. In other words, for any initial operating point we have $\lim_{t\to\infty} \beta(P_{fg}^{(t)}, P_{dg}^{(t)}) \leq \beta(P_{fg}^{*}, P_{dg}^{*})$ since $(P_{fg}^{(t)}, P_{dg}^{(t)})$ either enters $\Re_S$ in finite time or asymptotically approaches its boundary as $t \to \infty$.

Figure 3 illustrates some of the points discussed above. For a system with $n = 3$, $P_f = 0.4$, $P_d = 0.6$, and $\tau = 1$, Theorem 1 guarantees that all three cases will coexist since Eqs. (16) and (19) are both satisfied.

We begin with the initial point $(P_{fg}^{(M)}, P_{dg}^{(M)})$ = (44/125, 81/125) = (0.352, 0.648), for which GPE = 44/125 = 0.352. This initial point lies in the basin of the potential fixed point (P_{fg}^{*}, P_{dg}^{*}) = (8/35, 27/35) = (0.228571..., 0.771428...), for which GPE = 8/35 = 0.228571... . The iterates $(P_{fg}^{(t)}, P_{dg}^{(t)})$ first begin to converge to that point as t increases. However, because of truncation and round-off error in our computing machine, the 77-th iterate is perturbed into the basin of the potential 2-cycle consisting of the two points (784/4159, 3159/4159) = (0.188506..., 0.759557...) and

(1000/4159, 3375/4159) = (0.240442..., 0.811493...), for which GPE = 892/4159 = 0.214474... . The iterates then begin to converge to this potential 2-cycle. But the 227-th iterate is perturbed to a point in the fixed set near the second of the two listed points of the potential 2-cycle. Thereafter, the iterates are frozen at this point, (0.240442..., 0.811493...), for which the GPE is 0.214474... . The global probability of error has thus decreased from 0.352 to 0.214474..., although with exact arithmetic it should have decreased only to 0.228571... .

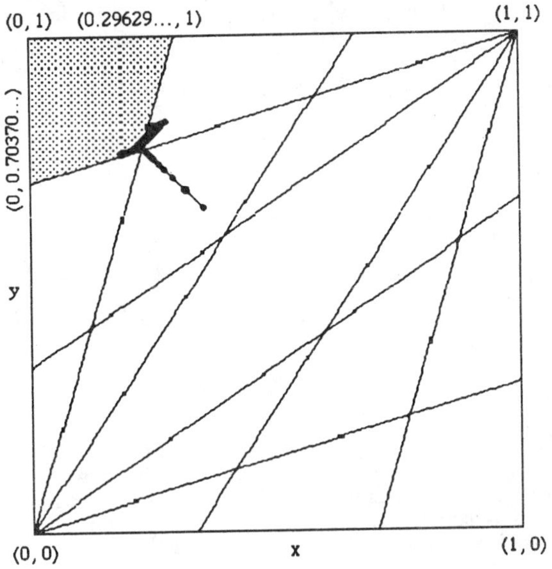

Fig. 3: The unit square S and its partition into polygons for which cases 2 and 3 of Theorem 1 both arise. Here n = 3, P_f = 0.4, P_d = 0.6, and τ = 1. The shaded region is the stopping set $\Re_S$. The various iterates are shown beginning with the initial point $(P_{fg}^{(M)}, P_{dg}^{(M)})$ = (44/125, 81/125) = (0.352, 0.648).

III. Conclusion

The effect of a 1-bit DFC memory on the performance of a distributed detection parallel architecture was quantified and demonstrated. Specifically, we studied the use of most recent decision in calculating the DFC's final decision. We showed that in stationary environments the 1-bit memory DFC will converge to a decision with probability one in finite time, and that the performance of this decision is quantified by way of a tight upper bound. More importantly, the 1-bit DFC memory system is shown with specific examples to outperform that of a system without memory and its performance can be accurately predicted. The price for the improved performance is the addition of hardware cost at the DFC when compared to the memoryless case. Further research is needed to study the functional properties of the resulting discrete-time system with the aim to evaluate the performance of the 1-bit DFC memory system in nonstationary environments, and to assess the effect of DFC-LDM feedback on detection performance.

References

[1] Z. Chair and P. K. Varshney, "Optimal data fusion in multiple sensor detection systems," *IEEE Transactions on Aerospace and Electronic Systems*, AES-22, pp. 98-101, 1986.

[2] W. Chang, *Distributed Detection with Limited Computational Resources*, Ph.D. dissertation, Ch. 4, Drexel University, June 1992.

[3] H. R. Hashemi and I. B. Rhodes, "Decentralized sequential detection," *IEEE Transactions on Information Theory*, IT-35, pp. 509-520, 1989.

[4] M. Kam, W. Chang and Q. Zhu, "Hardware complexity of binary distributed detection systems with isolated local Bayesian detectors," *IEEE Transactions on Systems, Man, and Cybernetics*, SMC-21, No. 3, pp. 565-571, 1991.

[5] J. Papastavrou and M. Athans, "Distributed detection by a large team of sensors in tandem," *IEEE Transactions on Aerospace and Electronic Systems*, AES-28, no. 3, pp. 639-653, 1992.

[6] ——, "On optimal distributed decision architectures in a hypothesis testing environment," *IEEE Transactions on Automatic Control*, AC-37, No. 8, pp. 1154-1169, 1992.

[7] A. R. Reibman and L. W. Nolte, "Optimal Detection and Performance of Distributed Sensor Systems," *IEEE Transactions on Aerospace and Electronic Systems*, AES-23, no. 1, pp. 24-30, 1987.

[8] P. F. Swaszek, "On the performance of serial network in distributed detection," *IEEE Transactions on Aerospace and Electronic Systems*, AES-29, no. 1, pp. 254-259, 1993.

[9] Z. B. Tang, K. R. Pattipati and D. L. Kleinman, "Optimization of detection networks: Part I — Tandem structures," *IEEE Transactions on Systems, Man, and Cybernetics*, SMC-21, No. 5, pp. 1044-1059, 1991.

[10] D. Teneketzis, "The decentralized Wald problem," *Proceedings of IEEE 1982 International Large-Scale Systems Symposium*, pp. 423-430, Virginia Beach, 1982.

[11] R. R. Tenney and N. R. Sandell, "Detection with distributed sensors," *IEEE Transactions on Aerospace and Electronic Systems*, AES-17, No. 4, pp. 501-509, 1981.

[12] J. N. Tsitsiklis, "Decentralized detection by a large number of sensors," *Mathematics of Control, Signals, Systems*, Vol.1, No. 2, pp. 167-182, 1988.

[13] J. N. Tsitsiklis and M. Athans, "On the complexity of distributed decision problems," *IEEE Transactions on Automatic Control*, AC-30, No. 5, pp. 440-446, 1985.

[14] H. V. Van Trees, *Detection, Estimation, and Modulation Theory*, New York: Wiley, 1969.

[15] R. Viswanathan, S. Thomopoulos and R. Tumuluri, "Optimal serial distributed decision fusion," *IEEE Transactions on Aerospace and Electronic Systems*, AES-24, No. 4, pp. 366-375, 1988.

Proceedings of the
American Control Conference
San Francisco, California • June 1993

A Low Communication Rate Scheme for Distributed Detection

Constantino Rago   Peter Willett   Yaakov Bar-Shalom
University of Connecticut
Storrs, CT 06269-3157 *

Abstract

In a practical distributed detection application a large number of resolution cells are continually being tested. A key observation is that most resolution cells will be empty and obviously so, and hence transmission, depending on the coarseness of quantization either of many local "no" decisions or of low-valued local likelihood ratios, is wasteful both of communication bandwidth and of fusion center attention. Here we consider a new scheme based on a "send/no-send" idea. The local sensors are assumed to "censor" their observations such that data about a cell deemed (locally) to be uninformative is simply not transmitted.

The main result is that with conditionally-independent sensor data and under a communication rate constraint, in order to minimize the probability of error, transmission should occur if and only if the local likelihood ratio value observed by the sensor does *not* fall in a single interval. With an appropriate redefinition of the average communication rate, a similar result can be derived under the Neyman-Pearson criterion.

For low prior probabilities of a target's presence in a given resolution cell, generally the most applicable case (and also, by symmetry, the case of a prior probability close to unity), the degradation in performance as measured against centralized decision-making is generally insignificant.

1 Introduction

Most treatments of distributed detection deal with the "parallel" topology, in which a group of sensors transmit some version of their observations to a central location for *fusion* into a global decision. Under the common assumption of conditionally-independent sensor data, the most effective transmission is a quantized version of the local likelihood ratio (*llr*). The severity of the bandwidth constraint on sensor-to-fusion-center communications determines the coarseness of the quantization: this may range from an essentially perfect version of the *llr* to a binary local decision. The literature on the subject is abundant, and in the interests of brevity we cite only [TS81, CV86, WW89].

In a practical application a large number of resolution cells are continually being tested. A great deal of data is presented to the fusion center, not only versions of the *llr*'s but also time, location, and Doppler "tags" to prevent loss of synchronization, and naturally the ability of the fusion center to adjudicate this must be considered when assigning the communication rate constraints. At any rate, one key observation is: most resolution cells will be empty and obviously so, and transmission either of many local "no" decisions or of low-valued *llr*'s is wasteful.

Thus motivated, in this paper we consider a new scheme based on a send/no-send idea. The local sensors are assumed to "censor" their observations such that data about a cell with an *llr* value deemed (locally) to be uninformative is simply not transmitted. In this approach it is clear that "tags" must accompany *each* transmission, and as such, intuition suggests that if data *is* transmitted, then it should be as little adulterated as possible by quantization.

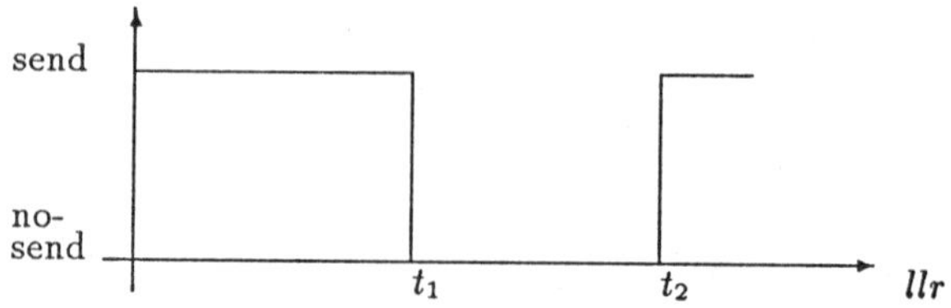

Figure 1: A Censoring Sensor.

The censoring idea is illustrated in Figure 1. In the previous argument the motivation was that the probability of H_1 (that is, that a resolution cell is indeed occupied) is low; Figure 1 is somewhat more general in that uninformative data need not necessarily refer to a small *llr*.

2 Formulation of the Problem

Suppose that we have N "independent" sensors; that is, sensors whose observations are independent conditioned on whether H (no target) or K (that a target is present) is true. Each sensor is connected, through some kind of channel, to a *Data Fusion Center (DFC)* and in this problem we impose the constraint that the average communication rate (see (2)) among the sensors and the *DFC* does not exceed a certain limit (communication rate constraint).

The basic idea behind the censoring scheme is to assign to each sensor two regions R_i and $\bar{R}_i$ (send and no-send regions for sensor $\#i$) such that if the *local likelihood ratio (llr)* of sensor $\#i$ belongs to the send region, the sensor sends the *llr* to the *DFC* and if not, the sensor does not send anything. We will assume that the regions R_i and $\bar{R}_i$ are such that the average communication rate constraint is satisfied.

Under this "censoring" scheme, the optimal fusion rule is a likelihood ratio test over the received and non-received *llr*'s given by

$$L_{FC}(l) = \prod_{i:l_i \in R_i} l_i \times \prod_{i:l_i \in \bar{R}_i} \frac{Pr(l_i \in \bar{R}_i|K)}{Pr(l_i \in \bar{R}_i|H)} \quad (1)$$

where $l = \{l_1, l_2, \ldots\}$ and l_i is the *llr* of sensor i. Note that the lack of a transmission from a given sensor does not mean that no information is sent, but rather that the information sent is less precise, *i.e.* the only information available in this case is that the *llr* belongs to the no-send region of that particular sensor.

*This research was supported by the Naval Undersea Warfare Center under ONT Grant N66604-92-C-1386

3 The Bayesian Case

The main concern in this "censoring" scheme is how to choose the send/no-send regions to minimize, in this case, the probability of error such that the communication rate constraint is satisfied.

To be specific, the average communication rate is given by

$$r = \pi_H \sum_i Pr(l_i \in R_i|H) + \pi_K \sum_i Pr(l_i \in R_i|K) \quad (2)$$

where π_H, π_K are the *prior* probabilities of the hypotheses, and the probability of error is naturally given by

$$P_e = \pi_H Pr(L_{FC} > \frac{\pi_H}{\pi_K}|H) + \pi_K Pr(L_{FC} \leq \frac{\pi_H}{\pi_K}|K) \quad (3)$$

The choice of the regions $\{R_i\}$ is in principle difficult; however, motivated by the well-known results on optimal quantization we give the following result:

Theorem 1 . *Given that the* llr*'s are conditionally independent, with probability density function $p_H(l)$*[1] *under H such that*
(i) $\exists$ *a parallelipiped* Λ : $p_H(l) > 0 \quad \forall l \in \Lambda$
(ii) *l is a continuous random variable under H*
and a communication rate constraint (as described by (2)) to be satisfied, then in order to minimize the probability of error, the exact value of the llr *should be sent iff it lies outside a specified interval corresponding to that sensor.*

Note that Theorem 1 states that the no-send region is a single interval (different, in general, for each sensor) over the likelihood ratio rather than some more general set.

Proof

We will concentrate on what happens if we modify the regions for only one of the sensors, with all the others' regions remaining unchanged. The change will be such that the average communication rate of the sensor in question remains unaltered.

Our goal is to show that the no-send region for each sensor is a single interval. Assume that for a particular sensor (sensor #1) we have a no-send region like the one shown in Figure 2 as scheme *I*, and we want to change this to a single interval region, as in scheme *II*. At the *DFC* we have a 'function' assigned to each sensor according to the optimal fusion rule given by (1). This function is depicted in Figure 3.

First, given ε, we need a criterion to choose the intervals ε_1 and ε_2 corresponding to the sensor under consideration. The criterion to be used here is the following:

Choose ε_1 and ε_2 such that the average communication rate under each hypothesis (a.c.u.e.h.) remains constant[2]. Using the definition of the average communication rate given by (2) the above criterion can be expressed as

$$\int_t^{t+\varepsilon} p_K(l)\, dl = \int_{t_1}^{t_1+\varepsilon_1} p_K(l)\, dl + \int_{t_2-\varepsilon_2}^{t_2} p_K(l)\, dl$$

$$\int_t^{t+\varepsilon} p_H(l)\, dl = \int_{t_1}^{t_1+\varepsilon_1} p_H(l)\, dl + \int_{t_2-\varepsilon_2}^{t_2} p_H(l)\, dl \quad (4)$$

[1]The following notation will be used:
l : likelihood ratio vector
l_i: likelihood ratio for sensor i

[2]It must be clear that this is an additional constraint, not present in the original problem. But given that we have two degrees of freedom (ε_1 and ε_2) and only one constraint, we can always choose this additional constraint, which will turn out to simplify the problem.

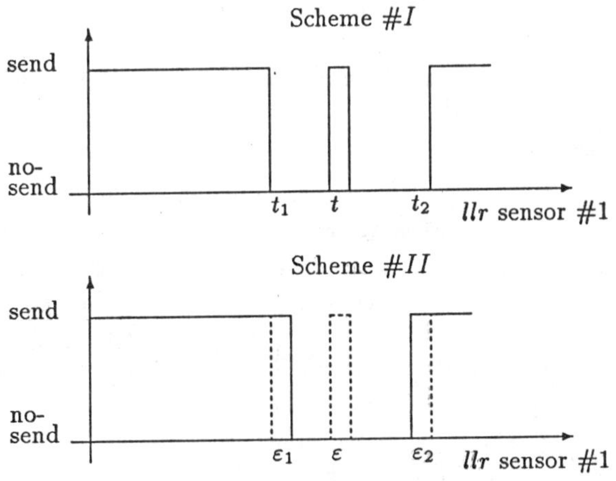

Figure 2: Two possible no-send regions for one of the sensors. Both schemes satisfy the communication rate constraint

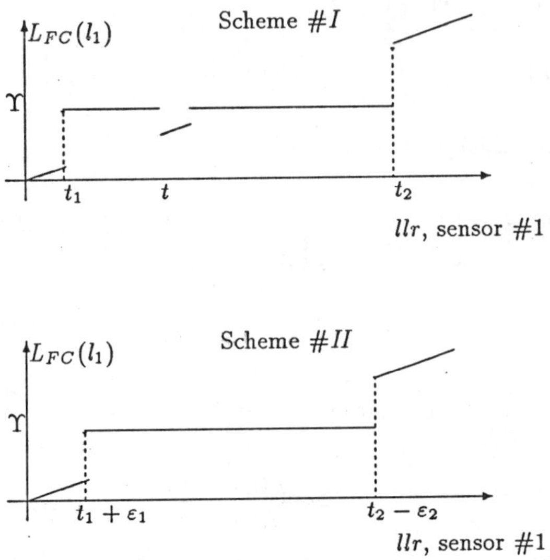

Figure 3: Function assigned in the *DFC* to the send–no-send regions for one of the sensors according to the optimal fusion rule.

where $p_K(l)$ and $p_H(l)$ are the density functions of the *llr* of the sensor in question under hypothesis K and H respectively.

The level assigned by the *DFC* to the no-send region of sensor #1 (*i.e.* if no data is transmitted to the DFC by the sensor in question) is given by

$$\Upsilon_1 = \frac{\int_{R_1} p_K(l_1)}{\int_{R_1} p_H(l_1)} \quad (5)$$

as can be seen from equation (1). We can prove that this level is the same for both schemes, since from (4) both numerator and denominator of (5) remain unmodified by the change in regions between scheme $\#I$ and scheme $\#II$.

The probability of error associated with each scheme (j = *scheme I or II*) is given by

$$P_e^j = \pi_K \int_{\Omega_H{}^j} p_K(l) + \pi_H \int_{\Omega_K{}^j} p_H(l) \quad (6)$$

Using the fact that the observations from one sensor are independent of the observations of the other, we can rewrite

(6) with the densities for sensor #1 in an explicit way:

$$P_e^j = \pi_K \int_{\Omega_H{}^j} p_K(l_1)\, p_K(\bar{l}_1) + \pi_H \int_{\Omega_K{}^j} p_H(l_1)\, p_H(\bar{l}_1) \quad (7)$$

where

$p_K(l_1)$ = prob. density function of the *llr* of sensor #1 under K

$p_K(\bar{l}_1)$ = joint prob. density function of the *llr* for the remaining sensors under K

$$\Omega_K^j = \{l : \frac{P_K(l)}{P_H(l)} > \tau\} = \{l : \frac{P_K(l_1)}{P_H(l_1)} > \tau \frac{P_H(\bar{l}_1)}{P_K(\bar{l}_1)}\}$$

and

$$\frac{P_K(l_n)}{P_H(l_n)} = \begin{cases} l_n \text{ for } l_n \in R_n^j \\ \Upsilon_n = \dfrac{\int_{\bar{R}_n} p_K(l_n)}{\int_{\bar{R}_n} p_H(l_n)} \text{ for } l_n \in \bar{R}_n^j \end{cases} \quad (8)$$

Using the fact that Ω_K and Ω_H are mutually exclusive sets, we can rewrite (7) as

$$P_e^j = \pi_K \left[1 + \int_{\Omega_K{}^j} \left(-p_K(l_1)\, p_K(\bar{l}_1) + \tau\, p_H(l_1)\, p_H(\bar{l}_1) \right) \right] \quad (9)$$

and using now the definition of Ω_K^j,

$$P_e^i = \pi_K \left[1 + \int_{\bar{l}_1} \int_{l_1 : \frac{P_K(l_1)}{P_H(l_1)} > \tau \frac{P_H(\bar{l}_1)}{P_K(\bar{l}_1)}} \left(-p_K(l_1)\, p_K(\bar{l}_1) + \tau\, p_H(l_1)\, p_H(\bar{l}_1) \right) \right] \quad (10)$$

Given that we have to integrate over all $\bar{l}_1$, we can make the following change of variables (which will turn out to simplify the notation):

$$u = \frac{P_K(\bar{l}_1)}{P_H(\bar{l}_1)} = \frac{P_K(u)}{P_H(u)} \quad (11)$$

(last equality follows from the fact that u is a *likelihood ratio* (see (8)). Now, we can rewrite eqn. (10) as:

$$P_e^i = \pi_K \left[1 + \int_u \int_{l_1 : \frac{P_K(l_1)}{P_H(l_1)} > \frac{\tau}{u}} \left(-p_K(l_1)\, dP_K(u) + \tau\, p_H(l_1)\, dP_H(u) \right) \right] \quad (12)$$

where $dP_K(u)$, $dP_H(u)$ are defined in the Radon-Nikodym sense.

To compare the difference in P_e between scheme *I* and *II* we need to compute (10) over all $\bar{l}_1$,or, equivalently, (12) over all u.

We have:

- for u such that:
  - either $\frac{\tau}{u} < t_1$
  - or $t_1 + \varepsilon_1 < \frac{\tau}{u} < t$
  - or $t + \varepsilon < \frac{\tau}{u} < t_2$
  - or $t_2 + \varepsilon_2 < \frac{\tau}{u} < t$

  the difference $(P_{e_{schemeI}} - P_{e_{schemeII}})$ due to the inner integral in (12) is 0 (because for every l_1 that belong to any of the above regions the value assigned to it in the *DFC* is the same for both schemes, see Fig. 3).

- for u such that: $t_1 < \frac{\tau}{u} < t_1 + \varepsilon_1$ then the difference $(P_{e_{schemeII}} - P_{e_{schemeI}})$ due to the inner integral in (12) is given by

$$\mathcal{A} : \quad \int_{t_1}^{\frac{\tau}{u}} [p_K(l_1)\, dP_K(u) - \tau\, p_H(l_1)\, dP_H(u)] \quad (13)$$

- for u such that: $t < \frac{\tau}{u} < t + \varepsilon$ then we have if $\Upsilon < t \rightarrow$ (see Fig. 3)

$$\mathcal{B}' : \quad \int_{\frac{\tau}{u}}^{t+\varepsilon} [p_K(l_1)\, dP_K(u) - \tau\, p_H(l_1)\, dP_H(u)] - \int_{t_2-\varepsilon_2}^{t_2} [p_K(l_1)\, dP_K(u) - \tau\, p_H(l_1)\, dP_H(u)] \quad (14)$$

if $\Upsilon > t \rightarrow$

$$\mathcal{B}'' : \quad \int_{t_1}^{t_1+\varepsilon_1} [p_K(l_1)\, dP_K(u) - \tau\, p_H(l_1)\, dP_H(u)] - \int_{t}^{\frac{\tau}{u}} [p_K(l_1)\, dP_K(u) - \tau\, p_H(l_1)\, dP_H(u)] \quad (15)$$

- for u such that: $t_2 - \varepsilon_2 < \frac{\tau}{u} < t_2$ then we have

$$\mathcal{C} : \quad -\int_{\frac{\tau}{u}}^{t_2} [p_K(l_1)\, dP_K(u) - \tau\, p_H(l_1)\, dP_H(u)] \quad (16)$$

Let us now analyze each of the above situations:

$\mathcal{A}$:

$$\int_{t_1}^{\frac{\tau}{u}} dP_K(u)\, p_H(l_1) \left[\frac{p_K(l_1)}{p_H(l_1)} - \tau \frac{dP_H(u)}{dP_K(u)} \right] = dP_K(u) \int_{t_1}^{\frac{\tau}{u}} p_H(l_1) \left[l_1 - \frac{\tau}{u} \right] \quad (17)$$

The integrand is negative over all the integration region, and hence the probability of error of scheme *II* is smaller than that of scheme I for u in that interval. An almost identical approach is valid for $\mathcal{C}$. Using the same argument as before, we see that the integral in (16) is now positive, and hence (16) is negative.

For $\mathcal{B}$, we have two different situations to analyze:

Case $\mathcal{B}'$: The first term in (14) is smaller than the integral over all ε, and using the relationships given by the communication rate constraint (a.c.u.e.h) (see (4)), we have the following equality:

$$\int_{\frac{\tau}{u}}^{t+\varepsilon} [p_K(l_1)\, dP_K(u) - \tau\, p_H(l_1)\, dP_H(u)] - \int_{t_2-\varepsilon_2}^{t_2} [p_K(l_1)\, dP_K(u) - \tau\, p_H(l_1)\, dP_H(u)] = \int_{t_1}^{t_1+\varepsilon_1} [p_K(l_1)\, dP_K(u) - \tau\, p_H(l_1)\, dP_H(u)] \quad (18)$$

Using the same arguments as for $\mathcal{A}$, it is clear that the last term is negative, *i.e.* :

$$\int_{t_1}^{t_1+\varepsilon_1} [p_K(l_1)\, dP_K(u) - \tau\, p_H(l_1)\, dP_H(u)] = dP_K(u) \int_{t_1}^{t_1+\varepsilon_1} p_H(l_1) \left[l_1 - \frac{\tau}{u} \right] \quad (19)$$

Now, u is such that (see (14)):

$t < \frac{\tau}{u} < t + \varepsilon$ hence, it is clear that the last term in (19) is negative.

In fact we were trying to find the sign of (14), but we can see that the positive term (the integral over ε) in (14) is smaller than in (18). Thus, $\mathcal{B}'$ has a negative contribution to the difference $P_{e_{schemeII}} - P_{e_{schemeI}}$.

Case $\mathcal{B}''$: Using again the relations given by (4), we can write:

$$\int_{t_1}^{t_1+\epsilon_1} [p_K(l_1)\, dP_K(u) - \tau\, p_H(l_1)\, dP_H(u)] - \int_{t}^{t+\epsilon} [p_K(l_1)\, dP_K(u) - \tau\, p_H(l_1)\, dP_H(u)] = - \int_{t_2-\epsilon_2}^{t_2} [p_K(l_1)\, dP_K(u) - \tau\, p_H(l_1)\, dP_H(u)] \quad (20)$$

but the right side integral is positive, making the right side term negative. Now, the positive term in (15) is smaller than in (20), then $\mathcal{B}''$ has a negative contribution to $P_{e_{schemeI}} - P_{e_{schemeII}}$. This process can be continued for each of the no-single intervals in the no-send region until the no-send region becomes a single interval.

Procedure: Therefore, in view of Theorem 1, the procedure of optimizing consist of minimizing (3) with respect to the (single) intervals $\bar{R}_i$ with the constraint (2).

4 The Neyman-Pearson case

In this section we will examine censoring under the Neyman-Pearson criterion. We need to reformulate the problem according to the fact that there are no reasonable *priors* associated with the hypotheses. The average communication rate must be redefined, and we shall use:

$$\mathrm{r} = Pr(send/H) = \sum_i Pr(l_i \in R_i|H) \quad (21)$$

This definition is supported by the fact that in most of the real situations (radar, sonar, etc.) π_K, if it were definable, would be very small.

Theorem 2 . *Given a probability of false alarm (α) and a communication rate constraint (as in (21)) to be satisfied, and under the same assumptions as Theorem 1, then in order to maximize the probability of detection, the exact value of the* llr *should be sent iff it lies outside a specified interval.*

Proof

As in the previous section we shall compare the probabilities of detection of a single and non-single no-send intervals for one of the sensor (see Figure 2), assuming that the send–no-send regions of the rest of the sensors remain unchanged. Given ε, we choose ε_1 and ε_2 such that the average communication rate under each hypothesis remains constant. As before, the level assigned by the *DFC* to the no-send region is the same in both schemes.

The probability of detection (β) is given by:

$$\beta = Pr(\text{decide } K/K) = \int_{\Omega_K} p_K(x) = \int_{\bar{l}_1} \int_{l_1 : \frac{P_K(l_1)}{P_H(l_1)} > \tau \frac{P_H(\bar{l}_1)}{P_K(\bar{l}_1)}} p_K(l_1)\, p_K(\bar{l}_1) \quad (22)$$

where τ is set by the false alarm probability (α):

$$\alpha = Pr(\text{decide } K/H) = \int_{\Omega_K} p_H(x) = \int_{\bar{l}_1} \int_{l_1 / \frac{P_K(l_1)}{P_H(l_1)} > \tau \frac{P_H(\bar{l}_1)}{P_K(\bar{l}_1)}} p_H(l_1)\, p_H(\bar{l}_1) \quad (23)$$

We can rewrite β as

$$\beta = \tau\alpha + \int_{\Omega_K} [p_K(x) - \tau\, p_H(x)] \quad (24)$$

$$= \tau\alpha + \int_{\bar{l}_1} \int_{l_1 : \frac{P_K(l_1)}{P_H(l_1)} > \tau \frac{P_H(\bar{l}_1)}{P_K(\bar{l}_1)}} [p_K(l_1)\, p_K(\bar{l}_1) - \tau\, p_H(l_1)\, p_H(\bar{l}_1)] \quad (25)$$

The integral in (25) is identical to that of (10) with the exception of the sign; as such the earlier procedure holds here with a *maximization* of the probability of detection in the last equation replacing the *minimization* of the probability of error in the former one.

Procedure: Therefore, in view of Theorem 2, the procedure of optimizing consist of minimizing (β) with respect to the intervals $\bar{R}_i$ with the constraint (21) and (23).

5 Numerical and Simulation Results

We present here a computational analysis for the *CA-CFAR* and *Gaussian* examples assuming that the *priors* are known (*i.e.* Bayesian case). For the first, the problem can be formulated as

$$\begin{aligned} \mathrm{H}: \Pr(X_i \le x) &= 1 - (1+x)^{-m} \\ \mathrm{K}: \Pr(X_i \le x) &= 1 - (1 + x/(1+S))^{-m} \end{aligned} \quad (26)$$

Here we have selected m (actually the number of "reference cells" used for CA-CFAR) to be 8, the SNR $S = 10dB$, and three identical sensors [3] ; note that X_i is not the local likelihood ratio but rather a monotone transformation of it. The observations of each of the three sensors are assumed to have identical and conditionally independent statistics. The problem has been analyzed both numerically and via Monte Carlo simulation. In the first case, the probability density function of the likelihood ratio at the *DFC* (1) was computed numerically, and according to the procedure summarized at the end of section 3, a minimization routine was used to determine the optimum no-send region and the corresponding probability of error was found. Then, the minimum average error for a finite set of possible no-send regions (each one satisfying the communication rate constraint) was evaluated via Monte Carlo runs. Both results are shown in Figure 4. We can see that even for a relatively small "average communication rate constraint" (defined as in equation (2)) the system performance is good for extreme priors; that is, low π_K or π_H. Note that the censoring system performs close to optimally when one hypothesis is much more probable than the other, which is the situation of interest here. The probability of error computed via Monte Carlo simulation is very near the one computed numerically. In Figure 5 we show the upper and lower thresholds of the "no-send" region over the data axis (equation 26). We observe that as $\pi_K \to 0$ the "no-send" region is any *llr* smaller than an upper threshold; as $\pi_K \to 1$ this eventually switches to any *llr* greater than a lower threshold. For some communication rate constraints there is a region of π_k for which both extremes of the no-send region are finite and non-zero.

In the *Gaussian* example, the problem can be formulated as

$$\begin{aligned} \mathrm{H}: \; p(X_i) &= \mathcal{N}(0,1) \\ \mathrm{K}: \; p(X_i) &= \mathcal{N}(1,1) \end{aligned} \quad (27)$$

[3] Based on the fact that the *llr*'s are conditionally independent, the total communication rate constraint is here assumed to be divided in equally among the sensors. It is at present open as to whether or not this is optimal.

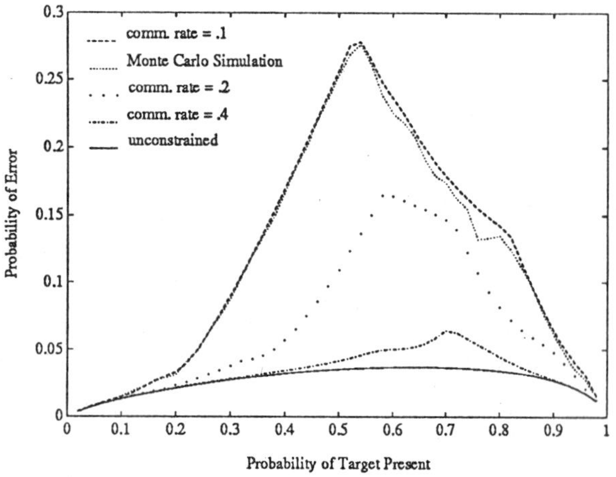

Figure 4: Probability of error for CA-CFAR problem (SNR = *10 dB*, 8-cell reference window, three sensors) versus prob. of target present for various communication rate constraint.

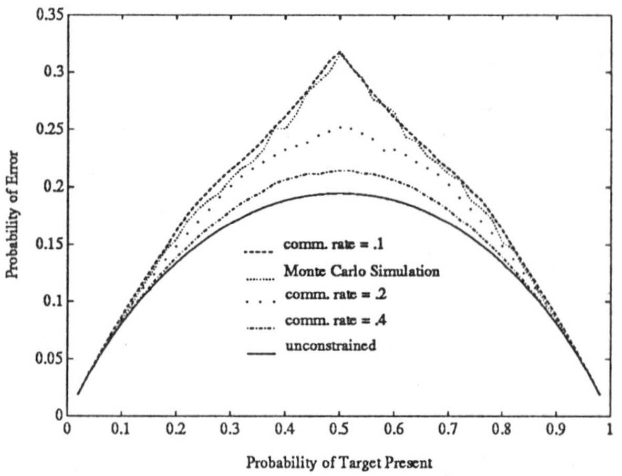

Figure 6: Probability of error for GAUSSIAN problem $\mu_H = 0$, $\mu_K = 1$, $\sigma = 1$, three sensors) versus prob. of target present for various communication rate constraint.

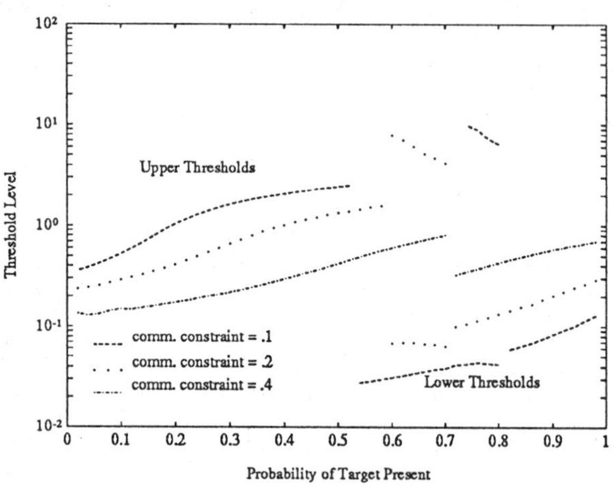

Figure 5: Upper and lower extremes for the no-send region in CA-CFAR problem (SNR = *10 dB*, 8-cell reference window, three sensors) for Various Communication Rate Constraints. (If lower threshold is not shown it is 0; if upper threshold is not shown it is ∞.)

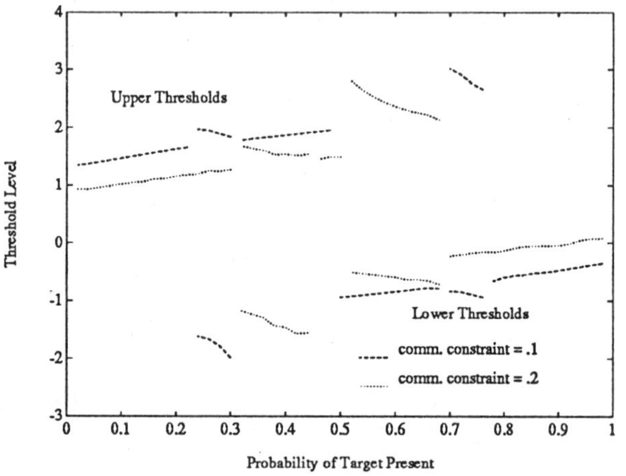

Figure 7: Upper and lower extremes for the no-send region in GAUSSIAN problem ($\mu_H = 0$, $\mu_K = 1$, $\sigma = 1$, three sensors) for Various Communication Rate Constraints. (If lower threshold is not shown it is $-\infty$; if upper threshold is not shown it is ∞.)

In Figures 6 and 7 we see the results for this example. The same conclusions as before apply to this case, with the difference being that the probability of error and no-send region are symmetric with respect to the *priors*.

6 Conclusions

The censoring scheme appears to represent a valid practical alternative to likelihood-ratio quantization, and is particularly well-suited to situations in which the prior probability of a target being present in a given resolution cell is small. The result that the no-send region is a single interval facilitates the processing of the received signal at the local sensors, and moreover, the design of the overall system is greatly simplified. The performance of the censoring scheme is very near to optimal for small π_K even with quite severe communication rate constraints.

The same conclusions, with an appropriate redefinition of the average communication rate, are valid for the Neyman-Pearson case.

References

[CV86] Z. Chair and P. Varshney. "Optimal Data Fusion in Multiple Sensor Detection". *IEEE Transactions on Aerospace and Electronic Systems*, AES-22(1):98–101, January 1986.

[TS81] R. Tenney and N. Sandell. "Detection with Distributed Sensors". *IEEE Transactions on Aerospace and Electronic Systems*, AES-17(4):501–510, July 1981.

[WW89] D. Warren and P. Willett. "Optimal Decentralized Detection for Conditionally Independent Sensors". *Proceedings of the 1989 American Control Conference*, June 1989.

Proceedings of the
American Control Conference
San Francisco, California • June 1993

Nonlinear Adaptive Joint Detection/Estimation for Multi-Radar Data Fusion

Thomas W. Hilands

Applied Research Laboratory
The Pennsylvania State University
University Park, PA 16802

Stelios C. A. Thomopoulos

Decision and Control Systems Laboratory
Dept. of Electrical and Computer Engineering
The Pennsylvania State University
University Park, PA 16802

Abstract. This paper addresses the problem of multi-sensor detection and high resolution signal parameter estimation using joint maximum a posteriori detection and high order nonlinear filtering techniques. The model-based fusion approach offers the potential for increased target resolution in range/azimuth space. The technique employs joint detection/estimation (JDE) filters for target detection and target parameter localization. The JDE approach segments the aggregate nonlinear model over the entire target resolution space into resolution subcells. This partitioning leads to extremely accurtate detection and parameter estimation. The proposed JDE approach has a built-in capability for automatic data alignment from multiple sensors, and can be used for centralized, noncentralized, and distributed data fusion.

1 Range and Azimuth Estimation from Noncolocated Sensors

Consider the situation of two spatially separated sensors, $s1$ and $s2$. The sensors are noncolocated. The colocated situation is examined in references [2] and [5]. Each of the two sensors attempts to detect and track objects coming into its respective area of coverage. The coverage of the two sensors is assumed to overlap in space, but not entirely. The sensor geometry is shown in Figure 1. In the overlap region the data received by the two sensors can be combined to get a more accurate estimate of target parameters or to estimate parameters that cannot be estimated with one sensor alone. In the overlap region the estimates from the individual sensors are combined to form improved target parameter estimates. We consider the case where each of the sensors may have different types of tracking devices such as optical trackers, various types of radars, etc. It is assumed that these sensors transmit a signal and process the echo returned from that signal. The signals are corrupted by additive Gaussian noise due to thermal effects within the receiver, and by clutter which may be due to non-Gaussian distortion such as sea clutter or other multipath spreading. Typical distributions used to model this distortion include the Rayleigh, Weibull or lognormal distributions. The thermal noise at the receiver is assumed to uncorrelated from sensor to sensor.

1.1 System Model

Assume that each sensor consists of a phased array or some other sensing device that can produce target angle estimates along with estimates of time delay. It is assumed that there are two separate measurements taken at each sensor - one measurement at each of the offset phase centers. The received signal at the pth sensor may be described by

$$\mathbf{z}_{p_k} = \mathbf{g}_{p_k} + \mathbf{u}_{p_k} + \mathbf{v}_{p_k} \qquad (1)$$

where $\mathbf{g}_{p_k}$ represents the received signal, $\mathbf{u}_{p_k}$ is the clutter, and $\mathbf{v}_{p_k}$ is the Gaussian noise at the kth sampling interval. Since there are two measurements observed at each sensor, the received signal can be more explicitly expressed as

$$\begin{bmatrix} z_{p1_k} \\ z_{p2_k} \end{bmatrix} = \begin{bmatrix} g_{p1_k} \\ g_{p2_k} \end{bmatrix} + \begin{bmatrix} u_{p1_k} \\ u_{p2_k} \end{bmatrix} + \begin{bmatrix} v_{p1_k} \\ v_{p2_k} \end{bmatrix} \qquad (2)$$

Two unknown delays, τ_{p1} and τ_{p2}, are introduced in the received signal $\mathbf{g}_{p_k}$. The delay τ_{p1} is the round-trip propagation time from the center of the sensor to the target and back to the sensor. From τ_{p1} the range to the target can be determined using the relationship

$$D_p = \frac{\tau_{p1}}{2\,c} \qquad (3)$$

where c is the speed of propagation. The delay τ_{p2} is the difference in time for the signal to reach from point P_{p1} to point P_{p2}. The difference in the propagation distance is given by $c\,\tau_{p2}$. The differential angle $\Delta\phi_p$ to the target from sensor p, which represents the difference between the sensor pointing angle ϕ_{p0} and the actual target angle ϕ_p, is then

$$\Delta\phi_p = \sin^{-1}\left(\frac{c\,\tau_{p2}}{d_p}\right) \qquad (4)$$
$$\phi_p = \phi_{p0} + \Delta\phi_p$$

where d_p is the distance between the two offset phase centers in the phased array for sensor p.

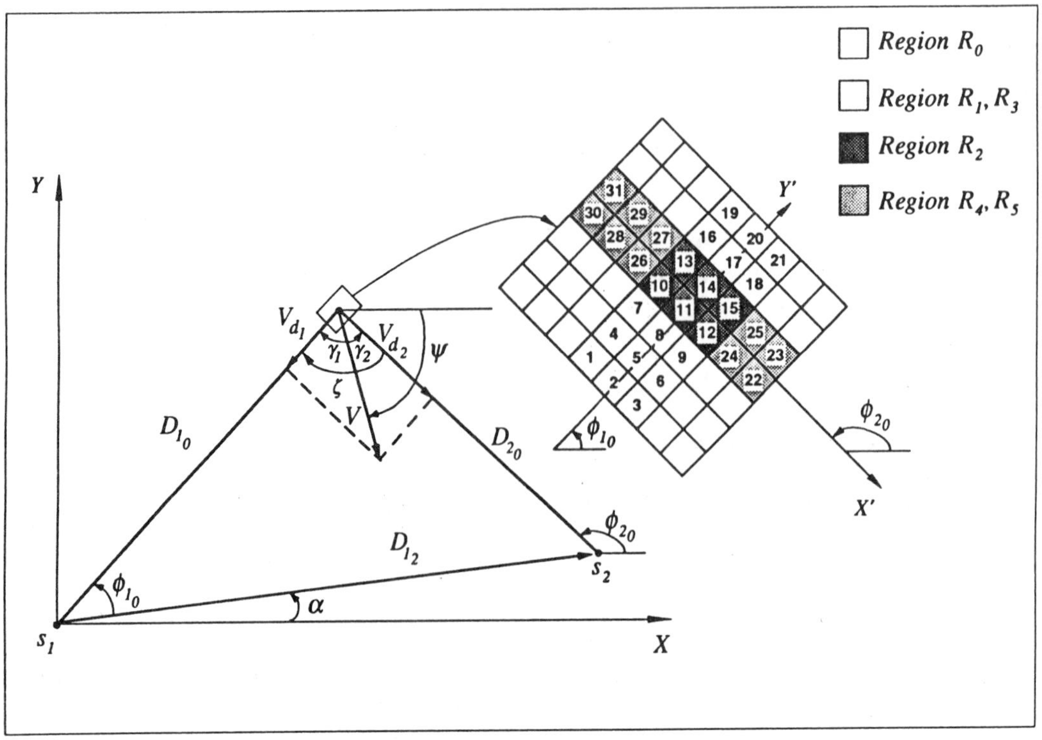

Figure 1 Sensor/Target Geometry for Multisensor Fusion

1.1.1 Single Observer Model

Using estimates of τ_{p1} and τ_{p2} from one sensor the target position can be estimated through the relations (3, and 4). Define the state variable vector for sensor p as $\mathbf{x}_{p_k} = [\tau_{p1_k}\ \tau_{p2_k}]^T$. It is assumed that the state does not change while the pulse is being reflected from it. Therefore the process dynamics are zero; that is, the state transition matrix is unity and there is no process noise. In terms of the state variables the received signal at the pth sensor is

$$\mathbf{g}_{p_k} = \begin{bmatrix} g_{p1_k} \\ g_{p2_k} \end{bmatrix} = \begin{bmatrix} a_{p1_k}(\mathbf{x}_{p_k})p_{p1_k}(\mathbf{x}_{p_k})r_{p1_k}(\mathbf{x}_{p_k}) \\ a_{p2_k}(\mathbf{x}_{p_k})p_{p2_k}(\mathbf{x}_{p_k})r_{p2_k}(\mathbf{x}_{p_k}) \end{bmatrix} \quad (5)$$

where

$$\begin{aligned} a_{pj_k}(\mathbf{x}_{p_k}) &= \frac{4A}{(c\,(x_{p_k}(1) - \kappa_j x_{p_k}(2)/2))^2} \\ p_{pj_k}(\mathbf{x}_{p_k}) &= 0.5 * (1 - \cos(2\pi\nu_p(kt_s - x_{p_k}(1) \\ &\quad + \kappa_j x_{p_k}(2)/2)/t_{w_p})) \\ r_{pj_k} &= \cos(\nu_p(\omega_p(kt_s - x_{p_k}(1) + \kappa_j x_{p_k}(2)/2))) \end{aligned} \quad (6)$$

for $j = 1, 2$. $\kappa_j = +1$ whenever $j = 1$. $\kappa_j = -1$ whenever $j = 2$. ν_p is the doppler velocity at (aasumed known in this case), A is the transmitted amplitude, and $a_{pj_k}(.)$ reflects attenuation due to spherical spreading loss. The definition of $p_{pj_k}(.)$ given above represents the Hanning pulse type with pulse width t_{w_p}. The EKF equations [4] for the constant state model given above are given by

$$\begin{aligned} K_{p_k} &= P_{p_{k-1|k-1}} H_{p_k}^T (G_{p_k} P_{p_{k-1|k-1}} G_{p_k}^T + R_{p_k}^{(2)})^{-1} \\ P_{p_{k|k}} &= (I_n - K_{p_k} G_{p_k}) P_{p_{k-1|k-1}} \\ \hat{\mathbf{x}}_{k|k} &= \hat{\mathbf{x}}_{k-1|k-1} + K_{p_k} \tilde{\mathbf{z}}_{p_k} \\ \tilde{\mathbf{z}}_{p_k} &= \mathbf{z}_{p_k} - \mathbf{g}_{p_k}(\hat{\mathbf{x}}_{k|k-1}) \end{aligned} \quad (7)$$

where $R_{p_k}^{(2)}$ is the measurement covariance, K_{p_k} is the filter gain, and G_{p_k} is the Jacobian of the measurement model. The EHOF [3,5] incorporates 3rd and 4th order estimation error and measurement error moments. However, the equations are very lengthy and are not presented here.

1.1.2 Double Observer Model

When information is available from two sensors, that is, whenever the target is in the overlap region, and the target is illuminated simultaneously by the two radars, the time delay estimates from each sensor can be combined to obtain a better estimate of target position.

Let X' and Y' denote the directions of a local coordinate system as shown in the insert in Figure 1. Let ϕ_{1_0} and ϕ_{2_0}, the pointing angles of the two sensors, be chosen such that $\phi_{2_0} - \phi_{1_0} = 90$ deg. In this case the direction X' points directly along the line of sight (LOS) of s_2, and perpendicular to the LOS of s_1. Likewise, Y' points directly along the LOS of s_1 and perpendicular to the LOS of s_2. X' is the in-track direction for s_1 and the cross-track direction for s_2. Y' is it in-track direction for s_2 and the cross-track direction for s_1. For small angles $\Delta\phi_p$ such that $\sin(\Delta\phi_p \approx 0)$, the position estimates in the X', Y' coordinate system, which can be found from either sensor, are given by

$$\begin{aligned} \hat{O}_{x'_1} &= D_{1_0} c\hat{\tau}_{12}/d_1 \\ \hat{O}_{x'_2} &= -(c\hat{\tau}_{21}/2 - D_{2_0}) \\ \hat{O}_{y'_1} &= (c\hat{\tau}_{11}/2 - D_{1_0}) \\ \hat{O}_{y'_2} &= D_{2_0} c\hat{\tau}_{22}/d_2 \end{aligned} \tag{8}$$

where D_{p_0} is the nominal range from sensor p to the center of the insert in Figure 1. The associated position error variances are given by

$$\begin{aligned} \sigma^2_{x'_1} &= D^2_{1_0} c^2 \mathrm{Var}[\tau_{12}]/d_1^2 \\ \sigma^2_{x'_2} &= c^2 \mathrm{Var}[\tau_{21}]/4 \\ \sigma^2_{y'_1} &= c^2 \mathrm{Var}[\tau_{11}]/4 \\ \sigma^2_{y'_2} &= D^2_{2_0} c^2 \mathrm{Var}[\tau_{22}]/d_2^2 \end{aligned} \tag{9}$$

If it is assumed that the time delay estimation errors have Gaussian distributions, then the maximum likelihood estimates of the target position in the overlap region D_2, which are the weighted sums of the estimates at each sensor, are given by

$$\hat{O}_{x'} = \frac{\sigma^2_{x'_2} D_{1_0} c\hat{\tau}_{12}/d_1 - \sigma^2_{x'_1}(c\hat{\tau}_{21}/2 - D_{2_0})}{\sigma^2_{x'_1}\sigma^2_{x'_2}} \tag{10}$$

$$\hat{O}_{y'} = \frac{\sigma^2_{y'_2}(c\hat{\tau}_{11}/2 - D_{1_0}) + \sigma^2_{y'_1} D_{2_0} c\hat{\tau}_{22}/d_1}{\sigma^2_{y'_1}\sigma^2_{y'_2}} \tag{11}$$

1.2 Joint Detection/Estimation

The joint detection/estimation (JDE) is an extension of a procedure originally described by Lainiotis [1]. The JDE technique is completely described in reference [5]. In the sequel we concentrate on the specific application of multisensor fusion. Assume that the target search region has been localized to the rectangular box shown in Figure 1. This box is subdivided into several resolution cells as shown in this figure. The beam pattern from sensor s_1 allows this sensor to detect a target and estimate its parameters if the target is located in resolution cells 1 through 21. Sensor s_2 can detect the target if it is in cells 11 through 15, 22 through 25, or 26 through 31. If the target is not located in any of these cells then the target is declared not present (or more precisely, not detectable) . This situation is represented by the null hypothesis H_0. The resolution cells are grouped into regions which will be used for minimum mean square error estimation. If the target is located in regions R_1 (resolution cells 1 through 9) or R_3 (resolution cells 16 through 21) only sensor s_1 can detect the target. Regions R_4 (resolution cells 22 through 25) and R_5 (resolution cells 26 through 31) correspond to the coverage area of sensor s_2 only. If the target is located in region R_2 (resolution cells 10 through 15) both sensors can detect the target and perform parameter estimation. The remaining area in the rectangle in Figure 1is designated as region R_0, where neither sensor can detect the target.

Let $\theta_i \in \Theta$ designate the parameter vector that describes the different combination of model uncertainty and initial condition uncertainty. The parameter vector θ_i is assumed to be time invariant. The parameter vector θ_i, $1 \leq i \leq 56$ is defined to be the ith resolution cell and is used to define 56 different combinations initial conditions and models. i corresponds to the range resolution cell number determined from the initial conditions on the two time delays from each sensor. θ_0 corresponds to the null hypothesis, i.e. noise only data.

Hypothesis H_i, representing the hypothesis that the target is located in resolution cell i, is defined by

$$H_i : \begin{cases} \mathbf{z}_{1_k} = \mathbf{g}_{1_k} + \mathbf{u}_{1_k} + \mathbf{v}_{1_k} \\ \mathbf{z}_{2_k} = \mathbf{g}_{1_k} + \mathbf{u}_{2_k} + \mathbf{v}_{2_k} \end{cases} \tag{12}$$

In regions R_1, R_2, and R_3, where sensor s_1 can detect the target, the component g_{1m_k} is defined by (5) as

$$g_{1m_k} = \begin{cases} a_{1m_k}(.)p_{1m_k}(.)r_{1m_k}(.) & \hat{\tau}_{1m_{i_k}} \leq k\,t_s \\ & k\,t_s < \hat{\tau}_{1m_{i_k}} + t_{w_1} \\ 0 & \text{otherwise} \end{cases} \tag{13}$$

In the regions R_0, R_4 and R_5, $g_{1m_k} = 0$, $\forall\ k$, $m = 1,2$. The delay $\hat{\tau}_{pm_{i_k}}$ is given by

$$\hat{\tau}_{pm_{i_k}} = \hat{\tau}_{p1_{i_k}} + \kappa_m \hat{\tau}_{p2_{i_k}} \tag{14}$$

where $\kappa_m = +1$ whenever $m = 1$, and $\kappa_m = -1$ whenever $m = 2$. In regions R_2, R_4, and R_5, where sensor s_2 can detect the target, the component g_{2m_k} is defined by (5) as

$$g_{2m_k} = \begin{cases} a_{2m_k}(.)p_{2m_k}(.)r_{2m_k}(.) & \hat{\tau}_{2m_{i_k}} \leq k\,t_s \\ & k\,t_s < \hat{\tau}_{2m_{i_k}} + t_{w_2} \\ 0 & \text{otherwise} \end{cases} \tag{15}$$

In the regions R_0, R_1 and R_3, $g_{2m_k} = 0$, $\forall\ k$, $m = 1,2$.

The initial conditions are given by

$$\begin{aligned} \hat{x}_{p_{0|0,\theta_i}} &= [\hat{\tau}_{p1_{i_0}}, \hat{\tau}_{p2_{i_0}}]^T \\ P_{p_{0|0,\theta_i}} &= \mathrm{Diag}\left[\mathrm{Var}[\hat{\tau}_{p1_{i_0}}], \mathrm{Var}[\hat{\tau}_{p2_{i_0}}],\right] \end{aligned} \tag{16}$$

The initial estimates $\hat{\tau}_{p1_{i_0}}, \hat{\tau}_{p2_{i_0}}, p = 1,2$ are chosen such that the position of the target for a signal received ate sensor p is at the center of resolution cell i. The variances $\mathrm{Var}[\hat{\tau}_{p1_{i_0}}]$ and $\mathrm{Var}[\hat{\tau}_{p2_{i_0}}]$ are determined based on a uniform distribution of the error within the cell.

Define $\mathbf{Z}_k = [\mathbf{z}_1, \mathbf{z}_2, \cdots \mathbf{z}_k]$, where $\mathbf{z}_k = [\mathbf{z}^T_{1_k}, \mathbf{z}^T_{2_k}]^T$, as the set of measurements up to time k, and let $p(\mathbf{z}_k|\mathbf{Z}_{k-1}, \theta_i)$ be the probability density function of $\mathbf{z}_k$ given the measurements $\mathbf{Z}_{k-1}$ and hypothesis H_i. The *a posteriori* probability of hypothesis H_i is given by

$$P(\theta_i|\mathbf{Z}_k) = \frac{P(\theta_i|\mathbf{Z}_{k-1})\,\Lambda_i(\mathbf{z}_k)}{\sum_{m=0}^{N} P(\theta_m|\mathbf{Z}_{k-1})\,\Lambda_m(\mathbf{z}_k)} \tag{17}$$

where $\Lambda_i(\mathbf{z}_k)$ is the likelihood ratio defined by

$$\Lambda_k(\mathbf{z}_k) = \frac{p(\mathbf{z}_k|\mathbf{Z}_{k-1}, \theta_k)}{p(\mathbf{z}_k|\mathbf{Z}_{k-1}, \theta_0)} \tag{18}$$

The minimum mean squared error estimate can be found by combining the estimates from all of the cells within a particular region. If the state vector $\mathbf{x}_k$ is common to all models the minimum mean squared error (MMSE) estimate can be used. The MMSE estimate for sensor p in region R_r can be expressed as

$$\hat{\mathbf{x}}^*_{p_k|k} = \sum_{\text{cell}_i \in R_r} P(\theta_i|\mathbf{Z}_k)\,\hat{\mathbf{x}}_{p_{k|k,\theta_i}}. \quad (19)$$

The most likely region is selected using the MAP criterion. Define as the hypothesis that the target is located in region R_r as I_r, $r = 0, 1, \cdots, 5$. The *a posteriori* probability associated with region R_r is the sum of the *a posteriori* probabilities of all of the cells in that region. This region-level probability is given by

$$P(I_r|\mathbf{Z}_k) = \sum_{\text{cell}_i \in R_r} P(\theta_i|\mathbf{Z}_k) \quad (20)$$

The most likely region is chosen such that

$$\text{Choose} \quad I_r \quad : \quad r = \text{argmax}_{r=0,\cdots,5,\theta_i \in \Theta} P(I_r|\mathbf{Z}_k) \quad (21)$$

1.2.1 Definition of Priors

The *a priori* probabilities of each hypothesis are based on the area coverage of the sensors. The total number of resolution cells shown in Figure 1 is 56. Of these, 25 are located in region R_0. All cells are assumed to have an equal probability containing the target. The *a priori* probabilities are given by $P(\theta_0) = 25/56$, $P(\theta_i) = 1/56$, $i = 1, 2, \cdots 31$. The probabilities associated with regions R_r, $r = 0, 1, \cdots, 5$ are given by $P(I_0) = 25/56$, $P(I_1) = 9/56$, $P(I_2) = 6/56$, $P(I_3) = 6/56$, $P(I_4) = 4/56$, and $P(I_5) = 6/56$.

1.3 Simulation Experiments

An experimental study was conducted to evaluate the performance of the multi-sensor fusion technique. In this evaluation the measurement noise consisted of 50% Log-normal Noise and 50% Gaussian noise. The nominal angles from sensors s_1 and s_2 to the target were $\phi_{1_0} = 45$ deg and $\phi_{2_0} = 135$ deg, respectively. The nominal range from s_1 to the target was $D_1 = 10$ miles. The nominal range from sensor s_2 to the target D_2 was chosen such that the received signal at s_2 was 5 dB higher than at s_1 for the same transmitted signal level and target strength.

The carrier frequencies used by the two sensors were the same at $f_c = 10 \times 10^6$. They both sample the signal at a rate $f_s = 100 \times 10^6$, and both signals have the same pulse width $t_{wp} = 12/f_s$, $p = 1, 2$. The resolution cell width is $1/f_s$ seconds. The associated initial error variance on time delays τ_{11_0} and τ_{21_0} is $t_s^2/12$. The corresponding range resolution cell width is $\Delta r_p = c/(2f_s)$. Thus, the initial variance for the angle-measurement delays is (4) $\text{Var}[\tau_{12_0}] = ((d_p c)/(2f_s D_p))^2/12$, $p = 1, 2$. d_p, the separation between phase centers at the sensor was chosen to be 3 feet for each sensor. Simulations were performed for SNR's (at sensor s_1) ranging from -10dB to 10dB. 500 random target positions were chosen at each SNR. Of these 500 trials, 228 target positions randomly chosen in region R_0, 91 in R_1, 54 in R_2, 44 in R_3, 40 in R_4, and 40 in R_5.

The probabilities of missed detection $P(I_0|I_r)$ and correct classification (i.e. not only detection of the target but correct localization at the region level) $P(I_r|I_r)$, $r = 1, \cdots, 5$ are displayed in Table 1. The probability of misclassification, which is not shown in this table, is given by $P(I_q|I_r) = 1 - P(I_r|I_r) - P(I_0|I_r)$, $q \neq r$. Sensor s_2 outperforms sensor s_1, which is to be expected since the SNR at s_1 is 5 dB higher than the SNR at sensor s_2. In the overlap region, R_2, the classification performance is much better than it is for any other region, with an 85% probability of correct classification.

Table 1. Probabilities of Missed Detection and Correct Classification - Region Level

SNR(dB)		Probability		
		$r = 1, 3$	$r = 2$	$r = 4, 5$
-10	$P(I_0\|I_r)$	0.40	0.074	0.16
	$P(I_r\|I_r)$	0.53	0.85	0.79
-5	$P(I_0\|I_r)$	0.16	0.019	0.024
	$P(I_r\|I_r)$	0.84	0.96	0.98
0	$P(I_0\|I_r)$	0.022	0.0	0.023
	$P(I_r\|I_r)$	0.98	1.0	0.98
5	$P(I_0\|I_r)$	0.0	0.0	0.0
	$P(I_r\|I_r)$	1.0	1.0	1.0
10	$P(I_0\|I_r)$	0.0	0.0	0.0
	$P(I_r\|I_r)$	1.0	1.0	1.0

The estimation results are shown in Figure 2. All results shown in this figure are in reference to the (X', Y') coordinate system. Figure 2(a) shows the average mean squared error for those detections in regions R_1 and R_3, in which only s_1 has coverage. Figure 2(c) shows similar results for regions R_4 and R_5, which are covered by sensor s_2. Figure 2(c) also illustrates the 5 dB performance for sensor s_2 over that for s_1. Figure 2(b) shows the results for both sensors in region R_2. In this region, as shown in Table 3 the proper cell is almost always found. Thus the cross-range estimation error variance should improve by about 6 dB (20log(2)) for sensor s_2, since the cross-range error for s_2 has been localized from 2 cells down to 1. Similarly, the cross-range error variance for sensor s_1 in Region R_2 is reduced by about 10 dB (20log(3)) since the target has been localized from 3 cells down to 1. This improvement is evident in Figure 2(b). Figure 2(d) shows the estimation results using the combined measurents obtained from (10, 11). Because of the larger variance in the cross-range error for each sensor and the fact that the intersection of the LOS's between the two sensors are perpendicular, the combined estimate consists of the X' estimate from sensor s_2 and the Y' estimate from sensor s_1.

2 Conclusion

A model-based adaptive detection/estimation approach has been presented for multi-sensor fusion. It is shown that excellent performance can be obtained for both target detection and target parameter estimation using this technique. A significant advantage of this technique is that each sensor can perform detection and parameter estimation in a decentralized mode. The final estimates and a *posteriori* probabilities from each sensor are processed by a centralized processor to derive the optimum estimate. The method provides an automatic referencing mechanism of the data from the different sensors (automatic data alignment) as long as the geometry and timing of the sweeping beams are known. For optimal target resolution performance, it is found that the lines of sight of the two sensors should be perpendicular to each other at any given time, requiring special synchronization.

References

1 D. G. Lainiotis, "Optimal Adaptive Estimation : Structure and Parameter Adaptation," *IEEE Trans. Automatic Control,* vol. AC-16, no. 2, pp. 160–170, April, 1971.

2 S. C. A. Thomopoulos and T. W. Hilands, "Nonlinear Adaptive Detection/Estimation for Single and Multiple Radar Processing," *IEEE MILCOM '92,* October 11-14, 1992, San Diego, CA.

3 T. W. Hilands and S. C. A. Thomopoulos, "High Order Filters for Estimation in Non-Gaussian Noise," *Canadian Conference on Electrical and Computer Engineering, CCECE-92,* Toronto, Canada, Sept. 13-16, 1992.

4 A. Gelb (Ed), *Applied Optimal Estimation,* MIT Press, 1974.

5 T. W. Hilands, "High Order Nonlinear Estimation with Signal Processing Applications," *Ph. D. Thesis,* The Pennsylvania State University, 1992.

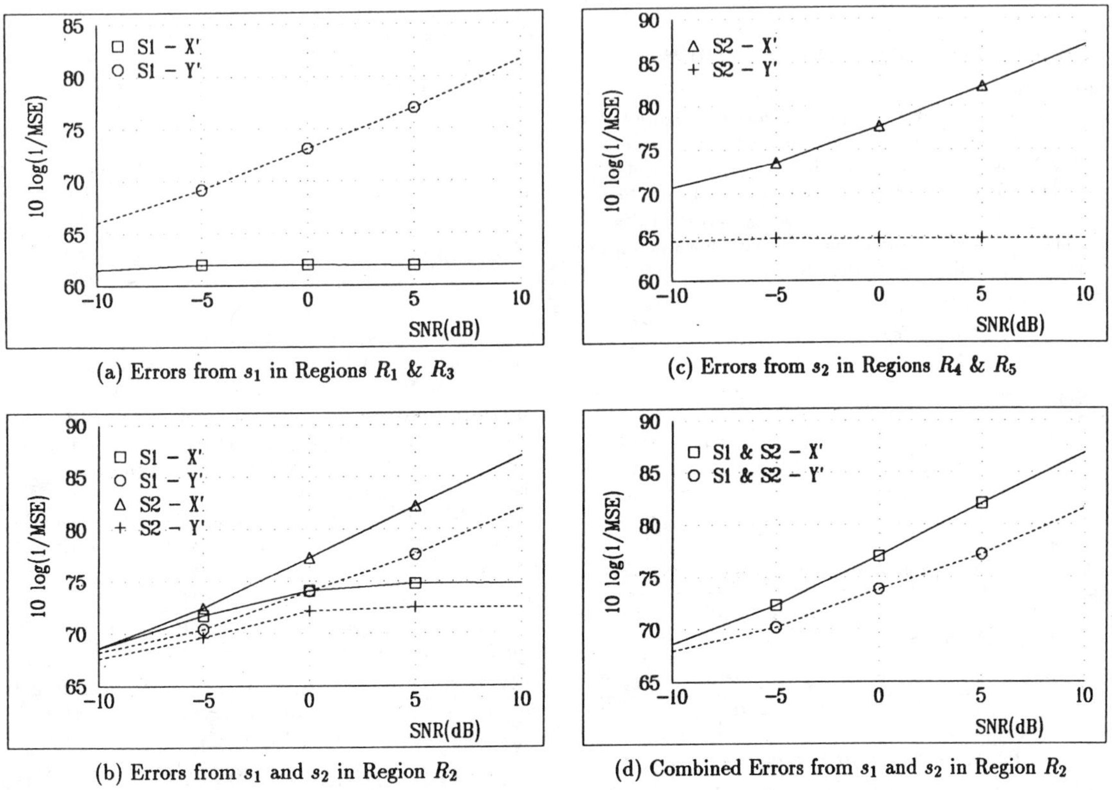

(a) Errors from s_1 in Regions R_1 & R_3

(c) Errors from s_2 in Regions R_4 & R_5

(b) Errors from s_1 and s_2 in Region R_2

(d) Combined Errors from s_1 and s_2 in Region R_2

Figure 2 Multisensor Fusion In-Track and Cross-Track Estimation Errors

Proceedings of the
American Control Conference
San Francisco, California • June 1993

A Nonparametric Training Algorithm for Decentralized Binary Hypothesis Testing Networks

John Wissinger Michael Athans
Department of Electrical Engineering and Computer Science
Massachusetts Institute of Technology
Cambridge, MA 02139

Abstract

We present a distributed nonparametric minimum-error training algorithm for networks of linear threshold classifiers performing decentralized binary hypothesis testing (detection). The training algorithm consists of communicating stochastic approximation algorithms. Knowledge of the network topology is required by the algorithm. We suggest that models of the variety in this study provide a paradigm for the study of adaptation in human decision making organizations.

1 Introduction

We have been attempting to develop a normative theory of training and adapatation in human decision making organizations by devising algorithms which train decentralized binary hypothesis testing (detection) networks to optimize a given measure of organizational performance [5].

In this paper, we propose that this problem may be solved in distributed fashion by a set of communicating stochastic approximation algorithms. In particular, we suggest that each decision agent, hereafter denoted decision maker (DM), solve a sequence of one-dimensional stochastic approximation subproblems, each of which is coupled to similar subproblems throughout the network. The decentralization is overcome through communication, which for the purposes of this paper we allow to occur in unrestricted fashion during training.

2 Example Network: Three-Member V

A representative network for which we will demonstrate the algorithm is the three-member V topology (3-Vee) shown in Figure 1. We consider the case of conditionally independent real-valued scalar observations. The decision criterion is the minimum probability of error criterion for DM C. Each DM chooses messages from the set $\{0, 1\}$.

The necessary conditions for optimality of the decision rules γ_A, γ_B, and γ_C under the above assumptions are well known and given by the following coupled likelihood ratio tests.
For DM C, given γ_A and γ_B:

$$\frac{p_{Y_C|H_1}(y_C|H_1)}{p_{Y_C|H_0}(y_C|H_0)} \underset{u_C=0}{\overset{u_C=1}{\gtrless}} \begin{cases} \eta\frac{(1-P_F^A)(1-P_F^B)}{(1-P_D^A)(1-P_D^B)} & \text{if } u_A = 0, u_B = 0 \\ \eta\frac{(1-P_F^A)P_F^B}{(1-P_D^A)P_D^B} & \text{if } u_A = 0, u_B = 1 \\ \eta\frac{P_F^A(1-P_F^B)}{P_D^A(1-P_D^B)} & \text{if } u_A = 1, u_B = 0 \\ \eta\frac{P_F^A P_F^B}{P_D^A P_D^B} & \text{if } u_A = 1, u_B = 1 \end{cases} \tag{2.1}$$

For DM A, given γ_B and γ_C:

$$\frac{p_{Y_A|H_1}(y_A|H_1)}{p_{Y_A|H_0}(y_A|H_0)} \underset{u_A=0}{\overset{u_A=1}{\gtrless}} \eta\frac{(1-P_F^B)[P_F^{C(10)} - P_F^{C(00)}] + P_F^B[P_F^{C(11)} - P_F^{C(01)}]}{(1-P_D^B)[P_D^{C(10)} - P_D^{C(00)}] + P_D^B[P_D^{C(11)} - P_D^{C(01)}]} \tag{2.2}$$

For DM B, given γ_A and γ_C:

$$\frac{p_{Y_B|H_1}(y_B|H_1)}{p_{Y_B|H_0}(y_B|H_0)} \underset{u_B=0}{\overset{u_B=1}{\gtrless}} \eta\frac{(1-P_F^A)[P_F^{C(01)} - P_F^{C(00)}] + P_F^A[P_F^{C(11)} - P_F^{C(10)}]}{(1-P_D^A)[P_D^{C(01)} - P_D^{C(00)}] + P_D^A[P_D^{C(11)} - P_D^{C(10)}]} \tag{2.3}$$

where $\eta = p_0/p_1$, (P_F^A, P_D^A) and (P_F^B, P_D^B) are the operating points of DMs A and B, and $(P_F^{C(ij)}, P_D^{C(ij)})$ denotes the operating point of DM C given it has received messages $u_A = i, u_B = j$ with $i, j \in \{0, 1\}$.

For the Gaussian detection problem, the decision rules of equations (2.1) - (2.3) may be reduced to an equivalent set of linear threshold rules for which we denote the observation threshold of DM A by α, DM B by β, and the thresholds of DM C by ξ_{ij}, for $i, j \in \{0, 1\}$.

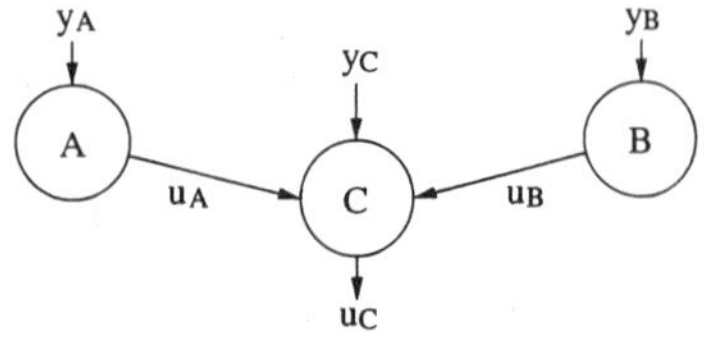

Figure 1: 3-Vee

3 The Network Training Algorithm

Training refers to the use of a set of correctly classified examples to minimize the imprecisely known probability of error function. Each training example consists of a set of observations for the network together with the desired network output, i.e. the acting hypothesis. We assume that during training the statistics according to which the observations are generated are stationary.

Roots of the equation

$$G(y) = \lambda_0 p_0 p_{Y|H_0}(y|H_0) + \lambda_1 p_1 p_{Y|H_1}(y|H_1) \tag{3.4}$$

where λ_0 and λ_1 are scalar constants, satisfy the necessary conditions for an observation threshold to minimize the Bayes risk, where λ_0 and λ_1 represent the costs of each type of error. The authors of [4] have shown, for a broad class of densities, that a sequence of points $\{\theta_k\}$ converging asymptotically (w.p.1) to a root of $G(y)$ is generated by a modified Robbins-Monro algorithm [2] of the form

$$\theta_{k+1} = \theta_k + \rho_k Z(y_k, \theta_k) \tag{3.5}$$

where θ_k is the threshold at time k, ρ_k is a decreasing positive stepsize, and $Z_k(y_k, \theta_k)$ is a random variable on the data given by

$$Z_k(y_k, \theta_k) = \begin{cases} +2L & \text{if } |\theta_k - y_k| \leq \delta_k,\ y_k \text{ from } H_0 \\ 0 & \text{if } |\theta_k - y_k| > \delta_k \\ -2(1-L) & \text{if } |\theta_k - y_k| \leq \delta_k,\ y_k \text{ from } H_1 \end{cases} \tag{3.6}$$

where y_k is the observation, δ_k is a decreasing positive window width, and $L = \lambda_0/(\lambda_0 + \lambda_1)$. Note the assumption that *a priori* the relative positions of H_0 and H_1 are known. This algorithm is actually a special case, using a rectangular window, of a more general algorithm which can employ several types of windows [3]. Furthermore, the Kiefer-Wolfowitz [1] approach yields algorithms similar in form to the above.

For 3-Vee, the roots of each of the following system of six coupled nonlinear equations (cf. (2.1)-(2.3)) satisfy the necessary conditions for optimality.

$$\begin{aligned} G_C^{00}(y_C) &= [(1-P_F^A)(1-P_F^B)]p_0 p_{Y_C|H_0}(y_C|H_0) \\ &+ [(1-P_D^A)(1-P_D^B)]p_1 p_{Y_C|H_1}(y_C|H_1) \\ G_C^{01}(y_C) &= [(1-P_F^A)P_F^B]p_0 p_{Y_C|H_0}(y_C|H_0) + [(1-P_D^A)P_D^B]p_1 p_{Y_C|H_1}(y_C|H_1) \\ G_C^{10}(y_C) &= [P_F^A(1-P_F^B)]p_0 p_{Y_C|H_0}(y_C|H_0) + [P_D^A(1-P_D^B)]p_1 p_{Y_C|H_1}(y_C|H_1) \\ G_C^{11}(y_C) &= [P_F^A P_F^B]p_0 p_{Y_C|H_0}(y_C|H_0) + [P_D^A P_D^B]p_1 p_{Y_C|H_1}(y_C|H_1) \\ G_B(y_B) &= [(1-P_F^B)(P_F^{C(10)} - P_F^{C(00)}) + P_F^B(P_F^{C(11)} - P_F^{C(01)})]p_0 p_{Y_B|H_0}(y_B|H_0) \\ &+ [(1-P_D^B)(P_D^{C(10)} - P_D^{C(00)}) + P_D^B(P_D^{C(11)} - P_D^{C(01)})]p_1 p_{Y_B|H_1}(y_B|H_1) \\ G_A(y_A) &= [(1-P_F^A)(P_F^{C(01)} - P_F^{C(00)}) + P_F^A(P_F^{C(11)} - P_F^{C(10)})]p_0 p_{Y_A|H_0}(y_A|H_0) \\ &+ [(1-P_D^A)(P_D^{C(01)} - P_D^{C(00)}) + P_D^A(P_D^{C(11)} - P_D^{C(10)})]p_1 p_{Y_A|H_1}(y_A|H_1) \end{aligned}$$

The coupling probabilities of each DM are constants, given that the decision rules of the other DMs are held fixed.

Given the statistics, one may uniquely solve this system of equations by iteration to a fixed point, provided that the system possesses a contraction property. Although we have been unable to prove this

*This work was supported by the National Science Foundation through an NSF Graduate Fellowship and under Grant NSF/IRI-8902755 (under a subcontract from the University of Connecticut)

property directly, our success with Gaussian simulations suggests, for that case at least, that the property may hold. We therefore propose a network training algorithm which solves the above system without knowledge of the statistics through iterative stochastic approximations. For 3-Vee, the thresholds $\xi_{ij}, i, j \in \{0, 1\}$ and β are initialized and held fixed while estimates of the corresponding operating points $(\hat{P}_F^{C(ij)}, \hat{P}_D^{C(ij)})$ and $(\hat{P}_F^B, \hat{P}_D^B)$ are obtained by measuring empirical relative frequencies over the training data. These estimated operating points are then communicated to DM A which computes the coupling coefficients $\hat{\lambda}_0 = [(1 - \hat{P}_F^A)(\hat{P}_F^{C(01)} - \hat{P}_F^{C(00)}) + \hat{P}_F^A(\hat{P}_F^{C(11)} - \hat{P}_F^{C(10)})]$ and $\hat{\lambda}_1 = [(1 - \hat{P}_D^A)(\hat{P}_D^{C(01)} - \hat{P}_D^{C(00)}) + \hat{P}_D^A(\hat{P}_D^{C(11)} - \hat{P}_D^{C(10)})]$, and then incorporates them as stepsize bias to solve for the corresponding root α of $G_A(y_A)$ using the local algorithm

$$\alpha_{k+1} = \begin{cases} \alpha_k + 2L\rho_k & \text{if } |\alpha_k - y_{A(k)}| \leq \delta_k,\ y_{A(k)} \text{ from } H_0 \\ \alpha_k & \text{if } |\alpha_k - y_{A(k)}| > \delta_k \\ \alpha_k - 2(1-L)\rho_k & \text{if } |\alpha_k - y_{A(k)}| \leq \delta_k,\ y_{A(k)} \text{ from } H_1 \end{cases} \tag{3.7}$$

with $L = \hat{\lambda}_0/(\hat{\lambda}_0 + \hat{\lambda}_1)$. Once the algorithm has generated a value of α, it is held fixed while the corresponding operating point $(\hat{P}_F^A, \hat{P}_D^A)$ is estimated. DM B then receives the estimated operating points from A and C, solves a local problem and so on. Local problems are solved in this manner in iterative fashion until some suitable criterion of convergence is met.

Due to space limitations, we present simulations only for the linear Gaussian case with parameters

$$\mu_0 = 1,\ \mu_1 = 3,\ \sigma_A^2 = \sigma_B^2 = \sigma_C^2 = 1,\ p_1 = 0.25 \tag{3.8}$$

Heuristics for choosing the stepsize and window sequences, as well as initial conditions for the local problem are discussed at length in [3]. For our simulations we used $\rho_k = 1/\sqrt{k}$ and $\delta_k = 2.25/\sqrt{k}$ as suggested in [4], and chose the value 2 as the initial condition for all subproblems as it lies in a region of significant probability density.

Figure 2 shows the paths travelled by the thresholds of 3-Vee, α, β, ξ_{00}, ξ_{01}, ξ_{10}, ξ_{11} during training. The paths for the exact successive approximation solution are shown along with the approximating paths resulting from the training algorithm. So that the paths of the exact successive approximation and the training would be comparable, both used the same initial values of $\beta = 0$, $\xi_{00} = 0$, $\xi_{01} = 1$, $\xi_{10} = 2$, $\xi_{11} = 3$. The spikes that appear on the graphs result from the fact that the initial steps of the window algorithm are large. Each spike marks the beginning of a new subproblem which is initiated after the DM receives the necessary coupling probabilities from the other DMs.

The simulations we present used 500 training examples for each subproblem, and each subproblem was rerun 15 times with independent noise on each pass and then averaged to smooth the curves. That is, each plotted threshold point represents an average over 15 points. In addition, at the end of each subproblem an additional 1000 trials were used to effectively estimate the coupling probabilities. Thus, the total number of trials is given by

$$\begin{aligned} \#\, trials &= (6 \text{ thresholds}) \cdot (15 \text{ subproblems/threshold}) \\ &\cdot\ [(500 \text{ trials/pass}) \cdot (15 \text{ passes/subproblem}) \\ &+\ (1000 \text{ estimation trials/subproblem})] = 765,000 \end{aligned}$$

including the averaging. We have made no attempt to minimize the required computation to this point.

4 Discussion

The number of trials required to adequately solve a given DM's subproblems depends on the noisiness of its observations, while the total number of subproblems which must be solved is highly dependent on the degree of coupling between the DMs and the overall size of the network. It is also clear that the algorithm requires the network LRTs in order to structure the computation of the coupling probabilities. This is equivalent to saying that each DM must know how it is tied in structurally to the organization, but it can be initially naive to the capabilities of the other DMs since it can infer them during training.

Distributed communicating stochastic approximation algorithms appear to be a viable methodology for determining the optimal observation thresholds in decentralized binary hypothesis testing networks. We are currently doing convergence analysis as well as investigating asynchronous implementations and techniques for minimizing the required communication. We believe that an understanding of the processes by which decision making organizations adapt to improve performance has been slow in coming, primarily because there is a notable lack of normative theory which addresses the inherent difficulties and fundamental limitations of learning in distributed environments. Enhancing this understanding is a long term goal of our research.

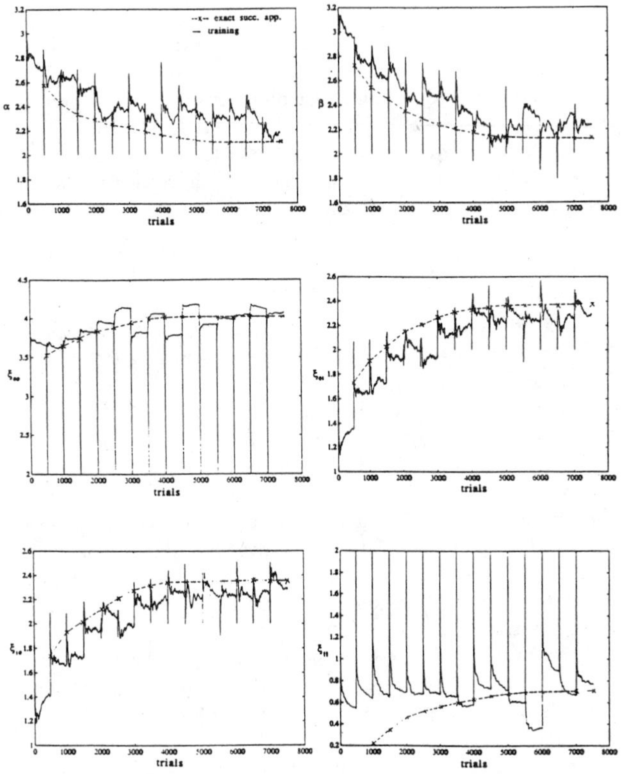

Figure 2: Motion of 3-Vee Thresholds during Training

References

[1] Kiefer, J. and J. Wolfowitz. Stochastic estimation of the maximum of a regression function. *Ann. Mathematical Statistics*, 23:462–466, 1952.

[2] Robbins, H. and S. Monro. A Stochastic Approximation Method. *Ann. Mathematical Statistics*, 22:400–407, 1951.

[3] Sklansky, J. and G. Wassel. *Pattern Classifiers and Trainable Machines*. Springer-Verlag, 1981.

[4] Wassel, G. and J. Sklansky. Training a One-Dimensional Classifier to Minimize the Probability of Error. *IEEE Trans. on Systems, Man, and Cybernetics*, SMC-2(4), Sept. 1972.

[5] Wissinger, J.W. *Training Algorithms for Decentralized Binary Hypothesis Testing Networks*. PhD thesis, M.I.T., expected Sept. 1993.

Proceedings of the
American Control Conference
San Francisco, California • June 1993

Variable Structure Control of Multi-Machine Power System

Govindaraju V. Subbarao
Nevada Power Company
6226 West Sahara Avenue
Las Vegas, NV 89151

Ashok Iyer
Electrical and Computer Engineering
University of Nevada-Las Vegas
Las Vegas, NV 89154

Abstract

Modern microprocessor capabilities permit the control designer to consider using relatively complicated nonlinear control algorithms, which would have been considered impractical in the past. The paper presents the results of a study of the variable structure control technique for the design of excitation and governor controllers for a multi machine power system. Control laws for rotor angle and field flux are derived. The closed loop system is shown to be asymptotically stable. The system can be transferred to a new operating condition corresponding to any desired terminal voltage V_t and tie-line power P_{tie}.

1 Introduction

The control of power systems consisting of interconnected networks of transmission lines linking generators and loads is an important problem. Ideally, the loads must be fed at constant voltage and frequency at all times. In practical terms, this means that both voltage and frequency must be held within close tolerances. It is also necessary that machines do not lose synchronism following a system fault. Random power impacts occur during the normal operation of a power system; this added power must be supplied by the generators. Further it is required to maintain a scheduled power exchange over the tie line in the interconnected system. The controller must be designed to perform these functions.

Some attempts have been made to design controllers for the nonlinear models of power systems[1]-[13]. In this paper, variable structure control theory is applied to the design of excitation and governor controllers using state variable feedback.

In a Variable Structure System, the control law is a discontinuous function of the state variables and switches when the trajectory crosses a prescribed hypersurface in the state space. The controller is such that the trajectories beginning from any initial condition are forced to the discontinuity surface and then are confined to it. The motion on the discontinuity surface is called the "Sliding Motion" and, interestingly, the motion during this phase is insensitive to uncertainty in the system.

Our objective in this paper is to design a nonlinear integrated excitation and governor control system so that the closed-loop system is stable in a large region in state space, and asymptotically tracks the nominal terminal voltage, frequency, and tie-line power flow under load and parameter variations. In this study, rotor angle δ and the generator voltage E are chosen as the controlled outputs for each generator. Indeed, δ and E are the basic variables which are directly influenced by the mechanical input torque to the synchronous machine and the field voltage, respectively. In stability analysis, δ is assumed to be an important variable. The controlled inputs are the governor valve and exciter-angle actuating signals.

The basic approach taken in this paper, is to control the rotor angle δ and the generator voltage E of each of the generators in the system using the variable structure control. Further, responses δ and E are independently controlled by the command inputs of the respective subsystems. The load fluctuations do not have any effect on E. E therefore stays at its nominal value even when the load is changing.

The organization of this paper is as follows. Section 2 presents the mathematical model of the system. Variable structure control is presented in Section 3. In Section 4, simulation results will be presented and Section 5 presents the conclusions.

2 Problem Formulation

The system model used as a basis for the development of the present paper is shown in Figure 1. It comprises of a three synchronous machines feeding into an interconnected power system. The mathematical model of the system of n interconnected generators is similar to that of Kakimoto *et al.*(1980) and is given in the appendix. From this, we can obtain the model for a system with $n = 3$. In an interconnected power system with more buses than generators, we can eliminate all the nodes and retain the nodes containing only the generators. Writing equations (24) to (28) in a vector form, the following representation of the power system model is obtained

$$\dot{x} = A(x) + Bu, \quad x \in M = R^{18} \tag{1}$$

where

$$x = \begin{bmatrix} x^1 \\ x^2 \\ x^3 \end{bmatrix}, \tag{2}$$

and

$$x^i = (\delta_i, \omega_i, E_i, E_{fdi}, P_{mi}, P_{gi})^T, i = 1,2,3 \tag{3}$$

$$A(x) = \begin{bmatrix} A_1(x) \\ A_2(x) \\ A_3(x) \end{bmatrix} \tag{4}$$

$$A_i(x) = \begin{bmatrix} \omega_i \\ \left[-d_i\omega_i + P_{mi} - \sum_{j=1}^{3} Y_{ij}E_iE_j \sin(\delta_{ij} + \theta_{ij})\right]/M_i \\ \left[-E_i + E_{fdi} + (x_{di} - x'_{di})\sum_{j=1}^{3} Y_{ij}E_j \cos(\delta_{ij} + \theta_{ij})\right]/T'_{d0i} \\ -E_{fdi}T_{ei} \\ (-P_{mi} + P_{gi})/T_{ti} \\ -P_{gi}/T_{gi} \end{bmatrix}, \tag{5}$$

$$u = \begin{bmatrix} u^1 \\ u^2 \end{bmatrix}, u^1 = \begin{bmatrix} u_{e1} \\ u_{e2} \\ u_{e3} \end{bmatrix}, u^2 = \begin{bmatrix} u_{g1} \\ u_{g2} \\ u_{g3} \end{bmatrix}, \quad u^1, u^2 \in R^3 \quad (6)$$

$$B = \begin{bmatrix} B_{11} & B_{12} \\ B_{21} & B_{22} \\ B_{31} & B_{32} \end{bmatrix} \quad (7)$$

$$B_{i1} = \begin{bmatrix} 0 & 0 & 0 \\ 0 & 0 & 0 \\ 0 & 0 & 0 \\ 0 & 0 & k_{ei}/T_{ei} \\ 0 & 0 & 0 \\ 0 & 0 & 0 \\ & & i\text{th column} \end{bmatrix}, \quad i = 1,2,3 \quad (8)$$

$$B_{i2} = \begin{bmatrix} 0 & 0 & 0 \\ 0 & 0 & 0 \\ 0 & 0 & 0 \\ 0 & 0 & 0 \\ 0 & 0 & 0 \\ 0 & 0 & 1/T_{gi} \\ & & i\text{th column} \end{bmatrix}, \quad i = 1,2,3 \quad (9)$$

We choose the rotor angle δ_i and the generator voltages E_i as the controlled outputs of the system. We note that δ_i and E_i are two important variables of the synchronous machine and the rotor angles δ_i play an important role in the stability analysis of the power system. Furthermore, if the outputs E_i and δ_i, i = 1,2,3, are analytic functions, and known over certain time interval and then, this information is sufficient to determine uniquely the complete state vector $x(t)$ for each t over this interval. Let the output vector be given by

$$y(t) = C(x) = \begin{bmatrix} E^T & \delta^T \end{bmatrix}^T, \quad y(t) \in R^6 \quad (10)$$

where

$$E = (E_1, E_2, E_3)^T, \quad E \in R^3 \quad (11)$$

$$\delta = (\delta_1, \delta_2, \delta_3)^T, \quad \delta \in R^3 \quad (12)$$

We consider reference models to generate the command rotor angle δ_r and generator voltage E_r to be tracked by the system of the form

$$\begin{aligned} &\delta_{ir}^{(4)} + f_{3i}\delta_{ir}^{(3)} + f_{2i}\delta_{ir}^{(2)} + f_{1i}\ delta_{ir}^{(1)} + f_{0i}(\delta_{ir} - R_{i2}) = 0 \\ &E_{ir}^{(2)} + f_{5i}E_{ir}^{(1)} + f_{4i}(E_{ir} - R_{i1}) = 0 \end{aligned} \quad (13)$$

where $\delta_{ir}^{(n)}$ indicates the nth order of the derivative of δ_{ir} and $E_{ir}^{(n)}$ indicates the nth order of the derivative of E_{ir}. The feedback parameters $f_{5i}, f_{4i}, \ldots, f_{0i}$ are functions of the natural frequencies ω_{ni} and the damping co-efficients ζ_i, and R_{i1}, R_{i2} are external inputs.

The transfer functions corresponding to the above equations are

$$\begin{aligned} \frac{\delta_{ir}(s)}{R_{i2}(s)} &= \frac{\omega_{n1i}^2\omega_{n2i}^2}{(s^2 + 2\zeta_{1i}\omega_{n1i}s + \omega_{n1i}^2)(s^2 + 2\zeta_{2i}\omega_{n2i}s + \omega_{n2i}^2)} \\ \frac{E_{ir}(s)}{R_{i1}(s)} &= \frac{\omega_{ni}^2}{(s^2 + 2\zeta\omega_{ni}s + \omega_{ni}^2)} \end{aligned} \quad (14)$$

where s denotes a Laplace transform variable. In view of (13) and (14)

$$\begin{aligned} f_{5i} &= 2\zeta\omega_{ni} \\ f_{4i} &= \omega_{ni}^2 \\ f_{3i} &= 2(\zeta_{1i}\omega_{n1i} + \zeta_{2i}\omega_{n2i}) \\ f_{2i} &= \omega_{n1i}^2 + 4\zeta_{1i}\zeta_{2i}\omega_{n1i}\omega_{n2i} + \omega_{n2i}^2 \\ f_{1i} &= 2(\zeta_{1i}\omega_{n2i} + \zeta_{2i}\omega_{n1i})\omega_{n1i}\omega_{n2i} \\ f_{0i} &= (\omega_{n1i}\omega_{n2i})^2 \end{aligned} \quad (15)$$

By proper choice of the parameters of (15) we can obtain desirable responses for δ and E.

We are interested in deriving a nonlinear state variable feedback control law using variable structure control such that in the closed loop system, the variables δ and E asymptotically track the reference trajectory. By a proper choice of the reference trajectory desirable attitude of the system can be attained.

3 Variable Structure System

In this section variable structure control laws for attitude control will be derived. In Variable Structure System(VSS) the control law is a discontinuous function of the state variables for the system and the structure of the system changes when the representative point crosses certain hypersurfaces in the state space.

Essential to the design of a variable structure control system is the selection of the switching surface. The control law is such that all the trajectories are attracted towards this surface, and after reaching the surface they slide on it. The structure of the controller changes when the trajectory crosses the switching surface.

3.1 Control Laws for δ_i

For the three machines in the system, we choose switching vectors of the form (for i = 1,2,3)

$$s_{1i} = \begin{bmatrix} P_{i1} & P_{i2} & P_{i3} & P_{i4} \end{bmatrix} \begin{bmatrix} e_{\delta i} \\ \dot{e}_{\delta i} \\ \ddot{e}_{\delta i} \\ \dddot{e}_{\delta i} \end{bmatrix} \quad (16)$$

where $e_{\delta i} = \delta_i - \delta_{ir}$. Notice that $s_{1i} \equiv 0$, implies that $e_{\delta i} \to 0$, as $t \to \infty$

We shall use a Lyapunov based approach to derive the control laws such that in the closed loop system the trajectory $e_{\delta i}$(t) reaches the surface s_{1i}=0 in a finite time and remains on it thereafter. We choose a Lyapunov function

$$V(s_{1i}) = | s_{1i} |$$

The function $V(s_{1i}) > 0$ for $s_{1i} \neq 0$. The control laws are chosen such that the derivative of V along the solutions of the closed loop system satisfies $\dot{V}(t) \leq -\epsilon_{1i} < 0$, whenever $s_{1i} \neq 0$. Now we compute the derivative of s_{1i} which in view of [14] is given by

$$\dot{s}_{1i} = P_{i1}\dot{e}_{\delta i} + P_{i2}\ddot{e}_{\delta i} + P_{i3}\dddot{e}_{\delta i} + P_{i4}\ddddot{e}_{\delta i} \quad (17)$$

Substituting the appropriate derivatives of δ_i we obtain

$$\dot{s}_{1i} = P_{i1}\dot{\delta}_i + P_{i2}\ddot{\delta}_i + P_{13}\dddot{\delta}_i + P_{i4}\ddddot{\delta}_i - P_{i1}\dot{\delta}_{ir} - P_{i2}\ddot{\delta}_{ir} - P_{i3}\dddot{\delta}_{ir} - P_{i4}\ddddot{\delta}_{ir} \quad (18)$$

We choose control laws of the form

$$u_{gi} = T_{gi}T_{ti}M_i\left[-P_{i1}\dot{e}_{\delta i} - P_{i2}\ddot{e}_{\delta i} - P_{i3}\dddot{e}_{\delta i} + P_{i4}\dddot{\omega}_{ir} - k_{1i}\text{sgn}(s)\right] \quad (19)$$

Where $k_{1i} > 0$ is to be determined later, and

$$\text{sgn}(s) = \begin{cases} 1, & s > 0 \\ 0, & s = 0 \\ -1, & s > 0 \end{cases}$$

The value of u_{gi} and appropriate values of $\delta_{ir}^{(n)}$ and $\delta_i^{(n)}$ can be substituted in (18). Now we can obtain the value of the gains k_{1i} such that $\dot{V}(t) < 0$ for the system.

3.2 Control Law for E_i

We choose switching vectors of the form

$$s_{2i} = Q_{2i}e_{Ei} + \dot{e}_{Ei} \tag{20}$$

where $e_{Ei} = E_i - E_{ir}$ and $Q_{2i} > 0$. Notice that $s_{2i} \equiv 0$, implies that $e_{Ei}(t) \rightarrow 0$, as $t \rightarrow \infty$

We shall use a Lyapunov based approach to derive the control laws such that in the closed loop system the trajectory $e_E(t)$ reaches the surface $s_{2i} = 0$ in a finite time and remains on it thereafter. We choose Lyapunov Functions

$$V(s_{2i}) = | s_{2i} |$$

The function $V(s_{2i}) > o$ for $s_{2i} \neq 0$. Now we compute the derivative of s_{2i} which in view of [14] is given by

$$\dot{s}_{2i} = Q_{2i}\dot{e}_{Ei} + \ddot{e}_{Ei} \tag{21}$$

Substituting the appropriate derivatives of E_i and E_{ir} we obtain

$$\dot{s}_{2i} = Q_{2i}\dot{E}_i + \ddot{E}_i - Q_{2i}\dot{E}_{ir} - \ddot{E}_{ir} \tag{22}$$

We choose the control laws of the form

$$u_{ei} = \frac{T_{ei}}{k_{ei}}(-Q_{2i}\dot{e}_{Ei} + \ddot{E}_{ir} - T'_{d0i}k_{2i}\text{sgn}(s)) \tag{23}$$

where $k_{2i} > 0$ is to be determined later, and sgn(s) is as described before.

The values of u_{ei} and appropriate values of E_i^n and E_{ir}^n can be substituted in (22). Now we can obtain the value of the gains k_{2i} such that $\dot{V}(t) < 0$ for the system. It is obvious that the command inputs R_{i2} and R_{i1} independently control δ_i and E_i respectively. The reference trajectories represent single-input and single-output systems. The parameters ω_{ni} and ζ_i are chosen to provide linear dynamic properties for the responses in δ_i and E_i.

The Variable Structure Control Law has been derived for the simplified model of the multi machine power system in which the unknown fluctuations in the load are zero *i.e.*, $\tilde{p}_v = 0$. In practice the system has unknown fluctuations in the load demand $\tilde{p}_v$ and parameter variation during operation of the power system. Under such system the reference trajectories used above may cause the system responses of δ_i and E_i to have small coupling. The load disturbances $\tilde{p}_v$ and parameter variations may cause the system to settle down with undesirable steady-state errors in δ_i and E_i. This problem can be overcome by designing a servo compensator as suggested in [6], for unknown constant disturbance. Also, to reduce the control effort, it could be held to a constant value and this may slow down the system.

4 Simulation Results

In this section, we present the results of digital simulation to evaluate the performance of the designed controller. The responses are presented for the system of equations (1), (19) and (23). The simulation studies are presented for the following values of the parameters:

$$\begin{array}{lll} \omega_{n1i} = 9.0 & \omega_{n2i} = 9.5 & \omega_{ni} = 4.0 \\ \zeta = 0.707 & \zeta_{1i} = 0.707 & \zeta_{2i} = 0.707 \\ P_{i1} = 250. & P_{i2} = 100. & P_{i3} = 10. \\ P_{4i} = 1. & Q_{2i} = 10. & \epsilon = 0.005 \end{array}$$

The above values can be tuned so that the desired fast responses without excessive requirements in T_{mi} and E_{fdi} are obtained.

4.1 Response to Perturbation in state

Figures 2 through 5 show the response of the closed loop system to perturbation in the initial state. The command inputs are $\delta_{1r} = 20^o, \delta_{2r} = 22^o, \delta_{3r} = 24^o$ and $E_{1r} = 1.0, E_{2r} = 1.0, E_{3r} = 1.0$ Figure 2 shows that the system rapidly returns to the equilibrium state from the perturbed condition of $\delta_1 = 62^o, \delta_2 = 60^o, \delta_3 = 58^o$ and $E_1 = 0.6, E_2 = 0.7, E_3 = 0.48$. The values of ω_i are set at $120^o s^{-1}$. Extensive simulation results for various perturbed initial states showed that well-damped response of the system are obtained. The response of the system can be made faster by increasing the natural frequencies ω_{ni}. However, this requires larger values of T_{mi} and E_{fdi}.

4.2 Response to stochastic load

Figures 6 and 7 show the response of the system to random load fluctuations. The random load fluctuations are assumed to be Gaussian noise with mean of 0.1 p.u and standard deviation of 0.003. The command inputs $\mathbf{x(0)}$ are as in the previous case.

The results of the simulation study can be summarized as follows:

1. The system rapidly attains its equilibrium state for large perturbations in state.
2. The rotor angle and field flux are independently controlled. The system state can be transferred to a new state corresponding to any desired terminal voltage and tie-line power flow.
3. The effect of stochastic disturbances on the response is small, and the response E_i remains unaffected.

5 Concluding Remarks

We have carried out an exploratory study of the applicability of variable structure control. The controlled variables are E_i and δ_i. In this system, δ_i and E_i are controlled by fourth and second-order differential equations respectively. The system was shown to be stable for large perturbations in the initial state. Desirable fast and well damped responses in δ_i and E_i were obtained. It was also shown that the system is stable under piecewise constant disturbance loads. Control laws were shown to be effective under stochastic load disturbances.

References

1. Iyer, S.N., and Cory, B.J., 'Optimal control of a turbogenerator including exciter and governor', *IEEE Transactions, 1971, PAS-90, pp. 2142- 2148*

2. Mukhopadhyay, B.K., and Malik, O.P., 'Optimal control of synchronous- machine excitation by quasilinearisation techniques' *Proceedings IEE, 1972, 119, (1), pp. 91-98*

3. Daniels, A.R., Lee, Y.B., and Pal, M.K., 'Non-Linear power system optimization using dynamic sensitivity analysis', *Proceedings IEE., 1976, 123,(4), pp. 365-370*

4. Daniels, A.R., Lee, Y.B., and Pal, M.K., 'Combined sub-optimal excitation and governing of a.c. turbogenerators using dynamic sensitivity analysis', *ibid., 1977, 124, (5) pp. 473-478*

5. Doraiswami, R., 'A nonlinear load-frequency control design', *IEEE Transactions, 1978, PAS-97, pp. 1278-1284*

6. Singh, S.N., 'Nonlinear state-variable-feedback excitation- and governor- control design using decoupling theory', *IEEE Proceedings, Vol.127,May 1980 pp. 131,141*

7. Ahmed, R., Villaseca, F.E., 'Transient stability hierarchical control in multimachine power systems', *IEEE Transactions on Power Systems, Vol. 4, No.4, October 1989, pp. 1438-1444*

8. Malik, O.P., Ashok Kumar, Hope. G.S., ' A load-frequency control algorithm based on a generalized approach', *IEEE Transactions on Power Systems, Vol.3, No.2, May 1988, pp. 375-382*

9. Romero, D.P., Heydt, G.T., 'An adaptive excitation system controller in a stochastic environment', *IEEE Transactions on Power Systems, Vol.PWRS-1, No.1, February 1986, pp. 168-175*

10. Subbarao, G.V., Iyer, A., 'Nonlinear Excitation and Governor control using sliding modes', *Accepted for publication in the American Control Conference, 1992*

11. Subbarao, G.V., Iyer, A., 'Nonlinear Excitation and Governor control using inverse control system', *Submitted for publication to the International Systems Science Conference, Wroclaw Poland 1992*

12. Anderson, J.H., and Raina, V.M., 'Power system excitation and governor design using optimal control theory', *International Journal of Control, 1972, 12, pp. 289-308*

13. Mello, F.P. de, and Concordia, C., 'Concepts of synchronous machine stability as affected by excitation control', *IEEE Transactions, 1969, PAS-88, pp. 316-329*

14. Paden, B.E. and Sastry, S.S., 'Calculus for computing Filippov's differential inclusion with application to the variable structure control of robot manipulators', *IEEE Transactions on Systems Circuit 34, pp.73-82,1987*

Appendix

Mathematical Model of the Power System

Synchronous Machine

$$M_i\ddot{\delta}_i + d_i\dot{\delta}_i = P_{mi} - \sum_{j=1}^{n} Y_{ij}E_iE_j\sin(\delta_{ij}+\theta_{ij}) \qquad (24)$$

$$T'_{d0i}\dot{E}_i = E_{fdi} - E_i + (x_{di} - x'_{di})\sum_{j=1}^{n} E_j\cos(\delta_{ij}+\theta_{ij}) \qquad (25)$$

Excitation System

$$T_{ei}\dot{E}_{fdi} = -E_{fdi} + k_{ei}u_{ei} \qquad (26)$$

Turbine and Governor

$$T_{ti}\dot{P}_{mi} = -P_{mi} + P_{gi} \qquad (27)$$

$$T_{gi}\dot{P}_{gi} = -P_{gi} + u_{gi}, i = 1,2,3 \qquad (28)$$

where $\delta_{ij} = \delta_i - \delta_j$ and for the generator i

P_{mi}	:	mechanical power input
M_i	:	angular momentum constant
d_i	:	damping power coefficient
$Y_{ij}\angle\theta_{ij}$	:	Post fault transfer admittance between ith and jth generator nodes
$E_i\angle\delta_i$	:	internal voltage (δ_i is the rotor angle)
E_{fdi}	:	Excitation voltage
T'_{d0i}	:	d-axis transient open circuit time constant
T_{ti}, T_{gi}, T_{ei}	:	turbine, governor, exciter time constants
u_{gi}, u_{ei}	:	governor, exciter, valve actuating signals
P_{gi}	:	governor output
ω_i	:	perturbation in frequency ($\dot{\delta}_i$)

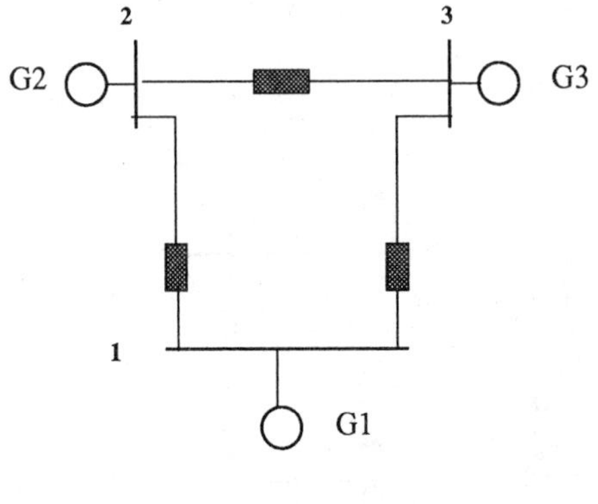

Figure 1: Multi-Machine Power System

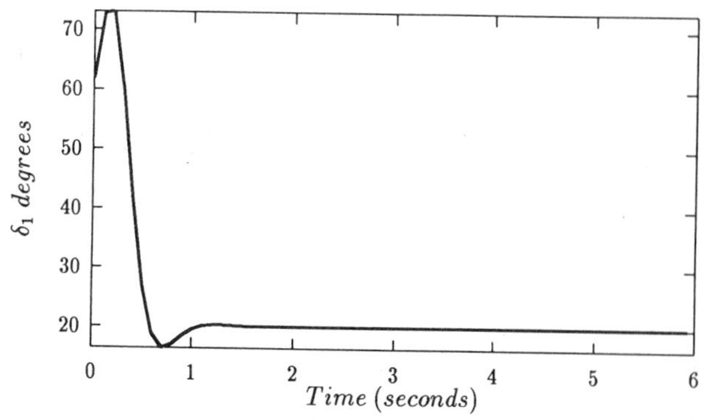

Figure 2: Petubation in State: Rotor Angle δ_1

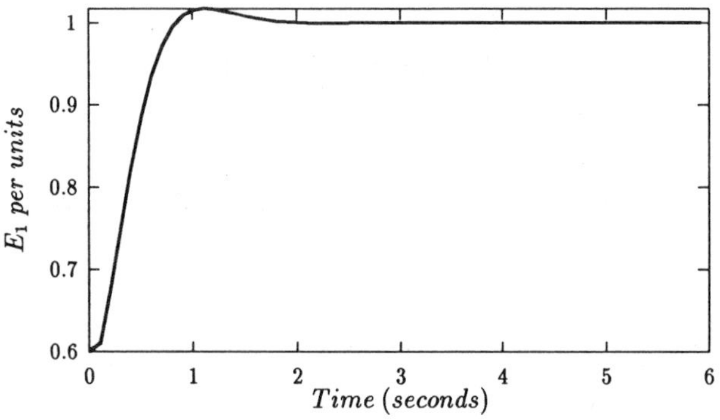

Figure 3: Petubation in State: E_1

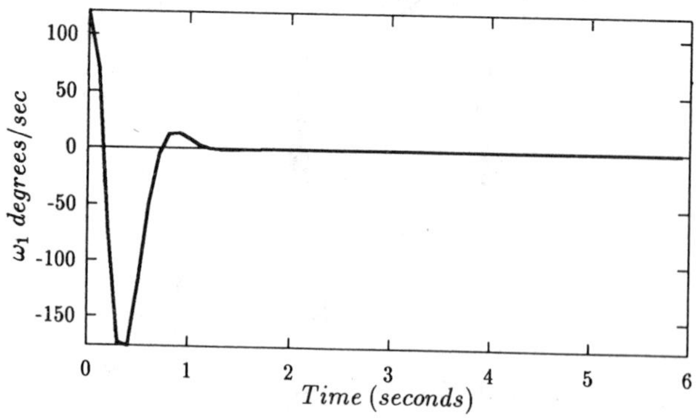

Figure 4: Petubation in State: ω_1

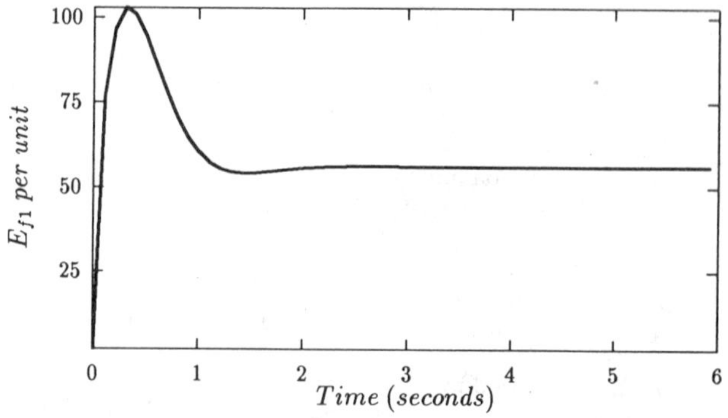

Figure 5: Petubation in State: E_{fd}

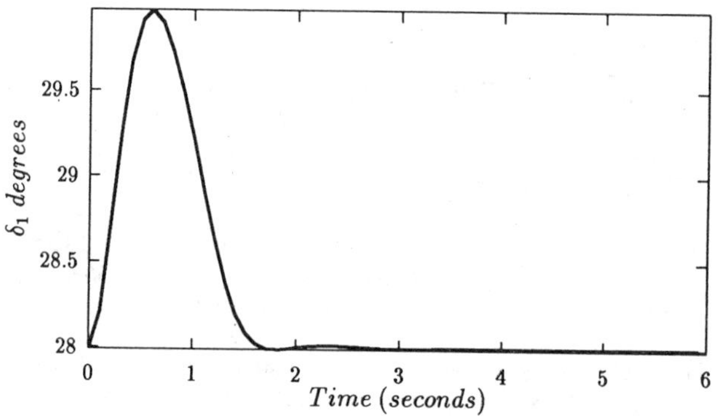

Figure 6: Response to Stochastic Load: Rotor Angle δ_1

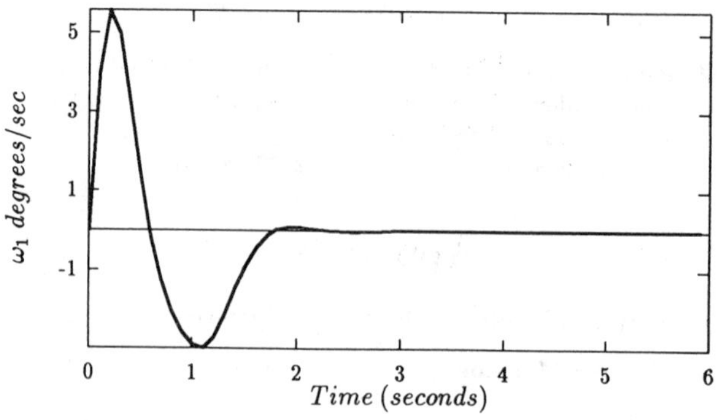

Figure 7: Response to Stochastic Load: ω_1

Proceedings of the
American Control Conference
San Francisco, California • June 1993

Sliding Mode Control of HAVE DASH II Missile Systems *

J. Huang, C.F. Lin
American GNC Corporation
9131 Mason Ave.
Chatsworth, CA 91311

Abstract: Sliding mode control is applied to design autopilot for bank-to-turn (BTT) missile systems. The design is compared with the feedback linearization approach and shows a significant improvement over the latter.

1. Introduction

The nonlinearity and uncertainty inherent in the HAVE DASH II missile dynamics have been a great challenge to the high performance autopilot design. In recent years, much attention has been focused on using linear optimal control methods to design missile autopilot [LL], [LJGEW], [W]. Although these advanced multivariable approaches are compared favorably to the classical one-loop-at-a-time method, they still manifest themselves incapabilities when performing large and rapid maneuvers. A natural step towards improving the autopilot's performance is to incorporate the more accurate nonlinear missile model into the design process. A typical nonlinear approach is the well-known feedback linearization approach [HSM] which uses the feedback and/or coordinates transform to linearize the nonlinear system, then addresses the design issues on the linearized system thus obtained. However, success of the feedback linearization approach is hinged on the availability of the accurate description of the model. Indeed, severe model uncertainty mainly due to the aerocoefficients may degrade the effectiveness of the feedback linearization approach. A more realistic approach should tolerate the model uncertainty to some degree. With this regard, some robust schemes such as sliding mode control have been proposed [SS].

In this paper, we will apply sliding mode method to design autopilot for the bank-to-turn HAVE DASH II missile system. The design will be carried out in two steps. First, a nonlinear inversion law is synthesized to decouple and linearize the input-output dynamics of a nominal missile system. Then based on this decoupled and linearized input-output relation, the sliding mode method is further applied to design a switching mechanism to account for the model uncertainty. The performance of the resulting controller is compared to that of the feedback linearization approach. It should be noted that similar approach has been applied to the control of aircraft in [SI]. However, our development is based on the more complicated missile model and the performance is evaluated using the full-scale six degree-of-freedom HAVE DASH II missile model.

*Research supported under USAF Contract No. F08630-91-C-0055, Air Force Armament Directorate, WL/MNAG

2. Formulation of Sliding Mode Controller

It is known that sliding mode control can be used to achieve trajectory tracking in presence of certain model uncertainty. In this section, we will formulate the sliding mode controller for a class of input-output feedback linearizable nonlinear systems. Details are referred to [SL]. We consider the system described by

$$\begin{aligned} \dot{x}(t) &= f(x(t)) + g(x(t))u(t) \\ y(t) &= h(x(t)) \end{aligned} \tag{2.1}$$

where $x(t)$ is the n-dimensional plant state, u is m-dimensional plant input, y is m-dimensional plant output, $f : R^n \rightarrow R^n$ and $g : R^n \rightarrow R^n \times R^m$, and $h : R^n \rightarrow R^m$ are smooth functions. Sliding mode controller for system (2.1) can be designed by the following steps.

1. Performing input-output feedback linearization. System (2.1) is said to be input-output feedback linearizable if there exist constants $\rho_1, \cdots, \rho_m$ and input-output mapping of the form

$$\begin{bmatrix} y_1^{(\rho_1)}(t) \\ y_2^{(\rho_2)}(t) \\ \vdots \\ y_m^{(\rho_m)}(t) \end{bmatrix} = B(x(t)) + A(x(t)) \begin{bmatrix} u_1(t) \\ u_2(t) \\ \vdots \\ u_m(t) \end{bmatrix} \tag{2.2}$$

where $u_i, y_i, i = 1, \cdots, m$ are components of u and y, $B : R^n \rightarrow R^m$ and $A : R^n \rightarrow R^m \times R^m$ are smooth with $A(x)$ invertible. For if this is the case, the following feedback control

$$u(t) = A^{-1}(x(t))(-B(x(t)) + v(t)) \tag{2.3}$$

where $v(t) = [v_1(t), \cdots, v_m(t)]^T \in R^m$, yields

$$y_i^{(\rho_i)}(t) = v_i(t), \;\; i = 1, \cdots, m \tag{2.4}$$

which clearly exhibits a decoupled linear input-output structure. The integers $\rho_1, \cdots, \rho_m$ are called *relative degree* of (2.1).

2. Specifying sliding surface. On the basis of the input-output linearized system (2.4), we can define m sliding surfaces s_i, $i = 1, \cdots, m$, as follows:

$$\begin{aligned} s_i(t) &= e_i^{(\rho_i-1)} + k_{i(\rho_i-1)}e_i^{(\rho_i-2)} \\ + &\cdots +k_{i2}e_i^{(1)} + k_{i1}e_i + k_{i0}\int e_i dt \end{aligned} \quad (2.5)$$

where $e_i = y_i - r_i$ with r_i the reference trajectories; and $k_{i(\rho-1)}, \cdots, k_{i0}$ are such that

$$\lambda^{\rho_i} + k_{i(\rho_i-1)}\lambda^{\rho_i-1} + \cdots + k_{i1}\lambda + k_{i0} \quad (2.6)$$

is Hulwitz polynomial.

3. Achieving sliding condition. The closed-loop system is said to satisfy the sliding condition if the following applies.

$$\frac{1}{2}\frac{ds_i^2}{dt} \le -\eta_i|s_i|, \quad (\eta_i > 0) \quad (2.7)$$

where $\eta_i, i = 1, \cdots, m$, are positive numbers. Note that sliding condition will make $s_i(t) = 0$ and $\dot{s}_i(t) = 0$ in a finite time. Since $\dot{s}_i(t) = 0$ is a stable differential equation, satisfaction of $\dot{s}_i(t) = 0$ by $e_i(t)$ in turn leads to aymptotic tracking.

Let

$$\dot{s} \overset{def}{=} \begin{bmatrix} \dot{s}_1 \\ \vdots \\ \dot{s}_m \end{bmatrix}, \quad Y^{(\rho)} = \begin{bmatrix} y_1^{(\rho_1)} \\ \vdots \\ y_m^{(\rho_m)} \end{bmatrix} \quad (2.8)$$

$$sgn(s) = [sgn(s_1), \cdots, sgn(s_m)]$$

where $sgn(\cdot)$ is the sign function. Then it can be verified that a control law that achieves the sliding condition (2.7) is given by

$$u = A^{-1}((\dot{s} - Y^{(\rho)}) - B - \lambda sgn(s)) \quad (2.9)$$

where $\lambda = diag\ [\lambda_1, \cdots, \lambda_m]$ with λ_i a positive number greater than given positive number η_i. Note that

$$\begin{aligned} (\dot{s}_i - y_i^{\rho_i}) &= -r_i^{\rho_i} + k_{i(\rho_i-1)}e_i^{(\rho_i-1)} \\ + &\cdots +k_{i2}e_i^{(2)} + k_{i1}e_i^{(1)} + k_{i0}e_i \end{aligned}$$

so $(\dot{s} - Y^{(\rho)})$ does not depend on u.

Remark 2-1: The integral term in (2.5) can be omitted by setting $k_{i0} = 0$. Since the sliding condition also implies $s_i(t) = 0$, the asymptotical tracking can still be achieved by the control law (2.9) as long as, for $i = 1, \cdots, m$, $k_{i(\rho-1)}, \cdots, k_{i1}$ are such that $\lambda^{\rho_i-1} + k_{i(\rho_i-1)}\lambda^{\rho_i-2} + \cdots + k_{i1}$ are Hulwitz.

Remark 2-2: The discontinuity of the sign function will cause *chattering* in the closed-loop system. In practice, the sign function $sgn(s_i)$ is often replaced by the saturation function $sat(\frac{s_i}{\epsilon_i})$ where

$$\begin{aligned} sat(x) = x, &\quad if|x| \le 1 \\ sat(x) = sgn(x), &\quad if|x| \ge 1 \end{aligned} \quad (2.10)$$

Remark 2-3: It is interesting to note that the above formulation include the feedback linearization or dynamic inversion as a special case. To see this, let $\lambda_i = 0$ in (2.9), then (2.9) is such that $\dot{s}_i = 0$ for $t \ge 0$. However, such a goal can be achieved by feedback linearization controllers only if there are no uncertainties in the plant model. By contrast, even in the presence of certain types of uncertainties, the sliding condition (2.7) can still be maintained by suitably choosing the values of λ_i [SL]. It should be also pointed out that unless $\sum_i^m \rho_i = n$, there is no guarantee for closed-loop stability since certain unobsolvable modes called zero-dynamics cannot be stabilized by the above controller. [I].

3. HAVE DASH II Missile Model

The rigid body motion equations of the HAVE DASH II missile in a body fixed frame are described by

$$\begin{aligned}
\dot{P} &= -\frac{I_{zz} - I_{yy}}{I_{xx}}QR + L/I_{xx} \\
\dot{Q} &= -\frac{I_{xx} - I_{zz}}{I_{yy}}PR + M/I_{yy} \\
\dot{R} &= -\frac{I_{yy} - I_{xx}}{I_{zz}}PQ + N/I_{zz} \\
\dot{\Psi} &= sin\Phi sec\Theta Q + cos\Phi sec\Theta R \\
\dot{\Theta} &= cos\Phi Q - sin\Phi R \\
\dot{\Phi} &= P + sin\Phi tan\Theta Q + cos\Phi tan\Theta R \\
\dot{V}_m &= \frac{1}{m}\{cos\alpha cos\beta(F_x + g_x) \\
&+ sin\beta(F_y + g_y) \\
&+ sin\alpha cos\beta(F_z + g_z)\} \\
\dot{\alpha} &= Q - (Pcos\alpha + Rsin\alpha)tan\beta \\
&+ \frac{1}{mV_m cos(\beta)}\{-sin\alpha(F_x + g_x) + cos\alpha(F_z + g_z)\} \\
\dot{\beta} &= Psin\alpha - Rcos\alpha \\
&+ \frac{1}{mV_m}\{-cos\alpha sin\beta(F_x + g_x) + cos\beta(F_y + g_y) \\
&- sin\alpha sin\beta(F_z + g_z)\}
\end{aligned} \quad (3.1)$$

where

$$\begin{aligned} g_x &= -mgsin\Theta \\ g_y &= mgcos\Theta sin\Phi \\ g_z &= mgcos\Theta cos\Phi \end{aligned}$$

In (3.1), P, Q, and R are the angular rates in the body fixed frame; V_m, α, and β are the missile velocity, angle of attack, and sideslip angle with respect to the body fixed frame; and θ, Φ, Ψ are pitch angle, roll angle, and yaw angle. The other parameters are three moments of the inertial about the body frame I_{xx}, I_{yy}, and I_{zz}, missile mass m, and gravity constant g. (F_x, F_y, F_z) and (L, M, N) are aerodynamic forces and rolling, pitching, and yawing moments, respectively, all about the body frame. They are given by

$$F_x = k_F\rho V_m^2 C_x, \quad F_y = k_F\rho V_m^2 C_y$$

$$F_z = k_F \rho V_m^2 C_z, \quad L = k_M \rho V_m^2 C_l$$
$$M = k_M \rho V_m^2 C_m, \quad N = k_M \rho V_m^2 C_n \qquad (3.2)$$

where ρ is the atmospheric density; k_F and k_M are constants determined by the missile's geometry; and C_x, C_y, C_z, C_l, C_m, and C_n are aerodynamic coefficients given in terms of an aerodynamic table. The functional form of the aerodynamic coefficients C_i, $i = x, y, z, l, m, n$ is given as follows

$$\begin{aligned} C_i &= C_{io}(\alpha, \beta, M_m) + C_{i\delta_e}(\alpha, \delta_e, M_m) \\ &+ C_{i\delta_a}(\alpha, \delta_a, M_m) + C_{i\delta_r}(\alpha, \delta_r, M_m) \end{aligned} \qquad (3.3)$$

where $M_m = V_m/c$ is Mach number with c being the speed of sound. δ_e, δ_a, and δ_r are the effective pitch, roll and yaw fin control deflections, respectively. They are converted from the corresponding commanded deflections $\delta_{ec}, \delta_{ac}, \delta_{rc}$ through actuator and fin mixer. The HAVE DASH II missile system has four tail fins arranged asymmetrically. The commanded deflections produce four fin deflection commands δ_{ic} according to

$$\begin{aligned} \delta_{1c} &= \delta_{ec} - \delta_{ac} + \delta_{rc} \\ \delta_{2c} &= -\delta_{ec} - \delta_{ac} + \delta_{rc} \\ \delta_{3c} &= -\delta_{ec} - \delta_{ac} - \delta_{rc} \\ \delta_{4c} &= \delta_{ec} - \delta_{ac} - \delta_{rc} \end{aligned}$$

These fin deflection commands $\delta_{ic}, i = 1, \cdots, 4$ are the inputs to the fin actuators which give the actual fin deflections $\delta_i, i = 1, \cdots, 4$, via a second order system

$$\frac{d}{dt}\begin{bmatrix} \delta_i \\ \dot{\delta}_i \end{bmatrix} = \begin{bmatrix} 0 & 1 \\ -\omega_a^2 & -2\zeta_a\omega_a \end{bmatrix}\begin{bmatrix} \delta_i \\ \dot{\delta}_i \end{bmatrix} + \begin{bmatrix} 0 \\ \omega_a^2 \end{bmatrix}\delta_{ic}$$

where $\zeta_a = 0.7, \omega_a = 35Hz$. It is assumed that the deflection limits of the fins are $\pm$ $25deg$. The deflection rates are limited by $\pm 400\ deg/sec$. Finally, the actual fin deflections are mixed to produce the effective pitch, roll and yaw fin deflections according to

$$\begin{aligned} \delta_e &= \frac{1}{4}(\delta_1 - \delta_2 - \delta_3 + \delta_4) \\ \delta_a &= -\frac{1}{4}(\delta_1 + \delta_2 + \delta_3 + \delta_4) \\ \delta_r &= \frac{1}{4}(\delta_1 + \delta_2 - \delta_3 - \delta_4) \end{aligned}$$

To put the missile model in the form described by (2.1), we need to approximate the aerodynamic coefficients by well defined affine functions as follows

$$\begin{bmatrix} C_x \\ C_y \\ C_z \end{bmatrix} \stackrel{def}{=} \begin{bmatrix} C_{x0} \\ C_{y0} \\ C_{z0} \end{bmatrix} + \begin{bmatrix} C_{xe} & C_{xa} & C_{xr} \\ C_{ye} & C_{ya} & C_{yr} \\ C_{ze} & C_{za} & C_{zr} \end{bmatrix}\begin{bmatrix} \delta_e \\ \delta_a \\ \delta_r \end{bmatrix} \stackrel{def}{=} C_{F0} + C_{Fu}u \qquad (3.4)$$

$$\begin{bmatrix} C_l \\ C_m \\ C_n \end{bmatrix} \stackrel{def}{=} \begin{bmatrix} C_{l0} \\ C_{m0} \\ C_{n0} \end{bmatrix} + \begin{bmatrix} C_{le} & C_{la} & C_{lr} \\ C_{me} & C_{ma} & C_{mr} \\ C_{ne} & C_{na} & C_{nr} \end{bmatrix}\begin{bmatrix} \delta_e \\ \delta_a \\ \delta_r \end{bmatrix} \stackrel{def}{=} C_{M0} + C_{Mu}u \qquad (3.5)$$

The entries of the matrices $C_{F0}, C_{Fu}, C_{M0}, C_{Mu}$ are generally functions of α, β and M_m. Using a simple curve fitting scheme based on the least square error criterion gives

$$C_{F0} = \begin{bmatrix} -0.57 + 0.0083\alpha \\ -0.21\beta \\ C_{z0}(\alpha, M_m) \end{bmatrix}, \quad C_{Fu} = \begin{bmatrix} 0.004 & 0 & 0 \\ 0 & 0 & 0.08 \\ -0.09 & 0 & 0 \end{bmatrix}$$

$$C_{M0} = \begin{bmatrix} 0.116\beta \\ C_{m0}(\alpha, M_m) \\ 0.08\beta \end{bmatrix}, \quad C_{Mu} = \begin{bmatrix} 0 & -0.127 & 0 \\ -0.675 & 0 & 0 \\ 0 & 0 & -0.584 \end{bmatrix}$$

where $C_{z0}(\alpha, M_m)$, and $C_{m0}(\alpha, M_m)$ are given as follows

$$\begin{aligned} C_{z0}(\alpha, M_m) &= C_{z1}(\alpha) + C_{z2}(\alpha)M_m \\ C_{m0}(\alpha, M_m) &= C_{m1}(\alpha) + C_{m2}(\alpha)M_m \end{aligned} \qquad (3.6)$$

with

$$\begin{aligned} C_{z1}(\alpha) &= -0.0015\alpha_3 + 0.0125\alpha^2 - 0.5052\alpha + 0.0429 \\ C_{z2}(\alpha) &= 0.0006\alpha_3 - 0.0138\alpha^2 + 0.1230\alpha - 0.0191 \\ C_{m1}(\alpha) &= -0.0055\alpha_3 + 0.2131\alpha^2 - 2.7419\alpha - 0.0381 \\ C_{m2}(\alpha) &= 0.0014\alpha_3 - 0.0623\alpha^2 + 0.8715\alpha - 0.4041 \end{aligned}$$

The other missile parameters are given by $G = 32.174\ ft/sec^2$, $m = 9.89\ slug$, $c = 968\ ft/sec$, $K_F = 0.1534\ ft^2$, $K_M = 0.0959\ ft^3$, $\rho = 5.124 \times 10^{-4}\ slugs/ft^3$, $I_{xx} = 1.1913\ slug\ ft^2$, $I_{yy} = 100.51\ slug\ ft^2$, and $I_{zz} = 100.57\ slug\ ft^2$, where c and ρ are computed at the altitude of 40,000 feet.

The performance output is chosen to be the following

$$\begin{aligned} y_1 &= Pcos\alpha + Rsin\alpha \stackrel{def}{=} P_s \\ y_2 &= \alpha \\ y_3 &= \beta \end{aligned} \qquad (3.7)$$

where P_s represents the roll rate with respect to the stability axis. The basic requiremnet for the closed-loop system is rapid and precise command following ability of P_s and α. Also, the sideslip angle β is required to be less than one degree.

4. Sliding Mode Controller

To make the design easier, we will assume the following

- The actuator dynamics are ignored, that is, we assume $\delta_e = \delta_{ec}$, $\delta_a = \delta_{ac}$, and $\delta_r = \delta_{rc}$.
- The variations of V_m is ignored, that is, we assume $\dot{V}_m = 0$.
- The coupling between the force and control deflections is ignored, that is, we assume $C_{Fu} = 0$.

Note that the first two assumptions are mainly made for convenience, which has been customarily practiced in autopilot design. The third assumption is based on the observation that the coupling between the force and control deflections are relatively small in comparison with the coupling between the moment and control deflections since the aileron, rudder, and elevator are principally moment producing devices. [RS].

Under the above assumptions, the missile system can be put into the standard form of (2.1) with $x = [P\ Q\ R\ V_m\ \alpha\ \beta\ \Psi\ \Phi\ \Theta]^T$, $u = [\delta_e\ \delta_a\ \delta_r]^T$, and $y = [P_s\ \alpha\ \beta]^T$. It can be easily verified that this system has a vector relative degree $(1,2,2)$. In fact, some calculations yield the following input-output relation

$$\begin{bmatrix} \dot{P}_s \\ \ddot{\alpha} \\ \ddot{\beta} \end{bmatrix} = \begin{bmatrix} B_1 \\ B_2 \\ B_3 \end{bmatrix} + \begin{bmatrix} A_{11} & A_{12} & A_{13} \\ A_{21} & A_{22} & A_{23} \\ A_{31} & A_{32} & A_{33} \end{bmatrix} \begin{bmatrix} \delta_e \\ \delta_a \\ \delta_r \end{bmatrix}$$

$$\stackrel{def}{=} B(x) + A(x)u \qquad (4.1)$$

with $A(x)$ given by

$$A(x) = k_M \rho V_m^2 \begin{bmatrix} \frac{\cos\alpha}{I_{xx}} & \frac{\sin\alpha}{I_{yy}} & 0 \\ -\frac{\cos\alpha \tan\beta}{I_{xx}} & \frac{1}{I_{yy}} & -\frac{\sin\alpha\tan\beta}{I_{zz}} \\ \frac{\sin\alpha}{I_{xx}} & 0 & -\frac{\cos\alpha}{I_{zz}} \end{bmatrix} C_{Mu} \qquad (4.2)$$

It can be checked that $A(x)$ is invertible for x in a neighborhood of $x = 0$. Therefore, the sliding mode controller can be readily synthesized using our general formulation (2.9). Specifically, the sliding surface is given, according to (2.5) with $k_{i0} = 0$, by

$$s = \begin{bmatrix} s_1 \\ s_2 \\ s_3 \end{bmatrix} = \begin{bmatrix} e_1 \\ \dot{e}_2 + k_{21}e_2 \\ \dot{e}_3 + k_{31}e_3 \end{bmatrix} \qquad (4.3)$$

where $e_1 = P_s - P_{sc}$, $e_2 = \alpha - \alpha_c$, and $e_3 = \beta$; and P_{sc} and α_c are commanded stability axis roll rate and angle of attack. Then

$$(\dot{s} - Y^{(\rho)}) = \begin{bmatrix} \dot{s}_1 - \dot{P}_s \\ \dot{s}_2 - \ddot{\alpha} \\ \dot{s}_3 - \ddot{\beta} \end{bmatrix} = \begin{bmatrix} -\dot{P}_{sc} \\ k_{21}(\dot{\alpha} - \dot{\alpha}_c) - \ddot{\alpha}_c \\ k_{31}\dot{\beta} \end{bmatrix}$$

The design parameters are given by $k_{21} = 20$, $k_{31} = 8$, $\lambda_1 = 100$, $\lambda_2 = 30$, $\lambda_3 = 16$. Finally, to alleviate the chattering due to the switching function, smoothing technique as described in Remark 2-2 is adopted. That is, replace $sgn(s_i)$ by $sat(s_i/\epsilon_i)$ with $\epsilon_1 = 1.0$, $\epsilon_2 = 0.5$, $\epsilon_3 = 0.5$. Note that all these parameters are selected largely on the trial-and-error basis.

The performance of this autopilot for a typical maneuver is shown in Figures 1 and 2 where all initial conditions are zero except that $V_m(0) = 2662 ft/sec$. The missile is required to roll at 90 degree per second in both moderate (10 degree) and large (20 degree) angles of attack. It is seen that the autopilot is quite capable of performing this maneuver. In both cases, the autopilot shows an excellent tracking ability to angle of attack command. The roll rate command following is also satisfactory though a nearly 10% overshoot in the roll rate response is observed when a 20 *deg* angle of attack change occurs. Other figures (not included for the reason of space) show that the induced sideslip angle is well below 0.2 *deg*.

It is interesting to make a comparison between the sliding mode controller and the feedback linearization controller. The feedback linearization controller can be obtained from (2.9) by letting $\lambda_i = 0$ and assigning appropriate values to k_{ij}. Figures 3 and 4 show the performance of the feedback linearization controller with $k_{10} = 55$, $k_{21} = 21$, $k_{20} = 225$, $k_{31} = 24$, $k_{32} = 350$. For a 10 *deg* angle of attack change, this controller performs almost as good as the sliding mode controller, however, For a 20 *deg* angle of attack change, a significant performance degradation in terms of about 50% overshoot in roll rate response is observed.

Acknowledgement

The authors wish to thank Johnny Evers of USAF Armament Directorate of Wright Laboratory for his suggestions and comments.

References

[HLCED] J. Hunag, C.F. Lin, J.R. Cloutier, J.H. Evers, and C.D. D'Souza, " Robust Feedback Linearization Approach to Autopilot Design" *Proceedings of the First Control Applications Conference* September, 1992.

[HSM] HUNT, L.R., SU R. AND G. MEYER, "Design for Multi-input Nonlinear Systems," *Differential Geometric Control Theory*, R.W. Brocket, R.S. Millman and H. Sussman eds., Birkhauser, pp. 268-298, 1983.

[I] ISIDORI, A, *Nonliner Control Systems*, Springer Verlag, 1989.

[LCEJW] LIN, C.F., J.R. CLOUTIER, J. EVERS, J. JUANG AND Q. WANG, "High Performance, Adaptive, Robust Bank to Turn Missile Autopilot Design," *Proceedings of AIAA Guidance, Navigation and Control Conference*, Vol. 3, pp 123 - 137, 1991.

[L] LIN, C. F., "Modern Navigation, Guidance, and Control Processing," *Prentice Hall*, 1991.

[LL] LIN, C.F. AND S.P. LEE, "Robust Missile Autopilot Design Using a Generalized Singular Optimal Control Technique," *J. of Guidance, Control and Dynamics*, Vol. 8, No. 4, pp 498-507, 1985.

[RS] ROMANO, J. J. AND S.N. SINGH, "I-O Map Inversion, Zero Dynamics and Flight Control" *IEEE Trans. on Aerospace and Electronnic Systems*, VOL. 26, NO. 6, pp 1022-1028, 1990.

[SI] SINGH, S.N. AND A. IYER, "Nonlinear Decoupling Sliding Mode Control and Attitude Control of Spacecraft," *IEEE Trans. on aerospace and Electronic Systems*, VOL. 25, No. 5, pp 621-633, 1989.

[SL] SLOTINE, J.-J. E. AND W. Li, Applied Nonlinear Control, *Prentice Hall*, 1991.

[SS] SLOTINE, J.-J. E. AND S.S. SASTRY, "Tracking Control of Nonlinear Systems Using Sliding Surfaces with Applications to Robot Manipulators," *Int. J. Control*, 39, 2, 1983.

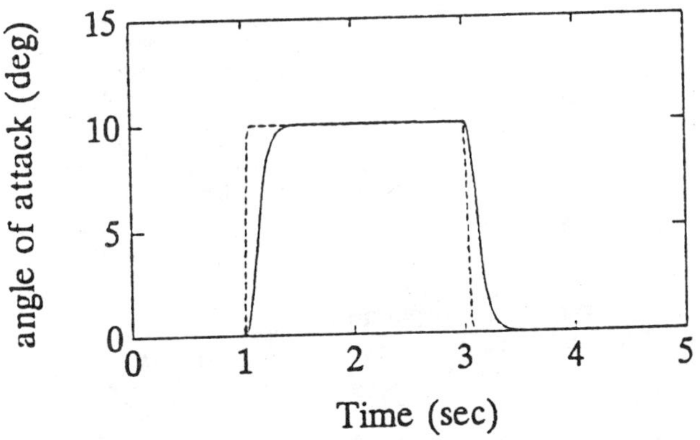

Figure 1a Angle of attack response (solid) (10 degree command) of sliding mode controller

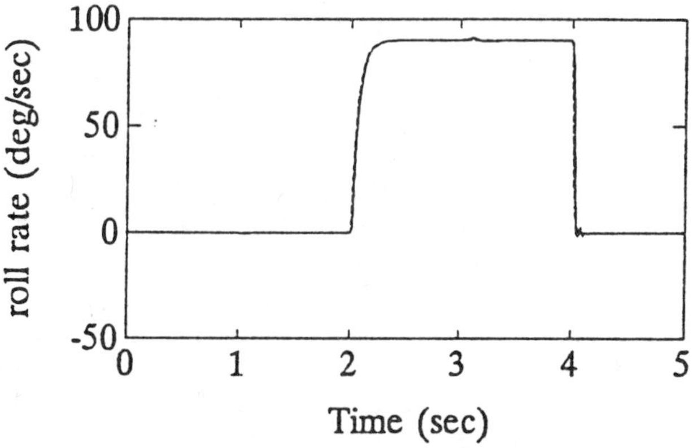

Figure 1b Roll rate response (solid) of sliding mode controller with a 10 degree angle of attack maneuver

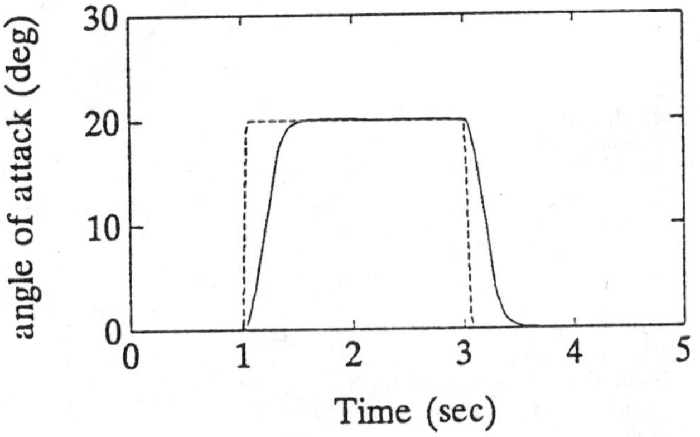

Figure 2a Angle of attack response (solid) (20 degree command) of sliding mode controller

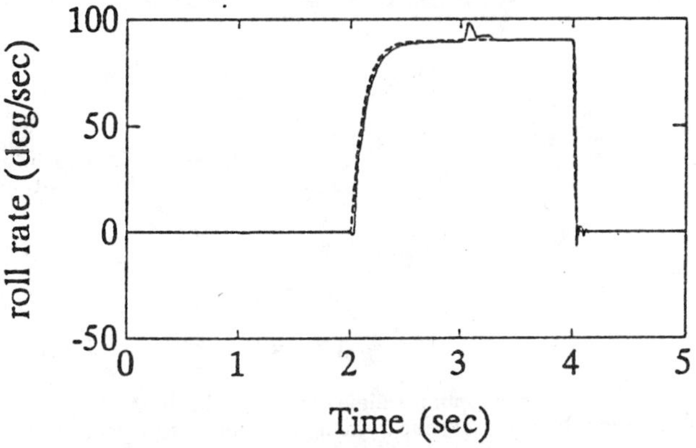

Figure 2b Roll rate response (solid) of sliding mode controller with a 20 degree angle of attack maneuver

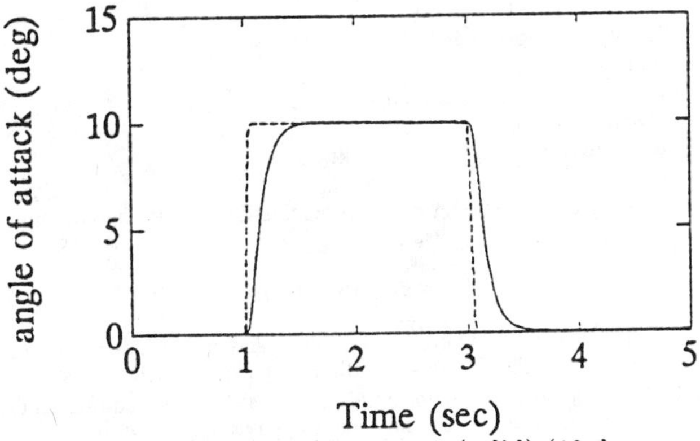

Figure 3a Angle of attack response (solid) (10 degree command) of feedback linearization controller

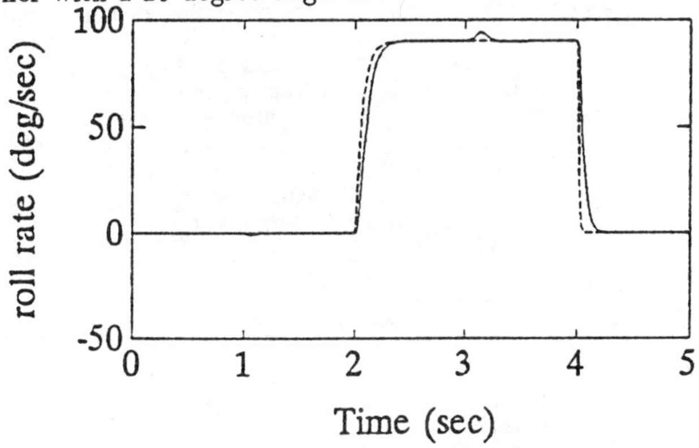

Figure 3b Roll rate response (solid) of feedback linearization controller with a 10 degree angle of attack maneuver

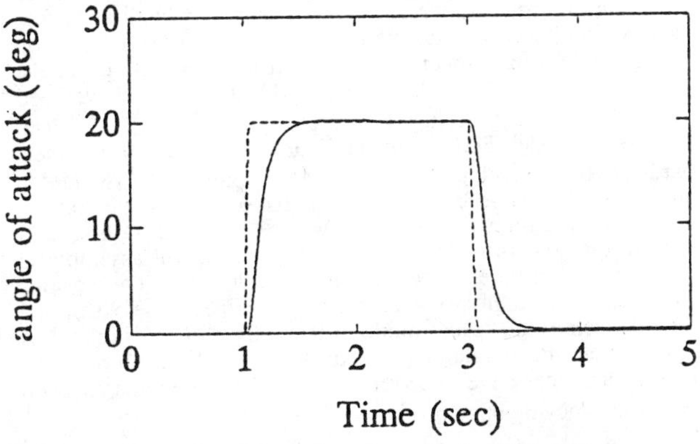

Figure 4a Angle of attack response (solid) (20 degree command) of feedback linearization controller

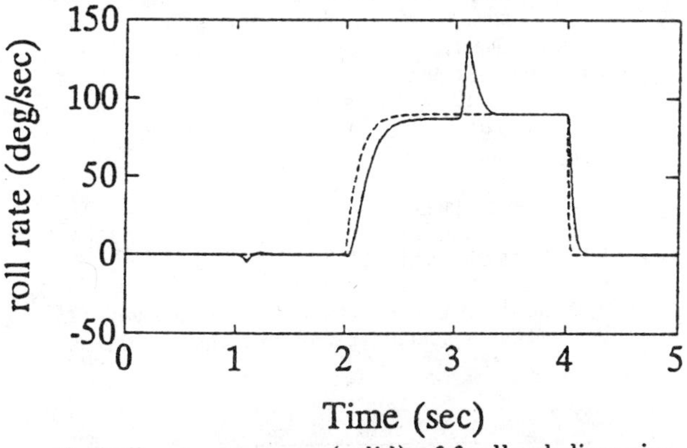

Figure 4b Roll rate response (solid) of feedback linearization controller with a 20 degree angle of attack maneuver

Proceedings of the
American Control Conference
San Francisco, California • June 1993

OPTIMAL SLIDING MODE CONTROL OF A FLEXIBLE SPACECRAFT UNDER STOCHASTIC DISTURBANCES

by

Alok Sinha[1]
Department of Mechanical Engineering
The Pennsylvania State University
University Park, PA 16802

and

David W. Miller[2]
Space Engineering Research Center
Massachusetts Institute of Technology
Cambridge, MA 02139

ABSTRACT

A new optimal sliding mode (OSM) controller is developed for a linear stochastic system and applied to the Middeck Active Control Experiment (MACE) which represents the control structure interaction problem for a precision spacecraft. The OSM controller minimizes the expected value of a quadratic objective function consisting of only states with the constraints that estimated states always remain on the intersection of sliding hyperplanes This controller is designed for two subsets of MACE problems: a single input, single output gimbal inertial pointing problem and a three input, three output torque wheel attitude control problem. Using numerical simulations, performance of the OSM controller is compared to that of the classical LQG controller. The OSM controllers are digitally implemented on the Development Model of MACE. The experimental results are shown to be in good agreement with theoretical results.

NOMENCLATURE

A: system matrix
B: input matrix
C: output matrix
E(.) : expected value
$F(S)$, $F_S(S)$ and $F_G(S)$: controller transfer functions
G : mxn matrix defining sliding hyperplanes
H : similarity transformation matrix
I_n : n-dimensional identity matrix
J, J_g, J_s : quadratic objective functions
K: defined by equation (38)
K_F: gain matrix for Kalman Filter
K_G : LQG controller gain matrix
L: disturbance matrix
m: number of inputs
n: number of states
p: number of outputs
P : defined by equation (7)
Q: symmetric positive semidefinite matrix
q(t): transformed state vector, defined by equation (23)
$q_1(t)$: vector containing first n-m elements of q(t)
$q_2(t)$: vector containing last m elements of q(t)
S(t): defined by equation (11)
s_i : variable defining ith sliding hyperplane
S: Laplace transformation variable
t: time
U(t): control input vector
V(t): state estimation error vector
X(t): state vector
$X_e(t)$: estimated state vector
Y(t): output vector
$\Delta(S)$: sensitivity function
$\Gamma(S)$: open loop transfer function
η: a positive number
μ: measure of boundary layer thickness
ν: η/μ
$\Psi(S)$: closed loop transfer function relating disturbance and output

1. INTRODUCTION

The active control of a flexible spacecraft is an important area of research. The future generation of spacecraft will consist of a highly flexible structure with multiple payloads[1]. The requirements on pointing accuracies for the attached payloads are going to be much higher. Hence, it is inevitable that the control bandwidth required for precision pointing will excite the flexible structural modes. This is known as control structure interaction (CSI). In addition, the controller for each payload must reject the disturbances caused by simultaneous maneuvering of other payloads. To develop design guidelines for a precision spacecraft with multiple payloads, the Middeck Active Control Experiment (MACE) is being developed by the Space Engineering Research Center at MIT[2]. The Development Model (DM) shown in Figure 1 is the first of three sets of hardware to be developed under the MACE program[3]. The DM is composed of a flexible bus which supports a two-axis gimballing payload, and a dummy mass which will be replaced by a second gimbal in the near future. A three-axis torque wheel assembly is placed for the attitude control of the flexible bus. The various identification and control experiments are scheduled to be performed in the middeck of the space shuttle in 1994. The control problem is set as a stochastic regulator problem where stochastic broadband torque disturbances have to be rejected in order to obtain a required pointing accuracy of a payload[4].

This paper deals with the development of a new optimal sliding mode (OSM) control system for a linear stochastic system

[1]Associate Professor, Member AIAA
[2]Principal Research Scientist, Member AIAA

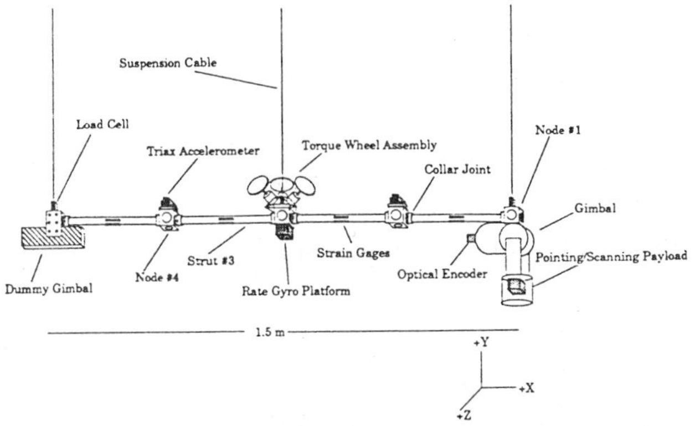

Figure 1: Development Model of MACE

and its application to the Development Model of MACE. Since all the states cannot be known for a flexible structure, the control law must be based on the measured outputs. The states are estimated using the well-known Kalman filter[5]. Then, m number of sliding hyperplanes are defined in the estimated state space, where m is the number of inputs. The control law is defined such that estimated states always remain on the intersection of the chosen set of hyperplanes, Figure 2. These hyperplanes are chosen to minimize a quadratic objective function J consisting of only states. This optimization task reduces to the solution of a standard LQ problem in n-m dimensions where n is the number of states. In other words, n-m closed-loop poles are determined by the optimal choice of sliding hyperplanes. The remaining m closed loop poles are governed by the thicknesses of boundary layers around hyperplanes. For a stochastic linear system, it is shown that the aforementioned control law minimizes the expected value of the quadratic objective function J. Here, the constraints for optimization are that all the

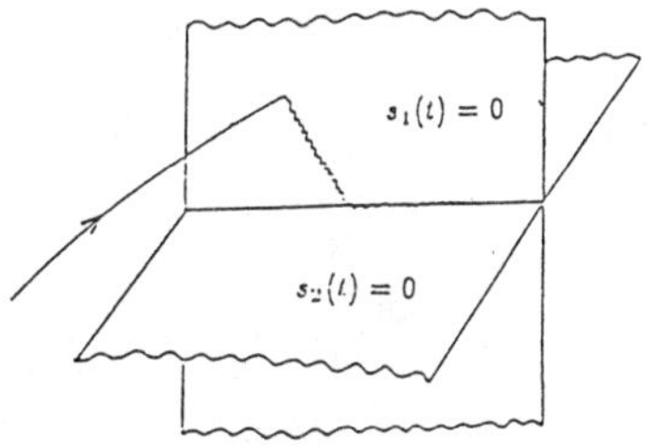

Figure 2: Sliding Manifold

estimated states are always on the intersection of sliding hyperplanes. Compared to the well-known LQG control[5] in which the objective function must contain the input term, the optimal sliding mode control law can be viewed as an alternate way of optimizing the system.

The sliding mode control technique was originally developed in the Soviet Union[6,7] and has recently attracted attention of researchers in other countries[8,9]. Sinha and Kao[10-11] have studied the asymptotic behavior of closed-loop systems inside boundary layers for a full-state feedback deterministic control of vibration in flexible structures. Kao and Sinha[12] examined the robustness of the sliding mode control system with estimated states to spillover phenomena caused by residual modes of vibration. However, they did not consider a stochastic system. Yurkovich et al.[13] have developed a model reference sliding mode control law for a deterministic flexible structure. They did not deal with the issue of optimality and their controller does not guarantee the behavior of structures at those locations where sensors are not mounted.

First, the theoretical development of OSM controller is presented for a linear stochastic system. Then, two subsets of MACE control problems are considered. The first control problem[3] deals with a single input, single output system which pertains to controlling the inertial angle of the gimbal mounted payload subject to stochastic torque disturbance in the gimbal. The second problem deals with the attitude control of the flexible bus by torque wheels under stochastic disturbances. In each case, the sensitivity of the OSM controller is compared to that of the LQG controller for the similar level of performance in terms of disturbance rejection. Lastly, experimental results are obtained by digitally implementing OSM controllers and are compared with theoretical results.

2. DEVELOPMENT OF SLIDING MODE CONTROL SYSTEM

Consider the following linear stochastic system:

$$\frac{dX(t)}{dt} = A\,X(t) + B\,U(t) + L\,\xi(t) \tag{1}$$

$$Y(t) = C\,X(t) + \theta(t) \tag{2}$$

where states $X(t) \in R^n$, input $U(t) \in R^m$ and output $Y(t) \in R^p$. It is assumed that (A,B) and (A,C) are controllable and observable, respectively. The plant disturbance vector $\xi(t)$ and the sensor noise vector $\theta(t)$ contain independent white noise processes with zero mean as their elements. Let their covariance matrices be defined as follows:

$$E(\,\xi(t)\,\xi^T(\tau)) = Q_0\,\delta(t-\tau) \tag{3}$$

$$E(\,\theta(t)\,\theta^T(\tau)) = R_0\,\delta(t-\tau) \tag{4}$$

where $\delta(t-\tau)$ is the dirac-delta function.

Using the Kalman filter, the estimated state vector $X_e(t)$ is given by the following relationship:

$$\frac{dX_e(t)}{dt} = A\,X_e(t) + B\,U(t) + K_F\,(\,Y(t) - C\,X_e(t)\,) \tag{5}$$

where the gain matrix K_F is given by

$$K_F = PC^TR_0^{-1} \tag{6}$$

$$PA^T + AP + Q_0 - PC^TR_0^{-1}CP = 0 \tag{7}$$

For m inputs, m hyperplanes passing through the origin of the estimated state space are defined as follows:

$$s_i(t) = g_i^T\,X_e(t);\; i = 1, 2, \ldots\ldots\ldots, m \tag{8}$$

If the estimated states never leave sliding hyperplanes, $\frac{ds_i}{dt} = 0$. This condition and the equation (5) yield the following relationship for the equivalent controller:

$$U_{eq}(t) = -\,(GB)^{-1}[\,G(A - K_FC)X_e(t) + GK_FY(t)] \tag{9}$$

where

$$G = [g_1, g_2, \ldots\ldots\ldots\ldots\ldots\ldots, g_m]^T \tag{10}$$

From (8) and (10),

$$S(t) = G\,X_e(t) \tag{11}$$

where

$$S(t) = [s_1(t), s_2(t), \ldots\ldots\ldots, s_m(t)]^T \tag{12}$$

The conditions for any initial state to reach the sliding manifold (intersection of sliding hyperplanes, Figure 2) are called the reaching conditions which are described as $s_i\frac{ds_i}{dt} < 0$; i = 1, 2, ..., m. To satisfy these reaching conditions, the control law is chosen as

$$U(t) = U_{eq}(t) - (GB)^{-1}\,\mathrm{diag}\,(\eta)\,\mathrm{sgn}\,(S(t)) \tag{13}$$

where diag (η) is a diagonal matrix with the ith diagonal equal to a positive number η_i. The ith element of the vector sgn (S(t)) is defined as follows:

$$\text{sgn}(s_i(t)) = \begin{cases} +1 \text{ if } s_i(t) > 0 \\ -1 \text{ if } s_i(t) < 0 \end{cases} \quad (14)$$

To eliminate the chattering behavior caused by the sgn function, a boundary layer[8] is introduced around each sliding hyperplane by replacing the sgn function in (13) by the saturation function. Hence, the control law (13) is modified to be

$$U(t) = U_{eq}(t) - (GB)^{-1} \text{diag}(\eta)\ \text{sat}(S(t)) \quad (15)$$

The ith element of sat(S(t)) is described as

$$\text{sat}(s_i(t)) = \begin{cases} \text{sgn}(s_i(t)) \text{ if } |s_i(t)| > \mu_i \\ s_i(t)/\mu_i \text{ otherwise} \end{cases} \quad (16)$$

where μ_i is a measure of the boundary layer thickness around the ith hyperplane. Although sat(S(t)) is a nonlinear function, the closed-loop system is linear inside boundary layers where it can be shown that

$$\frac{ds_i}{dt} = -\frac{\eta_i}{\mu_i} s_i(t) \quad (17)$$

For state estimation, $X_e(0)$ is typically set to zero. In this case, S(0) = 0 and the solution of equation (17) indicates that S(t) = 0. Therefore, estimated states will never leave hyperplanes and the resulting feedback control law will be linear. Using (9), (15) and (16), the effective linear control law is given by

$$U(t) = -(GB)^{-1}[G(A - K_F C + \frac{\eta}{\mu} I_n) X_e(t) + G K_F Y(t)] \quad (18)$$

Without any loss of generality, η_i and μ_i have been assumed to be η and μ, respectively. Note that the control law utilizes the direct feedback of the output in addition to the feedback of estimated states.

3. DYNAMICS OF THE CLOSED LOOP SYSTEM

Using (1), (5) and (18), the dynamics of the closed loop system can be described as follows:

$$\begin{bmatrix} \frac{dX(t)}{dt} \\ \frac{dV(t)}{dt} \end{bmatrix} = \begin{bmatrix} A-\Omega(A+\nu I_n) & \Omega(A+\nu I_n)-\Omega K_F C \\ 0 & A-K_F C \end{bmatrix} \begin{bmatrix} X(t) \\ V(t) \end{bmatrix} + \begin{bmatrix} L & -\Omega K_F \\ L & -K_F \end{bmatrix} \begin{bmatrix} \xi(t) \\ \theta(t) \end{bmatrix} \quad (19)$$

where

$$V(t) = X(t) - X_e(t) \quad (20)$$

$$\nu = \eta/\mu \quad (21)$$

and

$$\Omega = B(GB)^{-1}G \quad (22)$$

Equation (19) indicates that the eigenvalues of the closed-loop system are those of $A-\Omega(A+\nu I_n)$ and $A-K_FC$. The dynamics of the state estimation error V(t) is governed by the eigenvalues of $A-K_FC$. It is also clear that $A-\Omega(A+\nu I_n)$ is the closed-loop system matrix for the full-state regulator problem. Hence, the eigenvalue separation property holds[5].

Lemma 1: The m eigenvalues of $A-\Omega(A+\nu I_n)$ are $-\nu$ and the remaining n-m eigenvalues can be arbitrarily placed in the *S*-plane by a proper choice of G since the system (A,B) is controllable.

Proof: Let the columns of a matrix P_1 be composed of basis vectors of the null space[14-15] of B^T. Define a similarity transformation

$$q(t) = H\,X(t) \quad (23)$$

where

$$H = [P_1\ B]^T \quad (24)$$

From (1) and (23) and ignoring the disturbance,

$$\frac{dq(t)}{dt} = \underline{A}\, q(t) + \underline{B}\, U(t) \quad (25)$$

where

$$\underline{A} = H A H^{-1} \quad (26)$$

$$\underline{B} = H B \quad (27)$$

Because of the special structure of H, it can be seen that the first n-m rows of $\underline{B}$ will be zero. Hence, decomposing q(t) as $[q_1(t)^T\ q_2(t)^T]^T$ where $q_1(t)$ and $q_2(t)$ are n-m and m dimensional vectors, equation (25) can be written as

$$\begin{bmatrix} \frac{dq_1}{dt} \\ \frac{dq_2}{dt} \end{bmatrix} = \begin{bmatrix} A_{11} & A_{12} \\ A_{21} & A_{22} \end{bmatrix} \begin{bmatrix} q_1(t) \\ q_2(t) \end{bmatrix} + \begin{bmatrix} 0 \\ B_r \end{bmatrix} U(t) \quad (28)$$

or

$$\frac{dq_1}{dt} = A_{11}\, q_1(t) + A_{12}\, q_2(t) \quad (29)$$

$$\frac{dq_2}{dt} = A_{21}\, q_1(t) + A_{22}\, q_2(t) + B_r\, U(t) \quad (30)$$

Now, S(t) can be expressed as

$$S(t) = q_2(t) + K\, q_1(t) \quad (31)$$

For a full-state regulator problem, equation (11) will take the form of S(t) = GX(t). Hence, from (23) and (31),

$$G = [K\ I_m]\, H \quad (32)$$

Substituting (31) into (29) and using (17), system dynamics for the full state regulator problem can be represented as

$$\begin{bmatrix} \frac{dq_1}{dt} \\ \frac{dS}{dt} \end{bmatrix} = \begin{bmatrix} A_{11}-A_{12}K & A_{12} \\ 0 & -\nu I_m \end{bmatrix} \begin{bmatrix} q_1(t) \\ S(t) \end{bmatrix} \quad (33)$$

Using (23) and (31), it is recognized that X(t) and $[q_1^T\ S(t)^T]^T$ are related by similarity transformation. Since the closed loop system matrix for the full state regulator problem is $A-\Omega(A+\nu I_n)$ and the eigenvalues remain unchanged under similarity transformation, the eigenvalues of $A-\Omega(A+\nu I_n)$ are those of $A_{11}-A_{12}K$ and $-\nu I_m$. Hence, m eigenvalues of $A-\Omega(A+\nu I_n)$ are $-\nu$ and the remaining n-m eigenvalues are those of $A_{11}-A_{12}K$.

When S(t) = 0, $q_2(t) = -K\, q_1(t)$. In view of equation (29), K is a state feedback vector. Utkin and Yang[14] have shown that (A_{11}, A_{12}) is controllable if (A,B) is controllable. Hence, eigenvalues of $A_{11}-A_{12}K$ can be arbitrarily placed in the *S*-plane by a proper choice of K. Since the choice of K directly yields G (equation 32), it is clear that n-m eigenvalues of $A-\Omega(A+\nu I_n)$ can be arbitrarily placed by a proper choice of G. This completes the proof.

4. OPTIMAL CHOICE OF SLIDING HYPERPLANES OR THE MATRIX G

For the full-state and deterministic regulator problem, the

matrix G will be sought to minimize the following quadratic objective function:

$$J = \int_0^{\infty} X^T(t)QX(t)\,dt \tag{34}$$

where Q is symmetric and positive semidefinite. From (23) and (34),

$$J = \int_0^{\infty} q^T(t)\,(H^{-1})^T Q\, H^{-1} q(t)\,dt \tag{35}$$

Since the signs of eigenvalues are preserved under congruence transformation[15], the matrix $(H^{-1})^T QH^{-1}$ is symmetric and positive semidefinite. Define

$$(H^{-1})^T QH^{-1} = \begin{bmatrix} Q_1 & N \\ N^T & R \end{bmatrix} \tag{36}$$

Now, equation (35) can be written as

$$J = \int_0^{\infty} q_1{}^T(t)Q_1q_1(t)+2q_1{}^T(t)Nq_2(t)+q_2{}^T(t)Rq_2(t)\,dt \tag{37}$$

Equations (37) and (29) represent a standard LQ problem[14] provided $R > 0$. If Q is chosen to be positive definite, R is guaranteed to be positive definite because the signs of eigenvalues are preserved under congruence transformation. When Q is not positive definite; e.g., $Q = C^TC$ with $p < n$, R may not be positive definite. If R does not turn out to be positive definite as it will be seen in section 5, it has to be arbitrarily chosen to be a positive definite function. In this case, a new Q will be defined according to equation (36).

The gain matrix K which minimizes (37) is[5]

$$K = R^{-1}\,[A_{12}{}^TP_2 + N^T] \tag{38}$$

where

$$P_2(A_{11} - A_{12}R^{-1}N^T) + (A_{11}{}^T - N\,R^{-1}A_{12}{}^T)P_2 - P_2\,A_{12}\,R^{-1}\,A_{12}{}^T\,P_2 + Q_1 - NR^{-1}N^T = 0 \tag{39}$$

The optimal G is then obtained by substituting (38) into (32).

Lemma 2: For the stochastic system (1), (2) and (5), the G chosen on the basis of equation (38) minimizes the following function:

$$J_s = E\{\lim_{T\to\infty}\frac{1}{T}\int_0^T X(t)^TQX(t)\,dt\} \tag{40}$$

It should be noted that the constraint for minimization of the function (40) is $S(t) = G\,X_e(t) = 0$.

Proof:

For the Kalman filter, it is well-known[5] that

$$E(X_e(t)\,V^T(t)) = 0 \tag{41}$$

Using (41), it can be shown that

$$E(X(t)^TQX(t)) = E(X_e(t)^T\,Q\,X_e(t)) + \mathrm{tr}\,(Q\Sigma) \tag{42}$$

where

$$\Sigma = E(V(t)V(t)^T) \tag{43}$$

From (19), $\mathrm{tr}(Q\Sigma)$ is independent of the input U(t). Hence, the minimization problem described in Lemma 2 can be recast as follows:

Find G which minimizes

$$J_m = E\{\lim_{T\to\infty}\frac{1}{T}\int_0^T X_e(t)^TQX_e(t)dt\} \tag{44}$$

subject to equation (5) and $S(t) = G\,X_e(t) = 0$.

Equation (5) can be rewritten as

$$\frac{dX_e}{dt} = A\,X_e(t) + B\,U(t) + K_F\,\chi(t) \tag{45}$$

where

$$\chi(t) = Y(t) - C\,X_e(t) \tag{46}$$

It is recalled that the function $\chi(t)$ is known as the innovation process. It is well-known[16] that this is a white noise process with intensity R_0. Using the similarity transformation matrix $q_e(t)=HX_e(t)$, an equation similar to (29) is obtained:

$$\frac{dq_{e1}}{dt} = A_{11}\,q_{e1}(t) + A_{12}\,q_{e2}(t) + (HK_F)_{nm}\,\chi(t) \tag{47}$$

where $q_e(t) = [q_{e1}{}^T(t)\ q_{e2}{}^T(t)]^T$ and the matrix $(HK_F)_{nm}$ is the first n-m rows of the matrix HK_F. The corresponding form of the objective function (44) under the similarity transformation will be

$$J_m = E\{\lim_{T\to\infty}\frac{1}{T}\int_0^T q_{e1}{}^TQ_1q_{e1} + 2q_{e1}{}^TNq_{e2} + q_{e2}{}^TRq_{e2}\,dt\,\} \tag{48}$$

It should be recalled that $S(t) = q_{e2}(t) + Kq_{e1}(t)$. Using the stochastic regulator theory[16] with full state feedback, it is obvious that the matrix G (or K) which minimizes (37) also minimizes (48) which is same as (44). This completes the proof.

5. APPLICATION TO MACE

The optimal sliding mode control law is developed and digitally implemented for two subsets of the MACE control problem. The first problem deals with single input, single output payload inertial pointing and the second problem pertains to three input, three output attitude control. Using numerical simulations[17], performance of the optimal sliding mode controller is compared to that of an LQG controller for which the following objective function is minimized:

$$J_g = \lim_{T\to\infty} E\{\frac{1}{T}\int_0^T Y(t)^TY(t) + \rho\,U(t)^TU(t)dt\} \tag{49}$$

The LQG controller transfer function is described as follows:

$$U(S) = -\,F_G(S)\,Y(S) \tag{50}$$

where

$$F_G(S) = K_G(SI_n - A + BK_G + K_FC)^{-1}K_F \tag{51}$$

and K_G is the LQG controller gain matrix.

Using equations (5) and (18), the optimal sliding mode controller transfer function is obtained as follows:

$$U(S) = -F_S(S)\,Y(S) \tag{52}$$

where

$$F_S(S) = K_S(SI_n - A + BK_S + K_FC)^{-1}(K_F - B(GB)^{-1}GK_F) + (GB)^{-1}GK_F \tag{53}$$

and

$$K_S = (GB)^{-1}G(A + \nu I_n - K_F C) \quad (54)$$

The performance of the control system is measured by the magnitude of closed loop transfer function relating the disturbance and the output vectors. This transfer function is defined as

$$\Psi(S) = (I_p + \Gamma(S)\, F(S))^{-1}\, \Gamma(S) \quad (55)$$

where $\Gamma(S) = C(SI_n\text{-}A)^{-1}B + D$ is the open loop transfer function and $F(S)$ is the controller transfer function as defined by $F_S(S)$ and $F_G(S)$ for OSM and LQG controllers, respectively. The well-known sensitivity function[5] is defined as

$$\Delta(S) = (\, I_p + \Gamma(S)\, F(S))^{-1} \quad (56)$$

Anderson and Moore[5] have shown that a smaller $\Delta(S)$ implies a greater robustness to structured parametric uncertainties. For a SISO system, the function $\Delta(S)$ is the ratio of a percentage change in the closed-loop transfer function and the percentage change in the open loop transfer function.

The state space model of $F_S(S)$ is discretized using the tustin method for digital implementation with AC100[18]. The sampling frequency is taken to be 500 Hz. The experimental results are compared with theoretical results.

5.1 SINGLE INPUT, SINGLE OUTPUT SYSTEM

The objective is to inertially point the payload about the z-axis while a band limited white noise disturbance torque is introduced through the z-axis gimbal motor, which also provides the control input (torque). The response of the flexible bus in the x-y plane is included in the system model. The inertial angle of the payload is measured by the stabilized integral of a rate gyro signal. The stabilized integrator acts as a first order high pass filter at frequencies below 0.03 Hz and integrates the signal above 0.03 Hz.

MODEL

The dynamics of this single input, single output plant is obtained by experimentally measuring[3] the transfer function representing the ratio of stabilized integration of rate gyro signal and the voltage into the gimbal torque motor amplifier. This transfer function represents the dynamics of motor amplifier, gimbal/flexible bus, the rate gyro on the payload, eight pole 150 Hz Bessel anti-aliasing filter, the 0.03 Hz stabilized integrator and the 500 Hz digital delay. The SISO transfer function was then curve-fitted[3] using five complex poles, four complex zeros, a static gain and a time delay. This time delay represents all the delays associated with the processing delay, the anti-aliasing filters and rate gyro dynamics. A third order Pade approximation[17] is used to represent the effects of time delay. The state space model representing the measured transfer function is then developed for the controller design. The dimension of this state space model is 13.

CONTROLLER DESIGN

For the optimal sliding mode control, $Q = C^TC$ is chosen first. For this Q, R defined in equation (37) turns out be zero. Hence, R is arbitrarily taken to be a positive number and it plays the same role as ρ does for the LQG control, equation (49). The inverse of R can be described as a measure of the control authority.

First, R is chosen to be 4. The closed-loop transfer function $\Psi(S)$ relating the disturbance and the output is shown in Figure 3. This is overlayed with the open-loop transfer function calculated using the fitted model. Then, the LQG controller is designed with the same Kalman filter and $\rho = 0.01$ such that $E(YY^T)$ is almost the same as that for the OSM controller. The frequency response of the LQG closed loop transfer function $\Psi(S)$ is also shown in Figure 3. Both the controllers lead to similar levels of performance in terms of disturbance rejection. In Figure 4, LQG and OSM controller transfer functions are plotted. Focusing attention around 6 through 9 Hz, it is seen that the LQG controller results in plant inversion whereas the OSM controller does so to a lesser degree. The magnitudes of the sensitivity functions $\Delta(S)$ for both the controllers are presented in Figure 5. It can be concluded that the sensitivity of the LQG controller is greater than that of the OSM controller.

Next, results are examined for $R = 0.6$ and $\rho = 1e\text{-}4$, which lead to almost equal values of $E(YY^T)$ for both the controllers. Again, it is concluded that the OSM controller is less sensitive than the LQG controller for the similar level of performance, Figure 6.

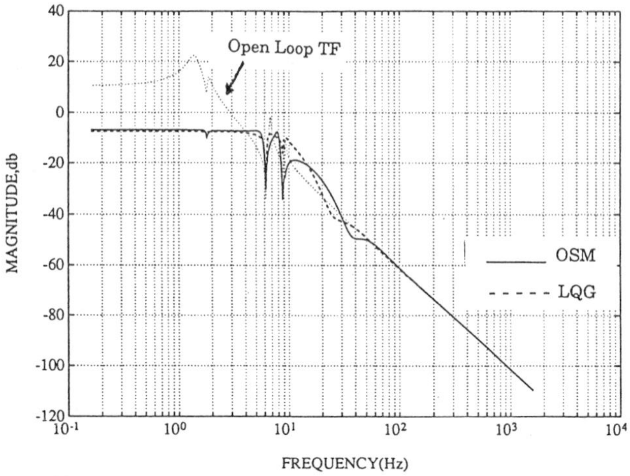

Figure 3: SISO Closed Loop Transfer Functions (R=4, ρ = 0.01)

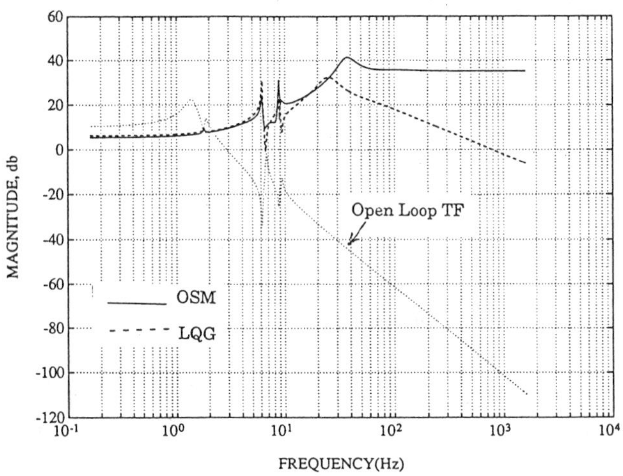

Figure 4: OSM and LQG Controller Transfer Functions

EXPERIMENTAL RESULTS

The OSM controllers for R = 4 and R = 0.6 have been digitally implemented. The experimental CLTF compares well with the theoretical CLTF, Figure 7. The reduction in the rms value of the inertial gimbal position is about 20 db. It should be noted that good performance is obtained with the controller derived on the basis of a model which was developed several months ago. LQG controllers which stabilized the plant when this model was new have subsequently been destabilizing due to shifts in dynamics caused by reassembly of the hardware. In this sense[3], the OSM controller seems to be more robust than the LQG controller.

5.2 THREE INPUT, THREE OUTPUT SYSTEM

The three inputs are independent torques produced by three torque wheels whereas the three outputs are the inertial angles of the flexible bus, which are obtained by the stabilized integration of rate gyros' signals. The broadband torque disturbances are also provided by torque wheels; i.e. L = B. The objective is to control the attitudes of the flexible bus under the torque disturbances.

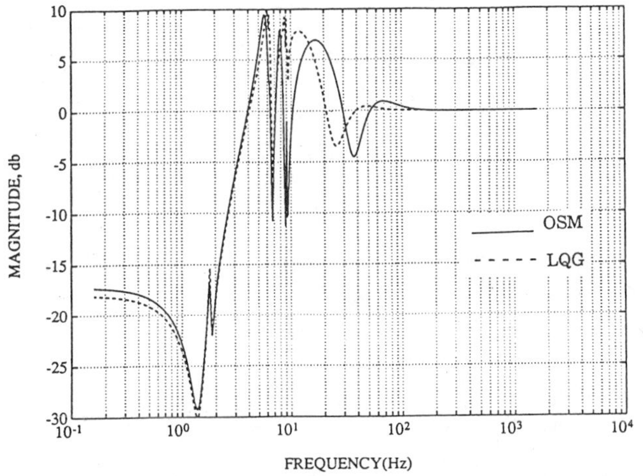

Figure 5: Magnitudes of Sensitivity Functions (R = 4, ρ = 0.01)

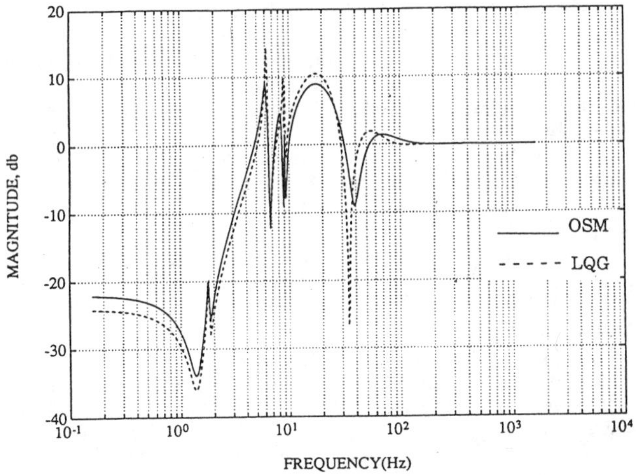

Figure 6: Magnitudes of Sensitivity Functions (R = 0.6, $\rho = 10^{-4}$)

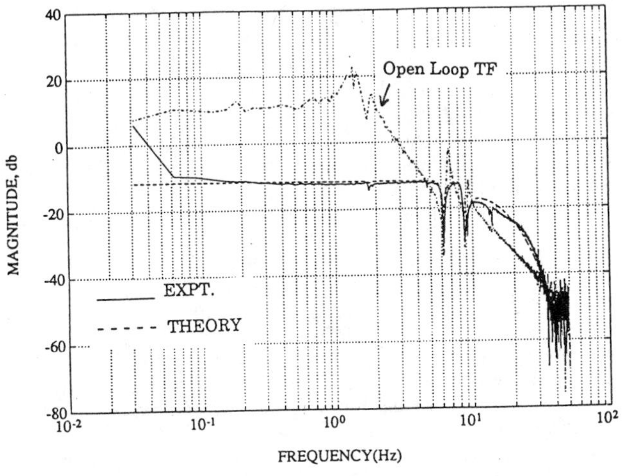

Figure 7: Experimental OSM Closed Loop Transfer Function (R = 0.6)

MODEL

The dynamic model is obtained by measuring three single input, three output (SITO) transfer functions by applying only one input at a time. On the basis of these three SITO transfer functions, a MIMO model is obtained. A total time delay of 15.2 msec was estimated to be present in each input channel. Each of these time delays is modeled by a fourth order Pade approximation. Excluding time delays, the order of the state space model is 52. Neglecting the higher modes, this model is reduced to have 36 states. This reduced order model is then augmented to include the state space model representing the Pade approximations for time delays. Hence, the controller is designed on the basis of a model with 48 states.

CONTROLLER DESIGN

For the OSM controller design, Q is again chosen to be C^TC. The corresponding R in equation (37) turns out to be nearly singular. Therefore, R is chosen to be $\rho_s I_3$ where ρ_s is a positive number.

In Figures 8-10, the magnitudes of the diagonal elements of the closed-loop transfer function matrix $\Psi(S)$ are shown for the OSM controller with ρ_s = 0.03. The maximum singular value of the corresponding sensitivity function $\Delta(S)$ is shown in Figure 11. In Figure 11, the maximum singular value of the sensitivity function $\Delta(S)$ is also plotted for a LQG controller with ρ = 0.01. This value of ρ is chosen so that the LQG controller led to almost same values of $E(YY^T)$ as those for the OSM controller. Comparing maximum singular values in Figure 11, it can be said that the LQG controller is more sensitive to plant parameter variations than the OSM controller.

EXPERIMENTAL RESULTS

The OSM controller is digitally implemented and the stochastic disturbance torque is introduced about only one axis at a time. The experimental results for the OSM controller with ρ_s = 0.03 are shown in Figures 8-10. It is clear that experimental results compare well with theoretical results. The reductions in the rms values of the angular positions are about 16.5 db in X-direction, about 17.25 db in y-direction and about 8.35 db in Z-direction. Although the LQG controller derived with ρ = 0.01 leads to similar levels of performance in theory, it led to an unstable closed-loop system when implemented.

6. SUMMARY AND CONCLUSIONS

A new optimal sliding mode (OSM) controller has been developed for a linear stochastic system. The states are estimated using the Kalman filter and m number of sliding hyperplanes are defined in the estimated state space where m is the number of inputs. It has been shown that m controller poles are determined by the thicknesses of boundary layers and remaining n-m poles are governed by the choice of sliding hyperplanes where n is the number of states. The sliding hyperplanes are chosen to minimize the expected value of a quadratic objective function consisting of only states. This task requires the solution of a LQ problem in n-m dimensions.

The OSM controller has been applied to the Development model of the Middeck Active Control Experiment(MACE). Two subsets of control problems have been considered: a single input, single output payload inertial pointing problem and a three input, three output attitude control problem. The results from numerical simulations indicate that the sensitivity function for the OSM controller is smaller than that for the LQG controller.

For both subsets of control problems, experimental closed-loop transfer functions relating the disturbance and the output compare well with theoretical results. The experimental results indicate that the OSM controller can result in significant reductions in the rms values of the outputs.

7. ACKNOWLEDGMENTS

This work was performed while the first author was on sabbatical at the MIT Space Engineering Research Center. The first author wishes to thank Professor E. F. Crawley for his help. The authors also thank Mr. E. Saarmaa for helping with the experiments.

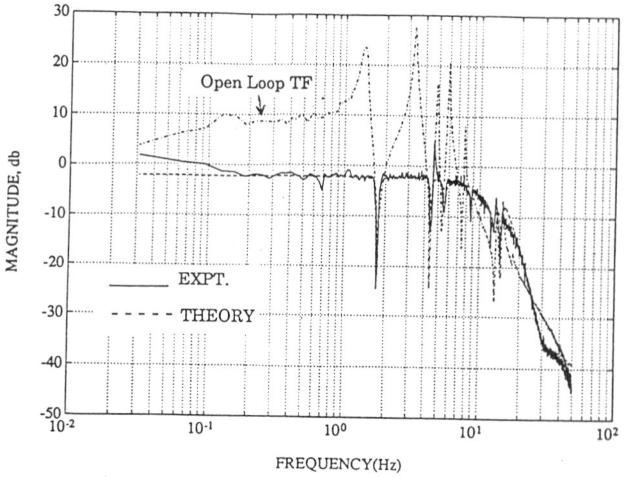

Figure 8: X-axis TITO Closed Loop Transfer Function with OSM Controller

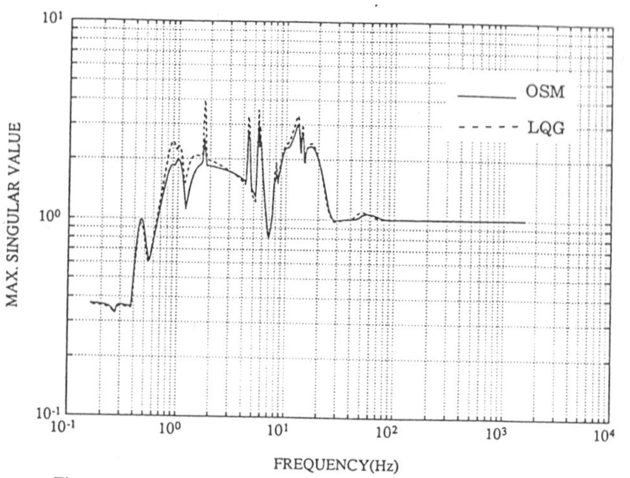

Figure 11: Maximum Singular Values of Sensitivity Functions for TITO System

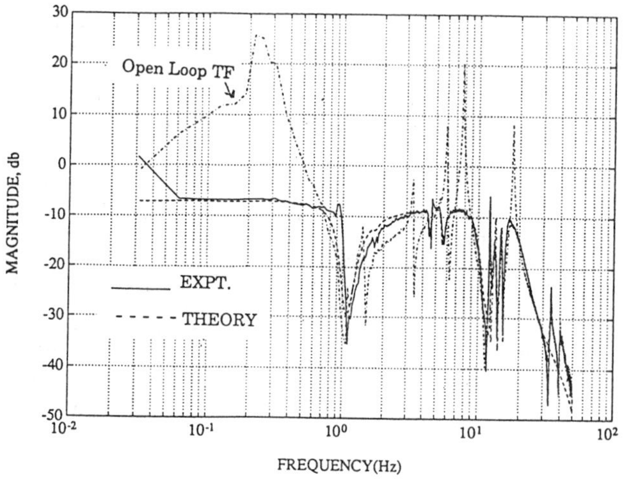

Figure 9: Y-axis TITO Closed Loop Transfer Function with OSM Controller

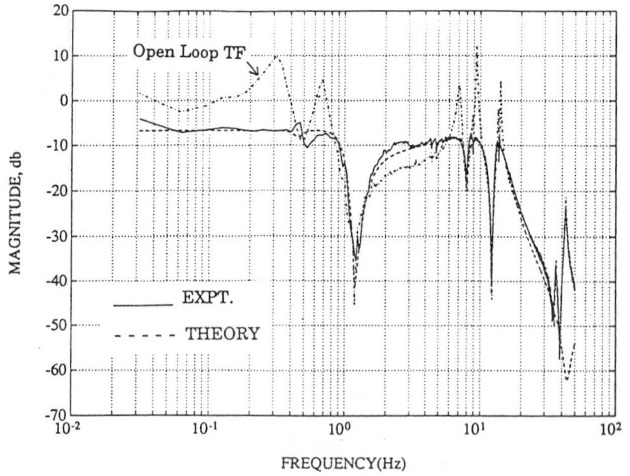

Figure 10: Z-axis TITO Closed Loop Transfer Function with OSM Controller

REFERENCES

[1]Laskin, R. A. and Sirlin, S. W., "Future Payload Isolation and Pointing System Technology," AIAA Journal of Guidance, Control and Dynamics, Vol. 9, No. 4, 1986, pp. 469 - 477.

[2]Miller, D. W., de Luis, J. and Crawley, E. F., "Dynamics and Control of Multipayload Platforms: The Middeck Active Control Experiment (MACE)," Paper # IAF-90-292, 41st Congress of the International Astronautical Federation, Dresden, GDR, October 1990.

[3]Miller D. W., Saarmaa, E. and Jacques, R. N., "Preliminary Structural Control Results from the Middeck Active Control Experiments (MACE)," AIAA Dynamics Specialists Conference, Dallas, TX, 1992.

[4]Mercadel, M., "The Middeck Active Control Experiment First Sample Problem: Sensor and Actuator Selection, Sensor and Actuator Pairing," SERC Report # 6 - 91 - R, MIT, Cambridge, MA, June 1991.

[5]Anderson, B. D. O. and Moore, J. B., "Optimal Control: Linear Quadratic Methods," Prentice Hall Inc., 1990.

[6]Utkin, V. I., "Variable Structure Systems with Sliding Modes: A Survey," IEEE Transactions on Automatic Control, Vol. AC-22, No. 2, 1977, pp. 212 - 222.

[7]Utkin, V. I., "Variable Structure Systems: Present and Future," Automation and Remote Control, Vol. 44, No. 9, 1983, pp. 1105-1119.

[8]Slotine, J. J. E., "The Robust Control of Robot Manipulators," International Journal of Robotic Research, Vol. 4, No. 2, 1985, pp. 49 - 64.

[9]Oz, H. and Mostafa, O., "Variable Structure Control System (VSCS) Maneuvering of a Flexible Spacecraft," The Journal of the Astronautical Sciences, Vol. 36, No. 3, 1988, pp. 311-344.

[10]Sinha, A. and Kao, C. K., "Independent Modal Sliding Mode Control of Vibration in Flexible Structures," Journal of Sound and Vibration, Vol. 147, No. 2, 1991, pp. 352 - 358.

[11]Kao, C. K. and Sinha, A., "Coupled Modal Sliding Mode Control of Vibration in Flexible Structures," AIAA Journal of Guidance, Dynamics and Control, Vol. 15, No. 1, 1992, pp. 65 - 73.

[12]Kao, C. K. and Sinha, A., "Sliding Mode Control of Vibration in Flexible Structures Using Estimated States," Proceedings of American Control Conference, Vol. 3, 1990, pp. 2467 - 2474.

[13]Yurkovich, S., Ozgunner, U., Al-Abbas, F., "Model Reference Sliding Mode Adaptive Control for Flexible Structures," The Journal of Astronautical Sciences, Vol. 36, No. 3, 1988.

[14]Utkin, V. I. and Yang, K. D., "Methods for Constructing Discontinuity Planes in Multidimensional Variable Structure Systems," Automation and Remote Control, Vol. 39, No. 10, 1978, pp. 1466 - 1470.

[15]Strang, G., "Linear Algebra and Its Applications," Hartcourt Brace Javanovich, Publishers, San Diego, 1988.

[16]Kwakernaak, H. and Sivan, R., "Linear Optimal Control Systems," John Wiley & Sons, Inc., 1972.

[17] PRO-MATLAB User's Guide, The Mathworks,Inc., 1990.

[18]Using the AC-100: AC-100 User's Guide v2.4.03A, Integrated Systems Inc., November 1990.

Proceedings of the
American Control Conference
San Francisco, California • June 1993

Sliding-Mode Controller Design for Spacecraft Attitude Tracking Maneuvers†

Yon-Ping Chen and Shih-Che Lo

Institute of Control Engineering
National Chiao Tung University
Hsinchu, Taiwan 30039, R.O.C

Abstract

This paper presents a robust sliding-mode control law to deal with the spacecraft attitude tracking problems. Two important natural properties related to the spacecraft model of motion are shown and then by using these properties and the second method of Lyapunov thoery, the system stability in the sliding mode can be easily achieved.

1 Introduction

Recently, some investigators [1,2,6] have applied the sliding-mode control (also called the variable-structure control) to the spacecraft attitude maneuvers, for example the detumbling and reorientation. In this paper, a new spacecraft sliding-mode controller is introduced to deal with the attitude tracking problems.

In the tracking controller design, we employ two important natural properties related to the system model. The first one is that the inertia matrix J is symmetric and positive-definite. Second, the matrix $T(\rho)$ in the kinematic equation satisfies $T(\rho) \geq \frac{1}{2}I$ where ρ is the Gibbs vector of Rodrigues attitude parameter and I is the identity matrix. Based on these two natural properties, a sliding vector is selected so that in the sliding mode the attitude tracking can be achieved and the control law can be easily derived to guarantee the reaching and sliding conditions. Besides, the direct method of Lyapunov stability theory is adopted to both the development of sliding-mode control law and the analysis of system stability in the sliding mode. As for the chattering caused by the practical implementation, it can be alleviated by the use of the sliding layer [6].

This paper is orgnized as follows. In the next section, the spacecraft model with two natural properties is presented. In Section 3, with these properties, a robust sliding-mode control law is designed for multiaxial attitude tracking maneuvers and the stability analysis of the system in the sliding mode is shown. Finally, Section 4 gives the concluding remarks.

2 Spacecraft Model Description

The mathematical model of a spacecraft is commonly composed of two sets of equations called the kinematic equations and dynamic equations which can be respectively described by [2,3]

$$\dot{\rho} = T(\rho)\omega \quad (1)$$
$$J\dot{\omega} = H\omega + \tau \quad (2)$$

where $\rho \in \Re^3$ is the Gibbs vector of Rodrigues attitude parameters, $\omega \in \Re^3$ represents the angular velocity, and $\tau \in \Re^3$ is the control input applied to the system. There are two important natural properties [1]:

(I) The inertia matrix J is symmetric and positive-definite,
(II) $T(\rho) \geq \frac{1}{2}I$,

which will be shown useful in the controller design. The inequality of (II) can be directly obtained from

$$x^T[T(\rho) - \frac{1}{2}I]x = \frac{1}{2}(\rho^T x)^2 \geq 0 \qquad \forall x \in \Re^3.$$

†*Research was supported by National Science Council, Taiwan, R.O.C. under the Contract NSC 80-E-sp-009-02D.*

3 Sliding-Mode Controller Design

The sliding-mode controller introduced here is to deal with the multiaxial attitude tracking maneuvers of the spacecraft modeled by (1) and (2). In the controller design, the required feedback signals ω and ρ are assumed to be measurable. Besides, to demonstrate the robustness of the controller, we allow the dynamic equations (2) to possess bounded input disturbances d and parameter variations ΔJ and ΔH; thus, the dynamic equations are rewritten as

$$J\dot{\omega} = H\omega + \tau + d \quad (3)$$

where $J = J_o + \Delta J$, $H = H_o + \Delta H$, and J_o and H_o represent the nominal parts of J and H, respectively. Note that the inertia matrix J is assumed to be time-invariant and its variation ΔJ, for example, may result from the change of payloads of the spacecraft.

The objective of the control are to drive the spacecraft such that $\rho(t) = \rho_d(t)$, i.e., the Gibbs vector tracks the given reference vector $\rho_d(t)$. In general, the design procedure of sliding-mode controller contains two fundamental steps:

Step 1. *Choose the sliding vector such that in the sliding mode the goal of control is achieved.*

Let us first define the errer signal as

$$\varepsilon(t) = \rho(t) - \rho_d(t) \quad (4)$$

and then choose the sliding vector as

$$s(t) = [\omega(t) - \hat{\omega}(t)] + K_p\varepsilon(t), \quad (5)$$

where $\hat{\omega}(t) = T^{-1}(\rho(t))\dot{\rho}_d(t)$, and K_p is a symmetric and positive-definite constant matrix whose eigenvalues will be shown later related to the rate of convergence of the error signal $\varepsilon(t)$. From the sliding-mode theory [7], once the reaching and sliding conditions are satisfied, the system is finally forced to stay in the sliding mode

$$s(t) = [\omega(t) - \hat{\omega}(t)] + K_p\varepsilon(t) = 0. \quad (6)$$

By using the kinematic equations (1) and premultiplying $T(\rho)$ into (6), we have

$$\dot{\varepsilon} + T(\rho)K_p\varepsilon = 0. \quad (7)$$

Let the candidate of Lyapunov function be

$$V_\varepsilon = \frac{1}{2}\varepsilon^T K_p \varepsilon. \quad (8)$$

Then, the derivative of V_ε is

$$\dot{V}_\varepsilon = \varepsilon^T K_p \dot{\varepsilon} = -(K_p\varepsilon)^T T(\rho)(K_p\varepsilon). \quad (9)$$

From property (II), we can further obtain

$$\dot{V}_\varepsilon \leq -\frac{1}{2}(K_p\varepsilon)^T(K_p\varepsilon) \leq 0, \quad (10)$$

and $\dot{V}_\varepsilon = 0$ only if $\varepsilon = 0$. Thus, V_ε is really a Lyapunov function so that the error signal ε will converge to zero. That means the Gibbs vector $\rho(t)$ can track $\rho_d(t)$ successfully. As for the angular velocity vector ω, we can easily derive $[\omega(t) - \hat{\omega}(t)] \to 0$ from (6). Next, let us further discuss about the choice of K_p.

Since K_p is symmetric and positive-definite, it can be decomposed as $K_p = U^T \Sigma U$, where U is the unitary matrix and $\Sigma = diag[\lambda_1\ \lambda_2\ \lambda_3]$ with λ_i's being the positive eigenvalues of K_p. Then the Lyapunov function becomes

$$V_\varepsilon = \frac{1}{2}[\lambda_1 \bar{\varepsilon}_1^2 + \lambda_2 \bar{\varepsilon}_2^2 + \lambda_3 \bar{\varepsilon}_3^2] \tag{11}$$

where $\bar{\varepsilon} = U\varepsilon$ and the derivative of V_ε in (10) can be rewritten as

$$\dot{V}_\varepsilon \leq -\frac{1}{2}[\lambda_1^2 \bar{\varepsilon}_1^2 + \lambda_2^2 \bar{\varepsilon}_2^2 + \lambda_3^2 \bar{\varepsilon}_1^2]. \tag{12}$$

From (11) and (12), we have

$$\dot{V}_\varepsilon = \frac{\dot{V}_\varepsilon}{V_\varepsilon} V_\varepsilon \leq -\frac{[\lambda_1^2 \bar{\varepsilon}_1^2 + \lambda_2^2 \bar{\varepsilon}_2^2 + \lambda_3^2 \bar{\varepsilon}_3^2]}{[\lambda_1 \bar{\varepsilon}_1^2 + \lambda_2 \bar{\varepsilon}_2^2 + \lambda_3 \bar{\varepsilon}_3^2]} V_\varepsilon \leq -\lambda_{min} V_\varepsilon, \tag{13}$$

where $\lambda_{min} = min\{\lambda_1, \lambda_2, \lambda_3\}$. As a result,

$$V_\varepsilon(\varepsilon(t)) \leq V_\varepsilon(\varepsilon(t_h)) e^{-\lambda_{min}(t-t_h)}, \tag{14}$$

where t_h denotes the time reaching the sliding mode. Since $\| \bar{\varepsilon} \| = \| U\varepsilon \| = \| \varepsilon \|$, from (11)

$$\frac{1}{2}\lambda_{min} \| \bar{\varepsilon} \|^2 \leq V_\varepsilon \leq \frac{1}{2}\lambda_{max} \| \bar{\varepsilon} \|^2 \tag{15}$$

where $\lambda_{max} = max\{\lambda_1, \lambda_2, \lambda_3\}$, (14) can be further extended to

$$\| \varepsilon(t) \| \leq \sqrt{\frac{\lambda_{max}}{\lambda_{min}}} \| \varepsilon(t_h) \| e^{-\frac{1}{2}\lambda_{min}(t-t_h)}. \tag{16}$$

This inequality implies the norm $\| \varepsilon \|$ of the tracking errors converge to zero related to an exponential rate of $\frac{1}{2}\lambda_{min}$. Note that if $\lambda_1 = \lambda_2 = \lambda_3 = \lambda$, i.e., $K_p = \lambda \cdot I$, (16) becomes

$$\| \varepsilon(t) \| \leq \| \varepsilon(t_h) \| e^{-\frac{\lambda}{2}(t-t_h)}$$

and from (6), $(\omega - \hat{\omega}) = -\lambda(\rho - \rho_d) = -\lambda\varepsilon$ or equivalently, $\| \omega - \hat{\omega} \| = \lambda \| \varepsilon \|$. That means $\| \omega - \hat{\omega} \|$ will converge to zero with the same rate $-\frac{\lambda}{2}$ as $\| \varepsilon \|$. Hence, in the next step, for simplicity we choose $K_p = \lambda I$ and then the sliding vector (5) becomes

$$s(t) = [\omega(t) - \hat{\omega}(t)] + \lambda[\rho(t) - \rho_d(t)]. \tag{17}$$

Step 2. *Design the control laws such that the reaching and sliding conditions are satisfied.*

From the truth that J is symmetric and positive-definite, the candidate of Lyapunov function is set as

$$V_s = \frac{1}{2}s^T J s \geq 0 \tag{18}$$

and $V_s = 0$ only when $s = 0$. Taking the first derivative of V_s and adopting (1), (3), and (17), we have

$$\dot{V}_s = s^T[H\omega + \tau + d - J\dot{\hat{\omega}} + \lambda J T(\rho)\omega - \lambda J \dot{\rho}_d] \tag{19}$$

Let the control law be

$$\tau = -H_o\omega + J_o\dot{\hat{\omega}} - \lambda J_o[T(\rho)\omega - \dot{\rho}_d] + \tau' \tag{20}$$

where

$$\begin{aligned} \dot{\hat{\omega}} &= \frac{d}{dt}(T^{-1}(\rho))\dot{\rho}_d + T^{-1}(\rho)\ddot{\rho}_d, \qquad (21) \\ \tau' &= \begin{bmatrix} \tau_1' & \tau_2' & \tau_3' \end{bmatrix}^T, \quad \tau_i' = -k_i \cdot sgn(s_i), \\ sgn(s_i) &= \begin{cases} 1 & s_i > 0 \\ -1 & s_i < 0 \end{cases} \quad i = 1, 2, 3. \end{aligned}$$

Then

$$\dot{V}_s = s^T[\delta + \tau'] = \sum_{i=1}^{3} -k_i|s_i|[1 - \frac{\delta_i}{k_i} sgn(s_i)] \tag{22}$$

where

$$\delta = \Delta H\omega + \Delta J\dot{\hat{\omega}} + \lambda \Delta J[T(\rho)\omega - \dot{\rho}_d] + d$$

Since the external disturbances d and uncertain parameters ΔJ and ΔH are all bounded, the upper bound of $|\delta_i|$ can be found and denoted as $\delta_i^{max}(\omega, \rho, \rho_d, \dot{\rho}_d, \ddot{\rho}_d, t)$. It is evident that if we choose $k_i = \delta_i^{max}(\omega, \rho, \rho_d, \dot{\rho}_d, \ddot{\rho}_d, t)$, for $i = 1, 2, 3$, then (22) becomes

$$\dot{V}_s = -\sum_{i=1}^{3} \delta_i^{max}|s_i|[1 - \frac{\delta_i}{\delta_i^{max}} sgn(s_i)] < 0$$

for $s \neq 0$. This implies V_s is really a Lyapunov function. Therefore, the reaching and sliding of the sliding mode $s = 0$ is guaranteed.

However, due to the existence of nonideality in the pratical implementation of the sign function $sgn(s_i)$, the control law τ in (20) always suffers from the chattering problem. To alleviate such undesirable performance, the sign function can be simply replaced by the saturation function [4]

$$sat(s_i, \epsilon) = \begin{cases} 1 & s_i > \epsilon \\ s_i/\epsilon & |s_i| < \epsilon \\ -1 & s_i < -\epsilon \end{cases}. \tag{23}$$

It is notice that the system is now no longer forced to stay in the sliding mode but be constrained within the sliding layer $|s_i| \leq \epsilon$. The cost of such substitution is a reduction in the accuracy of the desired performance.

4 Conclusion

In this paper, sliding-mode thoery is applied to the controller design for attitude tracking maneuvers of a spacecraft which generally possesses two important natural properties related to the inertia matrix J and matrix $T(\rho)$. With these properties and based on the direct method of the Lyapunov stability thoery, a new sliding vector is selected and two significant Lyapunov functions are introduced in the controller design. The convergent rate of the error signal is also dicussed in the first step of the design procedure. As for the chattering problem, the saturation functions are suggested to replaced the sign functions.

References

[1] Chen,Y.P., "Robust attitude and orbit control of satellites," Project Report for National Science Council, R.O.C., Grant No. 80-E-SP-009-02D, 1992.

[2] Dywer,T.A.W.III, and Sira-Ramirez,H., "Variable-Structure Control of Spacecraft Attitude Maneuvers," Journal of Guidance, Control, and Dynamics, Vol.11, No.3, 1988, pp.262-270.

[3] Kane,T.R., Likins,P.W., and Levinson,D.A., *Spacecraft Dynamics,* McGraw-Hill Book Co., New York, 1983.

[4] Slotine,J.E., "The robust control of robot manipulators," International Journal of Robotics Research, Vol.4, 1985, pp.49-64.

[5] Utkin,V.I., *Sliding Modes and Their Application to Variable Structure Systems,* MIR publishers, Moscow, 1978.

[6] Vadali,S.R., "Variable-Structure Control of Spacecraft Large-Angle Maneuvers," Journal of Guidance, Control, and Dynamics, Vol.9, 1986, pp.235-239.

Proceedings of the
American Control Conference
San Francisco, California • June 1993

Stability Analysis of a Piezoelectric Vibration Controller for an Euler-Bernoulli Beam

B. R. Patnaik
Graduate Student
Systems Design Engineering
University of Waterloo
biswa@now.uwaterloo.ca

G. R. Heppler
Associate Professor
Systems Design Engineering
University of Waterloo
heppler@dial.uwaterloo.ca

D. Wang
Assistant Professor
Elec. & Comp. Engineering
University of Waterloo
dwang@kingcong.uwaterloo.ca

Abstract

Piezoelectric actuators are capable of generating a distributed moment, and can be used to control the motion of a flexible structure. A simple piezoelectric damper is considered here for controlling the vibration of a cantilever Euler-Bernoulli beam. Asymptotic stability of the closed loop system is established via a distributed parameter extension of Liapunov's direct method.

Nomenclature

A_c effective cross sectional area

c piezoelectric constant

EI effective flexural modulus

$g_1(x)$, $g_2(x)$ beam initial deflection, velocity

$j = \sqrt{-1}$

J_t payload moment of inertia

K tip angular velocity feedback gain

L beam length

M_t payload mass

$u(t)$ control voltage

V Liapunov functional

$w(t,x)$ beam deflection

ρ effective volume mass density

$(\cdot)' = \frac{\partial}{\partial x}(\cdot)$

$\dot{(\cdot)} = \frac{\partial}{\partial t}(\cdot)$

Introduction

Bailey and Hubbard[1], and Plump et al.[2] have considered the problem of controlling the vibration of a cantilever Euler-Bernoulli beam by using a distributed piezoelectric actuator. The active damper configuration as shown in Fig. 1 consists of a layer of surface-bonded piezoelectric film which, when excited by a control voltage, produces a distributed moment which acts to damp out vibration. In the above

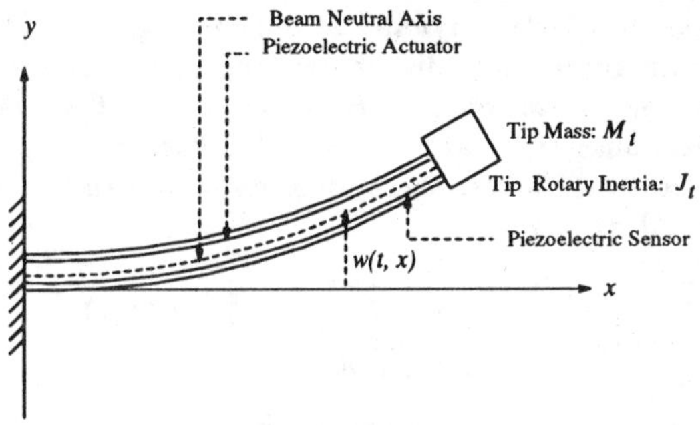

Figure 1: Schematic of Piezoelectric Active Damper

references the control algorithm is developed using Liapunov stability theory arguments, and the effectiveness of the controller has been verified through simulation and experiments. However the design and analysis of the proposed controller is theoretically inconclusive for two reasons. First of all it is not clear whether the chosen Liapunov candidate functional does indeed satisfy the desired properties of a Liapunov functional, and secondly no analytical investigation has been made as to the nature of stability. The objective of this paper is to resolve these two important issues.

In this paper a slightly different Liapunov functional is considered in order to arrive at a control algorithm similar to one proposed in [2]. By using a Liapunov-like stability theorem for distributed parameter systems[3] it will be shown that the closed loop system is asymptotically stable. The proof of stability follows the approach taken in [4, 5]. The novelty of this approach is that stability properties can be studied without assuming any kind of modal truncation of the actual distributed parameter plant.

State Variable Formulation

Bailey and Hubbard[1], and Plump et al.[2] show that the equation of motion which governs the behaviour of a distributed piezoelectric vibration damped beam, is given by

$$\frac{\partial^2}{\partial x^2}\left[EI\frac{\partial^2 w(t,x)}{\partial x^2} - c\,u(t,x)\right] + \rho A_c\frac{\partial^2 w(t,x)}{\partial t^2} = 0 \tag{1}$$

The control voltage $u(t,x)$ will be assumed to be uniform along the length of a uniform beam, in which case the above equation reduces to

$$EI\frac{\partial^4 w(t,x)}{\partial x^4} + \rho A_c\frac{\partial^2 w(t,x)}{\partial t^2} = 0 \tag{2}$$

where EI is the flexural stiffness, ρ is the volume mass density, and A_c is the cross sectional area of the beam. The transverse deflection of the beam is assumed small and is denoted by $w(t,x)$(see Figure 1).

In order to apply Liapunov stability theory we need to cast the system dynamical equations given in [1, 2] into an appropriate distributed parameter state variable representation [6]. By choosing the transverse deflection $w(t,x)$ and transverse velocity $\dot{w}(t,x)$ as the state variables, the system dynamics can be expressed as

$$\begin{bmatrix} \frac{\partial w(t,x)}{\partial t} \\ \frac{\partial \dot{w}(t,x)}{\partial t} \end{bmatrix} = \begin{bmatrix} 0 & 1 \\ -\frac{EI}{\rho A_c}\frac{\partial^4}{\partial x^4} & 0 \end{bmatrix}\begin{bmatrix} w(t,x) \\ \dot{w}(x,t) \end{bmatrix} \tag{3}$$

The beam is assumed to have some, possibly nonzero, initial deflection and initial velocity as expressed by the following general initial conditions:

$$w(0,x) = g_1(x) \tag{4}$$
$$\dot{w}(0,x) = g_2(x) \tag{5}$$

where $g_1(x)$ and $g_2(x)$ are some permissible shape functions. For example, Krall[7] considers $g_1(x)$ and $g_2(x)$ to be arbitrary smooth functions of x. The case of interest is that of a cantilever beam which has a continuous layer of piezoelectric film bonded to one side of the beam. The piezoelectric film has a spatially uniform feedback control voltage $u(t)$ applied along its length. For this case the appropriate boundary conditions have been shown to be [1]

$$w(t,0) = 0 \tag{6}$$
$$w'(t,0) = 0 \tag{7}$$
$$EI\,w''(t,L) = -J_t\,\ddot{w}'(t,L) + c\,u(t) \tag{8}$$
$$EI\,w'''(t,L) = M_t\,\ddot{w}(t,L) \tag{9}$$

The feedback control voltage $u(t)$ is expressed as

$$u(t) = F(w,\dot{w}) \tag{10}$$

where $F(\cdot,\cdot)$ is some linear spatial differential-integral operator yet to be determined. The exact form of $F(\cdot,\cdot)$ will become clear when the control law is derived via Liapunov's direct method.

From physical considerations it is known that the state space is a set of vectors with components which are real valued functions of the spatial variable x. For the system we are studying, a point in the state space is an ordered pair of functions $(w(x,t),\dot{w}(x,t))$, which physically represent the deflection, and the velocity profiles of the whole beam at some particular time t. However in order to apply the results from infinite dimensional stability theory to our specific problem, it is also necessary to put some restrictions on the set of points lying on a state trajectory. Formal definition of such a set is given below.

Definition 1 <u>*State Trajectory*</u>

Define a set $\gamma((w,\dot{w}); w(0,x),\dot{w}(0,x)) = \bigcup_{t\geq 0}\{(w(t,x),\dot{w}(t,x))\}$ *as the union of all points* $(w,\dot{w})$ *on a trajectory, which starts from an initial point* $(w(0,x),\dot{w}(0,x))$ *at time* $t=0$.

Henceforth the set $\gamma((w,\dot{w}); w(0,x),\dot{w}(0,x))$ will refer to a state trajectory of our dynamical system which is assumed to satisfy the conditions stated below.

Assumption 1 <u>*Compactness of state trajectory*</u>
The closed loop system defined by (3)–(10) is a dynamical system on some Banach space $\mathcal{B}$. *As well, there exists a set* $G \subseteq \mathcal{B}$ *in the neighborhood of the equilibrium point such that every trajectory* $\gamma((w,\dot{w}); w(0,x),\dot{w}(0,x)) \in G$ *lies in a compact set of* $\mathcal{B}$.

The physical nature of the system in question makes this a reasonable assumption.

The Liapunov Functional

The first step in deriving a suitable control law and establishing the stability of the system is to find a Liapunov Functional for the system (3)–(10).

Claim 1 *There exists a Liapunov Functional* $V : R^+ \times G \rightarrow R^+$ *for the dynamical systems described in(3)–(10).*

<u>*Proof:*</u>
Consider the total energy associated with the vibrating beam as the candidate Liapunov functional.

$$\begin{aligned} V(t,w,\dot{w}) &= Strain\ Energy + Kinetic\ Energy \\ &= \frac{1}{2}EI\int_0^L (w'')^2\,dx + \frac{1}{2}\rho A_c\int_0^L (\dot{w})^2\,dx \\ &+\frac{1}{2}M_t\,(\dot{w}(t,L))^2 + \frac{1}{2}J_t\,(\dot{w}'(t,L))^2 \end{aligned} \tag{11}$$

It is clear from the choice of the Liapunov functional that $V(t,w,\dot{w})$ is positive definite. In order for V to be a Liapunov functional it is necessary to show that the total time derivative of V is negative semidefinite. To do this, begin by differentiating(11) to obtain

$$\dot{V}(t, w, \dot{w}) = EI \int_0^L w'' \dot{w}'' \, dx + \rho A_c \int_0^L \dot{w} \, \ddot{w} \, dx$$
$$+ M_t \, \dot{w}(t, L) \, \ddot{w}(t, L) + J_t \, \dot{w}'(t, L) \, \ddot{w}'(t, L) \quad (12)$$

From (3) we have

$$\ddot{w}(t, x) = -\frac{EI}{\rho A_c} \, w''''(t, x) \quad (13)$$

Consider the second integral in the RHS of (12). Substitute for $\ddot{w}$ from (13) and then integrate by parts to obtain

$$\rho A_c \int_0^L \dot{w} \, \ddot{w} \, dx = -EI \left(\dot{w} w''' |_0^L - \int_0^L \dot{w}' \, w''' \, dx \right) \quad (14)$$

Substitute boundary conditions (6) and (9) into the first term of the RHS of (14) to get

$$\rho A_c \int_0^L \dot{w} \ddot{w} dx = -M_t \dot{w}(t, L) \ddot{w}(t, L) + EI \int_0^L \dot{w}' w''' dx \quad (15)$$

Integrating by parts again and using boundary conditions (7)–(8) yields

$$\rho A_c \int_0^L \dot{w} \, \ddot{w} \, dx = -M_t \, \dot{w}(t, L) \, \ddot{w}(t, L)$$
$$-J_t \, \dot{w}'(t, L) \, \ddot{w}'(t, L) - EI \int_0^L \dot{w}'' \, w'' \, dx$$
$$+c \, \dot{w}'(t, L) u(t) \quad (16)$$

Now replace the second term in the RHS of (12) with (16) to obtain

$$\dot{V}(t, w, \dot{w}) = c \dot{w}'(t, L) u(t) \quad (17)$$

In order to make $\dot{V}$ negative semidefinite choose the control voltage $u(t)$ as

$$u(t) = -K \, c \, \dot{w}'(t, L) \quad (18)$$

where $K > 0$ is the gain of the tip angular velocity feedback.

The control law (18) is similar but not identical to the control voltage used in [1, 2]. The non-linear form of the control voltage given in [1, 2] is also a valid choice; but it gives the impression that, in order to apply Liapunov's direct method, one needs to choose the magnitude of the control voltage sufficiently large. However Liapunov's direct method does not necessarily put any restriction on the magnitude of the control voltage. The measurement of $\dot{w}'(t, L)$ using a piezoelectric sensor is discussed in [8].

Next, combining (17) and (18) will give

$$\dot{V}(t, w, \dot{w}) = - K \, c^2 (\dot{w}'(t, L))^2 \quad (19)$$

which implies $\dot{V}$ is negative semidefinite, and therefore V is a valid Liapunov functional. *[Q.E.D.]*

Since $\dot{V} \leq 0$, the state trajectories $\gamma((w, \dot{w}); w(0, x), \dot{w}(0, x))$ are bounded, and the system is stable in the sense of Liapunov. In order to show asymptotic stability, we need to prove that $(w, \dot{w}) \to (0, 0)$ *as* $t \to \infty$. To prove this we need to construct a set $S = \{(w, \dot{w}) \in \overline{G} \mid \dot{V} \equiv 0\}$, where $\overline{G}$ is the closure of G. In the next section we consider an eigenfunction expansion of the solution $w(t, x)$, and obtain a result which will be used to construct the above set.

Eigenfunction Expansion

Begin by using the control law (18) in the moment boundary condition (8) and rewriting the system dynamics (3)–(10) as

$$EI \, w''''(t, x) + \rho A_c \, \ddot{w}(t, x) = 0 \quad (20)$$
$$w(t, 0) = 0 \quad (21)$$
$$w'(t, 0) = 0 \quad (22)$$
$$EI \, w''(t, L) + J_t \, \ddot{w}'(t, L) + c \, K \, \dot{w}'(t, L) = 0 \quad (23)$$
$$EI \, w'''(t, L) - M_t \, \ddot{w}(t, L) = 0 \quad (24)$$

$$w(0, x) = g_1(x) \quad (25)$$
$$\dot{w}(0, x) = g_2(x) \quad (26)$$

The above will allow us to demonstrate that for the chosen control law (18) the dynamical system (3)–(10) is asymptotically stable. To prove this, it is necessary to construct the set S as follows.

Claim 2 *If* $\dot{V} \equiv 0$ *then* $S = \{(w, \dot{w}) \in \overline{G} \mid \dot{w}'(t, L) \equiv 0\} = \{(0, 0)\}$.

Proof:
Suppose $\dot{V}(t, w, \dot{w}) = - K \, c^2 (\dot{w}'(t, L))^2 \equiv 0$.
As K, c are nonzero constants

$$\dot{w}'(t, L) = 0 \qquad \forall t \quad (27)$$

Therefore it must also be true that

$$\ddot{w}'(t, L) = 0 \qquad \forall t \quad (28)$$

The conditions (27)–(28) can be viewed as boundary conditions that have to be satisfied in addition to those given by (21)–(24). Then, in order to meet the forced and natural boundary conditions and the condition that $\dot{V} \equiv 0$ it is necessary from (20)–(24) and (27)–(28) that $w(t, x)$ satisfy the following.

$$EI \, w''''(t, x) + \rho A_c \, \ddot{w}(t, x) = 0 \quad (29)$$
$$w(t, 0) = 0 \quad (30)$$
$$w'(t, 0) = 0 \quad (31)$$
$$EI \, w''(t, L) = 0 \quad (32)$$
$$EI \, w'''(t, L) - M_t \, \ddot{w}(t, L) = 0 \quad (33)$$
$$\dot{w}'(t, L) = 0 \quad (34)$$

As a consequence of the boundary conditions being linear and homogeneous, the solution $w(t,x)$ can be assumed to be in variable separable form [7, 9], such that

$$w(t,x) = \psi(x)\, q(t) \tag{35}$$

Replacing w in (29)–(33) with (35) results in the following system of equations in $\psi(x)$ and $q(t)$:

$$\begin{aligned}
\ddot{q}(t) &= -\Omega^2 q(t) && (36)\\
\psi''''(x) &= \lambda^4\, \psi(x) && (37)\\
\psi(0) &= 0 && (38)\\
\psi'(0) &= 0 && (39)\\
\psi''(L) &= 0 && (40)\\
\psi'''(L) &= -\Omega^2 \frac{M_t}{EI}\, \psi(L) && (41)\\
j\Omega\psi'(L) &= 0 && (42)
\end{aligned}$$

where

$$\lambda^4 = \frac{\rho A_c \Omega^2}{EI} \tag{43}$$

The solution to (37) can be written as

$$\psi(x) = A \sin \lambda x + B \cos \lambda x + C \sinh \lambda x + D \cosh \lambda x \tag{44}$$

Boundary conditions (38)–(39) yield

$$\begin{aligned}
D &= -B && (45)\\
C &= -A && (46)
\end{aligned}$$

and (44) simplifies to

$$\psi(x) = A(\sin \lambda x - \sinh \lambda x) + B(\cos \lambda x - \cosh \lambda x) \tag{47}$$

The condition (42) holds if either $\Omega = 0$ or $\psi'(L) = 0$. First, we consider the trivial case when $\Omega = 0$. If $\Omega = 0$, then from (43) $\lambda = 0$, and therefore by (47) $\psi(x) \equiv 0$. This implies $w(t,x) = 0$ and $\dot{w}(t,x) = 0 \forall t$. Next we consider the nontrivial case when $\Omega \neq 0$ and $\psi'(L) = 0$. This along with (40) gives

$$A(\cos \lambda L - \cosh \lambda L) + B(-\sin \lambda L - \sinh \lambda L) = 0 \tag{48}$$

$$A(-\sin \lambda L - \sinh \lambda L) + B(-\cos \lambda L - \cosh \lambda L) = 0 \tag{49}$$

In order for the linear system in A and B in (48)–(49) to have a non-trivial solution, the determinant of the coefficient matrix should vanish, i.e.

$$-(\cos^2 \lambda L - \cosh^2 \lambda L) - (\sin \lambda L + \sinh \lambda L)^2 = 0$$

which may be further simplified to

$$\sin \lambda L \sinh \lambda L = 0 \tag{50}$$

Therefore the eigenvalues are given by

$$\lambda = \frac{n\pi}{L} \quad \textit{for } n = 0, 1, 2, \cdots \tag{51}$$

where $n = 0$ corresponds to the trivial case for which $\psi(x) \equiv 0$.

Consider the situation where $n \neq 0$ by substituting (51) into (48) and (49) such that

$$A = \frac{\sinh n\pi}{(-1)^n - \cosh n\pi} B \tag{52}$$

and

$$A = -\frac{(-1)^n + \cosh n\pi}{\sinh n\pi} B \tag{53}$$

respectively. Note that the relationships (52)–(53) between coefficients A and B are equivalent and depending upon convenience, they will be used interchangeably.

The eigenfunctions must also satisfy the condition (41). Using (47) to calculate $\psi'''(L)$ it is found that

$$\begin{aligned}
&\psi'''(L) = \\
&\lambda^3(\cos \lambda L + \cosh \lambda L) + B\, \lambda^3(\sin \lambda L - \sinh \lambda L)
\end{aligned}$$

Substituting for λ from (51) for the case $n \neq 0$ and using (53) the above expression can be simplified to

$$\begin{aligned}
&\psi'''(L) = \\
&-\left(\frac{n\pi}{L}\right)^3 [A((-1)^n + \cosh n\pi) + B \sinh n\pi] \\
&= -2\left(\frac{n\pi}{L}\right)^3 (-1)^n A
\end{aligned} \tag{54}$$

Similarly the RHS of (41) simplifies to

$$-\Omega^2 \frac{M_t}{EI} \psi(L) = -\frac{\Omega^2}{EI} M_t (2(-1)^n B) \tag{55}$$

The RHS of (55) may be further modified by making use of (43) and (51) to replace Ω^2 such that

$$-\Omega^2 \frac{M_t}{EI} \psi(L) = -2(-1)^n B \frac{M_t}{\rho A_c} \left(\frac{n\pi}{L}\right)^4 \tag{56}$$

The boundary condition (41) may now be re-expressed with the aid of (54) and (56) as

$$A = \frac{n\pi}{L} \frac{M_t}{\rho A_c} B \tag{57}$$

Comparing (52) and (57) we conclude that in order for A and B to assume non-trivial solutions, the following must hold true.

$$\frac{n\pi}{L} \frac{M_t}{\rho A_c} = \frac{\sinh n\pi}{(-1)^n - \cosh n\pi} \quad \textit{for } n = 1, 2, \cdots \tag{58}$$

However (58) cannot be true for any $n = 1, 2, \cdots$, since the right hand side of (58) is always negative and its left hand side is always positive. This is a contradiction.

Hence we must have the coefficients $A = B = C = D = 0$ which implies that all the eigenfunctions $\psi(x)$ are identically zero. Therefore $w(t,x) = 0$ and $\dot{w}(t,x) = 0 \, \forall \, t$. Hence $S = \{(0,0)\}$. [*Q.E.D.*]

Asymptotic Stability

As in the approach of Shifman[4] to prove asymptotic stability, the definition of an invariant set [10], and a theorem due to Hale[3] are needed. They are stated below.

Definition 2 *Invariant Set[10]*
A set $M(\mathcal{B})$ is said to to be invariant with respect to a given dynamical system if for any initial state $(w(0,x), \dot{w}(0,x)) \in M(\mathcal{B})$ its corresponding trajectory $\gamma((w,\dot{w}); w(0,x), \dot{w}(0,x))$ also lies in $M(\mathcal{B})$.

Note that $(w \equiv 0, \dot{w} \equiv 0)$ is the equilibrium state of our dynamical system and thus the set $\{(w \equiv 0, \dot{w} \equiv 0)\}$ is also an invariant set.

Theorem 1 *An Invariant Set Theorem[3]*
Suppose $\mathcal{U}$ is a dynamical system defined on some Banach space $\mathcal{B}$. If

1. *V is a Liapunov functional on a set $G \subseteq \mathcal{B}$*
2. *Any trajectory $\gamma((w,\dot{w}); w(0,x), \dot{w}(0,x)) \in G$ lies in a compact set of $\mathcal{B}$.*
3. *$S = \{(w,\dot{w}) \in \overline{G} \mid \dot{V} \equiv 0\}$, where $\overline{G}$ is the closure of G.*
4. *$M(\mathcal{B})$ is the largest invariant set in S of the dynamical system $\mathcal{U}$.*

then $\mathcal{U}(t; (w,\dot{w})) \to M$ as $t \to \infty$.

The aforementioned definition and theorem on an invariant set can be used to prove that the system of interest is asymptotically stable.

Claim 3 *The equilibrium state $(0,0)$ of the dynamical system (3)–(10) is asymptotically stable.*

Proof:
By Assumption 1, our system is a formal dynamical system and the state trajectories lie in some compact set.

The existence of a Liapunov functional V has been proved in Claim 1.

Since the trajectory must stay in in the invariant set $M(\mathcal{B}) \subseteq S$ for all time,we must find the invariant set $M(\mathcal{B})$. In Claim 2, it has been shown that $S = \{(0,0)\}$. Then by Definition 2, $M(\mathcal{B}) = \{(0,0)\}$. In other words $M(\mathcal{B})$ contains only the equilibrium state.

Then by applying Theorem 1, we conclude that $(w,\dot{w}) \to (0,0)$ as $t \to \infty$. Therefore by the definition of asymptotic stability[6], the equilibrium state $(0,0)$ of the closed loop system (3)–(10) is asymptotically stable. [*Q.E.D.*]

Conclusion

Using a Liapunov-like stability theorem[3] on a class of distributed parameter systems, it has been possible to prove asymptotic stability of a piezoelectric film actuated cantilever beam which uses the tip angular velocity of the beam as feedback. The analysis does not assume any kind of modal truncation of the plant. The effect of damping has not been considered in the model with the implicit assumption that any inherent structural/viscous damping will only result in a faster convergence of a state trajectory to the equilibrium state.

References

[1] Thomas Bailey and James E. Hubbard Jr. Distributed piezoelctric-polymer active vibration control of a cantilever beam. *J. Guidance*, 8(5):605–611, Sep-Oct 1985.

[2] J. M. Plump et al. Nonlinear control of a distributed system: Simulation and experimental results. *Journal of Dynamic Systems, Measurement and Control, Transactions of ASME*, 109:133–139, 1987.

[3] Jack K. Hale. Dynamical systems and stability. *Journal of Mathematical Analysis and Applications*, 26:39–59, 1969.

[4] J. J. Shifman. The control of flexible robots. Technical Report CUED/F-INFENG/TR 67, Cambridge University Engineering Department, Trumpington Street, Cambridge CB2 1PZ, U.K., May 1991.

[5] J. J. Shiffman. A tracking controller for the euler-bernoulli beam. In *IEEE International Conference on Robotics and Automation*, pages 928–933, Cincinnati, May 13-18 1990.

[6] P. K. C. Wang. Asymptotic stability of distributed parameter systems with feedback control. *IEEE Transactions on Automatic Control*, AC-11(1):46–54, January 1966.

[7] Allan M. Krall. Asymptotic stability of the euler-bernoulli beam with boundary control. *Journal of Mathematical Analysis and Applications*, 137:288–295, 1989.

[8] S. Hanagud, M. W. Obal, and A. J. Calise. Optimal vibration control by the use of piezoceramic sensors and actuators. In *27th AIAA/ASME/ASCE/AHS Structures, Structural Dynamics and Materials Conference*, pages 177–185, April 1986.

[9] Paul D. Ritger and Nicholas J. Rose. *Differential Equations with Applications*. McGraw-Hill, 1968.

[10] P. K. C. Wang. *Control of Distributed Parameter Systems*, volume 1 of *Advances in Control Systems, Theory and Applications*, chapter 3. Academic Press, New York, 1964.

Proceedings of the
American Control Conference
San Francisco, California • June 1993

EFFICIENT REORIENTATION OF A DEFORMABLE BODY IN SPACE: A FREE–FREE BEAM EXAMPLE

Ilya V. Kolmanovsky and N. Harris McClamroch*

Dept. of Aerospace Engineering
University of Michigan, Ann Arbor, MI 48109-2140

Abstract

It is demonstrated that the planar reorientation of a free–free beam in zero gravity space can be accomplished by periodically changing the shape of the beam using internal actuators. A control scheme is proposed in which electromechanical actuators excite the flexible motion of the beam so that it rotates in the desired manner with respect to a fixed inertial reference. The results can be viewed as an extension of previous work to a distributed parameter case.

1. Introduction

Following [8], we introduce the concept of a deformable body, for which distances between the points of the body can change during the motion. Examples of deformable bodies include both lumped and distributed parameter systems such as multilink rigid body interconnections and structures with distributed flexibility. The orientation of a deformable body with respect to a fixed inertial reference can be specified by a choice of body frame. In general, there are many ways to choose a body frame. For example, in the case of planar motion a body frame can be identified with any two distinct points in the body. The shape of a deformable body can be specified in terms of the position of the body relative to the body frame. Thus, an arbitrary motion of a deformable body can be separated into rigid body motion and shape change.

Assume that both linear and angular momenta about the center of mass of the body are conserved and equal to zero. These conditions hold if the body is in a circular orbit around the Earth or is in a free fall. As a consequence of angular momentum conservation, shape change and the rigid body motion are coupled. This coupling is inherently nonlinear. In particular, one may be interested in inducing a rotation of a deformable body with respect to a fixed inertial reference by periodically changing the shape of the body with internal (momenta preserving) actuators. Reorientation strategies for lumped parameter mechanical systems have been extensively studied in the literature [4, 5, 7, 8]. Reorientation schemes based on the use of internal actuators require a minimal use of fuel to achieve the desired reorientation maneuver.

*This research was supported by the National Science Foundation under Research Grant No. MSS-9114630 and the National Aeronautics and Space Administration under Research Grant NAG-1-1419.

In this paper we extend the aforementioned reorientation strategies to the case of flexible bodies. In particular, we are interested in a planar reorientation of a free–free beam in space using only electromechanical actuators. These electromechanical actuators, e.g. piezoelectric or shape memory actuators, do not change the angular momentum of the free–free beam but can be used to change the shape of the beam in a periodic way. Assuming that the angular momentum of the beam is always zero, oscillations in the shape of the beam can cause a rotation of the beam with respect to a fixed inertial reference. The rotation of the beam over one period depends only on the shape of the beam over one period and does not depend on the length of the period; hence this phenomenon is referred to as a geometric phase change.

The extension of existing strategies to the free–free beam case is not straightforward for several reasons. Classical models of uniform free–free flexible beams in zero gravity space result in complete decoupling of rigid body motion and flexible motion. Higher order nonlinear coupling between rigid body motion and flexible motion is captured in geometrically exact beam theories [9]. The resulting models, however, are complicated. The free–free beam is an infinite dimensional superarticulated system. Thus, an arbitrary shape change cannot be produced by a finite number of actuators. In addition, the body frame of the beam needs to be chosen so that the shape change is independent of the rigid body motion. Such a choice of body frame is natural for lumped parameter systems since variables specifying orientation are ignorable.

In this paper, we first address basic modeling issues. The dynamics which determine the shape of the free–free beam are assumed to be characterized by the Euler–Bernoulli equation, including material damping, with appropriate boundary conditions. The higher order coupling between the rigid body motion and the flexible motion is captured using the angular momentum expression which includes rotatory inertia and kinematically exact effects. A control scheme is proposed in which the actuators excite the flexible motion of the beam so that the beam rotates in the desired sense.

2. A Planar Free-Free Beam Model

Consider a uniform free–free beam of undeformed length $2L$ in space with zero angular momentum and zero linear momentum. Referring to Fig. 1 the motion of the beam is constrained to a plane defined by vectors $(\bar{e}_1, \bar{e}_3)$ where $(\bar{e}_1, \bar{e}_2, \bar{e}_3)$ is an orthonormal basis for an inertial frame whose origin is at the center of mass of the beam. Let $(\bar{i}, \bar{j}, \bar{k})$ be a rotating frame with its origin fixed at the origin of the inertial frame such that the vectors $(\bar{i}, \bar{k})$ lie in the plane $(\bar{e}_1, \bar{e}_3)$ and $\bar{j} = \bar{e}_2$. The straight line passing through the origin in the direction of vector $\bar{k}$ is called the reference line. Let the beam initially be at rest in a straight line configuration aligned with the reference line. Then, the location of each point on the line of mass centroids of the beam can be described in terms of the parameter $s \in [-L, L]$. This parameter s can be viewed as a label for each of the crossections. We assume that as the beam deforms the shape and the area of the crossections remain invariant. Following other researchers [1, 6, 9] we introduce three functions $u(s,t), y(s,t) : [-L, L] \times \Re \rightarrow \Re$ and $\psi(s,t) : [-L, L] \times \Re \rightarrow T^1$ such that $(u(s,t)+s, y(s,t))$ define the coordinates of the line of centroids in the deformed configuration with respect to the moving frame $(\bar{i}, \bar{k})$ at time t. The angle $\psi(s,t)$ between the normal to the crossection at s and $\bar{e}_3$ specifies the orientation of the crossection. The normal to the crossection at s is denoted by $\bar{t}_3$. We define the material basis $(\bar{t}_1, \bar{t}_2, \bar{t}_3)$ to be orthonormal so that $\bar{t}_1$ lies in the plane $(\bar{e}_1, \bar{e}_3)$. The crossection itself can be associated with the set of points (ξ_1, ξ_2) in a compact set $A \subset \Re^2$ such that $\xi_1\bar{t}_1 + \xi_2\bar{t}_2 + (u(s,t)+s)\bar{k} + (y(s,t))\bar{i}$ gives the location of any point on the beam as ξ_1 and ξ_2 vary through A and s varies from $-L$ to L.

Since the origin of the inertial frame is fixed at the center of mass of the beam we obtain

$$\int_{-L}^{L} y(s,t)ds = 0, \qquad (1)$$

$$\int_{-L}^{L} u(s,t)ds = 0. \qquad (2)$$

Let ρ denote the constant mass density per unit volume of the beam. We assume that the beam has a symmetric crossection so that the first moment of inertia of the crossection about the line of centroids is

$$\int_A \rho\xi_1 d\xi_1 d\xi_2 = 0. \qquad (3)$$

The second moment of inertia of the crossection about the line of centroids, referred to as the rotatory inertia, is

$$I_2 = \int_A \rho{\xi_1}^2 d\xi_1 d\xi_2. \qquad (4)$$

and assumed to be positive. The mass per unit length of the crossection is given by

$$m_0 = \int_A \rho d\xi_1 d\xi_2. \qquad (5)$$

We define the angle $\theta(t)$ between $\bar{e}_3$ and $\bar{k}$ so that $y(s,t)$ measured from the reference line satisfies the following orthogonality condition

$$\int_{-L}^{L} sy(s,t)ds = 0. \qquad (6)$$

The existence of the angle $\theta(t)$ follows from the geometry indicated in Fig. 1. This definition provides a separation between the motion which determines the shape of the beam, given by $y(s,t)$, $-L \le s \le L$, and the rotation of the beam as a whole, given by $\theta(t)$.

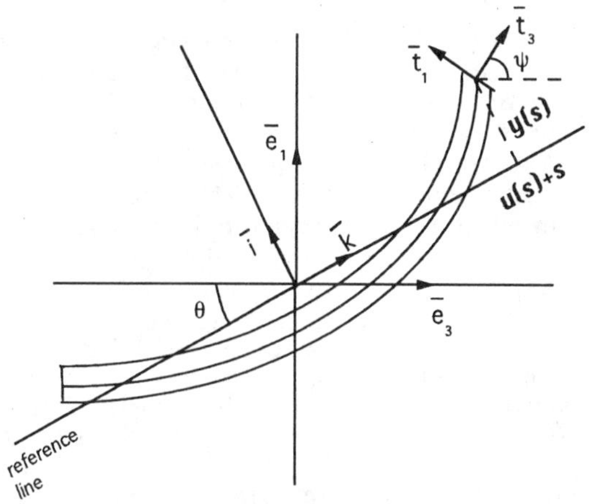

Fig 1. Planar Beam Model

We next develop a kinematically exact expression for the angular momentum of the free–free beam. Let $\bar{\varphi}(s, \xi_1, \xi_2, \theta, t)$ be the vector from the origin of the inertial frame to a point (s, ξ_1, ξ_2) on the beam at time t; then

$$\bar{\varphi} = (s\sin\theta + y\cos\theta + \xi_1\cos\psi + u\sin\theta)\bar{e}_1 + (\xi_2)\bar{e}_2 + (s\cos\theta - \xi_1\sin\psi - y\sin\theta + u\cos\theta)\bar{e}_3 \qquad (7)$$

where $\theta = \theta(t), y = y(s,t)$ and $\psi = \psi(s,t)$. The angular momentum about the origin of the inertial frame at time t is zero so that

$$\int_{-L}^{L}\int_A \rho\bar{\varphi} \times \frac{d\bar{\varphi}}{dt} d\xi_1 d\xi_2 ds = 0. \qquad (8)$$

Substituting equation (7) into equation (8) and using equations (4) and (5) we can express $\dot{\theta}$ in terms of y, u and α as

$$\dot{\theta} = \frac{\int_{-L}^{L}\{m_0 s\frac{\partial y}{\partial t} + I_2\dot{\alpha} + m_0(\frac{\partial y}{\partial t}u - \frac{\partial u}{\partial t}y)\}ds}{\int_{-L}^{L}\{-m_0 s^2 - m_0 y^2 - I_2\}ds} \qquad (9)$$

where $\alpha = \psi - \theta$ is the angle between the normal $\bar{t}_3$ to the crossection at s and the reference line.

Assume that the beam is unshearable and inextensible and that the deformations are small. This implies, using equation (2), that

$$u(s,t) = 0. \qquad (10)$$

and that

$$\alpha \approx y_s. \qquad (11)$$

We use the Euler–Bernoulli beam model to characterize the shape of the beam [3]. Thus $y(s,t)$ satisfies the Euler-Bernoulli equation of the form

$$m_0 y_{tt} + \gamma y_{tssss} + EI y_{ssss} = -\sum_{j=1}^{m} v_j(t)\delta'(s - s_j) \qquad (12)$$

with the boundary conditions

$$y_{ss}(-L) = y_{ss}(L) = 0, \tag{13}$$

$$y_{sss}(-L) = y_{sss}(L) = 0 \tag{14}$$

where $I = I_2/\rho$, E is Young's elasticity modulus, δ' is the distributional derivative of the delta function and where for simplicity we assume Kelvin-Voigt damping with a positive damping coefficient γ. In addition, $y(s,t)$ must satisfy conditions (1) and (6). Internal bending torques $v_j(t)$, $j = 1,\ldots,m$ are produced by m point actuators located at $s = s_j$ on the beam where $s_j \in [-L, L]$. These actuators change the shape of the beam but at the same time preserve the angular momentum. Although such actuators are capable of inducing relatively small displacements one can excite the beam periodically at a frequency near one of the lower resonant frequencies of the beam to obtain relatively large periodic shape change.

Using expressions (6), (10) and (11) in equation (9) we obtain

$$\dot{\theta} = \frac{-\int_{-L}^{L} I_2 y_{ts} ds}{\tau + \int_{-L}^{L} m_0 y^2 ds} \tag{15}$$

where $\tau = \frac{2}{3} m_0 L^3 + 2I_2 L$. This expression demonstrates the nonlinear coupling between the beam's shape and its rigid body motion. Expression (15) is non-integrable in the sense that if $y(s,t)$ is a periodic function of time, the integral of $\dot{\theta}$ over one period is, in general, non-zero.

We can expand the solution $y(s,t)$ to equation (12) in the series

$$y(s,t) = \sum_{i=1}^{\infty} w_i(s) q_i(t) \tag{16}$$

where $w_i(s), i = 1, 2, \ldots$ are the orthonormal *elastic* mode shapes of the Euler-Bernoulli model. The solution $y(s,t)$ satisfies equations (1) and (6), which can be viewed as orthogonality conditions for the rigid body modes and elastic modes. Expansion (16) provides the modal description

$$\ddot{q_i} + c_i \dot{q} + {\omega_i}^2 q = \sum_{j=1}^{m} b_{ij} v_j(t), i = 1, 2 \ldots \tag{17}$$

Equation (12), or equivalently equation (17), determines the shape of the beam and is called the shape space equation. Substituting equation (16) into equation (15) we obtain

$$\dot{\theta} = \frac{-I_2 \sum_{i=1}^{\infty} (J_i \dot{q_i})}{\tau + \sum_{i=1}^{\infty} {q_i}^2} \tag{18}$$

where $J_i = w_i(L) - w_i(-L)$. We note that (18) is, in general, non-integrable for any truncation of the infinite series in (16).

3. Asymptotic Reorientation Maneuvers

The goal is to accomplish asymptotic maneuvers, i.e. starting with $\theta(t_0) = \theta_0$, $y(s,t_0) = y_t(s,t_0) = 0$ we want to rotate the beam so that $\theta(t) \to \theta_d$, $y(s,t) \to 0$ and $y_t(s,t) \to 0$ as $t \to \infty$ for some desired angle θ_d.

Consider the periodic excitation of the beam at a single frequency ω as

$$v_j(t) = v_j^0 + v_j^\omega \cos(\omega t), j = 1, 2, \ldots, m \tag{19}$$

Since the shape space dynamics of the free–free beam is asymptotically stable, the steady-state motion of the beam is given by

$$q_i(t) = l_i + a_i \cos(\omega t + \phi_i) \tag{20}$$

where the parameters l_i, a_i and ϕ_i can be expressed in terms of v_j^ω and v_j^0 according to equation (17). The excitation function (19) should be sufficiently small so that the Euler–Bernoulli model for the shape space dynamics remains valid. Substituting equation (20) into equation (18) and integrating over one period we obtain the steady–state change in angle θ over one period is given by

$$\int_0^{\frac{2\pi}{\omega}} \frac{\varsigma_0 \cos(\omega t + \chi_0) dt}{1 + \varsigma_1 (\cos(\omega t + \chi_1) + \varsigma_2 \cos(2\omega t + \chi_2)} \tag{21}$$

for constants ς_0, ς_1, ς_2, χ_0, χ_1 and χ_2. Expression (21) implies that, in general, the change in angle θ in steady–state over one period is non-zero, thereby proving that a periodic change in shape of the beam results in a rotation of the beam. The steady-state difference $\theta(\frac{2\pi}{\omega}) - \theta(0)$ is referred to as the geometric phase. If $\sum_{i=1}^{\infty} q_i^2$ is small as compared with τ, we can approximate

$$\frac{1}{\tau + \sum_{i=1}^{\infty} q_i^2} \approx \frac{1}{\tau}(1 - \frac{\sum_{i=1}^{\infty} q_i^2}{\tau})$$

and thus using equation (20) we obtain

$$\theta(\frac{2\pi}{\omega}) - \theta(0) = \frac{2\pi}{\tau^2} \sum_{i=1}^{\infty} \sum_{j=1, j\neq i}^{\infty} a_i J_i l_j a_j \sin(\phi_j - \phi_i). \tag{22}$$

Although the geometric phase is generally non–zero, there are cases when the geometric phase is zero.

Proposition 4.1 Assume that the steady–state motion of the beam is described by equation (20). Then, $\theta(\frac{2\pi}{\omega}) - \theta(0) = 0$ if any of the following conditions hold:

1. $a_i = 0$ for all i
2. $l_i = 0$ for all i
3. $\phi_i = \phi_j$ for all i, j

The second statement of the proposition is the most important. It implies that for a non-zero geometric phase the beam should necessarily vibrate about a non-straight line reference configuration. It follows from expression (18) that in order to rotate the beam in the opposite direction it is sufficient to reverse the signs of v_j^{ω} and v_j^0.

We are now in a position to formulate a specific control strategy to accomplish the desired asymptotic maneuver. Starting at rest with $\theta(t_0) = \theta_0$ application of control law (19) results in a nonzero geometric phase change over one period. By repetition of cycles of motion as many times as necessary the beam can be caused to rotate closer and closer to θ_d. As $\theta(t)$ approach θ_d we can reduce the amplitude of the oscillations to zero in a way so that $\theta(t) \to \theta_d$ as $t \to \infty$.

The proposed control law is of the form

$$v_j(t) = \varepsilon_k \left[\bar{v}_j^0 + \bar{v}_j^{\omega} \cos(\omega t)\right], j = 1, \ldots, m, \quad (23)$$

where $\frac{2(k-1)\pi p}{\omega} \leq t - t_0 < \frac{2k\pi p}{\omega}$, $k = 1, 2, \ldots$; that is, the control excitation is an amplitude modulated function, where $\bar{v}_j^0$, $\bar{v}_j^{\omega}$ are constants and ε_k denotes the scalar amplitude modulation sequence that defines the control excitation on the k-th cycle. Each cycle is exactly p periods. The constants ω, $\bar{v}_j^0$, $\bar{v}_j^{\omega}$ can be chosen nearly arbitrary, although one approach is to choose $\bar{v}_j^0$, $\bar{v}_j^{\omega}$ to maximize geometric phase expression (22) where $a_i, l_i, \phi_i, i = 1, \ldots,$ are related to $\bar{v}_j^0$, $\bar{v}_j^{\omega}, j = 1, \ldots, m$ according to expressions (20) and (17), and $\bar{v}_j^0$, $\bar{v}_j^{\omega}$ are constrained in norm. In terms of $\bar{v}_j^0$, $\bar{v}_j^{\omega}, j = 1, \ldots, m$ this is a constrained mathematical programming problem which is linear in $\bar{v}_j^0$ (for fixed $\bar{v}_j^{\omega}$) and quadratic in $\bar{v}_j^{\omega}$ (for fixed $\bar{v}_j^0$). We will subsequently denote the maximum value of this constrained optimization problem as $\Delta\theta^*$.

The modulation sequence ε_{k+1} is defined in terms of an average of $\theta(t)$, over the k-th cycle, that is

$$\theta_k^{ave} = \frac{1}{2}(\max\theta(t) + \min\theta(t)) \quad (24)$$

where the maximum and minimum are over $\frac{2(k-1)\pi p}{\omega} \leq t - t_0 \leq \frac{2k\pi p}{\omega}$. We also introduce two auxilary variables $\theta_0^{ave} = \theta_0$ and $\varepsilon_0 = \text{sign}\left(\frac{\theta_d - \theta_0}{\Delta\theta^*}\right)$. We express ε_k in terms of θ_{k-1}^{ave} and ε_{k-1} as indicated below:

(A1) Compute

$$r_k = \left(\frac{\theta_d - \theta_{k-1}^{ave}}{\Delta\theta^*}\right)^{\frac{1}{3}}.$$

(A2) In case $|r_k| \geq |\varepsilon_{k-1}|$, if r_k and ε_{k-1} have the same signs then $\varepsilon_k = |\varepsilon_{k-1}|\text{sign}(r_k)$; if r_k and ε_{k-1} have opposite signs then $\varepsilon_k = \gamma_1|\varepsilon_{k-1}|\text{sign}(r_k)$, where $0 < \gamma_1 < 1$.

(A3) If $0 < |r_k| < |\varepsilon_{k-1}|$ then $\varepsilon_k = \gamma_2 r_k$, where $0 < \gamma_2 < 1$.

(A4) If $r_k = 0$ then $\varepsilon_k = \varepsilon_{k-1}$.

Proposition 4.2 If the proposed control law is of the form (23) where ε_k is selected according to steps **(A1)**–**(A4)**, then

$$\lim_{k\to\infty} \theta_k^{ave} = \theta_d, \lim_{k\to\infty} \varepsilon_k = 0.$$

Sketch of the Proof. The sequence $|\varepsilon_k|$ is non–increasing and bounded on $[0, 1]$. Therefore, there exists $b \in [0, 1]$ such that $b = \inf_k |\varepsilon_k|$. It can be shown that by construction of the sequence b must be zero.

Since $|\varepsilon_k| \to 0$ then $q_i(t) \to 0$ and $\dot{q}_i \to 0$ as $t \to \infty$. By continuity $\theta(t) \to \theta^{con}$ for some constant θ^{con} as $t \to \infty$. It can be shown that $\theta^{con} = \theta_d$. □

Finally, it follows from equations (24) and (20) that

$$\lim_{t\to\infty} \theta(t) = \theta_d, \lim_{t\to\infty} \begin{pmatrix} y(s,t) \\ y_t(s,t) \end{pmatrix} = 0, -L \leq s \leq L$$

The controller which we have constructed has two functions. Its main function is to excite the oscillations of the beam in such a way that the beam rotates in the desired sense. Subsequently, the controller serves to suppress the vibrations previously excited so that the free–free beam comes to rest with a desired orientation. Note that control law (23) is a non–smooth feedback control law [2].

4. Numerical Example

Consider a beam with half–length $L = 1[m]$, density per unit volume $\rho = 1400[kg/m^3]$ and square crossection with the side size $R = 0.1[m]$. Young's modulus of the beam is $E = 3.0 \times 10^6[N/m^2]$ and the Kelvin-Voigt damping coefficient is $\gamma = 0.2$. Two actuators are installed near both ends of the beam at $s_1 = -0.9[m]$ and $s_2 = 0.9[m]$. The maximal torque each of the actuators can produce is equal to $100[Nm]$. The excitation frequency $\omega = 13[Hz]$ is selected to lie between the first $10.6[Hz]$ and the second $29[Hz]$ resonant frequencies of the beam; $\bar{v}_j^0$ and $\bar{v}_j^{\omega}$, $j = 1, 2$ are chosen using expression (22) to maximize the geometric phase change over one period. For this example we choose $p = 5$ and $\gamma_1 = \gamma_2 = 0.9$. The first four elastic modes of the beam are used in our simulation.

We want to rotate the beam from $\theta_0 = 0.1[rad]$ at $t = 0[sec]$ to $\theta_d = 0[rad]$. The dependence of the angle $\theta(t)[rad]$ on time $t[sec]$ is shown for a part of the maneuver in Fig. 2. In this case the geometric phase change over one period in steady–state predicted by expression (22) is equal to -2.7465×10^{-4} $[rad]$ whereas its actual simulation value is equal to -3.0411×10^{-4} $[rad]$. The dependence of the modulation parameter ε on time is shown in Figure 3.

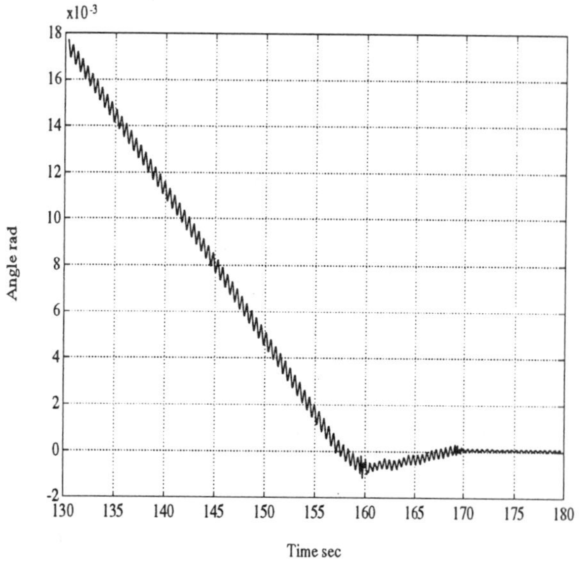

Fig 2. Asymptotic Reorientation Maneuver

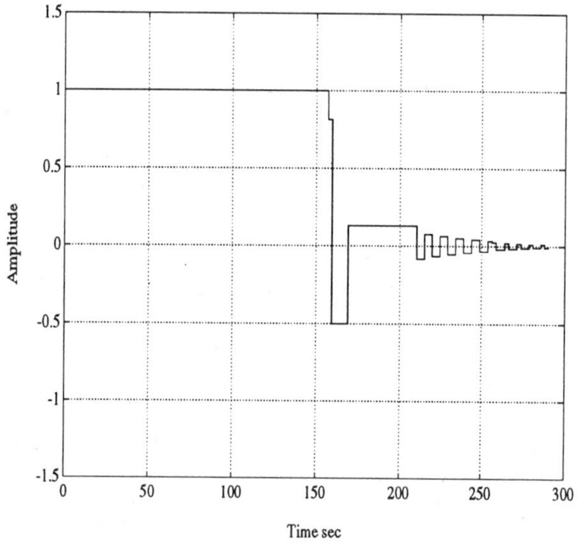

Fig 3. Amplitude Modulation Sequence

5. Conclusion

In this paper the angular momentum expression for a planar free–free beam in space is derived. It is shown how the general motion of the beam can be separated into rigid and elastic motions. The change of shape of the beam is described by the Euler–Bernoulli equation with free-free boundary conditions. Angular momentum conservation leads to the nonlinear dependence of the rigid motion on the shape of the beam. As shown this dependence is non–integrable in the sense that a periodic change in shape of the beam results in a non-zero rotation of the beam over one period. Approximate relationships expressing the average rate of rotation of the beam in terms of the amplitudes and phases of periodic excitation of the beam by internal actuators are derived. Finally, a control strategy for a planar asymptotic reorientation maneuver is developed.

A general treatment of the interplay between deformations and rotations of deformable bodies is given by Shapere and Wilczek [8]. Reyhanoglu and McClamroch [7] have developed a framework for reorientation of multibody systems in space. In this paper, we have used the framework developed by Shapere and Wilczek for the specific problem of reorientation of a free–free beam in space; our results represent, in a certain sense, the limiting case of the multibody results obtained by Reyhanoglu and McClamroch when the number of bodies increases without limit.

Although our study in this paper has been concerned with the ideal case of reorientation of a free–free beam in space, we note that the same ideas are applicable to reorientation of a wide class of deformable space structures, using only actuators embedded into the structure. In this sense, smart structures technology can be used to accomplish a variety of efficient reorientation maneuvers for space structures.

References

[1] J. Baillieul and M. Levi, "Constrained relative motions in rotational mechanics," *Arch. Rational Mech. Anal.*, Vol. 115, pp. 101–135, 1991.

[2] A. Bloch, M. Reyhanoglu and N. H. McClamroch, "Control and stabilization of nonholonomic dynamic systems," *IEEE Transactions on Automatic Control*, Vol. 37, No. 11, pp. 1746–1757, 1990.

[3] Y. G. Fung, *Foundations of Solid Mechanics*, Prentice-Hall, 1965.

[4] P. S. Krishnaprasad, "Geometric phases, and optimal reconfiguration for multibody systems," *Proc. of the American Control Conference*, Vol. 3, pp. 2440–2444, 1990.

[5] R. Murray and S. Sastry, "Steering nonholonomic systems using sinusoids," *Proc. of the 29-th Conference on Decision and Control*, Vol. 4, pp. 2097–2101, 1990.

[6] E. Reissner, "On a one-dimensional finite strain beam theory: the plane problem," *J. Appl. Math. Phys.*, Vol. 23, pp. 795-804, 1972.

[7] M. Reyhanoglu and N. H. McClamroch, "Planar reorientation maneuvers of space multibody systems using internal controls," *J. Guidance, Control and Dynamics*, Vol. 15, No. 6, pp. 1475–1480, 1992.

[8] A. Shapere and F. Wilczek,"Gauge kinematics of deformable bodies," *Geometric Phases in Physics*, World Scientific, Singapore, pp. 449–460, 1989.

[9] J. C. Simo and L. Vu-Quoc, "On the dynamics in space of rods undergoing large motions—A geometrically exact approach," *Computer Methods in Applied Mechanics and Engineering*, Vol. 66, pp. 125-161, North–Holland, 1988.

Proceedings of the
American Control Conference
San Francisco, California • June 1993

An Invariant Set Analysis of the Hub-Appendage Problem

Ranjan Mukherjee

Mechanical Engineering Department
Naval Postgraduate School
Monterey, CA 93943

John L. Junkins

Aerospace Engineering Department
Texas A&M University
College Station, TX 77843

1 Introduction

In the recent literature, an asymptotic stability theorem [1] for autonomous and periodic nonautonomous systems was used to prove the global asymptotic stability of the mass-spring-damper system and the damped Mathieu system. For such systems, the application of LaSalle's invariant set theorem [3] has been the conventional approach adopted to prove the global asymptotic stability. When the derivative of the Lyapunov function [2] vanishes, LaSalle's theorem [3] requires us to show that maximum invariant set of the system consists only of the equilibrium point as its entry. While it is always simple to identify the set of points Q where the derivative of the Lyapunov function vanishes, the maximum invariant set $I \subset Q$, is not always easy to identify. The main challenge of LaSalle's theorem [3] is therefore to sort out the maximum invariant set. For a distributed parameter system the dynamics is described by a hybrid set of ordinary and partial differential equations. For such a system, the sorting out of the maximum invariant set is not a trivial task.

The distributed parameter system consisting of a rigid hub with one or more cantilevered flexible appendages has appeared in the technical literature quite frequently [4], [5], [6]. The complete description of the system can be found in [4]. Under the assumption that the system undergoes anti-symmetric motion with deformation in unison (see Fig.2) a class of rest-to-rest manuevers was considered in [4]. For the particular Lyapunov function considered, the best choice of the control input only guaranteed the negative semi-definiteness of the derivative of the Lyapunov function. To conclude the global asymptotic stability using LaSalle's theorem, it would be necessary to formally prove that the maximum invariant set consists only of the equilibrium point. The global asymptotic stability of the system was claimed in [4] in the absence of this proof.

In this paper we consider the hub-appendage problem [4] with modifications. The modelling and successful control of such a system is expected to provide us with insight into the modelling and control of a general class of distributed parameter systems. Using a Lyapunov function approach and the asymptotic stability theorem in [1] we prove that global asymptotic stability of the system is guaranteed provided the system undergoes anti-symmetric motion with deformation in unison. In other situations like symmetric motion with deformation in opposition (see Fig.2), such a conclusion cannot be drawn.

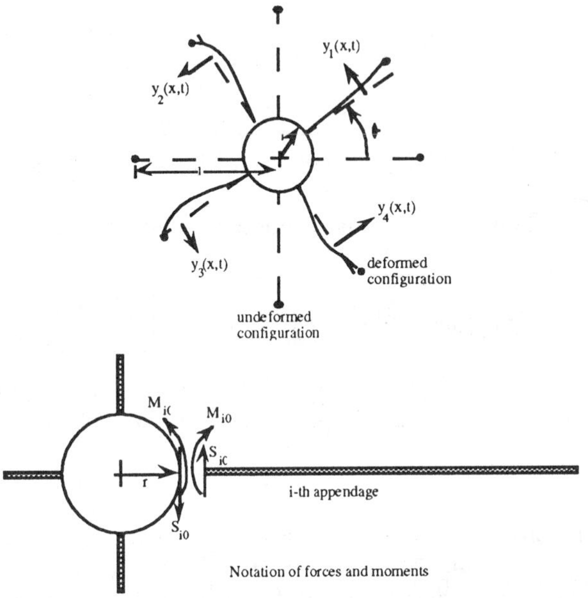

Figure 1. A distributed parameter autonomous system consisting of a rigid hub with four cantilevered flexible appendages.

2 The Hub-Appendage Problem

This example is taken from [4] with some modifications. The hybrid system of ordinary and partial differential equations governing the dynamics of the system, that has already been described in the introduction, are

$$I_{hub}\frac{d^2\theta}{dt^2} = u + \sum_{i=1}^{4}(M_{i0} - r\,S_{i0}) \qquad (1)$$

$$-(M_{i0} - r\,S_{i0}) = \int_r^l \rho x\left(\frac{\partial^2 y_i}{\partial t^2} + x\frac{d^2\theta}{dt^2}\right)dx \; +$$

$$m\,l\left(l\,\frac{d^2\theta}{dt^2}+\frac{\partial^2 y_i}{\partial t^2}\Big|_l\right),\quad i=1,2,3,4 \quad (2)$$

$$\rho\left(\frac{\partial^2 y_i}{\partial t^2}+x\frac{d^2\theta}{dt^2}\right)+EI\,\frac{\partial^4 y_i}{\partial x^4}=0,\quad i=1,2,3,4 \quad (3)$$

The boundary conditions on Eqs.(1), (2) and (3) are

$$y_i(t,r)=\frac{\partial y_i}{\partial x}\Big|_r=0,\quad i=1,2,3,4 \quad (4)$$

$$\frac{\partial^2 y_i}{\partial x^2}\Big|_l=0,\quad i=1,2,3,4 \quad (5)$$

$$\frac{\partial^3 y_i}{\partial x^3}\Big|_l=\frac{m}{EI}\left(l\,\frac{d^2\theta}{dt^2}+\frac{\partial^2 y_i}{\partial t^2}\Big|_l\right),\quad i=1,2,3,4 \quad (6)$$

The state of the system is described by a hybrid set of discrete and continuous variables

$$\mathbf{Z}=\left[\theta,\dot\theta,y_1(x,t),\cdots,y_4(x,t),\frac{\partial y_1(x,t)}{\partial t},\cdots,\frac{\partial y_4(x,t)}{\partial t}\right] \quad (7)$$

We choose the Lyapunov function V as

$$V=\frac{a_1}{2}I_{hub}\dot\theta^2+\frac{a_2}{2}(\theta-\theta_f)^2+\frac{a_3}{2}\sum_{i=1}^{4}\left[\int_r^l\rho\left(\frac{\partial y_i}{\partial t}+)\right]\right.$$
$$\left.[(x\dot\theta)^2\,dx+\int_r^l EI\left(\frac{\partial^2 y_i}{\partial x^2}\right)^2dx+m\left(l\dot\theta+\frac{\partial y_i}{\partial t}\Big|_l\right)^2\right] \quad (8)$$

in order to derive control laws that will drive the system to its desired state $\mathbf{Z}_{desired}=(\theta_f,0,0,\cdots,0,0,\cdots,0)$. In Eq.(10), a_1,a_2, and a_3 are positive constants. It can be shown [4], that the choice of $u(t)$ as

$$u=-(1/a_1)\quad\left[a_2(\theta-\theta_f)+a_4\dot\theta+(a_3-a_1)\right]$$
$$\left[\sum_{i=1}^{4}(r\,S_{i0}-M_{i0})\right],\quad a_4>0 \quad (9)$$

in Eq.(1), leads to $\dot V=-a_4\dot\theta^2$. Clearly, $\dot V$ is negative semidefinite and is equal to zero iff $\dot\theta=0$. To check for the asymptotic stability of the system using the theorem in [1], we first compute the higher-order derivatives of V. We find that when $\dot V=0$, the following condition always holds good

$$V^{(2k+1)}=-2^k a_4\left[\theta^{(k+1)}\right]^2,\quad V^{(i)}=0,\ i=1,2,\cdots,2k \quad (10)$$

for some positive integer k. In Eq.(12), $V^{(*)}$ denotes the $(*)$-th time derivative of V, and $\theta^{(*)}$ denotes the $(*)$-th time derivative of θ. Using Eq.(10) and the sufficient conditions of the asymptotic stability theorem [1], we conclude that the system is globally asymptotically stable if $\theta^{(k)}\neq 0$, for any positive integer k. In other words, if $\dot V=0$ at some time $t=T$, then the system will be globally asymptotically stable if θ is not a constant for all $t\geq T$, and is a constant only at the equilibrium point.

We now investigate the case where θ is a constant at a point other than at the equilibrium point where $\mathbf{Z}\neq\mathbf{Z}_d$. Let this constant be θ_C. Then Eqs.(1), (2) and (3) simplify to

$$u-\sum_{i=1}^{4}(r\,S_{i0}-M_{i0})=0 \quad (11)$$

$$-(M_{i0}-r\,S_{i0})=\int_r^l\rho x\,\frac{\partial^2 y_i}{\partial t^2}\,dx+m\,l\,\frac{\partial^2 y_i}{\partial t^2}\Big|_l,\quad i=1,2,3,4 \quad (12)$$

$$\rho\,\frac{\partial^2 y_i}{\partial t^2}+EI\,\frac{\partial^4 y_i}{\partial x^4}=0,\quad i=1,2,3,4 \quad (13)$$

The boundary conditions given by Eqs.(4) and (5) remain unchanged but the boundary condition given by Eq.(6) simplifies to

$$\frac{\partial^3 y_i}{\partial x^3}\Big|_l=\frac{m}{EI}\frac{\partial^2 y_i}{\partial t^2}\Big|_l,\quad i=1,2,3,4 \quad (14)$$

Also, the input to the system $u(t)$ defined by Eq.(9) can be simplified using Eq.(11) to

$$u=\sum_{i=1}^{4}(r\,S_{i0}-M_{i0})=\frac{a_2}{a_3}(\theta_f-\theta_C)\equiv C=constant \quad (15)$$

If we define $Y=\sum_{i=1}^{4}y_i$, then the above equation implies

$$\left[r\,\frac{\partial^3 Y}{\partial x^3}-\frac{\partial^2 Y}{\partial x^2}\right]_{x=r}=\frac{C}{EI}=\text{constant} \quad (16)$$

If we make the reasonable assumption that $Y(x,t)$ is of the form $Y(x,t)=F(x)\,G(t)$, then Eq.(16) leads to

$$G(t)\left[r\,\frac{\partial^3 F}{\partial x^3}-\frac{\partial^2 F}{\partial x^2}\right]_{x=r}=\text{constant} \quad (17)$$

Equation (17) implies that $G(t)$ is a constant. Summing Eqs.(13) and (14) over $i=1$ to $i=4$, we have

$$\rho\,\frac{\partial^2 Y}{\partial t^2}+EI\,\frac{\partial^4 Y}{\partial x^4}=0 \quad (18)$$

$$\frac{\partial^3 Y}{\partial x^3}\Big|_l=\frac{m}{EI}\frac{\partial^2 Y}{\partial t^2}\Big|_l \quad (19)$$

Since $Y(x,t) = F(x)G(t)$, and $G(t)$ is a constant, Eqs.(18) and (19) imply

$$\frac{\partial^4 Y}{\partial x^4} = 0 \quad \Longrightarrow \quad \frac{\partial^3 Y}{\partial x^3} = \text{constant} \qquad (20)$$

$$\left.\frac{\partial^3 Y}{\partial x^3}\right|_l = 0 \qquad (21)$$

From Eqs.(20) and (21) it follows that $(\partial^3 Y/\partial x^3) = 0$, which implies that $(\partial^2 Y/\partial x^2)$ is a constant. Additionally, the value of this constant can be shown to be zero from the boundary condition in Eq.(5). Proceeding in the same way and using the boundary conditions in Eq.(4) it is trivial to show that $(\partial Y/\partial x) = Y(x,t) = 0$. This implies from Eqs.(16) and (15) that $u = 0$ and $\theta_C = \theta_f$. Clearly, the maximum invariant set for the system comprises the set of points where $\theta = \theta_f$, $\dot{\theta} = 0$, and $\sum_{i=1}^{4} y_i(x,t) = 0$. If there exist functions $y_i(x,t) \neq 0, i = 1,2,3,4$ such that $Y = \sum_{i=1}^{4} y_i = 0$ holds good, then the set $S = \{\mathbf{Z} : V^{(j)}(\mathbf{Z}) = 0, \forall j = 1,2,\cdots,\infty\}$ contains entries other than the trivial solution $\mathbf{Z} = \mathbf{Z}_{desired}$. In such a situation we cannot claim global asymptotic stability of the equilibrium point. Such a situation may arise in the case of symmetric deformation in opposition, shown in Fig.2, where $y_1(x,t) = -y_2(x,t)$ and $y_3(x,t) = -y_4(x,t)$. In such a situation, the residual energy of the system remains trapped within the beams. There exists no net interacting moment between the hub and the beams and the hub remains motionless at its desired configuration $\theta = \theta_f$.

The case of anti-symmetric deformation in unison, shown in Fig.2, was considered in [4]. In this case, it is assumed that $y_1(x,t) = y_2(x,t) = y_3(x,t) = y_4(x,t)$. When $Y(x,t) = 0$, this implies $y_i(x,t) = 0$ for $i = 1,2,3,4$. Therefore, for anti-symmetric deformation in unison, it is quite simple to show that the set $S = \{\mathbf{Z} : V^{(j)}(\mathbf{Z}) = 0, \forall j = 1,2,\cdots,\infty\}$ contains only the equilibrium point $\mathbf{Z} = \mathbf{Z}_{desired}$. Consequently, we can establish the asymptotic stability property of the hub with the flexible appendages undergoing anti-symmetric deformation in unison under the input defined by Eq.(9). The control law given in Eq.(9) was used to stabilize the system to the equilibrium point in [4] but no formal proof for the asymptotic stability was provided.

3 Conclusion

The rest-to-rest maneuver of the distributed parameter system consisting of a rigid hub with four cantilevered flexible appendages was studied. The best choice of the control input resulted in the negative semi-definiteness of the derivative of the Lyapunov function. An invariant set analysis of the system was subsequently carried out using an asymptotic stability theorem [1]. The analysis establishes the fact that the hub-appendage system is globally asymptotically stable when the system undergoes anti-symmetric motion with deformation in unison.

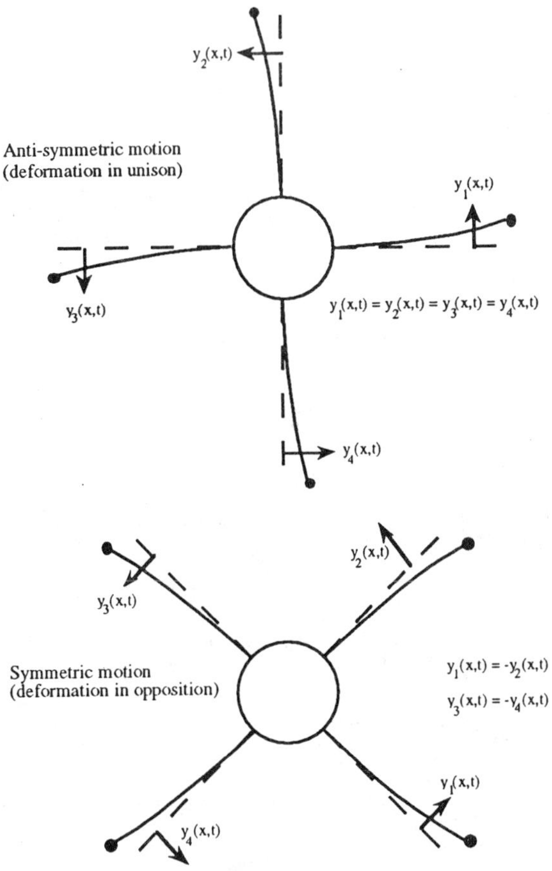

Figure 2. Anti-symmetric and symmetric motion of the system consisting of the rigid hub and four flexible appendages.

References

[1] Mukherjee, R., and Chen, D., "An asymptotic stability theorem for autonomous systems", Journal of Guidance, Control and Dynamics, (to appear).

[2] Lyapunov, A.M., "On the general problem of stability of motion", Kharkov Mathematical Society, Soviet Union (in Russian), 1892.

[3] LaSalle, J., and Lefschetz, S., "Stability by Lyapunov's Direct Method with Applications", Academic Press, New York, 1961.

[4] Junkins, J.L., Rahman, Z.H., and Bang, H., "Near-minimum time control of distributed parameter systems: Analytical and experimental results", Journal of Guidance, Control and Dynamics, Vol. 14, No. 2, pp. 406-415, 1991.

[5] Fujii, H., Ohtsuka, T., and Udou, S., "Mission Function Control for Slew Maneuver Experiment", Journal of Guidance, Control and Dynamics, Vol. 12, No. 6, pp. 858-865, 1989.

[6] Singh, G., Kabamba, P., and McClamroch, N., "Planar Time Optimal Slewing Maneuvers of Flexible Spacecraft", Journal of Guidance, Control and Dynamics, Vol. 12, No. 1, pp. 71-81, 1989.

Proceedings of the
American Control Conference
San Francisco, California • June 1993

NONLINEAR MODELING AND PARTIAL LINEARIZING CONTROL OF A SLEWING TIMOSHENKO-BEAM MANIPULATOR

King Yuan and Chen-Meng Hu
Department of Mechanical Engineering
National Taiwan University

Abstract

The modeling and control of a horizontally slewing inextensible Timoshenko-beam including the correct centrifugal stiffening effect and a tip payload are considered. Partial differential equations of motion and orthogonality conditions for the constrained modes are derived. A finite dimensional dynamic model simplified by using the orthogonality conditions is obtained. This nonlinear dynamic model places no restrictions on slenderness ratio, slewing angle, and rotational speed provided that the flexure deflections remain small. To achieve a joint angle trajectory tracking with rapid suppression of elastic vibrations, a nonlinear controller is designed using input-output linearization and elastic mode stabilization. The input-output linearization is used to generate a desired joint angle trajectory command. The elastic mode stabilization is designed based on the linear time-invariant part of the partially linearized system. Stability of the closed-loop system is investigated, and a sufficient condition for asymptotic stability is established. This stability condition justifies the existence of joint angle trajectory commands for accurate joint angle trajectory following and simultaneous vibration suppression.

1. Introduction

In this paper we present a physically valid nonlinear dynamic model for slewing beams, assuming that the axial beam vibrations are negligible but the motion-induced stiffening and softening terms are consistently retained. This dynamic model tends to provide a wide range of applicability, placing no restrictions on slenderness ratio, slewing angle, and rotational speed so long as the flexure deflections remain small in comparison with the length of the beam. The model will be validated through numerical simulations for a spin-up maneuver problem. Proceed with the model development, a partial linearizing feedback control to accomplish the joint angle tracking of a horizontally slewing Timoshenko beam is also considered. Unlike previous similar studies for the sole purpose of decoupling, e.g., Kwatny and Bennett (1988), Akhrif, Blankenship, and Bennett (1989) and Bennett, Akhrif, and Dwyer (1990), the partial linearizing control is used here to generate a desired joint angle trajectory command. Furthermore, a vibration stabilization control is also incorporated to quickly suppress the beam vibration. This elastic-mode stabilizer is designed using a linear quadratic regulator based on the linear time-invariant part of the partially linearied system. The stability of the overall closed-loop nonlinear system is then investigated and a sufficient condition to ensure asymptotic stability is presented. Several numerical simulations are carried out to demonstrate the feasibility and effectiveness of the proposed active control algorithms.

2. Equations of Motion of Slewing Beam

The horizontally slewing flexible beam depicted in Fig. 1 of total length L, area moment of inertia I, cross-sectional area A, density ϱ, Young's modulus E, shear modulus G and shear coefficient κ, is attached at one end to a payload of mass M_p and inertia J_p and on the other end a hub of inertia I_h, which in turn is connected to an actuctor that supplies a torque τ. Assume that the elastic deformations are small and that plane sections remain plane after deformation. To characterize the elastic deformations, we associate to each point on the neutral axis of the beam three quantities $u(x,t)$, $v(x,t)$ and $\phi(x,t)$. u and v are components of elastic displacement of the neutral axis. ϕ denotes the orientation of the beam cross-section. x is measured from the root of the beam.

The position vector at the point Q′ on the deformed neutral axis can be expressed as (see e.g., Choura et al., 1991)

$$\begin{aligned} \underline{r} &= [(a+x+u)cos\theta - vsin\theta]\underline{i} \\ &+[(a+x+u)sin\theta + vcos\theta]\underline{j} \end{aligned} \tag{1}$$

where $\underline{i}$ and $\underline{j}$ are unit vectors in the inertial frame, and $\theta(t)$ is the hub angular rotation.

The kinetic energy of the slewing beam, after integrating over the cross section, can be expressed as (see e.g., Simo and Vu-Quoc, 1986)

$$\begin{aligned} T &= \frac{1}{2}\int_0^L \varrho A\dot{\underline{r}}^T\dot{\underline{r}}dx + \frac{1}{2}\int_0^L \varrho I(\dot{\theta}+\phi_t)^2dx \\ &+\frac{1}{2}I_h\dot{\theta}^2 + \frac{1}{2}M_p\dot{\underline{r}}^T(L,t)\dot{\underline{r}}(L,t) \\ &+\frac{1}{2}J_p[\dot{\theta}+\phi_t(L,t)]^2 \end{aligned} \tag{2}$$

where the subscript t and dot indicate differentiation with respect to time t.

Assume further that the beam is inextensible, in the sense that the beam is much more rigid in the longitudnal direction than in the transverse direction, then $u(x,t)$ can be expressed as (see e.g., Baruh and Tadikonda, 1989)

$$u(x,t) = -\frac{1}{2}\int_0^x v_x^2(\sigma,t)d\sigma \tag{3}$$

where the subscript x denotes differentiation with respect to x. Eq. (3) implies that the stretch of the neutral axis due to axial vibration is negligible, but the effect of foreshortening is retained.

Substituting Eqs. (1) and (3) into Eq. (2), and retaining terms only up to quadratic in elastic variable v, we obtain

$$\begin{aligned} T &= \frac{1}{2}\int_0^L \{\varrho A[v_t^2 + v^2\dot{\theta}^2 + (a+x)^2\dot{\theta}^2 + 2(a+x)v_t\dot{\theta}] \\ &-v_x^2\dot{\theta}^2S(x)\}dx + \frac{1}{2}M_p[v^2(L,t)\dot{\theta}^2 \\ &+(a+L)^2\dot{\theta}^2 + 2(a+L)v_t(L,t)\dot{\theta} + v_t^2(L,t)] \\ &+\frac{1}{2}\int_0^T \varrho I(\dot{\theta}+\phi_t)^2dx + \frac{1}{2}I_h\dot{\theta}^2 \\ &\frac{1}{2}J_p[\dot{\theta}+\phi_t(L,t)]^2 \end{aligned} \tag{4}$$

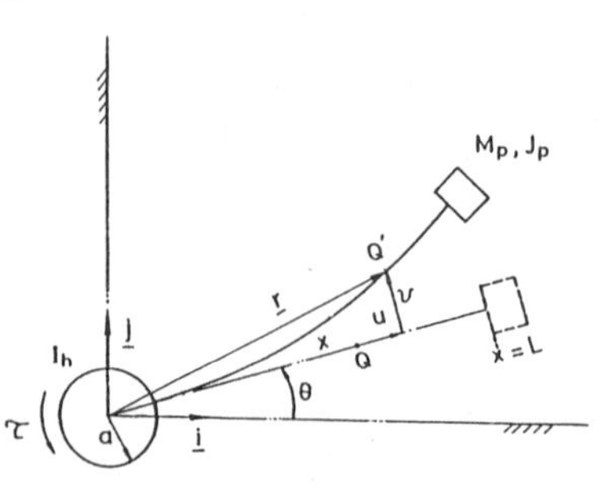

Fig. 1 Schematic of horizontally slewing flexible manipulator.

where

$$S(x) = \int_x^L \varrho A(a+x)dx + M_p(a+L) \quad (5)$$

Clearly the term $\dot{\theta}^2(t)S(x)$ represents an internal axial force arising from centrifugal effect. The potential energy of the slewing beam using linear strains can be written as

$$U = \frac{1}{2}\int_0^L EI\phi_x^2 dx + \frac{1}{2}\int_0^L \kappa GA(\phi - v_x)^2 dx \quad (6)$$

Note that the axial strain energy, which contains only terms higher than quadratic in elastic variable v, is not included in U for consistent formulation. It is also interesting to point out that in the so-called "effective load approach" (see e.g., Yigit et. al., 1988), the axial velocity is neglected in computing the kinetic energy, but a fictious axial force $\dot{\theta}^2(t)S(x)$ is assumed in computing the strain energy using linear strains. The equivalence of the inextensibility assumption (i.e., the bending foreshortening approach) and the effective load approach becomes obvious since they arise from the same physical origin and yield identical Lagrangian $T-U$.

Applying the extended Hamilton's principle

$$\int_{t_1}^{t_2} \delta(T-U)dt + \int_{t_1}^{t_2} \tau\delta\theta = 0 \quad (7)$$

we obtain the following equations of motion and the associated boundary conditions:

$$\begin{aligned}&\ddot{\theta}\{\int_0^L [\varrho A(v^2 + (a+x)^2) + \varrho I - Sv_x^2]dx \\ &+M_p[v^2(L,t) + (a+L)^2] + J_p + I_h\} \\ &+2\dot{\theta}\{\int_0^L (\varrho Avv_t - Sv_xv_{xt})dx \\ &+M_pv(L,t)v_t(L,t)\} \\ &+\int_0^L [\varrho A(a+x)v_{tt} + \varrho I\phi_{tt}]dx \\ &+M_p(a+L)v_{tt}(L,t) + J_p\phi_{tt}(L,t) = \tau \quad (8)\end{aligned}$$

$$\begin{aligned}&\varrho Av_{tt} - [\varrho Av + (Sv_x)_x]\dot{\theta}^2 + \kappa GA(\phi_x - v_{xx}) \\ &= -\varrho A(a+x)\ddot{\theta} \quad (9)\end{aligned}$$

$$\varrho I\phi_{tt} - EI\phi_{xx} + \kappa GA(\phi - v_x) = -\varrho I\ddot{\theta} \quad (10)$$

with the natural boundary conditions

$$\begin{aligned}&M_p[\dot{\theta}^2 v(L,t) - (a+L)\ddot{\theta} - v_{tt}(L,t)] - \dot{\theta}^2 S(L)v_x(L,t) \\ &-\kappa GA[v_x(L,t) - \phi(L,t)] = 0 \quad (11) \\ &J_p[\ddot{\theta} + \phi_{tt}(L,t)] + EI\phi_x(L,t) = 0 \quad (12)\end{aligned}$$

and the geometric boundary conditions

$$v(0,t) = 0 \quad (13)$$

$$\phi(0,t) = 0 \quad (14)$$

Although a number of researchers, e.g., Simo and Vu-Quoc (1986), Hanagud and Sarkar (1989), and Padilla and Flotow (1992), have argued that one has to use nonlinear strains or nonlinear strain-displacement relations to account for geometric stiffening, our linear strain approach does yield the stiffening and softening terms that are identical with those obtained by Simo and Vu-Quoc (1987) using second order nonlinear strains for the case of axially inextensible Timoshenko beams. Our approach, however, parallels to the work given by Boutaghou and Erdman (1991) for Euler-Bernoulli beams using the so-called Von-Karman geometric constraint. In this regard, within the framework of inextensible beams, our results represent a generalization for Timoshenko beams.

In the slewing beam problem it is common to choose the constrained mode expansion to obtain finite dimensional dynamic model. This is justifable if the beam-to-hub inertia ratio is very small (see e.g., Barbieri and Özgüner, 1988). When the rigid hub is constrained to be fixed and all external influences are set to zero, we obtain the classical Timoshenko-beam partial differential equations

$$\varrho Av_{tt} - \kappa GA(v_{xx} - \phi_x) = 0 \quad (15)$$

$$\varrho I\phi_{tt} - EI\phi_{xx} - \kappa GA(v_x - \phi) = 0 \quad (16)$$

and the clamped-mass boundary conditions

$$v(0,t) = 0 \quad (17)$$

$$\phi(0,t) = 0 \quad (18)$$

$$M_pv_{tt}(L,t) + \kappa GA[v_x(L,t) - \phi(L,t)] = 0 \quad (19)$$

$$J_p\phi_{tt}(L,t) + EI\phi_x(L,t) = 0 \quad (20)$$

The frequency equation and mode shapes can be determined by assuming $v(x,t) = v_i(x)e^{j\omega_i t}$ and $\phi_i(x,t) = \phi_i(x)e^{j\omega_i t}$, where $j = \sqrt{-1}$.

The orthogonality conditions between mode shapes can also be easily derived as

$$\begin{aligned}&\int_0^L (\varrho Av_iv_j + \varrho I\phi_i\phi_j)dx + M_pv_i(L)v_j(L) \\ &+J_p\phi_i(L)\phi_j(L) = m_i\delta_{ij} \quad (21) \\ &\int_0^L [EI\frac{\partial\phi_i}{\partial x}\frac{\partial\phi_j}{\partial x} + \kappa GA(\phi_i - \frac{\partial v_i}{\partial x})(\phi_j - \frac{\partial v_j}{\partial x})]dx \\ &= k_i\ \delta_{ij} \quad (22)\end{aligned}$$

where $i,\ j = 1,2,3,...,\delta_{ij}$ is the Kronecker delta, and m_i and k_i are defined by setting $i=j$ in Eqs. (21) and (22).

3. Finite Dimensional Dynamic Model

Let the assumed mode method based on the constrained mode expansion be applied to the small elastic deformations of a slewing beam. We write

$$v(x,t) = \underline{v}^T(x)\ \underline{\delta}(t) \quad (23)$$

$$\phi(x,t) = \underline{\phi}^T(x)\ \underline{\delta}(t) \quad (24)$$

where $\underline{v}(x) = [v_1(x),\cdots,v_n(x)]^T$, $\underline{\phi}(x) = [\phi_1(x),\cdots,\phi_n(x)]^T$, and $\underline{\delta}(t) = [\delta_1(t),\ \cdots,\ \delta_n(t)]^T$. Using the orthogonality conditions, it is possible to rewrite the kinetic energy and potential energy, i.e., Eqs. (4) and (6), in the following more suitable forms.

$$T = \frac{1}{2}(\dot{\theta}\ \dot{\underline{\delta}}^T)^T \begin{bmatrix} m_{rr}(\underline{\delta}) & \underline{m}_{re} \\ \underline{m}_{re}^T & \underline{M}_{ee}\end{bmatrix} (\dot{\theta}\ \dot{\underline{\delta}}^T) \quad (25)$$

$$U = \frac{1}{2}\ \underline{\delta}^T\underline{K}_{ee}\underline{\delta} \quad (26)$$

where

$$\begin{aligned}m_{rr}(\underline{\delta}) &= \int_0^L \varrho A(a+x)^2dx + \int_0^L \varrho Idx + I_h \\ &+M_p(a+L)^2 + J_p + \underline{\delta}^T\underline{N}\underline{\delta} \quad (27)\end{aligned}$$

$$\begin{aligned}\underline{N} &= \int_0^L \varrho A\underline{v}\underline{v}^Tdx + M_p\underline{v}(L)\underline{v}^T(L) \\ &- \int_0^L \varrho AS(x)\frac{\partial\underline{v}}{\partial x}\frac{\partial\underline{v}^T}{\partial x}\ dx \quad (28)\end{aligned}$$

$$\underline{m}_{re} = (\mu_1,\cdots,\mu_n)^T \quad (29)$$

$$\begin{aligned}\mu_i &= \int_0^L \varrho A(a+x)v_idx + \int_0^L \varrho I\phi_idx \\ &+ M_p(a+L)v_i(L) + J_p\phi_i(L) \quad (30)\end{aligned}$$

$$\underline{M}_{ee} = diag.(m_1,\cdots,m_n) \quad (31)$$

$$\underline{K}_{ee} = diag.(k_1,\cdots,k_n) \quad (32)$$

It is now straightforward using Lagrangian approach to arrive at the following finite dimensional nonlinear dynamic model for the slewing beam.

$$\begin{bmatrix} m_{rr}(\underline{\delta}) & \underline{m}_{re}^T \\ \underline{m}_{re} & \underline{M}_{ee} \end{bmatrix} \begin{pmatrix} \ddot{\theta} \\ \ddot{\underline{\delta}} \end{pmatrix} + \begin{bmatrix} 0 & \underline{0}^T \\ \underline{0} & \underline{K}_{ee} \end{bmatrix} \begin{pmatrix} \theta \\ \underline{\delta} \end{pmatrix} + \begin{bmatrix} n_r(\dot{\theta},\ \underline{\delta},\ \dot{\underline{\delta}}) \\ \underline{n}_e(\dot{\theta},\ \underline{\delta}) \end{bmatrix} = \begin{pmatrix} 1 \\ \underline{0} \end{pmatrix} \tau \tag{33}$$

where

$$n_r(\dot{\theta},\underline{\delta},\dot{\underline{\delta}}) = 2\dot{\theta}\ \dot{\underline{\delta}}^T\ \underline{N}\ \underline{\delta} \tag{34}$$

and

$$\underline{n}_e(\dot{\theta},\underline{\delta}) = -\dot{\theta}^2\ \underline{N}\ \underline{\delta} \tag{35}$$

For an Euler-Bernoulli beam free of payload, the terms involving rotary inertia, shear, and payload may be dropped. If we further drop the second order terms in elastic variables, Eq. (33) agrees with the single link special case (with immobile base) recently discussed by Padilla and Von Flotow (1992). This is again a surprising result since their dynamic equations were obtained through the use of nonlinear strain-displacement relations. It appears that the dilemma of consistent account of centrifugal stiffening is still an interesting open problem regardless of numerious papers published in this area in recent years.

Now let the torque applied to the slewing beam be generated by a DC servomotor, then τ can be expressed as (see e.g., Seraji, 1989)

$$\tau = N_g K_t \mathrm{I} - N_g^2 J_m \ddot{\theta} - N_g^2 D_m \dot{\theta} \tag{36}$$

where N_g is the gear reduction ratio, K_t is the motor torque constant, J_m is the motor inertia, D_m is the motor viscous damping coefficient, and I is the armature current. After substituting Eq. (36) into Eq. (33) and solving for $\ddot{\theta}$ and $\ddot{\underline{\delta}}$, we obtain the following open-loop equations for the combined motor-beam system.

$$\begin{aligned} \ddot{\theta} &= -[d_{rr}(\underline{\delta}) f_r(\theta,\dot{\theta},\underline{\delta},\dot{\underline{\delta}}) + \underline{d}_{re}^T(\underline{\delta}) \underline{f}_e(\theta,\dot{\theta},\underline{\delta},\dot{\underline{\delta}})] \\ &\quad + d_{rr}(\underline{\delta}) N_g K_t \mathrm{I} \end{aligned} \tag{37}$$

$$\begin{aligned} \ddot{\underline{\delta}} &= -[\underline{d}_{re}(\underline{\delta}) f_r(\theta,\dot{\theta},\underline{\delta},\dot{\underline{\delta}}) + \underline{D}_{ee}(\underline{\delta}) \underline{f}_e(\theta,\dot{\theta},\underline{\delta},\dot{\underline{\delta}})] \\ &\quad + \underline{d}_{re}(\underline{\delta}) N_g K_t \mathrm{I} \end{aligned} \tag{38}$$

where

$$d_{rr}^{-1}(\underline{\delta}) = m_{rr}(\underline{\delta}) + N_g^2 J_m - \underline{m}_{re}^T\ \underline{M}_{ee}^{-1}\ \underline{m}_{re} \tag{39}$$

$$\underline{d}_{re}(\underline{\delta}) = -d_{rr}(\underline{\delta})\ \underline{M}_{ee}^{-1}\ \underline{m}_{re} \tag{40}$$

$$\underline{D}_{ee}(\underline{\delta}) = \underline{M}_{ee}^{-1} - \underline{M}_{ee}^{-1}\ \underline{m}_{re}\ \underline{d}_{re}^T(\underline{\delta}) \tag{41}$$

$$f_r(\theta,\dot{\theta},\underline{\delta},\dot{\underline{\delta}}) = N_g^2 D_m \dot{\theta} + n_r(\dot{\theta},\underline{\delta},\dot{\underline{\delta}}) \tag{42}$$

$$\underline{f}_e(\theta,\dot{\theta},\underline{\delta},\dot{\underline{\delta}}) = \underline{C}_{ee}\dot{\underline{\delta}} + \underline{K}_{ee}\underline{\delta} + \underline{n}_e(\dot{\theta},\underline{\delta}) \tag{43}$$

and $\underline{C}_{ee} = diag.(2\zeta_1\omega_1,\cdots,2\zeta_n\omega_n)$ is a diagonal damping matrix included to account for the internal damping of the slewing beam.

4. Feedback Linearizing Joint Angle Control

Let the joint angle θ be the output and the current I be the input. The idea of input-output (or partial) linearization is to decouple rigid mode θ completely from the flexible modes $\underline{\delta}$ so that a linear time-invariant input-output relation is established. Let $\tilde{\theta} \triangleq \theta - \theta_d$ denotes the joint angle tracking error, where θ_d is the desired output trajectory. Inspection reveals that with the nonlinear feedback

$$\begin{aligned} \mathrm{I} &= [N_g K_t d_{rr}(\underline{\delta})]^{-1}\{d_{rr}(\underline{\delta}) f_r(\theta,\dot{\theta},\underline{\delta},\dot{\underline{\delta}}) \\ &\quad + \underline{d}_{re}^T(\underline{\delta}) \underline{f}_e(\theta,\dot{\theta},\underline{\delta},\dot{\underline{\delta}}) - a_1\dot{\theta} - a_2\theta - a_3\int_0^t \theta dt \\ &\quad + w_d + \delta w\} \end{aligned} \tag{44}$$

in which

$$w_d = \ddot{\theta}_d + a_1\dot{\theta}_d + a_2\theta_d + a_3\int_0^t \theta_d dt, \tag{45}$$

δw is a stabilizing signal to be determined later and a_1, a_2, a_3 are design parameters, Eqs. (37) and (38) can be reduced to

$$\ddot{\tilde{\theta}} + a_1\dot{\tilde{\theta}} + a_2\tilde{\theta} + a_3\int_0^t \tilde{\theta} dt = \delta w \tag{46}$$

$$\begin{aligned} &\underline{M}_{ee}\ddot{\underline{\delta}} + \underline{C}_{ee}\ \dot{\underline{\delta}} + (\underline{K}_{ee} - \dot{\theta}^2 \underline{N})\underline{\delta} \\ &= -\underline{m}_{re}(\ddot{\theta}_d - a_1\dot{\tilde{\theta}} - a_2\tilde{\theta} - a_3\int_0^t \tilde{\theta} dt) - \underline{m}_{re}\delta w \end{aligned} \tag{47}$$

Note that with $\delta w = 0$ the output (joint angle) tracking error converges to zero if a_1, a_2, and a_3 are properly chosen. It may be convenient to regard Eq. (45) as a third-order command genrator by letting $\dot{w}_d = a_3\theta_r(t)$, where $\theta_r(t)$ is a reference input, so as to produce the required joint angle trajectory command θ_d. However, as the joint angle follows the command trajectory, the internal dynamics (flexible modes) may not be desirable due to the small inherent material damping. It may not even be asymptotically stable if the material damping is neglected. Therefore, the use of δw to stabilize the flexible modes becomes necessary. Clearly, the decoupled joint angle response is disturbed once the stabilizing signal δw is applied. This may cause significant amount of joint angle tracking errors. To compensate this discrepancy, the command generator is chosen according to

$$\dddot{\theta}_d + a_1^*\ddot{\theta}_d + a_2^*\dot{\theta}_d + a_3^*\theta_d = a_3^*\theta_r(t) \tag{48}$$

where a_1^*, a_2^*, and a_3^* are design parameters. Note that a_1, a_2, and a_3 determine the decoupled joint angle response of partial linearizing feedback, while a_1^*, a_2^*, and a_3^* are used to generate the actual joint angle trajectory command.

It is worth to remark at this point that similar decoupling techniques have been employed by De Schutter et al. (1988). De Luca and Siciliano (1989), De Luca, Lucibello, and Ulivi (1989), Das and Singh (1990), Yuan and Lin (1990), Wang and Vidyasagar (1991) and others for Euler-Bernoulli-beam manipulators without taking account of centrifugal stiffening. However, a Timoshenko-beam manipulators including the correct centrifugal stiffening effect is considered here and the overall control scheme is also different.

5. Linear Stabilization of Elastic Vibrations

To track a desired joint angle trajectory with as little link vibration as possible, we define the error state vector as

$$\underline{e} = (\tilde{\theta}, \underline{\delta}^T, \dot{\tilde{\theta}}, \dot{\underline{\delta}}^T, \int_0^t \tilde{\theta} dt)^T \tag{49}$$

Then we have from Eqs. (46) and (47)

$$\dot{\underline{e}} = \underline{A}\underline{e} + \underline{B}\delta w + \underline{\psi}(\underline{e},t) \tag{50}$$

where

$$\underline{A} = \begin{bmatrix} 0 & \underline{0}_{1\times n} & 1 & \underline{0}_{1\times n} & 0 \\ \underline{0}_{n\times 1} & \underline{0}_{n\times n} & \underline{0}_{n\times 1} & \underline{I}_{n\times n} & \underline{0}_{n\times 1} \\ -a_2 & \underline{0}_{1\times n} & -a_1 & \underline{0}_{1\times n} & -a_3 \\ \underline{M}_{ee}^{-1}\underline{m}_{re}a_2 & -\underline{M}_{ee}^{-1}\underline{K}_{ee} & -\underline{M}_{ee}^{-1}\underline{m}_{re}a_1 & -\underline{M}_{ee}^{-1}\underline{C}_{ee} & \underline{M}_{ee}^{-1}\underline{m}_{re}a_3 \\ 1 & \underline{0}_{1\times n} & 0 & \underline{0}_{1\times n} & 0 \end{bmatrix} \tag{51}$$

$$\underline{B} = \begin{bmatrix} 0 \\ \underline{0}_{n\times 1} \\ 1 \\ -\underline{M}_{ee}^{-1}\underline{m}_{re} \\ 0 \end{bmatrix} \tag{52}$$

$$\underline{\psi} = \begin{bmatrix} 0 \\ \underline{0}_{n\times 1} \\ 0 \\ \underline{M}_{ee}^{-1}(\dot{\theta}^2\underline{N}\underline{\delta} - \underline{m}_{re}\ddot{\theta}_d) \\ 0 \end{bmatrix} \tag{53}$$

We now treat $\underline{\psi}$ as a disturbance and obtain a linear quadratic state feedback

$$\delta w = -\gamma^{-1}\underline{B}^T\ \underline{P}\underline{e} \tag{54}$$

for the linear time-invariant part of Eq. (50), by minimizing the performance index

$$J = \int_0^\infty e^{2\mu t}[\underline{e}^T\underline{Q}\underline{e} + \gamma(\delta w)^2]dt \tag{55}$$

where $\underline{Q} = \underline{Q}^T$ is at least positive semidefinite, γ is a positive constant, μ is a nonnegative constant, and $\underline{P}$ is the unique positive definite solution of the following algebraic Riccati equation

$$(\underline{A}^T + \mu \underline{I}_{2n+3})\underline{P} + \underline{P}(\underline{A} + \mu \underline{I}_{2n+3}) + \underline{Q}$$
$$-\gamma^{-1}\underline{P}\underline{B}\underline{B}^T\underline{P} = \underline{0} \quad (56)$$

where $\underline{I}_{2n+3}$ is the (2n+3) × (2n+3) identity matrix. The control current I is now obtained by the substitution of Eq. (54) into Eq. (44). The closed-loop system

$$\dot{\underline{e}} = (\underline{A} - \gamma^{-1}\underline{B}^T\underline{P})\underline{e} + \underline{\psi}(\underline{e}, t) \quad (57)$$

is asymptotically stable if $\underline{\psi} = 0$. This is the case when the error dynamics are linearized about the terminal equilibrium state (see e.g., Das and Singh (1990) and Yuan and Lin (1990) for Euler-Bernoulli manipulators without taking the correct centrifugal stiffening effect into account). Of course, only local stability is established in this case. Another exceptional case is obtained by setting $\underline{N} = \underline{0}$ in $\underline{\psi}$ intentionally in the dynamic modeling (see e.g., Wang and Vidyasagar (1991) for Euler-Bernoulli manipulators). Then it is trivially seen that Eq. (57) is globally asymptotic stable if $\ddot{\theta}_d(t) \to 0$ as $t \to \infty$. (Note that this includes the stable spin-up problem, i.e., $\dot{\theta}_d(t)$ = constant as $t \to \infty$, as a special case).

Now for $\underline{\psi} \neq \underline{0}$, a sufficient condition for asymptotic stability of Eq. (57) can be established as follows. Let $\lambda_1, \cdots, \lambda_{2n+3}$ be distinct eigenvalues of $\underline{\tilde{A}} = \underline{A} - \gamma^{-1}\underline{B}^T\underline{P}$. Let $\underline{\xi}_1, \cdots, \underline{\xi}_{2n+3}$ and $\underline{r}_1, \cdots, \underline{r}_{2n+3}$ be the associated eigenvectors and reciprocal base vectors. Then, under the coordinate transformation $\underline{e}(t) = [\underline{\xi}_1, \cdots, \underline{\xi}_{2n+3}]\ \underline{q}(t)$ the system modes can be solved from Eq. (57) to give

$$q_i(t) = e^{\lambda_i t} < \underline{r}_i, \underline{e}(0) > + \int_0^t e^{\lambda_i(t-\tau)} < \underline{r}_i, \underline{\psi}(\underline{e}(\tau), \tau) > d\tau$$
$$i = 1, 2, \cdots, 2n+3 \quad (58)$$

Taking the norms of both sides, we have for each i

$$| q_i(t) | \leq | \underline{r}_i | \{e^{\alpha_i t} | \underline{e}(0) | + \int_0^t e^{\alpha_i(t-\tau)} | \underline{\psi}(\underline{e}(\tau), \tau) | d\tau\} \quad (59)$$

where $\alpha_i = Re[\lambda_i(\underline{\tilde{A}})] < 0$. Note that stability is established if the time rate of change of the right hand side of Eq. (59) is non-positive. This leads to

$$\alpha_i | \underline{r}_i | \{e^{\alpha_i t} | \underline{e}(0) | + \int_0^t e^{\alpha_i(t-\tau)} | \underline{\psi}(\underline{e}(\tau), \tau) | d\tau\}$$
$$+ | \underline{r}_i | | \underline{\psi}(\underline{e}(t), t) | \leq 0 \quad (60)$$

In view of Eq. (59), Eq. (60) is always satisfied if

$$\alpha_i | q_i(t) | + | \underline{r}_i | | \underline{\psi}(\underline{e}(t), t) | \leq 0 \quad (61)$$

We thus obtain the following stability criterion

$$-\alpha_i |< \underline{\tilde{r}}_i, \underline{e}(t) >| \ \geq \ | \underline{\psi}(\underline{e}(t), t) | \quad \forall\, i = 1, 2, \cdots, 2n+3 \quad (62)$$

where $\tilde{\underline{r}}_i = \underline{r}_i / | \underline{r}_i |$. Other sufficient conditions for the asymptotic stability of systems such as Eq. (57) can be found in Patel, Toda, and Sridhar (1977), Ghaemmaghami and Juang (1989), and others. All these conditions including Eq. (62) can only be checked by trial and error numerical procedure. However, Eq. (62) has the advantage in predicting the mode(s) that most likely be driven by $\dot{\theta}_d(t)$ and $\ddot{\theta}_d(t)$ to the verge of instability.

The importance of this stability condition is not necessary that the controller must be designed to satisfy such criterion as the estimated bound on $\underline{\psi}$ may be very conservative. Rather its significance is that this stability condition justifies the existence of joint angle trajectory commands for stable joint angle trajectory following and simultaneous vibration suppression.

6. Simulation Results

Computer simulations for two flexible manipulators with different slenderness ratio L/r_g, where $r_g = \sqrt{I/A}$ is the cross-sectional radius of gyration, are considered. The system parameters are: $E = 6.8944 \times 10^{10} N/m^2$, $G = 2.6517 \times 10^{10} N/m^2$, $\varrho = 2766.67 Kg/m^3$, $\zeta_i = 0.01$, $L = 1.2m$, $A = 1 \times 10^{-4} m^2$, $k = 5/6$, $L/r_g = 1000$ or 5, $a = 0.05m$, $I_h = 0.5kg - m^2$, $M_p = 0.2kg$, $J_p = 5 \times 10^{-4} kg - m^2$, $N_g = 100$, $K_t = 0.5296 N - m/A$, $J_m = 8.4734 \times 10^{-4} Kg - m^2$, $D_m = 2.6971 \times 10^{-4} N - m - s$. The natural frequencies in Hz (Timoshenko beam/Euler-Bernoulli beam) for $L/r_g = 1000$ are: $\omega_1 = 1.3465/1.3465$, $\omega_2 = 11.9121/11.9129$, $\omega_3 = 35.0668/35.0726$, $\omega_4 = 66.1136/66.1309$. The natural frequencies in Hz (Timoshenko beam/Euler-Bernoulli beam) for $L/r_g = 5$ are: $\omega_1 = 1.9155 \times 10^2/2.3882 \times 10^2$, $\omega_2 = 9.0345 \times 10^2/2.1129 \times 10^3$, $\omega_3 = 1.9977 \times 10^3/6.2206 \times 10^3$, $\omega_4 = 3.0243 \times 10^3/1.1729 \times 10^4$. To generate a smooth command joint angle trajectory with almost zero overshoot, a third-order Bessel filter (Franklin, Powell, and Emami-Naeimi, 1991) is chosen according to

$$\dddot{\theta}_d + 2.4330\omega_r\ddot{\theta}_d + 2.4661\omega_r^2\dot{\theta}_d + \omega_r^3\theta_d = \omega_r^3\theta_r(t) \quad (63)$$

where ω_r is a design parameter adjustable for the rise time of a step reference input. The constants a_1, a_2, and a_3 in Eq. (45) are also chosen according to a third-order Bessel transfer function with poles located at $-0.9420\omega_0$, $-0.7455\omega_0 \pm j0.7112\omega_0$. Now the decoupled joint angle response of partial linearizing feedback depends only on ω_0, while the joint angle trajectory command is completely determined by ω_r.

(a) Verification of the Proposed Dynamic Modeling by a Spin-Up Maneuver.

Let the reference input be (Kane, Ryan, and Banerjee, 1986)

$$\theta_r(t) = \begin{cases} (\Omega/T)[t^2/2 + (T/2\pi)^2(cos(2\pi t/T) - 1)]rad & 0 < t \leq T \\ \Omega(t - T/2)\ rad & t \geq T \end{cases} \quad (64)$$

Consider the partial linearizing joint angle control with the following data: $L/r_g = 1000$, $\Omega = 10$ rad/sec, T = 5 sec, $\omega_0 = 4$ rad/sec, $\omega_r = 3.5$ rad/sec. Two elastic modes were used in the simulation. Fig. 2. compares the response for the two dynamic models with and without the stiffening correction term S(x). The occurance of unstable flexible modes predicted by the non-stiffening dynamic model is not unexpected since the steady state rotation has already exceeded the first bending natural frequency ($\omega_1 = 8.4603$ rad/sec) of the slewing beam. The small (practically invisible) amplitudes of steady-state oscillation of the flexible modes in the stiffening dynamic model case closely resemble that of Boutaghou and Erdman (1991). The linear elastic-mode stabilizer is therefore not needed in this case. It is important to remark at this point that the partial linearizing technique, which can be re-

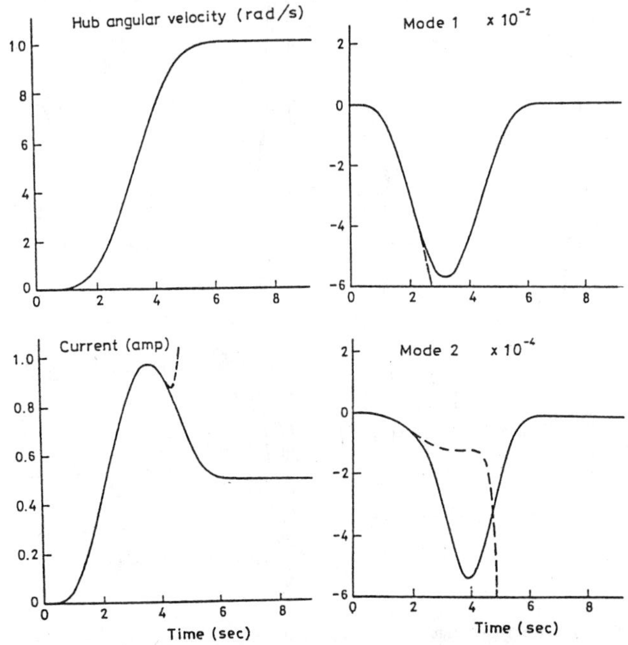

Fig. 2 Response of a spin-up maneuver (- - - without correct stiffening term , ——— with correct stiffening term).

garded merely as a method to compute the torque, provides a distinct and unique way of studying the spin-up maneuver problem. This is because the desired rigid rotation trajectory and its accompanied flexible dynamics are generated in a consistent manner by a required joint torque profile. In a conventional spin-up maneuver problem, the effect of flexible dynamics on the rigid rotation is almost always ignored.

(b) Joint Angle Trajectory Tracking and Linear Stabilization Control for a Large Slenderness Ratio Slewing Beam.

The feasibility of the proposed control strategy is demonstrated here through simulations using the following data: $L/r_g = 1000$, $\theta_r(t) = 1$, $\omega_0 = 4$ rad/sec, $\omega_r = 3.5$ rad/sec, Q = (10, 10^3, 10^3, 10, 10^3, 10^3, 1), $\mu = 1$, $\gamma = 0.3$. Two elastic modes were used in the controller design as well as in simulations. It is seen from Fig. 3 that although an exact joint angle tracking can be achieved without the elastic-mode stabilizer, the inherent material damping alone is not very effective for vibration suppression. The response of the closed-loop system including the linear elastic-mode stabilizer is also shown in Fig. 3. The results indicate that the elastic modes are rapidly damped out even with the presence of nonlinear disturbance $\underline{\psi}$. However, the exact joint angle tracking capability is slightly disturbed with only asymptotic tracking achieved. This suggests a tradeoff between vibration suppression and joint angle tracking accuracy. Simulations with the same type of controller but designed based on the Euler-Bernoulli beam model which are not shown herein, gave no significantly different results. This is to be expected, since the distinction between Timoshenko and Euler-Bernoulli beam models diminishes for a beam of very large slenderness ratio.

(c) Joint Angle Trajectory Tracking and Linear Stabilization Control for a Small Slenderness Ratio Slewing Beam.

To assess the significance of using Timoshenko beam model in obtaining acceptable performance for a slewing beam, several simulations were performed based on the following data: $L/r_g = 5$, $\theta_r(t) = 1$, $\omega_0 = 400$ rad/sec, $\omega_r = 350$ rad/sec, Q = diag. (10, 10^9, 10^9, 10, 10^{12}, 10^{12}, 1), $\mu = 0$, $\gamma = 0.01$. Two elastic modes were used in the controller design, but four elastic modes in simulations. Because the chosen beam has a bending stiffness 4 $\times 10^4$ times higher than the one used in part (b), the slewing beam will behave like a rotating rigid body for slow maneuvers. Therefore, a much rapid maneuver is studied here. The responses of both the partial linearizing control and the complete closed-loop system are shown in Fig. 4. The 3rd and 4th elastic modes (not shown) were found not of practical importance because their magnitudes are less than 10^{-6} and 10^{-9}, respectively, after 0.02 sec. Simulation results using the same type of controller but designed based on the Euler-Beroulli beam model are shown in Fig. 5. The response of the partial linearizing feedback is unstable because the effect of flexible dynamics on the rigid rotation can no longer be exactly cancelled out. Although the overall closed-loop system is asymptotically stable,

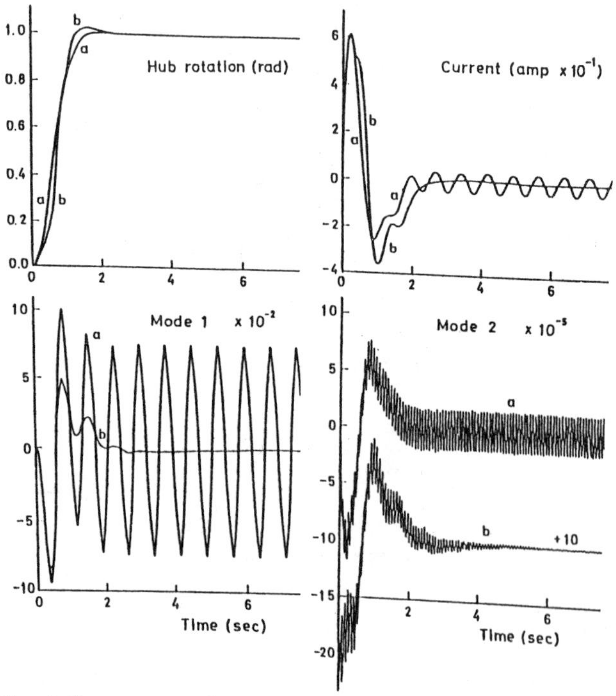

Fig. 3 Step response for a beam with slenderness ratio L/r_g = 100 (a: partial linearizing control only, b: with linear stabilization control).

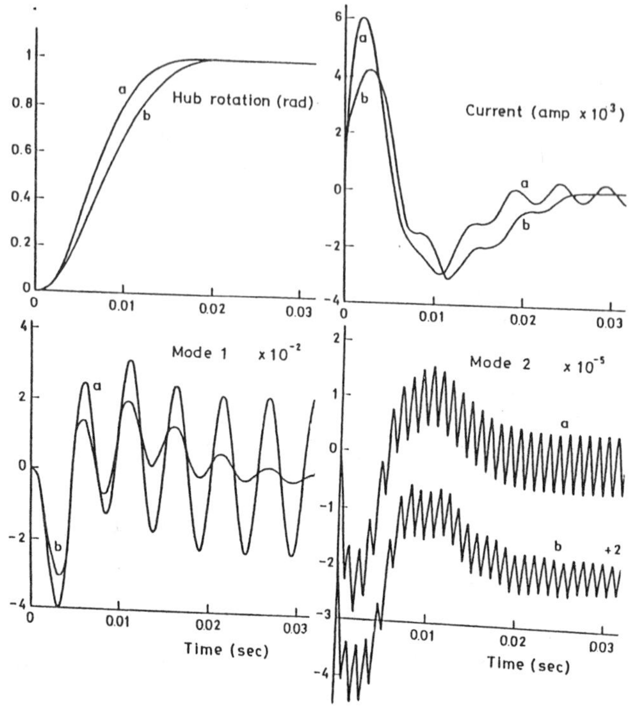

Fig. 4 Step response for a beam with slenderness ratio L/r_g = 5 (a: partial linearizing control only, b: with linear stabilization control): —— using Timoshenko beam based controller.

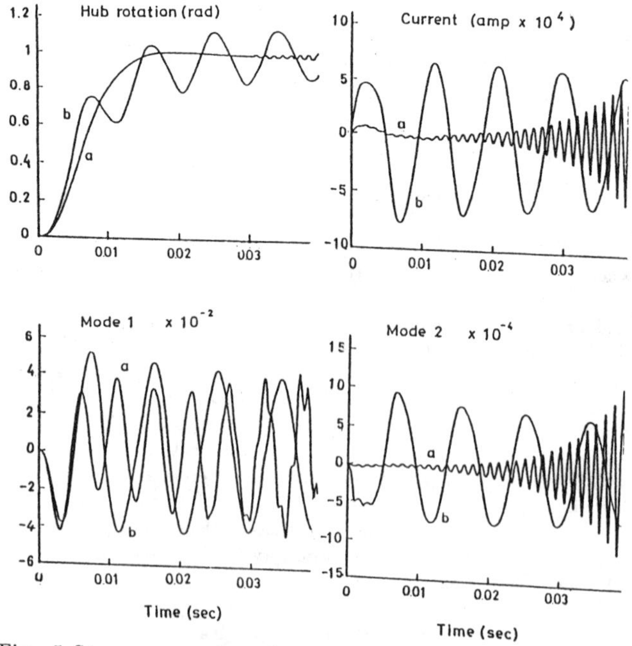

Fig. 5 Step response for a beam with slenderness ratio L/r_g = 5 (a: partial linearizing control only, b: with linear stabilization control): —— using Euler-Bernoulli beam based controller.

the response is not very satisfactory. The degration in performance is not unexpected since the controller based on the Euler-Bernoulli beam model has to cope with the more powerful ignored dynamics resulting from model simplication. However, an improved response can still be achieved for the same joint angle maneuver if a sufficiently slow joint angle trajectory command is adopted.

7. Concluding Remarks

In this paper, the partial differential equations of motion of a horizontally slewing inextensible Timoshenko beam have been derived explicitly with the inclusion of the correct centrifugal stiffening effect and a tip payload. The orthogonality conditions of the constrained modes have also been presented. A finite dimensional dynamic model of the combined motor-beam system simplified by using the orthogonality conditions was obtained. This new dynamic model places no restrictions on slenderness ratio, slewing angle, and rotational speed provided that the flexure deflections remain small. The validity of the dynamic model was then verified through numerical simulation of a spin-up problem. A controller design based on a combined partial linearizing joint angle control and linear elastic-mode stabilizer has also been studied. The stability of the overall closed-loop nonlinear system was then investigated and a sufficient condition for asymptotic stability has been obtained. The effectiveness of the proposed control algorithm have been demonstrated through numerical simulations. This study suggests that, with a properly selected joint angle trajectory command, an accurate joint angle trajectory tracking with rapid vibration suppression can be achieved. The sufficient condition for asymptotic stability guarantees the existence of such joint angle trajectory commands. However, no attempt has been made to search for the best joint angle trajectory command. Also, the issue of state estimation and robustness of the controller were not discussed in this paper. All these need to be examined for future research.

Acknowledgment

This research was supported by the National Science Council of R.O.C. under grant NSC 80-0422-E002-04.

References

[1] Akhrif, O., Blankenship, G.L., and Bennett, W.H., 1989, "Robust Control for Rapid Reorientation of Flexible Structures," *Proc. 1989 American Control Conference*, Pittsburg, PA., June, pp. 1142-1147.

[2] Barbieri, E. and Özgüner, U., 1988, "Unconstrained and Constrained Mode Expansions for a Flexible Slewing Link," *ASME J. of Dynamic Systems, Measurement and Control*, Vol. 110, No. 4, pp. 416-421.

[3] Baruh, H. and Tadikonda, S.S.K., 1989, "Issues in the Dynamics and Control of Flexible Robot Manipulators," *J. of Guidance, Control, and Dynamics*, Vol. 12, No. 5, pp. 659-671.

[4] Bennett, W.H., Akhrif, O., and Dwyer, T.A.W., 1990, "Robust Nonlinear Control of Flexible Space Structures," *Proc. 1990 American Control Conference*, San Diego, CA., May, pp. 2430-2436.

[5] Boutaghou, Z.E. and Erdman, A.G., 1991, "A Unified Approach for the Dynamics of Beams Undergoing Arbitrary Spatial Motion," *ASME J. of Vibration and Acoustics*, Vol. 113, pp. 494-502.

[6] Choura, S., Jayasuriya, S., and Medick, M.A., 1991, "On the Modeling and Open-Loop Control of a Rotating Thin Flexible Beam," *ASME J. of Dynamic Systems, Measurement, and Control*, Vol. 113, No. 1, pp. 26-33.

[7] Das, A. and Singh, S.N., 1990, "Dual Mode Control of an Elastic Robotic Arm: Nonlinear Inversion and Stabilization by Pole Assignment," *Int. J. Systems Sci.*, Vol. 21, No. 7, pp. 1185-1204.

[8] De Luca, A., Lucibello, P., and Ulivi, G., 1989, "Inversion Techniques for Trajectory Control of Flexible Robot Arms," . *J. of Robotic Systems*, Vol. 6, No. 4, pp. 325-344.

[9] De Luca, A., and Siciliano, B., 1989, "Trajectory Control of a Nonlinear One-Link Flexible Arm," *Int. J. Control*, Vol. 50, No. 5, pp. 1699-1715.

[10] De Schutter, J., Van Brussel, H., Adams, N., Froment, A., and Faillot, J.L., 1988, "Control of Flexible Robots Using Generalized Nonlinear Decoupling," 2nd IFAC Symp. on Robot Control (Syroco '88), Karlsruhe, FRG, Dec., pp. 113-118.

[11] Franklin, G.F., Powell, J.D., and Emami-Naeini, A. 1991, *Feedback Control of Dynamic Systems*, 2nd edition, Addison Wesley, Reading, Mass., pp.388-390.

[12] Ghaemmaghami, P. and Juang, J.N., 1989, "A Controller Design for Multi-body Large Angle Maneuvers," *Mech. Struct. & Mach.*, Vol. 17, pp. 33-52.

[13] Hanagud, S. and Sarkar, S., 1989, "Problem of the Dynamics of a Cantilever Beam Attached to a Moving Base," *J. of Guidance, Control, and Dynamics*, Vol. 12, No. 3, pp. 438-441.

[14] Kane, T.R., Ryan, R.R., and Bannerjee, A.K., 1987, "Dynamics of a Cantilever Beam Attached to a Moving Base," *J. of Guidance, Control, and Dynamics*," Vol. 10, pp. 139-151.

[15] Kwatny, H.G. and Bennett, W.H., 1988, "Nonlinear Dynamics and Control Issues for Flexible Space Platforms," *Proc. 27th IEEE Conf. on Decision and Control*, Austin, Texas, Dec., pp. 1702-1706.

[16] Padilla, C.E. and Von Flotow, A.H., 1992, "Nonlinear Strain-Displacement Relations and Flexible Multibody Dynamics," *J. of Guidance, Control, and Dynamics*, Vol. 15, No, 1, pp. 128-136.

[17] Patel, R.V., Toda, M., and Sridhar, B., 1977, "Robustness of Linear Quadratic State Feedback Designs in the Presence of System Uncertainty," *IEEE Trans. Automat. Contr.*, Vol. AC-21, pp. 945-949.

[18] Seraji, H., 1989, "Robust High Performance Control for Robotic Manipulators," *IEEE Int. Conf. Robotics and Automation*, Scottsdale, Arizona, April, pp. 1663-1669.

[19] Simo, J.C. and Vu-Quoc, L., 1986, "On the Dynamics of Flexible Beams Under Large Overall Motions The Plane Case: Part I," *ASME J. of Applied Mechanics*, Vol. 53, pp. 849-854.

[20] Simo, J.C. and Vu-Quoc, L., 1987, "The Role of Nonlinear Theories in Transient Dynamic Analysis of Flexible Structure," *J. of Sound and Vibration*, Vol. 119, pp. 487- 508.

[21] Wang, D. and Vidyasagar, M., 1991, "Control of a Class of Manipulators with a Single Flexible Link Part II: Observer-Controller Stabilization," *ASME J. of Dynamic Systems, Measurements and Control*, Vol. 113, pp. 662-668.

[22] Yigit, A., Scott, R.A., and Ulsoy, A. G., 1988, "Flexural Motion of a Rotating Beam Attached to a Rigid Body," *J. of Sound and Vibration*, Vol. 121, No. 2, pp. 201-210.

[23] Yuan, K. and Lin, L.C., 1990, "Motor Based Control of Manipulators with Flexible Joints and Links," *IEEE Int. Conf. on Robotics and Automation*, Cincinnati, Ohio, May, pp. 1809-1814.

Proceedings of the
American Control Conference
San Francisco, California • June 1993

Constrained Controllability of Linear Impulse Differential Systems

Z. Benzaid† and M. Sznaier‡

† Department of Mathematics
Embry Riddle Aeronautical University
Dayton Beach, FL 32114

‡Department of Electrical Engineering
University of Central Florida
Orlando Florida 32816

ABSTRACT

We consider the following linear impulse differential control system

$$\begin{cases} \dot{x} = A(t)x & t \neq t_k \\ \Delta x = B_k x(t_k) + C_k u_k & t = t_k \end{cases}$$

where the control sequences $\{u_k\}$ belong to some set of admissible controllers that is restricted either by norm or by range. We then give a necessary and sufficient condition for global null controllability of time-varying systems and some sufficient conditions for global null controllability for time-invariant systems with special structures.

I. INTRODUCTION

Many dynamical systems are characterized by the fact that at certain moments in their evolution they undergo rapid changes. Most notably this occurs in certain biological systems, population systems and even in control systems such as in pulse frequency modulated control systems. In modeling such systems it is more tractable and convenient to neglect the duration of these rapid changes and assume the state changes by jumps. The mathematical models of such processes are so-called differential systems with impulse effect, i.e., a system of ordinary differential equations, together with relations defining the jump condition [1]. More specifically the model is given by:

$$\begin{cases} \dot{x} = f(x,t) & \text{when } h(x,t) \neq 0 \\ \Delta x = j(x,t) & \text{when } h(x,t) = 0 \end{cases}$$

where $t \in R$ is the time variable, $x \in R^n$ is the state vector, $f:R^n \times R \to R^n$ and $j:R^n \times R \to R^n$ defines the jump condition. A point (x,t) in the extended phase space follows the solution trajectory of the differential system and as soon as it hits the hypersurface σ of equation $h(x,t) = 0$, the system incurs an instantaneous jump of 'size' $j(x,t)$.

In this note, we deal solely with deterministic, linear impulse systems whose instants of impulse effect are fixed, i.e., represented by a sequence of time hyperplanes $t = t_k$ where $\{t_k\}$ is a given time sequence.

$$(S) \quad \begin{cases} \dot{x} = A(t)x & t \neq t_k \\ \Delta x = x(t_k^+) - x(t_k) = B_k x(t_k) & t = t_k \end{cases}$$

where

$$k \in N, \quad A(\cdot) \in PC(R_+, R^{nxn}), \quad B_k \in R^{nxn}$$

$$\lim_{x \to \infty} t_k = +\infty$$

If $\det(I + B_k) \neq 0$ for all $k \in N$ and if U_k denotes the transition matrix of $\dot{x} = A(t)x$ on $t_{k-1} < t < t_k$ then the transition matrix ϕ of (S) is

$$\phi(t,s) = U_k(t_k^+) \prod_{j=k}^{i+1} (I+B_j) U_j(t_j, t_{j-1}^+)(I+B_i) U_i(t_i, s) \quad .$$

Consider now the following control problem:

$$(S) \quad \begin{cases} \dot{x} = A(t)x & t \neq t_k \\ \Delta x = B_k x(t_k) + C_k u_k & t = t_k \end{cases}$$

where $C_k \in R^{nxm}$ and $u_k \in U \subseteq R^m$ for $k \in N$ are the control vectors. The constrained null-controllability problem deals with the following question: Given an initial state $x(t_0) = x_0$ does there exist a sequence $\{u_k\}$ of admissible controllers that steers the system to the origin in a finite time T. In most treatment of constrained controllability the set of admissible controllers is restricted in various ways, either by norm or by range. In this note, we will give a necessary and sufficient condition for global null-controllability using controllers that are elements of unit balls of the sequence spaces ℓ_q^m (denoted by U_q). Furthermore, we provide some sufficient conditions for global null-controllability for systems with special properties.

II - RESULTS

We start this section by giving a general necessary and sufficient condition for global null-controllability. To motivate this basic criterion we introduce and briefly discuss a concept very similar to that of the reachable set. Consider the solution of system (S)

$$x(t,t_0,x_0) = \phi(t,t_0)x_0 + \sum_{t_0<t_i<t} \phi(t,t_i)C_i u_i$$

if we set $x(t, t_0, x_o) = 0$, we obtain using the nonsingularity of ϕ

$$x_0 = -\sum_{t_0<t_i<t} \phi(t_0,t_i)C_i u_i \quad .$$

We now let

$$R(t,t_0) = \left\{ x \in R^n : x = \sum_{t_0<t_i<t} \phi(t_0,t_i)C_i u_i \quad \text{for} \quad u_i \in U \right\} ,$$

clearly $R(t,t_0)$ consists of all initial positions $x_0 \in R^n$ that can be steered to the origin at or before time t. If there exists a time T such that $x_0 \in R(T, t_0)$ then system (S) is null-controllable for x_0. To achieve global null-controllability, a necessary and sufficient condition is

$$\bigcup_{t \geq t_0} R(t,t_0) = R^n \quad .$$

This last observation will translate in a divergence condition for global null-controllability analogous to Conti's [2] for differential systems without impulses. We omit the proof as it uses similar basic arguments from convex analysis.

Theorem 2.1: Assume $\det(I + B_i) \neq 0$ for all $i \in N$. Then (S) is globally null-controllable by means of U_q if and only if

$$\lim_{t_i \to \infty} \sum_{t_0<t_i} \|C_i^T \phi^T(t_0,t_i)y\|_2^P = +\infty \qquad \text{for all}$$

nonzero $y \in R^n$ where $\frac{1}{p} + \frac{1}{q} = 1$. Furthermore (S) is globally null-controllable by means of U_1 if and only if

$$\lim_{k \to \infty} \max_{1 \leq i \leq k} \|C_i^T \phi^T(t_0,t_i)y\|_2 = +\infty$$

for all nonzero $y \in R^n$.

Theorem 2.1 constitutes a complete characterization of global null-controllability and clearly demonstrates the dependence of controllability on the transition matrix Φ, the control matrices C_i's and the set of admissible controllers through the exponent p. To insure divergence of the infinite series, basically three conditions have to be met:

1. The products $C_i^T \phi^T(\cdot,t_i)y$ cannot be identically zero for nonzero $y \in R^n$, in other words, for the system to be controllable with constrained controls it has to be controllable with unconstrained controls.
2. The matrices $\phi^T(\cdot,t_i)$ do not decay to zero too rapidly, i.e., the solutions of (S) do not grow too fast for the restricted controller to keep up.
3. The exponent p has to be the proper one and hence the appropriate set of admissible controllers has to be used.

We conclude from the above remarks that if a system is stable in the sense of bounded transition matrix (but not necessarily asymptotically or exponentially stable) and in some sense uniformly controllable with unconstrained controllers, we would expect it to be globally null-controllable with certain classes of admissible controllers (see Sontag and Sussman [5]). Indeed the next theorem shows that this is in fact true but before we state and prove the theorem, let us introduce the well known concept of uniform controllability by giving a formal definition, see Kalman [4] for more general definitions.

Definition 2.1: (S) is uniformly controllable on $[t_0, \infty]$ if there exist a positive integer r and a positive real number α such that for all positive integers $n \geq t_0$ we have

$$\sum_{i=n}^{r+n} \phi(t_{r+n},t_i)C_iC_i^T\phi^T(t_{r+n},t_i) \geq \alpha I$$

in the sense of quadratic form.

Theorem 2.2: Assume $\det(I + B_i) \neq 0$ for all $i \in N$. If (S) is uniformly controllable on $[t_o, \infty]$ and stable then it is globally null-controllable by means of U_q for all $1 < q \leq \infty$. Moreover if the system is asymptotically or exponentially stable it is also controllable by means of U_1.

Proof: To prove global null-controllability we use the divergence condition given in theorem 2.1. Consider the infinite series

$$\sum_{i=1}^{\infty} \|C_i^T\phi^T(t_0,t_i)y\|_2^P \quad \text{where} \quad \frac{1}{p} + \frac{1}{q} = 1 \tag{2.1}$$

(2.1) can be rewritten as

$$\sum_{n=0}^{\infty} \sum_{i=nr}^{(n+1)r} \left\{\|C_i^T\phi^T(t_{(n+1)r},t_i)\,\phi^T(t_0,t_{(n+1)r})y\|_2^2\right\}^{\frac{p}{2}} \tag{2.2}$$

Using the assumption of uniform controllability we obtain

$$\sum_{i=1}^{\infty} \|C_i^T\phi^T(t_0,t_i)y\|_2^P \geq \sum_{n=0}^{\infty} \alpha^{\frac{p}{2}}\|\phi^T(t_0,t_{(n+1)r})y\|_2^P \tag{2.3}$$

From the assumption of stability we know that

$\|\phi(t,t_0)\| \leq K$ for some $K > 0$ and all $t \geq t_0$,

therefore

$$\|\phi^T(t_0,t_{(n+1)r})y\|_2 \geq \frac{\|y\|_2^2}{\|y^T\phi^T(t_{(n+1)r},t_0)\|_2} \geq \frac{1}{K}\|y\|_2 \tag{2.4}$$

Therefore inequality (2.3) becomes

$$\sum_{i=1}^{\infty} \|C_i^T\phi^T(t_0,t_i)y\|_2^P \geq \sum_{n=0}^{\infty}\left(\frac{\sqrt{\alpha}}{K}\right)^P \|y\|_2^P \tag{2.5}$$

The right side of (2.5) clearly diverges, hence we have global null-controllability by means of all U_q, $1 < q \leq \infty$. A similar argument can be applied to show that if (S) is asymptotically or exponentially stable then it is globally null-controllable by means of U_q, $1 \leq q \leq \infty$.

In case (S) is time-invariant then we have the following corollary:

Corollary 2.1: If (S) is a stable, time-invariant system and

1) $\det(I + B_i) \neq 0$ for all $i \in N$
2) A and B_i commute for all $i \in N$
3) $\text{rank}\,[C_i, AC_i, \ldots, A^{n-1}C_i] = n$ for all $i \in N$.

Then (S) is globally null-controllable by means of U_q for all $1 < q \leq \infty$. Furthermore if (S) is asymptotically stable then it is globally null-controllable for all $1 \leq q \leq \infty$.

Remark 2.1: Note that stability and uniform controllability does not necessarily imply global null-controllability by means of U_1, i.e., the unit ball of ℓ_1^m. Indeed consider the easy example:

$$\dot{x} = 0 \qquad t \neq t_k$$

$$\Delta x = u_k \qquad t = t_k$$

It is clear the only initial conditions x_0 that can be steered to zero are such that $-1 \leq x_0 \leq 1$.

In the case of constant systems, if we impose some structural and growth conditions, we can apply theorem 2.1 to obtain various other criteria that are sufficient for global null-controllability. More explicitly suppose that the B_i's commute with the coefficient matrix A and the products $(I + B_i)\,\Psi(t_{i+1}, t_i)$ do not grow too fast, where $\Psi(t, t_0) = \exp(A(t-t_0))$, then we obtain the following sufficiency condition:

Theorem 2.3: Assume

i) $\det(I + B_i) \neq 0$ for all $i \in N$
ii) A and B_i commute for all $i \in N$
iii) $\text{rank}\,[C_i, AC_i, \ldots, A^{n-1}C_i] = n$ for all $i \in N$
iv) $\|(I + B_i)\|\;\|\Psi(t_{i+1}, t_i)\| \leq \gamma_i$ where γ_i's satisfy

$$\sum_{i=1}^{n} \ln\gamma_i = o\left(\ln n^{\frac{1}{p}}\right) \quad \text{as} \quad n \to \infty.$$

Then (S) is globally null-controllable by means of U_q for all q such that $1 < q \leq \infty$. (Note: $\frac{1}{p} + \frac{1}{q} = 1$)

Proof: We again rely on the criterion given in theorem 2.1 to show global null-controllability. Proceeding similarly as in the proof of theorem 2.2 we have:

$$\sum_{i=1}^{\infty} \|C_i^T \phi^T(t_0,t_i)y\|_2^P \geq \sum_{n=0}^{\infty} \alpha^{\frac{P}{2}} \|\phi^T(t_0,t_{(n+1)r})y\|_2^P .$$

Now

$$\|\phi(t_{(n+1)r},t_0)\| = \| \prod_{i=(n+1)r}^{1} (I+B_i) \prod_{i=0}^{(n+1)r-1} \Psi(t_{i+1},t_i)\| \leq \prod_{i=1}^{(n+1)r} \gamma_i \tag{2.6}$$

Since

$$\|\phi^T(t_0,t_{(n+1)r})y\|_2 \geq \frac{\|y\|_2}{\|y^T \phi^T(t_{n+1)r},t_0)\|}$$

(2.6) implies that

$$\sum_{i=1}^{\infty} \|C_i^T \phi^T(t_0,t_i)y\|_2^P \geq \sum_{n=0}^{\infty} (\sqrt{\alpha})^P \prod_{i=1}^{(n+1)r} \left(\frac{1}{\gamma_i}\right)^P \|y\|_2^P \tag{2.7}$$

assumption (iv) implies that

$$\prod_{i=1}^{(n+1)r} \left(\frac{1}{\gamma_i}\right)^P = 0\left(\frac{1}{n}\right)$$ therefore the right hand side of (2.7) diverges. This proves the theorem.

Finally we end this note by giving one more application of theorem 2.1 to a system with a special structure. Suppose system (S) is given by

$$\begin{cases} \dot{x} = Ax & t \neq t_k \\ \Delta x = \alpha_k x(t_k) + C_k u_k & t = t_k \end{cases}$$

then the transition matrix ϕ becomes

$$\phi(t,t_0) = \prod_{i=1}^{k} (1+\alpha_i) e^{A(t-t_0)} .$$

We therefore obtain the following sufficiency condition:

Theorem 2.4: Assume

i) $\alpha_i \neq -1$ for all $i \in N$

ii) rank $[C_i, AC_i, \ldots, A^{n-1}C_i] = n$ for all $i \in N$

iii) $Re(\lambda_i) \leq 0$ for all eigenvalues λ_i of A

iv) $\sum_{i=1}^{n} |\alpha_i| \leq \ln n^{\frac{1}{P}}$ for all $n \in N$

Then (S) is globally null-controllable by means of U_q for all q such that $1 < q \leq \infty$.

Proof: Proceeding similarly as before, we have

$$\sum_{i=1}^{\infty} \|C_i^T \phi^T(t_0,t_i)y\|_2^P \geq \sum_{n=0}^{\infty} \alpha^{\frac{P}{2}} \prod_{i=1}^{(n+1)r} (1+|\alpha_i|)^{-P} \|e^{-A^T(t_{(n+1)r}-t_0)}y\|_2^P .$$

Without loss of generality assume that $t_{(n+1)r} = t_0 + (n+1)r$. Since $(1+|\alpha_i|) \leq e^{|\alpha_i|}$ the previous inequality assumes the form:

$$\sum_{i=1}^{\infty} \|C_i^T \phi^T(t_0,t_i)y\|_2^P \geq \sum_{n=0}^{\infty} \alpha^{\frac{P}{2}} \exp\left(-p \sum_{i=1}^{(n+1)r} |\alpha_i|\right) \|\exp(-A^T(n+1)r)y\|_2^P$$

We explicitly bound $\|\exp(-A^T(n+1))ry\|_2^2$ from below, indeed for all nonzero $y \in R^n$

$$\|\exp(-A^T t)y\|_2^2 \geq \exp(-2\beta t)t^{2\nu}(a+a(t))$$

where $\beta \in R$, $\nu \in N$ and a(t) depend in general on the jordan canonical form of A and the vector y and satisfy

1. $\min_{1 \leq i \leq s} Re(\lambda_i) \leq \beta \leq 0$

.2 $0 \leq \nu \leq \max_{1 \leq i \leq s}(n_i - 1)$ and $\begin{cases} a(t) \equiv 0 & \text{if } \nu = 0 \\ a(t) \to 0 & \text{as } t \to \infty \text{ if } \nu > 0 \end{cases}$

.3 $a>0$ where $A \sim \oplus \sum_{i=1}^{s} J_i$ where J_i $i=1,2,\cdots,s$

are jordon blocks of order n_i. Therefore

$$\sum_{i=1}^{\infty} \|C_i^T \phi^T(t_0,t_i)y\|_2^P \geq \sum_{n=0}^{\infty} \alpha^{\frac{P}{2}} \exp\left\{-P\left(\sum_{i=1}^{(n+1)r} |\alpha_i| + \beta(n+1)r\right)\right\} [(n+1)r]^{\nu P}(a+o(1))^{\frac{P}{2}} .$$

By assumptions (ii) and (iv) we obtain

$$\sum_{i=1}^{\infty} \|C_i^T \phi^T(t_0,t_i)y\|_2^P \geq \sum_{n=0}^{\infty} \alpha^{\frac{P}{2}} \frac{1}{(n+1)r} (a+o(1))^P$$

which is clearly a divergent series. This completes the proof of the theorem.

Remarks:

1. The assumption on the coefficient matrix A is that $Re(\lambda_i) \leq 0$ for all eigenvalues λ_i of A, therefore any repeated eigenvalue with zero real part gives rise to an unstable mode. So the theorem does take into consideration unstable systems (albeit polynomial growth instability).

2. Clearly in case (S) is asymptotically stable, i.e., $Re(\lambda_i) < 0$ for all eigenvalues λ_i of A then global null-controllability of (S) follows even if we used U_1 provided assumption (iv) is replaced

by $\sum_{i=1}^{n} |\alpha_i| < 2\beta(n+1)r$.

3. We can obtain a less conservative result if condition (iv) of the theorem is replaced by a condition that insures the divergence of the infinite product $(\Pi(1 + \alpha_i))^{-1}$.

4. If the jump matrix is constant, i.e., (S) has the form

$$\begin{cases} \dot{x} = Ax & t \neq t_k \\ \Delta x = Bx(t_k) + C_k u_k & t = t_k \end{cases}$$

and if A and B commute, then using similar arguments as above, it can be shown that (S) is globally null-controllable provided the Kalman rank condition holds and the moduli of the eigenvalues of $(I + B)\, e^A$ are less or equal to 1. (See [3])

III. CONCLUSION

In this note we gave a general necessary and sufficient condition for global null-controllability with constrained controls of differential systems with impulse effect. Relying on this criterion and the concept of uniform controllability in addition to certain growth conditions on the system transition matrix and the sizes of the jumps we obtain sufficiency conditions for global constrained controllability of certain stable and unstable systems.

LIST OF REFERENCES

1. D. D. Bainov and P. S. Simeonov, "*Systems with Impulse Effect: Stability, Theory and Applications*", Halsted Press, John Wiley and Sons, 1989.

2. R. Conti, "*Contributions to linear control theory*", J. Diff. Eqs., 1 (1965), 427-445.

3. M. E. Evans, "*Bounded control and discrete-time controllability*," Int. J. Systems Sci. 17 (1986), 943-951.

4. R. E. Kalman, "*Mathematical description of linear dynamical systems*," SIAM J.Control 1 (1963), 152-192.

5. E.D. Sontag and H.J. Sussman, "*Nonlinear output feedback design for linear systems with saturating controls*" 29th IEEE Conference on Decision and Control, Hawaii, 1990, p. 3414-3416.

Proceedings of the
American Control Conference
San Francisco, California • June 1993

A NEW METHOD FOR EVALUATING FLOQUET CHARACTERISTIC EXPONENTS OF PERIODIC LINEAR SYSTEMS[1]

J. Zhu[†,‡] and S. K. Vemula[†]

† Electrical and Computer Engineering Department
‡ Remote Sensing and Image Processing Laboratory
Louisiana State University, Baton Rouge, LA 70803

ABSTRACT

It is well-known that the stability of linear periodic (LP) systems can be assessed using Floquet Characteristic Exponents (FCE). In this paper, a new method is presented for evaluating FCE for nth-order scalar periodic linear systems based on a recently developed unified eigenvalue theory for linear time-varying (LTV) Systems [1]. The new theory allows FCEs to be evaluated from the DC term of the Fourier series of periodic PD-eigenvalues of a LP system. Comparing to the well-known Monodromy Matrix (MM) method and Infinite Dimensional Determinant (IDD) method for evaluating FCE, the solutions obtained by the new method have rapid local convergence. This new method also allow stability boundaries in the parameter space of a LP system to be evaluated and plotted directly. The new results shed some light on the general stability assessment problem for vector periodic linear systems and aperiodic LTV systems. Further studies along this direction are also discussed in this paper.

1. INTRODUCTION

It is well known that the stability of Linear Time-Varying (LTV) system of nth-order scalar form

$$y^{(n)} + \alpha_n(t)y^{(n-1)} + \cdots + \alpha_2(t)\dot{y}(t) + \alpha_1(t)y = 0 \qquad (1.1)$$

$$y^{(k)}(t_0) = y_k, \quad k = 1,2,\cdots,n-1, \quad y(t_0) = y_0, \quad t \geq t_0$$

and vector n-dimensional linear dynamical systems

$$\dot{\boldsymbol{x}} = \boldsymbol{A}(t)\boldsymbol{x}, \qquad \boldsymbol{x}(t_0) = \boldsymbol{x}_0, \qquad t \geq t_0 \qquad (1.2)$$

cannot be reliably assessed based solely on the Left-half-plane (LHP) confinement of the *frozen-time eigenvalues* (FTE) $\lambda_i(t)$ given by the roots of

$$\lambda^n + \alpha_n(t)\lambda^{n-1} + \cdots + \alpha_2(t)\lambda + \alpha_1(t) = 0$$

for (1.1) and

$$\det[\lambda \boldsymbol{I} - \boldsymbol{A}(t)] = 0$$

for (1.2). The failure of FTE stability criterion to be sufficient or necessary has been shown by [4], [9], [10], [11], [12].

Although precise stability analysis for general LTV systems (1.1) and (1.2) is a very difficult problem, it is well known that the stability of periodic LTV systems (1.1) satisfying $\alpha_i(t) = \alpha_i(t+T)$ and of (1.2) satisfying $\boldsymbol{A}(t+T) = \boldsymbol{A}(t)$ can be determined using the well-known Floquet Theory. Notice that the scalar periodic linear system (1.1) can always be converted to an equivalent vector system (1.2) by suitable choices of state variables. Thus we restate the celebrated Floquet theorem for the vector case as follows.

Theorem 1 (Floquet). Every periodic linear system (1.2) can be reduced to a Liner Time Invariant (LTI) system

$$\dot{\boldsymbol{z}} = \boldsymbol{B}\boldsymbol{z}, \qquad \boldsymbol{z}(t_0) = \boldsymbol{z}_0 \qquad (1.3)$$

via a stability preserving coordinate transformation

$$\boldsymbol{x} = \boldsymbol{L}(t)\boldsymbol{z} \qquad (1.3a)$$

where $\boldsymbol{L}(t)$ is a continuously differentiable, uniformly bounded, nonsingular (periodic) matrix and

$$\boldsymbol{B} = \boldsymbol{L}^{-1}(t)[\boldsymbol{A}(t)\boldsymbol{L}(t) - \dot{\boldsymbol{L}}(t)] \qquad (1.3b)$$

Then stability of periodic systems (1.2) is equivalent to that of the LTI system (1.3). □

The eigenvalues of $\boldsymbol{B}$ are known as the Floquet Characteristic Exponent (FCE). The difficulty with the Floquet method lies in finding analytically the coordinate transformation matrix $\boldsymbol{L}(t)$. However, well-known numerical algorithms exist for the solution of FCE, such as the Monodromy Matrix (MM) method and Infinite Dimensional Determinant (IDD) method, though they have certain limitations which will be mentioned later.

Monodromy Matrix Method: By virtue of the Floquet Theory, the state transition matrix (1.2) can always be expressed as

$$\boldsymbol{\Phi}(t,\tau) = \boldsymbol{L}(t)e^{\boldsymbol{B}(t-\tau)}\boldsymbol{L}^{-1}(\tau) \qquad (1.4)$$

where $\boldsymbol{L}(t)$ and $\boldsymbol{B}$ are as defined in (1.3a) and (1.3b). A monodromy matrix for (1.2) is defined to be $\boldsymbol{\Phi}(t_0+T,\ t_0)$, where T is the time period of the periodic system. Stability of the periodic system (1.2) is determined by the eigenvalues γ_i of the monodromy matrix which are known as the *Floquet Characteristic Multipliers* (FCM) and related to the FCEs μ_i by

$$\gamma_i = e^{\mu_i T} \qquad (1.5)$$

Consequently, the periodic system (1.2) is asymptotically stable *iff* all the FCM γ_i lie on the open unit disk $D_0 = \{\gamma;\ |\gamma| < 1\}$.

Numerical method based on monodromy matrix method are prone to quantization errors at low frequencies, as clearly indicated by the results presented in [12]. These errors could be corrected using the numerical method based on Hill-Type [2] Infinite Dimensional Determinant (IDD) which evaluates the FCE directly.

Infinite Dimensional Determinant Method: The IDD method was originally developed by Hill in [8] for second-order Mathieu equation

$$\ddot{y}(t) + (a - 2q\cos 2t)y(t) = 0$$

It is described here using the harmonic balance approach for periodic systems (1.2). Let $\boldsymbol{A}_k$ denote the Fourier coefficient of the kth harmonic $k\omega_0$, where $k \in \mathbb{Z}$, and $\omega_0 = \frac{2\pi}{T}$ is the fundamental frequency. Then (1.2) can be expressed in an infinite-dimensional state space representation by expanding $\boldsymbol{A}(t)$ and $\boldsymbol{L}(t)$ in (1.3b) into a Fourier series

$$\boldsymbol{A}(t) = \sum_{m \in Z} \boldsymbol{A}_m e^{jm\omega t} = \sum_{m \in Z} \boldsymbol{A}_m \zeta^m(t)$$

$$\boldsymbol{L}(t) = \sum_{m \in Z} \boldsymbol{L}_m e^{jm\omega t} = \sum_{m \in Z} \boldsymbol{L}_m \zeta^m(t)$$

where $\zeta(t) = e^{j\omega_0 t}$.

Thus, to find the FCE μ_i we need to solve the determinantal equation

$$\begin{aligned} 0 &= \det[\boldsymbol{B} - \mu \boldsymbol{I}] \\ &= \det \boldsymbol{L}^{-1}\det[(\boldsymbol{A} - \mu\boldsymbol{I})\boldsymbol{L} - \dot{\boldsymbol{L}}] \end{aligned} \qquad (1.6)$$

Since $\boldsymbol{L}(t)$ is nonsingular, (1.6) implies

$$\det[(\boldsymbol{A} - \mu\boldsymbol{I})\boldsymbol{L} - \dot{\boldsymbol{L}}] = 0 \qquad (1.7)$$

which is satisfied if

$$[(\mathcal{A} - \mathcal{N}) - \mu\mathfrak{I}]\overline{L}(t) = 0 \qquad (1.8)$$

where

$$\mathcal{N} = \mathrm{diag}[\ \cdots,\ -j\omega\boldsymbol{I}_n,\ 0.\boldsymbol{I}_n,\ j\omega\boldsymbol{I}_n,\ \cdots\ ]$$

$$\mathfrak{I} = \mathrm{diag}[\ \cdots,\ \boldsymbol{I}_n,\ \boldsymbol{I}_n,\ \boldsymbol{I}_n,\ \cdots\ ]$$

$$\mathcal{A} = \begin{bmatrix} \ddots & \vdots & \vdots & \vdots & \vdots & \iddots \\ \cdots & A_0 & A_{-1} & A_{-2} & A_{-3} & \cdots \\ \cdots & A_1 & A_0 & A_{-1} & A_{-2} & \cdots \\ \cdots & A_2 & A_1 & A_0 & A_{-1} & \cdots \\ \cdots & A_3 & A_2 & A_1 & A_0 & \cdots \\ \iddots & \vdots & \vdots & \vdots & \vdots & \ddots \end{bmatrix}$$

Equation (1.8) has a nontrivial solution $\overline{L}(t)$ *if and only if*

$$\Delta(\mu) = \det[(\mathcal{A} - \mathcal{N}) - \mu\mathfrak{I}] = 0 \qquad (1.9)$$

The IDD $\Delta(\mu)$ is known as Hill's determinant and the eigenvalues of $\mathfrak{H} = (\mathcal{A} - \mathcal{N})$ are the Floquet Characteristic Exponents μ_i, which stability of the periodic system (1.2). A problem of this method is that there is no general proof for the convergence of infinite dimensional determinantal equation (1.9), except for some special cases [6], [8]. Moreover, due to the logarithmic nature of (1.5), the FCEs μ_i are nonunique. Thus, as the order of truncation is increased to increase the accuracy of the FCE, the number of FCEs also increases.

Recently, a unified eigenvalue theory for LTV systems has been developed [1], [13], [14], [15], [16] based on a classical result of Floquet. In that new theory a necessary and sufficient stability criterion has been established for general nth-order scalar LTV systems (1.1) using the concept of *Parallel D-eigenvalues* (PD-eigenvalues) [1], [14]. The specialization of that stability result to the class of periodic linear system (1.1) allows FCE to be evaluated from the DC term of the Fourier series expansion of periodic PD-eigenvalues of (1.1).

[1] This work was supported by the National Science Foundation under Grant ECS-9110248.

In this paper, a new method is presented for evaluating FCE for nth-order scalar periodic linear systems (1.1) based on the unified eigenvalue theory. In this method, the Floquet Exponents are determined by applying the harmonic balance approach to a $(n-1)$th-order periodic nonlinear ordinary differential equation to find periodic PD-eigenvalues (known as the PD-characteristic equation for LTV systems). In doing so, a general expression for a PD-Characteristic equation in the frequency domain for nth-order periodic system (1.1) is obtained. This equation consists of nested frequency convolutions and point-wise multiplications. Using some effective notations, this *convolutional* equation can be represented by an infinite dimensional nonlinear *algebraic* equation. This nonlinear equation can be solved using Newton method for an finite order truncation of the Fourier series for the solution. A general expression for the Jacobian is also obtained for the Newton method. The algorithm is developed for an nth-order system, but exemplified here using 2nd-order systems. This algorithm has a rapid convergence rate for initial values in the domain of attraction for a solution. Comparing to the well-known Monodromy Matrix (MM) method and Infinite Dimensional Determinant (IDD) method for evaluating FCE, the solutions obtained by the new method have rapid local convergence and higher precision. The equations can be modified into a parametric form so that the stability boundaries of periodic systems can be obtained directly. The new results also shed some light on the general stability assessment problem for vector periodic linear systems and aperiodic LTV systems.

2. PRELIMINARY

In case of Linear Time-Invariant (LTI) systems, the roots of the characteristic equation are known as the eigenvalues which determine the stability of the LTI systems. Using an operator notation the scalar LTV system (1.1) can also be represented as

$$\mathfrak{D}_\alpha\{y\} = [\delta^n + \alpha_n(t)\delta^{n-1} + \cdots + \alpha_1(t)]\{y\} = 0 \quad (2.1)$$

where $\delta = d/dt$ is the derivative operator. The *Parallel D-Characteristic equation* for (1.1), which falls back to the conventional characteristic equation for LTI systems, is given by [1]

$$\mathfrak{D}_\rho^{n-1}\{\rho\} + \alpha_n(t)\mathfrak{D}_\rho^{n-2}\{\rho\} + \cdots + \alpha_3(t)\mathfrak{D}_\rho\{\rho\} + \alpha_2(t)\rho + \alpha_1(t) = 0 \quad (2.2)$$

where $\mathfrak{D}_\rho$ is an operator defined by $\mathfrak{D}_\rho = (\delta + \rho)$, $\mathfrak{D}_\rho^n = \mathfrak{D}_\rho \mathfrak{D}_\rho^{n-1}$, and $\rho(t)$ is called a *Parallel D-eigenvalue* (PD-eigenvalue) of (1.1).

It has been shown [1], [14] that a LTV system (1.1) is exponentially asymptotically stable if and only if the *extended-mean* of all PD-eigenvalues $\rho(t)$ for (1.1), i.e. the mean value of $\rho(t)$ over $[t_0, T]$ as $T \to \infty$, are in the left-half complex plane. Clearly, if a PD-eigenvalue is periodic with period T, then the extended-mean over $[t_0, \infty)$ can be replaced by the ordinary mean over any period $[t, t+T]$. The existence of periodic PD-eigenvalues for a periodic linear system (1.1) has been established in [1], [14], stated as follows.

Theorem 2.1.
Every nth-order periodic linear system (1.1) has a periodic PD-eigenvalue. □

It is well known that the stability of a periodic linear system (1.1) is governed by its Floquet Characteristic Exponents (FCE). There, the mean-value of a periodic PD-eigenvalue for a periodic linear system must somehow relate to its FCE. This is indeed the case, as shown in the following Theorem [1], [14].

Theorem 2.2.
Let $\rho(t)$ be a periodic PD-eigenvalue for the periodic linear system (1.1) with period T. Then the mean value of $\rho(t)$ given by

$$\mu_k = \frac{1}{T}\int_0^T \rho_k(t)dt = \sigma_k + j\omega_k \,. \quad (2.3)$$

coincides with a Floquet characteristic exponent for (1.1). □

By virtue of Theorem 2.2, FCE of a periodic linear system (1.1) can be evaluated from the mean-value of periodic PD-eigenvalues, provided that the quantity of such periodic PD-eigenvalues are related to the number of distinct FCEs. The following important Theorem 2.3 [1], [14] addresses this concern.

To facilitate the statement of Theorem 2.3, let $\rho(t)$ be a PD-eigenvalue of (1.1) and define

$$\xi(t) = \begin{bmatrix} \xi_1(t) \\ \xi_2(t) \\ \vdots \\ \xi_{n-1}(t) \end{bmatrix} = \begin{bmatrix} \rho(t) \\ \dot\rho(t) \\ \vdots \\ \rho^{(n-2)}(t) \end{bmatrix} . \quad (2.4)$$

Then the PD-characteristic equation (2.2) can be written into a state-variable (Phase-variable) format:

$$\dot\xi = \begin{bmatrix} \dot\xi_1 \\ \dot\xi_2 \\ \vdots \\ \dot\xi_{n-2} \\ \dot\xi_{n-1} \end{bmatrix} = \begin{bmatrix} \xi_2 \\ \xi_3 \\ \vdots \\ \xi_{n-1} \\ f(t, \xi_1, \xi_2, \cdots, \xi_{n-1}) \end{bmatrix} = F(t, \xi) \quad (2.5)$$

which will be called the *alternative PD-characteristic equation* for (1.1).

In the sequel, we shall denote by $\mathbb{S}$ the $(n-1)$-dimensional space $\mathbb{C}^{n-1}$ and denote by $\mathbb{S}_t$ the n-dimensional space $\mathbb{C}^{n-1}\times\mathbb{R}$, which will be called, respectively, the ***state space*** and the ***extended state space*** for the nonlinear alternative PD-characteristic equation (4-3.28). The collection of all trajectories defined by the solutions of (2.5) in $\mathbb{S}$ and $\mathbb{S}_t$ will be called the ***state portrait*** and the ***extended state portrait*** for (2.5), respectively.

Theorem 2.3.
Let F be the monodromy matrix for (1.1) in the Jordan canonical form having r Jordan blocks and h, $h \le r$, distinct eigenvalues γ_i, each shared by m_i Jordan blocks. Then the extended state space $\mathbb{S}_t$ contains h, and only h, *isolated* periodic *integral manifolds* S_i for (2.5), each of dimension m_i. Moreover, all (periodic) trajectories $\xi(t)$ in S_i have one and the same mean-value over one period, namely:

$$\frac{1}{T}\int_t^{t+T} \xi_1(\tau)d\tau = \boldsymbol{ln}\,\gamma_i = \mu_i \,, \quad (2.6a)$$

and

$$\frac{1}{T}\int_t^{t+T} \xi_k(\tau)d\tau = 0 \,, \qquad k = 2, 3, \cdots, n-1 \,, \quad (2.6b)$$

where μ_i is taken to be the principal value of $\boldsymbol{ln}\,\gamma_i$. □

Note that μ_i are the principal values of the FCE, and h is the number of distinct μ_i. The following graphical example is given to illustrate the implications of Theorem 2.3.

Example 2.1.
Consider the 3rd-order periodic linear system (1.1) with

$$\alpha_1(t) = -sin^3(t) + sin^2(t) + 3cos(t)sin(t) - cos(t) + 1 \quad (2.7a)$$
$$\alpha_2(t) = 3sin^2(t) - 2sin(t) - 3cos(t) + 1 \quad (2.7b)$$
$$\alpha_3(t) = -3sin(t) + 1 \,. \quad (2.7c)$$

The (alternative) PD-characteristic equation is given by (2.2) and (2.5) as

$$\dot\xi_1 = \xi_2 \quad (2.8a)$$
$$\dot\xi_2 = -(\xi_1^3 + 3\xi_1\xi_2 + \alpha_3(t)(\xi_1^2 + \xi_2) + \alpha_2(t)\xi_1 + \alpha_1(t)) \,. \quad (2.8b)$$

It can be verified that the monodromy matrix is given by

$$F = \begin{bmatrix} e^{-2\pi} & 0 & 0 \\ 0 & 1 & 0 \\ 0 & 0 & 1 \end{bmatrix}$$

By Theorem 2.3, the extended state portrait in $\mathbb{S}_t$ for the periodic PD-eigenvalues consists of an isolated 1-dimensional periodic manifold (trajectory) associated with $\gamma_1 = e^{-2\pi}$, and an isolated 2-dimensional periodic manifold associated with $\gamma_2 = \gamma_3 = 1$. Figure 2.1 shows the real-valued portion of these periodic manifolds (in the subspace of the reals in $\mathbb{S}_t$). The 1-dimensional isolated periodic trajectory initiated at $\xi_1(0) = -1$, $\xi_2(0) = 1$ is depicted in proportional aspect ration in Figure 2.2, and a typical (periodic) trajectory in the 2-dimensional periodic manifold initiated at $\xi_1(0) = 4, \xi_2(0) = -16$ is shown in Figure 2.3. It is interesting to note that the real parts of *all* the PD-eigenvalue trajectories $\rho(t) = \xi_1(t)$ in the 2-D periodic manifold have one and the same mean-value 0, which is the real part of the associated FCE. Moreover, this 2-D periodic manifold is an attractor, i.e. all the nonperiodic trajectories converge asymptotically to this periodic manifold as $t \to \infty$. Whereas the 1-dimensional periodic manifold is a repeller, i.e. an unstable limiting oscillation.

3. MAIN RESULTS

We are now in the position to develop the main results of this paper, namely, a new method for evaluating FCE for a nth-order scalar periodic linear system (1.1) by finding the mean value of its periodic PD-eigenvalues $\rho(t)$. Since the existence of periodic PD-eigenvalues has been established in theorem 2.1 and 2.3, we may represent them using Fourier series, provided that they are of L^2 class (i.e. square integrable)[2]. Then the DC term of the Fourier series would be the FCE.

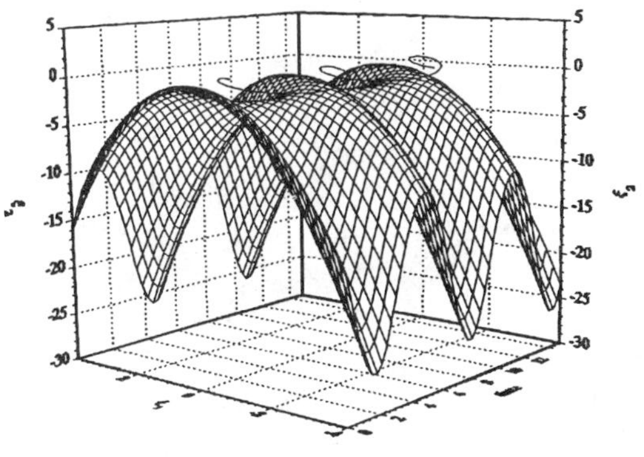

Figure 2.1. The Extended State Portrait of the Periodic Manifolds Containing Real-Valued Periodic PD-Eigenvalues for Example 2.1

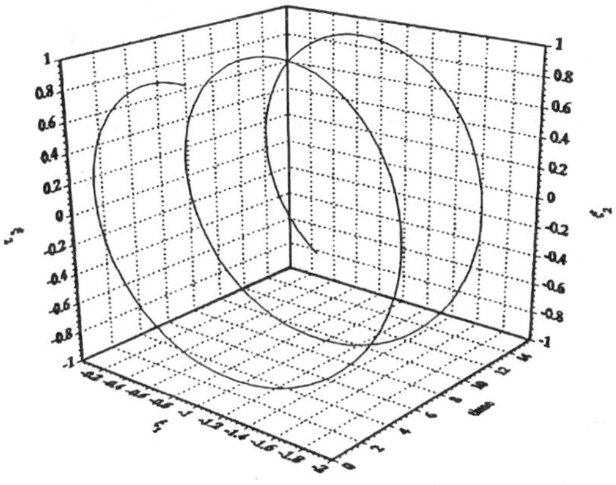

Figure 2.2. The Extended State Portrait of the Periodic PD-Eigenvalue on the Isolated 1-Dimensional Periodic Manifold for Example 2.1

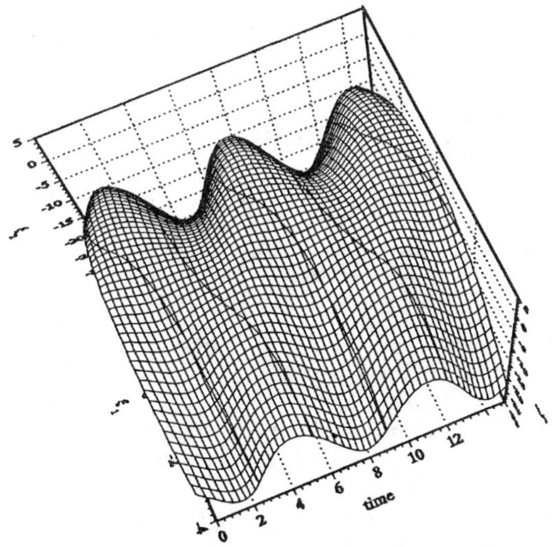

Figure 2.3. The Extended State Portrait of a Periodic PD-Eigenvalue Trajectory[3] on the Isolated 2-Dimensional Periodic Manifold for Example 2.1

[2] As shown in figure 2.3, a periodic PD-eigenvalue may have finite escape times where $\rho(t)$ goes to $-\infty$ and returns from $+\infty$. However, it can be shown that the rate of escape is $\frac{1}{t}$, so it is square integrable.

[3] Note that the five trajectory segments on the manifold belong to one and the same periodic trajectory initiated at $\xi_1(0)=4, \xi_2(0)=-16$. Thereafter, there is a finite escape-time between each segment of the trajectory where $\xi_1(t)$ goes to $-\infty$, and then comes back from $+\infty$, similar to the tangent function.

3.1 Theoretical Development.

The Fourier series representation for a periodic PD-eigenvalue $\rho(t)$ can be solved from the PD-characteristic equation using the well-known *harmonic balance* method. To that end, let $X(\omega)=\mathfrak{F}\{x(t)\}$ denote the Fourier transform[4] of a L^2 periodic function $x(t+T)=x(t)$. By the time differentiation and frequency convolution properties of Fourier transformation, we may write

$$\begin{aligned}\mathfrak{F}\{\rho(t)\} &= P(\omega)\\ \mathfrak{F}\{\mathfrak{D}_\rho\{\rho(t)\}\} &= \mathfrak{F}\{(\delta+\rho(t))\{\rho(t)\}\}\\ &= j\omega P(\omega)+P(\omega)*P(\omega)\\ &= \Phi_P\{P(\omega)\}\end{aligned} \tag{3.1}$$

where the frequency domain operator $\Phi_P\{\cdot\}$ is defined by

$$\Phi_P\{\cdot\} = (j\omega + P(\omega)*)\{\cdot\} \tag{3.2}$$

Using this notation the following lemma is readily verified by induction.

Lemma 3.1

Let $\mathfrak{D}_\rho$ and Φ_P be defined as before. Then

$$\mathfrak{F}\left\{\mathfrak{D}_\rho^k\{\rho(t)\}\right\} = \Phi_P^k\{P(\omega)\} \tag{3.3}$$

where $\Phi_P^k\{\cdot\}=\Phi_P\Phi_P^{k-1}\{\cdot\}$. □

As a direct consequence of lemma 3.1, we may transform the PD-characteristic equation (2.1) into frequency domain as

$$\begin{aligned}\Phi_P^{n-1}\{P(\omega)\}+A_n(\omega)*\Phi_P{}^{n-2}\{P(\omega)\}+\cdots+A_3(\omega)*\Phi_P\{P(\omega)\}+\\ +A_2(\omega)*P(\omega)+A_1(\omega)=0\end{aligned} \tag{3.4}$$

where $A_i(\omega)=\mathfrak{F}\{\alpha_i(t)\}, i=1,2,\cdots,n$, and $P(\omega)=\mathfrak{F}\{\rho(t)\}$.

In order to solve (3.1) for periodic PD-eigenvalue $\rho(t)$, note that the spectrum $X(\omega)=\mathfrak{F}\{x(t)\}$ for a L^2 periodic function $x(t+T)=x(t)$ is a comb function consisting of a sequence of equally spaced impulses given by

$$X(\omega)=2\pi\sum_{k=-\infty}^{\infty} x_k\delta(\omega-k\omega_0) \tag{3.5}$$

where $\omega_0=\frac{2\pi}{T}$ is the fundamental frequency of $x(t)$, and x_k, $k\in\mathbb{Z}$ are the coefficients of the Fourier series for $x(t)$. The inverse Fourier transform is then given by

$$\begin{aligned}\mathfrak{F}^{-1}\{X(\omega)\} &= \sum_{k=\infty}^{\infty} x_k e^{jk\omega_0 t}\\ &= x(t) \qquad \text{almost everywhere}^5\end{aligned} \tag{3.6}$$

which is the Fourier series expansion of $x(t)$.

As a consequence, the Fourier transformation of time-domain differentiation of a L^2 periodic $x(t)$ becomes

$$\begin{aligned}\mathfrak{F}\{\delta\{x(t)\}\} &= j\omega X(\omega)\\ &= j\omega\left[2\pi\sum_{k=-\infty}^{\infty} x_k\delta(\omega-k\omega_0)\right]\\ &= 2\pi\sum_{k=-\infty}^{\infty}(j\omega_k x_k)\delta(\omega-k\omega_0)\end{aligned} \tag{3.7}$$

where $\{\omega_k=k\omega_0\}$ is the harmonic sequence extracted from the continuous frequency function ω by the comb function $X(\omega)$.

Similarly, the Fourier transform of time-domain multiplication of two L^2 periodic functions $x(t)$, $y(t)$ is given by

$$\begin{aligned}\mathfrak{F}\{x(t)y(t)\} &= X(\omega)*Y(\omega)\\ &= 2\pi\sum_{k=-\infty}^{\infty}\left(\sum_{j=-\infty}^{\infty}(x_j y_{k-j})\delta(\omega-k\omega_0)\right)\\ &= 2\pi\sum_{k=-\infty}^{\infty}(x[k]*y[k])\delta(\omega-k\omega_0)\end{aligned} \tag{3.8}$$

where $x[k]=\{x_k\}$, $y[k]=\{y_k\}$ are the sequences of Fourier coefficients of $x(t)$, $y(t)$ respectively. Combining (3.7) and (3.8) yields

$$\begin{aligned}\mathfrak{F}^{-1}\{\Phi_P\{P(\omega)\}\} &= \mathfrak{F}^{-1}\{j\omega P(\omega)+P(\omega)*P(\omega)\}\\ &= j\sum_{k=-\infty}^{\infty}\left[(\omega_k x_k)+P[k]*P[k]\right]e^{jk\omega_0 t}\\ &= \mathfrak{D}_\rho\{\rho(t)\}\end{aligned} \tag{3.9}$$

To facilitate point-wise multiplication and discrete convolution of infinite sequences, we now define the following notations.

Definition 3.1

Let $x[k]=\{x_k\}$ be an infinite sequence. Define:

(i) the *sequence vector* for $x[k]$ by

$$\boldsymbol{x} = \text{col}\,[\ \cdots\ \ x_{-2}\ \ x_{-1}\ \ x_0\ \ x_1\ \ x_2\ \ \cdots\ ]$$

[4] We follow the definition of Fourier transform given in [3], which accommodates periodic time signals.

[5] It is well-known that if $x(t)$ is of L^2 class, then the Fourier expansion for $x(t)$ converges to $x(t)$ in L^2 norm. Having said so, we will hereafter drop the adjective *almost everywhere*.

(ii) *point-wise (p.w.) multiplicative matrix* for $x[k]$ by

$$\widetilde{X} = \text{diag}[\ \cdots,\ x_{-2},\ x_{-1},\ x_0,\ x_1,\ x_2,\ \cdots\ ]$$

(iii) *convolutional matrix* for $x[k]$ by

$$\widehat{X} = \text{toep}[\ \cdots,\ x_2,\ x_1,\ x_0,\ x_{-1},\ x_{-2},\ \cdots\ ]$$

where toep[$\cdots$] denotes the Toeplitz canonical form with the given center row elements. □

Now let $x[k]$, $y[k]$ be two infinite sequences represented by $\boldsymbol{x}, \boldsymbol{y}$ respectively. It is readily verified that the point-wise multiplication $z[k] = x[k] \cdot y[k]$ can be obtained using the conventional matrix-vector multiplication for the p.w. multiplicative matrix and the sequence vectors as follows:

$$\boldsymbol{z} = \boldsymbol{x} \cdot \boldsymbol{y} = \widetilde{X}\,\boldsymbol{y} = \widetilde{Y}\,\boldsymbol{x} \tag{3.10}$$

Similarly, the discrete convolution $w[k] = x[k]*y[k]$ can be obtained using the convolutional matrix and sequence vectors as follows:

$$\boldsymbol{w} = \boldsymbol{x}*\boldsymbol{y} = \widehat{X}\boldsymbol{y} = \widehat{Y}\boldsymbol{x} \tag{3.11}$$

Now define the harmonic (row) vector

$$\zeta(t) = [\ \cdots\ \ e^{-2j\omega_0 t}\ \ e^{-j\omega_0 t}\ \ e^{0}\ \ e^{j\omega_0 t}\ \ e^{2j\omega_0 t}\ \ \cdots\ ] \tag{3.12}$$

Then using (3.10)-(3.12), the convolutional equation (3.9) can be written as an infinite dimensional *algebraic* equation

$$\begin{aligned}\mathfrak{D}_\rho\{\rho(t)\} &= \mathfrak{F}^{-1}\{\Phi_P\{P(\omega)\}\} \\ &= \zeta(t)\Big[j\widetilde{\Omega} + \widehat{P}\Big]\boldsymbol{p}\end{aligned} \tag{3.13}$$

Denote by $\boldsymbol{\Psi}_P$ the infinite dimensional square matrix

$$\boldsymbol{\Psi}_P = j\widetilde{\Omega} + \widehat{P} \tag{3.14}$$

The following Lemma is readily proved by induction.

Lemma 3.2

Let $\rho(t)$ be a PD-eigenvalue of the PD-characteristic equation (2.1) and has the Fourier transform $P(\omega)$, then

$$\begin{aligned}\mathfrak{F}^{-1}\Big\{\Phi_P^k\{P(\omega)\}\Big\} &= \zeta(t)\boldsymbol{\Psi}_P^k\boldsymbol{p} \\ &= \mathfrak{D}_\rho^k\{\rho(t)\}\end{aligned} \tag{3.15}$$

Consequently, the PD-characteristic equation can be written as

$$\zeta(t)\Big[\boldsymbol{\Psi}_P^{n-1}\boldsymbol{p} + \widehat{\boldsymbol{A}}_n\boldsymbol{\Psi}_P^{n-2}\boldsymbol{p} + \cdots + \widehat{\boldsymbol{A}}_3\boldsymbol{\Psi}_P\boldsymbol{p} + \widehat{\boldsymbol{A}}_2\boldsymbol{p} + \boldsymbol{a}_1\Big] = 0 \tag{3.16}$$

where $\widehat{\boldsymbol{A}}_i$ is the conventional matrix for the sequence $\alpha_i[k]$ of Fourier coefficients of $\alpha_i(t)$ and $\boldsymbol{\alpha}_1$ is the sequence vector for $\alpha_1[k]$. Notice that the linear independence of the harmonic basis functions $e^{jk\omega_0 t}$ in $\zeta(t)$ equation (3.16) is satisfied if and only if the expression inside the bracket is zero. This is known as the harmonic balance condition. Thus we have proved the following Theorem 3.1.

Theorem 3.1

The harmonic balanced PD-characteristic equation for a nth-order periodic linear system (1.1) with L^2 coefficients $\alpha_i(t)$ is given by

$$\boldsymbol{\Psi}_P^{n-1}\boldsymbol{p} + \widehat{\boldsymbol{A}}_n\boldsymbol{\Psi}_P^{n-2}\boldsymbol{p} + \cdots + \widehat{\boldsymbol{A}}_3\boldsymbol{\Psi}_P\boldsymbol{p} + \widehat{\boldsymbol{A}}_2\boldsymbol{p} + \boldsymbol{a}_1 = 0 \quad \square \tag{3.17}$$

Remarks:

1. Note that the elements p_k of the sequence vector $\boldsymbol{p} = [\cdots\ p_{-1}\ p_0\ p_1\ \cdots]$ are the Fourier coefficients of periodic PD-eigenvalues. In particular, p_0 is a FCE of the periodic linear system (1.1).
2. The Fourier coefficients p_k when multiplied by 2π, are the intensities of the impulses constituting the frequency spectrum $P(\omega)$ for $\rho(t)$. Thus, Theorem 3.1 has in effect converted a time-domain nonlinear *differential* equation, i.e. the PD-characteristic equation (2.1) into a frequency domain nonlinear algebraic equation (3.17), though an infinite dimensional one.

3.2 Numerical method.

Having established the nonlinear harmonic balanced PD-characteristic equation (3.17), Newton's method can be used to solve for the solution. Newton's method solves a system of nonlinear algebraic equations $\boldsymbol{F}(\boldsymbol{p})$ using an iteration process given by

$$\boldsymbol{p}_{k+1} = \boldsymbol{p}_k - \boldsymbol{J}^{-1}(\boldsymbol{p}_k)\boldsymbol{F}(\boldsymbol{p}_k)$$

where $\boldsymbol{J}(\boldsymbol{p}_k)$ is the Jacobian of $\boldsymbol{F}(\boldsymbol{p})$ evaluated at $\boldsymbol{p}_k$ given by

$$\boldsymbol{J}(\boldsymbol{p}_k) = \big[(\partial f_i(\boldsymbol{F}(\boldsymbol{p}))/\partial p_j)\big]_{\boldsymbol{p}=\boldsymbol{p}_k}, \qquad \text{for } 1 \le i, j \le n.$$

Newton's method for nonlinear systems gives quadratic convergence [17], provided with sufficiently accurate initial values. For our case, let

$$\boldsymbol{F}(\boldsymbol{p}) = \boldsymbol{\Psi}_P^{n-1}\boldsymbol{p} + \widehat{\boldsymbol{A}}_n\boldsymbol{\Psi}_P^{n-2}\boldsymbol{p} + \cdots + \widehat{\boldsymbol{A}}_3\boldsymbol{\Psi}_P\boldsymbol{p} + \widehat{\boldsymbol{A}}_2\boldsymbol{p} + \boldsymbol{\alpha}_1 = 0 \tag{3.18}$$

A general expression of Jacobian for (3.18) is presented and proved in the following theorem 3.2.

Theorem 3.2

The Jacobian for an nth-order harmonic balanced PD-characteristic equation (3.18) can be written as

$$\begin{aligned}\mathfrak{J}\{\boldsymbol{F}(\boldsymbol{p})\} &= n\boldsymbol{\Psi}_P^{n-2}\widehat{\boldsymbol{P}} + j\widetilde{\Omega}\,\boldsymbol{\Psi}_P^{n-2} + \\ &\quad + \widehat{\boldsymbol{A}}_n\Big[(n-1)\boldsymbol{\Psi}_P^{n-3}\widehat{\boldsymbol{P}} + j\widetilde{\Omega}\,\boldsymbol{\Psi}_P^{n-3}\Big] + \cdots + \widehat{\boldsymbol{A}}_3\Big[2\widehat{\boldsymbol{P}} + j\widetilde{\Omega}\Big] + \widehat{\boldsymbol{A}}_2 \\ &= \widehat{\boldsymbol{A}}_2 + \sum_{k=0}^{n-2}\widehat{\boldsymbol{A}}_{k+3}\Big[(k+2)\boldsymbol{\Psi}_P^{n}\widehat{\boldsymbol{P}} + j\widetilde{\Omega}\,\boldsymbol{\Psi}_P^{n}\Big]\end{aligned} \tag{3.19}$$

where $\widehat{\boldsymbol{A}}_{n+1} = \mathfrak{I}$, and $\mathfrak{I}$ is the infinite dimensional identity matrix. □

Theorem 3.2 is a direct consequence of the following lemma.

Lemma 3.3

Let $\boldsymbol{\Psi}$ be defined as in (3.14). Then the Jacobian of $\boldsymbol{\Psi}_P^k\boldsymbol{p}$, (denoted $\mathfrak{J}(\boldsymbol{\Psi}_P^k\boldsymbol{p})$) is given by

$$\mathfrak{J}\{\boldsymbol{\Psi}_P^k\boldsymbol{p}\} = (k+1)\boldsymbol{\Psi}_P^{k-1}\widehat{\boldsymbol{P}} + j\widetilde{\Omega}\,\boldsymbol{\Psi}_P^{k-1} \tag{3.20}$$

Proof It is easy to show that (3.19) is true for $n = 1$. Lemma 3.3 then follows from the induction hypothesis

$$\mathfrak{J}\{\boldsymbol{\Psi}_P^{k-1}\boldsymbol{p}\} = k\boldsymbol{\Psi}_P^{k-2}\widehat{\boldsymbol{P}} + j\widetilde{\Omega}\,\boldsymbol{\Psi}_P^{k-2}$$

that

$$\begin{aligned}\mathfrak{J}\{\boldsymbol{\Psi}_P^k\boldsymbol{p}\} &= \mathfrak{J}\{\boldsymbol{\Psi}\boldsymbol{\Psi}_P^{k-1}\boldsymbol{p}\} \\ &= \mathfrak{J}\{\widehat{\boldsymbol{P}}\boldsymbol{\Psi}_P^{k-1}\boldsymbol{p} + j\widetilde{\Omega}\,\boldsymbol{\Psi}_P^{k-1}\boldsymbol{p}\} \\ &= \mathfrak{J}\{\widehat{\boldsymbol{P}}\boldsymbol{\Psi}_P^{k-1}\boldsymbol{p}\} + j\widetilde{\Omega}\ \mathfrak{J}\{\boldsymbol{\Psi}_P^{k-1}\boldsymbol{p}\} \\ &= \widehat{\boldsymbol{P}}\mathfrak{J}\{\boldsymbol{\Psi}_P^{k-1}\boldsymbol{p}\} + \boldsymbol{\Psi}_P^{k-1}\widehat{\boldsymbol{P}}\ \mathfrak{J}\{\boldsymbol{p}\} + j\widetilde{\Omega}\ \mathfrak{J}\{\boldsymbol{\Psi}_P^{k-1}\boldsymbol{p}\} \\ &= (k+1)\boldsymbol{\Psi}_P^{k-1}\widehat{\boldsymbol{P}} + j\widetilde{\Omega}\,\boldsymbol{\Psi}_P^{k-1}\end{aligned}$$

where we have used the commutativity properties of (3.10) to obtain

$$\mathfrak{J}\{\boldsymbol{\Psi}_P^n\widehat{\boldsymbol{P}}\boldsymbol{p}\} = \widehat{\boldsymbol{P}}\mathfrak{J}\{\boldsymbol{\Psi}_P^n\boldsymbol{p}\} + \boldsymbol{\Psi}_P^n\widehat{\boldsymbol{P}}\ \mathfrak{J}\{\boldsymbol{p}\}$$

□

4. EXAMPLES: SECOND-ORDER SYSTEMS

In this section we illustrate the use of our new results using second-order periodic linear systems of the form

$$\ddot{y}(t) + \alpha_2(t)\dot{y}(t) + \alpha_1(t)y = 0 \tag{4.1}$$

It can be derived from (2.1) that the PD-Characteristic equation for (4.1) is given by

$$\dot{\rho}(t) + \rho^2(t) + \alpha_2(t)\rho(t) + \alpha_1(t) = 0 \tag{4.2}$$

If $\alpha_2(t)$ and $\alpha_1(t)$ are periodic coefficients with time period T such that $\alpha_2(t+T) = \alpha_2(t)$, $\alpha_1(t+T) = \alpha_1(t)$, then according to theorem 2.3 the number of periodic integral manifolds for the PD-Characteristic equation is the same as the number of FCM. Moreover, the mean value of periodic PD-eigenvalues in these manifolds coincide with the corresponding FCM, which determines the stability of the periodic linear system (4.1).

By (3.17), the harmonic balanced PD-characteristic equation (3.17) for the second-order periodic linear system (4.1) can be written as

$$\boldsymbol{F}(\boldsymbol{p}) = (\widehat{\boldsymbol{P}} + j\widetilde{\Omega}\,)\,\boldsymbol{p} + \widehat{\boldsymbol{A}}_2\,\boldsymbol{p} + \boldsymbol{a}_1 = 0 \tag{4.3}$$

or more explicitly,

$$\begin{bmatrix} \ddots & \vdots & \vdots & \vdots & \iddots \\ \cdots & p_0 - j\omega & p_{-1} & p_{-2} & \cdots \\ \cdots & p_1 & p_0 & p_{-1} & \cdots \\ \cdots & p_2 & p_1 & p_0 + j\omega & \cdots \\ \iddots & \vdots & \vdots & \vdots & \ddots \end{bmatrix}\begin{bmatrix}\vdots \\ p_{-1} \\ p_0 \\ p_1 \\ \vdots\end{bmatrix} +$$

$$+\begin{bmatrix} \ddots & \vdots & \vdots & \vdots & \iddots \\ \cdots & a_{2,0} & a_{2,-1} & a_{2,-2} & \cdots \\ \cdots & a_{2,1} & a_{2,0} & a_{2,-1} & \cdots \\ \cdots & a_{2,2} & a_{2,1} & a_{2,0} & \cdots \\ \iddots & \vdots & \vdots & \vdots & \ddots \end{bmatrix}\begin{bmatrix}\vdots \\ p_{-1} \\ p_0 \\ p_1 \\ \vdots\end{bmatrix} + \begin{bmatrix}\vdots \\ a_{1,-1} \\ a_{1,0} \\ a_{1,1} \\ \vdots\end{bmatrix} = \boldsymbol{0}$$

Equation (4.3) is solved by Newton's method, where the Jacobian $\boldsymbol{J}(\boldsymbol{p})$ can be obtained from Theorem 3.2 as

$$\boldsymbol{J}(\boldsymbol{p}) = 2\widehat{\boldsymbol{P}} + j\widetilde{\Omega} + \widehat{\boldsymbol{A}}_2$$

$$= \begin{bmatrix} \ddots & \vdots & \vdots & \vdots & \iddots \\ \cdots & 2p_0 + a_{2,0} - j\omega & 2p_{-1} + a_{2,-1} & 2p_{-2} + a_{2,-2} & \cdots \\ \cdots & 2p_1 + a_{2,1} & 2p_0 + a_{2,0} & 2p_{-1} + a_{2,-1} & \cdots \\ \cdots & 2p_2 + a_{2,2} & 2p_1 + a_{2,1} & 2p_0 + a_{2,0} + j\omega & \cdots \\ \iddots & \vdots & \vdots & \vdots & \ddots \end{bmatrix} \tag{4.4}$$

To implement this algorithm finite order truncation has been taken. The computed solution tends to the true solution if the coefficients $\alpha_i(t)$ and the solution $\rho(t)$ are bandpass signals, which is usually the case. Let m be the order of truncation, then the frequency range covers $-m\omega_0$ to $+m\omega_0$, including the zeroth frequency component. So deleting the frequency harmonics outside $(-m\omega_0, +m\omega_0)$ results in a $(2m+1)$th-order nonlinear equation.

Example 1:

Consider system (4.1) with

$$\begin{aligned}\alpha_2(t) &= -2\sin t - 3 \\ \alpha_1(t) &= \sin^2 t + 3\sin t + 2 - \cos t\end{aligned}$$

The homogenetic PD-eigenvalues [1], [14] can be found analytically by

$$(\delta - (\sin t + 1))(\delta - (\sin t + 2)) = 0$$

which implies 1.0 and 2.0 are the real parts of Floquet Characteristic exponents.

i) PD-Characteristic solution method: Expanding the periodic coefficients $\alpha_1(t)$ and $\alpha_2(t)$ in Fourier series

$$\alpha_1(t) = -\frac{1}{4}e^{-j2\omega t} + (-\frac{1}{2} + j\frac{3}{2})e^{-j\omega t} + \frac{5}{2} + (-\frac{1}{2} - j\frac{3}{2})e^{j\omega t} - \frac{1}{4}e^{j2\omega t}$$

$$\alpha_2(t) = -je^{-j\omega t} - 3 + je^{j\omega t}$$

ii) IDD method: The system is transformed to the vector form (1.2) and the $A(t)$ matrix is expanded in Fourier series

$$A_{-2} = \begin{bmatrix} 0 & 0 \\ \frac{1}{4} & 0 \end{bmatrix}; \quad A_{-1} = \begin{bmatrix} 0 & 0 \\ \frac{1}{2} - \frac{3}{2}j & j \end{bmatrix}; \quad A_0 = \begin{bmatrix} 0 & 1 \\ -\frac{5}{2} & 3 \end{bmatrix}$$

$$A_1 = \begin{bmatrix} 0 & 0 \\ \frac{1}{2} + \frac{3}{2}j & -j \end{bmatrix} \quad A_2 = \begin{bmatrix} 0 & 0 \\ \frac{1}{4} & 0 \end{bmatrix}$$

The solution for FCE by both methods for different orders of truncation m are tabulated below.

Order of Truncation m	PD-Cha. eqn. method	IDD method
1	1.0, 2.0	0.6340, 2.3660
2	1.0, 2.0	1.0102, 1.9898
3	1.0, 2.0	0.9997, 2.0003
4	1.0, 2.0	1.0, 2.0
10	1.0, 2.0	1.0, 2.0

Note: The initial conditions for PD-Characteristic equation were chosen around one of the solutions of IDD method. It can be seen that FCE converges to the true value for 1st-order truncation by PD-Characteristic equation solution but for the 4th-order truncation by IDD method.

Example 2:

Consider a Lossless Mathieu equation of the form (4.1) with

$$\alpha_1(t) = a - 2q\cos 2t$$
$$\alpha_2(t) = 0$$

The harmonic balanced PD-Characteristic equation (3.17) is modified [7] into parametric form to obtain the stability boundaries of lossless Mathieu equation. The stability boundaries of lossless Mathieu equation found this way are shown in Figure 4.1 and are the same as the boundaries presented in [2]. The boundaries of Mathieu equation in [2] were obtained in a very time consuming way by choosing a particular point in the $a - q$ parameter space and finding whether it is in the domain of stability or not. Using our new method, the stability boundaries are evaluated directly from the modified harmonic balanced PD-characteristic equation given in [7]. It is interesting to note that these stability boundary curves are also bifurcation map of the aforementioned nonlinear equation given in [7].

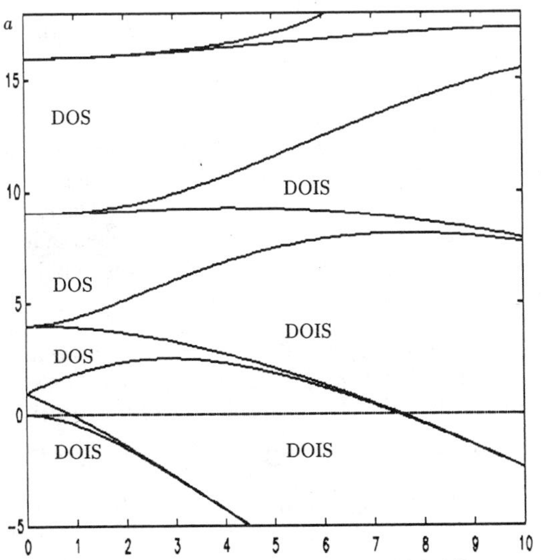

DOS - Domain of Stability, DOIS - Domain of InStability.

Figure 4.1. Stability diagram for the lossless Mathieu equation.

SUMMARY AND CONCLUSIONS

A new method for calculating Floquet Characteristic Exponent (FCE) has been developed in this paper, and its advantages over existing methods has been demonstrated by second-order examples. It has been observed from the examples that the solutions for FCE obtained by solving PD-Characteristic equation appear more accurate and converge faster because of the nonlinear terms involved in the evaluation. The new method also allows us to draw the stability boundaries directly which can aid in controller design with periodic time-varying feedback. The only shortcoming of this method is that it needs an initial condition in the domain of attraction for the solution. But, this can be easily circumvented by using the solution obtained by IDD, Monodromy matrix, or iteration method. In developing the new algorithm, the convolutional matrix notation allow frequency domain discrete convolutions to be represented as an infinite dimensional nonlinear algebraic equations. This sheds some light on solving periodic vector linear systems and the more general aperiodic scalar and vector LTV systems.

In order to implement the algorithm, finite order truncation of Fourier series for the system coefficients and the periodic PD-eigenvalues are inevitable. Therefore, there is a need to study convergence conditions, convergence rate and the minimum order of truncation for accurate estimation of FCE. Generalization of the new results of this paper for periodic scalar linear (1.1) to periodic vector linear systems (1.2) and to the more general aperiodic LTV systems (1.1), (1.2) are also being investigated.

REFERENCES

[1] Zhu, J., *A Unified Eigenvalue Theory for Linear Dynamical Systems*, Ph. D. Dissertation, ECE Dept., UAH, 1989 (3rd rev., 1992).

[2] Richards, J.A., *Analysis of Periodically Time-Varying systems*, Springer-Verlag, New York, 1983.

[3] Oppenheim, A. V. and Willsky, A.S., *Signals and Systems*, Prentice-Hall, 1983.

[4] Wu, M. Y., *A note on Stability of Linear Time-Varying Systems*, IEEE Transactions on Automatic Control, pp.162-162, Apr., 1974.

[5] Lamberto Cesari, *Asymptotic Behavior and Stability Problems in Ordinary Differential Equations*, Springer-Verlag, Berlin, 1959.

[6] Das, S.K. and Rajagopalan, P. K., *Infinite Determinant method for Stability Analysis of Periodic Systems*, IEE Proceedings, vol. 131, sept. 1984, pp.189-201.

[7] Zhu, J. and Vemula, S. K., *On Nonlinear Iterative Mappings whose Bifurcation Diagrams are Stability Boundaries of Periodic Linear Systems*, submitted.

[8] McLachlan, N.W., *Theory and Application of Mathieu functions*, Clarendon: Oxford U.P. 1947.

[9] Ilchmann, A., Owens, D.H. and Präetzel-Wolters, D., *Sufficient conditions for stability of linear time-varying systems*, Systems and Control letters, 9 (1987), pp. 157-163.

[10] Markus, L. and Yamabe, M., *Global stability criteria for differential systems*, Osaka Math. J., vol.12, pp.305-317, 1960.

[11] Vinogradov, R.E., *On a criterion for Instability in the sense of A. M. Lyapunov for solutions of ODE*, Dok. Akad. Nauk SSSR, vol.84, No.2, 1952.

[12] Zhu, J. Ray, S. and Vemula, S. K., *Further studies on Frozen-Time Eigenvalues in the Stability Analysis for Periodic Linear Systems*, Proc., IEEE 23rd SSST, pp. 355-360, 1991.

[13] Zhu, J. and Johnson, C.D., *New Results in the Reduction of Linear Time-Varying Dynamical Systems*, SIAM J. on Control and Optimizations, vol.27, No.3, 476-494,1989.

[14] Zhu, J. and Johnson, C.D., *Unified Canonical Forms for Matrices Over a Differential Ring*, Linear Aligebra and its Applications, pp. 201-248, 1991.

[15] Zhu, J. and Johnson, C.D., *Stability Analysis of Periodic Linear Dynamical Systems Using a New Time-Varying Eigenvalue Concept; Part I: Theoritical Aspects,* Proc., Southeastcon 89, 437-443, April, 1989.

[16] Zhu, J. and Johnson, C.D., *Stability Analysis of Periodic Linear Dynamical Systems Using a New Time-Varying Eigenvalue Concept; Part II: Computational Aspects,* Proc., Conference on Information Sciences and Systems, Baltimore, MD, March, 1989.

[17] Burden, R. L., Faires, J. D., and Reynolds, A. C., *Numerical Analysis*, Prindle, Weber and Schmidt, Boston, MA, 1981.

Proceedings of the
American Control Conference
San Francisco, California • June 1993

A Reachability Test for Systems over Polynomial Rings using Gröbner Bases

L.C.G.J.M. Habets
Eindhoven University of Technology
Department of Mathematics and Computing Science
P.O. Box 513
NL-5600 MB Eindhoven, The Netherlands

Abstract

Conditions for the reachability of a system over a polynomial ring are well known in the literature. However, verification of these conditions is in general a difficult problem. In this paper, the reachability problem is expressed in terms of polynomial ideals, and Gröbner Bases are used to carry out the test explicitly. Four different methods are proposed, and their effectiveness is compared. With one of these methods, it is also possible to obtain a right- or left-inverse of a general non-square polynomial matrix, often required in the design of feedback compensators.

1 Introduction

Systems over (polynomial) rings can be seen as a rather straightforward generalization of ordinary systems over fields. In the last three decades these systems have been investigated quite extensively (see for example [1] and [12]), not only because they highlight the most important system theoretic properties very clearly, but also because they have very interesting applications. For example, systems over polynomial rings can be used to model systems with varying parameters and time-delay systems. In the last case, some delay operators $\sigma_1, \ldots, \sigma_\ell$ are introduced which act on the state trajectory $x(t)$ and the input trajectory $u(t)$ of the system:

$$\sigma_i x(t) = x(t - \tau_i), \qquad \sigma_i u(t) = u(t - \tau_i), \tag{1}$$

where the τ_i, $(i = 1, \ldots, \ell)$, are ℓ incommensurate time-delays. A time-delay system can then be written as:

$$\begin{cases} \dot{x}(t) = A(\sigma_1, \ldots, \sigma_\ell)x(t) + B(\sigma_1, \ldots, \sigma_\ell)u(t), \\ y(t) = C(\sigma_1, \ldots, \sigma_\ell)x(t) + D(\sigma_1, \ldots, \sigma_\ell)u(t), \end{cases} \tag{2}$$

where the matrices $\hat{A} = A(\sigma_1, \ldots, \sigma_\ell)$, $\hat{B} = B(\sigma_1, \ldots, \sigma_\ell)$, $\hat{C} = C(\sigma_1, \ldots, \sigma_\ell)$ and $\hat{D} = D(\sigma_1, \ldots, \sigma_\ell)$ are all matrices over the polynomial ring $\mathbb{R}[\sigma_1, \ldots, \sigma_\ell]$. So the quadruple $\Sigma = (\hat{A}, \hat{B}, \hat{C}, \hat{D})$ can be seen as a system over the polynomial ring $\mathbb{R}[\sigma_1, \ldots, \sigma_\ell]$.

Several system theoretic concepts, which are well-known for systems over fields, such as reachability and observability, have been generalized to the systems over rings case. In this way it was possible to derive results on various problems such as pole-placement, stabilizability and input-output decoupling (see [9], [5] and [4] respectively), which are quite similar to the well-known results for systems over fields. However, in the existing literature almost no attention is paid to the computational aspects of systems over rings. In this article we fill in a part of this gap, and show how the reachability of a system over a polynomial ring can be tested explicitly.

Our approach to this problem is based on the use of Gröbner Bases. This is a very powerful technique from constructive commutative algebra for manipulating polynomial ideals. We describe how the reachability problem can be reformulated into terms of polynomial ideals, and how Gröbner Bases can be used to decide on this question. Other important issues are the computation of a right-inverse of the matrix $(zI - A \mid B)$, which is interesting from the control point of view, and a reformulation of our reachability test which is computationally more efficient.

Research supported by the Netherlands Organization for Scientific Research (NWO).

2 Reachability of systems over polynomial rings

Let $\mathcal{K}$ be an arbitrary field of characteristic zero, and let $\bar{\mathcal{K}}$ be the algebraic closure of $\mathcal{K}$. We denote the ring of all polynomials in ℓ indeterminates $\sigma_1, \ldots, \sigma_\ell$ with coefficients in $\mathcal{K}$ by $\mathcal{R} := \mathcal{K}[\sigma_1, \ldots, \sigma_\ell]$. Let A and B be $n \times n$ and $n \times m$ matrices respectively, which have all their entries in $\mathcal{R}$. Then we can consider the discrete time system over the ring $\mathcal{R}$ given by the equations

$$\begin{cases} x(t+1) &= Ax(t) + Bu(t), \\ x(0) &= x_0. \end{cases} \tag{3}$$

Now clearly $x(t) \in \mathcal{R}^n$ $(t \in \mathbb{Z}^+)$ and $u(t) \in \mathcal{R}^m$ $(t \in \mathbb{Z}^+)$. From a system theoretic point of view we call the system (3) reachable if for all $x_0, \bar{x} \in \mathcal{R}^n$ there exists a time instant $T \in \mathbb{Z}^+$ and an input sequence $u(0), u(1), \ldots, u(T-1)$ such that, starting the system in $x(0) = x_0$ and applying this input sequence, it reaches the state $\bar{x}$ at time T, i.e. $x(T) = \bar{x}$. It is easily shown (see for example [1]), that this property is satisfied iff the module generated by the columns of the matrix $(B \mid AB \mid \cdots \mid A^{n-1}B)$ is the free module $\mathcal{R}^n$. Based on the above interpretation, but nevertheless independent of it, reachability of systems over rings is defined as follows (compare [12]).

Definition 2.1 Let $\mathcal{R}$ be an arbitrary commutative ring, and $A \in \mathcal{R}^{n \times n}$, $B \in \mathcal{R}^{n \times m}$. Then the system $\Sigma = (A, B)$ is called *reachable* if the columns of the matrix

$$(B \mid AB \mid \cdots \mid A^{n-1}B) \tag{4}$$

span the free module $\mathcal{R}^n$.

The condition given in Definition 2.1 is rather difficult to check. Especially for systems over polynomial rings there are alternative characterizations of reachability which are more suitable for testing.

Theorem 2.2 *Let $\mathcal{R} = \mathcal{K}[\sigma_1, \ldots, \sigma_\ell]$ and suppose that $A \in \mathcal{R}^{n\times n}$ and $B \in \mathcal{R}^{n\times m}$. Consider the system $\Sigma = (A, B)$. Then the following four conditions are equivalent:*

(i) $\Sigma = (A, B)$ *is reachable,*

(ii) $(zI - A \mid B)$ *is right-invertible over* $\mathcal{R}[z]$,

(iii) $\forall(\bar\sigma_1, \ldots, \bar\sigma_\ell, \bar z) \in \bar{\mathcal{K}}^{\ell+1}\ \forall q^T = (q_1 \cdots q_n) \in \bar{\mathcal{K}}^n :$

$$q^T \cdot (\bar z I - A(\bar\sigma_1, \ldots, \bar\sigma_\ell) \mid B(\bar\sigma_1, \ldots, \bar\sigma_\ell)) = 0 \implies q^T = (q_1 \cdots q_n) = (0 \cdots 0), \quad (5)$$

(iv) $\forall(\bar\sigma_1, \ldots, \bar\sigma_\ell, \bar z) \in \bar{\mathcal{K}}^{\ell+1} :$

$$\mathrm{rank}(\bar z I - A(\bar\sigma_1, \ldots, \bar\sigma_\ell) \mid B(\bar\sigma_1, \ldots, \bar\sigma_\ell)) = n.$$

For the proof, see [1, ch. 2], [7], [8] and [11].
Condition *(ii)* in Theorem 2.2 is a very important characterization of reachability from the control point of view. In several control problems, such as the stabilization problem, the right-inverse of $(zI - A \mid B)$ can be used to design a compensator. The computation of such a right-inverse is therefore a very interesting question.
With help of condition *(iii)*, Lee and Olbrot ([8]) derived genericity conditions for the reachability of systems over polynomial rings. They showed that such a system is generically reachable if the number of inputs m to the system is strictly larger than the number of indeterminates ℓ in the polynomial ring $\mathcal{K}[\sigma_1, \ldots, \sigma_\ell]$. Moreover, if $m \leq \ell$, so when the number of inputs is smaller or equal to the number of indeterminates, a system is generically not reachable.

3 A reachability test using Gröbner Bases

The Gröbner Basis method is a technique from constructive commutative algebra to solve various questions on polynomial ideals, e.g. the membership problem and the solutions of a system of algebraic equations. It was introduced by B. Buchberger in 1965 and nowadays most computer-algebra packages contain software for the computation of Gröbner Bases. Good references are [3] for the algorithmic part of the problem, and [10] for a more theoretical point of view. Application in the field of systems theory, especially for nonlinear systems, were investigated by Forsman in [6].
A Gröbner Basis of a polynomial ideal is a set of polynomials of low complexity which generate the same ideal. First an ordering of the terms is introduced to measure the complexity. Based on this ordering a sort of reduction process is carried out, which generates polynomials of lower complexity. This process has very much in common with Euclidian Division, certainly in the one-indeterminate case. Let $p \in \mathcal{K}[x_1, \ldots, x_\ell]$ be a polynomial in ℓ indeterminates, and suppose that we have already introduced a term ordering on $\mathcal{K}[x_1, \ldots, x_\ell]$. Then the initial term of p, denoted by $\mathrm{in}(p)$, is the term in p of highest order. A Gröbner Basis of an ideal $\mathcal{I}$ can then be defined in the following way (compare [10, Def. 1.5.]):

Definition 3.3 Let $\mathcal{I}$ be an ideal in $\mathcal{K}[x_1, \ldots, x_\ell]$, $\mathcal{I} \neq \{0\}$. A finite subset G of $\mathcal{I}$ is a *Gröbner Basis* of $\mathcal{I}$ if the set

$$\mathrm{in}(G) = \{\mathrm{in}(g) \mid g \in G\}$$

generates the ideal $\mathrm{in}(\mathcal{I}) = \{\mathrm{in}(f) \mid f \in \mathcal{I}\}$.

As a direct consequence, a finite set of monomials (i.e. polynomials consisting of only one term) $\{m_1, \ldots, m_k\}$ is a Gröbner Basis of the ideal $\langle m_1, \ldots, m_k\rangle$ generated by these monomials (see [10]).
Gröbner Bases can be calculated using the algorithm of Buchberger (see [3]). In this way a so called auto-reduced Gröbner Basis is obtained. One can prove that an auto-reduced Gröbner Basis is unique (in the given term ordering) up to multiplication by non-zero constants from the field $\mathcal{K}$ (see [2]).

The next proposition shows how the reachability conditions of Theorem 2.2 can be translated in terms of polynomial ideals, and how Gröbner Bases can be used to carry out the reachability test explicitly.

Proposition 3.4 *Let $A \in \mathcal{R}^{n\times n}$ and $B \in \mathcal{R}^{n\times m}$ where $\mathcal{R} = \mathcal{K}[\sigma_1, \ldots, \sigma_\ell]$. Let $q^T = (q_1 \cdots q_n)$ be an n-vector of* <u>*indeterminates*</u>. *Define the row-vector p^T as*

$$p^T = (p_1 \cdots p_{n+m}) := q^T \cdot (zI - A \mid B). \quad (6)$$

Consider the elements p_i $(i = 1, \ldots, n+m)$ of p^T as polynomials in the ring $\mathcal{K}[\sigma_1, \ldots, \sigma_\ell, z, q_1, \ldots, q_n]$ (shorthand notation $\mathcal{K}[\sigma, z, q]$). Denote by $\mathcal{P}$ the ideal in $\mathcal{K}[\sigma, z, q]$, generated by the polynomials $p_1, \ldots, p_{n+m}$. Then

$(zI - A \mid B)$ *is right-invertible over* $\mathcal{R}[z]$,

$\Longleftrightarrow$

The auto-reduced Gröbner Basis of $\mathcal{P}$ consists precisely of the polynomials $q_1, \ldots, q_n$ (independent of the chosen term ordering).

Proof "$\Rightarrow$" Let $M(z)$ be a right-inverse of $(zI - A \mid B)$ over $\mathcal{R}[z]$. Right multiplication of (6) with $M(z)$ yields

$$p^T \cdot M(z) = q^T \cdot (zI - A \mid B) \cdot M(z) = q^T.$$

So each q_i $(i = 1, \ldots, n)$ can be written as a linear combination of p_j $(j = 1, \ldots, n+m)$, with coefficients in $\mathcal{K}[\sigma, z, q]$. So in $\mathcal{K}[\sigma, z, q]$ we have $\langle q_1, \ldots, q_n\rangle \subset \langle p_1, \ldots, p_{n+m}\rangle$. But, according to (6), $q^T \cdot (zI - A \mid B) = p^T$, and completely analogously we obtain $\langle p_1, \ldots, p_{n+m}\rangle \subset \langle q_1, \ldots, q_n\rangle$. So in the ring $\mathcal{K}[\sigma, z, q]$ we have $\mathcal{P} = \langle q_1, \ldots, q_n\rangle$, and because $q_1, \ldots, q_n$ are monomials in this ring, $q_1, \ldots, q_n$ form a Gröbner Basis of $\mathcal{P}$. Because none of these polynomials divides an other one, this basis is also auto-reduced.

"$\Leftarrow$" Define the ideal $\mathcal{Q} := \langle q_1, \ldots, q_n\rangle$ in $\mathcal{K}[\sigma, z, q]$. Then $\mathcal{P} = \mathcal{Q}$, hence their varieties are equal: $\mathcal{V}(\mathcal{P}) = \mathcal{V}(\mathcal{Q})$. This implies that $(p_1, \ldots, p_{n+m}) = 0$ if and only if $(q_1, \ldots, q_n) = 0$. Let now $(\bar\sigma, \bar z) := (\bar\sigma_1, \ldots, \bar\sigma_\ell, \bar z) \in \bar{\mathcal{K}}^{\ell+1}$, and let $\bar p$ denote the vector p, with $(\bar\sigma, \bar z)$ substituted for (σ, z). Then

$$\bar p^T = q^T \cdot (\bar z I - A(\bar\sigma) \mid B(\bar\sigma)).$$

Suppose that $\bar{p}^T = 0$. Because $\mathcal{V}(\mathcal{P}) = \mathcal{V}(\mathcal{Q})$, this implies that $q^T = 0$, and thus condition *(iii)* of Theorem 2.2 is satisfied. This implies that $(zI - A \mid B)$ is right-invertible over $\mathcal{R}[z]$. ∎

Combining the results of Theorem 2.2 and Proposition 3.4 it is easy to derive a reachability test for systems over the polynomial ring $\mathcal{R} = \mathcal{K}[\sigma_1, \ldots, \sigma_\ell]$. Let $\Sigma = (A, B)$. First compute the polynomials $p_1, \ldots, p_{n+m}$ in $\mathcal{K}[\sigma_1, \ldots, \sigma_\ell, z, q_1, \ldots, q_n]$ with help of formula (6). Compute an auto-reduced Gröbner Basis of $\langle p_1, \ldots, p_{n+m} \rangle$, using Buchberger's algorithm. If the Gröbner Basis consists precisely of the polynomials $q_1, \ldots, q_n$, the matrix $(zI - A \mid B)$ is right-invertible over $\mathcal{R}[z]$, so $\Sigma = (A, B)$ is reachable. Otherwise, when the Gröbner Basis contains other polynomials, $\Sigma = (A, B)$ is not reachable.

4 Computation of a right-inverse of $(zI - A \mid B)$

In the last section it was shown how the reachability of a system $\Sigma = (A, B)$ can be tested, by verifying the right-invertibility of the matrix $(zI - A \mid B)$ using Gröbner Bases. The computation of a right-inverse of $(zI - A \mid B)$ over $\mathcal{R}[z]$ is also very interesting for its own sake because this inverse is needed in the design of compensators for various control problems. In this section we show that the Gröbner Basis construction of the last section implicitly carries all the information needed to write down a right-inverse of $(zI - A \mid B)$ immediately.
Suppose that the system $\Sigma = (A, B)$ over $\mathcal{R}$ is reachable. Then $(zI - A \mid B)$ is right-invertible over $\mathcal{R}[z]$. Introduce again the row-vector $q^T = (q_1 \cdots q_n)$ of indeterminates and define:

$$p^T = (p_1 \cdots p_{n+m}) = q^T \cdot (zI - A \mid B).$$

Because $(zI - A \mid B)$ is right-invertible, the Gröbner Basis of $\langle p_1, \ldots, p_{n+m} \rangle$ is the set of polynomials $\{q_1, \ldots, q_n\}$. This set is obtained after application of Buchberger's algorithm. This algorithm does not only compute a Gröbner Basis, but also coefficients α_{ji} in $\mathcal{K}[\sigma, z, q]$ ($j = 1, \ldots, n+m; i = 1, \ldots, n$), such that

$$\forall i \in \{1, \ldots, n\} : q_i = \sum_{j=1}^{n+m} \alpha_{ji} p_j. \qquad (7)$$

Let $A(q)$ denote the $(n+m) \times n$ matrix over $\mathcal{K}[\sigma, z][q]$ such that the $(j, i)^{\text{th}}$ entry of $A(q)$ is α_{ji}. Then, according to (7): $q^T = p^T \cdot A(q)$. Substitution of $p^T = q^T \cdot (zI - A \mid B)$ yields for all q:

$$q^T = q^T \cdot (zI - A \mid B) \cdot A(q). \qquad (8)$$

Theorem 4.5 *Let M be an $n \times k$ matrix ($k \geq n$) with all entries in $\mathcal{R}[z] = \mathcal{K}[\sigma_1, \ldots, \sigma_\ell, z]$. Let $q^T = (q_1 \cdots q_n)$ be a row-vector of indeterminates. Suppose that $A(q)$ is an $k \times n$ polynomial matrix over $\mathcal{K}[\sigma_1, \ldots, \sigma_\ell, z][q_1, \ldots, q_n]$ such that*

$$q^T = q^T \cdot M \cdot A(q). \qquad (9)$$

Then the matrix $A(0)$, obtained by substitution of $(q_1 \cdots q_n) = (0 \cdots 0)$ in $A(q)$, is a right-inverse of M over $\mathcal{R}[z]$.

Proof Suppose that (9) holds true; then it also holds while replacing q by λq, where $\lambda \in \mathcal{K}\backslash\{0\}$, i.e.

$$\forall \lambda \in \mathcal{K}\backslash\{0\} : \lambda q^T = \lambda q^T \cdot M \cdot A(\lambda q).$$

Dividing both right- and left-hand side by λ yields:

$$\forall \lambda \in \mathcal{K}\backslash\{0\} : q^T = q^T \cdot M \cdot A(\lambda q).$$

Now $q^T \cdot M \cdot A(\lambda q) - q^T$ can be seen as an n-dimensional row-vector of polynomials in the indeterminate λ with coefficients in $\mathcal{K}[\sigma, z, q]$. For all $\lambda \neq 0$, these polynomials are zero, so they must be identically zero. Thus for $\lambda = 0$ we have: $q^T = q^T \cdot M \cdot A(0)$. Clearly $A(0)$ is an $k \times n$ matrix over $\mathcal{R}[z]$, while q^T is a row-vector of indeterminates. So, $A(0)$ is a right-inverse of M over $\mathcal{R}[z]$. ∎

Theorem 4.5 can be used to derive a right-inverse of $(zI - A \mid B)$ over $\mathcal{R}[z]$ from the matrix $A(q)$ over $\mathcal{K}[\sigma, z, q]$ defined in (7). From formula (8) and Theorem 4.5 we immediately see that substitution of $(q_1 \cdots q_n) = (0 \cdots 0)$ in $A(q)$ yields a right-inverse of $(zI - A \mid B)$ over $\mathcal{R}[z]$.

Remark 4.6 The method described above to compute a right-inverse of a polynomial matrix using Gröbner Bases, is not only valid in the case where the polynomial matrix has the special form $(zI - A \mid B)$. In the construction this special structure was never used. Therefore this method is also applicable in the general case. In this way Gröbner Bases can be used to test the right- and left-invertibility of non-square polynomial matrices and to compute left- and right-inverses of such matrices.

5 A recursive method to test reachability

Condition *(iii)* in Theorem 2.2 can also be used in a slightly different way. It is possible to reformulate the condition in order to get a sort of recursive method. This observation was already made by Lee and Olbrot in [8], where they used it to prove their result on genericity. This alternative condition is stated in the next lemma.

Lemma 5.7 *Let $\mathcal{R} = \mathcal{K}[\sigma_1, \ldots, \sigma_\ell]$, and suppose that $A \in \mathcal{R}^{n \times n}$ and $B \in \mathcal{R}^{n \times m}$. Consider the system $\Sigma = (A, B)$ over $\mathcal{R}$. Then*

$\Sigma = (A, B)$ *is reachable,*

$\Longleftrightarrow$

$$\forall (\bar{\sigma}, \bar{z}) = (\bar{\sigma}_1, \ldots, \bar{\sigma}_\ell, \bar{z}) \in \bar{\mathcal{K}}^{\ell+1}$$
$$\forall j \in \{1, \ldots, n\}\ \forall (q_{j+1} \cdots q_n) \in \bar{\mathcal{K}}^{n-j} :$$

$$(\underbrace{0 \cdots 0}_{j-1} | 1 | q_{j+1} \cdots q_n) \cdot (\bar{z}I - A(\sigma) \mid B(\sigma)) \neq 0. \qquad (10)$$

The condition of Lemma 5.7 is easily tested for each $j \in \{1, \ldots, n\}$ separately, using the Gröbner Basis method. Let $j \in \{1, \ldots, n\}$ and introduce the n-dimensional row-vector

$$q^T = (\underbrace{0 \cdots 0}_{j-1} | 1 | q_{j+1} \cdots q_n)$$

where $q_{j+1}, \ldots, q_n$ are considered as indeterminates. Define

$$p^T = (p_1 \cdots p_{n+m}) := q^T \cdot (zI - A \mid B).$$

The entries $p_1, \ldots, p_{n+m}$ of p^T can be seen as polynomials in $\mathcal{K}[\sigma_1, \ldots, \sigma_\ell, z, q_{j+1}, \ldots, q_n]$. When (A, B) is reachable, it follows from Lemma 5.7 that these polynomials do not have a common zero. According to the Hilbert-Nullstellensatz this implies that the ideal $\mathcal{P} = \langle p_1, \ldots, p_{n+m} \rangle$ is the whole ring $\mathcal{K}[\sigma_1, \ldots, \sigma_\ell, z, q_{j+1}, \ldots, q_n]$. Therefore it follows from Definition 3.3 that the auto-reduced Gröbner Basis of $\mathcal{P}$ consists of only one polynomial: the constant polynomial 1. (Here we made the assumption that the Gröbner Basis is normalized.)
Now the reachability of a system $\Sigma = (A, B)$ can be investigated by carrying out the test described above for each $j \in \{1, \ldots, n\}$. This leads to the following, in a sense recursive, algorithm.

Algorithm 5.8 Let $A \in \mathcal{R}^{n \times n}$ and $B \in \mathcal{R}^{n \times m}$. Then the algorithm below is a test for the reachability of the system $\Sigma = (A, B)$ over $\mathcal{R}$.

```
j := 1; G := {1};
while j ≤ n and G = {1} do
    q^T := (0···0 |1|q_{j+1} ··· q_n);   [0···0 of length j−1]
    p^T = (p_1 ··· p_{n+m}) := q^T · (zI − A | B);
    G := GröbnerBasis(⟨p_1,...,p_{n+m}⟩);
    j := j + 1;
od;
if G = {1}
    then Σ = (A, B) is reachable;
    else Σ = (A, B) is not reachable;
fi;
```

Algorithm 5.8 has one important advantage. The complexity of the computation of a Gröbner Basis is highly dependent on the number of indeterminates in the polynomial ring. Although in Algorithm 5.8 more Gröbner Bases have to be calculated, the number of indeterminates is in each step less than in the method of Section 3. Moreover, this number of indeterminates is decreasing in each step. Therefore it is possible that this algorithm is faster than the method of Section 3, especially for non-reachable systems. According to the proof in [8], Algorithm 5.8 will generically detect the non-reachability of such systems in the first step. Therefore it is much faster in this case than the method of Section 3. This is illustrated in Section 6, when the performances of both algorithms is compared. Note however that the method of Section 3 also yields a right-inverse of $(zI - A \mid B)$. This is not possible with Algorithm 5.8.

Remark 5.9 Algorithm 5.8 can be seen as a special case of the method of Section 3 (only the conclusions are derived in a different way) in the sense that in each step a number of the indeterminates $q_1, \ldots, q_n$ is substituted by some zeros and a one. In Algorithm 5.8 this is done in a special order (from q_1 to q_n), but this order does not make any difference for the problem under consideration. Therefore one can obtain alternative algorithms by changing the order of substitution. In this way it is possible to influence the computing-time by changing this order.

6 An example

In this section the effectiveness of the methods proposed in this paper, is illustrated with help of an example. Also a comparison of the performances of the various methods is made. Moreover, to illuminate the advantages and drawbacks of the algorithms derived in this paper very clearly, the performances are compared with a very simple method to test reachability. This rather straightforward method is introduced first.

Let A and B be matrices over the polynomial ring $\mathcal{R} = \mathcal{K}[\sigma_1, \ldots, \sigma_\ell]$ of size $n \times n$ and $n \times m$ respectively. Then an alternative method to test the right-invertibility of the matrix $(zI - A \mid B)$ over $\mathcal{R}[z]$ is the following. First compute all the $n \times n$ minors $r_1, \ldots, r_N$ of $(zI - A \mid B)$. Then it is clear (see for example [8, p. 111]) that $(zI - A \mid B)$ is right-invertible iff these minors do not have a common zero. According to the Hilbert-Nullstellensatz this implies that $\Sigma = (A, B)$ is reachable iff $\langle r_1, \ldots, r_N \rangle = \mathcal{R}[z]$, i.e. iff the ideal generated by the $n \times n$ minors $r_1, \ldots, r_N$ of $(zI - A \mid B)$ is the whole ring $\mathcal{R}[z]$. This last condition is easily verified with help of Gröbner Bases. According to Definition 3.3, the normalized auto-reduced Gröbner Basis of $\langle r_1, \ldots, r_N \rangle$ consists of only one polynomial in this case: the constant polynomial 1.

Example 6.10 Consider the matrices A, B and B_1 over the polynomial ring $\mathbf{R}[\sigma_1, \sigma_2]$ given by

$$A = \begin{pmatrix} \sigma_1 + 1 & \sigma_2 + \sigma_1 & \sigma_2 - \sigma_1 + 3 \\ \sigma_2 - 1 & \sigma_2 + 1 & \sigma_1 - 5 \\ {\sigma_1}^2 + 1 & 1 & \sigma_2 + 1 \end{pmatrix}, \tag{11}$$

$$B = \begin{pmatrix} \sigma_1 + \sigma_2 & \sigma_1 - 1 & 0 \\ 1 & {\sigma_2}^2 + 1 & \sigma_1 - 3 \\ 0 & \sigma_1 - \sigma_2 & \sigma_2 + 2 \end{pmatrix}, \tag{12}$$

and where B_1 consists of the first two columns of B. Based on the genericity conditions in [8], we expect $\Sigma = (A, B)$ to be reachable, but $\Sigma_1 = (A, B_1)$ not to be reachable. The reachability of both $\Sigma = (A, B)$ and $\Sigma_1 = (A, B_1)$ is now tested with four different methods:

Method 1 The method described in Section 3, based on the computation of a Gröbner Basis of $q^T \cdot (zI - A \mid B)$.

Method 2 Algorithm 5.8 in Section 5.

Method 3 A modification of Algorithm 5.8 as mentioned in Remark 5.9. The substitution order (from q_1 to q_n in Algorithm 5.8) is changed into the reverse direction (from q_n to q_1).

Method 4 The method based on the computation of a Gröbner Basis of the ideal generated by all the minors of $(zI - A \mid B)$, as explained at the beginning of this section.

The results of the application of these methods on this particular example are given in Table 1. First the conclusion (reachable/not reachable) is given, then the computing time (in CPU seconds) needed to arrive at the result. These experiments were made in the computer-algebra package MAPLE V, running on a Sun/Sparc Workstation with a 25MHz processor. To compute Gröbner Bases, we used the function *gbasis* from the *grobner* package, with the total-degree ordering and an automatic ordering of the indeterminates.

Table 1	$\Sigma = (A, B)$	$\Sigma_1 = (A, B_1)$
Method 1	reachable 55.7	not reachable 362.9
Method 2	reachable 20.3	not reachable 43.7
Method 3	reachable 19.7	not reachable 145.3
Method 4	reachable $158.6 \cdot 10^3$	not reachable 21.3

From Table 1 it is clear that the results obtained with Method 4 are rather extreme. Although this method is the fastest in the non-reachable case, it is very slow for the reachable system $\Sigma = (A, B)$. On the other hand, the Methods 1 to 3, as proposed in this paper, behave very well in both cases. Nevertheless, the performances of the Methods 1 to 3 also differ. In the reachable case, the recursive methods (Methods 2 and 3) are somewhat faster than Method 1, but the advantage becomes evident in the non-reachable case. Moreover, this example shows that the performances of these methods (the difference between Method 2 and Method 3) depend on the order of substitution.

Remark 6.11 The performances of the four different methods have also been compared on the basis of other test examples. The conclusions are almost the same. The methods proposed in this paper are far more effective than the simple method based on the computation of a Gröbner Basis of the ideal generated by the minors of the matrix $(zI - A \mid B)$. The recursive methods are in most cases somewhat better than the method of Section 3, certainly for non-reachable systems. In the recursive methods, the order of substitution does influence the computing time, but the relationship is not clear and probably problem dependent.

7 Conclusions

In this paper it was shown how the Gröbner Basis technique can be used to test the reachability of a system over a polynomial ring explicitly. Moreover, when a system $\Sigma = (A, B)$ is reachable, the same computations can be used to construct a right-inverse of the matrix $(zI - A \mid B)$. In test-examples the algorithm was very effective, and showed a better performance than a more straightforward method, based on the minors of $(zI - A \mid B)$. Finally, in the non-reachable case it is possible to speed up the computation by doing the test recursively.

Acknowledgement I would like to thank Malo Hautus and Henri Huijberts for their valuable suggestions and help during the accomplishment of this paper.

References

[1] J.W. Brewer, J.W. Bunce and F.S. Van Vleck, *Linear systems over commutative rings.* Lecture notes in pure and applied mathematics, vol. 104. New York, Marcel Dekker, 1986.

[2] B. Buchberger, Some properties of Gröbner Bases for Polynomial Ideals. *ACM SIGSAM Bull.*, vol. 10, No. 4, pp. 19-24, 1976.

[3] B. Buchberger, Gröbner Bases: An Algorithmic Method in Polynomial Ideal Theory. In N.K. Bose (ed.), *Multidimensional Systems Theory*, pp. 184-232. Dordrecht, Reidel, 1985.

[4] K.B. Datta and M.L.J. Hautus, Decoupling of multivariable control systems over unique factorization domains. *SIAM J. Control and Optimization*, vol. 22, pp. 28-39, 1984.

[5] E. Emre, On necessary and sufficient conditions for regulation of linear systems over rings. *SIAM J. Control and Optimization*, vol. 20, pp. 155-160, 1982.

[6] K. Forsman, *Constructive Commutative Algebra in Nonlinear Control Theory.* Linköping Studies in Science and Technology, Dissertations, No. 261. Linköping University, 1991.

[7] L.C.G.J.M. Habets, *Stabilization of time-delay systems: An overview of the algebraic approach.* EUT Report 92-WSK-02, Eindhoven University of Technology, 1992.

[8] E.B. Lee and A.W. Olbrot, On reachability over polynomial rings and a related genericity problem. *Int. J. Systems Sci.*, vol 13, pp. 109-113, 1982.

[9] A.S. Morse, Ring models for delay-differential systems. *Automatica*, vol. 12, pp. 529-531, 1976.

[10] F. Pauer and M. Pfeifhofer, The theory of Gröbner Bases. *L'Enseignement Mathématique*, vol. 34, pp. 215-232, 1988.

[11] Y. Rouchaleau, Régulation statique et dynamique d'un système héréditaire. In A. Bensoussan and J.L. Lions (eds.), *Analysis and Optimization of systems*, LNCIS vol. 44, pp. 523-547. Berlin, Springer Verlag, 1982.

[12] E.D. Sontag, Linear systems over commutative rings: a survey. *Ricerche di Automatica*, vol. 7, pp. 1-34, 1976.

Proceedings of the
American Control Conference
San Francisco, California • June 1993

COPRIMENESS OF POLYTOPES OF POLYNOMIALS

F.J. Kraus†, M. Mansour† and V. Kučera‡

† Automatic Control Laboratory, Swiss Federal Institute of Technology
ETH-Zentrum, CH-8092 Zürich, Switzerland
‡ Czech Academy of Sciences, Prague, Czech Republic

Abstract

In this paper necessary and sufficient conditions for the coprimeness of polytopes of polynomials are derived. For the special case of interval polynomials simplifications are introduced.

1. Introduction

In the analysis and synthesis of linear control systems where the transfer function of the uncertain plant is given by the ratio of two uncertain polynomials, it is important to determine if there is pole-zero cancellation. The work in this paper is motivated by the work in [1] on the solution of the polynomial equation

$$a(s)x(s) + b(s)y(s) = c(s) \qquad (1)$$

where $a(s), b(s), c(s)$ are given polynomials and $x(s), y(s)$ are unknown polynomials, and by the value set concept in the robust stability problem [2, 3, 4].
In the robust stability problem with parameter uncertainty we consider a family of polynomials $a(s,\Gamma)$ whose coefficients lie in a certain domain Γ in the coefficient space and give conditions such that the roots of the whole family lie inside a domain D in the complex plane. The problem of the coprimeness of two families of polynomials $a(s,\Gamma_a)$ and $b(s,\Gamma_b)$ is to find necessary and sufficient conditions such that the domain of the roots R_a and R_b are disjoint.
In the following sections we consider the coprimenes of a fixed polynomial with an edge- or polytope-uncertainty polynomial, coprimeness of two edge-uncertainty polynomials as well as two polytope-uncertainty polynomials. After that, the special case of interval polynomials is considered where necessary conditions, sufficient conditions and simplified necessary and sufficient conditions are derived.

2. Mathematical Preliminaries

The problem of common factors of two polynomials

$$\begin{aligned} a(s) &= a_0 + a_1 s + \dots + a_{n-1}s^{n-1} + a_n s^n \quad (2)\\ b(s) &= b_0 + b_1 s + \dots + b_{m-1}s^{m-1} + b_m s^m \quad (3)\end{aligned}$$

is a well known problem [5]. The complete solution of this problem is given by Silvester's resultant matrix

$$S(a,b) = \left[\begin{array}{cccccccc} a_0 & a_1 & a_2 & & \cdots & a_n & & \\ & a_0 & a_1 & & \cdots & a_{n-1} & a_n & \\ & & \ddots & & & & \ddots & \\ 0 & & & a_0 & a_1 & & \cdots & a_n \\ b_0 & b_1 & b_2 & & \cdots & b_m & & \\ & b_0 & b_1 & & \cdots & b_{m-1} & b_m & \\ & & \ddots & & & & \ddots & \\ 0 & & & b_0 & b_1 & & \cdots & b_m \end{array}\right] \begin{array}{l} \left.\vphantom{\begin{array}{c}a\\a\\a\\a\end{array}}\right\} m \\ \left.\vphantom{\begin{array}{c}b\\b\\b\\b\end{array}}\right\} n \end{array} \qquad (4)$$

The singularity of the matrix S indicates the existence of a common factor of $a(s)$ and $b(s)$. More precisely the degree ν of the g.c.d. of $a(s)$ and $b(s)$ is

$$\nu = m + n - rank(S) \qquad (5)$$

Using $a(s), b(s)$ and assuming $m \geq n$ we can form an auxiliary polynomial $f(z)$ and the critical nonlinear Hurwitz stability condition [6] as

$$f(z) = a_0 + b_0 z + a_1 z^2 + b_1 z^3 + \dots + b_m z^{2m+1} \qquad (6)$$

$$\det H_{2m} = 0 \qquad (7)$$

where H_{2m} is the Hurwitz matrix of order $2m \times 2m$ associated with $f(z)$.
Reordering H_{2m} to the blockdiagonal form it is easy to show, that the condition (7) is equivalent to

$$\det \left[\begin{array}{ccc} S & \vdots & 0 \\ \cdots & \cdots & \cdots \\ *\dots* & \vdots & D_1 \end{array}\right] = 0 \qquad (8)$$

where D_1 is a lower triangular matrix with diagonal elements $b_m I$. Therefore, the singularity of S and the condition (7) are idential.
This observation suggests the use of methods known for Hurwitz stability of $f(z)$ to investigate common roots of $a(s)$ and $b(s)$. The relation between H_{2m} and the roots of $f(z)$ is given by Orlando's formula [7]

$$\det H_{2m} = (-1)^{2m(2m+1)} b_m^{2m} \prod_{i<j}^{1,\dots,2m+1} (z_i + z_j) \qquad (9)$$

where z_i and z_j are roots of $f(z)$. A sufficient condition for H_{2m} to vanish is that $f(z)$ has imaginary roots. The critical nonlinear Hurwitz stability condition plays a crucial role in checking Hurwitz stability of an edge of polynomials.

$$f(z,\lambda) = (1-\lambda)f_0(z) + \lambda f_1(z) \ ; \ 0 \le \lambda \le 1 \quad (10)$$

This condition can be formulated as an eigenvalue problem [8]

$$Eig\left[H_0^{-1}H_1\right] \notin \mathbf{R}^- \quad (11)$$

where $\mathbf{R}^-$ denotes the negative real numbers and H_0, H_1 are the Hurwitz matrices associated with $f_0(z)$ and $f_1(z)$ respectively.
It has been shown in [9] that every root of $a(s,\Gamma_a)$ on the boundary of the domain of the roots R_a comes from a polynomial on one of the edges of the polytope Γ_a. This is the well known edge theorem which shall be used in the sequel.

3. Coprimeness Conditions

In this section we will investigate the existence of common factors for different combinations of uncertain polynomial families $a(s,\Gamma_a)$ and $b(s,\Gamma_b)$ where Γ_a and Γ_b are the regions of the uncertain coefficients of $a(s) \in a(s,\Gamma_a)$ and $b(s) \in b(s,\Gamma_b)$ respectively.

3.1. Edge Polynomials & Fixed One

Let $a(s,\alpha)$ be an edge polynomial family given by

$$a(s,\alpha) = (1-\alpha)a_0(s) + \alpha a_1(s) \qquad 0 \le \alpha \le 1 \quad (12)$$

where $a_0(s)$ and $a_1(s)$ are two fixed polynomials. Let $b(s)$ be also a fixed polynomial. This is the simplest case we consider.
Using the Silvester resultant matrix we obtain

$$S(a,b) = (1-\alpha)S(a_0,b) + \alpha S(a_1,b) \quad (13)$$

As $a_0(s), a_1(s), b(s)$ are fixed polynomials, S is just a function of α. To prove the nonsingularity of S, we use the idea of [8] and the equivalence of S and H_{2m} to get the following result.

Theorem 1: *Assume $a_0(s)$ and $b(s)$ are coprime. Then the polynomial family $a(s,\alpha)$ and $b(s)$ are coprime everywhere, if and only if*

$$Eig\left[S^{-1}(a_0,b)S(a_1,b)\right] \notin \mathbf{R}^- \quad (14)$$

There is also a simpler method to prove the coprimeness using the fact of $b(s)$ fixed. Let σ_i, $i = 1...m$ be the roots of $b(s)$. Then to check the coprimeness it is sufficient to show, that σ_i, $i = 1...m$ is not a root for any member of the family $a(s,\alpha)$. We get

Theorem 2: *The polynomial family $a(s,\alpha)$ and $b(s)$ are coprime if and only if for all $i = 1,2,...,m$*

$$\frac{a_0(\sigma_i)}{a_1(\sigma_i)} \notin \mathbf{R}^- \quad (15)$$

Proof: If $a(\sigma_i,\alpha)$ vanishes then $a_0(\sigma_i)/a_1(\sigma_i) = -\alpha/(1-\alpha)$ which is real negative. ∎

This test required the determination of the zeros of a polynomial. In general it is less accurate than the eigenvalue problem of theorem 1.

3.2. Polytope of Polynomials & Fixed One

In this subsection we generalize the results of the previous one. The polytope family

$$a(s,\Gamma) = \sum_{i=1}^{\nu} \gamma_i a_i(s) \quad (16)$$

with $\gamma_i \ge 0$ and $\sum_{i=1}^{\nu} \gamma_i = 1$ and $b(s)$ has a common factor if and only if some of the roots σ_i of $b(s)$ are also roots of $a(s,\Gamma)$. Hence we obtain

Theorem 3: *The polytope family $a(s,\Gamma)$ and $b(s)$ are coprime if and only if for all $\sigma_i, i = 1,2,...,m$ of $b(s)$ the polyeder*

$$a(\sigma_i,\Gamma) \not\ni 0 \quad (17)$$

Proof: With $s = \sigma_i$ we obtain the value set of $a(s,\Gamma)$ by $conv\{a_j(\sigma_i), j = 1,2,...,\nu\}$. This is a polyeder with at most ν corners in the complex plane. Because of the continuity of the mapping, every point inside of this polyeder correspond to at least one family member. If the origin is inside , then there exists a polynomial in the family such that $a(\sigma_i,\gamma^*) = 0$ and the coprimeness is lost. ∎

Let Γ_c denote the set of corners of Γ. Then it is easy to prove that only the corner polynomials must be checked.

Proposition 1: *The polyeder $a(\sigma_i,\Gamma)$ does not include the origin, if and only if there exists a straight line through the origin such that all corners $a(\sigma_i,\gamma); \gamma \in \Gamma_c$ lie strict on one side of this line.*

Note that the corners of the polyeder are a subset of the map of Γ_c. In this formulation the test of coprimeness is idential with the classification problem. It can be solved by linear programming methods.

3.3. Edge Polynomials & Edge Polynomials

In this subsection we shall investigate two different cases of edge polynomials

$$a(s,\alpha) = (1-\alpha)a_0(s) + \alpha a_1(s) \quad (18)$$
$$b(s,\beta) = (1-\beta)b_0(s) + \beta b_1(s) \quad (19)$$
$$0 \le \alpha \le 1 \text{ and } 0 \le \beta \le 1$$

In the first case there exists a relation between α, β say $\beta = \gamma(\alpha)$. The simplest one $\beta = \alpha$ shall be discussed in detail. But generalization to, for example, a polynomial dependency is easy to handle. In the second case α and β are independent.

a) $\alpha = \beta$

For the Silvester resultant matrix we obtain

$$S(a,b) = (1-\alpha)S(a_0,b_0) + \alpha S(a_1,b_1) \qquad (20)$$

which is an affine function of α. Thereby $S(a_0,b_0)$ and $S(a_1,b_1)$ are two fixed nonsingular matrices as coprimeness of (a_0,b_0) and (a_1,b_1) is assumed. The eigenvalue formulation (14) can be applied to get

Theorem 4: *The two edge polynomials $a(s,\alpha)$, $b(s,\alpha)$ are coprime if and only if*

$$Eig\left[S^{-1}(a_0,b_0)S(a_1,b_1)\right] \notin \mathbf{R}^- \qquad (21)$$

b) α and β independent.

Here the Silvester resultant matrix is given by

$$S(a,b) = S_0 + \alpha S_1 + \beta S_2 \qquad (22)$$

As far as we know there is no generalization of the eigenvalue problem for two independent variables. However, we can use the same procedure as in the case of stability testing for polynomial coefficient dependency [10].

1) Check corners for coprimeness

2) Check coprimeness of all edges for $\alpha \in \{0,1\}$ or $\beta \in \{0,1\}$. Necessary condition is, that $\det S$ has the same sign for all corners

3) Compute symbolically $p(\alpha,\beta) = \det S(a,b)$. Thereby $p(\alpha,\beta)$ is a polynomial in α,β whose structure can be given a priori

4) Solve the two equations

$$\frac{\partial p(\alpha,\beta)}{\partial \alpha} = 0 \quad , \quad \frac{\partial p(\alpha,\beta)}{\partial \beta} = 0 \qquad (23)$$

If a local extremum exists inside the region $0 < \alpha < 1, 0 < \beta < 1$ say at α^*, β^* and the associated value of $p(\alpha^*,\beta^*)$ is nonpositive for $p(0,0) > 0$ or is nonnegative for $p(0,0) < 0$, then at least one point with $p(\alpha,\beta) = 0$ exists inside the allowed parameter region and the coprimeness is lost.

In a more graphic-numerical oriented procedure one can use the root locus idea. Coprimeness of $a(s,\alpha), b(s,\beta)$ is identical with no intersection points of the two associated root loci.

3.4. Polytope of Polynomials & Polytope of Polynomials

Given $a(s,\Gamma_a), b(s,\Gamma_b)$ with two coefficient polytopes Γ_a, Γ_b. Associated with each is a root region R_a, R_b respectively. If there are no points in common i.e. $R_a \cap R_b = \emptyset$ where $\emptyset$ denotes the empty set, both families are coprime. From the edge theorem [9] we know, that the root boundary can be obtained just from the roots of the edges. Denote Γ_{ae}, Γ_{be} the sets of exposed edges and Γ_{ac}, Γ_{bc} the sets of corners of Γ_a and Γ_b respectively. Then we get

Theorem 5: *The families of polynomials $a(s,\Gamma_a)$, $b(s,\Gamma_b)$ are coprime if and only if*

i) $a(s,\Gamma_a)$ and $b(s,\gamma)$ are coprime for a $\gamma \in \Gamma_{bc}$

ii) $b(s,\Gamma_b)$ and $a(s,\gamma)$ are coprime for a $\gamma \in \Gamma_{ac}$

iii) $a(s,\mu)$ and $b(s,\nu)$ are coprime for any combination of the edges $\mu \in \Gamma_{ae}$ and $\nu \in \Gamma_{be}$

Proof: There are three different cases to check:

a) $R_b \subset R_a \;,\; \partial R_a \cap \partial R_b = \emptyset$

b) $R_a \subset R_b \;,\; \partial R_a \cap \partial R_b = \emptyset$

c) $\partial R_a \cap \partial R_b \neq \emptyset$

where ∂R denotes the boundary of R. With i) and ii) we check the possibility of case a) or case b). Otherwise, the only possibility for $\partial R_a \cap \partial R_b \neq \emptyset$ are common points on the root boundaries. Because of the edge theorem [9] there are a subset of the roots of the edges. Hence iii) covers the last case. ∎

From the practical point of view, it will be more suitable to check in i) and ii) not only one but all the corners. Also a significant reduction of iii) can be obtained if not all the exposed edges in the coefficient space are used but only those which are exposed in the value set. We give such a reduction in section 4 for the case of interval polynomials.

4. Special Cases and Simplifications

In this section we consider the special case of interval polynomials

$$\begin{aligned} a(s) &= a_0 + a_1 s + a_2 s^2 + a_3 s^3 + \ldots + a_n s^n \quad (24) \\ b(s) &= b_0 + b_1 s + b_2 s^2 + b_3 s^3 + \ldots + b_m s^m \quad (25) \\ &\text{where} \quad \underline{a}_i \le a_i \le \overline{a}_i \qquad i = 1,2,\ldots,n \\ &\text{and} \quad \underline{b}_j \le b_j \le \overline{b}_j \qquad j = 1,2,\ldots,m \end{aligned}$$

and give necessary conditions as well as sufficient conditions for the coprimeness of two interval polynomials. Also we show some simplifications w.r.t. the result obtained in the previous section.

4.1. Necessary Conditions

Theorem 6: *The interval polynomials $a(s)$ and $b(s)$ do not have common positive (negative) real roots if and only if for $\forall\lambda > 0$, ($\forall\lambda < 0$)*

$$\underline{a}(\lambda) = 0 \;\; or \;\; \overline{a}(\lambda) = 0 \qquad \underline{b}(\lambda)\,\overline{b}(\lambda) > 0$$
$$\underline{b}(\lambda) = 0 \;\; or \;\; \overline{b}(\lambda) = 0 \qquad \underline{a}(\lambda)\,\overline{a}(\lambda) > 0$$

thereby denote $\underline{a}(s), \overline{a}(s)$

$$\begin{aligned} \text{for } \lambda > 0 \quad \ldots \quad & \underline{a}(s) = \underline{a}_0 + \underline{a}_1 s + \underline{a}_2 s^2 + \underline{a}_3 s^3 + \ldots \\ \ldots \quad & \overline{a}(s) = \overline{a}_0 + \overline{a}_1 s + \overline{a}_2 s^2 + \overline{a}_3 s^3 + \ldots \\ \text{for } \lambda < 0 \quad \ldots \quad & \underline{a}(s) = \underline{a}_0 + \overline{a}_1 s + \underline{a}_2 s^2 + \overline{a}_3 s^3 + \ldots \\ \ldots \quad & \overline{a}(s) = \overline{a}_0 + \underline{a}_1 s + \overline{a}_2 s^2 + \underline{a}_3 s^3 + \ldots \end{aligned}$$

Proof: For no common negative real roots we consider the auxiliary polynomial $f(z)$

$$\begin{aligned} f(z) &= a_0 + b_0 z + a_1 z^2 + b_1 z^3 + \ldots + b_m z^{2m+1} \\ &= h(z^2) + z g(z^2) = a(z^2) + z\, b(z^2) \qquad (26) \end{aligned}$$

$f(z)$ has imaginary roots if and only if $h(\lambda)$ and $g(\lambda)$ i.e. $a(s)$ and $b(s)$ have common negative real roots. As the value set of $f(z)$ with $z = j\omega$ is a rectangle parallel to the axes [11], then $f(z)$ does not have imaginary root if and only if the origin does not lie on the four edges of the rectangle.

For no common positive real roots we consider the auxiliary polynomial

$$\begin{aligned} f^*(z) = a_0 + b_0 z - a_1 z^2 - b_1 z^3 + a_2 z^4 + b_2 z^5 - \\ - \ldots + (-1)^m b_m z^{2m+1} = h^*(z^2) + z g^*(z^2) \; (27) \end{aligned}$$

The proof is similar as the previous one with $-\lambda$ instead of λ. ∎

4.2. Sufficient Conditions

Theorem 7: *The interval polynomials $a(s)$ and $b(s)$ do not have common real roots if the four Kharitonov polynomials of $f(s)$ are either Hurwitz stable or Hurwitz antistable (all roots in the right half plane).*

Proof: The Hurwitz stability of the four Kharitonov polynomials is necessary and sufficient for the Hurwitz stability of the whole family [12]. According to Hermite-Bieler theorem $h(\lambda)$ and $g(\lambda)$ have simple negative real roots and interlacing which means that $a(s)$ and $b(s)$ have no common roots.

The antistability of the four Kharitonov polynomials means the antistability of the whole family, which according to an argument similar to Hermite-Bieler theorem $h(\lambda)$ and $g(\lambda)$ have simple positive real roots and interlacing. This means that $a(s)$ and $b(s)$ have no common roots. ∎

4.3. Reduction of the # of Critical Edges

The number of pairs of edges of Γ_a, Γ_b can be rather high. Therefore, a reduction of the number of edges which we have to check for coprimeness is very important from the practical point of view.

For the coprimeness test we need to use only such edges that supply a part of the root boundary. We call these the critical edges. For a given domain D only exposed edges of the value set w.r.t. ∂D determine the D-stability. Suppose now we have D that covers the root domain R_a of $a(s, \Gamma_a)$ i.e. $R_a \subset D$. Then all the edges of Γ_a, which are the preimages of the exposed edges of the value set of $a(s, \Gamma_a)$ w.r.t. ∂D are the critical edges. If we have no a priori knowledge about R_a we use the entire complex plain as D. The determination of the set of exposed edges w.r.t. ∂D is discussed in [3]. The generalization for any D, i.e. the partitioning of the complex plain in regions with the same set of exposed edges is discussed in [13]. For the case of interval polynomials the results in [14] can be used. In this case the partitions are conic sectors obtained from the root loci of

$$\frac{1}{s}, \frac{1}{s^2}, \frac{1}{s^3}, \ldots, \frac{1}{s^n}$$

The boundaries are straight lines through the origin whose angles are given by

$$\pi \left\{ 0, 1, \frac{i}{k} \mid 0 < i < k;\; k = 2, 3, \ldots, n \right\}$$

In every sector $2(n+1)$ exposed edges result. Without any a priori knowledge of R_a we have to use all the sectors. The union of the exposed edges of all the sectors are critical edges, (some of the exposed edges in different sectors can be the same. After the elimination of the repeated ones we obtain the desired minimal set).

The following table summarizes the obtained reduction for different non monic polynomial of order n,

n	2	3	4	5	6	7	8	9
K_1	12	32	80	192	448	1024	2304	5120
K_2	12	32	60	120	168	288	396	560
K_3	10	24	44	80	120	184	260	360

whereby K_1 is the total number of edges, K_2 is the union of exposed edges from the value sets and K_3 after the elimination of repeated edges [14] . The set of the critical edges can be given in advance independent of the actual parameter values.

Further reduction is possible using a priori knowledge of R_a. For example if $a(s, \Gamma_a)$ is investigated for Hurwitz stability only half of the sectors (left half plane) is to be used. This reduces the set of the critical edges to $K_3(n)/2$, similarly for $b(s, \Gamma_b)$. Furthermore, considering the robust stability of $a(s, \Gamma_a)$ w.r.t. some sector $\boldsymbol{S}$ we need to investigate only such exposed edges of $a(s, \Gamma_a)$ and $b(s, \Gamma_b)$ which are associated with partitions inside of $\boldsymbol{S}$. Obviously zeros of $b(s, \Gamma_b)$ outside of $\boldsymbol{S}$ cannot coincide with any zero of $a(s, \Gamma_a)$.

5. Example

Consider the coprimeness of the two edge polynomials

$$\begin{aligned} a(s, \alpha) &= s^2 + 4(1-\alpha)s + 4 \quad 0 \le \alpha \le 1 \\ b(s, \beta) &= s^2 + 2s + 1 + 6\beta \quad\;\; 0 \le \beta \le 1 \end{aligned}$$

Then the associated root loci are :

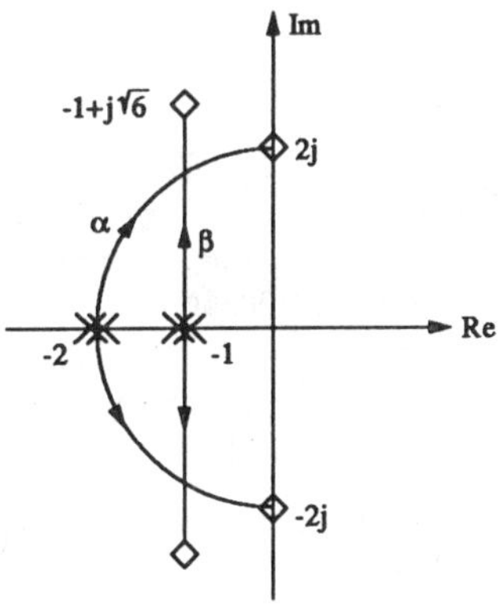

A common root exists for $\alpha^* = \frac{1}{2}, \beta^* = \frac{1}{2}$. Therefore, both families are not coprime. For the algebraic solution we obtain

$$p(\alpha,\beta) = \det \begin{bmatrix} 4 & 0 & 1-6\beta & 0 \\ 4-4\alpha & 4 & 2 & 1+6\beta \\ 1 & 4-4\alpha & 1 & 2 \\ 0 & 1 & 0 & 1 \end{bmatrix}$$

$$= 1 + 8\alpha + 12\beta + 16\alpha^2 + 36\beta^2 - 144\alpha\beta + 96\alpha^2\beta$$

This necessary condition at the corners is fulfilled

$$\begin{aligned} S_0 &= p(0,0) = 1 \ , \ S_1 = p(0,1) = 49 \\ S_2 &= p(1,0) = 25 \ , \ S_3 = p(1,1) = 25 \end{aligned}$$

For the edges we obtain

$$\begin{aligned} Eig\left[S_0^{-1}S_1\right] &= \{1,1,7,7\} \\ Eig\left[S_0^{-1}S_2\right] &= \{1,1,5,5\} \\ Eig\left[S_3^{-1}S_1\right] &= \{1,1,-0.76 \pm 1.1758i\} \\ Eig\left[S_3^{-1}S_2\right] &= \{1,1,-0.28 \pm 0.96i\} \end{aligned}$$

It is clear that the coprimeness of corners and edges is guaranteed. Inside of the α, β region we have

$$\frac{\partial p}{\partial \alpha} = 8 + 32\alpha - 144\beta + 192\alpha\beta = 0 \quad (28)$$

$$\frac{\partial p}{\partial \beta} = 12 + 72\beta - 144\alpha + 96\alpha^2 = 0 \quad (29)$$

This gives the solution $\alpha^* = \frac{1}{2}$, $\beta^* = \frac{1}{2}$ and $p\left(\frac{1}{2}, \frac{1}{2}\right) = 0$. Therefore according to the results in section 3, the two families are not coprime.

6. Conclusion

Necessary and sufficient conditions for the coprimeness of two polynomial families whose coefficients lie in polytopes are derived. It is shown that for the special case of interval polynomials a simplification can be obtained. Also simple necessary conditions as well as sufficient conditions can be obtained in this case. The result in this paper can be used in the analysis and synthesis of control systems.

References

[1] V. Kučera, *Discrete Linear Control: The Polynomial Equation Approach*, Wiley, Chichester, 1979.

[2] S. Dasgupta, P. J. Parker, B. D. O. Anderson, F. J. Kraus, and M. Mansour, "Frequency domain conditions for the robust stability of linear and nonlinear systems", *IEEE Transactions on Circuits and Systems*, vol. 38, pp. 389–397, 1991.

[3] F. J. Kraus and W. Truöl, "Robust stability of control systems with polytopical uncertainty: a Nyquist approach", *International Journal of Control*, vol. 53, pp. 967–983, 1991.

[4] M. Mansour, "Robust stability in systems described by rational functions", *in Control and Dynamic Systems*, vol. 51, pp. 79–128. Academic Press, 1992.

[5] S. Barnett, *Polynomials and linear control systems*, Marcel Dekker Inc., 1983.

[6] E. I. Jury, *Inners and Stability of Dynamic Systems*, R. E. Krieger Publ. Co., Florida, 1982.

[7] F. R. Gantmacher, *The theory of matrices*, Chelsea Publ. Co., New York, 2 edition, 1960.

[8] S. Bialas, "A necessary and sufficient condition for the stability of convex combinations of stable polynomials and matrices", *Bulletin of the Polish Academy of Sciences, Technical Sciences*, vol. 33, pp. 473–480, 1985.

[9] A. C. Bartlett, C. V. Hollot, and H. Lin, "Root locations of an entire polytope of polynomials: it suffices to check the edges", *Mathematics of Control, Signals and Systems*, vol. 1, pp. 61–71, 1988.

[10] M. Mansour and F.J. Kraus, "Robust stability of systems with nonlinear parameter dependency", *Proceedings of the 28th IEEE Conference on Decision and Control*, pp. 1931–1933, 1989.

[11] S. Dasgupta, "Kharitonov's theorem revised", *Systems & Control Letters*, vol. 11, pp. 381–384, 1988.

[12] V. L. Kharitonov, "Asymptotic stability of an equilibrium position of a family of systems of linear differential equations", *Differentsial'nye Uravneniya*, vol. 14, pp. 2086–2088, 1978.

[13] F. J. Kraus and M. Mansour, "Robust discrete control", *Proceedings of the European Control Conference, Grenoble*, 1991.

[14] F. J. Kraus and M. Mansour, "On robust stability of discrete systems", *Proceedings of the 29th IEEE Conference on Decision and Control*, vol. 2, pp. 421–422, 1990.

Proceedings of the
American Control Conference
San Francisco, California • June 1993

A STOCHASTIC DIFFERENTIAL GAMES APPROACH TO MIXED H_2/H_∞-CONTROL†

B. Bernhardsson
IMA, Univ. of Minnesota,
514 Vincent Hall, 206 Church Street S.E.,
Minneapolis, MN 55455
E-mail: bob@control.lth.se

P. Hagander
Department of Automatic Control
Lund Institute of Technology
P.O.Box 118, S-221 00 Lund, Sweden
Phone: +46 46 108786

1. Introduction

Standard H_∞-control can be applied to disturbance attenuation design, but it has then fundamental practical limitations. In H_∞-control the system is

$$\begin{aligned} \dot{x} &= Ax + B_1 d + B_2 u \\ y &= Cx + De \end{aligned} \tag{1}$$

Here d and e denote process and measurement disturbances, y measurement and $u = Ky$ control signals. The H_∞-control problem now optimizes system performance against worst disturbances d and e

$$\min_K \max_{d,e} \|z\|_2^2, \qquad \text{when } \|d\|_2^2 + \|e\|_2^2 \leq 1$$

where z describes some signals to be minimized. The constraint means that process disturbances and measurement noise can not both be large. It is unnatural to couple process disturbance and measurement noise in this way. It is better to assume that some signals are stochastic.

To make such a combination possible is now the goal for much research. There have been several slightly different attempts. The most promising result seems to be the three coupled Riccati equations developed by [5]. A similar result was obtained in [6]. In [3] a classical stochastic games approach is used to determine the finite time horizon version of these equations both in continuous and discrete time by completion of squares. The term *min-mix-control* is coined to emphasize the game theory background. The cornerstone is a generalization of a recent dynamic programming separation principle [2]. The approach makes it possible to unify several results and to gain insight. Explicit formulas for the value of the game are also determined. A simple but rich example illustrates the results.

2. A Recent Result

In the system (1) we replace $B_1 d$ by $B_0 w_0 + B_1 w_1$ and $Cx + De$ by $C_2 x + D_{20} w_0 + D_{21} w_1$, where w_0 is white noise. Introduce also $z^T = [(C_1 x)^T, u^T]$, and the game theory problem [5]

$$J = \min_K \sup_{w_1} E_{w_0} \left\{ \|z\|_2^2 - \gamma^2 \|w_1\|_2^2 \right\} \tag{2}$$

where the proper controller K also provides internal stability. For an early discussion on the importance of the information structures see [1]. Actually deterministic unit spectra signals w_0 are used in [5] instead of white noise. Their main result is

THEOREM 1—(Doyle *et al.*)
Given $\gamma > 0$, there exists a controller $K(s)$ which solves (2), if the following conditions hold:

- There exists a matrix $X \geq 0$ such that

  $$0 = A^T X + XA + C_1^T C_1 + X(\gamma^{-2} B_1 B_1^T - B_2 B_2^T) X$$

  and $A_c = A + B_1 F_1 + B_2 F_2$ is stable.
- There exist L, $Y \geq 0$, and $P \geq 0$ which satisfy

  $$\begin{aligned} 0 &= Y\{B_{0L} D_{20}^T + PC_2^T + \gamma^{-2} P(XB_1 + YB_{1L}) D_{21}^T\} \\ 0 &= YA_e + A_e^T Y + F_2^T F_2 - \gamma^{-2} Y B_{1L} B_{1L}^T Y \\ 0 &= A_e P + P A_e^T + B_{0L} B_{0L}^T \end{aligned}$$

  and $A_e = A + LC_2^T + \gamma^{-2} B_{1L}(B_1^T X + B_{1L}^T Y)$ is stable.

When these conditions hold, one such controller is

$$\begin{aligned} \dot{\check{x}} &= A\check{x} + B_2 u + B_1 F_1 \check{x} - L(y - C_2 \check{x} - D_{21} F_1 \check{x}) \\ u &= F_2 \check{x} \end{aligned}$$

The following compact notation is introduced here

$$\begin{aligned} B_{0L} &= B_0 + LD_{20}, \quad B_{1L} = B_1 + LD_{21} \\ F_1 &= \gamma^{-2} B_1^T X, \quad F_2 = -B_2^T X \end{aligned}$$

Warning. In the conference papers [4] and [7] these equations contained algebraic mistakes. The mistakes are corrected in the unpublished manuscript [5].

Remark. The coupling equation

$$0 = Y\{B_{0L} D_{20}^T + PC_2^T + \gamma^{-2} P(XB_1 + YB_{1L}) D_{21}^T\} \tag{3}$$

is linear in L, and for $Y > 0$, $B_1 D_{21}^T = 0$, and $B_0 D_{20}^T = 0$ it simplifies to

$$0 = PC_2^T + \gamma^{-2} PYLD_{21} D_{21}^T + LD_{20} D_{20}^T \tag{4}$$

3. A Simple Example

The feedback problem in Figure 1 gives a lot of insight into the behavior of min-mix control. The problem is given by

$$\begin{aligned} \dot{x} &= -x + w_1 + u, \quad x(0) = 0 \\ z &= \begin{pmatrix} x \\ u \end{pmatrix}, \quad y = x + \sigma w_0 \end{aligned} \tag{5}$$

† This work was partly supported by the Swedish Research Council for Engineering Sciences under contract 91-721

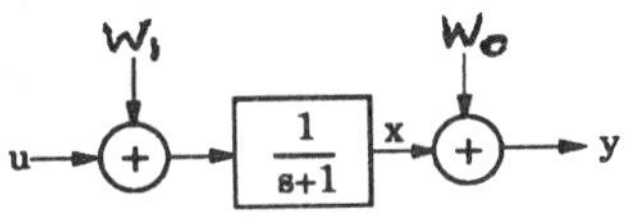

Figure 1. The system in Example 1

For large γ, actually $\gamma > \gamma_o = 1$, the min-mix controller is $K(s) = 0$, and the worst disturbance is $w_1 = 0$. The value of the game is then zero. For $1/\sqrt{2} < \gamma < 1$ there is a trade off between counteracting w_1 and introducing measurement noise w_0 into the process. For $\gamma < \gamma_\infty = 1/\sqrt{2}$ no controller could make the loss finite for the worst disturbance w_1, not even if the controller had full information of x and w_1. The min-mix equations of Theorem 1 reduce to

$$\begin{aligned} 0 &= -2X + 1 - X^2(1-\gamma^{-2}) \\ 0 &= 2A_eY + X^2 - \gamma^{-2}Y^2 \\ 0 &= 2A_eP + L^2\sigma^2, \quad L\sigma^2 = -P \\ A_e &= -1 + L + \gamma^{-2}(X+Y) \\ A_c &= -1 + (\gamma^{-2} - 1)X \end{aligned} \tag{6}$$

The controller is a strictly proper first order system

$$\begin{aligned} \dot{\hat{x}} &= A_c\hat{x} - L(y - \hat{x}) \\ u &= -X\hat{x} \end{aligned}$$

From (6) we get two solutions: $(L, P) = (0, 0)$ or $(L, P) = (2A_e, -2A_e\sigma^2)$. The solution with $L = 0$ can be used if $\gamma > \gamma_o = 1$. For $\gamma \searrow \gamma_o$ we then get that $A_e \nearrow 0$.

The other solution is valid for $\gamma_\infty < \gamma < \gamma_o$. For $\gamma \searrow \gamma_\infty = 1/\sqrt{2}$ we get $A_e = -\sqrt{2-\gamma^{-2}} \nearrow 0$ and $A_c \searrow -(\sqrt{7}+2)/3$, while $A_e \nearrow 0$ for $\gamma \nearrow \gamma_o = 1$.

The following situation is therefore verified: For $\gamma_\infty < \gamma < \gamma_o$ we use the solution $L = 2A_e$. Notice that L is independent of σ, which may be surprising. For large $\gamma > \gamma_o$ open loop control $L = 0$ should be used.

4. Completion of Squares Solution

To obtain the finite time horizon solution using Dynamic Programming like in [3] we introduce the "clever choices"

$$\begin{aligned} \dot{\hat{x}} &= A\hat{x} + B_2u + B_1F_1\hat{x} - L(y - C_2\hat{x} - D_{21}F_1\hat{x}) \\ u^* &= F_2\hat{x} \\ w_1^* &= F_1x + \gamma^{-2}B_{1L}^TY\tilde{x} \\ V(t, x, \tilde{x}) &= x^TXx + \tilde{x}^TY\tilde{x} + v(t) \\ v(t) &= \int_t^{t_f} \mathrm{Tr}\left(B_0^TXB_0 + B_{0L}^TYB_{0L}\right) d\tau \end{aligned} \tag{7}$$

where $\tilde{x} = x - \hat{x}$. Then we modify the symmetric X, Y, P–equations of Theorem 1 to dynamic Riccati equations:

$$\begin{aligned} -\dot{X} &= XA + A^TX + C_1^TC_1 - X(B_2B_2^T - \gamma^{-2}B_1B_1^T)X \\ -\dot{Y} &= YA_e + A_e^TY + XB_2B_2^TX - \gamma^{-2}YB_{1L}B_{1L}^TY \\ \dot{P} &= A_eP + PA_e^T + B_{0L}B_{0L}^T \\ X(t_f) &= 0, \quad Y(t_f) = 0, \quad P(t_0) = 0 \end{aligned}$$

Now completion of squares gives

$$\begin{aligned} f &:= \underset{w_0}{E}\left\{\frac{dV}{dt} + x^TC_1^TC_1x + u^Tu - \gamma^2w_1^Tw_1\right\} \\ &= |u - u^* - F_2\tilde{x}|^2 - |F_2\tilde{x}|^2 - \gamma^2|w_1 - w_1^*|^2 \end{aligned}$$

$w_1 = w_1^*$. The linear equation (3) for L guarantees that $\mathrm{Cov}(u - u^*, \tilde{x}|y^t) = 0$ in case of $w_1 = w_1^*$. Therefore $\min_u E_x f = 0$ is achieved for $u = u^*$. These are the two requirements in the separation principle in [2]. Notice the important second term in the expression (7) for w_1^*.

The game has the saddlepoint $\{u = u^*, w_1 = w_1^*\}$ and the value $J = V(t_0, x(t_0), \tilde{x}(t_0))$, provided the Riccati equations have solution over the interval (t_0, t_f). For the saddlepoint the closed loop dynamics is

$$\frac{d}{dt}\begin{pmatrix} x \\ \tilde{x} \end{pmatrix} = A_{cl}\begin{pmatrix} x \\ \tilde{x} \end{pmatrix} + \begin{pmatrix} B_0 \\ B_{0L} \end{pmatrix} w_0$$

$$A_{cl} = \begin{pmatrix} A_c & B_2B_2^TX + \gamma^{-2}B_1B_{1L}^TY \\ 0 & A_e \end{pmatrix}$$

5. Value of the Game for the Example

Consider $\gamma_\infty < \gamma < \gamma_o$. The finite horizon equations give with $P(t_0) = 0$, $P = L = 0$ as the optimal solution, unless the time interval is long enough for the Y-equation to explode. For time intervals that are long enough, the second stationary solution is obtained from the dynamic Riccati equation twopoint boundary-value problem after transients at both ends of the time interval. The value of the game for $x(t_0) = 0$, $\tilde{x}(t_0) = 0$ is $J = \int_{t_0}^{t_f} \sigma^2L^2Y\, d\tau$ with $J > 0$ for the second solution, $L \neq 0$ and $Y > 0$.

6. Conclusions

We strongly believe that intuition from the finite-time horizon results is necessary to fully understand the infinite horizon case, and that further study of the finite time horizon case will be rewarding. This is an open issue for future research.

7. References

[1] R. D. Behn and Y. C. Ho. "On a class of linear stochastic differential games." *IEEE Transactions on Automatic Control*, **AC-13:3**, pp. 227–240, 1968.

[2] P. Bernhard. "Information and strategies in dynamic games." *SIAM Journal on Control and Optimization*, **30:1**, pp. 212–228, 1992.

[3] B. Bernhardsson. *Theory for Digital and Robust Control of Linear Systems*. PhD thesis, Lund Institute of Technology, 1992.

[4] J. Doyle, K. Zhou, and B. Bodenheimer. "Optimal control with mixed H_2 and H_∞ performance objectives." In *American Control Conference*, pp. 2065–2070, 1989.

[5] J. Doyle, K. Zhou, K. Glover, and B. Bodenheimer. "Mixed H_2 and H_∞ performance objectives, ii: Optimal control.". Submitted, 1992.

[6] Nikoukhah, R. and F. Delebecque (1992): "On a stochastic differential game and its relationsip with mixed H_2/H_∞-control." In *American Control Conference*, pp. 1380–1384.

[7] K. Zhou, J. Doyle, K. Glover, and B. Bodenheimer. "Mixed mixed H_2 and H_∞ control." In *American Control Conference*, pp. 2502–2507, 1990.

Proceedings of the
American Control Conference
San Francisco, California • June 1993

Convergent On-Line Identification in H_∞ for Continuous Systems

Fu-Ming Lee[1], *I-Kong Fong*[1], and *Li-Chen Fu*[1,2]

Room 331, Department of Electrical Engineering[1]
Department of Computer Science and Information Engineering[2]
National Taiwan University, Taipei, Taiwan
10617, Republic of China

Abstract

In this paper, we formulate and solve two related on-line identification problems for stable linear time-invarient continuous systems. The first problem involves on-line identification of frequency responses of a system at an arbitrary finite set of frequency points from the available input and disturbed output timed data. The second problem involves on-line identification of the system model in H_∞ also from the available input and disturbed output timed data. Concrete convergent on-line algorithms are specified for these two problems. Each of these algorithms provides on-line not only an estimate of the system but also an explicit upper bound on the worst-case deterministic identification error.

1 Introduction

Due to the increasing need on relating the identification process to the design procedure of a robust controller for a system, considerable amount of research on system identification has already been under way to furnish results that not only give a nominal system model but also an upper bound on the model uncertainty, e.g., [2]-[4] [6]-[11] [13] [14] [16]. This research field is referred to as system identification for robust control design. We regard our paper as a contribution to this field.

The problem of "system identification in H_∞", which was introduced by Helmicki *et al.* [5] for continuous systems, is a particular worst-case deterministic identification problem. This problem is inspired by the recent advances in H_∞ robust control literature, and its formulation requires prior data of the frequency response of an unknown stable system at a specific finite set of frequency points. Generally speaking, the problem is to find an algorithm which maps the given data into an identified system model such that the worst-case identification error (over all possible data errors and all admissible unknown systems) converges to zero in H_∞-norm as both the data errors go to zero and the number of data points goes to infinity. Further, it is also an interest of this problem to derive an explicit upper H_∞-norm bound on the worst-case identification error. To date, several convergent algorithms with explicit error bounds have been proposed for solving the system identification in H_∞ problem, e.g. [1] [5]. However, they are classified as off-line algorithms because all the frequency response data are assumed priorly given.

In this paper, we formally formulate two related on-line identification problems for stable linear time-invariant single-input single-output continuous systems. These problems are a generalization of our recent paper for discrete systems [10]. The first problem involves on-line identification of frequency responses of a system at an arbitrary finite set of frequency points from the available input-output timed data. This problem will be referred to here as "on-line point-frequency response identification" (OLPFRI) and it is solved by using the continuous-time Fourier transform concept. The second problem formulated in this paper has a two-step structure. In the first step of the problem, the available input-output timed data are on-line mapped into finite point-frequency response estimates, and then they are on-line mapped into an identified system model in H_∞ in the second step. This problem will be referred to here as "on-line system identification in H_∞" (OLSIH) and it is solved by composing any arbitrary OLPFRI algorithm with any arbitrary system identification in H_∞ algorithm. Concrete on-line algorithms are specified for these two problems. Each of these algorithms provides on-line not only an estimate of the system but also an explicit upper bound on the worst-case deterministic identification error. The explicit upper bound is guaranteed to be monotonically decreasing with respect to time. Furthermore, the on-line algorithm is convergent for a large class of applied inputs.

The layout of this paper is as follows. In Section 2, notations are established and the problem of system identification in H_∞ is described. In Section 3, we formulate two related on-line identification problems precisely. In Section 4, concrete convergent on-line identification algorithems with explicit error bounds are specified for those problems fomulated in Section 3. To the end, Section 5 gives a conclusion.

2 Preliminaries

2.1 Notations

Let $\mathbf{I}_0$, $\mathbf{I}_+$, $\mathbf{R}_0$, $\mathbf{R}$, and $\mathbf{C}$ denote the set of nonnegative integers, positive integers, nonnegative real numbers, real numbers, and complex numbers, respectively. Let $\mathbf{C}^N$ denote the space of N dimensional complex vectors and let $\|x\|_\infty := \max_i |x_i|$ denote the norm in $\mathbf{C}^N$ space. For any $\sigma \leq 0$, define $C_\sigma := \{s \in \mathbf{C} : \mathrm{Re}(s) > \sigma\}$. Let normed spaces $L_1 := \{x : \mathbf{R}_0 \to \mathbf{R} \mid \|x\|_1 := \int_0^\infty |x(t)|dt < \infty\}$, and $L_\infty := \{x : \mathbf{R}_0 \to \mathbf{R} \mid \|x\|_\infty := \sup_{t\in\mathbf{R}_0} |x(t)| < \infty\}$, and $H_{\infty,C_\sigma} := \{G : \mathbf{C} \to \mathbf{C} \mid G$ is analytic in C_σ and $\|G\|_{\infty,C_\sigma} := \sup_{s\in C_\sigma} |G(s)| < \infty\}$. For any of the normed spaces $(X, \|\cdot\|_X)$ given above, we define $\bar{B}X(M) := \{x \in X : \|x\|_X \leq M\}$. In the case where $\sigma = 0$, we write H_∞ instead of H_{∞,C_0} and $\|G\|_\infty$ instead of $\|G\|_{\infty,C_0}$. Note that under these definitions the symbol $\|\cdot\|_\infty$ denotes the norms associated with each of the spaces $\mathbf{C}_\infty$, L_∞, and H_∞. However, each of these uses should be clear from context.

Finally, let

$$P_{(\infty,C_\sigma),M,\phi} := \{G \in \bar{B}H_{\infty,C_\sigma}(M) \ : \ |G(j\omega)| \leq \phi(\omega),\ \forall\, \omega \in \mathbf{R}\}$$

$$P_{C_\sigma,M} := \{G \in H_\infty : \int_0^\infty |g(v)|e^{-\sigma v}\, dv \leq M\}$$

$$P_{C_\sigma,M,\phi} := \{G \in P_{C_\sigma,M} : |G(j\omega)| \leq \phi(\omega),\ \forall\, \omega \in \mathbf{R}\}$$

where $\phi \in \Phi := \{\phi : \mathbf{R} \to \mathbf{R}_0 \mid \phi$ is continuous and satisfies $\lim_{|\omega|\to\infty} \phi(\omega) = 0\}$.

2.2 System Identification in H_∞

In the system identification in H_∞ problem formulated by Helmicki *et al.* [5], it is assumed that the given frequency response data are evaluated on a set of points which are bilinear transforms of uniformly spaced points on the unit circle. In this paper, we describe a more general problem of system identification in H_∞ for which the given frequency response data correspond to an arbitrarily specified set of frequencies.

Let

$$\Omega^N := \{\omega_k^N \in [0, \infty) : k = 1, \ldots, N\}$$

denote a given set of N distinct frequencies and $\{\Omega^N\}_{N=1}^\infty$ denote a given sequence of such sets. The system identification in H_∞ problem is precisely described as follows.

Given: (i) an information λ for which it is known that the true unknown plant $G \in P_\lambda \subset H_\infty$, (ii) a finite number N of frequency response estimates

$$E_k^N(G, \eta_k^N) := G(j\omega_k^N) + \eta_k^N$$

at frequencies $\omega_k^N \in \Omega^N, k = 1, \ldots, N$, where $\eta_k^N \in \mathbf{C}$ denotes the frequency response measurement error, and (iii) a real vector $\epsilon^N := [\epsilon_1^N, \ldots, \epsilon_N^N]$ for which it is known that

$$\eta^N := [\eta_1^N, \ldots, \eta_N^N] \in B^N(\epsilon^N)$$

where

$$B^N(\epsilon^N) := \{[x_1, \ldots, x_N] \in \mathbf{C}^N : |x_k| \leq \epsilon_k^N, \; k = 1, \ldots, N\}$$

Find: an algorithm A^N which maps the given information into an identified system model $G_{id}^N \in H_\infty$ in such a way that the worst-case identification error

$$e^N(\epsilon^N) := \sup\{\|G - G_{id}^N\|_\infty : G \in P_\lambda, \; \eta^N \in B^N(\epsilon^N)\} \quad (1)$$

satisfies

$$\lim_{N \to \infty, \|\epsilon^N\|_\infty \to 0} e^N(\epsilon^N) = 0 \quad (2)$$

In addition, derive an explicit upper bound $\bar{e}^N(\epsilon^N)$ on $e^N(\epsilon^N)$ as a function of λ, ϵ^N, and N.

As in [5], we define convergence as follows.

Definition 1 *An system identification in H_∞ algorithm A^N is said to be convergent if the error $e^N(\epsilon^N)$ satisfies (2).*

For solving the system identification in H_∞ problem, several convergent algorithms with explicit upper error bounds have been proposed for $G \in P_{(\infty, C_\sigma), M, \phi}$ [1] [5].

3 Problem Formulation

We assume that the available input-output timed data $\{u(\tau), y(\tau)\}_{\tau=0}^t$, $t \in \mathbf{R}_0$, are generated by a single-input signal-output system described by

$$y = g * u + d,$$

where $*$ stands for the usual convolution operator, g is the impulse response corresponding to a system G defined by

$$G(s) := \int_0^\infty g(t)e^{-st}dt,$$

u is an applied input, y is the observed output, and d is a disturbance. Note that d can be used to account for a variety of effects including nonzero initial conditions, input/output disturbances, measurement noise, etc.

3.1 On-Line Point-Frequency Response Identification

The OLPFRI problem is precisely formulated as follows.

Given: (i) an information λ for which it is known that the true unknown plant $G \in P_\lambda \subset H_\infty$, (ii) a level δ for which it is known that $d \in V_\delta$, (iii) a pair of input-output timed data, and (iv) a set Ω^N with N frequencies.

Find: an on-line algorithm $F_t^N|_{t=0}^\infty$ which maps the given information into N point-frequency response estimates, namely,

$$E_{k,t}^N(u, G, d) := G(j\omega_k^N) + \eta_{k,t}^N \quad (3)$$

at frequencies $\omega_k^N \in \Omega^N, k = 1, \ldots, N$, where $\eta_{k,t}^N \in \mathbf{C}$ accounts for the estimation error, in such a way that the worst-case estimation error

$$\epsilon_{k,t}^N(u, \delta) := \sup\{|\eta_{k,t}^N| : G \in P_\lambda, \; d \in V_\delta\} \quad (4)$$

satisfies

$$\lim_{t \to \infty, \delta \to 0} \epsilon_{k,t}^N(u, \delta) = 0 \quad (5)$$

In addition, derive an explicit upper bound $\bar{\epsilon}_{k,t}^N(u, \delta)$ on $\epsilon_{k,t}^N(u, \delta)$ as a function of λ, u, δ, N, and t.

As in Definition 1, we define convergence as follows.

Definition 2 *An OLPFRI algorithm $F_t^N|_{t=0}^\infty$ is said to be convergent if the error $\epsilon_{k,t}^N(u, \delta)$ satisfies (5).*

So far, only few convergent *single* point-frequency response identification algorithms with explicit upper error bounds have been proposed for $G \in P_{C_\sigma, M}$ in [5]. Different from those in [5], in this paper, we deal with a *general* on-line identification of arbitrary number of point-frequency responses of a system by applying *real* inputs. This problem is solved by using continuous-time Fourier transform concept. The detailed results are developed in Section 4.

3.2 On-Line System Identification in H_∞

The OLSIH problem is precisely formulated as follows.

Given: (i) an information λ for which it is known that the true unknown plant $G \in P_\lambda \subset H_\infty$, (ii) a level δ for which it is known that $d \in V_\delta$, and (iii) a pair of input-output timed data.

Find: (i) a sequence of frequency sets $\{\Omega^N\}_{N=1}^\infty$, and (ii) an on-line algorithm $A_t^N|_{t=0}^\infty := A^N \circ F_t^N|_{t=0}^\infty$, where the algorithm F_t^N first maps the given information into N point-frequency response estimates defined by (3) and then the algorithm A^N maps these N point-frequency response estimates into an identified system model $G_{id,t}^N \in H_\infty$ in such a way that the worst-case identification error

$$e_t^N(u, \delta) := \sup\{\|G - G_{id,t}^N\|_\infty : G \in P_\lambda, \; d \in V_\delta\} \quad (6)$$

satisfies

$$\lim_{t \to \infty, N \to \infty, \delta \to 0} e_t^N(u, \delta) = 0 \quad (7)$$

In addition, derive an explicit upper bound $\bar{e}_t^N(u, \delta)$ on $e_t^N(u, \delta)$ as a function of λ, u, δ, N, and t.

As in Definition 1, we define convergence as follows.

Definition 3 *An OLSIH algorithm $A_t^N|_{t=0}^\infty$ is said to be convergent if the error $e_t^N(u, \delta)$ satisfies (7).*

The OLSIH problem can be solved by composing any convergent OLPFRI algorithm with any convergent system identification in H_∞ algorithm. It is described precisely as follows.

Proposition 1 *Let $\{\Omega^N\}_{N=1}^\infty$ be a given sequence of frequency sets such that A^N is a convergent system identification in H_∞ algorithm with an explicit upper bound $\bar{e}^N(\epsilon^N)$ as described in Section 2.2, and $F_t^N|_{t=0}^\infty$ be a convergent OLPFRI algorithm with an explicit upper bound $\bar{\epsilon}_{k,t}^N(u, \delta)$ as described in Section 3.1, for each Ω^N, $N \in \mathbf{I}_+$. Then, the composite on-line algorithm $A_t^N|_{t=0}^\infty := A^N \circ F_t^N|_{t=0}^\infty$ is a convergent OLSIH algorithm and $\bar{e}_t^N(u, \delta) = \bar{e}^N(\bar{\epsilon}^N(t, u, \delta))$ is an explicit upper bound as described in Section 3.2, where $\bar{\epsilon}^N(t, u, \delta) := [\bar{\epsilon}_{1,t}^N(u, \delta), \ldots, \bar{\epsilon}_{N,t}^N(u, \delta)]$.*

Proof: It is clear that $\bar{e}_t^N(u, \delta) = \bar{e}^N(\bar{\epsilon}^N(t, u, \delta))$ is indeed an explicit upper bound on $e_t^N(u, \delta)$ as described in Section 3.2. In the following, we will show that the OLSIH algorithm $A_t^N|_{t=0}^\infty := A^N \circ F_t^N|_{t=0}^\infty$ is indeed convergent.

Because for each $\Omega^N, N \in \mathbf{I}_+$, $F_t^N|_{t=0}^\infty$ is a convergent OLPFRI algorithm, error $\epsilon_{k,t}^N(u, \delta)$ satisfies (5) and this implies

$$\lim_{t \to \infty, \delta \to 0} \|\epsilon^N(t, u, \delta)\|_\infty = 0$$

where

$$\epsilon^N(t, u, \delta) := [\epsilon_{1,t}^N(u, \delta), \ldots, \epsilon_{N,t}^N(u, \delta)]$$

Because A^N is a convergent system identification in H_∞ algorithm with respect to $\{\Omega^N\}_{N=1}^\infty$,

$$\sup\{\|G - G^N_{id,t}\|_\infty : G \in P_\lambda,\ \eta^N \in B^N(\epsilon^N(t,u,\delta))\} \to 0$$

as $N \to \infty$ and $\|\epsilon^N(t,u,\delta)\|_\infty \to 0$. Since

$$\begin{aligned} e^N_t(u,\delta) &:= \sup\{\|G - G^N_{id,t}\|_\infty : G \in P_\lambda,\ d \in V_\delta\} \\ &\le \sup\{\|G - G^N_{id,t}\|_\infty : G \in P_\lambda,\ \eta^N \in B^N(\epsilon^N(t,u,\delta))\} \end{aligned}$$

this implies that error $e^N_t(u,\delta)$ of algorithm $A^N_t := A^N \circ F^N_t$ satisfies (7), i.e., the OLSIH algorithm $A^N_t|^\infty_{t=0} := A^N \circ F^N_t|^\infty_{t=0}$ is convergent. □

4 Main Results

The OLPFRI problem is solved by using the continuous-time Fourier transform (CTFT) concept. Here, we denote the CTFT of any transformable element $x \in L_1$ as

$$X(j\omega) := \int_0^\infty x(\tau)e^{-j\omega\tau}d\tau,$$

denote the t-time CTFT of any signal x which is cotinuous almost everywhere (a. e.) as

$$X_t(j\omega) := \int_0^t x(\tau)e^{-j\omega\tau}d\tau,$$

and denote $\hat{X}_t(j\omega) := X_t(j\omega)/(t+\Delta)$, where $t \in \mathbf{R}_0$, $\omega \in \mathbf{R}$, and Δ is a small positive real number.

In the following, we will first develop several useful results so as to establish an error bound due to the estimation of the point-frequency response at frequency ω^N_k using $Y_t(j\omega^N_k)/U_t(j\omega^N_k)$.

Lemma 1 *Let $y = g * u + d$, where u, d, and g are continuous a. e., $u(\tau) = 0$ for all $\tau < 0$, and g is the impulse response corresponding to a system $G \in H_\infty$. At frequency ω^N_k, denote the CTFT of g by $G(j\omega^N_k)$ and denote the t-time CTFT of y, u, and d by $Y_t(j\omega^N_k)$, $U_t(j\omega^N_k)$, and $D_t(j\omega^N_k)$, respectively. Then, for any $t \in \mathbf{R}_0$ and any $\omega^N_k \in \mathbf{R}$,*

$$Y_t(j\omega^N_k) = G(j\omega^N_k)U_t(j\omega^N_k) - W_t(j\omega^N_k)$$

where

$$W_t(j\omega^N_k) = \gamma_t + U_t(j\omega^N_k)\int_t^\infty g(v)e^{-j\omega^N_k v}dv - D_t(j\omega^N_k)$$

with

$$\gamma_t = \int_0^t g(v)e^{-j\omega^N_k v}\int_{t-v}^t u(\tau)e^{-j\omega^N_k \tau}d\tau\, dv$$

Moreover, the magnitude of $W_t(j\omega^N_k)$ is bounded as follows:

$$|W_t(j\omega^N_k)| \le \bar{\gamma}_t + |U_t(j\omega^N_k)|\int_t^\infty |g(v)|\, dv + |D_t(j\omega^N_k)|$$

where

$$\bar{\gamma}_t = \int_0^t |g(v)|\int_{t-v}^t |u(\tau)|\, d\tau\, dv$$

Proof: Because $g(\tau) = u(\tau) = 0$ for all $\tau < 0$ and u, d, and g are continuous a. e., it can be shown that,

$$\begin{aligned} Y_t(j\omega^N_k) &= \int_0^t \left(\int_0^\infty g(v)u(\tau - v)\, dv\right) e^{-j\omega^N_k\tau}\, d\tau + D_t(j\omega^N_k) \\ &= \int_0^\infty g(v)e^{-j\omega^N_k v}\int_0^t u(\tau - v)e^{-j\omega^N_k(\tau - v)}\, d\tau\, dv + D_t(j\omega^N_k) \end{aligned}$$

and

$$\begin{aligned} &G(j\omega^N_k)U_t(j\omega^N_k) \\ &= \left(\int_0^\infty g(v)e^{-j\omega^N_k v}\, dv\right)\left(\int_0^t u(\tau)e^{-j\omega^N_k\tau}\, d\tau\right) \\ &= \int_0^\infty g(v)e^{-j\omega^N_k v}\int_0^t u(\tau)e^{-j\omega^N_k\tau}\, d\tau\, dv \end{aligned}$$

so that

$$\begin{aligned} W_t(j\omega^N_k) &= G(j\omega^N_k)U_t(j\omega^N_k) - Y_t(j\omega^N_k) \\ &= \int_0^\infty g(v)e^{-j\omega^N_k v}\left(\int_0^t u(\tau)e^{-j\omega^N_k\tau}d\tau \right. \\ &\quad \left. - \int_0^t u(\tau - v)e^{-j\omega^N_k(\tau - v)}d\tau\right) dv - D_t(j\omega^N_k) \\ &= \gamma_t + U_t(j\omega^N_k)\int_t^\infty g(v)e^{-j\omega^N_k v}dv - D_t(j\omega^N_k) \end{aligned}$$

The proof is thus completed by using the triangle inequality. □

Lemma 2 *Under the statement of Lemma 1, if $G \in P_{C_\sigma,M}$ for some $M < \infty$ and $\sigma < 0$, the magnitude of $W_t(j\omega^N_k)$ is bounded as follows:*

$$|W_t(\omega^N_k)| \le M\alpha_t + Me^{\sigma t}|U_t(j\omega^N_k)| + |D_t(j\omega^N_k)| \tag{8}$$

where

$$\alpha_t := e^{\sigma t}\int_0^t |u(\tau)|e^{-\sigma\tau}\, d\tau$$

which can be calculated on-line as follows:

$$\frac{d}{dt}\alpha_t = \sigma\alpha_t + |u(t)|,\ \alpha_0 = 0. \tag{9}$$

Furthermore, (i) α_t is bounded by some $\bar{B} < \infty$ for all $t \in \mathbf{R}_0$ if $u \in L_\infty$; (ii) $\lim_{t\to\infty}\alpha_t = 0$ if u is continuous and $u \in L_1 \cap L_\infty$.

Proof: Because both g and u are continuous a. e.,

$$\int_t^\infty |g(v)|e^{-\sigma t}\, dv \le \int_t^\infty |g(v)|e^{-\sigma v}\, dv \le M$$

so that

$$\int_t^\infty |g(v)|\, dv \le Me^{\sigma t}$$

and

$$\begin{aligned} &\int_0^t |g(v)|\int_{t-v}^t |u(\tau)|\, d\tau\, dv \\ &= \int_0^t |u(\tau)|\int_{t-\tau}^t |g(v)|\, dv\, d\tau \\ &\le \int_0^t |u(\tau)|\int_{t-\tau}^\infty |g(v)|\, dv\, d\tau \\ &\le \int_0^t |u(\tau)|Me^{\sigma(t-\tau)}\, d\tau = M\alpha_t \end{aligned}$$

for all $t \in \mathbf{R}_0$. Using the results of Lemma 1, we find that (8) is true. For all $t \in \mathbf{R}_0$, it can be shown that α_t can be calculated on-line as (9). Suppose (i) $u \in L_\infty$ and is bounded by some B, then

$$\alpha_t \le Be^{\sigma t}\int_0^t e^{-\sigma\tau}\, d\tau < -\frac{B}{\sigma} := \bar{B} < \infty$$

Suppose (ii) u is continuous and $u \in L_1 \cap L_\infty$, from Cor. 6.16 in [15], we know that

$$\int_0^\infty \alpha_t\, dt = \left(\int_0^\infty |u(t)|\, dt\right)\left(\int_0^\infty e^{\sigma t}\, dt\right) < \infty$$

Furthermore, because both α_t and $\frac{d}{dt}\alpha_t$ are bounded by some $\tilde{B} < \infty$ for all $t \in \mathbf{R}_0$, we know that $\lim_{t\to\infty}\alpha_t = 0$ by Cor. 1.2.2 in [12]. This completes the proof. □

Lemma 3 *Under the assumptions of Lemma 2, if $U_t(j\omega^N_k) \ne 0$ for some t,*

$$G(j\omega^N_k) - \frac{Y_t(j\omega^N_k)}{U_t(j\omega^N_k)} = \frac{W_t(j\omega^N_k)}{U_t(j\omega^N_k)}$$

and the magnitude of $W_t(j\omega^N_k)/U_t(j\omega^N_k)$ is bounded as follows:

$$\left|\frac{W_t(j\omega^N_k)}{U_t(j\omega^N_k)}\right| \le \beta^N_{k,t} := \frac{M\alpha_t}{|U_t(j\omega^N_k)|} + Me^{\sigma t} + \frac{|D_t(j\omega^N_k)|}{|U_t(j\omega^N_k)|} \tag{10}$$

Furthermore, (i) if $d \in \bar{B}L_1(\delta)$,

$$\beta_{k,t}^N \leq \bar{\beta}_{k,t}^{N,1} := \frac{M\alpha_t}{|U_t(j\omega_k^N)|} + Me^{\sigma t} + \frac{\delta}{|U_t(j\omega_k^N)|}$$

(ii) if $d \in \bar{B}L_\infty(\delta)$,

$$\beta_{k,t}^N \leq \bar{\beta}_{k,t}^{N,\infty} := \frac{M\alpha_t/(t+\Delta)}{|\hat{U}_t(j\omega_k^N)|} + Me^{\sigma t} + \frac{\delta t}{(t+\Delta)|\hat{U}_t(j\omega_k^N)|}$$

Proof: The proof of (10) simply follows the results of Lemma 1 and Lemma 2. If $d \in \bar{B}L_1(\delta)$,

$$|D_t(j\omega_k^N)| \leq \int_0^\infty |d(\tau)|\, d\tau \leq \delta$$

whereas if $d \in \bar{B}L_\infty(\delta)$,

$$|\hat{D}_t(j\omega_k^N)| \leq \frac{1}{t+\Delta}\int_0^t |d(\tau)|\, d\tau \leq \frac{\delta t}{t+\Delta}$$

and this completes the proof. □

Based on these developed results, a concrete OLPFRI algorithm is specified as follows.

Algorithm: *(OLPFRI, $F_t^N|_{t=0}^\infty$)*

Without loss of generality, we assume that there exists an arbitrary small $\varepsilon > 0$ such that $U_t(j\omega) \neq 0$, $\forall\, t \in [0, \varepsilon]$, $\forall\, \omega \in \mathbf{R}_0$. (i) In the case where $d \in \bar{B}L_1(\delta)$, for each $\omega_k^N \in \Omega^N$, let the initial point-frequency response estimate and the initial upper bound on the worst-case estimation error be, respectively, $E_{k,\varepsilon}^N = Y_\varepsilon(j\omega_k^N)/U_\varepsilon(j\omega_k^N)$ and $\bar{\epsilon}_{k,\varepsilon}^N = \bar{\beta}_{k,\varepsilon}^{N,1}$. For any $t > \varepsilon$, $t \in \mathbf{R}_0$, let the estimate and the upper bound be, respectively,

$$E_{k,t}^N = \begin{cases} \frac{Y_t(j\omega_k^N)}{U_t(j\omega_k^N)} & \text{if } U_t(j\omega_k^N) \neq 0 \text{ and } \bar{\beta}_{k,t}^{N,1} < \bar{\epsilon}_{k,t-}^N \\ E_{k,t-}^N & \text{otherwise} \end{cases} \quad (11)$$

and

$$\bar{\epsilon}_{k,t}^N = \begin{cases} \bar{\beta}_{k,t}^{N,1} & \text{if } U_t(j\omega_k^N) \neq 0 \text{ and } \bar{\beta}_{k,t}^{N,1} < \bar{\epsilon}_{k,t-}^N \\ \bar{\epsilon}_{k,t-}^N & \text{otherwise} \end{cases} \quad (12)$$

(ii) In the case where $d \in \bar{B}L_\infty(\delta)$, we replace $Y_t(\omega_k^N)$, $U_t(j\omega_k^N)$, and $\bar{\beta}_{k,t}^{N,1}$ in the algorithm by $\hat{Y}_t(j\omega_k^N)$, $\hat{U}_t(j\omega_k^N)$, and $\bar{\beta}_{k,t}^{N,\infty}$, respectively.

Remark 1: Because, for $t \in \mathbf{R}_0$,

$$\frac{d}{dt}Y_t(j\omega_k^N) = y(t)e^{-j\omega_k^N t},\ Y_0(j\omega_k^N) = 0,$$

$$\frac{d}{dt}\hat{Y}_t(j\omega_k^N) = -\frac{\hat{Y}_t(j\omega_k^N)}{t+\Delta} + \frac{y(t)e^{-j\omega_k^N t}}{t+\Delta},\ \hat{Y}_0(j\omega_k^N) = 0,$$

and α_t can be calculated on-line as (9), the algorithm $F_t^N|_{t=0}^\infty$ described by (11) and (12) for each of the two cases is indeed an on-line algorithm.

Theorem 1 *Let $y = g * u + d$, where u, d, and g are continuous a. e., $d \in V_\delta = \bar{B}L_1(\delta)$ or $d \in V_\delta = \bar{B}L_\infty(\delta)$, and g is the impulse response corresponding to a system $G \in P_{C_\sigma,M}$. If the input u satisfies the condition:*

(A1) *$u(\tau) = 0$ for all $\tau < 0$,*

the OLPFRI algorithm $F_t^N|_{t=0}^\infty$ described by (11) and (12) for each of the two cases guarantees that, for all $k = 1, \ldots, N$, the upper bound $\bar{\epsilon}_{k,t}^N$ on the worst-case estimation error $\epsilon_{k,t}^N(u,\delta)$ defined by (4) is monotonically decreasing with respect to t. In addition, if the input u satisfies the condition:

(A2) *For each $\omega_k^N \in \Omega^N$, u is continuous, $u \in L_1 \cap L_\infty$, and $\limsup_{t\to\infty} |U_t(j\omega_k^N)| > 0$ for the case where $d \in \bar{B}L_1(\delta)$, or $u \in L_\infty$ and $\limsup_{t\to\infty} |\hat{U}_t(j\omega_k^N)| > 0$ for the case where $d \in \bar{B}L_\infty(\delta)$,*

the algorithm $F_t^N|_{t=0}^\infty$ is convergent and $\lim_{t\to\infty,\delta\to 0} \bar{\epsilon}_{k,t}^N = 0$ for all $k = 1, \ldots, N$.

Proof: Assume that u satisfies the condition (A1). From the definition of $\bar{\epsilon}_{k,t}^N(u,\delta)$ described in (12), it is clear that $\bar{\epsilon}_{k,t}^N(u,\delta)$ is monotonically decreasing with respect to t. Furthermore, assume that u satisfies the condition (A2) for the case where $d \in \bar{B}L_1(\delta)$, then there exists a sequence $\{t_i\}_{i=1}^\infty$ with $\lim_{i\to\infty} t_i = \infty$ and an $L \in \mathbf{I}_+$ such that

$$|U_{t_i}(j\omega_k^N)| > 0,\ \forall\, \omega_k^N \in \Omega^N,\ \forall\, i \geq L.$$

From Lemma 2 and Lemma 3, we know that

$$\lim_{i\to\infty,\delta\to 0} \bar{\beta}_{k,t_i}^{N,1}(u,\delta) = 0$$

which implies

$$\lim_{t\to\infty,\delta\to 0} \bar{\epsilon}_{k,t}^N(u,\delta) = 0$$

Then, the error $\epsilon_{k,t}^N(u,\delta)$ satisfies (5), i.e., the algorithm $F_t^N|_{t=0}^\infty$ is convergent. The proof for the case where $d \in \bar{B}L_\infty(\delta)$ is similar to that for the case where $d \in \bar{B}L_1(\delta)$ and is omitted here. □

Remark 2: There exists a large class of signals which satisfy conditions (A1) and (A2) described in Theorem 1 for each of the two cases. Let S_1 be the set of impulse responses of all causal stable continuous systems which have no zeros on point $j\omega_k^N$ for all $\omega_k^N \in \Omega^N$. Because the CTFT $U(j\omega_k^N)$ of any element $u \in S_1$ is not equal to zero for all $\omega_k^N \in \Omega^N$, any element of S_1 will satisfy conditions (A1) and (A2) for the case where $d \in \bar{B}L_1(\delta)$. Suppose, for any $k = 1, \ldots, N$, $\omega_k^N = 2\pi q_k/p_k$ for some $q_k \in \mathbf{I}_0$ and $p_k \in \mathbf{I}_+$. Let $p = \prod_{k=1}^N p_k$ and

$$S_2 = \left\{ u : u(\tau) = \begin{cases} 0 & \text{for } \tau < 0 \\ 2\sum_{q=1}^N a_q \cos\omega_q^N \tau & \text{for } \tau \geq 0 \end{cases} \right\}$$

where $a_q \in \mathbf{R}$, $a_q \neq 0$, for all $q = 1, \ldots, N$. Because $u(\tau) = u(\tau + p)$ for any $u \in S_2$ and any $\tau \in \mathbf{R}_0$,

$$\begin{aligned} \hat{U}_{ip}(j\omega_k^N) &= \frac{1}{ip+\Delta}\sum_{\ell=0}^{i-1}\int_0^p u(\tau+\ell p)e^{-j\omega_k^N(\tau+\ell p)}\, d\tau \\ &= \frac{i}{ip+\Delta}\int_0^p u(\tau)e^{-j\omega_k^N \tau}\, d\tau = \frac{ipa_k}{ip+\Delta} \end{aligned}$$

for any $i \in \mathbf{I}_+$. Thus $\limsup_{t\to\infty} |\hat{U}_t(j\omega_k^N)| \geq |a_k| > 0$. Any element of S_2 will satisfy conditions (A1) and (A2) for the case where $d \in \bar{B}L_\infty(\delta)$.

Based on Proposition 1 and Theorem 1, several concrete OLSIH algorithms are specified as follows.

Algorithm: *(OLSIH, $A_t^N|_{t=0}^\infty$)*

Without loss of generality, we assume that there exists an arbitrary small $\varepsilon > 0$ such that $U_t(j\omega) \neq 0$, $\forall\, t \in [0, \varepsilon]$, $\forall\, \omega \in \mathbf{R}_0$. Let A^N be a convergent system identification in H_∞ algorithm, for example, an algorithm in [1] [5] for systems $G \in P_{(\infty, C_\sigma),M,\phi}$, with an explicit upper bound $\bar{e}^N(\epsilon^N)$ and associated sequence of frequency sets $\{\Omega^N\}_{N=1}^\infty$. For each $\omega_k^N \in \Omega^N$, let $F_t^N|_{t=0}^\infty$ be the OLPFRI algorithm with an explicit upper bound $\bar{\epsilon}_{k,t}^N$ described by (11) and (12) for each of the two cases. Define $E^N(t) := [E_{1,t}^N, \ldots, E_{N,t}^N]$ and $\bar{\epsilon}^N(t) := [\bar{\epsilon}_{1,t}^N, \ldots, \bar{\epsilon}_{N,t}^N]$. The composite on-line algorithm $A_t^N|_{t=0}^\infty := A^N \circ F_t^N|_{t=0}^\infty$ and the explicit upper error bound $\bar{e}_t^N$ are specified as follows. Let the initial identified system model and the initial upper bound on the worst-case identification error be, respectively, $G_{id,\varepsilon}^N = A^N(E^N(\varepsilon))$ and $\bar{e}_\varepsilon^N = \bar{e}^N(\bar{\epsilon}^N(\varepsilon))$. For any $t > \varepsilon$, $t \in \mathbf{R}_0$, let the identified system model and the upper bound be, respectively,

$$G_{id,t}^N = \begin{cases} A^N(E^N(t)) & \text{if } \bar{e}^N(\bar{\epsilon}^N(t)) < \bar{e}_{t-}^N \\ G_{id,t-}^N & \text{otherwise} \end{cases} \quad (13)$$

and

$$\bar{e}_t^N = \min\{\bar{e}^N(\bar{\epsilon}^N(t)),\ \bar{e}_{t-}^N\} \quad (14)$$

Theorem 2 *Let $y = g * u + d$, where u, d, and g are continuous a. e., $d \in V_\delta = \bar{B}L_1(\delta)$ or $d \in V_\delta = \bar{B}L_\infty(\delta)$, and g is the impulse response corresponding to a system $G \in P_{C_\sigma,M,\phi}$. If the input u satisfies the condition (A1) in Theorem 1, the OLSIH algorithm $A_t^N|_{t=0}^\infty$ described by (13) and (14) for each of the two cases guarantees that the upper bound $\bar{e}_t^N$ on the worst-case identification error $e_t^N(u,\delta)$ defined by (6) is monotonically decreasing with respect to t. In addition, if the input u satisfies the condition:*

(A3) *For each $\omega_k^N \in \Omega^N$ and each $N \in \mathbf{I}_+$, u is continuous, $u \in L_1 \cap L_\infty$, and $\limsup_{t\to\infty} |U_t(j\omega_k^N)| > 0$ in the case where $d \in \bar{B}L_1(\delta)$, or $u \in L_\infty$ and $\limsup_{t\to\infty} |\hat{U}_t(j\omega_k^N)| > 0$ in the case where $d \in \bar{B}L_\infty(\delta)$,*

the algorithm $A_t^N|_{t=0}^\infty$ is convergent. Moreover,

$$\lim_{t\to\infty, N\to\infty, \delta\to 0} \bar{e}_t^N = 0$$

if $e^N(\epsilon^N)$ satisfies $\lim_{N\to\infty, \|\epsilon^N\|_\infty \to 0} e^N(\epsilon^N) = 0$.

Proof: Because $G \in P_{C_\sigma,M,\phi}$, it follows from [5, Fact 2.1] that $G \in P_{(\infty,C_\sigma),M,\phi}$, i.e., $P_{C_\sigma,M,\phi} \subset P_{(\infty,C_\sigma),M,\phi}$. Thus, A^N is a convergent system identification in H_∞ algorithm for systems $G \in P_{C_\sigma,M,\phi}$. Also, since $P_{C_\sigma,M,\phi} \subset P_{C_\sigma,M}$, $F_t^N|_{t=0}^\infty$ is a convergent OLPFRI algorithm for a system $G \in P_{C_\sigma,M,\phi}$. Following the same argument in the proof of Proposition 1 and Theorem 1, it can be shown that Theorem 2 is true. □

5 Conclusion

In this paper, we formulate and solve two related on-line identification problems, namely, on-line point-frequency response identification and on-line system identification in H_∞, for a class of continuous systems from a worst-case deterministic standpoint. Concrete convergent on-line algorithms are specified for these two problems. Each of these algorithms provides on-line not only an estimate of the system but also an explicit upper bound on the worst-case deterministic identification error. Because a large class of applied inputs is admissible, the on-line system identification in H_∞ algorithm has execllent promise to be incorporated in an adaptive H_∞ robust control system as a robust estimator.

References

[1] H. Akçay, G. Gu, and P.P. Khargonekar, "A Class of Algorithms for Identification in H_∞: Continuous-Time Case", to be appeared in *IEEE TAC*.

[2] E.-W. Bai, "Adaptive Quantification of Model Uncertainties by Rational Approximation", *IEEE TAC*, Vol. 36, No. 4, pp. 441–453, 1991.

[3] J. Chen, C.N. Nett, and M.K.H. Fan, "Optimal Non-Parametric System Identification from Arbitrary Corrupt Finite Time Series: A Control-Oriented Approach", *ACC*, pp. 279–285, 1992.

[4] G.C. Goodwin, M. Gevers, and B. Ninness, "Quantifying the Error in Estimated Transfer Functions with Application to Model Order Selection", *IEEE TAC*, Vol. 37, No. 7, pp. 913–928, 1992.

[5] A.J. Helmicki, C.A. Jacobson, and C.N. Nett, "Worst-Case/Deterministic Identification in H_∞: The Continuous-Time Case", *IEEE TAC*, Vol. 37, No. 5, pp. 604–610, 1992.

[6] R.L. Kosut, M.K. Lau, and S. Boyd, "Set-Membership Identification of Systems with Parametric and Nonparametric Uncertainty", *IEEE TAC*, Vol. 37, No. 7, pp. 929–941, 1992.

[7] J.M. Krause and P.P. Khargonekar, "Parameter Identification in the Presence of Non-parametric Dynamic Uncertainty", *Automatica*, Vol. 26, No. 1, pp. 113–123, 1990.

[8] R.O. LaMaire, L. Valavani, M. Athans, and G. Stein, "A Frequency-Domain Estimator for Use in Adaptive Control Systems", *Automatica*, Vol. 27, No. 1, pp. 23–38, 1991.

[9] F.-M. Lee, I-K. Fong, and L.-C. Fu, "Parameter Identification of Systems with Uncertain Dynamics and Disturbances", *ACC*, pp. 2445–2449, 1992.

[10] F.-M. Lee, I-K. Fong, and L.-C. Fu, "Convergent On-Line Identification in H_∞ for Discrete Systems", to be appeared in *12th IFAC World Congress*, 1993.

[11] P.J. Parker and R.R. Bitmead, "Adaptive Frequency Response Identification", *26th IEEE CDC*, pp. 348–353, 1987.

[12] S. Sastry and M. Bodson, *Adaptive Control: Stability, Convergence, and Robustness*, Prentice-Hall, New Jersey, 1989.

[13] R.S. Smith and J.C. Doyle, "Towards a Methodology for Robust Parameter Identification", *ACC*, pp. 2394–2399, 1990.

[14] B. Wahlberg and L. Ljung, "Hard Frequency-Domain Model Error Bounds from Least-Squares Like Identification Techniques", *IEEE TAC*, Vol. 37, No. 7, pp. 900–912, 1992.

[15] R.L. Wheeden and A. Zygmund, *Measure and Integral: An Introduction to Real Analysis*, Marcel Dekker, New York, 1977.

[16] R.C. Younce and C.E. Rohrs, "Identification with Nonparametric Uncertainty", *IEEE TAC*, Vol. 37, No. 6, pp. 715–728, 1992.

Proceedings of the
American Control Conference
San Francisco, California • June 1993

Dissipative H_2/H_∞ Controller Synthesis

Wassim M. Haddad
Department of Mechanical and Aerospace Engineering
Florida Institute of Technology, Melbourne, FL

Dennis S. Bernstein and Y. William Wang
Department of Aerospace Engineering
The University of Michigan, Ann Arbor, MI

1 Introduction

In certain applications, such as the control of flexible structures, the plant transfer function is known to be positive real. This property arises if the sensor and actuator are colocated and also dual, for example, force actuator and velocity sensor or torque actuator and angular rate sensor. In practice, the prospects for controlling such systems is quite good since, if sensor and actuator dynamics are negligible, stability is unconditionally guaranteed so long as the controller is strictly positive real [1-3]. Although there is no general theory yet available for designing positive real controllers, a variety of techniques have been proposed based on H_2 theory [4-10] and H_∞ theory [11,12]. In this paper we focus on the H_2-based positive real controller synthesis method of Lozano-Leal and Joshi [7]. In [7] it is shown that if the plant is positive real and if the error and disturbance matrices satisfy certain constraints, then the LQG controller is also positive real. This approach is appealing in practice since it requires only standard LQG synthesis techniques. Our goal in this note is to extend the synthesis technique of [7] to include an H_∞ norm bound on the closed-loop transfer function [13]. This extension thus provides the control designer with more flexibility in specifying closed-loop system performance.

2 Preliminaries

In this section we establish definitions and notation. A square transfer function $G(s)$ is called *positive real* [14], p. 216, if 1) all poles of $G(s)$ are in the closed left half plane and 2) $G(s)+G^*(s)$ is nonnegative definite for $\mathrm{Re}[s]>0$. A square transfer function $G(s)$ is called *strictly positive real* or *dissipative* [15], [16] if 1) $G(s)$ is asymptotically stable and 2) $G(\jmath\omega)+G^*(\jmath\omega)$ is positive definite for all real ω. Recall that a minimal realization of a positive real transfer function is stable in the sense of Lyapunov [17], while a strictly positive real transfer function is asymptotically stable [15]. For notational convenience in this paper, G will denote an $l\times m$ transfer function with input $u\in\mathcal{R}^m$, output $y\in\mathcal{R}^l$, and internal state $x\in\mathcal{R}^n$. We will omit all matrix dimensions throughout, and assume that all quantities have compatible dimensions. Note that if the plant is positive real, then $l=m$ and the resulting compensator is square. Next we state the well-known positive real lemma [17], [18].

Lemma 2.1. The strictly proper transfer function $G(s)\overset{\min}{\sim}\left[\begin{array}{c|c}A&B\\\hline C&0\end{array}\right]$ is positive real if and only if there exist matrices Q_0 and L with Q_0 positive definite such that

$$AQ_0+Q_0A^{\mathrm T}=-LL^{\mathrm T},\tag{1}$$

$$Q_0C^{\mathrm T}=B.\tag{2}$$

This form of the positive real lemma is the dual of that given in [17], and the derivation is similarly dual. See [18] for further details on the dual positive real lemma. The dual version of Lemma 2.1 can be obtained by replacing A by $A^{\mathrm T}$ and B by $C^{\mathrm T}$. In this case $G(s)$ is positive real if and only if there exist matrices P_0 and $\hat L$ with P_0 positive definite such that

$$A^{\mathrm T}P_0+P_0A=-\hat L^{\mathrm T}\hat L,\quad P_0B=C^{\mathrm T}.\tag{3}$$

Recall that in the case in which $G(s)$ is strictly positive real it follows that $(A,\hat L)$ is observable [15]. Finally, we give a key definition and a lemma involving self-dual realizations.

Definition 2.1. Let $G(s)\overset{\min}{\sim}\left[\begin{array}{c|c}A&B\\\hline C&0\end{array}\right]$ be a positive real transfer function. Then $\left[\begin{array}{c|c}A&B\\\hline C&0\end{array}\right]$ is a *self-dual realization* of $G(s)$ if $A+A^{\mathrm T}\le 0$ and $B=C^{\mathrm T}$.

Self-dual realizations are convenient since conditions (1)-(3) are satisfied by $Q_0=P_0=I$ and $LL^{\mathrm T}=\hat L^{\mathrm T}\hat L=-(A+A^{\mathrm T})$. The next result due to [7] shows that positive real transfer functions always have self-dual realizations.

Lemma 2.2. Let $G(s)\overset{\min}{\sim}\left[\begin{array}{c|c}A&B\\\hline C&0\end{array}\right]$ be positive real and let positive-definite Q_0 and L satisfy (1), (2). Then $\left[\begin{array}{c|c}Q_0^{-1/2}AQ_0^{1/2}&Q_0^{-1/2}B\\\hline CQ_0^{1/2}&0\end{array}\right]$ is a self dual realization of $G(s)$.

3 Problem Statement and Main Results

In this section we begin by obtaining H_2 dynamic output-feedback controllers with constrained H_∞ disturbance attenuation. We then use this result to derive dissipative H_2/H_∞ controllers for a given positive real plant.

H_2/H_∞ Control Problem. Given the nth-order stabilizable and detectable plant

$$\dot x(t)=Ax(t)+Bu(t)+D_1w(t),\quad y(t)=Cx(t)+D_2w(t),\tag{4}$$

determine an nth-order dynamic compensator $G_c(s)\sim\left[\begin{array}{c|c}A_c&B_c\\\hline C_c&0\end{array}\right]$ of the form

$$\dot x_c(t)=A_cx_c(t)+B_cy(t),\,u(t)=C_cx_c(t),\tag{5}$$

that satisfies the following design criteria:

(i) the closed-loop system (4)-(5) given by $\tilde A\triangleq\begin{bmatrix}A&BC_c\\B_cC&A_c\end{bmatrix}$ is asymptotically stable;

(ii) the closed-loop transfer function $\tilde G(s)\sim\left[\begin{array}{c|c}\tilde A&\tilde D\\\hline\tilde E&0\end{array}\right]$ from the disturbance $w(t)$ to performance variables $z(t)=E_1x(t)+E_2u(t)$ satisfies the constraint $\|\tilde G(s)\|_\infty\le\gamma$, where $\gamma>0$ is a given constant, $\tilde D\triangleq\begin{bmatrix}D_1\\B_cD_2\end{bmatrix}$, and $\tilde E\triangleq[\ E_1\quad E_2C_c\ ]$; and ($iii$) the H_2 performance measure

$$J(A_c,B_c,C_c)\triangleq\lim_{t\to\infty}\frac1t\int_0^t[x^{\mathrm T}(s)R_1x(s)+u^{\mathrm T}(s)R_2u(s)]ds=\|\tilde G(s)\|_2^2\tag{6}$$

is minimized, where $R_1\triangleq E_1^{\mathrm T}E_1$, $R_2\triangleq E_2^{\mathrm T}E_2>0$, and $E_1^{\mathrm T}E_2=0$.

The basis for our approach is the mixed-norm H_2/H_∞ framework developed in [13]. For the case of equalized H_2/H_∞ weights, a full-order dynamic compensator satisfying design constraints (i), (ii), and providing a bound for (iii) is given by the following theorem. For convenience, define $V_1\triangleq D_1D_1^{\mathrm T}$, $V_2\triangleq D_2D_2^{\mathrm T}>0$, and assume $D_1D_2^{\mathrm T}=0$.

Theorem 3.1. Suppose there exist $n\times n$ nonnegative-definite matrices Q and P satisfying

$$0=AQ+QA^{\mathrm T}+V_1+\gamma^{-2}QR_1Q-QC^{\mathrm T}V_2^{-1}CQ,\tag{7}$$

$$0=(A+\gamma^{-2}QR_1)^{\mathrm T}P+P(A+\gamma^{-2}QR_1)+R_1-PBR_2^{-1}B^{\mathrm T}P+\gamma^{-2}PQC^{\mathrm T}V_2^{-1}CQP,\tag{8}$$

and let (A_c,B_c,C_c) be given by

$$A_c=A-QC^{\mathrm T}V_2^{-1}C-BR_2^{-1}B^{\mathrm T}P+\gamma^{-2}QR_1,\tag{9}$$

$$B_c=QC^{\mathrm T}V_2^{-1},C_c=-R_2^{-1}B^{\mathrm T}P.\tag{10}$$

Then $(\tilde A,\tilde D)$ is stabilizable if and only if $\tilde A$ is asymptotically stable. In this case the closed-loop transfer function $\tilde G(s)$ satisfies the H_∞ disturbance attenuation constraint and the H_2 performance criterion (6) satisfies the bound $J(A_c,B_c,C_c)\le\mathrm{tr}[QR_1+QC^{\mathrm T}V_2^{-1}CQP]$.

Note that using (9)-(10), the dynamic compensator (5) is given by

$$\dot x_c(t)=(A-QC^{\mathrm T}V_2^{-1}C-BR_2^{-1}B^{\mathrm T}P+\gamma^{-2}QR_1)x_c(t)+QC^{\mathrm T}V_2^{-1}y(t),\tag{11}$$

$$u(t)=-R_2^{-1}B^{\mathrm T}Px_c(t).\tag{12}$$

We now assume that the plant (4) is positive real and seek a strictly positive real controller within a negative feedback configuration.

Dissipative H_2/H_∞ Control Problem. Given the nth-order minimal positive real plant (4) determine an nth-order compensator $G_c(s)\sim\left[\begin{array}{c|c}A_c&B_c\\\hline C_c&0\end{array}\right]$ that satisfies the design criteria (ii) and (iii) with the additional property that $-G_c(s)\sim\left[\begin{array}{c|c}A_c&B_c\\\hline -C_c&0\end{array}\right]$ is strictly positive real. Note that in this case since the plant is positive real and the negative feedback compensator is strictly positive real, condition (i) is automatically satisfied [1]. We now present our main result which shows that if the design weights are chosen in a specific manner, then the controller is positive real. This choice of design weights is a direct generalization to the H_2/H_∞ problem of the H_2 design weights that were originally proposed in [7].

Theorem 3.2. Assume $G(s) \overset{\min}{\sim} \left[\begin{array}{c|c} A & B \\ \hline C & 0 \end{array}\right]$ is positive real, and let Q_0 and L satisfy (1), (2), where Q_0 is positive definite. Furthermore, assume that there exist $n \times n$ nonnegative-definite matrices Q and P satisfying (7), (8), where R_1, R_2, V_1, V_2, satisfy

$$V_1 = LL^{\mathrm{T}} + BR_2^{-1}B^{\mathrm{T}} - \gamma^{-2}Q_0R_1Q_0 > 0, V_2 = R_2, R_1 > C^{\mathrm{T}}R_2^{-1}C. \quad (13)$$

Then the negative feedback dynamic compensator $-G_c(s) \sim \left[\begin{array}{c|c} A_c & B_c \\ \hline -C_c & 0 \end{array}\right]$ given by (9)-(10) is strictly positive real and satisfies the design criteria (i), (ii). Furthermore, the H_2 performance criterion satisfies the bound $J(A_c, B_c, C_c) \leq \mathrm{tr}[QR_1 + QC^{\mathrm{T}}V_2^{-1}CQP]$.

Remark 3.1. Cross-weighting and cross-correlation terms were not included in either the H_2 case in [7] or the $\mathrm{H}_2/\mathrm{H}_\infty$ case in Theorem 3.2. In the H_2 case it can be shown that a cross-weighting term R_{12} and a cross-correlation term V_{12} can be allowed by replacing (13) by

$$V_1 = LL^{\mathrm{T}} + (1+\alpha)^2BR_2^{-1}B^{\mathrm{T}}, V_{12} = \alpha B, \quad (14)$$

$$V_2 = R_2, R_1 > R_{12}R_2^{-1}R_{12}^{\mathrm{T}} + C^{\mathrm{T}}R_2^{-1}C, \quad (15)$$

where $-2 \leq \alpha \leq 0$. In the $\mathrm{H}_2/\mathrm{H}_\infty$ case the terms R_{12} and V_{12} lead to additional complexity and thus are not considered here.

In order to apply Theorems 3.1 and 3.2, it is necessary to satisfy the positive real conditions (1), (2). For the case of a flexible structure with m force inputs and m velocity measurements, the colocated admittance, or driving point mobility, is characterized by $M\ddot{q} + C\dot{q} + Kq = B_0u, y = B_0^{\mathrm{T}}\dot{q}$, where M, C, and K are mass, damping and stiffness matrices, respectively, and B_0 is determined by the sensor/actuator locations. Choosing a realization for the system (3), (3) by

$$G(s) \sim \left[\begin{array}{c|c} \begin{bmatrix} 0 & I \\ -M^{-1}K & -M^{-1}C \end{bmatrix} & \begin{bmatrix} 0 \\ M^{-1}B_0 \end{bmatrix} \\ \hline \begin{bmatrix} 0 & B_0^{\mathrm{T}} \end{bmatrix} & 0 \end{array}\right]. \quad (16)$$

it follows that (1), (2) are satisfied by $Q_0 = \begin{bmatrix} K^{-1} & 0 \\ 0 & M^{-1} \end{bmatrix}$, $L = \begin{bmatrix} 0 \\ \sqrt{2}M^{-1}C^{1/2} \end{bmatrix}$, while (3), (3) hold with $P_0 = \begin{bmatrix} K & 0 \\ 0 & M \end{bmatrix}$, $\hat{L} = \begin{bmatrix} 0 & \sqrt{2}C^{1/2} \end{bmatrix}$ Thus $G(s)$ has the self-dual realization

$$G(s) \sim \left[\begin{array}{c|c} \begin{bmatrix} 0 & K^{1/2}M^{-1/2} \\ -M^{-1/2}K^{1/2} & -M^{-1/2}CM^{-1/2} \end{bmatrix} & \begin{bmatrix} 0 \\ M^{-1/2}B_0 \end{bmatrix} \\ \hline \begin{bmatrix} 0 & B_0^{\mathrm{T}}M^{-1/2} \end{bmatrix} & 0 \end{array}\right]. \quad (17)$$

4 Illustrative Numerical Example

For illustrative purposes consider a simply supported Euler-Bernoulli beam. The resulting state space model and problem data are

$$A = \underset{i=1,\ldots,5}{\text{block-diag}} \begin{bmatrix} 0 & 1 \\ -\omega_i^2 & -2\zeta\omega_i \end{bmatrix}, \quad \omega_i = i^2, \quad i = 1,\ldots,5, \quad \zeta = .01,$$

$$B = C^{\mathrm{T}} = \begin{bmatrix} 0 & 0.9877 & 0 & -0.309 & 0 & -0.891 & 0 & 0.5878 & 0 & 0.7071 \end{bmatrix}^{\mathrm{T}},$$

$$E_1 = \begin{bmatrix} 0 & 0.809 & 0 & -0.951 & 0 & 0.309 & 0 & 0.5878 & 0 & -1 \\ 0 & 0 & 0 & 0 & 0 & 0 & 0 & 0 & 0 & 0 \end{bmatrix},$$

$$E_2 = \begin{bmatrix} 0 & 1.9 \end{bmatrix}^{\mathrm{T}}, \quad R_1 = E_1^{\mathrm{T}}E_1, \quad D_1 = \begin{bmatrix} B & 0_{10\times 1} \end{bmatrix}, \quad D_2 = \begin{bmatrix} 0 & 1.9 \end{bmatrix},$$

$$V_2 = R_2 = D_2D_2^{\mathrm{T}} = E_2^{\mathrm{T}}E_2 = 3.61.$$

Note that with the above data, conditions (13) and (13) are not satisfied with strict inequality. Nevertheless, for $\gamma = \infty$ the H_2 controller was found to be positive real and yielded a closed-loop H_∞ performance of 14.13 dB (i.e., 14.13 dB above unity gain). Furthermore, for $\gamma = 12.02$ dB the $\mathrm{H}_2/\mathrm{H}_\infty$ positive real controller yielded a net H_∞ performance improvement of 2.65 dB (see Figure 1). This result is consistent with Theorem 1 of [19] which implies that the maximum ratio of the H_∞ performance of the optimal H_2 controller to the H_∞ performance of the optimal H_∞ controller can be no more than twice the number of right-half-plane transmission zeros for the transfer function between disturbances and measurements, and between control signals and performance variables. For the present problem with one nonminimum phase zero for the second transfer function, this bound corresponds to a factor of 2 (i.e., 6 dB). Finally, Figure 2 shows the gain and phase plots of the $\mathrm{H}_2/\mathrm{H}_\infty$ positive real controller.

[1] R. J. Benhabib, R. P. Iwens, and R. L. Jackson, "Stability of large space structure control systems using positivity concepts," *J. Guid. Contr.*, Vol. 4, pp. 487-494, 1981.

[2] S. M. Joshi, *Control of Large Flexible Space Structures*, New York: Springer-Verlag, 1989.

[3] W. M. Haddad and D. S. Bernstein, "Explicit construction of quadratic Lyapunov functions for the small gain, positivity, circle, and Popov theorems and their application to robust stability part I: Continuous-time theory," *Int. J. Robust Nonlinear Contr.*, to appear.

[4] M. J. Balas, "Direct velocity feedback control of large space structures," *J. Guid. Contr.*, Vol. 2, pp. 252-253, 1967.

[5] S. M. Joshi, "Robustness properties of collocated controllers for flexible spacecraft," *J. Guid. Contr.*, Vol. 9, pp. 85-91, 1986.

[6] M. D. McLaren and G. L. Slater, "Robust multivariable control of large space structures using positivity," *J. Guid. Contr. Dyn.*, Vol. 10, pp. 393-400, 1987.

[7] R. Lozano-Leal and S. M. Joshi, "On the design of dissipative LQG-type controller," *Proc. Conf. Dec. Contr.*, Austin, TX, pp. 1645-1646, 1988. Also in P. Dorato and R. K. Yedavalli, *Recent Advances in Robust Control*. New York: IEEE Press, 1990.

[8] G. Hewer and C. Kenney, "Dissipative LQG control systems," *IEEE Trans. Autom. Contr.*, Vol. AC-34, pp. 866-870, 1989.

[9] M. J. Jacobus, M. Jamshidi, C. Abdallah, P. Dorato and D. S. Bernstein, " Design of Strictly Positive Real, Fixed-Order Dynamic Compensators," *Proc. IEEE Conf. Dec. Contr.*, Honolulu, HI, pp. 3492-3495, 1990.

[10] J. D. Gardiner, "Stabilizing control for second-order models and positive real systems," *AIAA J. Guid. Contr. Dyn.*, Vol. 15, pp. 280-282, 1992.

[11] M. G. Safonov, E. A. Jonckheere, and D. J. N. Limebeer, "Synthesis of positive real multivariable feedback systems," *Int. J. Contr.*, Vol. 45, pp. 817-842, 1987.

[12] D. G. MacMartin and S. R. Hall, "Control of uncertain structures using an H_∞ power flow approach," *J. Guid. Contr. Dyn.*, Vol. 14, pp. 521-530, 1991.

[13] D. S. Bernstein and W. M. Haddad, "LQG control with an H_∞ performance bound: A Riccati equation approach," *IEEE Trans. Autom. Contr.*, Vol. AC-34, pp. 293-305, 1989.

[14] B. D. O. Anderson and S. Vongpanitlerd, *Network Analysis and Synthesis: A Modern Systems Theory Approach*, Englewood Cliffs, NJ: Prentice-Hall, 1973.

[15] J. Wen, "Time domain and frequency domain conditions for strict positive realness," *IEEE Trans. Autom. Contr.*, Vol. AC-33, pp. 988-992, 1988.

[16] R. Lozano-Leal and S. M. Joshi, "Strictly positive real transfer functions revisited," *IEEE Trans. Autom. Contr.*, Vol. AC-35, pp. 1243-1245, 1990.

[17] B. D. O. Anderson, "A system theory criterion for positive real matrices," *SIAM J. Contr. Optim.*, Vol. 5, pp. 171-182, 1967.

[18] B. D. O. Anderson, "Dual form of a positive real lemma," *Proc. IEEE*, Vol. 55, pp. 1749-1750, 1967.

[19] K. Zhou, "Comparison between H_2 and H_∞ controllers," *IEEE Trans. Autom. Contr.*, Vol. AC-37, pp. 1261-1265, 1992.

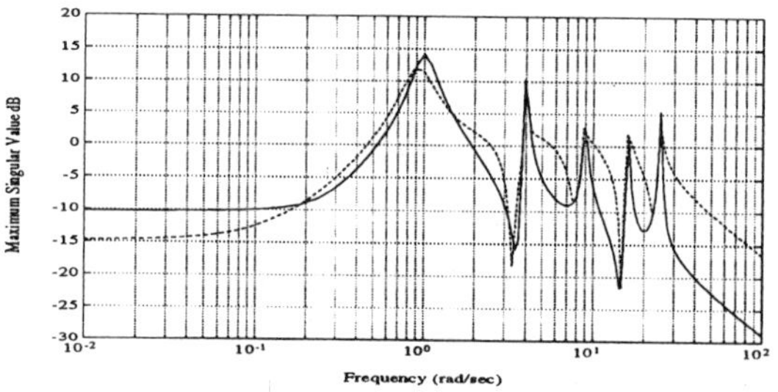

Figure 1: Comparison of $\| \tilde{G}(s) \|_\infty$ for H_2 Positive Real (Solid Line) and $\mathrm{H}_2/\mathrm{H}_\infty$ Positive Real (Dash Line) Controllers

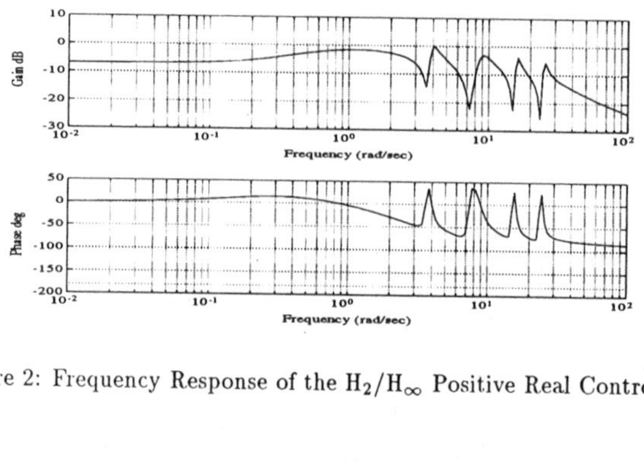

Figure 2: Frequency Response of the $\mathrm{H}_2/\mathrm{H}_\infty$ Positive Real Controller

Proceedings of the
American Control Conference
San Francisco, California • June 1993

Mixed H_2/H_∞ Control of Uncertain Systems

Riyanto BAMBANG†, Etsujiro SHIMEMURA†, Kenko UCHIDA†

†Department of Electrical Engineering, Waseda University
3-4-1 Ohkubo, Sinjuku-ku, Tokyo 169, JAPAN

Abstract: This paper considers mixed H_2/H_∞ control for linear systems with structured uncertainty via convex optimization. A generalized Riccati equation and a change of multivariable technique are emloyed in order to convexify the design problem. The resulting convex optimization problem is shown to be reducable to a Generalized Eigenvalue Minimization Problem.

1 Introduction

Mixed H_2/H_∞ control theory offers a way of combining disturbance attenuation which is guaranteed by H_∞-norm of a certain closed-loop transfer function, and quadratic performance which is measured by H_2-norm of another transfer function[2,3,5,7]. Due to inherent conservativeness of H_∞-norm measure for robust stability[11,14], however, mixed H_2/H_∞ design may not be of practical use when the designer know some of the structure of uncertainty. This form of uncertainty arises for example when there is real perturbation in the nominal model of the state space system or when modeling multiple (unstructured) uncertainty at different locations in the feedback loop[11,13]. There exist relatively a few works on mixed H_2/H_∞ control theory that were also devoted to deal with structured uncertainties. Yeh *et al.*[9] extends the standard mixed H_2/H_∞ to include real parameter variations using a surrogate system concept. Madiwale[6] discusses the problem of computing optimal values of a real block diagonal scaling matrix to reduce conservatism in the standard mixed H_2/H_∞ control theory, which may be considered as time domain approach to μ synthesis. The results of Madiwale however, requires iterations for updating scaling matrix where in each iteration a coupled Riccati equations need to be solved. At present, there is no efficient method for solving coupled Riccati equations other than homotopic continuation method. The approach of Yeh *et al.* also requires solving coupled Riccati equations.

In this paper, similar problem as that of Madiwale is discussed, but different approach is employed. We show that mixed H_2/H_∞ state feedback problem with diagonal structured uncertainties can be reduced to a convex optimization problem over a bounded subset of symmetric matrices as well as over diagonal matrices with certain structure, avoiding solving coupled Riccati equations. This extends mixed H_2/H_∞ control via convex optimization developed by Khargonekar and Rotea[3] to include structured uncertainty. This paper is a first step toward a more general and nonconservative mixed H_2/H_∞ robust performance design. All the proofs are omitted for lack of space.

2 Problem Formulation and Preliminaries

Consider finite-dimensional time-invariant linear system described by

$$\begin{aligned} \dot{x}(t) &= Ax(t) + B_1u_1(t) + B_2u_2(t) + B_3u_3(t) \\ z_1(t) &= C_1x(t) + D_{12}u_2(t) \\ z_2(t) &= C_2x(t) + D_{22}u_2(t) \\ z_3(t) &= C_3x(t) + D_{32}u_2(t) \\ y(t) &= x(t) \\ u_3(t) &= \Delta z_3(t), \end{aligned} \tag{2.1}$$

where $x(t) \in \mathbf{R}^{n_x}$ is the state; $u_1(t) \in \mathbf{R}^{n_{u_1}}$ is the disturbance; $u_2(t)$ is the control; $u_3(t) \in \mathbf{R}^{n_{u_3}}$ is the fictitious input; $z_1(t) \in \mathbf{R}^{n_{z_1}}$ is the performance variable associated with H_∞ constraint; $z_2(t) \in \mathbf{R}^{n_{z_2}}$ is the performance variable associated with H_2 criterion; $y(t) \in \mathbf{R}^{n_y}$ is the measurement; and $z_3(t) \in \mathbf{R}^{n_{z_3}}$ is the fictitious output. In the description (2.1), $n_{u_3} = n_{z_3}$. Let (A, B_2) be stabilizable. Assume that the perturbation matrix Δ consists of repeated scalar blocks and full blocks. Thus, Δ is a subset of the block structure $\mathbf{\Delta}$(a prescribed set of block diagonal matrices) defined by:

$$\mathbf{\Delta} := \{diag[d_1I_{r_1}, ..., d_sI_{r_s}, \Delta_{n_1}, ..., \Delta_{n_f}] :\ d_j \in \mathbf{C},\ \Delta j \in \mathbf{C}^{n_j \times n_j}\}, \tag{2.2}$$

where $\bar{\sigma}$ denotes maximum singular value. The two integers s and f in the above expression represent scalar and full blocks, respectively. The $i'th$ scalar blocks is $r_i \times r_i$, while the $j'th$ full blocks is $n_j \times n_j$. In other words, Δ takes the form of complex-valued, block diagonal perturbations, comprised of $d_i I_{ri}$ repeated scalar blocks, and Δ_{n_j} full blocks. The fullblocks can arise from multivariable neglected dynamics, while the repeated scalar blocks may represent affine parametric uncertainty in the nominal description of the system (2.1). We will need the bounded subsets of Δ, and we introduce the following notation

$$\mathbf{B\Delta} = \{\Delta \in \mathbf{\Delta} : \bar{\sigma}(\Delta) \leq 1\}. \tag{2.3}$$

Then for uncertainty block $\Delta \in \mathbf{\Delta}$ to be the subset of $\mathbf{B\Delta}$, we will require in (2.2) that $|d_j| \leq 1$ and $\bar{\sigma}(\Delta_j) \leq 1$. In this paper, it is assumed that we were given the plant description (2.1) (see [11,13] for the discussion on how the affine parametric uncertainty and/or unmodeled dynamic can be represented in the form of equation (2.1)).

The mixed H_2/H_∞ robust control problem considered in this paper is formulated as follows: for the plant given by (2.1), determine state feedback controller described by

$$u_2(t) = Kx(t) \tag{2.4}$$

such that the following design criteria are satisfied,

1. If $u_1(t)$ is an L_2 deterministic signal, the closed-loop transfer function from $u_1(t)$ to $z_1(t)$ satisfies
$$\sup_{\Delta \in \mathbf{B\Delta}} \|T_{z_1u_1}(s)\|_\infty < 1; \tag{2.5}$$
2. If $u_1(t)$ is a white noise signal with unit strength, the nominal H_2 performance criterion defined by
$$J := \lim_{T\to\infty} \mathcal{E}\{\frac{1}{T}\int_0^T [z_2(t)'z_2(t)]dt\} \tag{2.6}$$
is minimized, where $\mathcal{E}$ denotes the expectation;
3. The closed-loop system is asymptotically stable for all perturbations $\Delta \in \mathbf{B\Delta}$.

Suppose $T_{z_3u_3}(s)$ denotes the transfer function with compensator loop closed and uncertainty loop $u_3 \to y_3$ open. Then by the small gain theorem, the stability condition (3) is implied by

$$\|MT_{z_3u_3}M^{-1}\|_\infty < 1, \tag{2.7}$$

where M is a scaling matrix that is commute with Δ,

$$\begin{aligned} M \ :=\ & \{diag[M_1, ..., M_s, m_1I_{n_1}, ..., m_fI_{n_f}] :\ M_i \in \mathbf{C}^{r_i \times r_i}, M_i = M_i^* > 0, \\ & m_j \in \mathbf{R}, m_j > 0\}. \end{aligned} \tag{2.8}$$

The closed-loop system(depicted in Figure 1) can be written as

$$\begin{aligned} \dot{\tilde{x}} &= \tilde{A}\tilde{x} + \tilde{B}_1u_1 + \tilde{B}_3u_3 \\ z_1 = \tilde{C}_1\tilde{x},\quad & z_2 = \tilde{C}_2\tilde{x},\quad z_3 = \tilde{C}_3\tilde{x} \\ u_3 &= \Delta z_3, \end{aligned} \tag{2.9}$$

where

$$\tilde{A} = A + B_2K,\ \tilde{B}_1 = B_1,\ \tilde{B}_3 = B_3$$
$$\tilde{C}_1 = C_1 + D_{12}K,\ \tilde{C}_2 = C_2 + D_{22}K,\ \tilde{C}_3 = C_3 + D_{32}K.$$

Suppose that the nominal closed-loop system (2.9) is internally stable. Then under the absence of diagonal structured uncertainty, H_2 performance in (2.5) can be expressed as

$$J = \|T_{z_2u_1}\|_2^2 = tr\ [\tilde{C}_2'\tilde{C}_2P], \tag{2.10}$$

where P is positive definite solution to Lyapunov equation

$$\tilde{A}P + P\tilde{A}' + \tilde{B}_1\tilde{B}_1' = 0. \tag{2.11}$$

To this end, let us restrict the matrix M_i in (2.8) to be real symmetric matrices[18]. This introduces a certain conservativeness of the design. The following proposition gives a condition that guarantee the satisfaction of closed-loop stability and H_∞ performance bound for all structured perturbations. The proof is based on robust performance theorem of μ analysis[11] and characterization of H_∞-norm bound in terms of Riccati equation.

Proposition 2.1 *Consider the closed-loop system described in (2.9), with Δ given in (2.2). Suppose that the following condition is satisfied,*

$$\|\hat{M}\hat{C}(sI - \tilde{A})^{-1}\hat{B}\hat{M}^{-1}\|_\infty < 1 \tag{2.12}$$

where

$$\hat{M} := \begin{bmatrix} I & 0 \\ 0 & M \end{bmatrix},\ \hat{C} := \begin{bmatrix} \tilde{C}_1 \\ \tilde{C}_3 \end{bmatrix},\ \hat{B} := \begin{bmatrix} \tilde{B}_1 & \tilde{B}_3 \end{bmatrix}.$$

Then,

1. *The closed-loop system is asymptotically stable for all perturbations* $\Delta \in \mathbf{B\Delta}$;

2. *The worst-case disturbance attenuation satisfies*

$$\sup_{\Delta \in \mathbf{B\Delta}} \|T_{z_1 u_1}\|_\infty < 1;$$

3. *There exists* $\tilde{P} \geq 0$ *satisfying*

$$\tilde{A}\tilde{P} + \tilde{P}\tilde{A}' + \tilde{P}\tilde{C}_1'\tilde{C}_1\tilde{P} + \tilde{B}_1\tilde{B}_1' + \tilde{P}\tilde{C}_3'W\tilde{C}_3\tilde{P} + \tilde{B}_3W^{-1}\tilde{B}_3' = 0 \quad (2.13)$$

such that $[\tilde{A} + \tilde{P}(\tilde{C}_1'\tilde{C}_1 + \tilde{C}_3'W\tilde{C}_3)]$ *is asymptotically stable, where* $W := M'M$.

For convenience in stating some of the results of this paper, let us define

$$R(M,\tilde{P}) := \tilde{A}\tilde{P} + \tilde{P}\tilde{A}' + \tilde{P}\tilde{C}_1'\tilde{C}_1\tilde{P} + \tilde{B}_1\tilde{B}_1' + \tilde{P}\tilde{C}_3'W\tilde{C}_3\tilde{P} + \tilde{B}_3W^{-1}\tilde{B}_3' \quad (2.14)$$

Suppose that the condition in Proposition 2.1 is satisfied. Then, the following conditions can be easily verified[3,7],

$$0 \leq P \leq \tilde{P} \leq \hat{P}, \quad (2.15)$$
$$J \leq \tilde{J} := tr[\tilde{C}_2'\tilde{C}_2\tilde{P}], \quad (2.16)$$

where $\hat{P}$ denotes any real symmetric solution to the Riccati inequality $R(M,\hat{P}) < 0$, with R defined by (2.14). Note that $\tilde{J}$, which is given in terms of solution to Riccati equation $R(M,\tilde{P}) = 0$, is an upperbound to the quadratic cost J. Instead of minimizing the quadratic cost it self, we will minimize this upperbound in our optimization problem to be defined later.

The following result is direct generalization to that of [3, Lemma 2.1], the different being that in the present paper Riccati equation arising in the definition of the upper bound involves a scaling matrix, as well as an additional quadratic term.

Lemma 2.1 *Consider the closed-loop system described in (2.9) and let* T_{zu} *denote the transfer function matrix from* (u_1,u_3) *to* (z_1,z_2,z_3). *Suppose that* $\|\hat{M}\tilde{C}(sI-\tilde{A})^{-1}\tilde{B}\hat{M}^{-1}\|_\infty < 1$. *Then,*

$$\tilde{J}(T_{zu}) = inf\{tr(\tilde{C}_2'\tilde{C}_2\tilde{P}) : \tilde{P} = \tilde{P}' > 0 \ \ such\ that\ \ R(M,\tilde{P}) < 0\}. \quad (2.17)$$

Now, let the plant (2.1) be denoted by $\mathcal{P}$. We call a controller K *admissible* if K internally stabilizes the plant $\mathcal{P}$ *for all structured perturbations* $\Delta \in \mathbf{B\Delta}$. Introduce the following sets :

$$\begin{aligned}\mathcal{A}(\mathcal{P}) &:= \{K : K \text{ is admissible}\}\\ \mathcal{A}_\infty(\mathcal{P}) &:= \{K \in \mathcal{A}(\mathcal{P}) : \ \|\hat{M}\tilde{C}(sI-\tilde{A})^{-1}\tilde{B}\hat{M}^{-1}\|_\infty < 1,\\ &\qquad \hat{M} = \{diag\{I,M\}\},\ \ M \in \mathcal{M}\}. \quad (2.18)\end{aligned}$$

In the above expression, $\mathcal{M}$ is the set of matrices commuting with all elements of Q, where Q is the subset of $\mathbf{C}^{n_{u_3}\times n_{u_3}}$ describing the uncertainty structure, and every element Δ of Q has the form (2.2). Thus, every element M of $\mathcal{M}$ has the form (2.8).

In view of Proposition 2.1 and Lemma 2.1, we consider the following synthesis problem which may be considered as an extension of "suboptimal H_2/H_∞ controller synthesis" introduced by Khargonekar and Rotea[3] to the finite dimensional plant under the presence of diagonal structured uncertainty.

Synthesis Problem: "Compute the mixed performance measure

$$\theta_m(\mathcal{P}) := inf\{\tilde{J}(T_{zu}) : K \in \mathcal{A}_\infty(\mathcal{P})\}, \quad (2.19)$$

and, given any $\theta > \theta_m$, find a controller $K \in \mathcal{A}_\infty(\mathcal{P})$ such that $\tilde{J}(T_{zu}) < \theta$".

3 Convex Optimization Approach

In this section we will develop a convex optimization approach for solving the controller synthesis problem introduced above. Motivated by the result of [3], where it is proved that all memoryless state feedback mixed H_2/H_∞ controllers cannot be improved upon by the use of dynamic "full information" controllers, we are interested in the computation of constant state feedback matrices for the minimization of $\tilde{J}(\mathcal{P},K)$. The set of such controllers will be denoted by

$$\mathcal{A}_{\infty,s}(\mathcal{P}) := \{K \in \mathcal{A}_\infty(\mathcal{P}) : K \in \mathbf{R}^{n_{u_2}\times n_y}\}. \quad (3.1)$$

It will be shown that the optimal performance $\theta_m(\mathcal{P})$ defined in (2.19) is the value of (finite dimensional) convex optimization problem. Further, given any $\theta > \theta_m$, one can find K such that $\tilde{J}(\mathcal{P},K) < \theta$ by solving a convex programming problem.

Let Ξ denote the set of $n_x \times n_x$ real symmetric matrices, and define

$$\Omega := \{(X,M,\tilde{P}) \in \mathbf{R}^{n_{u_2}\times n_x} \times \mathbf{R}^{n_{u_3}\times n_{u_3}} \times \Xi : \tilde{P} > 0, M \in \mathcal{M}\}. \quad (3.2)$$

Observe that Ω is an open strictly convex subset of $\mathbf{R}^{n_{u_2}\times n_x} \times \mathbf{R}^{n_{u_3}\times n_{u_3}} \times \Xi$. Given $(X,M,\tilde{P}) \in \Omega$, define

$$f(X,M,\tilde{P}) := tr[(C_2\tilde{P} + D_{22}X)\tilde{P}^{-1}((C_2\tilde{P} + D_{22}X)'] \quad (3.3)$$

and, for $(X,M,\tilde{P}) \in \mathbf{R}^{n_{u_2}\times n_x} \times \mathbf{R}^{n_{u_3}\times n_{u_3}} \times \Xi$, let

$$\begin{aligned}\hat{R}(X,M,\tilde{P}) &:= A\tilde{P} + \tilde{P}A' + B_2X + X'B_2' + B_1B_1'\\ &+ (C_1\tilde{P} + D_{12}X)'(C_1\tilde{P} + D_{12}X)\\ &+ (MC_3\tilde{P} + D_{32}X)'(MC_3\tilde{P} + D_{32}X) + B_3(M'M)^{-1}B_3'. \quad (3.4)\end{aligned}$$

Define also the set of real matrices:

$$\Phi(\mathcal{P}) := \{(X,M,\tilde{P}) \in \Omega : \hat{R}(X,M,\tilde{P}) < 0\} \quad (3.5)$$

and consider the optimization problem

$$\tau(\mathcal{P}) := inf\{f(X,M,\tilde{P}) : (X,M,\tilde{P}) \in \Phi(\mathcal{P})\}. \quad (3.6)$$

The following result is a direct generalization of Theorem 4.1 of [3].

Theorem 3.1 *Consider the plant* $\mathcal{P}$ *defined in (2.1). Let* P *denote its transfer matrix, and* $\mathcal{A}_{\infty,s}(\mathcal{P})$ *denote the set of controllers defined in (3.1). Let* $\Phi(\mathcal{P})$ *be given by (3.5). Let* θ_m *and* $\tau(\mathcal{P})$ *be as defined in (2.19) and (3.6), respectively, with* K *restricted to be the subset of* $\mathcal{A}_{\infty,s}(\mathcal{P})$. *Then,*

$$\mathcal{A}_{\infty,m}(\mathcal{P}) \neq \emptyset \quad (3.7)$$

if, and only if,

$$\Phi(\mathcal{P}) \neq \emptyset \quad (3.8)$$

with $\emptyset$ *denote empty set. In this case,*

$$\theta_m(\mathcal{P}) = \tau(\mathcal{P}). \quad (3.9)$$

Furthermore, given any $\theta > \theta_m(\mathcal{P})$, *there exists* $(X,M,\tilde{P}) \in \Phi(\mathcal{P})$ *such that the state feedback gain* $K := X\tilde{P}^{-1}$ *satisfies*

$$K \in \mathcal{A}_{\infty,s}(\mathcal{P}) \ \ and\ \ \tilde{J}(T_{zu},K) \leq f(X,M,\tilde{P}) < \theta. \quad (3.10)$$

From Theorem 3.1, it follows that the computation of $\tau(\mathcal{P})$ involves a search over the set $\Phi(\mathcal{P})$, where X, M, and $\tilde{P}$ serve as the decision variables. On the other hand $\theta_m(\mathcal{P})$ is computed by solving nonlinear programming problem with only the real matrix K as the decision variable. We will show that the optimization problem defined in (3.6) is indeed a *convex problem*.

Theorem 3.2 *Let* f *and* Φ *be as defined in (3.3) and (3.5), respectively, and consider the optimization problem (3.6). Then, the set* Φ *is convex and the function* $f : \Phi \to \mathbf{R}^+$ *is convex and real analytic. Consequently, the optimization problem defined in (3.6) is convex.*

Remark 3.1
Under certain condition similar to that of Lemma 4.6 in [3], we can show that the set Φ defined in (3.5) is bounded. This condition is useful in guaranteeing that a numerical algorithm can be effectively used to solve (3.6).

Remark 3.2
While the result of this paper only guarantees to provide an optimized *nominal* H_2 *performance*, in view of the results of [16] it may be extended to the synthesis problem which provides, in addition to robust H_∞ performance, a robust H_2 performance by viewing structured uncertainty Δ as a single norm bounded (unstructured) uncertainty.

Let us consider again mixed H_2/H_∞ robust control synthesis for the state feedback plant $\mathcal{P}$. Suppose that $\theta > 0$ is given. From Theorems 3.1 and 3.2, we know that there exists $K \in \mathcal{A}_{\infty,s}(\mathcal{P})$ such that $\tilde{J}(T_{zu},K) < \theta$ if only if there exists $(X,M,\tilde{P}) \in \Phi$ such that $f(X,M,\tilde{P}) < \theta$. And in this case, the real matrix $K := X\tilde{P}^{-1}$ is a solution to the sub-optimal synthesis problem. The problem of finding $(X,M,\tilde{P}) \in \Phi$ such that $f(X,M,\tilde{P}) < \theta$ is a convex *feasibility program* which is a (nonsmooth) convex optimization problem[12].

4 Reduction To Generalized Eigenvalue Minimization Problem

In this section, we will show that the optimization problem defined in (3.6) can be reduced to Generalized Eigenvalue Minimization Problem(GEMP) developed in [12]. This is the problem of minimizing the maximum generalized eigenvalue of a(symmetric, symmetric positive-definite) pair of matrices that depend affinely on a variable x that is subject to some constraints. In [12], a fast and attractive algorithm based on Interior Point Method has been applied to solve efficiently GEMP.

In the general case, GEMP with variables $x \in \mathbf{R}^m$ and $\lambda \in \mathbf{R}$ takes the form

$$\min_{\substack{\lambda G(x) - F(x) > 0\\ G(x) > 0\\ H(x) > 0}} \lambda \quad (4.1)$$

or equivalently,

$$\min_{\substack{G(x) > 0\\ H(x) > 0}} \lambda_{max}(F(x),G(x)). \quad (4.2)$$

where λ_{max} denotes the generalized maximum eigenvalue. This is a function defined on a pair of matrices X,Y by $\lambda_{max}(X,Y) := max\{\lambda \in \mathbf{R} | det(\lambda Y -$

$X) = 0\}$. In (4.1) and (4.2), F ,G and H are symmetric matrices that depend affinely on $x \in \mathbf{R}^m$:

$$F(x) := F_0 + \sum_{i=1}^{m} x_i F_i,\ G(x) := G_0 + \sum_{i=1}^{m} x_i G_i,\ H(x) := H_0 + \sum_{i=1}^{m} x_i H_i (4.3)$$

where $F_i = F_i'$, $G_i = G_i' \in \mathbf{R}^{r\times r}$, and $H_i = H_i' \in \mathbf{R}^{s\times s}$. Matrices $F(x)$ and $G(x)$ may be complex Hermitian.

Let us turn our attention to the optimization problem defined in (3.6). Let us rewrite the objective function (3.3) as:

$$f(X,M,\tilde{P}) = tr(C_2\tilde{P}C_2' + C_2X'D_{22}' + D_2XC_2' + D_{22}X\tilde{P}^{-1}X'D_{22}'). \quad (4.4)$$

The last term $\Theta(X, M, \tilde{P} := D_{22}X\tilde{P}^{-1}X'D_{22}'$ in the above equation can be equivalently expressed as

$$\Theta(X,M,\tilde{P}) = \min_{\begin{bmatrix} S & D_{22}X \\ X'D_{22}' & \tilde{P} \end{bmatrix} > 0} tr(S).$$

Let us introduce the change of variable $\tilde{W} = (M'M)^{-1}$. Let us further define

$$\begin{aligned}
L_1(\lambda, X, \tilde{W}, \tilde{P}, S) &:= -tr(C_2\tilde{P}C_2' + C_2X'D_{22}' + D_{22}XC_2') - tr(S) + \lambda \\
L_2(\lambda, X, \tilde{W}, \tilde{P}, S) &:= -\begin{bmatrix} L_{2a} & L_{2b} \\ L_{2c} & L_{2d} \end{bmatrix} \\
L_3(\lambda, X, \tilde{W}, \tilde{P}, S) &:= \begin{bmatrix} S & D_{22}X \\ X'D_{22}' & \tilde{P} \end{bmatrix} \\
L(\lambda, X, \tilde{W}, \tilde{P}, S) &:= diag(L_1, L_2, L_3),
\end{aligned}$$

where

$$\begin{aligned}
L_{2a} &= -(A\tilde{P} + \tilde{P}A' + B_2X + X'B_2' + B_1B_1' + B_3\tilde{W}B_3') \\
L_{2b} &= [(C_1\tilde{P} + D_{12}X)' \quad (C_3\tilde{P} + D_{32}X)'] \\
L_{2c} &= L_{2b}' \\
L_{2d} &= \begin{bmatrix} I & 0 \\ 0 & \tilde{W} \end{bmatrix}.
\end{aligned}$$

Note carefully that $L_1(\lambda, X, \tilde{W}, \tilde{P}, S)$, $L_2(\lambda, X, \tilde{W}, \tilde{P}, S)$ and $L_3(\lambda, X, \tilde{W}, \tilde{P}, S)$ are affine matrix in the variables $(\lambda, X, \tilde{W}, \tilde{P})$.

Using the above constructions and employing the Schur complement formula, our optimization problem (3.6) can now be represented as

$$\min_{\substack{L(\lambda, X, \tilde{W}, \tilde{P}, S) > 0 \\ \tilde{W} \in \mathcal{M}}} \lambda. \quad (4.5)$$

Represented in the form of (4.1), symmetric affine matrices $F(x)$ and $G(x)$ for the optimization problem (4.5) are given by

$$\begin{aligned}
F(x) &:= diag([-tr(C_2\tilde{P}C_2' + C_2X'D_{22}' + D_{22}XC_2') - tr(S)], L_2, L_3) \\
G(x) &:= diag(1,0,0,0)
\end{aligned}$$

Vector x in (4.1) then contains the optimization variables which consist of the independent variables of $(\lambda, X, \tilde{W}, \tilde{P}, S)$. Since the constraint $L(\lambda, X, \tilde{W}, \tilde{P}, S) > 0$ has been expressed in terms of matrices that are affine in $(\lambda, X, \tilde{W}, \tilde{P}, S)$, the additional constraint $\tilde{W} \in \mathcal{M}$ in (4.5) can be handled easily using partition technique described on p. 57 in [11]. The GEMP can be effectively solved using Interior Point Method. Detailed algorithm as well as its convergence can be found in [12]. The definiteness requirement of $G(x)$ in (4.1) can be accomplished by simple modification(via the use of variable λ) of the above expression for $G(x)$, as well as by a minor modification on the algorithm of [12].

5 Conclusion

The problem of synthesizing mixed H_2/H_∞ robust controllers has been presented for finite dimensional linear time-invariant systems under the presence of structured uncertainty. This synthesis problem is well motivated since in addition to providing robust stability and robust H_∞ performance under the presence structured uncertainty, it also provides an optimized (nominal) quadratic performance. This suboptimal synthesis problem has been reduced to convex optimization problem over a bounded subset of symmetric matrices as well as diagonal matrix having certain structure, via the use of a Riccati equation and a change of variables. The resulting convex optimization problem has been reduced to the Generalized Eigenvalue Minimization Problem where a powerful algorithm based on interior point method(analytic center) has been developed to find its solution[12].

Acknowledgements: The first author would like to thank Prof. S.P. Boyd of Stanford Univ., USA, and Dr. El Ghaoui of ENSTA, France, for providing preprints of [12] and [15].

References

[1] Marshall, A.W. and Olkin, I., *Inequalities: Theory of Majorization and Its Application*, Academic Press, New York, 1979.

[2] Yeh, H.H., Banda, S.S. and Chang, B.C., "Necessary and Sufficient Conditions for Mixed H_2 and H_∞ Optimal Control", IEEE T.A.C., vol. 37, no. 3, pp. 355-357, 1992.

[3] Khargonekar, P.P. and Rotea, M.A., "Mixed H_2/H_∞ Control : A Convex Optimization Approach", IEEE T.A.C., vol. 36, no. 7, pp. 824-836, 1991.

[4] Boyd, S.P. and Barrat, C.H., "Linear Controller Design: Limits of Performance", Prentice Hall,1991.

[5] Doyle, J. et.al.,"Optimal Control with Mixed H_2 and H_∞ Performance Objectives", in Proc. American Control Conf.(ACC), pp. 2065-2070, 1989.

[6] Madiwale, A.N., "Reduction of Conservatism In Mixed H_2/H_∞ Design", Proc. 28th Conf. Decision and Control, pp. 923-925, 1989.

[7] Bernstein, D.S. and Haddad, W.M.,"LQG Control with an H_∞ Performance Bound : A Riccati Equations Approach", IEEE T.A.C., vol.34, no.3, pp. 293-305, 1989.

[8] Bambang, R., Shimemura, E. and Uchida, K., "Discrete-Time H_2/H_∞ Robust Control With State Feedback", Proc. 1991 ACC, 1991.

[9] Yeh, H., Banda, S., Sharon, A.H. and Barlett, A.C., "Robust Control Design with Real Parameter Uncertainty and Unmodelled Dynamics", J. Guidance, Control and Dynamics, vol. 13, no.2, pp. 1117-1125, 1990.

[10] Bambang, R., Shimemura, E. and Uchida, K., "Mixed H_2/H_∞ Control with Pole Placement: State Feedback Case", Proc. 1993 American Control Conf., 1993.

[11] Doyle, J.C., Packard, A., and Zhou, K., "Review of LFTs, LMIs, and μ", draft, 1991.

[12] Boyd, S., and El Ghaoui, L., "Method of Centers For Minimizing Generalized Eigenvalues", preprint, 1992.

[13] Steinbuch, M., Terlouw, J.C., and Bosgra, O.H., "Robustness Analysis for Real and Complex perturbations Applied to an Electro Mechanical System", Proc. IEE Pt. D, 1992.

[14] Fan, M.K.H., Tits, A.L., and Doyle, J.C., "Robustness in the Presence of Mixed Parametric Uncertainty and Unmodeled Dynamics", IEEE T.A.C., vol. 36, no. 1, pp. 25-38, 1991.

[15] Balakrishnan, V., Feron, E., Boyd, S. and El Ghaoui, L., "Computing Bounds For Structured Singular Value Via An Interior Point Algorithm", Proc. American Control Conf., 1992.

[16] Stoorvogel, A.A., "The Robust H_2 Control Problem: A Worst Case Design", Proc. 30th Conf. Decision and Control, pp. 194-199, 1991.

[17] Zhou, K. et al., "Mixed H_2 and H_∞ Performance Objectives I: Robust Performance Analysis", preprint, 1992

[18] Morton, B.G, "A Mu-Test For Robustness Analysis Of A Real Parameter Variation Problem", Proc. 1985 American Control Conf., pp.135-138, 1985.

[19] Kaminer I., Khargonekar, P.P. and Rotea, M., "Mixed H_2/H_∞ Control of Discrete-Time Systems via Convex Optimization", Proc. 1992 ACC, 1992.

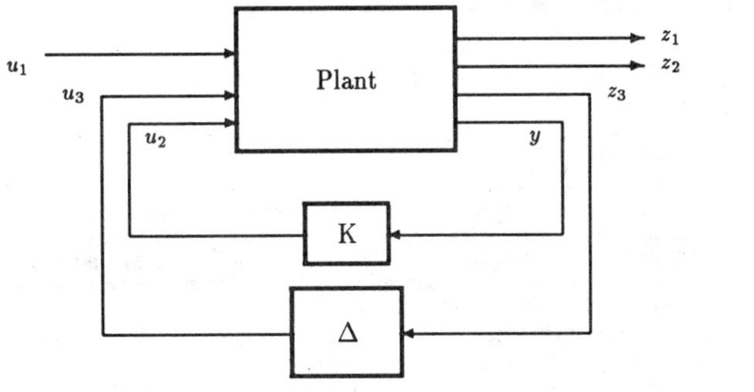

Figure 1: General framework for mixed H_2/H_∞ robust control design with structured uncertainty

Proceedings of the
American Control Conference
San Francisco, California • June 1993

H_2 controller design with an H_∞ bounded controller

Johan David[2] Bart De Moor[3]
Department of Electrical Engineering Katholieke Universiteit Leuven
Kardinaal Mercierlaan 94 B-3001 Leuven Belgium
tel: ++32/16/220931 fax: ++32/16/221855
email: david@esat.kuleuven.ac.be demoor@esat.kuleuven.ac.be

Abstract

In this paper the minimization of an H_2 norm is considered, when the controller is restricted to be linear, stable, finite dimensional and H_∞-norm bounded. It is also shown how this can be used in the design of a mixed H_2/H_∞ controller.

1 Introduction

In recent years there has been a lot of interest in the mixed H_2/H_∞ design problem (e.g. [1]-[6]). This problem is stated as minimizing an H_2-norm subject to the constraint that an H_∞-norm inequality has to be satisfied. In most papers, however, not the real H_2-norm is minimized but an upper bound. In this paper an other problem is considered first. The H_2-norm of a transfer function should be minimized using a linear, stable, finite dimensional controller that satisfies an H_∞-bound. Necessary conditions for this problem are derived, using a parameterization of this set of controllers of Steinbuch and Bosgra [5]. This can then be used to find controllers of a certain finite dimension that minimize a H_2-norm subject to a H_∞-norm constraint, as in the case of the general mixed H_2/H_∞ design problem.

2 Parameterization of H_∞ norm bounded transfer functions

In [5] Steinbuch and Bosgra describe a parameterization for strictly proper, stable, norm-bounded finite dimensional transfer functions:
Let the set Ω_γ^* be defined as

$$\Omega_\gamma^* = \{F(s) \mid \|F(s)\|_\infty < \gamma, F(s) \text{ stable, real rational,}$$

$$\text{strictly proper and of McMillan degree} \leq n\}$$

and consider the set Ω_γ

$$\Omega_\gamma = \{C(sI-A)^{-1}B | A = A_s + A_k, A_s = -\frac{1}{2}\gamma^{-2}BB^T$$

$$-\frac{1}{2}C^TC,\ A_k = -A_k^T \in \mathbb{R}^{n\times n}, B \in \mathbb{R}^{n\times n_w}, C \in \mathbb{R}^{n_z\times n}\}$$

Proposition 1 *[5]:* $\Omega_\gamma = \Omega_\gamma^*$.

[1] The following text presents research results obtained within the framework of the Belgian programme on interuniversity attraction poles initiated by the Belgian State - Prime Minister's Office - Science Policy Programming. The scientific responsibility is assumed by its authors.

[2] Johan David is a research assistant with the N.F.W.O. (Belgian National Fund for Scientific Research).

[3] Bart De Moor is a research associate with the N.F.W.O.

3 H_2 optimization with an H_∞ bounded controller

In this section necessary conditions are derived for a H_∞-norm bounded controller that minimizes an H_2-norm. We will call this problem a constrained H_2 problem.
Consider the following linear, time invariant plant:

$$\begin{aligned} \dot{x} &= Ax + B_1w + B_2u \\ z &= C_1x + D_{11}w + D_{12}u \\ y &= C_2x + D_{21}w + D_{22}u \end{aligned} \qquad (1)$$

Now find a dynamic, stable, strictly proper, H_∞-norm bounded controller K, $u = Ky$, that stabilizes the closed loop and such that the H_2-norm of the closed loop transfer function from w to z is minimized. K has to belong to Ω_γ. Without loss of generality γ can be taken $\gamma = 1$. The state space realization of the controller is then:

$$\begin{aligned} \dot{x}_c &= A_cx_c + B_cy \\ u &= C_cx_c \end{aligned} \qquad (2)$$

To make the 2-norm of the closed loop finite, D_{11} has to be 0. For notational reasons, we also assume $D_{22} = 0$. This is not a limitation, as the controller is strictly proper. This is shown e.g. in the paper of Glover and Doyle on H_∞ control [7].
From (1) and (2) the state space realization of the closed loop can be derived ($D_{11} = 0$ and $D_{22} = 0$):

$$\begin{pmatrix} \dot{x} \\ \dot{x}_c \end{pmatrix} = \begin{pmatrix} A & B_2C_c \\ B_cC_2 & A_c \end{pmatrix}\begin{pmatrix} x \\ x_c \end{pmatrix} + \begin{pmatrix} B_1 \\ B_cD_{21} \end{pmatrix} w$$

$$z = \begin{pmatrix} C_1 & D_{12}C_c \end{pmatrix}\begin{pmatrix} x \\ x_c \end{pmatrix}$$

Define

$$\overline{A} = \begin{pmatrix} A & B_2C_c \\ B_cC_2 & A_c \end{pmatrix} \quad \overline{B} = \begin{pmatrix} B_1 \\ B_cD_{21} \end{pmatrix}$$

$$\overline{C} = \begin{pmatrix} C_1 & D_{12}C_c \end{pmatrix}$$

The control objective can be expressed as $\min_{K\in\Omega_1}$ trace$\{\overline{C}^t\overline{C}S\}$ where S is the solution of $\overline{A}S + S\overline{A}^t + \overline{B}\overline{B}^t = 0$. Necessary conditions for this problem are given in the following lemma:

Lemma 1 *Necessary conditions for the constrained H_2 problem.*

Given the state space realization of (1), a stable, finite dimensional, strictly proper controller K, with H_∞-norm smaller than 1, that stabilizes the closed loop *and minimizes the H_2-norm of the closed loop transfer function from w to z satisfies the following equations:*

$$\overline{A}S + S\overline{A}^t + \overline{B}\overline{B}^t = 0$$
$$P\overline{A} + \overline{A}^t P + \overline{C}^t\overline{C} = 0$$

$$\begin{pmatrix} P_{12}^t & P_{22} \end{pmatrix}\begin{pmatrix} S_{12} \\ S_{22} \end{pmatrix} = \begin{pmatrix} S_{12}^t & S_{22} \end{pmatrix}\begin{pmatrix} P_{12} \\ P_{22} \end{pmatrix}$$

$$A_s + \frac{1}{2}B_cB_c^t + \frac{1}{2}C_c^tC_c = 0$$

$$B_c = \left[\begin{pmatrix} S_{12}^t & S_{22} \end{pmatrix}\begin{pmatrix} P_{12} \\ P_{22} \end{pmatrix}\right]^{-1}\begin{pmatrix} P_{12}^t & P_{22} \end{pmatrix}\begin{pmatrix} S_{11} \\ S_{12}^t \end{pmatrix}C_2^t$$

$$C_c\begin{pmatrix} S_{12}^t & S_{22} \end{pmatrix}\begin{pmatrix} P_{12} \\ P_{22} \end{pmatrix} - D_{12}^tD_{12}C_cS_{22}$$
$$= D_{12}^tC_1S_{12} + B_2^t\begin{pmatrix} P_{11}^t & P_{12} \end{pmatrix}\begin{pmatrix} S_{12} \\ S_{22} \end{pmatrix}$$

where $A_c = A_s + A_k$ with $A_s = A_s^t$ and $A_k = -A_k^t$. S and P have to be positive definite $S > 0$ and $P > 0$. The inverse has to exist.

The proof is straight forward using Lagrange multipliers.

4 Application to the mixed H_2/H_∞ problem

Using the above solution for the constrained H_2 problem with dynamic output feedback, the general mixed H_2/H_∞ problem can also be solved.

It is well-known that in general there is a set of solutions to the suboptimal H_∞ control problem [7], [8]. If there exists a solution, of course. Without loss of generality the H_∞ control problem can always be solved such that the H_∞-norm of the closed loop is smaller than 1. The set of controllers satisfying this condition is parameterized by a controller *generator* and a feedback Q. Where Q is a stable, H_∞-norm bounded transfer function.

This is used to solve the mixed H_2/H_∞ control problem. The state space realization is:

$$\begin{aligned} \dot{x} &= Ax + B_{w_1}w_1 + B_{w_2}w_2 + B_uu \\ z_1 &= C_{z_1}x + D_{z_1w_1}w_1 + D_{z_1w_2}w_2 + D_{z_1u}u \quad (3) \\ z_2 &= C_{z_2}x + D_{z_2w_1}w_1 + D_{z_2w_2}w_2 + D_{z_2u} \\ y &= C_yx + D_{yw_1}w_1 + D_{yw_2}w_2 + D_{yu}u \end{aligned}$$

Find a controller such that the closed loop from $\begin{pmatrix} w_1 & w_2 \end{pmatrix}^t$ to $\begin{pmatrix} z_1 & z_2 \end{pmatrix}^t$ is stable, $\|T_{z_1w_1}\|_2$ is minimized and $\|T_{z_2w_2}\|_\infty < 1$. The idea is now to calculate first the controller for the H_∞ part of the problem. Thus check if the H_∞ suboptimal problem is solvable, based on w_2, u, z_2 and y. If so, the controller generator, that is also a generalized system, is attached to the plant (3). Now concentrate on the H_2 problem.

Within the set of controllers that stabilize the closed loop and satisfy the H_∞ condition $\|T_{z_2w_2}\|_\infty < 1$, find the controller that minimizes the H_2-norm of $T_{z_1w_1}$. Therefore, we search for the transfer function Q, $r = Qv$, that minimizes the H_2-norm from z_1 to w_1.

The transfer function Q, however, should be such that it doesn't destabilize $T_{z_2w_2}$ and keeps the H_∞-norm less than or equal to 1. Therefore, we know from the H_∞ control theory, that Q has to be a stable transfer function such that $\|Q\|_\infty < 1$.

To obtain a finite H_2-norm the following conditions are needed:

1. $D_{z_1w_1} = 0$.
2. Q has to be strictly proper. A state space realization of Q is then:

$$\dot{x}_q = A_qx_q + B_qv$$
$$r = C_qx_q$$

Thus Q has to be stable, strictly proper and H_∞-norm bounded $\|Q\|_\infty < 1$. Thus Q has to be an element of Ω_1. So, the procedure explained in section 3 can be applied.

Find $Q \in \Omega_1$, such that $T_{z_1w_1}$ is stable and $\|T_{z_1w_1}\|_2$ is minimized. The closed loop will be stable. This is ensured by the H_∞ theory, if there is a stable solution ((A, B_u, C_y) has to be stabilizable and detectable). The H_∞ and H_2 part have the same feedback loop. So, if $T_{z_2w_2}$ is stabilized so will be $T_{z_1w_1}$.

From this derivation, it should also be clear that the lowest possible H_∞ norm, is the lowest possible norm that can be achieved for the H_∞-problem for $T_{z_2w_2}$.

5 Conclusions

In this paper we showed how the mixed H_2/H_∞ problem can be solved over the set of linear finite dimensional controllers. It is possible to solve this problem by first solving an H_∞ problem and then solving a constrained H_2 problem. Necessary conditions for the constrained H_2 problem are derived.

Numerical calculation based on a quasi-Newton optimization give a satisfying result. However, due to space limitations, these are not discussed further.

References

[1] D.S. Berstein and W.M. Haddad, "LQG control with H^∞ performance bound: A Riccati equation approach," *IEEE Trans. Autom. Contr.*, vol. 34, pp. 293-305,1989.

[2] J.C. Doyle, K. Zhou, and B. Bodenheimer, "Optimal control with mixed H_2 and H^∞ performance objectives," *Proc. ACC*, Pittsburgh, PA, p. 2065-2070, 1989.

[3] P.P. Khargonekar, and M.A. Rotea, "Mixed H_2/H_∞ control: A convex optimization approach," *IEEE Trans. Autom. Contr.*, Vol. 36, pp. 824-837, 1991.

[4] D. Mustafa, *Minimum Entropy H_∞ Control*, PhD Thesis, University of Cambridge, 1989.

[5] M. Steinbuch, and O. Bosgra, "Robust performance in H_2/H_∞ optimal control," Proc. 30 CDC, Brighton, pp. 549-550, 1991.

[6] H.-H. Yeh, S.S. Banda, B.-C. Chang, "Necessary and sufficient conditions for mixed H_2 and H_∞ optimal control," *IEEE Trans. Autom. Contr.*, vol. 37, pp. 355-358, 1992.

[7] K. Glover and J.C. Doyle, "State-space formulae for all stabilizing controllers that satisfy an H_∞ norm bound and relations to risk sensitivity," *Syst. Contr. Lett.*, vol. 11, pp. 167-172, 1988.

[8] K. Glover , D. Limebeer, J. Doyle, E. Kasenally, and M. Safanov, "A characterization of all solution to the H_∞ four block problem," *SIAM J. Control Optim.*, 29, pp. 283-324, 1991.

WM1 - 12:40

Proceedings of the
American Control Conference
San Francisco, California • June 1993

An (Almost) Exact Solution to General SISO Mixed $\mathcal{H}_2/\mathcal{H}_\infty$ Problems via Convex Optimization

Mario Sznaier
Electrical Engineering Dept.
University of Central Florida, Orlando, Fl 32816–2450
msznaier@frodo.engr.ucf.edu

Abstract

The mixed $(\mathcal{H}_2/\mathcal{H}_\infty)$ control problem can be motivated as a nominal *LQG* optimal control problem, subject to robust stability constraints, expressed in the form of an $\mathcal{H}_\infty$ norm bound. A related modified problem consisting on minimizing an *upper bound* of the $\mathcal{H}_2$ cost subject to $\mathcal{H}_\infty$ constraints was introduced in [1]. Although there presently exist efficient methods to solve this modified problem, the original problem remains, to a large extent, still open. In this paper we propose a method for solving general discrete-time SISO $(\mathcal{H}_2/\mathcal{H}_\infty)$ problems. This method involves solving a sequence of problems, each one consisting of a finite-dimensional convex optimization and an unconstrained Nehari approximation problem

1. Introduction

During the last decade, a large research effort has been devoted to the problem of designing robust controllers, capable of guaranteeing stability in the face of plant uncertainty. As a result, a powerful $\mathcal{H}_\infty$ framework has been developed, addressing the issue of robust stability in the presence of norm–bounded plant perturbations. Since its introduction, the original formulation of Zames [2] has been substantially simplified, resulting in efficient computational schemes for finding solutions. Of particular importance is [3] where a state–space approach is developed and an efficient procedure is given to compute suboptimal $\mathcal{H}_\infty$ controllers. In general, these controllers are preferred, since optimal $\mathcal{H}_\infty$ controllers may exhibit some undesirable properties. Since suboptimal controllers are seldom unique, the extra degrees of freedom available can then be used to optimize some performance measure. This leads naturally to a robust performance problem: design a controller guaranteeing a desired level of performance in the face of plant uncertainty. However, in spite of a large research effort [4], this problem has not completely been solved.

Alternatively, the extra degrees of freedom can be used to solve a problem of the form *nominal performance with robust stability*. In this case the controller yields a desired performance level for the nominal system while guaranteeing stability for all possible plant perturbations. A problem of this form that has been the object of much attention lately is the mixed $(\mathcal{H}_2/\mathcal{H}_\infty)$ control problem.

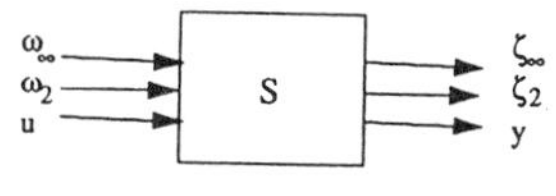

Figure 1: The Generalized Plant

Consider the system represented by the block diagram 1, where S represents the system to be controlled; the scalar signals w_∞ (a bounded power signal), w_2 (white noise) and u represent exogenous disturbances and the control action respectively; and ζ_∞, ζ_2 and y represent the regulated outputs and the measurements respectively. Then, the mixed $(\mathcal{H}_2/\mathcal{H}_\infty)$ control problem can be stated as: Given the nominal system (S), find an internally stabilizing controller

$$u(z) = K(z)y(z) \qquad (C)$$

such that the power semi–norm of the performance output $\|\zeta_2\|_P$ due to w_2 is minimized subject to the specification:

$$\sup_{w_\infty \in \mathcal{P},\ \|w_\infty\| \leq 1} \|\zeta_\infty\|_{\mathcal{P}} = \|T_{\zeta_\infty w_\infty}(z)\|_\infty \leq \gamma \qquad (P)$$

This work was supported in part by NSF under grant ECS–9211169 and by a grant from Florida Space Grant Consortium

Different versions of this problem have been studied recently. Bernstein and Haddad [1] considered the case where $w_2 = w_\infty$ and obtained necessary conditions for solving the *modified* problem of minimizing an *upper bound* of $\|T_{w_2\zeta_2}\|_2$, subject to the $\mathcal{H}_\infty$ constraint. In [5] and [6] the dual problem of minimizing this upper bound for the case $w_2 \neq w_\infty$, $\zeta_2 = \zeta_\infty$ was considered and sufficient conditions for optimality where given. Finally, in [7] these conditions where shown to be necessary and sufficient. However these conditions involve solving several coupled Riccati equations, and at this point there are no effective procedures for achieving this. In [8] Khargonekar and Rotea (see also [9] for the discrete–time version) showed that the modified problem can be cast into the format of a constrained convex optimization problem over a bounded set of matrices and solved using non–differentiable optimization techniques.

The approaches mentioned above provide a solution to the *modified* problem. However, at this time there is no information regarding the gap between the upper bound minimized in the modified problem and the true $\mathcal{H}_2$ cost. Very little work has been done concerning the original problem, which remains, to a large extent, still open. In [10] Rotea and Khargonekar addressed a *simultaneous* $(\mathcal{H}_2/\mathcal{H}_\infty)$ state–feedback control problem and showed that a solution to this problem, when it exists, also solves the mixed $(\mathcal{H}_2/\mathcal{H}_\infty)$ problem. Although this provides some insight into the structure of the problem, there are cases (most notably the case where $B_1 = B_2$) where the simultaneous problem provides little help in solving the original problem. Recently, mixed $(\mathcal{H}_2/\mathcal{H}_\infty)$ control using fixed–order controllers was analyzed using a Lagrange multipliers based approach and necessary conditions for optimality were obtained [11]. However, these conditions involve solving coupled non–linear matrix equations and finding the neutrally stable solution to a Lyapunov equation, which leads to numerical difficulties. Moreover, in [10] it was shown that even in the state–feedback case, the optimal controller must be dynamic, and it is conjectured that in the general case it may have higher order than the plant. This makes a fixed order appproach less attractive, since there is little a priori information on the order of the optimal controller.

In this paper we propose a solution to general discrete–time SISO mixed $(\mathcal{H}_2/\mathcal{H}_\infty)$ problems. Our approach resembles that of Boyd et. al. [12] in the sense that we use the Youla parametrization to cast the problem into a semi–infinite convex optimization form [13]. However, rather than approximately solving this problem by discretizing the constraints, we follow an approach in the spirit of [14] and [15] to show that the problem can be decoupled into a finite dimensional constrained optimization followed by the solution to an unconstrained Nehari approximation problem.

The paper is organized as follows: In section II we introduce the notation to be used and some preliminary results. Section III contains the proposed solution method. The main result of the session shows that the mixed $(\mathcal{H}_2/\mathcal{H}_\infty)$ problem can be solved by solving a sequence of modified problems, each one requiring the solution of a *finite dimensional* convex, constrained optimization problem and an unconstrained Nehari approximation problem. In section IV we present a simple design example. Finally, in section V, we summarize our results and we indicate directions for future research.

2. Preliminaries

2.1 Notation

By l_1 we denote the space of real sequences $\{q_i\}$, equipped with the norm $\|q\|_1 = \sum_{k=0}^{\infty} |q_k| < \infty$. Given a sequence $q \in l_1$ we will denote its Z–transform by $Q(z)$. $\mathcal{P}$ denotes the space of bounded power signals equipped with the seminorm: $\|u\|_P^2 = \lim_{k\to\infty} \frac{1}{2k} \sum_{l=-k}^{l=k} \|u_l\|^2$

$\mathcal{L}_\infty$ denotes the Lebesgue space of complex valued transfer matrices which are essentially bounded on the unit circle with norm

$\|T(z)\|_\infty \stackrel{\Delta}{=} \sup_{|z|=1} \sigma_{max}(T(z))$. $\mathcal{H}_\infty$ ($\mathcal{H}_\infty{}^-$) denotes the set of stable (antistable) complex matrices $G(z) \in \mathcal{L}_\infty$, i.e. analytic in $|z| \geq 1$ ($|z| \leq 1$). $\mathcal{H}_2$ denotes the space of complex matrices square integrable in the unit circle and analytic in $|z| > 1$, equipped with the norm:

$$\|G\|_2^2 = \frac{1}{2\pi} \oint_{|z|=1} Trace\{G(z)'G(z)\} z dz$$

where $'$ indicates transpose conjugate. The prefix $\mathcal{R}$ denotes real rational transfer matrices. Given $R \in \mathcal{L}_\infty$, $\Gamma_H(R)$ denotes its maximum Hankel singular value. Throughout the paper we will use packed notation to represent state-space realizations, i.e.

$$G(z) = C(zI - A)^{-1}B + D \stackrel{\Delta}{=} \left(\begin{array}{c|c} A & B \\ \hline C & D \end{array}\right)$$

Given two transfer matrices $T = \begin{pmatrix} T_{11} & T_{12} \\ T_{21} & T_{22} \end{pmatrix}$ and Q with appropriate dimensions, the lower *linear fractional transformation* is defined as:

$$\mathcal{F}_l(T, Q) \stackrel{\Delta}{=} T_{11} + T_{12}Q(I - T_{22}Q)^{-1}T_{21}$$

Finally, for a transfer matrix $G(z)$, $G^{\sim} \stackrel{\Delta}{=} G^T(\frac{1}{z})$.

2.2 Problem Transformation

Assume that the system S has the following state-space realization (where without loss of generality we assume that all weighting factors have been absorbed into the plant):

$$\left(\begin{array}{c|ccc} A & B_1 & B_2 & B_3 \\ \hline C_1 & D_{11} & D_{12} & D_{13} \\ C_2 & D_{21} & D_{22} & D_{23} \\ C_3 & D_{31} & D_{32} & D_{33} \end{array}\right) \qquad (S)$$

where D_{13} has full column rank, D_{31} has full row rank, and where the pairs (A, B_3) and (C_3, A) are stabilizable and detectable respectively. It is well known (see for instance [4]) that the set of all internally stabilizing controllers can be parametrized in terms of a free parameter $Q \in \mathcal{H}_\infty$ as:

$$K = \mathcal{F}_l(J, Q) \qquad (1)$$

where J has the following state-space realization:

$$\left(\begin{array}{c|cc} A + B_3F + LC_3 + LD_{33}F & -L & B_3 + LD_{33} \\ \hline F & 0 & I \\ -(C_3 + D_{33}F) & I & -D_{33} \end{array}\right) \qquad (J)$$

where F and L are selected such that $A + B_3F$ and $A + LC_3$ are stable. By using this parametrization, the closed-loop transfer functions $T_{\zeta_\infty w_\infty}$ and $T_{\zeta_2 w_2}$ can be written as:

$$\begin{aligned} T_{\zeta_\infty w_\infty} &= \mathcal{F}_l(T_\infty, Q) = T_{11}^\infty + T_{12}^\infty Q T_{21}^\infty \\ T_{\zeta_2 w_2} &= \mathcal{F}_l(T, Q) = T_{11} + T_{12}QT_{21} \end{aligned} \qquad (2)$$

where $T_i, T_i^\infty \in \mathcal{RH}_\infty$ and where T and T_∞ have the following state-space realizations:

$$T^\infty = \left(\begin{array}{cc|cc} A_F & -B_3F & B_1 & B_3 \\ 0 & A_L & B_1 + LD_{31} & 0 \\ \hline C_1 + D_{13}F & -D_{13}F & D_{11} & D_{13} \\ 0 & C_2 & D_{31} & 0 \end{array}\right)$$

$$T = \left(\begin{array}{cc|cc} A_F & -B_3F & B_2 & B_3 \\ 0 & A_L & B_2 + LD_{32} & 0 \\ \hline C_2 + D_{23}F & -D_{23}F & D_{22} & D_{23} \\ 0 & C_3 & D_{32} & 0 \end{array}\right) \qquad (3)$$

$$A_F = A + B_3F$$
$$A_L = A + LC_3$$

Moreover (see [15]), it is possible to select F and L in such a way that $T_{12}^\infty(z)$ and $T_{21}^\infty(z)$ are inner and co-inner respectively (i.e. $T_{12}^{\infty\sim}T_{12}^\infty = I$, $T_{21}^\infty T_{21}^{\infty\sim} = I$).

Remark 1: For the SISO case, equation (2) reduces to:

$$\begin{aligned} T_{\zeta_\infty w_\infty}(z) &= T_1^\infty(z) + T_2^\infty(z)Q(z) \\ T_{\zeta_2 w_2}(z) &= T_1(z) + T_2(z)Q(z) \end{aligned} \qquad (4)$$

where T_i, T_i^∞, Q are stable transfer functions and where T_2^∞ is inner. Since $\|.\|_\infty$ is invariant under multiplication by an inner function, we have:

$$\|T_{\zeta_\infty w_\infty}\|_\infty = \|T_1^\infty + T_2^\infty Q\|_\infty = \|R + Q\|_\infty \qquad (5)$$

where $R(z) \stackrel{\Delta}{=} T_1^\infty(z)T_2^{\infty\sim}(z)$ has all its poles outside the unit disk. A state-space realization of R in terms of the state-space realization of (S) is given in [15].

By using this parametrization the mixed $(\mathcal{H}_2/\mathcal{H}_\infty)$ problem can be now precisely stated as solving:

$$\mu^o = \inf_{Q \in \mathcal{H}_\infty} \|T_{\zeta_2 w_2}\|_2 = \inf_{q_i \in l^1} \left(\sum_{i=0}^{\infty} |t_i|^2\right)^{\frac{1}{2}} \qquad (\mathcal{H}_2/\mathcal{H}_\infty)$$

subject to:

$$\|T_1^\infty(z) + T_2^\infty(z)Q(z)\|_\infty \leq \gamma \qquad (6)$$

where $\{t_i\}$ and $\{q_i\}$ are the coefficients of the impulse responses of $T_{\zeta_2 w_2}$ and Q respectively.

3. Problem Solution

In this section we show that the mixed $(\mathcal{H}_2/\mathcal{H}_\infty)$ problem can be solved by solving a sequence of problems, each one requiring the solution of a finite dimensional convex optimization problem and an unconstrained Nehari extension problem.

3.1 A Modified $(\mathcal{H}_2/\mathcal{H}_\infty)$ Problem

Since all the solutions to a suboptimal Nehari extension problem of the form $\|R + Q\|_\infty \leq \gamma$ can be parametrized in terms of a free parameter $W(z) \in \mathcal{RH}_\infty$, $\|W\|_\infty \leq \gamma^{-1}$ problem $(\mathcal{H}_2/\mathcal{H}_\infty)$ can be thought of as an optimization problem inside the origin centered γ^{-1}-ball. However, even though the space $\mathcal{H}_\infty$ is complete, it is easily seen that the γ-ball is not compact. Thus a minimizing solution may not exist. Motivated by this difficulty, we introduce the following *modified* mixed $(\mathcal{H}_2/\mathcal{H}_\infty)$ problem. Let $\mathcal{H}_\delta = \{Q(z) \in \mathcal{H}_\infty : Q(z) \text{ analytic in} |z| \geq \delta\}$ and define the $(\mathcal{H}_2/\mathcal{H}_\delta)$ problem as follows: Given $T_1(z), T_2(z), T_1^\infty(z), T_2^\infty(z) \in \mathcal{RH}_\delta$, find

$$\mu_\delta^o = \min_{Q \in \mathcal{H}_\delta} \|T_{\zeta_2 w_2}\|_2 \qquad (\mathcal{H}_2/\mathcal{H}_\delta)$$

subject to:

$$\|T_1^\infty(z) + T_2^\infty(z)Q(z)\|_\delta \leq \gamma$$

where $\delta < 1$ and $\|Q\|_\delta \stackrel{\Delta}{=} \sup_{|z|=\delta} |Q(z)|$. In section 3.2 we will show that $(\mathcal{H}_2/\mathcal{H}_\delta)$, if feasible, always has a minimizing solution. Moreover, this optimal solution is rational (i.e. $Q \in \mathcal{RH}_\delta$).

Remark 2: From the maximum modulus theorem, it follows that any solution Q to $(\mathcal{H}_2/\mathcal{H}_\delta)$ is an admissible solution for $(\mathcal{H}_2/\mathcal{H}_\infty)$. It follows that μ_δ^o is an upper bound for μ^o.

Remark 3: Problem $(\mathcal{H}_2/\mathcal{H}_\delta)$ can be thought as solving problem $(\mathcal{H}_2/\mathcal{H}_\infty)$ with the additional constraint that all the poles of the closed-loop system must be inside the disk of radius δ. A parametrization of all achievable closed-loop transfer functions, such that T, T^∞ satisfy this additional constraint can be obtained from (1) by simply changing the stability region from the unit-disk to the δ-disk using the transformation $z = \delta\hat{z}$ before performing the factorization. Furthermore, by combining this transformation with the inner-coinner factorization, the resulting $T_2^\infty(z)$ satisfies $T_2^\infty(\delta z)T_2^\infty(\frac{1}{\delta z}) = 1$.

Next we show that a suboptimal solution to $(\mathcal{H}_2/\mathcal{H}_\infty)$, with cost arbitrarily close to the optimum, can be found by solving a sequence of truncated problems, each one requiring consideration of only a *finite* number of elements of the impulse response of $T_{\zeta_2 w_2}$. To establish this result we will show that: i) $(\mathcal{H}_2/\mathcal{H}_\infty)$ can be solved by considering a sequence of modified problems $(\mathcal{H}_2/\mathcal{H}_\delta)$. ii) Given $\epsilon > 0$, a suboptimal solution to $(\mathcal{H}_2/\mathcal{H}_\delta)$ with cost no greater than $\mu_\delta^o + \epsilon$ can be found by solving a truncated problem.

• **Lemma 1:** Consider an increasing sequence $\delta_i \to 1$. Let μ^o and μ_i denote the solution to problems $(\mathcal{H}_2/\mathcal{H}_\infty)$ and $(\mathcal{H}_2/\mathcal{H}_{\delta_i})$ respectively and assume that $\Gamma_H(R) < \gamma$. Then the sequence $\mu_i \to \mu^o$.

Proof: The proof, omitted for space reasons, follows from the maximum modulus theorem and continuity arguments.

Next we show show that, given $\epsilon > 0$, a suboptimal solution to $(\mathcal{H}_2/\mathcal{H}_\delta)$, with cost μ_δ^ϵ such that $\mu_\delta^o \le \mu_\delta^\epsilon \le \mu_\delta^o + \epsilon$ can be found by solving a truncated problem.

• **Lemma 2:** Let $\epsilon > 0$ be given. Then, there exists $N(\epsilon, \delta)$ such that if $Q \in \mathcal{H}_\delta$ satisfies the constraint $\|R + Q\|_\delta \le \gamma$ then it also satisfies $\sum_{i=N}^{\infty} |t_k|^2 \le \epsilon^2$, where t_k denote the coefficients of the impulse response of $T_{\zeta_2 w_2} = T_1 + T_2 Q$.

Proof: Since $Q \in \mathcal{H}_\delta$, $T_{\zeta_2 w_2}$ is analytic in $|z| \ge \delta$ and:

$$t_k = \frac{1}{2\pi j} \oint_{|z|=\delta} T_{\zeta_2 w_2}(z) z^{k-1} dz \tag{7}$$

Hence

$$\begin{aligned} |t_k| &\le \|T_{\zeta_2 w_2}\|_\delta \delta^k \\ \sum_{i=N}^{\infty} |t_k|^2 &\le \frac{\|T_{\zeta_2 w_2}\|_\delta^2 \delta^{2N}}{1 - \delta^2} \end{aligned} \tag{8}$$

If Q satisfies $\|R + Q\|_\delta \le \gamma$, since $\|.\|_\delta$ is submultiplicative, we have:

$$\begin{aligned} \|T_{\zeta_2 w_2}(z)\|_\delta &\le \|T_1\|_\delta + \|T_2\|_\delta \|Q\|_\delta \\ &\le \|T_1\|_\delta + \|T_2\|_\delta (\gamma + \|R\|_\delta) \stackrel{\Delta}{=} K \end{aligned} \tag{9}$$

The desired result follows by selecting $N \ge N_o = \frac{1}{2} \frac{log \epsilon^2 (1-\delta^2) - log K^2}{log \delta}$ ◇

• **Lemma 3:** Consider the following optimization problem:

$$\min_{Q \in \mathcal{H}_\delta} \left(\sum_{l=0}^{N-1} |t_i|^2 \right)^{\frac{1}{2}} = \|\underline{t}_1 + \tau \underline{q}\|_2^2 \qquad (\mathcal{H}_2/\mathcal{H}_\delta^\epsilon)$$

subject to:

$$\|R + Q\|_\delta \le \gamma$$

where:

$$\begin{aligned} \underline{t}_1 &\stackrel{\Delta}{=} (\, t_{1_o} \ \ \ldots \ \ t_{1\,N-1} \,)' \\ \tau &= \begin{pmatrix} t_{2_o} & 0 & \ldots & 0 \\ t_{21} & t_{20} & \ldots & 0 \\ \vdots & & \ddots & \\ t_{2\,N-1} & \ldots & & t_{2_o} \end{pmatrix} \\ \underline{q}^o &\stackrel{\Delta}{=} (\, q_o \ \ \ldots \ \ q_{N-1} \,)' \end{aligned} \tag{10}$$

and where q_k, t_{k_i} denote the kth element of the impulse response of $Q(z), T_i(z)$ respectively. Let Q^* and $T_{\zeta_2 w_2}^*$ denote the optimal solution and define $\mu_\delta^\epsilon = \|T_{\zeta_2 w_2}^*\|_2$. Then $\mu_\delta^o \le \mu_\delta^\epsilon \le \mu_\delta^o + \epsilon$

Proof: $\mu_\delta^o \le \mu_\delta^\epsilon$ is immediate from the definition of μ_δ^o. Denote by $T_{\zeta_2 w_2}^\epsilon$ and $T_{\zeta_2 w_2}^\delta$ the solution to problems $(\mathcal{H}_2/\mathcal{H}_\delta^\epsilon)$ and $(\mathcal{H}_2/\mathcal{H}_\delta)$ respectively and let t_i^ϵ, t_i^δ be the corresponding impulse responses. Then:

$$\begin{aligned} (\mu_\delta^\epsilon)^2 &= \|T_{\zeta_2 w_2}^\epsilon\|_2^2 = \sum_{i=0}^{\infty} |t_i^\epsilon|^2 = \sum_{i=0}^{N-1} |t_i^\epsilon|^2 + \sum_{i=N}^{\infty} |t_i^\epsilon|^2 \\ &\le \sum_{i=0}^{N-1} |t_i^\delta|^2 + \epsilon^2 \le \sum_{i=0}^{\infty} |t_i^\delta|^2 + \epsilon^2 = (\mu_\delta^o)^2 + \epsilon^2 \le (\mu_\delta^o + \epsilon)^2 \qquad \diamond \end{aligned}$$

By combining the results of Lemmas 1, 2 and 3, the following result is now apparent:

• **Lemma 4:** Consider an increasing sequence $\delta_i \to 1$. Let μ^o and $\mu_{\delta_i}^\epsilon$ denote the solution to problems $(\mathcal{H}_2/\mathcal{H}_\infty)$ and $(\mathcal{H}_2/\mathcal{H}_{\delta_i}^\epsilon)$ respectively. Then the sequence $\mu_{\delta_i}^\epsilon$ has an accumulation point $\hat{\mu}_\epsilon$ such that $\mu^o \le \hat{\mu}_\epsilon \le \mu^o + \epsilon$.

3.2 The $\mathcal{H}_\infty$ Performance Constraint

In the last section we showed that $(\mathcal{H}_2/\mathcal{H}_\infty)$ can be solved by solving a sequence of truncated problems. In principle these problems have the form of a semi-infinite optimization problem, and can be approximately solved by discretizing the unit-circle and applying outer approximation methods (see [13]). In this section we show that each problem $(\mathcal{H}_2/\mathcal{H}_\delta^\epsilon)$ can be *exactly* solved by solving a finite dimensional convex optimization problem and an unconstrained Nehari approximation problem. Moreover, since the solution to this Nehari approximation problem is rational, it follows that the solution to $(\mathcal{H}_2/\mathcal{H}_\delta^\epsilon)$ is also rational. The key to establish this result is to note that: i) the objective function of the truncated problem involves only the first N terms of the impulse response of Q and ii) If the first N terms of the impulse response of Q are fixed, the existence of Q such that $\|R + Q\|_\delta \le \gamma$ is equivalent to a finite dimensional convex constraint.

• **Theorem 1:** Let $R \stackrel{\Delta}{=} \left(\begin{array}{c|c} A_R & b_R \\ \hline c_R & d_R \end{array} \right) \in \mathcal{RH}_\infty^-$,with McMillan degree n, and $Q_F = \sum_{i=0}^{N-1} q_i z^{-i}$ be given. Then there exist $Q_R \in \mathcal{RH}_\infty$, such that $\|R + Q_F + z^{-N} Q_R\|_{\mathcal{H}_\infty} \le \gamma$, **iff** $\|\mathcal{Q}\|_2 \le \gamma$ where $\mathcal{Q}$, a symmetric matrix affine in the coefficients of Q_F, has the following form:

$$\begin{aligned} \mathcal{Q} &= W^{\frac{1}{2}} \begin{pmatrix} I & 0 \\ 0 & \mathcal{H}' \end{pmatrix} L_c^{\frac{1}{2}} \\ Lc &= \begin{pmatrix} L_{11}^C & L_{12}^C \\ L_{12}^{C\,\prime} & L_{22}^C \end{pmatrix} \\ L_{11}^C &= L_o^C \\ L_{12}^C &= -(\,(A_R')^{N-1} c_R' \quad (A_R')^{N-2} c_R' \ldots \quad c_R'\,) \\ L_{22}^C &= I_N \\ W'^{\frac{1}{2}} W^{\frac{1}{2}} &= \begin{pmatrix} L_o^0 & \mathcal{A} \\ \mathcal{A}' & I \end{pmatrix} \\ \mathcal{A} &= \left(A_R^{-N} b_R \quad A_R^{-(N-1)} b_R \ldots A_R^{-1} b_R \right) \\ \mathcal{H} &= \begin{pmatrix} h_N & h_{N-1} & \ldots & \ldots & h_1 \\ & h_N & h_{N-1} & \ldots & h_2 \\ & & \ddots & & \\ & & & h_N & h_{N-1} \\ & & & & h_N \end{pmatrix} \\ h_i &= q_{N-i} + b_R' (A_R')^{N-1-i} c_R' \qquad 1 \le i \le N-1 \\ h_N &= q_0 + d_R \end{aligned}$$

where L_o^0 and L_o^C are the solutions to the following Lyapunov equations:

$$\begin{aligned} A_R L_o^0 A_R' - L_o^0 &= b_R b_R' \\ A_R' L_o^C A_R - L_o^C &= (A_R')^N c_R' c_R (A_R)^N \end{aligned}$$

Proof: See [15].

Combining Lemma 3 and Theorem 1 yields the main result of this section:

• **Theorem 2:** A suboptimal solution to $(\mathcal{H}_2/\mathcal{H}_\delta)$, with cost $\mu_\delta \le \mu_\delta^\epsilon \le \mu_\delta + \epsilon$ is given by $Q^o = Q_F^o + z^{-N} Q_R^o$ where $Q_F^o = \sum_{i=0}^{N-1} q_i z^{-i}$, $\underline{q}^o = (q_o \ldots q_{N-1})'$ solves the following finite dimensional convex optimization problem:

$$\underline{q}^o = \underset{\substack{\underline{q} \in R^N \\ \|\mathcal{Q}\|_2 \le \gamma}}{\text{argmin}} \|\underline{t}_1 + \tau \underline{q}\|_2$$

and Q_R solves the unconstrained Nehari approximation problem

$$Q_R^o(\hat{z}) = \underset{Q_R \in \mathcal{RH}_\infty}{\text{argmin}} \|R(\hat{z}) + Q_F^o + \hat{z}^{-N} Q_R(\hat{z})\|_\infty$$

where R is defined in (5), $\underline{t}_1, \tau$ are defined in (10), N is selected according to Lemma 2, and $z = \delta \hat{z}$

3.3 Synthesis Algorithm

Combining Theorem 2 and Lemma 4, it follows that a suboptimal solution to $(\mathcal{H}_2/\mathcal{H}_\infty)$, with cost arbitrarily close to the optimum, can be found using the following iterative algorithm.

0) *Data:* An increasing sequence $\delta_i \to 1, \epsilon > 0, \nu > 0$.

1) Solve the unconstrained $\mathcal{H}_2$ problem (using the standard $\mathcal{H}_2$ theory) . Compute $\|T_{\zeta_\infty w_\infty}\|_\infty$. If $\|T_{\zeta_\infty w_\infty}\|_\infty \leq \gamma$ stop, else set $i = 1$.

2) For each i, find a suboptimal solution to problem $(\mathcal{H}_2/\mathcal{H}_{\delta_i})$ proceeding as follows:

   2.1) Let $z = \delta_i \hat{z}$ and consider the system $S(\hat{z})$

   2.2) Perform the factorization (2) to obtain $T_i(\hat{z}), T_i^\infty(\hat{z})$.

   2.3) Compute N from Lemma 2.

   2.4) Find $\hat{Q}(\hat{z})$ using Theorem 2.

3) Let $Q = \hat{Q}(\frac{z}{\delta_i}), K = F_l(J,Q)$. Compute $\|T_{\zeta_\infty w_\infty}(z)\|_\infty$. If $\|T_{\zeta_\infty w_\infty}(z)\|_\infty \geq \gamma - \nu$ stop, else set $i = i+1$ and go to 2.

Remark 4: At each stage the algorithm produces a feasible solution to $(\mathcal{H}_2/\mathcal{H}_\infty)$, with cost μ_i which is an upper bound of the optimal cost μ^o.

4. A Simple Example

Consider the simple system shown in figure 2, consisting of two unity masses coupled by a spring with constant $0.5 \leq k \leq 2$ but otherwise unknown. A control force acts on body 1 and the position of body 2 is measured, resulting in a non–colocated sensor actuator problem that embodies many of the pathologies and challenges present in realistic problems, such as control of complex aircraft and large space structures. This system has been used as a benchmark during the last few years at the American Control Conference [16–17] to highlight the issues and trade–offs involved in robust control design.

Assume that it is desired to design an internally stabilizing controller subject to the following performance specifications: i) the closed-loop system must be stable for all possible values of the uncertain parameter $k \in [0.5, 2]$. ii) the energy of the control action u in response to a white noise disturbance acting on m_2 should be minimized.

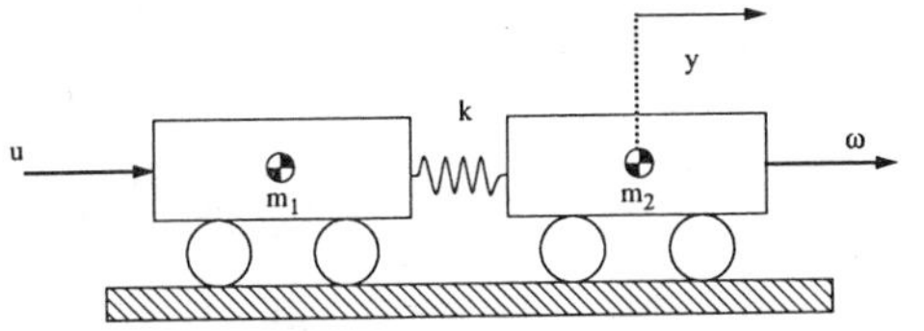

Figure 2: The ACC Robust Control Benchmark Problem.

In order to fit the problem into the $\mathcal{H}_\infty$ framework, the uncertain spring constant k is modeled as $k = k_o + \Delta$ (with $k_o = 1.25$ and $|\Delta| \leq 0.75$) and, following a standard procedure [18], Δ is "pulled out" of the system. The problem can be stated now as the problem of minimizing $\|T_{yw}\|_2$ over the set of all internally stabilizing controllers, subject to the constraint $\|T_{\zeta v}\|_\infty \leq \frac{4}{3}$. The system, with the uncertainty "pulled out", can be represented by the following state space realization:

$$A = \begin{pmatrix} 0 & 0 & 1 & 0 \\ 0 & 0 & 0 & 1 \\ -k_o & k_o & 0 & 0 \\ k_o & -k_o & 0 & 0 \end{pmatrix} \quad B = \begin{pmatrix} 0 & 0 & 0 \\ 0 & 1 & 0 \\ 1 & 0 & 1 \\ -1 & 0 & 0 \end{pmatrix}$$

$$C = \begin{pmatrix} 1 & -1 & 0 & 0 \\ 0 & 0 & 0 & 0 \\ 0 & 1 & 0 & 0 \end{pmatrix} \quad D = \begin{pmatrix} 0 & 0 & 1 \\ 0 & 0 & 0 \\ 0 & 0 & 0 \end{pmatrix}$$

In order to fit the problem into our framework, the system was discretized using sample and hold elements at the inputs and outputs, with a sampling time of 0.1 seconds. Finally, to remove the ill–conditioning caused by the poles on the unit circle, a bilinear transformation was used, constraining the poles of the closed–loop system to lie inside the $|z| \leq 0.95$ disk (i.e. $\delta = 0.95$) and the proposed design procedure was used with $\|T_{\zeta v}\|_\delta \leq 1.6$ and $N = 100$, resulting in a controller with 205 states.

Figure 3 shows the control action in response to an impulse disturbance acting on m_2 for the optimal $\mathcal{H}_\infty$ central controller, the optimal $\mathcal{H}_2$ and the mixed $\mathcal{H}_2/\mathcal{H}_\infty$ controllers, with the corresponding bode plots of $T_{\zeta v}$ shown in figure 4. These results are summarized in Table 1.

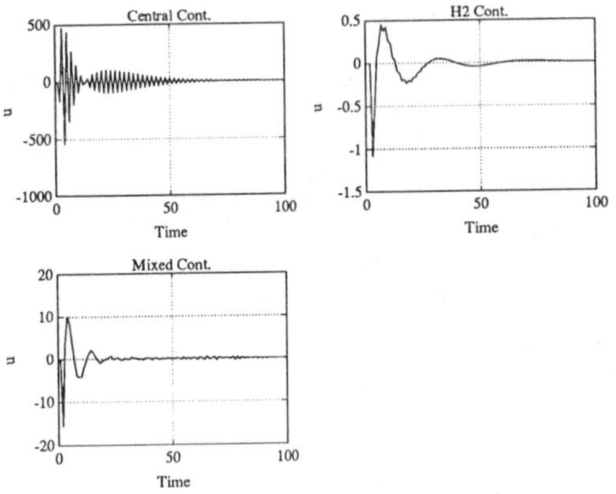

Figure 3: $T_{\omega u}$ Impulse Response for the $\mathcal{H}_\infty$, $\mathcal{H}_2$ and $\mathcal{H}_2/\mathcal{H}_\infty$ Cont.

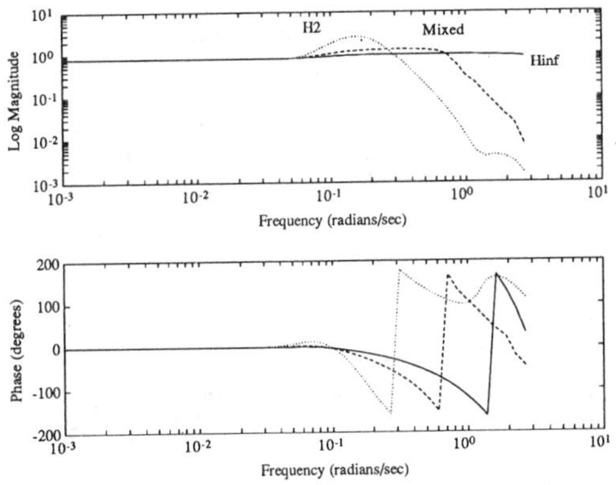

Figure 4: $T_{\zeta v}$ Frequency Response for the $\mathcal{H}_\infty$, $\mathcal{H}_2$ and $\mathcal{H}_2/\mathcal{H}_\infty$ Cont.

	$\|T_{\zeta v}\|_\infty$	$\|T_{uw}\|_2$
$\mathcal{H}_2$	2.604	1.5760
$\mathcal{H}_\infty$	0.9977	1085.2
$\mathcal{H}_2/\mathcal{H}_\infty$	1.292	22.6493

Table 1. $\|T_{\zeta v}\|_\infty$ and $\|T_{uw}\|_2$ for the example

Note that the actual value $\|T_{\zeta v}\|_\infty$ obtained with the mixed $\mathcal{H}_2/\mathcal{H}_\infty$ controller is 1.29. This is due to the fact that $\|T_{\zeta v}\|_\delta$ is an upper bound of $\|T_{\zeta v}\|_\infty$.

Table 2 shows a comparison between the optimal mixed $\mathcal{H}_2/\mathcal{H}_\infty$ controller and several reduced order controllers. It is interesting to notice that the controller can be reduced to 10th order with virtually no performance loss. Further reduction to a 3rd order controller only entails about 10% increase in the $\mathcal{H}_2$ cost. These results seem to support the conjecture of [11] that the mixed $\mathcal{H}_2/\mathcal{H}_\infty$ control problem results in controllers having higher dimension than the plant.

	$\|\|T_{\zeta v}\|\|_\infty$	$\|\|T_{uw}\|\|_2$
$\mathcal{H}_2/\mathcal{H}_\infty$	1.292	22.6493
10 ord.	1.281	22.8842
3 ord.	1.292	24.8594

Table 2. $\|T_{\zeta v}\|_\infty$ and $\|T_{uw}\|_2$ for reduced order controllers

5. Conclusions

In this paper we provide a sub-optimal solution to discrete-time mixed $(\mathcal{H}_2/\mathcal{H}_\infty)$ problems. Unlike previous approaches, our method yields a global minimum of the actual $\mathcal{H}_2$ cost rather than of an upper bound and it is not limited to cases where either the disturbances or the regulated outputs coincide. Although here we considered only the simpler case of a one-block $\mathcal{H}_\infty$ problems, we anticipate that the results will extend naturally to the 4-block case.

Perhaps the most severe limitation of the proposed method is that may result in very large order controllers (roughly $2N$), necessitating some type of model reduction. Hence, at this time, the proposed approach provides an analysis tool to establish the limits of performance of the plant, rather than a practical design tool. The example of section 4 suggests that substantial order reduction can be accomplished without performance degradation. Research is currently under way addressing this issue.

References

[1]. D. S. Bernstein and W. H. Haddad "LQG Control with an $\mathcal{H}_\infty$ Performance Bound: A Riccati Equation Approach," *IEEE Trans. Automat. Contr.*, Vol 34, 3, pp. 293–305, 1989.

[2]. G. Zames "Feedback and Optimal Sensitivity: Model Reference Transformations, Multiplicative Seminorms and Approximate Inverses," *IEEE Trans. Autom. Contr.* Vol 26, 4, pp. 301–320, 1981.

[3]. J. Doyle, K. Glover, P. Khargonekar and B. Francis "State-Space Solutions to Standard $\mathcal{H}_2$ and $\mathcal{H}_\infty$ Control Problems," *IEEE Trans. Autom. Contr.*, Vol 34, 8, pp. 831–846, August 1989.

[4]. K. Zhou and J. Doyle "Notes on MIMO Control Theory," Lecture Notes, California Institute of Technology, 1990.

[5]. J. Doyle, K. Zhou and B. Bodenheimer "Optimal Control with Mixed $\mathcal{H}_2$ and $\mathcal{H}_\infty$ Performance Objectives," *Proc. 1989 ACC*, Pittsburgh, PA, pp. 2065–2070

[6]. K. Zhou, J. Doyle, K. Glover and B. Bodenheimer "Mixed $\mathcal{H}_2$ and $\mathcal{H}_\infty$ Control," *Proc. 1990 ACC*, San Diego, CA, pp. 2502–2507

[7]. H. H. Yeh and S. S. Banda "Necessary and Sufficient Conditions for mixed $\mathcal{H}_2$ and $\mathcal{H}_\infty$ Optimal Control," *Proc. 29 IEEE CDC*, Hawaii, pp. 1013–1017, 1990.

[8]. P. P. Khargonekar and M. A. Rotea "Mixed $\mathcal{H}_2/H$ Control: A Convex Optimization Approach," *IEEE Trans. Autom. Contr.*, Vol 36, 7, pp. 824–837, 1991.

[9]. I. Kaminer, P. P. Khargonekar and M. Rotea "Mixed $\mathcal{H}_2/\mathcal{H}_\infty$ Control for Discrete Time Systems via Convex Optimization," *Proc. 1992 ACC*, Chicago, Il., June 24–26, pp. 1363–1367.

[10]. M. A. Rotea and P. P. Khargonekar "$\mathcal{H}_2$ Control with an $\mathcal{H}_\infty$ Constraint: The State Feedback Case," *Automatica*, Vol 27, 2, pp 307–316, 1991.

[11]. D. B. Ridgely, L. S. Valavani, M. A. Dahleh and G. Stein "Solution to the General Mixed $\mathcal{H}_2/\mathcal{H}_\infty$ Control Problem-Necessary Condition for Optimality," *Proc. of the 1992 ACC*, Chicago, Il., June 24–26, pp. 1348–1352.

[12]. S. Boyd et. al. "A New CAD Method and Associated Architectures for Linear Controllers," *IEEE Trans. Automat. Contr.*, Vol 33, 3, pp. 268–283, 1988.

[13]. C. Gonzaga and E. Polak "On Constraint Dropping Schemes and Optimality Functions for a Class of Outer Approximation Algorithms," *SIAM J. on Contr. and Opt.*, Vol 17, 4, pp. 477–493, 1979.

[14]. A. Sideris and H. Rotstein "H_∞ Optimization with Time Domain Constraints over a Finite Horizon," *Proc. of the 29th IEEE CDC*, Hawaii, Dec 5–7 1990, pp. 1802–1807.

[15]. M. Sznaier "A Mixed $l_\infty/\mathcal{H}_\infty$ Optimization Approach to Robust Controller Design," *Proc 1992 ACC*, Chicago, Il, pp. 727–732.

[16]. D. Bernstein and B. Wie, OrganizersInvited Session on "A Benchmark Problems for Robust $\mathcal{H}_2$ / $\mathcal{H}_\infty$ Control Design," Session WP-15, *Proc. of the 1990 ACC*, San-Diego, CA, May 23–25, pp. 961–973.

[17]. D. Bernstein and B. Wie, OrganizersInvited Session on "Benchmark Problems for Robust Control Design," Session TP-10, *Proc. of the 1991 ACC*, Boston, MA, June 26–28, pp. 1915–1936.

[18]. J. Doyle "Analysis of Feedback Systems with Structured Uncertainties," *IEE Proceedings, Part D*, Vol 129, pp. 242–250, 1982.

[19]. B. Francis "A Course in $\mathcal{H}_\infty$ Optimization Theory," *Vol 88 in Lectures Notes in Control and Information*, Springer-Verlag, New York, 1987.

Appendix: Some Numerical Considerations

In this appendix we give an alternative for computing $\mathcal{Q}$. Since this alternative expression does not involve increasing powers of A_R it is preferable in cases where N is large or A_R has large eigenvalues. From [15] it can be shown that:

$$
\begin{aligned}
L_c &= \begin{pmatrix} L_o^c & Y \\ Y' & I_N \end{pmatrix} = \begin{pmatrix} I & Y \\ 0 & I \end{pmatrix} \begin{pmatrix} W_{oR} & 0 \\ 0 & I \end{pmatrix} \begin{pmatrix} I & 0 \\ Y' & I \end{pmatrix} \\
L_o &= \begin{pmatrix} I & \mathcal{A} \\ 0 & \mathcal{H} \end{pmatrix} \begin{pmatrix} A_R^{-N} L_o^0 A_R'^{N} & 0 \\ 0 & I \end{pmatrix} \begin{pmatrix} I & 0 \\ \mathcal{A}' & \mathcal{H}' \end{pmatrix} \\
&= \begin{pmatrix} A_R^{-N} & \mathcal{A} \\ 0 & \mathcal{H} \end{pmatrix} \begin{pmatrix} L_o^0 & 0 \\ 0 & I \end{pmatrix} \begin{pmatrix} A_R^{-N} & 0 \\ \mathcal{A}' & \mathcal{H}' \end{pmatrix}
\end{aligned} \tag{C1}
$$

where:

$$
Y = -\begin{pmatrix} (A_R')^{N-1} c_R' & (A_R')^{(N-2)} c_R' & \dots & c_R' \end{pmatrix} \tag{C2}
$$

and $W_{oR} \triangleq L_o^c - YY'$ satisfies:

$$
A_R' W_{oR} A_R - W_{oR} = c_R' c_R
$$

(i.e. W_{oR} is the observability grammian of A_R). Since the spectral radius of $L_o L_c$ is invariant under a similarity transformation, it follows that $\mathcal{Q}$ can be replaced by:

$$
\mathcal{Q} = \begin{pmatrix} L_o^{0\frac{1}{2}} & 0 \\ 0 & I \end{pmatrix} \begin{pmatrix} A_R'^{-N} & A_R'^{-N} Y \\ \mathcal{A}' & \mathcal{A}'Y + \mathcal{H}' \end{pmatrix} \begin{pmatrix} W_{oR}^{\frac{1}{2}} & 0 \\ 0 & I \end{pmatrix} \tag{C3}
$$

where the only terms that contain powers $A_R^i, i = 1 \dots N$ are in $\mathcal{H}' + \mathcal{A}'Y$. Defining $\hat{H} \triangleq H + b_R'(A_R')^{-1} Y + b_R'(A_R')^{-1} c_R' e_N' = \begin{pmatrix} \hat{h}_1 & \dots & \hat{h}_N \end{pmatrix}$, yields:

$$
\begin{aligned}
\hat{h}_i &= q_{N-i} \qquad 1 \le i \le N-1 \\
\hat{h}_N &= q_0 + d_R
\end{aligned} \tag{C4}
$$

Hence, we have that

$$
\mathcal{H}' + \mathcal{A}'Y = \begin{pmatrix} \hat{h}_N & \hat{h}_{N-1} & \dots & \dots & \hat{h}_1 \\ & \hat{h}_N & \hat{h}_{N-1} & \dots & \hat{h}_2 \\ & & \ddots & & \\ & & & \hat{h}_N & \hat{h}_{N-1} \\ & & & & \hat{h}_N \end{pmatrix}
+ \begin{pmatrix} c_R A_R^{-1} b_R & c_R A_R^{-2} b_R & \dots & \dots & c_R A_R^{-N} b_R \\ & c_R A_R^{-1} b_R & c_R A_R^{-2} b_R & \dots & c_R A_R^{-(N-1)} b_R \\ & & \ddots & & \\ & & & c_R A_R^{-1} b_R & c_R A_R^{-2} b_R \\ & & & & c_R A_R^{-1} b_R \end{pmatrix} \tag{C5}
$$

which does not contain increasing powers of A_R.

Proceedings of the
American Control Conference
San Francisco, California • June 1993

Model Reference Robust Control of SISO Systems with Significant Unmodelled Dyamics

Zhihua Qu
Department of Electrical and Computer Engineering
University of Central Florida
Orlando, FL 32826, U.S.A.

Abstract

In this paper, a recently proposed control design technique, model reference robust control (MRRC) [10], is generalized to provide input-output robust control for much wider class of SISO systems. A system under consideration may contain not only parametric uncertainties, disturbances, uncertain high-order nonlinearities associated with output, but also unmodelled dynamics associated both input and output of the system. Unmodelled dynamics may be unstable and of infinite dimension. Common assumptions such as the order of nominal system, or bounds on system parameters, or coefficients in size-bounding functions on uncertainties and unmodelled dynamics are *not* needed in this paper. The apriori information required to apply the proposed design procedure includes relative degree of the nominal system, closed-form expression of bounding functions, and, for arbitrarily small tracking error of reference model output, the minimum-phase condition. Under the proposed control, the output tracking error can be made arbitrarily small to achieve any specified tracking accuracy. The distinct feature of MRRC is that neither uncertainties nor unmodelled dynamics are required to be small.

1 Introduction

Existing control scheme can be classified into two categories: state feedback control and output feedback control. Although state feedback control provides theoretically better stability and performance, input-output control is more attractive in practice since less feedback information is used. Most of the results on robust control based on Lyapunov technique are derived in the state space model. More specifically, robust state feedback controllers were designed in [1,4,12,13,14,15,16,23] for general nonlinear uncertain systems. Stabilization is usually the standard topic in this area [1,4,13,14,23]. Full state tracking is not achievable for most uncertain systems but only several special classes as reported in [12,15,16]. For most of engineering applications, output tracking may be sufficient. However, if output equation contains unknown parameter or uncertainty, state tracking does not include output tracking as a special case. Asymptotic output tracking results using state feedback have been reported in [19,20] for linear systems. However, the stability analysis therein imposed such restrictions as the disturbance being constant and the reference signal being generated from unit step function of time through either integration or differentiation.

The main shortcoming of designing robust control using state space model is that full state feedback is usually required. For many applications, output tracking is sufficient, and using feedback information more than output measurement is undesirable. This is because, although full state feedback control ensures better performance in theory, taking state measurement may be either expensive or simply impossible, and because noise introduced due to state measurement may make performance worse. Although recent advances have been made in [12,13,14,15,16,23] to provide less restrictive conditions, the matching conditions in [1,4] are still more or less required in designing full state feedback control. Meanwhile, such structural conditions are not needed for systems described by input-output model, which is another advantage of input-output control design. Based on these observations, a new robust control design approach, called model reference robust control (MRRC), has been recently proposed [10]. In [10], a system under investigation has a linear nominal part and is subject to nonlinearly bounded disturbances. The proposed MRRC controller in [10] requires apriori information on system order, relative order, bounds on unknown parameters, and bounding function on disturbances. Later, MRRC design has been extended in [11] to arbitrarily fast time-varying SISO systems. These two results show preliminarily that MRRC scheme combines the advantages of both robust control and model reference control under perfect knowledge.

In this paper, the MRRC technique is extended further to robustly stabilize systems whose orders are unknown and which contain not only significant disturbances and nonlinear uncertainties but also input-related and output-related unmodelled dynamics. The unmodelled dynamics may be unstable, of infinite dimension, and of arbitrarily large magnitude. Such an extension allows us to design robustly stabilizing control for virtually all system whose nominal system is linear and minimum-phase, which relative degree is arbitrary but fixed and known, and which dynamics are not internally unstable.

For now, the results in [10,11] and in this paper form a viable and novel control design scheme. As shown in [10], MRRC requires less feedback information than standard robust control results, can handle some of uncertainties which do not satisfy the generalized matching conditions in [23,16], and, as will be shown here, applicable to systems with significant unmodelled dynamics. It is worth mentioning here that robust control of systems with unmodelled dynamics has been discussed using singular perturbation technique, see [2] and the references therein. However, singular perturbation method inherently assumes that the unmodelled dynamics are much faster than the system dynamics and the resulting stability is always local. It is also worth noting that there is another input-output control design technique, the well-known model reference adaptive control scheme (MRAC) [7,9,18,21]. Preliminary comparison between MRRC and MRAC was given in [10]. It has been shown in [11] that MRRC guarantees global stability for fast time-varying systems while MRAC requires that time-varying parameters drift slow unless fast time-varying time functions are known. In a recent paper [8] on adaptive control of systems with unmodelled dynamics, besides some other assumptions, admissible unmodelled dynamics have to be sufficiently small, and disturbances have to be sector-bounded. More importantly, arbitrarily small tracking error can be achieved under MRRC while MRAC usually results in boundedness stability. Also, stability proof of MRRC, like standard robust control results, is a straightforward application of Lyapunov's direct method, while stability proof of MRAC for systems with high relative degree or with time-varying parameters or with unmodelled dynamics is very complicated. Therefore, MRRC is superior in many aspects than the existing control schemes.

This paper is organized as follows. A SISO system with significant unmodelled dynamics, basic assumptions, and MRRC problem are formulated in section two. Section three is devoted to find an equivalent closed loop system whenever perfect knowledge of the nominal system is available to design a perfect nominal control. The equivalent system is then used in section four to proceed MRRC design. Sections five contains an illustrative example.

2 Problem Formulation

To avoid unnecessary complexity, robust control design discussed in this paper is limited to systems whose nominal system is single-input single-output, time-invariant, and linear.

The system under consideration is given in Figure 1. Using a classic abuse of notation, the system can be described by the transfer function model:

$$y(t) = G_p(s)[1+\Delta G(s)][u(t)+\xi(y,t)], \tag{1}$$

where the symbol s denotes the differential operator in Laplace transform, $G_p(s)$ is a transfer function given by

$$G_p(s) \triangleq b_{p0}\frac{s^m + b_{p1}s^{m-1}+\cdots+b_{pm}}{s^n+a_{p1}s^{n-1}+\cdots+a_{pn}} \triangleq k_p\frac{B_p(s)}{A_p(s)},$$

$m \le n$, $\Delta G(s)$ denotes any possible unmodelled dynamics associated with input, and $\xi(y,t)$ denotes the sum of all other signals, injected into the system, which are possibly composed of time-varying disturbance, nonlinear uncertainty, or unmodelled dynamics associated with output.

With respect to the model of the controlled plant, we make the following assumptions:

A.1 Internal stabilizability: There is not unstable pole-zero cancellation in $\Delta G(s)$ or between $A_p(s)$ and $B_p(s)$. $\triangle$

A.2 The indices n and m are finite but not necessarily known. However, the relative degree $n_r = n - m \ge 0$ is arbitrary but fixed and known. Moreover, the sign of b_{p0} is assumed without loss of any generality to be positive. $\triangle$

A.3 The system is minimum phase. That is, all the roots of $B_p(s) = 0$ and $1+\Delta G(s) = 0$ are in strictly open left-half s-plane. Moreover, there exists constants $\gamma, C_{\Delta G}, C'_{\Delta G} > 0$ such that

$$\left|\mathcal{L}^{-1}\left\{\frac{\Delta G(s)}{1+\Delta G(s)}\right\}\right| \le C_{\Delta G}e^{-\gamma t} + C'_{\Delta G} \quad \forall t$$

or, more accurately, under zero initial conditions,

$$\left|\mathcal{L}^{-1}\left\{\frac{\Delta G(s)}{1+\Delta G(s)}z(s)\right\}\right| \le C_{\Delta G}\int_{t_0}^{t} e^{-\gamma(t-\tau)}|z(\tau)|d\tau + C'_{\Delta G}|z(t)| \quad \forall z(t)$$

where $\mathcal{L}^{-1}$ represents the operation of taking inverse Laplace transform. That is, zeros of $1+\Delta G(s-\gamma) = 0$ are stable for some known $\gamma > 0$. The constants $C_{\Delta G}$ and $C'_{\Delta G}$ are not required to be known. $\triangle$

A.4 The lumped uncertainty $\xi(y,t)$ is continuous and bounded as $\|\xi(y,t)\| \le \rho(y,t)$ for all (y,t), where $\rho(y,t)$, whose expression is known, is continuous with respect to its arguments, uniformly bounded with respect time, and locally uniformly bounded with respect to y. The symbol $\|\cdot\|$ denotes standard Euclidean norm [5,22]. $\triangle$

Remark 2.1: Assumption A.1 is obviously a necessary condition. In Assumption A.2, the indices n and m are not required to be fixed, but $n - m = n_r$ is constant. The trivial case that $n_r = 0$ can be treated in a similar fashion as the case that $n_r = 1$. $\diamond$

Remark 2.2: Assumption A.3 implies that $\Delta G/(1+\Delta G)$ is proper. This is true as long as $\lim_{s\to\infty}[1+\Delta G(s)] \ne 0$ (or, $\lim_{s\to\infty}\Delta G(s) \ne -1$). The equation $\lim_{s\to\infty}\Delta G(s) = -1$ means that the relative degree of the system is higher than that of $G_p(s)$. Since constant relative degree of the system is assumed, $\lim_{s\to\infty}\Delta G(s) \ne -1$ or $\Delta G/(1+\Delta G)$ being proper can be assumed without loss of any generality. Based on the same reasoning, $|\lim_{s\to\infty}\Delta G(s)| < \infty$ can be assumed. On the other hand, since the gain k_p is unknown, it can be further assumed without loss of any generality that $\lim_{s\to\infty}[1+\Delta G(s)] = 1$. The limit $\lim_{s\to\infty}\Delta G(s) = 0$ implies that ΔG is strictly proper, and in turn suffices that $\Delta G/(1+\Delta G)$ is strictly proper (i.e., $C'_{\Delta G} = 0$). Therefore, Assumption A.3 can be restated as, for any given finite constant η,

$$\left|\mathcal{L}^{-1}\left\{\frac{(s+\eta)\Delta G(s)}{1+\Delta G(s)}\right\}\right| \le C_{\Delta G}e^{-\gamma t} + C'_{\Delta G} \quad \forall t$$

or, more accurately, under zero initial conditions,

$$\left|\mathcal{L}^{-1}\left\{\frac{(s+\eta)\Delta G(s)}{1+\Delta G(s)}z(s)\right\}\right| \le C_{\Delta G}\int_{t_0}^{t} e^{-\gamma(t-\tau)}|z(\tau)|d\tau + C'_{\Delta G}|z(t)| \quad \forall z(t).$$

The above inequality with $\eta > 0$ will be used in this paper. $\diamond$

Remark 2.3: The only required information about $\Delta G(s)$ is the constant γ which can be viewed as the lower bound on time constants of zeros (except those in $B_p(s)$) of the system. Thus, for any finite dimensional system, γ can be arbitrarily chosen since finite number of zeros can all be included into $B_p(s)$. It is worth mentioning that $\Delta G(s)$ could be unstable, very slow in dynamics (γ being small), large in magnitude ($C_{\Delta G}, C'_{\Delta G}$ being large), and of infinite dimension as long as Assumption A.3 is satisfied. As an example, the following unmodelled dynamics of infinite dimension is admissible:

$$\frac{\Delta G(s)}{1+\Delta G(s)} = \mathcal{L}\left\{\sum_{i=1}^{\infty}\Delta g_i e^{-\Delta\gamma_i t}\right\},$$

where $\mathcal{L}$ denotes the operation of taking Laplace transform, $\Delta\gamma_i \ge \gamma > 0$, and the infinite series $\sum_{i=1}^{\infty}\Delta g_i$ is absolutely convergent. $\diamond$

Remark 2.4: Assumption A.3 also implies that zeros of $1+\Delta G$ are distinct. It is easy to generalize Assumption A.3 for the case that there are multiple zeros as long as an upper bound on multiplicity is known. However, multiple zeros of finite number can again be assumed to be included into $B_p(s)$, which implies that Assumption A.3 holds without loss of any generality. $\diamond$

Remark 2.5: The minimum phase condition in Assumption A.3 is introduced to guarantee good performance in tracking output of a reference model. It is known [3,8] that adaptive control is applicable to the so-called weakly non-minimum phase systems, in which only nominal system is

This work is supported in part by U.S. National Science Foundation under grant MSS-9110034.

required to be minimum phase but possible unmodelled dynamics are very small. There are two main differences between system (1) and those in [3,8]. First, the size of unmodelled dynamics considered here may be arbitrarily large. Second, unmodelled dynamics can be unstable and of infinite dimensional. These imply that is that the unmodelled dynamics in (1) are allowed to dominate the behavior of the overall system. It will be shown in an upcoming paper [17] that model reference robust control is applicable to weakly non-minimum phase systems that include those in [3,8] as special cases. ◇

Remark 2.6: The lumped uncertainty $\xi(y,t)$ may contain not only disturbances that are nonlinear functions of y but also additive unmodelled dynamics with respect to y (additive unmodelled dynamics associated with u will be studied in [17]). The function $\rho(y,t)$ bounds pointwise the magnitude of the uncertainty and, due to additive unmodelled dynamics, is in general a function of $y(\tau)$ for $0 < \tau \leq t$. For notational simplicity, a minor abuse of notation, $\rho(y,t)$, is used. The function $\rho(y,t)$ can usually be found by taking Euclidean norm with minimum apriori information. As an example, consider the uncertainty $\xi(y,t) = \Delta G'(s)(y + y^2) + \xi_0(t) + \xi_1(y)$, where $\Delta G'(s)$ is an unknown transfer function satisfying that $\Delta G'(s-\gamma')$ is stable, $\xi_0(t)$ is a time-varying, constant-bounded disturbance, and $\xi_1(y)$ is an uncertainty bounded by polynomial function of $|y|$ up to third order. It is obvious that $\Delta G'(s)$ being stable is necessary in order to have a well-defined bounding function $\rho(y,t)$ (if not, $\Delta G'(s)$ can not be treated as additive disturbance but included into the system). Then, the bounding function can be chosen to be $\rho(y,t) = C_1'[|y(t_0)| + y^2(t_0)]e^{-\gamma' t} + C_2'\int_{t_0}^t e^{-\gamma'(t-\tau)}[|y(\tau)| + y^2(\tau)]d\tau + C_3' + C_4'|y(t)| + C_5' y^2(t) + C_6'|y^3(t)|$ for some constants C_i'. Even if the bounding coefficients C_i' are unknown, the expression of bounding function is sufficient (and obviously necessary) to design a globally stabilizing control. ◇

Remark 2.7: It can be assumed without loss of any generality that $\rho(y,t)$ is differentiable (C^1 function) with respect to time. This is because, although the time derivative of $|y|$ is not well-defined around zero, choice of bounding function is not unique, $2|y| \leq 1 + y^2$, and the first-order derivative of $|y|^k$ is always well defined for $k > 1$. For instance, consider the example in the previous remark, one may choose

$$\rho(y,t) = C_1'[|y(t_0)| + y^2(t_0)]e^{-\gamma' t} + C_2'\int_{t_0}^t e^{-\gamma'(t-\tau)}[|y(\tau)| + y^2(\tau)]d\tau + C_3' + C_4' y^2(t) + C_5' y^4(t)$$

for another set of constants C_i' (Note again that C_i' are not required to be known). This choice guarantees differentiability of $\rho(y,t)$. An alternative way is to replace $|y|$ by $\sqrt{y^2+\varepsilon}$ for any $\varepsilon > 0$ in the expression of $\rho(y,t)$. ◇

Remark 2.8: The requirement of $\rho(y,t)$ being uniformly bounded with respect to time is necessary since it is introduced to exclude systems that can not be stabilized under finite control. As an example, consider $\xi(y,t) = t$. ◇

Remark 2.9: A relaxation of Assumption A.4 will be discussed later as Remark 4.6 on page 18. ◇

In many applications, certain information about the nominal plant, such as estimated values of or bounds on systems parameter, may be available. In this case, the following assumption can be made without loss of any generality.

Optional Assumption: The parameters of the system, a_{pi} and b_{pj}, are unknown constants but are bounded in known compact sets. Usually, compact sets are chosen to be intervals, that is, there are known constants $\underline{a}_{pi}$, $\overline{a}_{pi}$, $\underline{b}_{pj}$, and $\overline{b}_{pj}$ such that, for any $1 \leq i \leq n \leq \overline{n}$ and $0 \leq j \leq m \leq \overline{m}$, $\underline{a}_{pi} \leq a_{pi} \leq \overline{a}_{pi}$ and $\underline{b}_{pj} \leq b_{pj} \leq \overline{b}_{pj}$. Furthermore, denote the estimated values of a_{pi} and b_{pj} by $\hat{a}_{pi}$ and $\hat{b}_{pj}$. Apparently, the estimated values should be in the above compact sets. Also, the constants $C_{\Delta G}$ and $C'_{\Delta G}$ are assumed to be known. △

Remark 2.10: Since unmodelled dynamics can be of infinite order, an upper bound on the order of nominal system can always be assumed. As long as parameters of the nominal system are bounded in known sets, the controller to be proposed works for any choice of estimated values. Also, the proposed design procedure shows how to design robust controller even if bounds on the parameters are not available. That is, the above assumption is merely *optional*. ◇

The control objective in this paper is reference model following. That is, for any given bounded reference signal $r(t)$, the output of system (1) should track with good accuracy the output $y_m(t)$ of a reference model under the presence of $\xi(y,t)$ and $\Delta G(s)$. Let $Y_m(s)$ and $R(s)$ be Laplace transforms of $y_m(t)$ and $r(t)$ respectively, the reference model is then defined by transfer function

$$\frac{Y_m(s)}{R(s)} = b_{m0}\frac{1}{s^{n_r} + a_{m1}s^{n_r-1} + \cdots + a_{mn_r}} \triangleq k_m\frac{B_m(s)}{A_m(s)} \triangleq G_m(s), \tag{2}$$

where $k_m > 0$. The polynomial $A_m(s)$ is assumed to be Hurwitz [6]. We choose $n_m = n_r$ and $m_m = 0$ since, if not, different $G_m(s)$ can be generated by multiplying reference signal by a proper and stable transfer function. That is, it is trivial to generalize $G_m(s)$ such that $A_m(s)$ and $B_m(s)$ are Hurwitz polynomials of order n_m and m_m, respectively, as long as $n_m - m_m \geq n_r$.

Remark 2.11: The assumption $n_m - m_m \geq n_r$ can be removed. This can be done as follows. If $G_m(s)$ does not satisfy the assumption, find a transfer function $G_m'(s)$ which does. Then, proceed the following analysis using $G_m'(s)$, and the difference $[G_m(s) - G_m'(s)]R(s)$ can be treated as a "disturbance" which fits well in the proposed framework of robust control. ◇

In designing output feedback control, strictly positive real (SPR) transfer function [9] plays an important role. Detailed conditions for a transfer function to be SPR can be found on page 64 of [9]. Let

$$\overline{G}_m(s) = G_m(s)\alpha(s) \triangleq k_m\frac{\overline{B}_m(s)}{A_m(s)}, \tag{3}$$

where polynomial $\alpha(s)$ is monic, Hurwitz, and of degree $n_r - 1$. It is assumed without loss of any generality that $\overline{G}_m(s)$ be SPR. This is because, If $\overline{G}_m(s)$ is not SPR, a SPR reference model can be generated by rewriting $\overline{G}_m(s)r(t) = \overline{G}_m'(s)G'(s)r(t) \triangleq \overline{G}_m'(s)r'(t)$, where $\overline{G}_m'(s)$ is any SPR transfer function of relative degree zero. Since $G'(s)$ is stable and minimum-phase and since $r'(t) = G'(s)r(t)$, $r'(t)$ can be used as the reference input.

It should be noted that, throughout this paper, many discussions are proceeded using transfer functions. The transfer function method inherently assumes zero initial conditions for all internal variables. However, for a stable closed-loop linear system (in spite of the presence of uncertainty and unmodelled dynamics), non-zero initial conditions at most contribute additive, exponentially decaying terms. Such terms present no obstacle either for the consideration of model following, if added to system output, or for stability proof, if added to the derivative of Lyapunov function (Remark 4.10).

In the next section, we shall begin our discussion with control design under perfect knowledge of plant parameters. This discussion leads to an equivalent system which is more convenient for subsequent analysis and robust control design.

3 Perfect Nominal Control

In this section, we review briefly classical model reference control scheme for nominal system whose order and parameters are known exactly. Let us first look at the simple case that there is no disturbance, uncertainty, or unmodelled dynamics.

Under perfect knowledge of the nominal system, perfect tracking can be achieved whenever $d(t) \equiv 0$ and $\Delta G(s) \equiv 0$. The classical model reference control can be depicted by Figure 2 in which there are two auxiliary signals $w_1 \in \mathbf{R}^{n'-1}$ and $w_2 \in \mathbf{R}^{n'-1}$ satisfying

$$\dot{w}_1 = A_0 w_1 + B_0 u \tag{4}$$

$$\dot{w}_2 = A_0 w_2 + B_0 y \tag{5}$$

where $\alpha'(s)$ is a Hurwitz polynomial of order $n' - n_r$, $B_0 \in \mathbf{R}^{n'-1}$ is a constant vector such that the pair (A_0, B_0) is controllable, $A_0 \in \mathbf{R}^{(n'-1)\times(n'-1)}$ is a constant stable matrix such that

$$\det[sI - A_0] = \overline{B}_m(s)\alpha'(s) = \alpha(s)\alpha'(s) \triangleq A_o(s). \tag{6}$$

These two auxiliary signals are used to generate output feedback control given by

$$u(t) = kr(t) + \theta_0 y + \theta_1^T w_1 + \theta_2^T w_2 \tag{7}$$

where $k, \theta_0 \in \mathbf{R}$, $\theta_1, \theta_2 \in \mathbf{R}^{n'-1}$ are constant control parameters to be solved shortly. Under this control, the overall transfer function from $r(t)$ to $y(t)$ is easily shown to be

$$\left.\frac{Y(s)}{R(s)}\right|_{d(t)=\Delta G(s)\equiv 0} = \frac{kk_pB_p(s)A_o(s)}{A_p(s)[A_o(s) - D_1(s)] - k_pB_p(s)D_2(s)}, \tag{8}$$

where adj$(\cdot)$ denotes the adjoint matrix of the argument matrix, $D_1(s) = \theta_1^T \mathrm{adj}(sI - A_0)B_0$, and $D_2(s) = \theta_0 A_o(s) + \theta_2^T \mathrm{adj}(sI - A_0)B_0$.

Remark 3.1: In the case of perfect knowledge, we have $\overline{n} = n$ and $\overline{m} = m$; and we can choose $n' = n$. In the case that the system is unknown, we choose $n' = \overline{n}$ provided that the Optional Assumption holds. If the Optional Assumption can not be made, w_1 and w_2 will not be needed for control implementation (see Remarks 4.1 and 4.3), and $n' = n$ is chosen. In any case, the control $u(t)$ will *not* be chosen by (7) since expression (7) is not known. However, equation (7) allows us to find an equivalent system from which robust control is designed. This is analogous to model reference adaptive control. ◇

To ensure that $y(t)$ converges to $y_m(t)$ as time approaches infinity, as defined by perfect model following problem whenever the plant is perfect known, $d(t) \equiv 0$, and $\Delta G(s) \equiv 0$, we have to make the transfer function (8) be $G_m(s)$. That is, find control parameters θ_0, θ_1 and θ_2 such that

$$\left.\frac{Y(s)}{R(s)}\right|_{d(t)=\Delta G(s)\equiv 0} = G_m(s),$$

or, alternatively,

$$k_m A_p(s)[A_o(s) - D_1(s)] - k_m k_p B_p(s) D_2(s) = kk_pB_p(s)A_o(s)A_m(s). \tag{9}$$

The existence and uniqueness of solution of the above algebraic equation is guaranteed by the choice of n' in Remark 3.1. It is easy to see that the solution k satisfies

$$k = \frac{k_m}{k_p} = \frac{b_{m0}}{b_{p0}}, \tag{10}$$

where b_{m0} and b_{p0} are the leading parameters in the numerators of $G_p(s)$ and $G_m(s)$, respectively.

If there exists a disturbance $d(t)$ which is independent of y and bounded by constant, the closed-loop system is still stable but the output will not converge to the desired output under the control (7) since

$$\left.\frac{Y(s)}{D(s)}\right|_{r(t)=\Delta G(s)\equiv 0} = \frac{k_pB_p(s)[A_o(s) - D_1(s)]}{A_p(s)[A_o(s) - D_1(s)] - k_pB_p(s)D_2(s)} = G_m(s)\frac{A_o(s) - D_1(s)}{kA_o(s)}, \tag{11}$$

where $D(s)$ is the Laplace transform of $d(t)$. However, if $d(t) = \xi(y,t) \neq 0$ is a function of y, the closed system under (7) may not be stable.

If, in addition, there is unmodelled dynamics $\Delta G(s)$, it is easy to verify that

$$\left.\frac{Y(s)}{R(s)}\right|_{d(t)\equiv 0} = \frac{kk_pB_p(s)A_o(s)[1+\Delta G(s)]}{A_p(s)[A_o(s) - D_1(s)] - k_pB_p(s)D_2(s)[1+\Delta G(s)]} = G_m(s)\frac{1}{1 - H(s)\overline{\Delta G}(s)}, \tag{12}$$

$$\left.\frac{Y(s)}{D(s)}\right|_{r(t)\equiv 0} = G_m(s)\frac{A_o(s) - D_1(s)}{kA_o(s)}\frac{1}{1 - H(s)\overline{\Delta G}(s)}, \tag{13}$$

where

$$H(s) = 1 + \frac{k_pD_2(s)}{A_o(s)A_m(s)}, \qquad \overline{\Delta G}(s) = \frac{\Delta G(s)}{1+\Delta G(s)}.$$

Obviously, the control (7) is not effective in the presence of unmodelled dynamics. However, it follows from (12) and (13) that, under control (7), the system in Figure 2 is equivalent to that in Figure 3.

The question now is what control should be used if the plant is unknown and if $\xi(y,t) \neq 0$ (even if the plant parameters are known, control has to be redesigned to handle disturbance, uncertainty, and unmodelled dynamics). The answer to this question will be provided in the next section.

4 Robust Control Design

In this section, robust control design is proceeded for the case that the parameters of the plant are unknown, that $\Delta G(s) \neq 0$, and that $\xi(y,t) \neq 0$. No matter what control $u(t)$ is used, the total input to the plant is

$$\begin{aligned} \mho(t) &= u(t) + \xi(y,t) \\ &= \left\{k\left[r(t) + \frac{1}{k}(u - kr - \theta_0 y - \theta_1^T w_1 - \theta_2^T w_2)\right]\theta_0 y + \theta_1^T w_1 + \theta_2^T w_2\right\} + \xi(y,t) \\ &\triangleq u + d, \end{aligned} \tag{14}$$

where $u(t)$ is the robust control to be designed, θ_i are the unknown solution of (9), and w_i are auxiliary signals defined in (4) and (5). The scalar k in (14) is the unknown solution (10) but bounded. However, these unknowns can be handled by the proposed robust control scheme.

The term $[r(t) + \frac{1}{k}(u - kr - \theta_0 y - \theta_1^T w_1 - \theta_2^T w_2)]$ in (14) is now viewed as "the total reference input." Since the ideal parameter vector θ satisfies (9), it follows from the preceding discussion on perfect nominal control (Figure 3) that the plant output under total input (14) must be

$$
\begin{aligned}
y(t) &= \overline{G}_m(s)\left\{\frac{1}{\alpha(s)}\left[r(t)+\frac{1}{k}(u-kr-\theta_0 y-\theta_1^T w_1-\theta_2^T w_2)\right]\right.\\
&\left.+\frac{A_o(s)-D_1(s)}{k\alpha(s)A_o(s)}\xi(y,t)+\overline{\Delta G}(s)H(s)\overline{G}_m^{-1}(s)y(t)\right\}\\
&= G_m(s)r(t)+\overline{G}_m(s)\left[\frac{1}{\alpha(s)}u'(t)+d'\right]\frac{1}{k}, \qquad (15)
\end{aligned}
$$

where $\hat{k}$ and $\hat{\theta}_i$ are either zero, if the Optional Assumption is not imposed, or, if otherwise, the solution of (9) using the estimated value of system parameters $\hat{a}_{pi}$ and $\hat{b}_{pj}$, $\tilde{k}=k-\hat{k}$, $\tilde{\theta}_i=\theta_i-\hat{\theta}_i$, and

$$
\begin{aligned}
u'(t) &= u(t)-\hat{k}r-\hat{\theta}_0 y-\hat{\theta}_1^T w_1-\hat{\theta}_2^T w_2,\\
d'(y,r,u,t) &= \frac{1}{\alpha(s)}\left[-\tilde{k}r(t)-\tilde{\theta}_0 y-\tilde{\theta}_1 w_1-\tilde{\theta}_2^T w_2+\left(1-\frac{D_1(s)}{A_o(s)}\right)\xi(y,t)\right]\\
&+k\overline{\Delta G}(s)H(s)\overline{G}_m^{-1}(s)y(t).
\end{aligned}
$$

Remark 4.1: $u'(t)$ is the control to be designed, from which the overall control $u(t)$ can be determined. If the Optional Assumption does not hold, the order $n'=n$ is unknown, and in this case w_1 and w_2 can not be calculated. To guarantees that robust control is well defined, we set $\hat{k}=0$ and $\hat{\theta}_i=0$. Also, a bounding function for $d'(y,r,u,t)$ that does not require w_1 and w_2 has to be found (Remark 4.3). ◇

The problem of control design studied in this section is to find an input-output control $u'(t)$ (or equivalently $u(t)$) which compensates for the total uncertainty $d'(y,r,u,t)$ and therefore guarantees global stability. Lyapunov's direct method is used to show global stability in which process a proper robust control is formulated. To clarify ideas of robust control design, our discussion is divided into four parts. First, since Lyapunov method is based on state space representation, we shall find the system of output tracking error and then a workable state space model for the error system. The second part is to find a *known* bounding function for the total uncertainty $d'(y,r,u,t)$. The bounding function will be used in Lyapunov argument and in generating robust control. The robust control is then stated as the third part after determining the bounding function. These three parts will be proceeded in a sequence and serve as preparation for the last part, that is, to set up the stage for stating our main result, robust stability proof.

We are now in a position to make several definitions for deriving a state space model about the dynamics of output tracking error. First, let us define the output tracking error $e(t)$ to be $e(t)=y_m(t)-y(t)$, where $y_m(t)=G_m(s)r(t)$. Then, the dynamics of the output tracking error is described by

$$
e(t)=\overline{G}_m(s)\left[-\frac{1}{\alpha(s)}u'(t)-d'\right]\frac{b_{p0}}{b_{m0}}. \qquad (16)
$$

Second, let

$$
z_1=\frac{1}{\alpha(s)}u'(t) \qquad (17)
$$

be the intermediate control variable.

Third, let us introduce a new set of state variables z_i as the state in the controllable canonical realization of the transfer function $1/\alpha(s)$. We shall discuss the non-trivial case that $n_r\geq 1$. If $\alpha(s)=s^{n_r-1}+\alpha_1 s^{n_r-2}+\cdots+\alpha_{n_r-1}$, we define $\dot{z}_i=z_{i+1}$ for $i=1,\cdots,n_r-2$. If n_r is 1 or 2, no additional variable is needed. We can then rewrite (17) in terms of the state space equation as

$$
\begin{aligned}
\dot{z}_1 &= z_2, \quad \dot{z}_i=z_{i+1}, \quad \forall i=2,\cdots,n_r-2,\\
\dot{z}_{n_r-1} &= -\alpha_1 z_{n_r-1}-\cdots-\alpha_{n_r-1}z_1+u'(t)\\
&= -\alpha_1 z_{n_r}-\cdots-\alpha_{n_r}z_1+u(t)-\hat{k}r-\hat{\theta}_0 y-\hat{\theta}_1^T w_1-\hat{\theta}_2^T w_2,\\
z_1 &= \frac{1}{\alpha(s)}u'(t). \qquad (18)
\end{aligned}
$$

Forth, let the triple $\{\overline{A}_e,\overline{B}_e,\overline{C}_e\}$ denote the controllable canonical realization of the transfer function $\overline{G}_m(s)$, i.e.

$$
\dot{x}_e=\overline{A}_e x_e+\overline{B}_e[-z_1-d']\frac{b_{p0}}{b_{m0}} \qquad e=\overline{C}_e x_e. \qquad (19)
$$

Since $\overline{G}_m(s)$ is SPR, it follows from the Kalman-Yakubovich lemma in [5] that, given a symmetric positive definite (s.p.d.) matrix Q_e, there exists a s.p.d. matrix P_e such that

$$
\overline{A}_e^T P_e+P_e\overline{A}_e=-Q_e, \qquad P_e\overline{B}_e=\overline{C}_e^T. \qquad (20)
$$

The equations (18) and (19) form a state space model for (16). The relation (20) is important for designing input-output control and will be used in stability proof. This concludes the first phase of discussion.

The second phase of discussion is to find known bounding function for uncertainty. Define the following filtered auxiliary signals:

$$
\overline{r}=\frac{1}{\alpha(s)}r, \quad \overline{y}=\frac{1}{\alpha(s)}y, \quad \overline{w}_1=\frac{1}{\alpha(s)}w_1, \quad \overline{w}_2=\frac{1}{\alpha(s)}w_2, \quad y_1=\frac{1}{s+\eta}\overline{G}_m^{-1}(s)y, \qquad (21)
$$

for some $\eta>0$ arbitrarily chosen by the designer. Note that the transfer function $\overline{G}_m^{-1}(s)/(s+\eta)$ is stable and proper, and therefore can be implemented. Then, the total uncertainty $d'(y,r,u,t)$ can be rewritten as

$$
d'(y,r,u,t)=-\tilde{k}\overline{r}-\tilde{\theta}_0\overline{y}-\tilde{\theta}_1\overline{w}_1-\tilde{\theta}_2^T\overline{w}_2+\left(1-\frac{D_1(s)}{A_o(s)}\right)\frac{1}{\alpha(s)}\xi(y,t)+k(s+\eta)\overline{\Delta G}(s)H(s)y_1(t).
$$

Based on the above expression, we can determine a known bounding function, denoted by $g_1(y,r,u,t)$, on the size of $d'(y,r,u,t)$. Note that the bounding function is not unique and has different expressions, depending on what is known about the function and what the property the bounding function may have (such as differentiability). It follows from Assumptions A.3, A.4, and Remark 2.2 that the following inequalities hold:

$$
\left|\left(1-\frac{D_1(s)}{A_o(s)}\right)\frac{1}{\alpha(s)}\xi(y,t)\right|\leq(1+\|\theta_1\|\cdot\|e^{A_o t}B_0\|*)|h_1(t)|*\rho(y,t), \qquad (22)
$$

$$
\begin{aligned}
|k(s+\eta)\overline{\Delta G}(s)H(s)y_1(t)| &\leq |k|\left(C_{\Delta G}e^{-\gamma t}*+C'_{\Delta G}\right)(1+|k_p|\|\theta_0\||h_2(t)|*\\
&+\|\theta_2\|\|e^{A_o t}B_0\|*|h_2(t)|*)|y_1(t)|,
\end{aligned}
$$

$$
\left|\tilde{k}\overline{r}(t)\right|\leq|\tilde{k}||\overline{r}(t)|, \quad \left|\tilde{\theta}_0\overline{y}\right|\leq|\tilde{\theta}_0||\overline{y}(t)|, \quad \left|\tilde{\theta}_1\overline{w}_1(t)\right|\leq\|\tilde{\theta}_1\|\|\overline{w}_1(t)\|, \quad \left|\tilde{\theta}_2\overline{w}_2(t)\right|\leq\|\tilde{\theta}_2\|\|\overline{w}_2(t)\|,
$$

where $*$ denotes the operation of convolution, and $h_1(t)$ and $h_2(t)$ are the impulse responses of $1/\alpha(s)$ and $1/A_m(s)$, respectively. Again, non-zero initial conditions are neglected since they at most contribute exponentially decaying terms.

To represent a known bounding function, we need to introduce the following definition.

Definition: If $d(y,t)$ is an unknown continuous function. Then, $\|\|d(y,t)\|\|$ is a *known*, continuous function that bounds Euclidean norm of $d(y,t)$, that is, $\|d(y,t)\|\leq\|\|d(y,t)\|\|$ for all (y,t). △

Using the definition, the bounding function $g_1(y,r,u,t)$ can be chosen as follows:

(i) If the Optional Assumption holds,

$$
\begin{aligned}
g_1(y,r,u,t) &= \|\|\tilde{k}\|\|\cdot|\overline{r}(t)|+\|\|\tilde{\theta}_0\|\|\cdot|\overline{y}(t)|+\|\|\tilde{\theta}_1\|\|\cdot\|\overline{w}_1(t)\|+\|\|\tilde{\theta}_2\|\|\cdot\|\overline{w}_2(t)\|\\
&+(1+\|\|\theta_1\|\|\cdot\|e^{A_o t}B_0\|*)|h_1(t)|*\rho(y,t)+\|\|k\|\|(C_{\Delta G}e^{-\gamma t}*+C'_{\Delta G})(1+\\
&\|\|k_p\|\|\cdot\|\|\theta_0\|\|\cdot|h_2(t)|*+\|\|\theta_2\|\|\cdot\|e^{A_o t}B_0\|*|h_2(t)|*)|y_1(t)|, \qquad (23)
\end{aligned}
$$

where the upper bounds $\|\|\tilde{k}\|\|$, $\|\|\tilde{\theta}_0\|\|$, $\|\|\tilde{\theta}_1\|\|$, $\|\|\tilde{\theta}_2\|\|$, $\|\|k\|\|$, $\|\|k_p\|\|$, $\|\|\theta_0\|\|$, $\|\|\theta_1\|\|$, and $\|\|\theta_2\|\|$ on magnitudes of their arguments can be found using (9) under the Optional Assumption.

(ii) If the Optional Assumption is not valid, the bounding function can be chosen to be anything that contains higher-order nonlinear functions of the time function terms in that of case (i). One of the simplest choices of the bounding function is

$$
\begin{aligned}
g_1(y,r,u,t) &= k_g\left\{|\overline{r}(t)|^2+|\overline{y}(t)|^2+\|\|\overline{w}_1(t)\|\|^2+\|\|\overline{w}_2(t)\|\|^2+|h_1(t)|*\rho^2(y,t)\right.\\
&+\|\|e^{A_o t}B_0\|\|*|h_1(t)|*\rho^2(y,t)+e^{-\gamma t}*y_1^2(t)+e^{-\gamma t}*|h_2(t)|*y_1^2(t)\\
&+e^{-\gamma t}*\|\|e^{A_o t}B_0\|\|*|h_2(t)|*y_1^2(t)+y_1^2(t)\\
&\left.+|h_2(t)|*y_1^2(t)|+\|\|e^{A_o t}B_0\|\|*|h_2(t)|*y_1^2(t)\right\}, \qquad (24)
\end{aligned}
$$

where $k_g>0$ is a scalar gain whose value can be arbitrarily chosen by the designer. It will be shown later that global stability is always guaranteed for any choice of $k_g>0$ but tracking error becomes smaller if k_g becomes larger.

Remark 4.2: The function $g_1(y,r,u,t)$ is an implicit function of u since it depends only on a filtered version of $\overline{u}$. This is important in order to guarantees that the proposed robust control u (or u') is well-defined. If differentiability of $g_1(y,r,u,t)$ is needed, the form of the bounding function $g_1(y,r,u,t)$ should be modified in a similar way as that explained in Remark 2.7. ◇

Remark 4.3: If the Optional Assumption is assumed, $\overline{w}_1$, $\overline{w}_2$, $e^{A_o t}B_0$ can be calculated. since A_0 and B_0 are of order $\overline{n}-1$ and satisfy (6). Note that $\|\overline{w}_2\|\leq\|\|e^{A_o t}B_0\|\|*|\overline{y}(t)|\triangleq\|\|\overline{w}_2\|\|$. If the Optional Assumption does not hold, we have to bound $\overline{w}_1$ and $e^{A_o t}B_0$ since their order is unknown. This problem can be resolved as follows. Since $\alpha(s)$ and $\alpha'(s)$ are arbitrary Hurwitz polynomials chosen by designer (despite that the order of $\alpha'(s)$ is unknown), assume without loss of any generality that they have distinct roots p_{oi} satisfying $\mathrm{Re}(p_{oi})\leq-\gamma_o<0$. Then, let A_0 be diagonal and let B_0 be the vector in which every element is $1/(n-1)$, no matter what is the order of A_0 and B_0, we have $\|e^{A_o t}B_0\|\leq e^{-\gamma_o t}\triangleq\|\|e^{A_o t}B_0\|\|$. On the other hand, we have that, for any $\delta>0$,

$$
\overline{w}_{1i}=\frac{1}{n-1}\frac{1}{s+p_{oi}}\overline{u}=\frac{1}{n-1}\frac{s+\delta}{s+p_{oi}}\frac{1}{s+\delta}\overline{u},
$$

where $\overline{w}_{1i}$ denotes the i-th element in $\overline{w}_1$. Therefore, $\|\overline{w}_1\|$ can be easily bounded in terms of the signal $\frac{1}{s+\delta}\overline{u}$, that is, $\|\|\overline{w}_1\|\|$ can be found. ◇

Remark 4.4: The function $g_1(y,r,u,t)$ given by either (23) or (24) can be simplified further. For example, if $\|\|e^{A_o t}B_0\|\|=e^{-\gamma_1 t}$ and $|h_1(t)|=e^{-\gamma_2 t}$, then, $\|e^{A_o t}B_0\|*|h_2(t)|\leq Ce^{-\gamma_3 t}$ for some constants $C>0$ and $0<\gamma_3<\min\{\gamma_1,\gamma_2\}$. This implies that multiple convolution operations in (23) and (24) can always be reduced down to single convolution for the ease of implementation. ◇

The above choice of bounding function guarantees that either

$$
|d'(y,r,u,t)|-g_1(y,r,u,t)\leq 0 \qquad (25)
$$

whenever the Optional Assumption holds, or, if otherwise,

$$
|d'(y,r,u,t)|-g_1(y,r,u,t)\leq C_1(k_g) \qquad (26)
$$

for some unknown constant $C_1(k_g)$ satisfying $\lim_{k_g\to\infty}C_1(k_g)=0$. These two inequalities are crucial in stability analysis. The latter inequality is the basis for achieving global stability for any $k_g>0$ even if bounds on parameters are unknown. The second part of preparation is completed by making the following two additional observations on the process of finding bounding function.

Remark 4.5: There is no restriction on the choices of parameter estimates, $\hat{k}$, etc. If the Optional Assumption does not hold, that is, if the system is totally unknown, the parameter estimates plays no role in the control design by making the described choice of bounding function. However, if approximate information on parameters is available, non-zero choice of $\hat{k}$ can make $|\tilde{k}|$ smaller than $|k|$, which makes the bounding function have smaller coefficients. So, good estimates of parameters help to reduce the magnitude of control, but are not necessarily required for stability. ◇

Remark 4.6: It follows from the discussion in (22) that the lumped uncertainty $\xi(y,t)$ can be generalized. The generalized uncertainty $\xi(t,y,\dot{y},\ddot{y},\cdots)$ may depend on not only the output y but also derivatives of y provided that there exist a known Hurwitz polynomial $\beta(s)$ of order at most n_r-1 and a bounding function $\rho(y,t)$, which is function of y only, such that

$$
\left|\frac{1}{\beta(s)}\xi(t,y,\dot{y},\ddot{y},\cdots)\right|\leq\rho(y,t).
$$

As an example, consider the uncertainty $\xi(t,y,\dot{y})=3y^2\sin(\xi_0 y)\dot{y}$ where $\xi_0(t)$ is an unknown time-varying parameter. Then,

$$
\begin{aligned}
\left|\frac{1}{s+1}\xi(t,y,\dot{y})\right| &= \left|\int_{t_0}^{t}e^{-(t-\tau)}3y^2\sin(\xi_0 y)\dot{y}d\tau\right|\\
&\leq \int_{t_0}^{t}e^{-(t-\tau)}|d|y|^3|=|y|^3+e^{-(t-t_0)}|y(t_0)|^3+e^{-t}*|y|^3\triangleq\rho(y,t).
\end{aligned}
$$

We can make $\beta(s)$ be a factor of $\alpha(s)$. In this case, inequality (22) is still valid except that $h_1(t)$ is now the impulse response of $\beta(s)/\alpha(s)$. ◇

We are ready to introduce the robust design procedure. The following recursive mapping is used to generate the proposed robust controller:

$$
\begin{aligned}
\nu_1 &= \frac{\mu_1(e,y,r,u,t)|\mu_1(e,y,r,u,t)|^{r_1}}{|\mu_1(e,y,r,u,t)|^{r_1+1}+\epsilon_1^{1+r_1}}g_1(y,r,u,t),\\
\nu_2 &= e+\nu_1-z_1+\frac{\mu_2(e,y,r,u,t)|\mu_2(e,y,r,u,t)|^{r_2}}{|\mu_2(e,y,r,u,t)|^{r_2+1}+\epsilon_2^{1+r_2}}g_2(y,r,u,t),\\
\nu_i &= \nu_{i-2}-z_{i-2}+\nu_{i-1}-z_{i-1}+\frac{\mu_i(e,y,r,u,t)|\mu_i(e,y,r,u,t)|^{r_i}}{|\mu_i(e,y,r,u,t)|^{r_i+1}+\epsilon_i^{1+r_i}}g_i(y,r,u,t),\\
\nu_{n_r} &= \alpha_1 z_{n_r-1}+\cdots+\alpha_{n_r-1}z_1+\nu_{n_r-2}-z_{n_r-2}+\nu_{n_r-1}-z_{n_r-1}
\end{aligned}
$$

$$
\begin{aligned}
&\quad + \frac{\mu_{n_r}(e,y,u,t)|\mu_{n_r}(e,y,r,u,t)|^{\tau_{n_r}}}{|\mu_{n_r}(e,y,r,u,t)|^{\tau_{n_r}+1}+\epsilon_{n_r}^{1+\tau_{n_r}}} g_{n_r}(y,r,u,t),\\
u' &= \nu_{n_r}\\
u(t) &= \hat{k}r + \hat{\theta}_0 y + \hat{\theta}_1^T w_1 + \hat{\theta}_2^T w_2 + u',
\end{aligned}
\tag{27}
$$

where $i = 3, \cdots, n_r - 1$, $\epsilon_j > 0$ and $\tau_j \geq 0$, $j = 1, \cdots, n_r$, are constants, the constants τ_j are chosen such that the first order partial derivatives of ν_j with respect to their variables are well-defined, $g_1(y,r,u,t)$ is defined by either (23) or (24), $g_{k+1}(y,r,u,t) \triangleq |||\dot{\nu}_k|||$ denote bounding functions on $|\dot{\nu}_k|$ for $k = 1, \cdots, n_r - 1$, respectively, and

$$\mu_1(e,y,r,u,t) = 2eg_1(y,r,u,t), \qquad \mu_2(e,y,r,u,t) = 2(\nu_1 - z_1)g_2(y,r,u,t),$$

$$\mu_i(e,y,r,u,t) = 2(\nu_{i-1} - z_{i-1})g_i(y,r,u,t), \qquad \mu_{n_r}(e,y,r,u,t) = 2(\nu_{n_r-1} - z_{n_r} - 1)g_{n_r}(y,r,u,t).$$

Remark 4.7: Every intermediate control variable in (27) contains two parts. The first part is a linear control law since the nominal system is linear. The second portion is one of the standard nonlinear robust control laws given in [1,12,13,14,15,16]. The nonlinear robust control is to compensate for disturbance, uncertainty, and unmodelled dynamics. Again, w_1 and w_2 are not required by setting parameter estimates to be zero if the Optional Assumption is not valid. ◇

Remark 4.8: The procedure of deriving a globally stabilizing control requires in every step a bounding function $g_{i+1}(y,r,u,t)$ on $|\dot{\nu}_i|$. To find the bounding function, we shall first ensure that ν_i is differentiable (C^1 is sufficient since, by Remarks 2.7 and 4.1, the bounding function of $|\dot{\nu}_i|$ can be made differentiable again in the process of finding itself). Finite-time differentiability of ν_i can always be guaranteed by properly choosing $\tau_i > 0$ and $g_i(y,r,u,t)$. This can be seen from the discussion in Remark 2.7. Therefore, $\dot{\nu}_i$ can be calculated by differentiating by part. All first-order partial derivatives are known, and first-order time derivatives of the arguments are given by the following relations:

$$\dot{\bar{r}} = \frac{s}{\alpha(s)}r(t), \quad \dot{\bar{y}} = \frac{s}{\alpha(s)}y(t), \quad \dot{z}_i = z_{i+1}, \quad \forall i = 1, \cdots, n_r - 2, \quad \dot{\overline{w}}_1 = A_0\overline{w}_1 + B_0 z_1$$

$$\dot{\overline{w}}_2 = A_0\overline{w}_2 + B_0\overline{y}, \quad \dot{y} = sG_m(s)r(t) - \dot{e}, \quad \dot{e} = s\overline{G}_m(s)[-z_1 - d'(y,r,u,t)]\frac{b_{p0}}{b_{m0}},$$

in which there are uncertainties. However, using these relations, we can bound the magnitude of these first order derivatives. Note that $s\overline{G}_m(s)$ is proper. Then, the bounding function for $\dot{\nu}_i$ can be expressed in terms of products of the bounding functions of these first order time derivatives and the Euclidean norms of first order partial derivatives. Again, two expressions of the bounding function can be determined depending on whether the Optional Assumption holds. This process of finding bounding function is the same as that for determining $g_1(y,r,u,t)$ which bounds $d'(y,r,u,t)$. ◇

Remark 4.9: Some terms in the expression $\dot{\nu}_i$ do not depend on uncertainty or output derivatives. These terms are known, may not have to be bounded, and can be canceled exactly by choosing ν_{i+1} properly. However, to simplify the notation and expression, the mapping (27) does not contain these details. ◇

We can now state our main result, which proof is a straightforward application of Lyapunov's second method.

Theorem: *Suppose that the plant satisfies Assumptions A.1 to A.4. Then, under the robust control (27), the plant output tracking error e converges globally and exponentially to a residue set around the origin whose radius can be made to be arbitrarily small by making $\sum \epsilon_i$ small and, if applicable, k_g large. Moreover, the robust control u(t) defined in (27) is uniformly continuous and globally bounded.*

Proof: Choose V to be the Lyapunov function defined as

$$V = \frac{b_{m0}}{b_{p0}}x_e^T P_e x_e + \sum_{i=1}^{n_r-1}(z_i - \nu_i)^2,$$

where P_e is the solution of (20). Taking its time derivative along the trajectories of the system given by (18) and (19) yields

$$
\begin{aligned}
\dot{V} &= \frac{b_{m0}}{b_{p0}}x_e^T(P_e\overline{A}_e + \overline{A}_e^T P_e)x_e + 2x_e^T P_e \overline{B}_e[-z_1 - d'] + \sum_{i=1}^{n_r-1} 2(z_i - \nu_i)(\dot{z}_i - \dot{\nu}_i)\\
&= -\frac{b_{m0}}{b_{p0}}x_e^T Q_e x_e + 2e[-\nu_1 - d'] + 2(z_1 - \nu_1)(\nu_2 - e - \dot{\nu}_1)\\
&\quad + \sum_{i=2}^{n_r-2} 2(z_i - \nu_i)(\nu_{i+1} + z_{i-1} - \nu_{i-1} - \dot{\nu}_i)\\
&\quad + 2(z_{n_r-1} - \nu_{n_r-1})(u' - \alpha_1 z_{n_r-1} - \cdots - \alpha_{n_r-1}z_1 + z_{n_r-2} - \nu_{n_r-2} - \dot{\nu}_{n_r-1})\\
&\leq -\frac{b_{m0}}{b_{p0}}x_e^T Q_e x_e + 2|e|[|d'| - g_1(y,r,u,t)] + [|\mu_1(y,r,u,t)| - 2e\nu_1]\\
&\quad + \sum_{i=1}^{n_r-1} 2|z_i - \nu_i|[|\dot{\nu}_i| - g_{i+1}(y,r,u,t)] + \sum_{i=1}^{n_r-1}|\mu_{i+1}(y,r,u,t)|\\
&\quad + 2(z_1 - \nu_1)(\nu_2 - e) + \sum_{i=2}^{n_r-2} 2(z_i - \nu_i)(\nu_{i+1} + z_{i-1} - \nu_{i-1})\\
&\quad + 2(z_{n_r-1} - \nu_{n_r-1})(u' - \alpha_1 z_{n_r-1} - \cdots - \alpha_{n_r-1}z_1 + z_{n_r-2} - \nu_{n_r-2}).
\end{aligned}
\tag{28}
$$

It follows that

$$
\begin{aligned}
|\mu_1(e,y,r,u,t)| - 2e\nu_1 &= |\mu_1(e,y,r,u,t)| - \frac{|\mu_1(e,y,r,u,t)|^{\tau_1+2}}{|\mu_1(e,y,r,u,t)|^{\tau_1+1} + \epsilon_1^{1+\tau_1}}\\
&= \frac{|\mu_1(e,y,r,u,t)|\epsilon_1^{\tau_1}}{|\mu_1(e,y,r,u,t)|^{\tau_1+1} + \epsilon_1^{1+\tau_1}}\epsilon_1 \leq \epsilon_1.
\end{aligned}
$$

By mimicking the above derivation, we can show that

$$|\mu_2(e,y,r,u,t)| + 2(z_1 - \nu_1)(\nu_2 - e) \leq -2(z_1 - \nu_1)^2 + \epsilon_2,$$

$$|\mu_{i+1}(e,y,r,u,t)| + 2(z_i - \nu_i)(\nu_{i+1} + z_{i-1} - \nu_{i-1}) \leq -2(z_i - \nu_i)^2 + \epsilon_{i+1}, \qquad i \in \{2, \cdots, n_r - 2\},$$

$$
\begin{aligned}
&|\mu_{n_r}(e,y,r,u,t)| + 2(z_{n_r-1} - \nu_{n_r-1})(u' - \alpha_1 z_{n_r-1} - \cdots - \alpha_{n_r-1}z_1 + z_{n_r-2} - \nu_{n_r-2})\\
\leq\ & -2(z_{n_r-1} - \nu_{n_r-1})^2 + \epsilon_{n_r}.
\end{aligned}
$$

Substituting the above inequalities into (28) yields

$$
\begin{aligned}
\dot{V} &\leq -\frac{b_{m0}}{b_{p0}}x_e^T Q_e x_e - 2\sum_{i=1}^{n_r-1}(z_i - \nu_i)^2 + 2|e|[|d'| - g_1(y,r,u,t)]\\
&\quad + \sum_{i=1}^{n_r-1} 2|z_i - \nu_i|[|\dot{\nu}_i| - g_{i+1}(y,r,u,t)] + \sum_{j=1}^{n_r}\epsilon_j.
\end{aligned}
$$

Simplified expressions for $\dot{V}$ which are slightly different can be derived depending on whether the Optional Assumption holds. First, if the Optional Assumption is valid, it follows from (25) that

$$|e||d'(y,r,u,t)| - |e|g_1(y,r,u,t) \leq 0,$$

and, similarly,

$$|z_i - \nu_i||\dot{\nu}_i| - |z_i - \nu_i|g_{i+1}(y,r,u,t) \leq 0$$

for all $i = 1, \cdots, n_r - 1$. Therefore, we have

$$\dot{V} \leq -\frac{b_{m0}}{b_{p0}}x_e^T Q_e x_e - 2\sum_{i=1}^{n_r-1}(z_i - \nu_i)^2 + \sum_{j=1}^{n_r}\epsilon_j \leq \lambda V + \lambda\epsilon, \tag{29}$$

where $\lambda = \min\left\{\frac{\lambda_{min}(Q_e)}{\lambda_{max}(P_e)}, 2\right\}$, and $\epsilon = \frac{1}{\lambda}\sum_{i=1}^{n_r}\epsilon_i$. Now, letting $s(t) = \dot{V} + \lambda V - \lambda\epsilon$ yields $s(t) \leq 0$. It then follows that

$$V(t) = e^{-\lambda(t-t_0)}V(t_0) + \int_{t_0}^{t} e^{-\lambda(t-\tau)}(s(t) + \lambda\epsilon)d\tau \leq e^{-\lambda(t-t_0)}V(t_0) + \epsilon\left(1 - e^{-\lambda(t-t_0)}\right),$$

which approaches ϵ as $t \to \infty$. Therefore, V is uniformly ultimately bounded; all state variables including the output tracking error e converge globally and exponentially to their residue sets which radii are linearly proportional to ϵ.

$\dot{V}$ has a second expression if the Optional Assumption does not hold. It then follows from (26) that $|d'(y,r,u,t)| - g_1(y,r,u,t) \leq C_1(k_g)$, and, similarly, $|\dot{\nu}_i| - g_{i+1}(y,r,u,t) \leq C_{i+1}(k_g)$ for all $i = 1, \cdots, n_r - 1$. Therefore, we have

$$
\begin{aligned}
\dot{V} &\leq -\frac{b_{m0}}{b_{p0}}x_e^T Q_e x_e - 2\sum_{i=1}^{n_r-1}(z_i - \nu_i)^2 + 2|e|C_1(k_g) + 2\sum_{l=2}^{n_r}|z_l - \nu_l|C_l(k_g) + \sum_{j=1}^{n_r}\epsilon_j\\
&\leq -\frac{1}{2}\frac{b_{m0}}{b_{p0}}x_e^T Q_e x_e - \sum_{i=1}^{n_r-1}(z_i - \nu_i)^2 + \frac{2b_{p0}C_1^2(k_g)}{b_{m0}\lambda_{min}(Q_e)} + \sum_{l=2}^{n_r}C_l^2(k_g) + \sum_{j=1}^{n_r}\epsilon_j\\
&\leq \lambda V + \lambda\epsilon,
\end{aligned}
$$

where

$$\lambda = \min\left\{\frac{\lambda_{min}(Q_e)}{2\lambda_{max}(P_e)}, 1\right\} \qquad \epsilon = \frac{1}{\lambda}\left[\frac{2b_{p0}C_1^2(k_g)}{b_{m0}\lambda_{min}(Q_e)} + \epsilon_1 + \sum_{i=2}^{n_r}\left(\epsilon_i + C_i^2(k_g)\right)\right].$$

The above inequality is in the same form as (29), and consequently the same stability result follows even if the Optional Assumption does not hold.

It follows from system equation that, for any $\delta > 0$,

$$\frac{1}{s+\delta}\overline{u}(t) = \frac{1}{(s+\delta)\alpha(s)G_p(s)[1+\Delta G(s)]}y(t) - \frac{1}{(s+\delta)\alpha(s)}\xi(y,t).$$

Since the output is bounded and the system is minimum phase, the signal $\frac{1}{s+\delta}\overline{u}(t)$ is globally bounded. It then follows from (23), (24), Remark 4.3, and (27) that ν_1 and therefore z_1 are globally bounded. By induction, we can show global boundedness of the control $u(t)$ and all intermediate design (or fictitious control) variables ν_i. Therefore, the overall system is stable. Moreover, it follows from (27) that the control $u(t)$ and every intermediate design variable ν_i are all uniformly continuous. □

Remark 4.10: The proof of the above theorem is done under zero initial conditions. In the case there are non-zero I.C.s, the derivative of Lyapunov function will contain an additive term of magnitude $Ce^{-\lambda' t}\sqrt{V}$ for some constants $C, \lambda' > 0$. By triangle inequality, for any arbitrarily small $\kappa > 0$,

$$Ce^{-\lambda' t}\sqrt{V} \leq \kappa V + \frac{C^2}{4\kappa}e^{-2\lambda' t}.$$

Therefore, applying the procedure for solving (29) yields the same stability results. ◇

5 Illustrative Example

In this section, we shall present a simple example to illustrate the MRRC design approach and the effect of the resulting control in the presence of unmodelled dynamics.

Example: Consider the plant described by $G_p(s)[1 + \Delta G(s)]$ where $\Delta G(s)$ is strictly proper,

$$G_p(s) = k_p\frac{B_p(s)}{A_p(s)} = b_{p0}\frac{1}{s + a_{p1}},$$

and a_{p1} and b_{p0} are unknown parameters with $b_{p0} > 0$.

For this system, there are only two known information. First,

$$\left|\mathcal{L}^{-1}\left\{\frac{\Delta G(s)}{1 + \Delta G(s)}\right\}\right| \leq C_{\Delta G}e^{-0.1t}$$

for some unknown constant $C_{\Delta G}$. Second, the lumped uncertainty $\xi(y,t)$ is bounded by

$$|\xi(y,t)| \leq 1 + y^2 + e^{-t} * y^2 \triangleq \rho(y,t).$$

A stabilizing control can be designed using the MRRC approach which in general contains the following four steps:

Step (1): Choose a desired reference model and an appropriate filter $\alpha(s)$. Suppose that $G_m(s) = \frac{1}{s+1}$ and $\alpha(s) = 1$. It is easy to check that $\overline{G}_m(s) = G_m(s)$ is SPR.

Step (2): Generate, if desirable, the auxiliary signals. Note that, if an upper bound on the system order is unknown, this step must be skipped. For this example, no auxiliary signal is needed since $\alpha(s) = 1$.

Step (3): Find the bounding function $g_1(\cdot)$. Since the Optional Assumption is not imposed, there is no need to solve (9), and $u' = u$ (i.e., $\hat{k} = \hat{\theta}_0 = \hat{\theta}_1 = \hat{\theta}_2 = 0$) should be chosen. It follows from (24) that $g_1(y,r,u,t) = k_g\left\{r^2(t) + y^2(t) + \rho^2(y,t) + e^{-0.1t} * y^2(t)\right\}$, where $k_g > 0$ is a scalar gain, and the constant η is chosen to be 1.

Step (3): Determine robust control:

$$u = \nu_1 = \frac{\mu_1(e,y,u,t)}{|\mu_1(e,y,u,t)| + \epsilon_1}g_1(y,u,t) = \frac{eg_1^2}{|e|g_1 + \epsilon_1},$$

where $\epsilon_1 > 0$ is a constant, $\mu_1(e, y, u, t) = e(t)g_1(y, u, t)$.

The simulation was done using SIMNON© with the following choices:
Plant: $G_p(s) = \frac{1}{s-1}$, $\Delta G(s) = \frac{5}{s-2}$. Reference signal: $r(t) = \sin 2t$. Initial conditions: zero.
Lumped uncertainty: $\xi(y, t) = 0.25 \cos t + 0.5 \cos y + y \sin 2t + e^{-t} * [y^2 \sin(y \cdot t)]$.
Parameters in the controller: $k_g = 5.0$, $\epsilon_1 = 0.3$.

Simulation results will be shown in Figure 4. We note that the tracking error can be made smaller by choosing a smaller value for the design parameter ϵ_1.

Conclusion

The design method, MRRC (or I/O robust control), proposed recently in [10] is generalized in this paper for SISO systems containing significant disturbances, nonlinear uncertainties, and unmodelled dynamics. The newly designed robust control requires no information about controlled systems except relative degree of nominal system, minimum phase condition and a closed-form expression of bounding function on uncertainties. Any nonlinearly bounded uncertainty including disturbance and additive unmodelled dynamics with respect to output is admissible. The multiplicative unmodelled dynamics could be unstable, arbitrarily large, and of infinite dimension. The proposed MRRC can make the output tracking error arbitrarily small using always finite control magnitude. It is worth recalling that model reference robust control method has been successfully applied in [11] to systems with arbitrarily fast time-varying parameters. It will be shown in [17] that MRRC is applicable to weakly non-minimum phase systems as well. These results prove that MRRC is a viable control scheme that requires minimum information and handles much wider class of SISO systems than any other existing techniques for designing input-output tracking control.

Acknowledgement

The author is indebted to two anonymous reviewers for their useful comments.

References

[1] M.J.Corless and G.Leitmann "Continuous State Feedback Guaranteeing Uniform Ultimate Boundedness for Uncertain Dynamic Systems," *IEEE Trans. Automat. Contr.*, Vol.26, No.5, pp.1139-1144, May, 1981.

[2] M.J.Corless, "Controllers which guarantee robustness with respect to unmodelled flexibilities for a class of uncertain mechanical systems," *Int. J. of Adaptive Control and Signal Processing*, Vol.4, pp.565-579, 1990.

[3] P.A.Ioannou and K.S.Tsakalis, "A robust direct adaptive controller," *IEEE Transactions on Aotumatic Control*, Vol.31, Nov. 1986.

[4] S.Gutman, "Uncertain Dynamical Systems — A Lyapunov Min-Max Approach," *IEEE Trans. Automat. Contr.*, Vol.24, No.3, pp.437-443, June, 1979.

[5] H.K.Khalil, *Nonlinear Systems*, New York, Macmillan Publishing Company, 1991.

[6] T.Kailath, *Linear Systems*, Englewood Cliffs, Prentice Hall, Inc., 1980.

[7] Y.D.Landau, *Adaptive Control - The Model Reference Approach*, Marcel Dekker, 1979.

[8] S.M.Naik, P.R.Kumar, and B.E.Ydstie, "Robust continuous time adaptive control by parameter projection," *IEEE Transactions on Automatic Control*, Vol.37, No.2, pp.182-197, February, 1992.

[9] K.S.Narendra and A.M.Annaswamy, *Stable Adaptive Systems*, Prentice-Hall, 1989.

[10] Z.Qu and D.M.Dawson, "Model reference robust control of a class of SISO systems," *1992 American Control Conference*, Chicago, IL., pp.1182-1186, June, 1992.

[11] Z.Qu, et al., "Continuous input-output robust tracking control of SISO continuous time systems with fast time-varying parameters: A model reference approach," *The 31st IEEE Conference on Decision and Control*, pp.2767-2772, Tucson, Arizona, December, 1992.

[12] Z.Qu and D.M.Dawson, "Lyapunov direct design of robust tracking control for classes of cascaded nonlinear uncertain systems without matching conditions," *The 30th IEEE Conference on Decision and Control*, pp.2521-2526, Brighton, U.K. December 1991.

[13] Z.Qu and J.F.Dorsey, "Robust control of generalized dynamic systems without matching conditions," *Transactions of ASME, Journal of Dynamic Systems, Measurement, And Control*, Vol.113, No.4, pp.582-589, December, 1991.

[14] Z.Qu, "Global stabilization of nonlinear systems with a class of unmatched uncertainties," *Systems & Control Letter*, Vol.18, No.3, pp.301-307, May, 1992.

[15] Z.Qu and D.M.Dawson, "Robust control design of a class of cascaded nonlinear uncertain systems," *Control of Systems with Inexact Dynamic Models, 1991 ASME Winter Annual Meeting*, pp.63-71, Atlanta GA. December 1991.

[16] Z.Qu, "Robust control of nonlinear uncertain systems under generalized matching conditions," *Automatica*, Vol.29, No.4, July 1993.

[17] Z.Qu, "Model reference robust control of weakly non-minimum phase systems," submitted to *The 32nd IEEE Conference on Decision and Control.*

[18] S. Sastry and M. Bodson, *ADAPTIVE CONTROL: Stability, Convergence, and Robustness*, Prentice-Hall, Inc. 1989.

[19] W.E.Schmitendorf and B.R. Barmish, "Robust asymptotic tracking for linear systems with unknown parameters," *Automatica*, Vol. 22, pp.355-360, 1986.

[20] W.E.Schmitendorf and B.R. Barmish, "Guaranteed asymptotic output stability for systems with constant disturbance," *J. of Dynamic Systems, Measurement, and Control*, Vol. 109, pp.186-189, 1987.

[21] J.J.Slotine, *Applied Nonlinear Control*, Englewood Cliffs, NY, Prentice-Hall, Inc. 1991.

[22] G.W.Stewart, *Introduction to Matrix Computations*, New York: Academic 1973.

[23] J.S.Thorp and B.R. Barmish, "On guaranteed stability of uncertain linear systems via linear control," *J. of Optimization Theory and Applications*, Vol. 35, pp.559-579, 1981.

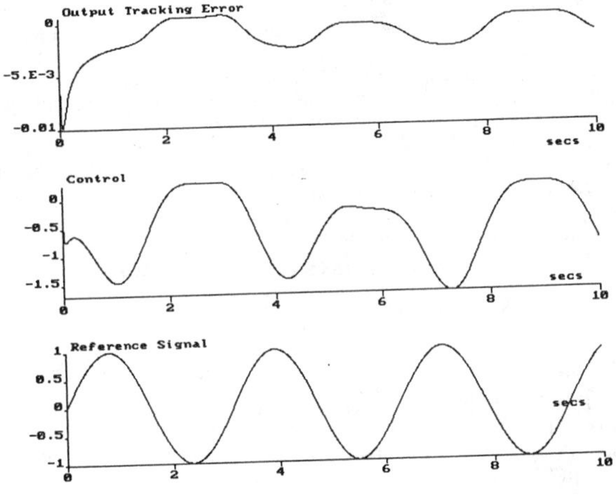

Figure 4: Simulation results of the illustrative example

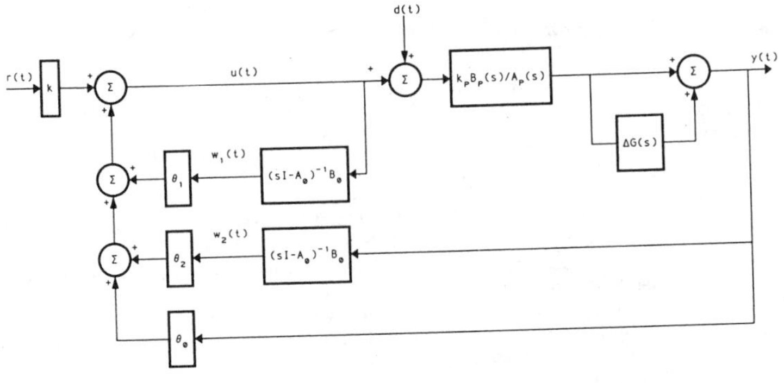

Figure 2: Tracking structure with perfect knowledge

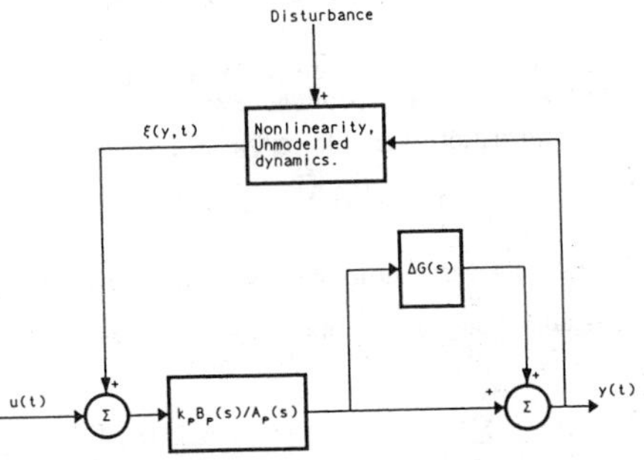

Figure 1: Block diagram of controlled plant

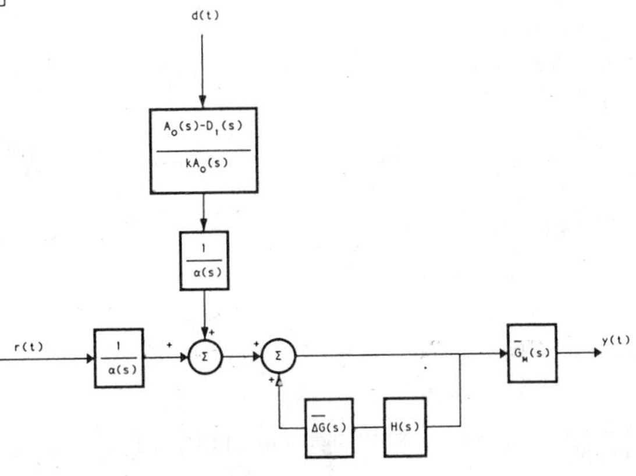

Figure 3: The closed loop system under perfect nominal control

Proceedings of the
American Control Conference
San Francisco, California • June 1993

Approximation of a parameter perturbation set by convex sets

M. Wang † *E. B. Lee †* *D. Boley ‡*

Control Science and Dynamical Systems Center
University of Minnesota
200 Union Street
Minneapolis, MN 55455

ABSTRACT

Estimating an admissible parameter perturbation set in a real parameter space is addressed; Norm bounds may be too conservative. Also Matrix pencil method suffers from numerical difficulties. An improved matrix measure method is suggested to approximate an admissible parameter perturbation set by a series of convex sets. Each of these sets can be computed by a matrix measure method which is easy to compute and is numerically stable.

1. Introduction

A great deal has been done to analyze the robust stability properties of systems. To do so first the robustness is parametrized by some geometric measurements, for example, by various norm bounds[Ma-J], [Pa-R], [Ye-R], [Zh-K], by distance from the nearest unstable systems [Va-L], or by some stability radii [Hi-D], and by some parameter space methods[Es-M], [Ho-C], [Wa-M].

In [Wa-M] we have shown how to compute an admissible parameter perturbation by matrix pencil method. However the computation is expensive when the dimension of a system is high; then the matrix measure method is introduced to approximate the admissible perturbation set, since the computation of matrix measure is easy and is numerically stable. Usually the estimate by matrix measure method is also conservative, so in this paper we develop a numerical method to characterize an admissible parameter perturbation set in a real parameter space and then to approximate this set by a family of convex sets, which can be computed via the matrix measure method.

Matrix measure is defined as (See, for example, [Wa-M])

$$\mu(A) = \lambda_{max}(\frac{A+A'}{2})$$

Here $\lambda_{max}(A)$ denotes the largest eigenvalue of the symmetric matrix A.

Different from eigenvalues of a matrix, the matrix measure of a matrix will change when the matrix is changed by a similarity transformation, i.e. generally for a nonsingular matrix T, $\mu(A) \neq \mu(T^{-1}AT)$.

For any stability matrix A, there always exists a similarity transformation T, such that $\mu(T^{-1}AT) < 0$. The relationship between matrix measure and similarity transformation provides a way to estimate a parameter perturbation set by a series of matrix measure computations. For our further development, we need the inertia theorem.

Define inertia of the matrix A by: $In(A) := (\pi(A), \nu(A), \delta(A))$; Here π, ν and δ are the numbers of characteristic roots of A with positive, negative and zero real parts respectively.

Theorem 1 [Ba- A]For a given complex matrix A, there exists a unique Hermitian H as the solution for:

$$A^*H+HA = C$$

where $C > 0$, iff the characteristic roots of A:
$\lambda_i(A)+\lambda_j(A) \neq 0$ for all $i \neq j$, and then $In(A) = In(H)$. □

Now we can use the inertia theorem to prove following result.

Proposition 2 $\lambda(A) \in C^-$ if and only if there exists a nonsingular T, such that $\mu(T^{-1}AT) < 0$.

Proof: The proof is constructive. Let B and C be any pair of matrices such that (A, B) is stabilizable and (A, C) is detectable. So there is a balanced realization transformation T for (A, B, I), such that under this similarity transformation: $\hat{A} = T^{-1}AT$, $\hat{B} = T^{-1}B$, and there is $P > 0$ for following equations:

$$\hat{A}'P+P\hat{A} = \hat{B}\hat{B}' \quad (1)$$

$$\hat{A}P+P\hat{A}' = T'T \quad (2)$$

Adding these two equations gives

$$(\hat{A}+\hat{A}')P+P(\hat{A}+\hat{A}') = -(\hat{B}\hat{B}'+T'T) < 0 \quad (3)$$

It follows that $\mu(\hat{A}) < 0$, since inertia of $(\hat{A}+\hat{A}')$ is as the same as the inertia of $-P$.

† : supported by Grants DMS9002019 and
‡ : supported by Grant CDA 9222922

2. Main result

For structured perturbation case we can study the robust stability in real parameter space. When $\Delta A = \sum_{i=1}^{k}\alpha_i E_i$, we can consider the robust stability in parameter vector α-space $\alpha = [\alpha_1\ \alpha_2, ..., \alpha_k]' \in R^k$. For a given system, matrix A is one of its realization. Any similarity ΔA is an allowable perturbation such that $A+\Delta A$ stays stable if and only if $\Delta A_T = T^{-1}\Delta AT$ is also an allowable perturbation to keep $T^{-1}AT+\Delta A_T$ stable. When $\Delta A = \sum_{i=1}^{k}\alpha_i E_i$, then $\Delta A_T = \sum_{i=1}^{k}\alpha_i T^{-1}E_i T$, so we can consider parameter perturbation tolerance in parameter α-space and estimate an admissible perturbation set in α-space through similarity transformations. Generally, if $\mu(A) > 0$, and under some similarity transformation T, $\hat{A} = T^{-1}AT$, with $\mu(\hat{A}) < 0$, then working with $\hat{A}$ might give a better estimation than directly working with A.

Example 1 [Ma-J] Consider a system as represented by an ordinary differential equation model in R^2:

$$\dot{x}=(A_0+\sum_{i=1}^{2}\alpha_i E_i)x \text{ with}$$

$$A_0=\begin{bmatrix} 0 & 1 \\ -2 & -2 \end{bmatrix}, E_1=\begin{bmatrix} 0 & 0 \\ 1 & 0 \end{bmatrix}, E_2=\begin{bmatrix} 0 & 0 \\ 0 & 1 \end{bmatrix}$$

By the matrix measure method suggested in [Wa-M], figure 1 compares two perturbation bound estimates in real parameter α-space. Dash curve is working with controller canonical form, the solid one is based upon some balanced realization.

It has been pointed out that matrix measure depends on similarity transformation, i.e. different realizations cause different matrix measure values. So from a single realization, the estimate of an admissible parameter perturbation set computed by matrix measure method usually is conservative. But the computation of the matrix measure is simple and is numerically stable. Can we improve the matrix measure method to get a better estimation? The answer is positive. In [Wa-M] we have defined an admissible parameter perturbation set

$$\Delta\Omega(A) = \left\{\Delta A \mid \lambda(A+\zeta\Delta A) \in C^-,\ \text{for all } \zeta \in [0, 1]\right\} \quad (7)$$

and then we applied matrix measure method to approximate this set by

$$\Delta\Omega_1(A) = \left\{\Delta A \mid \mu(P\Delta A) < 1\right\}. \quad (8)$$

where $P = Lyap(A, I)$, the solution of Lyapunov equation

$$A'P+PA = -I \quad (9)$$

By the subadditivity of the matrix measure $\mu(A)$, it is easy to porve that $\Delta\Omega_1(A)$ is a convex set. Now we redefine an admissible parameter perturbation set in a real parameter space which characterizes the robust stability behavior of a given system and is free from similarity transformations. Furthermore the set can be approximated by series of convex sets, each of them can be easily computed via matrix measure method addressed before.

Define an admissible parameter perturbation set

$$\Delta\Omega_A(\alpha) = \left\{\alpha \mid \Delta A = \sum_{i=1}^{k}\alpha_i E_i \in \Delta\Omega(A)\right\} \quad (10)$$

Under this definition, for a given system, the admissible parameter perturbation set will be independent of realization in the following sense: For any perturbation variable α with respect to a given system, $\alpha \in \Delta\Omega_A(\alpha)$ if and only if $\Delta A = \sum_{i=1}^{k}\alpha_i E_i \in \Delta\Omega(A)$.

Consider the fact that for a nonsingular matrix T, $\lambda(A) = \lambda(T^{-1}AT)$. So for any allowable perturbation $\Delta A = \sum_{i=1}^{k}\alpha_i E_i$ in $\Delta\Omega(A)$,

$$\lambda(A+\sum_{i=1}^{k}\alpha_i E_i) = \lambda(T^{-1}AT+\sum_{i=1}^{k}\alpha_i T^{-1}E_i T)$$

Let $\hat{A} = T^{-1}AT$, then $\hat{E}_i = T^{-1}E_iT$. Obviously for any $\hat{\alpha} \in \Delta\Omega_A(\alpha)$, $\Delta A = \sum_{i=1}^{k} \hat{\alpha}_i E_i \in \Delta\Omega(A)$ if and only if

$$\Delta\hat{A} = \sum_{i=1}^{k} \hat{\alpha}_i \hat{E}_i \in \Delta\Omega(\hat{A})$$

so

$$\Delta\Omega_A(\alpha) = \Delta\Omega_{\hat{A}}(\alpha) := \Delta\Omega(\alpha)$$

In the last equality, we omit the subscription for simplicity.

Denote $P_t := Lyap(A_t, I)$ as the solution of Lyapunov equation

$$A_t'P_t + P_tA_t = -I$$

here $A_t = T_t^{-1}AT_t$ and $P_t > 0$ due to the stability of A_t.

Define a convex set

$$\Delta\Omega_1(\alpha, T_t) = \left\{ \alpha \mid \mu(P_t \sum_{i=1}^{k} \alpha_i T_t^{-1} E_i T_t) < 1, P_t := Lyap(A_t, I) \right\}$$

Generally $\Delta\Omega_1(\alpha, T_j) \neq \Delta\Omega_1(\alpha, T_i)$ as long as $T_j \neq T_i$. So different from $\Delta\Omega(\alpha)$, $\Delta\Omega_1(\alpha, T_t)$ is a set which depends on the similarity transformation T_t. Notice that $\Delta\Omega_1(\alpha, T_t) \subset \Delta\Omega(\alpha)$, and we can use a series of similarity transformations to construct a union of $\Delta\Omega_1(\alpha, T_j)$'s to approximate $\Delta\Omega(\alpha)$, since each of these $\Delta\Omega_1(T_t)$'s is a convex set and is easy to compute by matrix measure method.

Proposition 3 For any nonsingular T_t with proper dimension, $\Delta\Omega_1(\alpha, T_t) \subset \Delta\Omega(\alpha)$. □

We use following theorem to summarize the relationship between $\Delta\Omega(A)$, $\Delta\Omega_1(A)$, $\Delta\Omega(T_t^{-1}AT_t)$, $\Delta\Omega_1(\alpha, A_t)$ and $\Delta\Omega(\alpha)$. Then we provide some algorithm to approximate $\Delta\Omega(\alpha)$ by $\cup_t \Delta\Omega_1(\alpha, A_t)$.

Theorem 4

$$(i)\quad \Delta\Omega(\alpha) = \left\{ \alpha \mid \Delta A = \sum_{i=1}^{k} \alpha_i E_i \in \Delta\Omega(A) \right\}$$

$$= \left\{ \alpha \mid \Delta A_t = \sum_{i=1}^{k} \alpha_i T_t^{-1} E_i T_t \in \Delta\Omega(A_t), A_t = T_t^{-1}AT_t \right\}$$

$$(ii)\quad \Delta\Omega_1(A) \subset \Delta\Omega(A);$$

$$(iii)\quad \cup_t \Delta\Omega_1(\alpha, T_t) \subset \Delta\Omega(\alpha).$$

Now we can use similarity transform to find a better estimate for the allowable perturbation in a real parameter space.

The matrix measure is varying, i.e. $\Delta\Omega_1(A) \neq \Delta\Omega_1(A_t)$, but $\Delta\Omega(\alpha)$ is invariant under similarity transformation T_t and the set $\Delta\Omega_1(\alpha, T_t)$ is contained in set $\Delta\Omega(\alpha)$.

Consider example 1 again, we use a series of T_t to construct a family of convex sets $\left\{ \Delta\Omega_1(\alpha, T_t),\ t = 1, 2, \ldots \right\}$ to approximate $\Delta\Omega(\alpha)$.

In Figure 2 we use $\left\{ \Delta\Omega_1(\alpha, T_t),\ t = 1, 2, \ldots 8. \right\}$ and the contour to approximate $\Delta\Omega(\alpha)$. In this example we parametrize T by θ and ϕ.

$$T(\theta, \phi) = \begin{bmatrix} 1 & \theta \\ \frac{1}{\theta} & \phi \end{bmatrix}$$

We choose 8 pairs of values for (θ, ϕ) and construct the corresponding $\Delta\Omega_1(\alpha, T(\theta, \phi))$, then the contour of these convex sets gives a good approximation to $\Delta\Omega(\alpha)$. Figure 2 shows all these $\Delta\Omega_1(\alpha, T(\theta, \phi))$'s.

Figure 1: (Example 1) Two perturbation bound estimates.

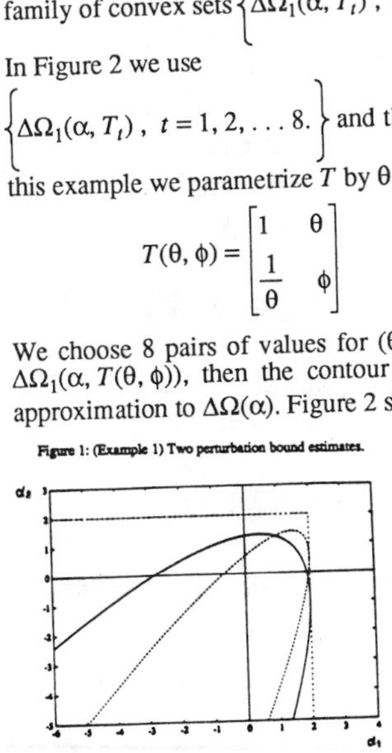

Figure 2 (Example 1) Convex approximation to $\Delta\Omega(A)$

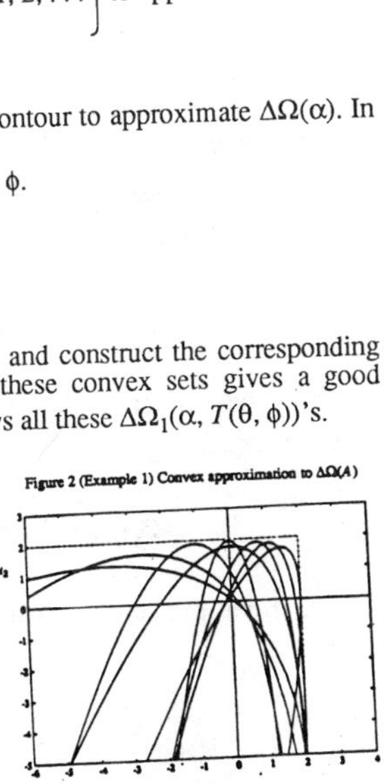

Figure 3 (Example 1) Convex approximation to $\Delta\Omega(A)$ — Contour

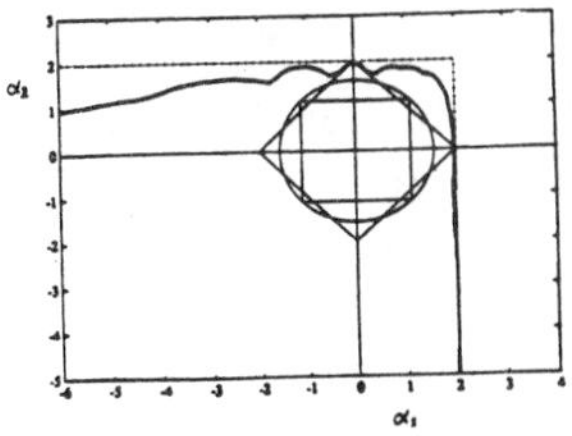

In Figure 3 the thick line presents the contour for the admissible perturbation set estimated by the convex sets $\cup_{t=1}^{8} \Delta\Omega_1(\alpha, T(\theta_t, \phi_t))$, the solid line shows the admissible sets given by norm bounds and the dash-point line denotes the actual region of the admissible parameter perturbation under which the stability remains.

We use an algorithm for allowable parameter perturbation as a summary for this section.

Algorithm 2: Convex approximation to allowable perturbation set in real parameter space.

1) Choose vector parameters $\theta_t = [\theta_{1t}, \theta_{2t}, \ldots, \theta_{rt}]$ and $\phi_t = [\phi_{1t}, \phi_{2t}, \ldots, \phi_{rt}]$ to parametrize similarity matrix $T = T(\theta_t, \phi_t)$.

2) For each pair of vector values of (θ, ϕ), to compute $T(\theta_t, \phi_t)^{-1}AT(\theta_t, \phi_t)$.

3) Compute $\Delta\Omega_1(\alpha, T(\theta_t, \phi_t))$ at a grid of (θ_k, ϕ_k)'s in the real parameter α-space.

4) The contour given by $\cup_t \Delta\Omega_1(\alpha, T(\theta_k, \phi_t))$ is an approximation of allowable perturbation set.

3. Conclusion

We have discussed the application of matrix measure method in linear time-invariant system for robust stability analysis and parameter perturbation estimate in real parameter spaces. The computation involved basically is to compute the maximal eigenvalues of real symmetric matrices, so this method is numerically stable and is easy to perform. Moreover if we can extend these results to complex matrices, then we can handle some problems in infinite dimensional systems, for example, delay systems and 2D systems. The example illustrates that the estimation given by matrix measure method is much better than those estimated by norm bounds. By this new method, a good estimation can be computed by parametrizing a similarity transformation matrix.

References:

[Ba-S] S. Barnett, Matrices in control theory with applications to linear programming, Van Nostrand Reinhold Co., New York, 1971.

[Es-M] M. Eslami, A unified approach to the stability robustness analysis of systems with multiple varying parameters, Technique report, UIC-EECS-90-3, Dept. of Electrical Engineering and Computer Science, The Univ. of Illinois at Chicago, April, 1990.

[Hi-D] D. Hinrichsen and A.J. Pritchard, Robustness measures for linear systems with application to stability radii of Hurwitz and Schur polynomials, Int. J. Control, vol.55, No.4, pp809-844, 1992.

[Ho-C] C. Hollot, D. P. Looze and A. C. Bartlett, Parameter uncertainty and unmodeled dynamics analysis via parameter space methods, IEEE Trans. AC-26, pp283-292, 1990.

[Ma-J] J. M. Martin, State space measures of robustness of pole locations for structured and unstructured perturbations, SIAM Conf. on linear algeb. San Francisco, CA, Dec. 1990.

[Pa-R] R. Patel and M. Toda, Quantitative measure of robustness for multivariable system, in Proc. Joint Automat. Contr. Conf. San Francisco, CA, paper TP8-A, 1980.

[Wa-M] M. Wang, E. B. Lee and D. Boley, Matrix pencil and matrix measure methods for robust stability in real parameter spaces, Proc. 30th IEEE Conf. Dec. Contr. Brighton, England, pp441-445, Dec. 1991.

[Va-L] C. Van Loan, How near is a stable matrix to an unstable matrix? Contemporary Mathematics, vol.47, pp465-478, 1985.

[Ye-R] R. Yedavalli, Improved measures of stability robustness for linear state space models, IEEE Trans. AC-30, pp557-579, 1985.

[Zh-K] K. Zhou and P. Khargonekar, Stability robustness bounds for linear state space models with structured uncertainty, IEEE Trans. AC-32, pp621-623, 1987.

Proceedings of the
American Control Conference
San Francisco, California • June 1993

Parametric Stability Margin for Multilinear Interval Control Systems

L. H. Keel
Center of Excellence in Information Systems
Tennessee State University
Nashville, TN 37203 - 3401

S. P. Bhattacharyya
Department of Electrical Engineering
Texas A&M University
College Station, TX 77843

Abstract

Recently, a necessary and sufficient condition to determine the robust stability of a multilinear interval control system has been reported in [1,2] as an extension of the well-known Box theorem [3] which deals with the linear affine case. This paper introduces a simple but computationally efficient algorithm, based on the above result, to check the robust stability of such systems. The method is also extended to find the parametric stability margin of such a system.

1. ROBUST STABILITY

Let $\mathbf{p} := [p_1\ p_2\ \cdots\ p_l]$ a vector of real parameters lying in the interval uncertainty set

$$\mathbf{\Pi} := \{p \mid p_i^- \le p_i \le p_i^+, \quad i = 1,2,\cdots,l\}. \tag{1}$$

Consider the polynomial

$$\delta(s,\mathbf{p}) := \delta_0(\mathbf{p})+\delta_1(\mathbf{p})s+\delta_2(\mathbf{p})s^2+\cdots+\delta_n(\mathbf{p})s^n \tag{2}$$

wherein the coefficients $\delta_i(\mathbf{p})$ are affine multilinear functions of $\mathbf{p}$. We shall refer to this type of polynomial as a multilinear interval polynomial. It is easy to show that any multilinear interval polynomial can be rewritten as

$$\delta(s) := \sum_{i=1}^{m} Q_i(s) \prod_{j=1}^{r} P_{ij}(s) \tag{3}$$

where $P_{ij}(s)$ are interval and $Q_i(s)$ are fixed polynomials. The necessary and sufficient condition for robust stability of the family $\delta(s)$ under the assumption that $P_{ij}(s)$ are independent is given below. Let $\mathcal{K}_{P_{ij}}(s)$ be the set of Kharitonov vertex polynomials [4] associated with the interval polynomial $P_{ij}(s)$ and $\mathcal{S}_{P_{ij}}(s,\lambda_j)$ the set of Kharitonov segment polynomials associated with interval polynomial $P_{ij}(s)$.

Theorem 1. [1,2] *The multilinear family $\delta(s)$ is Hurwitz stable if and only if the set of manifolds $\mathbf{M}_i$ for $i = 1,2,\cdots,m$ are Hurwitz stable where*

$$\mathbf{M}_l = \sum_{i=1,i\neq l}^{m} Q_i(s)\prod_{j=1}^{r}\mathcal{K}_{P_{ij}}(s) + Q_l(s)\prod_{j=1}^{r}\mathcal{S}_{P_{lj}}(s,\lambda_j) \tag{4}$$

for $\lambda_i \in [0,1]$ for all i.

Now let us define the new parameter vector

$$\underline{\lambda} := [\lambda_1\ \lambda_2\ \cdots\ \lambda_j], \tag{5}$$

then each manifold in $\mathbf{M}_l$ can be written as the polynomial set

$$\delta(s,\underline{\lambda}) := \delta_0(\underline{\lambda}) + \delta_1(\underline{\lambda})s + \cdots, \qquad \lambda_i \in [0,1] \tag{6}$$

where the coefficients $\delta_i(\underline{\lambda})$ are multilinear functions of $\underline{\lambda}$. Therefore, the problem of checking robust stability of a multilinear interval control system is reduced to checking the stability of the set of multilinear polynomials shown in eq. (6), as $\underline{\lambda}$ ranges over the positive unit hypercube in the first quadrant.

Let us define the set

$$\mathbf{\Delta} := \{\delta(s,\underline{\lambda}) \mid \lambda_i \in [0,1]\}. \tag{7}$$

Let $\mathbf{V}$ denote the vertices of the $\underline{\lambda}$ set,

$$\mathbf{V} := \{\underline{\lambda} \mid \lambda_i = 0 \text{ or } \lambda_i = 1, \text{ for all } i\} \tag{8}$$

$$\text{and } \mathbf{\Delta_V} := \{\delta(s,\underline{\lambda}) \mid \underline{\lambda} \in \mathbf{V}\} \tag{9}$$

denotes the set of vertex polynomials.

Note that $\mathbf{\Delta}$ is a continuum of polynomials whereas $\mathbf{\Delta_V}$ is a discrete set of polynomials and

$$\mathbf{\Delta_V} \subset \mathbf{\Delta}. \tag{10}$$

Fixing $s = s^*$, we let $\mathbf{\Delta}(s^*)$ denote the set of points $\delta(s^*,\underline{\lambda})$ in the complex plane obtained by letting $\underline{\lambda}$ range over $[0,1]$:

$$\mathbf{\Delta}(s^*) := \{\delta(s^*,\underline{\lambda}) \mid \underline{\lambda} \in [0,1]\}. \tag{11}$$

Likewise we have the discrete set of points in the complex plane

$$\mathbf{\Delta_V}(s^*) := \{\delta(s^*,\underline{\lambda}) \mid \underline{\lambda} \in \mathbf{V}\}. \tag{12}$$

We now state the well known Mapping Theorem [6].

Theorem 2. (Mapping Theorem [6]) *Under the assumption that $\delta_i(\underline{\lambda})$ are affine multilinear functions of $\underline{\lambda}$*

$$co\ \mathbf{\Delta}(s^*) = co\ \mathbf{\Delta_V}(s^*) \tag{13}$$

for each $s^* \in \mathbb{C}$ where $co\ (\cdot)$ indicates the convex hull of a set $(\cdot)$.

This theorem shows that the image set of the multilinearly parametrized interval family, evaluated at any point s^* is contained in the convex hull of the vertices evaluated at the same point. Although the convex hull of the vertices overbounds this set we can improve the accuracy of the approximation arbitrarily by introducing additional vertices. This is illustrated in Figures 1 to 4. The image set $\Delta(s^*)$ is contained in the convex hull of $\mathbf{R}(s^*) = co\ \mathbf{\Delta_V}(s^*)$ as shown in Figures 1 and 2. As shown in the subsequent figures (Figures 3, 4) this approximation can be improved by decomposing λ hypercube as a union of smaller boxes and thereby introducing additional vertices as shown in Figures A.1 and A.2.

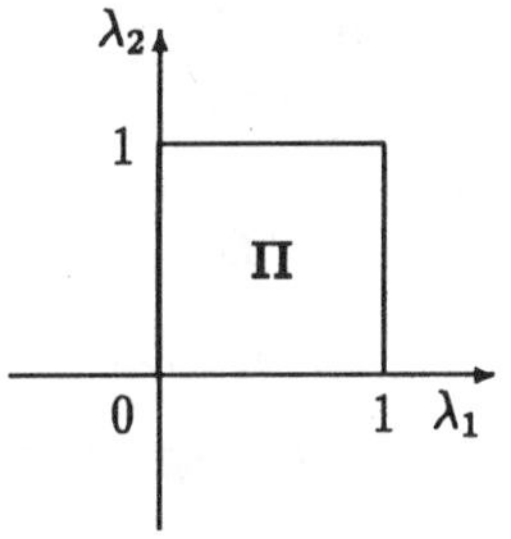

Figure A.1

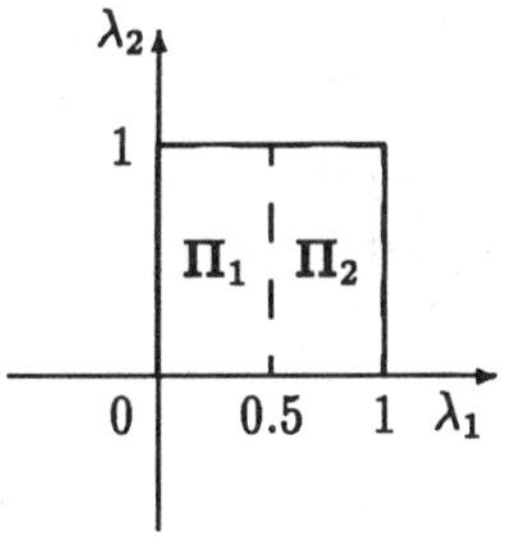

Figure A.2

From this theorem, we can easily establish the following corollary.

Corollary 1. *The multilinear polynomial set $\mathbf{\Delta}(s)$ is Hurwitz stable if the convex hull of $\mathbf{\Delta_V}(s)$ is Hurwitz stable. If the dependence of the coefficients $\delta_i(\mathbf{p})$ on $\mathbf{p}$ is linear the stability of $\mathbf{\Delta}(s)$ is equivalent to that of the convex hull of $\mathbf{\Delta_V}(s)$.*

If we define the set of convex combinations of the vertex polynomials in $\mathbf{\Delta_V}(s)$ by

$$\mathbf{E}(s) := \{\mu_{ij}\delta_i(s) + (1-\mu_{ij})\delta_j(s) \mid \mu_{ij} \in [0,1] \text{ and } \delta_i(s), \delta_j(s) \in \mathbf{\Delta_V}\}, \tag{14}$$

the stability of $co\ \mathbf{\Delta_V}(s)$ is equivalent to the stability of $\mathbf{E}(s)$. Since the set $\mathbf{E}(s)$ consists of line segments joining every pair of vertices in $\mathbf{\Delta_V}(s)$, its stability can be easily verified by the Segment Lemma [7]. The segment lemma basically determines if the phase difference of a pair of stable vertex polynomials reaches 180 degrees at some ω. If the phase difference does not reach 180° for any ω, the line segment joining the two vertices is Hurwitz stable. This condition is called the *Phase Condition.*

Using the above concepts we can easily prove the following. Let $\mathbf{\Delta}(j\omega)$ denote the complex plane image of the set $\mathbf{\Delta}(s)$ evaluated at $s = j\omega$.

Theorem 3. *The set of multilinear polynomials $\mathbf{\Delta}(s)$ is Hurwitz stable if i) for some $\omega \in [0, \infty)$, $0 \notin \mathbf{\Delta}(j\omega)$ and ii) the set of all corresponding line segments $\mathbf{E}(s)$ is Hurwitz stable.*

This theorem along with the previously given procedure for approximating the image set can be used to develop an efficient computational technique to check robust stability. We can also extend this result to the computation of the parametric stability margin of the multilinear interval control systems. This is done next.

2. PARAMETRIC STABILITY MARGIN

Consider a Hurwitz polynomial of the form

$$\delta(s) = \sum_{i=1}^{m} Q_i(s) \prod_{j=1}^{r} P_{ij}(s) \tag{15}$$

where $Q_i(s)$ are fixed and

$$P_{ij}(s) := p_{ij}^0 + p_{ij}^1 s + p_{ij}^2 s^2 + \cdots . \tag{16}$$

Let us assume that coefficients p_{ij}^k for $k = 0, 1, 2, \cdots$ are subject to variations. If we assume the variations in coefficients are bounded as

$$p_{ij}^k \in [p_{ij_0}^k - w_{ij}^k \epsilon, p_{ij_0}^k + w_{ij}^k \epsilon], \quad \epsilon \geq 0 \tag{17}$$

for a fixed value of the weights w_{ij} with $p_{ij_0}^k$ being the nominal values of the parameters, then the parametric stability margin is defined as the maximum value ϵ^* so that the multilinear polynomial $\delta(s)$ remains Hurwitz stable for all $\epsilon \in [0, \epsilon^*)$.

Let us recall the manifolds shown in eq. (4). From Theorem 1, the parametric stability margin of the polynomial in eq. (15) is equivalently defined as

$$\min\left\{\epsilon \mid \max\{\epsilon \mid M_l^k \in \mathcal{H}, \forall \lambda_i \in [0,1]\},\ l \in \underline{m}, k \in \underline{4}^{2r}\right\}. \tag{18}$$

Note that each manifold in $\mathbf{M}_l$ has the form of

$$\begin{aligned}
&Q_1(s)K_{P_{11}}^{i_{11}}(s)K_{P_{12}}^{i_{12}}(s)\cdots K_{P_{1r}}^{i_{1r}}(s) + \cdots \\
&+Q_{l-1}(s)K_{P_{l-11}}^{i_{l-11}}(s)K_{P_{l-12}}^{i_{l-12}}(s)\cdots K_{P_{l-1r}}^{i_{l-1r}}(s) \\
&+Q_l(s)S_{P_{l1}}^{i_{l1}}(s,\lambda_1)S_{P_{l2}}^{i_{l2}}(s,\lambda_2)\cdots S_{P_{lr}}^{i_{lr}}(s,\lambda_r) \\
&+Q_{l+1}(s)K_{P_{l+11}}^{i_{l+11}}(s)K_{P_{l+12}}^{i_{l+12}}(s)\cdots K_{P_{l+1r}}^{i_{l+1r}}(s) + \cdots
\end{aligned}$$

where $K^{k_{ij}}_{P_{ij}}(s)$ is the kth Kharitonov polynomial and $S^{k_{ij}}_{P_{ij}}(s,\lambda)$ is the kth segment polynomial associated with an interval polynomial $P_{ij}(s)$, respectively.

Using the sufficient condition developed in Theorem 3, we can develop the following computational procedure.For some $\hat{\epsilon}$, if all the corresponding line segments in $\mathbf{E}(s)$ are Hurwitz stable for all $\epsilon \in [0,\hat{\epsilon})$, then the actual parametric stability margin ϵ^* is always greater than or equal to $\hat{\epsilon}$. However, if we introduce additional vertex points the approximation of the image set by the convex hull of the vertices improves and so the difference $\epsilon^* - \hat{\epsilon}$ becomes smaller. This permits us to compute the parametric stability margin with arbitrary accuracy depending upon how much we want to refine the approximation and how much computational burden may be taken. From the above considerations, a bisection algorithm is developed as follows:

Bisection Method: ϵ
  For each fixed ϵ
    Find all manifolds for
    $(\lambda_1,\ldots,\lambda_r) \in \{(0,\cdots,0),\cdot,(1,\cdots,1)\}$
    IF all $\mathbf{E}(s)$ satisfy phase condition
      THEN forward bisection
      ELSE backward bisection
    ENDIF
Bisection Method stops when the section piece is small enough.

3. NUMERICAL EXAMPLES

Example 1. Consider the feedback system shown in Figure B.

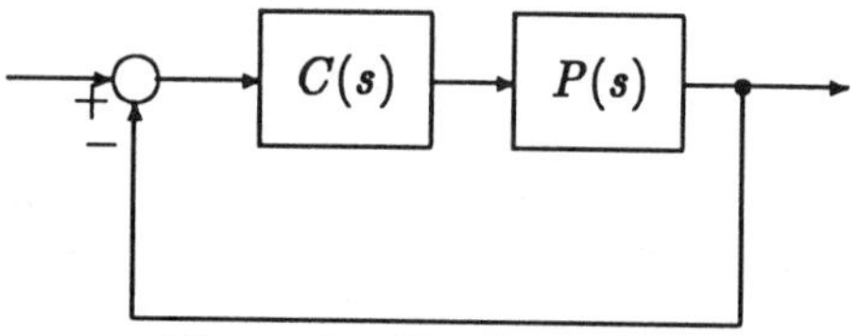

Figure B. Feedback System.

$$P(s) := \frac{n(s)}{d(s)} := \frac{n_1 s + n_0}{d_2 s^2 + d_1 s + d_0}$$
$$C(S) := \frac{n_c(s)}{d_c(s)} := \frac{s^2+2s+1}{s^4+2s^3+2s^2+s}$$

with its plant coefficient variations being bounded by

$n_1 \in [n_1^-, n_1^+]$ with the nominal value $n_1^0 = .15$
$n_0 \in [n_0^-, n_0^+]$ with the nominal value $n_0^0 = .95$
$d_2 \in [d_2^-, d_2^+]$ with the nominal value $d_2^0 = .95$
$d_1 \in [d_1^-, d_1^+]$ with the nominal value $d_1^0 = 1.9$
$d_0 \in [d_0^-, d_0^+]$ with the nominal value $d_0^0 = 2.0$

and
$$\begin{aligned}
[n_1^-, n_1^+] &= [n_1^0 - w_{n_1}\epsilon, n_1^0 + w_{n_1}\epsilon]\\
[n_0^-, n_0^+] &= [n_0^0 - w_{n_0}\epsilon, n_0^0 + w_{n_0}\epsilon]\\
[d_2^-, d_2^+] &= [d_2^0 - w_{d_2}\epsilon, d_2^0 + w_{d_2}\epsilon]\\
[d_1^-, d_1^+] &= [d_1^0 - w_{d_1}\epsilon, d_1^0 + w_{d_1}\epsilon]\\
[d_0^-, d_0^+] &= [d_0^0 - w_{d_0}\epsilon, d_0^0 + w_{d_0}\epsilon].
\end{aligned}$$

Then the characteristic polynomial is given by

$$\Pi := \{d(s)d_c(s) + n(s)n_c(s)\}$$

which shows that the parameters are entering into its coefficient linearly. As we stated in Corollary 1, the phase condition becomes necessary and sufficient in this case. The sets of Kharitonov polynomials associated with $n(s,\epsilon)$ and $d(s,\epsilon)$ are defined as follows:

$$\begin{cases} K_n^1(s,\epsilon) = n_0^- + n_1^- s, & K_n^2(s,\epsilon) = n_0^- + n_1^+ s\\ K_n^3(s,\epsilon) = n_0^+ + n_1^- s, & K_n^4(s,\epsilon) = n_0^+ + n_1^+ s \end{cases}$$

$$\begin{cases} K_d^1(s,\epsilon) = & d_0^- + d_1^- s + d_2^+ s^2\\ K_d^2(s,\epsilon) = & d_0^- + d_1^+ s + d_2^+ s^2\\ K_d^3(s,\epsilon) = & d_0^+ + d_1^- s + d_2^- s^2\\ K_d^4(s,\epsilon) = & d_0^+ + d_1^+ s + d_2^- s^2. \end{cases}$$

Thus we need to check the phase condition of the following set of vertex pairs: $\mathbf{E} := \mathbf{E}_1 \cup \mathbf{E}_2$ where

$$\begin{aligned}
\mathbf{E}_1 &:= \{(K_d^i(s,\epsilon)d_c(s) + K_n^j(s,\epsilon)n_c(s),\\
&\qquad K_d^i(s,\epsilon)d_c(s) + K_n^k(s,\epsilon)n_c(s))\}\\
\mathbf{E}_2 &:= \Big\{(K_d^j(s,\epsilon)d_c(s) + K_n^i(s,\epsilon)n_c(s),\\
&\qquad K_d^k(s,\epsilon)d_c(s) + K_n^i(s,\epsilon)n_c(s))\Big\}\\
&\text{for } i = 1,2,3,4 \text{ and}\\
&(i,k) \in \{(1,2),(1,3),(2,3),(3,4)\}.
\end{aligned}$$

Using a bisection method on ϵ, we have the parametric stability margin:

$$\epsilon^* = \max\{\epsilon \mid \mathbf{E} \in \mathcal{H},\ \forall\, \epsilon \in [0,\epsilon^*]\} = 0.146.$$

Example 2. Consider the following interconnected feedback system shown in Figure C. Let

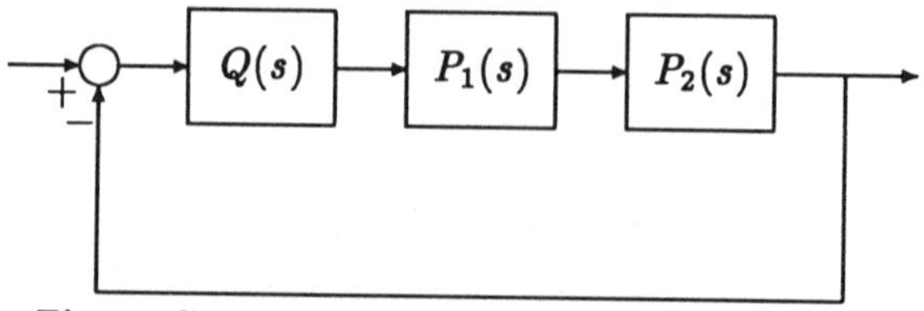

Figure C. Interconnected Feedback System.

$$Q(s) := \frac{Q_1(s)}{Q_2(s)} = \frac{s+2}{s+1}$$

$$P_1(s) := \frac{P_{11}(s)}{P_{21}(s)} = \frac{s^2+s+1}{s^3+a_2s^2+4s+a_0}$$
$$P_2(s) := \frac{P_{12}(s)}{P_{22}(s)} = \frac{6.6s^3+13.5s^2+15.5s+20.4}{s^3+b_2s^2+3.5s+2.4}$$

and let the set of parameters $\mathbf{p} = [a_2, a_0, b_2]$ vary as follows:

$$\begin{array}{ll} a_2 \in [a_2^-, a_2^+] & \text{with the nominal value } a_2^0 = -3.0 \\ a_0 \in [a_0^-, a_0^+] & \text{with the nominal value } a_0^0 = \ \ 2.0 \\ b_2 \in [b_2^-, b_2^+] & \text{with the nominal value } b_2^0 = \ \ 3.5 \\ \text{where } [a_2^-, a_2^+] & = [a_2^0 - w_{a_2}\epsilon, a_2^0 + w_{a_2}\epsilon] \\ \qquad [a_0^-, a_0^+] & = [a_0^0 - w_{a_0}\epsilon, a_0^0 + w_{a_0}\epsilon] \\ \qquad [b_2^-, b_2^+] & = [b_2^0 - w_{b_2}\epsilon, b_2^0 + w_{b_2}\epsilon] \end{array}$$

with $[w_{a_2}, w_{a_0}, w_{b_2}] = [1,1,1]$. The Kharitonov vertex and segment polynomials as follows:

$$\begin{aligned}
K^1_{P_{11}}(s,\epsilon) &= K^2_{P_{11}}(s,\epsilon) = K^3_{P_{11}}(s,\epsilon) \\
&= K^4_{P_{11}}(s,\epsilon) = P_{11}(s,\epsilon) \\
K^1_{P_{12}}(s,\epsilon) &= K^2_{P_{12}}(s,\epsilon) = K^3_{P_{12}}(s,\epsilon) \\
&= K^4_{P_{12}}(s,\epsilon) = P_{12}(s,\epsilon) \\
K^1_{P_{21}}(s,\epsilon) &= K^2_{P_{21}}(s,\epsilon) \\
&= a_0^- + 4s + a_2^+ s^2 + s^3 \\
K^3_{P_{21}}(s,\epsilon) &= K^4_{P_{21}}(s,\epsilon) \\
&= a_0^+ + 4s + a_2^- s^2 + s^3 \\
S^1_{P_{21}}(s,\epsilon) &= K^1_{P_{21}}(s,\epsilon) \\
S^2_{P_{21}}(s,\epsilon) &= S^3_{P_{21}}(s,\epsilon) \\
&= \lambda K^1_{P_{21}}(s,\epsilon) + (1-\lambda)K^3_{P_{21}}(s,\epsilon) \\
S^4_{P_{21}}(s,\epsilon) &= K^3_{P_{21}}(s,\epsilon) \\
K^1_{P_{22}}(s,\epsilon) &= K^2_{P_{22}}(s,\epsilon) \\
&= 2.4 + 3.5s + b_2^+ s^2 + s^3 \\
K^3_{P_{22}}(s,\epsilon) &= K^4_{P_{22}}(s,\epsilon) \\
&= 2.4 + 3.5s + b_2^- s^2 + s^3 \\
S^1_{P_{22}}(s,\epsilon) &= K^1_{P_{22}}(s,\epsilon) \\
S^2_{P_{22}}(s,\epsilon) &= S^3_{P_{22}}(s,\epsilon) \\
&= \lambda K^1_{P_{22}}(s,\epsilon) + (1-\lambda)K^3_{P_{22}}(s,\epsilon) \\
S^4_{P_{22}}(s,\epsilon) &= K^3_{P_{22}}(s,\epsilon).
\end{aligned}$$

The sets of manifolds to be checked for stability are:

$$\begin{aligned}
\mathbf{M} = \{ & Q_1(s)P_{11}(s,\epsilon)P_{12}(s,\epsilon) + \\
& Q_2(s)[\lambda_1 K^1_{P_{21}}(s,\epsilon) + (1-\lambda_1)K^3_{P_{21}}(s,\epsilon)] \\
& [\lambda_2 K^1_{P_{22}}(s,\epsilon) + (1-\lambda_2)K^3_{P_{22}}(s,\epsilon)]\}
\end{aligned}$$

We now solve the problem of checking these manifolds by overbounding this set by the convex hull of the vertices. After eliminating all duplicated segments, we have the following line segments which need to be checked. Note that the line segments listed below are functions of ϵ and our objective is to find the maximum value of ϵ so that all $\mathbf{E}(s,\epsilon^*)$ remain Hurwitz for all $\epsilon \in [0,\epsilon^*]$.

$$\begin{aligned}
E_1(s,\epsilon) = & (Q_1(s)P_{11}(s,\epsilon)P_{12}(s,\epsilon) + \\
& Q_2(s)K^3_{P_{21}}(s,\epsilon)K^3_{P_{22}}(s,\epsilon), \\
& Q_1(s)P_{11}(s,\epsilon)P_{12}(s,\epsilon) + \\
& Q_2(s)K^3_{P_{21}}(s,\epsilon)K^1_{P_{22}}(s,\epsilon)) \\
E_2(s,\epsilon) = & (Q_1(s)P_{11}(s,\epsilon)P_{12}(s,\epsilon) + \\
& Q_2(s)K^3_{P_{21}}(s,\epsilon)K^3_{P_{22}}(s,\epsilon), \\
& Q_1(s)P_{11}(s,\epsilon)P_{12}(s,\epsilon) + \\
& Q_2(s)K^1_{P_{21}}(s,\epsilon)K^3_{P_{22}}(s,\epsilon)) \\
E_3(s,\epsilon) = & (Q_1(s)P_{11}(s,\epsilon)P_{12}(s,\epsilon) + \\
& Q_2(s)K^3_{P_{21}}(s,\epsilon)K^3_{P_{22}}(s,\epsilon), \\
& Q_1(s)P_{11}(s,\epsilon)P_{12}(s,\epsilon) + \\
& Q_2(s)K^1_{P_{21}}(s,\epsilon)K^1_{P_{22}}(s,\epsilon)) \\
E_4(s,\epsilon) = & (Q_1(s)P_{11}(s,\epsilon)P_{12}(s,\epsilon) + \\
& Q_2(s)K^3_{P_{21}}(s,\epsilon)K^1_{P_{22}}(s,\epsilon), \\
& Q_1(s)P_{11}(s,\epsilon)P_{12}(s,\epsilon) + \\
& Q_2(s)K^1_{P_{21}}(s,\epsilon)K^3_{P_{22}}(s,\epsilon)) \\
E_5(s,\epsilon) = & (Q_1(s)P_{11}(s,\epsilon)P_{12}(s,\epsilon) + \\
& Q_2(s)K^3_{P_{21}}(s,\epsilon)K^1_{P_{22}}(s,\epsilon), \\
& Q_1(s)P_{11}(s,\epsilon)P_{12}(s,\epsilon) + \\
& Q_2(s)K^1_{P_{21}}(s,\epsilon)K^1_{P_{22}}(s,\epsilon)) \\
E_6(s,\epsilon) = & (Q_1(s)P_{11}(s,\epsilon)P_{12}(s,\epsilon) + \\
& Q_2(s)K^1_{P_{21}}(s,\epsilon)K^3_{P_{22}}(s,\epsilon), \\
& Q_1(s)P_{11}(s,\epsilon)P_{12}(s,\epsilon) + \\
& Q_2(s)K^1_{P_{21}}(s,\epsilon)K^1_{P_{22}}(s,\epsilon)).
\end{aligned}$$

Using a simple bisection method based algorithm we have

$$\begin{aligned}
\epsilon^* &= \max\{\epsilon | E_i(s,\epsilon) \in \mathcal{H}, \forall \epsilon \in [0,\epsilon^*], i = 1,\cdots,6\} \\
&= 0.6305.
\end{aligned}$$

4. CONCLUDING REMARKS

A simple technique to determine the parametric stability margin for multilinearly dependent interval control system has been given. The method is based on the multilinear generalization of the Box theorem. The method is powerful and reduces computational burden significantly. In fact, if used in conjunction with the Segment Lemma it completely eliminates frequency sweeping. Furthermore, by adding additional vertices one may achieve an arbitrarily high level of accuracy.

References

[1] H. Chapellat, L. H. Keel, and S. P. Bhattacharyya, "Stability margins for multilinear in-

terval control systems," in *Proceedings of the 30th IEEE Conference on Decision and Control*, (Brighton, U.K.), December 1991.

[2] S. P. Bhattacharyya and L. H. Keel, "Robust stability and control of linear and multilinear interval systems," *Control and Dynamic Systems*, vol. 51, pp. 31 – 78, 1992. Academic Press.

[3] H. Chapellat and S. P. Bhattacharyya, "A generalization of Kharitonov's theorem: robust stability of interval plants," *IEEE Transactions on Automatic Control*, vol. AC - 34, pp. 306 - 311, March 1989.

[4] V. L. Kharitonov, "Asymptotic stability of an equilibrium position of a family of systems of linear differential equations," *Differential Uravnen*, vol. 14, pp. 2086 – 2088, 1978.

[5] A. Katbab and E. I. Jury, "Robust Schur-stability of control systems with interval plants," *International Journal of Control*, vol. 51, no. 6, pp. 1343 - 1352, 1990.

[6] L. A. Zadeh and C. A. Desoer, *Linear Systems Theory*. New York: McGraw Hill, 1963.

[7] H. Chapellat and S. P. Bhattacharyya, "An alternative proof of Kharitonov's theorem," *IEEE Transactions on Automatic Control*, vol. AC - 34, pp. 448 – 450, April 1989.

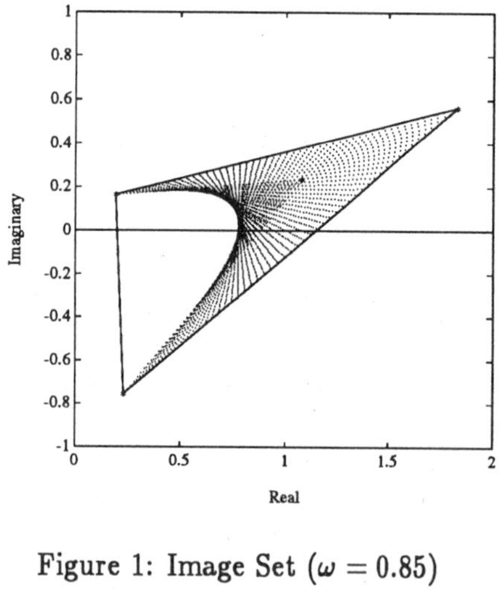

Figure 1: Image Set ($\omega = 0.85$)

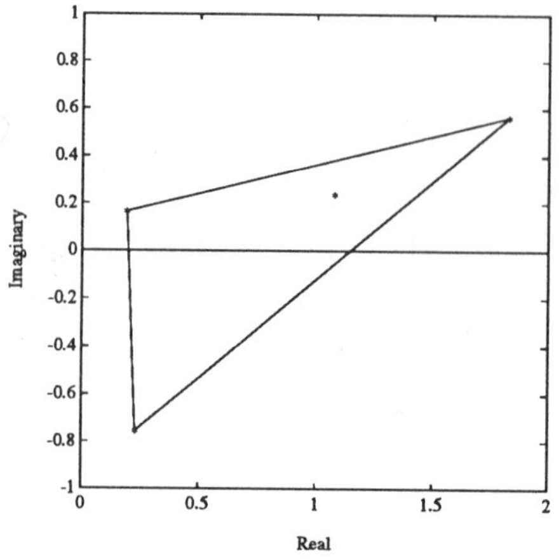

Figure 2: Convex Hull ($\omega = 0.85$)

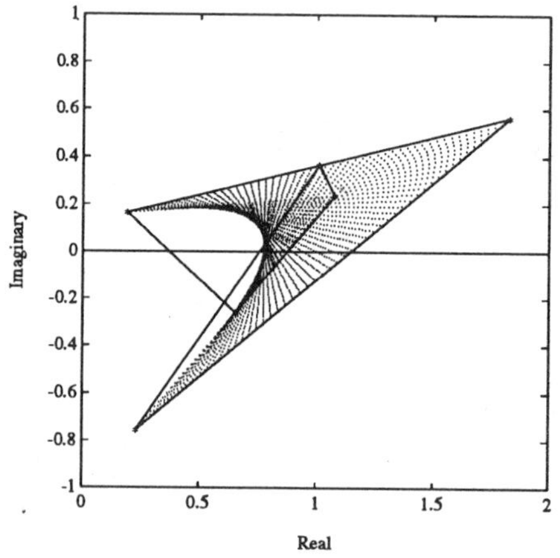

Figure 3: Image Set ($\omega = 0.85$)

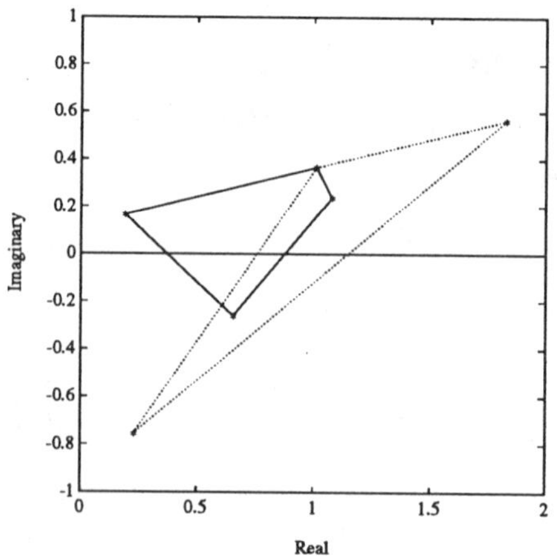

Figure 4: Convex Hull ($\omega = 0.85$)

Proceedings of the
American Control Conference
San Francisco, California • June 1993

Parametric Uncertainty Modeling using LFTs

Paul Lambrechts
Mechanical Engineering Systems and Control Group
Delft University of Technology, Mekelweg 2, 2628 CD Delft, The Netherlands
Jan Terlouw
Dutch National Aerospace Laboratory (NLR)
Anthony Fokkerweg 2, 1059 CM, Amsterdam, The Netherlands
Samir Bennani
Fac. of Aerospace Engineering, Section Stability and Control,
Delft University of Technology, Kluyverweg 1, 2629 HS Delft, The Netherlands
Maarten Steinbuch
Philips Research Laboratories
P.O.Box 80.000, 5600 JA Eindhoven, The Netherlands

Abstract

In this paper a general approach for modelling structured real-valued parametric perturbations is presented. It is based on a decomposition of perturbations into linear fractional transformations (LFTs), and is applicable to rational multi-dimensional (ND) polynomial perturbations of entries in state-space models. Model reduction is used to reduce the size of the uncertainty structure. The procedure will be applied for the uncertainty modelling of an aircraft model depending on altitude and velocity (flight envelope).

1 Introduction

In both robustness analysis and robust control system design the concept of the structured singular value μ as introduced by Doyle is of great importance [3]. It allows a high degree of detail in modelling the conditions under which the considered control system should operate satisfactorily, both in the sense of stability and performance. The calculation of μ for such models then results in a single number acting as an accurate measure in indicating whether the behaviour of the controlled system is satisfactory or not. The relevance of using the structured singular value instead of measures that do not reflect the structural properties of the plant uncertainties, like the ∞-norm or the 2-norm, can be found in literature; the latter may lead to arbitrarily conservative statements when practical examples are considered (see for instance [1, 15, 16, 6, 14]). In spite of this the use of μ has been seriously hampered by the considerable computational effort needed for its calculation with respect to a given uncertainty model. Recently developed methods for calculating close upper and lower bounds for the most general cases ([7, 8, 20]) now motivate the effort of modelling uncertainties in great detail. The main issue of this paper is to offer a complete procedure for setting up the general structure for the calculation of μ when uncertainties like real-valued parameter variations in state-space models and variations in operational conditions occur.

First, we will give some preliminary results on the use of Linear Fractional Transformations (LFTs) and their importance for uncertainty modelling, followed by a definition of the structured singular value μ and some relevant uncertainty sets. Section 3 then will present a procedure for parametric uncertainty modelling based on a state-space model in which uncertain entries may be given as rational multi-dimensional polynomial functions of a set of parameters. The usefulness of this procedure for practical problems will be demonstrated by means of an extensive example in section 4, after which some concluding remarks follow in section 5.

2 Preliminaries

This section will review some of the properties of Linear Fractional Transformations (LFTs) and the structured singular value μ along the lines of Doyle et al. [4, 5]. First we will give a definition of upper and lower LFTs and discuss some important possibilities of combining and rearranging them. Next we will consider the LFT concept as a framework for uncertainty modelling and within this framework we will give a definition of μ and some relevant uncertainty sets.

2.1 Definition of LFTs

We will consider matrices with entries that are fractions of polynomials in a complex-valued variable s; the space of all such real rational functions will be denoted as $\mathrm{R}(s)$, $M \in \mathrm{R}(s)^{p\times q}$ will denote that M is a $p \times q$ matrix with entries in $\mathrm{R}(s)$. Suppose this matrix M is partitioned as:

$$M = \begin{bmatrix} M_{11} & M_{12} \\ M_{21} & M_{22} \end{bmatrix} \quad \in \mathrm{R}(s)^{(p_1+p_2)\times(q_1+q_2)} \tag{1}$$

and let $\Delta_u \in \mathrm{R}(s)^{q_1\times p_1}$ and $\Delta_l \in \mathrm{R}(s)^{q_2\times p_2}$ be arbitrary. We will then define the *upper* and *lower* LFTs as operators on Δ_u and Δ_l respectively:

$$\begin{aligned} \mathcal{F}_u(M,\Delta_u) &:= M_{22} + M_{21}(I-\Delta_u M_{11})^{-1}\Delta_u M_{12} \\ \mathcal{F}_l(M,\Delta_l) &:= M_{11} + M_{12}(I-\Delta_l M_{22})^{-1}\Delta_l M_{21} \end{aligned} \tag{2}$$

Either LFT will be called *well defined* if the concerning inverse exists: $\det(I-\Delta_u M_{11}) \neq 0$ and $\det(I-\Delta_l M_{22}) \neq 0$. The matrix M is sometimes referred to as the coefficient matrix of the LFT. Note that if s is interpreted as the Laplace variable, a matrix with entries in $\mathrm{R}(s)$ can be seen as a multivariable transfer function of a linear time invariant finite dimensional system. In that case LFTs can be seen as operations resulting from feedback structures as given in fig.1; eq.2 then defines a closed loop transfer functions from w_M to z_M in both cases.

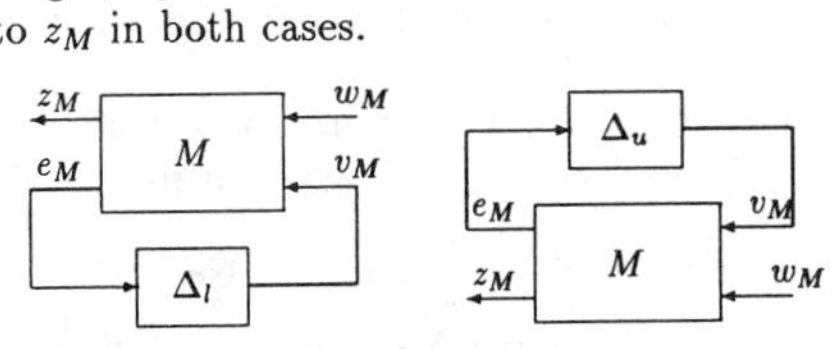

Fig. 1: Upper and lower LFT as feedback structure

An important reason for using the concept of LFTs in linear systems theory is that linear interconnections of LFTs can be rewritten as one single LFT. This implies that LFTs can be used to separately model specific details of the system under consideration after which a complete system description can be obtained by working out all connections. To demonstrate this we will first look at the two most basic connections between two LFTs: the cascade and parallel configurations. After that we will show a simple feedback configuration for one LFT which can also be rewritten into the standard form of fig.1. These three configurations will play an important role in the algorithmic approach to uncertainty modelling we will present in section 3.

Given matrices M and N partitioned as in eq.1: $M \in \mathrm{R}(s)^{p_M \times q_M)}$ and $N \in \mathrm{R}(s)^{p_N \times q_N}$, with $p_M := p_{M1} + p_{M2}$, $q_M := q_{M1} + q_{M2}$, $p_N := p_{N1} + p_{N2}$ and $q_N := q_{N1} + q_{N2}$. Let M and N be the coefficient matrices of the upper LFTs on $\Delta_M \in \mathrm{R}(s)^{q_{M1} \times p_{M1}}$ and $\Delta_N \in \mathrm{R}(s)^{q_{N1} \times p_{N1}}$ respectively and define the combined structure:

$$\Delta_{MN} = \begin{bmatrix} \Delta_M & 0 \\ 0 & \Delta_N \end{bmatrix} \quad \in \mathrm{R}(s)^{q_{MN} \times p_{MN}} \tag{3}$$

with $p_{MN} := p_{M1} + p_{N1}$ and $q_{MN} := q_{M1} + q_{N1}$. Then the cascade connection obtained by setting $w_M = z_N$ with $r := q_{M2} = p_{N2}$ (see fig.2) results in an upper LFT on Δ_{MN} with coefficient matrix:

$$M_c = \left[\begin{array}{cc|c} M_{11} & M_{12}N_{21} & M_{12}N_{22} \\ 0 & N_{11} & N_{12} \\ \hline M_{21} & M_{22}N_{21} & M_{22}N_{22} \end{array}\right] \in \mathrm{R}(s)^{(p_{MN}+r)\times(q_{MN}+r)} \tag{4}$$

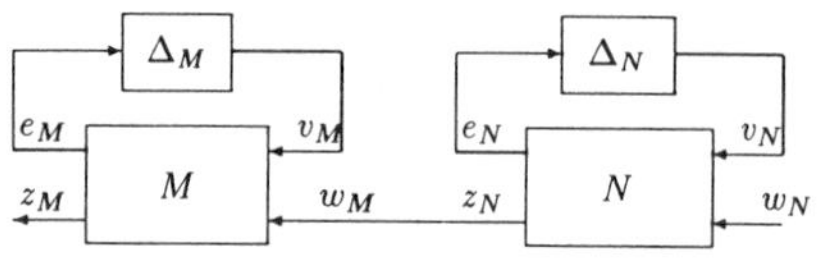

Fig. 2: Cascade connection of LFTs

The parallel connection obtained by setting $w_M = w_N$ and $z_{MN} = z_M + z_N$ with $r_q := q_{M2} = q_{N2}$ and $r_p := p_{M2} = p_{N2}$ (see fig.3) also results in an upper LFT on Δ_{MN}, this time with coefficient matrix:

$$M_p = \left[\begin{array}{cc|c} M_{11} & 0 & M_{12} \\ 0 & N_{11} & N_{12} \\ \hline M_{21} & N_{21} & M_{22} + N_{22} \end{array}\right] \in \mathrm{R}(s)^{(p_{MN}+r_p)\times(q_{MN}+r_q)} \tag{5}$$

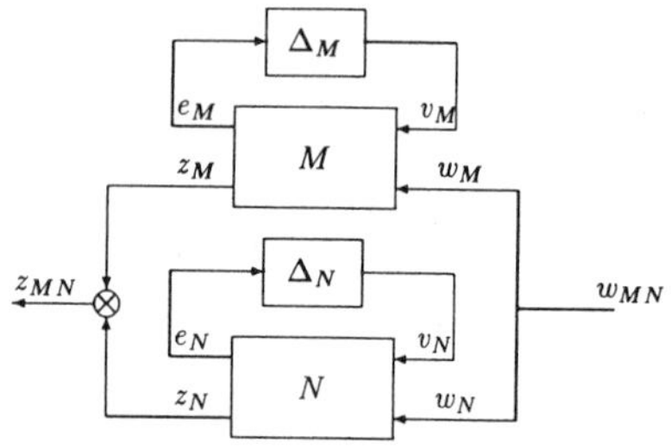

Fig. 3: Parallel connection of LFTs

Note that we have conveniently chosen the inputs and outputs of both LFTs to be compatible, but that it is also possible to connect only parts of input and output vectors by defining a further partitioning of M and N.

Next consider the feedback configuration given in fig.4 with M_{11} square ($p_1 = q_1$). In this case the coefficient matrix of the equivalent LFT can be calculated as:

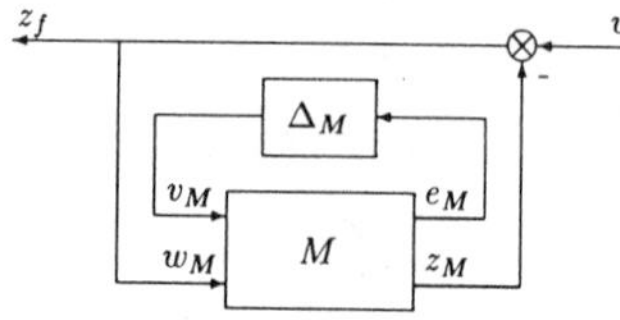

Fig. 4: An LFT in the feedback path

$$M_f = \left[\begin{array}{c|c} M_{f11} & M_{f12} \\ \hline M_{f21} & M_{f22} \end{array}\right] \quad \in \mathrm{R}(s)^{(p_2+p_1)\times(q_2+q_1)} \tag{6}$$

with:

$$\begin{array}{lcl} M_{f11} & := & M_{11} - M_{12}(I + M_{22})^{-1}M_{21} \\ M_{f12} & := & M_{12}(I + M_{22})^{-1} \\ M_{f21} & := & -(I + M_{22})^{-1}M_{21} \\ M_{f22} & := & (I + M_{22})^{-1} \end{array} \tag{7}$$

Clearly, for this coefficient matrix to be well defined we must have $\det(I + M_{22}) \neq 0$; note that with this condition we can write the transfer function from w_f to z_f both as $I/(I + \mathcal{F}_u(M, \Delta_M))$ or as $\mathcal{F}_u(M_f, \Delta_M)$ such that:

$$\mathcal{F}_u(M_f, \Delta_M) = I/(I + \mathcal{F}_u(M, \Delta_M)) \tag{8}$$

A more general form of this structure is known as the 'Redheffer Star-Product' [12].

2.2 Uncertainty descriptions with LFTs and the structured singular value

Another main advantage of the LFT concept is that it provides a framework for uncertainty modelling. The coefficient matrix can be seen as the part of a linear model that is assumed to be correct: the nominal model then results as an LFT on $\Delta = 0$. By taking $\Delta \in \mathbf{\Delta}$ with $\mathbf{\Delta} \subset \mathrm{R}(s)^{q \times p}$ a given subspace, it is then possible to specify a set of linear models rather than a single one. Especially if this set of models is closely related to physical properties of the system under consideration it thus provides a basis for non-conservative and trustworthy statements on robustness of controlled systems in the face of 'true' uncertainties.

A measure for determining whether all models within a specified set are stable was introduced by Doyle [3] as the structured singular value or μ and is based on a block-diagonal structure of $\mathbf{\Delta}$:

$$\begin{array}{rcl} \mathbf{\Delta} & = & \{\mathrm{diag}(\delta_1 I_{k_1}, \ldots, \delta_r I_{k_r}, \Delta_1, \ldots, \Delta_f) : \\ & & \delta_i \in \mathrm{R}(s), \Delta_i \in \mathrm{R}(s)^{k_{r+i} \times k_{r+i}}\} \end{array} \tag{9}$$

in which $\delta_i I_{k_i}, i = 1 \ldots r$ denote *repeated scalar* blocks and $\Delta_i, i = 1 \ldots f$ denote *full* blocks. Note that this implies that $\Delta \in \mathbf{\Delta}$ is square, although extensions to the non-square case are possible. As $\mathbf{\Delta} \subset \mathrm{R}(s)^{q \times p}$ we can consider the ∞-norm as a measure for the magnitude of an element of $\mathbf{\Delta}$ or one of its sub-blocks, with the ∞-norm of a matrix M defined as:

$$\|M\|_\infty := \sup_\omega \bar{\sigma}(M(j\omega)) \tag{10}$$

with $\bar{\sigma}$ denoting the largest singular value. We can then define the structured singular value as follows:

Definition 2.1 *Given a block-diagonal structure as in eq.9 and a compatible matrix $M \in \mathrm{R}(s)^{p \times q}$. $\mu_{\mathbf{\Delta}}(M)$ is then defined as:*

$$\mu_{\mathbf{\Delta}}(M) := \min\{\|\Delta\|_\infty : \Delta \in \mathbf{\Delta}, \det(I - \Delta M) = 0\}^{-1} \tag{11}$$

unless no $\Delta \in \mathbf{\Delta}$ makes $I - \Delta M$ singular in which case $\mu_{\mathbf{\Delta}}(M) := 0$.

Now if we consider a matrix M as given in eq.1 as the coefficient matrix of an upper LFT, then this definition implies that $\mu_{\mathbf{\Delta}}(M_{11})$ determines the 'smallest' $\Delta \in \mathbf{\Delta}$ for which the LFT is no longer well defined. If $\mathcal{F}_u(M, 0)$ and all $\Delta \in \mathbf{\Delta}$ are stable transfer function matrices, we may also interpret this Δ as the smallest one such that $\mathcal{F}_u(M, \Delta)$ is unstable.

We thus have the possibility to test the properties of a *set* of systems by constructing an appropriate LFT with Δ representing some bounded perturbations, normalizing Δ by incorporating scaling factors in M such that Δ becomes an element of a unit ball in $\mathbf{\Delta}$:

$$\mathrm{B}\mathbf{\Delta} = \{\Delta \in \mathbf{\Delta} : \|\Delta\|_\infty \leq 1\} \tag{12}$$

and finally determining whether $\mu \leq 1$. For an overview of such tests in the general case of eq.9 we refer to Doyle et al. [5]. Furthermore, we will not go into detail on computational issues with respect to μ but simply refer to recent developments as reported in [7, 8, 20]. We will concentrate on a restricted set of Δs that directly results from real valued parameter variations in state-space models as considered in section 3. For this purpose we define the set of Δs that are *square* and *diagonal* and consist only of *real-valued repeated scalar blocks*:

$$\mathbf{\Delta}_{rr} := \{\mathrm{diag}(\delta_1 I_{k_1}, \ldots, \delta_r I_{k_r}) : \delta_i \in \mathrm{R}\} \tag{13}$$

Again we can usually assume that the δ_is are bounded and that appropriate scaling factors are incorporated in the coefficient matrix such that Δ is further restricted to the bounded set:

$$\mathrm{B}\mathbf{\Delta}_{rr} := \{\mathrm{diag}(\delta_1 I_{k_1}, \ldots, \delta_r I_{k_r}) : \delta_i \in [-1, +1]\} \tag{14}$$

3 Parametric uncertainty modelling

In this paragraph we will consider the problem of state-space models with parametric uncertainty occurring as real rational ND-polynomials. This generalizes earlier results in parametric uncertainty modelling as given by Morton and McAfoos [11] and Steinbuch et al. [17, 18] In section 3.1 the problem will be formulated, which turns out to be an ND-realization problem. Section 3.2 discusses the existence of a solution and section 3.3 provides an algorithm for solving the realization problem by constructing an appropriate LFT.

3.1 Transformation of a state-space model to an LFT

Consider a vector $p = (p_1, ..., p_r) \in \mathrm{R}^r$ containing r bounded scalar parameters. Let the model of the perturbed system be given as a state-space realization in which the entries of the matrices depend on the parameter vector p:

$$\begin{aligned} \dot{x} &= A(p)x + B(p)u, \quad x \in \mathrm{R}^n, u \in \mathrm{R}^m \\ y &= C(p)x + D(p)u, \quad y \in \mathrm{R}^l \end{aligned} \tag{15}$$

With the $(n + l) \times (n + m)$ matrix $S(p)$ defined as:

$$S(p) := \begin{pmatrix} A(p) & B(p) \\ C(p) & D(p) \end{pmatrix} \tag{16}$$

we can write this as

$$\begin{pmatrix} \dot{x} \\ y \end{pmatrix} = S(p) \begin{pmatrix} x \\ u \end{pmatrix} \tag{17}$$

Now we would like to rewrite eq.16 using an upper LFT:

$$S(p) = M_{22} + M_{21}(I - \Delta_u M_{11})^{-1}\Delta_u M_{12} \tag{18}$$

with $\Delta_u \in \mathrm{B}\mathbf{\Delta}_{rr}$ (eq.14) and the matrices $M_{22}, M_{21}, M_{11}, M_{12}$ independent of Δ_u.
If we consider only the non-trivial case that $\delta_i \neq 0, \quad i = 1 \ldots r$ we can then define $\rho_i := 1/\delta_i$ and rewrite eq.18 as:

$$S(p) = M_{22} + M_{21} \left[\begin{bmatrix} \rho_1 I_{k_1} & & 0 \\ & \ddots & \\ 0 & & \rho_r I_{k_r} \end{bmatrix} - M_{11} \right]^{-1} M_{12} \tag{19}$$

Note that we now have transformed the problem of finding an LFT representation of eq.15 to an ND-realization problem [2].

3.2 Existence of a solution

Using a constructive algorithm we are now able to do the following statement.

A solution to the problem of transforming a state-space model with parametric uncertainty to an LFT exists
if
the entries of the state-space matrices are bounded and can be given as real rational ND-polynomials in the parameters.

Real rational varying entries in a state-space model can be described as LFTs individually. Based on the properties of the interconnection of LFTs, treated in subsection 2.1, these individual LFTs can be collected in one LFT afterwards. A detailed description of the algorithm will follow in section 3.3. Minimality of the obtained LFT can not be guaranteed since it is not straightforward to generalize the 1D concepts of controllability and observability to ND-systems. By for instance [9, 10, 13] 2D counterparts of these notions are considered, leading to the definition of local and global controllability and observability. As is well known, for 1D systems the minimality of a state-space description is equivalent to the property that such a realization is controllable and observable. By Kung and Levi [10] it is shown by means of an example that global observability and controllability does not imply minimality. However, by removing locally unobservable and uncontrollable perturbations the dimensions of the obtained LFT can be reduced substantially. This approach has been implemented in the algorithm given in the next section.

3.3 A procedure for the transformation

1. **Scaling the varying parameters**
Lower and upper bound vectors for the parameter vector p can be determined, denoted respectively as $\underline{p}$ and $\bar{p}$: Now define $p_o = (\underline{p}+\bar{p})/2$, $s = (\bar{p}-\underline{p})/2$, $\delta = (\delta_1 \ldots \delta_r)$, $\delta_i \in [-1, +1]$, such that $p_i = p_{oi} + s_i\delta_i$ for $i = 1 \cdots r$. Substitution of this result in eq.15 then gives scaled ND-polynomial expressions for all varying numerators and denominators. For instance, suppose a numerator is given as $n_{ij}(p_1, p_2) = p_1 p_2$, with $p_1 = p_{o1} + s_1\delta_1$ and $p_2 = p_{o2} + s_2\delta_2$. Then the scaled numerator is

$$n_{ij}(\delta_1, \delta_2) = p_{o1}p_{o2} + p_{o2}s_1\delta_1 + p_{o1}s_2\delta_2 + s_1 s_2\delta_1\delta_2 \tag{20}$$

2. **Individual varying terms as LFTs**
The varying parts of a numerator or denominator consist of a number of terms that can be written as seperate LFTs. For example, the scaled numerator $n_{ij}(\delta_1, \delta_2)$ given above has three varying terms resulting in three LFTs (see fig.5). Of course the same can be done with the varying terms in denominators.

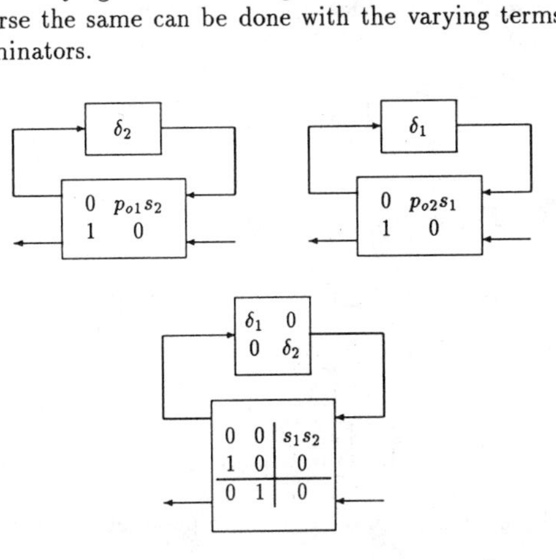

Fig. 5: The varying terms in the numerator n_{ij} written as LFTs

3. **Numerators of varying entries**
Using the fact that two parallel LFTs form again an LFT (see eq.5) the addition of all terms in each numerator can again be written as an LFT. Since we use upper LFTs, the nominal (constant) part of each numerator results in a feedthrough term, which can be incorporated in the M_{22} term of the combined LFT. The resulting LFT giving the numerator n_{ij} of eq.20 is depicted in fig.6.

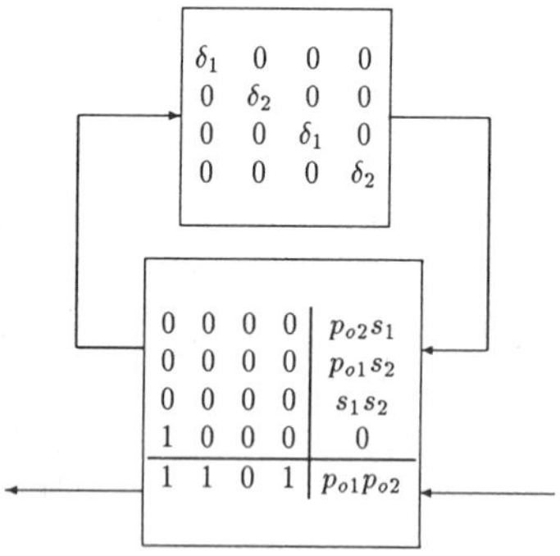

Fig. 6: The numerator n_{ij} given as a single LFT

4. **Denominators of varying entries**
To set up an LFT-description for denominator terms we should obtain an LFT of the *inverse* of an ND-polynomial. This inverse can be obtained by first setting up an LFT for the denominator as was done for the numerators in the previous step, subtracting 1 and putting the result in the feedback path as was done in fig.4. By means of eq.7 and eq.8 we can then find the desired LFT. The condition that the term $M_{22}+1$ is invertible corresponds with the restriction that the nominal parts of all the varying denominators of a state-space model must be unequal to zero, i.e. the entries of the nominal model must be bounded.

5. **Combining numerators and denominators of individual entries**
Cascade connection of the LFTs of each numerator-denominator pair found in the previous steps can be performed as in eq.4.

6. **Combining all varying entries**
We now have a complete description of all uncertain entries specified in eq.15 in the form of LFTs. Combining the LFTs for the A, B, C and D matrices separately is a simple excercise and results in fig.7 that can be rewritten as one single LFT with $\Delta = \text{diag}(\Delta_A, \Delta_B, \Delta_C, \Delta_D)$.

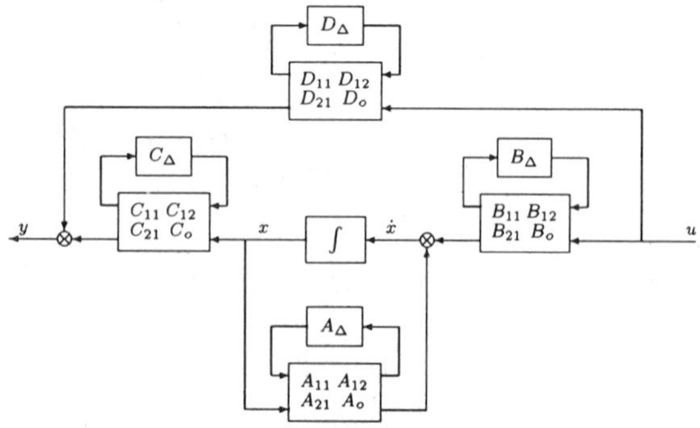

Fig. 7: LFT description of state-space parametric uncertainties

7. **Transformation to the real-repeated blockstructure**
Δ can be rearranged into the real-valued repeated scalar block structure of eq.13 by means of interchanging rows and columns of the LFT. Note that due to step 1 the entries of Δ are elements of $[-1,1]$, such that $\Delta \in \mathbf{B\Delta}_{rr}$.

8. **Reducing the dimension of Δ**
The resulting LFT can be set in state-space form in which the uncertainty inputs can be appended to u and the uncertainty outputs can be appended to y. It is well known that any uncontrollable and/or unobservable parts of this state-space model can be removed using a standard reduction technique, thus reducing the dimensions of the 'block of integrators'. The same procedure can be used to reduce the size of any of the real-repeated blocks in Δ. For this we can rewrite the LFT by considering x as an uncertainty input and $\dot{x}$ as an uncertainty output; this implies that the block of integrators is appended to Δ. Next we can separate the uncertainty block $\delta_1 I$ from Δ and consider its uncertainty inputs as 'pseudo-states' and its uncertainty outputs as 'pseudo-derivatives'. Removing the parts that are uncontrollable and/or unobservable when considering all other inputs and outputs will then reduce the size of $\delta_1 I$. This procedure can be repeated for all other real-repeated uncertainty blocks. Although a minimal realization can not always be obtained by this method, many examples have shown that an extensive reduction of dimensions can be achieved.

With these steps we now have an LFT description which is equivalent to the state-space system of eq.15. These steps have been implemented within the environment of PC Matlab such that the entire procedure can be performed interactively. In the next section an example is given.

4 Uncertainty modelling for the Phugoid approximation of the DHC2-Beaver aircraft.

The design example is based on the variations of aerodynamic coefficients and relative mass within the flight envelope, as they appear in the phugoid approximation of the Beaver aircraft. The phugoid motion is a low frequency badly damped oscillatory effect appearing in forward velocity and altitude of the aircraft. For good aircraft design it is important that the effect of the phugoid motion is minimized to ensure satisfactory handling and flying qualities, especially under instrument flight rules. Also for controller design it is important to find an accurate characterization of this effect. We will therefore start with the definition of the analytical phugoid model in which stability derivatives are defined that have been quantified accurately over the whole flight envelope by Tjee and Mulder [19].

In our example we are interested in modelling parameter variation of the aircraft in cruise flight conditions over the entire flight envelope. The flight envelope represents a set of flying conditions, in terms of velocity and altitude, under which the aircraft can operate. The goal of this exercise is to obtain an aircraft model that accurately represents all flight conditions that may occur and that may be used for stability and performance analysis and also can be used in robust controller synthesis. We will show that once the variations are explicitly defined, the model can be written as an LFT such that calculation of the structured singular value may provide a measure for the unwanted effect of the phugoid motion.

4.1 Modelling the phugoid motion

The aircraft model considered in this example is the linear approximation model of the phugoid motion and can be given in state-space form as:

$$\begin{aligned} \begin{bmatrix} \dot{u}(t) \\ \dot{\theta}(t) \end{bmatrix} &= A \begin{bmatrix} u(t) \\ \theta(t) \end{bmatrix} + \begin{bmatrix} 1 \\ 0 \end{bmatrix} w(t) \\ y(t) &= \begin{bmatrix} 0 & 1 \end{bmatrix} \begin{bmatrix} u(t) \\ \theta(t) \end{bmatrix} \end{aligned} \tag{21}$$

with:

$$A := \begin{bmatrix} \frac{V}{2\mu_c(\rho)\bar{c}} C_{X_u}(\rho, V) & -g_0/V \\ \frac{-V}{2\mu_c(\rho)\bar{c}} C_{Z_u}(\rho, V) & 0 \end{bmatrix} \tag{22}$$

The state vector $x = (u, \theta)$ represents the longitudinal component of the velocity vector (u) and the pitch angle (θ). The input vector w is added to demonstrate the possibility of modelling the effect of, for instance, air turbulence on the phugoid motion. As a measure of the effect of the phugoid motion we assume that the pitch angle θ can be measured. The terms C_{X_u} and C_{Z_u} represent the stablity derivatives which are known in terms of altitude (air density ρ) and velocity V. The accelleration of gravity is given as $g_0 = 9.80665$ m/s^2 and the factor $\mu_c = \frac{m}{\rho S \bar{c}}$ represents the relative aircraft mass with m denoting the nominal aicraft mass, S the wing area and $\bar{c}$ the mean aerodynamic chord of the wing profile. The air density ρ is assumed to depend on altitude h according to the Standard Atmosphere model:

$$\rho = \rho_0 \left[\frac{T_0}{T_0 + \lambda\, h}\right]^{\frac{M_0 g_0}{R_a \lambda}+1} \tag{23}$$

with $T_0 = 288.15$ K, $\lambda = -0.0065$ K/m, $R_a = 8314.32$ J/K·kmol and $M_0 = 28.9644$ kg/kmol.

4.2 Fitting the stability derivatives

To obtain a parametric description of the stability derivatives C_{X_u} and C_{Z_u} as a function of ρ and V we will use a 2 dimensional polynomial fitting procedure. Data regarding the stability derivatives for several combinations of ρ and V within the flight envelope is available from [19]. Although the area of the flight envelope is not square it can be approximated by means of polynomial fits of the nominal value and deviation of V as a function of ρ. Both the approximation of the area and the surfaces defined by C_{X_u} and C_{Z_u} can then be given as a function of two new parameters δ_x and δ_y varying between -1 and 1. For the approximation of the area, second order polynomial fits have been determined resulting in:

$$\begin{aligned} h &= 4000\ \delta_x + 6000 & \text{[ft]} \\ \rho &= -\ 1.25\text{e-}01\ \delta_x + 1.03 & \text{[kg/m}^3\text{]} \\ V &= -\ 3.57\ \delta_x^2\delta_y + 3.57\ \delta_x^2 - 3.50\ \delta_x\delta_y & \\ &\quad + 3.50\ \delta_x + 12.3\ \delta_y + 47.7 & \text{[m/s]} \end{aligned} \tag{24}$$

The flight envelope thus described is visualized in fig.8 as a function of δ_x. Polynomial fits for C_{X_u} and C_{Z_u} within this area and

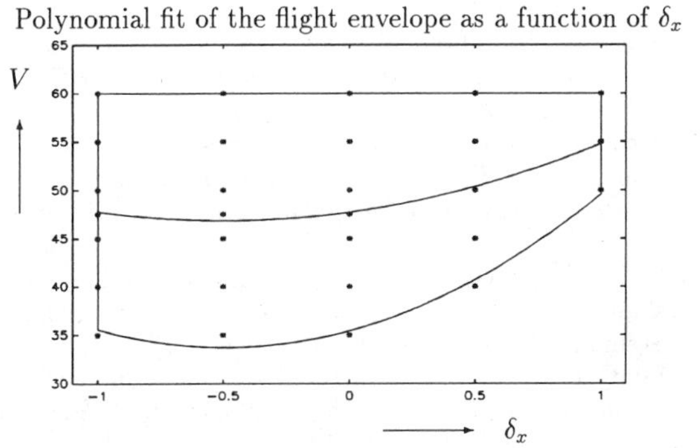

Fig. 8: Flight envelope and its approximation

with terms having a maximal order of 2 are given by:

$$\begin{aligned} C_{X_u} &= 5.95\text{e-}02\ \delta_x^2\delta_y^2 - 6.37\text{e-}02\ \delta_x^2\delta_y + 1.38\text{e-}02\ \delta_x^2 \\ &\quad + 3.97\text{e-}02\ \delta_x\delta_y^2 - 3.99\text{e-}02\ \delta_x\delta_y - 7.95\text{e-}04\ \delta_x \\ &\quad - 9.91\text{e-}02\ \delta_y^2 + 1.23\text{e-}01\ \delta_y - 0.14 \\ C_{Z_u} &= 1.02\text{e-}01\ \delta_x^2\delta_y^2 - 2.90\text{e-}01\ \delta_x^2\delta_y + 1.83\text{e-}01\ \delta_x^2 \\ &\quad + 1.09\text{e-}01\ \delta_x\delta_y^2 - 2.41\text{e-}01\ \delta_x\delta_y + 1.91\text{e-}02\ \delta_x \\ &\quad - 2.37\text{e-}01\ \delta_y^2 + 7.68\text{e-}01\ \delta_y - 1.43 \end{aligned} \tag{25}$$

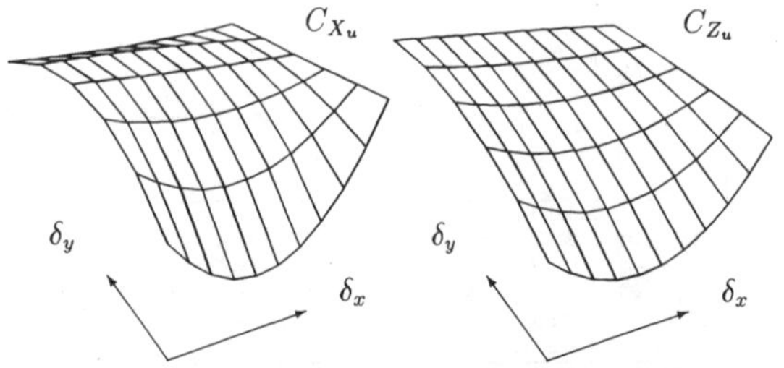

Fig. 9: Fitted surfaces of C_{X_u} and C_{Z_u}

and plotted in fig.9. Finally the relative aircraft mass can be determined as:

$$\mu_c = 7.43\ \delta_x + 60.9 \tag{26}$$

4.3 Results

Using the procedure of section 3 we arrive at an upper LFT description of the state-space model given in eq.21 with thirteen uncertainty inputs. and outputs

$$\begin{bmatrix} \dot{x} \\ \hline y_{\delta_{x1}} \\ \vdots \\ y_{\delta_{x6}} \\ y_{\delta_{y1}} \\ \vdots \\ y_{\delta_{y7}} \\ y \end{bmatrix} = \begin{bmatrix} A \\ \hline C \end{bmatrix} x + \begin{bmatrix} B_{\delta_1} & B_{\delta_2} & B_u \\ \hline D_{\delta_1} & D_{\delta_2} & D_u \end{bmatrix} \begin{bmatrix} u_{\delta_{x1}} \\ \vdots \\ u_{\delta_{x6}} \\ u_{\delta_{y1}} \\ \vdots \\ u_{\delta_{y7}} \\ w \end{bmatrix} \tag{27}$$

with:

$$A = \begin{bmatrix} -3.47\text{e-}02 & -2.06\text{e-}01 \\ 3.54\text{e-}01 & 0 \end{bmatrix} \tag{28}$$

$$B_{\delta_1} = \begin{bmatrix} -1.018\text{e-}01 & 8.25\text{e-}03 & 1.45\text{e-}01 & 1.89\text{e-}02 & 9.92\text{e-}03 & 2.07\text{e-}02 \\ 0 & -1.22\text{e-}01 & 0 & -4.47\text{e-}01 & -1.54\text{e-}01 & -2.74\text{e-}01 \end{bmatrix} \tag{29}$$

$$B_{\delta_2} = \begin{bmatrix} -1.17 & 9.61\text{e-}01 & 1.94\text{e-}02 & 0 & 0 & 0 & 0 \\ 3.04 & 3.70\text{e-}01 & 6.68\text{e-}03 & 0 & 0 & 0 & 0 \end{bmatrix} \tag{30}$$

$$B_u = \begin{bmatrix} 1 \\ 0 \end{bmatrix} \tag{31}$$

$$C = \begin{bmatrix} 0 & -1.48\text{e-}01 \\ 1.81\text{e-}01 & 0 \\ 0 & 0 \\ 0 & 0 \\ 0 & 0 \\ 0 & 0 \\ -3.05\text{e-}02 & -5.88\text{e-}03 \\ -1.48\text{e-}02 & 5.08\text{e-}02 \\ \hline -4.11\text{e-}03 & -1.40\text{e-}01 \\ -1.85\text{e-}02 & 0 \\ -1.48\text{e-}02 & 0 \\ -3.87\text{e-}03 & 0 \\ 3.00\text{e-}03 & 0 \\ \hline 0 & 1 \end{bmatrix} \tag{32}$$

$$D_{\delta_1} = \begin{bmatrix} 0 & 0 & 0 & 0 & 0 & 0 \\ -7.34\text{e-}02 & 0 & 1.05\text{e-}01 & 0 & 0 & 0 \\ 0 & -1.22\text{e-}01 & 0 & 0 & 0 & 0 \\ -7.14\text{e-}01 & 0 & 0 & 0 & 0 & 0 \\ 0 & 2.37\text{e-}01 & 0 & 0 & 0 & 0 \\ 0 & 0 & 0 & 5.57\text{e-}01 & 0 & 0 \\ \hline 0 & 0 & 0 & 0 & 5.20\text{e-}01 & 0 \\ -1.421\text{e-}02 & 5.29\text{e-}02 & 2.03\text{e-}02 & 1.90\text{e-}01 & 1.71\text{e-}01 & 2.16\text{e-}01 \\ 1.23\text{e-}01 & 1.98\text{e-}02 & -1.75\text{e-}01 & -5.00\text{e-}02 & 1.12\text{e-}01 & 1.36\text{e-}01 \\ -3.374\text{e-}01 & 4.96\text{e-}03 & 4.82\text{e-}01 & -2.62\text{e-}02 & 3.36\text{e-}02 & 4.04\text{e-}02 \\ 0 & 8.05\text{e-}02 & 0 & 4.15\text{e-}01 & -3.20\text{e-}01 & -2.81\text{e-}01 \\ 0 & 3.05\text{e-}02 & 0 & -4.24\text{e-}01 & -2.84\text{e-}01 & -2.78\text{e-}01 \\ 0 & -6.45\text{e-}02 & 0 & 1.79\text{e-}01 & 2.16\text{e-}02 & 2.55\text{e-}01 \\ \hline 0 & -7.33\text{e-}02 & 0 & 2.05\text{e-}01 & -8.07\text{e-}02 & -6.15\text{e-}01 \end{bmatrix} \tag{33}$$

$$
D_{\delta_2} = \left[\begin{array}{ccccccc}
0 & 0 & 0 & 0 & 0 & 0 & 0 \\
-1.02e{-}02 & 8.77e{-}02 & -2.41e{-}01 & 0 & 0 & 0 & 0 \\
0 & 0 & 0 & 0 & 0 & 0 & 0 \\
0 & 0 & 0 & 0 & 0 & 0 & 0 \\
0 & 0 & 0 & 0 & 0 & 0 & 0 \\
0 & 0 & 0 & 0 & 0 & 0 & 0 \\
0 & 0 & 0 & 0 & 0 & 0 & 0 \\
\hline
-1.33e{-}01 & -3.99e{-}01 & -1.50e{-}01 & 2.01e{-}01 & 1.55e{-}01 & 0 & 0 \\
1.69e{-}01 & 4.06e{-}02 & 1.01e{-}01 & 3.56e{-}01 & -7.59e{-}02 & 0 & 0 \\
5.64e{-}02 & 1.25e{-}01 & -2.14e{-}01 & 1.21e{-}01 & -3.41e{-}02 & 0 & 0 \\
3.27e{-}02 & 1.01e{-}01 & 3.53e{-}02 & -4.95e{-}02 & -9.58e{-}02 & 8.18e{-}02 & 8.65e{-}02 \\
-1.80e{-}02 & -2.19e{-}01 & -7.88e{-}02 & 3.49e{-}02 & -1.65e{-}02 & 3.34e{-}01 & -2.12e{-}02 \\
-3.86e{-}02 & -4.12e{-}02 & -1.34e{-}02 & -4.40e{-}02 & -1.57e{-}01 & 2.64e{-}01 & 2.72e{-}01 \\
\hline
2.24e{-}02 & -1.39e{-}01 & -5.14e{-}02 & 1.62e{-}01 & 8.95e{-}02 & 2.62e{-}03 & -1.49e{-}01
\end{array}\right] \qquad (34)
$$

$$
D_u = \left[0\ 0\ 0\ 0\ 0\ 0 \mid 0\ 0\ 0\ 0\ 0\ 0\ 0 \mid 0 \right]^T \qquad (35)
$$

To demonstrate the possibility of using the structured singular value μ as a measure for the worst case influence of disturbance input w on the phugoid motion, it will be calculated for the interconnection structure given in eq.27. The structure of the uncertainty block Δ for this LFT can be given according to eq.9 as $\mathbf{\Delta} = \text{diag}(\delta_x I_6, \delta_y I_7, \delta_w)$ with δ_x, δ_y the real parameter variations as defined before and δ_w a complex perturbation to express our demand to restrict the phugoid motion. We used a preliminary release of the MUSYN toolbox to calculate μ for this mixed real-repeated complex problem, resulting in a value of μ of 38.6. This value can be interpreted as the maximal amplification occurring in the transfer function matrix from w to y under the worst case conditions within the flight envelope and with the worst case disturbance w (a sine of frequency 0.27 rad/s). Note that our choice of disturbance input w and output y was arbitrary and just to demonstrate the procedure. A choice of inputs and outputs based on a physical interpretation of disturbances and the desired suppression of the phugoid motion is currently a research topic at the faculty of aerospace engineering.

5 Conclusions

The development of methods for analysis and design based on the structured singular value μ causes an increasing demand for the construction of accurate uncertainty models in the form of LFTs. Usually the knowledge concerning uncertainty in mathematical models of physical systems is available in terms of parameter variations. In state-space models this often appears as variations of entries that can be approximated accurately by means of ratios of ND-polynomials in independent variables which have a physical interpretation. In this paper an algorithm is presented which is used to transform a state-space model with this type of parametric uncertainty to an LFT description with a real-repeated perturbation matrix. Although the dimension of this perturbation matrix may initially be very high, a reduction procedure is proposed that usually decreases it significantly. However, this procedure does not guarantee minimality of the resulting structure. The proposed procedure has been applied to the uncertainty modelling for the phugoid approximation of the DHC2-Beaver aircraft resulting in an LFT description allowing the analysis of the influence of disturbances over the entire flight envelope. The procedure has been implemented in MatLab, such that uncertainty models can be set up in an interactive user-friendly manner.

Acknowledgements

Maarten Steinbuch wants to thank Mathew Newlin and Peter Young, both from California Institute of Technology, for providing a test version of their μ-analysis software for real and complex structures.

The authors also wish to thank Paula Rocha from Delft University of Technology fac. of Mathematics for her help in gaining a better understanding of developments in the area of 2D and ND system representations.

This research was sponsored by Philips Research Laboratories in Eindhoven, Delft University of Technology and National Aerospace Laboratory (NLR) in Amsterdam.

References

[1] Balas G.J., Packard A., Doyle J.C., "Theory and applications of robust multivariable control", in *H_∞ and μ Short Course, Musyn inc., Delft, june 25-28,* 1990.

[2] Bose N.K., *Applied multidimensional system theory.* Van Nostrand Reinhold Co., N.Y., 1982.

[3] Doyle J.C., "Analysis of feedback systems with structured uncertainties.", *IEE Proc., Part D, vol.129, no.6,* pp.242-250, 1982.

[4] Doyle J.C., Packard A., "Uncertain multivariable systems from a state space perspective.", in *Proc. American Control Conf.,* pp.2147-2152, 1987.

[5] Doyle J.C., Packard A., Zhou K., "Review of LFTs, LMIs and μ", in *Proc. IEEE Conf. on Decision and Control,* pp.1227-1232, 1991.

[6] Doyle J.C., Lenz K., Packard A., "Design examples using μ-synthesis: space shuttle lateral axis FCS during reentry", in *Proc. IEEE Conf. on Decision and Control,* pp.2218-2223, 1986.

[7] Fan M.K.H., Tits A.L., "Characterization and efficient computation of the structured singular value.", *IEEE Trans. on Automatic Control, vol.AC-31, no.8,* pp.734-743, 1986.

[8] Fan M.K.H., Tits A.L., Doyle J.C., "Robustness in the presence of mixed parametric uncertainty and unmodelled dynamics", *IEEE Trans. on Automatic Control, vol AC-36, no.1,* pp.25-38, 1991.

[9] Hinamoto T., "Realisation of a state-space model from 2D input output map.", *IEEE Trans. on Circuits & Systems, vol.CAS-27, no.1,* pp.36-44, 1980.

[10] Kung S., Levi B.C., "New results in 2D system theory, part II: 2D state-space models realisations and the notions of controllability, observability and minimality", in *Proc. of the IEEE, vol.65, no.6,* pp.945-961, 1977.

[11] Morton B.G., McAfoos R.M., "A μ-test for robustness analysis of a real-parameter variation problem.", in *Proc. American Control Conf.,* pp.135-138, 1985.

[12] Redheffer R., "Inequalities for a matrix Riccati equation", *J. of Mathematics and Mechanics, vol.8, no.3,* 1959.

[13] Roesser R.E., "A discrete state-space model for linear image processing", *IEEE Trans. on Automatic Control vol AC-20, no.1,* pp.1-10, 1975.

[14] Skogestad S., Morari M., Doyle J.C., "Robust control of ill-conditioned plants: high-purity distillation.", *IEEE Trans. on Automatic Control, vol.AC-33, no.12,* pp.1092-1105, 1988.

[15] Stein G., Doyle J.C., "Singular values and feedback: design examples", in *Proc. 16th Annual Allerton Conf. on Communication, Control and Computation, Univ. of Illinois,* pp.460-471, 1978.

[16] Stein G., Doyle J.C., "Beyond singular values and loop shapes", *J. of Guidance, vol.14, no.1,* pp.5-16, 1991.

[17] Steinbuch M., Terlouw J.C., Bosgra O.H., Smit S.G., "Uncertainty modelling and structured singular value computation applied to an electromechanical system", *IEE Proc., Part D, vol.139, no.3,* pp.301-307, 1992.

[18] Steinbuch M., Terlouw J.C., Bosgra O.H., "Robustness analysis for real and complex perturbations applied to an electro-mechanical system", in *Proc. American Control Conf.,* pp.556-561, 1991.

[19] Tjee R.T.H, Mulder J.A., "Stability and control derivatives of the De Havilland DHC-2 'BEAVER' aircraft", in *Techn. Univ. Delft, Report LR-556,* 1988.

[20] Young P.M., Newlin M.P., Doyle J.C., "μ analysis with real parametric uncertainty", in *Proc. IEEE Conf. on Decision and Control,* pp.1251-1256, 1991.

Proceedings of the
American Control Conference
San Francisco, California • June 1993

Robust Stability of Uncertain Generalized State-Space Systems

Chun-Hsiung Fang and Fan-Ren Chang

Department of Electrical Engineering
National Kaohsiung Institute of Technology
Kaohsiung 807, TAIWAN, R.O.C.

Department of Electrical Engineering
National Taiwan University
Taipei 107, TAIWAN, R.O.C.

Abstract

In this paper, we propose a new approach to analyze robust stability of uncertain continuous-time generalized state-space systems. Under structured perturbations, a sufficient condition checking whether the stability degree is larger than a specified value is provided.

1. Notations and introduction

$\rho(M)$: spectral radius of $M \in C^{n\times n}$.
$|M|_m$: modulus matrix of $M \in C^{n\times n}$.
$|M|$: determinant of matrix $M \in C^{n\times n}$.
$[t_{ij}]$: the (i,j)th element of $T \in \Re^{m\times n}$.
$T \geq N$: $[t_{ij}] \geq [n_{ij}]$ for $i = 1,2,\cdots,n,\ j = 1,2,\cdots,n$.
$Re(s)$: real part of a complex number s.

In recent years, there has been a growing interest in the system-theoretic problems of generalized state-space systems (or singular systems, or decriptor systems) due to the extensive applications of generalized state-space systems to large-scale systems, circuits, economics, control theory, and other areas [5,9, 10,16]. Several important and fundamental results, except about robustness property, in regular systems have been successfully extended to generalized state-space systems [1,6,7,8,12,17]. In this paper we consider a continuous-time perturbed generalized state-space system described by

$$E\dot{x}(t) = Ax(t) + \Delta Ax(t), \qquad Ex(0) = Ex_0 \tag{1}$$

where $E, A \in \Re^{n\times n}$ and ΔA stands for the perturbations. Here the matrix E may be singular. We will assume $rankE \equiv r \leq n$. Suppose the perturbation can be bounded by

$$|\Delta A|_m \leq kH \tag{2}$$

where k is a real positive number and H is a constant nonnegative matrix. The constant matrix H represents the highly-structured information for the additive perturbation matrix ΔA.

It is well-known that the system (1) contains three kinds of modes: finite dynamical modes, infinite dynamical modes, and infinite nondynamical modes [1,16]. The infinite dynamical modes can generate undesired impulse behaviors. Hence, to eliminate or to avoid inducing infinite dynamical modes is a key work in generalized state-space system control [1,10]. If we assume $deg\ |sE - A| = r$ and $\Delta A = 0$, the system (1) now has r finite dynamical modes, none of infinite dynamical modes, and $n-r$ infinite nondynamical modes. However, if the perturbation $\Delta A \neq 0$, it would possibly introduce dynamical infinite modes into system (1) since it can change the degree of $|sE - A - \Delta A|$. Furthermore, the perturbation ΔA can also possibly destroy the system regularity (i.e. $|sE - A - \Delta A|$ is identically zero).

2. Stability robustness

Lemma 1 : [1,16] The response of $E\dot{x}(t) = \hat{A}x(t)$ is said to be asymptotically stable and impulse free if and only if the following two conditions are satisfied

$$1)\quad deg\ |sE - \hat{A}| = rankE = r \tag{3}$$

and

$$2)\quad \textit{All roots of } |sE - \hat{A}| = 0 \textit{ have negative real parts} \tag{4}$$

Equation (4) in Lemma 1 can be rewritten as

$$|sE - \hat{A}| \neq 0 \ for\ all\ Re(s) \geq 0 \tag{5}$$

Note that when $E = I$ or E is nonsingular, the condition of equation (3) is always satisfied.

Lemma 2 : [11] For any $n \times n$ constant matrices X, Y, Z, $|X|_m \leq Z$, then

(a) $|XY|_m \leq |X|_m |Y|_m \leq Z\,|Y|_m$ (6)
(b) $|X+Y|_m \leq |X|_m + |Y|_m \leq Z + |Y|_m$ (7)
(c) $\rho(X) \leq \rho(|X|_m) \leq \rho(Z)$ (8a)
(d) $\rho(XY) \leq \rho(|X|_m|Y|_m) \leq \rho(Z\,|Y|_m)$ (8b)
(e) $\rho(X+Y) \leq \rho(|X+Y|_m) \leq \rho(|X|_m + |Y|_m) \leq \rho(Z + |Y|_m)$ (8c)

For the perturbed system (1), assume the pair $(E, \hat{A})$ is asymptotically stable and impulse free, one can expand $(sE - \hat{A})^{-1}$ as

$$(sE - \hat{A})^{-1} = \hat{G}_{sp}(s) + \hat{J} \tag{9}$$

where $\hat{G}_{sp}(s)$ is a strictly proper rational matrix which is analytic in right-half s-plane and $\hat{J}$ is a constant matrix. Denote by $\hat{G}(t)$ the impulse response of $\hat{G}_{sp}(s)$ and define

$$\hat{T} \equiv \int_0^\infty |\hat{G}(t)|_m\, dt \tag{10}$$

Lemma 3 : If the pair $(E, \hat{A})$ is asymptotically stable and impulse free, then

$$|(sE - \hat{A})^{-1}|_m \leq \hat{T} + |\hat{J}|_m, \quad for\ all\ Re(s) \geq 0 \tag{11}$$

Proof: Taking Laplace transform of $\hat{G}(t)$, we have

$$\hat{G}_{sp}(s) = \int_0^\infty \hat{G}(t)e^{-st}dt \tag{12}$$

By Lemma 2 and equation (9), it is easy to check

$$\begin{aligned} &|(sE - \hat{A})^{-1}|_m \\ &\leq |\hat{G}_{sp}(s)|_m + |\hat{J}|_m \quad for\ all\ Re(s) \geq 0 \\ &\leq \int_0^\infty |\hat{G}(t)e^{-st}|_m\, dt + |\hat{J}|_m \quad for\ all\ Re(s) \geq 0 \\ &\leq \int_0^\infty |\hat{G}(t)|_m\, dt + |\hat{J}|_m \quad for\ all\ Re(s) \geq 0 \\ &\leq \hat{T} + |\hat{J}|_m \end{aligned} \tag{13}$$

△△△

Let

$$A = \hat{A} - \alpha E \tag{14}$$

Lemma 4 : All finite eigenvalues of the pair (E, A) are located on the left of $-\alpha$ vertical line in complex plane if and only if The pair $(E, \hat{A})$ is asymptotically stable and impulse free.

Proof: This fact can be easily checked by

$$sE - A = \lambda E - \hat{A} \tag{15}$$

where

$$\lambda = s + \alpha \tag{16}$$

Theorem 1 : Assume the perturbation ΔA can be bounded by $| \Delta A |_m \leq kH$. The perturbed system (1) is impulse free and all its finite eigenvalues are located on the left of $-\alpha$ vertical line if all finite eigenvalues of the pair (E, A) lie on the left of $-\alpha$ vertical line and the following inequality

$$k < \frac{1}{\rho(\hat{T}H + | \hat{J} |_m H)} \tag{17}$$

is satisfied, where $\hat{T}$ is defined in equation (10) and $\hat{A}$ is constructed by equation (14).

Proof: By the determinant formula, we have

$$| sE - A - \Delta A | = | sE - A | \cdot | I - (sE - A)^{-1} \Delta A | \tag{18}$$

From Lemma 2, the following inequalities

$$\begin{aligned} &\rho((sE - A)^{-1} \Delta A) \\ &\leq \rho((sE - A)^{-1} kH) \quad for\ all\ Re(s) \geq -\alpha \\ &\leq \rho(| (sE - A)^{-1} |_m kH) \quad for\ all\ Re(s) \geq -\alpha \end{aligned} \tag{19}$$

are obvious since $| sE - A | = 0$ has no roots on the right of $-\alpha$ vertical line. From equation (13), (15), (19), and Lemma 2, we have

$$\begin{aligned} &\rho((sE - A)^{-1} \Delta A) \\ &\leq \rho(| \lambda E - \hat{A})^{-1} |_m kH) \quad for\ all\ Re(\lambda) \geq 0 \\ &\leq \rho(| \hat{T} |_m kH + | \hat{J} |_m kH) \quad for\ all\ Re(\lambda) \geq 0 \\ &\leq \rho(| \hat{T} |_m kH + | \hat{J} |_m kH) \quad for\ all\ Re(s) \geq -\alpha \end{aligned} \tag{20}$$

According to Lemma 3 and equation (18), we obtain $| sE - A - \Delta A | \neq 0$ for all $Re(s) \geq -\alpha$. That implies $| sE - A - \Delta A | \neq 0$ for all $Re(s) \geq -\alpha$.

The number of finite roots of $| sE - A - \Delta A | = 0$ could be determined by the degree of polynomial $| sE - A - \Delta A |$ or the degree of polynomial $| \lambda E - \hat{A} - \Delta A |$. By

$$| \lambda E - \hat{A} - \Delta A | = | \lambda E - \hat{A} || I - (\lambda E - \hat{A})^{-1} \Delta A | \tag{21}$$

it is not difficult to verify that the following identity

$$deg\ | \lambda E - \hat{A} - \Delta A | = deg(| \lambda E - \hat{A} || I - \hat{J} \Delta A |) \tag{22}$$

would hold if $I - \hat{J}$ is nonsingular. As long as inequality (17) is satisfied, we have $\rho(\hat{J}\Delta A) < 1$. This fact is from the following inequality

$$\rho(\hat{J}\Delta A) \leq \rho(k | \hat{J} |_m H) \leq \rho(k\hat{T}H + k | \hat{J} |_m H) \tag{23}$$

Therefore if inequality (17) holds, the number of roots of $| sE - A - \Delta A | = 0$ is equal to the number of roots of $| sE - A | = 0$. Furthermore, if inequality (17) is satisfied, equation (23) and (18) could guarantee the regularity of the perturbed system.

$\triangle\triangle\triangle$

3. Illustrative examples

Consider a continuous-time implicit system described as

$$\begin{bmatrix} 1 & 0 & 0 \\ 0 & 0 & 0 \\ 0 & 1 & 0 \end{bmatrix} \dot{x}(t) = \begin{bmatrix} 0 & 1 & 0 \\ 4 & 0 & -2 \\ -3 & -4 & 0 \end{bmatrix} x(t) + \Delta A x(t)$$

The pair (E, A) has finite eigenvalues at $\lambda_1 = -1$, $\lambda_2 = -3$. To check whether all finite eigenvalues lie on the left of -0.5 vertical line under perturbations, we obtain

$$\hat{T} = \begin{bmatrix} 2.8 & 0 & 0.8 \\ 2.4 & 0 & 0.8158 \\ 5.6 & 0 & 1.6 \end{bmatrix}, \quad \hat{J} = \begin{bmatrix} 0 & 0 & 0 \\ 0 & 0 & 0 \\ 0 & 0.5 & 0 \end{bmatrix}.$$

The following display the corresponding upper bound obtained by Theorem 1 for different structured perturbations:

$$if \quad H = \begin{bmatrix} 1 & 0 & 0 \\ 0 & 0 & 0 \\ 0 & 0 & 0 \end{bmatrix}, \quad \frac{1}{\rho(\hat{T}H + | \hat{J} |_m H)} = 0.3571;$$

$$if \quad H = \begin{bmatrix} 0 & 0 & 0 \\ 0 & 0 & 0 \\ 0 & 0 & 1 \end{bmatrix}, \quad \frac{1}{\rho(\hat{T}H + | \hat{J} |_m H)} = 2;$$

(in fact, the constant 2 is the exact upper bound,)

$$if \quad H = \begin{bmatrix} 1 & 1 & 0 \\ 1 & 1 & 0 \\ 0 & 0 & 0 \end{bmatrix}, \quad \frac{1}{\rho(\hat{T}H + | \hat{J} |_m H)} = 0.1923;$$

References

[1] D. J. Bender and A. J. Laub, "The linear-quadratic optimal regulator for descriptor systems," *IEEE Trans. Automat. Control*, vol 32, no 8, pp.672-687, 1987.

[2] B. S. Chen and C. C. Wong, "Robust linear controller design: time domain approach," *IEEE Trans. Automat. Control*, vol 32, pp.161-164, 1987.

[3] J. H. Chou, "Stability robustness of linear state space models with structured perturbations," *Systems & Control Letters*, vol 15, pp.207-210, 1990.

[4] J. D. Cobb, "Controllability observability, and duality in singular systems," *IEEE Trans. Automat. Control*, vol 29, pp.1076-1082, 1984.

[5] L. Dai, *Singular control systems - Lecture notes in control and information sciences*, Springer-Verlag, Berlin, 1989.

[6] C. H. Fang and F. R Chang, "Realization algorithm for constructing a controllable representation of a singular system with a special coordinate," *Int. J. Control*, vol 50, no 4, pp.1217-1226, 1989.

[7] C. H. Fang and F. R. Chang, "Deadbeat control in singular systems and its applications," *Control - Theory and Advanced Technology*, vol 6, no 3, pp.383-393, 1990.

[8] V. Kucera and P. Zagalak, "Fundamental theorems of state feedback for singular systems," *Automatica* vol 24, no 5, pp.653-658, 1988.

[9] F. L. Lewis, "A survey of linear singular systems," *J. Circuit, Syst., Signal Processing*, vol 5, no 1, pp.3-36, 1986.

[10] D. G. Luenberger, " Dynamic equations in descriptor form," *IEEE Trans. Automat. Control*, vol 22, pp. 312-321, 1977.

[11] J. M. Ortega, Numerical Analysis, Academic Press, New York, 1972.

[12] P. N. Paraskevopoulos and F. N. Koumboulis, "Decoupling and pole assignment in generalized state space systems," *IEE Pt.D*, vol 138, no 6, pp.547-560, 1991.

[13] A. Rachid, "Robustness of discrete systems under structured uncertainties," *Int. J. Control*, vol 50, pp.1563-1566, 1989.

[14] C. B. Soh, "Stability robustness measures of state-space models," *Int. J. System Sci.*, vol 22, no 10, pp.1867-1884, 1991.

[15] K. M. Sobel, S. S. Banda and H. H. Yeh, "Robust control for linear systems with structured state space uncertainty," *Int. J. Control*, vol 50, pp. 1991-2004, 1989.

[16] G. C. Verghese, B. C. Levy, and T. Kailath, "A generalized state-space for singular systems," *IEEE Trans Automat. Control*, vol 26, pp. 811-831, 1981.

[17] Y. Y. Wang, S. J. Shi, and Z. J. Zhang, "Pole placement and compensator design of generalized systems," *Systems & Control Letters* , vol 8, pp.205-209, 1987.

[18] R. K. Yedavalli, "Improved measures of stability robustness for linear state space models," *IEEE Trans. Automat. Control*, vol 30, pp.577-579, 1985.

Proceedings of the
American Control Conference
San Francisco, California • June 1993

ROBUST STABILITY RADII FOR PERTURBED DISCRETE-TIME CONSTRAINED SYSTEMS

Pin-Lin Liu
Department of Electrical Engineering,
Chien Kao Junior College of Technology,
Changhua 500, Taiwain, R. O. C.

Te-Jen Su
Department of Electronic Engineering,
National Kaohsiung Institute of Technology,
Kaohsiung, 807, Taiwain, R. O. C.

Abstract

This paper investigates the robust stability radius problem for perturbed discrete-time constrained systems. The main tool is so named stability radius of matrix in respect to the unit disk of the complex plane. The state feedback controller is designed to satisfy the requirement of stability under nonlinear saturation. An example is given to illustrate the application of our result.

1. Introduction

One practical approach to the problem of actuator saturation is the imposition of state and control limitations on the linear control. The problem of stabliity of a linear dynamic system with a saturating actuator has been consider by several researchers [2, 5 6]. A stabilizing saturated linear controller with constraints was developed by Gutman and Hagander [2] using a quadratic Lyapunov function to define a stability region. Pajunen and Erdol [5] proposed a time-varying stabilizing state space controller which allows the control to saturate. Su and Liu [6] have derived the stability conditions time-delay systems with actuator saturation. This paper investigates the stability criterion for perturbed discrete-time constrained systems by stability radius. The paper is organized as follows. In Sec. 2, the stability radius of the perturbed discrete-time systems is proposed. The problem formulation is presented in Sec. 3. The stability radius for the perturbed discrete-time constrained systems is summarized in Sec. 4. As an application, an example is illustrated in Sec. 5, and a conclusion is given in Sec. 6.

2. Stability radius of perturbed discrete-time systems

In this paper we choose a norm in complex space. This norm gives rise to matrix norm

$$\|A\| = \max_{\|x\|=1} [\, \|Ax\| \,] \tag{1}$$

Consider the following perturbed discrete-time system:

$$x(k+1)=(A+\Delta A)x(k), \tag{2}$$

where $x(k)$ is the n-dimensional state vector, A is an $n\times n$ time-invariant, nominally asymptotically stable matrix. ΔA is linear parametrical uncertainies with bound as $\|\Delta A\| \leq \alpha$. That is, the elements of the system matrix A are known exactly and all eigenvalues of A have magnitudes less than one. Let all eigenvalues of matrix A are inside the unit disk of the complex plane then positive value [3]

$$\rho(A)=\{\max_{0\leq\theta\leq 2\pi} [\, \|(e^{i\theta}I-A)^{-1}\| \,]\}^{-1}, \tag{3}$$

is said to be a complex stability radius of matrix A. The value $\rho(A)$ depends on the choice of the norm $\|x\|$, For example, if we use the induced Euclidean norm then show that [4]

$$\rho(A)=\min_{0\leq\theta\leq 2\pi} \{\sigma_{min}(e^{i\theta}I-A)\}, \tag{4}$$

where $\sigma_{min}(\gamma)$ is minimal singular value of matrix γ.

3. Problem formulation

Consider the following perturbed discrete-time system modelled with a saturating actuator as

$$x(k+1)=(A+\Delta A)x(k)+(B+\Delta B)\,sat((u(k)), \tag{5}$$

where $x(k)$ is the n-dimensional state vector, $sat(u(k))$ is the m-dimensional saturating control input to the plant, $u(k)$ is the m-dimensional control input to the actuator and A and B are the constant matrices of appropriate dimensions. ΔA, ΔB, are linear parametrical uncertainies with bound as $\|\Delta A\|\leq\alpha$, $\|\Delta B\|\leq\beta$, respectively. The operation rang of nonlinear saturation $sat(u_i(k))$ is considered inside the sector $[\, a_i, 1]$ which means that the graph of the nonlinearity lies between two straight lines passing through the origin with slopes a_i and 1, respectively, where $0\leq a_i\leq 1$ and $i=1, 2, \ldots m$. The saturating actuator $sat(u_i(k))$, where saturates at u_{iH} or u_{iL}, is defined as:

$$sat(u_i(k)) \begin{cases} u_{iH} & \text{if } 0<u_{iH}\leq u_i(k) \\ u_i(k) & \text{if } u_{iL}\leq u_i(k)\leq u_{iH} \\ u_{iL} & \text{if } u_i(k)\leq u_{iL}<0 \end{cases} \tag{6}$$

where the values of u_{iH} and u_{iL} are chosen to correspond to the actuator limitation; then following equation (7) is satisified [1]

$$\begin{aligned} &sat(u_i(k))-(1+a_i)u_i(k)/2 \\ &=(\Delta t_i(k)/2)u_i(k) \quad (i=1,2,\ldots m) \end{aligned} \tag{7}$$

where $\Delta t_i(k)$ is a real number which varies between $-(1-a_i)$ and $(1-a_i)$, i.e. $-(1-a_i)\leq\Delta t_i(k)\leq(1-a_i)$, then, we can obtain

$$sat(u(k))-[W/2]u(k)=(\Delta T/2)u(k) \tag{8}$$

where

$$sat(u(k))=[sat(u_1(k)),\ldots, sat(u_m(k))]^T,$$
$$W=diag[(1+a_1), (1+a_2),\ldots, (1+a_m)]$$

and $\Delta T(k)=diag[\Delta t_1(k),\ldots, \Delta t_m(k)]$ with the following property

$$|\Delta T(k)|_m\leq D, \tag{9}$$

where

$$D=diag[(1-a_1),\ldots, (1-a_m)]$$

without loss of generality, we assume (A, B) is controllable. In this paper, we pay attention to the following state feedback controller:

$$u(k)=-Fx(k), \tag{10}$$

where the state feedback matrix F has the appropriate dimension.

Then, the problem being treated here is to derive the stability condition under which the state feedback controller is a stabilizer, i.e. the state feedback controller makes the discrete-time saturating system to be asymptotically stable.

4. The stability rdaius for the perturbed discrete-time constrained systems

From (5), (8), and (10), we can obtain the resulting closed-loop discrete-time system as

$$x(k+1)=(A+\Delta A)x(k)+(BW/2)u(k)+(B+\Delta B)[sat(u(k))-Wu(k)/2]+(B+\Delta B)(Wu(k)/2)$$
$$=(A-BWF/2)x(k)+(\Delta A-\Delta BWF/2)x(k)-[(B+\Delta B)\Delta TF/2]x(k)$$
$$=A_Fx(k)+\Delta A_Fx(k)+\Delta B_Fx(k), \quad (11a)$$

where

$$A_F=A-(BWF)/2, \quad (11b)$$

and

$$\Delta A_F=\Delta A-(B\Delta TF)/2, \quad (11c)$$
$$\Delta B_F=-(B+\Delta B)\Delta TF/2. \quad (11d)$$

Then the problem becomes how to choose the state feedback gain F such that the resulting closed-loop discrete-time system (11a) is asymptotically stable.

Our result is summarized in the followinmg theorem to make the resulting closed-loop discrete-time system (11a) is asymptotically stable.

Lemma [2]

Let all eigenvalues of matrix A are inside the unit disk of the complex plane. All eigenvalues of all matrix $A+\Delta\tilde{A}$, where $\|\Delta\tilde{A}\|\leq\tilde{\alpha}$, are inside the unit disk if the value $\tilde{\alpha}<\rho(A)$.

Theorem

Let all eigenvalues of matrix A_F are inside the unit disk of the complex plane. All eigenvalues of all matrices $A_F+\Delta A_F+\Delta B_F$ are inside the unit disk if the value

$$\alpha+[\beta\Omega+\xi]/2<\rho(A_F). \quad (12)$$

where

$$\rho(A_F)=\min_{0\leq\theta\leq2\pi}[\sigma_{min}(e^{i\theta}I-A_F)],$$

$$\Omega=\|W\|+\|F\|,\quad \xi=(\|B\|\ \|D\|)\|F\|$$

Proof

$$\|\Delta A_F+\Delta B_F\|\leq\|\Delta A-\Delta BWF/2\|+\|-[(B+\Delta B)\Delta TF]/2\|$$
$$\leq\|\Delta A\|+[\|\Delta B\|\ \|W\|\ \|F\|+\|B+\Delta B\|\ \|\ |\Delta T|\ m\|\ \|F\|]/2$$
$$\leq\alpha+[\beta\|W\|\ \|F\|+(\|B\|+\beta)\|D\|\ \|F\|]/2$$
$$\leq\alpha+[\beta\Omega+\xi]/2$$
$$<\rho(A_F)$$

From lemma, the proof is completed. □

Remark

It showes that the larger the nonlinear saturation sector $[a_i,1]$ is the more conservative the stability condition (12) will be.

Algorithm

The following design algorithm can be used to select the control matrix F such that the resulting closed-loop discrete-time system (11a) is asymptotically stable.

step 1. By any pole-assignment method to design F, such that the matrix $A_F=A-BWF/2$ has the prescribed eigenvalues λ_i (i=1, 2,...,n) in the unit circle.

step 2. Check if the sufficient condition (12) is satisfied. If so, the design of state feedback controller for stabilizing a discrete-time saturating is obtained. If not, we shall set the eigenvalues closer to the center of the unit circle and then go to step 1.

5. Example

Consider the following perturbed discrete-time constrainted system:

$$x(k+1)=(A+\Delta A)x(k)+(B+\Delta B)sat((u(k))$$

where

$$A=\begin{bmatrix}0 & 1\\ -0.16 & -1\end{bmatrix},\quad B=\begin{bmatrix}1 & 0\\ 0 & 1\end{bmatrix},$$

$$\Delta A=\begin{bmatrix}[0.1\ \ -0.1] & 0\\ 0 & [0.1\ \ -0.1]\end{bmatrix},\quad \Delta B=\begin{bmatrix}[0.1\ \ -0.1] & 0\\ 0 & [0.1\ \ -0.1]\end{bmatrix}.$$

The nonlinear saturating characteristics belongs to the sector [1/2, 1], i.e. $a_1=a_2=1/2$.

Now, following the aforementioned design algorithm, if the eigenvalues of $A_F=A-(BWF)/2$ are assigned at $\lambda_1=0.049$ and $\lambda_2=-0.599$ by using u(k)=-Fx(k), where

$$F=\begin{bmatrix}-0.1 & 1\\ -0.12 & -0.5\end{bmatrix},$$

then we can obtain

$$\alpha+[\beta\Omega+\xi]/2=0.49151<\rho(A_F)=0.9236.$$

Thus, the stability condition (12) is satisfied. The state feedback controller is a stabilizer and the closed-loop discrete-time system with actuator saturation in (5) and (10) is asymptotically stable.

6. Conclusion

The sufficient robust stability condition is developed for perturbed discrete-time constrained systems. The stability radius is employed to treat this problem. A proposed state feedback control design algorithm can be used to select the control gain such that the perturbed discrete-time saturating system is asymptotically stable. Example shows that the method can easily be applied to the stability of the linear uncrtain discrete-time systems with actuator saturation.

References

[01] J. H. Chou, "Stabilization of linear discrete-time systems with actuator saturation," Systems & Control Letters 17 pp. 141-144, 1991.

[02] P.D. Gutman and P. Hagander, "A new dsign of constrained controllers for nonlinear systems," IEEE Trans. Automat. Control 30 pp. 22-33, 1985.

[03] D. Hinrichsen and A. J. Pritchard, "New robustness results for linear system under real perturbations," in Proc. 27th IEEE CDC, Austin, Texas, pp. 1375-1379, 1988.

[04] V. L. Kharitonov, "Stability radii and global stability of difference systems," in Proceeding 30th IEEE Conference on Decision and Control, Brighton, England, pp. 877-880, 1991.

[05] G.A. Pajunen and N. Erdol, "Time-varying saturating feedback control of linear systems under state and control constraints," in Proceeding 29th IEEE Conference on Decision and Control, Honolulu, Hawaii, pp. 3644-3645, 1990.

[06] T.J. Su, P.L. Liu, and J.T. Tsay, "Stabilization of delay-dependence for saturating actuator systems," in Proceeding 30th IEEE Conference on Decision and Control, Brighton, England, pp. 2891-2892, 1991.

Proceedings of the
American Control Conference
San Francisco, California • June 1993

Using Persistent Excitation with Fixed Energy to Stabilize Adaptive Controllers and Obtain Hard Bounds for the Parameter Estimation Error

Miloje S. Radenkovic
Department of Electrical Engineering
University of Colorado at Denver
Denver Colorado 80204.

B. Erik Ydstie
Department of Chemical Engineering
Carnegie Mellon University
Pittsburgh PA 15213.

Abstract.
We show that persistent excitation with fixed and finite energy can be used as a tool to stabilize adaptive control algorithms and obtain hard bounds for the parameter estimation errors. Two important instability problems in certainty equivalence adaptive control are solved by applying excitation. The first instability is parameter drift due to an unstable manifold which appears when the excitation level is not high enough. This problem has previously been studied using averaging and local analysis. Our results are global. The second instability is numerical, and due to a division with zero in the adaptive law. In the paper we show that the system parameters are estimated when the level of excitation is sufficiently high relative to the magnitudes of the external disturbances and the unmodelled dynamics. It follows that the singularity problem only can occur during the transient. The consequence of this is that we can implement a direct adaptive controller without requiring knowledge of the sign of the high frequency gain. The approach can be generalized to more complex adaptive laws and this, together with the fact that we obtain hard bounds for the parameter estimation error opens up for the possibility of designing robust controllers that are adaptive.

1 Introduction

In this paper we present the global stability analysis of a direct adaptive control system for which a persistent excitation condition is satisfied. By *global* we mean that the results are valid for all initial conditions. In this way the analysis complement the averaging methods which are initial condition dependent. Averaging, of course has been applied for the *local* analysis of adaptive systems with considerable success and sufficient as well as necessary conditions for stability of integral manifolds have been obtained by exploiting hyperbolicity [1], [10], [13].

It was early recognized that the parameter estimates in certainty equivalent adaptive control may drift, become unbounded or cross through regions where the control law calculation is ill-conditioned. The reason for this rather dissapointing behaviour is that the adaptive controller does not destabilize in such a way that excitation is generated. In the ideal case the parameters cannot diverge [3]. However, self stabilization of the estimator does not take place and in the non-ideal case small amplitude chaotic bursts as well as large transients and numerical instabilities may be observed [2], [14]. Numerous modifications to the certainty equivalence approach to adaptive control have been proposed to overcome these problems. For example, it has been shown that some of the problems can be solved by using artificial parameter bounding. In the case of leakage [4] and parameter projection [5] the parameters are constrained to belong to compact sets and additional measures are taken to ensure that the control law calculations are well behaved. Unfortunately, while boundedness of the input output signals can be established, these methods do not ensure that the parameter estimator is stabilized and large bursts are possible.

An alternative, and more direct method to solve the drift and singularity problems is to make sure that the estimator equations remain stable. It has been shown, using averaging analysis that a sufficient and necessary condition for such stabilization to take place is that the regression vector is persistently excited [13]. Since excitation is not automatically generated within the adaptive loop, the only possibility that remains is to generate the excitation externally. In this paper we do this by manipulating the reference signal using fixed and finite energy over a range of selected frequencies. Once excitation is generated this not only leads to stabilization of the adaptive loop, it also leads to good conditions for the estimator. The parameter drift is arrested and small parameter errors can be guaranteed. Reasonable system conditions can then be imposed to ensure that singularity problems in the solution of the Bezout identities do not arise and methods can be developed to start and stop the estimator. Thus we do not only solve the problem of adaptive stabilization; we also solve the problem of identifying parameters in an uncertain environment. The latter problem has attracked considerable attention in the recent literature. See for example the recent IEEE T-AC special issue on identification. However, we believe that results developed in this paper are among the first that can be applied for the identification of an open loop unstable plant.

We analyze a simple one step-step ahead predictive controller with gradient estimator. Two types of data normalization are used in the analysis. In one instance we use the exponentially weighted normalization [9] to show robustness of adaptive control with respect to unmodelled dynamics and bounded noise. This approach requires knowledge of an upper bound for the largest time constant for the closed loop system with an ideal controller. In order to relax this assumption we also analyse a second type of normalization sequence which does not require this type of a priori information. The idea here is to use the largest regressor up to time t to normalize the signals.

The results of the paper can be generalized to continuous time. Thus the projection used in [7] can be replaced with finite energy excitation of the reference.

2 Notation and Terminology

For a function $x : T \to R^+$, we define the following semi-norm

$$\|x(t)\|_\lambda = \left\{ \sum_{j=1}^{t} \lambda^{t-j} x(j)^2 \right\}^{1/2}, \qquad 0 < \lambda < 1$$

Here T is the set of positive integers while R^+ is the set of non-negative real numbers. When $\|x(t)\|_\lambda$ is bounded for all $t \geq 0$, x is said to be in l_2^λ.

H_∞ will denote the space of transfer functions $T(z)$, which are analytic and bounded outside and on the unit circle in the z plane. S^λ is the operator defined by

$$S^\lambda T(z) = T(\lambda^{1/2} z)$$

H_∞^λ is the space of transfer functions $T(z)$ such that $S^\lambda T(z) \in H_\infty$. In other words, $T(z) \in H_\infty^\lambda$, if $T(z)$ is analytic and bounded outside and on the circle $|z| = \lambda^{1/2}$ in the z-plane. For $T(z) \in H_\infty$, the H_∞ norm is defined by

$$\|T(z)\|_\infty = \max_{|z|=1} |T(z)|$$

Likewise, the norm of the H_∞^λ space is defined by

$$\|T(z)\|_\infty^\lambda = \|S^\lambda T(z)\|_\infty = \max_{|z|=1} |T(\lambda^{1/2} z)|$$

This norm is induced by the l_2^λ norm of the input and output signals of $T(z)$.

When performing majorizations in order to account for initial conditions, we use non-negative functions

$$\xi_i(t) = c_i \beta_i^t, \qquad 0 \leq c_i < \infty, \qquad 0 < \beta_i < 1$$

When confusion cannot arise we drop the subscripts.

3 Deterministic Adaptive Control and Major Assumptions

Let us consider the following discrete time SISO system with unmodelled dynamics

$$A(q^{-1})y(t+1) = B(q^{-1})[1+\Delta_1(q^{-1})]u(t) + A(q^{-1})\Delta_2(q^{-1})u(t) + w(t+1) \tag{1}$$

where $\{y(t)\}, \{u(t)\}$ and $\{w(t)\}$ are output, input and disturbance sequences, respectively, while q^{-1} represents the unit delay operator. The polynomials $A(q^{-1})$ and $B(q^{-1})$ describe the nominal system model, may be taken as being "centered" [15] and can be written as

$$A(q^{-1}) = 1 + a_1 q^{-1} + \ldots + a_{n_A} q^{-n_A}$$

$$B(q^{-1}) = b_0 + \ldots + b_{n_B} q^{-n_B}, \text{ with } b_0 \neq 0$$

In equation (1), $\Delta_i(q^{-1})$ for $i = 1, 2$, denote multiplicative and additive system perturbations. The transfer functions $\Delta_i(q^{-1})$ for $i = 1, 2$ are causal and $\Delta_1(q^{-1})$ is stable.

The aim is to simultanously stabilize the input-output behaviour of the system (1) and estimate the parameters of the nominal model to a given precision. This is the problem of identification of open loop unstable systems.

The nominal model is assumed to be stably invertible, the model mismatch small, the external perturbations bounded and the reference signal excited with sufficient energy in a selected range of frequencies. In order to develop the theory we will apply direct adaptive control to minimize the criterion

$$J = [y(t) - y^*(t)]^2$$

where $y^*(t)$ is the given reference signal.

To define the adaptive law it is convenient to write system (1) in the form

$$y(t+1) = \theta_0'\phi(t) + \gamma(t) \tag{2}$$

where

$$\theta_0' = (-a_1, -a_2, ..., -a_{n_A}, b_0, b_1, ..., b_{n_B})$$

is the vector of parameters that need to be estimated,

$$\phi(t)' = (y(t), y(t-1), ..., y(t-n_A+1), u(t), u(t-1), ..., u(t-n_B))$$

is the regression vector, and finally, the modelling error is defined so that

$$\gamma(t) = \Delta_0(q^{-1})u(t) + w(t+1) \tag{3}$$

with

$$\Delta_0(q^{-1}) = B(q^{-1})\Delta_1(q^{-1}) + A(q^{-1})\Delta_2(q^{-1})$$

From equation (2) it is obvious that when $\gamma(t) = 0$, the contol law

$$\text{Solve for} \quad u(t): \quad \theta_0'\phi(t) - y^*(t+1) = 0 \tag{4}$$

is optimal. Internal stability is ensured by the stable invertibility of $B(q^{-1})$.

In certainty equivalent adaptive control the parameter vector θ_0 is replaced by an estimate

$$\theta(t)' = (-\hat{a}_1(t), -\hat{a}_2(t), ..., -\hat{a}_{n_A}(t), \hat{b}_0(t), \hat{b}_1(t), ..., \hat{b}_{n_B}(t))$$

The following algorithm is used for estimating the unknown parameter θ_0.

$$\theta(t+1) = \theta(t) + \frac{\mu}{r(t)}\phi(t)e(t) \tag{5}$$

where

$$e(t) = y(t) - y^*(t) \tag{6}$$

is the tracking error. The algorithm gain sequence may be given by

$$r(t) = r_0 + n_\phi(t)^2, \text{ with } 0 < r_0 < \infty$$

and

$$n_\phi(t)^2 = \lambda n_\phi(t-1)^2 + \|\phi(t)\|^2 \tag{7}$$

where λ is a tunable parameter chosen so that $0 < \lambda < 1$. Note that this gain sequence is similar to the one proposed in [9]. In [15] the gain sequence is defined with $\lambda = 0$ so that

$$r(t) = r_0 + \|\phi(t)\|^2$$

In the current paper we also analyse an algorithm with gain sequence chosen so that

$$r(t) = r_0 + \max_{1 \le \tau \le t} \|\phi(\tau)\|^2 \tag{8}$$

This normalization sequence does not involve the parameter λ as is the case with n_ϕ defined by equation (7). On the other hand, $r(t)$ defined by equation (8) satisfies the same property as the sequence given by (7), namely $r(t) \ge \lambda r(t-1)$. As a consequence of this we should expect that the two algorithms behave in a similar fashion as long as $\phi(t)$ remains uniformly bounded. The main results concerning normalization sequence (7) are given in Theorem 5.1. The results concerning normalization sequence (8) are given in Theorem 5.2. The analysis for the normalization sequence (7) with $\lambda = 0$ can be carried out using the approach developed in [15] for the discrete time case and in [7] for the continuous time case.

Equation (4) is ill-defined when the estimate of b_0 is equal to zero and measures need to be taken to prevent large transients and instability of the algorithm. One approach, which is the one we follow here, is to depart from certainty equivalence on the event $A(t) = I_{\{|\hat{b}_0(t)| < \epsilon_1\}}$, where $I_{\{.\}}$ is the indicator function and ϵ_1 is specified below, and implement the law

$$\text{Solve for} \quad u(t): \quad \theta_c(t)'\phi(t) - y^*(t+1) = 0 \tag{9}$$

with

$$\theta_c(t)' = (-\hat{a}_1(t), -\hat{a}_2(t), ..., -\hat{a}_{n_A}(t), \epsilon(t)+\hat{b}_0(t), \hat{b}_1(t), ..., \hat{b}_{n_B}(t)) \tag{10}$$

Here

$$\epsilon(t) = \begin{cases} 0, & \text{if } |\hat{b}_0(t)| \ge \epsilon_1 > 0 \\ \epsilon_1 \text{sign}(\hat{b}_0(t)), & \text{if } |\hat{b}_0(t)| < \epsilon_1 \end{cases}$$

The sign function is defined so that $\text{sign}(x) = 1$ if $x \ge 0$ and $\text{sign}(x) = -1$ otherwise.

We show that due to the application of excitation

$$\sum_{t=1}^{\infty} A(t) < \infty$$

Other approaches to this problem include parameter projection [5] and algorithm switching [6].

Assumption A1: *(Concerning the reference signal and the disturbances)* There exist constants k_w and k_{y^*} so that for all $t \ge 1$:

$$|w(t)| \le k_w \quad \text{and} \quad |y^*(t)| \le k_{y^*}$$

In order to motivate the second assumption we develop closed loop expressions for the adaptive system. From equations (2) and (9) it follows that

$$e(t+1) = -z(t) + \gamma(t) \tag{11}$$

where

$$z(t) = \tilde{\theta}_c'(t)\phi(t) \tag{12}$$

and the control parameter error satisfies

$$\tilde{\theta}_c(t) = \theta_c(t) - \theta_0$$

From equations (9) and (12) we obtain

$$B(q^{-1})u(t) + q(1 - A(q^{-1}))y(t) = y^*(t+1) - z(t)$$

Combining this with equations (6) and (11) gives

$$B(q^{-1})u(t) = A(q^{-1})(-z(t) + y^*(t+1)) + (A(q^{-1}) - 1)\gamma(t) \tag{13}$$

Substituting this into equation (3) gives the closed loop

$$\gamma(t) = -\frac{\Delta_0(q^{-1})A(q^{-1})}{B(q^{-1}) - \Delta_0(q^{-1})(A(q^{-1}) - 1)}(z(t) - y^*(t+1)) + \tag{14}$$

$$+\frac{B(q^{-1})}{B(q^{-1}) - \Delta_0(q^{-1})(A(q^{-1}) - 1)}w(t+1)$$

The transfer function from the reference signal to the model error $\gamma(t)$ plays a signficant role in the stability analysis. It is assumed to be stable and have small gain. In order to discuss this assumption and perform the analysis define the following H_∞ norms:

$$C_{AB} = \left\|\frac{A(z)}{B(z)}\right\|_\infty^\lambda, \quad C_A = \left\|\frac{A(z) - 1}{B(z)}\right\|_\infty^\lambda$$

$$C_\gamma = \left\|\frac{\Delta_0(z)A(z)}{B(z) - \Delta_0(z)(A(z) - 1)}\right\|_\infty^\lambda$$

$$C_w = \left\|\frac{B(z)}{B(z) - \Delta_0(z)(A(z) - 1)}\right\|_\infty^\lambda$$

Assumption A2: *(Concerning the nominal system and unmodelled dynamics)*

1. There exists a positive number $\lambda_0 < 1$ so that the zeros of $B(z^{-1})$ and the poles of the transfer functions

$$H_0(z^{-1}) = \frac{\Delta_0(z^{-1})A(z^{-1})}{B(z^{-1}) - \Delta_0(z^{-1})(A(z^{-1}) - 1)}$$

and

$$H_1(z^{-1}) = \frac{B(z^{-1})}{B(z^{-1}) - \Delta_0(z^{-1})(A(z^{-1}) - 1)}$$

are inside a circle with radius λ_0.

2. The transfer function $H_0(q^{-1})$ has small gain in the sense that the inequality

$$\rho_1(\epsilon_1) = 1 - \frac{\mu}{2} - (1-\mu)C_\gamma - \frac{\mu}{2}C_\gamma^2 - \epsilon_1 C_u(1+C_\gamma) > 0$$

with

$$C_u = C_{AB} + C_A C_\gamma$$

is satisfied.

It is well known that the adaptive control algorithm described above is not stable. The problem is due to the presence of an unstable manifold along which the parameter estimates may drift to infinity. The problem can be avoided by applying parameter projection or leakage. However, these methods may give large transients and unrelented bursting, unless the region into which the parameters are projected is small or the leakage center is defined close to the optimal parameter values. An alternative method, which we explore here is to supply additional excitation. This approach has been shown to work well locally, and using averaging theory necessary and sufficient conditions for stability of integral manifolds have been established. The purpose of our analysis is to extend these results to be valid globally. In order to do this we introduce the following assumption about the level of excitation.

Define

$$\phi^*(t)' =$$

$$(y^*(t), ..., y^*((t-n_A+1), \frac{A(q^{-1})}{B(q^{-1})}y^*(t+1), ..., \frac{A(q^{-1})}{B(q^{-1})}y^*(t-n_B+1)) \quad (15)$$

Assumption A3: *(Persistent excitation)* For all sufficiently large N

$$\sum_{t=1}^{N} \lambda^{N-t}\phi^*(t)\phi^*(t)' \geq \delta_1^* I$$

where, for some δ_2^*

$$\frac{\delta_1^*}{2} - \left(n_1\Sigma_\gamma(\epsilon_1) + n_2\left[C_\gamma\Sigma_\gamma(\epsilon_1) + (C_\gamma k_{y^*} + (1+C_w)k_w)\frac{1}{(1-\lambda)^{1/2}}\right]\right)$$

$$= \delta_2^* > 0 \quad (16)$$

with

$$\Sigma_\gamma(\epsilon_1)^2 = \max\left\{\frac{16}{\rho_1(\epsilon_1)^2}[(1-\mu+\mu C_\gamma+\epsilon_1 C_u)\Sigma_1 + \epsilon_1(1+C_\gamma)\Sigma_2]^2;\right.$$

$$\left.\frac{\mu\Sigma_1}{\rho_1(\epsilon_1)}(\Sigma_1 + 2\epsilon_1\Sigma_2)\right\} \quad (17)$$

with

$$\Sigma_1 = \frac{k_{y^*}C_\gamma + k_w C_w}{(1-\lambda)^{1/2}} \text{ and } \Sigma_2 = \frac{k_{y^*}C_u + k_w C_A C_w}{(1-\lambda)^{1/2}}$$

The constants n_1 and n_2 are defined so that

$$n_1 = \left(\sum_{i=1}^{n_A}\lambda^{-i} + C_{AB}^2\sum_{i=1}^{n_B}\lambda^{-i}\right)^{1/2} \text{ and } n_2 = \left(\sum_{i=1}^{n_A}\lambda^{-i} + C_A^2\sum_{i=1}^{n_B}\lambda^{-i}\right)^{1/2}$$

Comments:

1. Assumption (A1) simply states that the reference and the disturbances should be uniformly bounded.

2. It is not difficult to see that Assumption (A2) can be written

$$(1-C_\gamma)\left(\left(1-\frac{\mu}{2}(1-C_\gamma)\right) - \epsilon_1 C_u\right) > 0$$

This relation is satisfied if

$$C_\gamma < 1 \quad (18)$$

and

$$1 - \frac{\mu}{2} + \frac{\mu}{2}C_\gamma - \epsilon_1 C_{AB} - \epsilon_1 C_A C_\gamma > 0 \quad (19)$$

Relationship (19) will be satisfied if ϵ_1 is selected so that

$$\epsilon_1 < \max\left\{(1-\frac{\mu}{2})\frac{1}{C_{AB}}; \frac{\mu}{2C_A}\right\} \quad (20)$$

and the admissible unmodelled dynamics is then specified by inequality (18).

3. Assumption (A3) is more complicated and essentially means the following: The intensities of the unmodelled dynamics C_γ, the external disturbances and the design parameter ϵ_1 should be small compared with the level of excitation. Moreover, $y^*(t)$ should have a spectral distribution function which is non-zero at $n_A + n_B + 1$ points (or more) and the transfer function of the nominal system model $B(z)/A(z)$ should be irreducible. This condition is not stronger than similar conditions introduced in deterministic adaptive control and coincides with those obtained from the application of the averaging analysis.

4. Since we do not know the magnitude of the disturbances, the intensity of the unmodelled dynamics and H_∞-norms C_{AB} and C_A, we cannot select ϵ_1 so that relationship (20) holds. The immediate consequence of this is that it is difficult to choose the right level of excitation and we are still some way off from the target of having a completely adaptive control algorithm. In the following we assume that ϵ_1 and the level of excitation is chosen so that this relationship holds true.

Constants, whose values are unimportant and do not depend on C_γ and C_w will be denoted by $C_i, i = 1, 2, \ldots$ Constants, whose values are unimportant, but depend on C_γ and C_w will be denoted by $\bar{C}_i, i = 1, 2, \ldots$

4 Technical Results

The following three results are usefull for future reference. Proofs of these results can be found in [12]. Lemma 4.1 simply states that all signals are bounded by the l_2^λ norm of the error signal $z(t)$, plus constants. Lemma 4.2 states that when the l_2^λ norm of $z(t)$ is small, then the signal vector $\phi(t)$ is persistently exciting. Finally, Lemma 4.3 states that under similar conditions the parameter error vector is small.

Lemma 4.1: Let Assumptions (A1) and (A2) hold. Then

1. $\|\gamma(t)\|_\lambda \leq C_\gamma\|z(t)\|_\lambda + h_1(t)$ where

$$h_1(t) = \frac{C_\gamma k_{y^*} + C_w k_w}{(1-\lambda)^{1/2}} + \xi_1(t)$$

2. $\|u(t)\|_\lambda \leq C_u\|z(t)\|_\lambda + h_2(t)$ with

$$h_2(t) = \frac{C_u k_{y^*} + C_A C_w k_w}{(1-\lambda)^{1/2}} + \xi_2(t)$$

3. $\|\phi(t)\|_\lambda \leq C_{\phi_1}\|z(t)\|_\lambda + h_3(t)$ where

$$h_3(t) = \frac{C_{\phi_1}k_{y^*} + C_{\phi_2}k_w}{(1-\lambda)^{1/2}} + \xi_3(t)$$

$$C_{\phi_1} = C_1(\lambda^{-1/2}(1+C_\gamma) + C_u), \text{ and } C_{\phi_2} = C_1 C_w(\lambda^{-1} + C_A)$$

$$C_1 = \left(\sum_{i=0}^{\max\{n_A, n_B+1\}}\lambda^{-i}\right)^{1/2}$$

4. If there exists finite t_0 so that for all $t \geq t_0$, $\|\theta_c(t)\| \leq f_\theta < \infty$ then

$$r(t) \leq \max\{C_\theta\|z(t-1)\|_\lambda^2, k_\theta + \xi_4(t)\}$$

with

$$C_\theta = 4\left(C_1\left(1+\frac{f_\theta C_1}{\epsilon_1}\right)(1+C_\gamma+C_u)\right)^2$$

and

$$k_\theta = 4\left(r_0^{1/2} + C_1\left(1+\frac{f_\theta C_1}{\epsilon_1}\right)\right)^2$$

$$\times\left(\left(\frac{(1+C_\gamma+C_u)k_{y^*} + C_w(1+C_A)k_w}{(1-\lambda)^{1/2}}\right)\left(1+\frac{k_{y^*}C_1}{\epsilon_1}\right)\right)^2$$

Proof: See [12].

By using equations (6), (11), (12) and (13), the measurement vector can be written in the from

$$\phi(t) = \phi^*(t) + \phi_w(t) + \phi_z(t) + \phi_\gamma(t) \quad (21)$$

where

$$\phi^*(t)' = (y^*(t), ..., \frac{A(q^{-1})}{B(q^{-1})} y^*(t+1), ...)$$

$$\phi_w(t)' = (w(t), ..., \frac{A(q^{-1})-1}{B(q^{-1})} w(t+1), ...)$$

$$\phi_z(t)' = (-z(t-1), ..., -\frac{A(q^{-1})}{B(q^{-1})} z(t), ...)$$

$$\phi_\gamma(t)' = (\gamma(t-1), ..., \frac{A(q^{-1})-1}{B(q^{-1})} \gamma(t), ...),$$

while $\phi^*(t)$ of course, is assumed to be persistently excited.
We are now ready to establish the following.

Lemma 4.2: Let Assumptions (A1)-(A3) hold. Then, for N_p sufficiently large on every subsequence $\{N_p\}$, where

$$\|z(N_p)\|_\lambda^2 \leq \Sigma_\gamma(\epsilon_1)^2 + \xi_5(N_p)$$

the following holds

$$\lambda_{\min}\left\{\sum_{t=1}^{N_p} \lambda^{N_p-t}\phi(t)\phi(t)'\right\} \geq \delta_2^* - \rho_0 > 0, 0 < \rho_0 << \delta_2^*$$

Here $\lambda_{\min}(\cdot)$ denotes the minimal eigenvalue of the corresponding matrix.

Proof: See [12].

We now have the following critical result.

Lemma 4.3: Let Assumptions (A1)-(A3) hold. Then on the subsequence $\{N_p\}$ where

$$\|z(N_p)\|_\lambda^2 \leq \Sigma_\gamma(\epsilon_1)^2 + \xi_6(N_p) \quad (22)$$

we have

$$\|\theta(N_p+1) - \theta_0\|^2 \leq d_0(\epsilon_1) + \xi_7(N_p)$$

where

$$d_0(\epsilon_1) = \frac{C_\phi^2}{(\delta_2^* - \rho_0)^2} \times$$
$$\times \left[\Sigma_\gamma(\epsilon_1)(1 + \mu(1 + C_\gamma) + \epsilon_1 C_u) + \right.$$
$$\left. + \frac{k_{y^*}(C_\gamma + C_u\epsilon_1) + C_w k_w(1 + \epsilon_1 C_A)}{(1+\lambda)^{1/2}}\right]^2 \quad (23)$$

with

$$C_\phi = C_{\phi 1}\Sigma_\gamma(\epsilon_1) + \frac{C_{\phi 1}k_{y^*} + C_{\phi 2}k_w}{(1-\lambda)^{1/2}} \quad (24)$$

Proof: See [12].

Comments: $\Sigma_\gamma(\epsilon_1)$ is small when C_γ and k_w are small. It follows that during the intervals where $\|z(t)\|_\lambda$ is of the order of $\Sigma_\gamma(\epsilon_1)$, excitation provided by the reference signal neutralizes the effect of the unmodelled dynamics and the external disturbances and prevents the parameter drift that otherwise causes instability of the estimator and the eventual destabilization of the loop. An exact statement of this property is given in Lemma 4.2.
The remaining question to answer is: "What happens when $\|z(t)\|_\lambda$ is not small?"

5 Main Results and Mathematical Formalization of Self Stabilization

Below we give the stability result for parameter estimation and direct adaptive control with persistent excitation.

Theorem 5.1: Let Assumptions (A1-A3) introduced in Section 3 hold and assume that the estimator is implemented with gain sequence (7) with $\lambda_0 \leq \lambda < 1$. Then there exist non-negative constants $\delta_1^*, C_\gamma, k_w$ and ϵ_1 so that

1.

$$\limsup_{t\to\infty} \|\theta(t) - \theta_0\|^2 \leq d_0(0) \text{ and } \quad \limsup_{t\to\infty} \|\theta_c(t) - \theta(t)\|^2 = 0$$

where $d(0)$ is given by equation (23) with $\epsilon_1 = 0$.

2.

$$\limsup_{t\to\infty} \sum_{j=1}^{t} \lambda^{t-j}|y(j+1) - y^*(j+1)|^2 \leq ((1+C_\gamma)\Sigma_D + \Sigma_1)^2$$

where Σ_1 is defined in Assumption A3 and

$$\Sigma_D^2 = \max\left\{\Sigma_\gamma(0)^2, \left[\frac{\lambda}{(1+d_0(0))C_\theta} + \frac{1}{\mu\rho_1(0)}\right] d_0(0)k_\theta\right\}$$
$$\times \exp\left(\frac{(1+d_0(0)C_\theta}{\lambda\mu\rho_1(0)}\right)$$

where $\Sigma_\gamma(0)^2$ is given by Assumption A2, $d_0(0)$ is given by equation (23) and $\rho_1(0)$ is given by Assumption A2 with $\epsilon_1 = 0$.

3.

$$\limsup_{t\to\infty} \|\phi(t)\|_\lambda \leq C_{\phi 1}\Sigma_D + \frac{C_{\phi 1}k_{y^*} + C_{\phi 2}k_w}{(1-\lambda)^{1/2}}$$

where $C_{\phi i}, i = 1, 2$ are defined under Statement 3 in Lemma 4.1.

Proof: We first determine a difference inequality which describes the behaviour of the parameter estimation error. From the estimation algorithm (5) we obtain

$$V(t+1) \leq V(t) + 2\frac{\mu}{r(t)}\tilde{\theta}(t)'\phi(t)e(t+1) + \frac{\mu^2}{r(t)}e(t+1)^2 \quad (25)$$

where $V(t) = \|\tilde{\theta}(t)\|^2$. From (11), the definition of the normalizing sequence and the above we then derive

$$V(t+1) \leq V(t) - 2\mu(1 - \frac{\mu}{2})\frac{z(t)^2}{r(t)} +$$

$$\frac{1}{r(t)}[2\mu(1-\mu)|z(t)\gamma(t)| + \mu^2\gamma(t)^2 + 2\mu|\epsilon(t)u(t)| \cdot |z(t) + \gamma(t)|] \quad (26)$$

We now show how global stability of the adaptive algorithm can be demonstrated by considering the following comparison function [11]

$$S(t+1) = V(t+1) + \frac{W(t+1)}{r(t)} \quad (27)$$

where

$$W(t+1) =$$

$$\mu\sum_{j=1}^{t} \lambda^{t-j}\left[\left(1 - \frac{\mu}{2} + (1-\mu)C_\gamma + \frac{\mu}{2}C_\gamma^2 + \epsilon_1 C_u(1+C_\gamma)\right) z(j)^2 - \right.$$

$$\left. -2(1-\mu)|z(j)\gamma(j)| - \mu\gamma(j)^2 - 2|\epsilon(t)u(t)| \cdot |z(t) + \gamma(t)|\right] \quad (28)$$

It will become clear in the analysis which follows that stability of the sequence $z(t)$ follows trivially whenever $W(t) \leq 0$. However, during these intervals the function $S(t)$ may increase, thus giving rise to bursting of the sequence $z(t)$. As a consequence of this, the function $W(t)$ becomes positive, forcing $S(t)$ to converge thus stabilizing $z(t)$. This mechanism does not rely on the use of external excitation, instead it is required that the parameters remain bounded and that singularities are avoided in order to prevent finite escape and ensure bounded growth of signals.
We now define sub-sequences τ_k and $\sigma_k, k \geq 1$ as follows

$$1 = \tau_1 < \sigma_1 < \tau_2 < \sigma_2 < ...\tau_k < \sigma_k < \tau_{k+1} < ...$$

so that

$$W(t+1) \leq 0 \text{ for } t \in Q_k, \quad \text{and } W(t+1) > 0 \text{ for } t \in T_k$$

with the intervals T_k and Q_k defined so that

$$Q_k = [\tau_k, \sigma_k), \quad T_k = [\sigma_k, \tau_{k+1}), \quad k \geq 1.$$

If $W(2) > 0$ set $\tau_1 = 0, \sigma_1 = 1$ and Q_k is defined for $k \geq 2$
If $W(t+1) > 0$ for all $t \geq 1$ define $\sigma_1 = 1$ and $\tau_2 = +\infty$
If $W(t+1) \leq 0$ for all $t \geq 1$ set $\tau_1 = 1$ and $\sigma_1 = +\infty$.

The proof is handled by considering three possible cases:

Case 1: For all finite k, we have $\tau_k < \infty$ and $\sigma_k < \infty$

Case 2: There exists a finite $k_0 \geq 0$, such that $\tau_{k_0} < \infty$ and $\sigma_{k_0} = +\infty$.

Case 3: There exists a finite $k_1 \geq 1$ so that $\sigma_{k_1} < \infty$ and $\tau_{k_1+1} = \infty$

In the first case $W(t+1)$ changes sign infinitely often. The main idea in analyzing this case is the following: During the time intervals Q_k the function $W(t+1)$ is non-positive and stability of the adaptive system follows directly from the definition of $W(t+1)$. During the intervals when $W(t+1) > 0$ the function $S(t)$ is non-increasing or strictly decreasing. It follows that such intervals only have a finite duration since $V(t)$ is non-negative. This is essentially the argument used in [15] to show that the normalization $r(t)$ can be replaced by $\|\phi(t)\|^2$. A similar development can be used here, however, in order to simplify the analysis we treat the case where the normalizing signal $r(t)$ is defined by equation (7) here and (8) under the heading of Theorem 5.2.

The two last cases are trivial since the sign of $W(t+1)$ eventually does not change. The complete details are given in [12].

We now give the main results for normalization sequence (8)

Theorem 5.2 Let assumptions A1-A3 hold and assume that the algorithm gain sequence is updated using equation (8). Then there exists $\delta_1^*, C_\gamma, k_w$ and ϵ_1 so that

1.

$$\limsup_{t\to\infty} \|\theta(t) - \theta_0\|^2 \leq d_0(0) \text{ and } \qquad \limsup_{t\to\infty} \|\theta_c(t) - \theta(t)\|^2 = 0$$

where $d(0)$ is given by equation (23) with $\epsilon_1 = 0$.

2.

$$\limsup_{t\to\infty} |y(t+1) - y^*(t+1)|^2 \leq$$

$$\left(\left(1 + \frac{C_\gamma}{(1-\lambda)^{1/2}}\right)\Sigma_{D1} + \frac{C_\gamma k_{y^*} + C_w k_w}{(1-\lambda)^{1/2}}\right)^2$$

where

$$\Sigma_{D1} = \max\{\Sigma_\gamma(0)^2; d_0(0)C_r\}$$

and C_r is a constant which decreases when C_γ and k_w decrease, while $\Sigma(0)$ is given by equation (17) with $\epsilon_1 = 0$.

Proof: See [12].

Remarks:

1. The advantage of the normalization signal given by equation (8) over that given by equation (7) is that we do not require a knowledge of the characteristic time constant λ_0.

2. From Assumptions A3 it follows that

$$\lim_{C_\gamma, k_w \to 0} \Sigma_1 = 0, \qquad \lim_{C_\gamma, k_w \to 0} \Sigma_\gamma(0) = 0, \qquad \lim_{C_\gamma, k_w \to 0} \delta_2^* = \delta_1^*/2,$$

From the definition of $d_0(\epsilon_1)$ in equation (23), the definition of Σ_D in Statement 2 of Theorem 5.1 and the analysis given above it then follows that

$$\lim_{C_\gamma, k_w \to 0} d_0(0) = 0, \qquad \lim_{C_\gamma, k_w \to 0} \Sigma_D = 0,$$

Consequently from Statements 1-2 of Theorem 5.1

$$\lim_{C_\gamma, k_w \to 0} \sum_{j=1}^{t} \lambda^{t-j} |y(j+1) - y^*(j+1)|^2 = 0,$$

and

$$\lim_{C_\gamma, k_w \to \infty} \|\theta(t) - \theta_0\| = 0$$

Similar results can be had from the expressions in Theorem 5.2. This implies that the tracking and parameter estimation errors are continuous with respect to the unmodelled dynamics and the disturbances in the sense that when the unmodelled dynamics and the external perturbations tend to zero, tracking and parameter estimation errors also tend to zero. Without the application of external excitation the uniform convergence of the parameter error cannot be expected.

3. When persistent excitation is applied the self-stabilization works in the following manner: Whenever the estimator produces parameters that cause the adaptive loop to become unstable, the controller stabilizes itself by producing excitation which results in parameter tuning. This tuning is the result of "self stabilization" and takes place even when the external signals are not excited.

4. There exists a finite level of excitation and a finite time τ_{k_2} so that the estimate of the high frequency gain, $\hat{b}_0(t)$ stays away from zero, i. e. $|\hat{b}_0(t)| \geq \epsilon_1$ for all $t \geq \tau_{k_2}$. This implies that the modification introduced to avoid division with small numbers is only used during a transient period.

6 Conclusions

In this paper we show that excitation with fixed and finite energy can be used to stabilize the estimator in a direct adaptive control algorithm. We show that the parameter estimates and the input output signals remain bounded when the level of excitation is sufficiently high relative to the magnitude of the external perturbations and the intensity of the unstructured unmodelled dynamics. We also show that the parameter estimates "converge" close to their optimal values. In other words, we show that it is possible to perform identification of open loop unstable systems and that we can bound the parameter estimation error. The results apply to systems that have a stably invertible nominal model. It is quite straight forward to generalize the results to a broader class of systems and to apply more complex control laws. A few practical problems remain to be solved. First, it is not clear how to develop algorithms to monitor performance and turn the estimation algorithm on and off. Second, while we have been able to develop guidelines for choosing excitation level through the definition of δ_2^*, these are not so easy to implement due to the fact that bounds on certain system H_∞ norms have to be known in advance for us to be able implement the approach.

References

[1] B. D. O. Anderson, R. R. Bitmead, C. R. Johnson, P. V. Kokotovic, R. L. Kosut,I. M. Y. Mareels, L. Praly and B. D. Riedle, *Stability of Adaptive Systems: Passivity and Averaging Analysis*, MIT-Press, Cambridge, MA, 1986.

[2] B. Egard, *Stability of adaptive controllers*, Springer-Verlag, New York, NY, 1979.

[3] G. C. Goodwin, P. J. Ramadage, and P. E. Caines, "Discrete time multivariable adaptive control," *IEEE Trans. Aut. Control*, vol 25, pp. 449–456, 1990.

[4] P. Ioannou and J. Sun, "Theory and design of robust direct and indirect adaptive control systems," *Int J. Control*, vol. 47, pp. 775–813, 1988.

[5] R. H. Middleton and Goodwin, G. C. and Hill, D. J. and Mayne, D. Q. "Design issues in adaptive control", *IEEE Trans. Automat. Contr.*, vol.33, pp. 50-58, 1988.

[6] A. S. Morse, D. Q. Mayne and G. C. Goodwin, "Applications of hysteresis switching in parameter adaptive control", *IEEE Trans. Automat. Contr.*, vol.37, pp. 1343-1354, 1992.

[7] S. J. Naik, P. R. Kumar and B. E. Ydstie, "Robust Continuous Time Adaptive Control with Parameter Projection", *IEEE Transactions on Auto. Control*, Vol T-AC 37, Jan. 1992, pp. 182-197.

[8] K. S. Narendra and A. M. Annaswamy, *Stable adaptive Systems*, Prentice Hall, NJ, 1989.

[9] L. Praly, "Robustness of model reference adaptive control," *Proc. 2nd Yale Workshop on Adaptive Systems*, 1983.

[10] L. Praly, "Topological orbital equivalence with asymptotic phase for a two time-scales discrete time system", *Mathematics of Control Systems and Signals*, Vol. 3, pp. 225-253, 1990.

[11] M. S. Radenkovic and A. N. Michel "Robust adaptive systems and self-stabilization", *IEEE Trans. Automat. Contr.*, vol.37, pp. 1355-1369, 1992.

[12] M. S. Radenkovic and B. E Ydstie. "Using persistent excitation with fixed energy to stabilize adaptive controllers and obtain hard bounds for the parameter estimation error", Technical report, Department of Electrical Engineering, Univeristy of Colorado Denver, Denver CO 80204.

[13] B. D. Riedle and P. V. Kokotovic "Integral manifolds of slow adaptation", *IEEE Trans. Automat. Contr.*, vol.31, pp. 316-324, 1986.

[14] C. E. Rohrs, L. Valevani, M. Athans and G. Stein, "Analytical verification of undesirable properties of direct model reference adaptive control algorithm", *Proc. 20th IEEE Conf. Decision and Control*, 2, pp. 1272-1284, San Diego, CA, 1981.

[15] B. E. Ydstie, "Transient performance and robustness of direct adaptive control", *IEEE Trans. Automat. Contr.*, vol.37, pp. 1091-1105, 1992.

Proceedings of the
American Control Conference
San Francisco, California • June 1993

Improvement of Transient Response in Adaptive Control Using Modified High Order Tuning

Li Wang, David R. Mudgett
Department of Electrical Engineering
The Pennsylvania State University
University Park, PA 16802

Abstract. Transient response has always been an important issue in adaptive control. A recent paper presents a useful method to control transient response, but it requires precise knowledge of the plant high frequency gain. The following paper shows how to use high order tuning to solve this problem without this prior knowledge, and recent work indicates that simplication of the tuning error, or "augmented" error, as well as elimination of additional prior knowledge requirements, may be possible.

1 Introduction

The problem of transient response control has always been an important issue in adaptive control. Good transient response in adaptive systems has been generally difficult to achieve, requiring extensive simulation and "tuning" of controller parameters to the problem at hand.

In a recent paper[1], Datta and Ioannou present a useful method to control transient response, by adding additional terms to the conventional certainty equivalence input for model reference adaptive control systems. However, at present, this approach requires *exact* prior knowledge of the controlled plant's high frequency gain, g , as well as the other "classical" process model assumptions, namely

(i) The plant has a stable inverse

(ii) An upper bound on plant dimension is known

(iii) The plant relative degree n^* is known precisely

(iv) Sign(g) is known

It turns out that the new control input of [1] is closely related to a different approach to adaptive control known as "high order tuning". This will be discussed in more detail in the next section. The purpose of this paper is to show how high order tuning may be used to obtain similar stability and transient response results to those given in [1] without precise knowledge of g. Precisely, exact knowledge of g is replaced by sign and upper bound knowledge.

2 High Order Tuning

The high-order paramenter adjustment method (more recently referred to as "High Order Tuning", reference [8]) was developed in 1986 [2]-[3] as a way to modify the standard certainty equivalence control law in such a way as to simplify the tuning error (often called the augmented error), used in classical model reference adaptive control laws. Consider the classical model reference tracking error equation (see, e.g. [5]), neglecting without loss of generality any additive linear combination of decaying exponentials:

$$e = gH(s)[u - \tilde{K}^{*\prime}\theta] \tag{1}$$

where $e = y_p - y_m$, y_p is the plant output, y_m is the reference model output, $H(s)$ is a known stable, rational, all-pole transfer function of order n^*, u is the plant control input, K^* is an unknown parameter vector, and θ is a vector of filtered plant inputs and outputs. The certainty equivalence control law and resulting error equation are given by

$$u = \hat{K}'\theta \tag{2}$$
$$e = gH(s)[\tilde{K}'\theta] \tag{3}$$

where $\tilde{K} = \hat{K} - K^*$. Using a result originally due to Monopoli [4], equation (3) can be rewritten as

$$e = g(\tilde{K}'\phi - \psi) \tag{4}$$

where $\phi = H(s)[\theta]$, and $\psi = \hat{K}'\phi - H(s)[\hat{K}'\theta]$ can be generated without derivatives of the process output; Therefore, by augmenting the tracking error, e , in the following manner,

$$\epsilon = \frac{e + \hat{g}(t)\psi}{1 + \gamma\phi'\phi} \tag{5}$$

where $\hat{g}(t)$ is a new parameter to be estimated and γ is a positive constant, then the augmented error ϵ satisfies

$$\epsilon = \frac{g\tilde{K}'\phi + \tilde{g}(t)\psi}{1 + \gamma\phi'\phi} \tag{6}$$

where $\tilde{g}(t) = \hat{g}(t) - g^*$. This is the starting point for analysis of the classical model reference algorithms, such as [5]-[6], using the parameter adjustment laws

$$\dot{\hat{K}} = -sign(g)\phi\epsilon \tag{7}$$
$$\dot{\hat{g}} = -\psi\epsilon \tag{8}$$

Consider now the idea of augmenting the original control input to eliminate the effect of ψ, instead of adding $\hat{g}\psi$ to the output to augment the tracking error. Defining, without loss of generality, $H(s) = \frac{1}{\alpha(s)}$, then we require

$$\begin{aligned} u &= \hat{K}'\theta + H^{-1}(s)[\psi] = \hat{K}'\theta + H^{-1}(s)[\hat{K}'\phi - H(s)(\hat{K}'\theta)] \\ &= \alpha(s)[\hat{K}'\phi] = \sum_{i=0}^{n^*} \frac{1}{i!}\hat{K}^{(i)\prime}\frac{d^i\alpha(s)}{ds^i}(\phi) \end{aligned} \tag{9}$$

Note since $\phi = \frac{1}{\alpha(s)}[\theta]$, that n^* derivatives of ϕ are available without differentiation. Hence, if n^* derivatives of $\hat{K}$ are available, this u can be physically realized without differentiators. High order parameter adjustment simply makes these derivatives available by choosing an adjustment law of the form

$$p(s)\dot{\hat{K}} = -sign(g)\phi\epsilon \tag{10}$$

where

$$\epsilon = \frac{e}{1 + \gamma\phi'\phi} = e - \gamma\phi'\phi\epsilon \tag{11}$$

The tracking error e satisfied simple equation

$$e = g\tilde{K}'\phi \tag{12}$$

however the analysis is slightly complicated by the high order parameter adjustment. The results of [2]-[3] show that this adaptive controller has the same global stability properties as the classical algorithms of [5]-[6].

This work was initially motivated by a desire to have a more natural tuning error than the conventional augmented error, to eliminate the additional estimated parameter, $\hat{g}$, and hopefully, eventually lead to progress in developing more generally applicable adaptive controllers. The elimination of $\hat{g}$ is important from the standpoint of verification of persistent excitation using external probing signals - see [7] - however this algorithm was basically put aside until recently.

Two very recent papers indicate that there may be an advantage to this approach. In [8], high order tuning is successfully applied to the classical LTI plant set, except that the relative degree may be either n^* or $n^* + 1$ instead of precisely n^* . In the same paper, global stability is also shown when applied to a $\leq n^{th}$ order plant with a simply structured nonlinearity.

Furthermore, in [1], a similar but slightly different approach is considered as a mechanism to improve the transient response of model reference adaptive systems with precisely known high-frequency gain, g. Referring to control input equation (9) above, instead of realizing the modified certainty equivalence control law by using derivatives of $\hat{K}$, made available by using a high-order parameter adjustment, u is realized as a lowpass filtered estimate of (9), ie.,

$$u = \hat{K}'\theta - \frac{H^{-1}(s)}{(1+\tau s)^{n^*}}[\epsilon m^2 + \psi] \tag{13}$$

where m^2 is a normalizing signal, a lowpass filtered estimate of $1+u^2+y^2$. Reference [1] shows that the resulting controller is stable and useful upper bounds on $|e|$ and $\frac{1}{t}\int_0^t e^2(\tau)d\tau$ are obtained.

Both the high-order tuning method of [2] – [3] and the approach of [1] seek to cancel the effect of ψ on the tracking error equation (4). High order tuning cancels it completely, whereas the controller of [1] cancels it at frequencies up to the cutoff of the filter $(\tau s+1)^{-n^*}$.

3 Control Law

The controller in this paper consist of the following:

- **Reference Model:** Without loss of generality, assume that the reference model is an all pole system with transfer function $W_m(s) = \frac{k_m}{(s+\lambda)\alpha(s)}$, where $\alpha(s)$ is a Hurwitz polynomial of degree (n^*-1), and all the $\alpha_i(s), i = 1, n^*-1$ are still Hurwitz, $\lambda > 0$. Then

$$\begin{aligned} \dot{x}_m &= A_m x_m + b_m r \\ y_m &= c_m x_m \end{aligned}$$

  where r is any piecewise-continuous input signal, and (A_m, b_m, c_m) is a canonical realization of $\frac{k_m}{(s+\lambda)\alpha(s)}$. For convenience, $\alpha(s)$ is chosen, for each $i = 1, 2, \ldots, n^*-1$, so that $\alpha_i(s) = \frac{d^i\alpha(s)}{ds^i}$ is strictly Hurwitz. This is not difficult; for example, choosing $\alpha(s) = (1+\tau s)^{n^*-1}$ works.

- **Plant:** The plant has transfer function $W_p(s) = k_p\frac{\alpha_p(s)}{\beta_p(s)}$, satisfying conditions $(i) - (iv)$ in the Introduction and in addition an upper bound on g is known:

$$\begin{aligned} \dot{x}_p &= A_p x_p + b_p u \\ y_p &= c_p x_p \end{aligned}$$

  where (A_p, b_p, c_p) is a canonical realization of $W_p(s)$.

- **Tracking Error e:**

$$e = y_p - y_m$$

- **Sensitivity function** θ:

$$\begin{aligned} \dot{\theta}_u &= \Lambda\theta_u + b_0 u \\ \dot{\theta}_y &= \Lambda\theta_y + b_0 y \end{aligned}$$

  where $\theta = [r, \theta_u', y_p, \theta_y'] \in R^{2n}$ and (Λ, b_0) is a stable controllable system of dimension $n-1$.

- **Filtered Sensitivity Function** ϕ:

$$\begin{aligned} \dot{H} &= A_H H + b_H\theta' \\ \phi_i &= c_H^i H \end{aligned}$$

  where $H = [h_1\, h_2 \ldots h_{2n}]$ is an $n^* * 2n$ matrix. For each $i = 0, 1, \ldots, n^*-1$ (A_H, b_H, c_H^i) is a canonical realization of $\alpha^i(s)/\alpha(s)$, $\alpha_i(s) = \frac{d^i\alpha(s)}{ds^i}$. Define $\phi = \phi_{n^*-1}$.

- **Control Input** u:

$$u = u_{HOT} - \frac{sign(g)}{|\overline{g}|}G(s)e \tag{14}$$

  where u_{HOT} is the standard high order tuning input discussed in section 2, given by $u_{HOT} = \alpha(s)[\hat{K}'\phi] = \sum_{i=0}^{i=n^*-1}\frac{1}{i!}\hat{K}'^{(i)}\phi_i$, $G(s) = \frac{F(s)}{1-F(s)W_m(s)}$, $F(s) = d\frac{W_M^{-1}(s)}{\beta(s)}$, $\beta(s)$ is any Hurwitz polynomial of degree n^*-1 chosen so that $\beta(s)-d$ is Hurwitz for any choice of $d \in [0,1)$, and $|\overline{g}|$ is a known upper bound on $|g|$.

- **Tuning Error,** ϵ:

$$\begin{aligned} \psi &= \hat{K}'\phi_{\beta\eta} - W_{\beta\eta}(s)(\hat{K}'\phi) && (15) \\ \dot{\sigma} &= -\lambda\sigma - \gamma|\overline{g}|\phi_{\beta\eta}'\phi_{\beta\eta}\epsilon + \hat{g}\psi && (16) \\ \epsilon &= e + \sigma && (17) \end{aligned}$$

  where $\phi_{\beta\eta} = W_{\beta\eta}(s)(\phi)$, $W_{\beta\eta}(s) = \frac{1-F(s)W_M(s)}{1-(1-\eta)F(s)W_M(s)} = \frac{\beta(s)-d}{\beta(s)-(1-\eta)d}$, and $\eta = \frac{|g|}{|\overline{g}|}$ and $0 \le \eta \le 1$,

- **High Order Parameter Adjustment Law:**

$$\begin{aligned} \dot{\hat{W}} &= -sign(g)\phi_{\beta\eta}\epsilon && (18) \\ \dot{\hat{g}} &= -\psi\epsilon && (19) \\ \hat{K} &= \frac{p_0}{p(s)}\hat{W} && (20) \\ \hat{K}^{i+1} &= \frac{p_0 s^i}{p(s)}\dot{\hat{W}}, \quad i = 0, 1, 2, \ldots n^*-2 && (21) \end{aligned}$$

  where $p(s)$ is any strictly Hurwitz polynomial $\sum_{i=1}^{n^*-1} p_i s^i$.

4 System Stability

Stability analysis follows the usual structure, such as given in textbook reference [9], and shows:

(i) Boundedness of all parameter estimates and L_2-norm boundedness of certain signals in the system.

(ii) Existence and uniqueness of solutions to the closed loop system

(iii) Boundedness of all closed-loop system states

(iv) Convergence of e(t) to zero as $t \to \infty$

(i). Using the control input equation (14), the tracking error is given by

$$\begin{aligned} e &= gW_m(s)(u - K'^*\theta) \\ &= g\frac{1}{s+\lambda}(\tilde{K}'\phi) - \frac{|g|}{|\overline{g}|}W_m(s)G(s)e \\ &= g\frac{W_{\beta\eta}(s)}{s+\lambda}(\tilde{K}'\phi) && (22) \end{aligned}$$

where $\tilde{K} = \hat{K} - K^*$. Similarly, the tuning error satisfies:

$$\dot{\epsilon} + (\lambda + \gamma|\overline{g}|\phi_{\beta\eta}'\phi_{\beta\eta})\epsilon = g(\tilde{K}'\phi_{\beta\eta}) + \tilde{g}\psi \tag{23}$$

Multiplying (23) by ϵ, substituting the parameter adjustment laws, and integrating both sides gives

$$\begin{aligned} &\frac{1}{2}\epsilon^2 + \lambda\int_0^t \epsilon^2 d\tau + \gamma|\overline{g}|\int_0^t \|\dot{\tilde{W}}\|^2 d\tau \\ = &-|g|\int_0^t \tilde{K}'\dot{\tilde{W}}d\tau \\ = &-|g|\int_0^t (\tilde{W}' - L(s)\dot{\tilde{W}}')\dot{\tilde{W}}d\tau - \int_0^t \tilde{g}\dot{\tilde{g}}d\tau \\ = &-|g|\|\tilde{W}\|^2 + |g|\int_0^t \dot{\tilde{W}}'L(s)\dot{\tilde{W}}d\tau - \tilde{g}^2 && (24) \\ \le &-|g|\|\tilde{W}\|^2 + |g|c_2\int_0^t \|\dot{\tilde{W}}\|^2 d\tau - \tilde{g}^2 + c_1 && (25) \end{aligned}$$

where $\tilde{K} = \frac{p_0}{p(s)}\tilde{W} = (1 - \frac{1-p(s)}{p(s)})\tilde{W} = \tilde{W} + \frac{q(s)}{p(s)}\dot{\tilde{W}} = \tilde{W} + L(s)\dot{\tilde{W}}$, $L(s) = \frac{q(s)}{p(s)}$; and c_1 , c_2 are positive numbers which depend only on the reference model $W_m(s)$ and initial conditions. Equation (25) follows from (24) by a lemma due to William and Byrnes [10].

Reorganizing (25) yields

$$\frac{1}{2}\epsilon^2 + \lambda\int_0^t \epsilon^2 d\tau + (\gamma|\overline{g}| - c_2|g|)\int_0^t \|\dot{\tilde{W}}\|^2 d\tau + |g|\|\tilde{W}\|^2 + \tilde{g}^2 \leq 0 \quad (26)$$

for $t \in R^+$. Thus choosing $\gamma > \frac{|g|}{|\overline{g}|}c_2$ yields $\epsilon \in L_2 \bigcap L_\infty[R^+]$, $\dot{\tilde{W}} \in L_2[R^+]$, $\tilde{W} \in L_\infty[R^+]$, $\tilde{g} \in L_\infty$. From this, it can be inferred that $\hat{K}^{(i)} \in L_2(R^+)$ for $i = 1, 2, \ldots n^* - 1$, and $\hat{K} \in L_\infty(R^+)$.

(ii). Defining $\hat{\kappa}' = [\hat{K}' \; \dot{\hat{K}}' \; \ldots \; \hat{K}^{(n^*-1)}]$, $\kappa^* = [K'^*, 0, \ldots, 0]$ and $\tilde{\kappa} = \hat{\kappa} - \kappa^*$, then it is straightforward but tedious to show that the closed-loop system satisfies a differential equation of the following form:

$$\dot{X}_e(t) = [A_e + B_e\tilde{\kappa}(t)C_e]X_e(t) + b_e\tilde{k}_r(t)r(t) \quad (27)$$

$$e(t) = c_e X_e(t) \quad (28)$$

where A_e, B_e, C_e, b_e are constants matrices. $X_e = [x_p' \; \theta_u' \; \theta_y' \; h_1' \; h_2' \; \ldots h_{2n}']'$ includes all the states of the closed loop system. Since $||\tilde{\kappa}||$ is bounded by step (i), a unique solution to the closed-loop system (27)-(28) exists, and all system states may grow at most exponentially.

(iii). The proof of this part followings the procedure in textbook [9]. In the sequel, certain notations in [9] are followed. Given a vector time function $f(t)$, then $sup||f(t)||$ denotes $sup_{\tau \leq t}||f(t)||$. The upper bar notation $\overline{f(t)}$ denotes the vector formed from $f(t)$ by deleting the reference input $r(t)$. The lower bar notation $\underline{f(t)}$ denotes the the vector formed from $f(t)$ by deleting both $r(t)$ and $y_p(t)$.

First assume that the norm of $||X_e||$ is not bounded. It is first shown that if certain components of this solution are not bounded, then they must grow at the same rate. This is used to establish a contradiction.

(a). Since Λ is asymptotically stable, then by lemma 2.6 of [9], it follows that:

$$\| \theta_u \| = O[sup|u|]$$

$$\| \theta_y \| = O[sup|y_p|]$$

(b). Similarly, since $W_m(s)$ is asymptotically stable, it follows that

$$\| \overline{\phi}_i \| = O[sup \| \overline{\theta} \|]; \quad i = \overline{1, n^* - 1}$$

Define $\overline{\Phi} = [\overline{\theta}, \overline{\phi}_1, \ldots, \overline{\phi}_{n^*-1}]$. Then:

$$sup \| \overline{\Phi} \| = O[sup \| \overline{\theta} \|], \qquad sup \| \Phi \| = O[sup \| \theta \|]$$

(c). The output of the plant y_p:

$$y_p = gW_m(s)[u - K^{*\prime}\theta] = W_m(s)[g\tilde{\kappa}'\Phi + \eta G(s)(\tilde{K}'\phi)]$$

where $\hat{\kappa}$, and $\hat{K}$ are bounded, and $W_m(s), G(s)$ are Hurwitz. Hence:

$$|y_p| = O[sup \| \Phi \|] = O[sup \| \overline{\Phi} \|] = O[sup \| \theta \|] = O[sup \| \overline{\theta} \|]$$

(d). Let $\underline{\theta} = [\theta_u' \; \theta_y']$. From (c),

$$\| \underline{\theta} \| \sim sup \| \overline{\theta} \|$$

(e). By lemma A.2 in the appendix, $\| \dot{\overline{\theta}} \| \leq c_1 \| \overline{\theta} \| + c_2$, where c_1, c_2 are positive constants. Then by corollary (2.7) of [9],

$$\| \theta_u \| = O[sup \| \overline{\theta} \|] = O[sup \| \underline{\theta} \|]$$

(f). Since $W_p(s)\theta_u = \theta_y$; $W_p(s)$ is minimum phase, by (e) and lemma 2.8 of [9], it follows that

$$\| \theta_u \| = O[sup \| \theta_y \|]$$

$$\| \theta_y \| \sim sup \| \underline{\theta} \|$$

(g). Similarly, since $\frac{\alpha^i(s)}{\alpha(s)}\overline{\theta} = \overline{\phi}_i$, $i = \overline{1, n^* - 1}$, and $\frac{\alpha^i(s)}{\alpha(s)}$ are minimum phase by construction, then by (e) and lemma 2.8 of [9], it follows that

$$\| \overline{\theta} \| = O[sup \| \overline{\Phi} \|]$$

$$\| \theta \| = O[sup \| \Phi \|]$$

(h). $W_{\beta\eta}(s)\phi = \phi_{\beta\eta}$ where $W_{\beta\eta}(s)$ is a proper Hurwitz minimum phase polynomial. Hence by Corollary [2.5] of [9], it follows that

$$sup \| \phi \| \sim sup \| \phi_{\beta\eta} \|$$

(i). From $(a) - (h)$ above, the following conclusions may be made for each $i = 0, 1, \ldots, n^* - 1$:

$$sup|y_p| \sim sup \| \theta_y \| \sim sup \| \overline{\theta} \| \sim sup \| \theta \| \sim sup \| \phi_i \|$$
$$\sim sup||h_i|| \sim sup \| \Phi \| \sim sup \| \phi_{\beta\eta} \|$$

(j). Note that

- $\epsilon \in L_2 \bigcap L_\infty$, hence $\epsilon = o[sup \| \phi \|]$.
- $\sigma = \frac{1}{s+\lambda}[\hat{g}\psi - |\overline{g}|\phi_{\beta\eta}'\phi_{\beta\eta}\epsilon]$

Now, $\frac{1}{s+\lambda}\hat{g}\psi = \frac{1}{s+\lambda}\hat{g}[\hat{K}'W_{\beta\eta}(s)\phi - W_{\beta\eta}(s)\hat{K}'\phi]$, where $\dot{\hat{K}} \in L_2[t_0, \infty)$, and $\hat{g}$ is bounded. Hence, by lemma 2.11 of [9], and the stability of $\frac{1}{s+\lambda}$

$$\frac{1}{s+\lambda}\hat{g}\psi = o[sup||\phi_{\beta\eta}||] \quad (29)$$

Further, $\frac{1}{s+\lambda}[\gamma|\overline{g}|\phi_{\beta\eta}'\phi_{\beta\eta}\epsilon] = \frac{1}{s+\lambda}[\gamma|\overline{g}|\phi_{\beta\eta}'\dot{\tilde{W}}]$, where $\dot{\tilde{W}} \in L_2[t_0, \infty)$.

Hence, $\frac{1}{s+\lambda}(\gamma|\overline{g}|\phi_{\beta\eta}'\phi_{\beta\eta}\epsilon) \in L_2[t_0, \infty)$, yielding $\sigma = o[sup||\phi_{\beta\eta}||]$.

Since $sup||\phi_{\beta\eta}|| \sim sup||\phi||$, then $\sigma = o[sup||\phi||]$.

(k). $e = \epsilon - \sigma$ where $\epsilon \in L_2 \bigcap L_\infty[t_0, \infty)$, and $\sigma = o[sup||\phi||]$ by step (j).

Hence $e = o[sup||\phi||]$. Similarly, $y_p = e + y_m = o[sup||\phi||]$.

This contradicts the equivalence in part (i). Therefore, all the states of the closed-loop system are bounded.

(iv). From (k), $e = o[sup||\phi||]$ and $||\phi||$ is bounded, so we have $e \to 0$ as $t \to \infty$.

5 Transient Response

In order to obtain specific bounds on the tracking error response, it is convenient to take $\beta(s) = (1+\tau s)^{n^*-1}$, as in [1], and to consider d as a function of the parameter τ. Specifically, we take $d(\tau) = (1-\tau)^{m(n^*-1)}$ where m is a positive integer. Then, the filter $W_{\beta\eta}(s)$ is given by:

$$W_{\beta\eta}(s) = \frac{(1+\tau s)^{n^*-1} - (1-\tau)^{m(n^*-1)}}{(1+\tau s)^{n^*-1} - (1-\eta)(1-\tau)^{m(n^*-1)}} \quad (30)$$

Note that if $0 < \tau \leq \frac{1}{m}$, the roots of $(1+\tau s)^n - (1-\tau)^{mn}$ are given by $-\frac{1}{\tau} + \frac{(1-\tau)^m}{\tau}e^{j\frac{2\pi k}{n}}$; $k = 0, 1, \ldots, n-1$, and that even as $\tau \to 0$, all roots are to the left of $s = -m, \forall n \in Z^+$. Furthermore, the roots of $(1+\tau s)^{n^*-1} - (1-\eta)(1-\tau)^{m(n^*-1)}$ are also to the left of $s = -m$, $\forall n \in Z^+$. Hence, $W_{\beta\eta}(s)$ is a proper transfer function with poles and zeros to the left of $s = -m$.

Now, the error response is given by equation (22)

$$e = \frac{g}{s+\lambda}W_{\beta\eta}(s)(\tilde{K}'\phi) \quad (31)$$

Defining the impulse response

$$h_{\beta\eta}(t) = L^{-1}[W_{\beta\eta}(s)] \quad (32)$$

where L denotes the Laplace transform, then

$$e(t) = h_{\beta\eta}(t) * L^{-1}[\frac{g}{s+\lambda}\tilde{K}'\phi] \quad (33)$$

where $*$ denotes convolution.

$||\tilde{K}'||$ and $||\phi||$ are bounded by finite constants by the results of Section 4. The choice of $W_{\beta\eta}(s)$ in (30) assures, for a sufficiently large value of m (depending only on n^*), that there is an upper bound on these constants that does not depend upon τ. Therefore, since $\lambda \geq 0$, it follows that $L^{-1}(\frac{1}{s+\lambda}\tilde{K}'\phi)$ is bounded above by some finite constant c_1 that does not depend upon τ.
Hence

$$|e(t)| \leq c_1 \int_0^t h_{\beta\eta}(\sigma)d\sigma \tag{34}$$

Now, factor $(1+\tau s)^{n^*-1} + (1-\eta)(1-\tau)^{m(n^*-1)}$ as $\prod_{i=1}^{n^*-1}(1+\beta_i s)$, where each β_i is a possibly complex number with positive real part. Without loss generality, assume that

$$\frac{1}{\tau} \leq \frac{Re(\beta_1)}{|\beta_1|} \leq \ldots \leq \frac{Re(\beta_{n^*-1})}{|\beta_{n^*-1}|} \tag{35}$$

Then

$$W_{\beta\eta}(s) = 1 - \left[\frac{A_1}{\beta_1 s+1} + \frac{A_2}{\beta_2 s+1} + \ldots + \frac{A_{n^*-1}}{\beta_{n^*-1}s+1}\right] \tag{36}$$

and

$$h_{\beta\eta}(t) = \delta(t) - \left[\frac{A_1}{\beta_1}e^{-\frac{t}{\beta_1}} + \frac{A_2}{\beta_2}e^{-\frac{t}{\beta_2}} + \ldots + \frac{A_{n^*-1}}{\beta_{n^*-1}}e^{-\frac{t}{\beta_{n^*-1}}}\right] \tag{37}$$

Integrating equation (35) yields:

$$\begin{aligned}\int_0^t h_{\beta\eta}(\sigma)d\sigma &= 1 + \left[A_1(e^{-\frac{t}{\beta_1}} - 1) + \ldots + A_{n^*-1}(e^{-\frac{t}{\beta_{n^*-1}}} - 1)\right] \\ &= 1 - (A_1 + \ldots + A_{n^*-1}) + A_1 e^{-\frac{t}{\beta_1}} + \ldots + A_{n^*-1}e^{-\frac{t}{\beta_{n^*-1}}} \qquad (38)\end{aligned}$$

Note that for each $i = \overline{1, n^*-1}$, $A_i = c_i \frac{\eta d}{1-(1-\eta)d}$, where c_i is a bounded function of η and τ. Hence

$$\begin{aligned}\int_0^t h_{\beta\eta}(\sigma)d\sigma &\leq \frac{1-d(\tau)}{1-(1-\eta)d(\tau)} + (|A_1| + |A_2| + \ldots |A_{n^*-1}|)e^{-\frac{Re(\beta_1)}{|\beta_1|^2}t} \\ &\leq \frac{1-d(\tau)}{1-(1-\eta)d(\tau)} + [|A_1| + |A_2| + \ldots + |A_{n^*-1}|]e^{-\frac{t}{\tau}} (39)\end{aligned}$$

Therefore $|e|$ is bounded by:

$$|e| \leq C_1\left(\frac{1-d(\tau)}{1-(1-\eta)d(\tau)} + \frac{C_2\eta d(\tau)}{1-(1-\eta)d(\tau)}e^{-\frac{t}{\tau}}\right) \tag{40}$$

and the mean square value of the tracking error is bounded by:

$$\begin{aligned}\frac{1}{t}\int_0^t e^2 d\sigma &\leq C_3\left(\left(\frac{1-d(\tau)}{1-(1-\eta)d(\tau)}\right)^2 \right. \\ &\left. + \frac{C_4\eta^2 d(\tau)^2}{(1-(1-\eta)d(\tau))^2}\frac{1}{t}(1-e^{-\frac{2t}{\tau}})\right) \qquad (42)\end{aligned}$$

where c_1, c_2, c_3, c_4 depend only on initial conditions.

Clearly, the bound on e and $\frac{1}{t}\int_0^t e^2(\sigma)d\sigma$ can be made as small as desired by letting $\tau \to 0$.

6 Conclusions

The controller presented here uses the classical "augmented"error approach to parameter tuning, as is the case in [1]. This avoids certain technical problems in showing stability and allows standard textbook results to be applied. However this appears not to be necessary, and we expect to obtain similar results using the normalized tracking error $\frac{e}{1+\phi'\phi}$ as the tuning signal, as is possible in the standard high order tuning approach. Work is also in progress to extend this type of result to more general classes of plants. It should also be pointed out that Papadakis [11] has recently solved this problem using a different approach. It is felt that high order tuning may offer an attractive alternative approach, especially considering Morse's high order tuner [8] for plants with uncertain relative degree.

A number of simulation experiments have also been performed, comparing the results here with those of [1] and a conventional model reference controller. Results have been quite favorable, and will be included in a future paper, after robustness issues have been considered.

Acknowledgments: The authors would like to thank Ioannis Papadakis for pointing out the results in [1] shortly after they were published, as well as an anonymous reviewer for highlighting the importance of the uniform bound of $||\phi||$ with respect to the parameter d.

7 References

[1]. A.Datta and P.A.Ioannou, "Performance improvement versus robust stability in model reference adaptive control," *Proceedings of the 30th CDC.* Brighton, England, pp 748-753, December, 1991.

[2]. D.R.Mudgett and A.S.Morse, "High-order parameter adjustment laws for adaptive stabilization," *Proceedings of the 1987 conference on Information Sciences and Systems,* Johns Hopkins University Baltimore, MD, pp. 314-317, March, 1987.

[3]. D.R.Mudgett, "Problems in Parameter Adaptive Control," Ph.D Dissertation, Department of Electrical Engineering, Yale University, 1988.

[4]. R.V.Monopoli, "Model reference adaptive control with an augmented error signal," *IEEE Transaction on Automatic Control* vol. AC-19, pp.474-484, October,1974.

[5]. A.S.Morse, "Global stability of parameter adaptive control systems," *IEEE Transactions on Automatic Control,* vol. AC-25, pp. 433-439, June, 1980.

[6]. K.S.Narendra, Y.H.Lin, and L.S.Valavani, "Stable adaptive controller design, Part II: Proof of stability," *IEEE Transactions on Automatic Control,* vol. AC-25, pp. 440-448, June, 1980.

[7]. S.Dasgupta, B.D.O. Anderson, and A.C.Tsoi, "Input conditions for continuous-time adaptive system problems," *Proceedings of the 22nd Conference on Decision and Control,* San Antonio, TX, pp. 211-216, December, 1983.

[8]. A.S.Morse, "High-order parameter tuners for the adaptive control of linear and nonlinear systems," preprint, to appear.

[9]. K.S.Narendra and A.M.Annaswamy, *Stable Adaptive Systems,* Englewood Cliffs, NJ, Prentice Hall, 1989.

[10]. J.C. Willems and C.I. Byrnes, "Global Adaptive Stabilization in the Absence of Information on the Sign of the Instantaneous Gain," *Proc. INRIA Conf. in Analysis and Optimization of Systems,* Springer Verlag, June 1984, pp. 49-57.

[11]. I.Papadakis, "Improvement performance of adaptive control using parameter mismatch compensation", Ph.D. thesis, Electrical Engineering Department, Penn State University, May, 1993.

APPENDIX

Lemma A.1:

$x_p = C\overline{\theta} + \delta(t)$, for some constant matrix C and some signal $\delta(t)$ which approaches to zero asymptotically.

Proof:
See Appendix $C.1$ in [9].

Lemma A.2:

$\| \dot{\overline{\theta}} \| \leq c_1 \| \overline{\theta} \| + c_2$, where c_1 and c_2 are positive constants.

Proof:
The components of $\overline{\theta}$, θ_u, y_p and θ_y satisfies the following differential equations:

$$\begin{aligned} \dot{\theta}_u &= \Lambda\theta_u + b_0[\hat{\kappa}'\Phi - \frac{sign(g)}{|\overline{g}|}G(s)(\tilde{K}'\phi)] \\ \dot{y}_p &= h_p^T A_p x_p + h_p^T b_p[\hat{\kappa}'\Phi - \frac{sign(g)}{|\overline{g}|}G(s)(\tilde{K}'\phi)] \\ \dot{\theta}_y &= \Lambda\theta_y + b_0 y_p \end{aligned} \tag{43}$$

This set of equations may be written as follows:

$$\begin{bmatrix} \dot{\theta}_u \\ \dot{y}_p \\ \dot{\theta}_y \end{bmatrix} = \begin{bmatrix} \Lambda + b_0\hat{K}_u' & b_0\hat{k}_y & b_0\hat{K}_y' \\ h_p^T b_p \hat{K}_u' & h_p^T b_p \hat{k}_y & h_p^T b_p \hat{K}_y' \\ 0 & b_0 & \Lambda \end{bmatrix} \begin{bmatrix} \theta_u \\ y_p \\ \theta_y \end{bmatrix} + \begin{bmatrix} 0 \\ h_p^T A_p \\ 0 \end{bmatrix} x_p$$

$$+ \begin{bmatrix} b_0 \\ h_p^T b_p \\ 0 \end{bmatrix} (\hat{\kappa}_1'\Phi_1 - \frac{sign(g)}{|\overline{g}|}G(s)(\tilde{K}'\phi) + \hat{k}_r r) \tag{44}$$

where $\hat{K}' = [\hat{k}_r,\ \hat{K}_u',\ \hat{k}_y,\ \hat{K}_y']$, $\hat{\kappa}_1' = [\hat{K}'^{(1)}\ \hat{K}'^{(2)}\ \dots\ \hat{K}'^{(n^*-1)}]$ and $\Phi_1' = [\phi_1'\ \phi_2'\ \dots\ \phi_{n^*-1}']$.
By Lemma A.1, $x_p = C\overline{\theta} + \delta(t)$ for some constant matrix C. Hence

$$\dot{\overline{\theta}} = [\overline{A} + \overline{B}_0\hat{K}']\overline{\theta} + \overline{B}_1(\hat{\kappa}_1'\Phi_1 - \frac{sign(g)}{|\overline{g}|}G(s)(\tilde{K}'\phi) + \hat{k}_r r) \tag{45}$$

where $\overline{A}$, $\overline{B}_0$ and $\overline{B}_1$ are constant matrices.

Since $\hat{K}$ and $\hat{\kappa}$ are bounded, and $\| \phi_i \| = O[sup \| \theta \|] = O[sup \| \overline{\theta} \|]$ for each $i = \overline{1, n^* - 1}$, then

$$\| \hat{\kappa}_1'\Phi_1 \| \leq c_1 \| \overline{\theta} \| + c_2 \tag{46}$$

for some bounded constants c_1, c_2.

Since $\tilde{K}$ bounded, and $G(s)$ is a stable transfer function for $d \in [0, 1)$, then

$$G(s)(\tilde{K}'\phi) = O[sup \| \phi \|] = O[sup \| \overline{\theta} \|] \tag{47}$$

Hence

$$G(s)(\tilde{K}'\phi) \leq c_3 \| \overline{\theta} \| + c_4 \tag{48}$$

Summarying (43), (44) and (45) with the fact that $k_r r$ is bounded yields the desired result.

Proceedings of the
American Control Conference
San Francisco, California • June 1993

On Certain Performance Issues Arising In Adaptive Control*

Kostas S. Tsakalis and Suttipan Limanond

Arizona State University
Department of Electrical Engineering
Tempe, AZ 85287-5706

Summary

In this note we address the problem of improving the performance of a class of Model Reference Adaptive Controllers (MRAC) under insufficient excitation and in the presence of perturbations, e.g., non-parametric uncertainty and bounded disturbances.

In such an environment, the global boundedness of a MRAC closed-loop (BIBO stability) has been established, without any excitation requirements, for both bounded disturbances and 'small' non-parametric uncertainty (e.g., see [1, 2] and references therein). In addition to this form of robust stability, the adaptive controller also guarantees robust tracking performance in a root-mean-square (RMS) sense. That is, the RMS value of the normalized tracking error is of order of the size of the non-parametric uncertainty and/or the RMS value of the external disturbances. Unfortunately, however, this weak performance measure is rarely reliable in assessing the effectiveness of the adaptive controller. Indeed, in the absense of sufficient excitation, even arbitrarily small perturbations may cause the adjustable parameters to drift away from their desired or actual values. Such a parameter drift can then produce large instantaneous tracking errors due to either a change in the excitation signal or the (local) destabilization of the closed loop system. This type of undesirable behavior, often referred to as burst phenomena, has been the subject of several studies (e.g., see [3, 4, 5, 6]).

A typical remedy of the bursting problem has been recognized in the form of absolute or relative dead-zones [7, 8]. The main idea of this approach is to cease adaptation when the estimation error becomes smaller than a threshold, derived as a conservative estimate of the worst-case upper bound of the perturbation entering the estimation algorithm of the adaptive controller. The net result of this approach is that if the threshold is chosen appropriately, the estimated parameters converge and the tracking error enters a residual set where its magnitude is proportional to the dead-zone threshold. We refer to this type of performance characterization as performance in a *lim sup* sense. Thus, for adaptive laws with dead-zone both the RMS and *lim sup* values of the tracking error are of the order of the threshold. (In the relative dead-zone case, all quantities are suitably normalized while the threshold should be sufficiently small to guarantee the BIBO stability of the closed-loop.) The need for a conservative selection of the dead-zone threshold, however, constitutes the main drawback of this approach in the sense that if the threshold is grossly overestimated, the RMS tracking performance may deteriorate unnecessarily.

It should be mentioned that tracking performance guarantees in the *lim sup* sense can also be obtained by requiring persistence of excitation [9, 10, 11, 12, 13] or appropriately shaping certain closed-loop sensitivity operators [14, 15]. The main limitation of the first approach is that it relies on the excitation properties of the reference input signal. On the other hand, the second approach is effective for disturbances or perturbations entering the closed-loop plant at a particular point but may still produce undesirable behavior in the general case.

In view of the previous discussion, it is natural to pose the question whether it is possible to construct an adaptive law that preserves the RMS tracking properties of laws with constant adaptation gains and provides tracking performance guarantees in the *lim sup* sense, similar to adaptive laws with dead-zones. Alternatively, we seek to construct an adaptive law that recovers the ideal case performance when the perturbations are removed while it provides *lim sup* performance guarantees for a wide class of perturbations, without any excitation requirements. The objective of this work is to present an adaptive law providing an affirmative answer to this problem.

The main idea of our approach is to use an a priori selected instantaneous bound on the effective perturbation to obtain and update on-line an estimate of the parametric uncertainty set (set-membership estimation). More specifically, each measurement together with the bound of the perturbation entering the adaptive law define a set as the intersection of two half-spaces in the M-dimensional parameter space where the actual or desired parameters must lie. Based on the available measurements, the parametric uncertainty set can then be defined as the intersection of all such sets. Although this conceptually simple defini-

*Supported by NSF RIA Grant No. ECS-9111346

tion leads to a computationally intractable task, suboptimal recursive solutions have been obtained e.g., see [16]. Such set-membership estimation algorithms estimate the parametric uncertainty set as an ellipsoid containing the set of parameters that are compatible with the measurements and the constraints.

At this point, one could select the center of this ellipsoid as an estimate of the adjustable parameters, an approach taken by [17, 18]. This design, although more effective in generic cases, results in a tracking error performance that is qualitatively similar to dead-zone algorithms with the same drawbacks. Other quite interesting techniques were discussed in [19, 20] where the controller was designed to optimize the worst-case performance for all plants in the updated uncertainty set but relying on persistence of excitation to ensure that this set becomes small enough for the controller design to be successful.

On the other hand, in our approach we generate this estimate of the parametric uncertainty set by means of an auxiliary estimator operating in a hybrid mode and use it as a projection set for the 'main' adaptive law that generates the estimates of the controller parameters. The properties of such an adaptive law are briefly summarized below:[1]

- For LTI plants, the ellipsoids generated by the set-membership estimator converge in finite time. Moreover, for any parameter vector contained in the final ellipsoid the associated estimation error or normalized estimation error in the case of non-parametric uncertainty, is bounded by $(\sqrt{M+1})d_z + \epsilon$, where M is the number of adjustable parameters, d_z is the instantaneous bound on the perturbation and ϵ is a constant that can be made arbitrarily small by an appropriate selection of design parameters.
- In the limit as $t \to \infty$, the controller parameters generated by the 'main' adaptive law remain ϵ-close to the intersection of the initial parametric uncertainty set and the final ellipsoid produced by the set-membership estimator. Consequently, the robust stability and RMS tracking performance bounds for such a MRAC are comparable to those of a MRAC using only projection and they become identical as the adaptation gain approaches zero. Furthermore, the tracking performance of this MRAC in the *lim sup* sense is $O[(\sqrt{M+1})d_z + \epsilon]$ while in the absence of perturbations the tracking error converges to zero.

Among the interesting features of this algorithm is that an estimate of parametric uncertainty is available at each time and is used as a constraint in updating the controller parameters. This set is updated in such a way that a measure of its size (e.g., volume) is nonincreasing and 'directional' excitation during transients as well as steady-state excitation can both serve to reduce parametric uncertainty and improve performance. The price paid for such a performance improvement is the requirement for a second estimator, which is not too severe in view of the improvements in the speed and computational power of microcomputers. Furthermore, at present these results are only applicable to the case of LTI plants. The possibility of extending of this algorithm to LTV plants, although nontrivial and quite interesting, is left as a topic of future research.

[1] Their derivation and precise statement involves a fair amount of technical details.

References

[1] P.A. Ioannou and J. Sun, "Theory and design of robust direct and indirect adaptive control schemes," *Int. J. Control*, Vol. 47, 775, 1988.

[2] K.S. Tsakalis, "Robustness of Model Reference Adaptive Controllers: An Input-Output Approach," *IEEE Trans. AC-37, 5*, 1992.

[3] B.D.O. Anderson, "Adaptive systems, lack of persistency of excitation and bursting phenomenon," *Automatica*, May 1985.

[4] G.J. Rey, C.R. Johnson and R.R. Bitmead, "Nonlinear interactions between signals and parameters in robust adaptive control," *Proc. 1990 ACC.*

[5] B.E. Ydstie, "Bifurcations and complex dynamics in adaptive control systems," *Proc. 25th CDC*, Dec. 1986.

[6] I.M.Y. Mareels and R.R. Bitmead, "Nonlinear dynamics in adaptive control: Chaotic and periodic stabilization," *Automatica*, Vol. 22, 641, 1986.

[7] B.B. Peterson and K.S. Narendra, "Bounded Error Adaptive Control," *IEEE Trans. Automat. Control*, Vol. AC-27, No. 6, pp. 1161–1168, 1982.

[8] R.H. Middleton, G.C. Goodwin, D. Hill and D. Mayne, "Design Issues in Adaptive Control," *IEEE Trans. Autom. Contr.*, vol. 33, No.1, Jan. 1988.

[9] B.D.O. Anderson, R.R. Bitmead, C.R. Johnson, P.V. Kokotovic, R.L. Kosut, I.M.Y. Mareels, L. Praly and B.D. Riedle, *Stability of Adaptive Systems: Passivity and Averaging Analysis*, MIT Press,1986.

[10] P. J. Gawthrop, *Continuous-Time Self-Tuning Control. Volume 1: Design*, John Wiley and Sons, 1987.

[11] P.A. Ioannou and G. Tao, "Dominant richness and improvement of performance of robust adaptive control," *Automatica*, Vol. 25, 287, March 1989.

[12] K. S. Narendra and A. M. Annaswamy, *Stable Adaptive Systems*. Prentice-Hall, 1989.

[13] S. S. Sastry and M. Bodson, *Adaptive Control: Stability, Convergence and Robustness*. Prentice-Hall, 1989.

[14] J. Sun, "A modified model reference adaptive control scheme for improved performance," *Proc. 1991 ACC.*

[15] A. Data and P.A. Ioannou, "Performance analysis and improvement in model reference adaptive control," *EE-Systems Dept., U.S.C. Report*, 1992.

[16] E. Fogel and Y.F. Huang, "On the value of information in system identification — Bounded noise case," *Automatica*, Vol. 18, 229, 1982.

[17] R. Lozano-Leal and R. Ortega, "Reformulation of the parameter identification problem for systems with bounded disturbances," *Automatica*, 1987.

[18] Tay, T.T. and M.H. Tan, "A robust adaptive performance enhancement controller using set membership identification," *IEEE Trans. AC-37, 10*, 1992.

[19] Polak, E., S.E. Salcudean, and D.Q. Mayne, "Adaptive control of ARMA plants using worst-case design by semi-infinite optimization," *IEEE Trans. AC-32, 5*, 1987.

[20] Kosut, R.L., "Adaptive control via parameter set estimation," *Int. J. ACSP*, Vol. 2., 371-400, 1988.

Proceedings of the
American Control Conference
San Francisco, California • June 1993

IMPROVED PERFORMANCE MRAC OF LINEAR AND NONLINEAR SYSTEMS

Ioannis N. M. Papadakis and **Stelios C. A. Thomopoulos**

Decision and Control Systems Laboratory
Department of Electrical and Computer Engineering
Pennsylvania State University
University Park, PA 16802

ABSTRACT

The problem of improved performance adaptive control (IPAC) of a class of linear and nonlinear systems is considered. A method for its solution is presented, the main feature of which lies in augmenting the "standard" model reference adaptive controller by a properly designed signal compensating for the effect of plant parameter uncertainty on the output error. One of the main performance improvement characteristics of the proposed IPAC is that the zero-state output error can be made arbitrarily small under standard model reference adaptive control (MRAC) assumptions in the case of linear systems while a similar result holds for a class of linearizable systems as well. The exponential convergence of the output and parameter errors in the presence of sufficiently rich reference inputs, remains a valid property of this controller which also achieves improved robustness in the presence of bounded disturbances and/or unmodeled dynamics as well as in the case of an adaptation switch-off.

1. INTRODUCTION

Since the first rigorous proofs of asymptotically stable adaptive control methods for linear systems [1-3], different methods with similar properties have been developed. In [4, 5], the issue of controller performance was addressed by using sufficiently rich reference inputs, in the presence of which, exponential convergence of the output and parameter errors to zero is guaranteed. However, this improvement in convergence results in a poorer transient performance if the desired reference trajectories are not sufficiently rich. Furthermore, since the exponential convergence is not uniform, the rate of convergence can be very small, so that large transients may still occur, especially in the case of large initial parameter uncertainty. Also, the stability and convergence results of [1-5] provide little or no information about the transient behavior of the system, allowing for unpredictably large overshoots, bursts, and low convergence rates.

The design of adaptive controllers with improved transient performance is therefore a problem of particular interest at the present stage of adaptive control. A useful result in this direction is that of [6], where a high-gain switching adaptive controller which provides an "arbitrarily good transient and steady-state performance" was introduced. Successful designs of adaptive controls with quantifiable transient behavior for linear systems have been introduced in [7-13]. In [9], performance improvement is achieved provided that the high frequency gain k_p of the plant is known. This requirement was relaxed in [11] and later in [10], to allow for performance improvement under some (not arbitrary) uncertainty on k_p. In this paper, we extend our previous results [11], as well as the results of [11], to achieve improved performance adaptive control for linear systems under the standard MRAC assumption regarding the high frequency gain k_p of the plant, i.e. knowledge of its sign and of an upper bound, by redesigning the compensation signal used for IPAC. We also show that under the assumptions of [21-22] regarding the admissible uncertainty on k_p the performance may be considerably improved by redesigning the shaping filters of the auxiliary signal used to provide parameter mismatch compensation. Another contribution of this paper is to clarify the effect of terms due to initial conditions, also resulting from stable operator inversions, on the internal signals of the closed adaptive system and on the output error.

2. IPAC FOR LINEAR SYSTEMS

Prior to describing the structure of the proposed IPAC, we first present in Section 2.1 some useful controller-independent results in MRAC. In Section 2.2, we give some necessary mathematical preliminaries and in Section 2.3 we introduce the IPAC and establish its properties.

2.1. Some Useful Controller-Independent Results in MRAC

Let the input - output relation of the plant ($u \to y_p$) and of the reference model ($r \to y_m$) be given by

$$y_p = k_p \frac{n_p(s)}{d_p(s)} [u] = \hat{P}(s)[u] \quad ; \quad y_m = k_m \frac{n_m(s)}{d_m(s)} [r] = \hat{M}(s)[r]. \qquad (2.1)$$

The control objective in MRAC is to design a control input u, so that the output y_p of the plant tracks the output y_m of the reference model. Consider the usual MRAC assumptions [4, 5] **(A1)** The polynomial $d_p(s)$ is monic and of degree n. **(A2)** The polynomial $n_p(s)$ is monic, Hurwitz and of degree $m < n$. **(A3)** The relative degree n^* [$= n - m$] of the plant is known. **(A4)** The polynomials $n_m(s)$, $d_m(s)$ are monic Hurwitz polynomials of degree q_m, p_m respectively, with $p_m \le n$, $n^* = p_m - q_m$ and $k_m > 0$. **(A5)** The input r(t) to the reference model is uniformly bounded, i.e. $r(t) \in L_\infty$. The following is a well known result in MRAC : Under the assumptions (A1)-(A5), the input-output relation of the plant may be expressed as

$$c_0^* y_p = \hat{M}[u] - \hat{M}[\theta^{*T}\bar{w}] + \varepsilon_{ic}(t) \qquad (2.2)$$

where $c_0^* = k_m/k_p$ and $\theta^{*T} = [c_0^* \ \bar{\theta}^{*T}] = [c_0^* \ c^{*T} \ d_0^* \ d^{*T}]$ is a constant parameter vector and

$$w_1 = \alpha(s)/\Lambda(s)[u] \quad , \quad w_2 = \alpha(s)/\Lambda(s)[y_p] \qquad (2.3)$$

$$\alpha(s) = [s^{n-2} \ldots s \ 1]^T; \ \Lambda(s) = n_m(s)\lambda(s); \ w^T = [r \ \bar{w}^T] = [r \ w_1^T \ y_p \ w_2^T]$$

$\lambda(s)$ is a monic Hurwitz polynomial of degree $n-q_m-1$ and $\varepsilon_{ic}(t)$ is a combination of exponentially decaying terms due to initial conditions of the plant and the observer. From (2.2), a controller - independent regressor equation may be obtained in different ways, one of which is described below. Define the signal $\tilde{e}$ by

$$\tilde{e} = c_0 y_p + \bar{\theta}^T \hat{M}[\bar{w}] - \hat{M}[u] = \theta^T \tilde{w} - \hat{M}[u] \qquad (2.4)$$

where $\theta^T = [c_0 \ \bar{\theta}^T]$ is a vector to be specified, and $\tilde{w}^T = [y_p \ \hat{M}[\bar{w}^T]]$. From (2.2) and (2.4) we have that the (available for measurement) signal $\tilde{e}$ satisfies

$$\tilde{e} = (\theta - \theta^*)^T [y_p \ \ M[\bar{w}^T]]^T + \varepsilon_{ic}(t) = \phi^T \tilde{w} + \varepsilon_{ic}(t) \qquad (2.5)$$

with the obvious definition for the parameter error vector ϕ. The vector θ becomes an estimate of θ^* if

$$\dot{\theta} = - \Pr[g \ \tilde{e} \ \tilde{w}/m^2] \quad ; \quad m = \sqrt{\rho + \gamma \ \tilde{w}^T \tilde{w}} \qquad (2.6)$$

where $g > 0$ is a constant and $\Pr[\cdot]$ is the usual projection operation [4] and ρ, γ are positive constants. In the presence of unmodeled dynamics, ρ must be modified as discussed in Section 2.3. The adaptation law (2.6) guarantees certain well known properties independently of the boundedness of $\tilde{w}$ or the presence of the term $\varepsilon_{ic}(t)$ [5].

2.2. Mathematical Preliminaries

Certain definitions and lemmas, useful in the analysis of the proposed IPAC, are stated below.

Definition 2.1 For any signal $z : \mathbb{R}^{\ge 0} \to \mathbb{R}^n$, and for any $\delta \ge 0$, $t \ge 0$, we define z_t and $\|z_t^\delta\|_2$ by

$$z_t(\sigma) = \begin{cases} z(\sigma) & \sigma \in [0, t] \\ 0 & \text{otherwise.} \end{cases} \quad ; \quad \|z_t^\delta\|_2 = \{\int_0^t \exp[-\delta(t-\sigma)][z^T(\sigma)z(\sigma)]d\sigma\}^{1/2}.$$

Definition 2.2 Let $\hat{H}(s)$ be a transfer matrix with causal and proper entries with entries analytic on $\mathrm{Re}[s] \ge -\delta/2$ for some $\delta \ge 0$ and let $u_t \in L_2$. Define the norm $\|\hat{H}\|_\infty^\delta$ by $\|\hat{H}\|_\infty^\delta = \sup\{\lambda_{max}[\hat{H}^*\hat{H}(j\omega-\delta/2)]\}^{1/2}$ where λ_{max} denotes the largest (necessarily real here) eigenvalue and $\hat{H}^*$ denotes the conjugate transpose of $\hat{H}$, and the norm $\|\hat{H}\|_2^\delta$ by $\|\hat{H}\|_2^\delta = \{\frac{1}{2\pi}\int_{-\infty}^{+\infty} \mathrm{tr}[\hat{H}^*\hat{H}(j\omega-\delta/2)]d\omega\}^{1/2}$.

Lemma 2.1 [9]

Let $z = \hat{H}(s)[x]$, where $\hat{H}(s)$ is a transfer matrix with causal and proper entries. If the entries of $\hat{H}(s)$ are analytic on $\mathrm{Re}[s] \ge -\delta/2$ for some $\delta \ge 0$

and $u \in L_{2e}$ then $\|z_t\|_2^\delta \leq \|\hat{H}\|_\infty^\delta \|x_t\|_2^\delta$. Furthermore, if the entries of $\hat{H}(s)$ are strictly proper then, $|z(t)| \leq \|\hat{H}\|_2^\delta \|x_t\|_2^\delta$.

2.3. IPAC : Controller Structure and Analysis

Consider the following control law

$$u = \theta^T w + FE \tag{2.7}$$

where the role of the *feedback error* signal FE is to compensate for the effect of the plant parameter uncertainty on the output error. In the absence of parameter mismatch compensation (FE = 0), the above controller reduces to the standard MRAC controller, widely used in MRAC literature [4-5]. In order to motivate the design of FE, we derive the output error equation associated with the control law (2.7) using (2.2). Note that an equally useful alternative parameterization also leading to a regressor with filtered versions of the control and of the plant output, is that of [1]. By using (2.2), (2.7) and by omitting the exponentially decaying term $\varepsilon_{ic}(t)$ as it bears no effect in our development regarding performance improvement (see discussion below), we obtain that

$$c_0^* e = \hat{M}[\phi^T w] + \hat{M}[FE] \;\; ; \; e = y_p - y_m \tag{2.8}$$

Let the feedback error signal FE be given by

$$FE = - \beta \hat{M}^{-1}\hat{F}_s[e] \tag{2.9}$$

where $\beta \neq 0$ is a constant to be specified, and $\hat{F}_s$ is a properly designed stable filter of relative degree n^*. By using (2.9) in (2.8), e satisfies the equation

$$\beta (\varepsilon + \hat{F}_s)[e] = \hat{M}[\phi^T w] \tag{2.10}$$

where $\varepsilon = c_0^*/\beta$ is a constant. From (2.10), in order to solve for e one needs to invert the operator $\varepsilon + \hat{F}_s$. Therefore, the stable, and of relative degree n^*, filter $\hat{F}_s$ should be such that $\varepsilon + \hat{F}_s$ is minimum phase. Furthermore, in order for $\hat{F}_s$ to lead to arbitrary performance improvement we require that $\|\hat{F}_s\|_\infty^\delta$ may also become arbitrarily large, as a function of some design parameter. One such filter (alternative choices are also possible) is given by

$$\hat{F}_s = (1 - \tau/\tau_{max})^{n^*}/[(\tau s + 1)^{n^*} - (1 - \tau/\tau_{max})^{n^*}] \tag{2.11}$$

where the design parameter τ satisfies $\tau \in (0, \tau_{max}]$ with $\tau_{max} > 0$ arbitrary. It can be easily shown [12] that the poles of $\hat{F}_s$ are in Re[s] < 0. From (2.11), we have that the poles of $1/(\varepsilon + \hat{F}_s)$ are in the left half plane if $|1 - \varepsilon|(1 - \tau/\tau_{max})^{n^*}/[|\varepsilon|\,|j\omega\tau + 1|^{n^*}] < 1$. For $\tau \in (0, \tau_{max}]$, we clearly have that $(1 - \tau/\tau_{max})^{n^*}/|j\omega\tau + 1|^{n^*} < 1 \;\forall\, \omega \in \mathbb{R}$ so that the stability condition is satisfied if $|1 - \varepsilon|/|\varepsilon| < 1$ which, in turn, holds for $\varepsilon > 1$. Therefore, the constant β in (2.9) should be a lower bound of c_0^* which implies that an upper bound of $k_p (= k_m/c_0^*)$ should be available. Having shown that $1/(\varepsilon + \hat{F}_s)$ is minimum phase and stable for $\varepsilon > 1$, we establish the properties of $\hat{F}_s$ which lead to performance improvement. A proof of the following lemma is given in [12]. For notational simplicity, the letter c is used throughout the paper as a generic symbol for a positive constant independent of τ.

Lemma 2.2 [12]

Let $\hat{W}$ be a strictly proper rational stable transfer function, analytic in $Re(s) \geq -\delta^*/2$ for some $\delta^* > 0$. Let $\hat{F}_s$ be given by (2.11) with $n^* \geq 1$ and $\tau \in (0, \tau_{max}]$ with $\tau_{max} > 0$ arbitrary. Then, $\forall\, \delta \in (0, \delta_1^*)$, for some small $\delta_1^* > 0$ and for $\varepsilon > 1$, **(a)** $\|1/(\varepsilon+\hat{F}_s)\|_\infty^\delta \leq c$; **(b)** $\|\hat{W}/(\varepsilon+\hat{F}_s)\|_\infty^\delta \leq c\,\tau$.

Based on Lemma 2.2, the following theorems state the performance improvement properties of the proposed IPAC method. The term "closed loop adaptive system" below, refers to the system described by (2.1), (2.3), (2.5)-(2.6) and (2.7), (2.9) with $\beta = k_m/k_{pmax}$, where k_{pmax} is a known upper bound of k_p. Abreviated versions of the proofs are included in the Appendix. The following assumption regarding k_p is introduced : **(A6)** The sign of the high frequency gain k_p of the plant is known (without loss of generality, we assume that k_p is positive). Furthermore, an upper bound k_{pmax} of k_p is also known. The assumptions (A1)-(A6) are usually referred to as standard MRAC assumptions due to their wide use in MRAC literature.

Theorem 2.1 (Main Result ; Ideal Case)

Under the assumptions (A1)-(A6) and for initial conditions in a ball M_0, i.e. $|\theta(0)| \leq M_0$ with $M_0 > 0$ arbitrary, all signals in the closed loop adaptive system with $\tau \in (0, \tau_{max}]$ and $\tau_{max} > 0$ arbitrary, are bounded. The output error satisfies $e \in L_2 \cap L_\infty$ and $\lim_{t\to\infty}[e(t)] = 0$. The output y_p of the plant and the output error are uniformly bounded with respect to τ and $t \geq 0$, and the output error e satisfies

$$\sup_{0\leq\sigma\leq t} |e(\sigma)| \leq c\,\tau \tag{2.12}$$

where $t \geq 0$ is arbitrary, and c is a positive constant which depends on M_0 but is independent of τ.

The above theorem implies that by using the FE signal given by (2.9), the performance improvement on the output error is achieved by reducing the value of τ. Note that (2.12) involves the steady state error, i.e. assuming that $\varepsilon_{ic}(t) = 0$ for all $t \geq 0$. Taking $\varepsilon_{ic}(t)$ into consideration does not alter the main result of the above theorem. The mathematically correct relation corresponding to (2.12), given here for the sake of completeness is $\sup_{t_0\leq\sigma\leq t} |e(\sigma)| \leq c\,\tau + c\,\exp(-a\,t_0)$ where the constant $a > 0$ is independent of τ, t and t_0 and exp(-at) decays as fast as $\varepsilon_{ic}(t)$. The presence of such a term is unavoidable, however it is important that it is uniformly bounded with respect to τ and that its rate of decay is essentially that of $\varepsilon_{ic}(t)$. Therefore our statement that the presence of the exponentially decaying term $\varepsilon_{ic}(t)$ does not affect performance improvement should be understood in this context. In general, the control u is **not** uniformly bounded with respect to τ. To show this, we derive expressions for the output error and the control, taking into account terms due to initial conditions. From (2.2), (2.7) and (2.9)

$$e = \frac{1}{\beta}\hat{M}(\varepsilon + \hat{F}_s)^{-1}[\phi^T w] + \frac{1}{\beta}(\varepsilon + \hat{F}_s)^{-1}[\varepsilon_{ic}(t)] \tag{2.13}$$

$$u = \theta^T w - \beta \hat{M}^{-1}\hat{F}_s[e]. \tag{2.14}$$

Noting that if $[A_1,b_1,c_1,d_1]$ is a state representation of the zero relative degree transfer function $\hat{M}^{-1}\hat{F}_s/(\varepsilon + \hat{F}_s)$ then $d_1 = c(1-\tau/\tau_{max})^{n^*}/\tau^{n^*}$, where c is a constant, we conclude that by decreasing τ, the initial magnitude $|d_1\varepsilon_{ic}(0+)|$ of the term $d_1\varepsilon_{ic}(t)$ in the resulting expression for u is increased. Therefore, although the proof of Theorem 2.1, given in the Appendix, guarantees that the output error is uniformly bounded with respect to τ, this is **not** the case with the control or w_1. This is a non-adaptive phenomenon characterizing high feedback-gain controllers. The above remark is general, in the sense that it also applies to the controls of [7-10, 11-13] despite that, as in [9, 11], the $\|\cdot\|_\infty^\delta$ norm of the compensating filter may be uniformly bounded with respect to τ. Similar remarks apply to the case of IPAC in the presence of bounded disturbances and/or unmodeled dynamics. The main conclusion is that, especially in the case of high-gain (adaptive or non-adaptive) controllers one should be careful in handling the contributions of terms due to initial conditions because their omission may lead to incorrect results. Arguments on uniform boundedness of signals in the closed loop are especially sensitive to such omissions. As is usually the case in control, the use of Laplace operators makes the analysis elegant and insightful, however one should be cautious to identify any gain-dependent contributions due to initial conditions or due to inversion(s) of minimum phase operators. A more detailed discussion of the above can be found in the proof of Theorem 2.1 in the Appendix.

The role of $\hat{F}_s$ in performance improvement becomes clear if (2.10) is solved with respect to the output error, and the resulting expression is substituted in (2.14), so that

$$u = \theta^T w - \{\hat{F}_s/(\varepsilon + \hat{F}_s)\}\,[(\theta - \theta^*)^T w] \qquad (2.15)$$

which shows that as τ is decreased the control "approaches" its nominal value, given by $\theta^{*T}w$. The performance improvement as implied by (2.15) is a direct result of the high-gain property of $\hat{F}_s$. The following theorem establishes the properties of the proposed IPAC in the event of an adaptation switch-off, i.e. $\dot{\theta} = 0$, $t \geq t_{so}$, where $t_{so} > 0$ denotes the adaptation switch-off time. A proof is given in the Appendix.

Theorem 2.2 (Adaptation Switch-Off)

Consider the assumptions (A1)-(A6), and the closed loop system (2.1), (2.3), (2.8) and (2.19) and let θ be fixed, i.e. $\dot{\theta} = 0$. There exists a constant $\tau^* > 0$ such that for any $\tau \in (0, \tau^*]$, the above closed loop system is stable and all signals in it are bounded. Furthermore, $|\hat{G}_c(j\omega) - \hat{M}(j\omega)| < c\,\tau \quad \forall\ \omega \in \mathbb{R}$ where $\hat{G}_c = y_p(s)/r(s)$ is the transfer function of the closed loop system.

The above theorem establishes the model-matching capability of the proposed IPAC uniformly in $\omega \in \mathbb{R}$, thus extending a related local robustness result in [7]. As expected, the value of τ^* is increased with increased parameter uncertainty $\|\phi\|$. The implication of the above theorem is that the output error may become arbitrarily small by reducing τ. For $\tau \leq \tau^*$, the role of the adaptation law is to ensure that the output error also converges asymptotically to zero as $t \to \infty$.

A description of the properties of the IPAC in the presence of bounded disturbances and/or unmodeled dynamics is given below. In this case, the input-output relation of the plant becomes $y_p = \{\hat{P}(1+\mu\hat{\Delta}_m)+\mu\hat{\Delta}_a\}[u + d_u]+d_y$ with $\mu \in (0, \mu^*]$ for some constant $\mu^* > 0$. The following additional assumptions specify the class of disturbances/modeling errors in the presence of which, "arbitrary" performance improvement follows. **(A7)** An upper bound $M_\theta > 0$ of $|\theta^*|$ is known. **(A8)** The transfer functions $\hat{\Delta}_m(s)$ and $\hat{\Delta}_a(s)$ are analytic in $Re(s) > -\delta_0$, for some $\delta_0 > 0$. **(A9)** The multiplicative uncertainty $\hat{\Delta}_m(s)$ is proper and satisfies $\|\hat{\Delta}_m\|_\infty^{\delta_1} < \infty$ for some $\delta_1 > 0$. **(A10)** There exists a rational transfer function W(s) with zeros and poles in $Re[s] < -\delta_2$ and relative degree not less than n^*, such that $\|\hat{W}^{-1}\hat{\Delta}_a\|_\infty^{\delta_2} < \infty$ for some $\delta_2 > 0$. Also, the additive uncertainty $\hat{\Delta}_a$ is strictly proper. **(A11)** The disturbances d_u, d_y and their time derivatives are bounded. Furthermore, d_y can always be represented as the output of a stable, proper, LTI filter with relative degree not less than n^*, with a bounded input. The adaptation law used in this case is given by (2.6), with $\rho = \rho(t) = \rho_0 + (s + \rho_1)^{-1}[u^2(t)]$ (*) and ρ_0, ρ_1 are positive constants to be specified. Note that, as in [11], if only bounded disturbances are present, i.e. $\mu = 0$, the presence of the filtered term in (*) is not necessary, i.e. $\rho = \rho_0$. The main performance improvement result of the proposed method in the presence of bounded disturbances and unmodeled dynamics is stated in the following theorem. The proof follows that of Theorem 2.1 and can be found in [13].

Theorem 2.3 (Performance Improvement ; Non-Ideal Case) [12, 13]

Consider (A1)-(A11), initial conditions in a ball M_0 and the closed loop adaptive system with ρ given by (*). There exist constants $\mu^* > 0$, $\rho_0^* > 0$, and $\rho_1^* > 0$ such that for any $\rho_0 \geq \rho_0^*$, $\rho_1 \in (0, \rho_1^*)$, and $\mu \in (0, \mu^*]$ all signals in the closed loop system with $\tau \in (0, \tau_{max}]$ and $\tau_{max} > 0$ arbitrary, are bounded. Furthermore, the output y_p of the plant is uniformly bounded with respect to τ and $t \geq 0$, and the output error, e, satisfies $\sup_{0 \leq \sigma \leq t} |e(\sigma)| \leq c\,\tau$ where $t \geq 0$ is arbitrary, and c is a positive constant which depends on M_0 but is independent of τ.

As implied by the above theorem, the proposed method achieves arbitrary performance improvement in the class of unmodeled dynamics described by (A7)-(A11). Note that if this class is enlarged, i.e. if some of (A7)-(A10) are relaxed, the corresponding performance improvement may not be arbitrary, i.e. $\tau \in [\tau_{min}, \tau_{max}]$ with $\tau_{min} > 0$. For example, if (A9) is relaxed, so that $\hat{\Delta}_m$ is not assumed to be proper but such that $\|\hat{W}\hat{\Delta}_m\|_\infty^{\delta_1} < \infty$ with $\hat{W}$ and δ_1 as in (A10), performance improvement is traded-off with robustness margins, as shown in [9] for the special case in which k_p is known. Note that the normalization signal in this case essentially guarantees that the contribution of the disturbances and/or the unmodeled dynamics is small in the mean, conforming with the normalizing signal approach.

Remarks

1) The performance improvement results of Theorems 2.1 and 2.3, hold if e(t) is replaced by any of its first n^*-1 time-derivatives.

2) The control (2.7) may be rewritten as $u = \theta_{new}^T w$ with θ_{new} given by

$$\theta_{new} = \theta_{new}(0) - \int_0^t Pr[g\,\frac{\tilde{e}}{m^2}\tilde{w}]\,d\sigma - \frac{\beta\,\hat{M}^{-1}\hat{F}_s[e]}{\delta_D(|w|) + w^T w}\,w$$

where $|w| = (w^T w)^{1/2}$ and $\delta_D(\cdot) : \mathbb{R}^{\geq 0} \to \{0, 1\}$ is the discrete impulse function, i.e. $\delta_D(x) = 1$ if $x = 0$ and $\delta_D(x) = 0$ if $x \neq 0$. Therefore, the use of the proposed IPAC introduces a "correction" term in the classical MRAC estimator as shown in the above expression.

3) The property of exponential convergence of all errors to zero in the presence of sufficiently exciting inputs holds in the presence of FE [11-13].

2.4. IPAC Under Some Uncertainty on k_p - Further Performance Enhancement

As we mentioned in the introduction, the result of [9] which requires k_p to be known were extended in [11] to include some uncertainty on k_p. In this section, we show that under similar constraints on the admissible uncertainty concerning k_p further improvement in performance can be achieved by redesigning the shaping filter of FE used in [11]. It is also shown that if the approach of Section 2.3 is used to achieve a similar performance enhancement, the resulting constraints on the admissible uncertainty on k_p parallel those of the previous cases. Using the MOEM notation [11] we denote $\tilde{\phi}_M = \tilde{\theta}_M - \tilde{\theta}_M^* = [\tilde{\phi}_0\ \bar{\phi}_M^T]^T$; $\tilde{w}_M = [-u\ \bar{w}^T]^T$; $\tilde{\theta}_M = [1/c_0\ \bar{\theta}^T/c_0]^T$; $\tilde{\theta}_M^* = [1/c_0^*\ \bar{\theta}^{*T}/c_0^*]^T$. By using (2.2), and by omitting $\varepsilon_{ic}(t)$, y_p may be expressed by $y_p = -\hat{M}[\tilde{\theta}_M^{*T}\tilde{w}_M]$ and since (2.7) implies that $r = -\tilde{\theta}_M^T\tilde{w}_M - FE/c_0$, (2.10) gives

$$e = \hat{M}[\tilde{\phi}_M^T\tilde{w}_M] + \hat{M}[FE/c_0] \qquad (2.16)$$

which does not involve c_0^* explicitly, motivating a different design for FE [11]. Consider FE given by $FE/c_0 = -[(1 + \hat{F})^{n^*} - 1][\tilde{\phi}_M^T\tilde{w}_M]$ which is clearly constructable if $\hat{F}$ is stable and of relative degree n^*. With this choice for FE, we have that $(1 + \hat{F})^{n^*}[e] = \hat{M}[\tilde{\phi}_M^T\tilde{w}_M]$ and by requiring $(1+\hat{F})\ (1-F_1) = 1$ where $F_1 = (1-\tau/\tau_{max})^{n^*}/(\tau s+1)^{n^*}$ we have that the corresponding error equation is $e = \hat{M}(1 - \hat{F}_1)^{n^*}[\tilde{\phi}_M^T\tilde{w}_M]$ which gives a performance improvement at the rate of τ^{n^*}, rather that τ as in all previous IPAC schemes. Not surprisingly, the above requirement for $\hat{F}$ gives that $\hat{F} = \hat{F}_1/(1 - \hat{F}_1) = \hat{F}_s$ where $\hat{F}_s$ is given by (2.11). Unfortunately, this approach does not lend itself to the IPAC of Section 2.3, i.e. under (A6). To see this, let FE be given by $FE = -\hat{M}^{-1}\Sigma[(\beta_i\,(\hat{F}_s)^i][e]]_{i=1}^{i=n^*}$. Sufficient conditions for stability are not difficult to obtain; one finds that such a set of conditions are $|\gamma_i| < 1/(n^* 2^{n^*-i})$ where $\gamma_i = \beta_i/c_0^* - \xi_i$, with $\xi_i = n^*!/[(i!)(n^*-i)!]$, $i \leq n^*$ which essentially constraints the maximum admissible relative uncertainty on k_p.

2.5. Simulation Results

We present simulation results using the IPAC described in Section 2.3. The plant and reference model transfer functions are given by

$\hat{P}(s) = 5(s+1)/(s^2+s-6)$, $\hat{M}(s) = (s+2)/(s^2+9s+20)$. The vector θ^* of nominal controller parameters is given by $\theta^* = [0.2\ 1\ -1.6\ -2]^T$. In the following simulations all initial conditions are identical. The initial conditions of the estimated parameters are $\theta(0) = [0.5\ 0.5\ -0.5\ -0.5]^T$. We have selected $M_\theta=10$, $\rho_0=10$, $\rho_1=1$, $g=50$, $\gamma=1$, $\tau_{max}=5$ and $k_{pmax}=10$, so that $\beta=0.1$ ($=k_m/k_{pmax}$). In each case, we plot the response of the uncompensated system (FE = 0) and that of the IPAC system with τ = 0.01, 1, 2, 4. Simulation results for an adaptive tracking problem are shown in Figures 2.1–2.3. The reference input is $r(t) = 100+\sin(t)+2\sin(3t)$. As shown in Figure 2.1, the performance improves as τ decreases, as expected from the analysis of Section 2.3. The control and the compensation signal (FE) are shown in Figures 2.2 and 2.3. In Figure 2.3, the effect of the initial conditions on FE as τ is decreased to 0.01 becomes more significant. Notice that the initial value of $|FE|$ is increased as τ is decreased, as predicted by the discussion in Section 2.3. As shown in Figure 2.2, the maximum magnitude of the IPAC is less than that of the uncompensated system. More simulation results can be found in [12-13].

3. IPAC FOR NONLINEAR SYSTEMS

In this section, we develop controllers for improved performance adaptive control for a class of nonlinear systems. As shown below, we draw heavily on the analysis of the IPAC problem for linear systems. We consider systems of the form

$$\dot{x} = f(x) + g(x)\, u \ ; \ y = h(x) \tag{3.1}$$

where $f, g : \mathbb{R}^n \to \mathbb{R}^n$, $u, y \in \mathbb{R}$, $x \in \mathbb{R}^n$ and $h : \mathbb{R}^n \to \mathbb{R}$, with globally exponentially stable zero dynamics [14, 15]. To illustrate our approach, we consider the case in which the functions g and h are a priori known and we assume that there exists a set of known functions $f_i(x) : \mathbb{R}^n \to \mathbb{R}^n$, $i = 1, \ldots, n_1$ and a set of (totally or partially unknown) constants θ_1^*, $\theta_2^*, \ldots, \theta_{n_1}^*$ such that $f(x) = \Sigma\{\theta_i^* f_i(x)\}_{i=1}^{i=n_1}$. Following the notation of [14], after differentiation we obtain that $\dot{y} = L_f h + L_g h\, u$. We assume that $L_g h \neq 0$, i.e. the system (3.1) is of relative degree one. The following results may be generalized for the higher relative degree case [14]. Denoting $\tilde{w}^T = -[L_{f_1} h\ L_{f_2} h \ldots L_{f_{n_1}} h]$; $\theta^{*T} = [\theta_1^*\ \theta_2^* \ldots \theta_{n_1}^*]^T$, $\dot{y}$ may be expressed in a regressor form as follows $\dot{y} = -\theta^{*T}\tilde{w} + L_g h\, u$ resulting in the identification equation $y_I = -\{s/(s+a)\}[y] + (s+a)^{-1}[L_g h\, u] = \theta^{*T} w$, $a > 0$, where $w = \{1/(s+a)\}[\tilde{w}]$ is a filtered version of the regressor $\tilde{w}$. Note that we have used the usual operator notation and we have, as before, neglected exponentially decaying terms due to initial conditions since they do not affect our results. The signal y_I can be measured since y is accessible and $a > 0$ is a known arbitrary constant. Let the signal $\tilde{e}$ be defined by $\tilde{e} = \theta^T w - y_I = \phi^T w$, where $\theta = \theta(t) \in \mathbb{R}^{n_1}$ is an estimate of θ. The parameter adaptation law is then given by $\dot{\phi} = -\tilde{e}\, w/(1 + \gamma w^T w)$. Motivated by [14], the control u is given by

$$u = (1/L_g h)(-\tilde{L_f h} + \upsilon) \ ; \ \tilde{L_f h} = \theta^T\tilde{w} \ ; \ \upsilon = \dot{y}_m + a(y_m - y) + FE \tag{3.2}$$

$$FE = \hat{M}_1^{-1}\hat{F}_q[y_I] - \hat{F}_q[\theta^T\tilde{w}] \ ; \ \hat{M}_1 = 1/(s+a) \tag{3.3}$$

which gives that $e = y - y_m = \hat{M}_1(1 - \hat{F}_q)[\phi^T\tilde{w}]$. Alternatively, one may select $FE = -\hat{M}_1^{-1}\hat{F}_s[e]$ where $\hat{F}_s$ is given by (2.11) with $n^* = 1$. Both designs lead to similar performance improvement results as stated by Theorem 3.1 below. The proof follows the steps of the proof of Theorem 2.1 and is given in [13].

Theorem 3.1

Consider the globally exponential minimum phase system (3.1) with f, g, h, $L_{f_i}h$, $i = 1,\ldots,n_1$, $L_g h$ continuous Lipschitz functions of x, and $\tilde{w} = \tilde{w}(x, \theta)$ having bounded partial derivatives in x and θ. Then for initial conditions in any ball M_0, by using the control and parameter update laws described above, all signals in the closed loop system for $\tau \in (0, \tau_{max}]$ with $\tau_{max} > 0$ arbitrary, are bounded. Furthermore, the output y_p of the plant and the output error are uniformly bounded with respect to τ and $t \geq 0$, and the output error e satisfies $\sup_{0\leq\sigma\leq t} |e(\sigma)| \leq c\,\tau$ where $t \geq 0$ is arbitrary, and c is a positive constant which depends on M_0 but is independent of τ.

CONCLUSION

A new method for improved performance adaptive control under standard model reference adaptive control assumptions was introduced, extending current results in this area. In this method, the standard model reference adaptive controller is augmented by a feedback error signal, designed to compensate for the effect of plant parameter uncertainty on the output error. By using the proposed method and under standard MRAC assumptions, performance improvement can be achieved in the ideal case as well as in the presence of bounded disturbances and/or unmodeled dynamics. Simulation results verify the analysis of the paper and demonstrate the potential of the parameter mismatch compensation approach for the design of adaptive controllers with improved performance characteristics. The parameter mismatch compensation approach applies also to a class of linearizable systems leading to IPAC with properties similar to its linear counterpart.

APPENDIX

Proof of Theorem 2.1 : The introduction of FE given by (2.9) does not affect the relative rates of growth of signals within the adaptive system. Therefore, the assumption that the signals in the adaptive system grow in an unbounded fashion leads to a contradiction, from which the facts that $e \in L_2 \cap L_\infty$ and $\lim_{t\to\infty}[e(t)] = 0$ follow, for any $\tau \in (0, \tau_{max}]$. In order to establish the uniform boundedness of e and y_p with respect to $\tau \in (0, \tau_{max}]$ we start with (2.2), (2.7) and (2.9) which give that

$$e = \frac{1}{\beta}\hat{M}(\varepsilon + \hat{F}_s)^{-1}[\phi^T w] + \frac{1}{\beta}(\varepsilon + \hat{F}_s)^{-1}[\varepsilon_{ic}(t)]. \tag{A.1}$$

where we have taken the term $\varepsilon_{ic}(t)$ in to account. For the control, we have that $u = P^{-1}[y_p] + \varepsilon_u(t)$, where $\varepsilon_u(t)$ is an exponentially decaying signal in the null space of $n_p(s)$ (i.e. $n_p(s)[\varepsilon_u(t)] = 0$) depending on the values of $u(0+),\ldots,u^{(m-1)}(0+)$, which are **not** uniformly bounded with respect to τ (see discussion in Section 2.3, below Thm. 2.1). However, one easily establishes that since ε_u is in the null space of $\hat{P}$, its presence does not affect y_p. Therefore, since we are ultimately interested in showing that y_p is uniformly bounded with respect to τ, replacing u with $u_1 = u - \varepsilon_u$ (which for notational convenience we denote below as u) leaves y_p unaltered. However, this should not be a source of confusion, leading one to extrapolate any boundedness results to the original control u. As we noted, $\varepsilon_u(t)$ is exponentially decaying but is **not** uniformly bounded with respect to τ. With this in mind we have that

$$\beta\, y_p = \hat{M}(\varepsilon + \hat{F}_s)^{-1}[\phi^T w] + \beta\,\hat{M}[r] + (\varepsilon + \hat{F}_s)^{-1}[\varepsilon_{ic}(t)]. \tag{A.2}$$

$$\beta\, u = \hat{P}^{-1}\hat{M}(\varepsilon + \hat{F}_s)^{-1}[\phi^T w] + \beta\,\hat{P}^{-1}\hat{M}[r] + \hat{P}^{-1}(\varepsilon + \hat{F}_s)^{-1}[\varepsilon_{ic}(t)]. \tag{A.3}$$

The terms due to $\varepsilon_{ic}(t)$ in the above equations are uniformly bounded with respect to τ and can therefore be omitted without changing our main performance result. Note that since $\varepsilon_{ic}(t)$ is defined for t>0–, the n^* differentiations implied by $\hat{P}^{-1}$ in (A.3) do not yield impulsive functions. Equation (A.3) may be written as

$$u = \frac{1}{\beta}\hat{P}^{-1}\hat{M}(\varepsilon+\hat{F}_s)^{-1}(s+\lambda)^{-1}[\dot{\bar{\phi}}^T w + \bar{\phi}^T\dot{w} + \lambda(\bar{\phi}^T w)] + \hat{M}^{-1}\hat{P}\{\frac{1}{\beta}(\varepsilon+\hat{F}_s)^{-1}[\phi_0 r] + r\} \tag{A.4}$$

where $\phi_0 = c_0 - c_0^*$, and $\lambda > \delta_{max}$, where $\delta_{max} > 0$ is such that $\hat{P}^{-1}\hat{M}(\varepsilon + \hat{F}_s)^{-1}$ is analytic on $Re(s) \geq -\delta_{max}$. For any $\delta \in (0, \delta_{max})$, by using Lemma 2.1 and the fact that the adaptation law (2.6) guarantees that $|\phi| \in L_\infty$, (A.2) and (A.4) imply that

$$\|y_{pt}^{\delta}\|_2 \leq c\,\tau\, s_f + c \ ; \ \|u_t^{\delta}\|_2 \leq c\,\tau\, s_f + c + c\,\| |\dot{\bar{\phi}}|\, s_f \|_2^{\delta}$$

where $s_f = \|y_{pt}^{\delta}\|_2 + \|u_t^{\delta}\|_2$ and c is used as a generic symbol for a non-negative constant that does not depend of τ. Thus one obtains that $s_f \leq c + c\,\tau\, s_f + c\,\| |\dot{\bar{\phi}}|\, s_f \|_2^{\delta}$ which implies that for $\tau \in (0, \tau^*)$, for some sufficiently small $\tau^* > 0$, i.e. $\tau^* < 1/c$, we may write $s_f \le c + c \, \| |\dot{\bar{\phi}}| \, s_f \|_2^{\delta}$. Squaring both sides and by using the Bellman-Gronwall Lemma [5], and since $|\dot{\bar{\phi}}| \in L_2 \cap L_\infty$, we conclude that $s_f \in L_\infty$ for $\tau \in (0, \tau^*)$. Since $\sup_{\tau^* \le \tau \le \tau_{max}} (s_f) \in L_\infty$, we have that $s_f \in L_\infty$ uniformly with respect to $\tau \in (0, \tau_{max}]$ and $t \ge 0$. We write (A.1) as

$$e = (1/\beta)\hat{M}(\varepsilon+\hat{F}_s)^{-1}[\phi_0 r] + (1/\beta)\hat{M}(\varepsilon+\hat{F}_s)^{-1}(s+\lambda)^{-1}[\dot{\bar{\phi}}^T\bar{w} + \bar{\phi}^T\dot{\bar{w}} + \lambda\,(\bar{\phi}^T\bar{w})]$$

and by using Lemmas 2.1 and 2.2 (b) and since $\|\hat{M}(\varepsilon+\hat{F}_s)^{-1}\|_{L_1} \le c$, we obtain that $|e(t)| \le c\,\tau\, s_f \le c\,\tau$. ■

Proof of Theorem 2.2 : From (A.3)

$$y_p = (1/\beta)\hat{M}(\varepsilon+\hat{F}_s)^{-1}\{[\Delta c_0 \; \Delta c^T \; \Delta d_0 \; \Delta d^T][r \; (\hat{\Gamma}[u])^T \; y_p \; (\hat{\Gamma}[y_p])^T]^T\}+\hat{M}[r] \quad (A.5)$$

where $\hat{\Gamma}(s)=a(s)/\Lambda(s)$ and $\Delta c_0 = c_0-c_0^*$, $\Delta c = c-c^*$, $\Delta d_0 = d_0-d_0^*$ and $\Delta c_0 = d-d^*$ are the components of the (constant) parameter error ϕ. From (A.5), after rearranging terms

$$y_p/r = \hat{M}\,[1 - (\Delta c_0/\beta)/(\varepsilon + \hat{F}_s]/(1 - \hat{R}) = \hat{G}_c \quad (A.6)$$

where $\beta\hat{R} = (\varepsilon+\hat{F}_s)^{-1}(\Delta c^T\hat{\Gamma}\hat{M}\hat{P}^{-1}) + (\Delta d_0)\hat{M}(\varepsilon+\hat{F}_s)^{-1} + \hat{M}(\varepsilon+\hat{F}_s)^{-1}(\Delta d^T\hat{\Gamma})$ is a strictly proper and stable transfer function. A condition for stability is given by $|\hat{R}(j\omega)| < 1$ where $|\hat{R}(j\omega)|$ denotes the magnitude of $\hat{R}(j\omega)$. Note that the poles of the transfer function $\hat{M}[1 - (\Delta c_0/\beta)/(\varepsilon + \hat{F}_s)]$ are in $Re(s) < 0$. Arguing as in the proof of Lemma 2.2, it can be shown that $|\hat{M}/(\varepsilon+\hat{F}_s)| \le c\,\tau$; $|(\Delta c^T\hat{\Gamma}\hat{M}\hat{P}^{-1})/(\varepsilon+\hat{F}_s)| \le c\,\tau \;\forall\; \omega \in \mathbb{R}$ so that $|\hat{R}(j\omega)| < c_1\tau$, for some constant $c_1 > 0$. Taking $\tau^* = 1/c_1$ completes the proof of the first part of the theorem since similar boundedness conclusions can be drawn for the control u as well. The proof of the second part of the theorem follows by using (A.6) to write $\hat{G}_c - \hat{M} = [\hat{M}\hat{R} - (\Delta c_0/\beta)\,\hat{M}/(\varepsilon + \hat{F}_s)]/(1 - \hat{R})$. The relative degree zero transfer function $1/(1-\hat{R})$ is well defined for $\tau = 0$, and $|1/(1-\hat{R})| \le c$, $\forall\, \omega \in \mathbb{R}$. Furthermore, for $\forall\, \omega \in \mathbb{R}$, we have that $|\hat{M}\hat{R}| \le c\tau$ and $|\hat{M}/(\varepsilon + \hat{F}_s)| \le c\tau$, so that $|\hat{G}_c - \hat{M}| \le c\tau$, for some constant $c > 0$. ■

REFERENCES

[1] A. S. Morse, "Global Stability of Parameter-Adaptive Control Systems," IEEE TAC, AC-25, No. 3, pp. 433-439, June 1980.

[2] K. S. Narendra, Y. H. Lin, and L. Valavani, "Stable Adaptive Controller Design," IEEE TAC, AC-25, pp. 440-448, June 1980.

[3] G. C. Goodwin, P. J. Ramadge, and P. E. Caines, "Discrete Time Multivariable Adaptive Control," IEEE TAC, AC-25, pp. 449-456, June 1980.

[4] S. Sastry and M. Bodson, *Adaptive Control, Stability, Convergence, and Robustness*, Prentice Hall, New Jersey, 1989.

[5] K. S. Narendra and A. M. Annaswamy, *Stable Adaptive Systems*, Prentice Hall, 1989.

[6] D. E. Miller and E. J. Davison, "An Adaptive Controller Which Provides an Arbitrarily Good Transient and Steady-State Response," IEEE TAC, AC 36, No. 1, pp. 68-81, January 1991.

[7] J. Sun, A. W. Olbrot, and M. P. Polis, "Robust Stabilization and Robust Performance Using Model Reference Control and Modeling Error Compensation," Proc. of ACC, Vol. 1, pp. 892-897, June 1991.

[8] J. Sun, "A Modified Model Reference Adaptive Control Scheme for Improved Performance," Proc. ACC, Vol. 1, pp. 150-155, June 1991.

[9] A. Datta and P. A. Ioannou, "Performance Improvement Versus Robust Stability in Model Reference Adaptive Control," Proc. of the CDC, Vol. 1, pp. 748-753, December 1992; also "Performance Improvement in Model Reference Adaptive Control," Dept. of EE, USC, Rept 91-05-01, May 1991.

[10] A. Datta and M. T. Ho, "Systematic Design of Model Reference Adaptive Controllers with Improved Transient Performance," Tech. Rept TAMU-ECE92-12, EE Dept., Texas A&M Univ., November 1992.

[11] I. N. M. Papadakis and S. C. A. Thomopoulos, "Modified Output Error Method with Parameter Mismatch Compensation for Improved Performance Adaptive Control," Proc.of the CDC, Vol. 4, pp. 3249-3254, December 1992; also Tech. Rept TR-DCSL-92-2/A, Dept. of ECE, PSU, July 1992.

[12] I. N. M. Papadakis, *"Improved Performance Adaptive Control Using Parameter Error Compensation,"* PhD Thesis, Dept. of ECE, PSU, December 1992.

[13] I. N. M. Papadakis and S. C. A. Thomopoulos, "Improved Performance Adaptive Control For Linear and Nonlinear Systems," 2nd Workshop on Adaptive Control, Cancun, Mexico, December 9-11, 1992; also full version of 1993 ACC paper.

[14] S. Sastry and A. Isidori, "Adaptive Control of Linearizable Systems," IEEE TAC, AC 34, No. 11, November 1989.

[15] A. Isidori, *Nonlinear Control Systems*, S. Verlag, Berlin, 1989.

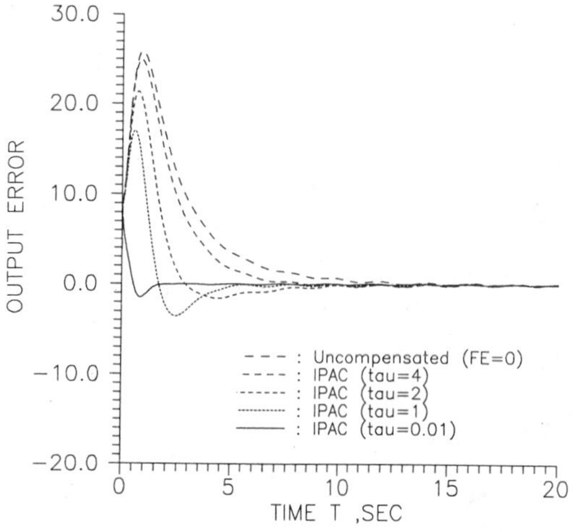

Figure 2.1

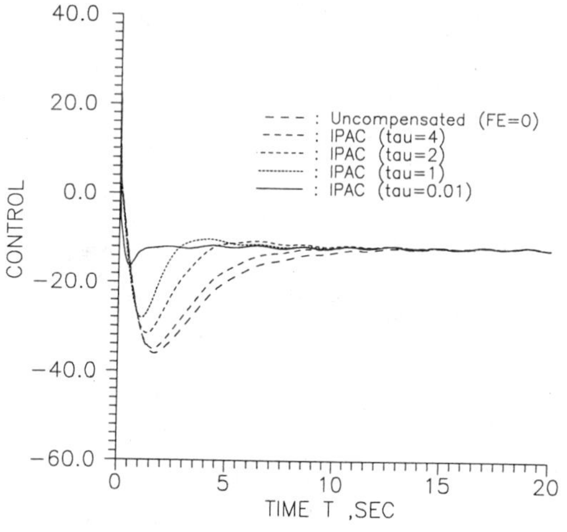

Figure 2.2

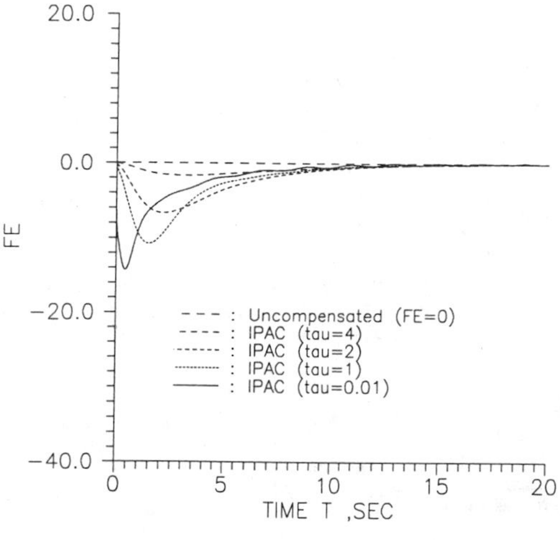

Figure 2.3

Proceedings of the
American Control Conference
San Francisco, California • June 1993

Transient Performance Improvement in Continuous-time Model Reference Adaptive Control: An L_1 Formulation[†]

Aniruddha Datta
Department of Electrical Engineering
Texas A & M University
College Station, TX 77843-3128
U.S.A

Abstract. This paper presents an L_1 formulation of the transient performance issue in model reference adaptive control. Specifically, it is shown that, in the case of known high frequency gain, the parametric uncertainty can be viewed as an input disturbance. Unlike as in standard L_1 optimal control, this disturbance cannot be apriori assumed to be bounded. Nevertheless, an L_1 optimal controller for the rejection of persistent bounded disturbances is designed, and is shown to be identical to a modified model refererence adaptive control scheme, proposed earlier for achieving performance improvement.

1 Introduction

Although the issue of transient performance of adaptive controllers is a very important one from a practical point of view, most of the existing results e.g. [1, 2] provide little or no information about it. To make matters worse, simulation experience suggests [3] that large parametric uncertainties can result in unacceptably poor transients.

Motivated by this empirical observation, in [4], we suggested a modified model reference adaptive control (MRAC) scheme which could be used to obtain arbitrarily improved transient performance in the ideal case, with known high frequency gain. This scheme was motivated from purely adhoc considerations and was not derived using any systematic methodology.

In this paper, we develop a systematic procedure for addressing the transient performance issue in model reference adaptive control. In particular, the effect of the parameter uncertainty is treated as an input disturbance. Using standard L_1 theory, it is then shown that one can design a sequence of suboptimal controllers that can lead to arbitrary performance improvement in the ideal case. Furthermore, the resulting controller is found to be exactly the same as the one proposed in [4].

The paper is organized as follows. In Section 2 we introduce some notation and mathematical preliminaries. This is followed in Section 3 by a brief description of a standard MRAC scheme. In Section 4, the performance improvement problem is formulated as an L_1 disturbance rejection problem, which is then solved using standard results. Section 5 establishes the equivalence between this solution and the earlier one obtained in [4]. Section 6 concludes the paper by discussing the main results and outlining some topics for future research.

2 Mathematical Preliminaries

In this section, we introduce some definitions and a lemma which is relevant to the results of this paper.

Suppose h is a distribution with support in the interval $[0, \infty)$ of the form

$$h(t) = \sum_{i=0}^{\infty} h_i \delta(t - t_i) + h_a(t) \tag{2.1}$$

where $0 \leq t_0 < t_1 \cdots$, δ denotes the unit impulse distribution, and $h_a(.)$ is Lebesgue measurable. The set $\mathcal{A}$ consists of all distributions h of the form (2.1) such that

$$\|h\|_{\mathcal{A}} = \sum_{i=0}^{\infty} |h_i| + \int_0^{\infty} |h_a(t)| dt \tag{2.2}$$

is finite. Note that $\mathcal{A}$ is precisely the set of impulse responses of BIBO stable systems.

Let $\hat{\mathcal{A}}$ denote the set of Laplace transforms of distributions in $\mathcal{A}$. Then clearly $\hat{\mathcal{A}}$ is a linear space. Suppose $F \in \hat{\mathcal{A}}$ and let f denote the inverse Laplace transform of F. Then we define

$$\|F\|_{\hat{\mathcal{A}}} = \|f\|_{\mathcal{A}} \tag{2.3}$$

Given a transfer function $H \in \hat{\mathcal{A}}$, it is well known [5] that $\|H\|_{\hat{\mathcal{A}}}$ is the induced norm of H viewed as an operator from L_∞ to L_∞. Next we state a result which is well known in the adaptive control literature.

[†]This work was supported by the National Science Foundation under Grant ECS-9210726

Lemma 2.1(Swapping Lemma) Let $\tilde{\theta}, w : R^+ \to R^n$ and let $\tilde{\theta}$ be differentiable. Let $W(s)$ be a proper stable rational transfer function with a minimal realization (A, b, c, d) i.e.

$$W(s) = c^T(sI - A)^{-1}b + d$$

Then

$$W(s)[\tilde{\theta}^T w] = \tilde{\theta}^T W(s)[w] + W_c(s)[(W_b(s)[w^T])\dot{\tilde{\theta}}] \tag{2.4}$$

where

$$W_c(s) = -c^T(sI - A)^{-1}, \; W_b(s) = (sI - A)^{-1}b$$

The proof of Lemma 2.1 can be found in [2].

3 A Standard MRAC Scheme

In this section, we consider a standard MRAC scheme and summarize its properties. The scheme consists of a model reference control algorithm and a parameter estimator using normalization and projection.

The plant to be controlled is described by the input-output pair u,y which are related by

$$y = G_0(s)[u] = k_p \frac{Z_0(s)}{R_0(s)}[u] \tag{3.1}$$

The control objective is to choose the control input u so that the output y of the plant tracks as closely as possible the output y_m of a stable reference model

$$y_m = W_m(s)[r] = k_m \frac{Z_m(s)}{R_m(s)}[r] \tag{3.2}$$

for any piecewise continuous, uniformly bounded reference input signal $r(t)$.

In order to meet the control objective, we make the following standard assumptions [1, 2] concerning the plant $G_0(s)$ and the reference model $W_m(s)$:

- (A1) $R_0(s)$ is a monic polynomial of degree n.
- (A2) $Z_0(s)$ is a monic Hurwitz polynomial of degree $m < n$.
- (A3) The constant k_p is known.*
- (A4) The relative degree $n^* = n - m$ is known.
- (A5) $Z_m(s)$, $R_m(s)$ are monic Hurwitz polynomials of degree q_m, p_m respectively with $p_m \leq n$, $n^* = p_m - q_m$ and $k_m > 0$.

We consider the following MRAC scheme that has been widely analyzed in the literature of adaptive control.

Control law:

$$u = \theta^T w + c_0 r, \; c_0 = \frac{k_m}{k_p} \tag{3.3}$$

where

$$\begin{aligned} w &= [w_1^T, w_2^T, y]^T, \; \theta = [\theta_1^T, \theta_2^T, \theta_3]^T \\ w_1 &= \frac{a(s)}{\Lambda(s)}[u], \; w_2 = \frac{a(s)}{\Lambda(s)}[y] \\ a(s) &= [s^{n-2}, s^{n-3}, \cdots s, 1]^T \\ \Lambda(s) &= Z_m(s)\lambda(s) \end{aligned}$$

where $\lambda(s)$ is a monic Hurwitz polynomial of degree $n - 1 - q_m$.

Adaptive law:

$$\dot{\theta} = \mathcal{P}r[-\gamma\epsilon\phi], \; \theta(0) \in C_\theta \tag{3.4}$$

$$\epsilon = \frac{[\theta^T\phi + c_0 y - W_m(s)[u]]}{m^2} \tag{3.5}$$

$$\phi = W_m(s)[w] \tag{3.6}$$

$$\frac{d}{dt}m^2 = -\delta_0(m^2 - 1) + u^2 + y^2, \; m^2(0) = 1 \tag{3.7}$$

*For the standard scheme, this assumption can be relaxed. However, the modified MRAC scheme in [4] required this assumption to be made.

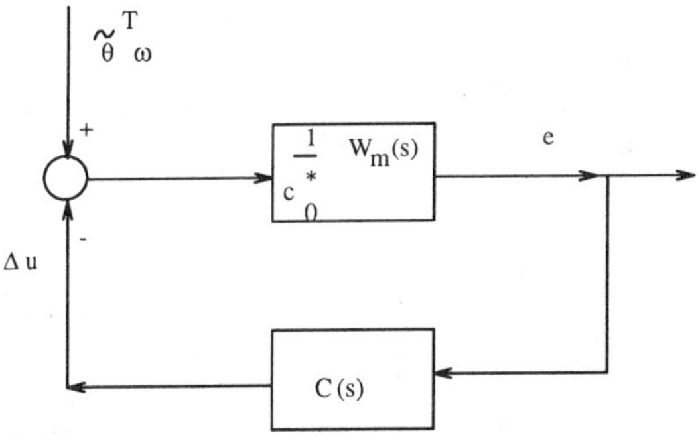

Figure 1: Design of L_1 Compensator

where $\gamma > 0$; $C_\theta = \{\theta \in R^{2n-1} | \, |\theta| \leq M_\theta\}$, $M_\theta > |\theta^*|$ is a design constant; θ^* is the desired controller parameter often referred to as the tuned parameter vector. The projection $\mathcal{P}r[.]$ operator is as defined in [6].

The design parameter $\delta_0 > 0$ is chosen so that $\lambda(s)$, $Z_m(s)$, $R_m(s)$ have all their roots in $\text{Re}[s] < -\frac{\delta_0}{2}$. The adaptive law (3.4) includes two rather standard by now modifications: a parameter projection and a special normalizing signal generated on line. Other modifications such as switching-σ, dead-zone etc. can also be used without changing the qualitative nature of the results of the paper.

The following theorem describes the properties of (3.3), (3.4) when applied to the plant (3.1).

Theorem 3.1: All the signals in the closed loop plant (3.1), (3.3), (3.4) are uniformly bounded and the tracking error $e(t) \triangleq y - y_m$ converges to zero as $t \to \infty$.

Proof: The proof is well known and is, therefore, omitted.

Theorem 3.1 fails to provide any information about the transient behaviour of the tracking error. This is what motivated us to propose an adhoc modification to the control law (3.3) [4] by exploiting the results of Sun [7] and the Swapping Lemma. In the next two sections, we will show how the modified MRAC scheme of [4] can be derived in a systematic way.

4 Performance Improvement as Input Disturbance Rejection

In this section, we show that the performance improvement issue is intimately related to the input disturbance rejection problem. From (3.1), (3.3), we can show that the tracking error e satisfies

$$e = \frac{1}{c_0^*} W_m(s) \left[\tilde{\theta}^T \omega\right], \; \tilde{\theta} \triangleq \theta - \theta^* \tag{4.1}$$

so that $\tilde{\theta}^T\omega$ effectively appears as a disturbance at the input of $\frac{1}{c_0^*}W_m(s)$. This input cannot be apriori assumed to be bounded, which means that auxiliary analysis will be required beyond what is usually carried out to solve the standard L_1 optimal disturbance rejection problem. Nevertheless, if the performance cannot be improved even after assuming $\tilde{\theta}^T\omega$ to be bounded, there is little or no hope that we will be able to do any better in the actual situation.

Accordingly, let us assume for the time being that $\tilde{\theta}^T\omega$ is bounded and design a controller to minimize the $\mathcal{A}$ norm of the closed loop transfer function from $\tilde{\theta}^T\omega$ to ϵ. The situation is depicted in Figure 1. Here Δu is an additional control input, and $C(s)$ is a stabilizing compensator for the system.

The set of all such stabilizing compensators can be conveniently parametrized using the Y-J-B-K parametrization [8] as follows. We first note that $N_p(s) = \frac{1}{c_0^*}W_m(s)$, $D_p(s) = 1$ is a coprime factorization of $\frac{1}{c_0^*}W_m(s)$ in the ring of stable rational transfer functions. Furthermore the Bezout Identity

$$N_p(s)X(s) + D_p(s)Y(s) = 1 \tag{4.2}$$

holds with $X(s) = 0$, $Y(s) = 1$. Thus the set of all stabilizing compensators for this system is given by

$$C(s) = \frac{X(s) + D_p(s)Q(s)}{Y(s) - N_p(s)Q(s)} \tag{4.3}$$

where $Q(s)$ ranges over the set of all stable rational transfer functions.

The resulting closed loop transfer function from $\tilde{\theta}^T\omega$ to e is given by

$$N_p(s)(1 - N_p(s)Q(s)) \tag{4.4}$$

Thus the problem of improving the L_∞ gain from $\tilde{\theta}^T\omega$ to e reduces to the problem of choosing a stable $Q(s) \in \mathcal{A}$ to minimize

$$||N_p(s)(1 - N_p(s)Q(s))||_{\hat{\mathcal{A}}} \tag{4.5}$$

The following Theorem gives a solution to this minimization problem.

Theorem 4.1: Suppose $N_p(s)$ is as already defined. Then

$$\inf_{Q(s)\in\hat{\mathcal{A}}} ||N_p(s)(1 - N_p(s)Q(s))||_{\hat{\mathcal{A}}} = 0$$

Furthermore, $Q(s) = \frac{N_p^{-1}(s)}{(\tau s+1)^{n^*}}$, $\tau > 0$ is an infimizing sequence in the sense that $||N_p(s)(1 - N_p(s)Q(s))||_{\hat{\mathcal{A}}} \to 0$ as $\tau \to 0$.

Proof: The proof can be completed as in [9] (Lemma 3.3).

5 Equivalence Between the Scheme of Section 4 and an Earlier One

In this section, we establish the equivalence between the scheme just derived and one proposed earlier in [4] for obtaining improved transient performance. From Figure 1, it follows that

$$\Delta u = -\left(X(s) + D_p(s)Q(s)\right) N_p(s) \left[\tilde{\theta}^T\omega\right] \tag{5.1}$$

Substituting for $X(s)$, $D_p(s)$, $N_p(s)$, $Q(s)$, we obtain

$$\Delta u = -\frac{1}{(\tau s+1)^{n^*}} \left[\tilde{\theta}^T\omega\right] \tag{5.2}$$

Using the Swapping Lemma and the fact that $\epsilon m^2 = \tilde{\theta}^T\phi$ we obtain

$$\Delta u = -\frac{W_m^{-1}(s)}{(\tau s+1)^{n^*}} \left[\epsilon m^2 + W_c(s)\left[\left(W_b(s)[\omega^T]\right)\dot{\theta}\right]\right] \tag{5.3}$$

which is precisely the modification to the control law proposed by us in [4].

We have just shown that the modified scheme of Section 4 is equivalent to our earlier scheme in [4]. Hence, we can proceed exactly as in [4] to argue that the modified MRAC scheme, derived here, does lead to improved transient performance. Due to space limitations, the details are omitted.

6 Concluding Remarks

In this paper, we have shown how the transient performance issue in adaptive control can be formulated as an optimal disturbance rejection problem. This formulation enables us to rederive in an elegant fashion a modified MRAC scheme that we proposed earlier for achieving performance improvement. We believe that the connection established here between a problem very specific to adaptive control and the extensively studied L_1 non-adaptive design methodology will result in a better understanding of the transient performance issue in adaptive control, perhaps leading to useful results in that area.

References

[1] K. S. Narendra and A. M. Annaswamy, *Stable Adaptive Systems*. Prentice Hall, 1989.

[2] S. Sastry and M. Bodson, *Adaptive Control: Stability, Convergence and Robustness*. Prentice Hall, 1989.

[3] Z. Zhang and R. R. Bitmead, "Transient Bounds for Adaptive Control Systems," in *Proc. 29th IEEE Conf. Decision Contr.*, 1990.

[4] A. Datta and P. A. Ioannou, "Performance Improvement Versus Robust Stability in Model Reference Adaptive Control," *Proceedings of the 30th IEEE Conference on Decision and Control*, 1082-1087, 1991.

[5] C. A. Desoer and M. Vidyasagar, *Feedback Systems: Input-Output Properties*. Academic Press, New York, 1975.

[6] G. C. Goodwin and D. Q. Mayne, "A Parameter Estimation Perspective of Continuous Time Model Reference Adaptive Control," *Automatica*, Vol. 23, No. 1, 57-70, 1987.

[7] J. Sun, "A Modified Model Reference Adaptive Control Scheme for Improved Performance," in *Proceedings of American Contr. Conf.*, 1991.

[8] D. C. Youla, H. A. Jabr and J. J. Bongiorno, "Modern Wiener-Hopf Design of Optimal Controllers — Part II: The Multivariable Case," *IEEE Trans. on Automat. Contr.*, Vol. AC-21, No. 6, 319-338, Jun. 1976.

[9] M. Vidyasagar, "Optimal Rejection of Persistent Bounded Disturbances," *IEEE Trans. on Automat. Contr.*, Vol. AC-31, No. 6, 527-534, Jun., 1986.

Proceedings of the
American Control Conference
San Francisco, California • June 1993

Bursting Phenomena in Extended-Least Squares Based Self-Tuning Control

Miloje S. Radenkovic
Dept. of Electrical Engineering
University of Colorado at Denver
Denver, Colorado 80204

Anthony N. Michel
Dept. of Electrical Engineering
University of Notre Dame
Notre Dame, IN 46556

Abstract

In this paper, bursting phenomena inherent to extended least-squares based self-tuning control are analyzed. It is shown that in the absence of external excitation and without imposing structural conditions on the system model, bursts of the tracking error and consequently drift of the parameter estimates are possible. Our analysis reveals the basic principle of learning and adaptation mechanisms: every increase of system disorder causes corresponding increases of system intelligence. On the other hand, every increase of system precision causes decreases of system intelligence.

1. Introduction

The original self-tuning controller proposed by Åström and Wittenmark [1], is based on the least-squares parameter estimator. Global stability of this self-tuning controller has been an open problem since 1973. Results representing a breakthrough in this direction were reported in [2,3]. By using the "Bayesian embedding" technique in [2], it is shown that the least-squares based adaptive tracker converges everywhere in the parameter space of θ_0, except on a certain set of Lebesgue measure zero. In [2], independence and the Gaussian property of the noise sequence is assumed. Excellent results are presented in [3], where the authors proved convergence of the extended least-squares based self-tuning controller, removing independence and the Gaussian assumption on the noise sequence. They also showed that the above set of measure zero in [2] is really an empty set.

In this paper we analyze bursting phenomena in the extended least-squares (ELS) self-tuning controller. With respect to the results presented in [3], contributions of the present paper include:

1. Two techniques, different and simpler than the one used in [3] are proposed for the analysis of the convergence properties of the ELS self-tuning controller. The proposed methods represent mathematical formulations of the bursting phenomena in the adaptive loop. The first method is very simple and is based on the evaluation of a bursting given by $\sum_{t=1}^{N} \| z(t) \|^2$, where $z(t)$ is related to the system tracking error. The second method formalizes the occurrence of a possible bursting in the condition number of the covariance matrix.

2. The analysis presented herein offers new insight into the physical phenomena in the adaptive loop. It will become clear that the phenomena which provide global stability of the adaptive system are self-excitation and self-stabilization mechanisms. This means that, whenever signals in the adaptive loop start to grow unboundedly, a self-excitation mechanism takes place as a consequence of which the condition number of the covariance matrix becomes bounded, and the system satabilizes itself. In other words, the basic principle behind the learning and adaptation process in self-tuning control is the following: when the disorder (instability) in the system increases, intelligence of the system increases also. Increased intelligence results in decreased disorder, i.e., in increased system precision. When the precision of the system increases, intelligence of the system decreases, thus making possible occurrence of a bursting and increased system disorder.

In the present paper we are not using external excitation nor are we imposing restrictions on the system model structure. Phenomena which may occur under these conditions are not considered in this paper.

2. Problem Statement

Let us consider the following discrete time multivariable system

$$A(q^{-1})y(t+1) = B(q^{-1})u(t) + C(q^{-1})\omega(t+1), \quad t \geq 1 \qquad (2.1)$$

where $\{y(t)\}, \{u(t)\}$ and $\{w(t)\}$ are l-dimensional system output, input and disturbance sequences, respectively, while q^{-1} represents the unit delay operator. Matrix polynomials $A(q^{-1}), B(q^{-1})$ and $C(q^{-1})$ are given by

$$\begin{aligned} A(q^{-1}) &= 1 + a_1 q^{-1} + \ldots + a_{n_A} q^{-n_A} \\ B(q^{-1}) &= b_0 + b_1 q^{-1} + \ldots + b_{n_B} q^{-n_B} \end{aligned} \qquad (2.2)$$

and

$$C(q^{-1}) = 1 + c_1 q^{-1} + \ldots + c_{n_C} q^{-n_C},$$

where a_i, b_i and c_i are $l \times l$ unknown matrices. It is assumed that the upper bounds of the orders n_A, n_B and n_C are known. Regarding system model (2.1) we introduce the following standard assumptions:

(A_1) $\{\omega(t), \mathcal{F}_t\}$ is a martingale difference sequence satisfying

$$\sup_t E\{\| \omega(t+1) \|^{2+\mu} | \mathcal{F}_t\} \leq k_\omega < \infty \quad (a.s.)$$

for some $\mu > 0$ and

$$\lim_{N\to\infty} \frac{1}{N} \sum_{t=1}^{N} \omega(t)\omega(t)^T = R > 0 \quad (a.s.) \qquad (2.3)$$

(A_2) $C(e^{i\lambda})^{-1} + C(e^{-i\lambda})^{-T} - I > 0, \quad \forall \lambda \in [0, 2\pi]$

(A_3) $\det B(z^{-1}) \neq 0, \quad \forall z : |z| \geq 1$

The problem considered in this paper is to stabilize system (2.1) by designing an adaptive controller so that the following functional criterion is minimized

$$J = \lim_{N\to\infty} \frac{1}{N} \sum_{t=1}^{N} [y(t) - y^*(t)][y(t) - y^*(t)]^T \qquad (2.4)$$

where $y^*(t)$ is a given l-dimensional reference signal. We will assume that the sequence $\{y^*(t)\}$ is (a.s.) bounded and $y^*(t+1)$ is $\mathcal{F}_t$ measureable. Two adaptive control schemes proposed in [3] will be analyzed.

Algorithm 1: Assuming that the high-frequence gain matrix b_0 is known and nondegenerate, control law $u(t)$ is defined by

$$u(t) = b_0^{-1}[y^*(t+1) - \hat{\theta}(t)^T \phi(t)] \qquad (2.5)$$

where $\hat{\theta}(t)$ is the estimate of

$$\theta_0^T = [-a_1, \ldots, -a_{n_A};\ b_1, \ldots, b_{n_B};\ c_1, \ldots, c_{n_C}], \qquad (2.6)$$

obtained by the following extended least-squares (ELS) algorithm

$$\begin{aligned} \hat{\theta}(t+1) &= \hat{\theta}(t) + p(t)\phi(t)[y(t+1) - y^*(t+1)], \quad t \geq 1 &(2.7) \\ p(t) &= p(t-1) - \frac{p(t-1)\phi(t)\phi(t)^T p(t-1)}{1 + \phi(t)^T p(t-1)\phi(t)}, \ p(0) = \\ &\quad p_0 I, p_0 > 0 &(2.8) \\ \phi(t)^T &= [y(t)^T, \ldots, y(t-n_A+1)^T; u(t-1)^T, \ldots, u(t-n_B)^T; \\ &\quad \hat{\omega}(t), \ldots, \hat{\omega}(t-n_C+1)] &(2.9) \end{aligned}$$

where

$$\hat{\omega}(t) = y(t) - b_0 u(t-1) - \hat{\theta}(t)^T \phi(t-1), t \geq 1; \ \hat{\omega}(t) = 0, \ t < 1. \quad (2.10)$$

Algorithm 2: In this case the high-frequency gain matrix b_0 is not known and

$$\theta_0^T = [-a_1, \ldots, -a_{n_A};\ b_0, b_1, \ldots, b_{n_B};\ c_1, \ldots, c_{n_C}] \qquad (2.11)$$

is estimated by the following ELS scheme

$$\hat{\theta}(t+1) = \hat{\theta}(t) + p(t)\phi(t)[y(t+1) - \hat{\theta}(t)^T\phi(t)], \quad t \geq 1 \tag{2.12}$$

$$p(t) = p(t-1) - \frac{p(t-1)\phi(t)\phi(t)^T p(t-1)}{1+\phi(t)^T p(t-1)\phi(t)}, p(0) = p_0 I, p_0 > 0 \tag{2.13}$$

$$\phi(t)^T = [y(t)^T, \ldots, y(t-n_A+1)^T;\ u(t)^T, \ldots, u(t-n_B)^T;\ \hat{\omega}(t)^T, \ldots, \hat{\omega}(t-n_C+1)^T] \tag{2.14}$$

$$\hat{\omega}(t) = y(t) - \hat{\theta}(t)^T\phi(t-1),\ t \geq 1;\ \hat{\omega}(t) = 0,\ t < 1. \tag{2.15}$$

According to [3], the control law is given by

$$u(t) = \hat{b'}_0(t)^{-1}\{y^*(t+1) + \hat{b}_0(t)u(t) - \hat{\theta}(t)^T\phi(t)\} \tag{2.16}$$

where $\hat{b'}_0(t)$ is chosen by the designer as

$$\hat{b'}_0(t) = \begin{cases} \hat{b}_0(t) \text{ if } \hat{b}_0(t)^T\hat{b}_0(t) \geq \frac{1}{\log r_\phi(t-1)}I; \\ \hat{b}_0(t) + V(t)U(t)^T\frac{1}{(\log r_\phi(t-1))^{1/2}}, \text{ otherwise }, \end{cases} \tag{2.17}$$

where

$$r_\phi(t) = \sum_{j=1}^{t} \| \phi(j) \|^2 + e, \tag{2.18}$$

while $V(t)$ and $U(t)$ are orthogonal matrices in the singular value decomposition of
$b_0(t)$, i.e.,

$$b_0(t) = V(t)\begin{bmatrix} \Sigma(t) & 0 \\ 0 & 0 \end{bmatrix}U(t)$$

where $\Sigma(t)$ is a positive definite diagonal matrix.

In both algorithms, we use for $\hat{\theta}(t)$ a finite arbitrary initial value $\hat{\theta}(0)$. Without loss of generality we also assume that $y(t) = 0, u(t) = 0$ and $\omega(t) = 0$ for $t < 1$.

For a discrete time signal $x(t), x(t) \in \Re$, we will use the norm

$$r_x(t) = \sum_{j=1}^{t} x(t)^2. \tag{2.19}$$

Also, throughout this paper we assume that all constants $C_i, K_i, i = 1,2,3,\ldots$, are nonnegative.

Note that the system model (2.1) can be written in the form

$$y(t+1) = \theta_0^T\phi(t) + I_g b_0 u(t) + q[C(q^{-1}) - 1](\omega(t) - \hat{\omega}(t)) + \omega(t+1) \tag{2.20}$$

where the indicator function I_g is given by

$$I_g = \begin{cases} 1, \text{ for Algorithm 1,} \\ 0, \text{ for Algorithm 2,} \end{cases} \tag{2.21}$$

and $\theta_0, \phi(t)$ and $\hat{\omega}(t)$ are defined by Eqs. (2.6), (2.9) and (2.10) for Algorithm 1 and by Eqs. (2.11), (2.14) and (2.15), for Algorithm 2. After substituting corresponding control laws (2.5) or (2.16) into (2.20) we derive

$$\begin{aligned} & y(t+1) - y^*(t+1) - \omega(t+1) \\ = & -z(t) + (1-I_g)\Delta\hat{b}_0(t)u(t) + q[C(q^{-1}) - 1] \\ \cdot & [\omega(t) - \hat{\omega}(t)] \end{aligned} \tag{2.22}$$

where

$$z(t) = -\tilde{\theta}(t)^T\phi(t),\ \tilde{\theta}(t) = \hat{\theta}(t) - \theta_0 \tag{2.23}$$

and

$$\Delta\hat{b}_0(t) = \hat{b'}_0(t) - \hat{b}_0(t). \tag{2.24}$$

For future reference we cite the following lemma [3,4].

Lemma 2.1: If assumptions $(A_1) - (A_3)$ hold, Algorithms 1 and 2 provide

1) $\| \hat{\theta}(t+1) - \theta_0 \|^2 \leq C_1[\log r_\phi(t)/\lambda_{\min}(t)]$ (a.s.) (2.25)

where $\lambda_{\min}(t)$ is the minimal eigenvalue of $p(t)^{-1}$.

2) $\sum_{t=1}^{N} \| \hat{\omega}(t) - \omega(t) \|^2 \leq C_2 \log r_\phi(N-1)$ (a.s.) (2.26)

3) $\sum_{t=1}^{N} \frac{\| z(t) \|^2}{1+\beta(t)} \leq C_3 \log r_\phi(N)$ (a.s.) (2.27)

where $r_\phi(t)$ is defined by (2.18), and

$$\beta(t) = \phi(t)^T p(t-1)\phi(t) \tag{2.28}$$

Proof: The first two statements are proved in [4], while the proof of (2.29) is given in [3].

By analyzing possible bursting phenomena, we will show in the next two sections that the following statements are valid for Algorithms 1 and 2:

1) $r_z(t) \leq \mathcal{O}\left\{t^{1-\epsilon+2\epsilon_0}\right\},\ 0 < \epsilon_0 << \epsilon/2,\ 0 < \epsilon < \frac{\mu}{2+\mu}$ (a.s.) (2.29)

where $r_z(t)$ is given by Eq. (2.19), when $x(t) = \| z(t) \|$, $z(t)$ is defined by (2.23), ϵ_0 is an arbitrarily small number, and μ is defined by Assumption (A_1);

2) $\sum_{i=1}^{t} \| y(i+1) - y^*(i+1) - \omega(i+1) \|^2 \leq \mathcal{O}\left\{t^{1-\epsilon+2\epsilon_0}\right\}$ (a.s.) (2.30)

3) $\lim_{N\to\infty} \frac{1}{N}\sum_{t=1}^{N}[y(t+1) - y^*(t+1)][y(t+1) - y^*(t+1)]^T = R$ (a.s.) (2.31)

where R is given by (2.3);

4) $\| \phi(t) \|^2 \leq \mathcal{O}(t^{1-\epsilon+2\epsilon_0})$ (a.s.) (2.32)

5) $\limsup_{N\to\infty} \frac{1}{N}\sum_{t=1}^{N}\left(\| y(t) \|^2 + \| u(t) \|^2\right) < \infty$ (a.s.) (2.33)

3. Bursting Phenomena and Performance of Algorithm 1

In order to establish convergence properties of this algoritm we need the following simple lemma.

Lemma 3.1: Let Assumptions $(A_1) - (A_3)$ hold. Then, for sufficiently large t,

1) $r_\phi(t) \leq C_4 r_z(t-1) + C_5 t$ (a.s.) (3.1)

2) $\liminf_{t\to\infty} r_\phi(t)/t \geq C_6 > 0$ (a.s.) (3.2)

3) $\beta(t) \leq o\left\{r_z(t-1) + t^{1-\epsilon}\right\}$ (a.s.) (3.3)

where $r_z(t)$ and ϵ are defined in (2.29), while $r_\phi(t)$ and $\beta(t)$ are given by (2.18) and (2.28), respectively.

Proof: The proof of this lemma is given in the Appendix.

The properties of Algorithm 1 are formulated in the next theorem, whose proof is based on the evaluation of the possible burstings of $r_z(t)$.

Theorem 3.1: Let Assumptions $(A_1)-(A_3)$ hold. Then, Algorithm 1 provides validity of the statements (2.29)-(2.33).

Proof: Statement (3) of Lemma 3.1 suggests analyzing possible burstings of $r_z(t)$. In this sense, let us define sequences τ_k and $\sigma_k, k \geq 1$ as

$$1 \triangleq \tau_1, < \sigma_1 < \tau_2 < \sigma_2 < \cdots < \tau_k < \sigma_k < \tau_{k+1} < \cdots \tag{3.4}$$

so that

$$r_z(t-1) \leq t^{1-\epsilon} \text{ for } t \in Q_k = [\tau_k, \sigma_k) \quad (a.s.) \tag{3.5}$$

and

$$r_z(t-1) > t^{1-\epsilon} \text{ for } t \in T_k = [\sigma_k, \tau_{k+1}) \quad (a.s.) \tag{3.6}$$

where ϵ is given in (2.29). If $r_z(0) > 1$, then we set in (3.4) $\tau_1 = 0$ and $\sigma_1 = 1$. For the sequences τ_k and σ_k we will analyze three cases:

Case 1: τ_k and σ_k are finite for all finite k,

Case 2: there exits a finite k_0 so that $\tau_{k_0} < \infty$ and $\sigma_{k_0} = +\infty$, and

Case 3: there exists a finite k_1 so that $\sigma_{k_1} < \infty$ and $\tau_{k_1+1} = +\infty$.

Case 2 is trivial and from (3.5) it follows that $r_z(t) \leq t^{1-\epsilon}$, (a.s.), for all $t \geq \tau_{k_0}$. From (A.11) in the Appendix we see that $r_z(t)$ is actually the order of $\| \omega(t) \|^2$. In this case the upper bound on $r_z(t)$ is stronger than the one established in [2]. It is difficult to prove that *Case 2* does not exist. Let us consider *Case 1*. From (3.5) and (3.6) it is obvious that in this case we need to evaluate $r_z(t)$ only for $t \in T_k$. From (3.3) and (3.6) we can derive that for sufficiently large k,

$$1+\beta(t) \leq \epsilon_1 \max\left\{r_z(t-1); t^{1-\epsilon}\right\} \leq \epsilon_1 r_z(t-1), \ \forall t \in T_k \ (a.s.) \quad (3.7)$$

where ϵ_1 is a small positive number satisfying

$$0 < \epsilon_1 < \frac{\epsilon_0(1-\epsilon)}{C_3(1-\epsilon+\epsilon_0)} \quad (3.8)$$

where ϵ_0 is an arbitrarily small number, $0 < \epsilon_0 < \epsilon/2$, while ϵ is defined in (2.29), and C_3 is the constant from (2.27). Such choice of ϵ_1 will be clear from the derivations that follow. Substituting (3.7) into (2.27) we obtain

$$\sum_{t=\sigma_k}^{N} \frac{\| z(t) \|^2}{\epsilon_1 r_z(t-1)} \leq C_3 \log r_\phi(N), \ \ N \in T_k, \quad (a.s.) \quad (3.9)$$

Since

$$\sum_{t=\sigma_k}^{N} \frac{\| z(t) \|^2}{r_z(t-1)} \geq \sum_{t=\sigma_k}^{N} \frac{r_z(t) - r_z(t-1)}{r_z(t-1)} \geq \sum_{t=\sigma_k}^{N} \int_{r_z(t-1)}^{r_z(t)} \frac{dx}{x} = \log \frac{r_z(N)}{r_z(\sigma_k - 1)}, \quad (3.10)$$

we derive from (3.9)

$$\log \frac{r_z(N)}{r_z(\sigma_k-1)} \leq \epsilon_1 C_3 \log r_\phi(N), \ \ N \in T_k \quad (a.s.). \quad (3.11)$$

By using (3.1) and (3.6), we can obtain for $N \in T_k$

$$\log r_\phi(N) \leq \log\{2C_{17} \max[r_z(N-1); N]\} \leq \log r_z(N-1)^{\frac{1}{1-\epsilon}} + C_{18}. \quad (3.12)$$

Substituting (3.12) into (3.11) yields,

$$\left(1 - \frac{\epsilon_1 C_3}{1-\epsilon}\right) \log r_z(N) \leq \log r_z(\sigma_k - 1) + C_{19}, \ N \in T_k \quad (a.s.) \quad (3.13)$$

or

$$r_z(N) \leq C_{20} r_z(\sigma_k - 1)^{\frac{1-\epsilon}{1-\epsilon-\epsilon_1 C_3}}, \ N \in T_k \quad (a.s.). \quad (3.14)$$

Let us now evaluate $r_z(\sigma_k - 1)$. From (3.3) and (3.5) it follows that

$$1 + \beta(\sigma_k - 1) \leq \epsilon_2 (\sigma_k - 1)^{1-\epsilon}, \ 0 < \epsilon_2 << 1 \quad (a.s.) \quad (3.15)$$

for sufficiently large k. Then from (2.27) we can derive

$$\begin{aligned} \| z(\sigma_k - 1) \|^2 &\leq (1 + \beta(\sigma_k - 1)) C_3 \log r_\phi(\sigma_k - 1) \\ &\leq \epsilon_2 C_3 (\sigma_k - 1)^{1-\epsilon} \log r_\phi(\sigma_k - 1) \end{aligned} \quad (3.16)$$

Since from (3.5), $r_z(\sigma_k - 2) \leq (\sigma_k - 1)^{1-\epsilon}$, relation (3.1) yields

$$\log r_\phi(\sigma_k - 1) \leq \log(\sigma_k - 1) + C_{21} \quad (a.s.) \quad (3.17)$$

and therefore, bŷ (3.16) we obtain for k sufficiently large,

$$\| z(\sigma_k - 1) \|^2 \leq C_{22} (\sigma_k - 1)^{1-\epsilon} \log(\sigma_k - 1) \quad (a.s.) \quad (3.18)$$

or

$$\begin{aligned} r_z(\sigma_k - 1) &= r_z(\sigma_k - 2) + \| z(\sigma_k - 1) \|^2 \\ &\leq (\sigma_k - 1)^{1-\epsilon} + C_{22}(\sigma_k - 1)^{1-\epsilon} \log(\sigma_k - 1) \\ &\leq C_{23} (\sigma_k - 1)^{1-\epsilon} \log(\sigma_k - 1). \end{aligned} \quad (3.19)$$

After substituting (3.19) into (3.14) we conclude that

$$r_z(N) \leq C_{24} (\sigma_k - 1)^{\frac{(1-\epsilon)^2}{1-\epsilon-\epsilon_1 C_3}} \{\log(\sigma_k - 1)\}^{\frac{1-\epsilon}{1-\epsilon-\epsilon_1 C_3}}, \ N \in T_k \quad (a.s.) \quad (3.20)$$

Since for sufficiently large k,

$$[\log(\sigma_k - 1)]^{\frac{1-\epsilon}{1-\epsilon-\epsilon_1 C_3}} \leq (\sigma_k - 1)^{\epsilon_0}, \ \ 0 < \epsilon_0 < \frac{\epsilon}{2} \quad (3.21)$$

we obtain from (3.20)

$$r_z(N) \leq C_{25} (\sigma_k - 1)^{1-\epsilon+2\epsilon_0}, N \in T_k \quad (a.s.) \quad (3.22)$$

where we have used the fact that by (3.8), $\frac{1-\epsilon}{1-\epsilon-\epsilon_1 C_3} < 1-\epsilon+\epsilon_0$ where, as it is stated with (3.8), ϵ_0 is an arbitrarily small constant, $0 < \epsilon_0 < \epsilon/2$. Finally, we see that (3.5) and (3.22) constitute statement (2.29). *Case 3*, when in (3.4) there exists k_1 so that $\sigma_{k_1} < \infty$ and $\tau_{k_1+1} = +\infty$, is impossible. Specifically, from (3.22) it follows that $r_z(t) \leq \mathcal{O}(\sigma_{k_1} - 1) < \infty$, (a.s.), for $t \geq \sigma_{k_1}$ which contradicts the fact that from (3.6) $r_z(t) > t^{1-\epsilon}$ for all $t > \sigma_{k_1}$.

From the previous analysis it is obvious that regarding $r_z(t)$, two possibilities exist:

1) $r_z(t) \leq \max_{1 \leq \tau \leq t} \| \omega(\tau) \|^2 = \mathcal{O}(t^{1-\epsilon})$ (a.s.), $t \geq 1$ (see Eq. (A.11) in the Appendix), or

2) $r_z(t)$ exibits burstings throughout the adaptation process.

Statements (2.30) and (2.31) of the theorem follow from (2.22), (2.26), and (2.29). The last two statements of the theorem are direct consequence of (2.29), (3.1) and (A.13) in the Appendix. Thus the theorem is proved. □

4. Bursting Phenomena and Performance of Algorithm 2

The following simple lemma is important for establishing convergence properties of Algorithm 2.

Lemma 4.1: Let the assumptions $(A_1) - (A_3)$ hold. Then for sufficiently large t,

1) $r_\phi(t) \leq K_1 r_z(t) + K_2 t$ (a.s.) (4.1)

$\liminf_{t\to\infty} \frac{r_\phi(t)}{t} \geq \delta_1 > 0$ (a.s.) (4.2)

where $r_\phi(t)$ is given by (2.18).

2) $\max_{1 \leq \tau \leq t} (\| y(\tau) \|^2 + \| u(\tau - 1) \|^2) \leq K_3 [r_z(t-1) + t^{1-\epsilon}]$ (a.s.) (4.3)

3) $\| z(t) \|^2 \leq K_5 \left\{[\log r_\phi(t-1)]^3 \bar{r}(t-1)\right\}$ (a.s.) (4.4)

where

$$\bar{r}(t) = \max\left\{r_z(t); (t+1)^{1-\epsilon}\right\}, \ \ 0 < \epsilon < \frac{\mu}{2+\mu} \quad (4.5)$$

where μ is defined in assumption (A_1).

Proof: The proof of the lemma is given in the Appendix.

Next, we analyze possible bursting phenomena and the performance of Algorithm 2, by making use of a method which differs from one used in the proof of Theorem 3.1.

Theorem 4.1: If Assumptions $(A_1) - (A_3)$ hold, then Algorithm 2 guarantees the validity of the statements (2.29)-(2.33).

Proof: Note that from Eq. (2.13), it follows that

$$d(t) = (1 + \beta(t)) d(t-1), \ d(t) = \det\{p(t)^{-1}\} \quad (4.6)$$

or

$$d_n(t) = (1 + \beta(t)) d_n(t-1) \left[\frac{\bar{r}(t-1)}{\bar{r}(t)}\right]^m, \ d_n(t) = \frac{d(t)}{\bar{r}(t)^m} \quad (4.7)$$

where m is an arbitrarily large finite positive number, and $\beta(t)$ and $\bar{r}(t)$ are defined by (2.28) and (4.5), respectively. The theorem will be proved by considering the behavior of $\beta(t)$ during the adaptation process. In doing so, possible bursts of $\beta(t)$ and their effects on $r_z(t)$ will be evaluated. Similarly, as in the proof of Theorem 3.1, let us define sequences τ_k and σ_k, so that (3.4) holds and

$$1 + \beta(t) \leq 3^m \left[\frac{\bar{r}(t)}{\bar{r}(t-1)}\right]^m, \ \ \forall t \in Q_k = [\tau_k, \sigma_k) \quad (a.s.) \quad (4.8)$$

and

$$1 + \beta(t) > 3^m \left[\frac{\bar{r}(t)}{\bar{r}(t-1)}\right]^m, \ \ \forall t \in T_k = [\sigma_k, \tau_{k+1}) \quad (a.s.) \quad (4.9)$$

If $1+\beta(1) > 3^m \left[\frac{\tilde{r}(1)}{\tilde{r}(0)}\right]^m$, then in (3.4) we set $\sigma_1 = 1$, and τ_k is defined for $k \geq 2$.

First we will analyze the case when in (3.4), $\tau_k < \infty$ and $\sigma_k < \infty$ for all finite k. The analysis will involve the following steps:

Step 1: evaluate $\tilde{r}(\sigma_k - 1)$, where $\tilde{r}(t)$ is given by (4.5);

Step 2: by using the result from Step 1, establish a lower bound for $d_n(\sigma_k - 1)$;

Step 3: based on the results from the previous step, establish a lower bound for $d_n(t)$ for all $t \in T_k$;

Step 4: by using Step 3, establish an upper bound of $r_z(t)$ for $t \in T_k$ and $t \in Q_k$.

Step 1: From (4.4), (4.5) and (4.8) we can obtain that for all $t \in Q_k$,

$$\begin{aligned} 1+\beta(t) &\leq 3^m \left[1 + \frac{\| z(t) \|^2}{\tilde{r}(t-1)} + \frac{(t+1)^{1-\epsilon} - t^{1-\epsilon}}{\tilde{r}(t-1)}\right]^m \\ &\leq 3^m \left\{1 + K_5[\log r_\phi(t-1)]^3 + \frac{1}{t^\epsilon \tilde{r}(t-1)}\right\}^m \\ &\leq K_{11}[\log r_\phi(t-1)]^{3m} \ (a.s.) \end{aligned} \tag{4.10}$$

where we have used the fact that by (4.2), $\log r_\phi(t-1) \to \infty$ when $t \to \infty$. Relations (2.27) and (4.10) imply

$$\sum_{t=\tau_k}^{N} \| z(t) \|^2 \leq K_{12}[\log r_\phi(N)]^{3m+1}, \quad \forall N \in Q_k \quad (a.s.) \tag{4.11}$$

and therefore, by (4.5), we can derive

$$\begin{aligned} &\tilde{r}(\sigma_k - 1) \leq \tilde{r}(\tau_k - 1) + K_{12}[\log r_\phi(\sigma_k - 1)]^{3m+1} + \sigma_k^{1-\epsilon} - \tau_k^{1-\epsilon} \\ &\leq 3\max\left\{\tilde{r}(\tau_k - 1);\ K_{12}[\log r_\phi(\sigma_k - 1)]^{3m+1}; \sigma_k^{1-\epsilon}\right\} (a.s.). \end{aligned} \tag{4.12}$$

Step 2:

Note that (4.7) implies

$$d_n(\sigma_k - 1) \geq d_n(\tau_k - 1)\left[\frac{\tilde{r}(\tau_k - 1)}{\tilde{r}(\sigma_k - 1)}\right]^m \quad (a.s.). \tag{4.13}$$

If in (4.12), $\tilde{r}(\sigma_k - 1) \leq 3\tilde{r}(\tau_k - 1)$, then from (4.13) it follows that

$$d_n(\sigma_k - 1) \geq \frac{1}{3^m} d_n(\tau_k - 1). \tag{4.14}$$

If in (4.12), $\tilde{r}(\sigma_k - 1) \leq 3K_{12}[\log r_\phi(\sigma_k - 1)]^{3m+1}$, then from the definition of $d_n(t)$ (Eq. (4.7)) we obtain

$$\begin{aligned} d_n(\sigma_k - 1) &\geq \frac{d(\sigma_k - 1)}{\{3K_{12}[\log r_\phi(\sigma_k - 1)]\}^{(3m+1)m}} \\ &\geq \frac{r_\phi(\sigma_k - 1)}{np_0^{n-1}\{3K_{12}[\log r_\phi(\sigma_k - 1)]\}^{(3m+1)m}} (a.s.) \end{aligned} \tag{4.15}$$

where we have used the fact that

$$d(t) \geq \lambda_{\max}(t)[\lambda_{\min}(t)]^{n-1}, \ \lambda_{\max}(t) \geq \frac{1}{n} r_\phi(t) \tag{4.16}$$

and that by (2.8), $\lambda_{\min}(t) \geq 1/p_0$. In (4.15) and (4.16) n is a dimension of the vector $\phi(t)$, while $\lambda_{\max}(t)$ and $\lambda_{\min}(t)$ denote the maximal and minimal eigenvalues of the matrix $p(t)^{-1}$. If in (4.12), $\tilde{r}(\sigma_k - 1) \leq 3\sigma_k^{1-\epsilon}$, then from the definition of $d_n(t)$ (Eq. (4.7)), (4.2) and (4.16) we conclude that

$$d_n(\sigma_k - 1) \leq \frac{1}{np_0^{n-1}} \cdot \frac{r_\phi(\sigma_k - 1)}{3^m \sigma_k^{(1-\epsilon)m}} \geq \delta_2 \frac{\sigma_k}{\sigma_k^{(1-\epsilon)m}}, \ \delta_2 > 0 \quad (a.s.). \tag{4.17}$$

Finally, from (4.14), (4.15) and (4.17) it is not difficult to see that

$$d_n(\sigma_k - 1) \geq \min\left\{\frac{1}{3^m} d_n(\tau_k - 1); \frac{\delta_2}{\sigma_k^{(1-\epsilon)m-1}}\right\} \quad (a.s.). \tag{4.18}$$

Step 3: From (4.7) and (4.9) it is not difficult to see that

$$d_n(t) \geq 3^m d_n(t-1) \geq 3^m d_n(\sigma_k - 1), \ \forall t \in T_k \quad (a.s.) \tag{4.19}$$

and therefore, by (4.18) it follows that

$$d_n(\tau_{k+1} - 1) \geq \min\left\{d_n(\tau_k - 1); \frac{3^m \delta_2}{\sigma_k^{(1-\epsilon)m-1}}\right\} \quad (a.s.) \tag{4.20}$$

and

$$d_n(t) \geq \min\left\{d_n(\tau_k - 1); \frac{3^m \delta_2}{\sigma_k^{m-1}}\right\}, \quad \forall t \in T_k \ (a.s.). \tag{4.21}$$

After iterative substitution of $d_n(\tau_k - 1)$ into (4.20), we obtain

$$d_n(\tau_{k+1} - 1) \geq \min\left\{d_n(\tau_2 - 1); \frac{3^m \delta_2}{\sigma_k^{(1-\epsilon)m-1}}\right\} \quad (a.s.). \tag{4.22}$$

In (3.4), two possibilities exist: $\tau_1 = 1$ or $\sigma_1 = 1$. If $\tau_1 = 1$, then from (4.20) for $k = 1$, we conclude that

$$d_n(\tau_2 - 1) \geq \min\left\{d_n(0); \frac{3^m \delta_2}{\sigma_1^{(1-\epsilon)m-1}}\right\} \quad (a.s.). \tag{4.23}$$

If $\sigma_1 = 1$, then from (4.19) we have $d_n(\tau_2 - 1) \geq 3^m d_n(0)$. This, together with (4.23) and (4.22) yield

$$d_n(\tau_{k+1} - 1) \geq 3^m \delta_2 / \sigma_k^{(1-\epsilon)m-1} \quad (a.s.) \tag{4.24}$$

where we have used the fact that $d_n(0) > 0$ and $\sigma_k \to \infty$ when $k \to \infty$. Substituting (4.24) into (4.21), we obtain

$$d_n(t) \geq 3^m \delta_2 / \sigma_k^{(1-\epsilon)m-1}, \ \forall t \in T_k \quad (a.s.). \tag{4.25}$$

Step 4: By using (4.7) and (4.1) we conclude from the previous relation that

$$\frac{3^m \delta_2 \tilde{r}(t)^m}{\sigma_k^{(1-\epsilon)m-1}} \leq d(t) \leq r_\phi(t)^n \leq K_{13}[r_z(t)^n + t^n], \ \forall t \in T_k (a.s.) \tag{4.26}$$

where $n = \dim(\phi(t))$. From (4.5) we see that $\tilde{r}(t) = (t+1)^{1-\epsilon}$ if $r_z(t) \leq (t+1)^{1-\epsilon}$, and $\tilde{r}(t) = r_z(t)$ if $(t+1) \leq r_z(t)^{1/1-\epsilon}$. When $\tilde{r}(t) = r_z(t)$, we obtain from (4.26)

$$\begin{aligned} r_z(t)^m &\leq K_{14}[r_z(t)^n + r_z(t)^{n/1-\epsilon}]\sigma_k^{(1-\epsilon)m-1} \\ &\leq K_{14}' r_z(t)^{\frac{n}{1-\epsilon}} \sigma_k^{(1-\epsilon)m-1} \ (a.s.) \end{aligned} \tag{4.27}$$

or

$$r_z(t)^{m-\frac{n}{1-\epsilon}} \leq K_{15}\sigma_k^{(1-\epsilon)m-1}, \text{ if } (t+1) \leq r_z(t)^{1/(1-\epsilon)} (a.s.). \tag{4.28}$$

Finally, for all $t \in T_k$ it follows that

$$r_z(t) \leq K_{16} \max\left\{(t+1)^{(1-\epsilon)}; \sigma_k^{(1-\epsilon)[(1-\epsilon)m-1]/[m(1-\epsilon)-n]}\right\} (a.s.). \tag{4.29}$$

Since m is an arbitrarily large finite positive number, we can choose it to satisfy $m \geq \left[\frac{(n-1)(1-\epsilon)+n\epsilon_0}{\epsilon_0(1-\epsilon)}\right] + 1$, where ϵ_0 is an arbitarily small positive number. Then from (4.29) we conclude that

$$r_z(t) \leq K_{17} t^{1-\epsilon+\epsilon_0}, \ \forall t \in T_k \quad (a.s.). \tag{4.30}$$

Since $r_z(t) = r_z(\tau_k - 1) + \Sigma_{\tau_k}^t \| z(j) \|^2$, $\forall t \in Q_k$, it follows from (4.1), (4.11) and (4.30) that the same upper bound as in (4.30) holds for all $t \in Q_k$. Thus, in the case when for all finite $k, \tau_k < \infty$ and $\sigma_k < \infty$, statement (2.29) of the theorem is proved. In the case where there exists a finite k_0 so that $\sigma_{k_0} < \infty$ and $\tau_{k_0+1} = +\infty$, relation (4.30) is valid for all $t \geq \sigma_{k_0}$. If there exists finite k_1 so that $\tau_{k_1} < \infty$ and $\sigma_{k_1} = +\infty$, it follows from (4.1) and (4.11) that for $t \geq \tau_{k_1}, r_z(t) \leq O[\log t]^{3m+1}$ (a.s.). Thus, the proof of statement (2.29) is completed. Statements (2.30) and (2.31) can easily be obtained from (2.29) and (2.22). Statements (2.32) and (2.33) follow from (2.29), (4.1) and (4.3). Thus the theorem is proved. □

For Algorithms 1 and 2, we established the following upper bound for $r_z(t)$,

$$r_z(t) \leq \mathcal{O}\left\{\gamma(t)t^{2\epsilon_0}\right\}, \ \gamma(t) = t^{1-\epsilon}, \ 0 < \epsilon < \frac{\eta}{2+\eta}, \ \epsilon_0 > 0 \quad (a.s.) \tag{4.31}$$

where η is defined in assumption (A_1), ϵ_0 is an arbitrarily small number, while $\gamma(t)$ actually represents the order of $\| \omega(t) \|^2$ (see (A.10) in the Appendix). By using different techniques, the same upper bound has been established in [3]. From the analyses presented in the proofs of Theorems 3.1 and 4.1, it is clear that there are bursting phenomena in the adaptive loop. Burstings either in $r_z(t)$ or $\beta(t)$ will cause corresponding fluctuations in other variables, such as parameter estimation error, condition number of the covariance matrix $p(t)$, etc. What is keeping the adaptive system globally stable is the *self-excitation mechanism* which takes place during bursting periods. In other words, whenever $r_z(t)$ starts to grow above $\gamma(t)$ (Eq. (4.31)), the PE condition in the adaptive loop will be satisfied. Consequently, $\tilde{\theta}(t)$ tends to zero, thereby forcing $r_z(t)$ to decrease. Let us analytically verfiy this statement. From (4.9) we see that for all $t \in T_k$, $1+\beta(t)$ is not bounded from above and therefore it can increase. As a consequence of this, at certain times $t_i, t_i \in T_k, r_z(t_i)$ will become larger than $\mathcal{O}\{\gamma(t_i)\}$. Let us consider the case when $r_z(t_i)$ becomes as large as $\mathcal{O}\{\gamma(t_i)t_i^{\epsilon_0/2}\}$, where $\epsilon_0 > 0$ is an arbitrarily small number. We have the following sequence of inequalities:

$$[\lambda_{max}(t_i)]^{n-1}\lambda_{min}(t_i) \geq \frac{\bar{r}(t_i)^m \delta_3}{\sigma_k^{(1-\epsilon)m-1}}, t_i \in T_k, \delta_3 > 0 \text{ (from (4.7) and (4.25))), and}$$

$$\bar{r}(t_i)^m \geq r_\phi(t_i)^{m(1-\epsilon)} r_\phi(t_i)^{m\epsilon_0/2} \text{ (from (4.5), (4.2) and the fact that } r_z(t_i) \geq t^{1-\epsilon-\frac{\epsilon_0}{2}}).$$

Since $\lambda_{max}(t) \leq \frac{1}{n} r_\phi(t)$, we obtain from the last two inequalities

$$\lambda_{min}(t_i) \geq \frac{r_\phi(t_i)^{m(1-\epsilon)}}{\sigma_k^{m(1-\epsilon)}} \cdot \frac{\sigma_k r_\phi(t_i)^{m\epsilon_0/2}}{r_\phi(t_i)^{n-1}} \tag{4.32}$$

which together with (4.2) yields

$$\lambda_{min}(t_i) \geq \delta_4 r_\phi(t_i)^{m\frac{\epsilon_0}{2}-n+1}, \delta_4 > 0 \quad (a.s.). \tag{4.33}$$

Using the fact that m is an arbitrarily large finite number it follows from (4.33) that whenever $r_z(t)$ grows larger than $\mathcal{O}\{\gamma(t)t^{\epsilon_0/2}\}$, $\lambda_{max}(t)/\lambda_{min}(t)$ becomes bounded. This means that on the subsequence $\{t_i\}$, the PE conditions are satisfied without external excitation and without imposing structural conditions on the matrix polynomials $A(q^{-1}), B(q^{-1})$ and $C(q^{-1})$. Therefore, as a consequence of the burstings in $r_z(t)$, internal excitation in the adaptive loop will cause $\| \tilde{\theta}(t_i) \|^2 \leq \mathcal{O}\{\log r_\phi(t_i)/r_\phi(t_i)\}$, (a.s.) (see Eq. (2.25)) which implies a decrease of $z(t_i)$. When $z(t)$ becomes small, the self-excitation property will vanish. Essentially, the basic principle behind the *self-excitation* mechanism is the following: whenever disorder of the system increases, the adaptive system becomes more intelligent, thereby producing better parameter estimates. Such estimates will force the system to have small $r_z(t)$. When the disorder of the system is decreasing and precision of the system is increasing, its intelligence decreases, thus making possible drift of the parameter estimates and appearance of burstings on $r_z(t)$ and $\beta(t)$.

6. Conclusion

In this paper two techniques are proposed for the convergence analysis of the ELS self-tuning controller. The presented methods are different than the one proposed in [3], and they provide physical insight into the bursting phenomena in the adaptive loop.

Acknowledgement: The authors wish to express their gratitude to Prof. P. Kumar for his valuable suggestions during the course of this research.

7. Appendix

Proof of Lemma 3.1: The proof of (3.1) is known and exists elsewhere in the literature. For the sake of completeness let us briefly sketch this proof. Note that for $I_g = 0$, (2.22) yields

$$r_y(t) \leq C_7[r_z(t-1) + r_\omega(t) + r_{y^*}(t) + \sum_{j=1}^{t-1} \| \omega(j) - \hat{\omega}(j) \|^2] \tag{A.1}$$

where $r_y(t), r_\omega(t)$ and $r_{y^*}(t)$ are given by (2.19) when $x(t) = \| y(t) \|^2, x(t) = \| \omega(t) \|^2$ and $x(t) = \| y^*(t) \|^2$, respectively.

Assumption (A_3) together with (2.1) imply that

$$r_u(t) \leq C_8[r_y(t+1) + r_\omega(t+1)] \tag{A.2}$$

where $r_u(t)$ is defined by (2.19) when $x(t) = \| u(t) \|^2$. On the other hand, from Eqs. (2.9) and (2.19) it follows that

$$r_\phi(t) \leq C_9 r_y(t) + r_u(t-1) + r_\omega(t) + \sum_{j=1}^{t} \| \hat{\omega}(j) - \omega(j) \|^2] + e. \tag{A.3}$$

Statement (1) of the lemma simply follows by combining (A.1), (A.2), (A.3) and (2.26) together with the facts that $r_{y^*}(t) \leq \mathcal{O}(t)$ and $r_\omega(t) \leq \mathcal{O}(t)$ (a.s.). The second statement of the lemma follows from assumption (A_1) and the proof is very well known in the literature on adaptive control. Let us prove (3.3). Since matrix $p(t)$ has limits, it follows from (2.8) that for any nonzero vector η, the following holds

$$\lim_{t\to 0} \frac{\eta^T p(t-1)\phi(t)\phi(t)^T p(t-1)\eta}{1+\beta(t)} = 0 \tag{A.4}$$

where $\beta(t)$ is given by (2.28). This implies that

$$\lim_{t\to\infty} \frac{\| p(t-1)\phi(t) \|^2}{1+\beta(t)} = 0, \text{ i.e., } \| p(t-1)\phi(t) \|^2 \leq o(1) + o\{\| \phi(t) \| \cdot \| p(t-1)\phi(t) \|\}. \tag{A.5}$$

Therefore, after simple manipulations we obtain

$$\beta(t) \leq \| \phi(t) \| \cdot \| p(t-1)\phi(t) \| \leq o(1) + o(\| \phi(t) \|^2). \tag{A.6}$$

Next, we establish upper bounds for $\| \phi(t) \|$. Note that (2.1) together with Assumption (A_3) yields

$$\| u(t-1) \|^2 \leq C_{10} \max_{1\leq\tau\leq t} \{\| y(\tau) \|^2 + \| \omega(\tau) \|^2\} \tag{A.7}$$

and (2.22) with $I_g = 0$, implies that

$$\| y(t) \| \leq \| z(t-1) \| + C_{11} \max_{1\leq\tau\leq t} \| \omega(\tau-1) - \hat{\omega}(t-1) \| + \| y^*(t) \| + \| \omega(t) \| . \tag{A.8}$$

Using (A.7) and (A.8) it follows from (2.9) that

$$\| \phi(t) \|^2 \leq C_{12} \max\{\| z(t-1) \|^2 + \| \omega(\tau) \|^2 + \| \omega(\tau-1) - \hat{\omega}(\tau-1) \|^2\} + C_{13}. \tag{A.9}$$

Note that Assumption (A_1) implies [3]

$$\| \omega(t) \|^2 = \mathcal{O}(t^{1-\epsilon}) \ (a.s.) \tag{A.10}$$

where ϵ is defined in (2.29). Since from (2.26) and (3.1),

$$\begin{aligned} \| \omega(t) - \hat{\omega}(t) \|^2 &\leq \mathcal{O}[\log r_\phi(t-1)] \leq \mathcal{O}\{\log C_{14} \max[r_z(t-2); t-1]\} \\ &\leq \mathcal{O}[\log r_z(t-2)] + \mathcal{O}[\log(t-1)], \end{aligned} \tag{A.11}$$

we obtain from (A.10) and (A.11)

$$\| \phi(t) \|^2 \leq C_{15} r_z(t-1) + C_{16} t^{t-\epsilon} \quad (a.s.) \tag{A.12}$$

and therefore by (A.6) statement (3.3) follows directly. Thus the lemma is proved. □

Proof of Lemma 4.1: The first statement of the lemma can be proved similarly as (3.1) and (3.2). In proving (4.1) and (4.2), the modified control law (2.16) does not create any difficulties since by (2.17), $\hat{b'}_0(t) - \hat{b}_0(t) \to 0$, when $t \to \infty$. Let us prove the second statement of the lemma. From (2.22), (2.26) and (A.10) we obtain

$$\| y(t+1) \| \leq \| z(t) \| + \mathcal{O}\left(t^{\frac{1-\epsilon}{2}}\right) + o(\| u(t) \|) + \mathcal{O}[\log r_\phi(t-1)]^{1/2} \quad (a.s.) \tag{A.13}$$

where we have used the fact that by (2.17), $\lim_{t\to\infty} \Delta\hat{b}_0(t) = 0$. It is not difficult to see that from (2.1) by Assumption (A_3) and (A.13),

$$\max_{1\leq\tau\leq t} \| u(\tau-1) \|^2 \leq K_6 \max_{1\leq\tau\leq t} \| z(\tau-1) \|^2 + \mathcal{O}(t^{1-\epsilon}) + \mathcal{O}[\log r_\phi(t-1)] \quad (a.s.). \tag{A.14}$$

Statement (4.3) follows from (4.1), (A.13) and (A.14). Statement (3) of the lemma is left to be proved. From (2.14), (4.3) and (2.25) it follows that

$$\| \hat{b}_0(t)u(t) - \hat{\theta}(t)^T\phi(t) \|^2 \leq K_7[r_z(t-1) + t^{1-\epsilon}] \log r_\phi(t-1) \quad (a.s.) \tag{A.15}$$

Eqs. (2.16) and (2.17) together with (A.15) imply

$$\| u(t) \|^2 \leq K_8[\log r_\phi(t-1)]^2[r_z(t-1) + t^{1-\epsilon}] \quad (a.s.) \tag{A.16}$$

Finally, from (2.14), (2.23), (2.25), (4.3) and (A.16) we conclude that

$$\begin{aligned} \| z(t) \|^2 &\leq \| \tilde{\theta}(t) \|^2 \| \phi(t) \|^2 \leq K_9[\log r_\phi(t-1)] \max_{1\leq\tau\leq t}[\| y(\tau) \|^2 + \| u(\tau) \|^2 \\ &+ \| \hat{\omega}(\tau) - \omega(\tau) \|^2 + \| \omega(\tau) \|^2] \\ &\leq K_{10}[\log r_\phi(t-1)]^3[r_z(t-1) + t^{1-\epsilon}] \quad (a.s.) \end{aligned} \tag{A.17}$$

which proves the lemma. □

References

[1] K. J. Åström and B. Wittenmark, "On Self-Tuning Regulators", *Automatica*, Vol. 9, pp. 195-199, 1973.

[2] P. R. Kumar, "Convergence of Adaptive Control Schemes Using Least-Squares Parameter Estimates", *IEEE Trans. Automat. Contr.*, Vol. AC-35, pp. 416-423, 1990.

[3] L. Guo and H. F. Chen, "The Åström-Wittenmark Self-Tuning Regulator Revisited and ELS-based Adaptive Trackers", *IEEE Trans. Automat. Contr.*, Vol. AC-36, pp. 802-812, 1991.

[4] H. F. Chen and L. Guo, "Convergence Rate of Least Squares Identification and Adaptive Control for Stochastic Systems", *Int. J. Contr.*, Vol. 44, pp. 1459-1476, 1986.

[5] S. Meyn and P. E. Caines, "The Zero Divisor Problem of Multivariable Stochastic Adaptive Control", *Syst. Contr. Lett.*, Vol. 6, No. 4, pp. 235-238, 1985.

[6] H. F. Chen and L. Guo, "Asymptotically Optimal Adaptive Control with Consistent Parameter Estimates", *SIAM J. Contr. Optimiz.*, Vol. 25, pp. 558-575, 1987.

[7] G. C. Goodwin and K. S. Sin, *Adaptive Filtering, Prediction and Control*, Englewood Cliffs, N.J.: Prentice-Hall, 1984.

Proceedings of the
American Control Conference
San Francisco, California • June 1993

A GAME-PLAYING FUZZY LOGIC CONTROLLER FOR SEMI-ACTIVE SUSPENSIONS

Dennis M. Briggs and Ka C. Cheok

Department of Electrical and Systems Engineering
School of Engineering and Computer Science
Oakland University, Rochester , Michigan 48309

Abstract

The idea of controlling physical systems with artificially-intelligent control methods has great appeal, and has been investigated heavily in the past. At the very least, they offer the chance to control effectively systems that are highly nonlinear and/or time-varying.

This paper describes attempts to fuse game-playing theory and binary-decision-tree pattern recognition methods to build a fuzzy logic parametric controller for a semi-active suspension system. The goal of the controller is to minimize (or defend against) the maximum possible transfer of road interaction forces to the vehicle. Simulation results show that the resulting system can provide the desired control actions to handle smoothly the irregularities in the road profile and the many nonlinearities inherent in the suspension system.

1. Introduction

The problem of control of semi-active suspension systems, for automotive and non-automotive applications, has been investigated using conventional methods such as optimal and adaptive control [2]. However, it is difficult to apply these techniques to highly nonlinear, time-varying systems for which there is no good closed-form model. Most control theory does not handle well the effects of natural nonlinear characteristics, saturation limits, and stiction.

In this paper, we present a fuzzy logic parametric control scheme that selects and implements a semi-active damper setting that has been determined by a heuristic game-playing search algorithm. The fusing of the fuzzy logic controller and the heuristic solution is achieved via the use of a binary decision tree classifier.

The proposed Game-Playing Parametric Control is a decision scheme which extends the ideas in [1] and selects a best parameter for the system depending on the control situation [5] [10]. The decision is based on an artificially-intelligent heuristic search that evaluates predicted performance of the control system. This paper shows how one part of game-playing theory, minimax search, can be used as a parametric control scheme for nonlinear systems.

Binary decision trees (BDTs) [4] [9] have long been used as a pattern recognition tool with applications in many areas. However, very little has been done with this technique in real-time control. While BDTs require discretizing of the output at some level, they lend themselves to today's von Neumann computers and provide the design engineer with a set of rules describing how the state space was partitioned as the BDT was trained.

The main idea behind this paper is to combine minimax game-playing techniques, BDTs and Fuzzy Logic, utilizing the best parts of these concepts to develop a parametric controller for the semi-active suspension system. Specifically, minimax is used to select the "best" shock setting against the worst road profile expected under normal conditions; the BDTs automatically observe the minimax decisions and generate the rules for the system; and the Fuzzy Logic system provides a continuous output to the plant being controlled. Note that in this process, the heuristics take the place of the knowledge engineering activity that is usually used in intelligent control.

The remainder of this paper is divided into the following sections: Problem Statement, Approach to Problem, System Description, Results, and Conclusions.

2. Problem Statement

The purpose of the project is to develop a continuous parametric controller for a simplified but nonlinear semi-active suspension system modeled for one wheel of a multi-wheeled vehicle. Interactions from other parts of the vehicle are not considered in this paper. The controller will be developed using the ideas introduced above; namely, minimax, BDTs, and Fuzzy Logic.

3. Approach To Problem

The basic approach to the problem is shown in Figure 1. Points in the *measure space* (i.e., those variables which can be measured and are useful) are selected by the designer for the minimax decision program, which determines the proper shock absorber damping setting for each point. The system described here uses the following variables in its measure space: wheel absolute vertical acceleration, suspension relative (between body and wheel) vertical displacement, and suspension relative vertical velocity. The selected points and the recommended shock settings from the minimax decision program are given to the BDT learning program. The BDT program generates a tree that divides the measure space into groups of similar shock settings, in the manner of most pattern recognition schemes. Since each path through the tree is a rule, the fuzzy logic generator can take the tree output and create fuzzy rules for the fuzzy controller. This is also the point where the discretized shock settings from the BDT are made continuous. The fuzzy controller then operates as do most controllers in similar schemes.

One characteristic of semi-active suspension systems is that since only the shock damping setting is controlled, little energy is put into the system by the controller. Therefore, stability problems are not of paramount concern here. However, other system maladies can occur, such as ringing or sudden jumps in acceleration, which could be felt by the passengers in the vehicle or could result in loss of vehicle control. It is the function of the minimax decision program to provide sufficient information to prevent or overcome these maladies.

4. System Description

This section describes each major block of the system shown in Figure 1.

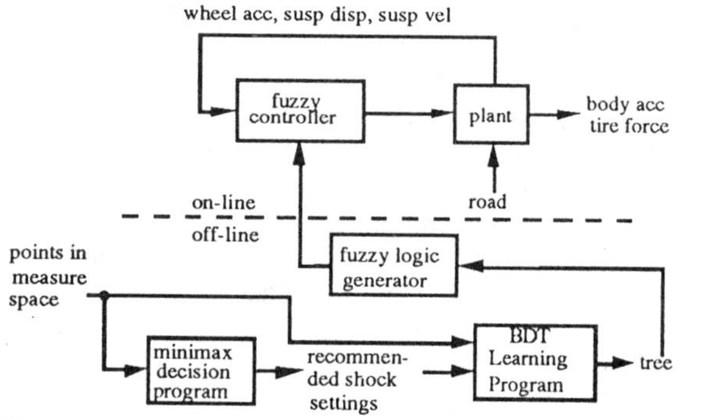

Figure 1. Minimax-BDT-Based Fuzzy Controller Architecture

Minimax Shock Curve Selection Program

The approach to handling the unknown disturbances from the road is similar to the minimax approach used in game-playing [8]. In games, the player and the opponent each have a finite number of possible moves, and each of the opponent's responses to each of the player's possible next moves is considered. In this application, the player is the controller and the opponent is the road. It is the purpose of the controller to be ready for whatever input the road may give to the system.

One difficulty of this approach is the spectrum of moves or values -- neither road nor controller is discrete. Both have essentially an infinite number of moves. For the purposes of generating a training set for the binary tree generator, the number of possible values of disturbance and control must be circumscribed.

The number of ways to generate a truncated set of values is clearly very large. The approach used for this paper is as follows:

Controller: four shock absorber damping curves were used: a minimum curve, a maximum curve, and two curves in between.

Road: three possible future road surface scenarios were considered (see Figure 2). The "plus" future consists of the road vertical acceleration jumping at t_1 from its initial value to a large positive value, and staying there until t_2. The "zero" future has the road acceleration moving at t_1 from its initial value to zero. In the "minus" future, the road acceleration jumps from its initial value to a large negative value, then to zero.

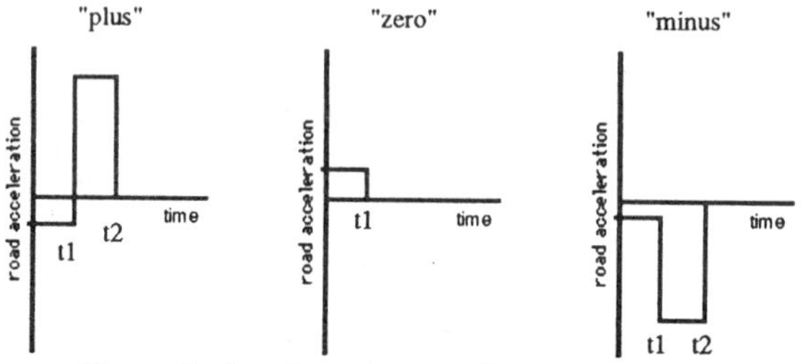

Figure 2. Road acceleration Future Scenarios

The basic procedure for generating a point in the training set consists of selecting a point in the measure space, generating the equivalent point in the state space, and then simulating the system for 100 ms at each combination of shock curve and road acceleration future. This creates the tree shown in Figure 3. For each curve, the maximum-cost future is chosen. Then, the curve with the smallest of the four maximum costs is selected and included in the training set. This is equivalent to a two-ply minimax search, and assures that the maximum damage will not exceed a certain amount, regardless of which future comes to pass.

It should be noted that this is not an optimal strategy. In fact, the minimax player says, "I will forego the best possible result in order to limit the potential damage done by my opponent." It is a defensive view of the situation, assuming that the road (or opponent) will always do what is worst for the suspension (or player).

Clearly, this defensive posture is a pessimistic view that is not fully warranted. It is impossible to say with certainty what the road will do, even in the next 100 ms. The road could, for example, move up or down in a way that actually helps the suspension provide a smooth ride and good handling. Some further improvements in strategy could be effected by utilizing this fact.

The minimaxing strategy may have some pitfalls [7] [8]. Further research is needed in this area to assure that a controller using it makes the proper choices.

BDT Learning Program

The BDT Learning Program [3] [4] creates binary decision trees by splitting the measure space into two groups, and then recursing on the groups just created, until all the groups have only one shock setting per group. This splitting of the measure space into groups is arranged into a BDT, each leaf of which consists purely of one shock setting. Normally, multiple leafs will contain the same shock setting. Some pruning of the tree usually follows, which reduces the computer load and actually increases the reliability of the pattern recognition process. For further details, see [1].

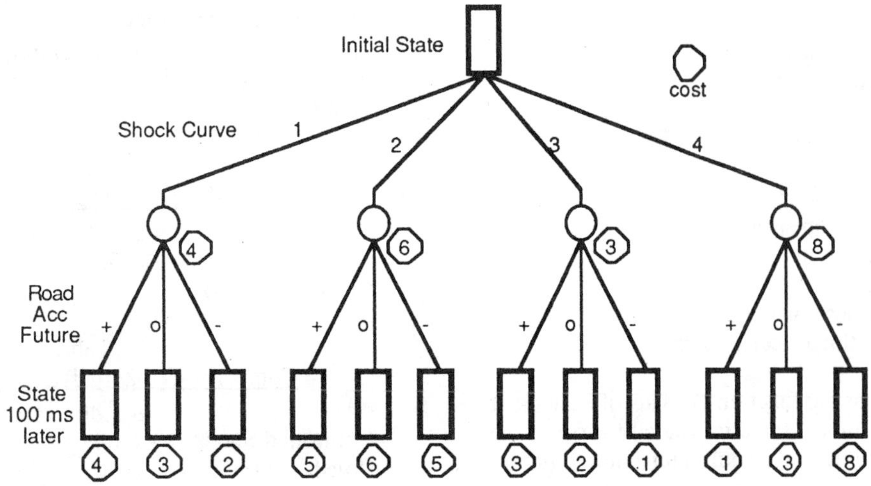

Figure 3
Minimax Search Applied to Shock Curve Selection
(In this case, select Curve 3)

Fuzzy Logic Generator

The Fuzzy Logic Generator takes the rules created by the BDT Learning Program and applies membership functions to each of the antecedents in each rule. It then creates code that implements standard fuzzy logic inferencing techniques. Each antecedent (such as velocity < -1000) causes the creation of two fuzzy assertions and associated membership functions. The assertion pair consists of two logical opposites, as shown in Figure 4.

Currently, all parameters, such as membership function shapes and inferencing techniques, are specified by the designer.

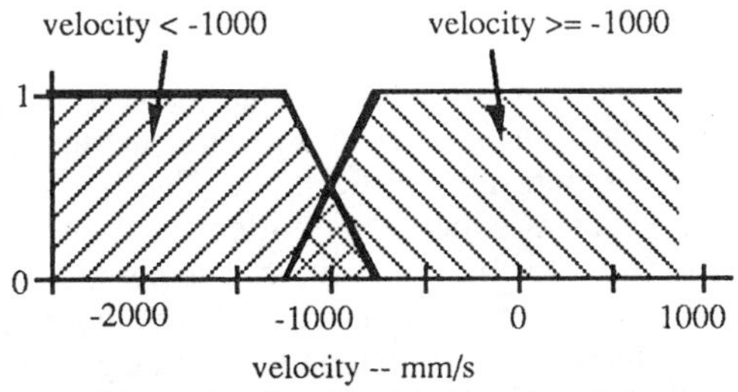

Figure 4. Membership Function Pair

Fuzzy Controller

The Fuzzy Controller implements the fuzzy rules discussed immediately above. The measured quantities are read in and the rules are applied to arrive at a crisp, continuous, output shock absorber setting.

Plant

The plant used in this paper is shown in Figure 5. The system has four states:

- relative velocity between body and wheel ($\dot{z}_{su}$)
- relative displacement between body and wheel (z_{su})
- relative velocity between wheel and road ($\dot{z}_{ur}$)
- relative displacement between tire and road (z_{ur})

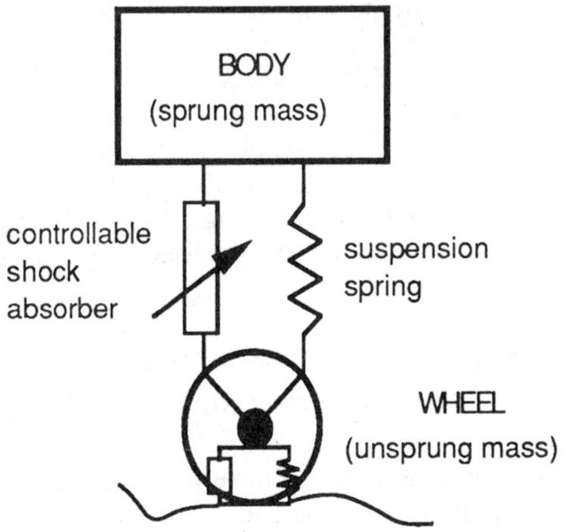

Figure 5. Plant to be controlled

These states are chosen to facilitate the simulation. The quantities used to determine effectiveness of the controller are body absolute acceleration (z_s), a measure of comfort, and force between the tire and the road (a measure of handling).

The equations governing the actions of the suspension are

shown below:

$$\ddot{z}_{ur} = \left(\frac{1}{M_u}\right)\left(-f_{td}\left[\dot{z}_{ur}\right] + f_{ts}\left[z_{ur}\right] + f_{sd}\left[\dot{z}_{su}\right] - f_{ss}\left[z_{su}\right]\right) - g - \ddot{z}_r$$

$$\ddot{z}_{su} = \left(\frac{1}{M_u}\right)\left(f_{td}\left[\dot{z}_{ur}\right] - f_{ts}\left[z_{ur}\right]\right) + \left(\frac{1}{M_u} + \frac{1}{M_s}\right)\left(-f_{sd}\left[\dot{z}_{su}\right] + f_{ss}\left[z_{su}\right]\right)$$

where s is sprung mass (body)
u is unsprung mass (wheel)
r is road
td is tire damping
ts is tire spring
sd is suspension damping
ss is suspension spring
z is vertical motion
M is mass
f is a nonlinear function
g is gravitational acceleration

The suspension damping function consists of a shock absorber with four nonlinear force-vs-velocity curves, a viscous damping function, and a coulomb friction function.

The tire damping function, always rather small, is forced to zero when the tire leaves the road. The tire spring function is linear in the normal range of operation, but goes to zero when the tire leaves the road. Additionally, there is a limit on the amount of tire spring compression (the wheel cannot dig into the road).

The suspension spring is approximately linear but the suspension travel hits limit stops at full compression (jounce) and extension (rebound).

A **Simulink** model was used to represent the system in both the minimax program and the simulation runs.

5. Results

This section shows the results obtained when using the proposed controller on several road disturbances. The controller was created with a training set generated by the minimax decision program using the following cost function:

$$J = k_1 * 2\text{-}norm(body\ absolute\ acc) + k_2 * max(body\ absolute\ acc), \quad k_1 + k_2 = 1$$

This function was used to minimize the acceleration and harshness experienced by the body as much as possible. The 2-norm term minimizes the general overall acceleration, while the max term minimizes the peak acceleration, which is somewhat related to harshness. Other cost functions tried include the Average Absorbed Power (which measures the amount of energy in a particular frequency band that is absorbed by the sprung mass, related to human fatigue), and a combination of body displacement, acceleration, and jerk.

In order for a particular shock control strategy to be considered further, it must prevent the suspension from causing the tire to be fully compressed, and prevent the suspension jounce and rebound limits from being hit, during all the maneuvers considered. Using these criteria, only the stiffest curve (curve 4) and the controlled shock qualified for further consideration. All other constant curves allowed the jounce limit to be reached, and curves 1 and 2 allowed the tire to be fully compressed, probably causing a blowout and actual wheel damage, along with loss of control.

Table 1
Comparison of Body Acceleration Costs

	St. Dn	Hole	St. Up	Bump
Controlled Shock	.052	.086	.074	.085
Const. Curve 4	.070	.099	.083	.096

Table 2
Comparison of Zero Tire Force Percentages

	St. Dn	Hole	St. Up	Bump
Controlled Shock	6.60	19.0	12.6	12.6
Const. Curve 4	8.10	23.4	15.7	20.0

The tables show the results of several simulation runs in which the vehicle travels at 50 mph and encounters the disturbances shown. The two qualifying strategies (controlled variable shock and stiff shock) are shown. The stiff shock is at the high-damping end of the variable-shock range. In both tables, lower numbers indicate better performance. When tire force is zero, the tire is airborne and can provide no lateral force, thus compromising handling. The advantage lies with the controlled shock in all cases.

A reasonable strategy for minimizing body movement is to allow the suspension to take up as much of the wheel motion as possible without actually hitting the jounce and rebound limits. When this happens, the body motion is minimized, and the wheel follows the bump profile much more closely, thus improving chances for good handling.

Figures 6-7 show in some detail what actually happens when the vehicle negotiates one of the disturbances; namely the ramped hole, at 50 mph. The hole is 200 mm deep, 3 meters wide at the bottom, and 10 meters wide at its rim. In Figure 6, curve 4 is so stiff that it does not allow the wheel to drop rapidly enough to keep the tire in contact with the road on the leading side of the hole. At the bottom of the hole, the tire once again establishes contact with the road, and keeps it without being fully compressed as the vehicle goes up the trailing side of the hole. After the hole is past, however, the body, which has been propelled upward by the trailing side, actually pulls the wheel off the road for about 7 meters of vehicle travel along the road. Neither the jounce nor the rebound limit is hit. In fact, the suspension did not come close to hitting its rebound limit.

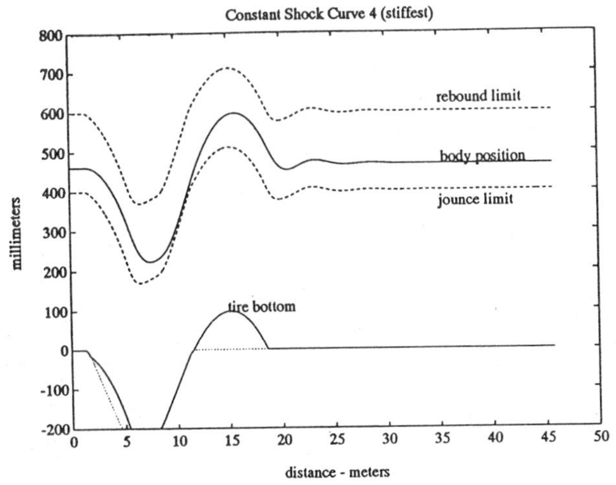

Figure 6. Stiffest Constant Shock Performance

Figure 7 shows the results of using the controlled shock. Note that both the jounce and rebound limits are approached very closely, indicating that more of the possible suspension travel is used to take up the wheel motion. This, as was stated before, improves chances for good performance. The more complete use of suspension travel is possible because the shock is not as stiff as curve 4 during some of the crucial parts of the maneuver. As a result, the tire is airborne for less time, and the body experiences less acceleration.

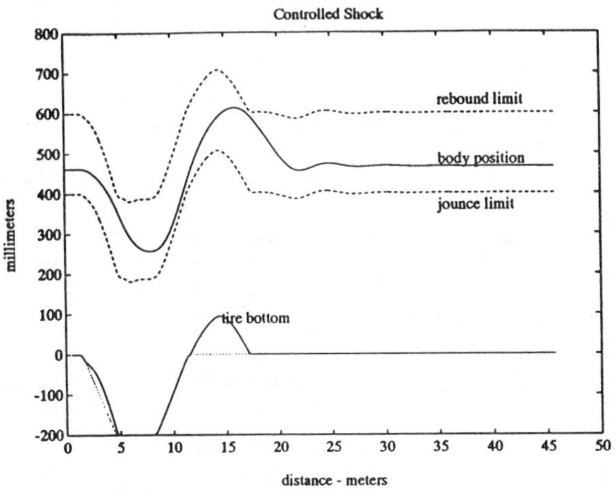

Figure 7. Controlled Shock Performance

6. Conclusions

This paper has shown the results of using a Fuzzy Logic parametric controller based on Game-Playing techniques and Binary Decision Tree concepts. It shows that this idea at its current very early development stage works quite well in the many situations studied in the simulations.

The challenge of any controlled shock is to work as well as a stiff shock when stiffness is called for, and as well as a soft shock when softness is called for. Further work is being done in this area, as well as in creating architectures that will allow automatic learning and improvement through self-criticism of current system performance.

7. References

1. D. M. Briggs, K. C. Cheok, N. Huang, R. E. Haskell, "A Heuristic Binary-Tree-Based Fuzzy Logic Controller for Semi-Active Suspensions", Robotics and Manufacturing, Proc. Fourth Intl. Symp. on Robotics and Manufacturing (ISRAM '92), SantaFe, NM, Nov. 1992, p. 637.
2. K. C. Cheok, N. K. Loh, H. D. McGee, T. Petit, "Optimal Model-Following Suspension with Microcomputerized Damping",*IEEE Trans. Ind. Elect.*, vol. 1E-32, no. 4, Nov. 1985.
3. R. Haskell, B. Mirshab, G. Castelino, "Calculating Shape Features in a Binary Image", paper presented at the Rochester Forth Conference, Rochester, NY, June 14-18,1988.
4. R. Haskell, G. Castelino, B. Mirshab,"Computer Learning using Binary Tree Classifiers",paper presented at Rochester Forth Conference, Rochester, NY,June 14-18,1988.
5. N. Huang, *Heuristic Optimal Control Systems: Theory and Applications*, Ph.D. Dissertation, Oakland University, Rochester , MI, 1991.
6. B. Kosko, *Neural Networks and Fuzzy Systems*,Prentice-Hall,Englewood Cliffs, NJ
7. Pearl, J., "On the Nature of Pathology in Game Searching", *Artificial Intelligence*, vol.20, no.4, pp.427-453.
8. Elaine Rich and Kevin Knight, *Artificial Intelligence*, McGraw-Hill, New York, 1991.
9. E. M. Rounds,"A Combined Nonparametric Approach to Feature Selection and Binary Decision Tree Design",Proc. 1979 IEEE Computer Soc. Conf. on Pattern Recognition and Image Processing, pp. 38-43, 1979.
10. J. C. Smith, K. C. Cheok, N. Huang, "Optimal Parametric Control of a Semi-Active Suspension System Using Neural Networks", Proc. 1992 American Control Conf.,Chicago, IL, June 1992, pp963-967.
11. L. Zadeh,"Outline of a New Approach to the Analysis of Complex Systems and Decision Processes",*IEEE Trans. Syst. Man Cybern.*,vol.SMC-3,pp28-44,1973.

Proceedings of the
American Control Conference
San Francisco, California • June 1993

Generalized Gain Scheduling Control of a Diesel Engine based on H_2 Optimization

Jin Jiang

Department of Electrical Engineering

University of Western Ontario

London, Ontario, N6A 5B9

CANADA

Abstract

A generalized gain scheduling control mechanism based on H_2 optimization techniques has been developed for a 2-cylinder water cooled Diesel engine. First, a set of linearized models is obtained for the engine operating at 3 different speeds and total of 15 loading conditions. It has been found that the behavior of the engine can best be characterized by a set of 5th order difference equations with appropriate time delays. The optimal controllers with a PID structure are then synthesized based on these mathematical models using off-line numerical optimization to minimize the H_2 norms of the closed-loop sensitivity functions. The designed control system has been implemented, and experiments have indicated that the performance of the Diesel engine with optimal controllers is much superior to that of the engine with the existing mechanical governor in terms of speed regulation, and disturbance rejection.

Introduction

Diesel engines have widely been used as power sources in practice. Diesel engine driven systems include automobiles, ships, and backup power generating stations to mention a few. However, control systems used on most of existing Diesel engines are still simple mechanical fly-wheel type of governors. The performance of these engines is usually limited by the inflexibilities of these governors. With the advance in computer technology and growing shortage of world energy resources, it is highly desirable to develop new control strategies to improve the performance of the existing engines in terms of speed regulation, robustness to load disturbance, and more importantly fuel economy. The main objective of this paper is to demonstrate how computer technology and modern control theory can be used to develop optimal control strategies for Diesel engines and to experimentally verify the developed schemes on an existing Diesel engine.

As it is well known, Diesel engines are highly nonlinear devices, their characteristics vary as a function of engine power output, speed, and ambient temperatures etc. Such nonlinear behaviors make the design of Diesel engine control systems very difficult. Furthermore, Diesel engines are inherently open-loop marginally stable systems in the sense that the engine speed will drift in the absence of feedback controllers, or the engine may stall when its operating speed is below certain value (1500 RPM for the current engine at no load).

It is also interesting to note that Diesel engines are inherent time-varying discrete-time systems in the sense that their speed is a function of fuel injection timing, compression and combustion processes which depend again on the instantaneous engine speed. It will be shown later that there is a pure time-delay between the movement of throttle positions and the engine speed change. This time-delay decreases as the engine speed increases. These undesirable properties make the design of optimal control systems for the engine even more challenging.

An optimal control of a Diesel engine speed governing loop has been formulated in [1]. Both 4-cylinder and 6-cylinder engines have been considered. A sample data model of the Diesel engine is constructed in a state-space form first. The cost function is then defined as a quadratic function of error in engine speed variables, control effort, and the air-fuel-ratio. This optimal control problem is solved by both dynamic programming and discrete minimum principle. This paper is theoretical in nature, and no attempts have been made to actually implement the developed control scheme on an actual engine.

In reference [2], a novel smoke sensor has been used in conjunction with tacho-generator to control the transient response of the Diesel engine. The engine fuel rack is controlled by a servo-motor drive. The control algorithms are of **PI** (Proportional and Integral) type whose parameters are so chosen that the engine overshoot and engine exhaust smoke are minimized. The control scheme has been evaluated on an actual Diesel engine under four operating speeds and three load conditions. A second order transfer function is assumed for the system from fuel rack to engine speed. However, the transfer function from fuel rack to engine smoke is found to be highly nonlinear. Therefore, a set of models has been used for the control system design at different load conditions.

Since almost all farm tractors are driven by Diesel engines, some research work has been done to design fuel efficient control systems for tractors. Among other things, optimal control of Diesel engine used in tractors has drawn a lot of attention, [3,4,5]. In above research publications and a Ph.D. dissertation, an optimal engine speed control system has been developed. The engine model from fuel rack to engine speed is identified first for various engine operating conditions. This model is a fifth-order **ARMA** (Auto-Regressive Moving Average) type. Lead-lag compensators are then designed, and the controller parameters are selected such that the **Integrated Absolute Error (IAE)** of the control loop is minimum. A microcomputer has been used to implement the designed control systems. The desired engine speed in this case is determined by a so-called Specific Fuel Consumption curve which depends not only on the engine speed controllers, but also on the gear ratio and traction control of the tractor as well.

In this paper, a set of dynamic models of the Diesel engine speed control loop is obtained first through dynamic system identification techniques under various engine speeds and power outputs. The models are in terms of difference equations with appropriate time-delays. Such parametric models are cross-checked by frequency response measurements before being used in controller designs.

Based on the derived mathematical models, H_2 optimal controllers have been designed, and the engine performance with these controllers have been evaluated by actual experiments on the engine under various engine operation conditions, such as sudden speed changes, ramp load disturbances, etc. The performance comparisons of the new control schemes with that of the original fly-wheel mechanical governor have indicated that tremendous improvements in terms of speed regulations and disturbance rejections have been achieved by the new control scheme. Since the controller parameters depend on both engine speed and power output, hence the term ***generalized gain scheduling controller*** has been used. By implementing the controller on a microcomputer, the controller gains can be adjusted automatically in response to the operated engine speed and power output on-line in real-time.

Construction of Diesel Engine Models

The specifications of the Diesel engine used in this paper are given as follows:

- Petter Diesel Model - PH2W
- 2 cylinder
- 15 Brake Horse Power at 1800 RPM
- Stroke 100 mm
- Cubic capacity per cylinder 0.659 litre

- Compression ratio 16.5:1.0
- Maximum Engine Speed 1800 RPM

There is a dynamometer which is permanently coupled to the engine main shaft for the purpose of simulating different loads on the engine. The load is varied by changing the field excitation of the dynamometer. The engine was designed to operate at a fixed speed with mechanical governors. However, this speed can be pre-set mechanically. Although the mechanical fly-wheel governor possesses certain speed regulation capabilities, the quality of such regulation is far from satisfactory. Although the designed speed of the engine is at 1800 RPM, the engine speed changes considerably as system environment varies, such as load, fuel quality, ambient and engine temperatures. The cooling system for the engine is via circulation of cool water through a heat exchanger.

The above engine and its related control systems have been upgraded. The major modifications are: (1) to install a DC-motor driven linear actuator to control the throttle position of the fuel injection pump through the movement of fuel rack position; (2) to couple a tacho-generator onto the engine secondary shaft (1/2 of the speed of the main shaft) for speed measurement through a flexible linkage and an electronic filter to minimize the torsional vibration in the measured engine speed signal; (3) to design and build an electronic circuit which is capable of generating various desired load patterns consistently by varying the strength of the field current of the dynamometer to simulate various engine load variations; and (4) to implement in real-time a computer data acquisition and control facilities for the engine measurement and controls.

The overall experimental set-up including computer based data acquisition system is shown in Figure 1. The signal generator has been used for engine frequency response measurements, it has also been used for generating various of load variation patterns for engine performance evaluations. However, it is not an essential part of the control system, therefore, dotted box has been used to represent it.

The parametric models of the engine are obtained by dynamic system identification methods. Since the engine is an open-loop marginally stable system, it is very dangerous and difficult to perform any open-loop tests. However, the control system designs call for the open-loop engine transfer function. One approach is to identify the closed-loop system (with appropriate controller in the loop) first, and then convert the closed-loop transfer function into an open-loop one. The second approach is to measure the signal from the inside of the engine control loop, such as the input signal to the linear actuator. Then, the open-loop engine transfer function can be calculated directly provided that an external probing signal is used to guarantee the identifiability. To minimize the computational cost, the second approach is used to identify the open-loop dynamic model of the engine in this research.

The identification procedures can be summarized as follows: A 9-bit PRBS of ±0.5 volts is generated and added to the nominal engine speed control signal at the speed set-point within the computer. The stabilizing controller for the engine is simply a proportional controller. The input signal used for system identification is the engine speed error signal which is the difference between the set-point speed control signal and the real-time measurement of the engine speed output from the tacho-generator. The system output signal for identification is the voltage measured at the output of the tacho-generator. The sampling period of 0.1 sec. is used in all the tests. Total of 400 data points are recorded for both input and output signals through RTI-815A Data Acquisition Unit. Based on the recorded data, ***PC MATLAB***™ and ***System Identification Tool Box*** from ***MathWork Inc.*** is used for deriving the parametric models of the engine in terms of difference equations.

The dynamic model of the engine can be represented by an ***ARMA (Auto-Regressive and Moving Average)*** model in terms of z-transform as shown in Eqns. (1) &(2). The data analysis indicates that to characterize the behavior of the engine at the speed of 1000 RPM, four units of time delays (0.4 sec.) have to be included in the model:

$$\frac{Speed(z^{-1})}{Error(z^{-1})} = \frac{b_4 z^{-4} + b_5 z^{-5} + b_6 z^{-6} + b_7 z^{-7}}{1 + a_1 z^{-1} + a_2 z^{-2} + a_3 z^{-3} + a_4 z^{-4} + a_5 z^{-5}} \quad (1)$$

However, when the engine speed increases to 1300 and 1500 RPM, the effective time delay reduces. Analysis indicates that three units of time delay is adequate to describe the engine dynamics at these two speed levels. Hence, the general form for the transfer function of the engine at 1300 and 1500 RPM is shown in Eqn. (2) in z-transform form:

$$\frac{Speed(z^{-1})}{Error(z^{-1})} = \frac{b_3 z^{-3} + b_4 z^{-4} + b_5 z^{-5} + b_6 z^{-6}}{1 + a_1 z^{-1} + a_2 z^{-2} + a_3 z^{-3} + a_4 z^{-4} + a_5 z^{-5}} \quad (2)$$

Since Diesel engines are nonlinear systems, the coefficients in Eqns.(1) & (2) are nonlinear functions of engine speeds and power outputs. Their respective values are obtained by least squares parameter estimation procedure, and tabulated in Table 1.

Fig 1. Computer based Diesel Engine Control System Setup

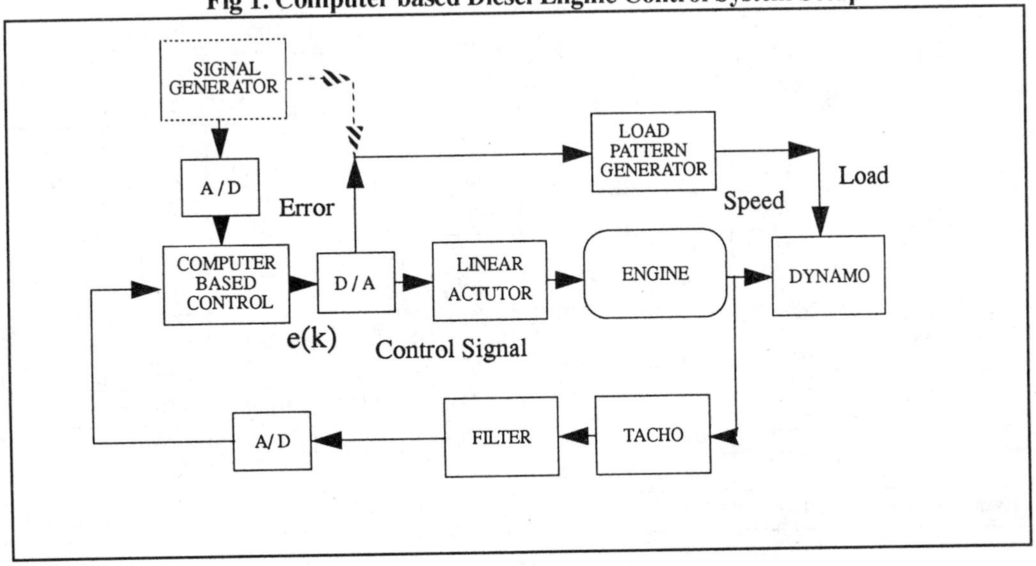

Generalized Gain Scheduling Control

Previous analysis indicates that Diesel engines are highly nonlinear systems. The direct consequence of such nonlinearities is that an *'optimal'* controller designed for one engine operating condition (speed and power output) may not work well when the engine is operating at another condition. In fact, under certain circumstances, even closed-loop system stability may be in jeopardy. One solution to such problem is to design a *'robust'* controller which performs reasonably well for all operating conditions. Because of the large variation of the engine dynamics at different speeds and power outputs, such a robust controller can never be optimal for all operating conditions. One of the simplest approaches to optimal controller designs is to divide the range of the engine operation into several different zones according to the engine speed and output power. An optimal controller is then designed for each of these zones. During the course of engine operation, depending on the engine operating condition, the most appropriate controller will be used, which provide the optimal engine performance in each zone. In this paper, the engine operations have been divided into 15 different zones as shown in Table 1.

It is important to mention that the optimality considered in the engine control system design is the quality of the transient responses, such as percentage overshoot, rise time, settling time etc. Such optimalities can be achieved by choosing appropriate PID controller parameters, K_p, K_I, and K_D to minimize H_2 norm of the engine speed error signal subject to step inputs, as follows, [6,7,8]:

$$J(K_p, K_I, K_D) = Min\int_0^{\infty}|e(t)|^2 dt \approx Min\sum_0^{\infty}|e(k)|^2 \quad (3)$$

where K_p, K_I, and K_D are proportional, integral and derivative gains of the PID controller. $e(k)$ is the engine speed error signal at sampling instance k as shown in Fig. 1.

The Optimization processes have been carried out numerically using the fifteen engine dynamic models given in Table 1. It should be noted that since the controller structure has been pre-specified as PID type, the Optimization process of Eqn.(3) is in fact a nonlinear one. ***MATRIXx Optimization Tool Box*** has been used to derive the appropriate controller parameters. The desirable controller parameters are also shown in a 3-D view in Fig. 2.

Since these controller parameters are obtained based solely on the linearized engine models, an important question is how well these controllers will perform on the actual test engine. To answer this crucial question, real-time experiments on the test engine using these controllers will be carried out under different engine operating conditions which is the subject of next section.

From the controller parameters in the above Tables, it is interesting to note that as engine speed and power output changes, the variation of the proportional controller gain K_P is relatively small. However, there is a large variation in integral controller gain K_I. The general changing pattern of K_I is that it decreases as engine load increases. The general changing pattern for derivative gain K_D is just opposite from that of K_I, i.e. as load increases, K_D decreases.

Performance Evaluations

Diesel engines with mechanical governors are usually designed to operate at a pre-specified speed which can be set mechanically via some limiting devices, therefore, it is not possible to perform any step response tests on the engine speed. Rather than introducing a step change in speed set-point of the engine, we will study the engine speed responses to various load variations.

The speed responses of the mechanical governor controlled Diesel engine to various load changes are shown in Figures 3 -- 5.

The underlying reasons for mechanical governors to have such poor control performance are (1) lack of integral actions in the mechanical governor, therefore, a finite speed error signal is required to pickup the additional engine loads. Hence, steady-state speed error; (b) large time constant of the mechanical governor

TABLE 1. Parameters of Engine Model at Different Speed and Output

Parameters	a_1	a_2	a_3	a_4	a_5	b_4	b_5	b_6	b_7
Loads	Engine Nominal Speed at 1000 RPM								
No Load	-1.7732	0.7077	0.2112	-0.2244	0.0916	0.0071	-0.0009	-0.0006	0.0022
0.7 Kwatt	-1.6952	0.6663	0.2459	-0.3750	0.1709	0.0104	0.0035	0.0011	0.0025
0.85 Kwatt	-1.7490	0.7618	0.1367	-0.2331	0.0990	0.0096	0.0051	0.0002	0.0017
1.2 Kwatt	-1.7972	0.7693	0.1586	-0.1655	0.0507	0.0089	0.0023	0.0002	-0.0007
2.0 Kwtt	-1.8665	1.0419	-0.1164	-0.1049	0.0643	0.0091	0.0044	0.00009	0.0022
Parameters	a_1	a_2	a_3	a_4	a_5	b_3	b_4	b_5	b_6
Loads	Engine Nominal Speed at 1300 RPM								
No Load	-2.0867	1.3388	-0.2887	0.0803	-0.0376	0.0135	-0.0019	-0.0053	0.0029
1.0 Kwatt	-2.0707	1.3438	-0.2270	-0.0586	0.0180	0.0136	0.0010	-0.0010	0.0029
2.5 Kwatt	-1.9778	1.2188	-0.2724	0.0760	-0.0403	0.0139	0.0041	0.0026	0.0014
3.0 Kwatt	-2.0399	1.3569	-0.3537	0.0755	-0.0341	0.0126	0.0040	0.0012	0.0034
3.7 Kwatt	-2.0169	1.2293	-0.1377	-0.0756	0.0055	0.0135	0.0036	0.0009	0.0030
Loads	Engine Nominal Speed at 1500 RPM								
No Load	-1.9115	0.8867	0.0872	-0.0009	-0.0533	0.0168	-0.0008	-0.0089	0.0018
0.7 Kwatt	-1.8508	0.8761	0.0055	0.0308	-0.0555	0.0168	0.0030	-0.0050	0.0029
1.85 Kwatt	-1.7552	0.7881	-0.1014	0.1812	-0.1069	0.0167	0.0060	-0.0010	0.0017
3.1 Kwatt	-1.7032	0.6956	0.0732	-0.0486	-0.0089	0.0167	0.0052	0.0018	0.0049
4.4 Kwatt	-1.6594	0.8301	-0.1701	-0.0501	0.0575	0.0156	0.0083	0.0049	0.0070

Fig 2. Three controller parameters for the engine at different operating conditions.

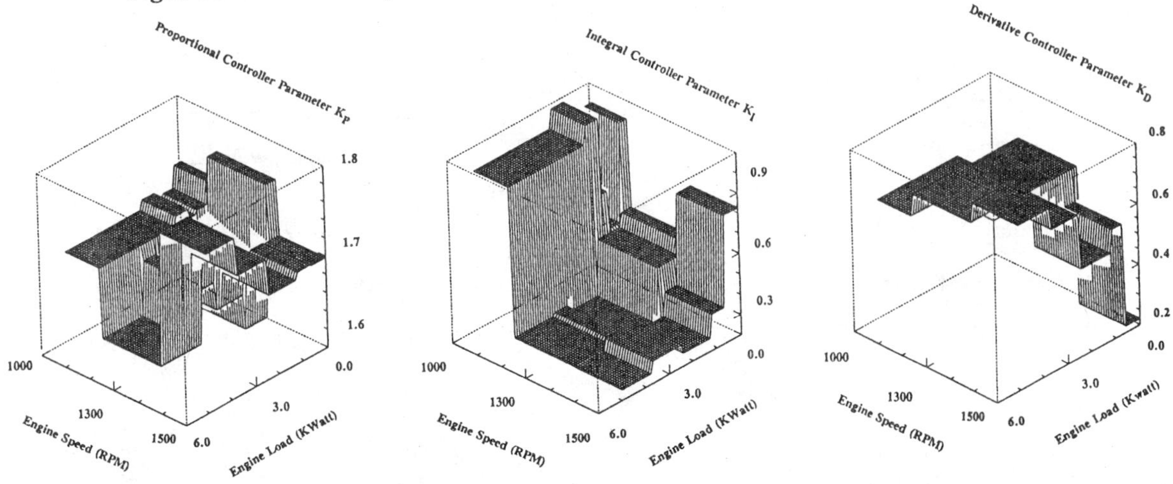

results in a sluggish responses to the engine speed change, as a consequence, the throttle position can not be adjusted instantaneously, which leads to a large speed variation. As is well known, when the engine speed is below a certain threshold value, the engine will stall eventually. Such unstable behaviors can best be seen in Figure 5. To completely understand how good the optimal controllers perform in actual engine environment, three types of tests have been conducted using optimal controllers.

The first group of tests is to investigate the speed regulation characteristics of the engine under constant torque output. Both Step and Ramp signals have been used as a speed change command signal. The purposes of the tests are to verify our controller designs, and to compare the engine responses at various speeds and loads. The second group of tests deals with the situations where the engine torque undergoes two types of variations: Step & Ramp changes, while the engine speed set-point is kept constant. Such tests are mainly used to study the disturbance rejection properties of the engine control loop. Finally, the power characteristics of the closed-loop engine control system have been investigated. By power characteristics we mean that the torque and the speed of the engine are changed simultaneously in the same direction with the same patterns, i.e. increased (decreased) in step or ramp fashions. In fact, such tests can put a lot of stress on the engine, particularly, the power characteristics of the engine. When step changes are used, the engine power variations will be as large as squared amount of that step change. On the other hand, if ramp changes are used, the engine power output will vary parabolically. Due to the space limitations, only selected results are presented here. Detailed results are available in Reference [9].

The step responses of the engine with optimal controllers have been performed by introducing a step change at engine set speed point. The magnitude of the step changes is 1.0 Volt, which corresponds to 168 RPM. The results are shown in Figure 6 where the engine was originally operating around 1000 RPM, and a speed change signal has been issued. As a result, the engine accelerates quickly and settles in the new speed.

An example of the engine speed responses to ramp input commands is shown in Figure 7. The ramp signal is generated by triangular waveforms. The Figure shows two engine speed responses at load of 1000 RPM. The upper graph has been obtained when the engine carries no external load, while the lower graph represents the same except that the initial engine power output is about 2 KWatt. Comparison of these two graphs indicates that the faster tracking can be obtained with lighter load. It appears that there is no steady-state tracking error even with ramp command inputs, however, this is not true in general for large load.

The performance of the engine under step load changes is shown in Figure 8 where the initial engine speed is 1000 RPM when an extra 1.05 KWatt load is being added. The performance of the engine under ramp load disturbances has also been studied. The load disturbance pattern and the corresponding engine speed response for the engine operating at a nominal speed of 1000 RPM are shown in Figure 9. The minimum and the maximum load variations are 0.075 KWatt and 1.62 KWatt, respectively. Under such load variations, the maximum speed deviation is only 43 RPM.

The third part of the experiments deals with the situations where the engine speed and the torque output are varied simultaneously in the same pattern. Figure 10 shows the torque and speed change patterns and corresponding speed response of the engine operating at a nominal speed of 1000 RPM. In this case, the speed variations is 1.0 Volt. which corresponds to 168 RPM, and the range of total power output is from 0.02 KWatt to 2.46 KWatt. The graph clearly indicates that the engine can maintain reasonably good transient and steady-state responses.

Conclusion

A generalized gain scheduling control scheme based on H_2 Optimization techniques has been developed for a Diesel engine. The designed scheme has been implemented on a microcomputer, and evaluated on a real engine. The results have indicated that the performance of the engine with the optimal controller is much superior to that with the existing engine governor.

References

[1] Flower, J. O., and Gupta, R. K., "Optimal Control Considerations of Diesel Engine Discrete Models," International Journal of Control, Vol. 19, No.6, pp. 1057-1068, 1974.

[2] Hong, G., and Collings, N., "Design of Diesel Smoke Feedback Control Using a Combination of Pl control Algorithm and Performance Optimization," SAE Technical Paper, No.#890387, 1989.

[3] Zhang, N., Perumpral, J. V., Byler, R. K., and Shaffer, S. D., "Diesel Engine Control Based on an ARMA Model," Transactions of the ASAE, Vol. 32, No.4, pp. 1112-1120, 1989.

[4] Zhang, N., Perumpral, J. V., and Byler, R. K., "Automatic Control System for Optimizing Diesel Engine Performance," Computers and Electronics in Agriculture, Vol. 2, pp. 31-46, 1987.

[5] Zhang, N., Microprocessor-Based Digital Controller Improving Tractor Operating Efficiency, Ph.D Dissertation, Virginia Polytechnic Institute and State University, 1987.

[6] Boyd, S. P., and Barratt, C. H., Linear Controller Design: Limits of Performance, Prentice Hall, Englewood Cliffs, New Jersey,1991.

[7] Anderson, B. D. O., and Moore, J. B., Optimal Control: Linear Quadratic Methods, Prentice Hall, Englewood Cliffs, New Jersey, 1990.

[8] Newton, Jr. G. C., Gould, L. A., and Kaiser, J. F., Analytical Design of Linear Feedback Controls, John Wiley & Sons, Inc. New York, 1957.

[9] Jiang, J., Development of an Optimal Fuel Efficient Digital Algorithm for Diesel Engine Controls, Final Project Report for Energy, Mine and Resources of Canada, May, 1992.

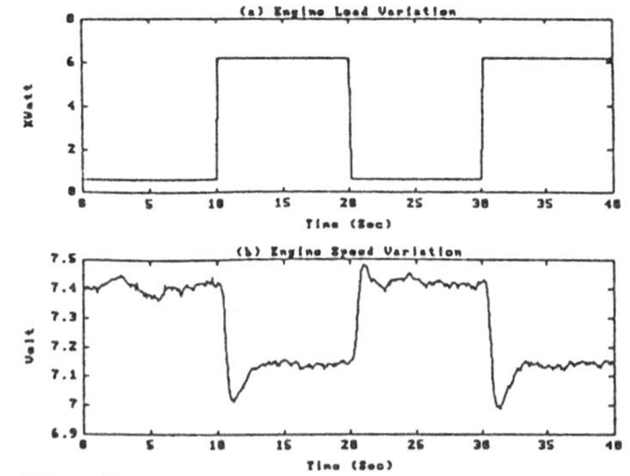

Fig. 3 Mechanical governor at step load change.

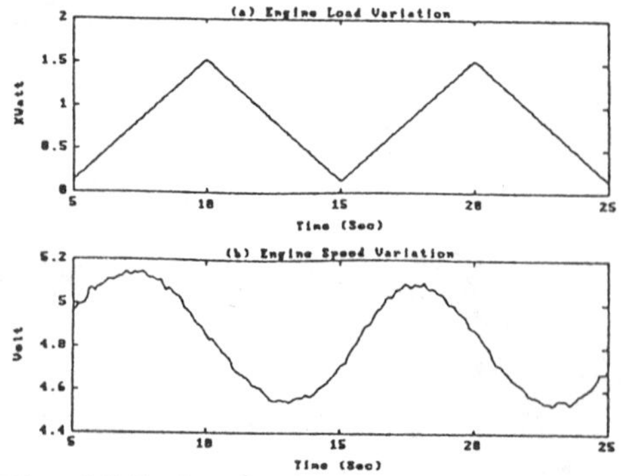

Fig. 4 Mechanical governor at ramp load change.

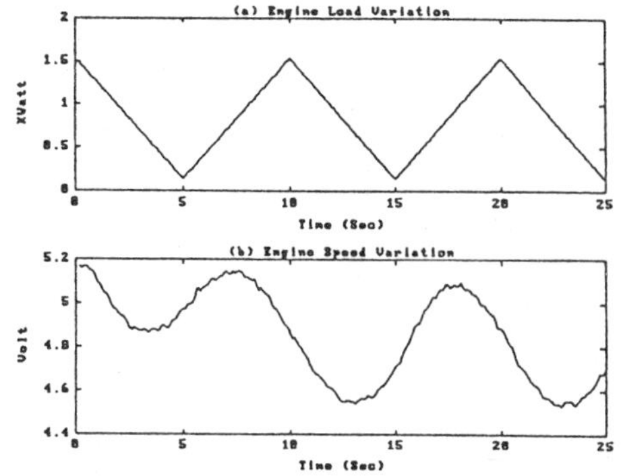

Fig. 5 Engine characteristics before stalling

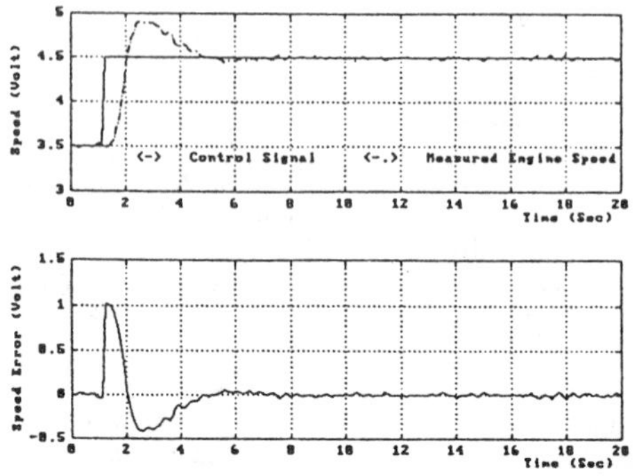

Fig. 6 Step input at 1000 RPM and no load.

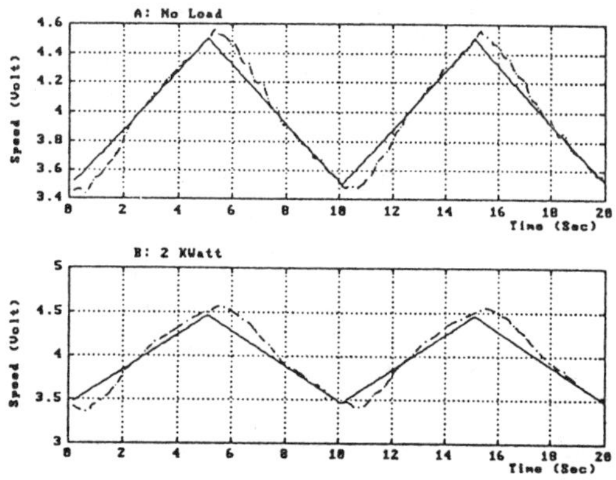

Fig. 7 Ramp input at 1000 RPM.

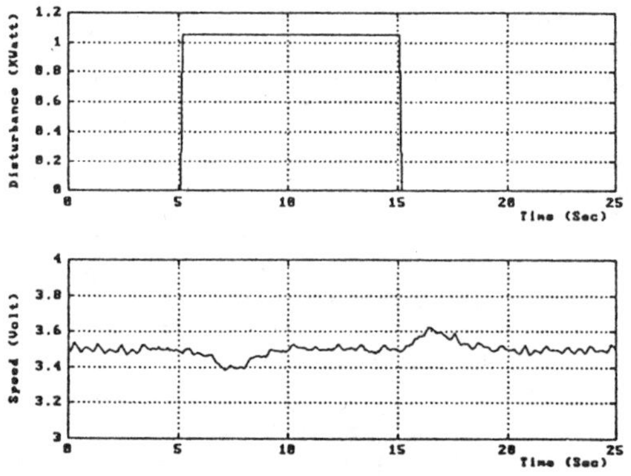

Fig. 8 Step load change at 1000 RPM.

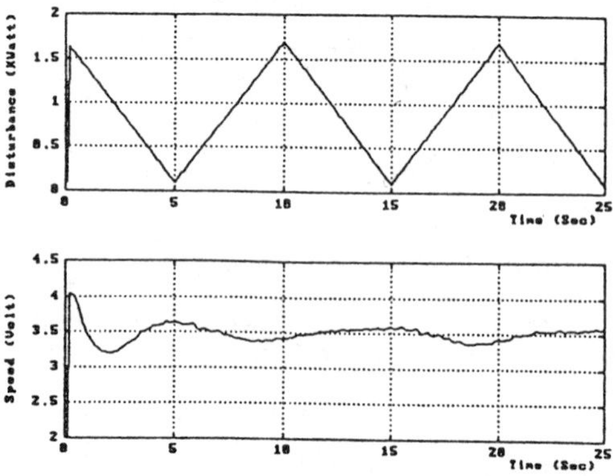

Fig. 9 Ramp load changes at 1000 RPM.

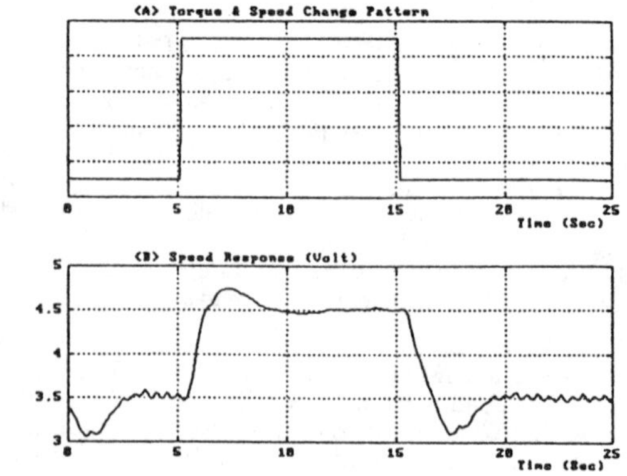

Fig. 10 Torque and speed changes at 1000 RPM.

Proceedings of the
American Control Conference
San Francisco, California • June 1993

Automotive Engine Idle Speed Control with Recurrent Neural Networks

G. V. Puskorius and L. A. Feldkamp

Research Laboratory, Ford Motor Company
Suite 1100, Village Plaza
23400 Michigan Avenue
Dearborn, Michigan 48124

ABSTRACT

This paper describes the development of recurrent neural network controllers for an automotive engine idle speed control (ISC) problem. Engine ISC is a difficult problem because of troublesome characteristics such as severe process nonlinearities, variable time delays, time-varying process dynamics and unobservable system states and disturbances. We demonstrate that recurrent neural network controllers can be trained to handle these difficulties gracefully while achieving good regulator performance for a representative model of a 4-cylinder, 1.6 liter engine. Empirical results clearly illustrate that neural network controllers with relatively large amounts of internal feedback provide more robust performance for the ISC problem than do neural network controllers that are static or contain limited internal recurrent connections.

1 Introduction

The automotive engine idle speed control problem has been extensively studied over the last dozen years [1, 2]. It has been shown that this problem lends itself to the application of a wide variety of techniques from both classical and modern control theory [1]. More recently, ISC with fuzzy logic has been investigated as a potentially attractive methodology for this problem that would allow automotive control engineers to deal directly with system nonlinearities [3, 4, 5]. In this paper, we investigate a neural network based approach to the development of controllers for ISC, and show that recurrent neural networks provide robust control performance for a wide range of operating conditions.

A number of characteristics complicate the design of controllers for ISC. The operation and regulation of an engine at idle is a highly nonlinear process. The idling process has time delays that vary inversely with engine speed and changes with time due to aging of components and environmental changes such as engine warm-up after a cold start. The measurement of system outputs occurs asynchronously with the calculation of control signals. We assume that the occurrence of plant disturbances, such as engagement of air-conditioner compressor, shift from neutral to drive in automatic transmissions, application and release of electric loads and power steering lock-up, are not directly observable. Other random or periodic disturbances may affect the idling process. The principal goal of ISC is to regulate the engine speed at a desired set point in the face of these unobserved disturbances.

We view neural networks as a powerful alternative for the synthesis of controllers for difficult problems such as ISC. We have previously shown that neural networks can be trained to act as controllers for realistic active suspension [6] and anti-lock braking (ABS) [7] models. These two problems exhibit some characteristics similar to the ISC problem. Both the active suspension and ABS problems are nonlinear, although the degree of nonlinearity is not as severe as in the ISC problem. Unobserved disturbances affect the active suspension system in the form of changes in road profile, while they affect ABS control in the form of changing road and vehicle/tire characteristics. Embedded in the ABS model were complications such as actuator dead zones and hysteresis. While the previously mentioned studies involved systems of only a single control input, the ISC problem as studied here has two control inputs.

The use of neural networks for the synthesis of system controllers offers a radical departure from classical and modern control theory approaches. A conventional approach to controller design is usually based upon analytical treatment of a mathematical system model, for which complications such as variable time delays and asynchronous sampling are often neglected in preliminary phases of analysis. On the other hand, a neural network approach to controller design is driven either directly with actual data from a physical system or with simulated data from a mathematical model of the system that includes the difficulties. Thus, the dynamical system model can be used as a simulation tool in off-line computer studies to establish reasonable neural network architectures for the control problem and to instantiate initial values for controller parameters before on-line adjustment of these parameters is performed for the real system. This paper describes the first step of this process, namely that of developing a neural network controller for a representative model of the ISC problem.

The remainder of this paper is organized as follows. In Section 2, we briefly discuss the engine model and the constraints that are imposed on its use for neural network training. A discussion of recurrent neural network architectures and their relationship to conventional control architectures is provided in Section 3. We describe neural network training details in Section 4, and provide a discussion of results in Section 5.

2 The Engine Model

The dynamic engine model employed in this study was derived from steady-state engine map data and empirical information by Powell [2], with revisions as described by Vachtsevanos et al. [5]. The engine model parameters are for a 1.6 liter, 4-cylinder fuel injected engine. The model is a two-input, two-output system where the system outputs are manifold pressure P in kPa and engine speed N in rpm, and where the control inputs are throttle angle θ and spark advance δ in degrees. Disturbances act on the engine in the form of an unobservable load torque disturbance T_d in N-m.

The evolution of the system is described by the following set of coupled equations:

$$\begin{aligned}
\dot{P} &= k_P(\dot{m}_{ai} - \dot{m}_{ao}), \quad k_P = 42.40 \\
\dot{N} &= k_N(T_i - T_L), \quad k_N = 54.26 \\
\dot{m}_{ai} &= (1 + 0.907\theta + 0.0998\theta^2)g(P) \\
g(P) &= \begin{cases} 1 & P < 50.6625 \\ 0.0197(101.325P - P^2)^{\frac{1}{2}} & P \geq 50.6625 \end{cases} \\
\dot{m}_{ao} &= -0.0005968N - 0.1336P \\
&\quad + 0.0005341NP + 0.000001757NP^2 \\
m_{ao} &= \dot{m}_{ao}(t-\tau)/(120N), \quad \tau = 45/N \\
T_i &= -39.22 + 325024m_{ao} - 0.0112\delta^2 + 0.635\delta \\
&\quad + (0.0216 + 0.000675\delta)N\,(2\pi/60) \\
&\quad - 0.000102N^2\,(2\pi/60)^2 \\
T_L &= (N/263.17)^2 + T_d\,.
\end{aligned}$$

For notational simplicity, explicit dependence on time is suppressed in these equations, except in the case of the delayed $\dot{m}_{ao}$. Refer to the references listed above for a more detailed discussion of these equations and engine dynamics.

For the purposes of this paper, the engine model is treated primarily as a black box that accepts control inputs and provides measured system states as outputs. Since the differential equations describing the performance of the engine exhibit *stiff* behavior in certain regions of operation, a backward Euler scheme with a step size of 1 ms is used for numerical integration. Control signals for throttle θ and spark advance δ are taken from ranges of 5–25 degrees and 10–45 degrees, respectively, and are computed in a background loop at 20 ms intervals. However, application of the computed control signals occurs only twice per engine revolution. Hence, when the engine speed is low, certain computed control signals may not be used; conversely, when the engine speed is high, the cycle time of the background loop is greater than the time interval between applications of control signals, and the same control command may be applied more than once. Measurements of manifold pressure and engine speed are made available at a rate of 4 measurements per engine revolution, where the current engine position is calculated from actual engine speeds. Measured manifold pressure P_m is corrupted by Gaussian noise of zero mean and standard deviation of 1 kPa, while measured engine speed N_m is corrupted by Gaussian noise of zero mean and standard deviation of 2.5 rpm. The application of control signals is delayed by at least 90 degrees (20 ms at 750 rpm) from the most recent measurements on which the control is based. Disturbances, ranging from 0 to 61 N-m, enter the system at a time resolution of 1 ms; hence, changes in disturbance input occur asynchronously with the application of control and the measurement of system outputs. It is noteworthy that the range of applied disturbances appears to be over twice as large as considered in some recent studies of ISC [3].

The primary goal of ISC is to maintain a constant engine speed while the system experiences unobserved disturbances. For the engine model described above, a set point of 750 rpm is desired. The two controls dynamically affect engine speed in distinctly different fashions. The throttle command θ has a large dynamic range (thousands of rpm), but its effect is delayed by a time inversely proportional to engine speed (for a steady-state engine speed of 750 rpm, the delay is 60 ms). On the other hand, the spark advance δ has an immediate effect on the engine speed, but its dynamic range is over an order of magnitude smaller than that of the throttle command. In addition to maintaining engine speed at 750 rpm, we would like to achieve a number of subjective secondary criteria. For example, it is desirable to maximize fuel efficiency while simultaneously minimizing vehicle vibrations. Fuel efficiency can be increased by operating the engine with an advanced spark angle. For the engine model described above, the spark advance that results in maximum brake torque (MBT) for a steady-state condition of 750 rpm is found to be 30.9 degrees. However, the spark advance must be retarded relative to this value if the spark advance control is to be useful in responding to torque load disturbances. Hence we choose, somewhat arbitrarily, a nominal spark advance of 22.9 degrees to allow rapid system response to unobserved torque disturbances while maintaining a reasonable level of fuel efficiency.

3 Neural Control Architectures

The general form of control architecture considered here is that of a feedback controller, where the control inputs are time-delayed measurements of manifold pressure P_m and engine speed N_m. We also consider the case in which explicit functions of the measured plant outputs are composed and used as controller inputs (e.g., integral and derivative terms of errors in engine speed). The feedback neural network controllers are specified by a generalized version of the recurrent multilayer perceptron (RMLP) architecture as described in [8]. A general RMLP architecture consists of layers of simple processing elements (nodes) arranged in a feedforward fashion with internal feedback connections between nodes of recurrent layers. Feedforward weights are constrained to only connect nodes of two successive layers, whereas feedback weights are constrained to connect nodes belonging to the same layer. In addition, we do not require that all nodes between successive layers be connected to one another, nor do we require complete interconnectivity between all nodes of a recurrent layer. Each node of the network transforms the weighted sum of its inputs by an output function (either the identity function for linear nodes or a bipolar sigmoidal function for nonlinear nodes). The input along feedback connections within a layer of the network is delayed by a unit time step, whereas the input along feedforward connections between layers can be used immediately.

RMLP architectures provide a number of useful characteristics that allow us to cope with complicating nonlinear dynamical system characteristics. For example, pure time delays can be conveniently represented by RMLP architectures [9]. Network architectures with internal recurrent connections can be used to encode and represent a system's internal hidden state. Furthermore, these architectures can also represent *strongly hidden state* [10], in which a system's output is a function of a potentially arbitrary number of past values of its inputs (e.g., consider the modeling of a flip-flop circuit). Finally, signal filtering and conditioning can be performed by neural control architectures with internal recurrent connections.

In addition to the useful properties described above, RMLP architectures can easily represent more traditional control architectures. Figure 1 shows a simple realization of a PID controller with a three-layer RMLP architecture. Linear output functions are used for all processing elements of this simple network. The single node in the first layer forms the error signal between the setpoint y_r and the measured system output y_m. The second layer consists of four linear nodes. The first node passes the error signal through without change by means of a connection of strength unity. The second node of this layer constructs the integral term, where the feedback weight α has a value slightly less than unity. The third and fourth

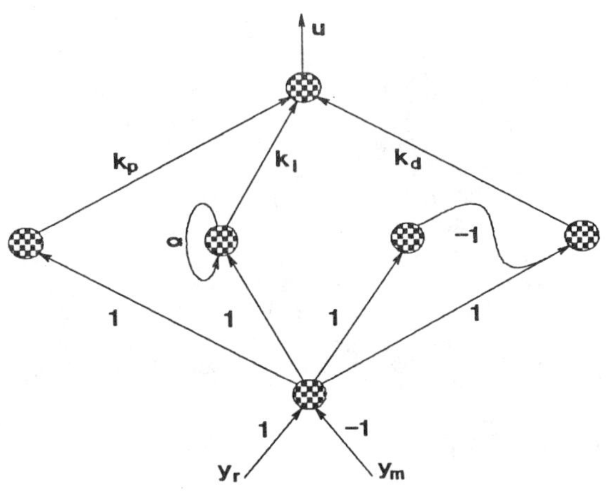

Figure 1: Realization of a PID controller with an RMLP architecture consisting of 3 layers of nodes with linear output functions.

nodes are used to form the difference between two successive error signals. The last layer consists of a single node that takes the weighted sum of the proportional, integral and derivative terms computed by the nodes in the second layer, and produces the output control signal. Note that this representation has a number of redundant connections; for example, with appropriate changes in the weights denoted by k_p and k_d, the feedforward weight connected to the fourth node of the middle layer may be eliminated. Further, we may allow the various connections in this architecture to be adjusted by a training procedure. More complex and elaborate recurrent network architectures, with a greater number of weights and nodes with nonlinear output functions, provide increased representational capabilities that are useful for difficult control problems as we demonstrate below.

4 Training Details

We employ a two step procedure for the training of neural controllers. In the first step, a neural network is trained to identify the input-output characteristics of the unknown dynamical system. In the second step, the trained identification network is used to provide estimates of the dynamic derivatives (also known as total partial derivatives or ordered derivatives) of plant outputs with respect to the trainable controller parameters. A neural network training algorithm based upon a decoupled extended Kalman filter (DEKF) is employed for training both identification and control networks as described in [6, 9, 11, 12]. For recurrent network architectures, we have shown [9] that the computational complexity of the DEKF algorithms is of the same order as that of gradient descent algorithms (real-time recurrent learning [13] or dynamic backpropagation [14]). Furthermore, empirical results clearly demonstrate that the training of feedforward and recurrent neural networks by the DEKF algorithms generally leads to superior results with less total training time and fewer presentations of training data than does training by pure gradient descent.

Training of neural controllers is performed in an indirect fashion by using the identification network to model the input-output behavior of the system. In this scheme, desired control signals are not known; rather, they must be inferred indirectly through a specification of the system's desired behavior, which is provided by a subjectively and empirically determined cost function. For the ISC problem, we choose a quadratic cost function consisting of four components. The first component penalizes deviations of engine speed from a set point of 750 rpm. The next three components penalize certain behaviors of the control signals. We include a term in the cost function that penalizes deviations of the spark advance from its desired set point of 22.9 degrees. The third and fourth components penalize large changes in throttle and spark angle, respectively, between two successive control time steps. These two components implement a *smoothness* constraint [15] that tends to discourage oscillatory behavior in the controls for dynamical systems with significant internal time delays. The contribution to the cost function at time step $n+1$ is given by

$$\begin{aligned} C(n+1) &= \frac{1}{2}\left(\beta_1(750 - N_m(n+1))^2 \right. \\ &\quad + \beta_2(22.9 - \delta(n))^2 \\ &\quad + \beta_3(\theta(n-1) - \theta(n))^2 \\ &\quad \left. + \beta_4(\delta(n-1) - \delta(n))^2\right), \end{aligned}$$

where the weighting factors are chosen empirically and are given by $\beta_1 = 1.6 \times 10^{-7}$ for $N_m(n+1) > 750$ and $\beta_1 = 2.4 \times 10^{-7}$ for $N_m(n+1) \leq 750$; $\beta_2 = 3.25 \times 10^{-7}$; $\beta_3 = 10^{-3}$; and $\beta_4 = 1.63 \times 10^{-5}$.

A critical step in training of neural controllers by gradient methods is to compute properly dynamic derivatives of plant and controller outputs with respect to the trainable controller parameters. We note that the evolution of the system state is defined recursively as a function of previous state. Furthermore, the computed control signals are also defined recursively as a function of measured system state, which is itself a function of previous state and previously applied control signals. Since the system state and computed control signals evolve in a recursive fashion, the dynamic derivatives of system state and controller outputs with respect to the trainable controller parameters should also be defined recursively as a function of dynamic derivatives from previous time steps. The temporal evolution and computation of the dynamic derivative of a component of plant output with respect to a controller parameter is illustrated diagrammatically in the sensitivity circuit of Figure 2. The dynamic derivatives that are thus computed can be used by gradient methods such as dynamic backpropagation [14, 16] and the Kalman filter based algorithms to update the controller's trainable parameters.

A simple identification network consisting of a single layer of 8 completely interconnected (recurrent) nodes with *linear* output functions was trained to model the input-output characteristics of the dynamical plant described above. The network has four inputs, consisting of linearly transformed values of measured system outputs, P_m and N_m, and linearly transformed values of control inputs, θ and δ. The output of the network is a prediction of the system output 20 ms into the future, corresponding to the background loop time for the calculation of control signals. The feedback weights of linear recurrent nodes are constrained to be less than unity in magnitude by treating them as the outputs of bipolar sigmoidal functions. This constraint tends to make the training process computationally stable for linear recurrent nodes. The control inputs and torque disturbances were varied through their entire ranges during training of the identification network. Since the torque disturbances are not observable, the prediction of system outputs by the identification network will be in error, particularly during large transitions in torque disturbance. However, for controller training to be effective we only require that on average the dynamic

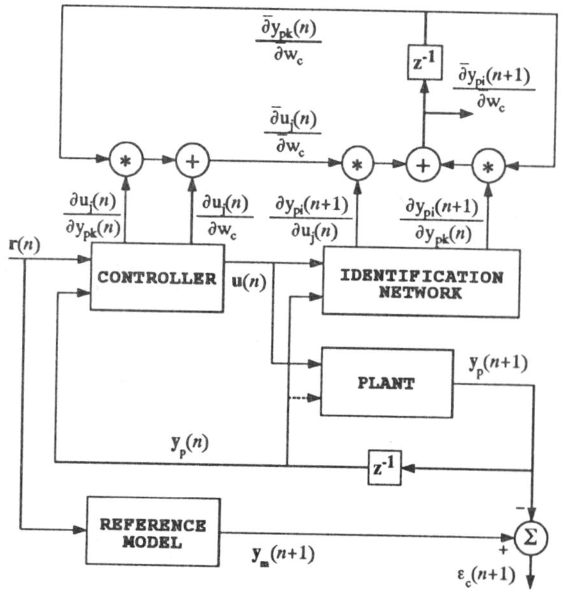

Figure 2: Recurrent derivative structure for controller training. This figure assumes that there are no internal feedback connections within either the identification or control networks, although there are external recurrent connections. The vertical lines emanating from the identification and control networks denote partial derivatives that are computed by backpropagation. The dynamic derivatives that this recurrent derivative structure produces are used with the error vector $\varepsilon_c(n+1)$ to update the weights of the controller.

derivatives of system outputs with respect to controller parameters be correct.

Control network architectures for the ISC problem were chosen on the basis of some limited experimentation. Controller inputs are linearly transformed values of a single time-delayed measurement of both manifold pressure and engine speed. The control network outputs range between ± 1 in magnitude, and are transformed into appropriate ranges for the throttle and spark commands before being applied to the plant. Initial weights of the control networks are chosen randomly from a zero-mean uniform distribution with maximum magnitude of 0.1.

We present results for two neural network control architectures. The first network consists of two layers of nodes, with two inputs, a hidden layer of 8 sigmoidal recurrent nodes, and 2 recurrent output nodes with sigmoidal output functions, where we chose to include all possible connections for the two layers. This recurrent network architecture consists of 110 trainable parameters. The second network architecture contains a linear recurrent preprocessing layer followed by a standard feedforward network. The inputs to the preprocessing layer are linearly transformed values of manifold pressure and error in engine speed. The preprocessing layer consists of seven linear nodes with limited interconnectivity. The first 3 nodes were chosen to encode proportional and derivative terms for manifold pressure, while the 4 remaining nodes construct proportional, integral and derivative terms for the error in engine speed. The connectivity pattern and the initial weight values are chosen in a fashion analogous to the middle layer of nodes in Figure 1. The remainder of the network consisted of three standard feedforward layers, with 10, 6 and 2 sigmoidal nodes from the preprocessing layer to the output layer. Only 5 of the 7 nodes in the preprocessing layer are connected to the following layer of 10 nodes (see Figure 1). This network architecture consists of 150 weights, and we allow all weights, including those of the preprocessing layer, to be trained. We will refer to the first architecture described above as a recurrent neural network controller and to the second architecture as a generalized PID neural network controller.

During training, torque disturbances are randomly selected from the range 0 to 61 N-m and are applied for times ranging between 1 and 2 seconds of simulated real time. The training sequence of load disturbances was chosen to be identical for the two network architectures. The dynamic derivatives are computed in a fashion similar to that shown in Figure 2, where we also employ a derivative discount factor of 0.99 for all recurrent derivatives of plant outputs with respect to trainable controller parameters in order to exponentially decay the effects of dynamic derivatives from time long past. The dynamic DEKF training algorithm is used to update the weights of the recurrent neural controller in a fashion similar to that described in [12, 17]. This algorithm updates the weights of the controller at each control time step (i.e., at 20 ms intervals). Training was carried out for a total of 100,000 training instances (approximately 30 minutes of simulated real time), although we observed that both neural controllers were capable of regulating the engine speed close to 750 rpm with minimal ringing in the applied control signals and measured system outputs after approximately 20,000 training instances.

5 Simulation Results

The behavior of the trained controllers was examined with an independent test sequence of torque disturbances generated in a fashion similar to that used for training. Representative results are shown in Figure 3. Qualitatively, the recurrent network architecture is seen to provide smoother behavior than the generalized PID network, both for deviations from the desired set point of 750 rpm and for oscillations in the control signals.

We also examine the robustness properties of the two trained controllers. The plant definition provided in Section 2 is altered by changing 5 parameters. The constants k_P and k_N are set to 38.16 and 59.69, respectively. The effect of throttle on the plant is altered by changing the intake mass air flow equation to $\dot{m}_{ai} = (1.2 + 0.907\theta + 0.12\theta^2)g(P)$. The load torque is given by $T_L = (N/236.85)^2 + T_d$. As a final complication, the measured manifold pressure has an offset of -10 kPa. The behavior of the two neural controllers, without any retraining, is shown in Figure 4, from which it is obvious that the recurrent neural controller provides significantly more robust performance that does the generalized PID controller. As a further comparison, we trained a simple linear neural network controller with 2 layers of nodes. The two inputs were manifold pressure and error in engine speed, the hidden layer consisted 7 linear preprocessing nodes as used in the generalized PID neural controller, and the output layer consisted of two linear nodes. This architecture provides a linear combination of PD terms for manifold pressure and PID terms for error in engine speed for both control signals. The performance of this linear controller was substantially inferior to that of either of the more complicated nonlinear neural network controllers.

We have tested the trained neural controllers for load disturbance sequences that had longer intervals of relatively constant disturbance, and found that the steady state behavior in engine speed and manifold pressure was constant except for small variations due to measurement

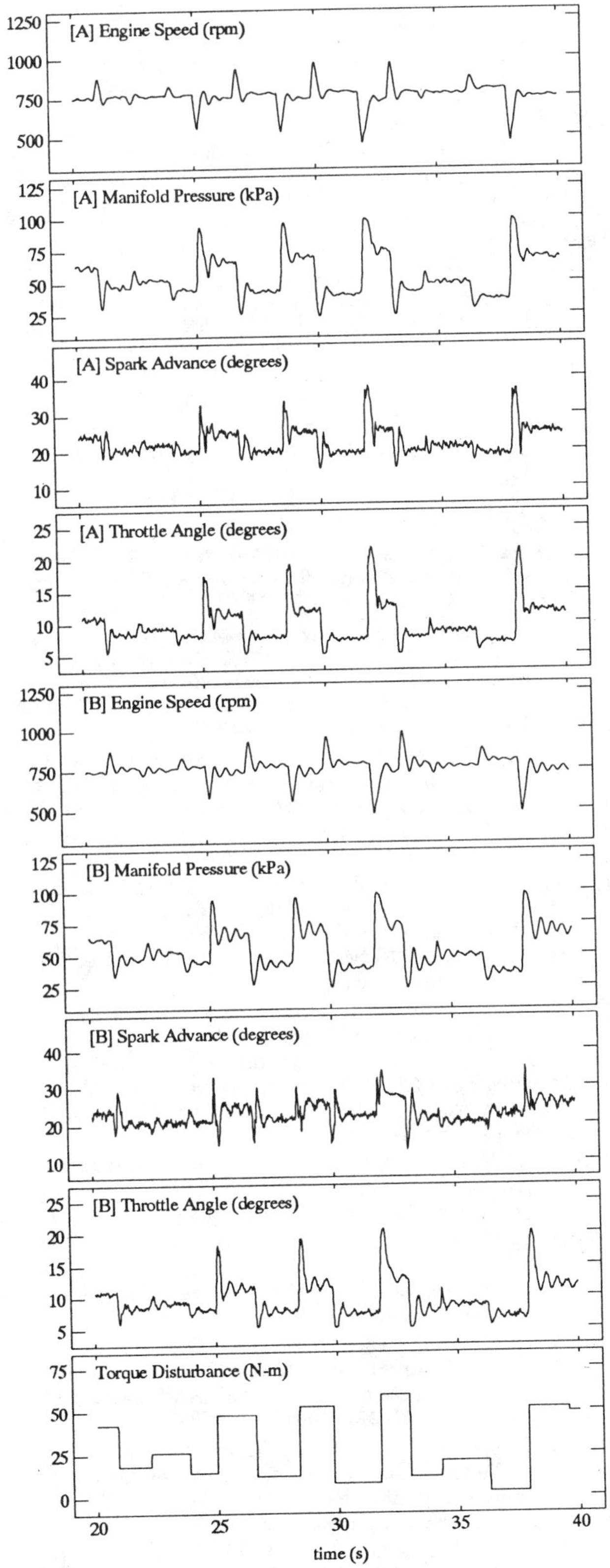

Figure 3: Comparative behavior of the recurrent and generalized PID neural controllers for a test sequence of load disturbances representative of those used during training. The imposed load disturbance is shown in the lowest panel. The upper four panels show the plant inputs and outputs for the recurrent neural controller [A], while the remaining panels demonstrate the input-output behavior of the generalized PID controller [B].

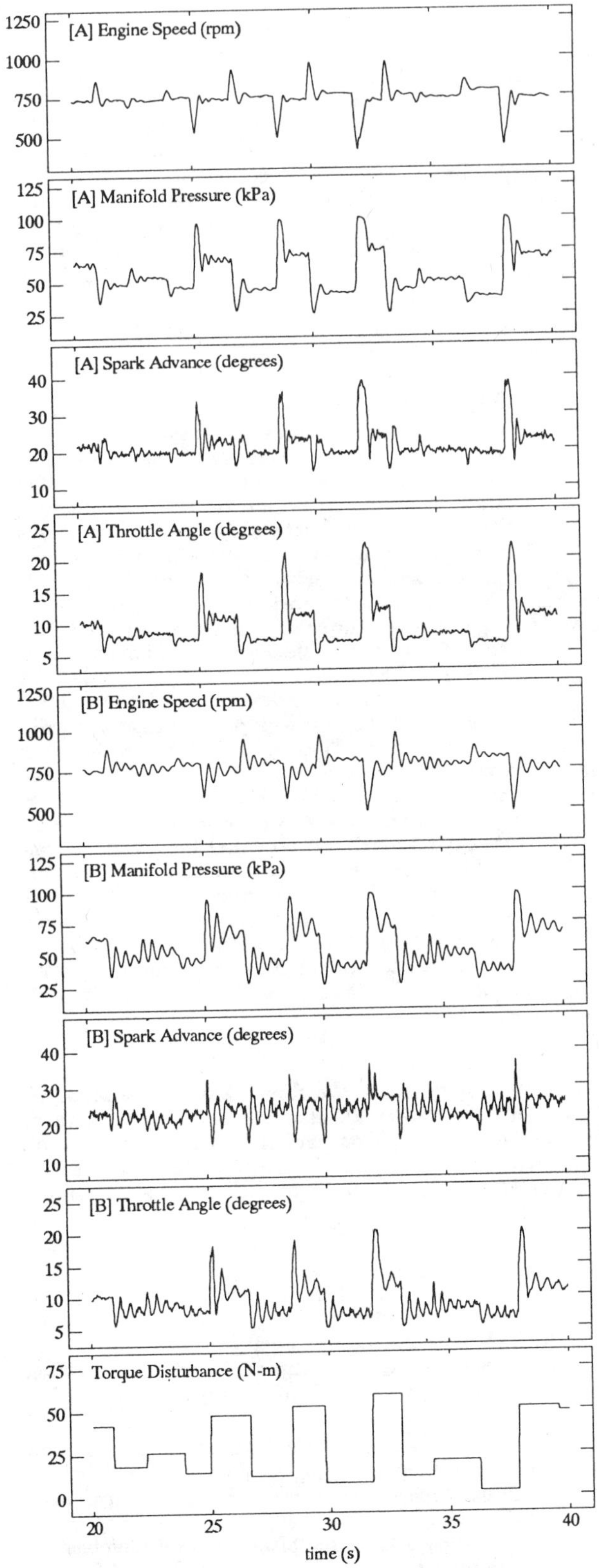

Figure 4: Comparative behavior of the recurrent [A] and generalized PID [B] neural controllers for a plant definition with altered parameters and an offset in measurement of manifold pressure. The organization of this figure is identical to that of Figure 3.

noise. Even in the unrealistic context of rapidly varying torque disturbances, e.g., switching back and forth between 5 and 55 N-m at a frequency of 1 Hz for 10 cycles, the recurrent neural network controller exhibits stable behavior and settles back to constant control after the disturbance is removed. We have also found that a recurrent neural control architecture containing as few as four recurrent nodes in a hidden layer followed by two recurrent output nodes (42 trainable parameters) was capable of achieving a reasonable level of performance for these various test sequences.

6 Conclusions

We have demonstrated that recurrent neural network architectures can be trained to provide robust control for an example idle speed control problem that is highly nonlinear and that contains complications such as asynchronous and multirate sampling and time delays that vary inversely with engine speed. Network control architectures of modest size (on order of 10 nodes and 100 trainable connections) utilizing only state information that is readily measurable are seen to provide excellent behavior for a wide range of load torque disturbances. We have attempted to include all troublesome plant characteristics in a simulation of the engine operating at idle so that controllers could be trained to deal with these characteristics directly, rather than through patches to analytically synthesized controllers. Since recurrent controllers that have been trained using a realistic simulation of the engine model operating at idle exhibit robust behavior to changes in plant dynamics and to errors in measurement of plant outputs, we can reasonably expect that these trained controllers would provide an adequate starting point for further on-line training with a real engine. Although we have assumed no *a priori* knowledge of the onset of torque load disturbances, feedforward information could easily be accommodated as an additional input for a neural network controller and could enhance significantly a controller's performance.

Acknowledgments: We would like to thank B. K. Powell of Ford Research Laboratory for sharing with us his immense expertise on engine dynamics and control. We are also indebted to G. Vachtsevanos and S. S. Farinwata of The Georgia Institute of Technology for providing details of the engine model used in this study.

References

[1] R. L. Morris and B. K. Powell (1983). Modern Control Applications in Idle Speed Control. *Proceedings of the 1983 American Control Conference*, vol. 1, 79–85.

[2] B. K. Powell and J. A. Cook (1987). Nonlinear Low Frequency Phenomenological Engine Modeling and Analysis. *Proceedings of the 1987 American Control Conference*, vol. 1, 336-340; J. A. Cook and B. K. Powell (1988). Modeling of an Internal Combustion Engine for Control Analysis. *IEEE Control Systems Magazine*, vol. 8, no. 4, 20–26.

[3] M. Abate and N. Dosio (1990). Use of Fuzzy Logic for Engine Idle Speed Control. *SAE Paper 900594*, 107–114; M. Abate (1991). An Application of Fuzzy Logic to Engine Control. *Proceedings of the Fuzzy and Neural Systems and Vehicle Applications '91 Conference*, Nov. 8–9, 1991, Tokyo.

[4] L. A. Feldkamp and G. V. Puskorius (1993). Application of a Trainable Fuzzy System to Idle-Speed Control. *Proceedings of the Second International Conference on Fuzzy Systems* (San Francisco 1993).

[5] G. Vachtsevanos, S. S. Farinwata and H. Kang (1992). A Systematic Design Method for Fuzzy Logic Control With Application to Automotive Idle Speed Control. *Proceedings of the 31st IEEE Conference on Decision and Control* (Tuscon, AZ 1992).

[6] L. A. Feldkamp, G. V. Puskorius, L. I. Davis, Jr., and F. Yuan (1992). Neural Control Systems Trained by Dynamic Gradient Methods for Automotive Applications. *Proceedings of the 1992 International Joint Conference on Neural Networks* (Baltimore 1992).

[7] L. I. Davis, Jr., G. V. Puskorius, F. Yuan, and L. A. Feldkamp (1992). Neural Network Modeling and Control of an Anti-Lock Brake System. *Proceedings of the Intelligent Vehicles '92 Conference* (Detroit 1992), 179–184.

[8] B. Fernandez, A. G. Parlos and W. K. Tsai (1990). Nonlinear Dynamic System Identification Using Artificial Neural Networks (ANNs). *International Joint Conference on Neural Networks* (San Diego 1990), vol. II, 133–141. New York: IEEE.

[9] G. V. Puskorius and L. A. Feldkamp (1992). Recurrent Network Training with the Decoupled Extended Kalman Filter Algorithm. *Proceedings of the 1992 SPIE Conference on the Science of Artificial Neural Networks* (Orlando 1992), 461–473.

[10] R. J. Williams (1990). Adaptive State Representation and Estimation Using Recurrent Connectionist Networks. *Neural Networks for Control*, eds. W. T. Miller III, R. S. Sutton and P. J. Werbos, chap. 4, 97–114. Cambridge, MA: MIT Press.

[11] G. V. Puskorius and L. A. Feldkamp (1991). Decoupled Extended Kalman Filter Training of Feedforward Layered Networks. *International Joint Conference on Neural Networks* (Seattle 1991), vol. I, 771–777. New York: IEEE.

[12] G. V. Puskorius and L. A. Feldkamp (1992). Model Reference Adaptive Control with Recurrent Networks Trained by the Dynamic DEKF Algorithm. *Proceedings of the 1992 International Joint Conference on Neural Networks* (Baltimore 1992), vol. II, 106–113. New York: IEEE.

[13] R. J. Williams and D. Zipser (1989). A Learning Algorithm for Continually Running Fully Recurrent Neural Networks. *Neural Computation* 1, 270–280.

[14] K. S. Narendra and K. Parthasarathy (1990). Identification and Control of Dynamical Systems Using Neural Networks. *IEEE Transactions on Neural Networks* 1, no. 1,4–27.

[15] M. I. Jordan (1989) Generic Constraints on Underspecified Target Trajectories. *International Joint Conference on Neural Networks* (Washington D.C. 1989), vol. I, 217–225. New York: IEEE.

[16] K. S. Narendra and K. Parthasarathy (1991). Gradient Methods for the Optimization of Dynamical Systems Containing Neural Networks. *IEEE Transactions on Neural Networks* 2, no. 2, 252–262.

[17] G. V. Puskorius and L. A. Feldkamp (1993). Practical Considerations for Kalman Filter Training of Recurrent Neural Networks. *Proceedings of the 1993 IEEE International Conference on Neural Networks* (San Francisco 1993).

Proceedings of the
American Control Conference
San Francisco, California • June 1993

CAD Tools for Nonlinear Control: Speed Control of a Car Engine

D.N. Godbole*
Dept. of Electrical Engineering
University of California, Berkeley

D. Swaroop†
Dept. of Mechanical Engineering
University of California, Berkeley

Abstract

A *feedback linearization* controller design is presented for the speed control of an automobile engine. Various difficulties encountered along the process and their proposed solutions are explained in detail. The ultimate goal of this project is to mechanise these calculations and develop a CAD package which will be able to solve a wide range of practical problems. The method proposed will be valuable in designing a controller by using most of the strategies from the rapidly growing *geometrical nonlinear control toolbox.*

1 Introduction

There has been a great deal of progress, over the past decade, in theoretical techniques for the control of nonlinear systems, the most popular of these being *feedback linearization* (for example [1]). However, at the moment, there are very few documented examples of practical systems being controlled by this technique. This seems to be because of the following difficulties with the methodology:

1. Most of the computations involved are symbolic and the symbolic packages available (e.g. Mathematica or Maple) are not numerically robust, since they involve differentiation.

2. The controller design methods are well developed for a model of a control system of the form

$$\begin{aligned} \dot{x} &= f(x) + \sum_{j=1}^{m} g_j(x) u_j \\ y_j &= h_j(x) \quad j = 1, \cdots, m \end{aligned} \tag{1}$$

where $x \in \Re^n, u \in \Re^m, y \in \Re^m$. $f(x), g_j(x)$ are smooth vector fields and $h_j(x)$ are smooth functions of x.

Many systems do not satisfy the above requirement for the following two reasons:

- Some parts of $f(x), g_j(x)$ or $h_j(x)$ may be given in the form of data tables, derived from experiments.
- The inputs may not enter the dynamical equations affinely.

We wish to address both these issues in this paper. A design methodology is presented which will describe a way to get around both the difficulties for most problems. We will first illustrate the method by way of an example: speed control of a car engine.

We will use a CAD package for nonlinear control system design called AP_LIN, developed at Berkeley. For a complete discussion of AP_LIN refer to [2].

2 Example: Speed control of a typical American Car Engine

To design a linearizing controller for the car engine, we will first obtain a model of the engine of the form of (1).

2.1 Model Development

The model development for applying feedback linearization is presented in detail in this section.

2.1.1 Physical Modeling

The following model is obtained from basic physical laws applied to the car engine.

$$\begin{aligned} \dot{m}_a &= M \cdot TC(\alpha) \cdot PRI(m_a) - \dot{m}_{ao}(m_a, \omega_e) \\ \dot{\omega}_e &= \frac{1}{J}[T_{net}(m_a, \omega_e) - C_a \omega_e^2 - T_{rr}] \end{aligned} \tag{2}$$

Where m_a is the mass of air in the intake manifold and ω_e is the engine speed in radian per second. The first equation describes the conservation of mass in the intake manifold. The second equations is obtained by applying Newton's law to the engine. The parameters in the model have the following meaning:

α	Throttle input angle
$TC(\alpha)$	Throttle characteristic
$PRI(m_a)$	describes choke flow relationship that occurs in the manifold.
J	Effective inertia referred to the engine side
C_a	Aerodynamic drag coefficient
T_{net}	Net engine torque.
$\dot{m}_{ao}$	Mass flow rate of air leaving the manifold.
M	represents the maximum air flow into the intake manifold.
T_{rr}	Rolling resistance.

A detailed discussion of this model is presented in [3]. Analytical expressions for *mass flow through the intake manifold* and the *net torque generated* are not known at this point. Extensive experiments are carried out on a test engine to obtain input/output data representing $TC(\alpha), PRI(m_a), T_{net}(m_a, \omega_e)$ and $\dot{m}_{ao}(m_a, \omega_e)$. In this model, α is the control variable and ω_e is the output variable. Since we are interested in the throttle control of the engine, we do not model dynamics of the brake sub-system.

2.1.2 Modeling of Numerical Data

In order to obtain an analytical model, we use AP_LIN to get polynomial approximations for the tabular experimental data. The best spline fit approximations of order 4 for the data are given by

$$\begin{aligned} TC(\alpha) &= -0.008 + 0.003\alpha + 7 \cdot 10^{-6}\alpha^2 + 9 \cdot 10^{-7}\alpha^3 \\ PRI(x_1) &= -6.651(\frac{x_1}{5})^4 + 9.8849(\frac{x_1}{5})^3 - 4.6538(\frac{x_1}{5})^2 \\ &\quad +0.4368(\frac{x_1}{5}) + 0.9874 \\ \dot{m}_{ao}(x_1, x_2) &= x_1 x_2[0.028x_1 - 0.003x_1^2 + 1 \cdot 10^{-4}x_2 \\ &\quad -5 \cdot 10^{-6}x_1 x_2 - 2 \cdot 10^{-7}x_2^2] \\ T_{net}(x_1, x_2) &= T_{ind} - T_{fr} \\ T_{ind}(x_1) &= x_1 \begin{pmatrix} 0.005x_1 + 0.017x_1^2 + 0.047x_1^3 + 0.08x_2 \\ +0.262x_1x_2 - 0.021x_2x_1^2 - 6 \cdot 10^{-4}x_2^2 \\ -4 \cdot 10^{-3}x_2^2 x_1 - 1 \cdot 10^{-6}x_2^3 \end{pmatrix} \\ T_{fr}(x_2) &= 0.141738\, x_2 + 23.5581 \end{aligned}$$

where $x_1 = m_a$ and $x_2 = \omega_e$

With these functions the approximation error is uniformly less than a prespecified ϵ [1] with $x_1 \in [0, 6]$ Kg, $x_2 \in [0, 500]$ rad/sec, $\alpha \in [0, \frac{\pi}{2}]$. As an example, we include a plot showing the actual and approximate throttle characteristic in fig(1).

In case of the above approximations, terms like $2 \cdot 10^{-7}x_2^2$ are not negligible as the engine speed x_2 is of the order of hundreds of radian per second.

Once we obtain an analytical model, it will be used to design approximate controller. From [4], we know that if the neglected terms are small enough, then the linearizing controller designed for the approximate system will provide satisfactory results for the original system.

2.1.3 Reduction of Model to Standard Form

The analytical model is not in the standard format (1). Specifically, we have powers of the input (α) upto the third order appearing in the dynamical equations. In order to get a model affine in u, we generate a set of test throttle inputs, u_{test}. The inputs in this set should be rich enough to excite all the modes of the system model. They should also cover the entire range of input magnitudes, $\alpha \in [0, \frac{\pi}{2}]$. One such

*Research supported in part by ARO under grant DAAL - 91-G-0191
†Research supported by PATH

[1] The choice of ϵ depends on the particular problem.

input for the car model is shown in fig(2).

The system (2) is simulated with these test inputs and then a polynomial approximation of the form of (1) is obtained. This model best approximates the input/output response of the system (2) for the set of test inputs u_{test}. This polynomial model is given by

$$\begin{aligned} \dot{x} &= f(x) + g(x)u \\ y &= h(x) \end{aligned} \qquad (3)$$

where $x \in \Re^2$, $y \in \Re$, and $u \in \Re$. With

$$\begin{aligned} f(x) &= \begin{bmatrix} -0.027x_2 + 7.0x_1 - 0.081x_1x_2 - 1.6{x_1}^2 \\ -0.024x_2 + 3.6x_1 - 0.009x_1x_2 + 0.371{x_1}^2 \end{bmatrix} \\ g(x) &= \begin{bmatrix} 1.6 + 0.009x_2 + 0.060x_1 \\ 0 \end{bmatrix} \\ h(x) &= [\ 0.100x_2\ ] \end{aligned}$$

The next step will be to design a controller for this model (3) and then apply it to actual system.

The controller yields an input $u_{control}$. The approximate polynomial model can be updated, from time to time, by including the control input $u_{control}$ into the set u_{test} and repeating the above procedure with this new set of test inputs.

2.2 Controller Design

After obtaining a model of the control system in the standard format, we design a linearizing controller by using AP_LIN. The computations are performed numerically and not symbolically. The relative degree of this model is 2. The static feedback controller renders the input to state map linear. The controller is given by

$$u = -A^{-1}(x)B(x) + A^{-1}(x)v \qquad (4)$$

where

$$\begin{aligned} A(x) &= \begin{bmatrix} 0.5551 + 0.002x_2 + 0.137x_1 - 0.9 \cdot 10^{-5}{x_2}^2 \\ +0.6 \cdot 10^{-3}x_1x_2 + 0.004{x_1}^2 \end{bmatrix} \\ B(x) &= \left[\begin{pmatrix} -0.010x_2 + 2.5x_1 - 0.037x_1x_2 \\ +0.2 \cdot 10^{-4}{x_2}^2 + 0.7 \cdot 10^{-4}x_1{x_2}^2 \end{pmatrix} \right] \end{aligned}$$

and the diffeomorphism:

$$\begin{bmatrix} y_1 \\ \dot{y}_1 \end{bmatrix} = \begin{bmatrix} 0.100x_2 \\ -0.002x_2 + 0.355x_1 - 0.9 \cdot 10^{-3}x_1x_2 + 0.037{x_1}^2 \end{bmatrix}$$

defines the linearizing change of coordinates

With this controller, the transfer function from v to y is linear and is of the form $\ddot{y}_i = v$

Now we may use any one of the linear control techniques to get the desired tracking performance. Here, we use a static feedback plus an integral controller to get the engine speed to track the reference trajectory.

$$v = -k_1(y_1 - y_{1d}) - k_2(\dot{y}_1 - \dot{y}_{1d}) - k_i \int_0^t (y_1 - y_{1d})dt$$

where $s^3 + k_2 s^2 + k_1 s + k_i = 0$ is a Hurwitz polynomial.

The above controller is in effect when the desired speed is greater than the actual speed. When we want to reduce the speed, v is made zero. The brake takes over while the throttle system decelerates according to its own zero input response.

3 Design Methodology using AP_LIN

Following are the steps in designing a controller

1. Enter the equations describing the dynamics
2. If there are any data tables, get the approximate analytical expressions using spline fits from AP_LIN.
3. If the analytical model is not in the standard form (1), simulate the analytical system around a test input trajectory and get an approximate polynomial model of the form of (1)
4. Design a controller using AP_LIN for this polynomial model
5. The polynomial model derived in step 3 may not be a good approximation for the input command we get from the linearizing controller. In this case, we can go back to step 3, add on this input command to the test inputs, and get an improved approximate polynomial model.

4 Results and Conclusions

Plots (3 and 4) represent step and sinusoidal response of the system (1) with the input generated by the linearizing controller (4). we use the gain values of $k_1 = 3, k_2 = 3$ and $k_i = 0.12$ to get these results. The response of the system can be changed by fine tuning these gain values.

Thus we present a methodology for applying various nonlinear control schemes to practical examples. This is already encorporated in a CAD package developed at Berkeley called AP_LIN. It still remains to be shown that this process of controller design converges after a finite number of iterations.

Acknowledgements: The authors would like to thank Prof. S. Shankar Sastry and Prof. J. K. Hedrick for their guidance and several helpful discussions during the course of this work.

References

[1] A. Isidori, *Nonlinear Control Systems.* Springer-Verlag, 2nd ed., 1989.

[2] R. R. Kadiyala, *AP_LIN: A CAD Tool Box for Nonlinear Control Design.* PhD thesis, Department of Electrical Engineering, University of California, Berkeley, California, 1992.

[3] D.Cho and J. Hedrick, "Automatic powertrain modelling for control," *ASME Journal of Dynamic Systems, Measurement and Control*, vol. Vol.111, no. No.4, 1989.

[4] J. E. Hauser, *Approximate Tracking for Nonlinear Systems with Application to Flight Control.* PhD thesis, Department of Electrical Engineering, University of California, Berkeley, California, 1989.

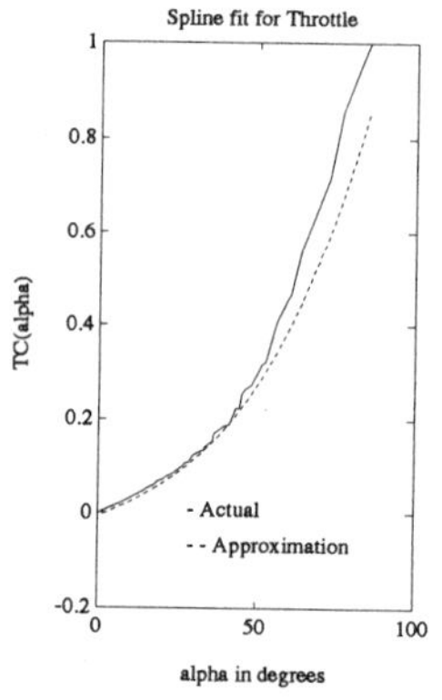

Fig. 1

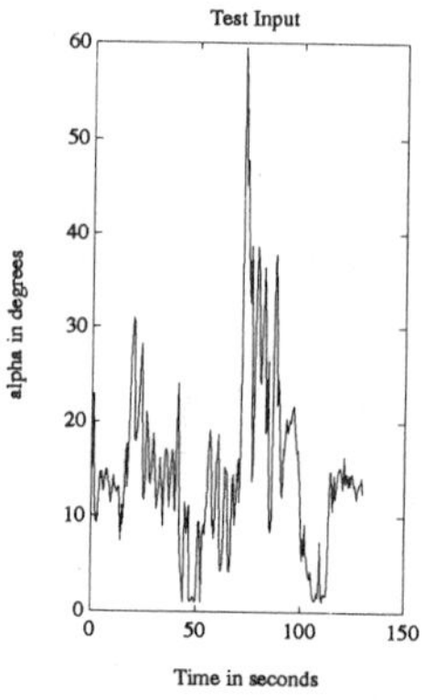

Fig. 2

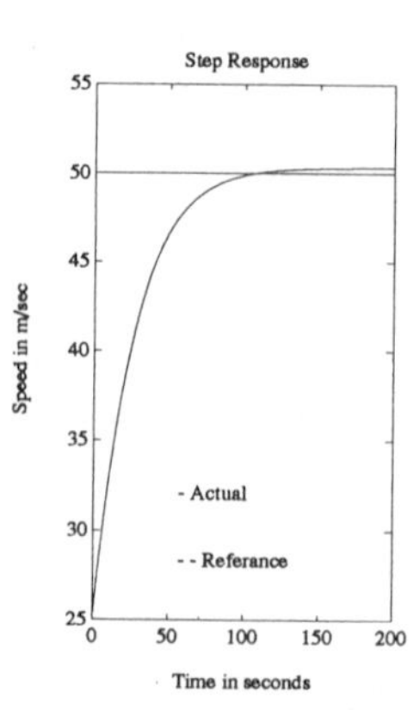

Fig. 3

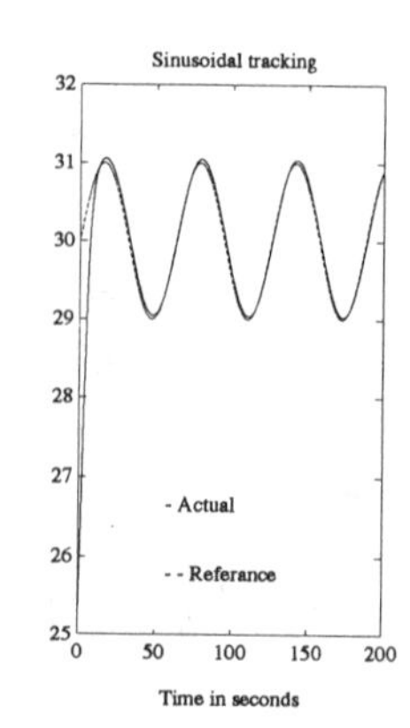

Fig. 4

Proceedings of the American Control Conference
San Francisco, California • June 1993

Design of A Control Panel Using a Sensory Engineering Approach

Kuang C. Wei
Ford Motor Co.
P.O. Box 2053
Dearborn, MI 48121
U. S. A.

Shouko Fujimoto
Komatsu Ltd.
Research Div.
Manda, Hiratsuka
Kanagawa, 254, Japan

Masahiro Ikeda
Komatsu Ltd.
Research Div.
Manda, Hiratsuka
Kanagawa, 254, Japan

ABSTRACT

This paper reports the design of an excavator's control panel with a sensory engineering approach. Nine panel designs were evaluated using the semantic differential method. Results showed the strength and weakness of each design, which can be incorporated by the designers into the final design.

1. INTRODUCTION

As product quality becomes more important in market place, manufacturers are constantly looking for ways to improve the quality of their products. Traditional measure of quality has mainly focused on product reliability and durability. After most of the traditional quality problems are solved, there is an emerging effort in Japan and Europe to explore a new horizon of quality measure. This is evidenced by the birth of a new engineering field, referred to here as 'sensory engineering', to study and include customer's feeling into the engineering of a product as a measurement of quality. Sensory engineering[a/] is a field which deals with the development of techniques to measure human's feelings towards different product designs and environment. These feelings are rooted in responses to different sensory, such as visual, auditory, tactile, taste, olfactory, etc. stimuli. Subjective measurements and characterization of these responses are correlated with product characteristics to identify appealing features which can be used for further product development and improvement. Application examples in automotive industry range from design of instrument panel, engine and road noise reduction, to vigilance enhancing system, etc. [1]-[5]. In this paper, the design of a control panel in an excavator was examined using this approach.

2. SEMANTIC DIFFERENTIAL (SD) METHOD

In the study of the meaning of words, Osgood found that the affective meaning of concepts would fall into a few major categories, or dimensions in a semantic space [6]. Difference between these concepts, as perceived by each human subject, can be quantified by examining their relative positions in this semantic space. The distance between the concepts in the semantic space thus can be used as a psychometrics to provide a quantitative measure for the feeling of a person or a population about these concepts. Even more interestingly, these major categories held remarkably consistent across different cultural groups from various countries in the world. Thereby, the method represents a powerful technique which can be used to measure customer's emotional feeling about a product or environment on a worldwide marketplace.

3. DESIGN OF AN EXCAVATOR'S CONTROL PANEL

The control panel, approx. 4.5'x9.5', consists of two portions: a LCD display and a functional control switch section, see Fig.1. The objective of the study

[a/]Also known as 'Kansei engineering' in Japan.

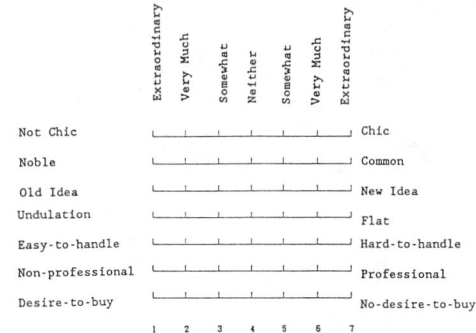

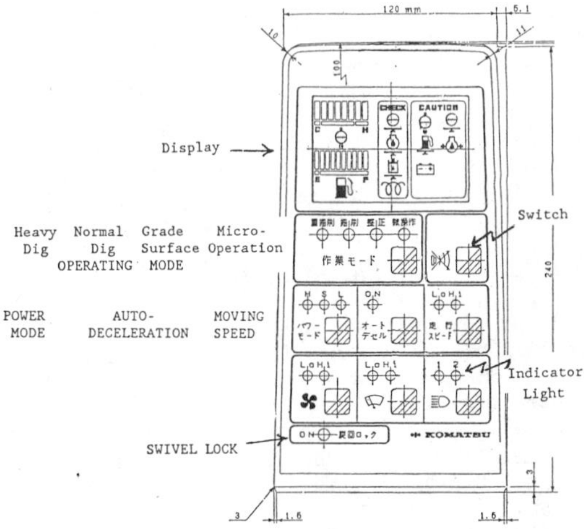

Fig. 1 Control Panel in Komatsu's PC200 Series Excavator

was to evaluate various panel designs derived by varying the display and switch layout pattern. These designs were presented as visual stimuli to the subjects for evaluation.

Selection of Semantic Adjectives

An extensive lists containing 439 adjective pairs was obtained through the courtesy of Professor M. Nagamachi of Hiroshima University. In order to provide a set of comprehensive and suitable descriptors of the panel, the list was refined to 79 adjective pairs. A portion of the adjectives is listed in Table 1. For a complete list and the selection procedure, see [7].

	Extraordinary	Very Much	Somewhat	Neither	Somewhat	Very Much	Extraordinary	
Not Chic								Chic
Noble								Common
Old Idea								New Idea
Undulation								Flat
Easy-to-handle								Hard-to-handle
Non-professional								Professional
Desire-to-buy								No-desire-to-buy
	1	2	3	4	5	6	7	

Table 1. A Partial List of SD Adjectives

Design Elements

Six elements of the panel were chosen for design variation, namely, size, shape, color, layout, switch type, and labeling language. A total of nine different designs were generated by varying these elements. A 3-D image of each design was created on a SUN computer workstation using a solid modeling software. Computer modeling of the control panel renders easy modification of the design, avoids the high cost of building prototypes, and provides the versatility in viewing the object from different angles. In the actual experiment, color images of each design were presented to the subjects for evaluation.

Experiment

Nine subjects participated in the subjective evaluation experiment. Subjects were asked to rate each design with the semantic adjective list using a 7-step scale. These ratings were later converted into numeric values ranging from 1 to 7 for analysis. A value of '1' represents the strongest association of feeling towards the left adjective, while '7' represents the strongest association with the opposite adjective located at the right end of the scale, see Table 1. During the experiment, the full view, the display portion, and the functional portion of the design were presented concurrently to the subjects for evaluation. In addition, the full-view image of the basic (current production) design was presented in parallel to provide as a reference. The experiment was administered in three sessions, three designs per session, with two ten-minute intermissions. It took the subjects about twelve min. to finish the seventy-nine questionnaires in each design evaluation. The whole experiment took about two hours.

4. ANALYSIS

Factor analysis was applied to the standardized scores from the first sixty-five questionnaires. Seven factors which accounted for 72% of the total variance in the scores were extracted. From the factor loadings, the following seven factor axes were formed: Sophistication & Freshness, Good Operability, Well Proportion, Heaviness & Rigidity, Individualistic, Relaxation, and Vividness. Radar plots which show the average factor scores over the nine subjects for each design were constructed to show main effects along each factor axis. Fig. 2 shows the mean scores received for the basic design. The two concentric circles represent the score of '0' and '3' respectively. The origin denotes the score of '-3'. The thin solid line represents the average score along each factor axis. The dotted and dashed line are the upper and lower value of 95% confidence interval. A higher value above '0' means the impression of the design towards the abstraction of that axis. For the negatively correlated axis, indicated with (-) as shown in 'Sophistication & Freshness' and 'Vividness' axes, the opposite is true. By examining the average scores received for each design along these seven factor axes, the strength/weakness of special design features were revealed. The factor which has very different score than the basic design is highlighted with solid underline, the one with some difference in scores is marked with dotted underline.

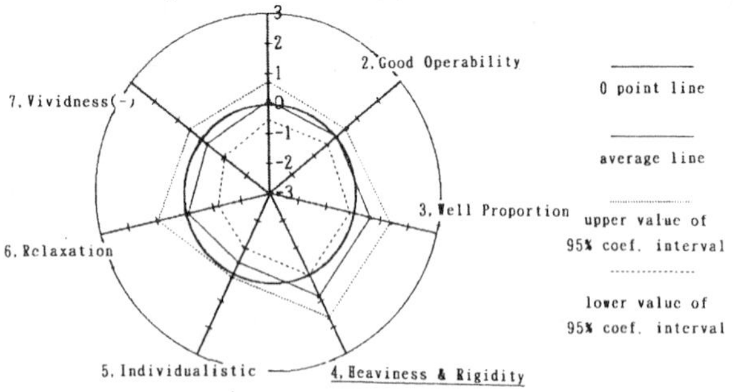

Fig. 2 Mean Scores for Basic Design

Mean scores for the reduced-size design is shown in Fig. 3. Strong impression can be seen along 'Well Proportion' axis, but poor impression on 'Operability'. In Fig. 4, the L-shaped 30°-neck 3-D designs, compared with the basic (planar) design, scored high in 'Freshness' and 'Operability'. Due to the space limitation, only sample figures are included here for illustration. For detailed figures and results, see [7].

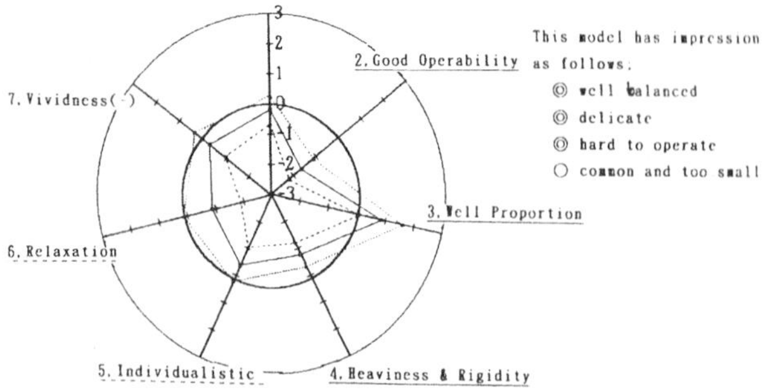

Fig. 3 Mean Scores for Reduced-Size Design

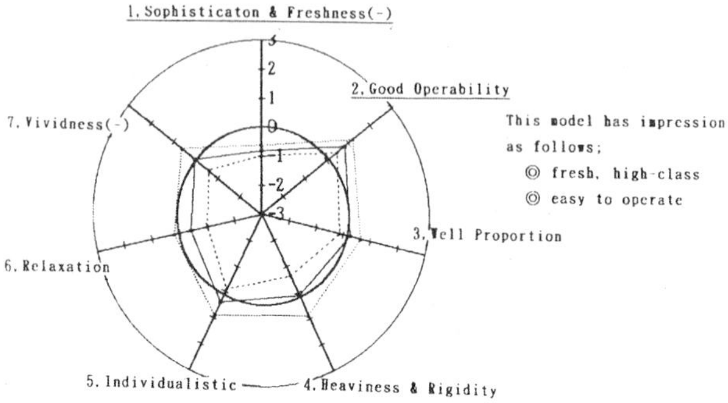

Fig. 4 Mean Scores for L-shaped Design

5. CONCLUSION

This paper discusses the use of a sensory engineering approach to the design of an excavator's control panel. It was found that the basic design was preferred over the reduced size design due to the perceived difficulty in operating a smaller panel. Both the L-shaped and the streamlined designs were preferred over the basic design due to the factors such as freshness, individualistic, and relaxation. These results show that the SD method provides an effective means to evaluate and characterize human's feelings about various product designs. These information can be utilized by the designer for in-time design modification to suit for the ultimate need of the customers.

ACKNOWLEDGEMENT

We like to thank Dr. F. Maaseidvaag and Mr. S. Murai for their encouragement and support to this work.

REFERENCES

[1] K. Kamiya, "Shape of Instrument Panel and Habitability," JSAE, Vol.98, No.5, 1984.

[2] M. Nagamachi, Kansei Engineering, Kaibundo Press, Japan, 1989, p.53.

[3] O. Kuroda and Y. Fujii, "An Approach to Improve Engine Sound Quality," SAE-880033, Feb., 1988.

[4] A. Kishi and S. Hata, "The Concept of Future Man-Machine System and the Evaluation Method of Vigilance," SAE-910114, Feb., 1991.

[5] E. Masuyama and S. Kobayashi, Sensory Evaluation, Kakiuchi Shuppan, Japan, 1989.

[6] C.E. Osgood, G.J. Suci, and P.H. Tannenbaum, "The Measurement of Meaning", University of Illinois Press, Champagne, IL, 1957.

[7] S. Fujimoto, M. Ikeda, and K. Wei, "Monitor Panel Design by the SD Method", Technical Report, Ford /Komatsu Technology Exchange Program, March, 1991.

Proceedings of the
American Control Conference
San Francisco, California • June 1993

Manipulability Measures of Cooperating Arms

Antonio Bicchi

Centro "E. Piaggio"
Facoltà di Ingegneria
Università di Pisa
56125 Pisa, Italia

Claudio Melchiorri

DEIS, Dip. di Elettronica,
Informatica e Sistemistica
Università di Bologna
40136 Bologna, Italia

Abstract

Manipulability ellipsoids are well known tools for the evaluation of the capability of a manipulator to perform a velocity/force task. Recently, extensions of the manipulability ellipsoids to cooperating arms have been proposed in the literature, even if these approaches may suffer of some limitations. In fact, it is believed that these techniques can not deal with general manipulation systems, e.g. when some of the arms have not full mobility in the task space (defective arms), or when different contact models must be assumed between the object and the arms.

In this paper, a new approach is presented for the measure of the manipulability of a multi-arm robotic system, considering the case of defective manipulators and general contact models. Examples are presented and discussed to illustrate the technique and compare it with previous methods.

1. Introduction

A well known method for the evaluation of a manipulator's aptitude to execute a specified velocity/force task is based on manipulability ellipsoids, [1]. Manipulability ellipsoids are defined by means of quadratic relations based on the Jacobian matrix $\mathbf{J}(\mathbf{q})$ of the considered manipulator. For single, serial link manipulators, the velocity and force ellipsoids are defined on the basis of the constraints $\dot{\mathbf{q}}^T\dot{\mathbf{q}} \leq 1$ and $\boldsymbol{\tau}^T\boldsymbol{\tau} \leq 1$ as:

$$\dot{\mathbf{x}}^T\,\mathbf{J}^{\dagger T}\,\mathbf{J}^{\dagger}\dot{\mathbf{x}} \leq 1, \qquad \mathbf{F}^T\,\mathbf{J}\,\mathbf{J}^T\mathbf{F} \leq 1, \tag{1}$$

respectively, where $\mathbf{J}^{\dagger}$ is a pseudo-inverse of the Jacobian, $\dot{\mathbf{x}}$, $\mathbf{F}$ are the velocity and force vectors in task space, and $\dot{\mathbf{q}}$, $\boldsymbol{\tau}$ the corresponding vectors in joint space. Eq. (1) defines the velocity/force ellipsoids, and represents the mappings of two unit balls in the joint spaces into the task space. The preferred directions in which tasks may be accomplished are given by the principal axes of the two ellipsoids, and may be computed with a singular value decomposition of the Jacobian matrix, $\mathbf{J} = \mathbf{U}\,\mathbf{S}\,\mathbf{V}^T$. The principal axes of the velocity ellipsoid are $\sigma_1\mathbf{u}_1, \ldots, \sigma_m\mathbf{u}_m$, where σ_i is the i-th singular value of $\mathbf{J}$, and $\mathbf{u}_i$ is the i-th column vector of $\mathbf{U}$. Dually, the principal axes of the force ellipsoid are $\mathbf{u}_1/\sigma_1, \ldots, \mathbf{u}_m/\sigma_m$.

In [2] and [3], two techniques are proposed to extend the concept of manipulability ellipsoid to the case of multiple-arm systems, as robotic hands, cooperating manipulators, or walking robots.

In [2], the manipulability velocity ellipsoid of a dual-arm system is defined by imposing on each arm the kinematic constraint deriving from the ellipsoids of both the manipulators. In practice, it is suggested to define an intersection of the two ellipsoids in order to obtain the velocity ellipsoid of the overall system. With this approach, for a two-arm system two (slightly) different results can be obtained, depending on the order used to intersect the original ellipsoids.

In [3], it is proposed to define the velocity/force ellipsoids imposing directly the constraints in the extended joint space formed by the arms. The Jacobian of the cooperating system is obtained composing the Jacobians of the single manipulators and the cooperation is modeled through the grasp matrix $\mathbf{G}$. Some problems may be encountered using this technique, as discussed in [4] and shown here in Section 4.

A comparison of these two techniques has been presented in [5], applied to the case of serial-parallel manipulators. However, some problems may be encountered using these two approaches for a general cooperating system. In fact, to our knowledge, the kinematic analysis of cooperating robotic systems presented in the literature has been mainly based on the assumption that every single arm has as many degrees-of-freedom (dof) as necessary to achieve arbitrary position/orientation in its task space. Moreover, also more general contact models besides the complete constraint contact (obtained by grippers) should be considered: for example the so called "soft-finger" contact, the "hard-finger" contact, and so on. In fact, an important application of cooperation between devices with "defective" kinematics is encountered in the analysis of *whole-limb* manipulation, that is manipulation using any link of the limbs. Examples of such devices are the MIT's Whole-Arm Manipulator (WAM), [6], or the University of Bologna UB Hand-II, [7].

In this paper a technique, based on the kinematic analysis discussed in [8], is presented and illustrated with some examples. This approach allows to overcome the above mentioned difficulties, and gives a measure of the manipulability capabilities of a general manipulation system.

2. Kinematic and Mobility Analysis

In [8] a technique has been presented aimed at solving

the problem of the kinematic and mobility analysis of general manipulation systems. The analysis considers a general cooperating system, i.e. an arbitrary number of limbs and an object which may be in contact with some or all of their links. Different contact models may be used to describe the interactions between the limbs and the object. As can be expected, each of these models will affect in a different manner the mobility capabilities of the system.

The kinematic constraints imposed by the i-th contact can be specified in terms of the relative velocities of two reference frames ${}^oC_i$ and ${}^mC_i$ both having the origin at the i-th contact centroid $\mathbf{c}_i$, and fixed to the object and to the robot link, respectively. In fact, for the n contact points on the object, we can write:

$$^o\dot{\mathbf{x}} = \mathbf{G}^T\dot{\mathbf{u}}, \tag{2}$$

where $\mathbf{u}$ is a 6-vector "twist", ${}^o\dot{\mathbf{x}}$ is a $6n$-vector where the velocities of the ${}^oC_i$ frames are stacked, and $\mathbf{G}$ is the $6 \times 6n$ grasp matrix.

Analogously, the linear and angular velocities of frame ${}^mC_i$ corresponding to joint velocities $\dot{\mathbf{q}}$ can be written in compact form as

$$^m\dot{\mathbf{x}} = \mathbf{J}\dot{\mathbf{q}}, \tag{3}$$

where $\mathbf{q}$ is a q-vector of joint coordinates, ${}^m\dot{\mathbf{x}}$ is a $6n$-vector where the velocities of the ${}^mC_i$ frames are stacked, and $\mathbf{J}$ is the $6n \times q$ Jacobian matrix.

Assuming a rigid-body model of the object and the links of the manipulators, the kinematic constraints imposed by contacts can be expressed as

$$\mathbf{H}\ ({}^o\dot{\mathbf{x}} - {}^m\dot{\mathbf{x}}) = 0 \tag{4}$$

where $\mathbf{H}$ is a selection matrix of suitable size that takes into account the type of contact. It is worth pointing out that (4) models bilateral constraints, and that unilateral or conic contact constraints can be considered in the assumption that the system of forces grasping the object is *force closure*. See [9] for a related discussion.

Substituting (2) and (3) in (4), we have

$$\mathbf{H}\mathbf{G}^T\dot{\mathbf{u}} - \mathbf{H}\mathbf{J}\dot{\mathbf{q}} = \tilde{\mathbf{G}}^T\dot{\mathbf{u}} - \tilde{\mathbf{J}}\dot{\mathbf{q}} = 0,$$

or in matrix form:

$$\begin{bmatrix} \tilde{\mathbf{G}}^T & -\tilde{\mathbf{J}} \end{bmatrix} \begin{bmatrix} \dot{\mathbf{u}} \\ \dot{\mathbf{q}} \end{bmatrix} = 0. \tag{5}$$

Let $\mathbf{Q} = \begin{bmatrix} \tilde{\mathbf{G}}^T & -\tilde{\mathbf{J}} \end{bmatrix}$, and define $\mathbf{C}$ as a matrix whose columns form a basis of the p-dimensional nullspace of $\mathbf{Q}$. Finally, partition $\mathbf{C}$ as $\mathbf{C} = \begin{bmatrix} \mathbf{C}_1^T & \mathbf{C}_2^T \end{bmatrix}^T$, where $\mathbf{C}_1$, and $\mathbf{C}_2$ are $6 \times p$, and $q \times p$ blocks, respectively.

The columns of $\mathbf{C}_1$ span the subspace of all possible rigid first-order differential motions of the object that do not break the contact constraints, and the columns of $\mathbf{C}_2$ span the corresponding subspace of joint motions. Moreover, by applying column operations only and partitioning appropriately, it is always possible to put the matrix $\mathbf{C}$ in the following form:

$$\begin{bmatrix} \mathbf{C}_1 \\ \mathbf{C}_2 \end{bmatrix} = \begin{bmatrix} \mathbf{C}_{11} & \mathbf{C}_{12} & \mathbf{O} \\ \mathbf{O} & \mathbf{C}_{22} & \mathbf{C}_{23} \end{bmatrix}. \tag{6}$$

Therefore, some coefficient vectors $\mathbf{x}_1$, $\mathbf{x}_2$, and $\mathbf{x}_3$ exist such that every possible pair of object velocity $\dot{\mathbf{u}}$ and joint velocity $\dot{\mathbf{q}}$ that comply with the kinematic and contact constraints of the multiple arm system can be written as

$$\begin{aligned} \dot{\mathbf{u}} &= \mathbf{C}_{11}\mathbf{x}_1 + \mathbf{C}_{12}\mathbf{x}_2 \\ \dot{\mathbf{q}} &= \mathbf{C}_{22}\mathbf{x}_2 + \mathbf{C}_{23}\mathbf{x}_3 \end{aligned}. \tag{7}$$

Mobility and Kinematic analysis

From (6) several interesting information may be deduced concerning the mobility and kinematics of the considered system. In particular:

- The mobility N_m of the system is equal to the rank of the $\mathbf{C}$ matrix, i.e. $N_m = \text{rank}(\mathbf{C})$;
- The connectivity N_c of the system is equal to the rank of the $\mathbf{C}_1$ block, $N_c = \text{rank}(\mathbf{C}_1)$;
- The indeterminacy N_i of the system is equal to the number of columns of $\mathbf{C}_{11}$, $N_i = \text{rank}(\mathbf{C}_{11})$. $\mathcal{R}(\mathbf{C}_{11})$, the indeterminacy subspace, is the subspace of object velocities that are not constrained by contacts. Note that $\mathcal{R}(\mathbf{C}_{11}) = \mathcal{N}(\tilde{\mathbf{G}}^T)$. These object motions can not be actuated directly by any combination of joint motions. Accordingly, if the object is moving along some direction in this subspace at some instant without external or unmodeled friction forces disturbing it, it will move indefinitely at constant speed in that direction [1].
- The redundancy N_r of the system is equal to the number of columns of $\mathbf{C}_{23}$, $N_r = \text{rank}(\mathbf{C}_{23})$. $\mathcal{R}(\mathbf{C}_{23})$ is the redundancy subspace, i.e. joint velocities that do not affect object velocities, but only modify the configuration of the manipulator arms. Note that $\mathcal{R}(\mathbf{C}_{23}) = \mathcal{N}(\tilde{\mathbf{J}})$.
- In the case that both $\mathbf{C}_{23}$ and $\mathbf{C}_{11}$ result empty ($N_i = N_r = 0$), there is a one-to-one correspondence between joint velocities in $\mathcal{R}(\mathbf{C}_{22})$ and object velocities in $\mathcal{R}(\mathbf{C}_{12})$, which can be written in parametric form as

$$\left\{ \begin{aligned} \dot{\mathbf{q}} &= \mathbf{C}_{22}\mathbf{x} \\ \dot{\mathbf{u}} &= \mathbf{C}_{12}\mathbf{x} \end{aligned} \right. \qquad \forall \mathbf{x} \in \mathcal{R}^{N_c}. \tag{8}$$

  In this case, the cooperating system is said to be "minimal".
- In the case $N_i = 0$ and $N_r > 0$, any desired velocity of the object in the feasible subspace $\mathcal{R}(\mathbf{C}_{12})$ can be obtained by means of infinitely many combinations of joint velocities. From (7) we obtain

$$\dot{\mathbf{q}} = \mathbf{C}_{22}\mathbf{C}_{12}^{+}\dot{\mathbf{u}} + \mathbf{C}_{23}\mathbf{y}, \qquad \forall \dot{\mathbf{u}} \in \mathcal{R}(\mathbf{C}_{12}), \tag{9}$$

  where $\mathbf{y} \in \mathcal{R}^{N_r}$ is a free coefficient vector. Any velocity $\dot{\mathbf{u}} \notin \mathcal{R}(\mathbf{C}_{12})$ can not be achieved by the system without breaking contact constraints. Note however that second- or higher-order differential motions in the forbidden directions may still be possible, see e.g. [11].

[1] However, some of these "free" motions can be indirectly controlled in some cases via exploitation of the dynamic couplings the object might have. For a related discussion, see e.g. [10].

- In case N_i is not zero ($\mathbf{C}_{11}$ is not empty), the object velocity corresponding to a given joint velocity is not uniquely determined by the quasi-static analysis. In fact, from (7),

$$\dot{\mathbf{u}} = \mathbf{C}_{12}\mathbf{C}_{22}^{+}\dot{\mathbf{q}} + \mathbf{C}_{11}\mathbf{y}, \qquad \forall\dot{\mathbf{q}} \in \mathcal{R}(\mathbf{C}_{22}), \quad (10)$$

where $\mathbf{y} \in \mathcal{R}^{N_i}$ is a free coefficient vector. The apparent physical non-sense of such indeterminacy is due to the assumed quasi-static model of the system, and can be solved by taking into account the object dynamics (see [10]).

3. Performance Evaluation

The technique for the mobility analysis presented in the previous section, summarized in (6), is an useful tool in studying techniques for the analysis of the kinetostatic properties of cooperating manipulation systems.

In the approach proposed here, we introduce an index of "efficiency" for the manipulation system in a given configuration which is defined as the ratio of an input effort and an output performance. In the velocity case, an input effort function for the system can be defined on the basis of the joint velocity vector $\dot{\mathbf{q}}$ (which is considered as the input to the system) as $f_i(\dot{\mathbf{q}}) = \dot{\mathbf{q}}^T\mathbf{W}_q\dot{\mathbf{q}}$. Analogously, an output performance function is defined in terms of $\dot{\mathbf{u}}$, the object's velocity vector, as $f_o(\dot{\mathbf{u}}) = \dot{\mathbf{u}}^T\mathbf{W}_u\dot{\mathbf{u}}$. $\mathbf{W}_q$ and $\mathbf{W}_u$ are symmetric, positive definite matrices of suitable size and physical dimensions. Therefore, the performance-to-effort ratio

$$R_v = \frac{f_o(\dot{\mathbf{u}})}{f_i(\dot{\mathbf{q}})} = \frac{\dot{\mathbf{u}}^T\mathbf{W}_u\dot{\mathbf{u}}}{\dot{\mathbf{q}}^T\mathbf{W}_q\dot{\mathbf{q}}} \quad (11)$$

may be used as a measure of the efficiency of the system in a particular configuration. Let's first consider the case of a single, non-redundant arm, for which the relation $\dot{\mathbf{u}} = \mathbf{J}\dot{\mathbf{q}}$ holds, being $\mathbf{J}$ the non-singular Jacobian matrix of the robot. Eq. (11) may be written as the Rayleigh quotient

$$R_v(\dot{\mathbf{q}}) = \frac{\dot{\mathbf{q}}^T\mathbf{J}^T\mathbf{W}_u\mathbf{J}\dot{\mathbf{q}}}{\dot{\mathbf{q}}^T\mathbf{W}_q\dot{\mathbf{q}}}. \quad (12)$$

As it is well known, the maximum (minimum) value of the Rayleigh quotient (12) corresponds to the maximum (minimum) generalized eigenvalue λ solving $(\mathbf{J}^T\mathbf{W}_u\mathbf{J})\,\dot{\mathbf{q}} = \lambda\,\mathbf{W}_q\,\dot{\mathbf{q}}$. Therefore, the directions (in the joint space) in which a maximum (minimum) efficiency is obtained are given by the generalized eigenvectors corresponding to the maximum (minimum) generalized eigenvalues given by (12). If λ_{max} is the maximum eigenvalue and $\dot{\mathbf{q}}_{max}$ the relative eigenvector, the corresponding direction in the task space is $\mathbf{J}\dot{\mathbf{q}}_{max}$. It may be easily verified that, in case the weighting matrices are assumed unitary, this result is the same as the one obtained with the ellipsoid approach, i.e. the direction given by the eigenvector corresponding to the maximum eigenvalue of the matrix $(\mathbf{J}\mathbf{J}^T)^{-1}$. In the following, it will be shown that this simple reformulation of Yoshikawa's manipulability ellipsoids, associated with the mobility analysis discussed in section 2, lends itself to a very straightforward generalization to multiple manipulation systems.

Minimal systems

Consider first minimal systems, i.e. assume that the submatrices $\mathbf{C}_{11}$ and $\mathbf{C}_{23}$ are empty, see (8). Although the system may not have full mobility in task space, there is a one-to-one relation between the motions of the joints and of the object. In this case, the Rayleigh quotient of velocity manipulability is defined as

$$R_v = \frac{\dot{\mathbf{u}}^T\mathbf{W}_u\dot{\mathbf{u}}}{\dot{\mathbf{q}}^T\mathbf{W}_q\dot{\mathbf{q}}} = \frac{\mathbf{x}^T\mathbf{C}_{12}^T\mathbf{W}_u\mathbf{C}_{12}\mathbf{x}}{\mathbf{x}^T\mathbf{C}_{22}^T\mathbf{W}_q\mathbf{C}_{22}\mathbf{x}}. \quad (13)$$

The maximum value of R_v is obtained for the maximum λ solving $\mathbf{C}_{12}^T\mathbf{W}_u\mathbf{C}_{12}\mathbf{x} = \lambda\mathbf{C}_{22}^T\mathbf{W}_q\mathbf{C}_{22}\mathbf{x}$. The corresponding generalized eigenvector $\mathbf{x}_{max}$ gives the direction, in the parameter $\mathcal{R}^{N_c}$ space, corresponding to which maximum performances are obtained. The corresponding directions in the task and joint velocity spaces are

$$\begin{aligned}\dot{\mathbf{u}}_{max} &= \mathbf{C}_{12}\mathbf{x}_{max}\\ \dot{\mathbf{q}}_{max} &= \mathbf{C}_{22}\mathbf{x}_{max}.\end{aligned} \quad (14)$$

Obviously, similar considerations apply for λ_{min}, the minimum generalized eigenvalue, and $\mathbf{x}_{min}$, the corresponding eigenvector. Note that (13) describes an ellipsoid in $\mathcal{R}^{N_c}$, the actual task space of the manipulation system at the given configuration.

Redundant systems.

In this case $\mathbf{C}_{23} \neq \mathbf{0}$, and there is a degree of arbitrarity in the choice of joint motions to achieve given object motions. However, according to our definition of an input effort function we will choose the joint motion that accomplishes the goal with minimum effort expenditure. Therefore, we want to solve the following constrained optimization problem:

$$\text{Min}_{\dot{\mathbf{q}}} \quad \dot{\mathbf{q}}^T\mathbf{W}_q\dot{\mathbf{q}}$$

$$\text{Such that} \quad \left\{\begin{aligned}\dot{\mathbf{q}} &= \mathbf{C}_{22}\mathbf{x} + \mathbf{C}_{23}\mathbf{y}\\ \dot{\mathbf{u}} &= \mathbf{C}_{12}\mathbf{x}\end{aligned}\right.$$

where $\mathbf{y} \in \mathcal{R}^{N_r}$ is a free vector to be determined. It is easy to verify, by equating the gradient of $\dot{\mathbf{q}}^T\mathbf{W}_q\dot{\mathbf{q}}$ to zero, that the minimum is obtained for

$$\mathbf{y} = -(\mathbf{C}_{23}^T\mathbf{W}_q\mathbf{C}_{23})^{-1}\mathbf{C}_{23}^T\mathbf{W}_q\mathbf{C}_{22}\mathbf{x} = -\mathbf{C}_{23q}^{+}\mathbf{C}_{22}\mathbf{x}$$

The corresponding optimal solution is

$$\begin{aligned}\hat{\dot{\mathbf{q}}} &= \mathbf{C}_{22}\mathbf{x} - \mathbf{C}_{23}\mathbf{C}_{23q}^{+}\mathbf{C}_{22}\mathbf{x}\\ &= (\mathbf{I} - \mathbf{C}_{23}\mathbf{C}_{23q}^{+})\mathbf{C}_{22}\mathbf{x} \quad = \hat{\mathbf{C}}_{22}\mathbf{x}\end{aligned}.$$

Therefore, the Rayleigh quotient for redundant systems is defined as

$$R_v(\mathbf{x}) = \frac{\mathbf{x}^T\mathbf{C}_{12}^T\mathbf{W}_u\mathbf{C}_{12}\mathbf{x}}{\mathbf{x}^T\hat{\mathbf{C}}_{22}^T\mathbf{W}_q\hat{\mathbf{C}}_{22}\mathbf{x}}. \quad (15)$$

If λ_{max}, $\mathbf{x}_{max}$ are the maximum generalized eigenvalue and the corresponding eigenvector, the "optimal" velocity vectors are

$$\begin{aligned}\dot{\mathbf{u}}_{max} &= \mathbf{C}_{12}\mathbf{x}_{max}\\ \dot{\mathbf{q}}_{max} &= \hat{\mathbf{C}}_{22}\mathbf{x}_{max}\end{aligned}. \quad (16)$$

Example. The 2 dof planar manipulator shown in fig. 1 is used as an example to illustrate the proposed technique. In this case, the original Yoshikawa's method can be used for the determination of the velocity ellipsoids. If the analysis is restricted to the linear x and y velocities, the resulting ellipsoid is shown in fig. 1.a. The principal semi-axes are defined, w.r.t. the end effector, by the two vectors:

$$\mathbf{v}_1 = [-1.376 \; 0.850]^T; \quad \mathbf{v}_2 = [-0.325 \; -0.526]^T.$$

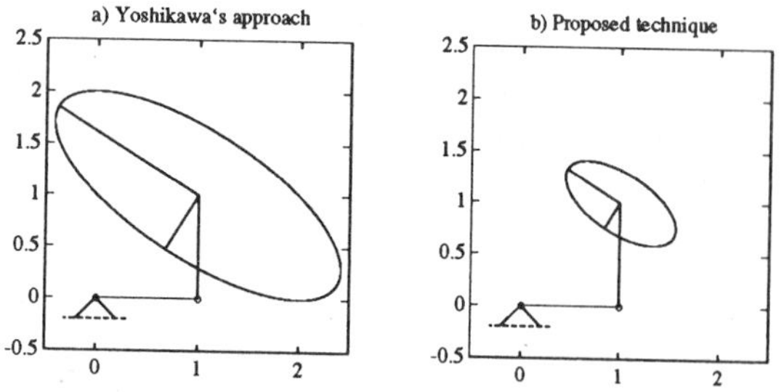

Figure 1: A 2-dof planar manipulator: comparison of Yoshikawa approach (a) and proposed technique (b).

In this case the $\mathbf{C}$ matrix, (6), results:

$$\mathbf{C} = \left[\; \mathbf{C}_1^T \mid \mathbf{C}_2^T \; \right]^T = \left[\begin{array}{cccccc|cc} -1 & 1 & 0 & 0 & 0 & 1 & 1 & 0 \\ -1 & 0 & 0 & 0 & 0 & 1 & 0 & 1 \end{array} \right]^T$$

and the system is minimal. Note that in this case $\mathbf{C}_1$ is equal to the Jacobian matrix of the manipulator. By using (13) and (14), with $\mathbf{W}_u$ and $\mathbf{W}_q$ identity matrices, one obtains the following maximum and minimum task and joint velocity vectors:

$$\dot{\mathbf{u}}_{max} = [-0.532 \;\; 0.329]^T \qquad \dot{\mathbf{u}}_{min} = [0.152 \;\; 0.246]^T$$
$$\dot{\mathbf{q}}_{max} = [0.329 \;\; 0.203]^T \qquad \dot{\mathbf{q}}_{min} = [0.246 \;\; -0.398]^T$$

The vectors $\dot{\mathbf{u}}_{max}$ and $\dot{\mathbf{u}}_{min}$ are shown in fig. 1.b. If the values are scaled in order to have $\dot{\mathbf{q}}^T\dot{\mathbf{q}} = 1$, the same result as in Yoshikawa's approach is obtained:

$$\dot{\mathbf{u}}_{max} = [-1.376 \;\; 0.850]^T \qquad \dot{\mathbf{u}}_{min} = [-0.325 \;\; -0.526]^T$$
$$\dot{\mathbf{q}}_{max} = [0.850 \;\; 0.526]^T \qquad \dot{\mathbf{q}}_{min} = [-0.526 \;\; 0.850]^T$$

4. Case Studies

Case 1. The first case study is shown in fig. 2. Two 2 dof manipulators hold an object. This example has been used also in [3]. Assuming a complete constraint contact model, the manipulability ellipsoids, as defined in [2] and [3], are shown in fig. 2.a and fig. 2.b, respectively. In this case, the only possible motion of the system is an instantaneous translation along the x axis. Note that the ellipsoids erraneously suggest possibility of motion along other directions. The $\mathbf{C}$ matrix, eq. (6), in this case results:

$$\mathbf{C} = \left[\begin{array}{cccccc|cccc} 1 & 0 & 0 & 0 & 0 & 0 & -1 & 1 & 1 & -1 \end{array} \right]^T,$$

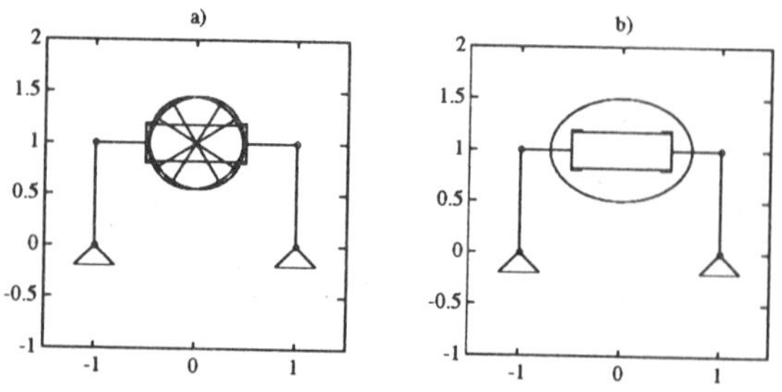

Figure 2: Two 2-dof planar manipulators: velocity ellipsoids computed as in [2] (a), and as in [3] (b).

confirming that only motions along the x direction are allowed. According to (8), the system is minimal. Eq. (13) and (14) give the following vectors for $\dot{\mathbf{u}}$ and $\dot{\mathbf{q}}$:

$$\dot{\mathbf{u}} = [0.5 \;\; 0]^T, \qquad \dot{\mathbf{q}} = [-0.5 \; 0.5 \; 0.5 \; -0.5]^T.$$

If a different contact model, for example the soft finger, is considered, and if the analysis is performed in the 6-dimensional space, motions along y are possible, as well as rotation about the z axis:

$$\mathbf{C} = \left[\begin{array}{cccccc|cccc} 1 & 0 & 0 & 0 & 0 & 0 & -1 & 1 & 1 & -1 \\ 0 & 1 & 0 & 0 & 0 & 0 & 0 & 2 & -2 & 0 \\ 0 & 0 & 0 & 0 & 0 & 1 & -1 & 0 & 0 & -1 \end{array} \right]^T.$$

In the 6-dimensional space, there are three eigenvalues and eigenvectors solutions of (13). Therefore, from (14) the following vectors, ordered by columns from λ_{max} to λ_{min}, are obtained:

$$\dot{\mathbf{u}} = \left[\begin{array}{ccc} -0.601 & -0.372 & 0.0 \\ 0.0 & 0.0 & -0.353 \\ 0.0 & 0.0 & 0.0 \\ 0.0 & 0.0 & 0.0 \\ 0.0 & 0.0 & 0.0 \\ -0.973 & 0.230 & 0.0 \end{array} \right], \quad \dot{\mathbf{q}} = \left[\begin{array}{ccc} 0.601 & 0.372 & 0.0 \\ 0.372 & -0.601 & -0.707 \\ 0.372 & -0.601 & 0.707 \\ 0.601 & 0.372 & 0.0 \end{array} \right].$$

Case 2. Let now consider the example shown in fig. 3, where two 3 degree-of-freedom planar manipulators hold an object. The manipulators operate in different planes, the first in $x - y$, while the second parallel to $y - z$. Assuming complete constraint contacts, the $\mathbf{C}$ matrix results:

$$\mathbf{C} = \left[\begin{array}{cccccc|cccccc} 0 & 1 & 0 & 0 & 0 & 0 & 0 & -1 & 1 & 0 & 1 & -1 \end{array} \right]^T.$$

Again, the system is minimal and (13)-(14) can be used, giving

$$\dot{\mathbf{u}} = 0.5[0 \; 1 \; 0 \; 0 \; 0 \; 0 \; 0]^T, \quad \dot{\mathbf{q}} = 0.5[0 \; -1 \; 1 \; 0 \; 1 \; -1]^T.$$

The result confirms that only movements along a line parallel to the y axis may be executed. Again, the approach proposed in [3] would misleadingly suggest non zero manipulability along directions where no motion is possible. If a soft-finger contact model is used, the mobility capabilities of the system change and

$$
\mathbf{C} = \left[\begin{array}{ccc|c}
0.5 & 0.0 & 0.0 & 0.0 \\
0.0 & 1.0 & -0.5 & 0.0 \\
0.0 & 0.0 & 0.0 & 0.0 \\
0.0 & 0.0 & 1.0 & 0.0 \\
-1.0 & 0.0 & 0.0 & 0.0 \\
0.0 & 0.0 & 0.0 & 0.0 \\
\hline
-1.0 & 0.0 & 0.0 & 0.0 \\
1.0 & 1.0 & 0.0 & 0.0 \\
0.0 & -1.0 & 0.0 & 0.0 \\
0.0 & 0.667 & -0.667 & 1.0 \\
0.0 & -0.333 & 0.333 & 1.0 \\
0.0 & 0.333 & -0.333 & -1.0
\end{array}\right]
$$

showing that the system has one degree of redundancy ($\mathbf{C}_{23} \neq \mathbf{0}$). In this case, by using (15) and (16), one obtains:

$$
\dot{\mathbf{u}} = \begin{bmatrix}
0.0 & 0.0 & 0.0 \\
0.374 & 0.534 & -1.037 \\
0.233 & -0.727 & -0.290 \\
0.152 & -0.077 & 1.462 \\
-0.233 & 0.727 & 0.290 \\
0.0 & 0.0 & 0.0
\end{bmatrix}
\dot{\mathbf{q}} = \begin{bmatrix}
-0.233 & 0.727 & 0.290 \\
0.758 & -0.269 & 0.135 \\
-0.526 & -0.457 & -0.425 \\
0.249 & 0.356 & -0.691 \\
-0.125 & -0.178 & 0.345 \\
0.125 & 0.178 & -0.345
\end{bmatrix}
$$

showing that maximum cooperation is achieved in a plane parallel to the $y - z$ plane (first elements of $\dot{\mathbf{u}}$ are null), as can be intuitively expected.

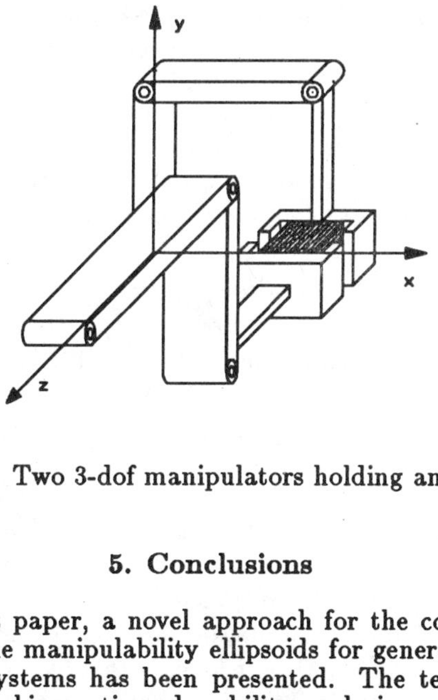

Figure 3: Two 3-dof manipulators holding an object.

5. Conclusions

In this paper, a novel approach for the computation of the manipulability ellipsoids for general cooperating systems has been presented. The technique relies on a kinematic and mobility analysis used to define the motion capabilities of a generic manipulation system, considering both different contact models between the object and the arms and the case in which some of the arms have not full motion capability in the task space. On this basis, it is possible to define performance-to-effort ratios for the system, and therefore compute the "preferred" directions in task and joint spaces by solving a generalized eigenvalue problem. The technique represents a generalization of Yoshikawa's original approach, giving the same results for single manipulators, and allows the application of these concepts to dexterous hands, cooperating manipulators, whole-arm devices.

Current activity is devoted to the extension of the presented method to the force case, and to the definition of tools for the workspace analysis (velocity/force polytopes).

Acknowledgments. This work has been supported by the CNR (Italian Research Council), under P.F.R., the special program on Robotics.

References

[1] T. Yoshikawa, "Manipulability of Robotic Mechanisms", Int. Jour. of Robotic Research, Vol. 4, No. 2, Summer 1985.

[2] S. Lee, "Dual Redundant Arm Configuration Optimization with Task-Oriented Dual Arm Manipulability", IEEE Trans. on Robotics and Automation, Vol. 5, No. 1, Feb. 1989.

[3] P. Chiacchio, S. Chiaverini, L. Sciavicco, B. Siciliano, "Global Task Space Manipulability Ellipsoids for Multiple-Arm Systems", Proc. IEEE Trans. on Robotics and Automation, Vol. 7, No. 5, Oct. 1991.

[4] C. Melchiorri, "Comments on 'Global Task Space Manipulability Ellipsoids for Multiple-Arm Systems' and Further Considerations", accepted for publication in the IEEE Trans. on Robotics and Automation, Sept. 1992.

[5] S. Lee, S. Kim, "Manipulabilities of Serial-Parallel Manipulator Systems", IEEE/RSJ Int. Conf. on Int. Robots and Systems, IROS'92, Raleigh, NC, July 1992.

[6] J.K. Salisbury, "Whole-Arm Manipulation", Proc. 4th. Int. Symp. on Robotics Research, Santa Cruz, CA, Aug. 1987.

[7] C. Melchiorri, G. Vassura, "Mechanical and Control Features of the University of Bologna Hand Version 2", IEEE/RSJ Int. Conf. on Int. Robots and Systems, IROS'92, Raleigh, NC, July 1992.

[8] A. Bicchi, C. Melchiorri, "Analysis of General Cooperating Manipulators", IEEE Int. Conf. on Robotics and Automation, Nice, F, 1992.

[9] Bicchi, A., "Optimal Control of Robotic Grasping", Proc. American Control Conference, ACC'92, Chicago, June 1992.

[10] Jain, A., and Rodriguez, G.: "Kinematics and Dynamics of Under-Actuated Manipulators", IEEE Conf. on Robotics and Automation, 1991.

[11] Nielsen, L., Canudas de Wit, C., and Hagander, P.: "Controllability Issues of Robots in Singular Configurations", Proc. IEEE Conf. on Robotics and Automation, 1991.

Proceedings of the
American Control Conference
San Francisco, California • June 1993

Force Regulation in Multiple Manipulator Systems

Mike J. Ryan, Steve H. Murphy, John T. Wen
Center for Intelligent Robotic Systems for Space Explorations
Rensselaer Polytechnic Institute
Troy, NY 12180

Abstract

An important advantage of multiple manipulator systems is the possibility to regulate the internal force in the payload. Common force control strategies include impedance control, position accommodation force control and Jacobian force control. This paper mainly considers the latter two schemes for which detailed dynamic models for the arms and the environment are not required. Comparison between these two methods are made and some experimental results on decentralized position accommodation force control are discussed.

1 Introduction

Multiple–manipulator systems significantly extend the capabilities of a single manipulator. With two or more manipulators a great number of significant tasks become feasible that would be extremely difficult, if not impossible with a single manipulator. This paper focuses on an important aspect of the multiple arm system control: regulation of the forces exerted by the manipulators on the payload. Successful force control will provide the capabilities necessary for many of the multi–arm tasks.

There have been various force control strategies, for example, for rigid grasping arms in [1, 2, 3, 4], and multiple fingers in [5, 6, 7, 8]. These strategies fall into the following categories:

1. Impedance control: The end effector is made to mimic a desired impedance through feedback linearization of the arm dynamics and direct force cancellation.

2. Position accommodation: The end effector is commanded to follow the arm trajectories corresponding to a desired impedance relation.

3. Jacobian force control: The arm is servoed directly based on the force error.

Direct force cancellation in impedance control can lead to instability due to the delay in force measurement [9]. Hence, we shall consider only the latter two cases. This paper will focus only on the position accommodation control as it is the first one that we have implemented experimentally. We will contrast its features to the Jacobian control whenever appropriate. In Section 2, we will describe the position accommodation and Jacobian force control methods and their comparison. In Section 3, some experimental results related to the decentralized force control are presented. A discussion on the force resolution issue in position accommodation control is given in Section 4.

2 Force Control Strategies

This paper focuses on two force control strategies: position accommodation control and Jacobian force control. We shall first consider these methods in the context of single arm force control (in contact with the environment) which is the basis of the decentralized multiple arm force control. Then the application to the multiple arm force control problem will be addressed.

Position Accommodation Control

Position accommodation control is similar in spirit to impedance control introduced in [10] where the end effector frame of the arm is commanded to mimic a desired mechanical impedance driven by the sensed force:

$$M_{des}\alpha_{des}+D_{des}v_{des}+K_{des}(x_{des}-x_{ref}) = -B(f-f_{des}), \quad (1)$$

However, in impedance control, feedback linearization and force cancellation are used to achieve this relationship exactly (at least in theory), but in position accommodation, any position controller can be used to follow the desired trajectory obtained from (1).

When this approach is used for force control, i.e., f_{des} is regarded as a force setpoint, K_{des} is usually set to zero in the constraint direction, so the desired setpoint will move beyond the constraint surface until the constraint force reaches the required setpoint. For the sake of illustration, consider a joint level proportion–derivative and gravity compensation

(PDG) controller:

$$\tau = -K_p(\theta - \theta_{des}) - K_v\dot{\theta} + k(\theta). \qquad (2)$$

To see the effect of this controller together with the desired impedance equation (1), consider the special case that the arm is in contact with an infinitely rigid environment and arm is in a motion equilibrium. In this case, we have the force balance equation $\tau = J^T f$. After linearization and substitution of the impedance equation and inverse kinematics, we have a second order equation

$$M_{des} J J^T \ddot{\eta} + D_{des} J J^T \dot{\eta} + B\eta = v \qquad (3)$$

where η is the integral of $\Delta f = f - f_{des}$ and v is a constant vector. If the parameters in the impedance equation are chosen so that (3) is a stable system, then η would tend to a constant (assuming that the arm never breaks off contact) and Δf would tend to zero as desired. However, the inclusion of M_{des} actually complicates matter. Depending on whether the left hand side of (3) is underdamped or overdamped, there may be oscillation in the force profile. Furthermore, this behavior depends on the robot configuration when contact occurs, due to the Jacobian terms in the equation. We recommend setting M_{des} to zero, so η would converge monotonically. In this case, the joint torque controller is of the form

$$\tau = -K_p(\theta - \theta_{ref}) - K_v\dot{\theta} - J^{-1} D_{des}^{-1} B \int_0^t \Delta f(s)\, ds. \qquad (4)$$

which is an integral force feedback controller with fixed spring and damper. As discussed in [11], integral force feedback possesses many desirable features (which agrees with the conclusion of an experimental investigation in [9]), especially in terms of robustness with respect to force measurement time delay when the environment is stiff.

Jacobian Based Direct Force Control

The position accommodation control converts the force error into a position error and performs joint servoing based on the position error. It is also possible to directly servo the joints based on the force error itself. The general form of the controller is

$$\tau = \tau_m + k(\theta) + J^T F \qquad (5)$$

where τ_m is a position control law (say, PD or PID) and F is the force controller. As discussed in [12], F can be chosen to be in either the feedforward or feedback form (or combination thereof). As mentioned before, integral force feedback is a particularly desirable choice, for both single arm and multiple arm force control.

The force control strategies described above can be applied to multiple arm control in two ways:

1. Decentralized: Each arm is controlled independently according to its own force control objective. In the position accommodation case, each arm has an impedance equation to follow:

$$M_{des\,i}\ddot{\delta x_i} + D_{des\,i}\dot{\delta x_i} + K_{des\,i}\delta x_i = A_i^T (f_i - f_{bias_i}) \qquad (6)$$

where A_i^T is the grasp Jacobian of the ith arm and $\delta x_i = x_i - x_{ref_i}$. This approach is the basis for the multiple–manipulator operating system KALI [13]. In general, x_{ref_i} and $f_{des\,i}$ should be chosen to satisfy the kinematic constraint. In the Jacobian force control case, a force setpoint $f_{des\,i}$ is specified for each arm.

2. Centralized: The arms are cooperatively controlled to allow for separate consideration of external and internal force control. In this case, all tip forces are propagated to a common frame C through the individual grasp Jacobian: $f_c = A^T f$. This force is used for the external force compliance.

   For internal force control, we extract an internal force variable ξ from $f = \widetilde{A^T}\xi$ where $\widetilde{A^T}$ is a full rank matrix whose range coincides with the null space of A^T. As explained in [14], the internal force can be parameterized by ξ, and strategies presented before can be used for its control.

While the decentralized force control system is inherently simple, it has distinct disadvantages: The decoupling of motion and force control cannot be achieved. Internal force control and external compliance cannot be independently specified. The system will compensate for the load gravity force as if it were an external force, requiring additional load compensation. The centralized force control system solves these difficulties at the expense of added calculations.

In general, position accommodation offers several advantages for multiple–manipulator systems:

- The basic controller for each manipulator remains unchanged. This is an advantage where existing manipulator controllers must be used and cannot be changed.
- Switching between controllers for cooperative modes and independent modes is not necessary.
- The calculation requirements are minimal.
- If the inverse kinematics function is sufficiently intelligent, then one manipulator may move through a singularity without necessarily adversely affecting the control of internal forces.
- The system will accommodate to external forces in the same manner as internal forces.

The disadvantages of such an approach are:

- Compliance is achieved through the controllers. Different controllers, PD vs PID for example, and different controller gains will require different impedance functions for equivalent performance.

- There is a potential for unstable interactions between the joint position control loop and the force compliance loop. If the joint controllers and force compliance calculations are digital and have the close bandwidths, then the interactions will be high, if the joint controllers are analog with much higher bandwidth, as is typical of most robot controllers, then the interactions are greatly diminished.

Overall this type of multiple-manipulator control represents one of the most straightforward implementations. As it can be implemented on many robotic systems it is a fundamental baseline to which other methods may be compared.

3 Experimental Results on Position Accommodation Control

Multiple arm control experiments have been conducted in the Center for Intelligent Robotic Systems for Space Explorations (CIRSSE) Dual Arm Laboratory at Rensselaer Polytechnic Institute. There are two PUMA560 type manipulators, each equipped with a Lord 15/50 force/torque sensor. The computer platform is a VME bus based system with five 68020 single board computers. The control software utilizes the CIRSSE-developed CTOS/MCS real time robot operating system. Only decentralized position accommodation has been experimented at this stage.

A block diagram of the software system is shown in Fig.1.

A number of experimental results are shown in this section. The following aspects of the decentralized position accommodation control are examined:

1. The effect of underlying controller (PD vs. PID).

2. Compression and tension tests.

Compliance Programming

We first test the ability of an unconstrained arm to follow a prescribed compliance. In Fig.2, good tracking of the desired trajectory is obtained before the arm begins to slow down. The deviates from the desired trajectory when it gets close to the steady state due to the effect of stick/slip friction.

Effect of Underlying Controller

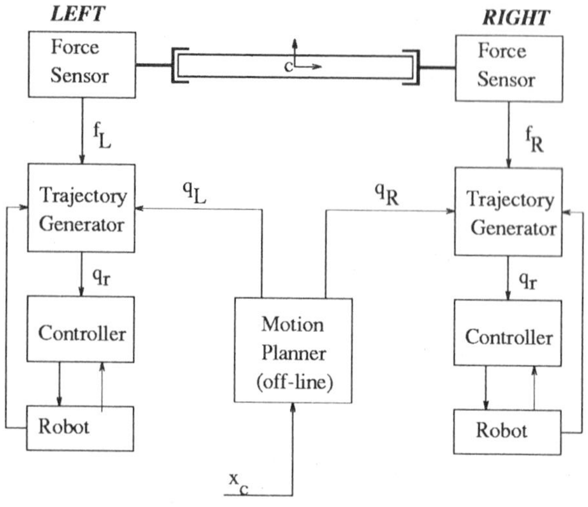

Figure 1: Architecture of Decentralized Dual Arm Position Based Force Control

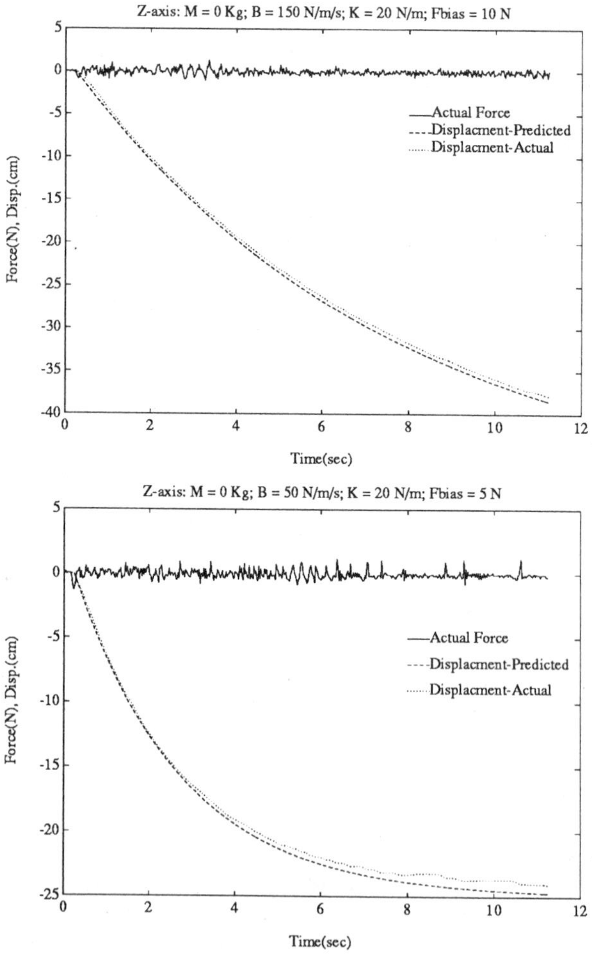

Figure 2: Tracking of Specified Compliance

A major drawback of the position accommodation force control is the dependence of the force control performance on the underlying position controller. For example, a good position controller may not perform well when it is used in the force control context. Fig.3 shows a force control experiment where the same impedance is specified, but the underlying controller is PD in one case and PID in the other. The results show a stable response for the PD case and an oscillatory response in the PID case, even though PID is the controller of choice for position control due to its better steady state response.

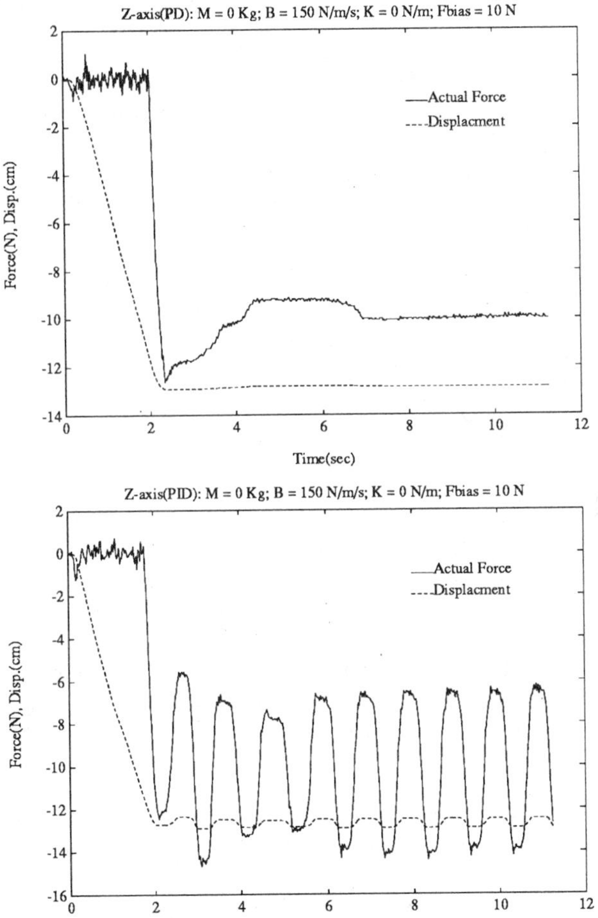

Figure 3: Comparison of PD and PID controllers

Compression and Tension Tests

Fig.4 shows the results of the arm pushing and pulling against each other (each with 5N force) along the longitudal axis of the held strut. The dash line shows the compliance in the closed kinematic chain and the variation in the force corresponds to the variation in the compression displacement variable. Note also the two arms show a net drift since there is no spring programmed in this case.

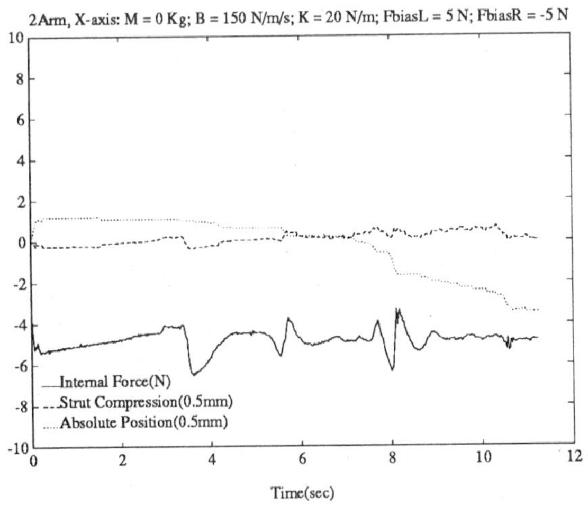

Figure 4: Compression and Tension Tests

Table 1: Approximate Force Resolution by Controller:

Parameter	PD	PID	Units
Lumped-Stiffness, k_l	99	9090	N/m
Force Resolution, Δf_l	0.01	0.9	N

4 Force Resolution Issue

For most robotic systems, the feedback of joint positions is done via optical encoders. The resolution of these encoders determines the absolute *positioning resolution* of the manipulator. This positioning resolution will correspondingly determine a *force resolution* related to the force mechanisms. The significance of the force resolution in relation to position accommodation control is discussed in this section.

The linear force resolution, Δf_l, of the manipulator can be approximated from the linear position resolution of the manipulator, Δp_l, and the lumped linear stiffness of the manipulator's position-controller, force sensor, and gripper, k_l, as $\Delta f_l = \Delta p_l \, k_l$ Estimating the linear positioning resolution of the PUMA arm to be $\Delta p_l \approx 0.1$[mm] [15], the approximate linear force resolution for both PD and PID position-controllers can be found, and is shown in Table 1 along with the estimated lumped-stiffness.

As can be seen in Table 1, there is a significant difference in the lumped-stiffness and corresponding force resolution between the PD and PID position-controllers. It can be inferred that this would greatly affect the performance of the position accommodation force control and was demonstrated to do so in the experiments shown in the previous section. The experimental runs with the PID controller showed sustained oscillations when contacting a rigid environment. These oscillations have been seen to persist even when heavily damped impedance parameters have been used, thus leading to the conclusion that the oscillations may have been caused *not* by too much forward-gain, but rather represented a *limit-cycle* behavior due to the coarseness of the force resolution.

To avoid the oscillations seen in Sec. 3, a PD position controller is used for most tasks. This brings out the quandary of position-based force control: for good positioning accuracy it is desired to have a very stiff manipulation mechanism(i.e. PID control), but this will correspondingly produce coarser force resolution. In practice, it may be necessary to switch controllers between free motion and contact tasks. This is one of the concept behind a *soft-servo* function in some industrial manipulators.

5 Conclusion

Two common multiple–arm force control strategies: position accommodation force control and Jacobian force control have been examined in this paper. While decentralized position accomodation has several advantages for implementation, experimental results have show many of the limitations: dry friction, effect of underlying position control law, and coupling between the position and force loops. We are currently conducting experimental investigation of centralized controller and Jacobian force control.

Acknowledgment

This work is supported by the Center for Intelligent Robotic Systems for Space Explorations at the Rensselaer Polytechnic Institute funded by the National Aeronautics and Space Administration under grant NAGW 1333.

References

[1] S. Hayati, "Hybrid position/force control of multi–arm cooperating robots," in *Proc. 1986 IEEE Robotics and Automation Conference*, (San Francisco, CA), pp. 1375–1380, Mar. 1986.

[2] J. Wen and K.Kreutz, "Stability analysis of multiple rigid robot manipulators holding a common rigid object," in *Proc. 27th IEEE Conference on Decision and Control*, (Austin, TX), 1988.

[3] P. Backes, "Dual–arm supervisory and shared control space servicing task experiments," in *Proc. AIAA Space Programs and Technologies Conference*, (Huntsville, AL), Mar. 1992.

[4] T. Alberts and D. Soloway, "Force control of a multiarm robot system," in *Proc. 1988 IEEE Robotics and Automation Conference*, (Philadelphia, PA), pp. 1490–1496, Apr. 1988.

[5] Y. Nakamura, K. Nagai, and T. Yoshikawa, "Mechanics of coordinative manipulation by multiple robotic mechanisms," in *Proc. 1987 IEEE Robotics and Automation Conference*, (Raleigh, NC), pp. 991–998, Mar. 1987.

[6] Z. Li, P. Hsu, and S. Sastry, "Grasping and dextrous manipulation with a multifingered robot hand," electronic research laboratory report, University of California, Berkeley, 1987.

[7] T. Yoshikawa and K. Nagai, "Manipulating and grasping forces in manipulation by multifingered robot hands," *IEEE Transactions on Robotics and Automation*, vol. 7, pp. 67–77, Feb. 1991.

[8] M. Uchiyama and P. Dauchez, "A symmetric hybrid position/force control scheme for the coordination of two robots," in *Proc. 1988 IEEE Robotics and Automation Conference*, (Philadelphia, PA), pp. 344–349, May 1988.

[9] R. Volpe, *Real and Artificial Forces in the Control of Manipulators: Theory and Experiments.* PhD thesis, Carnegie Mellon University, Pittsburgh, PA., Sept. 1990.

[10] N. Hogan, "Impedance control: An approach to manipulation: Part I – theory, Part II – implementation, Part III – applications," *ASME J. of Dyn. Sys., Meas. & Control*, pp. 1–24, 1985.

[11] J. Wen and S. Murphy, "Position and force control of robot arms," *IEEE Transactions on Automatic Control*, vol. 36, pp. 365–374, Mar. 1991.

[12] J. Wen and K. Kreutz-Delgado, "Motion and force control of multiple robotic manipulators," *Automatica*, to appear in 1992.

[13] V. Hayward and A. Topper, "Kali a control system for multiple arm robots," 1989.

[14] S. Murphy and J. Wen, "Force decomposition in robot force control," in *Proc. 1991 American Control Conference*, (Boston, MA), June 1991.

[15] M. J. Ryan, "Implementation of robotic force control with position accommodation," Master's thesis, Rensselaer Polytechnic Institute, Troy, NY., June 1992.

Proceedings of the
American Control Conference
San Francisco, California • June 1993

Experimental Demonstration of the Grasp Admittance Center Concept

A. A. Goldenberg K. B. Shimoga[1]

Robotics and Automation Laboratory
Department of Mechanical Engineering
University of Toronto, Toronto, ON, Canada, M5S 1A4.

Abstract

This paper demonstrates a new approach to achieving decoupled dynamic behavior in multifingered robotic hands. The approach is based on a new concept termed the **Grasp Admittance Center**. This concept is a generalized version of the *Compliance Center* concept, well known within the robotics literature for over a decade.

The proposed admittance center concept provides a framework for simultaneously achieving four useful features in robotic grasps[2]: (i) *decoupled*[3] *force-motion relationship* — a relationship between a motion imposed on the object and the reaction force that the object exerts to resist the motion; (ii) *decoupled time-response* — the motion response of the system to a force disturbance; and (iii) *stability* — the ability of the grasp to be in equilibrium despite disturbances. (iv) the task of assigning grasp dynamic behavior becomes transparent. These four features play important roles in the functioning of robotic hands, particularly when engaged in constrained manipulation tasks. Achieving these features in robotic grasps requires that the grasp impedance parameters[4] satisfy certain analytical conditions. These conditions are collectively referred to in this work as the admittance center concept.

Of the four advantages, conceptualizing the decoupled time response is difficult while the remaining 3 advantages are easily comprehendable. In view of this, the present work describes experiments wherein a carefully built passive compliant device emulates the dynamic behavior of multifingered grasps. The device is used to demonstrate the change in the time-response of 3 types of grasps: (i) a grasp in a general situation, (ii) a grasp with a compliance center only, and (iii) a grasp with an admittance center. The experimental results (photographic records) of the time-response of the 3 grasps clearly indicate the directionally decoupled dynamic behavior of an admittance center grasp, and the absence of such a behavior in general grasps and in grasps with a compliance center only. Such decoupled behavior is highly desirable in tasks involving constrained manipulation of delicate objects.

1 The Concept

The main objective of the research on robotic grasping, in general, is to use the robotic hands in the future to perform object handling tasks in a way similar to the humans. Thus far, the research in this area has focused mainly on the analysis and synthesis of grasps so as to achieve some essential properties such as the force-closure [14,15,18-20], equilibrium [1,2,4-6,8,10-13], and stability [1,4,5,8-10,12,13]. To successfully use the robotic hands in every-day tasks further requires regulation of their dynamic behavior. However, the research on static behavior itself is found to be very limited [3,6,16,17] while there is hardly any work on the dynamic behavior. The present work is concerned with the dynamic behavior of articulated grasps specifically when engaged in object manipulation tasks.

Extending Whitney's *Compliance Center* concept [24,25] to general articulated grasps, recent works [3,16,17] defined the *Grasp Compliance Center* as the origin of a coordinate frame in which a grasp will have a decoupled compliant behavior. Extending the concept to further include dynamic effects, our work in [21] conceptualized an *Accommodation Center* and a *Mobility Center* respectively as the origins of coordinate frames in which the grasp will have decoupled damping and decoupled inertial behaviors. When Compliance, Accommodation and Mobility Centers coincide in one coordinate frame, they yield what is termed an *Admittance Center*. For explanation on the related terminology, see Figure 1.

A grasp admittance center is completely specified by 5 parameters – the position and orientation of the admittance frame, and the three diagonal impedance matrices $\mathbf{M}, \mathbf{B}, \mathbf{K}$ that determine the dynamic behavior of the grasp [22]. The overall dynamic behavior of the grasp, described by $\mathbf{M}, \mathbf{B}, \mathbf{K}$, are derived primarily from the apparent dynamic behaviors of the fingers. Controlling the admittance center of a grasp during a task requires that the finger tips possess appropriate apparent impedances. This requires a method of computing the necessary finger tip impedances that lead to the desired grasp admittance center. This computational procedure is meaningfully referred to as the *synthesis* and it becomes an essential part of a hand control scheme. Such a synthesis algorithm was formulated and demonstrated via numerical examples in [24].

For a grasp to have an admittance center, analytically, it is necessary that (i) the matrices of grasp inertia, damping, stiffness, natural frequency and damping ratios, respectively denoted by $\mathbf{M}, \mathbf{B}, \mathbf{K}, \mathbf{\Lambda}$ and $\mathbf{\Gamma} \in R^{N\times N}$ are diagonal and the diagonal elements are positive, and (ii) all elements of $\mathbf{\Lambda}$ are equal and so are the elements of $\mathbf{\Gamma}$. Here, N is the number of degrees of freedom of the grasp. Physically, the above two conditions mean that the grasp can have different impedance behavior (force-motion relationship) on each degree of freedom but the dynamic behavior (natural frequency and damping ratio) on all degrees of freedom must be identical. Table 1 summarizes these analytical conditions.

In brief, a grasp with an admittance center will have a directionally decoupled dynamic behavior. Such a behavior is very useful during tasks involving dynamic manipulation of objects. This concept is also applicable to other closed kinematic chain robotic devices such as the cooperative multirobots as well as the multilegged mobile robots.

2 The Useful Features

A grasp with an admittance center will have 4 useful features, (i) stability — the ability of a grasp to return to to its nominal manipulation path if disturbed, (ii) decoupled force-motion relation — disturbance forces and motions result in motions and forces respectively on specific degrees of freedom only, (iii) decoupled time response — response to a step disturbance on any specific degree of freedom is restricted to that degree of freedom only, and (iv) the ease of specifying the grasp dynamic behavior. What follows is a brief description on how these features originate from the concept.

A Lyapunov approach based grasp stability analysis [21] indicated the necessary and sufficient conditions for a grasp to be stable are that the $\mathbf{M}, \mathbf{B}, \mathbf{K}$ of the grasp be positive definite. For an admittance center to exist, $\mathbf{M}, \mathbf{B}, \mathbf{K}$ must be diagonal with positive elements. Such $\mathbf{M}, \mathbf{B}, \mathbf{K}$ are already positive definite. The decoupled force-motion relation is achieved by the diagonality of $\mathbf{M}, \mathbf{B}, \mathbf{K}$. Hence, any motion error on any degree of freedom affects that degree of freedom only. The decoupled time-response of an admittance center grasp comes from the diagonality of $\mathbf{\Lambda}, \mathbf{\Gamma}$, specifically from the fact that $\mathbf{\Lambda}$ and $\mathbf{\Gamma}$ have identical eigenvalues. Last, the ease of specifying the grasp dynamic behavior comes from the fact that the impedance matrices need diagonal elements only to be specified and each diagonal element is responsible for the dynamic behavior of the grasp along one specific degree of freedom.

[1]Present address: Advanced Manipulators Laboratory, The Robotics Institute, Carnegie Mellon University, 5000 Forbes Avenue, Pittsburgh, PA 15213; Email: kshimoga@cs.cmu.edu

[2]A grasp is a system where an object is held by the fingers of a robotic hand.

[3]The behavior of a grasp is said to be decoupled if its response on a given degree of freedom is spurred by a disturbance experienced on that degree of freedom only.

[4]The spring, damper and mass coefficients are collectively called the impedance parameters.

Of the 4 features described, visualizing the stability, the decoupled force-motion relation, and the ease of specifying the dynamic behavior of the grasp are relatively easy. The other feature — decoupled time response and its importance in constrained manipulation tasks are hard to comprehend and hence are better clarified via a numerical example as below.

Consider a planar grasp for simplicity reasons, Figure 2, where, a peg grasped by fingers is being inserted into a hole. In this task, behavior of the peg-tip on its three degrees of freedom - along x and y and about z axes, are important. Let the apparent impedance matrices $\mathbf{K}, \mathbf{B}, \mathbf{M} \in R^{3\times3}$ of the pegtip in SI units be respectively,

$$\begin{aligned} \mathbf{K} &= \text{Diag}[\ 40.0 \quad 80.0 \quad 120.0\ ], \\ \mathbf{B} &= \text{Diag}[\ 0.8 \quad 1.6 \quad 2.4\ ], \\ \mathbf{M} &= \text{Diag}[\ 0.1 \quad 0.2 \quad 0.3\ ]. \end{aligned}$$

The resulting $\mathbf{\Lambda}, \mathbf{\Gamma} \in R^{3\times3}$ respectively are

$$\begin{aligned} \mathbf{\Lambda} &= \text{Diag}[\ 20.0 \quad 20.0 \quad 20.0\ ], \\ \mathbf{\Gamma} &= \text{Diag}[\ 0.2 \quad 0.2 \quad 0.2\ ]. \end{aligned}$$

Note that the conditions necessary for an admittance center to exist are satisfied.

At a given instant, let us assume that the peg tip should have been at P_0(0,0,0)mm, but due to some disturbing forces (say stick-slip phenomena), it is lagging behind at P_2(-5,0,0)mm. When the disturbing forces vanish, the peg will return to its equilibrium position P_0. The path it would take while doing so (as if the peg is unconstrained by the hole) for the two cases of with and without an admittance center are shown in Figures 3(a) and (b) respectively. Note that the return path of the peg with admittance center is a straight line and is coincident with the hole axis. Without an admittance center the path is curvaceous which implies that the motion of the peg has a component along the constrained y-axis. Since the peg is constrained to move within the hole, its tendency to move out of the hole in the constrained direction results in a reaction force. Figures 4(a) and (b) respectively show the reaction force at the peg tip for the cases of with and without an admittance center. This clearly demonstrates that the presence of an admittance center eliminates such undesirable forces in constrained manipulation tasks. If such forces happen to be relatively large and the manipulated object be fragile, the task itself might get aborted!

3 Experiments

3.1 A Compliant Device

Experimentally demonstrating the feature - *decoupled time-response* of a grasp is the goal of this section. A passive compliant device, shown in Figure 5 , has been built only for this purpose. Presented below is the principle behind the design of the device and a description on how the compliance center and the admittance center were achieved in the device.

Let us consider that the device (Figure 5a) has n springs (denoting the grasping fingers), connecting the inner square plate (denoting a grasped object) to the outer frame (denoting the grasping hand). The springs used are all identical whose stiffness, damping, and inertia be denoted by k, b, m respectively. The inner square plate is a pure mass without any compliance or damping. Excluding the rotational compliance for simplicity, the 2×2 stiffness matrix $\mathbf{K}$ of this plate, now on referred as the device, in the reference coordinate frame XOY is given by,

$$\mathbf{K} = \begin{bmatrix} \sum k_i C_i^2 & \sum k_i S_i C_i \\ \sum k_i S_i C_i & \sum k_i S_i^2 \end{bmatrix}, \tag{1}$$

where $S_i = \sin\alpha_i$, $C_i = \cos\alpha_i$ for $i = 1...n$, and α_i is the angle between the X-axis and the line of action of ith finger as shown in the sketch within Table 2. For a general procedure on obtaining $\mathbf{K}$, refer to Nguyen [17]. Further, one can obtain the matrix of damping $\mathbf{B}$ by simply replacing k_i in (1) above by b_i as,

$$\mathbf{B} = \begin{bmatrix} \sum b_i C_i^2 & \sum b_i S_i C_i \\ \sum b_i S_i C_i & \sum b_i S_i^2 \end{bmatrix}. \tag{2}$$

The apparent matrix of inertia $\mathbf{M}$ of the device is, however, the sum of two matrices — the overall inertia matrix of the device by virtue of the masses of the springs $\mathbf{M}_{spr}$, and the inertia matrix of the inner square plate itself $\mathbf{M}_{obj}$. They are respectively given by,

$$\mathbf{M}_{spr} = \begin{bmatrix} \sum m_i C_i^2 & \sum m_i S_i C_i \\ \sum m_i S_i C_i & \sum m_i S_i^2 \end{bmatrix} \tag{3}$$

and,

$$\mathbf{M}_{obj} = \begin{bmatrix} \frac{m_{obj} l^2}{12} & 0 \\ 0 & \frac{m_{obj} l^2}{12} \end{bmatrix}, \tag{4}$$

where, m_{obj} is the mass of the central plate (assumed to be thin for simplicity), and l is the length of each side of the (square) plate. Now, the overall inertia matrix $\mathbf{M}$ of the device is,

$$\mathbf{M} = \begin{bmatrix} \sum m_i C_i^2 + \frac{m_{obj} l^2}{12} & \sum m_i S_i C_i \\ \sum m_i S_i C_i & \sum m_i S_i^2 + \frac{m_{obj} l^2}{12} \end{bmatrix}. \tag{5}$$

What one must note here is that the overall impedance (stiffness, damping, and inertia) of the device (i.e. inner plate) is obtained from passive sources. In a real-life situation, such as in an articulated robotic hand, the apparent impedance of the grasp is obtained via regulating the closed-loop dynamic behavior of each finger using an impedance regulation scheme of the type described by Hogan [7].

3.2 A General Grasp

Consider a multifingered robotic grasp in a general situation. Its fingertip locations and impedances will be arbitrary. Consequently, the matrices $\mathbf{K}, \mathbf{B}$ and $\mathbf{M}$ will have non-zero diagonal elements and hence their dynamic behavior will be coupled. In such a grasp, neither a compliance center nor an admittance center will be present.

The dynamic behavior of such a grasp is demonstrated using the experimental device in Figure 5 as below. Since all springs used were identical, their configuration parameters (see Figure 6 and Table 2) were so chosen that the off-diagonal elements in $\mathbf{K}$ were both non-zero. As could be seen from (1),(2) and (5), $\mathbf{B}$ and $\mathbf{M}$ also will be non-diagonal when $\mathbf{K}$ is non-diagonal and the converse is true too. When $\sum S_i C_i = 0$ all 3 impedance matrices become diagonal. Else, all 3 remain non-diagonal which was true in our case.

The configuration of the device for this experiment was as follows. The 12 identical springs were arranged as shown in Figure 6a. The values of α for the 12 springs were as listed in the 1st row of Table 2. One can easily show that for these values, $\sum S_i C_i \neq 0$ and hence the impedance matrices were all non-diagonal. The time-response of the device was observed by disturbing the device reference frame origin O from the initial location P to a new location P' and released. The oscillatory path that the device takes (which is indicated by the LED - see Figure 5b) while returning to P was captured using time-exposure photography (exposure time 8 to 10 seconds). The time-response of device, in this general case, was as shown in Figure 7a. To infer from this figure is that an object held within an articulated robotic grasp whose closedloop dynamic behavior is arbitrary, it has a tendency to exhibit coupled dynamic behavior. That means, the grasped object, when disturbed, tends to oscillate along and about all degrees of freedom, including those on which the grasp was never disturbed. As pointed out earlier, this type of behavior is highly undesirable and may prove to be detrimental in close-fit insertion tasks involving delicate mating parts.

3.3 Grasp with a Compliance Center

A multifingered robotic grasp is said to have a compliance center when its stiffness matrix $\mathbf{K}$ is diagonal. In such a grasp, for the specified finger locations, each finger tip stiffness is so chosen and regulated that the off-diagonal elements in the resultant $\mathbf{K}$ matrix all vanish and hence the grasped object exhibits a decoupled force-displacement relation, strictly in a static situation. Note that this decoupling ceases to exist in a dynamic situation, i.e., when velocity and acceleration are non-zero.

The present experimental device was configured to simulate a grasp with a compliance center at its reference frame origin. For this, all springs in the device were arranged to be parallel to either of the axes (see Figure 6b). Thus, each spring contribute its compliance to one axis only. As a natural consequence, the off-diagonal elements in $\mathbf{K}$ all vanish and hence the device is said to have a compliance center. One must note that, diagonalizing

K in this device also leads to diagonal **B** and **M**. But this does not mean that an admittance center exists because, the resulting natural frequencies on all degrees of freedom may not be equal in general and the same might be true for the damping ratios (see Table 1 for conditions for admittance center existence).

The spring placements in the device, to simulate a grasp with a compliance center, is shown in Figure 6b. Of the 12 springs, 4 were placed parallel to X-axis and the remaining 8 were placed parallel to Y-axis. The values of α for the 12 springs in this case were as listed in the second row of Table 2. It is easy to show that for these values, $\sum S_i C_i = 0$ for $i = 1..12$ and hence **K** is diagonal. It could be further shown that due to the unequal number of springs on X and Y axes, the natural frequencies and the damping ratios on these axes will not be equal and hence the admittance center does not exist.

The time response of the device in this setting was studied as before. The return path of the point O (indicated by the LED) from P' to P was photographically recorded and is shown in Figure 7b. An important inference from this is that the presence of a compliance center is useful but only in a quasistatic situation. In a dynamic situation such as this, a grasp with only a compliance center will in no way different from a general grasp with arbitrary damping and inertia matrices. Therefore, such grasps face similar problems as general grasps in delicate insertion tasks.

3.4 Grasp with an Admittance Center

A robotic grasp is said to have an admittance center if the analytical conditions outlined in Table 1 are met with. To achieve such a grasp, each finger impedance must be regulated to be equal to the desired value, calculated apriori using the procedure formulated in [23]. The decoupled time-response in such a grasp comes by virtue of the fact that it has equal natural frequencies on all degrees of freedom and the same is true with damping ratios as well.

The spring settings on the device, in order to simulate such a grasp, is as shown in Figure 6c and the values of α were as listed in the third row of Table 2. That is, six springs were placed parallel to each of the two axes. As a result, $\mathbf{K}, \mathbf{B}$ and **M** became diagonal while all degrees of freedom had equal natural frequencies and equal damping ratios,

$$\omega_{nx} = \omega_{ny} = \frac{\sqrt{6k}}{\sqrt{6m + \frac{m_{obj} l^2}{12}}} \quad (6)$$

$$\xi_x = \xi_y = \frac{6b}{2\sqrt{6k + (6m + \frac{m_{obj} l^2}{12})}}, \quad (7)$$

where, $k = k_i \text{for} i = 1..n$, and the similar definition holds true for b and m as well. Therefore, an admittance center was present at the reference frame origin of the device. The time response of the device in this configuration, obtained as before, is shown in Figure 7c. The obvious observation is that a grasp with an admittance center would show its ability to confine its oscillations during the response to only those degrees of freedom on which it was disturbed, leaving all undisturbed degrees of freedom unaffected. An articulated grasp with such a property is highly desirable in constrained manipulation task, specifically in tasks involving insertion of delicate objects.

4 Conclusion

Presented in this paper are the results of the experiment where a carefully designed device was used to simulate the dynamic behavior of articulated multifingered robotic grasps. The goal was to demonstrate the usefulness of a concept called the *Grasp Admittance Center* - a notion that aims to make an articulated grasp exhibit a *directionally decoupled dynamic behavior*. An admittance center is conceptualized as the superposition of compliance, accommodation, and mobility centers in a desired coordinate frame. A grasp with an admittance center will have 4 useful features - (i) stability, (ii) decoupled force-motion relation, (iii) decoupled time-response, and (iv) the ease of specifying the dynamic behavior. These features are also useful to other closed kinematic chain robotic devices such as the cooperating multiarms and multilegged mobile robots engaged in non-quasistatic (dynamic) manipulation tasks.

Experiments were performed on the device to emulate the dynamic behavior of 3 types of grasps: (i) a general grasp, (ii) a grasp with a compliance center, and (iii) a grasp with an admittance center. The springs were used in the device to simulate the fingers of a robotic hand whose impedances are regulated. Three types of grasps were emulated by varying the spring locations and their configuration parameters and this is equivalent to changing the fingertip location and tip impedance in an articulated grasp. The time response of the 3 grasps were recorded using extended exposure photography. The results clearly demonstrate the difference in time-response of the grasps. The general grasp shows a strongly coupled dynamic response to a disturbance and so was the grasp with a compliance center, because no consideration was given to the damping and the inertial properties of the grasp. The grasp with an admittance center clearly demonstrates a decoupled dynamic behavior, which was expected based on the theoretical analysis performed earlier [21]. Results recommend that a robotic grasp involved in delicate insertion tasks must be controlled to have an admittance center at an appropriate location on the grasped object. Failure to do so may prove to be detrimental to the successful completion of the task.

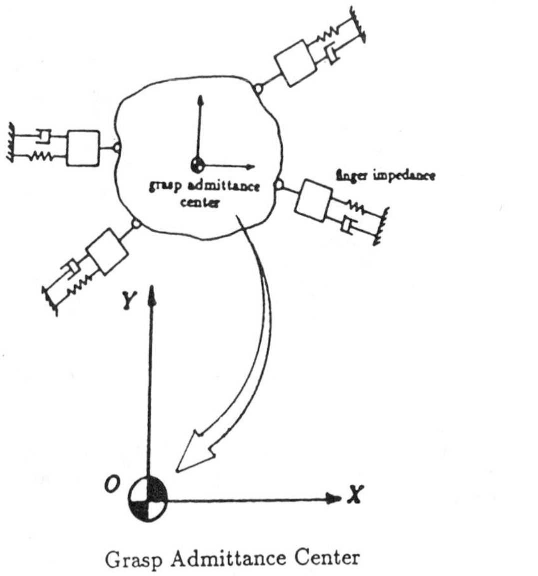

Grasp Impedance Matrices : A collective terminology for the siffness, damping, and inertia matrices of a grasp.

Grasp Admittance Center : The origin of a frame in which the grasp impedance matrices will be diagonal and the dynamic behavior of the grasp will be identical on all degrees of freedom.

Grasp Admittance Frame : The coordinate frame in which, the grasp admittance center exists or intended to exist.

Admittance Center Parameters : The 5 parameters that completely specify a grasp admittance center, viz., the location of the admittance frame origin, the frame orientation, the matrices of desired apparent stiffness, damping, and inertia.

Figure 1: *Compliance, Accommodation and Mobility Centers exist and are coincident at O. Also given above are the terminology related to the admittance center.*

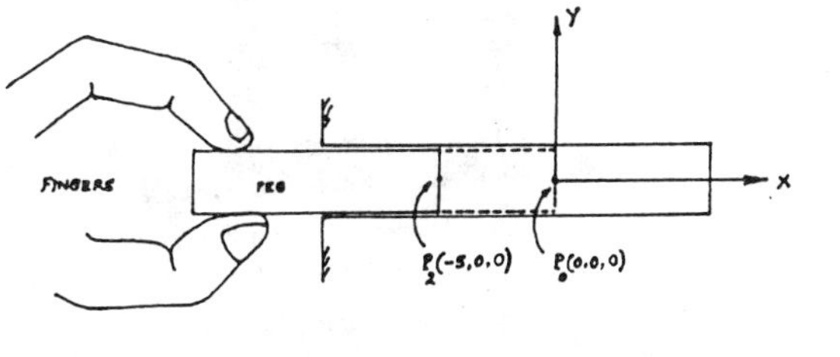

Figure 2: *Planar peg insertion task (details in Section 3).*

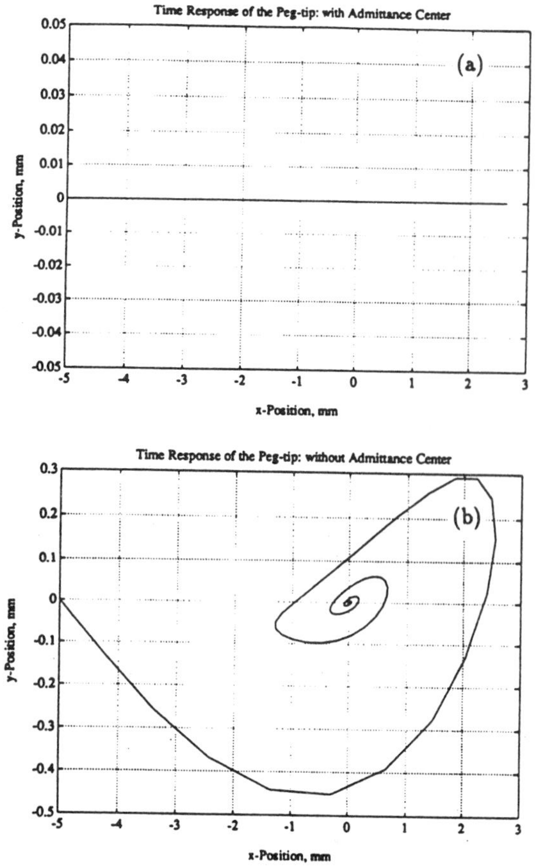

Figure 3: *Simulated time response of the peg tip – (a) with admittance center, (b) without admittance center, (details in Section 2).*

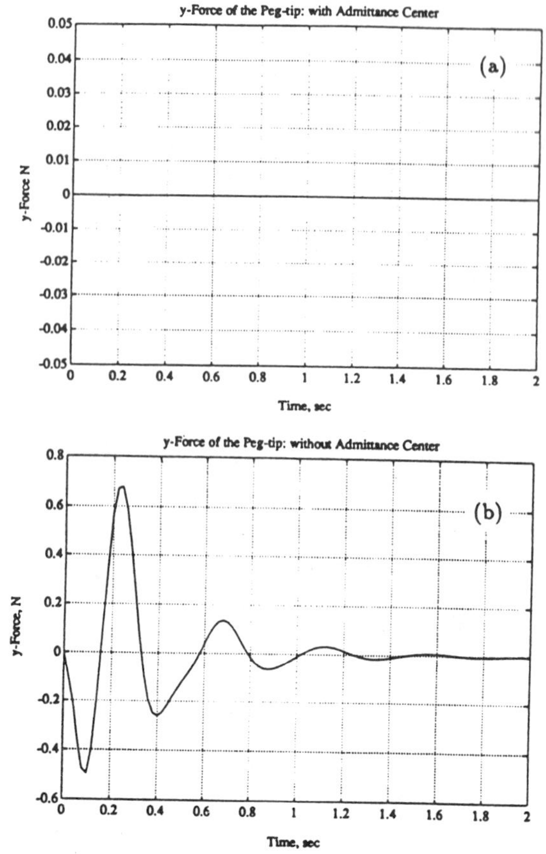

Figure 4: *Force resulting from the tendency of the peg to move laterally out of the hole – (a) with admittance center, (b) without admittance center, (details in Section 2).*

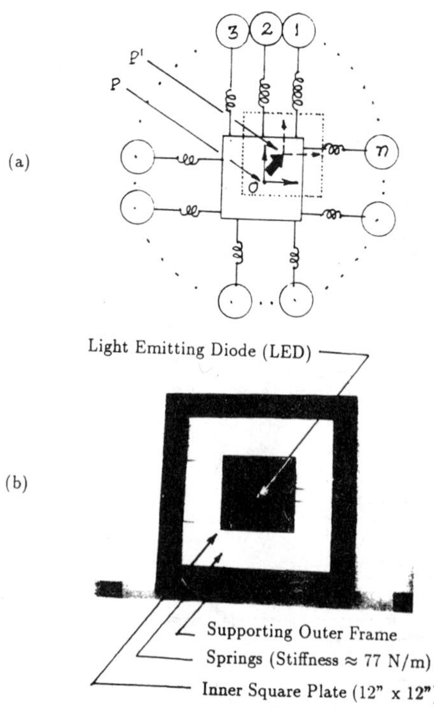

Figure 5: *The experimental device that simulates the dynamic behavior of an articulated robotic grasp: (a) a schematic of the device in arbitrary configuration, (b) a view of the actual device.*

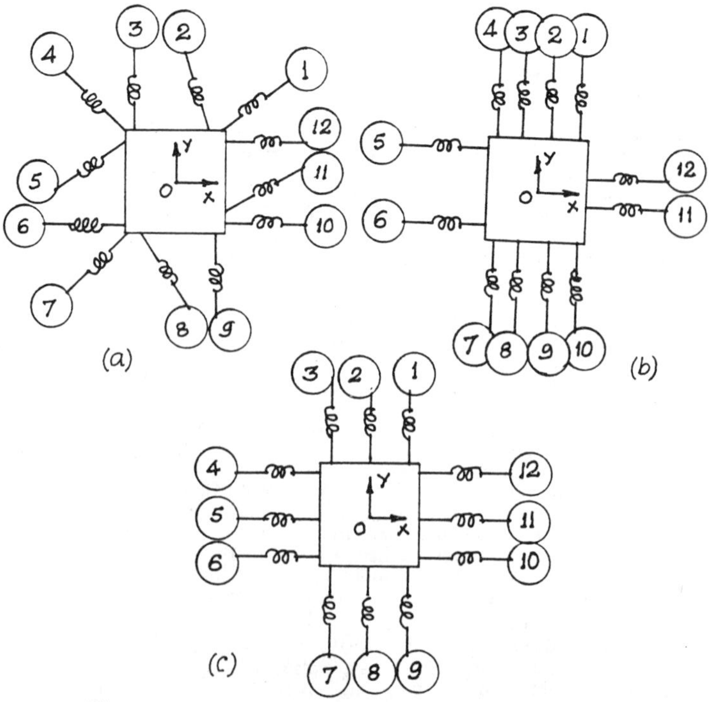

Figure 6: *The configuration of the springs in the device when it simulated the dynamic behavior of a grasp (a) in its general form, (b) with a compliance center, and (c) with an admittance center. Also see Table 2 for the values of angle α of springs in each case.*

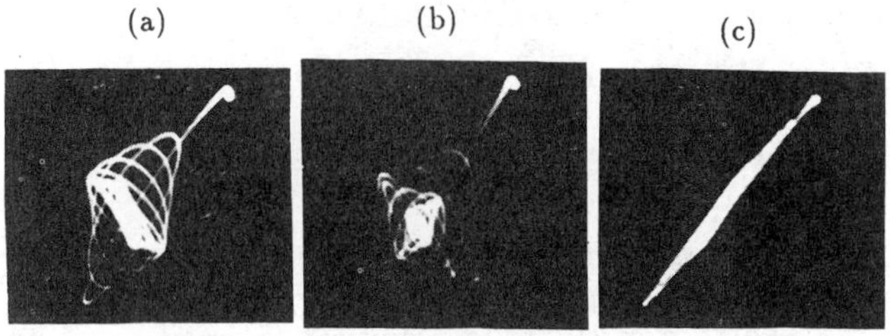

Figure 7: *The time-response plots of 3 grasps simulated by the experimental device: (a) grasp in its general form, (b) grasp with a compliance center, and (c) grasp with an admittance center.* **Note:** *The above photographs, in fact, are the motions of the LED placed at the center of our experimental device's reference frame origin O (see Figure 5b). In the above, the bright spot on the right top is the point P' to which the reference frame origin O was displaced to and released from. Another bright spot in the center is the rest point P to which O returns to after the oscillations subside.*

Table 1: *The analytical conditions that must be satisfied in order for an admittance center to exist: column 1 shows the concerned matrices, column 2 shows the necessary conditions on these matrices, and column 3 shows the useful features originating when conditions in column 3 are satisfied.*

Matrices	*Necessary Condition(s)*	*Useful Feature*
$\mathbf{M}, \mathbf{B}, \mathbf{K}$	Positive Definiteness	Stability
$\mathbf{M}, \mathbf{B}, \mathbf{K}$	Diagonality	Decoupled Force-Motion Relation
$\mathbf{\Lambda}, \mathbf{\Gamma}$	Diagonality Identical Diagonal Entries	Decoupled Time Response

Table 2: *The values of α (see sketch below) of the 12 springs used in the experimental device in each of the 3 settings: (a) a general grasp, (b) a grasp with a compliance center, and (c) a grasp with an admittance center. All angles above are in degrees. For schematics of the device in these settings, refer to Figure 6.*

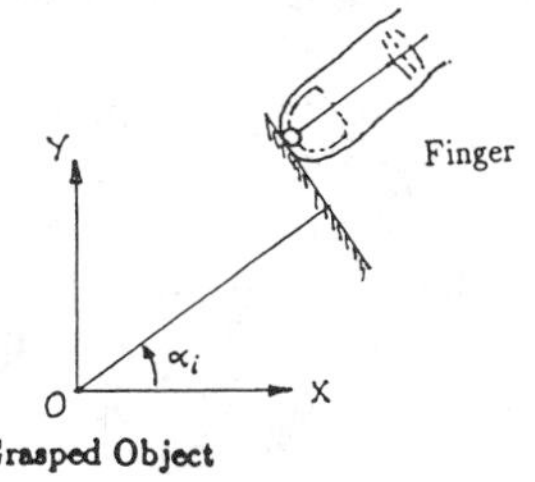

	Spring #											
Configuration	1	2	3	4	5	6	7	8	9	10	11	12
Figure 6 (a)	30	80	90	150	200	180	225	300	270	360	400	360
Figure 6 (b)	90	90	90	90	180	180	270	270	270	270	360	360
Figure 6 (c)	90	90	90	180	180	180	270	270	270	360	360	360

All angles above are in *degrees*. For schematics of the device in these settings, refer to Figure 6.

References

[1] Abel J.M., Holzmann W. and McCarthy J.M., 1985, "On Grasping Planar Objects withe Two Articulated Fingeres," *IEEE Transaction on Robotics and Automation*, vol. RA-1, No. 4, pp. 211-214.

[2] Baker, B.S., Fortune, S., and Grosse, E., 1985, "Stable Prehension with a Multifingered Hand," *Proc. 1985 IEEE Int. Conf. on Robotics and Automation*, St. Luis, MS, March, pp. 570-575.

[3] Cutkosky M.R. and Kao I., 1989, "Computing and Controlling the Compliance of a Robot Hand," *IEEE Trans. Robotics and Automation*, vol. RA-5, no. 2, pp. 151-165.

[4] Cutkosky, M.R., and Wright, P.K., 1986,"Friction, Stability, and the Design of Robotic Fingers," *International Journal of Robotics Research*, vol. 5, no. 4, pp. 20-37.

[5] Fearing, R.S., 1986, "Simplified Grasping and Manipulation with Dexterous Robot Hands," *IEEE Journal of Robotics and Automation*, vol. RA-2, no. 4, December, pp. 188-195.

[6] Hanafusa, H., and Asada, H., 1982a, "Stable Prehension by a Robot Hand with Elastic Fingers," in Brady M., et al (Eds), *Robot Motion: Planning and Control*, MIT Press, Cambridge, MA, pp. 322-335.

[7] Hogan N., 1985, "Impedance Control: An Approach to Manipulation, Part I-III," *ASME J. Dyn. Sys., Meas., and Control*, vol. 107, pp. 1-24.

[8] Holzmann W. and McCarthy J.M., 1985 "Computing the Friction Forces Associated with a Three-Fingered Grasps," *IEEE Transaction on Robotics and Automation*, vol. RA-1, No. 4, pp. 206-210.

[9] Jameson J.W. and Leifer L.J., 1986, "Quasi-static analysis : A Method for predicting Grasp Stability," *IEEE Int. Conf. on Robotics and Automation*, San Fransisco, CA, April, pp. 876-883.

[10] Kerr J. and Roth B., 1986a, " Analysis of Multifingered Hands," *The Int. J. of Robotics Research*, vol. 4, No. 4, Winter, pp. 3-17.

[11] Kobayashi, H., 1985, "Control and Geometrical Considerations for an Articulated Robot Hand," *The Int. Jl. of Robotics Research*, vol. 4, no. 1, Spring, pp. 3-12.

[12] Kumar V. and Waldron K., 1987, "Sub-Optimal Algorithms for Force Distribution in Multifingered Grippers," *IEEE Int. Conf. on Robotics and Automation*, Raleigh, NC, March/April, pp. 252-257.

[13] Li Z. and Sastry S., 1988, "Dexterous Hands : Grasping and Manipulation," *Workshop on Dexterous Hands, IEEE Int. Conf. on Robotics and Automation*, Philadelphia, PA, April, pp. 69-106.

[14] Markenscoff X., Ni L., and Papadimitriou C.H., 1990, "The geometry of grasping," *Int. J. Robotics Research*, vol. 9, no. 1, pp. 61-74.

[15] Markenscoff X., and Papadimitriou C.H., 1990, " Optimum grip of a polygon," *Int. J. Robotics Research*, vol. 8, no. 2, pp. 17-29.

[16] Mason M.T. and Salisbury J.K., 1982, *Articulated Hand and Mechanics of Manipulation*, Cambridge: MIT Press, MA.

[17] Nguyen, V., 1986, "The Synthesis of Stable Grasps in the Plane," *Proc. 1986 IEEE Int. Conf. on Robotics and Automation*, San Francisco, CA, March, pp. 884-889.

[18] Nguyen, V., 1988, "Constructing Force Closure Grasps," *Int. J. of Robotics Research*, vol. 7, no. 3, pp. 3-16.

[19] Park Y.C. and Starr G.P., 1990, "Grasp Synthesis of Polygonal Objects," *Proc. 1990 IEEE Int. Conf. Robotics and Automation*, Cincinnati, OH, May, pp. 1574-1580.

[20] Pollard N.S. and Lozano-Perez T., 1990, "Grasp stability and feasibility of an arm with an articulated hand," *Proc. 1990 IEEE Int. Conf. Robotics and Automation*, Cincinnati, OH, May, pp. 1581-1585.

[21] Shimoga K.B. and Goldenberg A.A., 1991, "Grasp Admittance Center: A Concept and Its Implications," *Proc. 1991 IEEE Int. Conf. on Robotics and Automation*, Sacramento, CA, April 7-12, pp. 674-679.

[22] Shimoga K.B. and Goldenberg A.A., 1991, "Grasp Admittance Center: Choosing Admittance Space Parameters," *Proceedings of the American Control Conf.*, Boston, MA, June 26-28, pp. 2527-2532.

[23] Shimoga K.B. and Goldenberg A.A., 1992, "Constructing Multifingered Grasp to Achieve An Admittance Center," *To appear in Proc. 1992 IEEE International Conference on Robotics and Automation*, Nice, France, May 10-15.

[24] Whiteny D.E., 1984, "Quasistatic Assembly of Compliantly Supported Rigid Bodies," *ASME J. of Dyn. Sys., Meas., and Control*, vol. 104, March, pp. 65-77.

[25] Whitney D.E. and Nevins J.L., 1979, "What is the Remote Center of Compliance and What can it do ?," *Proc. 9th Int. Symp. on Ind. Robots*, March, pp. 135-143.

Proceedings of the
American Control Conference
San Francisco, California • June 1993

Task-Oriented Kinematic Control of Two Cooperative 6-DOF Manipulators

Pasquale Chiacchio Stefano Chiaverini Bruno Siciliano

Dipartimento di Informatica e Sistemistica
Università degli Studi di Napoli Federico II
Via Claudio 21, 80125 Napoli, Italy

Abstract—*The kinematic control problem for a system of two cooperative 6-dof manipulators is addressed in this paper. First, a kinematic model of the system is obtained which allows a clear description of the task in terms of absolute and relative variables. Then, a suitable inverse kinematics scheme is designed to compute the joint variable trajectories corresponding to a given trajectory for the above cooperative task variables. The effectiveness of the technique is demonstrated by two case studies for two cooperative PUMA 560 robot manipulators; one regards a typical coordinated motion for the system, the other is aimed at illustrating the redundancy resolution features of the scheme.*

1. Introduction

An effective control strategy for a system of two robots holding a common object must properly take into account the mechanical constraints imposed by the contact between each arm and the object. It can be recognized that both the absolute motion of the object and the internal forces acting between the two end-effectors should be controlled. Also, the presence of kinematic redundancy into the system should be properly handled.

Several works addressed the problem of coordinated control of a two-arm robot system, e.g. [1], which designed control systems that improve on the performance of previous schemes of master/slave fashion [2], or else of leader-follower type [3]. Further schemes were developed which regarded the cooperative system from a global point of view, i.e. operating with object space coordinates, and allowed control of absolute object motion and of internal forces [4–6].

A drawback of the above schemes is that the interpretation of cooperative task space variables is not always straightforward; from the user's point of view, it would be preferable to define variables that are directly related to the assigned cooperative task. In this context, a two-stage kinematic control strategy can be devised which presents the cascade of a kinematic inversion block for the task variables characterizing the cooperation and a conventional control in the joint space. One advantage of a two-stage control strategy is also the capability of solving kinematic redundancy. This approach was developed for two planar arms [7,8] and is here generalized to the case of two cooperative 6-dof manipulators.

The contribution of this work is to obtain a kinematic model of the cooperative system which allows a clear description of the task in terms of absolute and relative components. In particular, an effective definition of meaningful (absolute and relative) orientation variables is given which overcomes the major difficulty in previous cooperative task descriptions.

Further, a closed-loop inverse kinematics scheme [9,10] is developed to compute the joint variable trajectories corresponding to a given trajectory for the above cooperative task variables. The scheme uses the Jacobians relative to the task variables which, by virtue of the above kinematic description, can be expressed in terms of the end-effector Jacobians for the single arms.

A system composed by two cooperative PUMA 560 robot manipulators is considered to work out two case studies. In the first one, a trajectory is assigned to the task variables realizing a coordinated motion for the system. In the second one, the system is made kinematically redundant by considering a reduced number of task variables, and the features of the scheme to perform redundancy resolution are demonstrated.

2. Task description

The choice of a functional task description for multiple arm systems manipulating a common object is crucial to the development of effective control systems that achieve true cooperation between the arms.

Consider a system of two spatial manipulators. The location of each end-effector can be described by six task space variables, three for position and three for a minimal representation of orientation. This indicates that, if the manipulators have to cooperate, a number of twelve task space variables should be defined to fully describe the kinematics of the system.

The trivial choice would be to consider the two end-effector locations. However, in this way the system is regarded as composed by two independent manipulators and management of coordination is left to the user.

Another possibility would be to adopt as task variables those derived from a kineto-static object level description of the system which is based on the so-called grasp matrix mapping end-effector forces into external object forces [4]. One drawback of this description regards the representation of orientation. In fact, the kinematic variables are originated from the composition of linear and angular velocities of the two end-effectors; a problem then arises in view of the non-integrability of angular velocities. Further, even if a minimal representation of orientation is found, this would not have a clear meaning to the user.

In the following an effective description is established which unambiguously characterizes the cooperative task as well as allows the user to give an immediate specification of the task in terms of meaningful variables.

It can be recognized that the typical task of a cooperative two-arm system is to manipulate a common object. Therefore, it is natural to define not only a set of variables specifying the absolute motion of the object but also a set of variables describing the relative location between the end-effectors which in turn characterizes the object grasp. Obviously, both the absolute and relative variables include position and orientation.

Consider a system of two cooperative manipulators. For each manipulator ($i = 1, 2$), let $\boldsymbol{p}_i^b$ be the (3×1) vector denoting the end-effector position. Let also $\boldsymbol{R}_i^b$ be the (3×3) rotation matrix expressing the end-effector orientation. Both quantities are expressed in a common base frame (superscript "b").

The end-effector linear velocity is directly given as the time derivative of the position vector, that is $\dot{\boldsymbol{p}}_i^b$. The end-effector angular velocity is given by the (3×1) vector $\boldsymbol{\omega}_i^b$, which is related to the time derivative of the rotation matrix $\boldsymbol{R}_i^b$ through the relationship

$$\dot{\boldsymbol{R}}_i^b = \boldsymbol{S}(\boldsymbol{\omega}_i^b)\boldsymbol{R}_i^b, \tag{1}$$

where $\boldsymbol{S}(\cdot)$ is the (3×3) skew-symmetric operator performing the vector cross product.

The absolute position of the cooperative system can be defined as the origin of a suitable frame attached to the object (denoted by subscript "a"), which has to be expressed as a function of the positions of the two end-effectors. One simple choice is

$$\boldsymbol{p}_a^b = \frac{1}{2}(\boldsymbol{p}_1^b + \boldsymbol{p}_2^b), \tag{2}$$

whose time derivative gives the absolute linear velocity

$$\dot{\boldsymbol{p}}_a^b = \frac{1}{2}(\dot{\boldsymbol{p}}_1^b + \dot{\boldsymbol{p}}_2^b). \tag{3}$$

In order to define the absolute orientation of the system, consider the matrix operator $\boldsymbol{R}_k(\vartheta)$ expressing the rotation by the angle ϑ about the axis aligned with the unit vector $\boldsymbol{k} = (\,k_x \quad k_y \quad k_z\,)^{\mathrm{T}}$. Note also that the following property holds:

$$\dot{\boldsymbol{R}}_k(\lambda\vartheta) = \lambda\dot{\boldsymbol{R}}_k(\vartheta), \tag{4}$$

where λ is a constant. The rotation matrix giving the absolute orientation is then defined as

$$\boldsymbol{R}_a^b = \boldsymbol{R}_1^b\boldsymbol{R}_{k_{12}^1}^1(\vartheta_{12}/2), \tag{5}$$

where $\boldsymbol{k}_{12}^1$ and ϑ_{12} are respectively the unit vector and the angle that realize the rotation described by $\boldsymbol{R}_2^1$. Therefore, the above choice corresponds to make a rotation about the axis $\boldsymbol{k}_{12}^1$ by an angle which is half the angle needed to align $\boldsymbol{R}_2^b$ with $\boldsymbol{R}_1^b$. By differentiating (5) and using (1,4), it can be shown that the absolute angular velocity is given by

$$\boldsymbol{\omega}_a^b = \frac{1}{2}(\boldsymbol{\omega}_1^b + \boldsymbol{\omega}_2^b). \tag{6}$$

The relative position between the two end-effectors can be defined as

$$\boldsymbol{p}_r^b = \boldsymbol{p}_2^b - \boldsymbol{p}_1^b, \tag{7}$$

whose time derivative is

$$\dot{\boldsymbol{p}}_r^b = \dot{\boldsymbol{p}}_2^b - \dot{\boldsymbol{p}}_1^b. \tag{8}$$

Nevertheless, notice that for the user it is more convenient to assign the relative position in the object frame, i.e. $\boldsymbol{p}_r^a$. If this is the case, the relative position in the base frame can be computed as

$$\boldsymbol{p}_r^b = \boldsymbol{R}_a^b\boldsymbol{p}_r^a \tag{9}$$

with $\boldsymbol{R}_a^b$ as in (5). Further, the relative linear velocity in the base frame is given by

$$\dot{\boldsymbol{p}}_r^b = \boldsymbol{R}_a^b\dot{\boldsymbol{p}}_r^a + \boldsymbol{S}(\boldsymbol{\omega}_a^b)\boldsymbol{p}_r^b \tag{10}$$

with $\boldsymbol{\omega}_a^b$ as in (6).

The relative orientation between the two end-effectors can be defined in the end-effector frame of either manipulator —say the first one— according to the above choice for the relative position, i.e.

$$\boldsymbol{R}_r^1 = \boldsymbol{R}_2^1. \tag{11}$$

The resulting relative angular velocity is

$$\boldsymbol{\omega}_r^1 = \boldsymbol{\omega}_2^b - \boldsymbol{\omega}_1^b \tag{12}$$

which is notefully related to quantities expressed in the base frame.

3. Closed-loop inverse kinematics scheme

The above task space description constitutes the basis for a kinematic control scheme. This requires the solution of an inverse kinematics problem, that is finding the joint variable trajectories corresponding to given trajectories for the absolute and relative task variables. These trajectories will then constitute the reference inputs to some joint space control scheme.

Any algorithmic solution to the inverse kinematics problem is based on the computation of the Jacobian relative to the task variables of interest. Since these variables have been expressed as a function of the position and orientation of the two end-effectors, the sought Jacobian can be related to the Jacobians of the single manipulators.

Without loss of generality, consider a system of two cooperative 6-dof manipulators. For each manipulator, let $\boldsymbol{q}_i$ indicate the (6×1) vectors of joint variables. The geometric Jacobian $\boldsymbol{J}_i^b(\boldsymbol{q}_i)$ is the (6×6) matrix relating the joint velocity vectors $\dot{\boldsymbol{q}}_i$ to the linear and angular end-effector velocities in the base frame as

$$\begin{pmatrix} \dot{\boldsymbol{p}}_i^b \\ \boldsymbol{\omega}_i^b \end{pmatrix} = \boldsymbol{J}_i^b(\boldsymbol{q}_i)\dot{\boldsymbol{q}}_i \qquad i = 1, 2. \tag{13}$$

At this point, combining (3,6) and taking into account (13) yields

$$\begin{pmatrix} \dot{\boldsymbol{p}}_a^b \\ \boldsymbol{\omega}_a^b \end{pmatrix} = \boldsymbol{J}_a^b(\boldsymbol{q}_1, \boldsymbol{q}_2)\begin{pmatrix} \dot{\boldsymbol{q}}_1 \\ \dot{\boldsymbol{q}}_2 \end{pmatrix}, \tag{14}$$

where the (6×12) absolute Jacobian matrix is defined as

$$\boldsymbol{J}_a^b = (\,\tfrac{1}{2}\boldsymbol{J}_1^b \quad \tfrac{1}{2}\boldsymbol{J}_2^b\,). \tag{15}$$

Further, combining (8,12) and taking into account (13) yields

$$\begin{pmatrix} \dot{p}_r^b \\ \omega_r^1 \end{pmatrix} = J_r^b(q_1, q_2) \begin{pmatrix} \dot{q}_1 \\ \dot{q}_2 \end{pmatrix}, \qquad (16)$$

where the (6 × 12) relative Jacobian matrix is defined as

$$J_r^b = (-J_1^b \quad J_2^b). \qquad (17)$$

The inverse kinematics algorithm used is the closed-loop scheme based on the computation of the inverse of the manipulator Jacobian [9]. In the general case, the joint velocity solution can be written in the form

$$\dot{q} = J^{-1}(v_d + Ke) \qquad (18)$$

where q is the vector of joint variables, J is the Jacobian —assumed to be square and singularity-free— associated to the velocity mapping, v_d is the desired task velocity, K is a suitable diagonal positive gain matrix, and e is the error between the desired and actual task variables.

The closed-loop inverse kinematics scheme based on (18) avoids the typical numerical drift of open-loop resolved-rate schemes. The solution can be made robust with respect to singularities of J by resorting to a damped least-squares inverse of the matrix [11].

Further, if the system possesses redundant degrees of freedom —due either to the presence of additional joint variables or to relaxation of some task variables— the Jacobian becomes a low rectangular matrix. In this case, the solution is modified into [10]

$$\dot{q} = J^{\dagger}(v_d + Ke) + (I - J^{\dagger}J)\dot{q}_0 \qquad (19)$$

where $J^{\dagger}$ denotes the pseudoinverse of J, and the operator $(I - J^{\dagger}J)$ projects the vector of arbitrary joint velocities $\dot{q}_0$ (aimed at exploiting the redundant degrees of freedom) into the null space of J so as not to interfere with the primary end-effector task.

The above algorithms can be keenly applied to solve the inverse kinematics for the cooperative system at issue. In detail, define

$$q = \begin{pmatrix} q_1 \\ q_2 \end{pmatrix}. \qquad (20)$$

If the system is non-redundant, solution (18) is applied. The Jacobian is

$$J = \begin{pmatrix} J_a^b \\ J_r^b \end{pmatrix}, \qquad (21)$$

where J_a^b, J_r^b are given as in (15,17). The error is

$$e = \begin{pmatrix} e_a \\ e_r \end{pmatrix}. \qquad (22)$$

The absolute error has a translation and an orientation component and is given by

$$e_a = \begin{pmatrix} p_{ad}^b - p_a^b \\ \frac{1}{2}(S(n_a^b)n_{ad}^b + S(s_a^b)s_{ad}^b + S(a_a^b)a_{ad}^b) \end{pmatrix}, \qquad (23)$$

where p_{ad}^b is the desired absolute position specified by the user in the base frame, p_a^b is the actual absolute position that can be computed as in (2), $n_{ad}^b, s_{ad}^b, a_{ad}^b$ are the column vectors of the rotation matrix R_{ad}^b giving the desired absolute orientation specified by the user in the base frame, and n_a^b, s_a^b, a_a^b are the column vectors of the rotation matrix R_a^b in (5). The relative error is given by

$$e_r = \begin{pmatrix} R_a^b p_{rd}^a - p_r^b \\ \frac{1}{2}(S(n_r^1)n_{rd}^1 + S(s_r^1)s_{rd}^1 + S(a_r^1)a_{rd}^1) \end{pmatrix}. \qquad (24)$$

The rotation R_a^b is aimed at expressing the desired relative position p_{rd}^a, assigned by the user in the object frame, in the base frame; in this way, if an error occurs on the object frame orientation this does not affect the specification of the desired relative position between the two end-effectors. Further in (24), p_r^b can be computed as in (7), $n_{rd}^1, s_{rd}^1, a_{rd}^1$ are the column vectors of the rotation matrix R_{rd}^1 giving the desired relative orientation specified by the user in the end-effector frame of the first manipulator, and n_r^1, s_r^1, a_r^1 are the column vectors of the rotation matrix R_r^1 in (11). Finally, the desired velocity is

$$v = \begin{pmatrix} v_a \\ v_r \end{pmatrix}. \qquad (25)$$

The absolute velocity term is given by

$$v_a = \begin{pmatrix} \dot{p}_{ad}^b \\ \omega_{ad}^b \end{pmatrix}, \qquad (26)$$

where $\dot{p}_{ad}^b$ and ω_{ad}^b are respectively the desired absolute linear and angular velocities specified by the user in the base frame. The relative velocity term is given by

$$v_r = \begin{pmatrix} R_a^b \dot{p}_{rd}^a + S(\omega_a^b)R_a^b p_{rd}^a \\ \omega_{rd}^1 \end{pmatrix}, \qquad (27)$$

where $\dot{p}_{rd}^a$ is the desired relative linear velocity specified by the user in the object frame and ω_{rd}^1 is the desired relative angular velocity specified by the user in the end-effector frame of the first manipulator. Notice that the expression of the translational part of the relative velocity presents an additional term which is a consequence of having assigned the relative position in the object frame.

On the other hand, if the system is redundant, solution (19) is applied. In this case, the rows in the Jacobian matrix (21) corresponding to the relaxed task variables have to be canceled and J becomes a low-rectangular matrix. The analogous components in the error vector (22) and desired velocity (25) have to be canceled accordingly; the dimension of matrix K is reduced accordingly. Concerning the choice of $\dot{q}_0$ in (19), this is taken as

$$\dot{q}_0 = k_c \nabla_q c(q) \qquad (28)$$

where c is a constraint function of the joint variables that is optimized locally and k_c is a signed constant.

4. Case studies

A system of two cooperative PUMA 560 manipulators is considered to develop two case studies. Discrete-time simulations of the inverse kinematics algorithms (18) and (19) have been run in MATLAB at 1 [ms] sampling time. To gain numerical robustness to the occurrence of kinematic singularities, a damped least-squares is used in lieu of the pure (pseudo)inverse of the relevant Jacobian.

A non-redundant system is analyzed in the first case study, i.e. twelve cooperative task variables are considered, and a coordinated motion is specified for the system. The bases of the two manipulators are respectively located at $(0 \quad -0.1501 \quad 0)^{\mathrm{T}}$ [m] and $(1.4331 \quad 0.1501 \quad 0)^{\mathrm{T}}$ [m] with reference to a common base frame. The initial joint configurations are $q_1 = (0 \quad -2\pi/5 \quad 9\pi/10 \quad 0 \quad 0 \quad 0)^{\mathrm{T}}$ [rad] and $q_2 = (\pi \quad -2\pi/5 \quad 9\pi/10 \quad 0 \quad 0 \quad 0)^{\mathrm{T}}$ [rad]. The initial rotation matrices $\boldsymbol{R}_1^b, \boldsymbol{R}_2^b$ are chosen as identity matrices so as to refer to suitable tool frames aligned with the base frame; of course, the orientation of the two end-effectors may differ but the algorithms will embed proper rotation matrices to pass from the end-effector frames to the user-defined tool frames. With these values, the initial absolute position is $\boldsymbol{p}_a^b = (0.7166 \quad 0 \quad 0.4310)^{\mathrm{T}}$ [m] and the initial relative position is $\boldsymbol{p}_r^a = (0.1 \quad 0 \quad 0)^{\mathrm{T}}$ [m]. Also, the initial absolute rotation matrix is $\boldsymbol{R}_a^b = \boldsymbol{I}$ and the initial relative rotation matrix is $\boldsymbol{R}_r^1 = \boldsymbol{I}$; this is a direct consequence of the convenient choice made above for $\boldsymbol{R}_1^b, \boldsymbol{R}_2^b$. The final absolute position is displaced at $(0.05 \quad 0 \quad 0.05)^{\mathrm{T}}$ [m] from the initial one while the final relative position is displaced at $(-0.02 \quad 0 \quad 0)^{\mathrm{T}}$ [m] from the initial one. As regards the orientation, a rotation of $\pi/4$ [rad] along the y-axis of the base frame is assigned for the final absolute orientation while a rotation of 0.1 [rad] along the z-axis of the initial $\boldsymbol{R}_1^b$ is assigned for the final relative orientation. The trajectories for the desired variables are generated by using an interpolating polynomial of fifth order with null initial and final velocities and accelerations; the duration time is 1 [s]. The feedback gain matrix in (18) is $\boldsymbol{K} = \text{block diag}\{500\boldsymbol{I}_6, 1000\boldsymbol{I}_6\}$ where $\boldsymbol{I}_6$ means the (6×6) identity matrix.

The results are plotted in Figs. 1–4. The norm of position and orientation components of both absolute and relative errors (Figs. 1,2) demonstrate the tracking capabilities of the inverse kinematics scheme; the error peaks occurring in the starting phase are due to the effort paid to exit from the wrist singularities of both manipulators. The time history of the joint variables is shown in Figs. 3,4.

Reconfiguration of a redundant system is analyzed in the second case study. The cooperative system is made redundant by relaxing the absolute position, i.e. nine task variables are considered which have to remain constant. The initial configuration of the system is the same as in the previous case study. The constraint function in (28) is

$$c(\boldsymbol{q}) = \frac{1}{4}\boldsymbol{u}^{\mathrm{T}}\left(\boldsymbol{J}_{t1}^b(\boldsymbol{J}_{t1}^b)^{\mathrm{T}} + \boldsymbol{J}_{t2}^b(\boldsymbol{J}_{t2}^b)^{\mathrm{T}}\right)\boldsymbol{u}$$

where the subscript "t" refers to the translational part of the single arm Jacobians. Minimizing this function is equivalent to maximizing the intersection of the global task space external force manipulability ellipsoid [16] along the task space direction specified by the unit vector $\boldsymbol{u}$; in this case, it is $\boldsymbol{u} = (1 \quad 0 \quad 0)^{\mathrm{T}}$ describing the x-axis of the base frame. The constant in (28) is $k_c = -10$.

The results are plotted in Figs. 5–8. The time history of the function in Fig. 5 demonstrates the effective exploitation of redundant degrees of freedom to minimize the given constraint. This is obtained by means of a reconfiguration of the system; the absolute position (Fig. 6) changes while the errors (Figs. 7,8) show that all the other task variables are practically unaffected.

ACKNOWLEDGMENTS

This work was supported by *Consiglio Nazionale delle Ricerche* under contracts no. 92.01064.PF67 and no. 92.01105.PF67.

REFERENCES

[1] M. Uchiyama, N. Iwasawa, and K. Hakomori, "Hybrid position/force control for coordination of a two-arm robot," *Proc. 1987 IEEE International Conference on Robotics and Automation*, Raleigh, NC, pp. 1242–1247, 1987.

[2] E. Nakano, S. Ozaki, T. Ishida, and I. Kato, "Cooperational control of the anthropomorphous manipulator 'MELARM'," *Proc. 4th International Symposium on Industrial Robots*, Tokyo, J, pp. 251–260, 1974.

[3] J.Y.S. Luh and Y.F. Zheng, "Constrained relations between two coordinated industrial robots for motion control," *International Journal of Robotics Research*, vol. 6, n. 3, pp. 60–70, 1987.

[4] M. Uchiyama and P. Dauchez, "A symmetric hybrid position/force control scheme for the coordination of two robots," *Proc. 1988 IEEE International Conference on Robotics and Automation*, Philadelphia, PA, pp. 350–356, 1988.

[5] Z. Li, P. Hsu, and S. Sastry, "Dynamic coordination of a multiple robotic system with point contact," *Proc. 1988 American Control Conference*, Atlanta, GA, pp. 505–510, 1988.

[6] J.T. Wen and K. Kreutz, "Motion and force control for multiple cooperative manipulators," *Proc. 1989 IEEE International Conference on Robotics and Automation*, Scottsdale, AZ, pp. 1246–1251, 1989.

[7] P. Chiacchio, S. Chiaverini, and B. Siciliano, "Dexterous reconfiguration of a two-arm robot system," *Proc. IEE International Conference on Control '91*, Edinburgh, GB, pp. 347–351, March 1991.

[8] P. Chiacchio, S. Chiaverini, and B. Siciliano, "Cooperative control schemes for multiple robot manipulator systems," *Proc. 1992 IEEE International Conference on Robotics and Automation*, Nice, F, pp. 2218–2223, 1992.

[9] B. Siciliano, "A closed-loop inverse kinematic scheme for on-line joint-based robot control," *Robotica*, vol. 8, pp. 231–243, 1990.

[10] P. Chiacchio, S. Chiaverini, L. Sciavicco, and B. Siciliano, "Closed-loop inverse kinematics schemes for constrained redundant manipulators with task space augmentation and task priority strategy," *International Journal of Robotics Research*, vol. 10, no. 4, pp. 410–425, 1991.

[11] Y. Nakamura and H. Hanafusa, "Inverse kinematic solution with singularity robustness for robot manipulator control," *ASME J. of Dynamic Systems, Measurements, and Control*, vol. 108, pp. 163–171, 1986.

[12] P. Chiacchio, S. Chiaverini, L. Sciavicco, and B. Siciliano, "Global task space manipulability ellipsoids for multiple arm systems," *IEEE Transactions on Robotics and Automation*, vol. 7, no. 5, pp. 678–685, 1991.

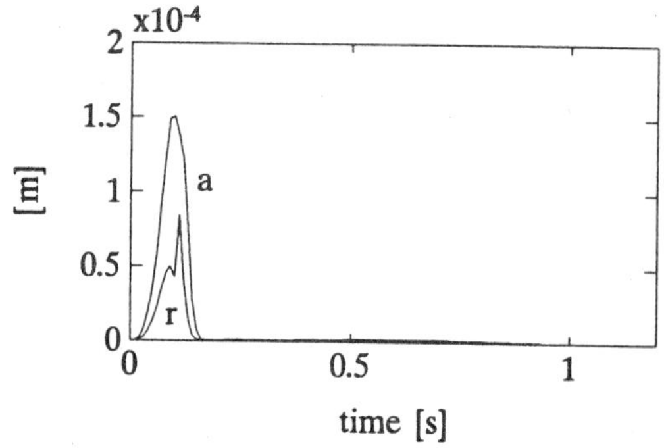

Fig. 1 — Norm of position errors; (a) absolute, (r) relative.

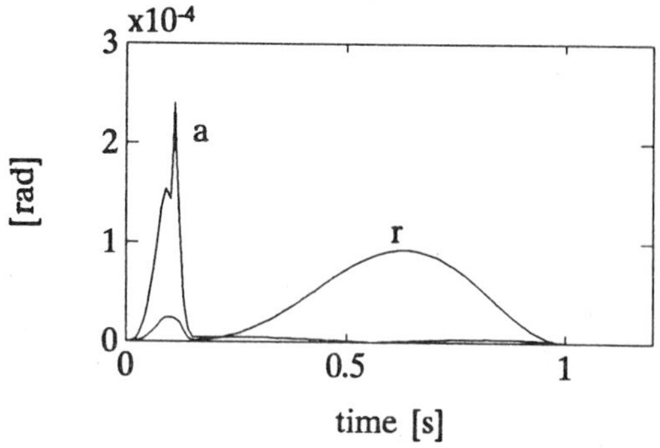

Fig. 2 — Norm of orientation errors; (a) absolute, (r) relative.

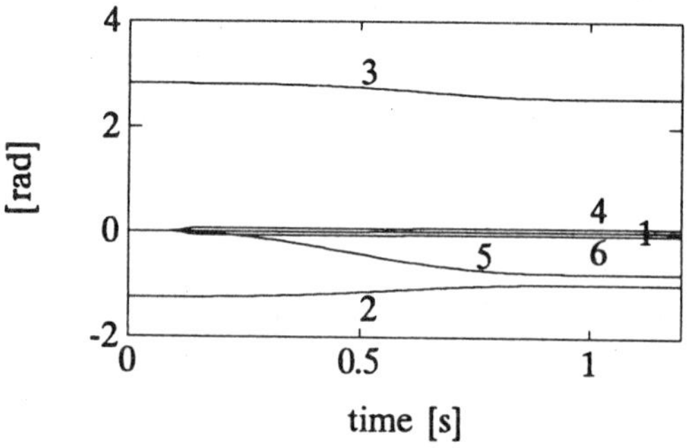

Fig. 3 — Joint variables of manipulator # 1.

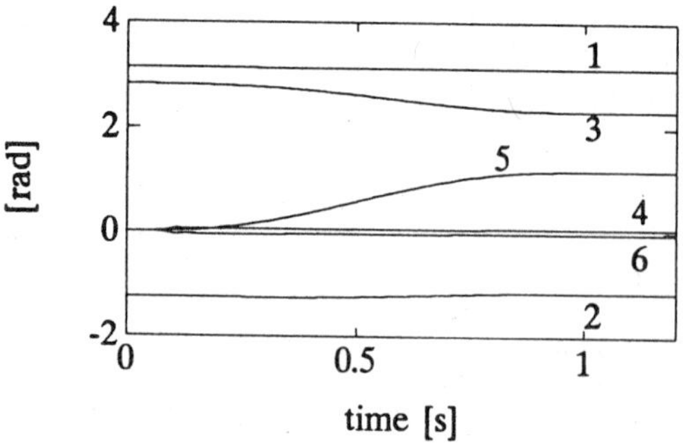

Fig. 4 — Joint variables of manipulator # 2.

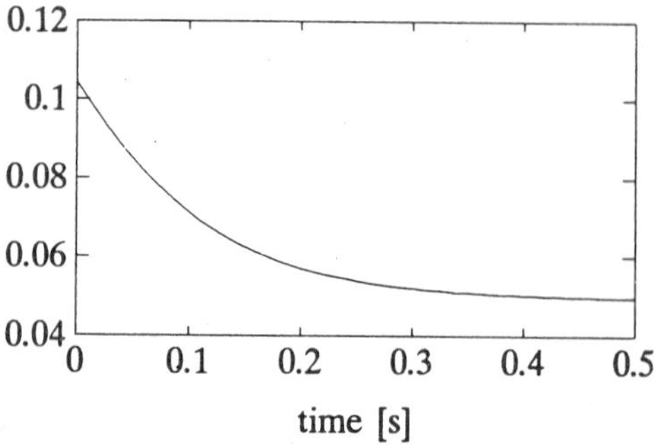

Fig. 5 — Constraint variable.

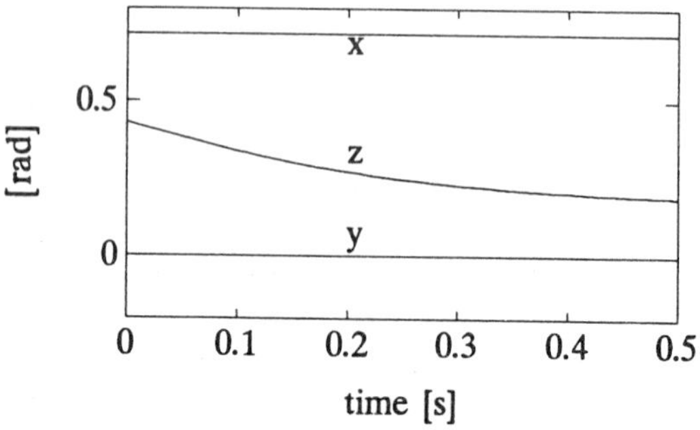

Fig. 6 — Absolute position coordinates.

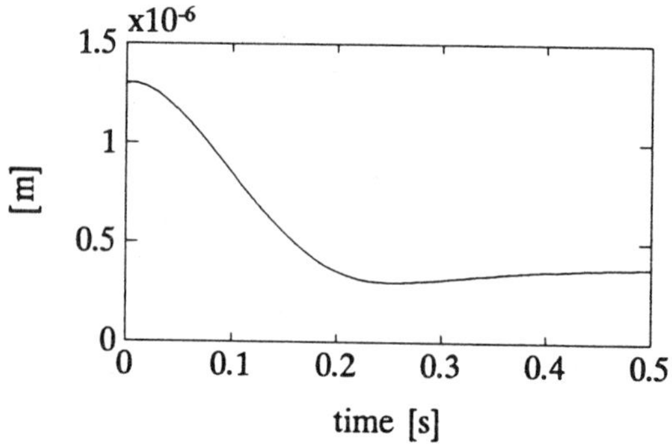

Fig. 7 — Norm of relative position error.

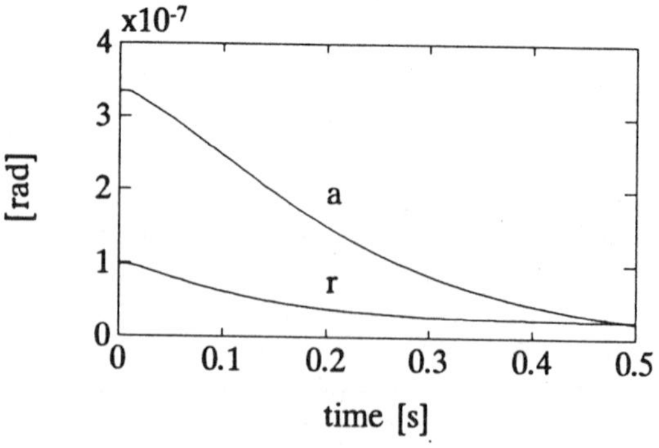

Fig. 8 — Norm of orientation errors; (a) absolute, (r) relative.

Proceedings of the
American Control Conference
San Francisco, California • June 1993

Adaptive Resolution of Conflicts in Multimanipulator Systems

Ping Hsu †

Department of Electrical Engineering
San Jose State University
San Jose, CA 95192

Abstract

The main problem of controlling a multiple manipulator system is the conflicting actions between the manipulators. This conflicting action is often due to geometric modeling error or, in the case of independently controlled system, mismatch between the reference trajectories of the controllers. The proposed control scheme resolves the conflicting actions via a 'mutual learning' process. The adaptive mechanism of each controller modifies its reference trajectory so as to adapt to others. It is shown that a common reference trajectory will eventually be reached by all the controllers. This adaptation process is carried out without explicit communication between the controllers. The proposed scheme was verified by computer simulations and experiments on a dual-manipulator system.

1. Introduction

A great deal of research efforts have been devoted to the control of multiple manipulator systems in recent years (see, for example, [1]-[8]). This trend was motivated by the fact that a multiple manipulator system provides higher flexibility in automated manufacturing and unstructured environment. Most the existing control schemes are model based and centralized. Here we define 'centralized' as a single controller oversees and controls the operation of each and every manipulator in the system. Under the ideal condition of having an exact mode of the system, a properly designed centralized controller is able to avoid the conflicting actions between the manipulators [6]. In a real system, however, modeling errors always exist and, in the case of a multiple manipulator system controlled by a number of independent controllers, a real-time communication channel between the controllers at servo level is not always available or desirable (the requirement of such a channel makes the system less flexible). In these cases, conflicting actions are prone to occur. Consider the following two conditions:

(1) If the distance between two manipulators' bases is not precisely known, an attempt of cooperatively lifting an object will result in excessive compression or stretching force. In a fixed configuration multi-manipulator system, such a modeling error can be eliminated by a careful verification process. For a greater flexibility in task planning, it is desirable to have a low-level controller that is capable of adjusting the system model so as to adapt to the environment.

(2) When a number of independently controlled manipulators engaging a cooperative task, the controllers may be instructed to follow a number of mismatched trajectories. This is the case when each controller has an independent trajectory planner which accepts high-level command (e.g., move object X from point A to point B) from a common task planner. The case of two human operators using two joysticks to steer two manipulators to carry a single object is also an example of this condition.

The objective of this research is to develop a 'self-adjusting' controller capable of minimizing the conflicting actions between manipulators due to modeling error or discrepancy in the reference trajectories as described in the above two conditions. By lumping the geometric modeling error into the mismatch between reference trajectories, we are able to treat the problems associated with these two conditions in the same way. For example, the modeling error of the distance between two bases of the manipulators in the earlier example can be treated in the same way as treating a system with an exact model but two conflicting reference trajectories.

In developing the proposed scheme, we first linearize each manipulator's dynamics in the end-effector coordinate space by nonlinearity cancellation. This step simplifies the problem so that a linear adaptive scheme can be applied. The philosophy of the proposed scheme is different from the typical adaptive scheme in that a typical adaptive scheme estimates an unknown parameter vector while the proposed scheme minimizes the difference between trajectory parameter vectors via a 'mutual learning' process.

The following is an outline of this paper. Dynamic equation of a multiple manipulator system with a linearizing control law is derived in Section 2.1. In Section 2.2 and 2.3 the adaptive mechanism is introduced and the over-all system behavior is rigorously established. The parameter convergence property is discussed in Section 2.4. A simulation result is presented in Section 3 and experimental results are presented in Section 4.

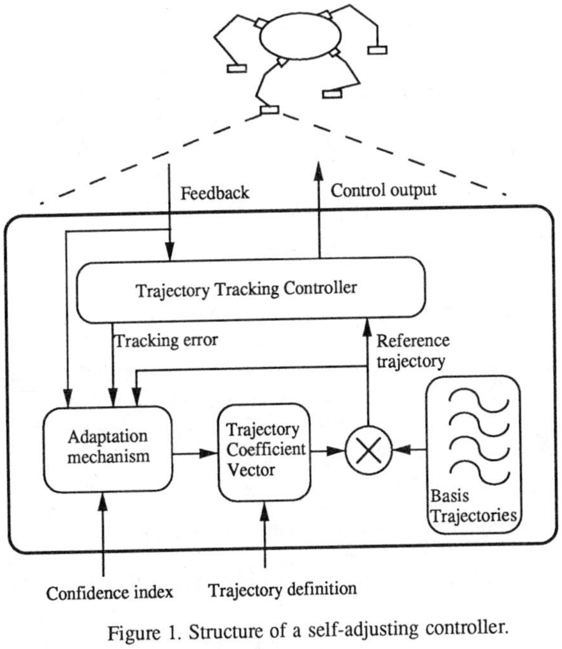

Figure 1. Structure of a self-adjusting controller.

† Research supported by NSF under Research Initiation grant No. MSS-8909732

2. Controller Structure

Consider a system of n manipulators carrying an object as shown in Figure 1. Each manipulator is controlled by a dedicated controller. In each controller, there are four elements: a *trajectory tracking controller*, a *basis function set*, a *trajectory vector*, an *adaptation mechanism*. These elements will be discussed in the following sections.

2.1 Trajectory Tracking Controller

The dynamic equation of the ith mechanical manipulator in a multiple manipulator system can be written in the following form

$$M_i\ddot{X}_i + N_i = [J_i^T]^{-1}\tau_i \tag{1}$$

where X is the position and orientation of the object being carried, M is a configuration dependent mass matrix, N represents centrifugal, Coriolis, gravitational force, τ is the input joint torque vector, and J is the configuration dependent Jacobian matrix of the manipulator's forward kinematic function. Manipulator dynamics described by (1) can be linearized by the "Resolved Acceleration" control law [9] or, in a more general term, the "Exact Linearization" method [10] as follows. Consider the following linearizing trajectory tracking control law

$$\tau_i = (J_i^T)\left[M_i(\ddot{X}_{ri}-K_v\dot{E}_i-K_pE_i) + N_i\right] \tag{2}$$

where X_{ri} is the reference trajectory, $E_i \triangleq X-X_{ri}$ is the tracking error, and K_v and K_p are constant diagonal matrices. For simplicity, we only consider the control of one of the coordinate system variables (e.g., x coordinate in the $X=[x,y,z]^T$ coordinate system) in the sequel. With the control law (2), the closed loop system equation takes the following form

$$\ddot{x} = \ddot{x}_{ri} - k_v\dot{e}_i - k_pe_i \tag{3}$$

or

$$\ddot{e}_i + k_v\dot{e}_i + k_pe_i = 0 \tag{4}$$

where only one of the coordinate variables is shown. With properly chosen k_v and k_p, equation (4) guarantees the convergence of the tracking error.

If (i) all manipulators' grippers are rigidly attached to the object, (ii) the same object coordinate x is used by all controllers, (iii) mass of the object is negligible (when compared to the masses of the manipulators) or it is modeled as part of the gripper mass of the manipulators, and (iv) all controllers are running the same control law (2) (the configuration dependent terms are different for each manipulator, of course), then the closed loop dynamic of the entire multiple manipulator system can be expressed as

$$\ddot{e} + k_v\dot{e} + k_pe = 0. \tag{5}$$

This case can be thought of as a single controller implemented in a parallel fashion. We now consider the case that x_{ri} $(1 \le i \le n)$ are not identical. From the assumption that all grippers are rigidly attached to the object and all controllers use the same object coordinate x, we can combine equation of the form (3) for $1 \le i \le n$ as follows

$$\ddot{x} = \frac{1}{n}\sum_{i=1}^{n}\left[\ddot{x}_{ri} - k_v\dot{e}_i - k_pe_i\right] \tag{6}$$

$$= \left[\ddot{x}_{r1} - k_v\dot{e}_1 - k_pe_1\right] + \frac{1}{n}\sum_{i=2}^{n}\left[\ddot{\xi}_{i1} + k_v\dot{\xi}_{i1} + k_p\xi_{i1}\right]$$

where $e_1 \triangleq x-x_{r1}$ represents the tracking error of the first manipulator and $\xi_{i1} \triangleq x_{ri}-x_{r1}$ is the mismatch between the first controller's reference trajectory and that of the ith controller. The second equality in (6) is obtained with the substitution

$$e_i = x_i-x_{ri} = (x-x_{r1})-(x_{ri}-x_{r1}) = e_1-\xi_{i1}.$$

Equation (6) can be rearranged into the following from:

$$\ddot{e}_1 + k_v\dot{e}_1 + k_pe_1 = \frac{1}{n}\sum_{i=2}^{n}\left[\ddot{\xi}_{i1} + k_v\dot{\xi}_{i1} + k_p\xi_{i1}\right]. \tag{7}$$

The above equation describes how the error dynamics of the first manipulator is affected by the mismatches of the reference trajectories. A similar expression can be obtained for each manipulator in the system.

2.2 Basis Functions and Trajectory Vector

As indicated in Figure (1), the task trajectory is generated by linearly combining elements of a bounded linearly independent basis function set $(W(t))$, i.e.,

$$x_{ti}(t) = \Phi_i^TW(t) \tag{8}$$

where Φ_i is the trajectory vector of the ith controller. This parameter is to be set by the ith *task planner* which determines a task trajectory for performing a certain task. The task planning process is executed mostly by way of computer algorithms which will not be discussed in this paper. The task trajectory x_{ti} is then fed to a second-order system of the following form:

$$\ddot{x}_{ri} + k_v\dot{x}_{ri} + k_px_{ri} = x_{ti} \tag{9}$$

The state variables of this second-order system $(x_{ri}, \dot{x}_{ri})$ and $\ddot{x}_{ri}$ are used as reference signals by the *trajectory tracking controller* described earlier in Section 2.1.

2.3 Adaptation Mechanism

The adaptation mechanism (as shown in Figure (1)) adjusts the trajectory vector so that all Φ_i eventually converge to a common value (i.e., a common reference trajectory) so that the error equation (5) is realized. This property will be shown in this section.

From (8), (9), and the definition $\xi_{i1} \triangleq x_{ri}-x_{r1}$, we see that

$$\ddot{\xi}_{i1} + k_v\dot{\xi}_{i1} + k_p\xi_{i1} = x_{ti} - x_{t1} \tag{10}$$

$$= (\Phi_i-\Phi_1)^TW \triangleq \Psi_{i1}^TW$$

Substituting (10) into (7), we obtain

$$\ddot{e}_1 + k_v\dot{e}_1 + k_pe_1 = \frac{1}{n}\sum_{i=2}^{n}\Psi_{i1}^TW. \tag{11}$$

The state space form of the above equation is

$$\dot{e}_1 = Ae_1 + b(\sum_{i=2}^{n}\Psi_{i1})^TW \tag{12}$$

where

$$e_1 \triangleq \begin{bmatrix} e_1 \\ \dot{e}_1 \end{bmatrix}, \; A \triangleq \begin{bmatrix} 0 & 1 \\ -k_p & -k_v \end{bmatrix}, \text{ and } b \triangleq \begin{bmatrix} 0 \\ 1/n \end{bmatrix} \tag{13}$$

Similarly, a general expression of e_j is obtained:

$$\dot{e}_j = Ae_j + b(\sum_{i=1, i\neq j}^{n}\Psi_{ij})^TW, \quad 1 \le j \le n. \tag{14}$$

Summing all equations of the form of (14), we get the following combined error equation

$$\frac{d}{dt}\left[\sum_{i=1}^{n}e_i\right] = A\left[\sum_{i=1}^{n}e_i\right] \tag{15}$$

where we used the fact that $\Psi_{ij} = -\Psi_{ji}$. Since A is exponentially stable, the above equation implies that

$$\sum_{j=1}^{n}e_j = 0 \tag{16}$$

at steady state. We now show that, if each trajectory parameter is updated according to the following update law,

$$\dot{\Phi}_i = Wb^TPe_i \tag{17}$$

then all e_i converge to zero. The P matrix in the above equation satisfies the following equation.

$$PA + A^TP = -Q, \text{ where } P,Q>0. \tag{18}$$

Consider the following Lyapunov function.

$$V_i=\frac{1}{2}e_i^T P e_i+\frac{(n-1)^2}{n}\left[\frac{1}{n-1}\sum_{j=1,j\neq i}^{n}\Phi_j-\Phi_i\right]^T\left[\frac{1}{n-1}\sum_{j=1,j\neq i}^{n}\Phi_j-\Phi_i\right] \tag{19}$$

The time derivative of V_i is

$$\begin{aligned}\dot{V}_i &= -\frac{1}{2}e_i^T Q e_i + W^T\left[\sum_{j=1,j\neq i}^{n}\Psi_{ji}\right]b^T P e_i + \qquad (20)\\ &\frac{(n-1)^2}{n}\left[\frac{1}{n-1}\sum_{j=1,j\neq i}^{n}\Phi_j-\Phi_i\right]^T\left[\frac{1}{n-1}Wb^T P\sum_{j=1}^{n}e_j-\frac{n}{n-1}Wb^T P e_i\right]\\ &= -\frac{1}{2}e_i^T Q e_i + W^T\left[\sum_{j=1,j\neq i}^{n}\Psi_{ji}\right]b^T P e_i\\ &\quad -\frac{(n-1)}{n}\left[\sum_{j=1,j\neq i}^{n}\Psi_{ji}\right]^T\left[\frac{n}{n-1}Wb^T P e_i\right]\\ &= -\frac{1}{2}e_i^T Q e_i\end{aligned}$$

where the second equality is from equation (16) and the fact that $\Psi_{ij}=-\Psi_{ji}$. Note that since the convergence of (15) is independent of the adaptation process, the above Lyapunov analysis is valid. Form (14), (19), (20), and the boundness assumption on the $W(t)$, we conclude that $\dot{e}_i$ is bounded and, hence, e_i converges to zero.

Remarks:

(1) In the above analysis, the interaction forces between the manipulators and the object are not considered. In general, proper response in motion control does not imply good behavior in force response. A high conflicting force and a good tracking performance can coexist. The proposed scheme is, however, immune from this undesirable situation. Note that if e_i converges to zero, the actuator force prescribed by the linearizing control law (2) will be limited to an acceleration feedforward term and a nonlinear cancellation term. Both of these terms will behave properly if the manipulator trajectory (i.e., the manipulator configuration) is properly controlled .

(2) Control law (2) and update law (17) of the ith controller do not require the state variables of other controllers.

(3) An interpretation of the Lyapunov function (19) is as follows. Each controller can be thought of as a spring-damper mechanism attached to the mass on one end and an imaginary point on the other end. This imaginary point moves along the task trajectory $x_{ti}(t)$. The second term in the Lyapunov function, i.e.,

$$\left[\frac{1}{n-1}\sum_{j=1,j\neq i}^{n}\Phi_j-\Phi_i\right]^T\left[\frac{1}{n-1}\sum_{j=1,j\neq i}^{n}\Phi_j-\Phi_i\right] \tag{21}$$

represents the distance between the ith imaginary steering point and a point representing the combined effect of all other steering points.

2.4 Parameter Convergence

Recall that $W(t)$ is a set of bounded linearly independent functions. If this independence is uniform in time, $W(t)$ satisfies a persistent excitation condition [8]. This condition, (19), and (20), guarantee that

$$\lim_{t\to\infty}\left[\frac{1}{n-1}\sum_{j=1,j\neq i}^{n}\Phi_j-\Phi_i\right] = 0, \qquad \text{for all } i. \tag{22}$$

The above equation can be arranged in a matrix form as follows

$$\lim_{t\to\infty}\begin{bmatrix} -I & \frac{I}{n-1} & \cdot & \frac{I}{n-1}\\ \frac{I}{n-1} & -I & \cdot & \frac{I}{n-1}\\ \cdot & \cdot & \cdot & \cdot\\ \frac{I}{n-1} & \frac{I}{n-1} & \cdot & -I\end{bmatrix}\begin{bmatrix}\Phi_1\\ \Phi_2\\ \cdot\\ \Phi_n\end{bmatrix} = 0 \tag{23}$$

where I is the identity matrix conform to Φ_i. It can be verified that the null space of the above matrix is the span of all vectors of the form $[\Phi_o,\Phi_o,\cdots,\Phi_o]^T$ where Φ_o is an arbitrary vector in the parameter space. This result implies that all parameter vectors converge to a common one. Note that this property is unlike in a typical adaptive control scheme where the parameter vector is updated to approach to a 'true' parameter vector.

It may appear that the control scheme has no control of the final common trajectory parameter vector (i.e., Φ_o). The following analysis shows that final trajectory is 'optimal' in a sense. Consider the following definitions:

$$\Delta\Phi_j \triangleq \lim_{t\to\infty}\Phi_j(t)-\Phi_j(0). \tag{24}$$

$\Delta\Phi_j$ is the amount of change of the jth parameter in the adaptation process. If all the initial error in (15) are set to zero, then

$$\sum_{j=0}^{n}\Delta\Phi_j = \int_0^\infty\left[\sum_{j=0}^{n}\dot{\Phi}_j\right]dt = \int_0^\infty\left[Wb^T P\sum_{j=0}^{k}e_j\right]dt = 0 \tag{25}$$

where we used equation (16) and (17). This equation implies that the point (in the parameter space) corresponding to the final trajectory is at the center of mass of the system of the points corresponding to the initial trajectory parameters as shown in the following figure.

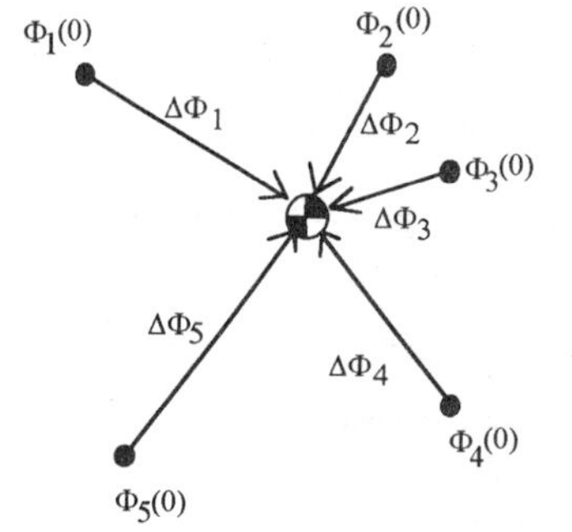

Figure 2. Relative position of the initial and the final parameter vectors.

3. Simulations

A simulation package SIMNON is used in simulating the proposed adaptive scheme. We simulated a 3-manipulator system. The trajectory in each controller is determined by the inner product of a two-dimensional parameter vector with the following base set

$$W(t) = \left[\cos(2t),\ \sin(5t)\right]^T.$$

In this particular simulation, the parameters' initial conditions are set to $\Phi_1(0)=[5,1]^T$, $\Phi_2(0)=[1,5]^T$, and $\Phi_3(0)=[-1,-1]^T$. Figure 3 shows the reference trajectories determined by these initial conditions without the proposed adaptation process. Figure 4 shows the diminishing differences between the trajectories as the adaptation mechanism adjusting the parameters. Further convergence of the reference trajectories is shown in Figure 5 which is a continuation of Figure 4. Figure 6 and 7 show the convergence of the parameters and the tracking errors. Figure 8 is a plot of parameters' trajectory in the parameter space. It's easy to see that the final parameter is located at the center of mass of the triangle determined by the initial conditions.

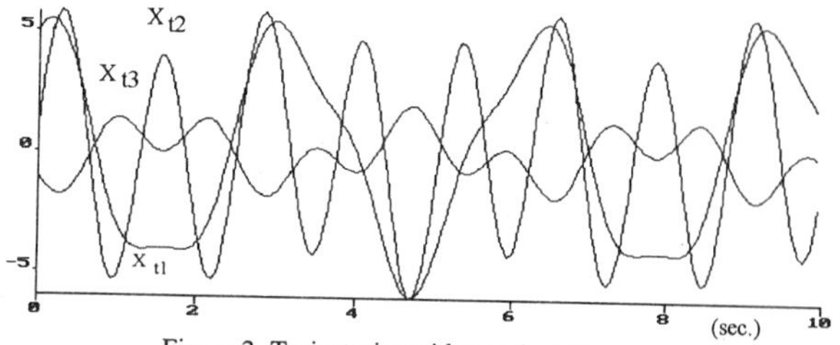

Figure 3. Trajectories without adaptation.

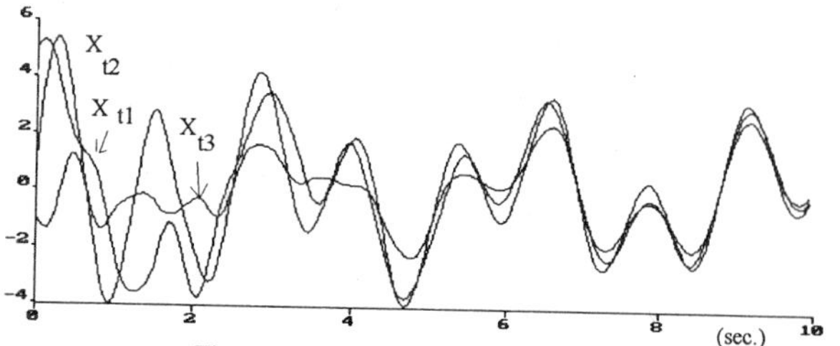

Figure 4. Trajectories with adaptation.

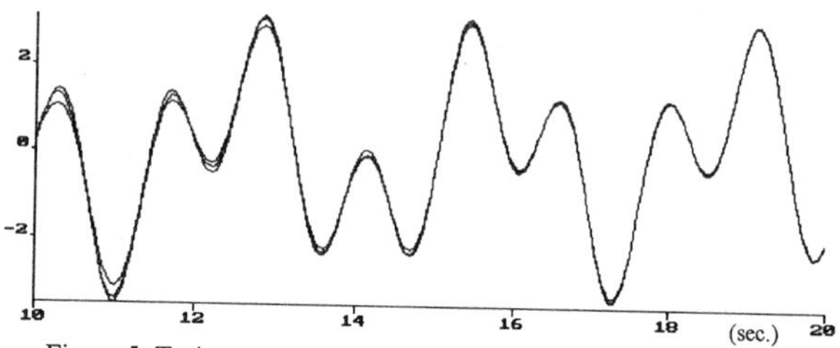

Figure 5. Trajectory with adaptation (continued from Figure 4).

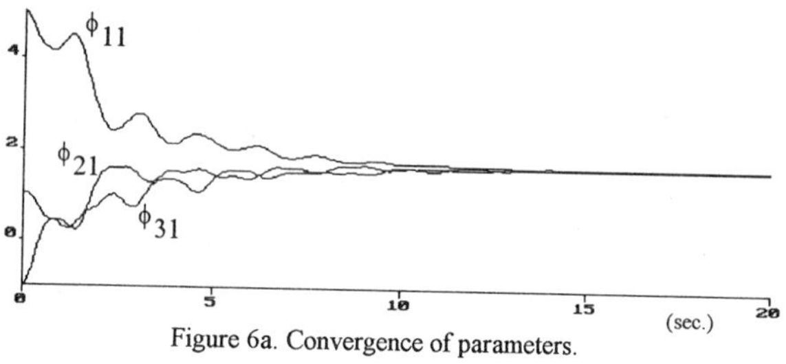

Figure 6a. Convergence of parameters.

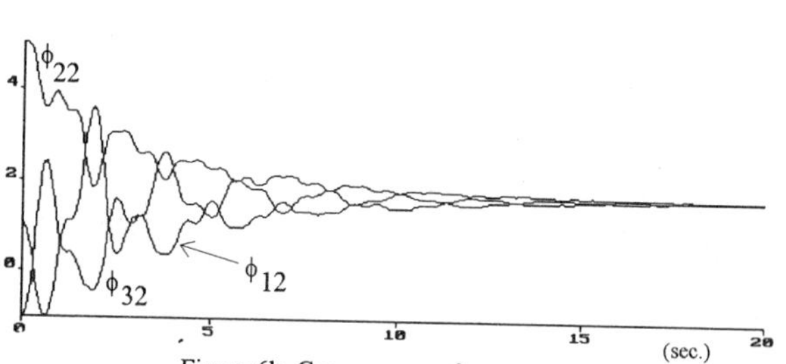

Figure 6b. Convergence of parameters.

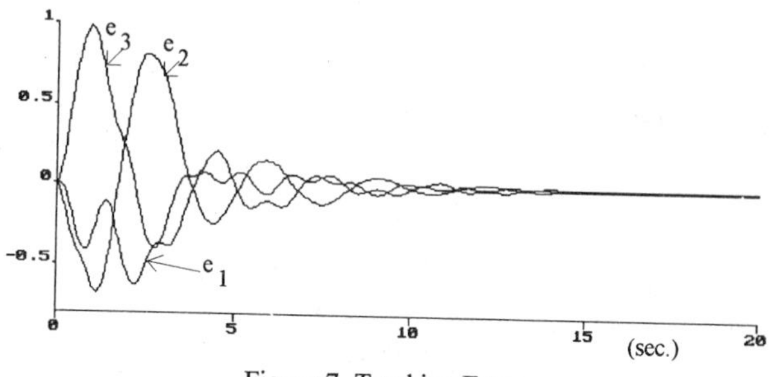

Figure 7. Tracking Error.

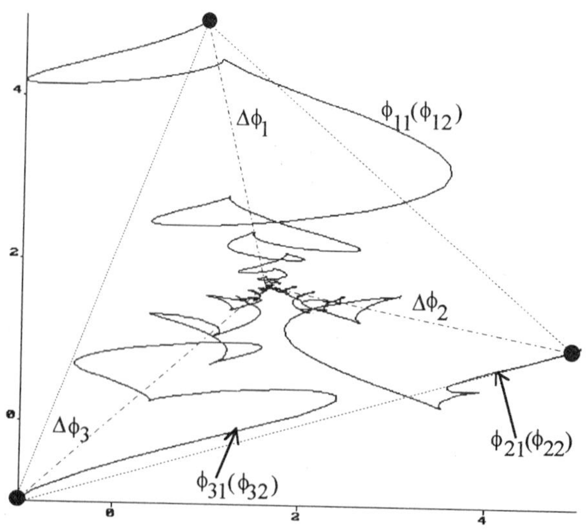

Figure 8 Pararameter trajectories in the parameter space

4. Experimental Results

A planar dual-manipulator system is used for testing the proposed scheme. The manipulators are direct-drive SCARA type. The control algorithm is implemented on a TMS320C30 based processor board which resides on an IBM PC bus. A more detailed description on this system can be found in [6]. The control variables are x and y coordinates of the contact point of the two manipulators. The task trajectories in the x and y direction of each controller are

$$x_t(t) = a_1 + a_2\sin(3.14t)$$

$$y_t(t) = a_3 + a_4\cos(3.14t)$$

Figure 9 to 11 are results from a typical experiment. The parameter vector (i.e., $[a_1, a_2, a_3, a_4]$) of two controllers are initially set at different values. As shown in Figure 9, corresponding parameters converge to each other. The gap between the final values of the corresponding parameters is due to a threshold function on the tracking error in the adaptation mechanism. This threshold function keeps the parameters from drifting. In this experiment, the threshold level was set at 2mm. Figure 10 shows the convergence of the reference trajectories in the x and y direction. Figure 11a and 11b show the x and y direction tracking errors. The large initial tracking errors on both controllers indicate the conflicting actions.

To test the scheme's ability to adapt to modeling error, we moved the manipulators 2cm closer than the model in the control program and repeated the same experiment. In this experiment, as indicated in Figure 12, the x direction reference trajectories of the two controllers converge to 2cm of each other to compensate for the modeling error. The tracking error in this experiment is similar to the one shown in Figure 11.

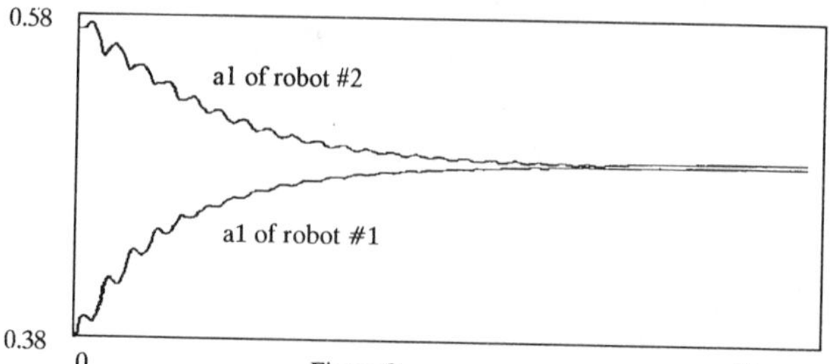

Figure 9a.

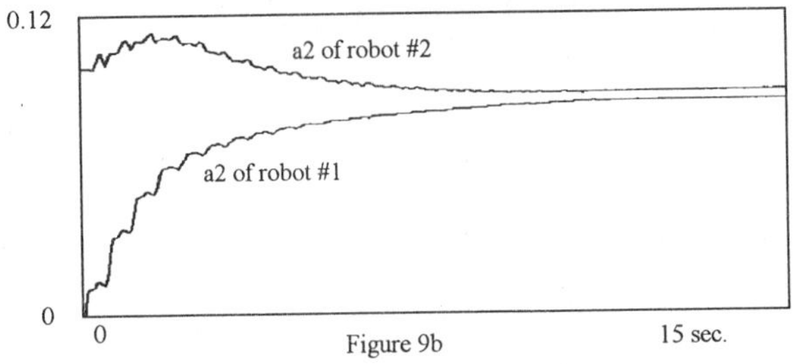

Figure 9b

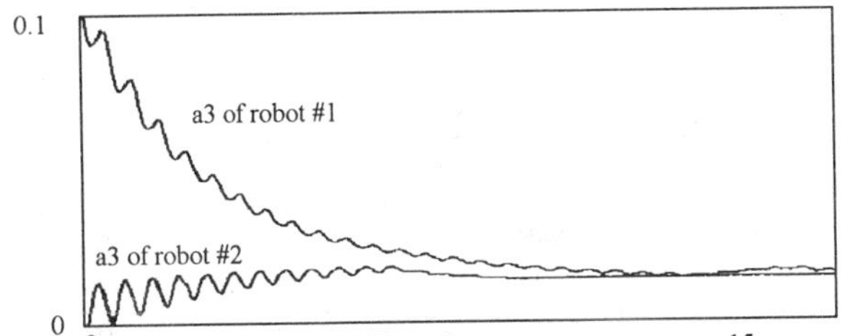

Figure 9c

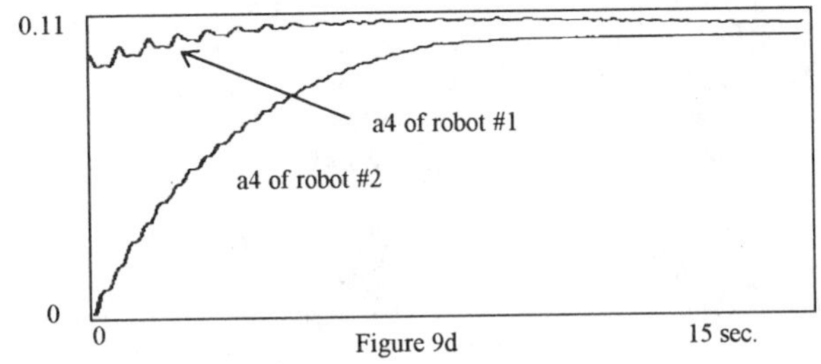

Figure 9d

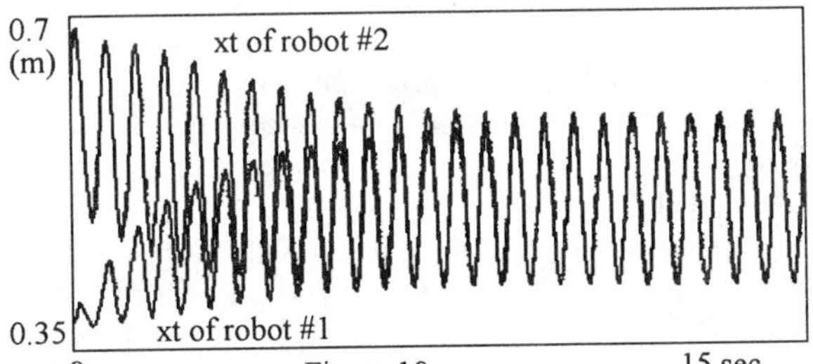

Figure 10a

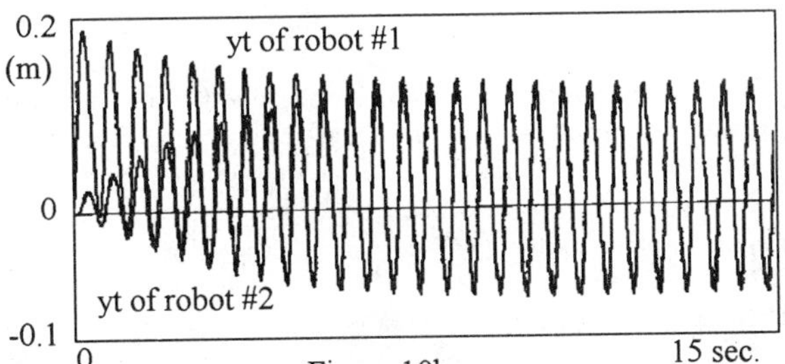

Figure 10b

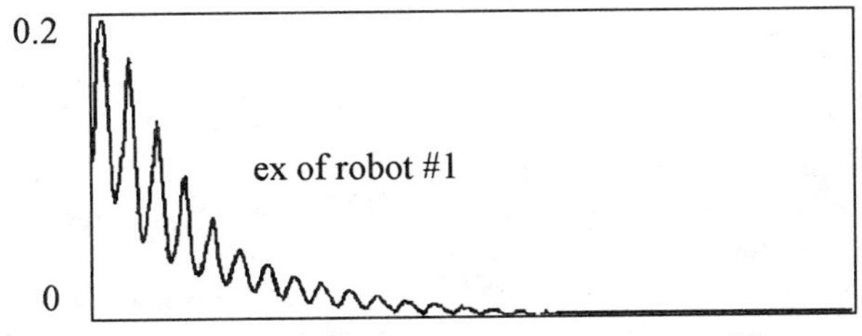

Figure 11a

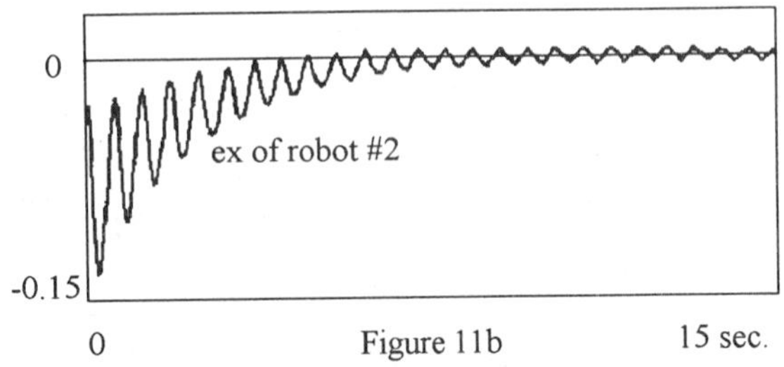

Figure 11b

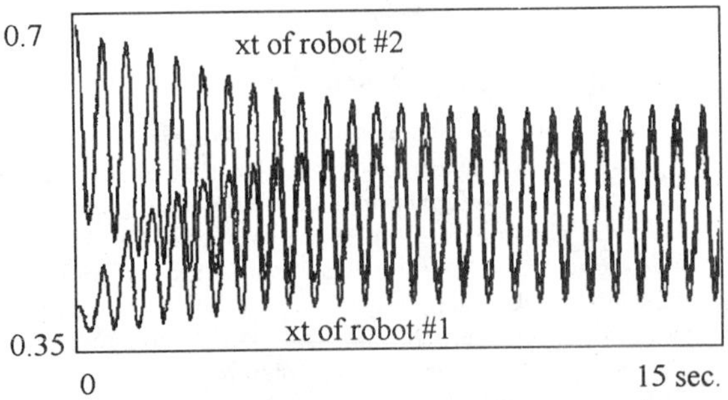

Figure 12. Reference trajectories with 2cm modeling error.

5. Summary

An adaptive control scheme for a multiple manipulator system is proposed. In this scheme, each controller updates its reference trajectory so as to accommodate other controllers' trajectories. A common reference trajectory will be eventually reached as the result of this 'mutual learning' process. The scheme is tested by computer simulations and actual experiment.

6. References

[1] Nakamura,Y., K. Nagai and T. Yoshikawa. 1987. "Mechanics of coordinative manipulation by multiple robotic mechanisms." Proc. *IEEE Int. Conf. on Robotics and Automation.* pp991-998.

[2] Zheng Y.F. and J.Y.S. Luh. 1988. "Optimal Load Distribution for Two Industrial Robots Handing a Single Object." Proc. *IEEE Int. Conf. on Robotics and Automation,* pp344-349.

[3] Kim, K.I. and Y.F. Zheng "Unknown Load Distribution of Two Industrial Robots", *1991 IEEE International Conference on Robotics and Automation.* Sacramento, California. April 1991. pp. 992-997.

[4] Pittelkau, M.E. 1988. "Adaptive Load-Sharing Force Control for Two-arm Manipulators," Proc. *IEEE Int. Conf. on Robotics and Automation,* pp498-503.

[5] Hsu, P., "Coordinated Control of Multi-Manipulator Systems", *1989 IEEE International Conference on Robotics and Automation.* Phoenix, Arizona. May 1989. pp.1234-1239.

[6] Hsu, P. and Steven Su "Coordinated Control of Multi-Manipulator Systems -- Experimental Results", *1992 IEEE International Conference on Robotics and Automation.* Nice, France, May 1992. pp.2199-2204.

[7] Tao, J.M. and J.Y.S. Luh, "Position and Force Control for Two Coordinating Robots", *1991 IEEE International Conference on Robotics and Automation.* Sacramento, California. April 1991. pp. 176-181.

[8] Kumar, V., X. Yun, E. Paljug, and N. Sarkar, "Control of Contact Conditions for Manipulation with Multiple Robotic Systems", *1991 IEEE International Conference on Robotics and Automation.* Sacramento, California. April 1991. pp. 170-175.

[9] Luh, J.Y.S., M.W. Walker, and R.P.C. Paul. 1980. "Resolved-Acceleration Control of Mechanical Manipulators." *IEEE Tans. AC 25, 3.* pp468-474.

[10] Isidori, Alberto. *Nonlinear Control System.* Springer-Verlag, 1989.

WM6 - 11:00

Proceedings of the
American Control Conference
San Francisco, California • June 1993

A Direct Adaptive Control Scheme for Disk File Servos [1]

James McCormick and *Roberto Horowitz*

Computer Mechanics Laboratory
Department of Mechanical Engineering
University of California at Berkeley
Berkeley, CA 94720

Abstract

This paper presents a direct adaptive control scheme for disk file track following servos. The scheme is designed to enhance the performance of a fixed observer based controller in the face of plant uncertainty and operating in a stochastic environment. The compensator used in each disk file is individually tuned with the use of an add-on adjustable FIR filter, **Q**, utilizing a linear fractional transformation (LFT) known as the Youla-Kucera parameterization. Similarly, the difference between the actual disk drive dynamics and the nominal model is characterized by an unknown transfer function, **S**, using the Youla-Kucera parameterization applied to the plant rather than to the compensator. The adaptive scheme utilizes two parameter adaptation algorithms running simultaneously. An recursive least squares (RLS) algorithm is used to identify the transfer function **S** which quantifies the mismatch between the actual disk file and the nominal disk file model. A second parameter adaptation algorithm is used to identify the finite impulse response (FIR) compensator **Q**. The goal of the overall adaptive controller is to minimize the specified $\mathcal{H}_2$ cost.

1 INTRODUCTION

Conventional servo systems for mechanical positioning devices, such as disk file actuators, are fixed in the sense that the compensator structure and its parameters are constant. Generally the same compensator is used in different units of the same product line. A so called *nominal model* is used as the controlled plant when designing the compensator. This nominal model encompasses the dynamic behavior of the average system in the product line. Moreover, some assumptions must be made regarding the nature and intensity of the stochastic disturbances which affect the system. These assumptions are generally referred to as the noise model. In most cases, a unique fixed compensator cannot accommodate the variations that exist within different units of a product line, nor the different operating conditions that a particular unit is subjected to, while functioning in an optimal manner.

The presence of dynamic variations in the product line motivates the need for a robust feedback controller design. We will assume in this paper that a nominal compensator has been designed which is robust to all plant variations within a product line. In the proposed control scheme an add-on compensator is inserted in the feedback loop which acts in tandem with the nominal compensator. The parameters of the add-on compensator are adjusted by a direct Parameter Adaptation Algorithm (PAA), in order to attain an optimal system performance for that particular plant. Thus, in this manner, the overall control system is capable of maintaining a high level of performance in the presence of variations in the dynamics of the units of the product line, under different operating conditions.

The scheme presented in this paper is inspired by the ideas presented in [11] and [12]. [11] introduced a direct adaptive disturbance estimate feedback (DEF) controller which feeds back a disturbance estimate via an adaptive add-on compensator, using the Youla-Kucera parametrization [14, 7, 13]. However, the add-on Youla parameter in the case of the DEF controller only parameterizes the set of stabilizing controllers for the nominal plant, rather than for the actual plant. As a result, constraining the add-on Youla parameter **Q** to be rational and stable does not necessarily results in an overall stabilizing controller for the actual plant. This problem was addressed in [12], where the idea of estimating a plant Youla parameter was introduced, utilizing dual results to the class of stabilizing controllers. This idea was exploited in [12, 6] in the formulation of indirect adaptive control schemes where the plant-Youla parameter, **S**, is identified and the controller-Youla parameter **Q** is subsequently synthesized.

This paper presents a new direct adaptive control scheme for stochastic regulators in which the plant Youla parameter **S**, the noise model, and the controller Youla parameter **Q** are simultaneously updated using two recursive parameter adaptation algorithms. As in [11] the controller Youla parameter **Q** is realized as a Finite Impulse Response (FIR) filter. However, this scheme differs from the one presented in [11] in that the add-on adaptive compensator does parametrize a set of stabilizing controllers for the actual plant. Moreover, the adaptive scheme does not require the on-line solution of either a Bezout or a Riccati equation, as in [12, 6] and many other indirect adaptive schemes for stochastic systems [4]. It is however necessary that the nominal compensator be robust to all possible dynamic variations in the product line and that the parameter estimation algorithm for the plant Youla parameter **S** generate asymptotically stable linear time varying filters.

This paper is organized as follows. In section 2 we review some well known results in control theory that are used in the formulation of adaptive control law. In section 3 the solution of an optimal FIR filter **Q** which minimizes an $\mathcal{H}^2$ cost function and adaptive schemes for estimating the Youla plant parameter **S** are presented. The overall adaptive control algorithm is presented in section 4. A simulation study is presented in Section 5. Conclusions are given in section 6.

2 Preliminaries

In this paper we will consider *discrete time* feedback systems as the one shown in Fig. 1, where **G** denotes the plant rational and proper transfer function, **K** denotes the compensator real rational and proper transfer function, and the plant and compensator outputs, $y(k)$, $u(k) \in \Re^m$ and k is the sampling time control index. The disturbance input $w(k) = [w_1^T(k)\ w_2^T(k)]^T$ in Fig. 1 form a

[1]This work was supported by the IBM Corporation and a Research Grant from the U.C. Berkeley Computer Mechanics Laboratory

sequence of zero mean Gaussian stochastic vectors. We will use the notation $[\mathbf{G},\mathbf{K}]$ to denote the feedback system in Fig. 1. In general functions and filters in the time domain will be expressed as arguments of k or the delay operator, q^{-1}. The z-transform of a sequence $\{y(k)\}_1^\infty$, will be denoted by $\mathbf{y} := \mathcal{Z}[\{y(k)\}_1^\infty]$. In this paper we will use bold letters to denote Z-domain variables to distinguish them from their time domain counterparts. We will generally not include the z argument when using z-domain variables, unless it necessary for clarity.

In the disk file servo control problem, the signal $\mathbf{w}_2$ in Fig. 1 is referred to as the *track runout*, while the error signal $\mathbf{e}_2$ in the same figure is referred to as the *Position Error Signal* (PES). The closed loop sensitivity transfer function between $\mathbf{w}_2$ and e2 is commonly referred to as the *error rejection transfer function*. The frequency response of this transfer function is of paramount significance in specifying the performance of the servo system. In this paper we will consider as the performance criterion a (possibly frequency weighted) $\mathcal{H}_2$ cost functional of the position error signal and the control effort. Thus, defining the regulated variable z by

$$z = \begin{bmatrix} P_1 & P_{12} \\ P_{12}^T & P_2 \end{bmatrix} \begin{bmatrix} e_2 \\ u \end{bmatrix} = P \begin{bmatrix} e_2 \\ u \end{bmatrix}, \tag{2.1}$$

where P is weighting matrix. The control objective consists in designing the compensator $\mathbf{K}$ so that the feedback system $[\mathbf{G},\mathbf{K}]$ is stable and the variance

$$E\{|z|^2\} = E\{|z(k)|^2\} = \lim_{N\to\infty} 1/N \sum_{k=0}^{N} z^T(k)z(k) \tag{2.2}$$

is minimized. Notice that, if $P_{12} = P_2 = \mathbf{0}$ and $P_1 \geq 0$, the problem consists in the solution of a minimum variance servo. If the parameters of the plant and the noise model of the system are known, the solution of this problem is the well known Linear Quadratic Gaussian (LQG) compensator (cf. [8]). However, we assume in this paper that neither the plant parameters nor the noise model are known.

We will now introduce an additional condition regarding the class of plants that will be considered in this paper. Let us first define the *nominal feedback system* $[\mathbf{G}_o,\mathbf{K}_o]$, such as the one in Fig. 1, with the rational and proper transfer functions $\mathbf{G}_o$ and $\mathbf{K}_o$ in place of $\mathbf{G}$ and $\mathbf{K}$ respectively.

Definition 1 *The class $\mathcal{G}$ is the set of all rational and proper plants* $\mathbf{G}$ *in Fig. 1 which are stabilized by the nominal compensator* $\mathbf{K}_o$.

Assumption 2.1 *All plants to be controlled by the adaptive compensator,* $\mathbf{K}$ *belong to the class $\mathcal{G}$, where both* $\mathbf{G}_o$ *and* $\mathbf{K}_o$ *are known.*

In disk file actuator servo systems, the class $\mathcal{G}$ can be the set of all disk file actuators in a product line. In most cases, it is not difficult to satisfy the above assumption. Notice that we do not assume nor require that the performance of the nominal feedback system $[\mathbf{G}_o,\mathbf{K}_o]$ be optimal.

We will use the symbols $\mathcal{R}_p^m$ to denote the class of all $m \times m$ rational and proper transfer functions, $\mathcal{RH}_\infty^m$ to denote the class of all $m \times m$ rational, proper and stable (i.e. all poles inside the unit circle) transfer functions and $\mathcal{F}_n^m$ the class of all $m \times m$ finite impulse response filters of order n. [2]

Linear fractional transformations (LFT) were developed as a means for standarizing many different feedback arrangements. We will use this terminology to describe our control scheme. A linear fractional transformation (LFT) is denoted by:

$$F_L(\mathbf{J},\mathbf{Q}) = \mathbf{J}_{11} + \mathbf{J}_{12}\mathbf{Q}(\mathbf{I} - \mathbf{J}_{22}\,,\mathbf{Q})^{-1}\mathbf{J}_{21} \tag{2.3}$$

$$\mathbf{J} = \begin{bmatrix} \mathbf{J}_{11} & \mathbf{J}_{12} \\ \mathbf{J}_{21} & \mathbf{J}_{22} \end{bmatrix} \in \mathcal{R}_P^{2m}, \qquad \mathbf{Q} \in \mathcal{R}_P^m, \tag{2.4}$$

whenever $det(\mathbf{I} - \mathbf{J}_{22}\mathbf{Q}) \neq 0$, and is depicted in Fig. 2

The adaptive compensator, $\mathbf{K}$ in the feedback structure $[\mathbf{G},\mathbf{K}]$ depicted in Fig. 1 is given be the LFT structure in (2.3) with the additional constraints that $\mathbf{J}_{11} = \mathbf{K}_o$ and $\mathbf{Q} \in \mathcal{F}_N^m$. The parameters of the finite impulse response filter $\mathbf{Q}$ will be updated by a PAA which will be defined in Section 4. Notice that, if $\mathbf{Q} = \mathbf{0}$, $\mathbf{K} = \mathbf{K}_o$. The parameters of the blocks $\mathbf{J}_{21}$ and $\mathbf{J}_{22}$ of the transfer function $\mathbf{J}$ in (2.4) will be updated by another PAA. This will be described in Section 3.2. Both PAA's are recursive least square algorithms, and can be updated simultaneously.

In order to continue with the formulation of $\mathbf{K}$, it is necessary to review some basic results in factorization theory.

2.1 Youla-Kucera Parametrizations

Let us consider the nominal feedback system $[\mathbf{G}_o,\mathbf{K}_o]$. As mentioned earlier, we assume that the transfer functions $\mathbf{G}_o$ and $\mathbf{K}_o$ are known and that the feedback system is stable. Utilizing well known results from factorization theory (cf. [13, 3]) $\mathbf{G}_o$ and $\mathbf{K}_o$ can be factorized by

$$\mathbf{G}_o = \mathbf{N}_o\mathbf{M}_o{}^{-1} = \tilde{\mathbf{M}}_o^{-1}\tilde{\mathbf{N}}_o\,, \quad \mathbf{K}_o = \mathbf{U}_o\mathbf{V}_o{}^{-1} = \tilde{\mathbf{V}}_o^{-1}\tilde{\mathbf{U}}_o\,, \tag{2.5}$$

where $\mathbf{N}_o$, $\mathbf{M}_o$, $\tilde{\mathbf{M}}_o$, $\tilde{\mathbf{N}}_o$, $\mathbf{U}_o$, $\mathbf{V}_o$, $\tilde{\mathbf{U}}_o$ $\tilde{\mathbf{V}}_o \in \mathcal{RH}_\infty^m$ and the pairs $(\mathbf{N}_o, \mathbf{M}_o)$, $(\tilde{\mathbf{N}}_o, \tilde{\mathbf{M}}_o)$, $(\mathbf{U}_o, \mathbf{V}_o)$, $(\tilde{\mathbf{U}}_o, \tilde{\mathbf{V}}_o)$, are coprime. That is, any common divisors of the coprime pairs are units in $\mathcal{RH}_\infty^m$.

An important result in factorization theory is that if the nominal feedback loop $[\mathbf{G}_o,\mathbf{K}_o]$ is stable, then the factorizations for $\mathbf{G}_o$ and $\mathbf{K}_o$ can be choosen such that the following Bezout identity is satisfied.

$$\begin{bmatrix} \tilde{\mathbf{V}}_o & -\tilde{\mathbf{U}}_o \\ -\tilde{\mathbf{N}}_o & \tilde{\mathbf{M}}_o \end{bmatrix} \begin{bmatrix} \mathbf{M}_o & \mathbf{U}_o \\ \mathbf{N}_o & \mathbf{V}_o \end{bmatrix} = \begin{bmatrix} \mathbf{I} & \mathbf{0} \\ \mathbf{0} & \mathbf{I} \end{bmatrix} \tag{2.6}$$

Assumption 2.2 *The nominal plant and controller factorizations in (2.5) and (2.5) are known and satisfy (2.6).*

There exist many ways to generate a set of coprime factorizations for the nominal plant and the nominal controller (c.f. [10, 12]).

A dual result to parametrizing the class of all stabilizing controllers for the nominal plant, $\mathbf{G}_o$, is to parametrized the class $\mathcal{G}$ of all plants which can be stabilized by the nominal controller $\mathbf{K}_o$. This result is immediate upon interchanging the role of controller and plant [12]. This class can be parametrized by the following LFT

$$\mathbf{G}(\mathbf{S}) = \mathbf{G}_o + \tilde{\mathbf{M}}_o^{-1}\mathbf{S}(\mathbf{I} + \mathbf{M}_o{}^{-1}\mathbf{U}_o\mathbf{S})^{-1}\mathbf{M}_o{}^{-1} \tag{2.7}$$

for all $\mathbf{S} \in \mathcal{RH}_\infty^m$. Any plant from the class $\mathcal{G}$ can be parametrized by Eq. (2.7) for some $\mathbf{S} \in \mathcal{RH}_\infty^m$. Moreover, for any $\mathbf{S} \in \mathcal{RH}_\infty^m$ the plant parametrized by Eq. (2.7) belongs to the class $\mathcal{G}$. We will refer to the transfer function $\mathbf{S}$ as the *plant Youla parameter*.

Consider now a plant $\mathbf{G} \in \mathcal{G}$ given by the transfer function $\mathbf{G}(\mathbf{S})$ in (2.7), with $\mathbf{S} \in \mathcal{RH}_\infty^m$ known. It is then possible to generate the following set of coprime factorizations for $\mathbf{G}(\mathbf{S})$.

$$\begin{aligned} \mathbf{G}(\mathbf{S}) &= \mathbf{N}\mathbf{M}^{-1}\,,\ \mathbf{N} = \mathbf{N}_o + \mathbf{V}_o\mathbf{S}\,,\ \mathbf{M} = \mathbf{M}_o + \mathbf{U}_o\mathbf{S} \\ \mathbf{G}(\mathbf{S}) &= \tilde{\mathbf{M}}^{-1}\tilde{\mathbf{N}}\,,\ \tilde{\mathbf{N}} = \tilde{\mathbf{N}}_o + \mathbf{S}\tilde{\mathbf{V}}_o\,,\ \tilde{\mathbf{M}} = \tilde{\mathbf{M}}_o + \mathbf{S}\tilde{\mathbf{U}}_o\,. \end{aligned} \tag{2.8}$$

[2] The superscript m will be droped from these symbols, when the dimension of the transfer functions can be determine from the contex.

The factorizations in Eq. (2.8) satisfy the double Bezout identity, Eq. (2.6), with $\mathbf{M}$, $\mathbf{N}$, $\tilde{\mathbf{M}}$, and $\tilde{\mathbf{N}}$ replacing $\mathbf{M}_o$, $\mathbf{N}_o$, $\tilde{\mathbf{M}}_o$, and $\tilde{\mathbf{N}}_o$ respectively. This can be verified by direct substitution. Moreover, given the factorization $\mathbf{N}$, in terms of $\mathbf{S}$ as in (2.8), it is possible to generate the class of all stabilizing controllers for the actual plant, $\mathbf{G}(\mathbf{S})$ as given by

$$\mathbf{K}(\mathbf{Q}) = F_L(\mathbf{J_K},\mathbf{Q}) = \mathbf{K}_o + \tilde{\mathbf{V}}_o^{-1}\mathbf{Q}(\mathbf{I} + \mathbf{V}_o{}^{-1}\mathbf{N}\mathbf{Q})^{-1}\mathbf{V}_o{}^{-1}, \quad (2.9)$$

where $\mathbf{Q} \in \mathcal{RH}_\infty^m$ and the block $\mathbf{J_K}$ is defined by

$$\mathbf{J_K}(\mathbf{S}) = \begin{bmatrix} \mathbf{K}_o & \tilde{\mathbf{V}}_o^{-1} \\ \mathbf{V}_o{}^{-1} & -\mathbf{V}_o{}^{-1}\mathbf{N}_o - \mathbf{S} \end{bmatrix} \in \mathcal{R}_p{}^{2m}. \quad (2.10)$$

We will refer to the transfer function $\mathbf{Q}$ as the *controller Youla parameter*. Also notice that we have made the dependance of $\mathbf{J_K}$ on $\mathbf{S}$ explicit in (2.10). Fig. 3 shows a block diagram of the feedback system which generates the class of stabilizing controlles for the plant $\mathbf{G}(\mathbf{S})$. The compensator $\mathbf{K}(\mathbf{Q},\mathbf{S}) = F_L(\mathbf{J_K}(\mathbf{S}),\mathbf{Q})$, with $\mathbf{J_K}(\mathbf{S})$ given by (2.10) and $\mathbf{Q} \in \mathcal{RH}_\infty^m$, will be a stabilizing controller for the plant $\mathbf{G}(\mathbf{S})$. The control structure in Fig. 3 will serve as the basis of the adaptive control scheme presented in this paper.

3 $\mathcal{H}_2$ Minimization Using Q

In the previous section we presented a feedback structure which generates the class of stabilizing controlles for the actual plant $\mathbf{G}$, when the *plant Youla parameter* $\mathbf{S}$ is known. In this section we will show how this structure can be used to obtain a Recursive Least Squares (RLS) algorithm for estimating the parameters for the controller Youla parameter $\mathbf{Q}$ which minimizes the variance $E\{z^Tz\}$ in (2.2) when the plant Youla parameter $\mathbf{S}$ and noise model are *known*, and $\mathbf{Q}$ is constrained to be a FIR filter.

In order to obtain a solution to this problem, we will express the tracking error signal, e_2, in terms of it's innovations filter (c.f. [4]) and the control input $\mathbf{u}$. Assuming zero initial conditions and that $\mathbf{S} \in \mathcal{RH}_\infty^m$, we can describe this input/output dynamics as follows

$$\mathbf{e}_2 = \mathbf{G}(\mathbf{S})\mathbf{u} + \tilde{\mathbf{L}}\Omega \quad (3.1)$$

where $\mathbf{e_2}$ and $\mathbf{u}$ are the z-transforms of e_2 and u respectively, $\tilde{\mathbf{L}}$ is the innovations model for the actual plant with input noise w_1 and output noise w_2, while $\omega(k)$ is the innovations signal and Ω is the z-transform of ω.

Let us for the moment assume that $\mathbf{G}(\mathbf{S})$ and $\tilde{\mathbf{L}}$ in (3.1) are known and that the innovations signal ω is measurable. By the separation principle of the LQG theory, the controller which minimizes $E\{|z|^2\}$ also minimizes its estimate, $E\{|\hat{z}|^2\}$, where

$$\hat{z}(k) = P\begin{bmatrix} \hat{e}_2(k) \\ u(k) \end{bmatrix} = P\begin{bmatrix} \hat{e}_2(k) - \omega(k) \\ u(k) \end{bmatrix}. \quad (3.2)$$

We will now obtain an expression for the regulating signal estimate $\hat{\mathbf{z}}$ in terms of the compensator $\mathbf{Q}$ and the innovations signal. To do this, we first assume that that a compensator $\mathbf{K}(\mathbf{Q},\mathbf{S}) = F_L(\mathbf{J_K}(\mathbf{S}),\mathbf{Q})$ in (2.10), shown in Fig. 3 is used in the system $[\mathbf{G},\mathbf{K}]$. Thus, the auxiliary control signal $\mathbf{u}_q$ in Fig. 3 can be expressed as follows

$$\mathbf{u}_q = \tilde{\mathbf{Q}}\mathbf{r}', \quad (3.3)$$
$$\mathbf{r} = \mathbf{V}_o{}^{-1}\mathbf{e}_2 - \mathbf{V}_o{}^{-1}\mathbf{N}_o\mathbf{u}_q, \quad \mathbf{r}' = \mathbf{r} - \mathbf{S}\mathbf{u}_q \quad (3.4)$$

As shown in ([9],using the spectral factoraization theorem, the innovations filter for the signal $\mathbf{r}'$ is given by

$$\mathbf{L}^T(z^{-1})\mathbf{L}(z) = \tilde{\mathbf{L}}^T(z^{-1})\tilde{\mathbf{M}}^T(z^{-1})\tilde{\mathbf{M}}(z)\tilde{\mathbf{L}}(z).$$

Consequently, $\mathbf{u}_q$ in (3.3) and the regulating signal estimate $\hat{\mathbf{z}}$ can be expressed in terms of the innovations Ω as follows

$$\mathbf{u}_q = \mathbf{Q}\Omega = \tilde{\mathbf{Q}}\mathbf{L}\Omega, \quad (3.5)$$
$$\hat{\mathbf{z}} = P\left\{\begin{bmatrix} \mathbf{V}_o \\ \mathbf{U}_o \end{bmatrix}\mathbf{L} - \begin{bmatrix} I \\ 0 \end{bmatrix} + \begin{bmatrix} \mathbf{N} \\ \mathbf{M} \end{bmatrix}\mathbf{Q}\right\}\Omega, \quad (3.6)$$

Eq. (3.6) reveals the well known result that the sensitivity and complementary sensitiviy transfer functions are affine in the controller Youla parameter $\mathbf{Q}$ (c.f. [2]). Instead of solving the minimization problem $\min_{\mathbf{Q}\in\mathcal{RH}_\infty^m} E\{|z|^2\}$, herein we constrain $\mathbf{Q}$ to be a FIR filter of order n_Q, (e.g. $\mathbf{Q} \in \mathcal{F}_{n_Q}^m$) and redefine the optimization problem as

$$\min_{\mathbf{Q}\in\mathcal{F}_{n_Q}^m} E\{|\hat{z}|^2\} = \min_{\mathbf{Q}\in\mathcal{F}_{n_Q}^m} \| P\left\{\begin{bmatrix} \mathbf{V}_o \\ \mathbf{U}_o \end{bmatrix}\mathbf{L} - \begin{bmatrix} I \\ 0 \end{bmatrix} + \begin{bmatrix} \mathbf{N} \\ \mathbf{M} \end{bmatrix}\mathbf{Q}\right\}\|_2 \quad (3.7)$$

The solution of Eq. (3.7) can be obtained in closed form (c.f. [2]) when the plant Youla parameter $\mathbf{S}$ and the innovations filter $\mathbf{L}$ are known.

3.1 Determination of the optimal FIR filter Q (S and L known, SISO case)

In order to simplify the derivation of our adaptive control scheme, we only consider in this paper the solution of (3.7) when the plant and compensator transfer functions in the feedback system $[\mathbf{G}(\mathbf{S}),\mathbf{K}(\mathbf{Q})]$ are SISO. Thus, we will limit ourselves to the case where $\mathbf{G}_o, \mathbf{K}_o, \in \mathcal{R}_p{}^1$, $\mathbf{S} \in \mathcal{RH}_\infty^1$ and $\mathbf{Q} \in \mathcal{F}_N^1$. We also asumme in this section that the plant Youla parameter $\mathbf{S}$ the innovations filter $\mathbf{L}$ are known and the innovations signal is available These assumption is subsequently removed in section 3.2.

Under the assumption that $\mathbf{Q} \in \mathcal{F}_N^1$, the filters in the last term of Eq. (3.7) can commute and a solution is readedly available using Wiener filtering theory (cf. [5]). Define the signals $d(k), x(k) \in \mathcal{R}^2$ by

$$d(k) = P\left\{\begin{bmatrix} V_o(q^{-1}) \\ U_o(q^{-1}) \end{bmatrix} L(q^{-1}) - \begin{bmatrix} 1 \\ 0 \end{bmatrix}\right\}\omega(k) \quad (3.8)$$
$$x(k) = -P\begin{bmatrix} N(q^{-1}) \\ M(q^{-1}) \end{bmatrix}\omega(k), \quad (3.9)$$

and regressor matrix $X(k) \in \mathcal{R}^{N\times 2}$ by

$$X(k) = [x(k)\, x(k-1) \cdots x(k-n_Q)]^T. \quad (3.10)$$

Let the solution of (3.7) be given by

$$Q^o(H^o;q^{-1}) = h_0^o + h_1^o q^{-1} + \cdots + h_{n_Q}^o q^{-n_Q}, \quad (3.11)$$

where $H^o = [h_0^o\, h_1^o \cdots h_{n_Q}^o]^T$ is the optimal parameter vector. From Eqs. (3.6), (3.11)-(3.10), and the orthogonality principle, the optimal cost (3.7) is given by

$$\min_{\mathbf{Q}\in\mathcal{F}_N^1} E\left\{|\hat{z}(k)|^2\right\} = E\left\{|\hat{z}^o(k)|^2\right\} = E\left\{|d(k) - X^T(k)H^o|^2\right\}, \quad (3.12)$$

where H^o is such that

$$E\{X(k)\hat{z}^o(k)\} = E\{X(k)d(k)\} - E\{X(k)X^T(k)\}H^o = 0. \quad (3.13)$$

In this paper we will assume that $E\{X(k)X^T(k)\}$ is positive definite. The optimal FIR parameter vector can be estimated using linear FIR adaptive filters such as the least mean squares (LMS) or the recursive least squares (RLS) algorithms (c.f. [5]).

3.2 Estimation of the plant Youla parameter and whitening filter (SISO case)

In the previous section the optimal $\mathcal{H}_2$ **Q** FIR filter solution of (3.12) was presented, when the plant Youla parameter **S** and the whitening filter **L** are assumed known. In this section, we will discuss PAA for estimating these filters and for generating an unbaised estimate of the innovation signal $\omega(k)$. This is achieved by identifying an ARMAX model which has as its deterministic input the auxiliary input $\mathbf{u}_q$, as random noise the innovations Ω, and as output the residual **r** signal in Fig. 3.

$$\mathbf{r} = \mathbf{S}\mathbf{u}_q + \mathbf{L}\Omega\,. \tag{3.14}$$

Recall that **r** is generated by Eq. (3.4). As in the previous section, for simplicity we constraint the transfer functions $\mathbf{S}, \mathbf{L} \in \mathcal{RH}^1_\infty$ and represent the filters $S(q^{-1})$ and $L(q^{-1})$ as follows

$$S(q^{-1}) = \frac{B(q^{-1})}{A(q^{-1})}\,, \qquad L(q^{-1}) = \frac{C(q^{-1})}{A(q^{-1})}\,, \tag{3.15}$$

where the polynomials

$$\begin{aligned} A(q^{-1}) &= 1 + a_1 q^{-1} + \ldots + a_{n_A} q^{-n_A} \\ B(q^{-1}) &= b_0 + b_1 q^{-1} + \ldots + b_{n_B} q^{-n_B} \\ C(q^{-1}) &= 1 + c_1 q^{-1} + \ldots + c_{n_C} q^{-n_C} \end{aligned} \tag{3.16}$$

are unknown. Notice that $A(q^{-1})$ and $C(q^{-1})$ are Hurwitz. Eq. (3.14) can be rewritten as follows

$$r(k) = \psi(k-1)^T\theta + \omega(k)\,, \tag{3.17}$$

where

$$\begin{aligned} \theta &= [a_1 \ldots a_{n_A}\ b_0 \ldots b_{n_B}\ c_1 \ldots c_{n_C}\ ]^T \\ \psi(k) &= [-r(k) \ldots -r(k-n_A+1)\ u_q(k) \ldots u_q(k-n_B+1)\ \omega(k) \ldots]^T\,. \end{aligned} \tag{3.18}$$

We will use Pseudo Linear Regression (PLR) algorithms (c.f. [4]) based on Eq. (3.17) to estimate the parameters of the filters $S(q^{-1})$, $L(q^{-1})$ and the innovation signal $\omega(k)$. For this purpose let us define the parameter estimate the regressor vector

$$\begin{aligned} \hat\theta(k) &= [\hat a_1(k) \ldots \hat a_{n_A}(k)\ \hat b_0(k) \ldots \hat b_{n_B}(k)\ \hat c_1(k) \ldots \hat c_{n_C}(k)]^T \\ \phi(k) &= [-r(k) \ldots\ldots -r(k-n_A+1)\ u_q(k) \ldots u_q(k-n_B+1)\ \eta(k) \ldots]^T\,, \end{aligned} \tag{3.19}$$

where the *a-posteriori* and *a-priori* estimation errors are respectively defined by

$$\begin{aligned} \eta(k) &= r(k) - \phi(k-1)^T\hat\theta(k) & (3.20) \\ e(k) &= r(k) - \phi(k-1)^T\hat\theta(k-1)\,. & (3.21) \end{aligned}$$

$\hat\theta(k)$ may be updated by a stochastic gradient (SG) or a recursive least squares (RLS) PAA algorithm (c.f. [4]). Following we describe the RLS algorithm

$$\begin{aligned} \hat\theta(k) &= \hat\theta(k-1) + \frac{F_S(k-1)\phi(k-1)}{1+\phi^T(k-1)F_S(k-1)\phi(k-1)}e(k) \\ F_S(k) &= F_S(k-1) + \frac{F_S(k-1)\phi(k-1)\phi^T(k-1)F_S(k-1)}{1+\phi^T(k-1)F_S(k-1)\phi(k-1)} \end{aligned} \tag{3.22}$$

We also introduce standard assumptions regarding the model (3.14)-(3.16) (c.f. [4])

Assumption 3.1 *The following is known about the system (3.14)-(3.16): A1) An upper bound is known for the polynominal orders n_A n_B and n_C. A2) $[1/C(q^{-1}) - 1/2]$ is very strictly passive. A3) The innovations has the following statistical characteristics*

$$E\{\omega(k)|\Omega_{k-1}\} = 0\,, E\{\omega(k)^2|\Omega_{k-1}\} = \sigma^2\,,\ \sup_N \frac{1}{N}\sum_{k=1}^{N} w(k)^2 < \infty \ a.s. \tag{3.23}$$

where Ω_k represents the observations up and until the sampling instance k and a.s. signifies almost surely.
A4) $\lim\sup_{k\to\infty} \frac{\lambda_{max}F_S(k)}{\lambda_{min}F_S(k)} < \infty$.

Remark: The periodic regularization of the gain matrix F_S may be necessary to guarantee A4).

4 Overall Adaptive Scheme (SISO)

We now introduce a direct adaptive control scheme to obtain an estimate to solution to Eq. (3.7), when the Youla plant parameter $\mathbf{S} \in \mathcal{RH}^1_\infty$, the innovations filter $\mathbf{L} \in \mathcal{RH}^1_\infty$, and the innovations signal $\omega(k)$ are unknown. This is achived by combining the identification scheme in Section 3.2 with a recursive FIR PAA algorithm for estimating the optimal Wiener FIR $Q^o(H^o; q^{-1})$ in Section 3.1. A block diagram of the overall adaptive feedback system $[\mathbf{G}(\mathbf{S}), \mathbf{K}(\hat{\mathbf{Q}}, \hat{\mathbf{S}})]$ is shown in Fig. 4.

The auxiliary control signal $u_q(k)$ in Fig. 4 is given by

$$u_q(k) = \hat Q(\hat H(k); q^{-1})\eta(k) = X^T_\eta(k)\hat H(k)\,, \tag{4.1}$$

where the $\eta(k)$, given by (3.20), is the *a-posteriori* error signal of the RLS identification scheme described in Section 3.2, and the controller regressor vector $\mathbf{X}_\eta(k)$ and parameter vector $\hat H(k)$ are

$$\begin{aligned} X_\eta(k) &= [\eta(k)\,\eta(k-1)\ \cdots\ \eta(k-n_Q)]^T & (4.2) \\ \hat H(k) &= [\hat h_0(k)\,\hat h_1(k)\ \cdots\ \hat h_{n_Q}(k)]^T\,. & (4.3) \end{aligned}$$

The FIR controller parameter vector $\hat H(k)$ is updated by a RLS PAA. In this scheme estimates of the signals $d(k)$ and $X(k)$ in Eqs. (3.8) and (3.9) are generated utilizing the following time varying filters $\hat S(\hat\theta(k); q^{-1})$ and $\hat L(\hat\theta(k); q^{-1})$

$$\hat S(\hat\theta(k); q^{-1}) = \frac{\hat B(\hat\theta(k); q^{-1})}{\hat A(\hat\theta(k); q^{-1})}\,, \quad \hat L(\hat\theta(k); q^{-1}) = \frac{\hat C(\hat\theta(k); q^{-1})}{\hat A(\hat\theta(k); q^{-1})}\,, \tag{4.4}$$

which are the estimates of the **S** and **L** filters in (3.15). The polynomials $\hat A(\hat\theta(k); q^{-1})$, $\hat B(\hat\theta(k); q^{-1})$ and $\hat C(\hat\theta(k); q^{-1})$ are as in (3.16), only that the parameter estimate $\hat\theta(k)$ which is updated by (3.19), is used instead of the unknown parameter θ in (3.18). The following input-output notation is used in the definition of time varying filters

$$y(k) = \frac{\hat B(k; q^{-1})}{\hat A(k; q^{-1})}u(k) \quad\Rightarrow\quad y(k) = -\hat A'(k; q^{-1})y(k) + \hat B(k; q^{-1})u(k)\,,$$

where $\hat A'(k; q^{-1}) = \hat A(k; q^{-1}) - 1$.
Also $y(k) = G_1(k; q^{-1})G_2(k; q^{-1})u(k) = G_1(k; q^{-1})\bar u(k)$, where $\bar u(k) = G_2(k; q^{-1})u(k)$.

The estimates of the signals $d(k)$ and $x(k)$ in Eqs. (3.8) and (3.9) are generated as follows

$$\begin{aligned} \hat d(k) &= P\left\{\begin{bmatrix} V_o(q^{-1}) \\ U_o(q^{-1}) \end{bmatrix} \hat L(\hat\theta(k); q^{-1}) - \begin{bmatrix} 1 \\ 0 \end{bmatrix}\right\}\eta(k) & (4.5) \\ \hat x(k) &= -P\begin{bmatrix} \hat N(\hat\theta(k); q^{-1}) \\ \hat M(\hat\theta(k); q^{-1}) \end{bmatrix}\eta(k)\,, & (4.6) \end{aligned}$$

and

$$\hat X(k) = [\hat x(k)\,\hat x(k-1)\ \cdots\ \hat x(k-n_Q)]^T\,, \tag{4.7}$$

where estimates $\hat N(\hat\theta(k); q^{-1})$ and $\hat M(\hat\theta(k); q^{-1})$ are given by

$$\begin{aligned} \hat N(\hat\theta(k); q^{-1}) &= N_o(q^{-1}) + V_o(q^{-1})\hat S(\hat\theta(k); q^{-1}) \\ \hat M(\hat\theta(k); q^{-1}) &= M_o(q^{-1}) + U_o(q^{-1})\hat S(\hat\theta(k); q^{-1}) \end{aligned} \tag{4.8}$$

The controller parameter vector $\hat H(k)$ in Eq. (4.1) is updated by the following RLS PAA

$$\hat{H}(k) = \hat{H}(k-1) + F_Q(k)\hat{X}(k)\,[\hat{d}(k) - \hat{X}^T(k)\hat{H}(k-1)] \quad (4.9)$$

$$F_Q(k) = \frac{1}{\lambda_Q(k)}\Big\{F_Q(k-1) - F_Q(k-1)\hat{X}(k)\times [\lambda_Q(k)I + \hat{X}^T(k)F_Q(k-1)\hat{X}(k)]^{-1}\hat{X}^T(k)F_Q(k-1)\Big\}$$

$$F_Q(0) > 0\,, \qquad 0 < \lambda_Q \le 1\,,$$

or the following LMS PAA

$$\hat{H}(k) = \hat{H}(k-1) + \mu(k)\hat{X}(k)\,[\hat{d}(k) - \hat{X}^T(k)\hat{H}(k-1)] \quad (4.10)$$

$$\mu(k) > 0$$

Remarks:

1) The adaptive scheme in this section consists of two adaptive algorithms running in parallel. The PAA given by Eqs. (3.19)-(3.22) identifies the plant Youla parameter and the noise model.

The PAA given by (4.9) or (4.10) updates the parameters of the FIR filter $\hat{Q}(\hat{H}(k); q^{-1})$.

2) A projection must be used in the PAA's given by Eqs. (4.9) or (4.10) so that the FIR filter parameter vector $\hat{H}(k)$ remains bounded, in order to guarantee the stability of the feedback system $[\mathbf{G(S)}, \mathbf{K}(\hat{\mathbf{Q}}, \hat{\mathbf{S}})]$.

3) A second projection must be used in the PAA given by Eqs. (3.19)-(3.22), so that the polynomial $\hat{A}(\hat{\theta}(k); q^{-1})$ remains Hurwitz for all k and the filters in (4.4) remain asymptotically stable. This guarantees that the signals $\hat{d}(k)$ and $\hat{x}(k)$ remain bounded.

4) The forgetting factor, λ_Q in Eqs. (4.9) must remain $0 < \lambda_Q(k) < 1$, and $\mu(k) > 0$ until the signals $\hat{d}(k)$ and $\hat{x}(k)$ in (4.5) and (4.6) are nearly stationary. The signal $\delta_\theta(k) = |\hat{\theta}(k) - \hat{\theta}(k-1)|^2$ can be monitored to determine when this happens.

5) In the simulation and experimental results that were conducted, we initially set the signal $u_q(k)$ to be a random input, in order to start the identification algorithm (3.19)-(3.22), after a number of itterations, the control law and adaptation algorithm (4.1)-(4.9) is turned on.

6) We have observed that the convergence of the RLS algorithms is superior to that of the combination of stochastic gradiant and LMS schemes.

The following theorem shows that the adaptive feedback control system $[\mathbf{G(S)}, \mathbf{K}(\hat{\mathbf{Q}}, \hat{\mathbf{S}})]$ in Fig. 4 remains stable under mild assumptions.

Theorem 4.1 *Consider the feedback control system* $[\mathbf{G(S)}, \mathbf{K}(\hat{\mathbf{Q}}, \hat{\mathbf{S}})]$ *in Fig. 4 with the controller parameters being updated by the PAA's (3.19)-(3.22) and (4.9). Under Assumption 3.1, if in addition a projection algorithm is used in the PPA in Eqs. (4.9) such that* $|\hat{H}(k)| \le h_{max} < \infty$ *where* h_{max} *is known such that* $|H^o| < h_{max}$ *and* H^o *is the solution of (3.13), then*

$$\lim_{N\to\infty} \frac{1}{N}\sum_{k=1}^{N}[\eta(k) - w(k)]^2 = 0\,, \quad \lim_{N\to\infty}\sum_{k=1}^{N}|\hat{\theta}(k) - \hat{\theta}(k-m)|^2 < \infty \quad (4.11)$$

$$\lim_{N\to\infty} \frac{\hat{\theta}^T(N)F_S{}^{-1}(N)\hat{\theta}(N)}{N} < \infty\,, \quad \lim_{N\to\infty}\frac{1}{N}\rho(N-1) \le \infty \ a.s. \quad (4.12)$$

$$\rho(k) = \rho(k-1) + \phi^T(k)\phi(k)\,. \quad (4.13)$$

Proof: See section 5.3.1 of [9]. Straightforward calculations show that, under $|\hat{H}(k)| \le h_{max} < \infty$ and the control law (4.1), all conditions in theorem 8.5.2 and lemma 8.5.2 in [4] are satisfied.

The next set of results provide an insight on the self optimizing properties of the adaptive system $[\mathbf{G(S)}, \mathbf{K}(\hat{\mathbf{Q}}, \hat{\mathbf{S}})]$ in Fig. 4. Let us first define the signal $\hat{z}_o(k)$ as follows

$$\hat{z}_o(k) = \hat{d}(k) - \hat{X}(k)\hat{H}(k) \quad (4.14)$$

The PAA algorithms for $\hat{H}(k)$ given by the RLS Eq. (4.9) and the LMS Eq. (4.10) PAA's minimize $E\{|\hat{z}_o(k)|^2\}$, as $k \to \infty$ when the signals $\hat{d}(k)$ and $\hat{X}(k)$ are stationary and $k\lambda_q(k) \to k, k\mu(k) \to \mu_o$. Unfortunately, the signals $\hat{d}(k)$ and $\hat{H}(k)$ in (4.5)-(4.7) are not stationary, since they are generated by time varying filters. Thus, we cannot rigorously prove that these PAA minimize $E\{|\hat{z}_o(k)|^2\}$ under these conditions. However, from the convergence results in theorem 4.1, we can assume that these signals are *asymptotically stationary*, in that $\lim_{k\to\infty} E\{\hat{X}(k)\hat{d}(k)\} = E_{\hat{X}\hat{d}}$ and $\lim_{k\to\infty} E\{\hat{X}(k)\hat{X}^T(k)\} = E_{\hat{X}\hat{X}}$. Let us define the time varying optimal parameter vector $\hat{H}^o(k)$ as the solution to

$$E\{\hat{X}(k)\hat{d}(k)\} - E\{\hat{X}(k)\hat{X}^T(k)\}\hat{H}^o(k) = 0\,. \quad (4.15)$$

As shown in [1], the LMS PAA in (4.10) will track the optimal parameter vector $\hat{H}^o(k)$ with a finite maximum error norm. Under the assumption that the higher order moments of $\hat{d}(k)$ and $\hat{X}(k)$ are uniformly bounded, and that $E\{\sum_{j=k}^{k+p}\hat{X}^T(j)\hat{X}(j)\}$ is positive definite for some integer p, there exist positive constants β, β', μ_M so that

$$\lim_{k\to\infty} \sup E\{|\hat{H}^o(k) - \hat{H}(k)|^2\} \le \beta\mu + \beta'(L/\mu)^2\,, \forall\,\mu \in (0, \mu_m),$$

$$L = \sup_k |\Delta\hat{H}^o(k)|\,,\ \Delta\hat{H}^o(k) = \hat{H}^o(k) - \hat{H}^o(k-1)\,. \quad (4.16)$$

Similar results exist for the RLS PAA in (4.9) (c.f. [5]). The second term in the bound of (4.16), reflects the deteriorating effect of nonstationarity in the convergence of the controller parameter estimate $\hat{H}(k)$ to the optimal $\hat{H}^o(k)$. The bound (4.16) is very conservative in light of the definition of L. However, under the assumption that the signals $\hat{d}(k)$ and $\hat{H}(k)$ are asymptotically stationary, it follows that $|\Delta\hat{H}^o| \to 0$ and, from the analysis in [1], as $k \to \infty$, the effects of early changes in $\Delta\hat{H}^o$ on $E\{|\hat{H}^o - \hat{H}|^2\}$ are not significant.

Lemma 4.1 *Under the assumptions of theorem 4.1, if a projection scheme is utilized in the PAA for* $\hat{\theta}(k)$ *so that the polynomial* $\hat{A}(\hat{\theta}(k); q^{-1})$ *is updated so that* $L(\hat{\theta}(k); q^{-1})$ *and following time varying filters*

$$W(\hat{\theta}(k); q^{-1}) = P\begin{bmatrix}\mathbf{N}(\hat{\theta}(k); q^{-1})\\ \mathbf{M}(\hat{\theta}(k); q^{-1})\end{bmatrix} = \left[\begin{array}{c|c} A_w(\hat{\theta}(k)) & B_w(\hat{\theta}(k)) \\ \hline C_w(\hat{\theta}(k)) & D_w(\hat{\theta}(k))\end{array}\right]_T$$

$$W_C(\hat{\theta}(k); q^{-1}) = \left[\begin{array}{c|c} A_w(\hat{\theta}(k)) & A_w(\hat{\theta}(k)) \\ \hline C_w(\hat{\theta}(k)) & C_w(\hat{\theta}(k))\end{array}\right]_T$$

$$W_B(\hat{\theta}(k); q^{-1}) = \left[\begin{array}{c|c} A_w(\hat{\theta}(k)) & B_w(\hat{\theta}(k)) \\ \hline I & 0\end{array}\right]_T \quad (4.17)$$

are asymptotically stable, then

$$\lim_{N\to\infty}\frac{1}{N}\sum_{k=1}^{N}|[\hat{z}(k) - \hat{z}_o(k)] + \Delta q(k)|^2 = 0 \ \text{, where,} \quad (4.18)$$

$$\Delta q(k) = \hat{Q}(\hat{H}(k); q^{-1})W(\hat{\theta}(k); q^{-1})\eta(k) - W(\hat{\theta}(k); q^{-1})\hat{Q}(\hat{H}(k); q^{-1})\eta(k)$$

$$= W_C(\hat{\theta}(k); q^{-1})[X_\eta^{*T}(k)\Delta\hat{H}(k)]$$

$$X_\eta^*(k) = W_B(\hat{\theta}(k); q^{-1})X_\eta(k)\,,\ \Delta\hat{H}(k) = \hat{H}(k) - \hat{H}(k-1)\,. \quad (4.19)$$

Proof: See the proof of lemma 5.1 in [9].

Remarks:

1) Notice that if $k\lambda_q(k) \to k$ or $k\mu(k) \to \mu_o$ as $k \to \infty$, $\lim_{N\to\infty}\frac{1}{N}\sum_{k=1}^{N}|\Delta\hat{H}(k)|^2 = 0$ and $\lim_{N\to\infty}\frac{1}{N}\sum_{k=1}^{N}|\Delta q(k)|^2 = 0$.

2) From Lemma 4.1 we can conclude that if the PAA's Eq. (4.9) or (4.10) converge such that $\hat{Q}(\hat{H}(k); q^{-1})$ converges to a filter $Q^*(q^{-1})$ which minimizes $E\{|\hat{z}_o(k)|^2\}$, $Q^*(q^{-1})$ is also the solution of (3.7).

5 Simulation Study

A computer simulation study was performed to evaluate the adaptive scheme developed in this paper. A simple but frequently used nominal model for magnetic disk file actuators is the double integrator plant. The nominal compensator in this simulation study consists of a state feedback and state obeserver based compensator. The model chosen to describe the *'actual'* file actuator is that of a system containing an unidentified lightly damped resonance mode

$$G_a(s) = \frac{k_a\omega_a^2}{s^2(s^2 + 2\zeta_a\omega_a s + \omega_a^2)}, \quad \mathbf{G(S)} = (1 - z^{-1})Z\left(\frac{G_a(s)}{s}\right) \qquad (5.1)$$

ω_a is the unknown resonant frequency, ζ_a is the damping ratio and k_a is a constant gain, which can differ from the nominal system gain, k.

When $\mathbf{G}_o$ and $\mathbf{G(S)}$ are as described above, an observer based compensator is used as the nominal compensator, and the factorization given by [10] are used, $\mathbf{S}$ given by Eq. (2.7) is a sixth order transfer function. A computer program was coded in the *Matrix$_x$* simulation language which implemented the algorithm described in Section 4. The response of the $[\mathbf{G(S)}, \mathbf{K}_o]$ feedback system and the adaptive $[\mathbf{G(S)}, \mathbf{K}(\hat{\mathbf{Q}}, \hat{\mathbf{S}})]$ system in Fig. 4 were tested under uncorrelated white noise random input disturbances w1 and w2. Different choices of the design parameters n_A (the order of $\hat{S}(\hat{\theta}(k); q^{-1})$), were tested. The order of the the FIR adaptive filter, $\hat{Q}(\hat{H}(k); q^{-1})$ was 12 and the regulated variable weighting matrix was $P = [1\ 0.01]$. Also simulated for benchmark purposes was the response of the feedback system $[\mathbf{G(S)}, \mathbf{K}_{opt}]$, where $\mathbf{K}_{opt}$ is the exact LQG compensator for the plant $\mathbf{G(S)}$, and the self-tuning LQG scheme described in [6]. The cost $J = E\{|z|^2\}$ was calculated for the fixed feedback systems and for the adaptive and self-tuning systems, once the adaptive controller parameters had converged to some fixed values. The results are shown in the following table.

$J_{[\mathbf{G(S)},\mathbf{K}_o]}$	$J_{[\mathbf{G(S)},\mathbf{K}_e]}$	$J_{[\mathbf{G(S)},\mathbf{K}(\hat{Q},\hat{S})],6}$	$J_{[\mathbf{G(S)},\mathbf{K}(\hat{Q},\hat{S})],4}$	$J_{ST,6}$
0.4525	0.2226	0.2312	0.2479	0.3058

where $[\mathbf{G(S)}, \mathbf{K}(\hat{Q}, \hat{S})], 6$ and $[\mathbf{G(S)}, \mathbf{K}(\hat{Q}, \hat{S})], 4$ denote the adaptive scheme presented in this paper, with the order of $\hat{S}(\hat{\theta}(k); q^{-1})$ respectively equal to 6 and 4, and $J_{ST,6}$ is the cost resulting from the indirect self-tuning LQG scheme in [6].

6 Conclusions

A direct adaptive control scheme which consists of two recursive PAA algorithms running simultaneously has been described. The scheme is designed to enhance system performance of a nominal disk file servo, in the face of plant uncertainty. One PAA is used in the identification of a stable factorization for the perturbed plant $\mathbf{G(S)}$. The other PAA generates a FIR filter that minimizes the variance of the regulated variable.

References

[1] E. Eweda and O. Macchi. Tracking error bounds of adaptive nonstationary filtering. *Automatica*, 21:293–302, 1985.

[2] B. A. Francis. On the wiener-hopf approach to optimal feedback design. *Systems and Control Letters*, 2(4):197–201, 1982.

[3] B. A. Francis. *A Course in H_∞ Control Theory*, volume 88 of *Lecture Notes in Control and Information Systems*. Springer Verlag, 1987.

[4] G. Goodwin and K. S. Sin. *Adaptive Filtering Prediction and Control.* Prentice-Hall, 1984.

[5] S. Haykin. *Adaptive Filter Theory.* Prentice-Hall, Second Edition, 1991.

[6] R. Horowitz and J. McCormick. A self-tuning control scheme for disk file servos. *IEEE Transactions on Magnetics*, 27:4490–4495, 1991.

[7] V. A. Kucera. *Discrete Linear Control: The Polynomial Equation Approach.* John Wiley, 1979.

[8] H. Kwakernaak and R. Sivan. *Linear Optimal Control Systems.* Wiley-Interscience, 1972.

[9] J. McCormick. *Performance Enhancements of Disk File Servos Through Adaptive Control.* PhD thesis, University of California at Berkeley, 1992.

[10] C. N. Nett, C. A. Jacobson, and M. J. Balas. A conection between state space and doubly coprime fractional representations. *IEEE Transactions on Automatic Control*, 29:831–832, September 1984.

[11] T. Tay and J. Moore. Enhancement of fixed controllers via adaptive-q disturbance estimate feedback. *Automatica*, 27, No. 1:39–54, 1991.

[12] T. T. Tay, J. B. Moore, and R. Horowitz. Indirect adaptive techniques for fixed controller performance enhancement. *International Journal of Control*, 1989. To appear.

[13] M. Vidyasagar. *Control Systems Synthesis: A Factorization Approach.* MIT Press, 1985.

[14] D. Youla, H. Jabr, and J. Biongiorno. Modern wiener-hopf design of optimal controllers, part ii: The multivariable case. *IEEE Transactions on Automatic Control*, 21:319–338, 1976.

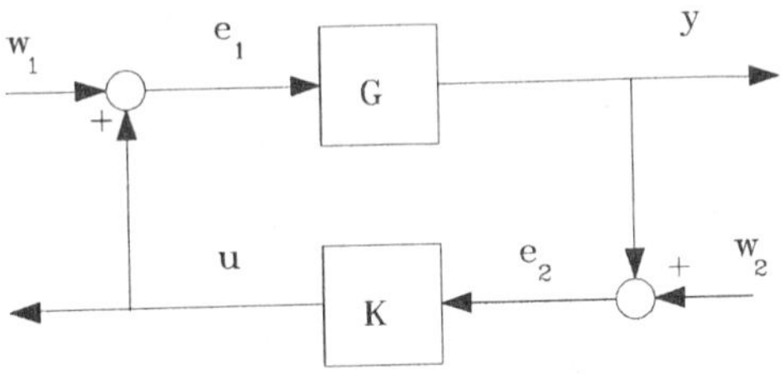

Figure 1: $[\mathbf{G}, \mathbf{K}]$ Feedback System

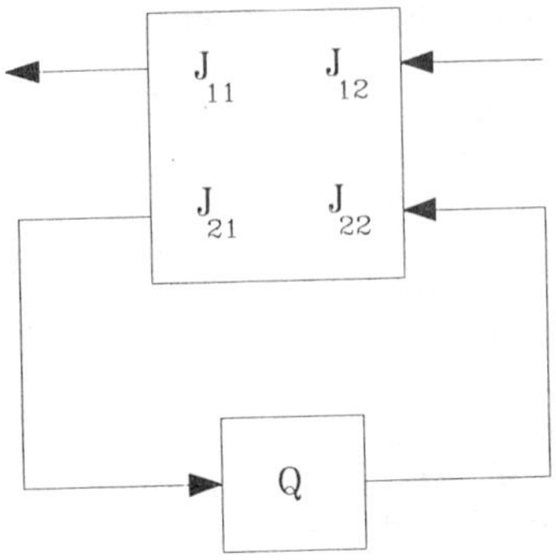

Figure 2: Linear Fractional Transformation (LFT)

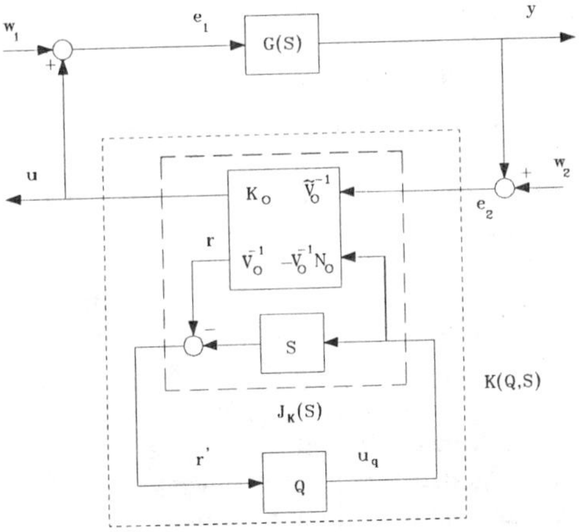

Figure 3: The class of stabilizing controllers for $\mathbf{G(S)}$

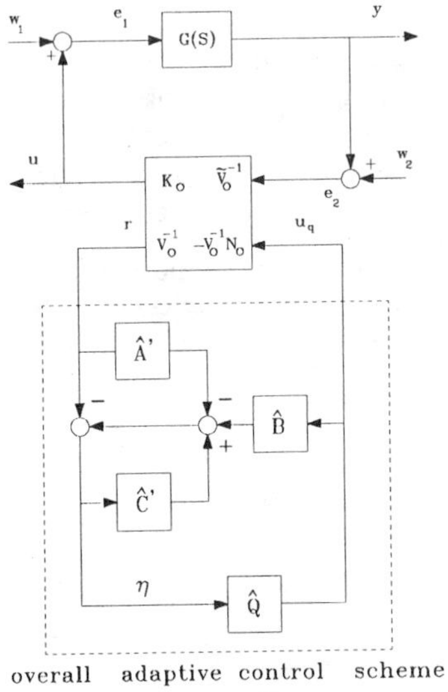

Figure 4: Overall Adaptive Control System

Proceedings of the
American Control Conference
San Francisco, California • June 1993

Integration of Machine Learning and Sensor–Based Control in Intelligent Robotic Systems *

Gerald DeJong Seth Hutchinson Mark W. Spong
University of Illinois
Urbana, Illinois

Abstract

This paper discusses the integration of machine learning and sensor–based control in intelligent robotic systems. Our research is interdisciplinary and combines techniques of explanation–based control with robust and adaptive nonlinear control, computer vision, and motion planning. Our intent in this research is to go beyond the strict hierarchical control architectures typically used in robotic systems by integrating modeling, dynamics, and control across traditional levels of planning and control at all levels of intelligence. Our ultimate goal is to combine analytical techniques of nonlinear dynamics and control with artificial intelligence into a single new paradigm in which symbolic reasoning holds an equal place with differential equation based modeling and control.

1 Introduction

The development of robots which are capable of complex, autonomous behavior such as adapting to changes and uncertainties in their environments, planning and executing strategies to carry out tasks without human intervention, and learning from past experience to improve future performance is one of the ultimate goals of robotics research. Achieving this goal would have tremendous impact in many areas of engineering. It is clear that many of the research problems that need to be solved to achieve this goal lie in the area broadly classified as intelligent control, and consist of modeling and control of uncertain nonlinear dynamical systems, and the integration of machine learning with sensor–based, real–time control.

Despite recent advances in robust and adaptive nonlinear control theory, present day robot manipulators and mobile robots are incapable of more than the most rudimentary of intelligent behaviors. Part of the reason for this is the fact that the intelligent execution and control of complex tasks by mechanical devices is difficult to accomplish within the traditional differential equation based trajectory tracking paradigms of modern control theory. Trajectory generation and tracking control techniques are suitable for a limited class of tasks, such as spray painting, arc welding, or palletizing, but they are ill–suited to more complex tasks for which mathematical models are unavailable, poorly known, or too complex to be practical. Examples of complex tasks for which simple mathematical models and simple trajectories are not easily described include building a house, repairing a satellite, navigating through a network of pipes to inspect for corrosion, repairing downed power lines, cleaning up hazardous waste, and many others.

An *intelligent* robotic system would possess a symbolic reasoning capability and would thus be able to reason about the *qualitative* behavior of the system. While symbolic reasoning of this sort has been a mainstay of the Artificial Intelligence community for many years, control theorists have strongly criticized traditional symbolic AI paradigms of reasoning about action and change for their neglect of real–world effects faced by a robotic system, such as dynamic uncertainties, disturbances, noisy measurements, bandwidth limitations, etc. The classic examples of inserting a peg into a hole, and stacking blocks are applications where success or failure depends not only on reasoning about the sequence of motions necessary to accomplish the task but also upon understanding and controlling the interaction forces, the dynamics of the robot and its environment, etc. In spite of the obvious need and advantages of integrating planning and control, current robotic systems tend to be hierarchical instead, with high level task planners at the top which compute trajectories without utilizing information about the dynamics of the process, and low level servo systems at the bottom, which are designed simply to track the trajectories presented to them.

To date AI and vision research has failed to exploit the analytical results and techniques from control theory. The new paradigm that we will explore is based fundamentally on the belief that Intelligent Control of Robotic Systems is not possible without integrating the three areas of machine learning, sensing, and control theory. Some specific elements of this new paradigm

*This research is partially supported by The National Science Foundation and the Electric Power Research Institute under the joint NSF/EPRI Intelligent Control Initiative, Grant number ECS-9216428

are:

1. Planning must take into account what information the sensing system can robustly and quickly deliver. In particular, since general purpose vision currently is not possible in real-time, an intelligent control system must move beyond the traditional role of merely "observing" sensor data and take an active role in planning the sensing strategies to be used.
2. The sensing system should exploit techniques from control theory to aid in the acquisition and processing of sensor data. For example, an important problem in current robotics research is using a moveable camera to obtain vision feedback for end-effector servo control. This tracking problem could be greatly aided by the use of control theoretic methods, both for image plane feature tracking, and for controlling the motions of the tracking camera. Sensing is thus a key element to bridge the AI—Control Theory gap.
3. Planning must take into account the performance limits of the control system. For example, one of the well-known ways that an adaptively controlled system can become unstable is if the reference trajectory excites the unmodeled dynamics. Thus a hierarchical system in which planning takes place independently of control can fail dramatically if adaptive control is used in an attempt to increase it's performance.
4. Control techniques must be developed to cope with uncertainties in the system beyond the usual cases of unknown parameters and unknown high frequency components. To this end, symbolic techniques can be used to diagnose model inadequacies and to suggest appropriate refinements in response to observed responses.
5. Machine learning techniques must be developed to suggest general descriptions of systematic behavior underlying world observations. This capability is essential if intelligent robotic systems are to perform effectively in novel situations, or in environments that change dynamically in unexpected ways.

The intent of our research is to increase the scope of control theory to embrace applications which cannot be solved with classical, modern, fuzzy logic, or neural net control systems. In particular, we believe that the AI area of planning (reasoning about perception, action, and world change) and the discipline of control theory (modeling, sensing, and actuation) are designed to serve the same purpose. In both, the task is to construct a strategy to transform a system from a given (perhaps unknown) initial state to a desired final state.

2 Task Control

Task Control involves the integration of control theory and AI planning into a new synthesis. We focus on hybrid systems for which no full adequate mathematical model can be given. An illustrative example is a robot working in a complex environment in which friction, inelastic collisions, and other uncertainties dominate. Traditionally, robot control is viewed as separate from trajectory generation, grasping, etc. which are relegated to a separate planner. A more natural viewpoint, however, is to consider the robot, for which an adequate model can be constructed, and the robot's environment, which cannot be adequately described mathematically, as a single integrated system. In fact, such a viewpoint is taken by most of control theory (excluding robotics). One does not, for example, imagine the position of a valve in a chemical plant to be the output of the control system. One typically wishes to control the level of a chemical, not the position of a valve whose effect varies with other factors. No control engineer would say "Ah, well, that's a planning problem. I only control actuators." Yet that is just the response given by robotics control engineers.

Why is robotics different? Why not view the robot-environment as a single plant? One reason might be that it seems to make a convenient dividing line. This is traceable to the "general-purposeness" of robots. The chemical plant actuator will never find itself in a different environment. It always controls a particular flow of a particular fluid. Plant engineers are not allowed to redo the plumbing on a daily or hourly schedule so that at one moment the valve controls the flow of a high pressure liquid of a certain density and viscosity and another time a low pressure gas. In non-robotic control, the changes in environment are simple and can be circumscribed and modeled. This cannot be said of robots, which by their very nature are general purpose. A robot may be at one time quickly moving a heavy object grasped far from its center of mass in which little path accuracy is required, at another time applying a force to an unmoving tower to steady it, and still later precisely positioning a small part. The environment changes so drastically and so quickly that attempting to analyze "the environment" as a single plant is ludicrous from a control theory point of view.

3 Machine Learning

Recently, a new technique called explanation-based control [3] has been advanced. It appears to be a promising vehicle to bridge the current gap between the symbolic reasoning methods that underlie AI planning and the existence of continuous changes in the world, a cornerstone of control theory.

Explanation-based control employs machine learning techniques, primarily explanation-based learning [4,10] over a symbolic axiom set representing background knowledge of the world. The ontology of the symbolic logic is inspired by control theory and permits the representation of simultaneously and continuously varying world quantities. The predicates are based on work in qualitative reasoning [5,2,8,14]. Basically, the approach involves 1) observing a human or specialized control system expert as it solves a problem currently beyond the learning system's capabilities, 2) constructing a symbolic qualitative explanation for why the expert's behavior results in the desired profile of effects, 3) symbolically generalizing the explanation in standard EGGS fashion [11], 4) calibrating the concept with the quantitative points observed from the expert's behavior, 5) using numerical interpolation between observed points to efficiently estimate the world's behavior, 6) quantitatively refining the planning concept with additional observed world points derived from the concept's use, 7) symbolically refining the concept by conjecturing an alternative explanation when world observations contradict the current explanation.

Through symbolic explanation (which identifies relevant inputs and state variables) coupled with numeric interpolation (to generalize the expected world behavior beyond the observed sample points) an explicit empirically derived numeric approximation of the world's inverse dynamics is formed. These explicit functions can be employed in control applications. The crucial point is that no differential equation model of the world's behavior is used. Rather, the system relies upon a symbolic axiom set describing the world's qualitative behavior. In many applications for which an adequate quantitative differential equation model of the world is too complex or unknown, one may still be able to provide an adequate qualitative description in symbolic terms. Furthermore, preliminary experience with the approach indicates that it may be tolerant of some non-linearities in the world, and may exhibit a certain robustness without the usual concomitant sluggishness.

Some form of stability analysis is most crucial; an analog to controllability and observability are also desirable. These are the primary research issues we intend to pursue for explanation-based control.

4 Adaptive Control

In the past decade important strides have been made in the design and analysis of robust and adaptive controllers for robotic manipulators using various mathematical tools, such as Lagrangian and Hamiltonian mechanics, passive network synthesis, Lyapunov methods, differential geometric control theory, singular perturbations and integral manifolds. The design and analysis of Intelligent Controllers requires the broadening of such tools to encompass real-time vision feedback, machine learning and AI planning techniques. This is a nontrivial task. To begin with, adaptive control in conjunction with real-time vision feedback is a completely open area of research in robotics. Adaptive control is attractive because it holds out the promise of improved performance over a wide range of payloads. However, until the robustness properties of adaptive robot control are fully understood, industrial designers will be reluctant, even unwise, to use them. Given the complicated behavior that can arise from adaptive control of even a simple first order linear system[9], it should not be surprising that a complete understanding of the robustness fo adaptive control of nonlinear systems as complicated as multi-link, multi-sensor robotic manipulators is still lacking. With the inclusion of vision feedback in the control loop the problem of robustness of adaptive control becomes even more complicated. With the further integration of explanation based learning directly into the feedback loops, perhaps operating in multiple time scales, we are faced with a class of nonlinear systems for which few prior results are available to help in the analysis or design.

It is known that the stability of adaptive systems are highly sensitive to disturbances and unmodeled dynamics. These arise in the robotics context from several sources. External disturbances include many types of interaction with the environment. For example, robotic assembly has been described as a sequence of controlled collisions with the environment. These collision forces can be viewed as disturbances to the controller. A repetitive task, for example, subjects the robot to periodic forcing which, even in non-adaptive control, can excite complex nonlinear dynamic behavior, such as period doubling bifurcations and chaos[15].

Unmodeled dynamics include actuator/sensor dynamics, joint flexibility, link flexibility, and environment dynamics. Environment dynamics arise in force and impedance controlled tasks such as assembly and grinding and will become increasingly important in future applications.

Several so-called "instability mechanisms" in adaptive control have been identified [7]. Among the mechanisms leading to instability are:

1) Reference trajectories which are "too fast." If the bandwidth of the reference trajectory is in the same frequency range as the unmodeled dynamics, then these unmodeled dynamic modes can be excited, leading to instability.

2) Parameter drift. In typical parameter adaptive controllers the estimated parameters are not guaranteed to converge to their true values, but only to remain bounded, without additional persistency of excitation conditions.

3) High gain instability. This type of instability, when the controller gains excite unmodeled dynamics, is actually due to a loss of passivity from the rigid robot case and can occur even for nonadaptive algorithms

4) Fast adaptation instability. This type of instability occurs when the gains in the parameter update law are too large.

5) Neglected time delays. It has been known since the mid 1960's that small time delays in data transmission in systems such as bilateral force reflecting teleoperators can be destabilizing.

In addition to these, there are a number of instability mechanisms that are directly attributable to the introduction of vision sensing into the control loop.

6) Lens Distortion. The geometric correspondence between points in the 3D space and points in an image is typically approximated by either perspective projection (which reflects an ideal thin lens assumption) or by orthographic projection (which holds only when the distance from the camera to the object is much greater than the lens focal length). Neither of these approximations account for limited depth of field, vignetting, and non-linear distortions of the image as the radial distance from the focal center increases.

7) Image Plane Quantization Effects. The camera image plane is actually a discrete array of sensors. Therefore, the coordinates of object features used for visual tracking are actually quantized versions of the true coordinates of those features.

8) Motion Induced Blur in Image Formation. If there is relative motion between the camera and the object being imaged, then the resulting image will be blurred.

9) Low Frequency Vision Sampling. To date, the fastest sampling rate that has been reported in the literature on visual servo control is still well below video rate. Such slow sampling rates have severe implications for system stability.

5 Experimental Research

We are developing a testbed system that can be used as an experimental platform to test our theoretical results. The testbed will be built around a planar, three-degree-of-freedom robot arm equipped with a wrist force/torque sensor and a real-time vision system. The camera may either be mounted away from the arm or eye-in-hand, depending on the research problem being investigated.

We will focus initially on *Robotic Air Hockey*, i.e., controlling a puck sliding on a surface, as the application to test our theoretical results. This application contains many of the fundamental research issues in intelligent control that are of interest to us. For example, the motion trajectory of the arm cannot be planned off-line and presented to the control system in a hierarchical fashion. Real-time planning in conjunction with real-time vision are an absolute necessity for this application. In addition, this is an application where an accurate model of the dynamics of the environment is difficult to obtain because of large uncertainty in friction combined with high sensitivity of the puck motion to initial conditions. To be more specific, one would expect large amounts of uncertainty and variation over time in the friction characteristics of the table and puck. In addition, irregularities in the table surface and bumpers would make it difficult to obtain a mathematical model of the environment sufficiently precise to enable accurate predictions of puck motion. When this large uncertainty is combined with the expected high sensitivity of the puck motion to changes in initial imposed forces and velocities, it appears that traditional motion planning and tracking control schemes would be difficult or impossible to apply successfully. On the other hand, this application appears eminently suited to learning through repeated trials in combination with real-time adaptive vision feedback control.

Another area where this experimental set-up will facilitate cross-disciplinary research is in the nature and control of the interaction forces between the puck and the robot. Of course, it is only through the forces imparted to the puck during collision with the paddle held by the robot that the puck is controlled. Issues of force feedback control are thus of prime importance in this research. In this application, however, the time of contact between the puck and paddle are of extremely short duration, and *force control*, as it is traditionally conceived, has little meaning. Instead, the force information collected during impact must be combined with the information about the resulting puck motion as determined by the vision system and the information about the arm motion as determined by the joint encoders to modify the arm motion during repeated impacts. Standard learning control methods are not likely to succeed, however, because it is impossible to recreate the puck trajectory over two successive trials.

In our previous research we have developed and exploited the so-called network approach to force control[1] including the hybrid impedance control framework. In the hybrid impedance control framework we are able to control both force levels (i.e., track force trajectories) and simultaneous control the end-effector impedance. We may be able to apply these same techniques in the present context. For example, by repeated trials the robot may be able to learn the optimal impedance to use while imparting a desired force to the puck. Ultimately, such knowledge will pay tremendous benefits in numerous industrial settings, such as in robotic assembly applications, or robotic handling of radioactive waste or fuel rods in a nuclear power plant.

There are many interesting problems in robust and adaptive nonlinear control that arise in this example. The dynamics of this process are complex enough that they cannot simply be ignored in the learning and planning phase. For example, the intermittent, impulsive, and repetitive nature of the interaction forces, when combined with adaptive control may induce interesting and complex behaviors, such as bifurcations, chaotic motion, and bursting. Thus the control designer must be aware of the potential for such nonlinear phenomena and how the actions of motion planning and learning may excite them.

The Robotic Air Hockey application contains numerous interesting and fundamental problems in computer vision. For example, understanding the physics of puck motion in the image plane is necessary for accurate tracking and for commanding motion of the arm. Issues such as camera placement to maximize the visual analog of manipulability [16] need to be understood. In other words, it is desirable that "small puck motion" translate to "large image motion" in order to increase the sensitivity of the vision sensor. However, it is also desirable that "large puck motion" translate to "small image motion" in order to reduce the amount of information that the vision system needs to process in real–time. Understanding this and other trade-offs are fundamental for this application.

References

[1] Anderson, R.J., and Spong, M.W., "Hybrid Impedance Control of Robots, *IEEE J. of Robotics and Automation*, Vol. 4, no. 5, pp.549-556, Oct. 1988.

[2] D. Bobrow (ed.), *Qualitative Reasoning about Physical System.* MIT Press, Boston, 1985.

[3] G. F. DeJong, "Explanation-based control: An approach to reactive planning in continuous domains," In *Proceedings of the Workshop on Innovative Approaches to Planning, Scheduling and Control*, San Diego, CA, November 1990.

[4] G. F. DeJong and R. J. Mooney, "Explanation-based learning: An alternative view," *Machine Learning*, 1(2):145–176, 1986.

[5] K. D. Forbus, "Qualitative process theory," *Artificial Intelligence*, 24:85–168, 1984.

[6] Ghorbel, F., Fitzmorris, A., and Spong, M.W., "Robustness of Adaptive Control of Robot Manipulators: Theory and Experiment," *Workshop on Nonlinear and Adaptive Control: Application to Robotics*, Grenoble, France, Nov. 21-23, 1990, invited plenary paper.

[7] Ioannou, P.A., and Kokotovic, P.V., "Instability Analysis and Improvement of Robustness of Adaptive Control," *Automatica*, 20 (1984), pp.583-594.

[8] B. J. Kuipers, "Qualitative simulation," *Artificial Intelligence*, 29:289–338, 1986.

[9] Middleton, R.H., and Kokotovic, P.V., "Boundedness Properties of Simple Indirect Adaptive Control Systems," *IEEE Trans. on Automatic Cont.*, Vol. AC-37, No. 12, pp. 1989–1994, Dec. 1992.

[10] Thomas M. Mitchell, Richard M. Keller, and Smadar T. Kedar-Cabelli, "Explanation-based generalization: A unifying view," *Machine Learning*, 1(1):47–80, January 1986.

[11] R. J. Mooney and S. W. Bennett, "A domain-independent explanation-based generalizer," In *Proceedings of the National Conference on Artificial Intelligence*, pages 551–555, Philadelphia, PA, August 1986.

[12] Ortega, R., and Spong, M.W., "Adaptive Motion Control of Rigid Robots: A Tutorial," *Proc. IEEE Conference on Decision and Control*, Austin, TX, Dec. 1988.

[13] Reed, J.S., and Ioannou, P.A., "Instability Analysis and Robust Adaptive Control of Robotic Manipulators," *Proc. 27th IEEE Conf. on Decision and Cont.*, Austin, Dec. 1988.

[14] D. Weld and J. deKleer (ed.), *Readings in qualitative reasoning about physical systems.* Morgan Kaufmann, 1990.

[15] Ydstie, B.E., and Golden, M.P., "Chaos and Strange Attractors in Adaptive Control Systems," *Proc. IFAC World Congress on Automatic Control*, Munich, July, 1987.

[16] Yoshikawa, T., "Manipulability of Robotic Mechanisms," *The International Journal of Robotics Research*, Vol. 4, No. 2, pp. 3-9, Summer, 1985.

Proceedings of the
American Control Conference
San Francisco, California • June 1993

Intelligent Control Using Active-Adaptive Information Sources

Anuradha Annaswamy and Haruhiko Asada
Center for Information-Driven Mechanical Systems
Department of Mechanical Engineering
MIT
Cambridge, MA 02139

Abstract

In this paper, we report preliminary results of a framework within which to view intelligent controllers. Our premise is that an intelligent control system differs from a traditional control approach primarily in its usage of information. Unlike a traditional feedback control system, an intelligent controller uses a variety of information sources in a flexible form which are updated on-line as and when necessary. Motivated by the human decision process which activates various new information sources on-line in order to resolve difficult and confusing situations, we propose a framework wherein the controller can update the vector information sources based on knowledge and experience gained on-line, even as the system is in operation, and appropriately reorganize the control structure automatically. In particular, we shall focus on the contigency situations, examine candidates for contingent variables that needed to be added to the existing outputs, and propose a measure of persistent excitation to evaluate the information content of each contingent variable.

1. Introduction

A significant feature that distinguishes an intelligent control system from a traditional control system is in the usage of information available. A traditional feedback control system collects information from predetermined sources, describes the system with a set of state variables, and generates a control input using a fixed functional relationship between the measured signals and control actions. Such a format where the functional relationship, the information sources, and the state-variables are predetermined, is used even in advanced control systems such as adaptive and learning control. The objective of advanced controllers is to fine tune the functional relationship by using the predetermined information sources [11]. Our premise is that an intelligent control system differs from a traditional control approach primarily in its usage of information. The former uses a variety of information sources, identifies useful information on-line, and augments the variables by including the new information sources.

Such an active and adaptive usage of information sources will lead to a new approach to control problems that cannot be dealt with effectively by traditional control methods. When the degree of uncertainty and ambiguity present in the system becomes large, fundamental difficulties exist in selecting state variables and effective sources of information. At the time of control design, it is difficult to foresee all possible operating conditions of a complex system under which the controller must function. In control of fluid and thermal systems, for example, the system often has to deal with various physical phenomena, mixture of different phases and many special cases. If the system dynamics is subjected to such variations, it may simply not be possible to encompass all of them in a single dynamic model. Depending on variations in the system dynamics as well as on operating conditions, significant variables and useful information are substantially different. Attempts to generate a comprehensive and an exhaustive collection of variables and information sources may lead to a huge and useless mathematical description with a large number of variables and parameters. Hence, there is a basic inadequacy in the traditional control system methodology which requires that the complete set of variables necessary for describing the system behavior be delineated prior to its operation in order to take a control action.

To motivate an alternate, intelligent control methodology which overcomes the aforementioned difficulties, we focus on the human decision making process as a metaphor. When humans face difficult cases and confusing situations, they often seek new information that resolves the difficulty and ambiguity, rather than adhere to predetermined control rules and fixed information sources. Instead of using a fixed mapping from inputs to outputs, humans expand the input space as and when required, by activating various information sources. Human experience indicates that the input space is continuously modified, augmented, or even reduced when new and useful information is learned through experience. In addition to just learning a fixed form of input-output relationship, humans also learn as to what is useful information, explore new information sources, and organize the decision making process by incorporating the new information in their knowledge base. In this paper, we present a new formulation of an intelligent control system that possesses the ability not only to function as a traditional feedback control system which meets performance specifications, but also to cope with various phenomena and unpredictable phase changes by seeking pertinent information and using it appropriately in the controller structure. The information sources that constitute the intelligent control system are thus updated actively to include new information and restructured adaptively to cope with a higher degree of uncertainty and ambiguity.

The major goal of this paper is to determine how a control system can find useful information sources based on experience gained on-line, even as the system is in operation, and appropriately reorganize the control structure. In general, determining a set of significant variables for describing a system's behavior is a classical modeling problem as long as the variables are to be determined off-line. There are numerous methods for off-line determination of significant variables. In regression analysis, statistical methods such as the Backward Elimination method using the coefficient of determination and F-statistics have been developed to extract significant variables from sample data [6]. In estimation theory, techniques for obtaining reduced-order models based on the principle of prediction error have been existing for years [5,8]. These are primarily off-line modeling techniques that have been well grounded on pattern recognition, signal processing and traditional control methods. On the other hand, techniques for the on-line determination of significant information are very few. Relevant techniques can be found in the field of machine vision and artificial intelligence. Recently, a concept of active vision has been developed in order to acquire useful information pertinent to present contexts and situations [2]. For instance, the motion of a camera is coordinated with the image understanding and decision making processes. By activating panning, zooming and focusing drives, the camera seeks useful information actively depending on the context, goal and situation of the system [1]. The remarkable feature in active vision is that those variables and parameters extracted from the images are not predetermined but are attained on-line as the system recognizes the significance of those variables. In this paper, we will explore a new approach to intelligent control using a notion similar to that in active vision. We will formulate a procedure wherein significant variables which are locally active can be detected on-line, and develop a method for evaluating the relative information content of these variables based on a measure of persistent excitation.

2. A Framework of Intelligent Control

In this paper, we deal with systems that have a high degree of uncertainty and complexity characterized by the following:

- The system has to deal with various phases of plant conditions including special cases and contingencies that cannot be predicted a priori;
- While some special cases can be predicted, there may be several others present that may not be amenable to generate a low-order plant model due to dimensionality limits;
- Though a large amount of data may be available, it may not be possible to ascertain the phase of plant conditions that are producing each piece of information.

To cope with these issues, we propose an intelligent control method that allows the system to:

- detect substantial phase changes in plant conditions and inadequacies of the control structure due to the phase change,
- Identify on-line the variables that are significant and evaluate their information content in each phase of plant conditions, and
- re-organize the controller by incorporating the new variables.

Figure 1 shows the overall organization of the proposed intelligent control system. The system consists of the traditional control loop shown by the dotted line and the higher-level controller, termed "organizer". In the traditional control loop, all available information acquired from the sensors is collected and fed back into the control block, which computes the necessary action to be introduced into the plant. The basic structure of this control loop is determined based on a priori knowledge and data of the plant, while the sensors are appropriately designed so as to provide the necessary information to the controller. During this design process, we examine plant dynamics and describe the dominant behavior of the system by selecting a set of significant variables. In this paper, such variables describing the dominant system behavior are referred to as global variables. In the traditional control loop shown in Figure 1, these global variables are fed back to the controller, which leads to adequate performance for "normal" plant conditions.

When the system undergoes substantial phase changes, the set of global variables may not be sufficient to describe its behavior. In such an event, the sensors may not provide all the necessary information leading to the controller's response becoming erratic and inconsistent, and as a result, the system performance could deteriorate significantly. We propose an *intelligent controller* to detect this shortcoming by using a structure as shown in Fig. 1. The organizer modifies the bank of sensor outputs by adding significant new information when an erratic and inconsistent behavior is detected. More specifically, the organizer carries out the following tasks:

1. Determine whether or not the system performance is repeatedly deteriorating;
2. If so, commence to restructure the controller; The restructuring operation consists of the following:
   (a) The organizer requests the information processing unit to monitor new variables that are not included in the set of global variables.
   (b) The organizer evaluates the information content of each of the new variables relative to that of the global variables in order to obtain new information regarding the system that is independent of and uncorrelated to the original set of variables. This is done by attaching a *measure of persistent excitation* to each of the new variables that provides its information content.
   (c) The organizer incorporates both the new variables and their measures of persistent excitation into the traditional feedback loop and re-organizes the low-level controller.

The new variables to be incorporated into the feedback controller during a phase shift are referred to as contingent variables. Unlike the original set of global variables, contingent variables are not relevant to the dominant plant behavior under normal plant conditions, but are pertinent only to a specific phase of plant conditions which are often difficult to foresee a priori. In this paper, we assume that a set of candidates for contingent variables are provided to the organizer and discuss the procedure by which the organizer determines which of the variables among the candidates are more significant and pertinent to the current plant conditions. An assumption is also made that phase changes do not occur frequently and that once it does occur, the time-constants of the system are sufficiently large so that a large observation period is available to monitor the system characteristics when it is in its new phase. For example, in many thermal systems such as air conditioning systems, the various physical phenomena undergo a variety of phase changes, but these changes are slow and not frequent, compared with the computational speed of the controller.

In order to evaluate the information content of the variables, we shall use the concept of persistent excitation and develop a measure of persistent excitation of candidate variables which is relative to the information content of the global variables. Before describing the details of the procedure by which the organizer updates itself and the controller, we shall discuss, in the next section, the concept of persistent excitation.

3. A Persistent Excitation Condition

The concept of persistent excitation has been around since the sixties, when it arose naturally in the context of system identification. It was generally recognized at that time that the input signal should be such that it excites all the modes of the plant to be identified so that the plant parameters can all be identified. In 1966, a formal statement relating persistent excitation to parameter convergence was given by Åström and Bohlin [3]. Other equivalent statements regarding the convergence of parameters in terms of linear independence of sensitivity functions over an interval, nonsingularity of the autocovariance matrix of inputs, and the frequency content of the input signal have also been made over the years [7,9,4]. Persistent excitation has played a major role in the design of adaptive systems in both adaptive identification and control, to provide conditions under which the parameters of an adaptive observer converge to their true values in the former and the adaptive control parameters to the desired value in the latter.

Yet another instance where persistent excitation figured prominently was while establishing robustness properties of adaptive systems. It was realized that in the presence of disturbances, parameter convergence is essential to establish boundedness of all signals in the adaptive loop; local stability follows in the presence of persistent excitation and the boundedness is global if the measure of persistent excitation is large compared to the magnitude of the disturbance present [10].

The importance of persistent excitation in the afore-mentioned control problems stems from the fact that the property of persistent excitation is related, in principle, to the information content of the signals in the system. Persistent excitation, as defined and used in the above contexts, directly provides information regarding the system parameters and such information leads to better robustness in the presence of disturbances. In this paper, we exploit such a property of persistent excitation to ascertain the information content of contigent variables and to attach to each one of them a measure of persistent excitation to provide the extent of information each variable can provide.

3.1 Definitions

The following are some of the definitions of persistent excitation that have been introduced in the literature: A time-varying vector $u : \mathbb{R}^+ \rightarrow \mathbb{R}^n$ is said to be persistently exciting if constants t_0, T_0 and α exist such that

$$\int_t^{t+T} u(\tau)u^T(\tau)d\tau \geq \alpha I \quad \forall\, t \geq t_0 \qquad (1)$$

Several equivalent statements can be derived for Eq. (1) and the following are useful for our discussion here:

There exist positive constants t_0, T_0 and ϵ_0 such that for all unit vectors $w \in \mathbb{R}^n$,

$$(1)\ \frac{1}{T_0}\int_t^{t+T_0} w^T u(\tau)u^T(\tau)w d\tau \geq \epsilon_0^2\ \forall\, t \geq t_0 \qquad (2)$$

or

$$(2)\ \frac{1}{T_0}\int_t^{t+T_0} |u^T(\tau)w| d\tau \geq \epsilon_0\ \forall\, t \geq t_0 \qquad (3)$$

or

$$(3)\ \lambda_{\min}\left[\frac{1}{T_0}\int_t^{t+T_0} u(\tau)u^T(\tau)d\tau\right] \geq \epsilon_0^2\ \forall\, t \geq t_0 \qquad (4)$$

where $\lambda_{\min}(A)$ corresponds to the minimum eigenvalue of A. It was shown that when u satisfies the condition in Eq. (1) or its equivalent, then the origin $x = 0$ of the vector differential equation

$$\dot{x} = -u(t)u^T(t)x \qquad (5)$$

is uniformly asymptotically stable. We note that the error differential equation is directly relevant to the identification of an n-vector θ defined by the input-output relation

$$y(t) = \theta^T u(t)$$

using a parameter estimate $\widehat{\theta}$ specified by the differential equation

$$\dot{\widehat{\theta}} = u(t)(y(t) - u^T(t)\widehat{\theta})$$

if $x(t) \triangleq \widehat{\theta}(t) - \theta$.

A few remarks are in order regarding the definition of persistent excitation. We note that all the definitions above correspond to a property of an n-dimensional vector in an n-dimensional space. It is required that over every interval $[t, t+T_0]$, the vector $u(t)$ must have a component along every direction w in $\mathbb{R}^n$. Hence, the dimensionality of the space in which the persistent excitation is being evaluated is of considerable importance. For instance, a scalar constant $u(t) \equiv u_0$ is persistently exciting in $\mathbb{R}^1$ but if $u(t) = [u_0\ \ u_0]^T \in \mathbb{R}^2$, it is not persistently exciting in $\mathbb{R}^2$. Similarly, $u(t) = [\sin t\ \ \cos t]^T$ is persistently exciting in $\mathbb{R}^2$ but $u(t) = [\sin t\ \ \cos t\ \ \sin(t+\phi)]^T$ is not persistently exciting in $\mathbb{R}^3$ for any phase value ϕ. Hence, we note that the "linear independence" of the various components of a vector is central to its persistent excitation. While all the above conditions are required to be satisfied for all $t \geq t_0$, corresponding definitions of persistent excitation over a finite interval of time can also be given.

3.2 Statement of the problem

Our objective in this paper is to select contingent variables which are such that they provide the best possible useful information in a contingent situation when a phase change occurs. As mentioned in the introduction, it is assumed that the system remains in its new phase with a sufficiently large time-constant so that a large observation interval $[t_0, t_n]$ is available. We assume that, to begin with, a set of variables $\{z_1, z_2, \ldots, z_m\}$ have been identified as possible candidates in a region $\mathcal{X}^t$. The problem is to select contingent variables $x_1, x_2, \ldots, x_n$, $n < m$, all of which contribute to useful information regarding the phase change.

We propose an iterative procedure, consisting of n stages, to accomplish this objective. At each stage, observations are made over an interval $[t_i, t_{i+1}]$, where $t_i < t_{i+1}$, $i = 0, \ldots, n-1$. Suppose that at stage i, the vector of state-variables $\phi_i = [x_1, x_2, \ldots, x_{i-1}]^T$ has been identified to contribute significantly, that it is persistently exciting, with

$$\frac{1}{T_0} w_i^T \left[\int_t^{t+T_0} \phi_i(\tau)\phi_i^T(\tau)\, d\tau \right] w_i \geq \epsilon_i^2 \qquad \forall\, t \geq t_0$$

for all unit vectors $w_i \in \mathbb{R}^i$, where ϵ_i is the *measure* of persistent excitation of ϕ_i. The problem is to select x_i from a set of candidate contingent variables $L_i = \{z_1' \ldots, z_p\}$, where $p = m - i + 1$ so that the updated $\phi_{i+1} = [\phi_i^T, x_i]^T$ is maximally persistently exciting in $\mathbb{R}^{i+1}$. Starting from $i = 1$, such a procedure can be followed and repeated for $i = 2, \ldots, n$.

At each stage i, we require x_i to be such that

$$w_{i+1}^T \left[\frac{1}{T_0} \int_t^{t+T_0} \phi_{i+1}(\tau)\phi_{i+1}^T(\tau) d\tau \right] w_{i+1} \geq \epsilon_{i+1}^2 \quad (6)$$

for all $t \in [t_i, t_{i+1}]$, and for all unit vectors $w_{i+1} \in \mathbb{R}^{i+1}$. Therefore x_i is chosen as simply that variable in the set L_i which maximizes the measure ϵ_{i+1} in Eq. (6). These computations must be carried out for all the variables in L_i, which can be done either in parallel, or sequentially over subintervals $[t_i', t_{i+1}']$ of $[t_i, t_{i+1}]$. By proceeding in this manner, at stage n, we obtain variables $x_1, x_2, \ldots x_n$, and to each x_i a vector ϕ_i and a measure ϵ_i of persistent excitation are associated.

We note that Eq. (6) is computationally intensive and infeasible to implement on-line especially as i becomes large. Note, however, that the iterative procedure used implies that at each stage i, a persistently exciting vector ϕ_i in $\mathbb{R}^i$ is available with a measure of persistent excitation ϵ_i, and is updated using x_i to form an $i+1$-dimensional vector ϕ_{i+1}. The problem can therefore be restated as the determination of x_i such that

$$\frac{1}{T_0} w_{i+1}^T \left[\int_t^{t+T_0} \phi_{i+1}(\tau)\phi_{i+1}^T(\tau) d\tau \right] w_{i+1} \text{ is a maximum} \quad (7)$$

for all $t \in [t_i, t_{i+1}]$, $\forall$ unit vectors $w_{i+1} \in \mathbb{R}^{i+1}$ given that

$$\frac{1}{T_0} w_i^T \left[\int_t^{t+T_0} \phi_i(\tau)\phi_i^T(\tau) d\tau \right] w_i \geq \epsilon_i^2 \quad (8)$$

for all $t \in [t_i, t_{i+1}]$, $\forall$ unit vectors $w_i \in \mathbb{R}^i$. This is achieved by choosing x_i for which the measure p_i of persistent excitation is a maximum, where p_i is defined as

$$\frac{1}{T_0} \int_\Omega x_i^2\, d\tau \geq p_i^2 \quad (9)$$

where Ω is the union of all intervals $[\bar{t}_j, \bar{t}_{j+1}]$ in $[t, t+T_0]$ over which

$$\left\| \int_{\bar{t}_j}^{\bar{t}_{j+1}} \phi_i x_i\, d\tau \right\| \leq \epsilon \quad (10)$$

where ϵ is an arbitrarily small positive constant, i.e., x_i is uncorrelated with ϕ_i. By proceeding in stages, where at the end of each stage i, we selecte a contingent variable x_i and a measure of persistent excitation p_i, we can determine contingent variables $x_1, x_2, \ldots, x_n$, with measures of persistent excitation $p_1, p_2, \ldots, p_n$ which correspond to the information content of x_i.

4. The Organizer and Persistent Excitation

The above discussion indicates that starting from candidate variables in a set L_i, n variables can be determined which can be transmitted to the controller. Their measures of persistent excitation indicate the significance of the information in a given region $\mathcal{X}_t$. In order to implement the above procedure as an on-line method for a dynamic system, we propose the following approach. The candidate variables can be divided into several groups so that each group of candidate variables can be observed or estimated by the information processing unit at the same time. The organizer requests the information processing unit to evaluate different groups of candidate variables sequentially and their measures of persistent excitation, so that variables that correspond to the large measures can be used as contingent variables. The unique feature of the proposed method is that there are bidirectional interactions between the organizer and the information processing unit (and hence the bank of sensors); the organizer specifies the information processor which variables to observe, while the information processor provides observed data to the organizer so that the organizer can evaluate the persistent excitation of each variable in real time. Unlike the traditional control, the information used in the controller is not predetermined, but is selectively altered depending on actual plant conditions. In this sense, the information sources of the proposed control system are actively and adaptively modified on-line, hence active-adaptive information sources.

5. Concluding Remarks

Preliminary results pertaining to a framework for designing intelligent controllers were reported. With the premise that an intelligent control system differs from a traditional control approach primarily in its usage of information, we proposed an architecture wherein the controller uses information sources in a flexible form which are updated on-line as and when necessary. When unforseen changes occur in the system leading to contingency situations, candidate variables which contribute new information regarding the system were evaluated. A procedure by which the information content of these variables can be determined using the concept of persistent excitation was described. Work is currently under investigation to determine control strategies which can effectively make use of the contingent variables and their measures of persistent excitation.

References:

[1] A.L. Abbot and N. Ahuja, "Surface Reconstruction by Dynamic Integration of Focus, Camera Vergence and Stereo," *Proceedings of the 2nd International Conference on Computer Vision*, pp. 532-543, 1988.

[2] I.W. Aloimonos and A. Bandyapadhyay, "Active Vision," *International Journal of Computer Vision*," vol. 1, pp. 333-356, 1988.

[3] K.J. Åström and T. Bohlin, "Numerical Identification of Linear Dynamic Systems from Normal Operating Records," In *Theory of Self-Adaptive Control Systems*, Plenum Press, New York, 1986.

[4] P. Eykhoff (Ed.), "Identification and System Parameter Estimation," *Proceedings of the 3rd IFAC Symposium*, North Holland Publishing Company, Amsterdam, 1973.

[5] G.C. Goodwin and K. Sin, Adaptive Filtering, Prediction, and Control, Prentice-Hall, 1984.

[6]. R.F. Gunst and R.L. Mason, "Regression Analysis and Its Application," In Statistics: Textbooks and Monographs, vol. 34, Marcel Dekker, New York, 1980.

[7] P.M. Lion, "Rapid Identification of Linear and Nonlinear Systems," *AIAA Journal*, vol. 5, p. 1835, 1967.

[8] L. Ljung, *System Identification*, Prentice-Hall, Englewood Cliffs, NJ, 1987.

[9] J.M. Mendel, Discrete Techniques of Parameter Estimation, Marcel Dekker, New York, 1973.

[10] K.S. Narendra and A.M. Annaswamy, "Robust Adaptive Control in the Presence of Bounded Disturbances," *IEEE Transactions on Automatic Control*, vol. 31, 1986.

[11] K.S. Narendra and A.M. Annaswamy, Stable Adaptive Systems, Prentice-Hall, Englewood Cliffs, NJ, 1989.

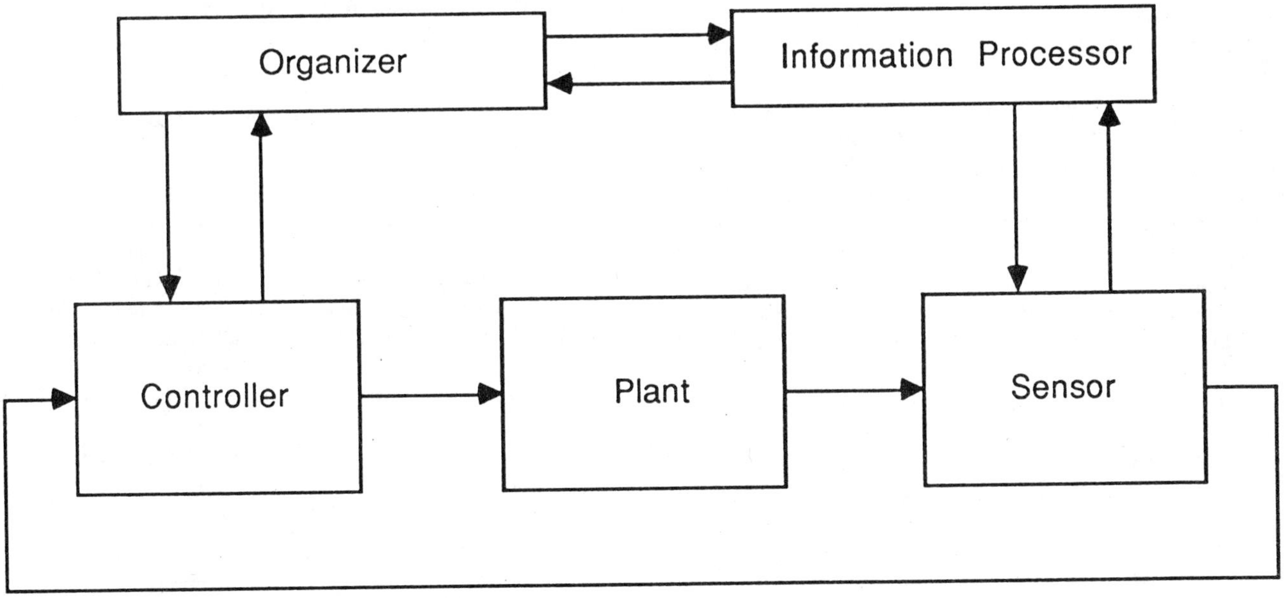

Figure 1. An Intelligent Controller

Proceedings of the American Control Conference
San Francisco, California • June 1993

A Nodal Link Perceptron Network with Applications to Control of a Free–Flying Robot *

Nader Sadegh

The George W. Woodruff School of Mechanical Engineering
Georgia Institute of Technology, Atlanta Georgia 30332

Abstract

Tracking control of a class of nonlinear systems using a Perceptron Neural Network (PNN) with local basis functions is presented. The basic structure of the PNN and its main properties are first stated. A novel discrete–time control strategy is introduced that employs the PNN for direct on–line estimation of the required feedforward control input. The developed controller is then applied for end point tracking control of a nonholonomic (free–flying) robot. The simulation results of this application demonstrate a perfect tracking performance after the network is fully trained.

1 Introduction

The applications of perceptron neural networks to control of nonlinear systems has been the subject of many research works in recent years [2, 6, 4, 7]. The main advantage of using the PNN as a controller is twofold: 1) complex nonlinear, even "table–look–up", control algorithms can be dynamically mapped onto the PNN, and recalled instantly when demanded; 2) the learning capability of the PNN enables the resulting controller to adapt itself to possible variations in the plant (i.e., system under control) dynamics while in operation.

In this paper, we introduce a perceptron network with "local" basis functions [7] referred to as the Nodal Link Perceptron Network (NLPN). The NLPN approximates nonlinear functions using a number of local multi–linear splines. As a result of its local basis functions, the NLPN has some key advantages over the conventional multi–layered perceptron networks: 1) its size and number of layers can be configured more easily and systematically, 2) it learns functional relationships faster, and 3) it may be trained based on information form one region of the input space without corrupting the previously learned information in more distant regions [3].

Following its theoretical development, the NLPN controller is applied to a 2–link free–flying manipulator for tracking control of its end–point. The novelty of the proposed control scheme lies in that it controls three degrees of freedom (end–point cartesian coordinates and base orientation) using only two internal torque inputs. No existing computed torque controller is known to accomplish such a task as effectively. The employed NLPN takes the desired state of the manipulator as input and, once trained, generates the required actuation inputs. The weights of the network are trained using the desired trajectory information, and the corresponding tracking errors.

This paper is organized as follows: Section 2 introduces the architecture and main properties of the NLPN. The NLPN control law is formulated in section 3. Section 4 discusses the application of the NLPN controller to a 2–link free–flying robot.

*This work was supported by the National Science Foundation under grant MSS-8910427.

2 Nodal Link Perceptron Network

In this section we present a Functional Link Perceptron Network (FLPN) [5, 8, 7] with *local* basis functions, which is used for identification and dynamic storage of nonlinear functions (see Fig. 1). This network for reasons to be made clear in the sequel will be referred to as the Nodal Link Perceptron Network (NLPN). The results obtained in this section will be subsequently used for the control of nonlinear dynamical systems to be introduced.

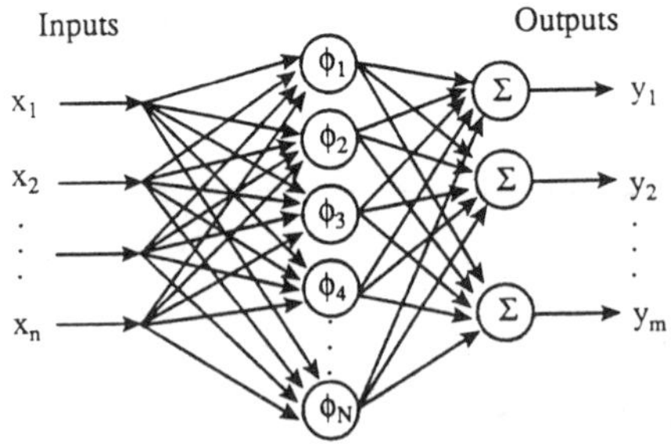

Figure 1: Functional Link Perceptron Network

To formulate the problem, let A be a compact simply connected subset of $\mathbb{R}^n$ referred to as the *input* space. Define $\mathcal{L}^m(A)$ to be the space of (Lebesgue) measurable functions $f : A \subset \mathbb{R}^n \to \mathbb{R}^m$ such that the "sup" norm of f, denoted by $\|f\|_A$, is bounded, i.e., $\|f\|_A := \sup_{\mathbf{x}\in A} |f(\mathbf{x})| < \infty$.

Without loss of generality, we assume that the input space is reshaped so that $A = [\alpha_1, \beta_1] \times \cdots \times [\alpha_n, \alpha_n]$. Furthermore, each interval $[\alpha_i, \beta_i]$ is divided into N_i equal sub-intervals which in turn partitions A into $\prod_{i=1}^n N_i$ identical rectangular prisms. We refer to the corners of these prisms as the nodal points of A. It can be easily seen that this partitioning of A results in $N := \prod_{i=1}^n (N_i + 1)$ nodal points. Defining the index set $\mathcal{I} := \{(i_1, \ldots, i_n) : i_j = 0, \ldots, N_j\}$ then the i-th ($i \in \mathcal{I}$) partition of A is

$$A_i = \{\mathbf{x} \in A : i_j - 1 \leq \frac{x_j - \alpha_j}{\beta_j - \alpha_j} N_j \leq i_j,\ j = 1, \ldots, n\}$$

if $1 \leq i_j \leq N_j$ and $A_i = \emptyset$ otherwise. Subsequently, the *normal* coordinates of $\mathbf{x} = [x_1 \ \cdots \ x_n]^T \in A_i$ are defined to be

$$\bar{x}_j^i := \frac{x_j - \alpha_j}{\beta_j - \alpha_j} N_j - i_j + 1, \quad j = 1, \ldots, n$$

where each $\bar{x}_j^i$ is a real number between 0 and 1. The i-th ($i \in \mathcal{I}$) nodal point of A, denoted by $\mathbf{a}^i$, is a point whose j-th coordinate is given by $\mathbf{a}_j^i = \alpha_j + [(\beta_j - \alpha_j) i_j / N_j]$.

We are now in position to describe the structure of the NLPN in detail.

Definition 1 An $N_1 \times \cdots \times N_n$ dimensional NLPN is a three-layered perceptron network whose output vector $\mathbf{y} \in \mathbb{R}^m$ is related to its input vector $\mathbf{x} \in A$ according to

$$\mathbf{y} = f_{\mathbf{W}}(\mathbf{x}) := \sum_{i \in \mathcal{I}} \mathbf{w}_i \phi_i(\mathbf{x}) \qquad (1)$$

where ϕ_i's are the basis (or activation) functions in the hidden layer and $\mathbf{w}_i \in \mathbb{R}^m$ is the vector of interconnection *weights* from the i-th hidden node to the output layer. Defining the index set $\mathcal{E}$ as

$$\mathcal{E} = \{(e_1, \ldots, e_n) : e_j = 1 \text{ or } 0,\ j = 1, \ldots, n\}$$

then the i-th basis function is given by

$$\phi_i(\mathbf{x}) = \begin{cases} \prod_{j=1}^n [(1 - e_j)\bar{x}_j + e_j(1 - \bar{x}_j] & \text{if } \mathbf{x} \in A_{i+e} \\ \text{for some } e \in \mathcal{E} & \\ 0 & \text{otherwise} \end{cases}$$

where $\bar{x}_j$ is the j-th normal coordinate of $\mathbf{x}$ in A_{i+e}. [1]
The set
$\mathcal{F} := \{f \in \mathcal{L}^m(A) : \ f = \sum_{i \in \mathcal{I}} \mathbf{w}_i \phi_i;\ \mathbf{w}_i \in \mathbb{R}^m\}$
which consists of all possible functions generated by the NLPN, is referred to as the (functional) range of the NLPN. In addition, the set of all functions in $\mathcal{L}^m(A)$ that can be approximated to within ε by the NLPN is denoted by $\mathcal{F}_\varepsilon$:

$$\mathcal{F}_\varepsilon := \{f \in \mathcal{L}^m(A) : \ \|f - f_{\mathbf{W}}\|_A \leq \varepsilon \quad \text{for some } f_{\mathbf{W}} \in \mathcal{F}\}$$

[1]the notation $i + e$ means $(i_1 + e_1, \ldots, i_n + e_n)$.

Example 1 The basis functions for $n = 2$ can be more explicitly expressed as follows:

$$\phi_{(i_1,i_2)}(x) = \begin{cases} \bar{x}_1\bar{x}_2 & \text{if } x \in A_{(i_1,i_2)} \\ (1 - \bar{x}_1)\bar{x}_2 & \text{if } x \in A_{(i_1+1,i_2)} \\ \bar{x}_1(1 - \bar{x}_2) & \text{if } x \in A_{(i_1,i_2+1)} \\ (1 - \bar{x}_1)(1 - \bar{x}_2) & \text{if } x \in A_{(i_1+1,i_2+1)} \\ 0 & \text{otherwise} \end{cases}$$

The following proposition reveals the rationale behind the definition of the proposed basis functions:

Proposition 1 *Each basis function $\phi_i(\mathbf{x})$ is well defined and continuous on A. Moreover, the value of f_w at the i-th nodal point of A equals $\mathbf{w}_i$: $f_{\mathbf{W}}(\mathbf{a}_i) = \mathbf{w}_i$. Thus $\mathbf{w}_i$'s are simply the nodal values of the function $f_{\mathbf{W}}$ stored in the NLPN.*

Since each basis function ϕ_i is multilinear, the NLPN approximates a nonlinear function by a piecewise multilinear function with the same nodal values. This property can be used to prove the following proposition:

Proposition 2 *Let $\mathcal{F}$ be the functional range of an $N_1 \times \cdots \times N_n$ dimensional NLPN. For any differentiable $f \in \mathcal{L}^m(A)$ there exists a $f_{\mathbf{W}} \in \mathcal{F}$ such that $\|f - f_{\mathbf{W}}\|_A = \sum_{j=1}^n O(h_j^2)$ where $h_j = (\beta_j - \alpha_j)/N_j$.*

Remark 1 Proposition 2 implies that any function $f \in \mathcal{L}^m$ can be approximated to within a prescribed accuracy by an NLPN with a sufficiently "large" number of nodes. In particular, the total number of nodal points, N, of the NLPN can be estimated based on the approximation tolerance, and an upper bound on the second-order variations of the function in question.

Remark 2 One drawback associated with this network is that the number of nodal points, N, grows exponentially as a function of the dimension n. However, if the network is constructed based on the assumption that the functions of interest are *linearly separable* this problem can be alleviated. By linearly separable, we mean that a function $f(x_1, \ldots, x_n)$ can be well approximated by a linear combination of lower dimensional functions. Letting the fixed integer $r < n$ denote the dimension of these functions, then it is assumed that $f \approx \sum_{\kappa \in \mathcal{K}} f_\kappa(x_{\kappa_1}, \ldots, x_{\kappa_r})$ where

$$\kappa \in \mathcal{K} = \{(\kappa_1, \ldots, \kappa_r) : 1 \leq \kappa_1 < \cdots < \kappa_r \leq n\}$$

It can be easily seen that a total number of $n!/[(n-r)!r!]$ NLPN's, each with an r dimensional input space, are needed to approximate f. Thus the total number of nodal points to approximate f has only a *polynomial* growth rate in n for a fixed r.

The input-output equation of the NLPN (1) can be more compactly expressed as

$$f_{\mathbf{W}}(\mathbf{x}) = \mathbf{W}^T \Phi(\mathbf{x})$$

where $\mathbf{W}^T := [\mathbf{w}_i]_{i \in \mathcal{I}} \in \mathbb{R}^{m \times N}$ and $\Phi(\mathbf{x}) := [\phi_i]_{i \in \mathcal{I}} \in \mathbb{R}^N$. Because of the local nature of the basis functions, at most 2^n components of $\Phi(\mathbf{x})$ are nonzero for any $\mathbf{x} \in A$. To exploit this property, we define $\mathbf{W}_i^T := [\mathbf{w}_{i+e}]_{e\in\mathcal{E}} \in \mathbb{R}^{m\times 2^n}$ and $\Phi_i(\mathbf{x}) := [\phi_{i+e}]_{e\in\mathcal{E}} \in \mathbb{R}^{2^n}$. Then the local representation of $f_\mathbf{W}$ becomes

$$f_\mathbf{W}(\mathbf{x}) = \mathbf{W}_i^T \Phi_i(\mathbf{x}) \quad \text{if } \mathbf{x} \in A_i \tag{2}$$

3 The NLPN Control Law

In this section we apply the NLPN to control a class of discrete–time nonlinear dynamical systems governed by the difference equation

$$\mathbf{x}_{k+1} = \mathbf{F}(\mathbf{x}_k, \mathbf{u}_k) \tag{3}$$

where $\mathbf{x}_k \in \mathbb{R}^{n_s}$ and $\mathbf{u}_k \in \mathbb{R}^m$ $(m \geq n_s)$ are the state and input vectors at discrete time k, respectively, and $\mathbf{F}(.,.)$ is a smooth function. This class, as we shall see, can also be used to incorporate the dynamic model of a nonlinear continuous–time plant subjected to a suitable discrete–time control strategy.

Let $\{\mathbf{x}_{dk}\}_{k=0}^{\infty}$ be a sequence of desired states that is confined to a compact set $A_d \in \mathbb{R}^{n_s}$. The control objective is to find a control sequence $\{\mathbf{u}_k\}_{k=0}^{\infty}$ that forces $\mathbf{x}_k$ to asymptotically converge to $\mathbf{x}_{dk}$ as $k \to \infty$. The control law to be proposed consists of two primary components: static feedback and feedforward. As we shall see a suitable NLPN will be used to generate the feedforward part of the control input.

To insure the controllability of the plant along the desired trajectory, we make the following assumptions:

Assumption 1

a) The Jacobian and controllability matrices, $\mathbf{J}(\mathbf{x})$ and $\mathbf{Q}(\mathbf{x})$, defined by

$$\mathbf{J}(\mathbf{x}) := \frac{\partial \mathbf{F}}{\partial \mathbf{x}}(\mathbf{x}, 0), \quad \text{and} \quad \mathbf{Q}(\mathbf{x}) := \mathbf{J}(\mathbf{x})^{-1}\frac{\partial \mathbf{F}}{\partial \mathbf{u}}(\mathbf{x}, 0),$$

respectively, are well defined and full–rank for all $\mathbf{x} \in A_d$.

b) The system is *controllable* along the desired trajectory in the following sense: There exists a continuous function $\Psi : A_d \times A_d \to \mathbb{R}^m$ such that if $\mathbf{u}_k$ is set to $\Psi(\mathbf{x}_{dk}, \mathbf{x}_{d,k+1})$, then $\mathbf{x}_{d,k+1} = \mathbf{F}(\mathbf{x}_{dk}, \mathbf{u}_k)$.

The following control law, referred to here as the NLPN control law, has been shown to achieve the aforementioned control objective [8]:

$$\mathbf{u}_k = -\mathbf{Q}_{dk}^{+}\left[\mathbf{e}_k + \mathbf{J}_{dk}^{-1}\hat{\mathbf{f}}_k\right] \tag{4}$$

where $\mathbf{J}_{dk} := \mathbf{J}(\mathbf{x}_{dk})$ and $\mathbf{Q}_{dk} := \mathbf{Q}(\mathbf{x}_{dk})$. The term $\hat{\mathbf{f}}_k$ is the feedforward input at time k generated by an NLPN (see definition1) with an $n \leq 2n_s$ dimensional input space A:

$$\hat{\mathbf{f}}_k = \hat{\mathbf{W}}_{i,k}^T \Phi_i(\underline{\mathbf{x}}_{dk}) \quad \text{if } \underline{\mathbf{x}}_{dk} \in A_i \tag{5}$$

where A_i is the i–th partition of A, $\underline{\mathbf{x}}_{dk}$ is networks's input at time k, which is a function of $\mathbf{x}_{dk}$ and $\mathbf{x}_{d,k+1}$, and $\Phi_i(.) \in \mathbb{R}^{2^n}$ is the i–th (local) vector of basis functions, as defined in the preceding section. The corresponding weight matrix, $\hat{\mathbf{W}}_{i,k}$, of the NLPN is updated using the following *modified* delta rule [7]:

$$\hat{\mathbf{W}}_{i,k+1} = \hat{\mathbf{W}}_{i,k} + c_k \Phi_{i,k-1}\bar{\mathbf{e}}_k^T \tag{6}$$

$$\bar{\mathbf{e}}_k = \mathbf{e}_k - c_{k-1}\Phi_{i,k-1}^T \Phi_{i,k-2}\, \bar{\mathbf{e}}_{k-1} \tag{7}$$

where $\Phi_{i,k} = \Phi_i(\underline{\mathbf{x}}_{dk})$, and $0 < c_k\ |\Phi_k|^2 < 2$.

Remark 3 As can be seen, the NLPN controller requires knowledge of the Jacobian and controllability matrices. However, as justified in [8], only an approximate knowledge of these matrices often suffices in practice.

Remark 4 The NLPN control law is composed of two components: state feedback and feedforward. The first term in eq. (5) represents the feedback component with a time varying gain, $\mathbf{Q}_{dk}^{+}$. The feedforward component, $\hat{\mathbf{f}}_k$, which is the output of the NLPN, is "learned" as a function of the desired state. See Fig. 2 for a block diagram representation of the NLPN control law.

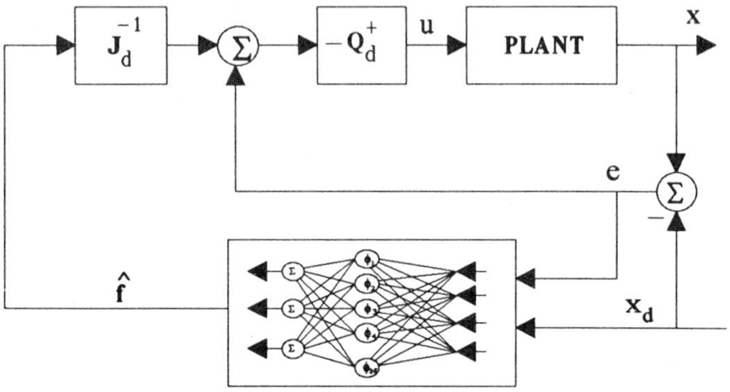

Figure 2: Block Diagram of the NLPN Controller

To guarantee the exponential convergence of the network's training algorithm, we assume that the desired state is chosen such that the vector of basis functions, Φ_k, is *Persistently Exciting*:

Assumption 2 The sequence $\Phi_k = \Phi(\underline{\mathbf{x}}_{dk})$ is Persistently Exciting (PE). That is, there exist $\alpha > 0$ and integer $s \geq 1$ such that the matrix

$$\sum_{k=k_0}^{k_0+s-1} \Phi_k \Phi_k^T \geq \alpha \mathbf{I}$$

for all integer $k_0 \geq 0$.

Remark 5 The examination of the above PE condition may be computationally difficult because of the size of the matrix involved. However, as in the formulation of the training law, it is possible to obtain a sufficient condition based the local representation of the network since most of the elements of Φ_k are zero at any given time k.

The main stability properties of the NLPN control law are summarized in the theorem below [8]:

Theorem 1 *Consider the dynamical system $\mathbf{x}_{k+1} = \mathbf{F}(\mathbf{x}_k, \mathbf{u}_k)$ subjected to the control laws given by eqs. (4) and (6) with assumptions 1 and 2 satisfied. Defining*

$$\mathbf{f}(\mathbf{x},\mathbf{z}) := -\frac{\partial \mathbf{F}}{\partial \mathbf{u}}(\mathbf{x},0)\ \Psi(\mathbf{x},\mathbf{x}+\mathbf{z})$$

let ε_t be the smallest positive scalar for which $\mathbf{f} \in \mathcal{F}_{\varepsilon_t}$. There exist positive scalars $\bar{e}_0$, $\bar{\mathrm{f}}_0$, $\bar{\varepsilon}_t$, and $\bar{\varepsilon}_d$ such that if $|\mathbf{e}_0| \leq \bar{e}_0$, $\|\hat{\mathbf{f}}_0 - \mathbf{f}\|_A \leq \bar{\mathrm{f}}_0$, $\varepsilon_t \leq \bar{\varepsilon}_t$, and $\varepsilon_d := \sup_k |\mathbf{u}_{dk}| \leq \bar{\varepsilon}_d$, then $\mathbf{e}_k$ and $\mathbf{u}_k$ are bounded for all k. Moreover, $\lim_{k\to\infty} |\mathbf{e}_k| = O(\varepsilon_t)$.

Remark 6 More simply stated, the theorem implies that if the desired task and the network size are properly selected, then for a sufficiently small initial tracking error, $\mathbf{e}_0$, and functional estimation error, $\|\hat{\mathbf{f}}_0 - \mathbf{f}\|_A$ (or equivalently $\tilde{\mathbf{W}}_0$), the tracking error, $\mathbf{e}_k$, and control input, $\mathbf{u}_k$, are bounded sequences. In addition, the magnitude of the tracking error at steady-state is on the order of the approximation tolerance, ε_t.

4 Application to a Free–Flying Robot

In this section we will show that it is possible to transform the equations of motion of a free-flying robot into a discrete-time equation of the form used as the plant model in the NLPN control law. For simplicity we only consider a two-link robot with $n = 3$ and $p = 2$; the extensions to higher degrees of freedom is straightforward but messy, and is not discussed here.

Consider the 2-link manipulator shown in Fig. 3. Let q_i, $i = 0, 1, 2$ denote the angular displacements of the base, link 1 relative to the base, and link 2 relative to link 1, respectively.

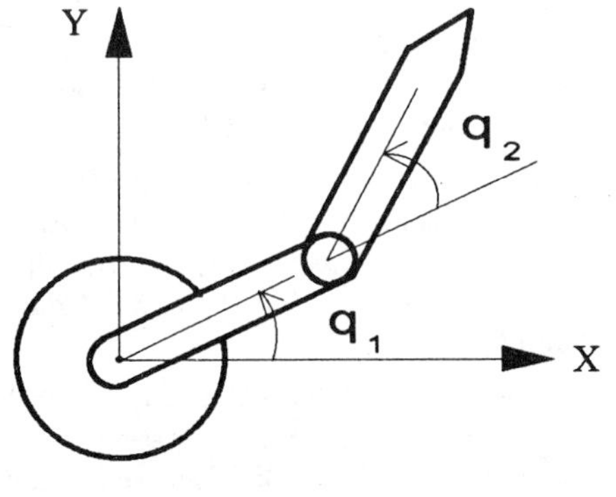

Figure 3: 2-Link Free–Flying Manipulator

In the absence of any external torques, by the law of conservation of angular momentum we have

$$M_0(q_2)\dot{q}_0 + M_1(q_2)\dot{q}_1 + M_2(q_2)\dot{q}_2 = 0$$

where

$$\begin{aligned} M_2(q_2) &= I_2 + m_2 l_{c2}^2 + m_2 l_1 l_{c2} \cos(q_2) \\ M_1(q_2) &= M_2(q_2) + I_1 + m_1 l_{c1}^2 + m_2 l_1^2 + m_2 l_1 l_{c2} \cos(q_2) \\ M_0(q_2) &= I_0 + M_1(q_2) \end{aligned}$$

In the above equations I_i is the moments of inertia of link i (link 0 is the base) about its centroid, m_i and l_i are the mass and length of link i, respectively, and l_{ci} is the distance between the centroid of link i and its center of rotation. Defining the state vectors $\mathbf{x} = [q_1\ q_2\ q_3]^T$, then the state equation for this system is

$$\dot{\mathbf{x}} = g_1(\mathbf{x})u_1 + g_2(\mathbf{x})u_2 \tag{8}$$

where $u_i = \dot{q}_i$, $i = 1, 2$, are the control inputs, and

$$\begin{aligned} g_1(\mathbf{x}) &= \begin{bmatrix} -\frac{M_1(q_2)}{M_0(q_2)} & 1 & 0 \end{bmatrix}^T \\ g_2(\mathbf{x}) &= \begin{bmatrix} -\frac{M_2(q_2)}{M_0(q_2)} & 0 & 1 \end{bmatrix}^T \end{aligned}$$

To discretize the differential equation (8), let T denote the state sampling time. The inputs $u_1(t)$ and $u_2(t)$ are chosen to be piecewise constant on $[kT, (k+1)T]$ and are collectively identified with $\mathbf{u}_k = [u_{1k}\ u_{2k}\ u_{3k}]^T \in \mathrm{IR}^3$. The relationship between the inputs $u_1(t)$ and $u_2(t)$ over the time interval $[kT, (k+1)T]$ and $\mathbf{u}_k$ is as follows:

$$\begin{aligned} u_1(t) &= (u_{1k} - 2\mu)\sigma_k^1 + \mu(1 - \sigma_k^1) \\ u_2(t) &= \sigma_k^2 u_{2k} + \sigma_k^3 u_{3k} \end{aligned}$$

where

$$\sigma_k^j(t) = \begin{cases} 1 & \text{if} \quad kT + (j-1)\delta \leq t < kT + j\delta \\ 0 & \text{otherwise} \end{cases}$$

$\delta = T/3$, and $\mu \neq 0$ is a free control parameter, which, for example, can be chosen to minimize a weighted norm of the input. Integrating eq. (8) from $t = kT$ to $t = (k+1)T$ gives $\mathbf{x}_{k+1}$ as a function of $\mathbf{x}_k$ and $\mathbf{u}_k = [u_{1k} \cdots u_{3k}]$:

$$\mathbf{x}_{k+1} = \mathbf{F}(\mathbf{x}_k, \mathbf{u}_k)$$

where the map $\mathbf{F} : \mathrm{IR}^3 \times \mathrm{IR}^2 \rightarrow \mathrm{IR}^3$ is the corresponding state transition map. Using proposition (3.1) in [7] it can be seen that the Jacobian matrix $\mathbf{J}(\mathbf{x}) = \mathbf{I}$ and that the controllability matrix, $\mathbf{Q}(\mathbf{x})$, is given by

$$\mathbf{Q}(\mathbf{x}) = \begin{bmatrix} \delta g_1 & \mathbf{b} & \mathrm{Ad}_{g_1}^{\delta}(\mathbf{b}) \end{bmatrix}(\mathbf{x}) \tag{9}$$

$$\mathbf{b}(\mathbf{x}) = \mu \int_0^{\delta} \mathrm{Ad}_{g_1}^{t}(g_2)(\mathbf{x})\, dt$$

The "Ad" operation on vector fields g_1 and g_2 can be computed using the following Taylor series expansion known as the Lie series [7, 1]:

$$\mathrm{Ad}_{g_1}^{t}(g_2)(\mathbf{x}) = \sum_{k=0}^{\infty} \frac{t^k}{k!} \mathrm{ad}_{g_1}^{k}(g_2)(\mathbf{x}) + o(|t|^k) \tag{10}$$

where $\mathrm{ad}_{g_1}(g_2)$ (also denoted by $[g_1, g_2]$) is the Lie bracket of g_1 and g_2 defined by

$$\mathrm{ad}_{g_1}(g_2)(\mathbf{x}) = \frac{\partial g_2}{\partial \mathbf{x}} g_1 - \frac{\partial g_1}{\partial \mathbf{x}} g_2 \tag{11}$$

and $\mathrm{ad}_{g_1}^{k}(g_2) = \mathrm{ad}_{g_1}(\mathrm{ad}_{g_1}^{k-1}(g_2))$.

Straight forward computations shows that for the two-link manipulator under consideration we have

$$g_3(\mathbf{x}) := \mathrm{ad}_{g_1}(g_2)(\mathbf{x}) = \frac{-2l_1 l_{c_2} I_0 m_2 \sin(q_2)}{M_0(\mathbf{x})^2} \begin{bmatrix} 1 & 0 & 0 \end{bmatrix}^T$$

and $\mathrm{ad}_{g_1}^k(g_2) = \mathbf{0}$ for $k \geq 2$. Using this in eq. (9) gives

$$\mathbf{Q}(\mathbf{x}) = \begin{bmatrix} g_1 & g_2 + (\delta\mu/2)g_3 & g_2 + (3\delta\mu/2)g_3 \end{bmatrix} \delta$$

It can be easily seen that $\mathbf{Q}(\mathbf{x})$ is invertible if and only if $q_2 \neq 0$, which is the case when the manipulator is in a nonsingular configuration. The NLPN control law in this case becomes

$$\mathbf{u}_k = -\mathbf{Q}_{dk}^{-1}(\mathbf{e}_k + \hat{\mathbf{f}}_k) \quad (12)$$

with $\hat{\mathbf{f}}_k$ given by eqs. (5)–(7).

4.1 Simulation Example

The performance of the NLPN controller was simulated on a free–flying robot with the following parameters: $l_1 = l_2 = 1$, $l_{c_1} = 1/2$, and $l_{c_2} = 2/3$ m.; $m_1 = m_2 = 1$ Kg.; $I_0 = 2.5$, $I_1 = 1/12$, and $I_2 = 1/6$ Kg–m^2. The sampling time $T = 0.12$ sec., and $\delta = T/3 = 0.04$ sec. The desired state of the manipulator was chosen so that its end–effector would follow the ellipsoid $(x/1.3)^2 + (y/1.6)^2 = 1$ in 6 seconds while the base maintained its initial orientation at every sampling instant. From the physics of the problem, it can be easily seen that the desired feedforward input is only a function of the second joint angle and the desired incremental angular motion of links 1 and 2. Therefore, the input vector of the NLPN may be selected as $\underline{\mathbf{x}}_{dk} = [q_{2k}\ \Delta q_{1k}\ \Delta q_{2k}] \in \mathbb{R}^3$ where q_{ik} is the desired angular position of the i–th link at time k, and $\Delta q_{ik} = q_{i,k+1} - q_{ik}$. The simulations were performed using an $8 \times 8 \times 8$ dimensional NLPN with the input space $A = [1.3, 1.8] \times [0, 0.2] \times [-0.1, 0.1]$. The simulation results in Fig. 4 shows that the NLPN controller forces the tracking error $\mathbf{e}_k = \mathbf{x}_k - \mathbf{x}_{dk}$ to zero asymptotically.

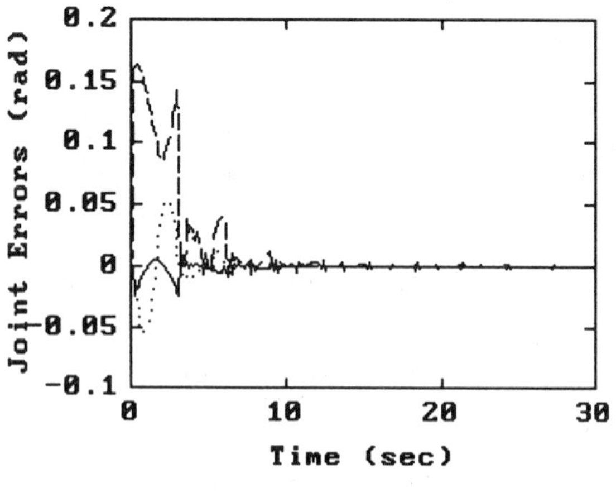

Figure 4: Joint Tracking Errors vs. Time
e_1: —, e_2: - - -, e_3: · · ·

5 Conclusions

A tracking controller for nonlinear dynamical systems, which employs a Nodal Link Perceptron Network (NLPN), was introduced. The basic structure and the properties of the NLPN were first discussed. It was subsequently shown that the NLPN could be used to generate the feedforward control input for tracking control of a large class of discrete–time nonlinear systems. Finally, the NLPN controller was applied for end point tracking control of a free–flying 2–link manipulator with only two internal actuators. The simulation results of this application confirmed the theoretical assertions of the paper.

References

[1] Krener, A.J., "$(\mathrm{Ad}_{f,g})$, $(\mathrm{ad}_{f,g})$ and Locally $(\mathrm{ad}_{f,g})$ Invariant and Controllability Distributions," *Siam J. Control and Optimization*, vol. 23, No. 4, pp. 523–549, July 1985.

[2] Kwato, M., K. Furukawa, and R. Suzuki, "A Hierarchical Neural–Network Model for Control and Learning of Voluntary Movement," *Biological Cybernetics*, vol. 57, pp. 169–185, 1987.

[3] Lane, S.H., D.A. Handelman, and J.J. Gelfand, "Theory and Development of Higher–Order CMAC Neural Networks," *IEEE Control System Magazine*, vol. 12, no. 2, April 1992.

[4] Narendra, K.S. and K. Parthasarathy, "Identification and Control of Dynamical Systems Using Neural Networks," *IEEE Trans. on Neural Networks*, vol.1, no.1, March 1990.

[5] Pao, Y.–H., *Adaptive Pattern Recognition and Neural Networks*, Addison–Wesley, 1989.

[6] Psaltis, D., S. Athanasios, and A.A. Yamamura, "A Multilayered Neural Network Controller," *IEEE Control Systems Magazine* April, 1988.

[7] Sadegh, N., "A Perceptron Network for Functional Identification and Nonlinear Control," *Proceedings of the 1992 American Control Conference*, Chicago, Illinois, June 1992. Also, Submitted to the *IEEE Transactions on Neural Networks.*

[8] Sadegh, N., "Nonlinear Identification and Control via Neural Networks," Symposium of Systems with Inexact Dynamic Models, *the ASME Winter Annual Meeting*, December 1–6, 1991, Atlanta, GA.

[9] Sadegh, N. and K. Guglielmo, "A New Repetitive Controller for Mechanical Manipulators," *International Journal of Robotics Research*, vol. 8, August 1991.

Proceedings of the
American Control Conference
San Francisco, California • June 1993

Learning Control of Non-Linear Power Transmission Mechanisms - The Electronic Flywheel

Jwu-Sheng Hu
Assistant Professor
Department of Mechanical Engineering
Wayne State University

Abstract

To reduce velocity variation due to nonlinear dynamic effect in mechanisms, passive devices such as the mechanical flywheel is usually used. The velocity variation can also be suppressed by precise control of the power source. In this paper, a learning control algorithm is developed for velocity control of non-linear power transmission mechanisms. The algorithm is separated into two versions. In the first version, the reference velocity is designed such that at steady state, the nonlinear dynamic effect is periodic in time. In such case, only one functional has to be learned to control the velocity. The second version of the controller extends the first one to deal with the reference velocity which results in an aperiodic dynamic effect at steady state.

1. Introduction

Mechanical systems are very important in industrial machinery. Modern design of mechanisms combine electrical, hydraulic, pneumatic actuators as well as sensory devices to perform complex tasks. A successful example is the robot manipulator. In the area of mechanism design, one of the crucial elements is to control the transmission of force. Without modern control technology, most of the control tasks are achieved in a passive manner - combining kinematic and dynamic design of machine elements. While advanced motion controllers have been applied to robot manipulators, there are still many types of systems in which modern control techniques can be used. Although they share the same kinematic and dynamic principles, the nature of the task and control issues are not necessary the same as robot manipulators.

In this paper, we consider the speed control problem of one-degree-of-freedom mechanisms. Typical operations of this kind of mechanisms are rotation-to-rotation translation such as a gear train and linear-to-rotation or rotation-to-linear translation such as a slider-crank mechanism. The transmission mechanisms are used not only to perform specific tasks, but also to improve efficiency. For example, electric motors usually operate most efficiently within a certain speed range. Therefore, a gear train has to be used for tasks in other speed ranges. Another example is to use a slider-crank mechanism to perform a reciprocal motion which involves repeated start/stop movements. However, the complexity of the kinematic design results in complex dynamic behavior of the mechanisms. In such cases, additional components are used to achieve desired operation. The most common example of such components is the flywheel. A large flywheel can reduce the speed variation due to nonlinear dynamic effects. Flywheels are usually designed for a specific speed operation and consume a significant amount of the energy. In this paper, an alternative design of flywheel is proposed which is based on the application of active feedback control to the power source, i.e., torque control of an electric motor used in variable-inertia nonlinear mechanisms. The effect of feedback control is equivalent to adding an "electronic flywheel" to the system without the disadvantage associated with the inertia and friction of ordinary flywheels. Furthermore, use of microprocessor-based controllers allows more flexibility in the operation of the system.

One particular idea similar to the electronic flywheel is the "electronic governor" in a DC motor (Kenjo and Nagamori, 1985). The principle of an electronic governor is based on the dynamic coupling effect between electrical and mechanical systems. Consequently, speed control can be achieved by regulating voltage through internal feedback circuits. The feedback controller is usually designed by assuming a constant load and may not be able to accommodate a non-linear mechanism.

The computed torque and adaptive control methods in the robotics research can be applied directly to the transmission mechanisms. However, unlike most robot manipulators, transmission mechanisms do not have motion sensors at every joint. As a result, the requirement to solve complex kinematic relations in both these methods makes them unappealing in practice. A close look at most transmission mechanisms shows that the their nonlinear dynamics are position (angle) dependent. Therefore, the nonlinear dynamics can be viewed as a function with bounded domain and range. If the function is known in advance, it can be used as a direct cancellation signal which is essentially the computed torque method. A more advanced design is to learn the function during the course of control actions. In such cases, a functional is adapted in time as compared with adapting parameters in conventional adaptive control. Adaptive learning of a functional has been proposed by Messner et al (1991) In this paper, a simpler learning algorithm for speed tracking of transmission mechanism is proposed. The control law is implemented based on the angular information and is characterized as "learning in the angular domain". Three functional to be learned are the generalized inertia, Coriolis and centripetal forces, and gravitational force. It is interesting to notice that the combined effect of these forces may not be periodic even though the velocity is periodic. In such cases, the time-domain repetitive control technique (Hara et al, 1988; Tomizuka et al, 1988) cannot be applied. For certain periodic speed trajectories where the nonlinear dynamics are also periodic in time, the control law can be further simplified so that only one functional is learned. As demonstrated later, the nonlinear dynamics are not necessarily periodic in time even if the speed of one of the joints is periodic.

The control systems are demonstrated on a four-bar linkage mechanism which exhibits most of the complex dynamic characteristics appearing in many mechanical systems

2. Dynamic Model of Transmission Mechanisms

The dynamic model of a one-degree-of-freedom mechanism, neglecting joint clearances, can be written as

$$m(\theta)\ddot{\theta} + c(\theta)\dot{\theta}^2 + p(\theta) + f(\theta,\dot{\theta}) = \tau \qquad (1)$$

where θ can be either angular or linear displacement, $m(\theta)$ is the generalized inertia, $c(\theta)\dot{\theta}^2$ represents the Coriolis and centripetal forces, $p(\theta)$ is the gravitational force, $f(\theta,\dot{\theta})$ is the friction force and τ is the actuator force or torque. The generalized coordinate q cannot be arbitrarily chosen. It must be selected such that the mechanism's configuration is uniquely determined. As an example, consider a four-bar linkage shown in Fig. 1. The kinematic constraints are expressed as

$$l_3 cos(\theta_3) = l_1 - l_2 cos(\theta_2) + l_4 cos(\theta_4) \qquad (2a)$$

$$l_3 sin(\theta_3) = l_4 sin(\theta_4) - l_2 sin(\theta_2) \qquad (2b)$$

$$\dot{\theta}_3 = \frac{l_2 sin(\theta_2 - \theta_4)}{l_3 sin(\theta_4 - \theta_3)}\dot{\theta}_2 \qquad (3a)$$

$$\dot{\theta}_4 = \frac{l_2 sin(\theta_2 - \theta_3)}{l_4 sin(\theta_4 - \theta_3)}\dot{\theta}_2 \qquad (3b)$$

If we choose θ_2 (the crank's angle) as the generalized coordinate, by substituting Eq.(2a,b) and (3a,b), the kinetic energy

$$K_E = \frac{1}{2}I_2\dot{\theta}_2^{\,2} + \frac{1}{2}m_3 l_2 r_3 cos(\theta_2 - \theta_3)\dot{\theta}_2\dot{\theta}_3$$

$$+\frac{1}{2}m_3 r_3^{\,2}\dot{\theta}_3^{\,2} + \frac{1}{2}I_3\dot{\theta}_3^{\,2} + \frac{1}{2}I_4\dot{\theta}_4^{\,2}$$

can be transformed into

$$K_E = \frac{1}{2}m(\theta_2)\dot{\theta}_2^{\,2}$$

Similarly, the potential energy is

$$V = m_2 g\, sin(\theta_2) r_2 + m_3 g(l_2 sin(\theta_2) + r_3 sin(\theta_3)) + m_4 g\, sin(\theta_4) r_4$$

$$= V(\theta_2)$$

Using the Largrange equation, a dynamic equation similar to Eq.(1) can be derived. Notice that in Eq.(1), the inertia, Coriolis, and centripetal terms satisfy

$$c(\theta) = \frac{1}{2}\frac{\partial}{\partial\theta}m(\theta) \tag{4}$$

Eq.(4) is nothing but the special case of skew-symmetry property observed by Arimoto et al (1983) and Koditchek (1984) in the robot dynamics. The one-dimensional version of the skew symmetry property is very easy to prove by knowing that

$$c(\theta)\dot{\theta}^2 = \frac{d}{dt}m(\theta)\dot{\theta} - \frac{\partial}{\partial\theta}K_E$$

3. The Application of Computed Torque and Adaptive Control Methods

The computed torque method, which directly cancels the non-linearity in Eq.(1) (i.e., Coriolis, centripetal and gravitational forces), has been proposed in robotics research (Craig 1986). The algorithm can be written as follows,

$$\tau = p(\theta) + f(\theta,\dot{\theta}) + c(\theta)\dot{\theta}\dot{\theta}_d + m(\theta)\ddot{\theta}_d - k_d\dot{\tilde{\theta}} - k_p\tilde{\theta} \tag{5}$$

where

$\tilde{\theta} = \theta - \theta_d$, θ_d : the reference position

It requires the knowledge of the parameters such as the link length and inertia to implement Eq.(5). For open-loop robots, this requirement can be removed by using the adaptive control technique. This technique involves a reparameterization of the dynamic equation (Slotine and Li, 1986). However, in a closed-loop mechanism, the kinematic relationship needs to be solved since it is not likely to measure the coordinate of each joint. Therefore, the parameters such as the link length in a four-bar linkage has to be known in order to apply the adaptive control. In this case, reparameterization can be shown as

$$p(\theta) + c(\theta)\dot{\theta}\dot{\theta}_d + m(\theta)\ddot{\theta}_d = W(\theta,\dot{\theta},\dot{\theta}_d,\ddot{\theta}_d)\Theta \tag{6}$$

where $W(\cdot)$ is a known vector and Θ contains the unknown parameters. The control law is devised as follows (Slotine and Li, 1986)

$$\tau = W(\theta,\dot{\theta},\dot{\theta}_d,\ddot{\theta}_d)\hat{\Theta} + f(\theta,\dot{\theta}) - k_d\dot{\tilde{\theta}} - k_p\tilde{\theta} \tag{7}$$

$$\dot{\hat{\Theta}} = -\gamma W^T\dot{\tilde{\theta}}$$

In Eq.(7), instead of the composite error (or distance to the sliding surface) as commonly used in the robotics research, the velocity error is used to drive the parameter estimation algorithm. Stability of the algorithm is still guaranteed. However, a large part of the transmission mechanisms are designed to transmit momentum (or energy). Position regulation in these cases is not a concern. Hence, Eq.(5) and (7) can be applied by simply dropping the last term in the control input.

4. Learning Control in The Angular Domain:

The objective of the learning controller is to track a velocity profile without knowing the specific structure of a mechanism. The velocity profile is assumed to be periodic (including constant velocity). Without loss of generality, the coordinate measured in a mechanism is assumed to be a joint angle. Since the nonlinear functions ($m(\theta)$, $c(\theta)$, and $p(\theta)$) only depend on the angle, they can be viewed as functional whose domain is the angular period. Let the period be ϕ. We can define a projection $\Phi_1: R \rightarrow [0,\phi]$ such that

$$\theta = n\phi + \Phi_1(\theta),\ \ 0 \le \Phi_1(\theta) \le \phi,\ \ n: \text{integer}$$

As demonstrated later, the nonlinear function to be learned is defined as

$$g(t) = m(\theta(t))\ddot{\theta}_d(t) + c(\theta(t))\dot{\theta}_d^{\,2}(t) + p(\theta(t)) \tag{8}$$

Using the projection Φ_1, Eq.(8) is transformed into the following functional

$$w(u,t)\big|_{u=\Phi_1(\theta)} = m(\theta)\ddot{\theta}_d(t) + c(\theta)\dot{\theta}_d^{\,2}(t) + p(\theta) \tag{9}$$

The desired velocity and acceleration, as functions of time, can be represented as functions of the desired angle. Since tracking of the desired angle in time domain is not necessary for a closed-loop mechanism, it can be treated as an independent variable (independent of time). In that case, there is no difference between the desired angle and the actual angle. This also corresponds to the case when the desired velocity and acceleration are designed as functions of the angle (i.e., configuration dependent instead of time dependent). Therefore, Eq.(8) can be rewritten as

$$w(u,\theta)\big|_{u=\Phi_1(\theta)} = m(\theta)\ddot{\theta}_d(\theta) + c(\theta)\dot{\theta}_d^{\,2}(\theta) + p(\theta) \tag{10}$$

Let the time-domain period of the desired velocity be T. This implies that Eq.(9) is a periodic functional with period T. Denoting α as the angular period, i.e.,

$$\int_t^{t+T} \dot{\theta}_d(\tau)d\tau = \alpha$$

Eq.(10) is also a periodic functional with period α. Suppose $\phi=\lambda\alpha$, Eq.(10) can be simplified to a functional with only one variable if λ is a rational number, i.e., $\lambda=m/h$, m,h: integers.. The domain can be derived as the least common multiplier of ϕ. and α ($h\phi$ or $m\alpha$). Defining a new projection as

$$\theta = nh\phi + \Phi(\theta),\ \ 0 \le \Phi(\theta) \le h\phi,\ \ n: \text{integer}$$

Eq.(9) can then be written as

$$w(u)\big|_{u=\Phi(\theta)} = m(\theta)\ddot{\theta}_d(\theta) + c(\theta)\dot{\theta}_d^{\,2}(\theta) + p(\theta) \tag{11}$$

The cases of λ being irrational or rational correspond to the function $g(t)$ being periodic or aperiodic (Berge et al., 1984) at steady state (i.e., $\dot{\theta}(t) = \dot{\theta}_d(t)$). It can be shown that the nonlinear functions $m(\theta(t))$, $c(\theta(t))$ and $p(\theta(t))$ are periodic in time if and only if λ is a rational number. Moreover, the period can be calculated as hT which is also the period of $g(t)$. As an example, consider the four-bar linkage (Fig. 1) with θ_2 as the generalized coordinate. The nonlinear functions have an angular period $\phi=2\pi$. Consider the following two desired velocities:

$$(1)\ \dot{\theta}_d = 20\pi + 10\sin(10\pi t)\ \text{rad/sec} \tag{12a}$$

$$(2)\ \dot{\theta}_d = 20\pi - 10\sin(10t)\ \text{rad/sec} \tag{12b}$$

The first case has a time period $T=0.2$sec and an angular period $\alpha=4\pi$. Therefore, the period of $g(t)$ is 0.4sec and the domain of the functional (Eq.(11)) is 4π. The second case has an angular period of $4\pi^2$ which results in an aperiodic $g(t)$. This example can be better illustrated by examining their steady-state phase diagrams. The phase plane is considered as the circular area of a cylinder. The circumference represents the angle (0 to 2π) while the longitudinal axis represents the velocity. Fig.2 and 3 depict the phase diagrams by unfolding the cylinder. In the first case (Fig.2), it is clear that the trajectory is periodic with angular period 4π. The trajectory in the second case results in a chaotic motion on the phase plane as shown in Fig. 3. The trajectory will be dense on the phase plane eventually.

We first consider the learning controller design when λ is a rational number. As indicated by Eq.(11), the functional to be learned depends only on angle. To represent the functional, an angular index is created as the following,

$$\theta^*(t) = \int_{t_0}^{t} \left|\dot{\theta}(t)\right| dt - mh\phi \tag{13}$$

where m is an integer such that $0 \le \theta^*(t) < h\phi$. The control law for tracking of a periodic velocity profile is proposed as

$$\tau(t) = -K_d\dot{\tilde{\theta}}(t) - K_s sign(\dot{\tilde{\theta}}(t)) + \hat{w}(\theta^*(t),t) \tag{14a}$$

$$\frac{\partial}{\partial t}\hat{w}^*(u,t) = -\Gamma\dot{\tilde{\theta}}(t)\delta(u-\theta^*(t)),\ \ \delta(\cdot): \text{Dirac delta function} \tag{14b}$$

$$\hat{w}(u,t) = \begin{cases} \hat{w}^*(u,t) & \text{if}\ \ \underline{W} - \gamma < \hat{w}^*(u,t) < \overline{W} + \gamma \\ \hat{w}^*(u,t-T) & \text{otherwise} \end{cases} \tag{14c}$$

$$T:\ \int_{t-T}^{t} \left|\dot{\theta}(t)\right| dt = h\phi \tag{14d}$$

$$K_d > \underset{\theta}{Max}\left|c(\theta)\right| + \delta_1,\ \ K_s \ge \underset{\theta,\dot{\theta}}{Max}\left|f(\theta,\dot{\theta})\right| + \delta_2 \tag{14e}$$

$$\overline{W} = \underset{\theta^*\in[0,h\phi]}{Max}\ w(\theta^*),\ \ \underline{W} = \underset{\theta^*\in[0,h\phi]}{Min}\ w(\theta^*) \tag{14f}$$

The proof of stability of the above control algorithm is shown in the Appendix. The learning gain Γ can be adjusted to achieve a desired convergence rate. Notice that $\hat{w}^*(u,t)$, which is intended to learn $w(u)$ in Eq.(11), is a functional in time. The argument u has the range of $[0,h\phi]$ and the functional is updated at the point $u = \theta^*(t)$ every time instant. In Messner's work (1991), a smooth Hilbert-Schmdt kernel is used in order to guarantee stability. As a result, the overall functional has to be updated every time. Eq.(14) is more like the conventional repetitive control where only one point within the functional is updated. However, to guarantee the boundness of the functional, Eq.(14c) has to be imposed.

When λ is not a rational number, the nonlinear functional cannot be represented by a functional with one argument (Eq.(11)). However, the function $m(\theta)$, $c(\theta)$ and $p(\theta)$ still depend solely on the angle and can be viewed as three different functional. Therefore, the idea of functional adaptation shown in Eq.(14) can be utilized to learn those functional. In this case, the angular index is defined as

$$\theta^*(t) = \int_{t_0}^{t} |\dot{\theta}(t)| dt - m\phi \quad (15)$$

where m is an integer such that $0 \le \theta^*(t) < \phi$. The control law is proposed as the following,

$$\tau(t) = -K_d \dot{\tilde{\theta}}(t) - K_s sign(\dot{\tilde{\theta}}(t)) + \hat{w}_1(u,t)\ddot{\theta}_d + \hat{w}_2(u,t)\dot{\theta}_d\dot{\theta} + \hat{w}_3(u,t) \quad (16a)$$

$$\frac{\partial}{\partial t}\hat{w}_i^*(u,t) = -\Gamma_i \alpha_i(t)\dot{\tilde{\theta}}(t)\delta(u - \theta^*(t)), \; i = 1,2,3 \quad (16b)$$

$$\hat{w}_i(u,t) = \begin{cases} \hat{w}_i^*(u,t) & \text{if } \underline{W}_i - \delta < \hat{w}_i^*(u,t) < \overline{W}_i + \delta \\ \hat{w}_i^*(u,t-T) & \text{otherwise} \end{cases} \quad (16c)$$

$$T: \int_{t-T}^{t} |\dot{\theta}(t)| dt = \phi \quad (16d)$$

$$\alpha_1(t) = \ddot{\theta}_d(t), \;\; \alpha_2(t) = \dot{\theta}_d(t)\dot{\theta}(t), \;\; \alpha_3(t) = 1, \quad (16e)$$

$$K_d > 0, \; K_s \ge \underset{\theta,\dot{\theta}}{Max}|f(\theta,\dot{\theta})| + \delta_2 \quad (16f)$$

$$\underline{W}_i \le \underset{\xi\in[0,\phi]}{Min}|b_i(\xi)| - \gamma_i, \;\; \overline{W}_i \ge \underset{\xi\in[0,\phi]}{Max}|b_i(\xi)| + \gamma_i$$

where

$$b_1(\xi) = m(\xi), \;\; b_2(\xi) = c(\xi), \;\; b_3(\xi) = p(\xi),$$

The time interval T in Eq.(16d) is defined as the smallest positive number such that $\theta^*(t) = \theta^*(t-T)$. Proof of the stability of this control algorithm is given in the Appendix. The functional $\hat{w}_i(\cdot)$ is intended to learn the angle dependent functions $m(\theta)$, $c(\theta)$ and $p(\theta)$. From Eq.(16b), the functional are updated only when the angular index is encountered.

A major difference in implementing Eq.(14) and (16) is that in Eq.(14), all the parameters can be expressed as functions of the angular index (Eq.(13)). In Eq.(16), however, two angular indices are needed. One of them is defined in Eq.(15) and the other one is used to index the desired velocity and acceleration. Alternatively, the desired velocity and acceleration can also be represented in time. In that case, an internal clock in the controller is required.

5. Simulation Examples

To simulate the learning control law in digital computers, discrete approximation to both Eq.(14) and (16) is necessary, especially for Eq.(14b) and (16b). Assume that the angular velocity is not zero and the domain of u is digitized into N segments. Eq.(14b) can be approximated as

$$\hat{w}^*(u_j,t_k)\Big|_{u_j=\theta^*(t_k)} - \hat{w}^*(u_j,t_k - h_k)\Big|_{u_j=\theta^*(t_k)} = -\Gamma h_k \dot{\tilde{\theta}}(t_k) \quad (19)$$

$$\approx -\Gamma_1 \dot{\tilde{\theta}}(t_k) \text{ for large } N$$

where

$$u_j = j\frac{h\phi}{N}, \;\; t_k = t_{k-1} + h_k, \text{ and } \theta^*(t_k) = \theta^*(t_{k-1}) + \frac{h\phi}{N}$$

Similar results can be derived for Eq.(16b) also. The parameters of the four-bar linkage considered in the simulation is listed in the following

LINK #	1	2	3	4
Length (mm)	283.7	44.45	240.0	240.0
Mass (kg)	-	0.8	0.2	0.2
Inertia (kg-mm^2)	-	5268.8	3840	3840

Table 1 Parameters of the four-bar linkage

The mass centers are assumed to be half of the links' length and the gravitational acceleration is 9.8 kgm/sec^2. The desired velocity of the crank for the first example is shown in Eq.(12a) which requires only one learning algorithm (Eq.(14)). The initial velocity is 30 rad/sec. Fig. 4 shows the crank's velocity and the convergence of error is shown in Fig. 5. The nonlinear function learned by the algorithm is shown in Fig. 6 where the horizontal axis depicts the angular index (number of revolutions of the crank). Notice that due to a large initial error, the updated functional value is larger than the upper bound and the functional value is assigned as the one in the previous period (zero initially). After the velocity approaches the desired one, the updated functional value falls within the bounds and learning is activated. The second example uses the velocity profile in Eq.(12b) and implements the controller in Eq.(16). Figure 7 shows the tracking result of the velocity profile and Fig.8 the convergence of velocity errors.

6. Conclusion

In this paper, motion control of transmission mechanisms is discussed. Two types of control algorithms are presented. The objective is to use modern control techniques to achieve speed regulation of non-linear transmission mechanisms in order to save energy by eliminating flywheels. The controller proposed is of learning type which learns the non-linear dynamic of a mechanism. One of the novelty of the learning control algorithms presented in this paper is to learn the nonlinearity in the angular domain. Although the controller is designed in the continuous time domain, the best way to implement it is by using digital microprocessors. The angle information can be obtained from pulse generating sensors such as an optical encoder. The width of the generated pulses determines the sampling time. As a consequence, the digital control system runs at an asynchronous fashion. More research will be conducted toward this direction so as to make the controller a practical proposition.

Reference:

S. Arimoto and F. Miyazaki, 1984, "On The Stability of PID Feedback with Sensory Information", Int. Symp. Robotics Research, Bretton Woods, MIT Press.

Pierre Berge, Yves Pomeau, and Christian Vidal, 1984, *Order Within Chaos*, John Wiley & Sons.

J. Craig, 1986, Introduction to Robotics: Mechanics and Control, Addison-Wesley.

S. Hara, Y. Yamamoto, T. Omata and M. Nakano, 1988, "Repetitive Control System: A New Type of Servo System for Periodic Exongenous Signals", IEEE Transactions on Automatic Control, AC-33(7):659-668, July.

T. Kenjo and S. Nagamori, 1985, Permanent-Magnet and Brushless DC Motors, Oxford University Press.

Dan Koditschek, 1984, "Natural Motion of Robot Arms", IEEE Conf. Decision and Control, Las Vegas.

W. Messner, R. Horowitz, W.W. Kao and M. Boals, 1991, "A New Adaptive Learning Rule", IEEE Transactions of Automatic Control, AC-33(1):50-58, January.

J.J.E. Slotine and W. Li, 1986, "On the Adaptive Control of Robot Manipulators", ASME Winter Annual Meeting, Anaheim.

J.J.E. Slotine and W. Li, 1991, *Applied Nonlinear Control*, Prentice-Hall.

M. Tomizuka, T.C. Tsao and K.K. Chew, 1988, "Discrete-Time Domain Analysis and Synthesis of Repetitive Controllers", American Control Conference, pp. 860-866.

Appendix

Stability proof of the learning controller (Eq.(17)):

The nonlinear dynamics which are periodic in the angular domain are defined in Eq.(11).

$$w(u)\big|_{u=\theta} = m(\theta)\ddot{\theta}_d(\theta) + c(\theta)\dot{\theta}_d^2(\theta) + p(\theta)$$

where $u \in [0,h\phi]$. Consider the following Lyanpunov functional

$$V = \frac{1}{2}m(\theta)\dot{\tilde{\theta}}^2 + \frac{1}{2}\int_{\Phi}\Gamma^{-1}\tilde{w}^2(\lambda,t)d\lambda \quad (A1)$$

where

$$\tilde{w}(\lambda,t) = \hat{w}(\lambda,t) - w(\lambda)$$

and $\hat{w}(\lambda,t)$ is the estimated functional. Differentiating Eq.(A1) and substituting Eq.(1) and (17), we have

$$\dot{V} = -[K_d + c(\theta)\dot{\theta}_d]\dot{\tilde{\theta}}^2 - [K_s sign(\dot{\tilde{\theta}}) + f(\theta,\dot{\theta})]\dot{\tilde{\theta}} + \hat{w}(\theta^*(t),t)\dot{\tilde{\theta}} - [m(\theta)\ddot{\theta}_d + c(\theta)\dot{\theta}_d^2 + p(\theta)]\dot{\tilde{\theta}} + \int_\Phi \Gamma^{-1}\tilde{w}(\lambda,t)\frac{\partial}{\partial t}\hat{w}(\lambda,t)d\lambda \quad \text{(A2)}$$

If $\underline{W} - \gamma < \hat{w}^*(\theta^*(t),t) < \overline{W} + \gamma$, Eq.(A2) becomes

$$\dot{V} = -\delta_1\dot{\tilde{\theta}}^2 - \delta_2\left|\dot{\tilde{\theta}}\right| + \tilde{w}(\theta^*(t),t)\dot{\tilde{\theta}} - \int_\Phi \tilde{w}(\lambda,t)\dot{\tilde{\theta}}\delta(\lambda - \theta^*(t))d\lambda$$
$$\le -\delta_1\dot{\tilde{\theta}}^2 - \delta_2\left|\dot{\tilde{\theta}}\right| \quad \text{(A3)}$$

If $\hat{w}^*(\theta^*(t)) < \underline{W} - \gamma$ or $\hat{w}^*(\theta^*(t),t) > \overline{W} + \gamma$, we will have

$$\left|w(\theta^*(t)) - \hat{w}(\theta^*(t))\right| + \gamma < \left|w(\theta^*(t)) - \hat{w}^*(\theta^*(t),t)\right|$$

Consequently,

$$[w(\theta^*(t)) - \hat{w}(\theta^*(t),t)]^2 + \gamma^2 < [w(\theta^*(t)) - \hat{w}^*(\theta^*(t),t)]^2 \quad \text{(A4)}$$

Let the second term in Eq.(A1) be V_2 when $\hat{w}(\theta^*(t),t) = \underline{W}$ or $\overline{W}$ and V_2^* when $\hat{w}(\theta^*(t),t) = \hat{w}^*(\theta^*(t),t)$. The following relation can be established by using Eq.(A4).

$$\frac{d}{dt}V_2 = \lim_{\Delta t\to 0}\frac{1}{\Delta t}\frac{1}{2}\Gamma^{-1}\int_\Phi (w(\lambda) - \hat{w}(\lambda,t))^2 d\lambda$$
$$= \lim_{\Delta t\to 0}\frac{1}{\Delta t}\frac{1}{2}\Gamma^{-1}\int_\Phi [(w(\lambda) - \hat{w}(\lambda,t))^2 - (w(\lambda) - \hat{w}(\lambda,t-\Delta t))^2]\delta(\lambda - \theta^*(t))d\lambda$$
$$= \lim_{\Delta t\to 0}\frac{1}{\Delta t}\frac{1}{2}\Gamma^{-1}[(w(\theta^*(t)) - \hat{w}(\theta^*(t),t))^2 - (w(\theta^*(t)) - \hat{w}(\theta^*(t),t-\Delta t))^2]$$
$$< \lim_{\Delta t\to 0}\frac{1}{\Delta t}\frac{1}{2}\Gamma^{-1}[(w(\theta^*(t)) - \hat{w}^*(\theta^*(t),t))^2 - (w(\theta^*(t)) - \hat{w}(\theta^*(t),t-\Delta t))^2]$$
$$= \frac{d}{dt}V_2^*$$

Therefore, the Lynapunov functional is decreasing since it's derivative is less than zero when $\hat{w}(\theta^*(t),t) = \hat{w}^*(\theta^*(t),t)$ as shown in Eq.(A4).

From the above discussion, the Lyanpunov function is bounded, i.e.,

$$\lim_{t\to\infty} V(t) < \infty$$

Since $\hat{w}(\theta(t)$ is bounded (Eq.(17c)) and the integration limit of the second term in the Lyanpunov function is finite (Eq.(A1)), the velocity error is also bounded ($\dot{\tilde{\theta}}(t) \in L_\infty$). This implies that the acceleration error bounded ($\ddot{\tilde{\theta}}(t) \in L_\infty$). Furthermore, from Eq.(A3), we have

$$\dot{V} \le -\delta_1\dot{\tilde{\theta}}^2$$

As a result,

$$\int_{t_0}^{\infty}\dot{\tilde{\theta}}^2(\tau)d\tau \le -\frac{1}{\delta_2}\int_{t_0}^{\infty}\dot{V}(\tau)d\tau = -\frac{1}{\delta_2}[V(\infty) - V(t_0)] < \infty$$

which implies $\dot{\tilde{\theta}}(t) \in L_2$. Therefore, the asymptotic convergence of $\dot{\tilde{\theta}}(t)$ is guaranteed by the Barlabat's lemma (Slotine and Li, 1991).

Stability proof of the learning controller (Eq.(18)):

Considering the Lyanpunov functional

$$V = \frac{1}{2}m(\theta)\dot{\tilde{\theta}}^2 + \frac{1}{2}\int_\Phi \Gamma_1^{-1}\tilde{w}_1^2(\lambda,t)d\lambda + \frac{1}{2}\int_\Phi \Gamma_2^{-1}\tilde{w}_2^2(\lambda,t)d\lambda + \frac{1}{2}\int_\Phi \Gamma_3^{-1}\tilde{w}_3^2(\lambda,t)d\lambda$$

where

$$w_1(\lambda)\big|_{\lambda=\theta^*(t)} = m(\theta^*(t)),\quad w_2(\lambda)\big|_{\lambda=\theta^*(t)} = c(\theta^*(t)),$$
$$w_3(\lambda)\big|_{\lambda=\theta^*(t)} = p(\theta^*(t)),$$

and

$$\tilde{w}_i = \hat{w}_i - w_i$$

The proof is essentially the same as the previous one since the derivative of the Lyanpunov functional satisfies

$$\dot{V} = -K_d\dot{\tilde{\theta}}^2 - [K_s sign(\dot{\tilde{\theta}}) + f(\theta,\dot{\theta})]\dot{\tilde{\theta}} + \sum_{i=1}^{3}[\tilde{w}_i(\theta^*(t),t)\alpha_i(t) + \int_\Phi \Gamma_i^{-1}\tilde{w}_i(\lambda,t)\frac{\partial}{\partial t}\hat{w}_i(\lambda,t)d\lambda]$$
$$\le -K_d\dot{\tilde{\theta}}^2 - \delta_2\left|\dot{\tilde{\theta}}\right|$$

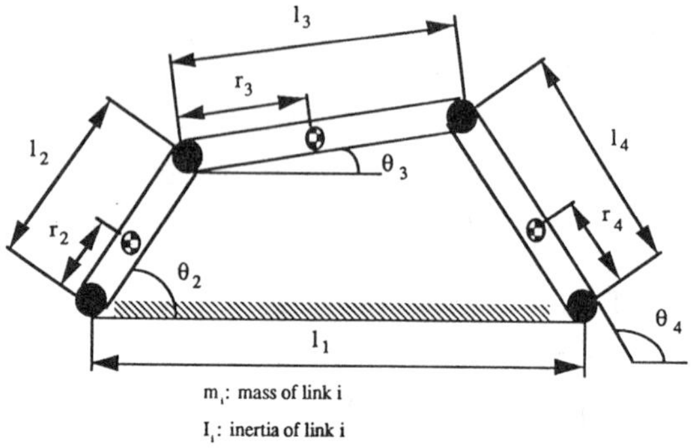

Figure 1 The four-bar linkage

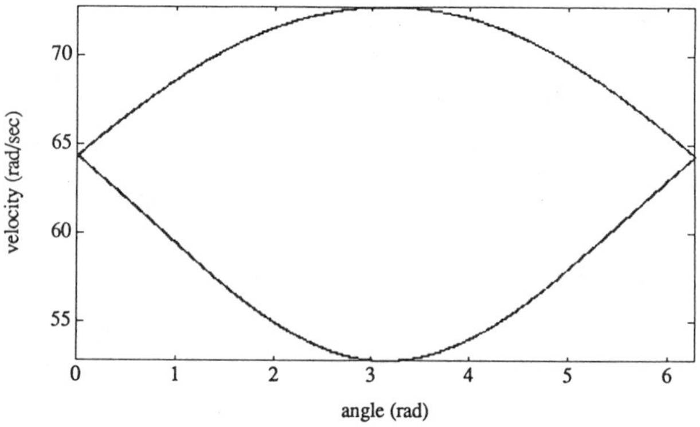

Figure 2 Steady state phase diagram of the trajectory in Eq.(12a)

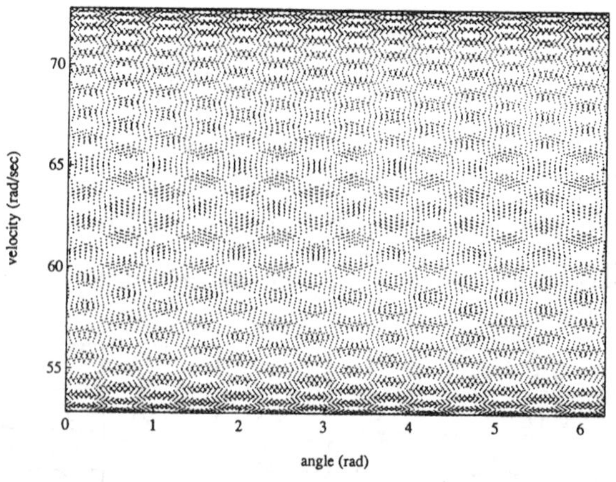

Figure 3 Steady state phase diagram of the trajectory in Eq.(12b)

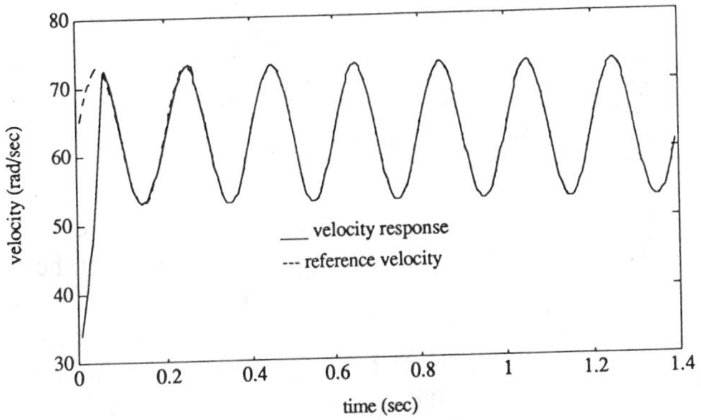

Figure 4 Velocity trajectory of the crank under learning control (periodic disturbance case)

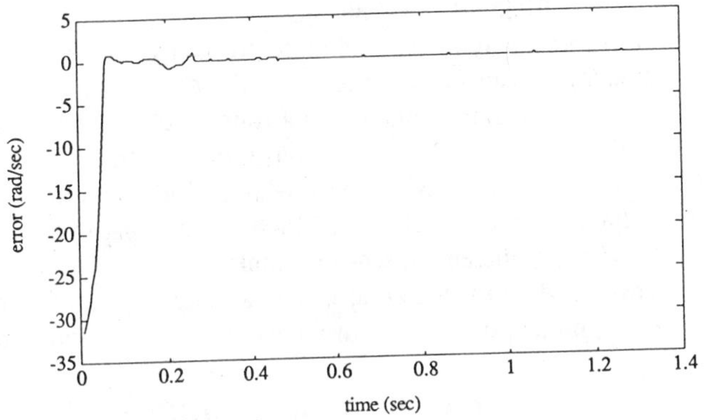

Figure 5 Convergence of velocity errors (periodic disturbance case)

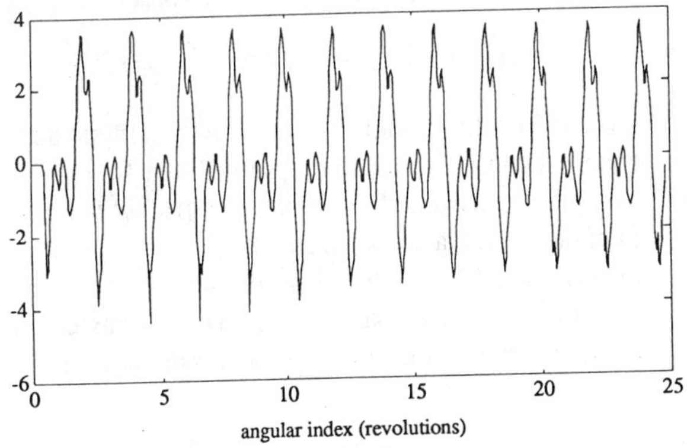

Figure 6 The function learned by the controller (periodic disturbance case)

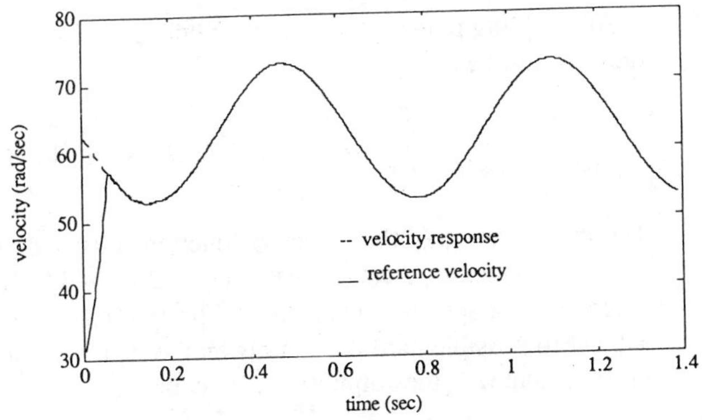

Figure 7 Velocity trajectory of the crank under learning control (non-periodic disturbance case)

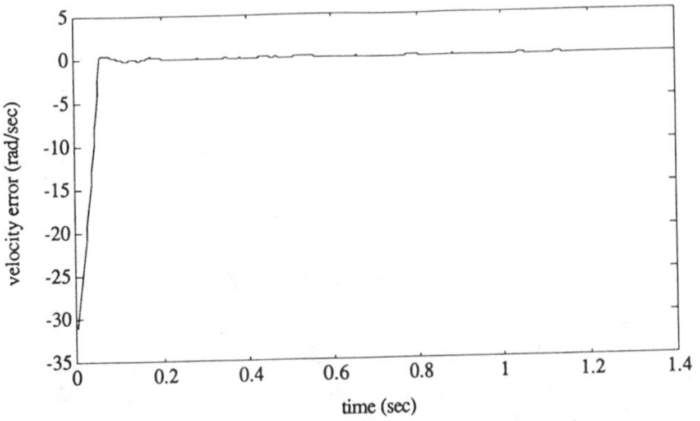

Figure 8 Convergence of velocity errors (non-periodic disturbance case)

Proceedings of the
American Control Conference
San Francisco, California • June 1993

Output Constraint Softening for SISO Model Predictive Control

Evanghelos Zafiriou* and Hung-Wen Chiou

Department of Chemical Engineering and Institute for Systems Research
University of Maryland, College Park, MD 20742

Abstract

The presence of constraints in the on-line optimization problem solved by Model Predictive Control algorithms results in a nonlinear control system, even if the plant and model dynamics are linear. This is the case both for physical constraints, like saturation constraints, as well for performance or safety constraints on outputs or other variables of the process. Performance constraints can usually be softened by allowing violation if necessary. This is advisable, as hard constraints can lead to stability problems. The determination of the necessary degree of softening is usually a trial-and-error matter. This paper utilizes a theoretical framework that allows to relate hard as well as soft constraints to closed-loop stability. We focus on the special case of output constraints for single-input single-output systems and develop a non-conservative condition. This condition allows the determination of the appropriate amount of softening either numerically or via a suitable Nyquist plot.

1. Introduction

A major attraction of Model Predictive Control is the ability to include constraints in the control problem formulation by simply carrying out an optimization subject to satisfaction of these constraints. The standard formulation in the literature is to list constraints on inputs, outputs and possibly other variables, and handle these constraints as hard ones, i.e., constraints that have to be satisfied before any objective is optimized. The presence of these constraints, however, complicates the question of stability. Closed-loop stability cannot be assumed simply because the on-line optimization finds a solution. Furthermore, the constraints of the on-line optimization, even if they are not physical constraints, result in a nonlinear closed-loop system in spite of the fact that the process dynamics are usually assumed to be linear. Zafiriou (1990) suggested a framework that allows the translation of robust stability of the constrained, and therefore nonlinear, closed-loop system into robustness conditions for a set of linear systems.

In this paper we focus on the case where output constraints are imposed over the prediction horizon. Although the idea behind the development in the paper can be applied to the general multi-input multi-output case (Zafiriou and Chiou, 1992), we will limit the discussion here to the single-input single-output case, since in this case a non-conservative and simple to use condition can be obtained. Zafiriou and Marchal (1991) showed in detail how hard output constraints can result in very aggressive controllers. Ricker *et al.*(1989) suggested that softening such constraints may help avoid these problems. Since not all constraints can be softened, as is the case, e.g., for saturation constraints, one needs a framework that can deal with a mix of hard and soft constraints. Zafiriou (1991) extended his original framework to include the effect of softening on closed-loop stability. In that paper a conservative sufficient closed-loop contraction condition was developed for the SISO case. In this paper we use a different approach that results in a nonconservative condition.

2. Closed-loop Stability

An impulse response model is used to describe the process:

$$\tilde{y}(k) = H_1 u(k-1) + H_2 u(k-2) + \ldots + H_N u(k-N) \quad (1)$$

where $\tilde{y}$ is the model output, u is the input and N the truncation number, i.e., it is assumed that $H_i = 0$ for $i > N$. The plant is assumed to be open-loop stable. Other types of models can also be used, e.g., step response models (Garcia and Morshedi, 1986) or state space descriptions (Li *et al.*, 1989; Ricker, 1990). The z-transfer function, $\tilde{p}^*(z)$, describing the process model is related to (1) through

$$\tilde{p}^*(z) = \sum_{i=1}^{N} H_i z^{-i} \quad (2)$$

At sampling point k, the following optimization is carried out on-line:

$$\min_{\Delta u(k),\ldots,\Delta u(k+M-1)} \sum_{l=1}^{P} [e(k+l)^2 + D^2 \Delta u(k+l-1)^2] \quad (3)$$

The minimization of the objective function is carried out over the values of $\Delta u(k)$, $\Delta u(k+1)$,..., $\Delta u(k+M-1)$, where M is a specified parameter. The minimization is subject to possible hard constraints on the inputs u, their rate of change Δu, the outputs y and other process variables

*Author to whom correspondence should be addressed. E-mail: zafiriou@src.umd.edu

usually referred to as associated variables. The details on the formulation of the optimization problem can be found in Prett and Garcia (1988). After the problem is solved on-line at k, only the optimal value for the first input $\Delta u(k)$ is implemented and the problem is solved again at $k+1$. The optimal $u(k)$ depends on the tuning parameters of the optimization problem, the current output measurement $y(k)$ and the past inputs $u(k-1),\ldots, u(k-N)$ that are involved in the model output prediction. Let f describe the $u(k)$ that is obtained by adding $u(k-1)$ to the $\Delta u(k)$ that is the result of the optimization solved at sampling point k :

$$u(k)=f(y(k), u(k-1), \ldots, u(k-N); r_P(k), d(k)) \quad (4)$$

where $r_P(k)$ includes all the values of the reference signal (setpoint) during the prediction horizon from $k+1$ to $k+P$ and $d(k)$ is the disturbance effect at the output at k.

For linear model dynamics, Zafiriou (1990) showed that the *constrained* MPC is *piece-wise linear*, meaning that the dynamics of MPC for a certain constraint set J_i active, are those of a discrete linear controller. This linear controller, denoted $c_{J_i}(z)$, depends explicitly only on J_i; it depends only implicitly on the past and current values of the plant inputs and outputs. These values together with external inputs (setpoints, disturbances) determine the J_i that corresponds to a sampling point. However, if at different sampling points the Quadratic Program (QP) solution results in the same J_i, the MPC dynamics at those points are those of the *same* linear controller. The expression for the c_{J_i} is given by:

$$c_{J_i}(z)=\frac{-(\nabla_y f)_{J_i}}{1-(\nabla_{x_1} f)_{J_i} z^{-1}-\ldots-(\nabla_{x_N} f)_{J_i} z^{-N}} \quad (5)$$

where x_j are the states of the system, defined as:

$$x_j(k)=u(k-j), \quad 1 \leq j \leq N \quad (6)$$

A necessary condition for the closed-loop operator mapping the states of the system (plant + controller) from one sampling point to the next, is that each of these linear controllers gives a closed-loop stable system. Note that the contraction property implies closed-loop stability. For more details and discussion the reader is referred to Zafiriou (1990).

In this paper we consider the case of output constraints only. These are defined over a future prediction horizon:

$$y_L \leq y(k+l) \leq y_U, \quad w_b \leq l \leq w_e \quad (7)$$

where y_L, y_U are the lower and upper limits respectively. In Zafiriou and Marchal (1991) the expressions for the c_{J_i} are given for special cases of combinations of points in the horizon, at which the hard constraints may become active at the optimum of the on-line optimization. It is also shown that for many important cases, the corresponding c_{J_i} result in an unstable closed-loop system, regardless of the values of the tuning parameters of the objective function. In such cases the only option is to soften the constraints by allowing violation by an amount ϵ. In the formulation here, the same violation variable $\epsilon \geq 0$ is used for all the points in the constraint window. Hence the output constraints are softened to be:

$$y_L-\epsilon \leq y(k+l) \leq y_U+\epsilon, \quad w_b \leq l \leq w_e \quad (8)$$

The term $W^2\epsilon^2$ is added to the objective function, where W is the weight that determines the extent of softening. For $W=\infty$ we get hard constraints. $W=0$ corresponds to completely removing the constraints. For a nonzero finite W, and when the on-line QP results in a nonzero ϵ, then at the optimum for at least one of the points in the constraint window, say for $N_a \in [w_b, w_e]$, we will have $y(k+N_a)=y_U+\epsilon$ or $y(k+N_a)=y_L-\epsilon$. Otherwise a smaller ϵ would reduce the objective function, while still satisfying the constraints. This point is the one for which satisfaction of the constraint presents the greatest difficulty.

We will consider the case $M=1$, which is the usual choice for the unconstrained case, but which for the case of hard output constraints was shown to be a risky one in Zafiriou and Marchal (1991). Let the subscripts u and h correspond to the unconstrained and hard constrained cases, respectively, and f_u, f_h the result of the MPC optimization for these cases as defined in (4). Then by carrying out the computations it can be shown that when the constraint is softened, we have for the coefficients of the c_{J_i} (from (5)) that corresponds to the softened constraint at $k+N_a$:

$$\nabla_{x_j} f_s=\frac{1}{1+G^{-1}S_{N_a}^2 W^2} \nabla_{x_j} f_u + \frac{G^{-1}S_{N_a}^2 W^2}{1+G^{-1}S_{N_a}^2 W^2} \nabla_{x_j} f_h \quad (9)$$

for $j=1,\ldots,N$ and also for ∇_y, where the subscript s stands for soft. S_{N_a} is the value of the open-loop unit-step response of the process model at the N_a sampling point. G is the Hessian of the quadratic objective defined in (3). Note that both f_u and f_s correspond to the constraint at $k+N_a$. The closed-loop poles for each of these cases are the roots of the characteristic polynomials obtained from the numerator of $(1+\tilde{p}c_{J_i})$:

$$r_{J_i}=1-(\psi_1)_{J_i} z^{-1}-\ldots-(\psi_N)_{J_i} z^{-N}, \quad 1 \leq j \leq N \quad (10)$$

where

$$(\psi_j)_{J_i}=(\nabla_{x_j} f)_{J_i}+(\nabla_y f)_{J_i} H_j, \quad 1 \leq j \leq N \quad (11)$$

We know that for the unconstrained case (Garcia and Morari, 1982) a value $M=1$ combined with a large horizon P will result in a stable control system. (The use of the D weight also helps.) Let us assume that this has been accomplished and therefore the closed-loop characteristic polynomial $r_u(z)$ has roots inside the unit circle:

$$r_u(z)=1-\psi_{1,u} z^{-1}-\ldots-\psi_{N,u} z^{-N}$$

On the other hand, $r_h(z)$ is often unstable, and for $M = 1$ the parameters of the objective function have no effect of it:

$$r_h(z) = 1 - \psi_{1,h} z^{-1} - \ldots - \psi_{N,h} z^{-N}$$

Softening of the constraint allows us to tune W for stability. Define

$$\delta_{N_a} = \frac{G^{-1} S_{N_a}^2 W^2}{1 + G^{-1} S_{N_a}^2 W^2} \quad (12)$$

Note that $\delta_{N_a} = 0$ for $W = 0$ (unconstrained); $\delta_{N_a} \rightarrow 1$ for $W \rightarrow \infty$ (hard constraint). Equation (9) can be re-written as:

$$\nabla f_s = (1 - \delta_{N_a}) \nabla f_u + \delta_{N_a} \nabla f_h$$

Combined with (11) yields:

$$\psi_{j,s} = (1 - \delta_{N_a}) \psi_{j,u} + \delta_{N_a} \psi_{j,h}$$

We can now use (10) to obtain:

$$\begin{aligned} r_s(z) = & \ (1 - \delta_{N_a}) r_u(z) + \delta_{N_a} r_h(z) \\ & = r_u(z) + \delta_{N_a} (r_h(z) - r_u(z)) \end{aligned}$$

We can assume at this point that the tuning parameters of the on-line objective function have been selected to yield a stable unconstrained system ($r_u(z)$). However, $r_h(z)$ may be unstable and therefore the appropriate degree of softening, defined by the value of W, can be obtained by answering the question of which is the largest δ_{N_a} (≤ 1) for which $r_s(z)$ is stable. Let $z = e^{i\theta}$. As δ_{N_a} increases from zero, if $r_h(z)$ is unstable, eventually $r_u(e^{i\theta}) + \delta_{N_a}(r_h(e^{i\theta}) - r_u(e^{i\theta})) = 0$ for some θ. This is the largest δ_{N_a} that we can accept from this analysis:

$$\delta_{N_a} = \frac{r_u(e^{i\theta})}{r_u(e^{i\theta}) - r_h(e^{i\theta})}$$

This value can be computed from a Nyquist plot of $\frac{r_u}{r_u - r_h}$. If $r_h(z)$ unstable, $\frac{r_u}{r_u - r_h}$ will cross the real axis at least once between 0 and 1. The smallest such value is the largest δ_{N_a} for which the nominal system remains stable. (12) then yields the largest W. The dependence on N_a comes form the dependence of r_h on the point in the constraint window, for which the constraint may be predicted active at the optimum of the optimization. Each point in the window will result in a different value for W. The smallest value should be used. From Zafiriou and Marchal (1991) we know:

$$r_h(z) = 1 - \frac{H_{N_a+1}}{S_{N_a}} z^{-1} - \ldots - \frac{H_N}{S_{N_a}} z^{-N+N_a}$$

Alternatively, W can be directly obtained from a different Nyquist plot. By substituting (12) into $r_u(e^{i\theta}) + \delta_{N_a}(r_h(e^{i\theta}) - r_u(e^{i\theta})) = 0$ we obtain

$$r_u(e^{i\theta}) + G^{-1} S_{N_a}^2 W^2 r_h(e^{i\theta}) = 0$$

which yields

$$W^2 = -\frac{1}{G^{-1} S_{N_a}^2} \frac{r_u(e^{i\theta})}{r_h(e^{i\theta})} \quad (13)$$

A Nyquist plot of $\frac{r_u}{r_h}$ is obtained. If it does not intersect the negative real axis, any W is acceptable, and therefore the corresponding constraint can be made hard. Otherwise the intersect nearest 0 gives W from (13).

3. Example

The example is the top SISO part of the heavy oil fractionator defined in the Shell Standard Control Problem (Prett and Garcia, 1988). The output is the top end point concentration and the input is the top draw. It is used to demonstrate how the technique described in the previous section can be used for computing the largest softening weight W. This is a case where the use of a hard constraint for the output prediction on the first point in the window (after the time delay) gives rise to instability of the control system. The process model is:

$$\frac{4.05 e^{-27s}}{50s + 1}$$

For a sampling time of 4 minutes, the discrete model is:

$$\frac{0.0802(z + 2.8828) z^{-7}}{z - 0.92312}$$

Notice that there is an unstable zero in the discrete model. It becomes an unstable root of $r_h(z)$, when the hard constraint is set on the first possible point after the time delay:

$$-0.5 \leq y(k+7) \leq 0.5$$

This root at -2.8828 cannot be moved via tuning of the MPC parameters, as long as the constraint remains a hard one. As a result instability occurs during operation for which the constraint becomes active at the optimum of the optimization. This is illustrated by simulating the response to step output disturbances. The simulations (figures 1 and 2) show that enlarging the prediction horizon is useless for stabilizing the control sytem. The tuning parameters for the simulations are: $D = 0$, $M = 1, P = 8$ (figure 1), $P = 60$ (figure 2). The unconstrained simulations with the same tuning parameters are shown in figures 3, 4.

We now proceed with softening the constraint at $k + 7$ ($N_a = 7$). The weight W is deternimed with the method developed in the previous section. The largest values are obtained from the Nyquist plots in figures 7 and 8. For $P = 8$, we get $W = 3.6$ and for $P = 60$, $W = 290$. The simulation with a soft constraint at $k+7$ for the case $P = 8$, $W = 3.6$ is shown in figure 5. The control system is closed-loop stable and the constraint bounds are essentially satisfied. For the case with $P = 60$, $W = 290$, the simulation is shown in figure 6. The control system is stable and its performance with respect to constraint satisfaction is clearly better than that of the unconstrained case, shown in figure 4.

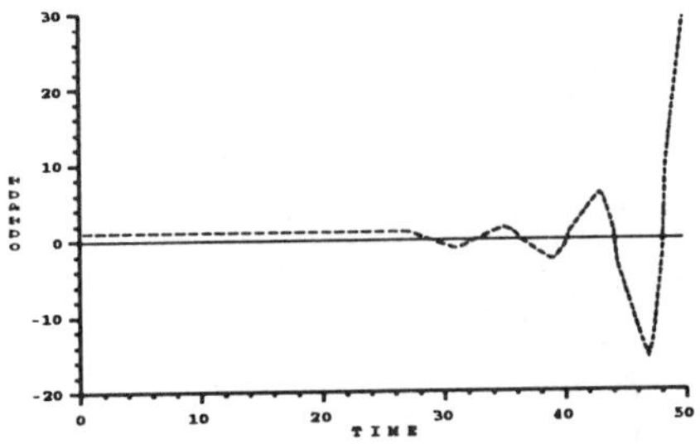

Figure 1 (a): The output of the hard constraint simulation with $P = 8$

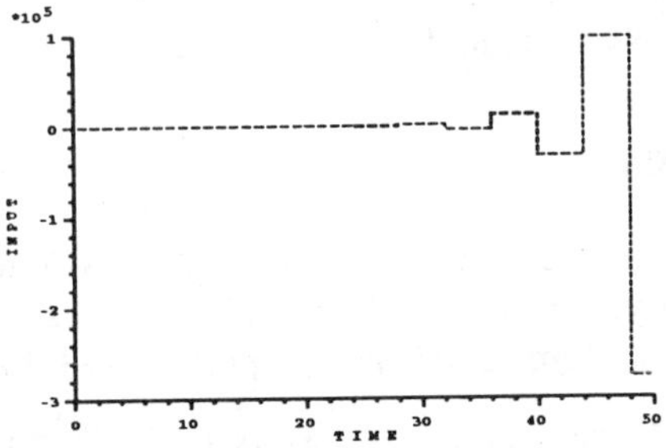

Figure 1 (b): The input of the hard constraint simulation with $P = 8$

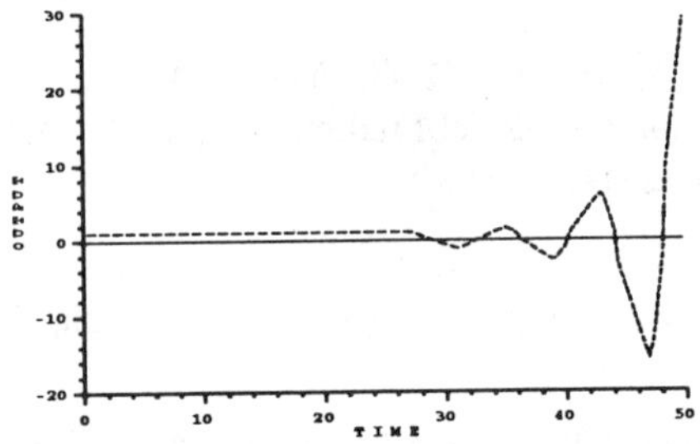

Figure 2 (a): The output of the hard constraint simulation with $P = 60$

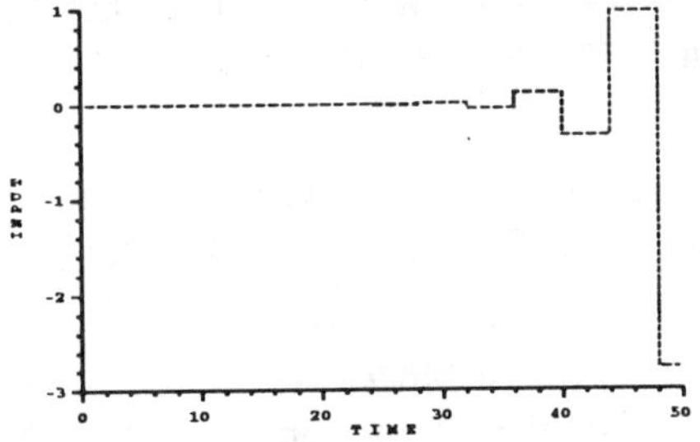

Figure 2 (b): The input of the hard constraint simulation with $P = 60$

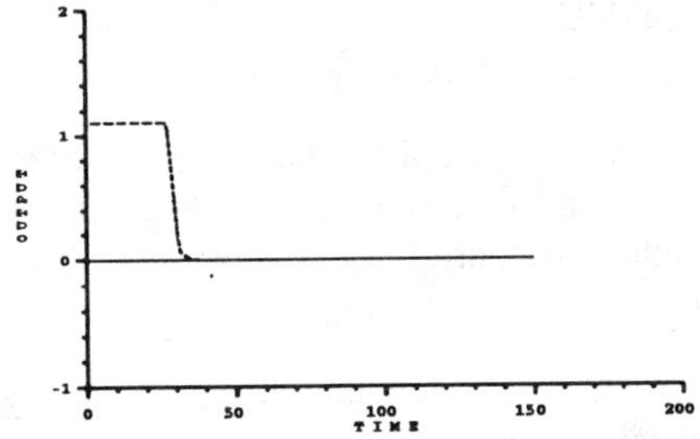

Figure 3 (a): The output of the unconstrained simulation with $P = 8$

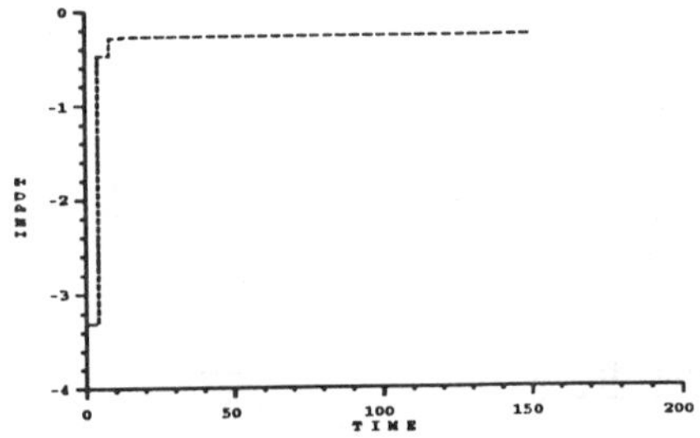

Figure 3 (b): The input of the unconstrained simulation with $P = 8$

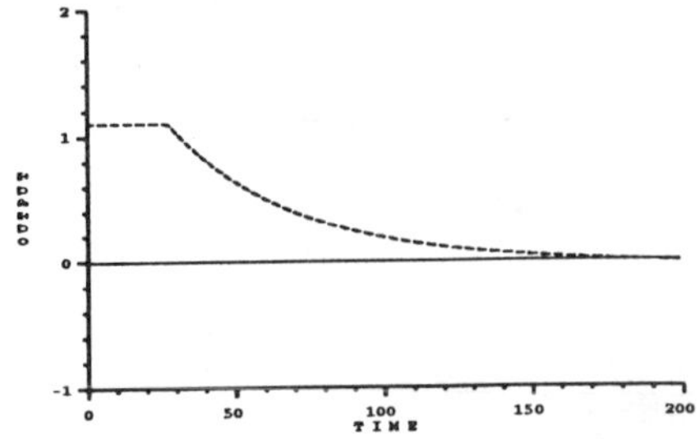

Figure 4 (a): The output of the unconstrained simulation with $P = 60$

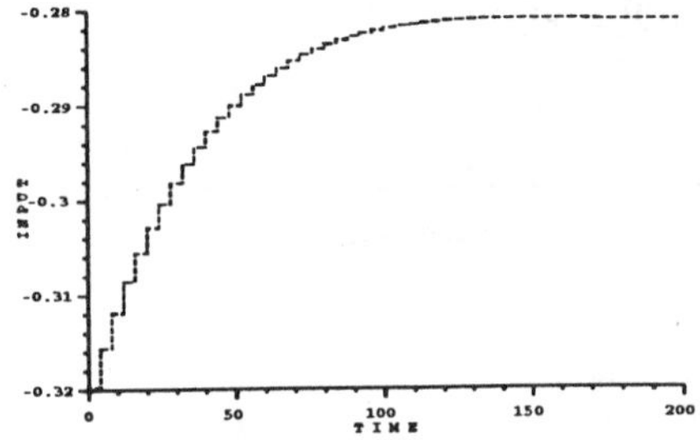

Figure 4 (b): The input of the unconstrained simulation with $P = 60$

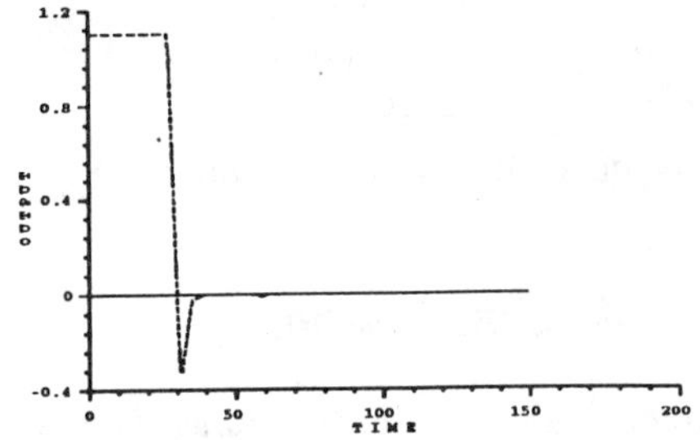

Figure 5 (a): The output of the soft constraint simulation with $P = 8,\ W = 3.6$

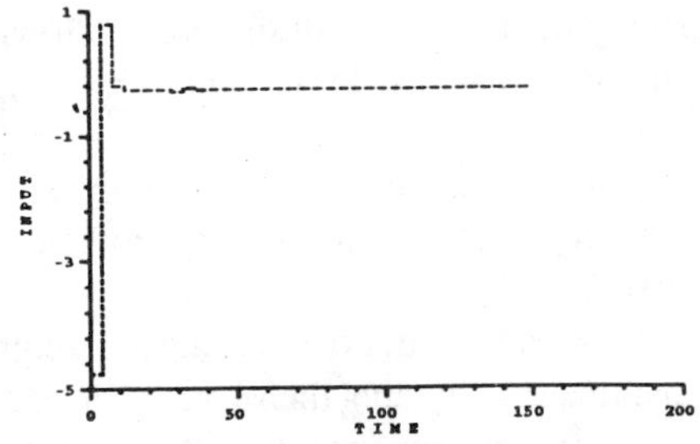

Figure 5 (b): The input of the soft constraint simulation with $P = 8,\ W = 3.6$

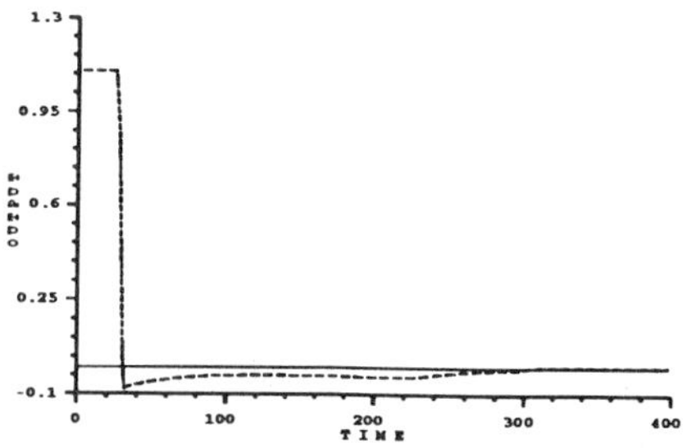

Figure 6 (a): The output of the soft constraint simulation with $P = 60,\ W = 290$

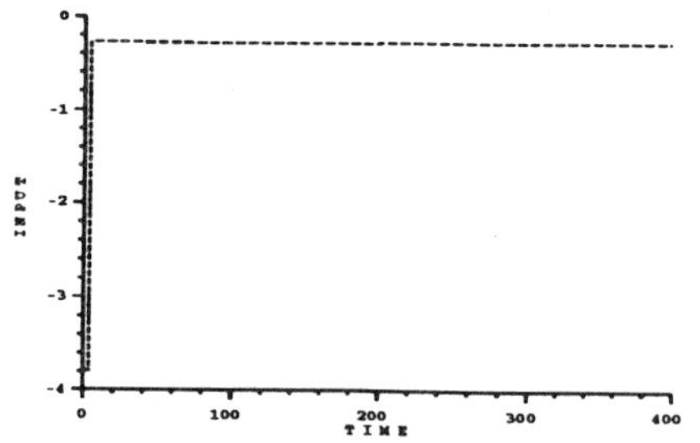

Figure 6 (b): The input of the soft constraint simulation with $P = 60,\ W = 290$

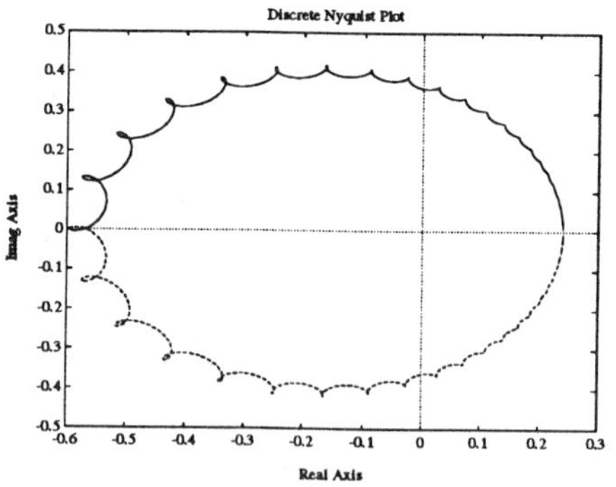

Figure 7: The Nyquist plot for the case with $P = 8$

4. Conclusions

This paper provides a method for obtaining the weights used in softening output constraints of MPC algorithms. The technique results in the largest weight (hardest constraint) that will not cause any stability problems. The task can be carried out as a second design step following the design of the unconstrained MPC algorithm. Thus, although the control system is nonlinear because of the constraint, the methods that have been developed in the literature for designing unconstrained controllers can still be used in the first step.

The method is based on the idea of handling the weights as "uncertain" parameters. Finding their largest value can be thought of as a robust stability problem. As a result the technique can be extended to MIMO systems, as well as to the case where model-plant mismatch exists.

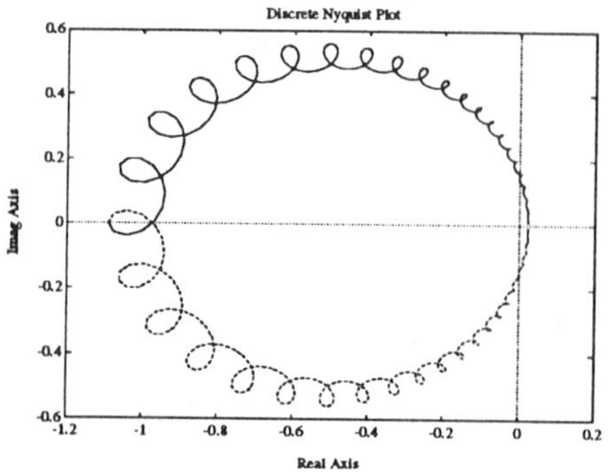

Figure 8: The Nyquist plot for the case with $P = 60$

References

[1] C. E. Garcia and M. Morari, "Internal Model Control. 1. A Unifying Review and Some New Results," *Ind. Eng. Chem. Proc. Des. Dev.*, **21**, pp. 308-323, 1982.

[2] C. E. Garcia and A. M. Morshedi, "Quadratic Programming Solution of Dynamic Matrix Control (QDMC)", *Chem. Eng. Commun.*, **46**, pp. 73-87, 1986.

[3] S. Li, K. Y. Lim and D. G. Fisher, "A State Space Formulation for Model Predictive Control," *AIChE J.*, **35**, pp. 241-249, 1989.

[4] D. M. Prett and C. E. Garcia, *Fundamental Process Control*, Butterworth Publishers, Stoneham, MA, 1988.

[5] N. L. Ricker, T. Subrahmanian and T. Sim, "Case Studies of Model-Predictive Control in Pulp and Paper Production", *in Model Based Process Control– Proc. of the 1988 IFAC Workshop*, T. J. McAvoy, Y. Arkun and E. Zafiriou, eds., Pergamon Press, Oxford, 1989.

[6] N. L. Ricker, "Model Predictive Control with State Estimation," *Ind. Eng. Chem. Res.*, **29**, pp. 374-382, 1990.

[7] E. Zafiriou, "Robust Model Predictive Control of Processes with Hard Constraints", *Comp. Chem. Eng.*, **14**, pp. 359-371, 1990.

[8] E. Zafiriou, "On the Closed–Loop Stability of Constrained QDMC," *Proc. Amer. Control Conf.*, pp. 2367-2372, Boston, MA, June 1991.

[9] E. Zafiriou and H.-W. Chiou, "On the effect of Constraint Softening on the Stability and Performance of Model Predictive Controllers," Annual AIChE mtg., Paper No. 123f, Miami Beach, FL, Nov. 1992.

[10] E. Zafiriou and A. L. Marchal, "Robust Stability of SISO Quadratic Dynamic Matrix Control with Hard Output Constraints," *AIChE J.*, **37**, pp. 1550-1560, 1991.

Proceedings of the
American Control Conference
San Francisco, California • June 1993

Solving the Model Predictive Control Problem with Soft Constraints

James D. Feher and Kelvin T. Erickson

Department of Electrical Engineering
University of Missouri-Rolla, Rolla, Missouri 65401

ABSTRACT

This paper will demonstrate how the convexity and quadratic nature of the soft constrained model predictive control problem can be used to solve for its unique minimum in a finite number of steps. A mathematical formulation for this problem will be given that leads to a new convergent minimization algorithm. This algorithm will then be compared to a traditional method of steepest descent type algorithm in an example.

INTRODUCTION

This paper investigates the use of soft constraints as applied to model predictive controllers. Soft constraints will be applied by adding a penalty function to the objective function being minimized. This approach will yield an algorithm that converges to an *exact* solution in a *finite* number of steps.

Model predictive control with hard constraints is usually handled as a standard quadratic program (QP) with linear constraints (Ricker, 1991). However, when soft constraints are added to the problem, the objective function becomes nonlinear. Li and Biegler (1988) formulated a model predictive controller with hard and soft constraints as a nonlinear QP. Their method is a successive quadratic programming approach that uses an Armijo line search (Armijo, 1966) to control the search direction step size.

The method proposed here is closest to penalty function methods of nonlinear programming (Fletcher, 1987). Each of the soft system constraints will correspond to a penalty given by the distance squared from the solution to the constraint, if the constraint is violated. The constraints considered are linear and can be viewed as hyperplanes in the solution space. This finite number of hyperplanes divide the solution space up into a finite number of convex components. The functional form of the sum of all of the penalties changes for each separate component. This introduces nonlinearities that complicate the problem.

A development for the minimization problem will first be given. This will then be used to generate an algorithm that will solve the soft constrained problem for the unique minimum in a finite number of steps. An example comparing both the Armijo and the newly developed algorithm for the solution of the minimization of a soft constrained quadratic function will be given.

MATHEMATICAL FORMULATION

While many different MPC strategies exist, their mathematical representations are all very similar. Here the model predictive control problem will be generalized so as to focus more on the problem of working with the soft constraints. The MPC system is given by,

$$\mathbf{y} = \mathbf{A}\mathbf{m} + \mathbf{b}. \tag{1}$$

$\mathbf{A}$ is a (q x r) matrix given by the model of the system, $\mathbf{m}$ an (r x 1) input vector whose element in the ith row is m_i, $\mathbf{y}$ a (q x 1) output vector, and $\mathbf{b}$ a (q x 1) vector of output predictions. The problem then centers on minimizing V(m),

$$\min_{\mathbf{m}} V(\mathbf{m}) = \min_{\mathbf{m}}\left[(\mathbf{s}- \mathbf{A}\mathbf{m}- \mathbf{b})^T\Gamma(\mathbf{s}- \mathbf{A}\mathbf{m}- \mathbf{b})+ \mathbf{m}^T\Delta\mathbf{m}\right] \tag{2}$$

Here $\mathbf{s}$ is a setpoint vector and Γ and Δ are weighting matrices. Bounds, limits, or constraints existing for the inputs and the outputs of the system can be represented as $\alpha_{iL} \leq m_i \leq \alpha_{iU}$ and $y_{jL} \leq y_j \leq y_{jU}$ where α_{iL} and α_{iU} represent lower and upper input bounds and where y_{jL} and y_{jU} the bounds on the outputs. Each of these 2(r+q) constraints can be thought of as a r-1 dimensional hyperplane in $\mathbb{R}^r$, the r-dimensional space where $\mathbf{m}$ resides. It is best to have the constraints expressed in terms of the solution space, in this case the system input. Using equation (1), the output constraints can be represented as input constraints, $\alpha_{Li} \leq m_i \leq \alpha_{Ui}$ and $\beta_{Lj} \leq \mathbf{a}_j^T\mathbf{m} \leq \beta_{Uj}$, where $\mathbf{a}_j$ is the jth row of $\mathbf{A}$.

While constraints can be violated for the soft constrained case, it certainly is not desired. A way to minimize any constraint violation in the solution is to add the following distance squared penalty to the original quadratic function to be minimized

$$P(\mathbf{m}) = \sum_{i=1}^{r}\{p_{ILi}(\mathbf{m})\frac{(\mathbf{e}_i^T\mathbf{m} - \alpha_{Li})^2}{\|\mathbf{e}_i\|^2} + p_{IUi}(\mathbf{m})\frac{(\mathbf{e}_i^T\mathbf{m} - \alpha_{Ui})^2}{\|\mathbf{e}_i\|^2}\}$$
$$+\sum_{j=1}^{q}\{p_{OLj}(\mathbf{m})\frac{(\mathbf{a}_j^T\mathbf{m} - \beta_{Lj})^2}{\|\mathbf{a}_j\|^2} + p_{OUj}(\mathbf{m})\frac{(\mathbf{a}_j^T\mathbf{m} - \beta_{Uj})^2}{\|\mathbf{a}_j\|^2}\} \tag{3}$$

where α, β, and $\mathbf{a}_j$ are defined above and the $\mathbf{e}_i$ vectors are

$$\mathbf{e}_1^T= [1\ 0 \cdots 0],\ \mathbf{e}_2^T= [0\ 1\ 0 \cdots 0],\ \cdots,\ \mathbf{e}_r^T= [0 \cdots 0\ 1].$$

The p_{ILi}, p_{IUi}, p_{OLj} and p_{OUj} are characteristic functions that have a value of one if the corresponding constraint is violated and zero if it is satisfied. Thus the solution space is composed of the union of a finite number of subsets defined by the violation or satisfaction of the linear constraints. These subsets, or components, form at most 3^{r+q} convex subsets in the solution space.

The penalty function, P(m), will be added to the original function to be minimized, V(m). It can be shown that the penalty function is convex. V(m) is strictly convex, so the sum of V(m)+P(m) will be strictly convex, and the solution to the minimization problem will be unique. The following minimization problem will be quadratic as well, $\min_{\mathbf{m}} [V(\mathbf{m}) + P(\mathbf{m})]$.

APPROACH TO THE PROBLEM

The solution of this problem is basically the main idea behind the paper. A previous approach by Feher and Erickson (1992) yielded an algorithm that solved for the unique minimum of the soft constrained problem by searching each separate component. The number of components to check, at most 3^{r+q}, is finite, but can be large. In addition, there was no guarantee that the algorithm would converge monotonically, an advantage if it would have to be terminated prematurely, a possibility for real-time control.

Definition: Let $P_{\mathbf{m}_i}$ be the penalty such that the characteristic function is determined using $\mathbf{m}_i$.

ALGORITHM

0.) Choose any point $\mathbf{m}_0 \in \mathbb{R}^n$.
1.) Solve for the critical point of V + $P_{\mathbf{m}_i}$, $\mathbf{m}_{cpi}$.
2.) If $(V+P)(\mathbf{m}_i) > (V+P)(\mathbf{m}_{cpi})$ then $\mathbf{m}_{i+1} = \mathbf{m}_{cpi}$, go to 1.
3.) If $\mathbf{m}_i = \mathbf{m}_{cpi}$, then $\mathbf{m}_i$ is the minimum for V+P, stop.
4.) Form the line segment, $\lambda\mathbf{m}_{cpi} + (1-\lambda)\mathbf{m}_{cpi}$, $\lambda \in [0,1]$. Let $\mathbf{m}_{i+1}$ equal the minimum of V+P along this line segment. Return to step 1.

The algorithm will converge to the unique minimum monotonically in a finite number of steps. It is clear that $f(\mathbf{m}_i) > f(\mathbf{m}_{i+1}) > 0$, so the algorithm generates a positive, monotonically decreasing sequence, bounded below by $f(\mathbf{m}_{min})$, where $\mathbf{m}_{min}$ is the unique minimum of f. If $\mathbf{m}$ is in the same component as $\mathbf{m}_{min}$, then the next iteration will yield the unique minimum.

Definition: Let $f = V+P$, $\lambda \in [0,1]$, $\mathbf{m}, \mathbf{m}_{cp} \in \mathbb{R}^n$, and $\nabla(V+P_{\mathbf{m}})(\mathbf{m}_{cp}) = 0$. Define a the new function, df, such that

$$df(\mathbf{m}) = f(\mathbf{m}) - f(\mathbf{m}_\lambda).$$

Where $\mathbf{m}_\lambda$ is minimum of f along the line segment $\lambda\mathbf{m}_{cp} + (1-\lambda)\mathbf{m}$.

There is a bound on the number of components, therefore step 2 can be used only a finite number of times. It also can be shown that a positive real ϵ exits such that df is bounded below by ϵ for all $\mathbf{m}$ not in the same component as $\mathbf{m}_{min}$ (Feher, 1993). So, step 4 also can only be used a bounded number of times, **N**, where

$$\mathbf{N} = [\text{least integer greater than } f(\mathbf{m}_0) - f(\mathbf{m}_{min})]/\epsilon.$$

Since either step 2 or step 4 must be used for each new iteration, there is a bound on the number of iterations in reaching the unique minimum.

EXAMPLE

The square system following the form of Equations 1 and 2 will be examined.

$$\mathbf{y} = \begin{bmatrix} 0.3 \\ -0.2 \end{bmatrix} \qquad \mathbf{A} = \begin{bmatrix} 1 & 0.8 \\ 0.5 & -0.2 \end{bmatrix}$$

with $\mathbf{b} = \mathbf{0}$, $\Gamma = \mathbf{I}$ and $\Delta = \mathbf{0}$.
The soft constraints are given by:

$$\begin{bmatrix} -1 \\ 1 \end{bmatrix} < \mathbf{y} < \begin{bmatrix} 1 \\ 1.5 \end{bmatrix} \qquad \begin{bmatrix} 0 \\ -0.4 \end{bmatrix} < \mathbf{m} < \begin{bmatrix} 0.5 \\ 0 \end{bmatrix}.$$

A traditional steepest descent algorithm, specifically the Armijo search, was applied to this problem as was the new algorithm. Both were given the same starting point, the minimum for V. The Armijo method was stopped when the points from consecutive iterations were within a distance of 0.1 of each other.

The contour plot shown in Figure 1 shows the paths taken by each of the convergence methods. These algorithms were run using MATLAB on an IBM-compatible computer. As shown in Figure 1, the new algorithm converged to the ***exact*** minimum in two iterations, while the method using the Armijo search required three iterations to come within the stopping distance, and yield an approximate solution.

CONCLUSION

The algorithm obtained here offers obvious advantages over traditional steepest descent methods. The most important being that the algorithm obtained always yields the *unique* minimum in a *finite* number of steps. Traditional methods converge, however, not necessarily to the exact minimum. Also, a decision must be made on when to stop the algorithm. This may require specific knowledge of the system in order to achieve acceptable results. These issues combined, illustrate the advantage of using this new algorithm when solving the soft constrained problem for model predictive controllers.

REFERENCES

Armijo, L., "Minimization of functions having Lipschitz continuous first partial derivatives," *Pacific Journal of Mathematics*, vol. 16, pp. 1-3, 1966.

Erickson, K. T. and Otto, R. E., "Development of a Multivariable Forward Modeling Controller," Proceedings of the IFAC Workshop on Model Based Process Control, June, 1988, Atlanta, Georgia.

Feher, J. D. and Erickson, K. T., "Model Predictive Control with Soft Constraints," *AIChE Annual Conference*, Miami Beach, Florida, November, 1992.

Feher, J. D., "Forward Modeling Control with Soft Constraints," Dissertation for Ph.D., University of Missouri-Rolla, 1993.

Fletcher, R., Practical Methods of Optimization, John Wiley & Sons Ltd., 1987.

Li, W. C. and Biegler, L. T., "Process control strategies for constrained nonlinear systems," *Ind. Eng. Chem. Research,* 27, 1421-1433, 1988.

Ricker, N. L., Subrahmanian, T. and Sim, T., "Case studies of model-predictive control in pulp and paper production," *Model Based Predictive Control - Proc. of the IFAC Workshop on Model Based Process Control,* 1989.

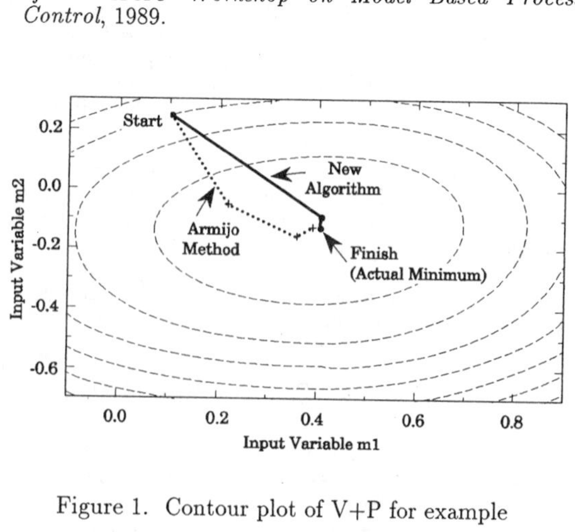

Figure 1. Contour plot of V+P for example

Proceedings of the
American Control Conference
San Francisco, California • June 1993

Robust Stability of Constrained Model Predictive Control

Zhi Q. Zheng Manfred Morari *

Chemical Engineering, 210-41
California Institute of Technology
Pasadena, CA 91125

Abstract

A new design technique for a robust model predictive controller is proposed using an uncertainty description expressed in the time-domain. Robust stability of the resulting closed-loop system is guaranteed for a set of Finite Impulse Response (FIR) models. Both necessary and sufficient conditions for asymptotic stability are stated. If the uncertainty is described as lower and upper bounds on impulse response coefficients, then the resulting optimization problem can be cast as a linear program of moderate size.

1 Introduction

Model Predictive Control (MPC), also known as moving horizon control and receding horizon control, has become an attractive feedback strategy. The underlying principle of MPC is to determine some future control moves that optimize some open-loop performance objective on a time interval extending from the current time (or some future time) to the current time (or the future time) plus a prediction horizon. Although more than one control move is generally calculated, only the first one is implemented. At the next sampling time interval, the output measurement is used to update the predictions and the same calculations are repeated.

Rawlings *et al* [9] showed for the state feedback case that nominal stability could be guaranteed by using an infinite receding horizon. Zafiriou [10] analyzes the contraction properties of the closed-loop system for constrained MPC. Assuming upper and lower bounds on each impulse response coefficient, Genceli *et al* [5] showed how to robustly stabilize a set of SISO systems. Some efforts [2, 3] have been made to achieve robustness by modifying the "min" optimization problem that is solved on-line to a "min-max" problem that minimizes the objective function maximized over all possible plants. The computational issues of the "min-max" problem for some specific uncertainty description has been explored by [1, 2]. However, the problem is that robust stability may not be guaranteed by solving the "min-max" problem. The reason is that feedback from the uncertain plant is not taken into account in the formulation of the optimization problem which is an open-loop minimization of the objective function over all possible plants. Due to the feedback, the "worst-case" plant at each sampling time may be different [7]. In this paper, we propose to solve a modified "min-max" problem which guarantees robust stability of the closed-loop system.

The paper is organized as follows. Section 2 presents the preliminary and the main results are presented in Section 3. If the uncertainty is described as lower and upper bounds on each impulse response coefficient, we show that the optimization problem can be formulated as a linear program in Section 4. Examples are presented in Section 5 to demonstrate the characteristics of the proposed method. Section 6 concludes the paper.

Notation $\Re^n$ and $\Re^{n\times n}$ denote the set of real vectors of dimension n and the set of real $n\times n$ matrices, respectively. x' denotes the transpose of x. $|\cdot|_1$ denotes the 1-norm on $\Re^n$, *i.e.* $|x|_1 = \sum_{i=1}^n |x_i|\ \forall\ x \in \Re^n$. $\|\cdot\|_1$ denotes the 1-norm on $\Re^{n\times n}$, *i.e.* $\|x\|_1 = \max_j \sum_{i=1}^n |x_{ij}|\ \forall\ x \in \Re^{n\times n}$. It can be easily shown that $\|\cdot\|_1$ is the operator norm induced by $|\cdot|_1$ [8]. I is the identity matrix of dimension of $n\times n$. For $x, y \in \Re^n$, $x \le y$ if and only if $x_i \le y_i, i = 1, 2, \cdots, n$. For $A, B \in \Re^{n\times n}, A \le B$ if $A_{ij} \le B_{ij}, i, j = 1, 2, \cdots, n$. $\max_{y(k+i|k)} \Leftrightarrow \max_{y(k+i|k)\in Y(k+i|k)}$.

2 Preliminary

Consider the system

$$y(k+1) = y(k) + \sum_{i=1}^{N} g_i(k+1)\Delta u(k) \qquad (1)$$

where y and u are the output and the input of the system, respectively, and $g(k+1) \equiv [g_1(k+1) \cdots g_N(k+1)] \in \Pi\ \forall\ k$. Π is generally obtained from some identification methods (*e.g.* [4, 6]). At each sampling time k, m control moves are calculated as follows.

$$\min_{\Delta u(k|k),\cdots,\Delta u(k+m-1|k)} \ \max_{y(k+i|k), i=l,\cdots,N+m-1} \Phi_k \qquad (2)$$

*Author to whom all correspondence should be addressed: phone (818)356-4186, fax (818)568-8743, e-mail: MM@IMC.CALTECH.EDU subject to

$$|\Delta u(k+i|k)| \le \Delta u^{max}, \qquad i = 0,1,\cdots,m-1$$
$$u^{min} \le u(k+i|k) \le u^{max}, \qquad i = 1,2,\cdots,m$$

and

$$\Phi_k = \max_{i\in\{l,\cdots,N+m-1\}} |\Gamma_y[r(k+i) - y(k+i|k)]|_1 + \sum_{j=0}^{m-1} |\Gamma_u \Delta u(k+j|k)|_1 \quad (3)$$

where

$\Delta u(k+i|k) \in \Re^n$ denotes the control move at time $k+i$ evaluated at time k and $\Delta u(k) \equiv \Delta u(k|k)$;

$y(k+i|k) \in \Re^n$ is the output at time $k+i$ predicted at time k and $y(k|k)$ is the output measured at time k. $y(k+i|k) \in Y(k+i|k)$;

$Y(k+i|k) = \{y(k+i|k) : y(k+i|k) = y(k+i-1|k) + g(k+i)\begin{bmatrix}\Delta u(k+i-N)\\ \vdots \\ \Delta u(k+i-1|k)\end{bmatrix}, g(k+i) \in \Pi,$ $y(k+i-1|k) \in Y(k+i-1|k)\}$ for any integer i and $Y(k|k) = \{y(k|k)\}$;

$r(k+i) \in \Re^n$ is the set-point at time $k+i$;

Γ_y and Γ_u are positive definite diagonal and positive semidefinite diagonal $n \times n$ matrices, respectively; and

l is the start of the prediction horizon to be minimized. As pointed out by Campo [2] for $l = 1$, the algorithm does not reject persistent disturbances for systems exhibiting inverse response characteristics. Therefore, l can be adjusted to handle systems with inverse response, dead time, etc. Obviously, $1 \le l \le N+m-1$.

Remark 1 *The system is assumed to be linear time varying (LTV) in the sense that g_i in Equation (1) varies with time. Since the system settles in N steps and only m controls are calculated, the maximum over the horizon from $k+l$ to $k+N+m-1$ equals the maximum over the infinite horizon starting from $k+l$. Effectively the objective function (3) uses the 1-norm spatially and the ∞-norm temporally. The control moves are calculated to minimize the "worst-case" value of the objective function.*

Remark 2 *When output constraints are present, all results hold provided that a feasible solution to the optimization problem (2) exists.*

3 Robust Stability of Constrained MPC

Throughout the paper, we will assume that the set-point r is constant such that the zero steady-state error is feasible for all plants in the model set.[1]

[1] If r is time-varying for $t \le T < \infty$, then we can take the initial time to be T.

Theorem 1 *Optimization of (2) without the inequality constraints at each sampling time k results in a closed-loop system which is robustly BIBO stable for all finite $m \ge 1$ and $1 \le l \le N+m-1$.*

Proof: Let J_k be the optimal value of the objective function (3) at time k. We want to show $J_{k+1} \le J_k$. At time $k+1$, the objective function is evaluated again to determine the optimal control moves. Let

$$\Delta U^*_{k+1} = \begin{bmatrix}\Delta u^*(k+1|k+1)\\ \vdots \\ \Delta u^*(k+m-1|k+1)\\ \Delta u^*(k+m|k+1)\end{bmatrix} = \begin{bmatrix}\Delta u(k+1|k)\\ \vdots \\ \Delta u(k+m-1|k)\\ \Delta u(k+m|k)=0\end{bmatrix}$$

Since ΔU^*_{k+1} may not be the optimal solution, $J_{k+1} \le J^*_{k+1}$ where J^*_{k+1} is the value of the objective function for ΔU^*_{k+1}.

$y(k+1|k+1)$ is measured at time $k+1$ and $Y(k+1|k+1) = \{y(k+1|k+1)\}$. Since $y(k+1|k+1) \in Y(k+1|k)$, $Y(k+1|k+1) \subseteq Y(k+1|k)$. Similarly, from the definition of $Y(k+i|k)$ and $\Delta u^*(k+i|k+1) = \Delta u(k+i|k)$, we can conclude $Y^*(k+i|k+1) \subseteq Y(k+i|k), i = 2,\cdots$. Therefore, $\max_{y(k+i|k+1)\in Y^*(k+i|k+1)} |\Gamma_y[r - y(k+i|k+1)]|_1 \le \max_{y(k+i|k)\in Y(k+i|k)} |\Gamma_y[r - y(k+i|k)]|_1, i = 1,2,\cdots \Rightarrow J^*_{k+1} \le J_k$.

Therefore, $J_{k+1} \le J_k$ and the objective function is bounded for all times. Since Γ_y is a positive definite diagonal matrix, the output must be bounded for all times. For any finite m, since the open-loop plant settles down in N steps and the prediction horizon is infinite, u must also be finite.

QED

Define the steady state gain as $G(k) = \sum_{i=1}^{N} g_i(k)$. The following two theorems set conditions on the set of models in terms of $G(k)$ for perfect tracking.

Theorem 2 *If $\min_x \max_{g(k)\in\Pi} |r - \Gamma_y G(k)x|_1 = |r|_1$ for $r \in \Re^n$ and Γ_u is positive definite, then starting from a steady state $\Delta u(k|k) = 0, k = 1,2,\cdots$.*

Proof: We need only to show $\Delta u(1|1) = 0$. If $\Delta u(1|1) = 0$, then starting from a steady state $\Delta u(k|k) = 0$ for $k = 2,3,\cdots$.

$J_1 = |\Gamma_y r|_1$ if $\Delta u(1+i|1) = 0, i = 0,1,\cdots,m-1$. Suppose $\Delta u(1|1) \ne 0$, then the set of the steady state output predictions contains $G(1)\sum_{i=0}^{m-1} \Delta u(1+i|1)$. We have

$$J_1 > \min_x \max_{g(1)\in\Pi} |\Gamma_y(r - G(1)x)|_1$$

$$= \min_{x} \max_{g(1)\in\Pi} |\Gamma_y r - \Gamma_y G(1)x|_1$$
$$= |\Gamma_y r|_1$$

The strict inequality follows from the fact that the second term in the objective function is non-zero since $\Delta u(1|1) \neq 0$. Therefore, $\Delta u(1|1) = 0$ is the only optimal solution.

QED

Remark 3 *If Γ_u is semidefinite, $\Delta u(k|k) = 0, k = 1, 2, \cdots$, may not be the only solution for some uncertainty descriptions.*

Remark 4 *For SISO systems, the condition $\min_x \max_{g(k)\in\Pi} |r - \Gamma_y G(k)x|_1 = |r|_1$ for $r \in \Re^n$ becomes that two plants in the model set have different steady-state gain signs or that a plant in the model set has zero steady state gain. Under the condition, no trajectory can be tracked. However, some subset of trajectories may be tracked if the condition fails.*

Theorem 3 *If there exists a nonsingular steady state gain matrix $G_0 \in \Re^{n\times n}$ resulting from some $g \in \Pi$ such that $\max_{g(k)\in\Pi} ||I - \Gamma_y G(k)G_0^{-1}||_1 < 1$, then the closed-loop system is asymptotically stable, i.e. the tracking error approaches zero asymptotically, for some m, l and Γ_u.*

Proof: Let us show this theorem for $m = 1, l = N$, and $\Gamma_u = 0$. The optimal value of the objective function becomes

$$J_k = \min_{\Delta u(k|k)} \max_{y(k+N-1|k)} |\Gamma_y[r - y(k+N-1|k)]|_1 \quad (4)$$

Given the optimal control move $\Delta u(k-1|k-1)$, define

$$2\delta = \max_{y(k+N-2|k-1)} \sum_{i=1}^{n} \Gamma_{y_{ii}}[r_i - y_i(k+N-1|k)] - \min_{y(k+N-2|k-1)} \sum_{i=1}^{n} \Gamma_{y_{ii}}[r_i - y_i(k+N-1|k)].$$

Then

$$J_{k-1} = |\Gamma_y(r - y_0)|_1 + \delta \text{ for some } y_0 \in \Re^n. \quad (5)$$

Let $\Delta u^*(k|k) = \alpha G_0^{-1}\Gamma_y(r - y_0), 0 < \alpha \leq 1$. α can always be chosen such that $\Delta u^*(k|k)$ is feasible (see Remark 5). $\Delta u^*(k|k)$ may not be optimal. We have

$$\begin{aligned}
J_k^* &= \max_{y(k+N-1|k)} |\Gamma_y[r - y(k+N-1|k)]|_1 \\
&\leq \max_{y(k+N-2|k-1)} \max_{g(k)\in\Pi} F \\
&\leq \delta + \max_{g(k)\in\Pi} |\Gamma_y[r - y_0 - G(k)\Delta u^*(k|k)]|_1 \\
&= \delta + \max_{g(k)\in\Pi} |(I - \alpha\Gamma_y G(k)G_0^{-1})\Gamma_y(r - y_0)|_1 \\
&\leq \delta + \max_{g(k)\in\Pi} ||(I - \alpha\Gamma_y G(k)G_0^{-1})||_1 |\Gamma_y(r - y_0)|_1 \\
&\leq \delta + \beta|\Gamma_y(r - y_0)|_1 \\
&\leq (1-\beta)\delta + \beta J_{k-1}
\end{aligned}$$

where

$$F = |\Gamma_y[r - y(k+N-2|k-1) - G(k)\Delta u^*(k|k)]|_1$$

and

$$\begin{aligned}
\beta &= \max_{g(k)\in\Pi} ||(I - \alpha\Gamma_y G(k)G_0^{-1})||_1 \\
&\leq \max_{g(k)\in\Pi} ||(\alpha I - \alpha\Gamma_y G(k)G_0^{-1})||_1 + (1-\alpha)||I||_1 \\
&\leq \alpha \max_{g(k)\in\Pi} ||I - \Gamma_y G(k)G_0^{-1})||_1 + (1-\alpha) < 1.
\end{aligned}$$

Therefore, $J_k \leq (1-\beta)\delta + \beta J_{k-1}$. Suppose that $J_k \to J \neq 0$ as $k \to \infty$. Then $\Delta u(k|k) \to 0$ (see Remark 6) and therefore $\delta \to 0$ as $k \to \infty$. For sufficiently large k, $J_k < J$ which contradicts the assumption that $J_k \to J$ as $k \to \infty$. Therefore, $J_k \to 0$ as $k \to 0$ and the tracking error approaches zero asymptotically for some m, l, and Γ_u.

QED

Remark 5 *Choosing α sufficiently small guarantees that $|\Delta u^*(k+1|k+1)| \leq \Delta u^{max}$. Also, by assumption that the steady state input for all plants in the model sets does not violate the constraints and $u(k) + G_0^{-1}\Gamma_y(r - y_0)$ is the steady state input for some plant in the model set, we have $u^{min} \leq u(k) + G_0^{-1}\Gamma_y(r - y_0) \leq u^{max}$. Since $u^{min} \leq u(k) \leq u^{max}$, $u^{min} \leq u(k) + \Delta u^*(k+1|k+1) \leq u^{max}$ for all $0 < \alpha \leq 1$.*

Remark 6 *If the solution to (4) is not unique, then we can always make it unique by choosing Γ_u to be arbitrarily small.*

Remark 7 *For SISO systems, the sufficient condition for asymptotic stability becomes that all plants in the model set have the same steady-state gain sign. This condition is also necessary. The condition is trivially satisfied if there is no uncertainty associated with the nominal model and the steady state gain matrix of the nominal model is not singular.*

Remark 8 *Theorem 3 states the condition that all trajectories can be tracked while Theorem 2 states the condition that no trajectory can be tracked. Therefore, naturally there is a gap between these two conditions. For the cases where neither condition is satisfied, some subset of trajectories may be tracked.*

4 Impulse Response Uncertainty

The results obtained in the previous section hold for any uncertainty description expressed in the time-domain. However, when considering the computational complexity of the optimization problem, some uncertainty description may be preferred. The optimization problem (2) can be cast as a linear program for the uncertainty description considered below. Some details are omitted because of the space limitation. Consider the following uncertainty description.

$$\Pi = \{g_i : |g_i - g_{i0}| = |\Delta g_i| \le \Delta g_i^{max}, \Delta g_i \in \Re^{n\times n}, \quad i = 1, \cdots, N\} \qquad (6)$$

Then,

$$\max_{y(k+i|k)} |\Gamma_y [r(k+i) - y(k+i|k)]|_1$$
$$= \max_{y(k+i-1|k)} \max_{\Delta g(k+i)} |\Gamma_y[r(k+i) - y(k+i-1|k) - (g^0 + \Delta g(k+i))\Delta u^i]|_1$$

$$= \max_{y(k+i-1|k)} \left|\Gamma_y \left[r(k+i) - y(k+i-1|k) - g^0\Delta u^i\right]\right|_1 + \left|\Gamma_y \Delta g^{max} |\Delta u^i|\right|_1$$

where

$g^0 = [g_{N0} \cdots g_{10}]'$,
$\Delta g(k+i) = [\Delta g_N(k+i) \cdots \Delta g_1(k+i)]'$, and
$\Delta u^i = [\Delta u(k+i-N) \cdots \Delta u(k+i-1|k)]'$.

The first equality follows from the definition while the second equality follows from the fact that the maximum must occur at one of the extreme points and that $\Delta g(k+i)$ belongs to the set if and only if $-\Delta g(k+i)$ belongs to the set. Repeating this process i times, we obtain

$$\max_{y(k+i|k)\in Y(k+i|k)} |\Gamma_y[r(k+i) - y(k+i|k)]|_1$$
$$= |\Gamma_y[r(k+i) - y(k|k)] - H_i\Delta U_k]|_1 + |L_i|\Delta U_k||_1$$
$$= |C_{ki} - H_i\Delta U_k|_1 + |L_i|\Delta U_k||_1, i = 1, \cdots, N + m - 1$$

where $\Delta U_k = [\Delta u(k-N) \cdots \Delta u(k+m-1|k)]'$, C_{ki} are constant vectors, and H_i and L_i are constant matrices. All terms involving Δg^{max} are combined to obtain the second term. The reason why we can do this is that each element of $\Gamma_y \Delta g^{max}$ is nonnegative and that $|A|x||_1 + |B|x||_1 = |(A+B)|x||_1$ if each element of A and B is nonnegative.

Thus, the optimization problem (2) is equivalent to the following optimization problem.

$$\min_{\Delta u_k} \theta \qquad (7)$$

such that

$$\begin{array}{ll} \alpha(i) + \beta(i) + \gamma \le \theta & i = l, \cdots, N+m-1 \\ |C_{ki} - H_i\Delta U_k|_1 = \alpha(i) & i = l, \cdots, N+m-1 \\ |L_i|\Delta U_k||_1 = \beta(i) & i = l, \cdots, N+m-1 \\ \sum_{j=0}^{m-1} |\Gamma_u \Delta u(k+j|k)|_1 = \gamma & \\ |\Delta u(k+i|k)| \le \Delta u^{max} & i = 0, 1, \cdots, m-1 \\ u^{min} \le u(k+i|k) \le u^{max} & i = 0, 1, \cdots, m-1 \end{array}$$

By introducing extra variables, the constraints can be converted into the form $Ax \le b$. Every equality constraint can be replaced by two inequalities. For example, $x = y \Leftrightarrow x \ge y$ *and* $-x \ge -y$. Therefore, the above optimization can be cast a linear program. The total number of variables is $2 + (n+2)(N + m - l) + 2mn$ and the total number of constraints is $1 + (3 + 2n)(N + m - l) + 5mn$.

5 Examples

We present two SISO examples to demonstrate the characteristics of the proposed algorithm. Example 1 shows that the Robust Model Predictive Control (RMPC) algorithm proposed in [2, 3] does not guarantee robust stability of the closed-loop system. Example 2 illustrates the effects of the tuning parameters m and l. $\Gamma_y = 1$ and $\Gamma_u = 0$ for both examples.

Example 1 *The set of plants is given by*
$\mathcal{G} = \{G : G = g_1 q^{-1} + g_2 q^{-2}, .5 \le g_1 \le 1, .4 \le g_2 \le .6\}$

Figure 1 shows the simulated results for the RMPC scheme proposed by Campo [2, 3] and the method proposed here when the actual plant $G = 0.75q^{-1} + 0.5q^{-2}$. Our algorithm is slightly more sluggish than Campo's algorithm though the performance for both algorithms is reasonable.

Figure 2 shows the simulated results for the two methods when the actual plant $G = q^{-1} + 0.4q^{-2}$. In this case, Campo's algorithm results in an unstable closed-loop system.

Example 2 *The actual plant is given by*

$$G = \frac{-0.25 + 0.65q^{-1}}{q - 0.6}$$

g_{i0} *denotes the* i^{th} *impulse coefficient of* G. *The set of plants is given by*

$$\mathcal{G} = \{G : G = \sum_{i=1}^{N} g_i q^{-1}, |g_i - g_{i0}| \le 0.05|g_{i0}|\}$$

Since the plant exhibits inverse response characteristics, l must be larger than one to provide any non-zero control. Selecting $l = 2$ is sufficient for this example. As shown in Figure 3 ($N = 15$), the response for $m = 2$ is faster than that for $m = 1$. In general, the larger m is, the faster is the response, but the more expensive is the computation.

6 Concluding Remarks

We proposed a new MPC design technique which guarantees robust stability of the closed-loop system. The plant uncertainty is incorporated directly into the formulation. Both necessary and sufficient conditions for asymptotic stability are stated. If the uncertainty is described as lower and upper bounds on each impulse response coefficient, the optimization can be formulated as a linear program. Computational complexity for more general uncertainty descriptions is under study. We are also investigating how unmeasured disturbances and state estimation affect the closed-loop stability.

7 Acknowledgement

Partial support from the National Science Foundation

and the Department of Energy is gratefully acknowledged.

References

[1] J. C. Allwright and G. C. Papavasiliou. On linear programming and robust model-predictive control using impulse-responses. *Systems & Control Letters*, 18:159–164, 1992.

[2] P. J. Campo. *Studies In Robust Control Of Systems Subject To Constraints.* PhD thesis, California Institute of Technology, Pasadena, 1990.

[3] P. J. Campo and M. Morari. Robust model predictive control. In *Proceedings of the 1987 American Control Conference*, pages 1021–1026, 1987.

[4] E. Fogel and Y. F. Huang. On the value of information in system identification – bounded noise case. *Automatica*, 18(2):229–238, 1982.

[5] H. Genceli and M. Nikolaou. Robust stability analysis of constrained model predictive control. In *AIChE Annual Meeting*, Miami, FL, November 1992.

[6] R. L. Kosut, M. Lau, and S. Boyd. Identification of systems with parametric and nonparametric uncertainty. In *Proceedings of American Control Conf.*, pages 2412–2417, 1990.

[7] J. H. Lee and M. Morari. Robust model predictive control. In *AIChE Annual Meeting*, November 1991.

[8] M. Morari and E. Zafiriou. *Robust Process Control.* Prentice-Hall, Inc., Englewood Cliffs, N.J., 1989.

[9] J. B. Rawlings and K. R. Muske. The stability of constrained receding horizon control. *IEEE Transactions on Automatic Control*, 1992. Submitted.

[10] E. Zafiriou. Robust model predictive control of processes with hard constraints. *Computers and Chemical Engineering*, 14:359–371, 1990.

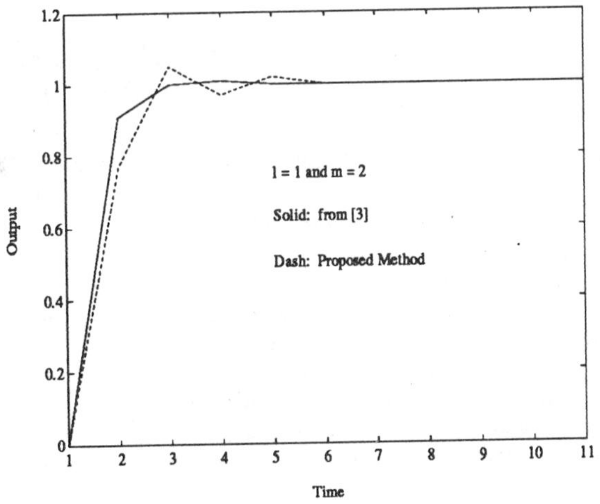

Figure 1: Closed-loop Response for Set-point Change

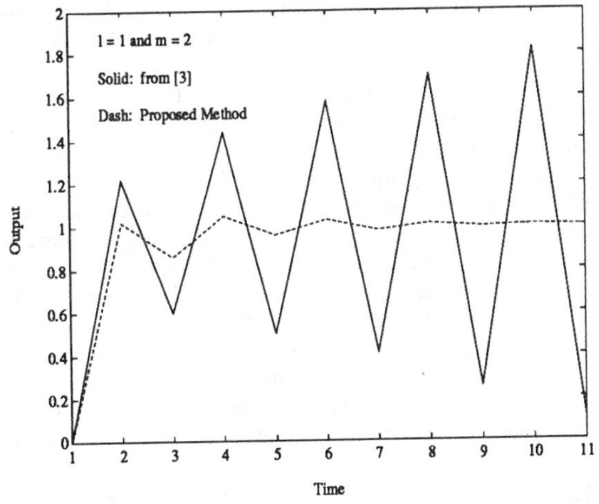

Figure 2: Closed-loop Response for Set-point Change

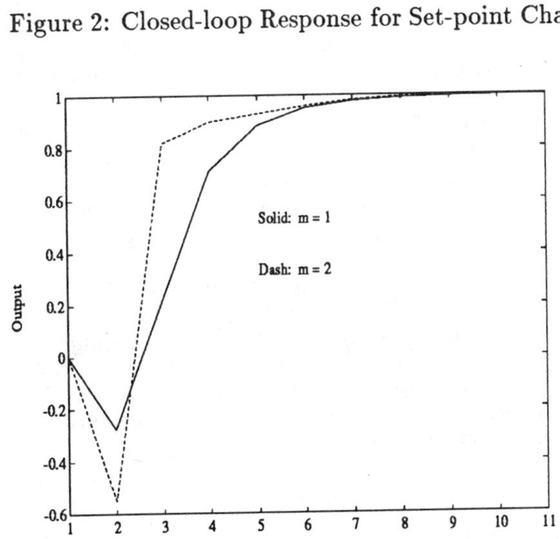

Figure 3: Effect of m on Closed-loop Response

Proceedings of the
American Control Conference
San Francisco, California • June 1993

Generalized Predictive Control Algorithms with Guaranteed Frozen-Time Stability and Bounded Tracking Error

Thomas Jolly and Joseph Bentsman*
Department of Mechanical & Industrial Engineering, University of Illinois at Urbana-Champaign
1206 West Green Street, Urbana, Illinois 61801, USA

Abstract

In its present form, for a fixed plant model GPC (generalized predictive control) guarantees stability only for two specific choices of horizons in the cost function. In one instance, GPC has been shown to result in a deadbeat control law while in the other, the control law has been shown to converge to that given by the solution of the corresponding algebraic Riccati equation. However a lower bound on the costing horizon that results in a stabilizing controller is not known *a priori*. This paper presents sufficient conditions for stability of closed loop systems that result from implementing solutions of the finite horizon LQ problem for arbitrary fixed costing horizons. On this basis, a class of predictive control laws that ensures frozen-time stability of the closed loop system is proposed. When the plant is required to track a known reference signal that is bounded, the sufficient conditions for frozen-time stability of the closed loop are used to derive a controller structure that guarantees the tracking error to be bounded.

1 : Introduction

The GPC law is derived by minimizing a cost function that is expressed explicitly in terms of predictions of future plant outputs and control increments. Implementation of the control at each step is based on the so called receding horizon strategy, where only the first control signal is used before a new control sequence is computed at the next instant. In the non-adaptive case if computation of the control sequence is based on a fixed horizon and only the first control signal is used at each step, implementing the receding horizon strategy results in a time-invariant controller gain. To account for changes in reference inputs and/or plant deadtime, the costing horizons may be adjusted online without updating the plant model per se[13]. This leads to non-constant controller gains corresponding to each set of horizons used in the cost function.

This paper presents theoretical analysis and design of the SPC (stabilizing predictive control) law that guarantees frozen-time stability of time-varying systems which result from implementing a receding horizon control strategy for a fixed plant model for a given value of the costing horizon. For tracking known reference signals, the paper presents a controller structure that guarantees the error between plant output and reference signal to be bounded regardless of the costing horizon used.

2 : State-Space Formulation of GPC

The plant is chosen to be described by a CARIMA model:

$$A(q^{-1})\,y_t = B(q^{-1})\,u_{t-1} + \frac{C(q^{-1})}{\Delta}\,\xi_t \qquad (2.1)$$

where $\Delta \triangleq (1-q^{-1})$ and ξ_t is white noise with zero mean and unit variance. $A(q^{-1})$, $B(q^{-1})$, and $C(q^{-1})$ are polynomials in the backward shift operator q^{-1}. $A(q^{-1})$ is monic and $C(q^{-1})$ is assumed to have all zeros strictly within the unit circle with $\deg(C(q^{-1})) \leq \deg(A(q^{-1}))$. Development of GPC when the plant is represented by (2 .1) may be found in [12]. In the deterministic case, (2 .1) can be reformulated as:

$$\left.\begin{aligned} x_{t+1} &= Fx_t + G\Delta u_t \\ y_t &= Hx_t \end{aligned}\right\} \qquad (2.2)$$

with $x_t \in \Re^n$, where $n = 1 + n_a$ and $n_a \triangleq \deg(A(q^{-1}))$. The system matrices are:

$$F = \begin{bmatrix} -\tilde{a}_1 & 1 & 0 & . & 0 & 0 \\ -\tilde{a}_2 & 0 & 1 & . & 0 & 0 \\ . & . & . & . & . & . \\ -\tilde{a}_{na} & 0 & 0 & . & 0 & 1 \\ -\tilde{a}_n & 0 & 0 & . & 0 & 0 \end{bmatrix},\quad G = \begin{bmatrix} b_0 \\ b_1 \\ . \\ b_{na-1} \\ b_{na} \end{bmatrix},\quad K = \begin{bmatrix} c_1-\tilde{a}_1 \\ c_2-\tilde{a}_2 \\ . \\ c_{na}-\tilde{a}_{na} \\ -\tilde{a}_n \end{bmatrix},$$

and $H = \begin{bmatrix}1 & 0 & . & . & 0 & 0\end{bmatrix}$. If it is desired that the plant output be brought to zero, a deterministic cost function may be defined as:

$$J_{GPC} = \sum_{j=1}^{N} \gamma\left[\hat{y}_j\right]^2 + \sum_{j=0}^{N-1} \lambda\left[\Delta u_j\right]^2 . \qquad (2.3)$$

In (2 .3), $\hat{y}_j$ and Δu_j are weighted for the same finite horizon N.

2.1 : Prediction of Future Outputs

The predicted state of the system N steps into the future will be the sum of the free state response due to the current state x_0 and the forced state response due to future control increments.

$$\begin{Bmatrix} \hat{x}_1 \\ \hat{x}_2 \\ . \\ \hat{x}_N \end{Bmatrix} = \begin{bmatrix} F \\ F^2 \\ . \\ F^N \end{bmatrix} x_0 + \begin{bmatrix} G & 0 & . & 0 & 0 \\ FG & G & : & 0 & 0 \\ . & . & . & . & . \\ F^{N-1}G & F^{N-2}G & . & FG & G \end{bmatrix} \begin{Bmatrix} \Delta u_0 \\ \Delta u_1 \\ . \\ \Delta u_{N-1} \end{Bmatrix} \qquad (2.4)$$

The predicted outputs N steps into the future are given by:

$$\hat{\boldsymbol{y}}^T \triangleq \left[\hat{y}_1\ \hat{y}_2\ .\ .\ \hat{y}_N\right]^T = \left[H\hat{x}_1\ H\hat{x}_2\ .\ .\ H\hat{x}_N\right]^T \qquad (2.5)$$

Defining $\boldsymbol{u} \triangleq \left[\Delta u_0\ \Delta u_1\ .\ .\ \Delta u_{N-1}\right]^T$ and combining (2 .4) and (2 .5), we have: $\hat{\boldsymbol{y}} = \boldsymbol{\Phi}\ x_0 + \boldsymbol{G}\ \boldsymbol{u}$ (2.6)

$$\text{where } \boldsymbol{\Phi} \triangleq \begin{bmatrix} HF \\ HF^2 \\ . \\ HF^N \end{bmatrix} \text{ and } \boldsymbol{G} \triangleq \begin{bmatrix} HG & 0 & . & 0 \\ HFG & HG & : & 0 \\ . & . & . & . \\ HF^{N-1}G & HF^{N-2}G & . & HG \end{bmatrix}.$$

In (2 .6) $\hat{\boldsymbol{y}} \in \Re^N$, $\boldsymbol{\Phi} \in \Re^{N\times n}$, $x_0 \in \Re^n$, $\boldsymbol{G} \in \Re^{N\times N}$ and the vector of future controls is $\boldsymbol{u} \in \Re^N$. $\boldsymbol{\Phi}x_0$ is the predicted free response and $\boldsymbol{Gu}$ is the predicted forced response due to future controls.

2.2 : Derivation of the Control Law

The cost function (2 .3) to be optimized may be rewritten using (2 .6) as:

$$\begin{aligned} J_{GPC} &= \gamma\,\hat{\boldsymbol{y}}^T\hat{\boldsymbol{y}} + \lambda\,\boldsymbol{u}^T\boldsymbol{u} \\ &= \gamma\left[\boldsymbol{\Phi}x_0 + \boldsymbol{Gu}\right]^T\left[\boldsymbol{\Phi}x_0 + \boldsymbol{Gu}\right] + \lambda\,\boldsymbol{u}^T\boldsymbol{u}\,. \end{aligned} \qquad (2.7)$$

Minimizing (2 .7) with respect to **u**, the optimal control vector is:

$$\boldsymbol{u}_{opt} = -\left[\gamma\,\boldsymbol{G}^T\boldsymbol{G} + \lambda I\right]^{-1}\gamma\,\boldsymbol{G}^T\,\boldsymbol{\Phi}x_0\,. \qquad (2.8)$$

Since GPC uses a receding horizon control strategy, the control increment that is actually implemented is the first element of the $\Re^N$vector on the right hand side of (2 .8).

Remark 1: If only N_u future control increments are penalized in (2 .3) where $N_u < N$, then $\boldsymbol{G} \in \Re^{N\times N_u}$ and $\left[\gamma\,\boldsymbol{G}^T\boldsymbol{G} + \lambda I\right]$ is of reduced dimension $(N_u \times N_u)$.

Remark 2: If as in the LQ regulator problem, all states from $j = 0$ to $j = N$ are included in the cost function, (2 .3) may be rewritten as

$$J_{GPC}^{ext} = \sum_{j=0}^{N} \gamma\left[\hat{y}_j\right]^2 + \sum_{j=0}^{N-1} \lambda\left[\Delta u_j\right]^2 . \qquad (2.9)$$

Since $\hat{y}_0$ is equal to the known current output y_0, the predicted state vector $\hat{x}_0$ is independent of $\boldsymbol{u}$. Since $\hat{y}_0$ does not affect future control increments, the optimal control vector that minimizes (2 .9) is therefore equal to (2 .8).

3 : Comparison between GPC and LQ Optimal Control

Even though GPC is not amenable to rigorous stability and performance analysis in its present form, it may be treated as a special case of LQ control by embedding it into the framework of LQ optimal control. Assuming complete state information for the deterministic plant model (2 .2), the quadratic cost function to be minimized with respect to $\boldsymbol{u}$ is :

$$J_{LQ} = x_N^T P_0 x_N + \sum_{j=0}^{N-1}\left[x_j^T Q x_j + \Delta u_j^T R \Delta u_j\right] \qquad (3.1)$$

where $P_0 \geq 0$, $Q \geq 0$, and $R > 0$.

* Author to whom correspondence should be addressed

The equivalence of LQ control and GPC have been studied by Bitmead et al.[1] by assuming full state information and posing both the LQ and GPC cost functions in a regulator framework. Under certain assumptions on the weighting matrices and costing horizons, LQ and GPC cost functions are shown to be identical.

The control vector $\boldsymbol{u}$ given by GPC is generated on the basis of information $\{\Delta u_{t-1},\ x_t : t \le 0\}$ whereas that given by the LQ control law is computed using the information $\{\Delta u_{t-1},\ x_t : t \le j\}$. Therefore the solution sequences computed by the GPC and LQ control laws will be equal only when $j = 0$ where their computation is based on the same information.

4 : Properties of Receding Horizon Control Strategies

Asymptotic stability properties of the infinite horizon LQG controller are well documented [4], [5] through properties of the associated ARE (algebraic Riccati equation). The techniques suggested by Bitmead et al.[11] are used to connect solutions of the RDE for the finite horizon problem to the corresponding ARE for the infinite horizon case.

4 .1 : Monotonic Properties of Finite Horizon LQ Control

Consider the deterministic plant model (2 .2) and the cost function for the LQ regulator problem to be minimized given by (3 .1). The associated RDE can be rewritten as:

$$P_{t+1} = F^T P_t F - F^T P_t G \left[G^T P_t G + R\right]^{-1} G^T P_t F + Q \qquad (4\,.1)$$

for $t = 0, \ldots, N-1$. It has been shown[6], [7] that subject to conditions of stabilizability and detectability of the original system and conditions on the weighting matrices in the cost function, P_t of (4 .1) $\rightarrow \overline{P}$ as $t \rightarrow \infty$. However, the choice of the costing horizon N to guarantee stability and its dependence on terminal state weighting P_0 is not clear. Poubelle et al.[10] rewrite the RDE in (4 .1) as the so called FARE (fake algebraic Riccati equation):

$$P_t = F^T P_t F - F^T P_t G \left[G^T P_t G + R\right]^{-1} G^T P_t F + \overline{Q}_t \qquad (4\,.2)$$

$$\text{where:} \quad \overline{Q}_t \triangleq Q + \left[P_t - P_{t+1}\right] . \qquad (4\,.3)$$

Bitmead et al.[1] have translated the concept of stability of the ARE solution to "frozen-time" stability of each solution of the RDE (4 .2). It has been shown[11] that if the solution P_t of the RDE in (4 .1) is monotonically non-increasing at one time instant, then it is monotonically non-increasing at all subsequent time instants.

4 .2 : Stability of Receding Horizon LQ controllers

Conditions for guaranteed "frozen-time" asymptotic stability of the closed loop independent of the costing horizon N when finite horizon control gains are implemented as a receding horizon strategy are given by Bitmead et al.[1] using monotonically non-increasing properties of P_t. However, there is no indication how the initial condition P_0 of the RDE (4 .1) and consequently $\overline{Q}_0$ must be selected to guarantee stability of the closed loop system matrix. The following lemma gives a choice for P_0 which will guarantee that $P_2 \le P_1 \le P_0$ where P_1 and P_2 are successive solutions of (4 .1).

***Lemma* 4 .1**: Let P_1 and P_2 be successive solutions to the RDE (4 .1). If the initial condition P_0 to (4 .1) is chosen to be the unique solution of the ARE given by:

$$\overline{P}_0 = F^T \overline{P}_0 F - F^T \overline{P}_0 G \left[G^T \overline{P}_0 G + R\right]^{-1} G^T \overline{P}_0 F + \overline{Q}_0 \qquad (4\,.4)$$

where $\overline{Q}_0 = Q + \varepsilon^2 I$ and $\varepsilon \ge 0$, then $P_2 \le P_1 \le P_0$.

Proof: The ARE (4 .4) can be rewritten as an RDE:

$$P^1_{t+1} = F^T P^1_t F - F^T P^1_t G \left[G^T P^1_t G + R\right]^{-1} G^T P^1_t F + Q^1 \qquad (4\,.5)$$

where $Q^1 \triangleq \overline{Q}_0 = Q + \varepsilon^2 I$, and $P^1_t \equiv \overline{P}_0 \ \forall\ t \ge 0$.

$$\text{Then,} \quad P^1_0 = P^1_1 = P^1_2 = \ldots = \overline{P}_0 . \qquad (4\,.6)$$

The RDE (4 .1) can be rewritten as:

$$P^2_{t+1} = F^T P^2_t F - F^T P^2_t G \left[G^T P^2_t G + R\right]^{-1} G^T P^2_t F + Q^2 \qquad (4\,.7)$$

where $Q^2 \triangleq Q$. Now define $\tilde{Q} \triangleq Q^2 - Q^1 = -\varepsilon^2 I$ and $\tilde{P}_t \triangleq P^2_t - P^1_t$. Since $P^1_0 = \overline{P}_0$, the first iteration of (4 .5) yields:

$$P^1_1 = F^T \overline{P}_0 F - F^T \overline{P}_0 G \left[G^T \overline{P}_0 G + R\right]^{-1} G^T \overline{P}_0 F + Q^1 .$$

Let the initial condition of (4 .7) be $\overline{P}_0$. The first iteration of (4 .7) yields $P^2_1 = F^T \overline{P}_0 F - F^T \overline{P}_0 G \left[G^T \overline{P}_0 G + R\right]^{-1} G^T \overline{P}_0 F + Q^2$.

$$\text{Then,} \quad \tilde{P}_1 = P^2_1 - P^1_1 = Q^2 - Q^1 = -\varepsilon^2 I . \qquad (4\,.8)$$

$$\text{From (4 .6) and (4 .8) we have} \quad P^2_1 - \overline{P}_0 = -\varepsilon^2 I . \qquad (4\,.9)$$

Since the initial condition of (4 .7) is chosen as $P^2_0 = P_0 = \overline{P}_0$, we have from (4 .9):

$$P^2_1 - P^2_0 = -\varepsilon^2 I \Rightarrow P^2_1 - P^2_0 \le 0 \Rightarrow P_1 \le P_0 . \qquad (4\,.10)$$

Since P^1_1 and P^2_1 are solutions of (4 .5) and (4 .7) respectively, by *Lemma A* of the Appendix, we have:

$$\tilde{P}_2 = \overline{F}_1^{1T} \tilde{P}_1 \overline{F}_1^1 - \overline{F}_1^{1T} \tilde{P}_1 G [G^T P^2_1 G + R]^{-1} G^T \tilde{P}_1 \overline{F}_1^1 + \tilde{Q} .$$

From (4 .8), $\overline{F}_1^{1T} \tilde{P}_1 \overline{F}_1^1 - \overline{F}_1^{1T} \tilde{P}_1 G [G^T P^2_1 G + R]^{-1} G^T \tilde{P}_1 \overline{F}_1^1 \le 0$.

$$\text{Define} \quad M \triangleq -\left[\overline{F}_1^{1T} \tilde{P}_1 \overline{F}_1^1 - \overline{F}_1^{1T} \tilde{P}_1 G [G^T P^2_1 G + R]^{-1} G^T \tilde{P}_1 \overline{F}_1^1\right]$$

where $M \ge 0$. We then have:

$\tilde{P}_2 = P^2_2 - P^1_2 = -M + \tilde{Q} = -M - \varepsilon^2 I$. From (4 .6) and (4 .9), we have:

$$\tilde{P}_2 = P^2_2 - \overline{P}_0 = -M - \varepsilon^2 I = -M + P^2_1 - \overline{P}_0$$

$$\Rightarrow \quad P^2_2 - P^2_1 = -M \le 0$$

$$\Rightarrow \quad P^2_2 \le P^2_1 \Rightarrow P_2 \le P_1 . \qquad (4\,.11)$$

(4 .10) and (4 .11) complete the proof. Q.E.D.

The following theorem gives a sufficient condition for asymptotic stability of the "frozen-time" closed loop at each iteration step of the RDE by suggesting a choice of P_0 that will force P_t to be monotonically non-increasing $\forall\ t \ge 0$.

***Theorem* 4 .1**

Consider the plant (2 .2), the LQ cost function (3 .1), and the associated RDE:

$$P_{t+1} = F^T P_t F - F^T P_t G \left[G^T P_t G + R\right]^{-1} G^T P_t F + Q . \qquad (4\,.12)$$

Assume that $[F, G]$ is stabilizable, $\left[F, Q^{1/2}\right]$ is detectable, $Q \ge 0$, $R > 0$. Then the "frozen-time" closed loop system matrix given by:

$$\overline{F}_t = F - G \left[G^T P_t G + R\right]^{-1} G^T P_t F \qquad (4\,.13)$$

has all eigenvalues strictly within the unit circle $\forall\ t \ge 0$ if the initial condition P_0 to the RDE (4 .12) is chosen to be the unique solution of the ARE given by:

$$\overline{P}_0 = F^T \overline{P}_0 F - F^T \overline{P}_0 G \left[G^T \overline{P}_0 G + R\right]^{-1} G^T \overline{P}_0 F + \overline{Q}_0 \qquad (4\,.14)$$

where $\overline{Q}_0 = Q + \varepsilon^2 I$, and $\varepsilon \ge 0$.

Proof: Since $Q \ge 0$ and $\varepsilon \ge 0$, we have $\overline{Q}_0 = Q + \varepsilon^2 I \ge Q \ge 0$. Since $\left[F, Q^{1/2}\right]$ is detectable, $\left[F, \overline{Q}_0^{1/2}\right]$ is also detectable. This satisfies conditions for the existence of a unique, maximal $\overline{P}_0 \ge 0$ which is the stabilizing solution to the ARE (4 .14). By *Lemma* 4 .1, if the initial condition P_0 of (4 .12) were chosen to be equal to $\overline{P}_0$, then $P_2 \le P_1 \le P_0$. Now the monotonicity properties[1] of P_t are invoked to conclude that the frozen-time closed loop system (4 .13) will be asymptotically stable $\forall\ t \ge 0$. Q.E.D.

Remark 3 : In (4 .14) if $R = 0$, i.e. no constraint is placed on control effort, then the terminal weighting $\overline{P}_0$ that is sufficient to guarantee stability of the closed loop system matrix can be made arbitrarily close to Q. The implication is that for guaranteed stability, a trade-off exists between chosing the amount of control effort and the costing on the terminal state.

The receding horizon control strategy involves implementation of the control Δu_0 at each step. The corresponding constant closed loop system matrix for a given costing horizon N will be:

$$\overline{F}_{N-1} = F - G \left[G^T P_{N-1} G + R\right]^{-1} G^T P_{N-1} F . \qquad (4\,.15)$$

If the conditions of *Theorem* 4 .1 are satisfied, (4 .15) will have all its eigenvalues strictly within the unit circle. This results in asymptotic stability of the frozen-time closed loop system (4 .15).

5 : Stability under Generalized Predictive Control

Consider a plant that is represented in its observable canonical form (2 .2) and the problem of minimizing the cost function:

$$J_{GPC} = \sum_{j=1}^{N} \gamma \left[y_j\right]^2 + \sum_{j=0}^{N-1} \lambda \left[\Delta u_j\right]^2$$
$$= \sum_{j=0}^{N-1} \left[\gamma\, x_j^T H^T H x_j\right] + \gamma\, x_N^T H^T H x_N + \sum_{j=0}^{N-1} \lambda\, \Delta u_j^T \Delta u_j \,. \quad (5.1)$$

Remark 4 : Note that x_0 which is the initial state is known from the current output. Therefore changing the lower limit of summation in the first term of (5 .1) to $j = 0$ does not change the optimal solution.

Theorem 5 .1

Consider the plant (2 .2) which is both stabilizable and detectable and the cost function to be minimized in (5 .1). If the weighting matrix of the final state x_N used in the cost function is chosen to be the unique solution $\overline{P}_0$ of the ARE:

$$\overline{P}_0 = F^T\overline{P}_0F - F^T\overline{P}_0G\left[G^T\overline{P}_0G + \lambda\, I\right]^{-1}G^T\overline{P}_0F + \overline{Q} \quad (5.2)$$

where $\overline{Q} = \gamma\, H^TH + \varepsilon^2 I$, and $\varepsilon \geq 0$, then the frozen–time closed loop system matrix with GPC will have all eigenvalues strictly within the unit circle.

Proof: When the system is represented in its observable canonical form (2 .2), the matrix H is of the form $\begin{bmatrix}1 & 0 & 0 & . & . & 0\end{bmatrix}$. Then we have $\overline{Q} = \gamma\, H^TH + \varepsilon^2 I \geq \gamma\, H^TH \geq 0$ since both $H^TH \geq 0$ and $\varepsilon \geq 0$. Since $[F\,,H]$ is detectable, $\left[F\,,\overline{Q}^{1/2}\right]$ is also detectable. Then by *Theorem* 4 .1 , $\overline{P}_0$ exists as a unique solution to the ARE (5 .2). Using this value of $\overline{P}_0$ as the initial condition to the corresponding RDE:

$$P_{t+1} = F^TP_tF - F^TP_tG\left[G^TP_tG + \lambda\, I\right]^{-1}G^TP_tF + \gamma H^TH \quad (5.3)$$

will necessarily ensure, by the same arguments as in the proof of *Theorem* 4 .1 , that all successive solutions P_t of the RDE (5 .3) will be monotonically non–increasing. This ensures that the closed loop resulting from implementing subsequent solutions $P_t\ \forall\ t \geq 0$ will have all eigenvalues strictly within the unit circle. When the weighting matrices $P_0 = \gamma\, H^TH,\ \ Q = \gamma\, H^TH$, and $R = \lambda\, I$, the GPC cost function (5 .1) is identical to the cost function (3 .1) for the LQ regulator problem. Therefore the LQ control signal obtained after N–1 iterations of the RDE (5 .3) will be equivalent to that given by GPC. Since the receding horizon strategy of GPC implements this control increment, the resulting closed loop system matrix will have all eigenvalues within the unit circle. Q.E.D.

6 : Design of Stabilizing Predictive Controller (SPC)

Consider the plant model (2 .2) and the cost function (5 .1). Let $\overline{P}$ be the stabilizing solution to the corresponding infinite horizon LQ regulator problem ARE which is given by:

$$\overline{P} = F^T\overline{P}F - F^T\overline{P}G\left[G^T\overline{P}G + \lambda\, I\right]^{-1}G^T\overline{P}F + \overline{Q} \quad (6.1)$$

where $\overline{Q} = \gamma\, H^TH + \varepsilon^2 I$ and $\varepsilon \geq 0$. The following theorem presents the stabilizing predictive control law that produces a frozen–time stable closed loop system for any value of the costing horizon.

Theorem 6 .1

Consider the plant model (2 .2). Let $\overline{P}$ be the stabilizing solution to the ARE (6 .1) and $\overline{W} \triangleq \left[\overline{P} - \gamma\, H^TH\right]$. Then the control law given by:

$$\boldsymbol{u} = -\left[\gamma\, \boldsymbol{G}^T\boldsymbol{G} + \Omega + \lambda\, I\right]^{-1}\left[\gamma\, \boldsymbol{G}^T\boldsymbol{\Phi} + \Psi\right] x_0 \quad (6.2)$$

with

$$\Omega = \Pi^T\overline{W}\Pi,\ \Psi = \Pi^T\overline{W}F^N,\ \Pi = \left[F^{N-1}F^{N-2}.\ .\ I\right]\boldsymbol{G}, \quad (6.3)$$

and $\boldsymbol{G}, \boldsymbol{\Phi}$ defined in (2 .6) minimizes the cost function (5 .1), and the closed loop system with this control law has all eigenvalues strictly within the unit circle for any value of the costing horizon N.

Proof: *Theorem* 5 .1 states that in order to produce a stabilizing predictive controller that minimizes the cost function (5 .1), the weighting on the terminal state in (5 .1) should be equal to the stabilizing solution of the ARE (6 .1). Since $\overline{P}$ is the stabilizing solution to (6 .1), the modified cost function when the terminal state is weighted by $\overline{P}$ is:

$$J_{GPC}^{mod} = \sum_{j=0}^{N-1} \left[\gamma\, x_j^TH^THx_j\right] + x_N^T\overline{P}x_N + \sum_{j=0}^{N-1} \lambda\, \Delta u_j^T\Delta u_j\,. \quad (6.4)$$

Adding and subtracting $\gamma\, x_N^TH^THx_N$ from (6 .4), we have:

$$J_{GPC}^{mod} = \sum_{j=0}^{N} \left[\gamma\, x_j^TH^THx_j\right] + x_N^T\left[\overline{P} - \gamma H^TH\right]x_N + \sum_{j=0}^{N-1} \lambda\, \Delta u_j^T\Delta u_j$$
$$= J_{GPC}^{reg} + x_N^T\left[\overline{P} - \gamma\, H^TH\right]x_N$$
$$= \gamma\left[\boldsymbol{\Phi}x_0 + \boldsymbol{Gu}\right]^T\left[\boldsymbol{\Phi}x_0 + \boldsymbol{Gu}\right] + \lambda\, \boldsymbol{u}^T\boldsymbol{u} + x_N^T\, \overline{W}\, x_N$$

where $\boldsymbol{\Phi} \in \Re^{N\times n}$, $x_0 \in \Re^n$, $\boldsymbol{G} \in \Re^{N\times N}$, $\boldsymbol{u} \in \Re^N$ are as defined in (2 .6), and $x_N^T\, \overline{W}\, x_N$ is the augmented terminal cost with $\overline{W} \triangleq \left[\overline{P} - \gamma\, H^TH\right]$. Simplifying, we have:

$$J_{GPC}^{mod} = \gamma\, x_0^T\, \boldsymbol{\Phi}^T\boldsymbol{\Phi}\, x_0 + 2\,\gamma\, \boldsymbol{u}^T\boldsymbol{G}^T\boldsymbol{\Phi}\, x_0 + \boldsymbol{u}^T\left[\gamma\, \boldsymbol{G}^T\boldsymbol{G} + \lambda\, I\right]\boldsymbol{u} + x_N^T\, \overline{W}\, x_N\,. \quad (6.5)$$

The augmented terminal cost can be obtained using (2 .4) as:

$$x_N^T\, \overline{W}\, x_N = x_0^T\, \Theta\, x_0 + 2\,\boldsymbol{u}^T\Psi\, x_0 + \boldsymbol{u}\,\Omega\,\boldsymbol{u} \quad (6.6)$$

where $\Psi \in \Re^{N\times n}$ and $\Omega \in \Re^{N\times N}$ are given in given (6 .3). Using (6 .6) in (6 .5), the modified cost function is:

$$J_{GPC}^{mod} = x_0^T\left[\gamma\, \boldsymbol{\Phi}^T\boldsymbol{\Phi} + \Theta\right]x_0 + 2\,\boldsymbol{u}^T\left[\gamma\, \boldsymbol{G}^T\boldsymbol{\Phi} + \Psi\right]x_0 + \boldsymbol{u}^T\left[\gamma\, \boldsymbol{G}^T\boldsymbol{G} + \Omega + \lambda\, I\right]\boldsymbol{u}\,. \quad (6.7)$$

Finally, minimization of (6 .7) yields the optimal control vector:

$$\boldsymbol{u}_{opt} = -\left[\gamma\boldsymbol{G}^T\boldsymbol{G} + \Omega + \lambda I\right]^{-1}\left[\gamma\boldsymbol{G}^T\boldsymbol{\Phi} + \Psi\right]x_0\,. \qquad \text{Q.E.D.}$$

Remark 5 : In terms of the system matrix F and the augmented terminal state weighting matrix $\overline{W}$, the matrix $\Theta \in \Re^{n\times n}$will be equal to $\left(F^N\right)^T\overline{W}\,F^N$.

Remark 6 : For a fixed plant, the ARE (6 .1) needs to be solved just once. The matrices Ω, $\boldsymbol{\Phi}$, and Ψ will have to be recomputed when the costing horizon N is changed.

Remark 7 : If the plant model is time–invariant and the costing horizon N is fixed, the controller gain matrix in (6 .2) becomes time–invariant.

6 .1 : Simulation Results for SPC

To demonstrate the stabilizing properties of SPC, two separate plant models are considered. In all simulations, unit weighting is assumed on both the states and control increments in the cost function.

6 .1 .1 : Minimum Phase Unstable Plant: A third order minimum phase plant with two unstable poles at $z_{1,2} = -1.1, 1.6$ is controlled using both GPC and SPC. The transfer function of the open loop plant is $\dfrac{0.2 - 0.1q^{-1}}{1 - 0.8q^{-1} - 1.61q^{-2} + 0.528q^{-3}}$. GPC fails to stabilize the closed loop when $N_p \leq 13$. Figure 1 shows the response of the plant under SPC when $N = 1$ and $\varepsilon = 0$. Note that when $\varepsilon = 0$, we have $\overline{Q} = \gamma\, H^TH$, and the SPC law will therefore be equal to the stabilizing control law given by the corresponding infinite horizon LQ problem for all choices of N.

In Figure 2 when $\varepsilon = 100$, SPC brings the plant output to zero within 6 sampling intervals even when $N = 1$. This indicates that SPC exhibits better stability characteristics than GPC. Comparing Figure 2 with infinite horizon LQ control (Figure 1 where $\varepsilon = 0$), SPC is seen to exhibit better performance. For a given value of $\varepsilon > 0$, as N is increased, the SPC law approaches the infinite horizon control law. This can be seen by comparing the response in Figure 3 where $N = 6$ with that of Figure 2 where $N = 1$. Simulations indicate that the plant output is stable when $N_u < N$ even though *Theorem* 5 .1 does not guarantee stability under such choice of horizons.

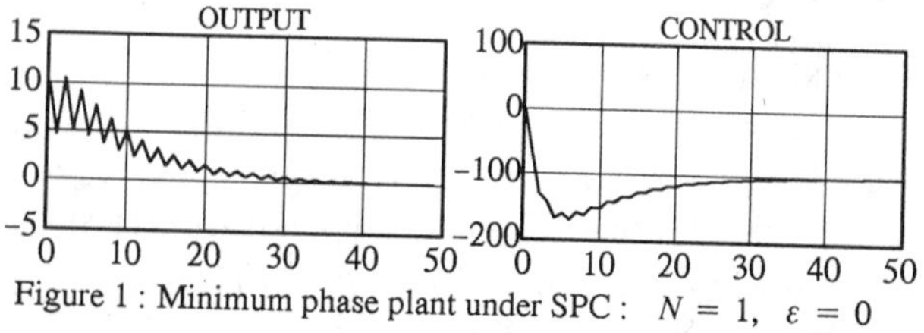

Figure 1 : Minimum phase plant under SPC : $N = 1,\ \ \varepsilon = 0$

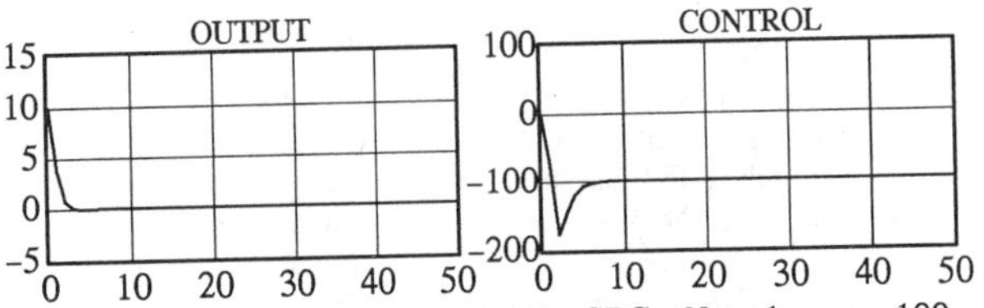

Figure 2 : Minimum phase plant under SPC : $N = 1, \quad \varepsilon = 100$

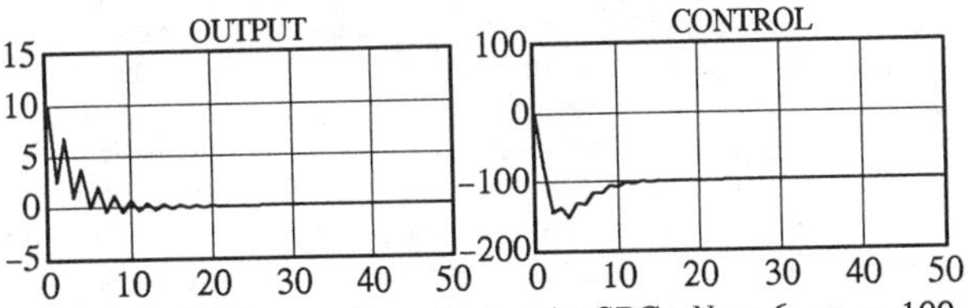

Figure 3 : Minimum phase plant under SPC : $N = 6, \quad \varepsilon = 100$

6 .1 .2 : Non-Minimum Phase Unstable Plant: The plant has a zero at $z = 1.3$ with two unstable poles at $z_{1,2} = 1.25, 1.4$. The zero lies between the two unstable poles, yielding an open loop transfer function $\frac{1 - 1.3q^{-1}}{1 - 2.65q^{-1} + 1.75q^{-2}}$. Due to the non-minimum phase zero, GPC cannot stabilize the plant unless the costing horizons are very large. However SPC is seen to stabilize the closed loop when $N = 1$ (Figure 4). Simulations indicate that the closed loop system is stable under SPC even when $N_u < N$.

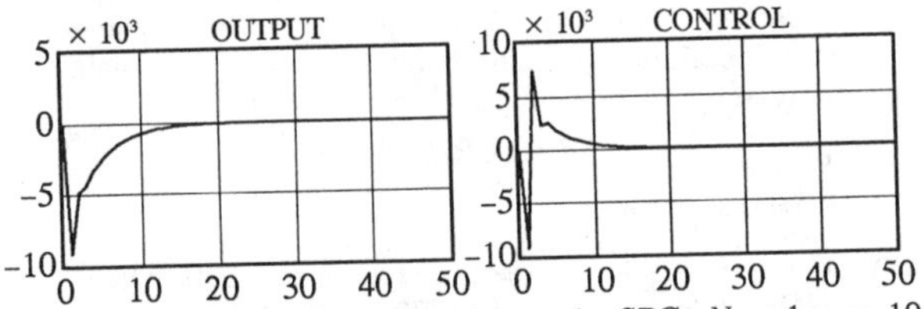

Figure 4 : Non-minimum phase plant under SPC : $N = 1, \varepsilon = 10$

7 : The Tracking Problem in a Regulator Setup

If the output of the plant (2 .2) is to track a known reference signal $\boldsymbol{r} \in \Re^N$, the cost function (5 .1) for the corresponding tracking problem can be rewritten as:

$$J_{GPC} = \sum_{j=0}^{N} \gamma\, [y_j - r_j]^T [y_j - r_j] + \sum_{j=0}^{N-1} \lambda\, \Delta u_j^T \Delta u_j \,. \qquad (7.1)$$

Since $\boldsymbol{r}$ is known, it may be represented by a state model with dimension equal to N as:

$$\left.\begin{aligned} x_{t+1}^r &= F^r x_t^r + G^r \xi_t \\ r_t &= H^r x_t^r \end{aligned}\right\} \qquad (7.2)$$

$$\text{where } F^r = \begin{bmatrix} 0 & 1 & 0 & . & 0 & 0 \\ 0 & 0 & 1 & . & 0 & 0 \\ \cdot & \cdot & \cdot & \cdot & \cdot & \cdot \\ 0 & 0 & 0 & . & 0 & 1 \\ 0 & 0 & 0 & . & 0 & 0 \end{bmatrix},\ G^r = \begin{bmatrix} 0 \\ 0 \\ \cdot \\ 0 \\ 1 \end{bmatrix}, \text{ and } H^r = \begin{bmatrix} 1 \\ 0 \\ \cdot \\ 0 \\ 0 \end{bmatrix}^T. \qquad (7.3)$$

The initial value of the state vector x_t^r is taken as $x_0^r = \left[r_0 \;.\;.\; r_{N-2}\; r_{N-1}\right]^T$ and the reference model is driven by zero mean white noise ξ_t. Using (2 .2) and (7 .2) with $X_t^{trk} \triangleq \begin{Bmatrix} x_t \\ x_t^r \end{Bmatrix}$, the combined state equations can be rewritten as:

$$X_{t+1}^{trk} = \begin{bmatrix} F & 0 \\ 0 & F^r \end{bmatrix} X_t^{trk} + \begin{bmatrix} G \\ 0 \end{bmatrix} \Delta u_t + \begin{bmatrix} 0 \\ G^r \end{bmatrix} \xi_t \qquad (7.4)$$

$$\text{and} \qquad y_t - r_t = \begin{bmatrix} H & -H^r \end{bmatrix} X_t^{trk} \,. \qquad (7.5)$$

Since the reference model is deadbeat, the system (7 .4) is stabilizable even though it is not controllable from Δu_t. Using (7 .4) and omitting the terms independent of Δu_j, (7 .1) may be rewritten as:

$$J_{GPC} = \sum_{j=0}^{N} \gamma X_j^{trk^T} [H \; -H^r]^T [H \; -H^r] X_j^{trk} + \sum_{j=0}^{N-1} \lambda \Delta u_j^T \Delta u_j \quad (7.6)$$

8 : Predictive Controller with Bounded Tracking Error

The results of Section 5 will be used to derive a predictive controller that will guarantee the tracking error of the frozen-time closed loop system to be bounded for any value of the costing horizon. The RDE for the regulator problem posed by (7 .4) and (7 .6) can be written as $\hat{P}_{t+1} = \hat{F}^T \hat{P}_t \hat{F} - \hat{F}^T \hat{P}_t \hat{G} \left[\hat{G}^T \hat{P}_t \hat{G} + R\right]^{-1} \hat{G}^T \hat{P}_t \hat{F} + \hat{Q}$ and at each iteration step:

$$\hat{P}_t = \begin{bmatrix} P_t^{11} & P_t^{12} \\ P_t^{12^T} & P_t^{22} \end{bmatrix}. \qquad (8.1)$$

$\hat{F} = \begin{bmatrix} F & 0 \\ 0 & F^r \end{bmatrix}$, $\hat{G} = \begin{bmatrix} G \\ 0 \end{bmatrix}$, $\hat{Q} = \gamma [H \; -H^r]^T [H \; -H^r]$ and $R = \lambda I$.

Since F^r is stable by construction, the assumptions that $\lambda > 0$, $[F, G]$ is stabilizable, and $\left[F, \gamma^{1/2} H\right]$ is detectable will together imply the stabilizability and detectability of the combined system (7 .4) – (7 .5). If $\gamma \geq 0$, the existence of $\hat{P}_\infty$ as $t \to \infty$ is guaranteed.

Consider the combined state equations (7 .4) - (7 .5) and the cost function (7 .6) to be minimized. Let $\hat{P}_{ss}$ be the steady-state solution to the corresponding infinite horizon ARE given by:

$$\hat{P}_{ss} = \hat{F}^T \hat{P}_{ss} \hat{F} - \hat{F}^T \hat{P}_{ss} \hat{G} \left[\hat{G}^T \hat{P}_{ss} \hat{G} + \lambda I\right]^{-1} \hat{G}^T \hat{P}_{ss} \hat{F} + \hat{Q}_{ss} \quad (8.2)$$

where $\hat{Q}_{ss} = \gamma\, [H \; -H^r]^T [H \; -H^r] + \varepsilon^2 I$ and $\varepsilon \geq 0$. Then, P_{ss}^{11} and P_{ss}^{12} of (8 .2) will satisfy:

$$P_{ss}^{11} = F^T P_{ss}^{11} F - F^T P_{ss}^{11} G \left[G^T P_{ss}^{11} G + \lambda I\right]^{-1} G^T P_{ss}^{11} F + \left[\gamma H^T H + \varepsilon^2 I\right] \qquad (8.3)$$

$$\text{and } P_{ss}^{12} = F^T P_{ss}^{11} F^r - F^T P_{ss}^{11} G \left[G^T P_{ss}^{11} G + \lambda I\right]^{-1} G^T P_{ss}^{12} F^r - \gamma H^T H^r \qquad (8.4)$$

respectively. The following theorem presents the control law that will guarantee the tracking error of the frozen-time closed loop system to be bounded for any choice of the costing horizon.

Theorem 8 .1

Consider the plant model (2 .2), the reference model (7 .2), and the cost function (7 .1) to be minimized. Let P_{ss}^{11} and P_{ss}^{12} be the solutions to (8 .3) and (8 .4) respectively and $\overline{W}_{ss} \triangleq \left[P_{ss}^{11} - \gamma H^T H\right]$. Then the control law given by :

$$\boldsymbol{u} = \left[\gamma \boldsymbol{G}^T \boldsymbol{G} + \Omega_{ss} + \lambda I\right]^{-1} \left\{ \gamma \boldsymbol{G}^T \boldsymbol{r} - \left[\gamma \boldsymbol{G}^T \boldsymbol{\Phi} + \Psi_{ss}\right] x_0 - \gamma \Pi^T H^T r_N - \Pi^T P_{ss}^{12} x_N^r \right\} \qquad (8.5)$$

with

$$\Pi = \left[F^{N-1} F^{N-2} .\, .\, I\right] G,\ \Omega_{ss} = \Pi^T \overline{W}_{ss} \Pi,\ \Psi_{ss} = \Pi^T \overline{W}_{ss} F^N \quad (8.6)$$

and $\boldsymbol{G}, \boldsymbol{\Phi}$ defined in (2 .6) will minimize (7 .1), and the tracking error of the closed loop system with this control law will be bounded.

Proof: *Theorem* 5 .1 is applied to (7 .4) and (7 .6) after setting the terminal state weighting of (7 .6) equal to the stabilizing solution of the ARE (8 .2). Then the predictive control law derived using this modified cost function will generate a frozen-time closed loop matrix for the combined system (7 .4) with all eigenvalues strictly within the unit circle. This implies that the output error $e_t \triangleq [y_t - r_t]$ will be bounded as $t \to \infty$ provided r_t is bounded.

Since $\hat{P}_{ss}$ is the solution to the ARE (8 .2), the modified cost function obtained when the terminal state in (7 .6) is weighted by $\hat{P}_{ss}$ is:

$$J_{GPC}^{mod} = J_{GPC} + X_N^{trk^T} \hat{P}_{ss} X_N^{trk} - \gamma \left[y_N - r_N\right]^2 . \qquad (8.7)$$

Using (2 .6), the GPC cost function (7 .1) can be written as:

$$\begin{aligned} J_{GPC} &= \gamma \left[\hat{\boldsymbol{y}} - \boldsymbol{r}\right]^T \left[\hat{\boldsymbol{y}} - \boldsymbol{r}\right] + \lambda\, \boldsymbol{u}^T \boldsymbol{u} \\ &= \gamma \left[\Phi x_0 + \boldsymbol{G}\boldsymbol{u} - \boldsymbol{r}\right]^T \left[\Phi x_0 + \boldsymbol{G}\boldsymbol{u} - \boldsymbol{r}\right] + \lambda\, \boldsymbol{u}^T \boldsymbol{u} \\ &= 2\gamma\, \boldsymbol{u}^T \boldsymbol{G}^T \left[\Phi x_0 - \boldsymbol{r}\right] + \boldsymbol{u}^T \left[\gamma\, \boldsymbol{G}^T \boldsymbol{G} + \lambda I\right] \boldsymbol{u} + \mathrm{T}. \end{aligned} \qquad (8.8)$$

where T represents the terms that are independent of $\boldsymbol{u}$. Using the block matrix form of $\hat{P}_{ss}$ and the predicted state equations (2 .4), the second term on the right hand side of (8 .7) can be rewritten as:

$$X_N^{trk^T} \hat{P}_{ss} X_N^{trk} = x_N^T P_{ss}^{11} x_N + 2\, x_N^T P_{ss}^{12} x_N^r + x_N^{r\,T} P_{ss}^{22} x_N^r$$
$$= 2\, \boldsymbol{u}^T \Pi^T \left[P_{ss}^{11} F^N x_0 + P_{ss}^{12} x_N^r \right] + \boldsymbol{u}^T \Pi^T P_{ss}^{11} \Pi\, \boldsymbol{u} + \mathrm{T}. \quad (8.9)$$

where $\Pi = \left[F^{N-1} \; F^{N-2} \; . \; . \; I \right] G$. The third term on the right hand side of (8 .7) can be written as:

$$\gamma \left[y_N - r_N \right]^2 = \gamma \left[HF^N x_0 + H\Pi\, \boldsymbol{u} - r_N \right]^2$$
$$= 2\, \boldsymbol{u}^T \Pi^T \left[\gamma\, H^T H F^N x_0 - \gamma\, H^T r_N \right] + \gamma\, \boldsymbol{u}^T \Pi^T H^T H \Pi \boldsymbol{u} + \mathrm{T}. \quad (8.10)$$

From (8 .8) – (8 .10) we have:

$$J_{GPC}^{mod} = 2\boldsymbol{u}^T \left\{ \left[\gamma \boldsymbol{G}^T \Phi + \Psi_{ss} \right] x_0 - \gamma \boldsymbol{G}^T \boldsymbol{r} + \gamma \Pi^T H^T r_N + \Pi^T P_{ss}^{12} x_N^r \right\}$$
$$+ \boldsymbol{u}^T \left[\gamma \boldsymbol{G}^T \boldsymbol{G} + \Omega_{ss} + \lambda\, I \right] \boldsymbol{u} + \mathrm{T}. \quad (8.11)$$

where Ω_{ss} and Ψ_{ss} are as in (8 .6). Finally, minimization of (8 .11) with respect to $\boldsymbol{u}$ gives the optimal control vector (8 .5). Q.E.D.

Remark 8 : The costing horizon N depends on the length of future reference input data that is known. $x_N^r \in \Re^N$ in the control law corresponds to reference inputs ouside the horizon N.

Remark 9 : For a fixed plant, P_{ss}^{11} and P_{ss}^{12} needs to be solved just once. The matrices Φ, Ω_{ss} , and Ψ_{ss} will have to be recomputed when the costing horizon N is changed.

Remark 10 : The control input is the sum of a feedback control signal and a prefilter control signal as shown in Figure 5 . For a time-invariant plant with a fixed costing horizon N, the feedback and prefilter gains are also time-invariant.

Remark 11 : Steady state tracking error may be eliminated by including an internal model i.e. an integrator, in the feedback loop[4].

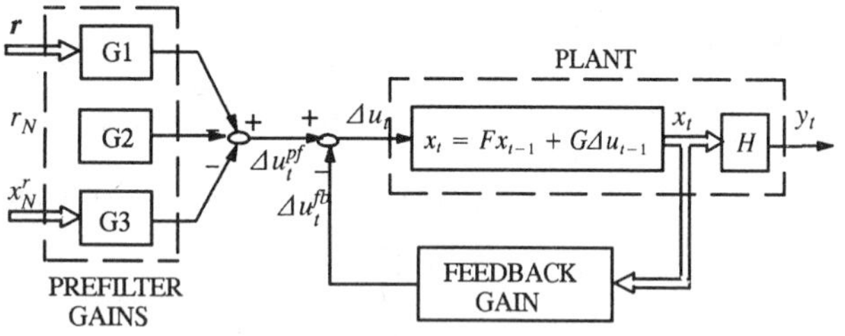

Figure 5 : Structure of the SPC for reference tracking

8 .1 : Simulation Results

A non-minimum phase plant $\dfrac{1 + 1.2q^{-1}}{1 + 0.3q^{-1} - 1.8q^{-2}}$ with two unstable poles at $z_{1,2} = 1.2, -1.5$ is required to track a step reference input of magnitude 10. Due to the unstable zero at $z = -1.2$, GPC leads to instability in the output unless the costing horizons are large. When the plant is controlled using SPC, the plant output and consequently the tracking error is bounded (Figure 6) even when $N_p = N_u = N = 1$. As N is increased to 3 in Figure 7 , improved step response performance is achieved since the tracking error is reduced. Simulations indicate that the tracking error is bounded for all values of the costing horizons. The tracking performance is seen to improve for larger values of N.

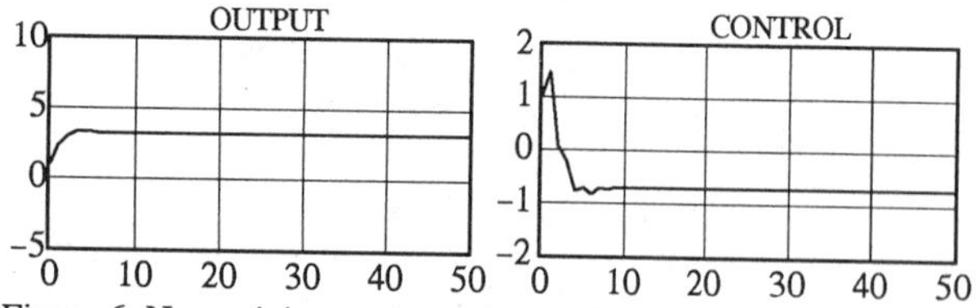

Figure 6 :Non-minimum phase plant under SPC : $N = 1, \varepsilon = 0.01$

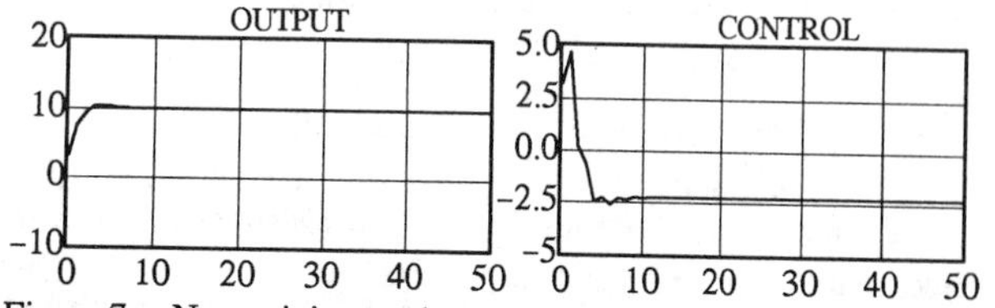

Figure 7 : Non-minimum phase plant under SPC : $N = 3, \varepsilon = 0.1$

9 : Conclusions

Using the equivalence of GPC and LQ control, sufficient conditions for stability of the frozen–time closed loop system are satisfied by modifying the GPC cost function with an augmented weighting on the terminal state. Minimizing the modified cost function results in a stabilizing predictive control (SPC) law that will guarantee frozen–time stability of the closed loop system. When the predicted outputs and future controls are penalized for the same number of steps for a fixed plant, this control law results in frozen–time stable closed loop systems regardless of the costing horizon. Conditions for the controller to guarantee frozen–time stability of the closed loop system when the control horizon is less than the prediction horizon are at present unknown. Simulation studies demonstrate the stabilizing properties of SPC to be superior to that of GPC and performance superior to that of infinite horizon LQ control. When the plant is required to track a known reference signal, the state of the plant is augmented by a suitable state model of the reference signal and the cost function for the tracking problem is then reformulated in terms of the combined states. The stabilizing predictive control law which guarantees frozen–time stability of the combined system then guarantees bounded tracking error whenever the reference signal is bounded. This is achieved by incorporating prefilter gains that account for future values of the reference signal. Simulation results show that the stabilizing predictive controller with prefilter tracks a step reference with bounded tracking error regardless of the length of the costing horizon. By guaranteeing frozen–time closed loop stability and bounded tracking error for arbitrary costing horizons, the predictive controller designs presented in this paper make the implementation and tuning of predictive control algorithms easier, at the same time retaining the possibility of optimizing control under constraints.

REFERENCES

[1] R.R. Bitmead, M.Gevers, and V. Wertz *Adaptive Optimal Control: The Thinking Man's GPC*, Prentice Hall, 1990

[2] K.W. Lim and K.V. Ling. Generalized Predictive Control of a Heat Exchanger, *IEEE Control Syst. Magazine*, October 1989

[3] D.W. Clarke. Application of Generalized Predictive Control to Industrial Processes, *IEEE Control Syst. Magazine*, April 1988

[4] B.D.O. Anderson and J.B. Moore, *Optimal Control: Linear Quadratic Methods*, Prentice Hall, 1990

[5] A.E. Bryson, Jr. and Yu-Chi Ho, *Applied Optimal Control: Optimization, Estimation, and Control*, Hemisphere Publishing Corporation, 1975

[6] W.H. Kwon and A.E. Pearson, A Modifiied Quadratic Cost Problem and Feedback Stabilization of a Linear System, *IEEE Trans. on Automatic Controls*, Vol. AC-22, October 1977

[7] W.H. Kwon and A.E. Pearson, On Feedback Stabilization of Time-Varying Discrete Linear Systems, *IEEE Trans. on Automatic Controls*, Vol. AC-23, June 1978

[8] C.E. de Souza, M.Gevers, and G.C. Goodwin, Riccati Equations in Optimal Filtering of Nonstabilizable Systems having Singular State Transition Matrices, *IEEE Trans. on Aut. Controls*, Vol. AC-31, 1986

[9] V. Peterka, Predictive and LQG Optimal Control: Equivalences, Differences and Improvements, *Control of Uncertain Systems, Proceedings of an International Workshop*, Bremen, June 1989

[10] M-A. Poubelle, R.R. Bitmead, and M.R. Gevers, Fake Algebric Riccati Techniques and Stability, *IEEE Trans. Automatic Controls*, Vol.33, April 1988

[11] R.R. Bitmead, M.R. Gevers, I.R. Peterson, and R.J. Kaye, Monotonicity and stabilizability properties of solutions the Riccati difference Equation: Propositions, lemmas, theorems, fallacious conjectures and counterexamples, *Systems & Control Letters*, Vol. 5, April 1985

[12] D.W. Clarke, C. Mohtadi, and P.S. Tuffs, Generalized Predictive Control, Part I and II, *Automatica*, Vol.23, No.2, 1987

[13] J.W. MacArthur, An End-Time-Constrained Adaptive Horizon Control Policy, Submitted for publication in *Journal of Dynamic Systems, Measurement, and Control*, 1992

[14] C.E. de Souza, Monotonicity and Stabilizability results for the Solution of the Riccati Difference Equation, *Proc. Workshop on the Riccati Equation in Cont., Syst. and Signals*, Como, Italy, 38–41, 1989

APPENDIX

***Lemma A* [14] :** Let P_t^1 and P_t^2 be the solutions of two RDEs (4 .1) with the same F, G and R matrices but with possibly different Qs: Q^1 and Q^2 respectively. Then the matrix $\tilde{P}_t = P_t^2 - P_t^1$ satisfies the equations:

$$\tilde{P}_{t+1} = \overline{F}_t^{1\,T} \tilde{P}_t \overline{F}_t^1 - \overline{F}_t^{1\,T} \tilde{P}_t G (G^T P_t^2 G + R)^{-1} G^T \tilde{P}_t \overline{F}_t^1 + \tilde{Q}$$

or: $$\tilde{P}_{t+1} = \overline{F}_t^{1\,T} \tilde{P}_t \overline{F}_t^1 - \overline{F}_t^{1\,T} \tilde{P}_t G (G^T \tilde{P}_t G + \tilde{R}_t)^{-1} G^T \tilde{P}_t \overline{F}_t^1 + \tilde{Q}$$

where $\overline{F}_t^1 \triangleq F - G(G^T P_t^1 G + R)^{-1} G^T P_t^1 F$, $\tilde{Q} \triangleq Q^2 - Q^1$, and $\tilde{R}_t \triangleq G^T P_t^1 G + R$.

Proof: See [14].

Proceedings of the
American Control Conference
San Francisco, California • June 1993

Integrated State Estimation, Fault Detection and Diagnosis for Nonlinear Systems

Douglas Robertson
Jay H. Lee

Department of Chemical Engineering
Auburn University, Auburn, AL 36849

March 15, 1993

1 Introduction

Increased competition from abroad and fast-changing market conditions are demanding today's chemical plants to be designed and operated more interactively than ever before with reduced safety margins. This has led to many difficult control problems involving large-scale, interactive, time-varying systems with tight performance specifications and active constraints. Today's process control engineers are facing a new challenge since these problems cannot be solved via traditional feedback control techniques. While Model Predictive Control (MPC) (see Garcia *et al.*, 1989 for review) has provided the engineers with a powerful tool to meet this challenge, many *ad hoc* fixes and adjustments previously performed by plant operators or engineers are no longer sufficient to maintain the integrity of such a complex, multi-variable control system in today's dynamic operating environment. Hence, the use of large-scale, optimization-based control methods like MPC requires reliable, computer-based process monitoring, failure detection and diagnosis schemes.

While the term "fault" implies certain abnormality in the operating condition, faults are more generally defined as substantial degradation in the closed-loop performance caused by gradual or abrupt changes in plant parameters or equipment errors. Fault detection deals with determination of existence of a fault while fault diagnosis attempts to locate the root of the problem. Fault detection, diagnosis and other aspects of process monitoring have received substantial amount of interest due to the aforementioned trends in process operation. Past efforts have included both qualitative approaches involving expert systems and artificial intelligence (Kramer and Palowitch, 1987; Venkatasubramanian and Chan, 1989) to quantitative approaches involving estimation and filtering (Willsky, 1976). Since the latest trend of MPC is to use state estimation techniques for prediction, it seems natural to integrate into MPC the latter approach to fault detection and diagnosis. One inherent difficulty in estimating faults is that, since a fault necessarily implies substantial (possibly abrupt) deviation from the steady-state conditions, proper estimation should be based on nonlinear models with nonstationary inputs.

While many estimation techniques have been proposed (see Willsky, 1976 for review), the most popular methods have been the Kalman filter and the extended Kalman filter (EKF). EKF (Cox, 1964) is a straightforward application of the time-varying linear Kalman filter theory to nonlinear systems by approximating a nonlinear model with a discrete, time-varying linear model obtained via local linearization at each time step. Although not guaranteed to converge for the original nonlinear filtering problem, the EKF has been found effective in many chemical process applications since the local linearization assumption is valid as long as the states and parameters do not change substantially within each sampling interval (Park and Himmelblau, 1983; Watanabe and Himmelblau, 1984; Li and Olson, 1991). However, there are substantial shortcomings of the EKF as a fault detection and diagnosis tool. As the degree of nonlinearity increases, the locally linearized model is valid over a smaller range of operating conditions. If changes in the states or parameters fall outside of this range, the EKF can provide poor estimates.

Several estimation strategies formulated as optimization problems have been proposed, based on statistical methods (for example, the most likelihood). In these methods, the state equations are entered explicitly into the optimization as constraints. Jazwinski (1970) presents a least squares formulation for the optimal "batch" state estimation problem that leads to the Kalman filter for linear systems. Several authors (Jang *et. al.*, 1986; Tjoa and Biegler, 1991) have reported good success with using the least squares formulation for parameter identification. In a similar spirit, Lee *et. al* (1992b) proposed a constrained, receding horizon state estimation method formulated as Quadratic Programming (QP). In their method, additional state / noise constraints are imposed and a fixed-size moving estimation window is employed to keep the optimization size from growing without bounds. They show that the estimates resulting from the optimization are equivalent to those of the standard Kalman filter in the case of linear systems with no constraints. A significant advantage of their optimization approach over the traditional Kalman filter is that constraints on the estimated variables and state disturbances can be entered into the optimization, leading to more reliable estimates.

In this paper, we extend the constrained receding horizon state estimation method by Lee *et. al* (1992) to nonlinear systems to develop an integrated state estimation, fault detection and diagnosis technique. The nonlinear state equations are discretized via orthogonal collocation and entered as algebraic constraints to the quadratic objective, yielding a Nonlinear Programming (NLP) problem that can be solved via standard algorithms like the Sequential Quadratic Programming (SQP). The use of the nonlinear model enables more reliable detection of sudden as well as gradual faults of substantial magnitudes and the state and noise constraints make the resulting estimates more robust with respect to gross sensor errors and other types of failures. The proposed technique is applied to a CSTR with a first-order exothermic reaction.

2 Model

A general nonlinear system can be represented by the following differential equations:

$$\dot{x} = f(x, u, p) \quad (1)$$
$$y = g(x, p) \quad (2)$$

where x is the state vector, u the manipulated input vector, y the output vector, and p the vector containing the unmeasured disturbances and fault parameters.

An interval T can be chosen over which p and u are assumed to be constant. To simplify the presentation, this interval will be chosen as the sampling time T_s in this paper; however, any interval of the form T_s/n (n a positive integer) will work. The model can now be written in discrete form as

$$x_k = \tilde{f}_{T_s}(x_{k-1}, u_{k-1}, p_{k-1}) \quad (3)$$
$$y_k = g(x_k, p_k) \quad (4)$$

where $\tilde{f}_{T_s}(x_{k-1}, u_{k-1}, p_{k-1})$ denotes the terminal state vector resulting from integrating the ODE (1) for one sample interval with the initial condition x_{k-1} and the constant inputs of $u = u_{k-1}$ and $p = p_{k-1}$. The vector p can be modelled by the following stochastic process:

$$x_k^w = A^w x_{k-1}^w + B^w w_{k-1} \quad (5)$$
$$p_k = C^w x_k^w + p_{bias} \quad (6)$$

where w_k is discrete-time white noise with covariance Q.

The measurement vector $\hat{y}_k$ is a discrete sampling of the output vector y corrupted by measurement noise and is of the form

$$\hat{y}_k = g(x_k, p_k) + \nu_k \quad (7)$$

where x_k is the state vector at time k and ν_k is white noise with covariance R.

Equations (3)-(7) can be combined to obtain the following augmented model:

$$\begin{bmatrix} x_k \\ x_k^w \end{bmatrix} = \begin{bmatrix} \tilde{f}_{T_s}(x_{k-1}, u_{k-1}, C^w x_{k-1}^w + p_{bias}) \\ A^w x_{k-1}^w \end{bmatrix} + \begin{bmatrix} 0 \\ B^w \end{bmatrix} w_{k-1} \quad (8)$$
$$\hat{y}_k = g(x_k, C^w x_k^w + p_{bias}) + \nu_k \quad (9)$$

Notice that we have modelled the fault parameters and unmeasured disturbances as states. The problem of fault detection is now one of state estimation and will be treated as such. For most cases, disturbances or parameters are modelled adequately as independent random walk processes. In this case, the matrices A^w, B^w, and C^w are identity matrices of appropriate size. The zero-mean random variable vector w_{k-1} then represents the changes in the parameters from time $k-1$ to k.

3 Extended Kalman Filter

The extended Kalman filter uses a time-varying linear model obtained by linearizing the discrete model (8)-(9) with respect to the current state estimates at each time step. The EKF provides the state estimates through the following equations:

Model Update:

$$\begin{bmatrix} x_{k|k-1} \\ x_{k|k-1}^w \end{bmatrix} = \begin{bmatrix} \tilde{f}_{T_s}(x_{k-1|k-1}, u_{k-1}, C^w x_{k-1|k-1}^w) \\ A^w x_{k-1|k-1}^w \end{bmatrix} \quad (10)$$

Measurement Correction:

$$\begin{bmatrix} x_{k|k} \\ x_{k|k}^w \end{bmatrix} = \begin{bmatrix} x_{k|k-1} \\ x_{k|k-1}^w \end{bmatrix} + L_k\left(\hat{y}_k - g(x_{k|k-1}, C^w x_{k|k-1}^w)\right) \quad (11)$$

where

$$\begin{aligned} L_k &= P_{k|k-1}\Xi_k^T(\Xi_k P_{k|k-1}\Xi_k^T + R)^{-1} \\ P_{k|k-1} &= \Phi_{k-1}P_{k-1|k-1}\Phi_{k-1}^T + \Gamma^w Q(\Gamma^w)^T \\ P_{k|k} &= (I - L_k\Xi_k)P_{k|k-1} \end{aligned} \quad (12)$$

and

$$\Phi_{k-1} = \begin{bmatrix} A_{k-1} & B_{k-1}C^w \\ 0 & A^w \end{bmatrix} \quad \Gamma^w = \begin{bmatrix} 0 \\ B^w \end{bmatrix}$$
$$\Xi_k = \begin{bmatrix} C_k & C_k^p C^w \end{bmatrix}$$
$$A_{k-1} = \exp\left(\tilde{A}_{k-1}T_s\right)$$
$$B_{k-1} = \int_0^{T_s} \exp\left(\tilde{A}_{k-1}\tau\right) d\tau \cdot \tilde{B}_{k-1}$$
$$\tilde{A}_{k-1} = \left.\frac{\partial f(x,u,p)}{\partial x}\right|_{x=x_{k-1|k-1}, u=u_{k-1}, p=C^w x_{k-1|k-1}^w}$$
$$\tilde{B}_{k-1} = \left.\frac{\partial f(x,u,p)}{\partial p}\right|_{x=x_{k-1|k-1}, u=u_{k-1}, p=C^w x_{k-1|k-1}^w}$$
$$C_k = \left.\frac{\partial g(x,p)}{\partial x}\right|_{x=x_{k|k-1}, p=C^w x_{k|k-1}^w}$$
$$C_k^p = \left.\frac{\partial g(x,p)}{\partial p}\right|_{x=x_{k|k-1}, p=C^w x_{k|k-1}^w}$$

Note that $\frac{\partial f}{\partial x}$ and $\frac{\partial f}{\partial p}$ represent the Jacobian matrices for f with respect to x and p respectively. $P_{0|0}$ is the covariance of the error in the initial state estimates. The notation $\{\cdot\}_{\ell|k}$ denotes the most likely value of a vector at time ℓ based on measurements up to time k.

4 Receding Horizon Estimator

The "batch" state/parameter estimation problem at time k can be stated as follows:

> Given the initial state and parameter/unmeasured disturbance estimates $x_{0|0}$ and $x_{0|0}^w$ and model (8)-(9), find the most likely values for x_0^e ($\equiv x_0 - x_{0|0}$), $(x_0^w)^e$ ($\equiv x_0^w - x_{0|0}^w$), and temporally independent sequences $(w_0, \ldots, w_{k-1})$ and $(\nu_1, \ldots, \nu_k)$ based on the measurement sequence $(y_1, \ldots, y_k)$

The "optimal" batch estimation problem can be formulated as the following quadratic optimization:

$$\min_{X^e_{0|k},\, w_{\ell-1|k},\, \nu_{\ell|k}} \quad \sum_{\ell=1}^{k} \nu_{\ell|k}^T R^{-1} \nu_{\ell|k} + w_{\ell-1|k}^T Q^{-1} w_{\ell-1|k} + (X^e_{0|k})^T P_{0|0}^{-1} X^e_{0|k} \tag{13}$$

$$\text{s.t.} \quad \begin{aligned} \nu_{\ell|k} &= y_\ell - g(x_{\ell|k}, C^w x^w_{\ell|k} + p_{bias}) \\ x_{\ell|k} &= \tilde{f}_{T_s}(x_{\ell-1|k}, u_{\ell-1|k}, C^w x^w_{\ell-1|k} + p_{bias}) \\ x^w_{\ell|k} &= A^w x^w_{\ell-1|k} + B^w w_{\ell-1|k} \end{aligned}$$

where $X^e_{0|k} = \left[(x^e_{0|k})^T \; ((x^w_{0|k})^e)^T\right]^T$ is the error vector for the initial state estimate. The matrices Q, R, and $P_{0|0}$ are the covariances of w, ν, and X^e respectively. The optimality is in the sense of maximizing the conditional probability density function of the state estimates. For linear systems, the above optimization yields an explicit solution a recursive form of which is the well-known Kalman filter (see Jazwinski, 1970). When $P_{0|0}^{-1} = 0$ and $Q^{-1} = 0$, this method is similar to the optimization-based estimation methods previously proposed (Jang *et al.*, 1986; Tjoa and Biegler, 1991). The differential constraints arising from the state equation can be transformed into algebraic constraints via orthogonal collocation (for an excellent reference of this technique see Villadsen and Michelsen, 1978). By using Lagrange interpolation polynomials, the optimization variables become the state values at the collocation points. Prior known bounds on the states and noise can be entered as inequality constraints to improve the robustness of the method.

As the number of measurements grows, the size of the optimization increases without bound. To prevent this problem, the method can be modified to employ a fixed-size moving window. The *receding horizon* state estimation problem at time k with horizon size of N is formulated as follows:

$$\min_{X^e_{k-N|k},\, w_{k+\ell-1-N|k},\, \nu_{k+\ell-N|k}} \quad \sum_{\ell=1}^{N} \nu_{k+\ell-N|k}^T R^{-1} \nu_{k+\ell-N|k} + w_{k+\ell-1-N|k}^T Q^{-1} w_{k+\ell-1-N|k} + (X^e_{k-N|k})^T P^{-1}_{k-N|k-N} X^e_{k-N|k} \tag{14}$$

$$\text{s.t.} \quad \begin{aligned} \nu_{k+\ell-N|k} &= y_\ell - g(x_{k+\ell-N|k}, C^w x^w_{k+\ell-N|k} + p_{bias}) \\ x^w_{k+\ell-N|k} &= A^w x^w_{k+\ell-N-1|k} + B^w w_{k+\ell-N-1|k} \\ x_{k+\ell-N|k} &= \tilde{f}_{T_s}(x_{k+\ell-N-1|k}, u_{k+\ell-N-1|k}, C^w x^w_{k+\ell-N-1|k} + p_{bias}) \end{aligned}$$

At the beginning of the estimation, the number of measurements is allowed to grow until it reaches the size of the horizon (*i.e.*, $t = N$). At this time the initial estimates $x_{0|0}$ and $x^w_{0|0}$ are replaced by $x_{1|1}$ and $x^w_{1|1}$ and the weighting matrix $P_{0|0}^{-1}$ is replaced by $P_{1|1}^{-1}$. At present, the covariance matrix $P_{\ell|\ell}$ is updated via Eq. (12) used for the EKF (the choice of the initial covariance matrix has little effect when the horizon size is chosen sufficiently large; however, alternate methods are currently being investigated). The first measurement is discarded and replaced by the current one. The optimization (of constant size) proceeds in this manner for all future time steps.

Our experience has been that, if the only constraints are the state equation, a horizon of one works as well as any. In this case the computational requirement is close to that of the extended Kalman filter, and the improvement in performance is proportional to the degree of nonlinearity of the problem.

5 Example

We use a CSTR with a first-order reaction to compare the two approaches. The CSTR model was used by Jang *et al.* to compare their horizon method with the EKF. Our augmented model contains four states (two of which are parameters to be estimated) and is given by

$$\begin{bmatrix} \dot{C} \\ \dot{T} \\ U_k \\ (E_a)_k \end{bmatrix} = \begin{bmatrix} \frac{q}{V}(C_0 - C) - kC\exp(\frac{-E_a}{T}) \\ \frac{q}{V}(T_0 - T) - \frac{\Delta H}{\rho C_P} kC \exp(\frac{-E_a}{T}) - \frac{UA}{\rho C_P V}(T - T_c) \\ U_{k-1} \\ (E_a)_{k-1} \end{bmatrix} + \begin{bmatrix} 0 \\ 0 \\ w^1_{k-1} \\ w^2_{k-1} \end{bmatrix} \tag{15}$$

where w^1 and w^2 represent the respective changes in U and E_a from one sampling time to the next. The constant parameters are $q = 10\text{cm}^3/\text{s}$, $V = 1000\text{cm}^3$, $C_0 = 6.5 \times 10^{-6}\text{gmol/cm}^3$, $k = 7.86 \times 10^{12}\text{s}^{-1}$, $\Delta H = -27000$ cal/ gmol, $\rho = 0.001\text{g/cm}^3$, $C_p = 1.0$ cal/ (g K), $A = 10\text{cm}^2$, $T_0 = 350$ K, and $T_c = 340$ K. The steady state values of the four states are $C_{ss} = 1.525 \times 10^{-7}\text{gmol/cm}^3$, $T_{ss} = 460.92$ K, $U_{ss} = 5 \times 10^{-4}\text{cal/(cm}^2$ s K), and $(E_a)_{ss} = 14090$ K. The initial states are $C(O) = 3.531 \times 10^{-7}$, $T(0) = 440.9$, $U(0) = 5 \times 10^{-4}$, and $E_a(0) = 14090$.

The initial estimates and covariance matrices used in simulation are

$$\mathbf{X}_{0|0} = \begin{bmatrix} 3.753 \times 10^{-7} \\ 446.5 \\ 4.76 \times 10^{-4} \\ 13377 \end{bmatrix} \qquad \mathbf{P}_{0|0} = \begin{bmatrix} 0.2 & & & \bigcirc \\ & 100 & & \\ & & 0.5 & \\ \bigcirc & & & 10^6 \end{bmatrix}$$

$$\mathbf{R} = \begin{bmatrix} 0.1 & 0 \\ 0 & 10 \end{bmatrix} \qquad \mathbf{Q} = \begin{bmatrix} 0.06 & 0 \\ 0 & 10^{-5} \end{bmatrix}$$

The initial state error was generated by random noise of covariance $\mathbf{P}$. Measurements, corrupted by noise of covariance $\mathbf{R}$, of both states were made at 1 s intervals. The parameter E_a remained constant throughout the simulation while U stepped from 5×10^{-4} to 8×10^{-4} at $t = 100$ s. A horizon of 1 s was used for the receding horizon estimator, yielding a computational load close to that of the EKF. The state equations and non-negativity bounds were the only constraints used in solving the NLP.

Figure 1 illustrates the performance of the EKF and receding horizon estimator. Both perform well as the simulation progresses; however, in all cases, the EKF is slower to converge. For the parameter U large error occurs for the first 40 seconds. This can be attributed to the locally linearized model being a poor representation of the actual process for this time period. Other simulations with different noise characteristics showed the same trend: the receding horizon estimator has better initial response with performance nearly identical to the EKF as time progresses. This example illustrates the potential of the receding horizon estimator; however, since the EKF performs well in this case, the improvement is marginal.

We are currently examining cases where the EKF fails. By exploiting the ability of the receding horizon estimator to use a larger horizon size and entering constraints on the states, disturbances and noise, the receding horizon estimator can outperform the EKF. Other current research topics include finding a better way to update the covariance matrix for the initial state error and investigating the trade-off between performance and computational load for different methods of formulating the NLP (*e.g.* number of collocation points, horizon size, step size of the SQP algorithm, *etc.*)

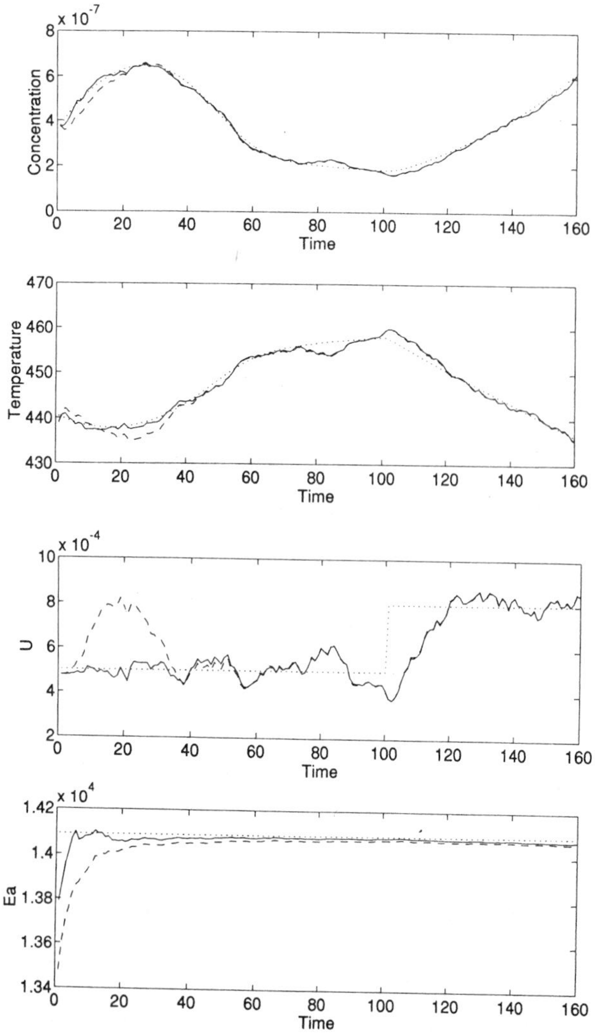

Figure 1: Parameter and State Estimation with EKF and RHE: true value (....); RHE (___); EKF (- - -)

References

[1] Cox, H. "On the Estimation of State Variables and Parameters for Noisy Dynamic Systems", *IEEE Trans. Autom. Control*, **23**, pp. 149-160, 1987.

[2] Garcia, C. E.; Prett, D. M.; Morari, M. "Model Predictive Control: Theory and Practice - a Survey", *Automatica*, **25**, pp. 335-348, 1989.

[3] Kramer, M. A.; Palowitch, B. L. "A Rule-Based Approach to Fault Diagnosis Using the Signed Directed Graph", *AIChE J.*, **33**, pp. 1067, 1987.

[4] Jang, S. S.; Joseph, B.; Mukai, H. "Comparison of Two Approaches to On-Line Parameter and State Estimation of Nonlinear Systems", *Ind. Eng. Chem. Process Des. Dev.*, **25**, pp. 809-814, 1986.

[5] Jazwinski, A. H. *Stochastic Processes and Filtering Theory*, Academic, New York (1970)

[6] Lee, J. H.; Robertson, D.; Rawlings, J. B. "Receding Horizon State Estimation and Its Application to Model Predictive Control" presented at AIChE Annual Meeting, Nov., 1992b.

[7] Li, R.; Olson, J. H. "Fault Detection and Diagnosis in a Close-Loop Nonlinear Distillation Process: Application of Extended Kalman Filters", *Ind. Eng. Chem. Res.*, **30**, 898-908, 1991.

[8] Park, S.; Himmelblau, D. M. "Fault Detection and Diagnosis via Parameter Estimation in Lumped Dynamic Systems", *Ind. Eng. Chem. Proc. Des. Dev.*, **22**, pp. 482-487, 1983.

[9] Tjoa, I. B.; Biegler, L. T. "Simultaneous Solution and Optimization Strategies for Parameter Estimation of Differential-Algebraic Equation Systems", *Ind. Eng. Chem. Res.*, **30**, pp. 376-385, 1991.

[10] Venkatasubramanian, V.; Chen, K. "A Neural Network Methodology for Process Fault Diagnosis", *AIChE J.*, **12**, pp. 1993, 1989.

[11] Villadsen, J.; Michelsen, M. L. *Solution of Differential Equation Models by Polynomial Approximation*, Prentice-Hall, Englewood Cliffs, NJ (1978).

[12] Watanabe, K.; Himmelblau, D. M. "Incipient Fault Diagnosis of Nonlinear Processes with Multiple Causes of Faults", *Chem. Eng. Sci.*, **39**, pp. 491-508, 1984.

[13] Willsky, A. S. "A Survey of Design Methods for Failure Detection in Dynamic Systems", *Automatica*, **12**, pp. 601-611, 1976.

Proceedings of the
American Control Conference
San Francisco, California • June 1993

Model Predictive Control of Multivariable Nonlinear Processes in Continuous-Time

Masoud Soroush and Costas Kravaris

Department of Chemical Engineering
The University of Michigan
Ann Arbor, MI 48109-2136

Abstract

This paper concerns the synthesis of continuous-time feedback control systems for multivariable nonlinear processes with deadtimes. A general model predictive control law, that minimizes a quadratic performance index in the presence of input constraints and process deadtimes, is derived. The issue of deadtime compensation for a class of nonlinear multivariable systems is studied and an explicit control law is derived. Connections between the derived control law and (a) the globally linearizing control (GLC) and (b) the linear internal model control (IMC) are established. The theory is illustrated by a CSTR example.

1 Introduction

Since the mid eighties, nonlinear process control has advanced mainly within the two popular research directions: the model predictive approach, and the geometric approach. The key advantage of the model predictive control (MPC) has been its appealing intuitive interpretation and its explicit account for input and state constraints, whereas the key advantage of the geometric approach has been its solid theoretical justification.

The scope of this paper is twofold:

(i) Using the model predictive approach, a continuous-time control law is derived for general nonlinear processes with deadtimes (in output measurements).

(ii) Concrete theoretical connections between the derived MPC law and the continuous-time GLC and IMC are established. It is shown that the model predictive and geometric approaches can lead to identical feedback controllers.

An advantage of the present MPC method over previous MPC methods is that, in many special cases, the minimization problem has an explicit analytical solution, which greatly reduces the computational effort of the controller in the search for an optimal control action.

This article briefly presents the generalization of the SISO results of our previous work [11] for multivariable nonlinear processes. The details of this work are given in [10].

First a review of some continuous-time nonlinear controller synthesis results (derived within the geometric framework) will be given. Then, controller synthesis formulas will be derived in continuous-time on the basis of model predictive considerations. This approach involves derivation of output prediction equations via truncated Volterra series and formulation of a set of reference trajectories. A control law that minimizes a quadratic performance index will then be synthesized. The control law will be simplified in a number of special cases. Finally, the performance of the derived control law will be illustrated by a CSTR example.

2 Preliminaries

In this paper, we consider continuous-time nonlinear square (equal numbers of inputs and outputs) MIMO systems described by a state-space model of the form

$$\left\{ \begin{array}{rcl} \dot{x}(t) & = & f(x(t)) + \sum_{j=1}^{m} g_j(x(t))u_j(t) \\ y(t) & = & \begin{bmatrix} h_1(x(t-\theta_1)) \\ \vdots \\ h_m(x(t-\theta_m)) \end{bmatrix} \end{array} \right. \tag{1}$$

where θ_i is the deadtime in the ith output, and $x = [x_1 \ \cdots \ x_n]^T$, $u = [u_1 \ \cdots \ u_m]^T$ and $y = [y_1 \ \cdots \ y_m]^T$ are the vectors of state variables, manipulated inputs, and controlled outputs, respectively. It is assumed that $x \in X \subset \mathbb{R}^n$, and $u \in U \subset \mathbb{R}^m$, where X and U are open connected sets that contain the equilibrium point, and $g_1(x)$, $\cdots$, $g_m(x)$, $h(x) = [h_1(x) \ \cdots \ h_m(x)]^T$ and $f(x)$ are analytic vector functions on X.

In a more compact vector notation, the differential equations in Eq.1 can take the form $\dot{x} = f(x) + g(x)u$, where $g(x) = [g_1(x) \ \cdots \ g_m(x)]$. The delay-free part of the system of Eq.1 is

$$\left\{ \begin{array}{rcl} \dot{x}(t) & = & f(x(t)) + \sum_{j=1}^{m} g_j(x(t))u_j(t) \\ y^*(t) & = & \begin{bmatrix} h_1(x(t)) \\ \vdots \\ h_m(x(t)) \end{bmatrix} \end{array} \right. \tag{2}$$

Consider a system of the form of Eq.2. The **relative order** r_i of the output y_i^* with respect to the manipulated input vector u is defined as the smallest integer r_i for which

$$\left[L_{g_1} L_f^{r_i-1} h_i(x) \ \cdots \ L_{g_m} L_f^{r_i-1} h_i(x) \right] \not\equiv [0 \ \cdots \ 0]$$

If such an integer does not exist, $r_i = \infty$. For a system of the form of Eq.2 with finite relative orders $r_1, \cdots, r_m$, the matrix

$$\mathcal{C}(x) \triangleq \begin{bmatrix} L_{g_1} L_f^{r_1-1} h_1(x) & \cdots & L_{g_m} L_f^{r_1-1} h_1(x) \\ \vdots & \ddots & \vdots \\ L_{g_1} L_f^{r_m-1} h_m(x) & \cdots & L_{g_m} L_f^{r_m-1} h_m(x) \end{bmatrix}$$

is called the **characteristic matrix** of the system of Eq.2.

3 The Geometric Approach

In this section, for completeness, some controller synthesis formulas, which have been derived in the geometric framework, are reviewed.

Proposition 1 [10]: *Consider the system described by Eq.1 and assume that its delay-free part possesses finite relative orders $r_1, \cdots, r_m$ and nonsingular characteristic matrix $C(x)$ on X. Then, the dynamic system*

$$\left\{\begin{array}{rcl} \dot{w}(t) & = & f(w(t)) + g(w(t))\{[\gamma_{1r_1} \cdots \gamma_{mr_m}]C(w(t))\}^{-1} \\ & & \bullet\left\{v(t) - h(w(t)) - \sum_{i=1}^{m}\sum_{\ell=1}^{r_i}\gamma_{i\ell}L_f^{\ell}h_i(w(t))\right\} \\ u(t) & = & \{[\gamma_{1r_1} \cdots \gamma_{mr_m}]C(w(t))\}^{-1} \\ & & \bullet\left\{v(t) - h(w(t)) - \sum_{i=1}^{m}\sum_{\ell=1}^{r_i}\gamma_{i\ell}L_f^{\ell}h_i(w(t))\right\} \end{array}\right. \quad (3)$$

where the reference input $v(t)$ is given by

$$v(t) = e(t) + \begin{bmatrix} h_1(w(t-\theta_1)) \\ \vdots \\ h_m(w(t-\theta_m)) \end{bmatrix}, \quad (4)$$

and $\gamma_{i\ell} = [\gamma_{i\ell}^1 \cdots \gamma_{i\ell}^m]^T$ are m-vector adjustable constant parameters with $det[\gamma_{1r_1} \cdots \gamma_{mr_m}] \neq 0$, represents an n-th order state-space realization of a dynamic error-feedback controller that induces the linear input/output behavior

$$\begin{bmatrix} y_1(t+\theta_1) \\ \vdots \\ y_m(t+\theta_m) \end{bmatrix} + \sum_{i=1}^{m}\sum_{\ell=1}^{r_i}\gamma_{i\ell}\frac{d^{\ell}y_i(t+\theta_i)}{dt^{\ell}} = y_{sp}(t) \quad (5)$$

to the closed-loop system operating on X.

The controller realization of Eq.3 represents a dynamic error-feedback controller with implicit integral action. This control structure is depicted in Figure 1. Kravaris and Daoutidis [4] have shown that this control structure can also be used for SISO open-loop stable nonlinear processes whose delay-free parts are nonminimum-phase.

Remark 1: The input/output stability of the closed-loop system under the controller of Proposition 1 will be guaranteed, if the parameters $\gamma_{i\ell}$, $\ell = 1, \cdots, r_i$, $i = 1, \cdots, m$ are chosen so that the roots of the characteristic equation

$$det\left\{I_m + \left[\left(\sum_{\ell=1}^{r_1}\gamma_{1\ell}s^{\ell}\right)\left(\sum_{\ell=1}^{r_2}\gamma_{2\ell}s^{\ell}\right)\cdots\left(\sum_{\ell=1}^{r_m}\gamma_{m\ell}s^{\ell}\right)\right]\right\} = 0$$

lie in the left half of the complex plane. If the closed-loop system is input/output stable, and in addition, the zero dynamics of the process and the open-loop process are locally asymptotically stable, then the local internal stability of the closed-loop system will be guaranteed.

Remark 2: In the case that input/output decoupling:

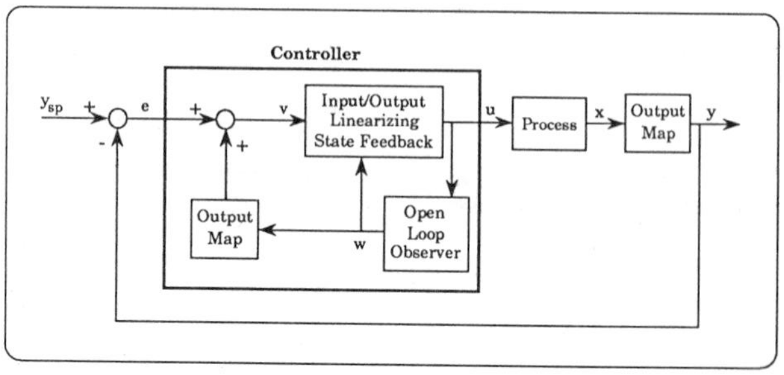

Figure 1: GLC-error feedback (reduced-order) structure.

$$y_i(t) + \gamma_{i1}^i\frac{dy_i(t)}{dt} + \cdots + \gamma_{ir_i}^i\frac{d^{r_i}y_i(t)}{dt^{r_i}} = y_{sp_i}(t-\theta_i), \quad i = 1, \cdots, m, \quad (6)$$

is meaningful and desirable, it can be achieved by setting the tuning parameters γ_{ij} according to

$$\gamma_{ij}^{\ell} = 0, \quad \ell \neq i, \ \ell = 1, \cdots, m, \ j = 1, \cdots, r_i, \ i = 1, \cdots, m \quad (7)$$

with $\gamma_{ir_i}^i \neq 0$, $i = 1, \cdots, m$.

4 The Model Predictive Approach

Two common and important features of MPC techniques are (a) the explicit use of a process model for the prediction of the future trends of the process outputs, and (b) the calculation of a sequence of controller actions that minimize a desirable performance index oven a time horizon.

Considering the continuous-time system of Eq.1, we see that, at any given point in time t_0, one can

(a) integrate the differential equations in Eq.1 [$\dot{x}(t) = f(x(t)) + g(x(t))u(t)$] initialized at a given $x(t_0)$, and predict the output $y_1(t), \cdots, y_m(t)$ for all possible input trajectories $u_1(t), \cdots, u_m(t)$,

(b) formulate an optimal control problem for the selection of the "best" $u(t)$ (that minimizes a desired performance index over a given time horizon). This optimization problem can in principle be solved on-line with considerable computational effort.

In connection with the two common features of MPC techniques, there are two important concerns: (a) the deterioration of the quality of output prediction as the prediction horizon becomes larger (because of the presence of modeling errors and process disturbances), and (b) the computational effort that is needed for numerically solving the optimization problem on-line. These concerns imply that prediction equations for the outputs should be simple and explicit, and accurate in the vicinity of t_0 but could lose accuracy for large times, like for example a truncated power series in $(t - t_0)$. Then, given such prediction equations, one can follow a desired MPC approach (e.g., Dynamic Matrix Control (DMC)-type approach [1, 8], or Model Algorithmic Control (MAC)-type approach [5, 6, 9]) to calculate the "best" $u(t)$.

In this paper, we follow a MAC-type approach, which involves:

1. for each output y_i, determining the "smallest prediction horizon" beyond which the output y_i is affected by the manipulated input vector u,
2. defining a set of reference trajectories, which the controller will try to force the outputs to follow,
3. deriving the control law by minimizing an appropriate quadratic performance index that depends on the reference trajectories.

The reference trajectories, the weights of the deviations of predicted outputs from their desired trajectories and the input penalties will be "tunable".

Suppose for a moment that the process is delay-free ($\theta_i = 0$, $i = 1, \cdots, m$). In this case, we can derive such prediction equations (simple, explicit, and accurate in the vicinity of t_0) by using the Volterra series [7]: One can substitute truncated Taylor series for $u_1(t), \cdots, u_m(t)$, do an appropriate truncation of the Volterra series, and obtain "closed-loop" prediction equations. The result is as follows:

$$\hat{y}(t) \approx y(t_0) + \begin{bmatrix} \sum_{\ell=1}^{P_1}\mathcal{B}_{1\ell}(x(t_0), \mathcal{U}(t_0))\frac{(t-t_0)^{\ell}}{\ell!} \\ \vdots \\ \sum_{\ell=1}^{P_m}\mathcal{B}_{m\ell}(x(t_0), \mathcal{U}(t_0))\frac{(t-t_0)^{\ell}}{\ell!} \end{bmatrix} \quad (8)$$

where the superscript $\hat{}$ is used to indicate closed-loop prediction,

$$\mathcal{U}(t) \triangleq \left[u_1(t) \quad \frac{du_1(t)}{dt} \quad \cdots \quad \frac{d^{P_1-1}u_1(t)}{dt^{P_1-1}} \quad \vdots \quad \cdots \quad \vdots \quad u_m(t) \quad \frac{du_m(t)}{dt} \quad \cdots \quad \frac{d^{P_m-1}u_m(t)}{dt^{P_m-1}} \right]^T$$

and $\mathcal{B}_{i\ell}(x, \mathcal{U}(t))$ are determined recursively from

$$\begin{aligned}
\mathcal{B}_{i(\ell+1)}(x,\mathcal{U}(t)) &= \left[L_f + \sum_{k=1}^{m} u_k(t) L_{g_k} + \frac{\partial}{\partial t} \right] \mathcal{B}_{i\ell}(x,\mathcal{U}(t)), \\
& \qquad \ell = 1, 2, \cdots, \; i = 1, \cdots, m \\
\mathcal{B}_{i1}(x,\mathcal{U}(t)) &= L_f h_i(x) + \sum_{j=1}^{m} u_j(t) L_{g_j} h_i(x), \qquad i = 1, \cdots, m
\end{aligned}$$

In the case that none of the state variables can be measured on-line and process is open-loop stable, the state variables can be estimated from on-line simulation of the process dynamics

$$\dot{x}_c(t) = f(x_c(t)) + \sum_{j=1}^{m} g_j(x_c(t)) u_j(t)$$

where the subscript c indicates estimates of the states x calculated from model simulations (as opposed to the actual process states x). Note that the region of validity of the power series prediction of $\hat{y}_i(t)$ (time horizon over which the truncation of $\hat{y}_i(t)$ is sufficiently accurate) will be a function of P_i. The larger the P_i, the larger the region of validity of the power series prediction of $\hat{y}_i(t)$. P_i is referred to as the **order** of the prediction for the output y_i.

4.1 Smallest Order of Output Prediction and Output Prediction Equations

Equation 8 implies that, for a process with nonsingular characteristic matrix $\mathcal{C}(x_c)$, the relative order r_i is the smallest order of prediction for output y_i, which is affected by the manipulated input vector.

Consider processes governed by Eq.1. Given the process state histories, the closed-loop prediction of the output y_i for $t_0 \leq t \leq t_0 + \theta_i$ can be obtained from

$$\hat{y}_i(t) = y_i(t_0) - h_i(x_c(t_0 - \theta_i)) + h_i(x_c(t - \theta_i))$$

whereas for $t \geq t_0 + \theta_i$ from (analog of Eq.8 for $P_i = r_i$ and a system with deadtime θ_i in its ith output):

$$\hat{y}_i(t) = y_i(t_0) - h_i(x_c(t_0 - \theta_i)) + \sum_{\ell=0}^{r_i} L_f^\ell h_i(x_c(t_0)) \frac{[t - (t_0 + \theta_i)]^\ell}{\ell!} + \sum_{j=1}^{m} L_{g_j} L_f^{r_i - 1} h_i(x_c(t_0)) u_j(t_0) \frac{[t - (t_0 + \theta_i)]^{r_i}}{r_i!} + h.o.t.$$

The above equation for all the outputs, in a vector form, becomes:

$$\hat{y}(t) = y(t_0) - \begin{bmatrix} h_1(x_c(t_0 - \theta_1)) \\ \vdots \\ h_m(x_c(t_0 - \theta_m)) \end{bmatrix} + \begin{bmatrix} \sum_{\ell=0}^{r_1} L_f^\ell h_1(x_c(t_0)) \frac{[t - (t_0 + \theta_1)]^\ell}{\ell!} \\ \vdots \\ \sum_{\ell=0}^{r_m} L_f^\ell h_m(x_c(t_0)) \frac{[t - (t_0 + \theta_m)]^\ell}{\ell!} \end{bmatrix} + diag\left\{ \frac{[t - (t_0 + \theta_i)]^{r_i}}{r_i!} \right\} \mathcal{C}(x_c(t_0)) u(t_0) + h.o.t. \quad (9)$$

where x_c is calculated from on-line simulation of the process model.

Remark 3: For a process with a diagonal characteristic matrix:

$$\mathcal{C}(x_c(t_0)) = diag\left\{ L_{g_i} L_f^{r_i - 1} h_i(x_c(t_0)) \right\}$$

the prediction equations of Eq.9 simplify to

$$\hat{y}_i(t) = y_i(t_0) - h_i(x_c(t_0 - \theta_i)) + \sum_{\ell=1}^{r_i} L_f^\ell h_i(x_c(t_0)) \frac{[t - (t_0 + \theta_i)]^\ell}{\ell!} + L_{g_i} L_f^{r_i - 1} h_i(x_c(t_0)) u_i(t_0) \frac{[t - (t_0 + \theta_i)]^{r_i}}{r_i!} + h.o.t.$$

$i = 1, \cdots, m$.

4.2 Reference Trajectories

Reference trajectory y_{d_i} is a desired trajectory which the controller, beyond the deadtime θ_i, will try to force the output y_i to follow. Therefore, the reference trajectory y_{d_i} will refer to the desired behavior of the output y_i beyond the deadtime θ_i. Because of the need for output functional controllability [2] of the process along the trajectories, each reference trajectory y_{d_i} at time $t_0 + \theta_i$ has to match the predicted value of the output y_i after the deadtime θ_i:

$$\hat{y}_i(t_0 + \theta_i) = y_i(t_0) - h_i(x_c(t_0 - \theta_i)) + h_i(x_c(t_0)),$$

the ith component of the inherent speed, acceleration and so on of the system at time $t_0 + \theta_i$ as predicted by the model. Furthermore, we are interested in exponential-type trajectories (which are solutions of linear ordinary differential equations). In particular, we choose the vector of the reference trajectories to be the solution of

$$\left\{ \begin{aligned}
& y_d(t) + \sum_{i=1}^{m} \sum_{\ell=1}^{r_i} \gamma_{i\ell} \frac{d^\ell y_{d_i}(t)}{dt^\ell} = y_{sp} \\
& \text{subject to the initial conditions:} \\
& \quad y_{d_i}(t_0 + \theta_i) = \hat{y}_i(t_0 + \theta_i) \\
& \quad \frac{dy_{d_i}(t_0 + \theta_i)}{dt} = L_f h_i(x_c(t_0)) \\
& \quad \vdots \qquad\qquad\qquad\qquad , \quad i = 1, \cdots, m \\
& \quad \frac{d^{r_i - 1} y_{d_i}(t_0 + \theta_i)}{dt^{r_i - 1}} = L_f^{r_i - 1} h_i(x_c(t_0))
\end{aligned} \right. \quad (10)$$

The $O\left[t - (t_0 + \theta_i)\right]^{r_i}$ truncations of the Taylor-series expansions of the trajectories $y_{d_1}(t), \cdots, y_{d_m}(t)$ defined by Eq.10, in a vector form, can be written as:

$$\begin{aligned}
y_d(t) = y(t_0) - \begin{bmatrix} h_1(x_c(t_0 - \theta_1)) \\ \vdots \\ h_m(x_c(t_0 - \theta_m)) \end{bmatrix}
+ \begin{bmatrix} \sum_{\ell=0}^{r_1 - 1} L_f^\ell h_1(x_c(t_0)) \frac{[t - (t_0 + \theta_1)]^\ell}{\ell!} \\ \vdots \\ \sum_{\ell=0}^{r_m - 1} L_f^\ell h_m(x_c(t_0)) \frac{[t - (t_0 + \theta_m)]^\ell}{\ell!} \end{bmatrix} + diag\left\{ \frac{[t - (t_0 + \theta_i)]^{r_i}}{r_i!} \right\} \\
\bullet \left[\gamma_{1r_1} \cdots \gamma_{mr_m} \right]^{-1} \left[y_{sp} - y(t_0) + \begin{bmatrix} h_1(x_c(t_0 - \theta_1)) \\ \vdots \\ h_m(x_c(t_0 - \theta_m)) \end{bmatrix} - h(x_c(t_0)) - \sum_{i=1}^{m} \sum_{\ell=1}^{r_i - 1} \gamma_{i\ell} L_f^\ell h_i(x_c(t_0)) \right] + h.o.t. \quad (11)
\end{aligned}$$

which can be used as the solution of Eq.10 for sufficiently small time horizons beyond the deadtimes.

Remark 4: If the characteristic matrix $\mathcal{C}(x_c(t_0))$ is diagonal (see also Remark 3), it will be meaningful to set the adjustable parameters γ_{ij} according to Eq.7. In this case, the above $O\left[t - (t_0 + \theta_i)\right]^{r_i}$ truncations (Eq.11) simplify to:

$$y_{d_i}(t) = y_i(t_0) - h_i(x_c(t_0 - \theta_i)) + \sum_{\ell=0}^{r_i - 1} L_f^\ell h_i(x_c(t_0)) \frac{[t - (t_0 + \theta_1)]^\ell}{\ell!} + \frac{y_{sp_i} - y_i(t_0) + h_i(x_c(t_0 - \theta_i)) - h_i(x_c(t_0)) - \sum_{\ell=1}^{r_i - 1} \gamma_{i\ell}^i L_f^\ell h_i(x_c(t_0))}{\gamma_{ir_i}^i} \bullet \frac{[t - (t_0 + \theta_i)]^{r_i}}{r_i!} + h.o.t., \quad i = 1, \cdots, m.$$

4.3 Formulation of the Optimization Problem-Derivation of Control Law

Consider the following optimization problem:

$$\min_{u(t_0)}\left\{\sum_{\ell=1}^{m} q_\ell \,\|y_{d_\ell}(t)-\hat{y}_\ell(t)\|_\ell^2+\sum_{\ell=1}^{m}\rho_\ell\,|u_\ell(t_0)|^2\right\}$$

subject to the constraints

$$u_{l_\ell}\le u_\ell\le u_{h_\ell},\qquad \ell=1,\cdots,m$$

where $\|.\|_\ell$ is any function norm over a finite time interval of the form $[t_0+\theta_\ell,\ t_0+\theta_\ell+T_{h_\ell}]$, q_ℓ and ρ_ℓ are positive adjustable constant parameters.

In contrast to the SISO case [11], the above minimization problem in the presence of input constraints, in general, does not have an analytic solution; it should be solved numerically on-line to obtain the optimal controller action. Therefore, the control law is represented by

$u(t_0)$ is the solution of the minimization problem

$$\min_{u(t_0)}\left\{\sum_{\ell=1}^{m} q_\ell \,\|y_{d_\ell}(t)-\hat{y}_\ell(t)\|_\ell^2+\sum_{\ell=1}^{m}\rho_\ell\,|u_\ell(t_0)|^2\right\}$$

subject to the constraints

$$u_{l_\ell}\le u_\ell\le u_{h_\ell},\qquad \ell=1,\cdots,m \qquad (12)$$

where $\hat{y}_\ell(t)$ and $y_{d_\ell}(t)$ for sufficiently short time horizons are given by Eqs.9 and 11, and x_c is obtained by simulating

$$\dot{x}_c(t_0)=f(x_c(t_0))+g(x_c(t_0))u(t_0)$$

In this dynamic error-feedback control law, $\|.\|_\ell$, T_{h_ℓ} with $T_{h_\ell}\ge 0$, q_ℓ with $q_\ell\ge 0$, ρ_ℓ with $\rho_\ell\ge 0$ and $\gamma_{i\ell}=[\gamma_{i\ell}^1\cdots\gamma_{i\ell}^m]^T$ with $det[\gamma_{1r_1}\cdots\gamma_{mr_m}]\ne 0$ are adjustable.

Remark 5: If the characteristic matrix $C(x_c(t_0))$ is diagonal, it will be meaningful to set the adjustable parameters γ_{ij} according to Eq.7. In this case, we saw (in Remarks 3 and 4) that both the output prediction $\hat{y}_i(t)$ and the reference trajectory $y_{d_i}(t)$ depend **only** on the input u_i, and therefore, one can find an analytic solution to the minimization problem of Eq.12:

$$\begin{aligned} u_1(t_0) &= \mathcal{S}_1\left[\widehat{\Psi}_1(x_c(t_0),e(t_0))\right]\\ &\ \vdots\\ u_m(t_0) &= \mathcal{S}_m\left[\widehat{\Psi}_m(x_c(t_0),e(t_0))\right]\end{aligned}$$

Here

$$\mathcal{S}_i[w]\triangleq\begin{cases} u_{l_i}, & if\ \ w<u_{l_i}\\ w, & if\ \ u_{l_i}\le w<u_{h_i},\qquad i=1,\cdots,m\\ u_{h_i}, & if\ \ w\ge u_{h_i}\end{cases}$$

are saturation functions and

$$\widehat{\Psi}_i(x_c(t_0),e(t_0))\triangleq\frac{L_{g_i}L_f^{r_i-1}h_i(x_c(t_0))}{\left(L_{g_i}L_f^{r_i-1}h_i(x_c(t_0))\right)^2+\rho_i'}$$

$$\bullet\frac{e_i(t_0)+h_i(x_c(t_0-\theta))-h_i(x_c(t_0))-\sum_{\ell=1}^{r_i}\gamma_{i\ell}^iL_f^\ell h_i(x_c(t_0))}{\gamma_{ir_i}^i}$$

where

$$\rho_i'\triangleq\frac{\rho_i\,(r_i!)^2}{\|[t-(t_0+\theta_i)]^{r_i}\|_i^2}.$$

This control law can be written as (since t_0 is completely arbitrary):

$$\begin{aligned} u_1(t) &= \mathcal{S}_1\left[\widehat{\Psi}_1(x_c(t),e(t))\right]\\ &\ \vdots\\ u_m(t) &= \mathcal{S}_m\left[\widehat{\Psi}_m(x_c(t),e(t))\right]\end{aligned}$$

where x_c is obtained by simulating

$$\dot{x}_c(t)=f(x_c(t))+\sum_{j=1}^{m}g_j(x_c(t))u_j(t)$$

4.4 Special Cases of the Control Law

Special Case I: No input constraints

In the absence of input constraints, the m-dimensional quadratic minimization problem of Eq.12 has a closed-form explicit analytic solution, which is the following control law:

$$u(t_0)=\Psi(x_c(t_0),e(t_0))$$

$$\triangleq\left\{[C(x_c(t_0))]^T diag\{q_i\alpha_i(T_{h_i})\}C(x_c(t_0))+diag\{\rho_i\}\right\}^{-1}$$

$$\bullet[C(x_c(t_0))]^T diag\{q_i\alpha_i(T_{h_i})\}[\gamma_{1r_1}\ \cdots\ \gamma_{mr_m}]^{-1}$$

$$\bullet\left\{e(t_0)+\begin{bmatrix}h_1(x_c(t_0-\theta_1))\\ \vdots\\ h_m(x_c(t_0-\theta_m))\end{bmatrix}-h(x_c(t_0))-\sum_{i=1}^{m}\sum_{\ell=1}^{r_i}\gamma_{i\ell}L_f^\ell h_i(x_c(t_0))\right\}\qquad(13)$$

where

$$\alpha_i(T_{h_i})\triangleq\frac{\|[t-(t_0+\theta_i)]^{r_i}\|_i^2}{(r_i!)^2}$$

Since t_0 is completely arbitrary, this control law can be written as

$$u(t)=\Psi(x_c(t),e(t))$$

where x_c is obtained by simulating

$$\dot{x}_c(t)=f(x_c(t))+g(x_c(t))u(t)$$

Special Case II: No penalty on u, and no input constraints

In this case, the control law is obtained by setting $\rho_i=0$, $i=1,\cdots,m$ in Eq.12. The resulting controller has the form:

$$u(t)=\{[\gamma_{1r_1}\ \cdots\ \gamma_{mr_m}]C(x_c(t))\}^{-1}$$

$$\bullet\left\{e(t)+\begin{bmatrix}h_1(x_c(t-\theta_1))\\ \vdots\\ h_m(x_c(t-\theta_m))\end{bmatrix}-h(x_c(t))-\sum_{i=1}^{m}\sum_{\ell=1}^{r_i}\gamma_{i\ell}L_f^\ell h_i(x_c(t))\right\}$$

where x_c is obtained by simulating

$$\dot{x}_c(t)=f(x_c(t))+g(x_c(t))u(t)$$

which is exactly the **GLC-error feedback** controller of Eq.3 with x_c replacing w.

Remark 6: In this case, because there is no constraint and no input penalty to prevent it, the output vector exactly matches the reference trajectory vector at **every** point in time. For this reason, in closed-loop, the output vector follows exactly the same differential equation that generates y_d:

$$\begin{bmatrix}y_1(t+\theta_1)\\ \vdots\\ y_m(t+\theta_m)\end{bmatrix}+\sum_{i=1}^{m}\sum_{\ell=1}^{r_i}\gamma_{i\ell}\frac{d^\ell y_i(t+\theta_i)}{dt^\ell}=y_{sp}(t)$$

Special Case III: No dead-time and no input constraints

In this case, the control law is obtained by setting $\theta_i=0$, $i=1,\cdots,m$ in Eq.13. The resulting controller has the form:

$$u(t)=\left[[C(x_c(t))]^T diag\{q_i\alpha_i(T_{h_i})\}C(x_c(t))+diag\{\rho_i\}\right]^{-1}$$

$$\bullet[C(x_c(t))]^T diag\{q_i\alpha_i(T_{h_i})\}[\gamma_{1r_1}\ \cdots\ \gamma_{mr_m}]^{-1}$$

$$\bullet\left\{e(t)-\sum_{i=1}^{m}\sum_{\ell=1}^{r_i}\gamma_{i\ell}L_f^\ell h_i(x_c(t))\right\}$$

where x_c is obtained by simulating

$$\dot{x}_c(t)=f(x_c(t))+g(x_c(t))u(t)$$

This control law does not allow u_j, $j=1,\cdots,m$ to become unbounded. The above controller can further be simplified by setting $q_i=1/\alpha_i(T_{h_i})$, $i=1,\cdots,m$. In this case, the corresponding controller takes the form:

$$u(t) = \left[[\mathcal{C}(x_c(t))]^T \mathcal{C}(x_c(t)) + diag\{\rho_i\}\right]^{-1} [\mathcal{C}(x_c(t))]^T$$
$$\bullet [\gamma_{1r_1} \cdots \gamma_{mr_m}]^{-1} \left\{ e(t) - \sum_{i=1}^{m}\sum_{\ell=1}^{r_i} \gamma_{i\ell} L_f^{\ell} h_i(x_c(t)) \right\}$$
where x_c is obtained by simulating
$$\dot{x}_c(t) = f(x_c(t)) + g(x_c(t))u(t)$$

Remark 7: Conditions for input/output stability and internal stability of the closed-loop system (under the controller of Eq.12) in the absence of input constraints and penalties on inputs are the same as those given in Remark 1. At the present time, the theoretical properties of the closed-loop system (under the controller of Eq.12) in the presence of an input constraint or penalty are unknown.

5 Error-Feedback Control of Linear Systems

In this section, the controller of Case II (Proposition 1) is applied to multivariable time-invariant linear systems described by a state-space model of the form

$$\left\{ \begin{array}{rcl} \dot{x}(t) & = & Ax(t) + Bu(t) \\ \begin{bmatrix} y_1(t) \\ \vdots \\ y_m(t) \end{bmatrix} & = & \begin{bmatrix} c_1 x(t-\theta_1) \\ \vdots \\ c_m x(t-\theta_m) \end{bmatrix} \end{array} \right. \quad (14)$$

where A, B and c_ℓ are nxn, nxm, 1xn matrices, respectively. This class of systems is a special case of Eq.1 for $f(x(t)) = Ax(t)$, $g(x(t)) = B$, and

$$\begin{bmatrix} h_1(x(t-\theta_1)) \\ \vdots \\ h_m(x(t-\theta_m)) \end{bmatrix} = \begin{bmatrix} c_1 x(t-\theta_1) \\ \vdots \\ c_m x(t-\theta_m) \end{bmatrix}.$$

For the delay-free part of this system, the relative order r_i is the smallest integer for which $c_i A^{r_i-1} B \neq [0 \cdots 0]$, and the characteristic matrix is given by

$$\mathcal{C} = \begin{bmatrix} c_1 A^{r_i-1} B \\ \vdots \\ c_m A^{r_i-1} B \end{bmatrix}.$$

The delay-free part of the system of Eq.14 is assumed to have finite relative orders and nonsingular characteristic matrix.

The input/output behavior of the system of Eq.14, in the s-domain, can be represented by

$$y(s) = diag\left\{e^{-\theta_i s}\right\} H(s)u(s) \quad (15)$$

Here $H(s)$ is the matrix transfer function of the delay-free part of the system, given by

$$H(s) = C\,(sI_n - A)^{-1}\,B \quad (16)$$

where $C = [c_1 \cdots c_m]^T$. Applying the controller of Case II to the system of Eq.14, we obtain the following linear error-feedback controller:

$$\left\{ \begin{array}{l} \dot{x}_c(t) = \left\{ A - B\left\{[\gamma_{1r_1} \cdots \gamma_{mr_m}]\mathcal{C}\right\}^{-1} \left(C + \sum_{i=1}^{m}\sum_{\ell=1}^{r_i} \gamma_{i\ell} c_i A^{\ell} \right) \right\} x_c(t) \\ \quad + B\left\{[\gamma_{1r_1} \cdots \gamma_{mr_m}]\mathcal{C}\right\}^{-1} \left(\begin{bmatrix} c_1 x_c(t-\theta_1) \\ \vdots \\ c_m x_c(t-\theta_m) \end{bmatrix} + e(t) \right) \\ u(t) = \left\{[\gamma_{1r_1} \cdots \gamma_{mr_m}]\mathcal{C}\right\}^{-1} \\ \quad \bullet \left\{ e(t) + \begin{bmatrix} c_1 x_c(t-\theta_1) \\ \vdots \\ c_m x_c(t-\theta_m) \end{bmatrix} - \left(C + \sum_{i=1}^{m}\sum_{\ell=1}^{r_i} \gamma_{i\ell} c_i A^{\ell} \right) x_c(t) \right\} \end{array} \right. \quad (17)$$

which is a minimal-order state-space realization of the s-domain multivariable controller

$$u(s) = [H(s)]^{-1}$$
$$\bullet \left\{ \left[\left(\sum_{\ell=1}^{r_1} \gamma_{1\ell} s^{\ell} \right) \cdots \left(\sum_{\ell=1}^{r_m} \gamma_{m\ell} s^{\ell} \right) \right] + I_m - diag\left\{e^{-\theta_i s}\right\} \right\}^{-1} e(s) \quad (18)$$

where $H(s)$ is given by Eq.16. The transfer function of Eq.18 is **exactly** the controller derived from standard synthesis methods (e.g., IMC [3]) for a requested closed-loop response of the form

$$y(s) = diag\left\{e^{-\theta_i s}\right\} \left\{ I_m + \left[\left(\sum_{\ell=1}^{r_1} \gamma_{1\ell} s^{\ell} \right) \cdots \left(\sum_{\ell=1}^{r_m} \gamma_{m\ell} s^{\ell} \right) \right] \right\}^{-1} y_{sp}(s)$$

Note that, in the continuous-time IMC controller of Eq.18, the matrix transfer function

$$\left\{ I_m + \left[\left(\sum_{\ell=1}^{r_1} \gamma_{1\ell} s^{\ell} \right) \cdots \left(\sum_{\ell=1}^{r_m} \gamma_{m\ell} s^{\ell} \right) \right] \right\}^{-1}$$

is the IMC filter, which is exactly the transfer function of the differential equation of the set of reference trajectories defined by Eq.10.

Remark 8: In the case that input/output decoupling is meaningful and desirable, it is achieved by setting γ_{ij}^{ℓ} according to Eq.7. In this case, the controller of Eq.18 simplifies to the following multivariable IMC controller

$$u(s) = [H(s)]^{-1}\, diag\left\{ \frac{1}{\gamma_{ir_i}^{i} s^{r_i} + \cdots + \gamma_{i1}^{i} s + 1 - e^{-\theta_i s}} \right\} e(s)$$

which has a diagonal matrix filter of the form:

$$diag\left\{ \frac{1}{\gamma_{ir_i}^{i} s^{r_i} + \gamma_{i(r_i-1)}^{i} s^{r_i-1} + \cdots + \gamma_{i1}^{i} s + 1} \right\}$$

and induces the decoupled input/output response

$$y_i(s) = \frac{e^{-\theta_i s}}{\gamma_{ir_i}^{i} s^{r_i} + \gamma_{i(r_i-1)}^{i} s^{r_i-1} + \cdots + \gamma_{i1}^{i} s + 1} y_{sp_i}(s)$$

$i = 1, \cdots, m$, to the closed-loop system.

6 Illustrative Example: Application to a CSTR

Consider a well-mixed CSTR, in which the following parallel reactions

$$A \xrightarrow{k_1} U_1$$
$$A \xleftarrow{k_{-1}} U_1$$
$$A \xrightarrow{k_2} U_2$$
$$A \xrightarrow{k_3} U_3$$
$$A \xrightarrow{k_4} U_4$$
$$A \xrightarrow{k_d} D$$

take place. U_1, U_2, U_3 and U_4 are undesirable side products, and D is the desired product. The dependence of k_1, k_{-1}, k_2, k_3, k_4 and k_d on temperature are given by $k_i = Z_i \exp(-E_{a_i}/RT)$, $i = 1, -1, 2, 3, 4$, and $k_d = Z_d \exp(-E_{a_d}/RT)$, respectively. It is assumed that the feed to the reactor does not contain U_1, U_2, U_3, U_4 or D.

6.1 Mathematical Model and Control Problem

Energy and species mass balances for the reactor (under standard assumptions) give the reactor model:

$$\left\{ \begin{array}{l} \dfrac{dC_A}{dt} = R_A(C_A, C_{U_1}, T) + \dfrac{C_{A_i} - C_A}{\tau} \\ \dfrac{dC_{U_1}}{dt} = R_{U_1}(C_A, C_{U_1}, T) - \dfrac{C_{U_1}}{\tau} \\ \dfrac{dT}{dt} = \dfrac{R_H(C_A, C_{U_1}, T)}{\rho c} + \dfrac{T_i - T}{\tau} + \dfrac{Q}{\rho c V} \end{array} \right. \quad (19)$$

where the rate expressions $R_A(C_A, C_{U_1}, T)$, $R_{U_1}(C_A, C_{U_1}, T)$ and $R_H(C_A, C_{U_1}, T)$ are given by

$$\begin{array}{rcl} R_A(C_A, C_{U_1}, T) & = & k_{-1} C_{U_1}^{n_{-1}} - \sum_{\ell=1,2,3,4,d} k_\ell C_A^{n_\ell} \\ R_{U_1}(C_A, C_{U_1}, T) & = & k_1 C_A^{n_1} - k_{-1} C_A^{n_{-1}} \\ R_H(C_A, C_{U_1}, T) & = & -(-\Delta H_1) k_{-1} C_{U_1}^{n_{-1}} + \sum_{\ell=1,2,3,4,d} (-\Delta H_\ell) k_\ell C_A^{n_\ell} \end{array}$$

The parameters of the reactor model are given in Tables 1 and 2.

Figure 2 depicts the reaction selectivity $\mathcal{S}$, defined by

$$\mathcal{S} = \frac{k_d C_A^{n_d}}{k_1 C_A^{n_1} + k_2 C_A^{n_2} + k_3 C_A^{n_3} + k_4 C_A^{n_4} - k_{-1} C_{U_1}^{n-1}}$$

versus the concentration C_A and temperature T at steady-state conditions. As Figure 2 shows, the selectivity $\mathcal{S}$ has a global maximum at the point $(C_A, T) = (1, 400)$.

The control problem is to maintain the concentration C_A and the temperature T at the point $(C_A, T) = (1, 400)$, where the selectivity $\mathcal{S}$ is maximum (i.e., $\mathcal{S} = 1$). The manipulated inputs are the inlet concentration of species A (C_{A_i}) and the heat input to the reactor (Q). It is assumed that the heat input and the inlet concentration are bounded: $|Q| \le Q_{max}$ and $0 \le C_{A_i} \le C_{A_{i_{max}}}$.

Table 1. Kinetic parameters of the CSTR model.

R	=	8.345×10^0	$kJ.kmol^{-1}.K^{-1}$
Z_1	=	3.906×10^0	s^{-1}
Z_{-1}	=	9.000×10^3	s^{-1}
Z_2	=	3.906×10^0	$m^6.kmol.^{-2}.s^{-1}$
Z_3	=	4.933×10^9	$m^6.kmol.^{-2}.s^{-1}$
Z_4	=	4.933×10^9	s^{-1}
Z_d	=	2.499×10^6	$m^3.kmol^{-1}$
E_{a_1}	=	2.000×10^4	$kJ.kmol^{-1}$
$E_{a_{-1}}$	=	6.000×10^4	$kJ.kmol^{-1}$
E_{a_2}	=	2.000×10^4	$kJ.kmol^{-1}$
E_{a_3}	=	1.000×10^5	$kJ.kmol^{-1}$
E_{a_4}	=	1.000×10^5	$kJ.kmol^{-1}$
E_{a_d}	=	6.000×10^4	$kJ.kmol^{-1}$
$-\Delta H_1$	=	4.000×10^4	$kJ.kmol^{-1}$
$-\Delta H_2$	=	5.500×10^4	$kJ.kmol^{-1}$
$-\Delta H_3$	=	5.000×10^4	$kJ.kmol^{-1}$
$-\Delta H_4$	=	6.200×10^4	$kJ.kmol^{-1}$
$-\Delta H_d$	=	6.000×10^4	$kJ.kmol^{-1}$
$n_1 = n_{-1}$	=	1.000×10^0	
$n_2 = n_3$	=	3.000×10^0	
n_4	=	1.000×10^0	
n_d	=	2.000×10^0	

Table 2. Other parameters of the CSTR model.

τ	=	3.000×10^2	s
V	=	1.000×10^{-2}	m^3
ρ	=	1.000×10^3	$kg.m^{-3}$
c	=	4.200×10^0	$kJ.kg^{-1}.K^{-1}$
T_i	=	2.952×10^2	K
$C_{A_{i_{max}}}$	=	6.000×10^0	$kmol.m^{-3}$
Q_{max}	=	1.000×10^1	$kJ.s^{-1}$

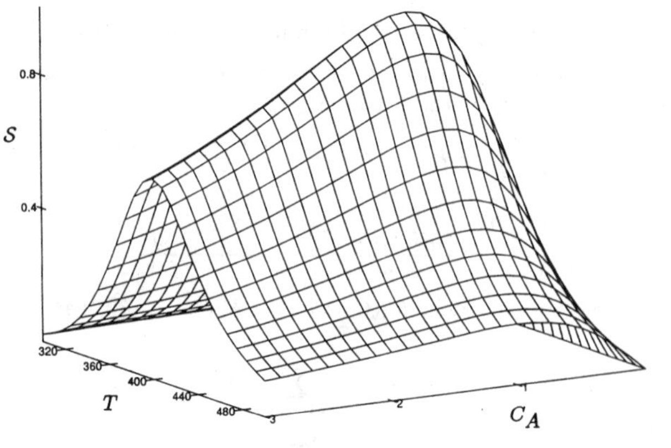

Figure 2: 3-dimensional plots of selectivity versus temperature (T) and concentration of A (C_A) at steady-state conditions.

6.2 Controller Synthesis and Implementation

Let $y_1 = C_A$, $y_2 = T$, $u_1 = C_{A_i}/C_{A_{i_{max}}}$ $(0 \le u_1 \le 1)$, and $u_2 = Q/Q_{max}$ $(|u_2| \le 1)$. The relative orders $r_1 = 1$ and $r_2 = 1$, and the characteristic matrix is

$$\mathcal{C} = \begin{bmatrix} \dfrac{C_{A_{max}}}{\tau} & 0 \\ 0 & \dfrac{Q_{max}}{\rho c V} \end{bmatrix}$$

which is nonsingular everywhere on $\mathbb{R}^3$. In this case, since the characteristic matrix is diagonal, the controller of Remark 5 can be implemented. The tuning parameters are chosen as follows: $\gamma_{11}^1 = 1.0 \times 10^1\ s$, $\gamma_{11}^2 = \gamma_{21}^1 = 0$, and $\gamma_{21}^2 = 2.0 \times 10^2\ s$. Therefore, the controller of Remark 5, for this specific example, becomes:

$$u_1 = \begin{cases} 0, & if\ \ \Psi_1(C_{A_c}, C_{U_{1c}}, T_c, e_1) < 0 \\ \Psi_1(C_{A_c}, C_{U_{1c}}, T_c, e_1) & if\ \ -1 \le \Psi_1(C_{A_c}, C_{U_{1c}}, T_c, e_1) < 1 \\ 1, & if\ \ \Psi_1(C_{A_c}, C_{U_{1c}}, T_c, e_1) \ge 1 \end{cases} \tag{20}$$

$$u_2 = \begin{cases} -1, & if\ \ \Psi_2(C_{A_c}, C_{U_{1c}}, T_c, e_2) < -1 \\ \Psi_2(C_{A_c}, C_{U_{1c}}, T_c, e_2) & if\ \ -1 \le \Psi_2(C_{A_c}, C_{U_{1c}}, T_c, e_2) < 1 \\ 1, & if\ \ \Psi_2(C_{A_c}, C_{U_{1c}}, T_c, e_2) \ge 1 \end{cases} \tag{21}$$

where

$$\Psi_1(C_{A_c}, C_{U_{1c}}, T_c, e_1) = \frac{e_1 - \gamma_{11}^1 \left[R_A(C_{A_c}, C_{U_{1c}}, T_c) - \dfrac{C_{A_c}}{\tau} \right]}{\gamma_{11}^1 \dfrac{C_{A_{max}}}{\tau}}$$

$$\Psi_2(C_{A_c}, C_{U_{1c}}, T_c, e_2) = \frac{e_2 - \gamma_{21}^2 \left[\dfrac{R_H(C_{A_c}, C_{U_{1c}}, T_c)}{\rho c} + \dfrac{T_i - T_c}{\tau} \right]}{\gamma_{21}^2 \dfrac{Q_{max}}{\rho c V}}$$

and C_{A_c}, $C_{U_{1c}}$ and T_c are obtained from on-line simulation of the process model (Eq.19).

6.3 Simulation Results

Using the operating conditions given in Table 3, the closed-loop process (under the controller of Eqs.20 and 21) was simulated.

Figures 3a and 3b depict the start-up profiles of the controlled outputs and manipulated inputs under the controller of Eqs.20 and 21. As these two figures show, both manipulated inputs initially hit their upper constraints; the heat input remains at its upper constraint for a much longer time. Despite the long stay of the heat input at its upper constraint, the temperature response is very sluggish. Note that in order to force the inlet concentration C_A to hit its upper constraint, the value of γ_{21}^2 was chosen to be very small (10 s). Overall, these two figures show the satisfactory ("optimal") performance of the nonlinear controller in the presence of the active input constraints. Figure 3a also shows that, under open-loop operation, the process goes to the desirable steady-state operating point, and the very sluggish C_A profile has a large overshoot.

7 Notation

A	=	reactant
c	=	heat capacity of reacting mixture, $kJ.kg^{-1}.K^{-1}$
C_A	=	concentration of reactant A, $kmol.m^{-3}$
C_{A_i}	=	inlet concentration of reactant A, $kmol.m^{-3}$
$C_{A_{i_{max}}}$	=	maximum inlet concentration of A, $kmol.m^{-3}$
$C_{A_{i_{ss}}}$	=	steady-state inlet concentration of A, $kmol.m^{-3}$
$C_{A_{ss}}$	=	steady-state concentration of A, $kmol.m^{-3}$
C_D	=	concentration of desired product, $kmol.m^{-3}$
$C_D(0)$	=	start-up concentration of desired product, $kmol.m^{-3}$

Table 3. Operating conditions of the CSTR.

$C_A(0) = C_{A_c}(0)$	=	0.000×10^0	$kmol.m^{-3}$
$C_{U_1}(0) = C_{U_{1c}}(0)$	=	0.000×10^0	$kmol.m^{-3}$
$T(0) = T_c(0)$	=	2.952×10^2	K
$C_{A_{ss}}$	=	1.000×10^0	$kmol.m^{-3}$
$C_{U_{1_{ss}}}$	=	5.844×10^{-1}	$kmol.m^{-3}$
T_{ss}	=	4.000×10^2	K
$C_{A_{i_{ss}}}$	=	5.687×10^0	$kmol.m^{-3}$
Q_{ss}	=	5.942×10^0	$kJ.s^{-1}$

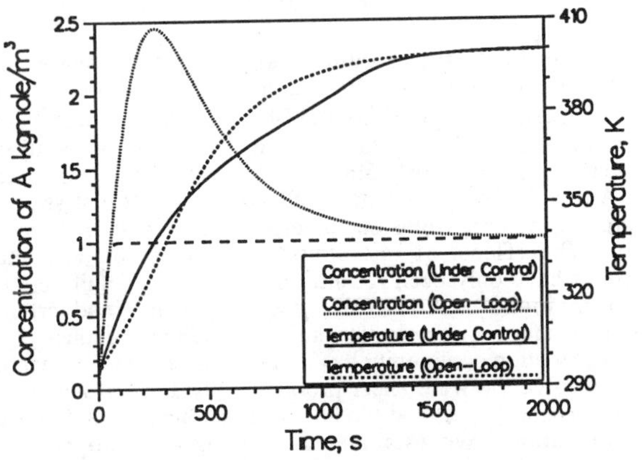

Figure 3a: Start-up profiles of the outputs.

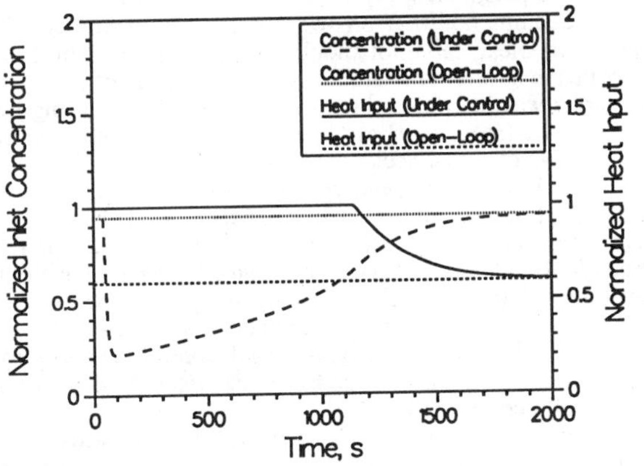

Figure 3b: Start-up profiles of the manipulated inputs.

C_{U_ℓ} = concentration of undesired product U_ℓ, $kmol.m^{-3}$
$C_{U_\ell}(0)$ = start-up concentration of undesired product U_ℓ, $kmol.m^{-3}$
D = desired product
e = error $\triangleq y_{sp} - y$
E_{a_d} = activation energy for desired reaction, $kJ.kmol^{-1}$
E_{a_ℓ} = activation energy for undesired reaction $\ell = -1, 1, \cdots, 4$, $kJ.kmol^{-1}$
n_d = order of the desired reaction
n_ℓ = order of the undesired reaction ℓ
q_i = penalty on the mismatch $(y_{d_i}(t) - \hat{y}_i(t))$
Q = heat input to jacket, $kJ.s^{-1}$
Q_{max} = maximum heat input to jacket, $kJ.s^{-1}$
Q_{ss} = steady-state heat input to jacket, $kJ.s^{-1}$
r_i = relative order of controlled output y_i
R = universal gas constant, $kJ.kmol^{-1}.K^{-1}$
R_A = rate of production of A, $kmol.m^{-3}.s^{-1}$
R_H = overall rate of heat production by reactions, $kJ.kmol^{-1}$
R_{U_1} = rate of production of U_1, $kmol.m^{-3}.s^{-1}$
S = reactor-jacket heat transfer area, m^2
t = time, s
T = reactor temperature, K
$T(0)$ = start-up reactor temperature, K
T_i = temperature of inlet stream, K
T_{ss} = steady-state reactor temperature, K
u = manipulated input vector
U = overall heat transfer coefficient, $kJ.m^{-2}.s^{-1}.K^{-1}$
U_1, U_2, U_3, U_4 = undesired products
V = volume of the reacting mixture, m^3
x = vector of state variables
y = vector of output variables
y_d = vector of reference trajectories
y_{sp} = vector of output set-points
Z_d = frequency factor for desired reaction, $m^6.kmol^{-2}.s^{-1}$
Z_{-1}, Z_1, Z_4 = frequency factors for undesired reactions −1, 1 and 4, s^{-1}
Z_2, Z_3 = frequency factors for undesired reaction 2 and 3 $m^6.kmol^{-2}.s^{-1}$

Greek letters

$-\Delta H_d$ = heat of desired reaction, $kJ.kmol^{-1}$
$-\Delta H_\ell$ = heat of undesired reaction ℓ, $kJ.kmol^{-1}$
$\gamma_{j\ell}$ = m-vector tunable parameters
ρ = density of reacting mixture, $kg.m^{-3}$
ρ_j = penalty on the controller action u_j
τ = CSTR residence time, s

References

[1] Cutler, C. R., and B. L. Ramaker, "Dynamic Matrix Control-A Computer Control Algorithm," *AIChE National Meeting, Houston, Texas* (1979).

[2] Hirschorn, R. M., "Invertibility of Multivariable Nonlinear Control Systems," *IEEE Trans. Automat. Contr.*, AC-24, 855 (1979).

[3] Holt, B. R., and M. Morari, "Design of Resilient Processing Plants V. The Effect of Deadtime on Dynamic Resilience," *Chem. Eng. Sci.*, 40(7), 1229 (1985).

[4] Kravaris, C., and P. Daoutidis, "Output Feedback Controller Realizations for Nonlinear Open-loop Stable Processes," *Proc. of ACC*, FA1 (1992).

[5] Mehra, R. K., R. Rouhani, and R. Praly, "New Theoretical Developments in Multivariable Predictive Algorithmic Control," *Proc. of ACC*, FA9-B (1980).

[6] Mehra, R. K., and R. Rouhani, "Theoretical Considerations on Model Algorithmic Control for Nonminimum Phase Systems," *Proc. of ACC*, TA8-B (1980).

[7] Nijmeijer, H., and A. J. van der Schaft, "Nonlinear Dynamical Control Systems," *Springer-Verlag*, 121 (1990).

[8] Prett, D. M., and R. D. Gillette, "Optimization and Constrained Multivariable Control of a Catalytic Cracking Unit," *AIChE National Meeting, Houston, Texas* (1979).

[9] Richalet, J., A. Rault, J. L. Testud, and J. Papon, "Model Predictive Heuristic Control: Application to Industrial Processes," *Automatica*, **14**, 413 (1978).

[10] Soroush, M., "Studies in Nonlinear Control and Optimal Design with Experimental Application to Polymerization Reactors," *Ph.D. Thesis, The University of Michigan, Ann Arbor* (1992).

[11] Soroush, M., and C. Kravaris, "A Continuous-Time Formulation of Nonlinear Model Predictive Control," *Proc. of ACC*, p.821 (1992).

Proceedings of the
American Control Conference
San Francisco, California • June 1993

Aircraft Flight Control in Wind Shear Using Partial Dynamic Inversion

Sandeep S. Mulgund* and Robert F. Stengel**
Department of Mechanical and Aerospace Engineering
Princeton University, Princeton, NJ 08544

Abstract

A flight control law based on partial inversion of the longitudinal dynamics of a twin-jet transport aircraft is presented. The controller is partitioned into a slow-time-scale and a fast-time scale to simplify its design. Three types of controllers are developed: airspeed/climb rate, groundspeed/climb rate, and throttle/climb rate. For microburst encounters during approach to landing, it is found that a combination of airspeed and groundspeed regulation is quite effective for controlling the flight path to touchdown. Regulation of groundspeed to a nominal value in the performance-increasing region of the microburst prevents an inadvertent reduction in thrust, while regulation of airspeed to a nominal value in the performance-decreasing area of the microburst prevents excessive airspeed loss. The throttle/climb rate controller is used for aborted-landing encounters. The combination of groundspeed and airspeed control is used until the decision is made to abort the landing, at which point maximum throttle and a specified positive climb rate are commanded.

Nomenclature

D	Drag
E_s	Specific Energy
F	Nondimensional wind shear hazard index
g	Acceleration due to gravity
h	Altitude
I_{yy}	Moment of Inertia about body y-axis
L	Lift
m	mass
M	Pitching Moment
q	Pitch rate
r	Rate of climb
R	Radius of downdraft column
s	Laplace variable
t	Time
T	Engine Thrust
$\mathbf{u}$	Aircraft control vector
U_{max}	Maximum horizontal wind speed
V_a	Airspeed
V_i	Groundspeed
w_x	Wind component along the x-axis
w_h	Wind component along the h-axis
W	Weight
x	Distance along x-axis
$\mathbf{x}$	Aircraft state vector
$\mathbf{y}$	Control system command vector
z_{max}	Altitude of maximum outflow
α	Angle of attack
γ	Flight Path Angle
δ_E	Elevator deflection
δ_T	Throttle setting
Δx	Range from core
θ	Pitch Attitude

Superscripts

$\dot{( )}$ Time derivative

Subscripts

a, A Air-mass referenced quantity
c Commanded value
i, I Inertially-referenced quantity

Introduction

Severe low-altitude wind variability represents an infrequent but significant hazard to aircraft taking off or landing. During the period from 1964 to 1985, *microburst wind shear* was a contributing factor in at least 26 civil aviation accidents involving nearly 500 fatalities and over 200 injuries [1]. A microburst is a strong localized downdraft that strikes the ground, creating winds that diverge radially from the impact point. The effects of microburst wind shear on airplane dynamics have only been recently understood in detail, and it has been found that effective recovery from inadvertent encounters may require counterintuitive piloting techniques [2].

The aviation community has initiated an extensive research effort to solve the wind shear problem. The Federal Aviation Administration (FAA) and the National Aeronautics and Space Administration have established an integrated program to address the wind shear problem through focused research and development programs [3,4]. The FAA's *Wind Shear Training Aid* [5] recommends that on recognizing an encounter with severe wind shear, the pilot should command maximum thrust and rotate the aircraft to an initial target pitch angle of 15°. This pitch target was identified through rigorous analyses using full six-degree-of-freedom flight simulators and wind models representative of actual accident cases [6].

Optimal trajectory analysis (OTA) has been used to identify the limits of aircraft performance in wind shear and to determine the control strategies required to achieve such performance [7-12]. Computation of these trajectories requires global knowledge of the flow field. Since this is not possible in practice, OTA results are not immediately useful for real-time aircraft control. Consequently, feedback control laws employing local wind-field knowledge have been developed for near-optimal flight control [13-15].

The goal of this research is to bridge the gap between the performance achieved using OTA and that attainable using feedback control based on local (and possibly forward-look) wind field knowledge. In a recent paper [16] we presented an optimization study for jet-transport encounters with microburst wind shear on final approach. The objective was to execute an escape maneuver that maintained safe ground clearance and an adequate stall margin during the climb-out. A quadratic cost function penalizing deviations in climb rate from a positive nominal value and elevator deflection rate produced qualitatively good escape trajectories. A minimum airspeed constraint prevented excessive airspeed loss in severe microbursts. While the results provided a qualitative picture of the nature of optimal control in a microburst, they were not immediately useful for real-time use. This study was thus undertaken to develop control logic that approximated the performance realized in the optimal trajectories. This paper addresses the control issue; that is, given a flight path and airspeed or groundspeed command in a windshear environment, a control law that generates the appropriate throttle and elevator commands is developed. The controller is designed using *partial dynamic inversion* [17-23]. A combination of groundspeed, airspeed, and climb-rate control [24] produced qualitatively reasonable trajectories in microburst encounters on final approach.

---

* Graduate Research Assistant
** Professor
Presented at the 1993 American Control Conference, June 2-4, 1993, San Francisco, CA.

Effect of Wind Shear on Airplane Dynamics

Aircraft Model and Equations of Motion

A three degree-of-freedom model of a twin-jet transport aircraft is used for this study. The aircraft has a gross weight of 85,000 lb and maximum takeoff thrust of 24,000 lb. Its aerodynamic coefficients are complex nonlinear functions of altitude, Mach number, incidence angles, rotation rates, control deflections, configuration changes (such as gear and flap deflection), and ground proximity. Effects of wind shear on aircraft motion and aerodynamics are modeled using the technique described in [25, 26]. The relevant reference frames used to describe the aircraft's position, orientation, and velocity are presented in Fig. 1. Flight is assumed to take place in a vertical plane over a flat Earth, and a coordinate system fixed to the ground is defined as the inertial reference frame. On the basis of these assumptions, the equations of motion are:

$$\dot{x} = V_a \cos\gamma_a + w_x \quad (1)$$

$$\dot{h} = V_a \sin\gamma_a + w_h \quad (2)$$

$$\dot{V}_a = \frac{T}{m}\cos\alpha_a - \frac{D}{m} - g\sin\gamma_a - \dot{w}_x\cos\gamma_a - \dot{w}_h\sin\gamma_a \quad (3)$$

$$V_a\dot{\gamma}_a = \frac{T}{m}\sin\alpha_a + \frac{L}{m} - g\cos\gamma_a - \dot{w}_h\cos\gamma_a + \dot{w}_x\sin\gamma_a \quad (4)$$

$$\dot{\alpha}_a = q - \dot{\gamma}_a \quad (5)$$

$$I_{yy}\dot{q} = M \quad (6)$$

The effect of wind shear on airplane energy state can be described compactly. First define the specific energy (energy per unit weight) as the sum of air-mass relative kinetic energy and inertial potential energy:

$$E_s = \frac{V^2}{2g} + h \quad (7)$$

Differentiating this expression and substituting from eqs. 1-3,

$$\dot{E}_s = V_a\left(\frac{T\cos\alpha_a - D}{W} - \frac{\dot{w}_x}{g}\cos\gamma_a - \frac{\dot{w}_h}{g}\sin\gamma_a + \frac{w_h}{V_a}\right) \quad (8)$$

The first term is recognizable as the airplane's specific excess power. The three wind terms describe wind shear impact on airplane energy state, and they may be combined into a single scalar quantity called the "F-Factor," [3] as follows:

$$F = \frac{\dot{w}_x}{g}\cos\gamma_a + \frac{\dot{w}_h}{g}\sin\gamma_a - \frac{w_h}{V_a} \quad (9)$$

The vertical shear term is typically quite small and often neglected. The effect of wind shear on airplane performance is thus expressed as an effective reduction in available specific excess power due to horizontal and vertical shears and downdrafts. Regions where F is negative are considered to be *performance-increasing* shears, while regions where F is positive are *performance-descreasing*. F values of more than 0.15 cancel the climb gradient capability of most jet transports.

The equations of motion can be expressed using inertial-axis variables as well. First define

$$\Delta\alpha = \alpha_i - \alpha_a \quad (10)$$

Then

$$\dot{x} = V_i\cos\gamma_i \quad (11)$$

$$\dot{h} = V_i\sin\gamma_i \quad (12)$$

$$\dot{V}_i = \frac{T}{m}\cos\alpha_i - \frac{D}{m}\cos(\Delta\alpha) - \frac{L}{m}\sin(\Delta\alpha) - g\sin\gamma_i \quad (13)$$

$$V_i\dot{\gamma}_i = \frac{T}{m}\sin\alpha_i + \frac{L}{m}\cos(\Delta\alpha) - \frac{D}{m}\sin(\Delta\alpha) - g\cos\gamma_i \quad (14)$$

$$\dot{\alpha}_i = q - \dot{\gamma}_i \quad (15)$$

Lift, drag, pitching moment and thrust are expressed as,

$$L = \bar{q}S_{ref}C_L \quad (16)$$

$$D = \bar{q}S_{ref}C_D \quad (17)$$

$$T = T_{max}(V_a)\delta_T \qquad 0 \le \delta_T \le 1 \quad (18)$$

$$M = \bar{q}S_{ref}\bar{c}C_M \quad (19)$$

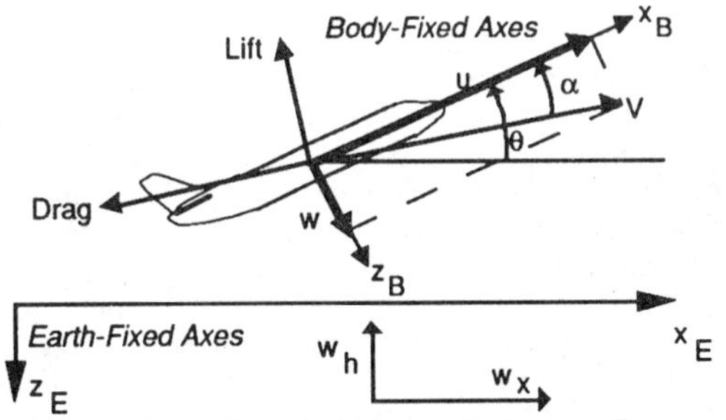

Figure 1. Coordinate System and Reference Frames.

The wind components and spatial gradients used in the equations of motion are obtained from the Oseguera-Bowles downburst model [27]. This analytic time-invariant model represents an axisymmetric stagnation point flow, and it permits simulation of microbursts of varying size and strength through specification of the radius of the downdraft column, the maximum outflow, and the altitude of maximum outflow.

Nonlinear Flight Control

This description of nonlinear control methods is necessarily brief. More complete treatments can be found in [28,29]. The following derivation is from [30]. Given a system of the form,

$$\dot{\mathbf{x}} = \mathbf{f}(\mathbf{x}) + \mathbf{G}(\mathbf{x})\mathbf{u} \quad (20)$$

where $\mathbf{x}$ is n x 1 and $\mathbf{u}$ is m x 1, we define an m-dimensional output vector,

$$\mathbf{y} = \mathbf{H}(\mathbf{x}) \quad (21)$$

It is possible to define a nonlinear feedback control law that provides output decoupling of the elements of $\mathbf{y}$ or their derivatives such that $\mathbf{y}^{(d)} = \mathbf{v}$. The new control input $\mathbf{v}$ can be chosen to place the system poles in desired locations (for example, to achieve desired specifications on response overshoot and settling time). The vector $\mathbf{y}^{(d)}$ is expressed as,

$$\mathbf{y}^{(d)} = \mathbf{f}^*(\mathbf{x}) + \mathbf{G}^*(\mathbf{x})\mathbf{u} = \mathbf{v} \quad (22)$$

and d is the *relative degree of differentiation* required to identify a direct control effect on each element of the output vector. The inverse control law then takes the form,

$$\mathbf{u} = [\mathbf{G}^*(\mathbf{x})]^{-1}[\mathbf{v} - \mathbf{f}^*(\mathbf{x})] \quad (23)$$

and the closed-loop dynamics of the system take the form,

$$\dot{\mathbf{x}} = \mathbf{f}(\mathbf{x}) + \mathbf{G}(\mathbf{x})[\mathbf{G}^*(\mathbf{x})]^{-1}[\mathbf{v} - \mathbf{f}^*(\mathbf{x})] \quad (24)$$

While the expression of the inverse control law appears simple, its implementation can be quite complex. Evaluation of the functions $\mathbf{f}^*(\mathbf{x})$ and $\mathbf{G}^*(\mathbf{x})$ requires that a full, d-differentiable model of the aircraft dynamics be included in the control system. The controller can be simplified if the system can be partitioned into slow and fast-time-scale subsystems [31]. The separation of the dynamics into fast and slow time-scales is a natural consequence of the underlying physics. For the aircraft problem, it is assumed that the pitch rate evolves faster than the flight path and velocity. This is consistent with the time-scale separation between the phugoid and short-period modes of an aircraft's longitudinal dynamics [32]. This technique has been applied to the flight control problem [19-23]. In the present study, the effects of wind shear are explicitly considered in the inversion. The structure of the inverse control law is now derived.

Controller Design

Inertial Speed/Climb Rate Control Mode

The objective is to control climb rate and inertial speed by partially inverting the aircraft dynamical equations. The output vector is,

$$\mathbf{y}(t) = \begin{bmatrix} \dot{h}(t) \\ V_i(t) \end{bmatrix} \quad (25)$$

The controller is partitioned into an outer loop and an inner loop. The control commands generated by the outer loop are pitch rate q_c and commanded engine thrust T_c. Although aircraft lift does depend on δ_E, the effect is small and is not a primary path of aerodynamic control. It has been shown [33] that inverse control laws exploiting these weak aerodynamic effects either generate unreasonably large control deflections in response to small state perturbations, or destabilize the system by canceling the nonlinear equivalent of non-minimum phase transmission zeros. Thus for the present design, elevator contribution to lift is included when L is calculated in the simulation, but the controller does not exploit the effect.

The engine dynamics are modeled as a first-order lag:

$$\dot{T} = \frac{1}{\tau}(T_c - T) \tag{26}$$

The time constant τ is set to 2 sec. The inverse controller is developed by differentiating eq. 25 until the control inputs T_c and q_c appear linearly. Two differentiations are required. Although lift and drag are in principle dependent on q, its contribution is very small and an inverse controller that exploits this unsteady aerodynamic effect would command very large pitch rates in response to small state perturbations. Hence for the purposes of the inversion, lift and drag are not considered to be functions of pitch rate. When lift and drag are calculated for simulation, pitch rate effects are included. However, the inverse controller is derived as though pitch rate has no effect on lift or drag. In order to complete the inversion, time-rate-of-change of lift and drag are expressed as,

$$\dot{L} \equiv E_1 + E_2 q_c \tag{27}$$

$$\dot{D} \equiv F_1 + F_2 q_c \tag{28}$$

The pitch rate q_c is now treated as a control input. The expressions for E_1 and E_2 are developed from the aircraft aerodynamic coefficients. Differentiating eq. 25 twice and substituting from eqs. 10-15 one obtains,

$$\ddot{\mathbf{y}} = \mathbf{f}_I^* + \mathbf{G}_I^* \mathbf{u} = \mathbf{v} \tag{29}$$

where

$$\mathbf{f}_I^* = \begin{bmatrix} f_1 \\ f_2 \end{bmatrix} \quad \mathbf{G}_I^* = \begin{bmatrix} g_{11} & g_{12} \\ g_{21} & g_{22} \end{bmatrix} \quad \mathbf{u} = \begin{bmatrix} T_c \\ q_c \end{bmatrix} \quad \mathbf{v} = \begin{bmatrix} v_1 \\ v_2 \end{bmatrix} \tag{30}$$

The f_i and g_{ij} are determined by differentiating the original motion equations. Rearranging eq. 29,

$$\mathbf{u} = \left[\mathbf{G}_I^*\right]^{-1}(\mathbf{v} - \mathbf{f}_I^*) \tag{31}$$

It remains to determine the nature of the new control input $\mathbf{v}$ and the means by which the desired pitch rate q_c is achieved.

Desired Outer-Loop Dynamics

The form of the control inputs v_1 and v_2 must be specified. Presently, proportional-derivative control is used. Thus,

$$\ddot{h}(t) = v_1 = k_1\left[\dot{h}_{com}(t) - \dot{h}(t)\right] - k_2\ddot{h}(t) \tag{32}$$

$$\ddot{V}_i(t) = v_2 = k_3\left[V_{i_{com}}(t) - V_i(t)\right] - k_4\dot{V}_i(t) \tag{33}$$

where $\dot{h}_{com}$ and V_{com} are the commanded altitude rate and inertial speed, respectively. Now define r(t) as follows:

$$r(t) \equiv \dot{h}(t) \tag{34}$$

Substituting eq. 34 into eq. 32, and taking the Laplace transforms of eqs. 32 and 33, one obtains,

$$r(s) = \frac{k_1}{s^2 + k_2 s + k_1} r_{com}(s) \tag{35}$$

$$V_i(s) = \frac{k_3}{s^2 + k_4 s + k_3} V_{i_{com}}(s) \tag{36}$$

By choosing the gains k_i appropriately, the outer-loop response of the aircraft can be shaped as desired. The nonlinear dynamics of the aircraft have thus been transformed into those of a pair of second-order linear systems using the technique described here. The method used to achieve the commanded pitch rate q_c is now described.

Inner-Loop Dynamics

The inner-loop control law generates the pitch rate q_c commanded by the outer-loop controller. We define

$$\Delta q(t) \equiv q(t) - q_c(t) \tag{37}$$

The inner-loop controller regulates Δq to zero. For the aircraft to respond to speed or climb-rate commands with the dynamics of eqs. 35 and 36, the inner-loop controller must generate the required pitch rate on a time-scale much shorter than that of the outer-loop dynamics. As a practical matter, the inner-loop dynamics should be chosen to have a time constant that is at least 3 to 5 times faster than the outer loop. The inner-loop dynamics take the form,

$$\Delta\dot{q} = v_3 = -k_5 \Delta q \tag{38}$$

If the time-scales of the two controllers are sufficiently separated, on the inner-loop time scale, $\dot{q}_c \approx 0$. Assuming this approximation to be an equality,

$$\dot{q} + k_5 q = k_5 q_c \tag{39}$$

Taking the Laplace transform of this expression,

$$q(s) = \frac{k_5}{s + k_5} q_c(s) \tag{40}$$

The constant k_5 can be chosen to achieve a sufficiently fast response. The validity of this technique depends on adequate time-scale separation between the inner- and outer-loop dynamics [34]. Elevator bandwidth limits place a constraint on the time constant achievable in eq. 40. The necessary elevator deflection is calculated by inverting the pitch-rate dynamics. From eqs. 6 and 19,

$$\dot{q} = \frac{\bar{q} S_{ref} \bar{c}}{I_{yy}} C_M \tag{41}$$

The pitching moment can be written as

$$C_M = C_{M_o} + C_{M_{\delta_E}} \delta_E \tag{42}$$

where C_{M_o} consists of several terms dependent on altitude, mach number, lift coefficient, engine thrust, angle of attack, angle of attack rate, and pitch rate. Combining eqs. 38, 41 and 42,

$$\delta_E = \frac{1}{C_{M_{\delta_E}}}\left(\frac{I_{yy} v_3}{\bar{q} S_{ref} \bar{c}} - C_{M_o}\right) \tag{43}$$

The inertial speed/climb rate controller development is thus complete. The airspeed/climb rate controller is now presented.

Airspeed/Climb Rate Control Mode

In this mode, the objective is to regulate airspeed and climb rate about nominal values. The output vector is

$$\mathbf{y}(t) = \begin{bmatrix} \dot{h}(t) \\ V_a(t) \end{bmatrix} \tag{44}$$

As before, the output is differentiated twice. We thus obtain,

$$\ddot{\mathbf{y}} = \mathbf{f}_A^* + \mathbf{G}_A^* \mathbf{u} = \mathbf{v} \tag{45}$$

where

$$\mathbf{f}_A^* = \begin{bmatrix} a_1 \\ a_2 \end{bmatrix} \quad \mathbf{G}_A^* = \begin{bmatrix} b_{11} & b_{12} \\ b_{21} & b_{22} \end{bmatrix} \quad \mathbf{u} = \begin{bmatrix} T_c \\ q_c \end{bmatrix} \quad \mathbf{v} = \begin{bmatrix} v_4 \\ v_5 \end{bmatrix} \tag{46}$$

so that

$$\mathbf{u} = \left[\mathbf{G}_A^*\right]^{-1}(\mathbf{v} - \mathbf{f}_A^*) \tag{47}$$

Several wind component time-derivatives are needed in the calculation of a_2. They are computed using spatial derivatives obtained directly from the Oseguera-Bowles model. In practice, it would be necessary to estimate the wind derivatives from available inertial and air-data measurements. For this preliminary study, it is assumed that they are known exactly.

The form of the outer-loop dynamics of the airspeed/climb rate controller is identical to that of the inertial speed/climb rate controller and is not described further. The same inner-loop dynamics are used for both the groundspeed and airspeed controllers.

Control Issues in the Microburst Environment

In a classical microburst, the aircraft typically first encounters a performance-increasing headwind. If airspeed is regulated about a nominal value, a reduction in thrust would be commanded, leaving the aircraft in a precarious situation once the headwind is replaced by a performance-decreasing downdraft and tailwind. Therefore, airspeed should not be regulated blindly in a microburst. Inertial speed control, subject to a minimum airspeed constraint, might be desirable during a final approach in a microburst [35]. Control of inertial speed would prevent too high a touchdown velocity, while the minimum airspeed constraint would maintain an adequate stall margin in the convective wind shear environment. During takeoff or in an escape maneuver initiated on approach, airspeed control is a concern, since the airplane's ability to climb or maintain altitude depends on its speed with respect to the local air mass. A conservative strategy during an escape would be to command full throttle. The control law should be structured so that an inadvertent reduction in thrust is not commanded in the performance-increasing area of the microburst. One possible solution is to regulate the minimum of airspeed and groundspeed to a nominal value [24], as discussed below. In an escape maneuver, full throttle and a desired climb rate can be commanded, so that the aircraft's full performance capability is utilized as soon as possible.

Groundspeed/Airspeed Control Law

In [24], Park and Psiaki present a throttle control law that regulates the minimum of airspeed and groundspeed to a nominal value in a microburst environment. The same nominal value was set for both airspeed and groundspeed, and a thrust feedback loop was designed to keep the minimum of the two speeds at this nominal value. In still air, airspeed and groundspeed are identical, and the control law behaves like an airspeed controller. In the performance-increasing area of the microburst, groundspeed is less than airspeed, and a reduction in thrust is not commanded. In the tailwind area, airspeed is the minimum of the two speeds, and thrust is increased while the aircraft is in a performance-decreasing shear. This control structure is extended here into a throttle/pitch control law for flight path tracking in microburst wind shear.

The controller structure is developed by rewriting eqs. 29 and 45 with slightly different notation:

$$\ddot{\mathbf{y}}_I = \mathbf{f}_I^* + \mathbf{G}_I^* \mathbf{u}_I = \mathbf{v}_I \quad (48)$$

$$\ddot{\mathbf{y}}_A = \mathbf{f}_A^* + \mathbf{G}_A^* \mathbf{u}_A = \mathbf{v}_A \quad (49)$$

The same nominal value is used for the commanded airspeed and groundspeed for the purposes of calculating the elements of $\mathbf{v}_I$ and $\mathbf{v}_A$. During a microburst encounter, the aircraft responds with the dynamics of either eq. 48 or eq. 49, depending on the relative magnitude of T_{c_I} and T_{c_A}. If $T_{c_I} > T_{c_A}$ then $T_c = T_{c_I}$ and $q_c = q_{c_I}$. Conversely if $T_{c_A} > T_{c_I}$ then $T_c = T_{c_A}$ and $q_c = q_{c_A}$. In other words, the throttle setting and commanded pitch rate depend on the relative magnitude of the thrust commands generated by the airspeed/climb-rate controller and the groundspeed/climb-rate controller.

In the event of throttle saturation, complete output variable independence cannot be maintained. Saturation injects discontinuities into the system, and the resultant response may not look anything like the desired dynamics [33]. However, partial independence can be maintained by dropping one of the comand variables from the command set, and including the saturation effect into the calculation of the inverse dynamics of the remaining command variable [18]. Presently, the controller is configured to maintain climb rate tracking in the event of throttle saturation. Full command-variable independence is recovered once the commanded thrust drops below the maximum available.

During an escape maneuver, the command vector is

$$\mathbf{y}_{escape}(t) = \begin{bmatrix} T(t) \\ \dot{h}(t) \end{bmatrix} \quad (50)$$

This output vector is slightly different than the previous two, since its components are of different order. No number of differentations of the first element will bring out a dependence on q. It is differentiated once to make T_c appear linearly. The second element is differentiated twice as before. During an escape maneuver, full throttle and a desired climb rate are commanded.

Controller Evaluation

The groundspeed/airspeed control law is evaluated during a microburst encounter on approach to landing. The aircraft is required to track a reference climb rate through the encounter. The microburst had a core radius of 3790 ft, a maximum horizontal wind speed of 46 ft/sec, and a maximum outflow altitude of 109 ft. The aircraft was initialized on the glide slope 9400 ft from the core, at an altitude of 985 ft with an airspeed of 253 ft/sec (150 kt). The initial groundspeed was 247 ft/sec, and this was the nominal airspeed and groundspeed value used in the control law. Figure 2 presents altitude and F-Factor vs. Range from core. It can be seen that the aircraft successfully tracks the target climb rate through the encounter. The peak F-Factor experienced by the aircraft is about 0.14, so this is a moderately strong microburst. Most reactive wind shear detection systems trigger an alert when the estimated F-Factor exceeds 0.1. Figure 3 presents airspeed, groundspeed and throttle setting vs. range. The aircraft tracks the reference groundspeed until $\Delta x \approx$ -1000 ft, at which it switches over to airspeed/climb-rate tracking. It is able to do so without saturating the throttle.

The recovery control logic was evaluated in a more severe microburst. It had a core radius of 3000 ft, a maximum horizontal wind speed of 46 ft/sec, and a maximum outflow velocity of 60 ft/sec, and a maximum outflow altitude of 150 ft. The aircraft was initialized on the glide slope at an altitude of 765 ft, 7500 ft from the core. The reference groundspeed was 253 ft/sec. Figure 4 presents altitude and F-Factor vs. range. The aircraft tracked the approach climb rate until F exceeded 0.1, at which point a 5 ft/sec recovery climb rate was

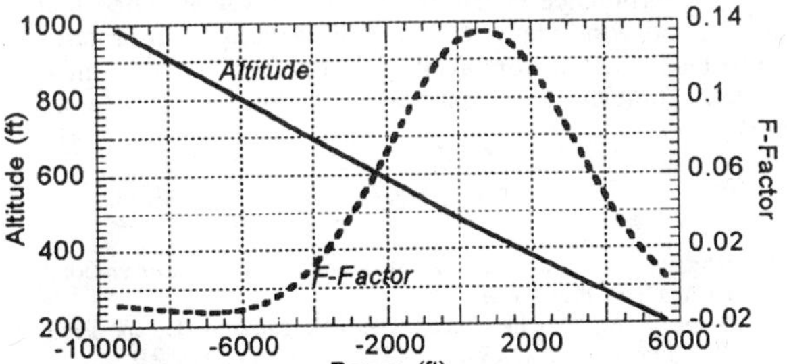

Figure 2. Altitude and F-Factor vs. Range - Landing Case.

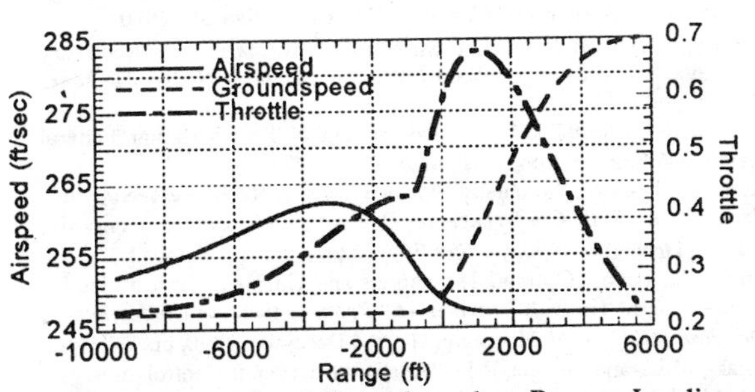

Figure 3. Airspeed and Groundspeed vs. Range - Landing Case.

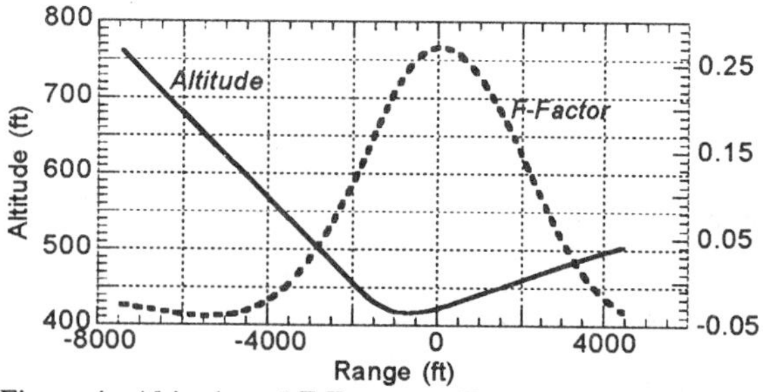

Figure 4. Altitude and F-Factor vs. Range - Aborted Landing.

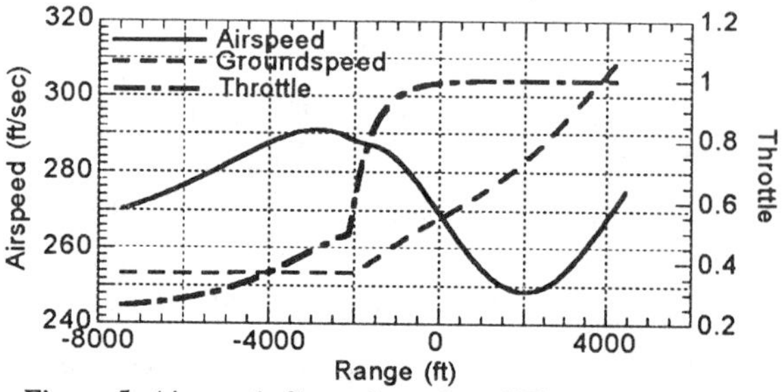

Figure 5. Airspeed, Groundspeed, and Throttle vs. Range - Aborted Landing.

commanded. From the latter part of the trajectory, it is apparent that the aircraft was able to track the target climb rate through the shear. The peak F experienced by the aircraft was about 0.27, which exceeds the maximum climb-gradient capability of most jet transports. As such, this was a quite severe microburst.

Conclusions

A windshear flight control law based on partial inversion of longitudinal aircraft dynamics has been presented. The approach control logic used a combination of groundspeed/airspeed and climb-rate control. The combination of groundspeed and airspeed control was chosen for its ability to overcome the limitations of either airspeed or groundspeed control. Climb-rate following was maintained even in the event of throttle saturation. During aborted-landing encounters, the command variables were throttle setting and climb rate.

Future work will assess the robustness of the controller to uncertainty in the aerodynamic model. The performance of the controller in turbulence is also uncertain. It was assumed that the aircraft and wind states were known exactly -- in practice they must be estimated from available inertial and air-data measurements. The estimation issue will be addressed in a future paper.

References

1. Townsend, J., "Low-Altitude Wind Shear and Its Hazard to Aviation," National Academy Press, Washington, 1983.
2. Hinton, David A., "Flight Management Strategies for Escape From Microburst Encounters," NASA TM 4057, Washington D.C., 1988.
3. Bowles, Roland L., "Reducing Windshear Risk Through Airborne Systems Technology," *Presented at the 17th Congress of the Intl. Council of the Aeronautical Sciences*, Stockholm, Sweden, 1990.
4. Hinton, David A., "Piloted-Simulation Evaluation of Recovery Guidance for Microburst Wind Shear Encounters," NASA TP 2886, Washington D.C., 1989.
5. *Windshear Training Aid*, U.S. Department of Transportation, Federal Aviation Administration, Washington D.C., 1987.
6. Kupcis, Edgars A., "Manually Flown Windshear Recovery Technique," *Proc. of the 29th Conference on Decision and Control*, Honolulu, Hawaii, December 1990, pp. 758-759.
7. Miele, A., et al., "Optimal Trajectories and Guidance Trajectories for Aircraft Flight Through Windshears," *Proc. of the 29th Conference on Decision and Control*, Honolulu, Hawaii, December 1990, pp. 737-746.
8. Psiaki, M.L., and Stengel, R.F., "Analysis of Aircraft Control Strategies for Microburst Encounter," *Journal of Guidance, Control, and Dynamics*, Vol. 8, No. 5, Sept.-Oct. 1985, pp. 553-559.
9. Psiaki, Mark L., "Control of Flight Through Microburst Wind Shear Using Deterministic Trajectory Optimization," Ph.D. Thesis, Princeton University, Report No. 1787-T, 1987.
10. Psiaki, M.L., and Stengel, R.F., "Optimal Aircraft Performance During Microburst Encounter," *Journal of Guidance, Control, and Dynamics*, Vol. 14, No. 2, March-April 1991, pp. 440-446.
11. Zhao, Y., and Bryson, A.E., "Optimal Paths Through Downbursts," *Journal of Guidance, Control, and Dynamics*, Vol. 13, No. 5, Sept.-Oct. 1990, pp. 813-818.
12. Mulgund, S.S., and Stengel, R.F., "Target Pitch Angle for the Microburst Escape Maneuver," AIAA Paper 92-0730, *Presented at the 30th Aerospace Sciences Meeting*, Reno, NV, Jan. 1992. (Also to appear in the *Journal of Aircraft*)
13. Zhao, Y., and Bryson, A.E., "Control of an Aircraft in Downbursts," *Journal of Guidance, Control, and Dynamics*, Vol.13, No.5, Sept.-Oct. 1990, p. 819.
14. Miele, A., et al., "Guidance Strategies for Near-Optimum Takeoff Performance in Wind Shear," *Journal of Optimization Theory and Applications*, Vol, 50, No. 1, July 1986.
15. Miele, A., et al., "Optimization and Gamma/Theta Guidance of Flight Trajectories in a Windshear," *Presented at the 15th ICAS Congress*, London, Sept. 1986.
16. Mulgund, S.S., and Stengel, R.F., "Optimal Recovery from Microburst Wind Shear," AIAA Paper 92-4338, *Proc. of the 1992 Atmospheric Flight Mechanics Conference*, Hilton Head, SC, Aug. 1992. *(*Also to appear in the *Journal of Guidance, Control, and Dynamics)*
17. Morton, B.G., Elgersma, M.R., et al, "Nonlinear Flying Quality Parameters Based on Dynamic Inversion," AFWAL-TR-87-3079, Honeywell Systems and Research Center, Minneapolis, MN, Oct. 1987.
18. Lane, Stephen, and Stengel, R.F., "Flight Control Using Non-linear Inverse Dynamics," *Automatica*, Vol. 24, No. 4, pp. 471-483, 1988.
19. Menon, P.K.A., et al, "Nonlinear Flight Test Controllers for Aircraft," *Journal of Guidance*, Vol. 10, No. 1, Jan-Feb 1987.
20. Menon, P.K.A., et al, "A Two-Time-Scale Autopilot for High Performance Aircraft," *Presented at the 1991 AIAA Guidance, Navigation, and Control Conference*, New Orleans, Aug. 1991.
21. Meyer, G., and Cicolani, L., "Application of Nonlinear System Inverses to Automatic Flight Control Designs -- System Concepts and Flight Evaluations", in *Theory and Application of Optimal Control in Aerospace Systems*, AGARD -- AG251, pp. 10.1-10.29.
22. Hauser, J., Sastry, S., and Meyer, G., "Nonlinear Control Design for Slightly Non-minimum Phase Systems: Application to V/STOL Aircraft," *Presented at the IFAC Conference NOLCOS '89*, Capri, Italy, June 1989.
23. Elgersma, M., and Morton, B., "Partial Inversion of Noninvertible Nonlinear Aircraft Models," Honeywell Systems Research Center, Minneapolis, MN, Aug. 1989.
24. Psiaki, M., and Park, K., "Thrust Laws for Microburst Wind Shear Penetration," Journal of Guidance, Control, and Dynamics, Vol. 15, No. 4, July-Aug. 1992.
25. Frost, W., and Bowles, R., "Wind Shear Terms in the Equations of Aircraft Motion," *J. of Aircraft*, Vol.21, No.11, Nov.1984, pp.866-872.
26. Stengel, R.F., *Course Notes for MAE 566: Aircraft Dynamics*, Princeton University, Princeton, NJ, Jan. 1990.
27. Oseguera, R.M., and Bowles, R.L., "A Simple, Analytic 3-Dimensional Downburst Model based on Boundary Layer Stagnation Flow," NASA TM 100632, Washington D.C., 1988.
28. Singh, S.N., and Rugh, W.J., "Decoupling in a Class of Nonlinear Systems by State Feedback," *ASME J. Dyn. Syst. Meas. Cont.*, Series G, Vol. 94, No. 1972, pp. 323-329.
29. Isidori, A., *Nonlinear Control Systems*, Springer-Verlag, Berlin, 1989.
30. Stengel, R.F., "Toward Intelligent Flight Control," *Presented at the NATO-AGARD Workshop on Stability in Aerospace Systems*, Toulouse, France, June 23-26, 1992.
31. Chow, J. and Kokotovic, P., "Two-Time-Scale Feedback Design of a Class of Nonlinear Systems," *IEEE Transactions on Automatic Control*, Vol. AC-23, No. 3, June 1978.
32. Etkin, B., *Dynamics of Atmospheric Flight*, Wiley, New York, 1972.
33. Lane, Stephen, "Theory and Development of Adaptive Flight Control Systems Using Nonlinear Inverse Dynamics," Ph.D. Thesis, Princeton University, Report No. 1806-T, 1988.
34. Van Buren, M.A., and Mease, K.D., "Aerospace Plane Guidance Using Time-Scale Decomposition: A Geometric Approach," *Proc. of the 1991 AIAA Guidance, Navigation, and Control Conf.*, Vol. 1, pp. 370-379.
35. Zhao, Y., and Bryson, A.E., "Approach Guidance in a Downburst," *J. of Guidance, Control, and Dynamics*, Vol.15, No.4, July-Aug. 1992.

Proceedings of the
American Control Conference
San Francisco, California • June 1993

Analysis and Resonance Stabilization of Bifurcation Phenomena in Aircraft Flight

Mark A. Pinsky and Bill Essary
Dept. of Mathematics, University of Nevada, Reno
Reno, Nevada 89557

Abstract

This paper addresses a theoretical framework for a unified methodology which allows analysis of nonlinear stability and efficient control of high-dimensional nonlinear plants modeling aircraft flight. It is shown that analysis of nonlinear transition phenomena (bifurcations) is central to revealing the limitation of robust control (i.e., an accurate estimate of the basin of stability). Omitting transition behavior causes over control and provides a very local stabilization. Analysis and control of bifurcations of aircraft flight are given in the spirit of the generalized normal forms method which provides one with the nonreduceable system preserving stability characteristics of the initial plant. Stabilization of a plants bifurcations is then given in terms of the resonance control methodology.

1. Introduction

A modern aircraft is designed to attain high speed and maneuverability. As an aircraft becomes faster and more maneuverable, however, it becomes more difficult to control at or near the extrema of the flight envelope. Previous research concentrated primarily on analysis/control of aircraft flight at a high angle of attack. The phenomena of a high incident flight such as stall, spin entry, flat and steep spin, nose slice and wing rock have been interpreted as instability of steady state solutions of governing nonlinear dynamic equations. Observed instabilities were described in terms of elementary bifurcations in a number of publications (Abed and Lee, 1989, 1990, Adams, 1972, Carroll and Mehra, 1982, Cochran and Ho, 1983, Gerrard and Jordan, 1979, Kwatny, et al., 1990, Mehra, et al., 1977, and Young, et al., 1989) . In spite of the fact that different types of steady state and Hopf bifurcations in aircraft flight dynamics have been observed, present knowledge in this field is far from providing a comprehensive understanding of such and more complex phenomena.

One of the main objectives of dynamical analysis of aircraft is to facilitate design of a stabilizing control. Several techniques using feedback linearization were introduced for design of a stabilizing robust control (Banks, 1988, Isidori, 1985, and Nijmeijer and van der Schaft, 1990) for nonlinear systems. In other words, one generates an additional torque in order to simplify the mathematical description of the system. After linearization another control loop is designed to stabilize the linear system.

The past two decades have demonstrated that nonlinear dynamics are richer and more complex than linear ones (Arnold, 1983, Guckenheimer and Holmes, 1983). In fact, just local bifurcation behavior cannot be captured by a linear system. In many important practical cases stability can be characterized from the local point of view. Notice that all known types of aircraft instabilities can be described in terms of the local bifurcations of known steady state solutions. Thus in order to investigate and stabilize an aircraft's instabilities we concentrate on designing an efficient feedback for the close to critical nonlinear systems with a linear part having eigen-values on or close to the imaginary axis.

Design of stabilizing feedback control for the critical dynamical systems (faced with bifurcations) has been studied by several authors. Existence of smooth feedback which asymptotically stabilizes an equilibrium point was studied by Brockett, 1983. His consideration rests on Lyapunov functions. Aeyels, 1984, 1985, 1986, studied the same problem for a critical nonlinear system which exhibits Hopf bifurcation. His approach was based on the center manifold reduction to the standard Hopf bifurcation problem in two dimensions. Works of bifurcation control have been reported by Carroll and Mehra, 1982, Kwatny, et al., 1990, and Mehra, et al., 1977. Abed and Fu, 1986, 1987, obtain sufficient conditions for local smooth feedback stabilization in the critical cases when the linearized system has either a pair of pure imaginary eigen-values or a single zero eigen-value.

In the last approach the design of stabilizing feedback control rests on the closed form first order approximation of transition behavior of a plant which undergoes either Hopf or elementary stationary bifurcations. In fact, the closed form approximation of bifurcation phenomena is available only in cases of elementary bifurcations and ensures relatively local stabilization.

While certain phenomena have been analyzed in isolation, there exists a clear need for a unified approach in order to analyze systematically an aircraft's unstable behavior. A suitable methodology would provide detection, qualitative classification, and quantitative confirmation of unstable aircraft behavior and would develop guidelines for stabilizing them.

2. The Resonance Normal Forms Concept

We are concerned with developing an effective generic method for analysis of the local bifurcations of a broad class of multidimensional and multiparametric dynamical systems (such as aircraft dynamical models). Let us begin a short comparative analysis of known approaches to this subject.

A governing equation in the local nonlinear dynamics can be specified in the following form:

$$\dot{x} = A(\mu)x + \varepsilon f(x,t,\mu,\varepsilon) \tag{1}$$

where $x \in R^n$ is a vector of state variables, $0 < \varepsilon < 1$ is a small parameter which corresponds to a size of a chosen neighborhood of equilibrium, A is an n x n matrix with simple spectrum which is represented in the diagonal form, $f = \{f_1, ..., f_n\}$, $\mu \in R^m$ is a vector of control parameters. Transition of stability of an equilibrium occurs if eigen-values of A cross the imaginary axis. In such critical cases the dominant linear terms compensate each other and the transition behavior is determined by small nonlinear terms. It is clear that in critical cases feedback linearization is not an adequate approach.

Let us observe the three basic techniques that have been used in order to approximate solutions of (1). The most primitive way to improve the linear approximation of (1) is to iterate solutions of the linearized equation successfully. The iterations work out easily for a very broad class of dynamical systems but lead to rapidly divergent series in all practically interesting situations. Divergence is an intrinsic property of such kinds of series which occurs due to so called resonance components in f.

The averaging method is considered as one of the deepest techniques for local nonlinear analysis. However, the use of averaging requires preliminary transformation of an initial system to amplitude-phase variables and also becomes complicated in the case of bifurcations (multiple resonance) (Arnold, 1983, Guckenheimer and Holmes, 1983).

The most natural approach for analysis of (1) in the case of bifurcations is the Poincare normal forms method which has become an essential tool in modern qualitative bifurcation theory (Arnold, 1983). Notice that Poincare resonance nonlinear normal forms and linear normal forms via feedback linearization are absolutely distinct from each other. The Poincare method acts in the cases when $f(x=0,\cdot,\cdot,\cdot)=0$ and f is a power series. For such a system a normal forms method specifies the simplest canonical form which preserves the stability characteristics of an initial plant. The normal form is deduced from the original system by nonlinear change of variables adapted to the structure of the system. The normalized change of variables is addressed as a recursively defined power series which is poorly computed (Arnold, 1983). While the Poincare method has been used widely for topological classification of bifurcations, its practical applications are limited due to a lack of computability.

3. Generalized Normal Forms Method and Averaging Normal Forms

We briefly describe here a more general approach to finding normal forms which is computationally efficient and is applicable to a broader class of systems than established algorithms. Write an equation in the form:

$$\dot{x} = Ax + \varepsilon f(x,t,\varepsilon) \tag{2}$$

where f is a power series in x periodic with respect to t and A is as in (1). Note that we do not have to assume here that $f(0,t,\varepsilon) = 0$. As above we attempt to simplify (2) with the aid of a close to identity change of variables:

$$x = y + \varepsilon r(y,t,\varepsilon)$$

Suppose that in the new variables (2) takes the form:

$$\dot{y} = Ay + \varepsilon B(y,t,\varepsilon) \tag{3}$$

From (2) and (3) we get:

$$Ar - r_{,y}Ay - r_{,t} = -f(y+\varepsilon r) + B + \varepsilon r_{,y}B \tag{4}$$

where $r_{,y}$ is the Jacobian with respect to y and $r_{,t}$ is a partial derivative of r with respect to t. We consider (4) as a system of partial differential equations with respect to r. We seek a particular solution of (4) satisfying an additional condition:

$$\|f\| \to 0 \Rightarrow \|r\| \to 0$$

where $\|\cdot\|$ is a certain norm of a vector valued function. In other words, we are looking for a particular solution such that the norm of r tends to zero if the norm of f tends to zero also. For small ε one can try to approximate the solution of (4) by iterations:

$$Ar_1 - r_{1,y}Ay - r_{1,t} = -f(y)$$
$$Ar_k - r_{k,y}Ay - r_{k,t} = -f(y+\varepsilon r_{k-1}) + B_k + \varepsilon r_{k-1,y}B_{k-1}, \quad k>1 \tag{5}$$

Note that (5) represents a set of linear partial differential equations with respect to r_k. Let us write a characteristic equation for (5) :

$$\dot r_1 = Ar_1 + f(y,t) - B_1 \tag{6}$$
$$\dot r_k = Ar_k + f(y+\varepsilon r_{k-1}) - \varepsilon r_{k-1,y}B_{k-1} - B_k, \quad k>1 \tag{7}$$
$$\dot y = Ay \tag{8}$$

It follows from (8) that $y = e^{At}c$, where c is a constant vector.

We split the time-dependent terms in (6)-(8) into two distinct groups, namely, resonance and nonresonance terms.

Definition: F(t) is called a resonance perturbation if

$$F(t) = e^{At}N(c)$$

where $N(c) \in R^n$ is a vector dependent upon c, otherwise F is called a nonresonance perturbation. In order to annihilate nonresonance terms we set: $B_k = e^{At}N_k(c)$. Recalling that $c=e^{-At}y$, one is able to write:

$$B_k(y,t) = e^{At}N_k(e^{-At}y).$$

It is easy to verify that the last formula generalizes the Poincare resonance condition and agrees with it if f admits Poincare's assumptions. Note also, that B_k becomes time invariant if f does not include time.

Observe that (6)-(8) coincide with the set of linear ODEs given by naive iterations if one sets B_k=0, $k \geq 1$. As mentioned before, the resonance terms present in these recursive sequences force the iterations to diverge on large time intervals. The problem with naive iterations is that they do not distinguish between resonance and nonresonance terms. In spite of this, one can use the available B_k to annihilate resonance terms in (6)-(8) and place them into the normal form (3).

Because the resonance terms are exceptional, the normalization yields significant reduction of the initial nonlinear system. Moreover, the normal forms admit complementary reduction in the amplitude-phase variables.

Let us write the normal form equation in such a way:

$$\dot y = Ay + \varepsilon e^{At}N(e^{-At}y,\varepsilon) + O(\varepsilon^K)$$

Addressing a slow variable c(t) by the formula $y(t) = e^{At}c(t)$, one obtains:

$$\dot c = \varepsilon N(c,\varepsilon) + O(\varepsilon^K)$$

Assume now that all eigen-values of A are complex conjugate:

$$\lambda_k = \alpha_k + I\omega_k; \quad \bar\lambda_k = \alpha_k - I\omega_k, \quad k=1,\dots,n/2, \quad I=\sqrt{-1}$$

Let us represent a complex diagonal matrix $A = \alpha + I\beta$ and introduce $y = e^{I\beta t}c(t)$, where related c_k are chosen as complex conjuate couples:

$$c_k(t) = a_k(t)e^{I\rho_k(t)}, \quad \bar c_k(t) = a_k(t)e^{-I\rho_k(t)}, \quad k=1,\dots,n/2$$

Assume also, that vector $\lambda=\{\lambda_1, \dots,\lambda_{n/2}\}$ is not resonant. Namely, there is no vector m satisfying the Poincare resonance condition $\lambda_s= (m;\lambda)$, s=1,...,n/2. In this case we get:

$$\dot a = \alpha a + \tfrac{1}{2}\varepsilon(N(a,\varepsilon) + \bar N(a,\varepsilon)) + O(\varepsilon^K)$$
$$\dot\rho = \tfrac{-I}{2a}\varepsilon(N(a,\varepsilon) - \bar N(a,\varepsilon)) + O(\varepsilon^K) \tag{9}$$

where $a = \{a_1, \dots a_{n/2}\}$, $r = \{r_1, \dots, r_{n/2}\}$ and $\alpha = \{\alpha_1, \dots, \alpha_{n/2}\}$. Note that the remarkable feature of the above equations is that the right-hand-sides of (9) are independent of ρ, and also $a \geq 0$.

For zero eigen-values, related eigen-vectors occur as slow variables directly. Assume that critical eigen-values consist of both a number of zero eigenvalues and a certain number of noncomensurable complex conjugate couples. In this case an averaging normal form also assumes the form (9). In fact, the vector of slow variables consists of additional components corresponding to zero eigen-vectors.

In the face of additional resonances: $\lambda_s = (m; \lambda)$, s = 1, ..., p conforming combinations of phase variables, namely

$$\psi_s = (m;\rho) - \rho_s, \quad s=1,\dots,p \tag{10}$$

play the same part as additional amplitude variables. Defining by (10) the new variables $\psi =\{\psi_1, \dots, \psi_p\}$ and leaving the same notation for the remaining variables, we write (9) in a modified form

$$\dot a = \alpha a + \tfrac{1}{2}\varepsilon(N(a,\psi,\varepsilon) + \bar N(a,\psi,\varepsilon)) + O(\varepsilon^K)$$
$$\dot\psi = \tfrac{-I}{2a}\varepsilon(N(a,\psi,\varepsilon) - \bar N(a,\psi,\varepsilon)) + O(\varepsilon^K)$$
$$\dot\rho = \tfrac{-I}{2a}\varepsilon(N(a,\psi,\varepsilon) - \bar N(a,\psi,\varepsilon)) + O(\varepsilon^K)$$

Thus additional p resonances yield additional p active variables (ψ) in the averaging normal form.

4. Estimation of Residual Terms

We present here a simple upper bound on residual terms that guides the formulation of sufficient conditions for local stability of a steady state solution.

Terminating iterations (6)-(8) on the k-th step by setting $r_{k+1} = r_k$ gives the residual term of the form: $E = B_{k+1} = Ar_k - \dot r_k + \gamma(y+\varepsilon r_k) - \varepsilon r_{k,y}B_k$. It is clear that $E = R(a, \rho, \varepsilon)$ depends on both amplitude and phase variables. Therefore, (9) can be written in the following form:

$$\dot a = \alpha a + \tfrac{1}{2}\varepsilon(N(a,\varepsilon) + \bar N(a,\varepsilon)) + \varepsilon^K E(a,\rho,\varepsilon)$$
$$\dot\rho = \tfrac{-I}{2a}\varepsilon(N(a,\varepsilon) - \bar N(a,\varepsilon)) + \varepsilon^K e(a,\rho,\varepsilon) \tag{11}$$

where amplitudes $a \in R^{n_1}$ and phases $\rho \in R^{n_2}$ (n_1-n_2 is the number of zero eigen-values in matrix α). E and e are periodic functions with respect to each ρ_k, k = 1, ..., p, with noncomensurable periods T_k:

$$E(a,\rho_k + T_k) = E(a,\rho_k), \quad e(a,\rho_k + T_k) = e(a,\rho_k)$$

It is important to notice that the above equations are given by the closed form change of variables and are therefore accurate. Let us show that the residuals E and e can be effectively bounded.

Indeed, the upper bounds are:

$$E \leq \max_{\rho_1 \in [0;T_1]} \dots \max_{\rho_n \in [0;T_n]} E(a,\rho,\varepsilon) = E^0(a,\varepsilon)$$
$$e \leq \max_{\rho_1 \in [0;T_1]} \dots \max_{\rho_n \in [0;T_n]} e(a,\rho,\varepsilon) = e^0(a,\varepsilon)$$

Using these bounds we can formulate asymptotic stability conditions for a steady state solution of (11) using a Lyapunov function which is addressed in amplitude variables. Observe that in the majority of engineering problems, the residual turns out to be insignificantly small and stability is governed by the resonance part of (11).

5. Resonance Stabilization

We outline briefly the essential steps in design of the resonance control. We assume that a plant is represented by equations of the averaging normal form:

$$\dot{a} = \alpha a + \varepsilon Q(a,\varepsilon) + \varepsilon^K E(a,\rho,\varepsilon) + V$$
$$\dot{\rho} = \varepsilon q(a,\varepsilon) + \varepsilon^K e(a,\rho,\varepsilon) + v$$

where uncertain values v and V ($v_{min} < v < v_{max}$, $V_{min} < V < V_{max}$) initialize bounded uncertainties.

It is assumed that possible error involved in an approximation of the steady state solution has been estimated and has been formally added to the bounds of unmodeled dynamics. We also assume that the origin of coordinates is shifted to coincide with steady state solutions.

Assign $G(a) = \alpha a + \varepsilon Q(a,\varepsilon) + \varepsilon^K E(a,\rho,\varepsilon) + V + v(a)$ and $G^0(a) = \alpha a + \varepsilon Q(a,\varepsilon) + \varepsilon^K E^0(a,\varepsilon) + V + v(a)$ where feedback V(a) is addressed in amplitude variables.

Choose a Lyapunov function L=L(a) and design feedback to satisfy in a certain neighborhood of a steady state solution the Lyapunov criteria for asymptotic stability.

$$\sum_{i=1}^{n_1} \frac{\partial L}{\partial a_i} G_i(a,\rho,\varepsilon) \le -D, \quad a_0 \le a \le -\mu,\ \mu \le a \le a^0,\ \mu > 0$$
$$\sum_{i=1}^{n_1} \frac{\partial L}{\partial a_i} G_i(a,\rho,\varepsilon) \le 0, \quad |a| < \mu$$

where vector D>0 is assigned the degree of relative stability, vectors a_0, a^0 initialize a basin of stability, and μ is a small positive value. Note that in the last relation equality is achieved only for a=0. The above condition consists of ρ and thus would be difficult to verify. Recalling that $\partial L/\partial a_i > 0$, we are able to simplify this inequality. In fact, using the upper bounds on the residual we get:

$$\sum_{i=1}^{n_1} \frac{\partial L}{\partial a_i} G_i^0(a,\rho,\varepsilon) \le -D, \quad a_0 \le a \le -\mu,\ \mu \le a \le a^0,\ \mu > 0$$
$$\sum_{i=1}^{n_1} \frac{\partial L}{\partial a_i} G_i^0(a,\rho,\varepsilon) \le 0, \quad |a| < \mu, \tag{12}$$

There are a few ways to determine a feedback V(a) that satisfies the above inequality. A simple control design procedure is shown below in an example.

The final step is to map feedback V(a) from the amplitude to the original state variables. This step is rather routine because the truncated averaging normal form is linked with the initial equations by an invertible mapping given in closed form.

While a variety of Lyapunov functions can be adapted in feedback design, we will show that the most simple one $L = \sum_{i=1}^{n_1} a_i^2$ provides us with a controller which yields exponential decay of the amplitude variables with the desired rates. The amplitudes a_i are nonnegative when all critical/close to critical eigen-values are complex conjugate with nonzero imaginary parts and there are no additional resonances imposed.

In this case a_0=0 and (12) is true if

$$G_i^0(a) \le -d,\ \mu \le a \le a^0$$
$$G_i^0(a) \le 0,\ 0 \le a < \mu$$

Rewrite this inequality in the form:

$$\dot{a}_i \le -d_i,\ \mu \le a \le a^0$$
$$\dot{a}_i \le 0,\ 0 \le a < \mu \tag{13}$$

Thus the resonance stabilization allows us to control least rates (d_i) of exponential decay of the amplitude variables which is one of the principle concerns in engineering applications.

Suppose now that all critical eigen-values are real numbers close or equal to zero. In this case (12) holds but there is no reason to assume that a_i>0. In particular for a single zero eigen-value(12) is reduced to:

$$aG^0(a) \le -D,\ a_0 \le a \le -\mu,\ \mu \le a \le a^0$$
$$aG^0(a) \le 0,\ |a| < \mu$$

In order to conform with this relation G(a) should possess the property:

$$\text{sign } G(a) = -\text{sign } a$$

The last relation agrees if G(a) is chosen for example as an appropriate smooth odd function.

In the case of multiple zero/close-to-zero eigen-values (12) is reduced to

$$\sum_{i=1}^{n_1-n_2} a_i G_i^0(a) \le -D,\ a_0 \le a \le -\mu,\ \mu \le a \le a^0$$
$$\sum_{i=1}^{n_1-n_2} a_i G_i^0(a) \le 0,\ |a| < \mu \tag{14}$$

This relation agrees if sign $G_i^0(a) = -\text{sign } a_i$, $G_i^0(a=0) = 0$, $|G_i^0(a)| < d_i$, $a_0 \le a \le -\mu$, $\mu \le a \le a_0$ where rates of decay d_i are determined from (14).

The general case when both complex and real critical eigen-values persist can be broken out into the two special cases mentioned above. The given stability conditions do not shape the procedure of control design uniquely. We reveal with the following example one of the possible ways to choose a resonance stabilizing feedback.

6. Resonance Control of the Hopf Bifurcation

Write the equations in the form:

$$\dot{x}_1 = x_2$$
$$\dot{x}_2 = -x_1 + \varepsilon(x_2 - x_2^3)$$

The eigen-values of the linearized system ($\lambda_1 = I$, $\lambda_2 = -I$) are a pure imaginary couple and satisfy the resonance condition: $\lambda_1 + \lambda_2 = 0$. The resonance condition is violated for any small $\varepsilon \ne 0$ and occurs suddenly in the case when $\varepsilon = 0$. Indeed, the normal forms in the resonance and nonresonance cases are essentially distinct. In order to find a normal form which smoothly depends upon the parameter ε, one has to treat the small linear term εx_2 as part of the function f. Thus the associated linearized system is:

$$\dot{x}_1 = x_2$$
$$\dot{x}_2 = -x_1$$

The first order approximation of the resonance normal form for $\varepsilon = 0.1$ is:

$$\dot{z}_1 = (0.05 + I)z_1 - 0.15 z_1^2 z_2 + O(\varepsilon^2)$$
$$\dot{z}_2 = (0.05 - I)z_2 - 0.15 z_1 z_2^2 + O(\varepsilon^2)$$

The variables $\{z_1, z_2\}$ are coupled with $\{x_1, x_2\}$ by the nonlinear change of variables:

$$x = Ty$$
$$y_1 = z_1 - 0.025Iy_2 - 0.025Iy_1^3 + 0.075Iy_1y_2^2 - 0.0125Iy_2^3$$
$$y_2 = z_2 + 0.025Iy_1 + 0.025Iy_2^3 - 0.075Iy_1^2y_2 + 0.0125Iy_1^3$$

In amplitude-phase variables $\{a, \rho\}$

$$z_1 = a(t)e^{It + I\rho(t)}$$
$$z_2 = a(t)e^{-It - I\rho(t)}$$

the normal form is represented as follows:

$$\dot{a} = 0.05a - 0.15a^3 + \varepsilon^2 E(a,\rho)$$
$$\dot{\rho} = \varepsilon^2 e(a,\rho)$$

where residuals E(a, ρ) and e(a, ρ) are determined in the second iteration.

It is clear that the trivial solution is unstable in this case, while the system possesses a stable limit circle. In order to stabilize the trivial solution of the above system by feedback we determine the upper bound of E(a, ρ):

$$E(a,\rho) < E^0 = 0.00928a^3 + 0.034599a^5 + 0.00253a^7 + 0.0002a^9$$

Combining the resonance and error terms one gets:

$$g(a) = 0.05a - 0.14072a^3 + 0.034599a^5 + 0.00253a^7 + 0.0002a^9$$

Observe that a constant value is not a resonant component and thus both u(0) = 0 and g(0) = 0. We choose a control u(a) which ensures that:

$$G^0(a) = g(a) + u(a) \le -d, \text{ for } a > \mu$$
$$G^0(a) \le 0, \text{ for } 0 \le a < \mu \tag{15}$$

In other words, control should ensure asymptotic stability for all $a \ge 0$, and outside of a small regime about zero (initialized by vector μ), the least rate of decay of the amplitude variable should be equal to d . Choose

$$u(a) = ka - 0.035a^5 - 0.0026a^7 - 0.00021a^9$$

in order to overcome small positive nonlinear terms in g(a); at the same time the prime resonance nonlinear term remains the same.

Let μ=0.005 and d=0.1. Then determining k that satisfies (15), we get

$$u(a) = -2.04965a - 0.035a^5 - 0.0026a^7 - 0.00021a^9$$

Mapping this function back to the original variables is introduced control in measurable initial coordinates. Figure 1b shows the initial system with unstable equilibrium and figure 1a displays the effect of the designed stabilizing control. On figure 1c we display both uncontrolled and controlled amplitudes as well as stabilizing feedback versus time.

7. Analysis and Control of an Aircraft Model

In this section we analyze and control the lateral oscillations experienced by a slender-wing aircraft at a high angle of attack. The considered model was adopted from Cochran and Ho, 1983, which they termed aircraft B. The obtained averaging normal form reveals the failure of linearization in critical cases.

The governing equations are written in the form (1) where :

$$A = \begin{bmatrix} \frac{\rho SVC_{y_l}}{m} & \frac{g\cos(\alpha)}{V} & \sin(\alpha) + \frac{\rho SsC_{y_p}}{m} & -\cos(\alpha) + \frac{\rho SsC_{y_r}}{m} \\ 0 & 0 & 1 & \tan(\alpha) \\ q_x V(I_z C_{t_l} + I_{xz} C_{n_l}) & 0 & q_x s(I_z C_{t_p} + I_{xz} C_{n_p}) & q_x s(I_z C_{t_r} + I_{xz} C_{n_r}) \\ q_x V(I_{xx} C_{t_l} + I_x C_{n_l}) & 0 & q_x s(I_{xz} C_{t_p} + I_x C_{n_p}) & q_x s(I_{xz} C_{t_r} + I_x C_{n_r}) \end{bmatrix}$$

$$f = \begin{bmatrix} \frac{(\rho bSV) C_{y_3} \beta^3}{2m} \\ 0 \\ q_x V(I_z C_{t_3} + I_{xz} C_{n_3})\beta^3 \\ q_x V(I_{xz} C_{t_3} + I_x C_{n_3})\beta^3 \end{bmatrix}$$

with β the sideslip angle, ϕ the roll angle, p the roll rate and r the yaw rate. The value of listed parameters were taken from table 2 in Cochran and Ho, 1983, with the exception of:

$$I_{xx} = 2182 \quad kg/m^2, \quad C_{t_3} = -2.0$$

along with angle of attack α = 1.25 degrees and speed V = 71.25 m/s.

With these parameters the equations of motion take the form:

$$\dot{x}_1 = -0.126927x_1 - 1.98427x_1^3 + 0.0432864x_2 + 0.947983x_3 - 0.314497x_4$$
$$\dot{x}_2 = x_3 + 3.01834x_4$$
$$\dot{x}_3 = -16.9354x_1 - 161.428x_1^3 - 0.358942x_3 + 1.04395x_4$$
$$\dot{x}_4 = -5.16107x_1 - 25.4932x_1^3 - 0.212874x_3 + 0.00577748x_4 \tag{16}$$

where $x = (\beta\ \phi\ p\ r)^T$.

The eigen-values of the system (16) linearized are:

$$\lambda = \{-0.00181506 + 3.83335\ I, -0.00181506 - 3.83335\ I,$$
$$-0.47646, -8.61259\ 10^{-7}\}$$

Notice that both the real portion of the complex conjugate pair and the last eigen-value in the above list are close to zero. These relevant small linear terms in (16) are adjoint to f such that the principle linear part in (16) becomes critical. As was mentioned, the normal form of such a critical system preserves behavior of the initial system in a sufficiently large neighborhood of the steady state solution.

Calculation of the first order normal form for this system gives:

$$\dot{z}_1 = (-0.00181506 + 3.83335\ I)z_1 + (-0.308908 + 3.11451\ I)z_1^2 z_2$$
$$+ (-0.000967355 + 0.00975318\ I)z_1 z_4^2$$
$$\dot{z}_2 = (-0.00181506 - 3.83335\ I)z_2 + (-0.308908 - 3.11451\ I)z_1 z_2^2$$
$$+ (-0.000967355 - 0.00975318\ I)z_2 z_4^2$$
$$\dot{z}_3 = -0.47646z_3 + 0.474638z_1 z_2 z_3 + 0.000743172z_3 z_4^2$$
$$\dot{z}_4 = -8.61259\ 10^{-7} z_4 + 0.103323z_1 z_2 z_4 + 5.39267\ 10^{-5} z_4^3$$

The variable z is determined by a cumbersome nonlinear transformation which is obtained with the aid of the designed symbolic software.

Addressing amplitude-phase variables by the formula:

$$z_1 = a(t)e^{I(3.83335t + \rho(t))}$$
$$z_2 = a(t)e^{-I(3.83335t + \rho(t))}$$
$$z_3 = z_3; \quad z_4 = z_4$$

we get

$$\dot{a} = -0.00181506a - 0.308908a^3 - 0.000967355az_4^2$$
$$\dot{\rho} = 3.11451a^2 + 0.00975318z_4^2$$
$$\dot{z}_3 = -0.47646z_3 + 0.474638a^2 z_3 + 0.000743172z_3 z_4^2$$
$$\dot{z}_4 = -8.61259\ 10^{-7} z_4 + 0.103323a^2 z_4 + 5.39267\ 10^{-5} z_4^3 \tag{17}$$

The first and last equations denote projection of the system on the center manifold which characterizes stability properties of the system. Thus the remaining two equations can be disregarded in stability analysis.

While (17) remains nonintegrable, it admits clear qualitative analysis. Numerical integration of (17) shows that amplitude a decays slowly, while z_4 grows slowly in magnitude.

In order to estimate the error involved in the normal form reduction, we map these solutions to the original coordinate basis (see figure 2a) and compare them with direct numerical simulations of the initial equations. In fact, on the displayed time interval the error remains less than 10^{-3}. Smooth nonlinear feedback control that ensures exponential decay of a and z_4 coordinates with an assigned rate of convergence to zero can be introduced as a function of two critical variables: a and z_4 only.

Computing the second iteration, we find the error residual of (17) and compute an upper bound on the residual. Recall that the upper bound is a strictly increasing function and so reaches it's maximum value at the boundry of stability: $0 \le a < a^0$, $|z_4| \le z_4^0$. Thus,

$$g_1 = -0.0181506a - 0.308908a^3 - 0.0000967355az_4^2 + \max(E_1(a^0, z_4^0))$$
$$g_2 = 0.103323a^2 z_4 + 5.39267\ 10^{-5} z_4^3 + \max(E_2(a^0, z_4^0))$$

Control u = {u_1, u_2} is chosen as follows:

$$u_1 = k_1 z_1$$
$$u_2 = k_2 z_2 - 0.103323 a^2 z_4 - 5.39267\ 10^{-5} z_4^3$$

Note that in the first equation the resonance nonlinear terms enhance stability and so remain unchanged while the nonlinear term in the last equation destabilizes the system and thus has been annihilated by feedback. The coefficients k_1=-20.0025 and k_2=-20.00025 are chosen to satisfy (13) and (14) correspondingly with d=0.1. The computation has been completed for:

$$\mu_1 = 0.025,\ \mu_4 = 0.025,\ a^0 = 0.25,\ z_4^0 = 0.25,$$
$$\max(E_1) = 2.17986\ 10^{-5},\ \max(E_2) = 1.32859\ 10^{-7}$$

The figure 2b displays the result of resonance stabilization in the original coordinate frame. On figure 2c we display both uncontrolled and controlled amplitudes and stabilizing feedback versus time.

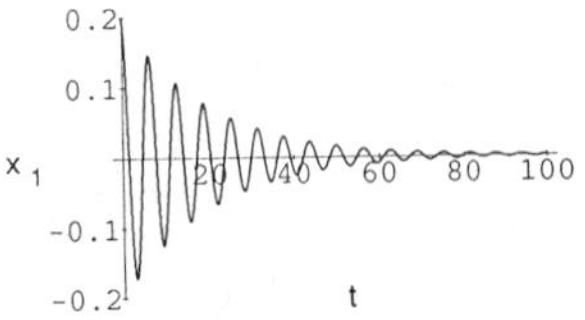

Figure 1a: Analytical solution of the controlled Van der Pol equations

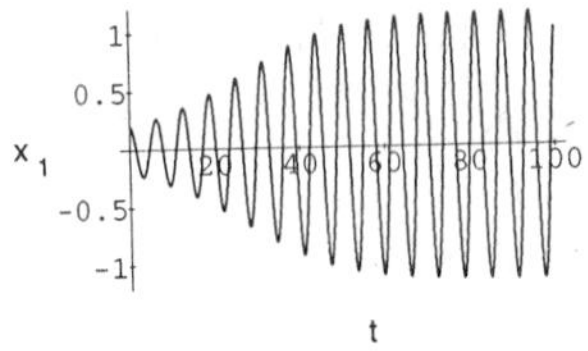

Figure 1b: Runge Kutta solution of the Van der Pol equations

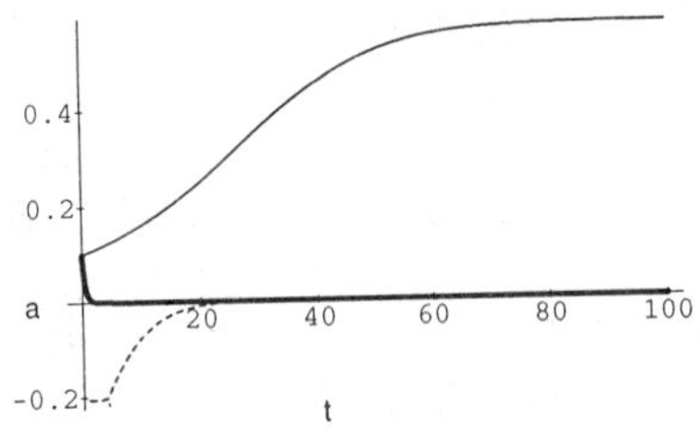

Figure 1c: Combined graph of uncontrolled Amplitude (solid), controlled Amplitude (thick), and control force (dashed)

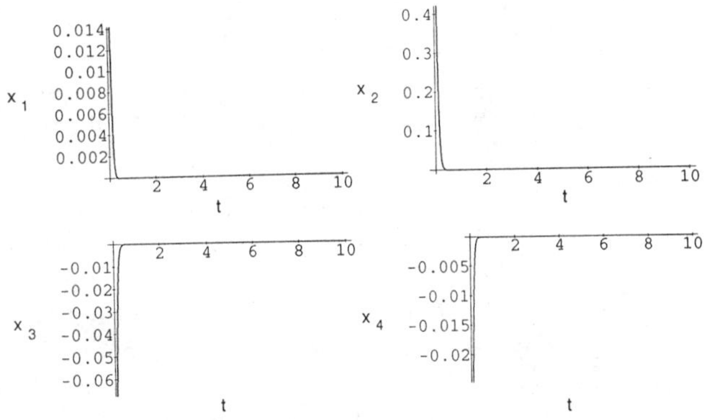

Figure 2a: Analytical solution of controlled Model B equations

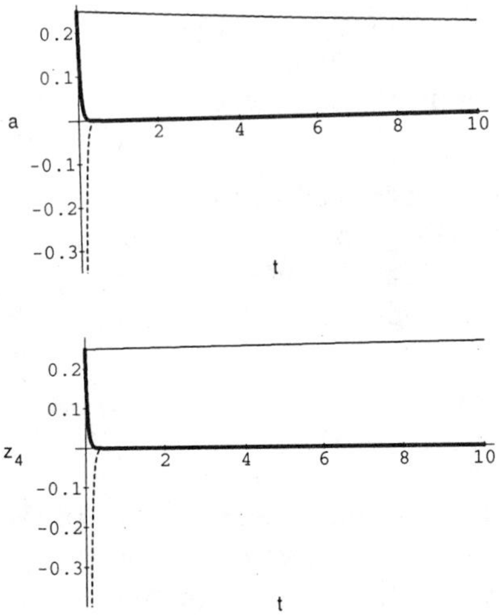

Figure 2b: Model B combined graph of uncontrolled Amplitudes of unstable modes (solid), controlled Amplitudes (thick), and control forces (dashed)

References

Abed, E.H. and J.-H. Fu, 1986, "Local feedback stabilization and bifurcation control, I. Hopf bifurcation," System and Control Letters, Vol. 7, pp. 11-17.

Abed, E.H. and J.-H. Fu, 1987, "Local feedback stabilization and bifurcation control, II. Stationary bifurcation," Systems and Control Letters, Vol. 8, pp. 467-473.

Abed, E.H. and Lee, H., 1989, "Washout filters in the bifurcation control of high alpha flight dynamics," ACC, Vol. 1, pp. 206-211.

Abed, E.H. and Lee, H.-C., 1990, "Nonlinear Stabilizing control of high angle-of-attack flight dynamics using bifurcation control," American Control Conference, Vol. 3, pp. 2235-2238.

Adams, W.M., 1972, "Analytic Prediction of Airplane Equilibrium Spin Characteristics," NASA TN D-6926.

Aeyels, D., 1984, "Local and global controllability for nonlinear systems," Systems Control Letters, Vol. 5 pp. 19-26.

Aeyels, D., 1985, "Stabilization of a class of nonlinear systems by a smooth feedback control," Systems and Control Letters, Vol. 5, pp. 289-294.

Aeyels, D., 1986, "Local and global stabilizability for nonlinear systems," in Theory and Applications of Nonlinear Control Systems, C.I. Byrnes and A. Lindquist (editors), pp. 93-105, North-Holland, Amsterdam.

Arnold, V.I., 1983, *Geometrical methods in the theory of ordinary differential equations*, Springer-Verlag, New York.

Banks, S.P., 1988, *Mathematical theories of nonlinear systems*, Prentice Hall International Series in Systems and Control Engineering, M.J. Grimble, ed., Prentice Hall International (UK).

Brockett, R.W., 1983, *Asymptotic stability and feedback stabilization, Differential geometric control theory*, in: R.W. Brockett, R.S. Milmann, and H.J. Sussman, eds., Progress in Mathematics, Birkhauser, Boston.

Carroll, J.V. and R.D. Mehra, 1982, "Bifurcation analysis of nonlinear aircraft dynamics," J. Guidance, Vol. 5, pp. 529-536.

Cochran, J.E. Jr. and C.-S. Ho, 1983, "Stability of aircraft motion in critical cases," J. Guidance, Vol. 6, pp. 272-279.

Gerrard, W.L. and J.M. Jordan, 1977, "Design of nonlinear automatic flight control systems," Automatica, Vol. 13, pp. 497-505.

Guckenheimer, J. and Holms, P., 1983, *Nonlinear oscillations, dynamical systems, and bifurcations of vector fields*, Springer-Verlag, New York.

Isidori, A., 1985, *Nonlinear Control Systems: An Introduction*, Vol. 72, Lecture Notes in Control and Information Sciences, M. Thoma, ed., Springer-Verlag Berlin.

Kwatny, N.G., Bennett W.H. and Berg J., 1990, "Local Regulations of nonlinear dynamics," American Control Conference, Vol. 2, pp. 1707-1712.

Mehra, R.K., W.C. Kessel and J.V. Carroll, 1977, "Global Stability and Control Analysis of aircraft at High Angles-of-Attack," ONRCR-215-248-1, U.S. Office of Naval Research, Arlington, VA.

Nijmeijer, H. and A.J. van der Schaft, 1990, *Nonlinear Dynamical Control Systems*, Springer-Verlag, New York.

Young, J.W., Schy, A.A., and Johnson, K.G., 1980, "Pseudosteady-State Analysis of Nonlinear Aircraft Maneuvers," NASA TP-1758.

Proceedings of the
American Control Conference
San Francisco, California • June 1993

Flight Control Design By Nonlinear Servomechanism Theory *

J. Huang, C.F. Lin
American GNC Corporation
9131 Mason Ave.,
Chatsworth, CA 91311

Abstract: A new approach to the high performance missile autopilot design based on the nonlinear servomechanism theory is proposed. This approach coupled with the analytic gain scheduling leads to an effective means to account for the nonlinearity and uncertainty in the missile system.

1. Introduction

Recently, there have been increasing attentions on the high performance missile autopilot design using various nonlinear approaches ranging from gain scheduling, [SG], [NRR], robust feedback linearization [HLGED]. These papers emphasized the need to more directly incorporate the nonlienarity and uncertainty of missile systems into the design process.

In this paper, we will propose a new approach to missile autopilot design using the recently developed nonlinear servomechanism theory [HR]. This approach will be illustrated on the pitch autopilot design for the bank-to-turn HAVE DASH missile system. Several features are intended in the design. First, an analytic gain scheduling mechanism is incorporated into the design of the feedback stabilizer in order to achieve a satisfactory performance over an expanded flight envelop. Second, two designs, namely, servo-regulator and robust servo-regulator are conducted, respectively. The latter design incorporates the integral of the tracking error in the feedback loop. This robust scheme coupled with the analytic gain scheduling leads to an effective means to account for the nonlinearity and uncertainty in the missile system.

This paper is organized as follows. In section 2, we review the methodology of the state feedback nonlinear servo-regulator. In Section 3, we detail the design steps for the pitch autopilots and present the simulation results.

2. Review of Nonlinear Servomechanism Theory

Briefly, by servomechanism design, we mean the problem of asymptotical tracking a class of reference trajectories, perhaps, in presence of a class of disturbances. The servomechanism theory for linear systems was developed in 1970s [D] and has been extended to the nonlinear systems recently [HR], [IB]. Here we only give a review of the most basic part of the theory, that is, state feedback servo-regulator design for the case of constant reference and disturbance.

Consider a plant described by

$$\begin{aligned} \dot{x}(t) &= f(x(t), u(t), w(t)), \;\; x(0) = x_0 \\ y(t) &= h(x(t), u(t), w(t)), \;\; t \geq 0 \end{aligned} \tag{2.1}$$

where $x(t)$ is the n-dimensional plant state, $u(t)$ is the m-dimensional plant input, $y(t)$ is the p-dimensional plant output, and $w(t)$ is the q-dimensional constant disturbance signal. Our problem can be described as follows. Given a constant p-dimensional reference input r, design a state feedback controller of the form

$$u(t) = k(x(t), r(t), w(t)) \tag{2.2}$$

such that the closed-loop system is internally stable in the sense to be clarified later and satisfies

$$\lim_{t \to \infty} e(t) = 0 \tag{2.3}$$

where $e(t) = y(t) - r(t)$ is the tracking error.

For simplicity, all the functions involved in this setup are assumed to be smooth and defined globally on the appropriate Euclidean spaces, with the value zero at the respective origins. All our results are stated locally in terms of open neighborhoods of origins of appropriate Euclidean spaces.

The problem can be approached as follows. First, find two sufficiently smooth functions $\mathbf{x}:\Gamma \to R^n$, $\mathbf{u}:\Gamma \to R^m$ such that $\mathbf{x}(0,0) = 0$, $\mathbf{u}(0,0) = 0$, where Γ is an open neighborhood of the origin in R^{p+q}, such that for $(r, w) \in \Gamma$

$$\begin{aligned} 0 &= f(\mathbf{x}(r,w), \mathbf{u}(r,w), w) \\ r &= h(\mathbf{x}(r,w), \mathbf{u}(r,w), w) \end{aligned} \tag{2.4}$$

Equation (2.4) can be viewed as a *static decoupling* condition. It is clear that $\mathbf{x}$ and $\mathbf{u}$ corresponding to those equilibrium points of the plant that yield zero steady state tracking error. For this reason, the functions $\mathbf{u}(r, w)$ and $\mathbf{x}(r, w)$ are called *zero-error constrained input* and, respectively, *zero-error constrained equilibrium manifold.*

*Research supported under USAF Contract No. F08630-91-C-0055, Air Force Armament Directorate, WL/MNAG

By the implicit function theorem, the existence of $\mathbf{x}(r,w)$ and $\mathbf{u}(r,w)$ is guaranteed by the following condition

$$rank \begin{bmatrix} \frac{\partial f}{\partial x}(0,0,0) & \frac{\partial f}{\partial u}(0,0,0) \\ \frac{\partial h}{\partial x}(0,0,0) & \frac{\partial h}{\partial u}(0,0,0) \end{bmatrix} = n+p \qquad (2.5)$$

The second step is to design the controller to satisfy the following two requirements.

Requirement 1:

$$k(\mathbf{x}(r,w),r,w) = \mathbf{u}(r,w) \qquad (2.6)$$

Under this requirement, we have

$$\begin{aligned} f(\mathbf{x}(r,w),k(\mathbf{x}(r,w),r,w),w) &= f(\mathbf{x}(r,w),\mathbf{u}(r,w),w) = 0 \\ h(\mathbf{x}(r,w),k(\mathbf{x}(r,w),r,w),w) &= h(\mathbf{x}(r,w),\mathbf{u}(r,w),w) = r \end{aligned}$$

That is, $\mathbf{x}(r,w)$ is still the equilibrium of the closed-loop system.

Requirement 1: The closed-loop system is (locally) stable in the sense that all the eigenvalues of the matrix

$$\frac{\partial f(\mathbf{x}(r,w),k(\mathbf{x}(r,w),r,w),w)}{\partial x}$$

have negative real parts for each $(r,w) \in \Gamma$.

Clearly, such a closed-loop system has the property that, for each $(r,w) \in \Gamma$, there corresponds an asymptotically stable equilibrium $\mathbf{x}(r,w)$ that annihilates the tracking error. Thus for initial state x_0 sufficiently close to $\mathbf{x}(r,w)$, the trajectory of the closed-loop system will asymptotically approach $\mathbf{x}(r,w)$, and the output $y(t)$ will asymptotically approach r with the transient decay determined by the eigenvalue placement.

The controller satisfying the above two requirements will be called a *servo-regulator* in the sequel. The following result gives a constructive proof of the existence of a servo-regulator.

Theorem 1: Suppose the plant satisfies equation (2.5) and the pair

$$\frac{\partial f}{\partial x}(\mathbf{x}(r,w),\mathbf{u}(r,w),w), \quad \frac{\partial f}{\partial u}(\mathbf{x}(r,w),\mathbf{u}(r,w),w) \qquad (2.7)$$

is controllable, then there exists a state feedback servo-regulator of the form (2.2).

Proof: By condition (2.5), there exist smooth functions $\mathbf{x}(r,w)$ and $\mathbf{u}(r,w)$ satisfying (2.4) locally. Furthermore by condition (2.7), there exists a smooth matrix $K(r,w)$ such that the eigenvalues of the matrix

$$\frac{\partial f}{\partial x}(\mathbf{x}(r,w),\mathbf{u}(r,w),w) + \frac{\partial f}{\partial u}(\mathbf{x}(r,w),\mathbf{u}(r,w),w)K(r,w) \qquad (2.8)$$

have negative real parts. Letting

$$k(x,r,w) = \mathbf{u}(r,w) + K(r,w)(x - \mathbf{x}(r,w)) \qquad (2.9)$$

gives the desired controller.

Remark 2.1: It should be noted that the gain matrix $K(r,w)$, being a function of (r,w), is capable of stabilizing all the equilibrium points parameterized by each $(r,w) \in \Gamma$, thus resulting in a closed-loop system insensitive to the variations of the equilibrium point. This feature is called the *analytic gain scheduling*. It is of particular interest in the flight control design where the plant parameters undergo significant variations with respect to the trimed conditions so that a fixed gain controller can hardly deliver the desired performance. It can also be shown that the gain scheduling mechanism is able to achieve guaranteed tracking-error for slowly varing reference input and disturbance [HR].

Remark 2.2: In case there exist parameter variations in the plant description, The static decoupling condition only holds for the nominal plant. To guarantee the zero tracking error in the presence of the plant uncertainty, internal model principle can be utilized. Specifically, the plant will be augmented by a q-dimensional compensator of the form

$$\dot{z} = h(x,u,w) - r \qquad (2.10)$$

As a result, the controller takes the form

$$u = k(x,z,r,w) \qquad (2.11)$$

It is known that under the conditions of Theorem 1, the pair

$$\begin{bmatrix} \frac{\partial f}{\partial x}(\mathbf{x}(r,w),\mathbf{u}(r,w),w) & 0 \\ \frac{\partial h}{\partial x}(\mathbf{x}(r,w),\mathbf{u}(r,w),w) & 0 \end{bmatrix}, \quad \begin{bmatrix} \frac{\partial f}{\partial u}(\mathbf{x}(r,w),\mathbf{u}(r,w),w) \\ \frac{\partial h}{\partial u}(\mathbf{x}(r,w),\mathbf{u}(r,w),w) \end{bmatrix}$$

is controllable [HR]. Thus there exist smooth function $K_x(r,w)$ and $K_z(r,w)$ such that

$$\begin{bmatrix} \frac{\partial f}{\partial x}(\mathbf{x}(r,w),\mathbf{u}(r,w),w) & 0 \\ \frac{\partial h}{\partial x}(\mathbf{x}(r,w),\mathbf{u}(r,w),w) & 0 \end{bmatrix} + \begin{bmatrix} \frac{\partial f}{\partial u}(\mathbf{x}(r,w),\mathbf{u}(r,w),w) \\ \frac{\partial h}{\partial u}(\mathbf{x}(r,w),\mathbf{u}(r,w),w) \end{bmatrix} [K_x(r,w) \quad K_z(r,w)]$$

have negative real parts. It can be verified that the controller

$$\begin{aligned} k(x,z,r,w) &= \mathbf{u}(r,w) + K_x(r,w)(x - \mathbf{x}(r,w)) \\ &+ K_z(r,w)(z - \mathbf{z}(r,w)) \end{aligned} \qquad (2.13)$$

where $\mathbf{z}(r,w)$ is a smooth function, achieves asymptotic tracking and disturbance rejection. Moreover, asymptotic stability of the closed-loop system implies $\lim_{t\to\infty} \dot{z}(t) = 0$, that is, $\lim_{t\to\infty} y(t) = r$. Therefore, regardless of the parameter variations in the plant, asymptotical tracking and disturbance rejection can still be achieved as long as the stability property described by requirement 2 for the augmented plant is maitained. In this sense, we say (2.13) is a *robust servo-regulator*. Clearly, this scheme is an extension of the well-known linear PID controller to the nonlinear setting.

3. Pitch Controller Design

The pitch dynamics of the missile system is described by

$$\dot{V}_m = \frac{1}{m}\{cos\alpha F_x + sin\alpha F_z)$$

$$\dot{\alpha} = Q + \frac{1}{mV_m}\{-sin\alpha F_x + cos\alpha F_z\}$$
$$\dot{Q} = M/I_{yy} \quad (3.1)$$

where V_m, α, and Q are, respectively, the missile's velocity, angle of attack, and pitch angular rate, all with respect to a body fixed frame; m and I_y are the missile's mass and the moment of inertial; F_x and F_z are forces along the X and Z axes, and M is the pitch moment. The forces and moment have the following functional form

$$\begin{aligned} F_x &= k_F \rho V_m^2 C_x(\alpha, \delta_e, M_m) \\ F_z &= k_F \rho V_m^2 C_z(\alpha, \delta_e, M_m) \\ M &= k_M \rho V_m^2 C_m(\alpha, \delta_e, M_m) \end{aligned} \quad (3.2)$$

Here C_x, C_z, and C_m are aerocoefficients given in a table; ρ is the atmospheric density; k_F and k_M are constants depending on the missile's geometry; $M_m \stackrel{def}{=} V_m/c$ is Mach number with c being the speed of sound; δ_e is the effective pitch fin control deflection. The fin control deflection is produced by the commanded fin deflection δ_c through a second order actuators

$$\frac{d}{dt}\begin{bmatrix} \delta_e \\ \dot{\delta}_e \end{bmatrix} = \begin{bmatrix} 0 & 1 \\ -\omega_a^2 & -2\zeta_a\omega_a \end{bmatrix} + \begin{bmatrix} 0 \\ \omega_a^2 \end{bmatrix} \delta_{ec} \quad (3.3)$$

It is assumed that the fin deflection and deflection rate limits are $\pm 25\ deg$ and $\pm 400\ deg/sec$, respectively.

Various parameters in (3.1) through (3.3) are given as follows

$$\begin{aligned} G &= 32.174\ ft/sec^2, \quad m = 9.89\ slug \\ c &= 968\ ft/sec, \quad K_F = 0.1534\ ft^2 \\ K_M &= 0.0959\ ft^3, \quad \rho = 5.124 \times 10^{-4}\ slugs/ft^3 \\ I_{yy} &= 100.5\ slug\ ft^2, \quad \zeta_a = 0.7 \\ \omega_a &= 35\ H_z \end{aligned}$$

where c and ρ are computed at the altitude of $40,000\ ft$.

It is well known that the pitch maneuvers are realized by developing the appropriate angle of attack. The major concern with the autopilot design is the dramatic variations of the aerocoefficients with respect to the angle of attack and Mach number. Reflecting these thoughts, we choose the angle of attack as the output. The basic objective is to have the angle of attack α rapidly and precisely track the commanded angle of attack α_c.

Model for Design

To put the above objective under the framework suitable for servo-regulator design, we will first approximate the aerocoefficients C_x, C_y, and C_z by analytic functions as follows:

$$\begin{aligned} C_x &= C_{x0}(\alpha) + C_{xe}\delta_e \\ C_z &= C_{z1}(\alpha) + C_{z2}(\alpha)M_m + C_{ze}\delta_e \\ &\stackrel{def}{=} C_{z0}(\alpha, M_m) + C_{ze}\delta_e \\ C_m &= C_{m1}(\alpha) + C_{m2}(\alpha)M_m + C_{me}\delta_e \\ &\stackrel{def}{=} C_{m0}(\alpha, M_m) + C_{me}\delta_e \end{aligned} \quad (3.4)$$

where

$$\begin{aligned} C_{x0}(\alpha) &= -0.57 + 0.0083\alpha \\ C_{z1}(\alpha) &= -0.0015\alpha^3 + 0.0125\alpha^2 - 0.5052\alpha + 0.0429 \\ C_{z2}(\alpha) &= 0.0006\alpha^3 - 0.0138\alpha^2 + 0.1230\alpha - 0.0191 \\ C_{m1}(\alpha) &= -0.0055\alpha^3 + 0.2131\alpha^2 - 2.7419\alpha - 0.0381 \\ C_{m2}(\alpha) &= 0.0014\alpha^3 - 0.0623\alpha^2 + 0.8715\alpha - 0.4041 \\ C_{xe}(\alpha) &= 0.004, \quad C_{ze}(\alpha) = 0.09, \quad C_{me}(\alpha) = -0.675 \end{aligned}$$

These function are obtained using curve fitting technique based on the least square error criterion. They are valid for $0\ deg \leq \alpha \leq 25\ deg$ and $2.0 \leq M_m \leq 3.0$. Figure 1 compares the approximate aerocoefficients C_m with the true table data.

Next, to make design easier, we will treat the Velocity V_m (equivalently the Mach number M_m) as a constant disturbance, and ignore the actuator's dynamics, that is, assume $\delta_e = \delta_c$. Thus our design will be based on a second order nonlinear system given by, after substituting (3.4) and $V_m = cM_m$ into (3.1).

$$\begin{aligned} \dot{\alpha} &= Q + \frac{k_F \rho c M_m}{m}\{-sin\alpha(C_{x0}(\alpha) + C_{xe}\delta_e) \\ &+ cos\alpha(C_{z0}(\alpha, M_m) + C_{ze}\delta_e)\} \\ &\stackrel{def}{=} f_1(\alpha, Q, \delta_e, M_m) \\ \dot{Q} &= \frac{k_M \rho c^2 M_m^2}{I_{yy}}(C_{m0}(\alpha, M_m) + C_{me}\delta_e) \\ &\stackrel{def}{=} f_2(\alpha, Q, \delta_e, M_m) \\ y &= \alpha \stackrel{def}{=} h(\alpha) \end{aligned} \quad (3.5)$$

Clearly, with $x = (\alpha, Q)$, $u = \delta_e$, $y = \alpha$, $w = M_m$, and $r = \alpha_c$, equation (3.5) is exactly in the form of (2.1).

Servo-Regulator

The first step of the design is to solve the zero-error constrained input and the zero-error constrained equilibrium manifold as defined in equation (2.4) which, in this case, takes the form

$$\begin{aligned} 0 &= f_1(\alpha(\alpha_c, M_m), \mathbf{Q}(\alpha_c, M_m), \delta_e(\alpha_c, M_m), M_m) \\ 0 &= f_2(\alpha(\alpha_c, M_m), \mathbf{Q}(\alpha_c, M_m), \delta_e(\alpha_c, M_m), M_m) \\ 0 &= h(\alpha) - \alpha_c \end{aligned} \quad (3.6)$$

simple calculations give

$$\alpha(\alpha_c, M_m) = \alpha_c$$
$$\delta_e(\alpha_c, M_m) = -\frac{C_{m0}(\alpha_c, M_m)}{C_{me}}$$
$$\begin{aligned} \mathbf{Q}(\alpha_c, M_m) = -\frac{k_F \rho c M_m}{m}\{-sin\alpha_c(C_{x0}(\alpha_c) \\ + C_{xe}\delta_e(\alpha_c, M_m)) + cos\alpha_c(C_{z0}(\alpha_c, M_m) + C_{ze}\delta_e(\alpha_c, M_m) \end{aligned}$$

and

$$\frac{\partial f_1}{\partial \alpha}(\alpha_c, M_m) = \frac{k_F \rho c M_m}{m}\{-cos\alpha_c(C_{x0}(\alpha_c)$$

$$
\begin{aligned}
&+ \quad C_{xe}\delta_e(\alpha_c, M_m)) \\
&- \quad sin\alpha_c \frac{\partial C_{x0}}{\partial \alpha}(\alpha_c) - sin\alpha_c(C_{z0}(\alpha_c, M_m) \\
&+ \quad C_{ze}\delta_e(\alpha_c, M_m)) + cos\alpha_c \frac{\partial C_{z0}}{\partial \alpha}(\alpha_c, M_m)) \\
&\stackrel{def}{=} \quad a_{11}(\alpha_c, M_m)
\end{aligned}
$$

$$
\begin{aligned}
\frac{\partial f_1}{\partial Q}(\alpha_c, M_m) &= 1 \stackrel{def}{=} a_{12}(\alpha_c, M_m) \\
\frac{\partial f_2}{\partial \alpha}(\alpha_c, M_m) &= \frac{k_M \rho c^2 M_m^2}{I_{yy}} \frac{\partial C_{m0}}{\partial \alpha}(\alpha_c, M_m) \\
&\stackrel{def}{=} a_{21}(\alpha_c, M_m) \\
\frac{\partial f_2}{\partial Q}(\alpha_c, M_m) &= 0 \stackrel{def}{=} a_{22}(\alpha_c, M_m) \\
\frac{\partial f_1}{\partial \delta_e}(\alpha_c, M_m) &= \frac{k_F \rho c M_m}{m}(-C_{xe} sin\alpha_c + C_{ze} cos\alpha_c) \\
&\stackrel{def}{=} b_1(\alpha_c, M_m) \\
\frac{\partial f_2}{\partial \delta_e}(\alpha_c, M_m) &= \frac{k_M \rho c^2 M_m^2 C_{me}}{I_{yy}} \stackrel{def}{=} b_2(\alpha_c, M_m)
\end{aligned}
$$

For notational simplicity, let $v = (\alpha_c, M_m)$, let

$$
A(v) = \begin{bmatrix} a_{11}(v) & a_{12}(v) \\ a_{21}(v) & a_{22}(v) \end{bmatrix}, \quad B(v) = \begin{bmatrix} b_1(v) \\ b_2(v) \end{bmatrix} \tag{3.7}
$$

Then it is easy to verify that $A(v)$ and $B(v)$ is controllable for all $0\ deg \leq \alpha_c \leq 25\ deg$ and $2.0 \leq M_m \leq 3.0$. Assume that the desired closed-loop eigenvalues are given by the roots of Hurwitz polynomial $s^2 + d_1 s + d_2$. Let $|sI - A(v)| = s^2 + c_1(v)s + c_2(v)$. Then using the well known *Bass-Gura formula* gives the desired feedback gain $K(v) = (K_1(v)\ \ K_2(v))$ as follows

$$
K(v) = (C(v) - D)P^{-1}(v)W^{-1}(v) \tag{3.8}
$$

where $D = (d_1, d_2)$, $C(v) = (c_1(v), c_2(v))$, and

$$
P(v) = \begin{bmatrix} 1 & c_1(v) \\ 0 & 1 \end{bmatrix}, \quad W(v) = [B(v)\ \ A(v)B(v)]
$$

In fact, let $K(v) = (K_1(v), K_2(v))$, then (3.7) gives

$$
\begin{aligned}
K_1(v) &= \frac{-(d_1 + a_{11}(v))(a_{21}(v)b_1(v) - a_{11}(v)b_2(v))}{b_1(v)(a_{21}(v)b_1(v) - a_{11}(v)b_2(v)) - b_2^2(v)} \\
&+ \frac{(d_2 + a_{21}(v))b_2(v)}{b_1(v)(a_{21}(v)b_1(v) - a_{11}(v)b_2(v)) - b_2^2(v)} \\
K_2(v) &= \frac{(d_1 + a_{11}(v))b_2(v) - (d_2 + a_{21}(v))b_2(v)}{b_1(v)(a_{21}(v)b_1(v) - a_{11}(v)b_2(v)) - b_2^2(v)}
\end{aligned}
$$

Finally, gives the desired controller:

$$
\begin{aligned}
k(\alpha, Q, \alpha_c, M_m) &= \delta_e(\alpha_c, M_m) + K_1(\alpha_c, M_m)(\alpha - \alpha_c) \\
&+ K_2(\alpha_c, M_m)(Q - \mathbf{Q}(\alpha_c, M_m))
\end{aligned}
$$

Remark 3.1: It is assumed that the angle of attack is available for feedback. If this is not the case, the normal acceleration can be used for feedback.

The performance of the above controller is evaluated using both the approximate aerocoefficients (3.4) and the true aerocoefficient table. The simulations are shown in Figure 2 and 3, respectively, The desired closed-loop characteristic polynomial coefficients are $d_1 = 21, d_2 = 250$, which is equivalent to 0.7 damping ratio and 16 rad/sec natural frequency. All initial conditions are zero except that $V_m(0) = 2662 ft/sec$. The commanded angle of attack is a series of step commands with the magnitudes being 10, 15, 20 degrees, respectively. As shown by Figure 2, where the approximate aerocoefficients are used for simulation, the autopilot exhibits, to a great extent, a uniform performance in terms of the rise time, overshoot, and settling time despite the fact that a wide range of flight conditions (from $\alpha = 0$ to $\alpha = 20$, and $M_m = 2.75$ to $M_m = 2.45$) are transversed. This is attributed to the uniform closed-loop pole pattern with respect to α_c and M_m rendered by the gain scheduling technique. On the other hand, the zero steady state tracking error for all flight conditions is achieved by satisfying the static decoupling condition (2.4). Nevertheless, when the true aerocoefficient table is used for simulation as is the case shown in Figure 3, a small steady state error for $\alpha_c = 20\ deg$ is observed. This performance degradation is clearly due to the violation of the static decoupling condition which is in turn due to the uncertainty arising from the rough approximation of aerocoefficients as shown in Figure 1.

Robust Servo-Regulator

To account for the tracking error arising from the model uncertainty, the robust acheme as described in Remark 2.2 will be employed. To begin with, adjoin the compensator

$$
\dot{z}(t) = \alpha - \alpha_c \tag{3.9}
$$

to the system (3.5). Let

$$
A_c(v) = \begin{bmatrix} a_{11}(v) & a_{12}(v) & 0 \\ a_{21}(v) & a_{22}(v) & 0 \\ 1 & 0 & 0 \end{bmatrix}, \quad B_c(v) = \begin{bmatrix} b_1(v) \\ b_2(v) \\ 0 \end{bmatrix} \tag{3.10}
$$

which represents the linearization of the augmented system along each $(\alpha_c, M_m) \in \Gamma$. Then by Remark 2.2, there exist 3-dimensional smooth row vectors $K(v) = (K_1(v)\ \ K_2(v)\ \ K_3(v))$ such that $A_c(v) + B_c(v)K(v)$ has desired pole pattern. In fact, let the desired closed-loop characteristic polynomial be $s^3 + d_1 s^2 + d_2 s + d_3$, then again $K(v)$ can be obtained using the Bass-Gura formula. The controller, according to (2.11), takes the form

$$
\begin{aligned}
k(\alpha, Q, z, \alpha_c, M_m) &= \delta_e(\alpha_c, M_m) + K_1(\alpha_c, M_m)(\alpha - \alpha_c) \\
&+ K_2(\alpha_c, M_m)(Q - \mathbf{Q}(\alpha_c, M_m)) \\
&+ K_3(\alpha_c, M_m)(z - \mathbf{z}(\alpha_c, M_m))
\end{aligned} \tag{3.11}
$$

Again, the performance of the robust controller is evaluated using both the approximate aerocoefficients (3.4) and the true aerocoefficients table. The results are shown in Figure 4 and 5, respectively. The desired closed-loop characteristic polynomial is given by $(s^2 + 2 \times 0.7s^2 + 21^2)(s - 8)$. Comparing Figures 4 and 5, it is seen that this autopilot retains the uniform performance regardless of the model uncertainty. Note that in this case, the transient responses are still shaped by the gain scheduling technique. However, the zero-steady state tracking error is achieved by employing the internal model principle.

Acknowledgement

The authors wish to thank Johnny Evers of USAF Armament Directorate of Wright Laboratory for his suggestions and comments.

References

[D] E.J. Davison "The Robust Control of a Servomechanism Problem for Linear Time-Invariant Multivariable Systems," *IEEE Transactions on Automatic Control*, Vol. 35, No.2, pp. 131 - 140, 1990.

[HLCED] J. Hunag, C.F. Lin, J.R. Cloutier, J.H. Evers, and C.D. D'Souza, " Robust Feedback Linearization Approach to Autopilot Design" *Proceedings of the First Control Applications Conference* September, 1992.

[HR] J. Huang and W.J. Rugh, "On a Nonlinear Multivariable Servomechanism Problem," *Automatica*, Vol. 26, No. 6, pp. 963-972, 1990.

[IB] A. Isidori and C.I. Byrnes, "Output Regulation of Nonlinear Systems", *IEEE Transactions on Automatic Control*, Vol. 35, No.2, pp. 131 - 140, 1990.

[L] C. F. Lin, "Modern Navigation, Guidance, and Control Processing," *Prentice Hall*, 1991.

[RNR] R.T. Reichert, R.A. Nichols, and W.J. Rugh, " Nonlinear Scheduling Approach for H-infinity/Mu-Synthesis Controllers", presented in *American Control Conference*, June 1992.

[SC] J. Shamma, and J.R. Cloutier, "A Linear Parameter Varying Approach to Gain Scheduled Missile Autopilot Design", *Proceedings of American Control Conference*, pp 1317-1321, June 1992.

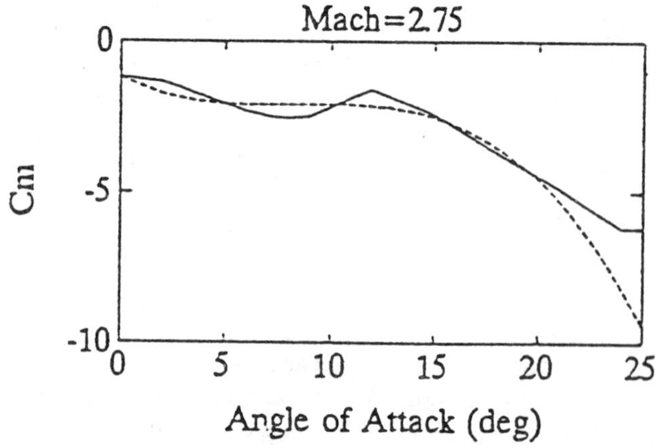

Figure 1 The approximate C_m (dashed) versus the true table data (solid) when $\delta_e = 0$

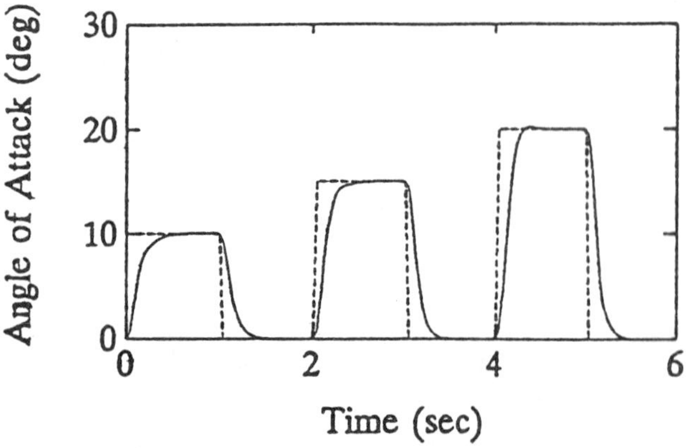

Figure 2 Performance of the servo-regulator simulated on the approximate aerocoefficients

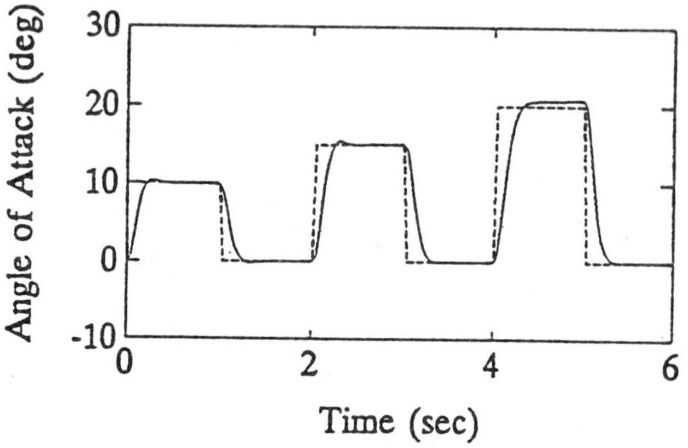

Figure 3 Performance of the servo-regulator simulated on the true aerocoefficient table

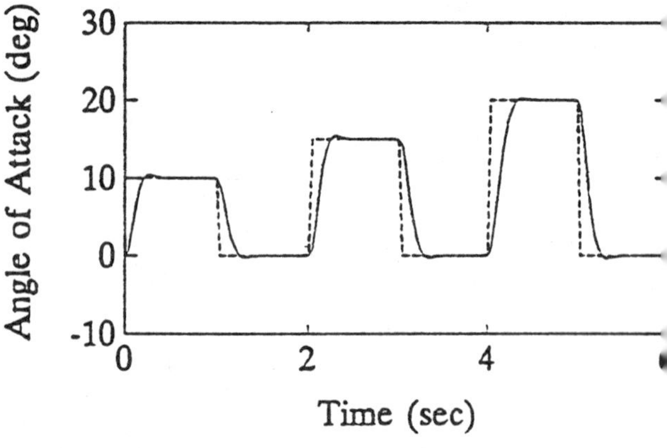

Figure 4 Performance of the robust servo-regulator simulated on the approximate aerocoefficients

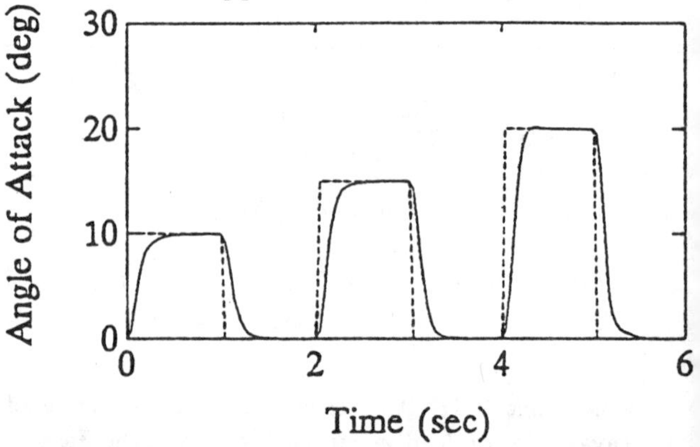

Figure 5 Performance of the robust servo-regulator simulated on the true aerocoefficient table

Proceedings of the
American Control Conference
San Francisco, California • June 1993

Full Conventional Envelope Longitudinal Axis Flight Control with Thrust Vectoring

James M. Buffington*, Andrew G. Sparks*, and Siva S. Banda†
WL/FIGC Bldg 146, 2210 Eighth St, Ste 21
Wright-Patterson AFB, Ohio 45433-7531
Tel: (513) 255-8680, Facsimile: (513) 476-4000
buff@falcon.flight.wpafb.af.mil

ABSTRACT

A full conventional envelope longitudinal axis control design is presented for a thrust-vectoring fighter aircraft. An inner-outer loop modular control structure is used to provide good flying qualities in the presence of highly structured uncertainty across a wide flight envelope. Simple, low-order control laws are designed for a version of an F-18 aircraft model. A minimal-order H_∞ design algorithm is used to aid in the design of an inner loop equalization controller. Structured singular value synthesis is used to design outer loop implicit model-following controllers. Structured singular values are used to analyze stability robustness to structured parametric uncertainty and actuator and sensor unmodeled dynamics. Nonlinear simulation is used for aircraft control system performance evaluation for large amplitude commands.

INTRODUCTION

Historically, the trend of flight control industry has been to use well-established single loop classical control system design techniques due to the inherent simple control structures. However, these methods provide no good means for guaranteed robustness to simultaneous structured uncertainties. The most natural approaches for addressing multiple structured uncertainties are robust multivariable control techniques.

Initial control gains obtained from multivariable design methods must be tuned to achieve performance objectives. Expensive and time-consuming "re-tuning" of the high-order control gains is required during configuration changes in the aircraft design process. Therefore, simple low-order flight control systems are necessary that do not sacrifice performance objectives and guarantee robustness to structured uncertainty. Simple control structures will also ease implementation difficulties, gain-scheduling for example, corresponding to the use of high-order controllers. The control law design presented in this paper develops low-order controllers that require minimal tuning and implementation effort while guaranteeing system robustness.

Other implementation difficulties inherent in multivariable controllers involve redundant control effectors. The addition of control effectors, such as thrust vectoring nozzles, presents the problem of allocating commands between effectors to obtain the desired response. Generally, multivariable control methods generate actuator commands without considering the possibility of redundant effectors "fighting" each other, i.e. redundant effector commands of opposite signs. This paper discusses the use of a control selector within the controller addressing these issues.

In [1], the design of a fixed H_∞ controller for a fighter aircraft flying a Herbst-type maneuver with multiple control effectors is presented. One condition along the maneuver trajectory is chosen as nominal and several other conditions along the trajectory are used to develop uncertainty models. Reference [2] considered the Herbst-type maneuver of [1] and presented longitudinal and lateral/directional axes designs at a single flight condition along the maneuver. Structured singular value or μ-synthesis was used to design a controller formulated in an implicit model-following framework allowing for direct incorporation of flying qualities specifications into the design.

This paper is an extension of [1] and [2] in that a model-following framework is used in an inner-outer loop control structure to provide a full envelope capability for the aircraft. The design goal is to obtain acceptable longitudinal aircraft flying qualities, despite modeling uncertainties, using conventional aerodynamic control effectors and thrust vectoring for a wide flight envelope.

In the following sections, the problem addressed in this paper is defined, and a description of the aircraft model is given. The body of the paper begins with descriptions of the controller structure and design. Subsections are organized in the natural order of the design process. These subsections are organized to present background theory followed by application of the theory . Flying qualities, robustness, and nonlinear analyses of the control design are then presented followed by a summary of conclusions.

PROBLEM AND MODEL DESCRIPTION

This paper addresses robust longitudinal stabilization for the full conventional flight envelope of a fighter aircraft. The conventional flight envelope is defined as the subsonic Mach regime between sea level and 40,000 ft. Dynamic pressure ranges from 50 psf to 1000 psf. These limitations correspond to angles of attack up to approximately 25 deg. Figure 1 shows the conventional flight envelope with design and analysis model flight conditions indicated.

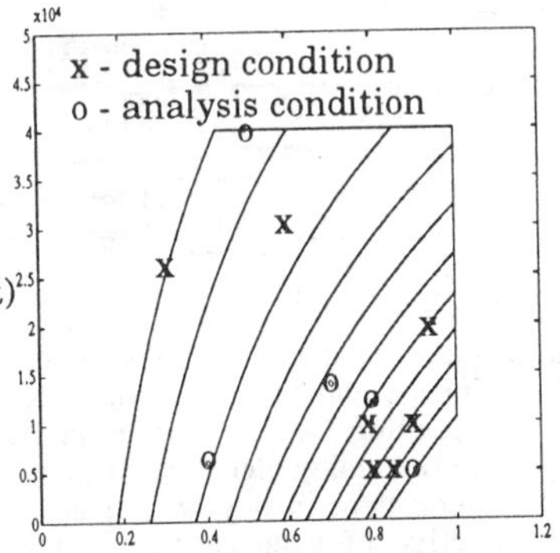

Figure 1: Flight Envelope

A high-fidelity nonlinear 6 DOF model of a modified F-18 aircraft augmented with thrust vectoring nozzles is used for nonlinear simulations and linear model generation at trim conditions for control design. Leading and trailing edge flaps are scheduled with angle of attack to provide optimum lift-to-drag ratio. The nonlinear aircraft model has detailed aerodynamic, propulsion, actuator, and sensor FORTRAN modules. The extensive aerodynamic and propulsion databases were obtained from well documented flight and wind tunnel testing and augmented with thrust vectoring test data. The actuator models include rate and position limits. The sensors are modeled with infinitely fast dynamics.

As alluded to above, the nonlinear model is linearized at trim conditions to generate state-space models for design. The linear models have ten state variables that represent the aircraft dynamics within a small region around the trim condition. For the flight envelope of interest, the longitudinal and lateral/directional dynamics are sufficiently decoupled to partition the dynamics into a fifth order model for the longitudinal axis and a fifth order model for the lateral/directional axes. This paper describes only the longitudinal dynamics model described by angle of attack (α), pitch rate (q), velocity (u), altitude (h), and pitch angle (θ) state variables. Since the pilot controls the trajectory states (u, h θ),

* Aerospace Engineer, Control Dynamics Branch, Member AIAA
† Aerospace Engineer, Control Dynamics Branch, Associate Fellow AIAA

they are eliminated from the linear models resulting in two state short-period longitudinal linear models of the following form:

$$\begin{bmatrix} \dot{\alpha} \\ \dot{q} \end{bmatrix} = \begin{bmatrix} Z_\alpha & 1 \\ M_\alpha & M_q \end{bmatrix} \begin{bmatrix} \alpha \\ q \end{bmatrix} + \begin{bmatrix} Z_{\delta_E} & Z_{\delta_{PTV}} \\ M_{\delta_E} & M_{\delta_{PTV}} \end{bmatrix} \begin{bmatrix} \delta_E \\ \delta_{PTV} \end{bmatrix}$$

$$= A \begin{bmatrix} \alpha \\ q \end{bmatrix} + B \begin{bmatrix} \delta_E \\ \delta_{PTV} \end{bmatrix} \qquad (1)$$

where δ_E is the elevator deflection, δ_{PTV} is the thrust vectoring nozzle deflection in the pitch axis, Z_α, $Z_{\delta E}$, and $Z_{\delta PTV}$ are z-direction force derivatives, and M_α, M_q, $M_{\delta E}$, and $M_{\delta PTV}$ are the pitch moment derivatives. Short-period longitudinal linear models of this form are generated at the design conditions indicated by figure 1.

CONTROLLER STRUCTURE AND DESIGN

The longitudinal axis manual flight control system generates elevator and pitch thrust vector commands from angle-of-attack commands. These control effector commands stabilize the short period aircraft dynamics across a wide conventional flight envelope.

The structure of the longitudinal flight control system is modular, where each control module is designed for a specific purpose. Figure 2 shows this modular control structure.

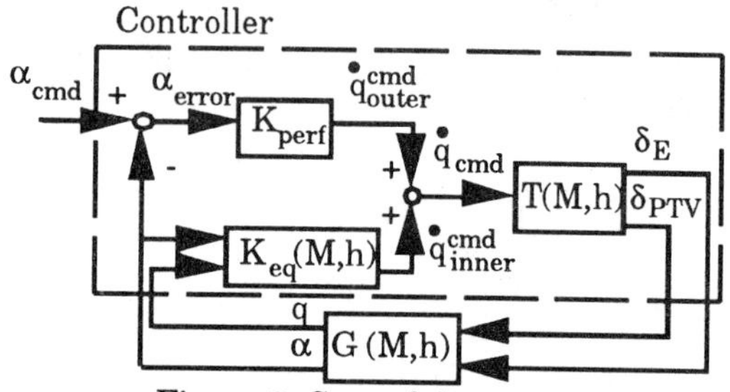

Figure 2: Control Structure

There are three control system modules: the nonlinear control selector (T), the inner equalization controller (K_{eq}), and the outer performance controller (K_{perf}). The controlled plant is represented by the remaining element of figure 2 (G), and Mach number and altitude dependency is indicated by (M,h). The design and objective of each control system component is described in detail in the following sections.

Control Selector

The idea behind the control selector is to introduce generalized controls in cases where there are redundant control effectors [1]. Generalized controls keep the force-moment generation accounting decoupled from the remaining control system (i.e. inner and outer loop components) . The control selector dictates how the control effectors will generate the necessary forces and moments commanded by the rest of the control system. Preserving the rotational accelerations due to an actual control command (u) and a generalized control command (u^*) results in

$$B^* u^* = Bu, \qquad (2)$$

where B is the actual control distribution matrix, and B^* is the generalized control distribution matrix. Therefore, the mapping from the generalized controls to the control effectors,

$$u = Tu^*, \qquad (3)$$

becomes the control selector

$$T = B^\# B^* \qquad (4)$$

where $B^\#$ is the pseudo-inverse of B. Note that if B has full row rank, then B^* is exactly obtainable, and the realization of the control selector, T, and open-loop plant, G, is $\tilde{G}$ (A,B^*,C,0) which is used as the design model for the inner loop equalization controller in the next section.

The actual control surface commands for the longitudinal control system are elevator and pitch thrust vector commands, and the generalized control is pitch acceleration

$$u = \begin{bmatrix} \delta_E \\ \delta_{PTV} \end{bmatrix} \qquad u^* = \dot{q}_{cmd} \qquad B^* = \begin{bmatrix} 0 \\ 1 \end{bmatrix}. \qquad (5)$$

Practical implementation issues, such as blending of thrust vectoring commands, are also addressed within the control selector. Consider the following partitioning of the control distribution matrix

$$B = [B_{aero} \;\; B_{tvec}], \qquad (6)$$

where B_{aero} is the aerodynamic control effector partition, and B_{tvec} is the thrust vectoring effector partition. A daisy-chain method is used to generate thrust vector commands. Thrust vectoring is used only when the aerodynamic surfaces are not able to generate the necessary forces and moments required for commanded maneuvers. Nonlinear elements, such as position and rate limiters, are required to implement the daisy-chain thus making the control selector nonlinear. Figure 3 shows the structure of the nonlinear control selector.

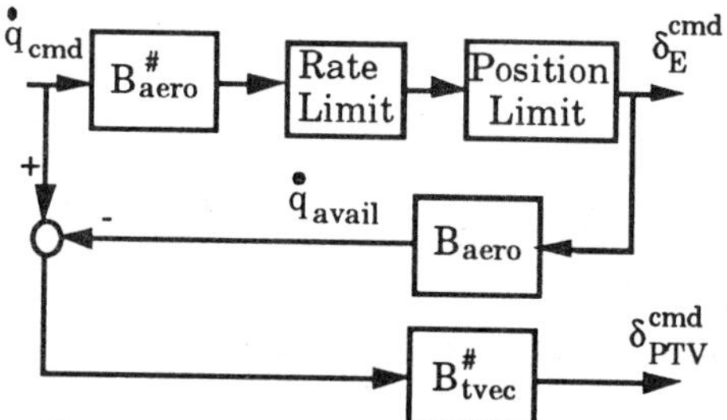

Figure 3: Nonlinear Control Selector

A limited elevator command (δ^{cmd}_E) is generated from a pitch acceleration command ($\dot{q}_{cmd}$) via the pseudo-inverse of the aerodynamic control distribution partition ($B^\#_{aero}$) and elevator rate and position limits. An achievable pitch acceleration ($\dot{q}_{avail}$) is computed from the limited elevator command using the aerodynamic control distribution (B_{aero}). The difference of the commanded and achievable pitch acceleration is transformed to a pitch thrust vector command (δ^{cmd}_{PTV}) using the pseudo-inverse of the thrust vector control distribution partition ($B^\#_{tvec}$).

Minimal-Order H_∞ Inner Equalization Controller

The purpose of the inner loop equalization controller is, as the name suggests, to equalize the aircraft dynamics across the flight envelope between angle of attack response and commanded pitch acceleration. In other words, the goal of the inner loop is to reduce the variation of the aircraft dynamics between operating conditions, thereby reducing the modeling uncertainty between flight condition dependent aircraft models. Successfully reducing the modeling uncertainty provides a greater possibility that one robust performance controller will control the aircraft across all operating conditions. Therefore, an effective inner loop controller must be designed to reduce the relative error between aircraft models. The relative error of a given linear model (P) and a nominal linear model (P_0) is given by

$$\Delta = (P - P_0)P_0^{-1}, \qquad (7)$$

where P_0 is a nonsingular reference transfer function. Summarizing Safanov and Chiang's robustness theorem [3], an outer loop stabilizing controller of P_0 will stabilize P provided the maximum singular value of the relative error is less than unity across the controller bandwidth.

A minimal-order H_∞ design algorithm [4],[5] is used to generate controllers that equalize the dynamics across the flight envelope. The controller has the Luenberger observer-based structure shown in figure 4 and has dimension equal to the number of plant states minus the number of plant measurements.

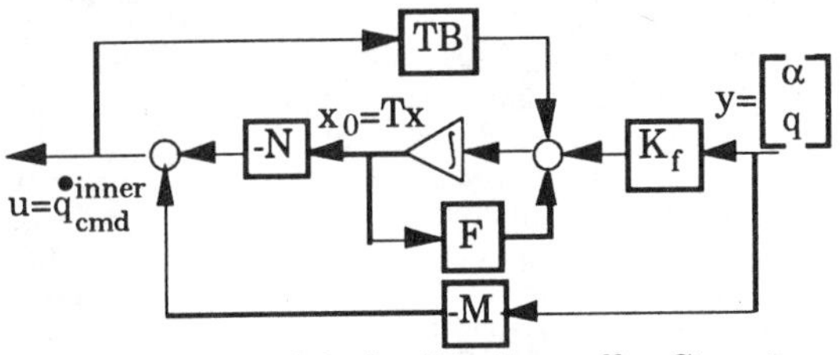

Figure 4: Minimal-Order H_∞ Controller Structure

Controllers are designed using the minimal-order H_∞ design method at the discrete flight conditions of figure 1. A linear model of the control selector (T), the open loop aircraft dynamics (G), and the inner equalization controller (K_{eq}) is represented by P. Since P is a function of flight condition, the equalization controller must be scheduled against a slowly-varying flight condition-dependent parameter [6], such as dynamic pressure, or must be robust across the flight envelope. Because the aircraft dynamics vary greatly across a wide envelope, it is highly unlikely one robust controller can be designed. Thus, the inner equalization controller gains are scheduled across the flight envelope as functions of dynamic pressure.

The performance weight used in the inner loop design represents the inverse of the desired equalized dynamics. The desired equalized dynamics are chosen to be close to the dynamics of the high dynamic pressure flight conditions to prevent positive feedback from diminishing the fast dynamics at high dynamic pressure conditions. With a first order performance weight augmented to the open-loop aircraft dynamics, the number of design states becomes three, and the number of inputs and outputs remains at one and two respectively. Therefore, the order of the equalization controller is one (# of states - # of measurements). The performance weight used for the inner equalization design is

$$W_{eq} = \frac{510(s+10)}{s+100}. \qquad (8)$$

The resulting controller elements are

$$F = -40 \quad K_f = [1 \quad 1] \qquad T = [0 \quad .0247 \quad 0]$$

$$N = N(\bar{q}) \qquad M = [M_1(\bar{q}) \quad M_2(\bar{q})]. \qquad (9)$$

Only three control parameters require scheduling with dynamic pressure ($\bar{q}$). The elements of N and M are fit using least-squares polynomial curve-fits, linear in dynamic pressure:

$$N(\bar{q}) = -.312\,\bar{q} + 461$$

$$M_1(\bar{q}) = -.058\,\bar{q} + 50.5 \qquad M_2(\bar{q}) = -.006\,\bar{q} + 8.11 \qquad (10)$$

The controller given by eqs.(9) and (10) provides closely matched frequency responses of the closed inner-loop transfer function (P) from $\dot{q}^{outer}_{cmd}$ to α across the flight envelope as shown in figure 5.

To analyze the variation of aircraft dynamics at different flight conditions, the relative error defined by eq.(7) is computed for a given linear model (P) and a nominal linear model (P_0). In order to evaluate the relative error between these equalized models, the closed inner-loop model (P) at 0.95 Mach and 20 kft is arbitrarily chosen as the nominal model (P_0). Figure 6 shows the maximum singular values of the model errors relative to P_0 across the flight envelope at design conditions given in table 1. Since the closed inner-loop errors relative to the nominal condition are less than unity for all frequencies and across the flight envelope, P_0 is used as the open outer-loop design plant for the performance controller.

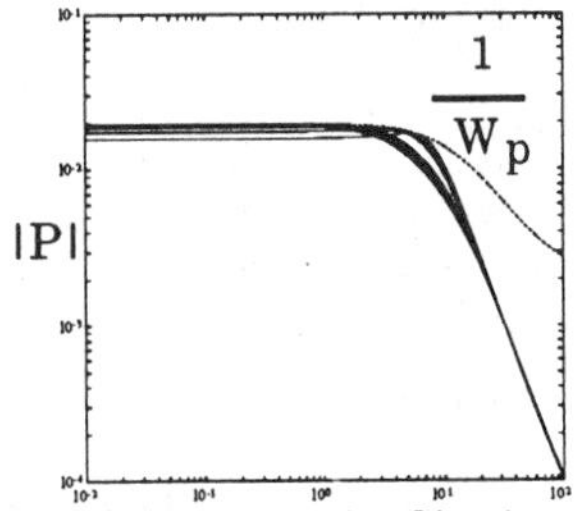

Frequency (rad/sec)
Figure 5: Full Envelope Equalization

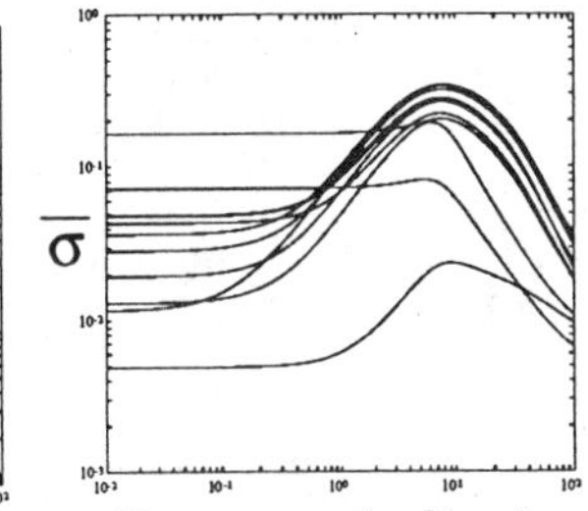

Frequency (rad/sec)
Figure 6: Closed Inner-Loop Errors

μ-Synthesis Outer Performance Controller

The general output feedback H_∞ design problem is to find a controller K(s) such that the disturbance to controlled output transfer function (T_{zw}) is bounded [7]. The structured singular value (μ) of a matrix $M \in C^{n \times n}$ is defined as the inverse of the size of the smallest destabilizing perturbation of a given structure [8], [9]. Combination of general output feedback H_∞ design theory and structured singular value analysis theory form a design technique known as μ-synthesis [10], [11]. By scaling the H_∞ system, the bound on T_{zw} can be reduced. Using this idea, the D-K iteration synthesis technique is defined by

$$\underset{\text{Stabilizing } K(s)}{min} \left\{ \underset{\underline{D}(s) \in \mathbf{D}}{min} \| \underline{D}(s)\, F_l(P,K)\, \underline{D}(s)^{-1} \|_\infty \right\}, \qquad (11)$$

where $\underline{D}(s)$ is a real-rational, stable, minimum phase transfer function that approximates the D scales over frequency since optimum D-scaling is performed at each frequency. $F_l(P,K)$ is the lower linear fractional transformation [12] of the design plant P and stabilizing controller K.

The purpose of the outer performance controller is to generate a pitch acceleration command from an angle-of-attack command that produces a desired robust angle-of-attack response from the aircraft. This problem is formulated as an implicit model-following problem, where the ideal model to be followed is chosen to be a second-order filter based on desired flying qualities

$$\frac{\alpha_{ideal}}{\alpha_{cmd}} = \frac{\omega^2_{ideal}}{s^2 + 2\,\zeta_{ideal}\,\omega_{ideal}\,s + \omega^2_{ideal}}. \qquad (12)$$

Using this ideal model-following approach, the outer performance controller design model is developed in figure 7.

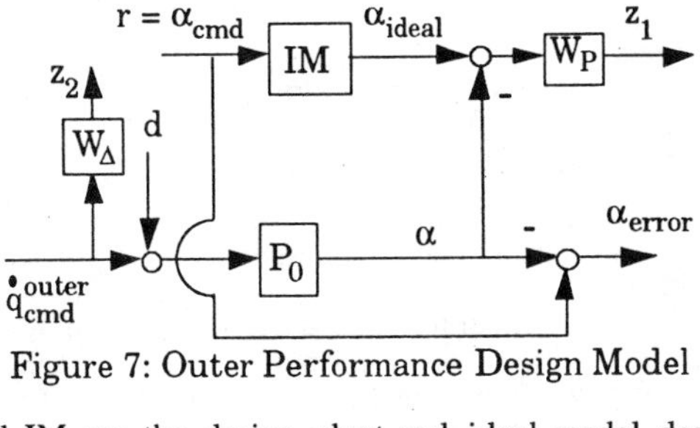

Figure 7: Outer Performance Design Model

P_0 and IM are the design plant and ideal model described previously, and W_P and W_Δ are design weights.

The robust performance controller (K_{perf}) for P_0 is designed using μ-synthesis with the performance and input uncertainty weights set as follows

$$W_P = \frac{.25s + 50}{s + 5} \qquad W_\Delta = \frac{10s + 1000}{s + 10000}. \tag{13}$$

Unlike the responses in the lateral/directional axes, the desired pitch response is not uniform across the flight envelope; the pilot would like to feel a faster response at higher speeds. To account for the different performance requirements, two robust performance controllers are designed using two ideal models based on eq.(12): 1) a low dynamic pressure controller using a slow ideal model (ζ_{ideal}=.8, ω_{ideal}=3 rad/sec), and 2) a high dynamic pressure controller using a fast ideal model (ζ_{ideal}=.8, ω_{ideal}=5 rad/sec). The choice of the ideal model parameters is based upon flying quality requirements [13]. Implementation of the two outer-loop performance controllers is achieved through a simple linear blending parameter (δ_b) that generates a combination of controller commands as shown in figure 8.

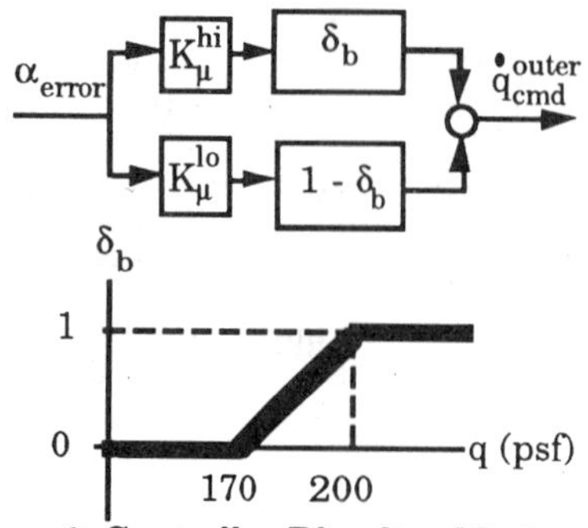

Figure 8: Controller Blending Mechanism

Structured singular value synthesis typically generates controllers of an order much higher than the original plant because of the design weights and the frequency dependent scalings. Truncation of a minimal balanced realization [14] of the low and high dynamic pressure controllers reveals that the original 13th-order controllers are feasibly reduced to 4th-order controllers without destroying the original robustness.

ANALYSIS OF RESULTS

This section describes the results and analysis of the results from implementation of the control system described in the previous section. Flying quality results based on low-order equivalent short-period approximations are first presented. Robustness to unmodeled dynamics and parametric uncertainties is then assessed, and finally nonlinear time responses are presented.

Flying Qualities Analysis

Several flying qualities measures are used to analyze the handling characteristics of the aircraft and the designed control system. The measures for short-term pitch response are given in terms of low-order equivalent systems (LOES) that represent pitch rate response to pilot stick deflection inputs.

$$\frac{q}{\delta_{stick}} = \frac{K_q\left(s + \frac{1}{T_{\theta 2}}\right)e^{-\tau_e s}}{s^2 + 2\zeta_{sp}\omega_{sp}s + \omega_{sp}^2}, \tag{14}$$

where ζ_{sp} is equivalent short-period damping, ω_{sp} is equivalent short-period frequency, $T_{\theta 2}$ corresponds to the pitch rate zero , and τ_e is equivalent pitch time delay. Details of LOES and acceptable values of the LOES parameters are given in [13]. The complete scheduled flight control system, full-order actuator models, and second-order aircraft short-period models are used to generate high-order closed-loop aircraft linear models. Low-order equivalent systems are generated from the high-order models using an equivalent system transfer function matching program.

All LOES parameters of eq.(14) meet Category A Level 1 flying quality specifications for all flight conditions of figure 1.

Robustness Analysis

Structured singular value analysis techniques are used to analyze stability robustness of the control system design to uncertainties corresponding to unmodeled actuator and sensor dynamics, parameters in the plant model, and blending of high and low dynamic pressure outer performance controllers.

A high-order detailed elevator actuator model is reduced to a simple 4th-order model to avoid very small time-step integration during nonlinear simulation. The reduced order actuator model is used in the analysis model, and the difference between the high-order and low-order models represents the unmodeled actuator dynamics. The actual error dynamics between these models are fit to a real rational transfer function that represents the weighting function for the actuator uncertainty

$$W_E = \frac{.63s^2 + 3.03s + .078}{s^2 + 68.4s + 1900}. \tag{15}$$

The angle of attack and pitch rate sensor dynamics are captured entirely as unstructured uncertainty. The sensor dynamics are estimated from flight test data and fit to real rational transfer functions representing measurement uncertainty weighting functions

$$W_\alpha = \frac{21.9s^2 + 1120s + 91100}{s^2 + 574s + 1140000}$$

$$W_q = \frac{.745s^3 + 152s^2 + 95.9s + 1.38}{s^3 + 626s^2 + 173000s + 235000}. \tag{16}$$

An extensive aerodynamic uncertainty database, developed from wind tunnel and flight test data, is used to generate structured uncertainty models. For simplicity, the uncertainty model for each state-space element,

$$\Delta A = \begin{bmatrix} \pm.02|A(1,1)| & 0 \\ \pm.04|A(2,1)| & \pm2|A(2,2)| \end{bmatrix}$$

$$\Delta B = \begin{bmatrix} \pm.22|B(1,1)| & \pm.22|B(1,2)| \\ \pm.04|B(2,1)| & \pm.04|B(2,2)| \end{bmatrix}, \tag{17}$$

is held constant at the worst flight condition case thus making the parameter uncertainty models conservative in a sense.

Recall from previous sections that for better flying qualities, high and low dynamic pressure performance controllers are designed and implemented by blending both controller commands with the blending parameter δ_b. The blending mechanism is normalized such that the blending parameter for analysis, $\bar{\delta}_b$, varies between -1 and 1. Therefore analyzing robustness to the parameter $\bar{\delta}_b$ is equivalent to analyzing robustness for all outer-loop controller command combinations.

Figure 9 shows the robustness analysis model including the structure of the uncertainty as well as the normalization weighting elements. Figure 10 shows the robust stability plots of the structure shown in figure 9 for all analysis conditions of figure 1. It is interesting to note the absence of a peak near the short period frequency suggesting insensitivity of the short period dynamics to the given uncertainty structure. The peak at approximately 40 rad/sec corresponds to sensitivity to angle of attack measurements.

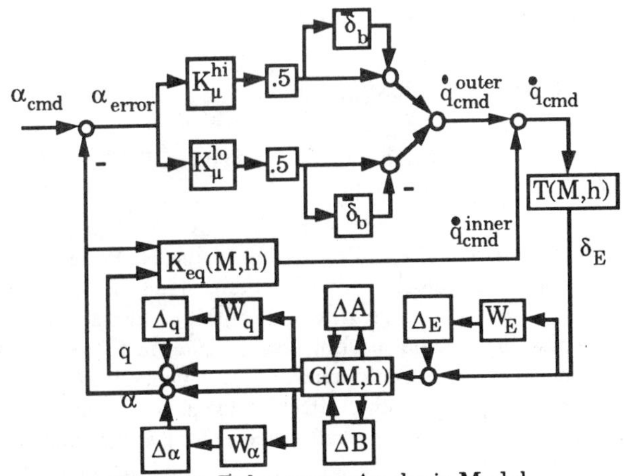

Figure 9: Robustness Analysis Model

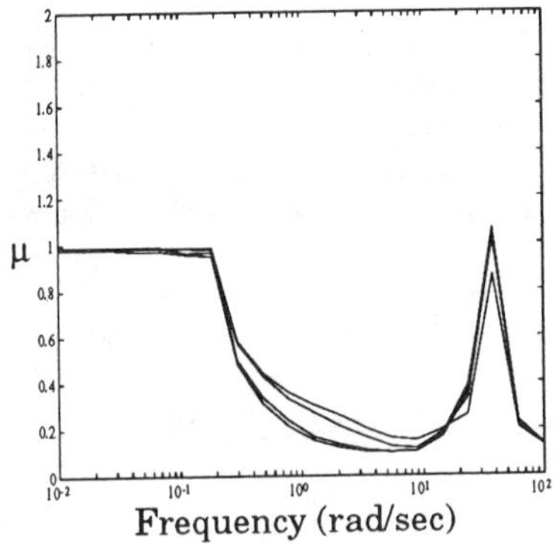

Figure 10: Robust Stability

Nonlinear Analysis

Figure 11 shows the nonlinear time responses for a 10 deg. angle of attack step input at 0.3 Mach and 10 kft that requires pitch thrust vectoring.

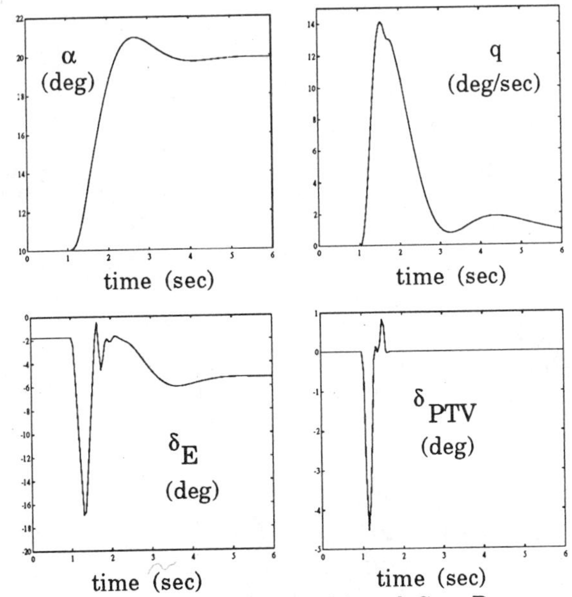

Figure 11: Nonlinear Angle of Attack Step Response

This maneuver is severe enough to rate saturate the elevator and thus engage the thrust vectoring commands through the logic of the nonlinear control selector without going unstable and still maintaining good performance.

CONCLUSIONS

A simple inner-outer loop control structure is presented for robust flight control design. Daisy-chaining is used as a practical mechanism for blending thrust vector commands with conventional elevator commands. H_∞ and structured singular value theories are used to design and analyze a control system that accounts for desired flying qualities using an implicit angle of attack ideal model. The full conventional envelope controller is robust to parametric uncertainty and unmodeled dynamics and performs well in the nonlinear simulation. The flight control design presented is a good first step toward high angle of attack supermaneuvering control design.

REFERENCES

[1] R. Y. Chiang, M. G. Safanov, K. P. Madden, and J. A. Tekawy, " A Fixed H^∞ Controller for a Supermaneuverable Fighter Aircraft Performing the Herbst Maneuver," *Presented at the 29th IEEE Conference on Decision and Control*, Honolulu HI, Dec. 1990.

[2] A. Sparks and S. Banda, "Application of Structured Singular Value Synthesis to a Fighter Aircraft," *Proceedings of the 1992 American Control Conference*, Chicago IL, pp. 1301-1305, Jun. 1992.

[3] M. G. Safanov and R. Y. Chiang, "Model Reduction for Robust Control: A Schur Relative Error Method," *International Journal of Adaptive Control and Signal Processing*, 1988, Vol.2, pp.259-272.

[4] H. H. Yeh, J. L. Rawson, and S. S. Banda, "Robust Control Design with Real-Parameter Uncertainties," *Proceedings of the 1992 American Control Conference*, Chicago IL, pp. 3249-3256, Jun. 1992.

[5] J. M. Buffington, H. H. Yeh, and S. S. Banda, "Robust Control Design for an Aircraft Gust Attenuation Problem," *Proceedings of the 31st Conference on Decision and Control*, Tucson AZ, pp.560-561, Dec. 1992.

[6] J. S. Shamma and M. Athans, "Gain Scheduling: Potential Hazards and Possible Remedies," *IEEE Control Systems Magazine*, June 1992, Vol.12, No.3, pp.101-107.

[7] J. Doyle, K. Glover, P. Khargonekar, and B. Francis, "State-Space Solutions to Standard H_2 and H_∞ Control Problems," *IEEE Transactions on Automatic Control*, Aug. 1989, Vol.34, No.8, pp. 831-847.

[8] J. C. Doyle, J. Wall, and G. Stein, "Performance and Robustness Analysis for Structured Uncertainty," *Proceedings of the 21st IEEE Conference on Decision and Control*, Orlando FL, pp.629-636, Dec. 1982.

[9] J. C. Doyle, "Analysis of Feedback Systems with Structured Uncertainties," *IEEE Proceedings*, Vol. 129, Part D, No. 6, pp.242-250, Nov. 1982.

[10] J. C. Doyle, "Structured Uncertainty in Control System Design," *Proceedings of the 24th IEEE Conference on Decision and Control*, Ft. Lauderdale FL, pp. 260-265, Dec. 1985.

[11] G. J. Balas, A. K. Packard, J. C. Doyle, K. Glover, and R. Smith, "Development of Advanced Control Design Software for Researchers and Engineers," *Proceedings of the 1991 American Control Conference*, Boston MA, pp. 996-1001, Jun. 1991.

[12] J. Doyle, A. Packard, and K. Zhou, "Review of LFTs, LMIs, and μ," *Proceedings of the 30th IEEE Conference on Decision and Control*, Brighton UK, pp. 1227-1232, Dec. 1991.

[13] Military Standard - Flying Qualities of Piloted Airplanes, MIL-STD-1797A, 30 Jan. 1990.

[14] J. M. Maciejowski, Multivariable Feedback Design, Addison-Wesley Publishing Company, Wokingham UK, 1989, p. 392.

Proceedings of the
American Control Conference
San Francisco, California • June 1993

A Full-Authority 4D Guidance Algorithm for Conventional Aircraft

Ilie Stiharu-Alexe*, Carmen Stiharu-Alexe+

Laboratoire d'Automatique de Grenoble, ENSIEG, B.P. 46, 38402 Saint Martin d'Heres, FRANCE

Abstract

A full-authority 4D guidance algorithm for a conventional aircraft is developed using Nonlinear Inverse Dynamics (NID) theory. The control task is simplified by the use of a forced singular perturbation, overall system dynamics being separated into fast and slow reduced-order systems. An analytical solution to inverting the slow time-scale dynamics is found through the Inverse Kinematics Problem (IKP). The algorithm's performance is evaluated in the terms of the tracking error.

1. Nomenclature

F_x, F_y, F_z	- aerodynamic forces in body frame
g	- acceleration of gravitation
I_x, I_y, I_z, J_{xz}	- moments of inertia
L, M, N	- roll moment, pitch moment, yaw moment
$C_{(.)}$	- nondimensional force coefficient
m	- mass
ρ	- air density
S	- equivalent surface
T_m	- maximum engine thrust
U, V, W	- velocity components in body frame
P, Q, R	- roll rate, pitch rate, yaw rate
V_N, V_E, V_D	- inertial velocity components (north, east, down, respectively)
X_N, X_E, X_D	- inertial position coordinates
α	- angle of attack
β	- sideslip
Δ_e, Δ_t, Δ_a, Δ_r	- elevator, thrust, aileron, rudder controls
Φ, Θ, Ψ	- roll attitude, pitch attitude, yaw attitude
Superscripts	
D	- desired value
Subscripts	
B	- body frame
I	- inertial frame
W	- wind frame

2. Introduction

A typical task for a conventional aircraft maneuver is that of tracking a 4D trajectory defined by several waypoints. Using the singular perturbation theory to separate overall system dynamics into a fast and a slow reduced-order systems, the tracking algorithm developed in this paper results in control laws allowing for a great flexibility in trajectory definition. Control laws that are based upon NID offer the potential for providing improved level of safety and performance in all flight conditions over the competing designs developed using linearizing assumptions. This is due to the NID controller's more accurate representation of the forces and moments that arise in response to large state and control perturbations. The difficulty in position control lies in the fact that strict application of the NID differentiation techniques leads one to using the force generating effect of the control surfaces to control the conventional aircraft which is not the most practical way to use controls that are primarily moment generating devices. In order to avoid this practical inconvenient, the NID technique is used to control only body attitude [1] Φ,Θ,Ψ, by the means of elevator, aileron and rudder, which are assumed to be only moment generating devices [2]. The thrust, assumed to be only force generating device, is used to control body forces in the slow system by solving the IKP. A particularity of this approach consists of a linear feedback control, at the slow system level, meant to minimize the tracking error according to a proportional navigation criterion. Finally, the algorithm's performance is evaluated in terms of the tracking error.

*Assistant Professor in Aeronautics

+Lecturer in Aeronautics

3. System Model

A six-degree-of-freedom conventional aircraft model [3] is used as the basis for the algorithm development. The inertial position and velocity dynamics are presented as follows:

$$\begin{pmatrix} \dot{x}_N \\ \dot{y}_E \\ \dot{z}_D \end{pmatrix} = \begin{pmatrix} V_N \\ V_E \\ V_D \end{pmatrix} \tag{1}$$

$$\begin{pmatrix} \dot{x}_N \\ \dot{y}_E \\ \dot{z}_D \end{pmatrix} = L_{IB} \begin{pmatrix} U \\ V \\ W \end{pmatrix} \tag{2}$$

$$\begin{pmatrix} \dot{V}_N \\ \dot{V}_E \\ \dot{V}_D \end{pmatrix} = L_{IB} \begin{pmatrix} f_x \\ f_y \\ f_z \end{pmatrix} + \begin{pmatrix} 0 \\ 0 \\ g \end{pmatrix} \tag{3}$$

$$\begin{pmatrix} \dot{U} \\ \dot{V} \\ \dot{W} \end{pmatrix} = \begin{pmatrix} f_x - QW + RV \\ f_y - RU + PW \\ f_z - PV + QU \end{pmatrix} \tag{4}$$

$$f_x = F_x / m, \; f_y = F_y / m, \; f_z = F_z / m \tag{5}$$

where L_{IB} is the body-to-inertial frame transformation matrix. The dominant force control in Eq.(3) is the thrust control which controls the longitudinal force f_x and the normal force f_z. The attitude dynamics are represented by:

$$\begin{pmatrix}\dot{P}\\ \dot{Q}\\ \dot{R}\end{pmatrix} = \begin{pmatrix}(E_p I_z + E_r J_{xz})/(I_x I_z - J_{xz}^2)\\ (M + J_{xz}(R^2 - P^2) + (I_z - I_x)PR)/I_y\\ (E_r I_x + E_p J_{xz})/(I_x I_z - J_{xz}^2)\end{pmatrix} \tag{6}$$

$$E_p = J_{xz}PQ - (I_y - I_z)QR + L \tag{7}$$

$$E_r = -J_{xz}QR + (I_x - I_y)PQ + N \tag{8}$$

$$\begin{pmatrix}\dot{\Phi}\\ \dot{\Theta}\\ \dot{\Psi}\end{pmatrix} = \begin{pmatrix}1 & \sin\Phi tg\Theta & \cos\Phi tg\Theta\\ 0 & \cos\Phi & -\sin\Phi\\ 0 & \sin\Phi\sec\Theta & \cos\Phi\sec\Theta\end{pmatrix}\begin{pmatrix}P\\ Q\\ R\end{pmatrix} \tag{9}$$

where the moment terms L, M and N in Eq.(6) are largely functions of the longitudinal and lateral controls Δ_e, $\Delta_a$and Δ_r. One important assumption made in this model is that the elevator, aileron and rudder are primarily moment generating controls and as such do not make a significant contribution to the body forces. Only the thrust control is assumed to be a direct force control. This assumption, supported by the fast and slow time-scale controller approach, has been justified for the conventional aircraft model by the fact that the control forces caused by ailerons, rudder and elevator make certain input-output maps nearly singular [2], [6].

4. Approach to the 4D Guidance Algorithm

The singular perturbation theory is used to reduce the large 12th order system into two small systems having slow and fast dynamics. The main separation is made between the position dynamics Eq.(1)-(5), and the attitude dynamics Eq.(6)-(9), in order to control the slow states X_N, Y_E, Z_D, V_N, V_E, V_D and the fast states P, Q, R, Φ, Θ, Ψ. To accomplish that the system state equations are written in the form:

$$\dot{x} = f(x,z,u,\varepsilon,t) \tag{10}$$

$$\varepsilon\dot{z} = g(x,z,u,\varepsilon,t) \tag{11}$$

where ε is a small parameter, x represents the slow time-scale dynamics and z represents the fast dynamics. For the slow time scale, ε=0, Eq.(11) becomes algebraic $g(\bar{x},\bar{z},\bar{u},0,t) = 0$, where $\bar{x},\bar{z},\bar{u}$ are solutions to the approximate Eq.(10) and Eq.(11) with ε=0. The algebraic equation (11) may be solved for $\bar{z}$ as a function of $\bar{x}$ and $\bar{u}$:

$$\bar{z} = G(\bar{x},\bar{u},t) \tag{12}$$

substituting Eq. (12) in Eq. (10) yields:

$$\dot{\bar{x}} = f[\bar{x},G(\bar{x},\bar{u},t),\bar{u},0,t] = f(\bar{x},\bar{u},t) \tag{13}$$

Setting ε to zero causes the fast dynamics to became algebraic, implying that the dynamics responds instantaneously in the slow time-scale. This results in the slow time-scale problem in which the dynamic equations for the body attitude are replaced by algebraic equations i.e. $\dot{\bar{\Phi}} = \dot{\bar{\Theta}} = \dot{\bar{\Psi}} = 0$.

In this algebraic equations $\bar{\Phi},\bar{\Theta},\bar{\Psi}$ are used to represent the slow time-scale values of the body attitudes. An interpretation of this solution is that in the slow time-scale the fast states have already reached their steady-state values. Because of the assumption that the system dynamics have a block-triangular form [4], the only control to be considered in the slow dynamics is the thrust control. Meanwhile at this level the steady-state values $\bar{\Phi},\bar{\Theta},\bar{\Psi}$ appears as pseudo controls for the fast time-scale system. Therefore, the position dynamics are controlled through the body attitude and thrust controls. Then the aircraft will be controlled using throttle to adjust the magnitude of the thrust vector and body attitude controls to orient the thrust vector in the desired direction. Since the vehicle is in moment equilibrium in the slow time-scale, the moment generated by the throttle is trimmed out by the elevator control. Fig. 1 presents the block diagram of the two time-scale controllers. The slow time-scale controller is designed to track the X_N (t), Y_E(t), Z_D(t) position coordinates through attitude references and the thrust control Δ_{tc}. The fast time-scale controller tracks attitude references of the slow time-scale system using Δ_{ec}, Δ_{ac}, Δ_{rc} controls. First order actuator dynamics are considered in conjunction with adequate limitations of displacements and rates for simulation purposes.

5. Nonlinear Inverse Dynamics

Fig. 2 presents the block diagram of the fast time-scale system controlled according to the NID differentiation technique [5], [6]. For this approach the fast system dynamics are considered of the form:

$$\dot{z} = A(z) + B(z)u_f \tag{14}$$

$$y = Cz \tag{15}$$

where $y = [\Phi, \Theta, \Psi]^T$ represents the controlled state and $u = [\Delta_{ec}, \Delta_{ac}, \Delta_{rc}]^T$ the fast time-scale system control vector. As the NID technique requires, the controlled states are successively differentiated two times until control terms appear. That can be written in a compact form:

$$y^{<2>} = A^*(z) + B^*(z)u_f \tag{16}$$

with A^* and B^* presented in [7]. A sufficient condition for the existence of an inverse system model to Eq.(14) and Eq.(15) is that B in Eq.(16) be nonsingular [8]. In this case the inverse system model takes the form:

$$\dot{z} = [A(z) - B(z)F(z)] + B(z)G(z)v \tag{17}$$

$$u_f = -F(z) + G(z)v \tag{18}$$

where $v = y^{<2>}$ is the input of the inverse system, u is the output and $G(x)=[B(x)]^+$, $F(x)=[B(x)]^+A(x)$ with $(.)^+$ the pseudo inverse of the matrix. Applying the NID control law, Eq.(18), to the original system of Eq.(14) - (15) leaves it in the integrator-decoupled form $y^{<2>}=v$. Setting:

$$v = -P_1 y^{<1>} - P_0(y - y_D) \tag{19}$$

with P_k chosen as constant diagonal matrices, gives the original system the decoupled linear, time invariant dynamics

$$y^{<2>} + P_1 y^{<1>} + P_0 y = P_0 y_D \tag{20}$$

where y_D is the attitude pseudo control.

6. Slow Time-Scale Controller

The slow time-scale system is designed to track the $X_N^D(t), Y_E^D(t), Z_D^D(t)$ position coordinates of a desired trajectory thaught as a smooth path passing over imposed waypoints. A specific requirement for a performant tracking, according to the aircraft class, is that the maximum acceleration on the trajectory does not exceed the value imposed by the Admissible Load Factor (ALF). In order to test this technical requirement, at the level of the slow system, the reference acceleration converted into the body axis is bound to the value resulted from ALF (Fig. 3).

The main task of the slow time-scale controller is to supply with thrust and attitude commands $\overline{\Phi}, \overline{\Theta}, \overline{\Psi}$. On this purpose the left-hand side of Eq.(3) is replaced by the desired acceleration vector Eq.(21). At the slow time-scale body Euler angles in Eq.(21) are represented by their steady-state values $\overline{\Phi}, \overline{\Theta}, \overline{\Psi}$.

$$\begin{pmatrix} a_N^D \\ a_E^D \\ a_D^D - g \end{pmatrix} = L_{IB} \begin{pmatrix} f_x \\ f_y \\ f_z \end{pmatrix} \quad (21)$$

$$a^D = L_{IB} f \quad (21a)$$

Solving Eq.(21) for $\overline{\Phi}, \overline{\Theta}, \overline{\Psi}$ is the inverse kinematics problem [9,10] because the rotation matrix must be found. Since L_{IB} is purely a rotation transformation, the magnitudes of the acceleration vector a^D and the body specific force vector f must be equal in order to find a solution for the Euler angles. The thrust control is used to adjust the magnitude of the body forces because it is a direct force generating control and appears in the slow time-scale dynamics in f_x and f_z.

7. Solution to the Inverse Kinematics Problem

The solution of the IKP relies on the factorization:

$$L_{BI} = L_{BW} L_{WI} \quad (22)$$

where $L_{WI}(\Psi_W, \Theta_W, \Phi_W)$ is the inertial-to-wind transformation matrix and $L_{WB}(0, -\alpha, -\beta)$ is the body-to-wind transformation matrix.The use of the wind frame allows us to rewrite Eq.(21) in a more adequate way for aircraft:

$$f_{xW} = F_{xW}/m, \; f_{yW} = F_{yW}/m, \; f_{zW} = F_{yW}/m \quad (23)$$

exploiting the fact that the aerodynamic forces are primarily expressed in that frame. At this point Eq.(23) contains five unknowns: $\Theta_W, \Psi_W, \Phi_W, f_{xW}$ and f_{zW}. While f_{xW} and f_{zW} are strictly connected to the attack angle α and thrust, f_{yW} can be considered with its current value found from the aerodynamic model (or from sensed acceleration).

If the atmosphere is assumed to be at rest, the desired inertia velocity components can be related to the desired air speed V^D, heading Ψ_W, and flight-path angle Θ_W as follows:

$$V^D = (V_N^{D^2} + V_E^{D^2} + V_D^{D^2}) \quad (24a)$$

$$\Theta_W = \sin^{-1}(-V_D^D / V^D) \quad (24b)$$

$$\Psi_W = \tan^{-1}(V_D^D / V^D) \quad (24c)$$

Eq.(23) and Eq.(24) have been written with respect to the desired trajectory, i.e., the desired acceleration and speed. Considering the fact that currently the aircraft is not on the desired trajectory, a feedback was designed to minimize the tracking error using a proportional navigation criterion. This last one is implemented by means of two tracking errors defined with respect to the wind frame, the lateral deviation LD and the vertical deviation VD:

$$LD = -(X_N^D - X_N)\sin\Psi_W + (Y_E^D - Y_E)\cos\Psi_W \quad (25)$$

$$VD = Z_D^D - Z_D \quad (26)$$

Thus, before using the heading and flight-path angle in Eq.(23), their values are corrected according to a proportional law:

$$\Psi_W^c - \Psi_W = \Delta\Psi_W = K_1 \, LD \quad (27)$$

$$\Theta_W^c - \Theta_W = \Delta\Theta_W = K_2 \, VD \quad (28)$$

where K_1[rad/m] and K_2[rad/m] are linear feedback gains. Equating the three components from Eq.(23) yields:

$$a_N^D \cos\Theta_W^c \cos\Psi_W^c + a_E^D \cos\Theta_W^c \sin\Psi_W^c - a_D^D \sin\Theta_W^c = f_{xW} \quad (29)$$

$$a_N^D(\sin\Phi_W \sin\Theta_W^c \cos\Psi_W^c - \cos\Phi_W \sin\Psi_W^c) + a_E^D(\sin\Phi_W \sin\Theta_W^c \sin\Psi_W^c - \cos\Phi_W \cos\Psi_W^c) + a_D^D \sin\Phi_W \cos\Theta_W^c + V\Delta\dot{\Psi}_W = f_{yW} \quad (30)$$

$$a_N^D(\cos\Phi_W \sin\Theta_W^c \cos\Psi_W^c + \sin\Phi_W \sin\Psi_W^c) + a_E^D(\cos\Phi_W \sin\Theta_W^c \sin\Psi_W^c - \sin\Phi_W \cos\Psi_W^c) + a_D^D \cos\Phi_W \cos\Theta_W^c - V\Delta\dot{\Theta}_W = f_{zW} \quad (31)$$

Beside the components due to the desired acceleration on the trajectory, the left-hand side of Eq.(29)-(31) includes also small correction terms due to the instantaneous rotation on the transient comeback trajectory. Eq.(30) offers a solution for Φ_W, while Eq.(29) and Eq.(31), may be used to determine f_{xW} and f_{zW}. Considering a simplified representation for the aerodynamic forces:

$$f_{xW} = \rho S V^2/(2m)\left[C_{x0} + K_{p1}(C_{z0} + C_{z\alpha}\alpha + C_{z\delta e}\Delta_e)^2\right] + (T_m \cos\alpha)\Delta_{tc} \quad (32)$$

$$f_{zW} = \rho S V^2/(2m)\left[C_{z0} + C_{z\alpha}\alpha + C_{z\delta e}\Delta_e\right] + (T_m \sin\alpha)\Delta_{tc} \quad (33)$$

the attack angle α and thrust command Δ_{tc} are easily computed Assuming that the aircraft must track the trajectories with zero sideslip, i.e., β=0, an analytical solution for the steady-state attitudes is then provided based upon Eq.(22):

$$\overline{\Theta} = \sin^{-1}(\sin\Theta_W^c \cos\alpha + \cos\Phi_W \cos\Theta_W^c \sin\alpha) \quad (34a)$$

$$\overline{\Phi} = \sin^{-1}\left[(\sin\Phi_W \cos\Theta_W^c)/\cos\overline{\Theta}\right] \quad (34b)$$

$$\overline{\Psi} = \cos^{-1}((\cos\Theta^{c}_{W}\cos\Psi^{c}_{W}\cos\alpha - (\cos\Phi_{W}\sin\Theta^{c}_{W}\cos\Psi^{c}_{W} + \sin\Phi_{W}\sin\Psi^{c}_{W})\sin\alpha) / \cos\overline{\Theta}) \qquad (34c)$$

8. Practical Implementation

For the algorithm implementation a simulation program [11] with a nonlinear rigid-body model [12], cvasistatic linearized aerodynamics, simplified trim calculation, and first-order engine dynamics was used. A set of desired 4D trajectories defined by waypoints and estimated times of arrival (ETA) was used to verify the tracking performances. A large number of simulations allowed for the tuning of the algorithm parameters in order to minimize the tracking error. Thus the gains of the slow time-scale controller have been established at K_1=0.1 rad/m and $K_2 = 2\ 10^{-5}$ rad/m, and the dynamics of the NID controller are defined by a damping ratio of 0.7 and a response time of 3 s.

Fig. 4 presents a simulation case which considers a desired trajectory generated by a cubic Spline interpolation over five waypoints between 5000m and 5400m. Fig. 4a shows the desired flight path in the horizontal plane. Fig.4b points out a 35m maximum error in altitude tracking. The airspeed evolution during this maneuver is depicted in Fig.4c.

Figures 4d-4f allow for a comparison between the slow-time commanded attitudes and the actual attitudes of the aircraft. Note that the pitch and roll attitudes are tracked to within 0.5 deg and the heading to within 1 deg.

Fig. 5 shows comparatively the cross track distance (XTK) and the 4D track error. The influence of the atmospheric turbulence [10] upon XTK is analysed in Fig. 6. It results that the atmospheric turbulence considered with a Dryden model in standard conditions raises the maximum error to within 5%.

9. Conclusions

Nonlinear inverse dynamics theory has been used to design a full-authority inertial position guidance algorithm for a conventional aircraft. According to the singular perturbation method, a time separation between the inertial position and attitude dynamics was made in order to simplify the control task. Unique to this approach is the control law development for the thrust command in conjunction with a specific solution to the inverse kinematics problem to carry out nonlinear inverse control. The thrust command is used as a force control to adjust the magnitude of the thrust vector while the body attitude pseudocommands are used to orient the same vector in the desired direction.

We can conclude that the full-authority algorithm previously presented assures very good tracking performances, over the entire flight envelope, for the class of transport aircraft considered for simulation. The small number of the algorithm tuning parameters also allows for a great flexibility with regard to different classes of aircraft. The time-scale separation together with the specific solution to the inverse kinematics problem open further possibilities to accomplish the control task by using either a nonlinear transformation or a predictive algorithm.

References

[1]Isidori A.,"Nonlinear Control Systems"An Introduction, 2nd Edition, Springler-Verlag, 1989.

[2]Singh, S.W.,"Decoupling with Nearly Singular I-O Maps and Control of Aircraft", *Proceedings of the IEEE 27th Conference on Decision and Control,* Austin, TX, December 1988, pp.706-711.

[3]Etkin,B., "Dynamics of Atmospheric Flight", John Wiley & Sons New York, 1972.

[4]Meyer,G., Cicolani, L., "Application of Nonlinear System Inverses to Automatic Flight Control Design-System Concepts and Flight Evaluation", *Theory and Application of Optimal Control in Aerospace Systems,* AGARDograph 251, 1980.

[5]Singh,N.S., Schy,A.A, "Output Feedback Nonlinear Decoupled Control Synthesis and Observer Design for Manoeuvring Aircraft",*International Journal of Control,*Vol.31, No. 4, 1980.

[6]Lane,S.H., Stengel,R.F., "Flight Control Design Using Nonlinear Inverse Dynamics", *Proceedings of American Control Conference,* 1988.

[7]Stiharu-Alexe I., Stiharu-Alexe C., "On Nonlinear Inverse Dynamics Control in 4D Aircraft Guidance",*L.A.Grenoble Rapport No. 92-127, Grenoble, France, 1992.*

[8]Singh,N.S., Rugh,W.J., "Decoupling in a Class of Nonlinear System by State Variable Feedback", Journal of Dynamic Systems Measurement and Control, Dec., 1972.

[9]Kato,O., Sugiura,I., "An Interpretation of Airplane General Motion and Control Inverse Problem", Journal of Guidance and Control, Vol. 9,No. 2,1986.

[10]McRuer,D., Ashikenas,I., Graham,D., "Aircraft Dynamics and Automatic Control", Princeton University Press, 1973.

[11]Stiharu-Alexe,I., Stiharu-Alexe,C., Constantinescu,C., "ACAV Integration of the Simulation in the Control Analysis and Design of Atmospheric Vehicle Autopilots", *Proceedings of WMC'93 Conference,* San-Diego, C.A., 1993.

[12]Wanner,J.C., "Dynamique du vol et pilotage des avions", ONERA Paper, 1983.

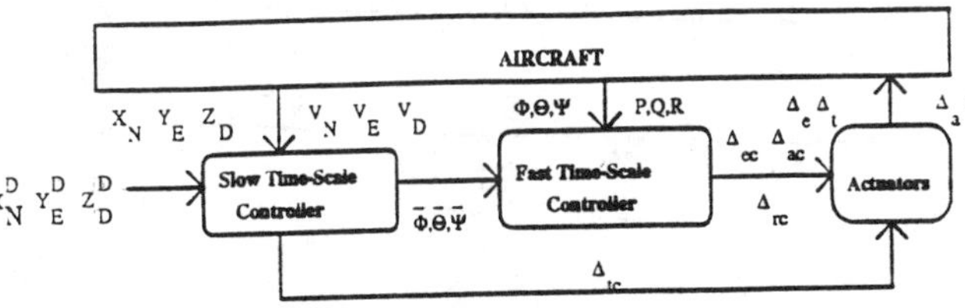

Fig.1

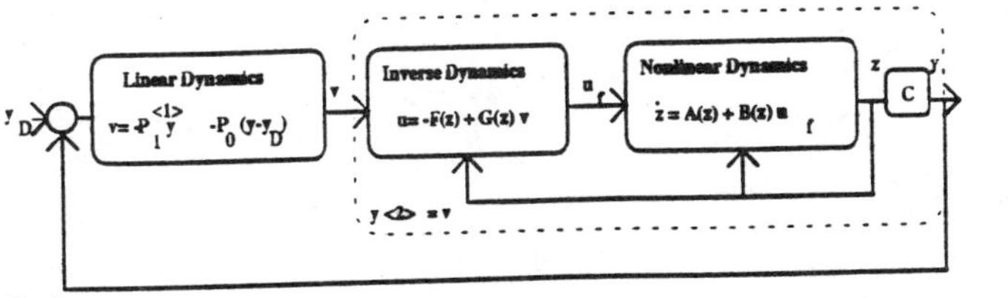

Fig. 2

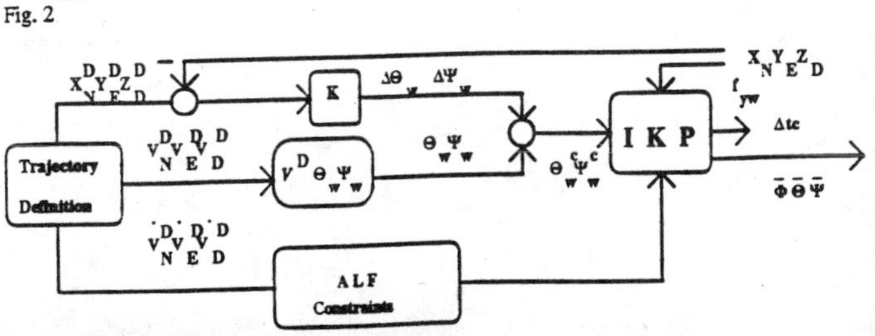

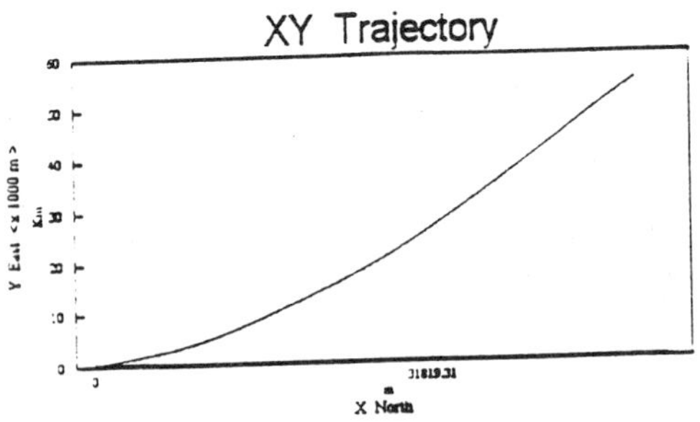

Fig.4a.

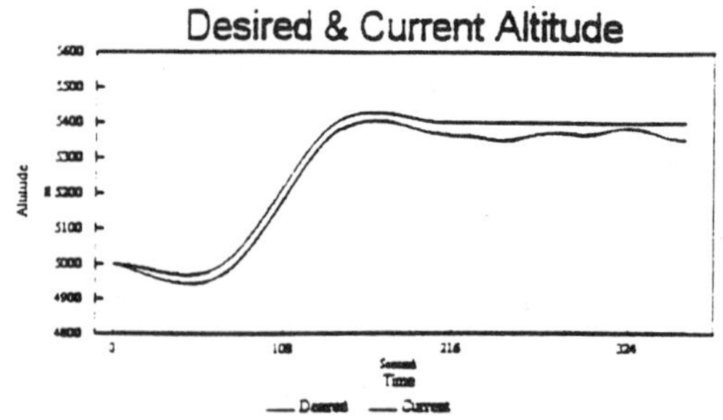

Fig.4b.

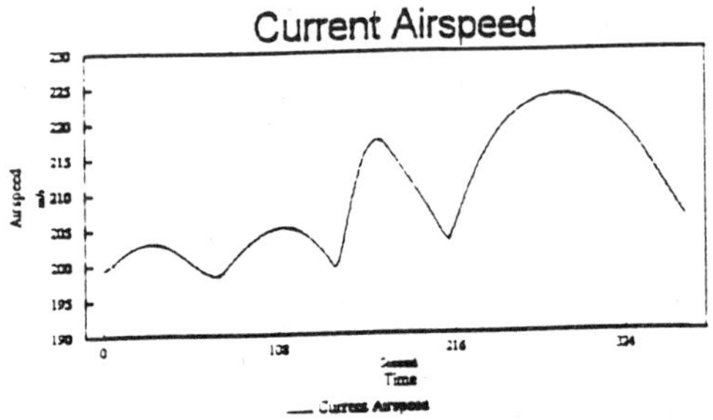

Fig.4c.

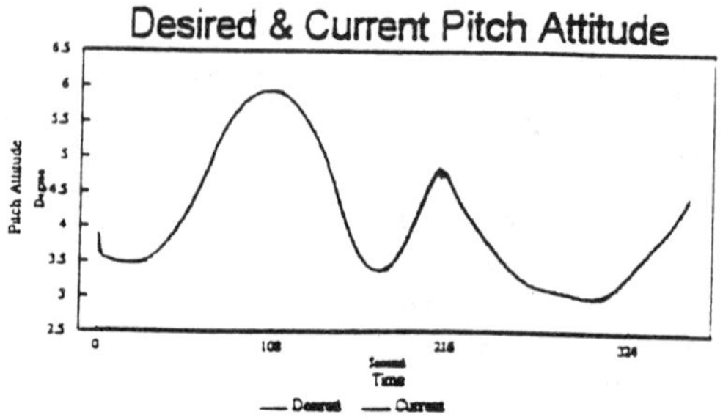

Fig.4d.

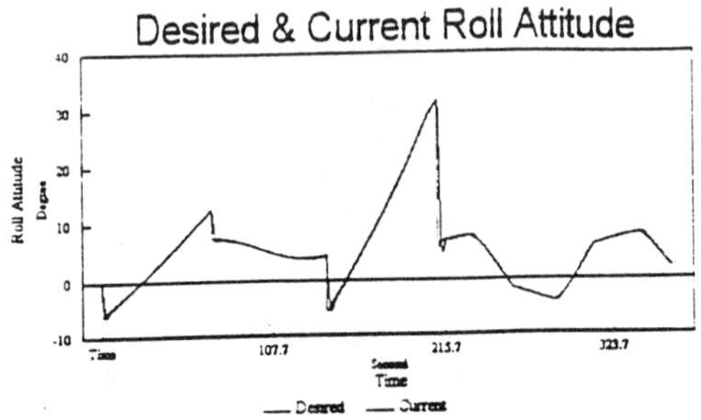

Fig.4e.

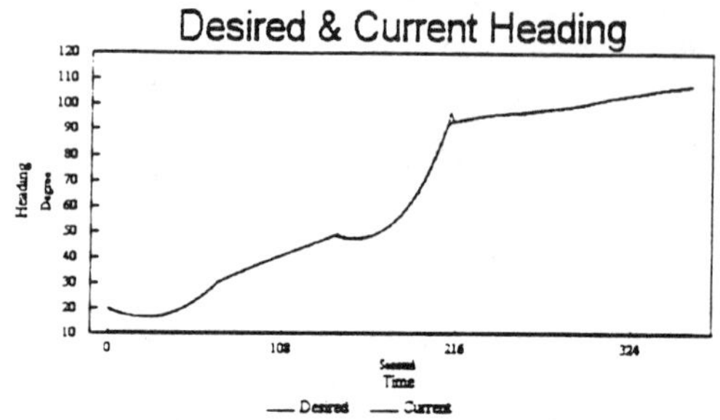

Fig.4f.

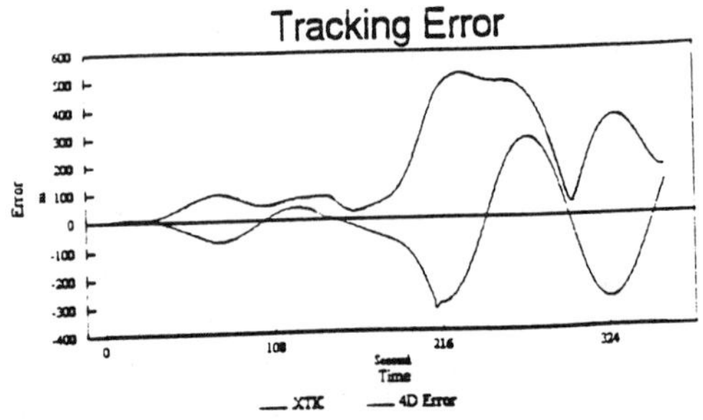

Fig.5.

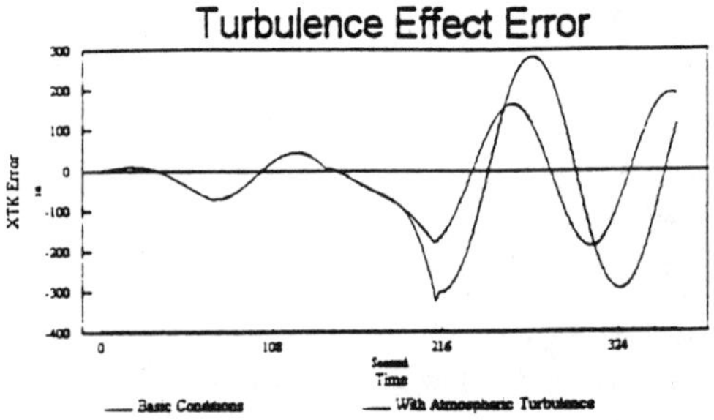

Fig.6.

Proceedings of the
American Control Conference
San Francisco, California • June 1993

GLOBAL ATTITUDE REPRESENTATION AND ITS LIE BRACKET [1]

Kuang-Yow Lian[†], Li-Sheng Wang[‡], and Li-Chen Fu[†]

Department of Electrical Engineering[†]

Institute of Applied Mechanics[‡]

National Taiwan University, Taipei, Taiwan, R.O.C.

Abstract

Global representation and various properties of the rigid body attitude, i.e., $SO(3)$, are investigated in this paper. The representations, Euler-Lagrange equation, and Hamilton's equation on the second bundle of $SO(3)$ are formally given. For its important role in nonlinear control theory, the global representation of Lie bracket on $T((SO(3))^m \times \mathcal{R}^n)$, a general tangent bundle of the product space of $SO(3)$ and Euclidean spaces, is also provided. As an application, the global controllability of spacecraft system with three gas jets is then easily guaranteed through this framework.

1 Introduction

The techniques in dealing with attitude problem have been applied in various areas, such as attitude determination and control for the spacecraft, pointing of aircraft and helicopter, and the orientation control of a single or multiple manipulators , etc. Literature on this subject is very rich and keeps growing at a steadily rapid rate, while the study of the motions of rigid-body systems keeps being one of the main streams in classical mechanics. Mathematically the attitude of a rigid body could be modeled as 3×3 rotation matrices, or *Special Orthogonal Group* $SO(3)$. Unlike the flat space $\mathcal{R}^3$, i.e., Euclidean space, the $SO(3)$ has intrinsically the structure of a smooth manifold. There are many studies on its mathematical structure and its representations [2, 7, 13, 14]. Due to the singularity problems of local representations on $SO(3)$, it has been observed that the global representations become more important on modeling and designing control laws and observers, etc., for systems on $SO(3)$.

Among the various representations of attitude, or $SO(3)$, three Euler angles are the most familiar and classical one. However, they are local coordinates of the manifold $SO(3)$, and, accordingly, subject to the problem of singularities. Three global representations for the attitude of a rigid body which are often mentioned are as follows: rotation matrix (or $SO(3)$) which consists of nine parameters with six constraints; Euler parameters (or quaternion) of four with one constraint; and Cayley-Klein parameters (or $SU(2)$) which is eight parameters with five constraints. Let q be a quaternion. By construction, the q and -q denote the same rotation, it can be shown that $SO(3)$, $SU(2)$ and the set of quaternions are isomorphic with each other [9] . In some literature, the quaternion is usually adopted for its minimal number of parameters and its long history which can be traced back to Hamilton, 1853, cf.[7]. It can be also conveniently used in numerical computation.

The rotation group $SO(3)$ is sometimes viewed as too complex to work with directly [22]. However, since the structure of the $SO(3)$ are gradually realized, the rotation matrix representation become more powerful in many problems, and can be conveniently applied to perform stability analysis [18, 19, 20], attitude determination, and optimal control [10]. The advantages of such representation reside on its brevity, clarity, and strong geometric interpretation.

The rest of this paper is organized as follows. Some notations and preliminaries are given in section II. Section III and IV present the representations of the second tangent and cotangent bundles of $SO(3)$, and then derives the Euler-Lagrange equation and Hamilton's equation on $SO(3)$. These materials can be viewed as the extension of the work [18, 19].

The Lie bracket computation is required in many important techniques or principles in control theory, for instance: accessibility property, controllability property, equivalence theorem, Bang-Bang theorem, and optimality conditions. In section V, we shall demonstrate the technique of computing Lie bracket based on the rotation matrix representation of $SO(3)$.

As an application of the results developed in the previous sections, in section VI we prove a controllability theorem for the spacecraft system. Although the same results have been obtained in [6, 8], the method adopted here is more systematic and straight.

[1] This work was partially supported by National Science Council, Republic of China, under grant NSC 81-0401-E-002-551 and NSC 82-0422-E-002-045

2 Notations and Preliminaries

Let the operator $\hat{}$ defined by

$$\widehat{\begin{pmatrix} w_1 \\ w_2 \\ w_3 \end{pmatrix}} = \begin{pmatrix} 0 & -w_3 & w_2 \\ w_3 & 0 & -w_1 \\ -w_2 & w_1 & 0 \end{pmatrix}$$

to denote the natural isomorphism between $\mathcal{R}^3$ and the space of 3×3 skew-symmetric matrices $so(3)$. To facilitate the subsequent development, several identities which can be straightforwardly verified are summarized below: for some $a,\ b,\ c \in \mathcal{R}^3$ and some $M \in \mathcal{R}^{3\times3}$

$$\begin{aligned} \hat{a}b &= a \times b. \\ \left[\hat{a},\ \hat{b}\right] &= \hat{a}\hat{b} - \hat{b}\hat{a} = \widehat{a \times b}. \\ A\hat{a}A^\top &= \widehat{Aa}, \quad \text{for } A \in SO(3). \\ \mathrm{tr}(\hat{a}\hat{b}\hat{c}) &= -(a \times b)\cdot c \ = \ -a \cdot (b \times c). \\ \mathrm{tr}(\hat{a}\hat{b}) &= 2a \cdot b. \\ \mathrm{tr}(\hat{a}^\top M \hat{a}) &= a \cdot M^o a, \end{aligned}$$

where if

$$M = \begin{pmatrix} M_{11} & M_{12} & M_{13} \\ M_{21} & M_{22} & M_{23} \\ M_{31} & M_{32} & M_{33} \end{pmatrix},$$

then

$$M^o = \begin{pmatrix} M_{22}+M_{33} & -M_{12} & -M_{13} \\ -M_{21} & M_{11}+M_{33} & -M_{23} \\ -M_{31} & -M_{32} & M_{11}+M_{22} \end{pmatrix}.$$

Moreover, in order to have $\mathrm{tr}(\hat{a}^\top M \hat{b}) = a \cdot M^o b$ the matrix M needs to be symmetric.

Let $\{e_1, e_2, e_3\}$ and $\{b_1, b_2, b_3\}$ be orthonormal bases of spatial (or inertial) frame and of body frame, respectively, both satisfying the right-hand rule. In particular, $e_i = \sum_{j=1}^{3} A_{ij} b_j$ for some $A = [A_{ij}]$ which satisfies that $A^\top A = I$ and $\det A = 1$. Then, for a vector with coordinates x observed at body frame, its coordinate y with respect to the spatial frame is given by $y = Ax$. Linear transformations of this sort, also known as rotation matrices, form the *special orthogonal group* $SO(3)$.

If we take the time derivative on both sides of $A^\top A = I$, we get

$$\frac{d}{dt} A^\top A = \dot{A}^\top A + A^\top \dot{A} = (A^\top \dot{A})^\top + (A^\top \dot{A}) = 0,$$

which implies that $A^\top \dot{A}$ is a skew-symmetric matrix, i.e., an element of $so(3)$. Hence, if we define $A^\top \dot{A} = \hat{\Omega}$, then we obtain the kinematic relationship

$$\dot{A} = A\hat{\Omega}. \tag{1}$$

In mechanics, the variable Ω corresponds to the instantaneous angular velocity of the body motion in body coordinates. But if we take the time derivative on both sides of $AA^\top = I$, then it satisfies

$$\dot{A} = \hat{\omega} A$$

for some $\omega \in \mathcal{R}^3$. Hence we have the relation $\omega = A\Omega$ since

$$\hat{\omega} = A\hat{\Omega}A^\top = \widehat{A\Omega}.$$

It explains that ω is the instantaneous angular velocity of the body motion in inertial coordinates.

3 Representations of the Second Bundle of $SO(3)$

Equation (1) implies that elements in the tangent bundle $TSO(3)$ can be characterized as $(A, A\hat{u})$, where $A \in SO(3)$, $u \in \mathcal{R}^3$. The trace pairing in $GL(n)$ (general linear group) which can be defined as $\langle A, B\rangle = \frac{1}{2}\text{tr}(A^\top B)$ provides us with a standard way to define elements in $T^*SO(3)$. For every $A\hat{u} \in T_A SO(3)$, we could let $A\hat{a} \in T_A^* SO(3)$, and

$$\begin{aligned}\langle A\hat{a}, A\hat{u}\rangle &= \frac{1}{2}\text{tr}(\hat{a}^\top A^\top A\hat{u}) = \frac{1}{2}a \cdot (A^\top A)^\circ u = \frac{1}{2}a \cdot 2Iu \\ &= a \cdot u\,,\end{aligned}$$

where $a \cdot u$ denotes the Euclidean inner product on $\mathcal{R}^3$. Accordingly, the pairing of $T^*SO(3)$ and $TSO(3)$ mimic the pairing on $\mathcal{R}^3$. In mechanics, angular momentum Π can be thought as a linear functional which maps the angular velocity Ω to a real number. This suggest that the elements in $T^*SO(3)$ which denotes the angular momentum can be written as

$$(A, A\hat{\Pi}).$$

Associated with $(A, A\hat{\Omega}) \in TSO(3)$, we have $\langle A\hat{\Pi}, A\hat{\omega}\rangle = \Omega \cdot \Pi$. It is the double of the kinetic energy.

Now, we turn to the representation of the second tangent bundle of $SO(3)$. The intrinsic reason for dealing with second tangent bundle is because all the natural models in mechanics are second order system. In general, let $(A\hat{u}, w) \in T_{(A,A\hat{\Omega})}TSO(3)$ for some u, $w \in \mathcal{R}^3$. Then, it should be clear that this tangent vector is generated by the curve

$$\left(Ae^{\epsilon\hat{u}}, Ae^{\epsilon\hat{u}}(\hat{\Omega} + \epsilon\hat{v})\right) \in TSO(3)$$

which passes through $(A, A\hat{\Omega})$ at $\epsilon = 0$, and hence we have

$$w = \left.\frac{d}{d\epsilon}\right|_{\epsilon=0} Ae^{\epsilon\hat{u}}(\hat{\Omega} + \epsilon\hat{v}) = A(\hat{u}\hat{\Omega} + \hat{v}).$$

Consequently, any elements in $TTSO(3)$ can be written as

$$\left(A, A\hat{\Omega}, A\hat{u}, A(\hat{u}\hat{\Omega} + \hat{v})\right).$$

Likewise, we also look for a canonical representation of an element in $T^*TSO(3)$, which is the dual space of the second tangent bundle of $SO(3)$. So, let $\gamma(A, A\hat{\Omega}) = (\alpha, \beta) \in T^*_{(A,A\hat{\Omega})}TSO(3)$, then we should have

$$\gamma(A, A\hat{\Omega})\left(A\hat{u}, A(\hat{u}\hat{\Omega} + \hat{v})\right) = a \cdot u + b \cdot v \qquad (2)$$

for some a, $b \in \mathcal{R}^3$. Thus, from the trace pairing mentioned above, it can be verified that

$$\begin{aligned}\alpha &= A(\hat{b}\hat{\Omega} + \hat{a}),\\ \beta &= A\hat{b},\end{aligned}$$

satisfy (2, which in turn yields the representation of elements in $T^*TSO(3)$ as

$$\left(A,\ A\hat{\Omega},\ A(\hat{b}\hat{\Omega} + \hat{a}),\ A\hat{b}\right).$$

On the other hand, since in Hamiltonian mechanics, we deal mainly with cotangent bundle or momentum-phase space. Hence, we need also to have parameterization on $TT^*SO(3)$. Similar to the above argument, an element in $T_{(A,A\hat{\Pi})}T^*SO(3)$ can be written as

$$\left(A\hat{u}, A(\hat{u}\hat{\Pi} + \hat{v})\right).$$

We could then have

$$\left(A(-\hat{\Pi}\hat{b} + \hat{a}), A\hat{b}\right)$$

as the representation for elements in $T^*_{(A,A\hat{\Pi})}T^*SO(3)$ such that

$$\begin{aligned}&\langle\left(A(-\hat{\Pi}\hat{b} + \hat{a}), A\hat{b}\right), \left(A\hat{u}, A(\hat{u}\hat{\Pi} + \hat{v})\right)\rangle \\ &= \frac{1}{2}\text{tr}\left((-\hat{\Pi}\hat{b} + \hat{a})^\top A^\top A\hat{u} + \hat{b}^\top A^\top A(\hat{u}\hat{\Pi} + \hat{v})\right) \\ &= \frac{1}{2}\text{tr}\left((-\hat{b}\hat{\Pi}\hat{u} - \hat{b}\hat{u}\hat{\Pi}\right) + \frac{1}{2}\text{tr}\left(\hat{a}^\top\hat{u} + \hat{b}^\top\hat{v})\right) \\ &= a \cdot u + b \cdot v.\end{aligned}$$

where the trace pairing has been used. In summary, we obtain the following result:

Proposition 1 *The elements in $TTSO(3)$, $T^*TSO(3)$, $TT^*SO(3)$, $T^*T^*SO(3)$ can be represented by*

$$\begin{aligned}\left(A\hat{u}, A(\hat{u}\hat{\Omega} + \hat{v})\right) &\in T_{(A,A\hat{\Omega})}TSO(3),\\ \left(A(\hat{b}\hat{\Omega} + \hat{a}), A\hat{b}\right) &\in T^*_{(A,A\hat{\Omega})}TSO(3),\\ \left(A\hat{u}, A(\hat{u}\hat{\Pi} + \hat{v})\right) &\in T_{(A,A\hat{\Pi})}T^*SO(3),\\ \left(A(-\hat{\Pi}\hat{b} + \hat{a}), A\hat{b}\right) &\in T^*_{(A,A\hat{\Pi})}T^*SO(3),\end{aligned} \qquad (3)$$

respectively. □

Remark: The elements in $T^*_{(A,A\hat{\Omega})}TSO(3)$ can be also represented by

$$\left(A(-\hat{\Omega}\hat{b} + \hat{a}), A\hat{b}\right),$$

and similarly $\left(A(\hat{b}\hat{\Pi} + \hat{a}), A\hat{b}\right)$ for $T^*_{(A,A\hat{\Pi})}T^*SO(3)$. However, the representations given in (3) are more natural in the derivation of dynamics. This will become clear in the following sections. □

4 Euler-Lagrange Equation and Hamilton's Equation on $SO(3)$

Before going to present Euler-Lagrange equation on $TSO(3)$ and Hamilton's equation on $T^*SO(3)$, we first introduce the concept of Fréchet differential with respect to $SO(3)$.

Let M and N be smooth manifolds and $F : M \longrightarrow N$ a smooth map between them. Each one-parameter family $C = \{\phi(\epsilon) : \epsilon \in I\}$ on M, where I is an interval on $\mathcal{R}$ and $0 \in I$, is transformed by F to a one-parameter curve $\tilde{C} = F(C) = \{F(\phi(\epsilon)) : \epsilon \in I\}$ on N. Thus F induces a map transforming the tangent vector $\frac{d\phi}{d\epsilon}$ at $x = \phi(0)$ to the corresponding tangent vector $\frac{d}{d\epsilon}|_{\epsilon=0}F(\phi(\epsilon))$ at the image point $F(x) = F(\phi(0))$. We can write

$$DF \cdot \dot{\phi}(0) = \left.\frac{d}{d\epsilon}\right|_{\epsilon=0} F(\phi(\epsilon)),$$

where $DF(x)$ is call the differential of F at x.

Now, consider

$$\begin{aligned}F : SO(3) &\longrightarrow N\\ A &\longmapsto F(A),\end{aligned}$$

then we have

$$D_A F(A) \cdot A\hat{u} = \left.\frac{d}{d\epsilon}\right|_{\epsilon=0} F(Ae^{\epsilon\hat{u}}).$$

where $A\hat{u} \in TSO(3)$. This formula can be applied to obtain the gravity gradient torque from the gravitational potential energy. We consider the motion of a rigid body $\mathcal{B}$ moving in a central inverse-square gravitational force field that is generated by a massive body $\mathcal{B}_e$. Let E and C be the origins of the spatial frame and the body frame which are centering at $\mathcal{B}_e$ and $\mathcal{B}$, respectively. The gravitational potential energy of the rigid body can be expressed as

$$V(B, r) = \int_{\mathcal{B}} \frac{-GM_e}{|r + B\bar{q}|} dm(\bar{q}), \qquad (4)$$

where r represents the vector from E to C in spatial coordinates, $\bar{q}$ from C to a mass element of rigid body in body coordinates, G is the universal gravitational constant, and M_e is the total mass of $\mathcal{B}_e$. We now derive the corresponding gravity-gradient torque in the following.

Since $D_B V(B, r) \in T_B^* SO(3)$, we denote it by $B\hat{a}$. Let $B\hat{u}$ in $T_B SO(3)$. We have

$$\begin{aligned}D_B V(B) \cdot B\hat{u} &= \left.\frac{d}{d\epsilon}\right|_{\epsilon=0} V(Be^{\epsilon\hat{u}})\\ &= \left.\frac{d}{d\epsilon}\right|_{\epsilon=0} \int_{\mathcal{B}} \frac{-GM}{|r + Be^{\epsilon\hat{u}}\bar{q}|} dm(\bar{q})\\ &= \int_{\mathcal{B}} \frac{GM}{|r + B\bar{q}|^2} \left.\frac{d}{d\epsilon}\right|_{\epsilon=0} |r + Be^{\epsilon\hat{u}}\bar{q}| dm(\bar{q})\\ &= \int_{\mathcal{B}} \frac{GM(r + B\bar{q})^\top B\hat{u}\bar{q}}{|r + B\bar{q}|^3} dm(\bar{q}),\end{aligned} \qquad (5)$$

where the following formula has been used,

$$\left.\frac{d}{d\epsilon}\right|_{\epsilon=0} |x+h(\epsilon)| = \left.\frac{d}{d\epsilon}\right|_{\epsilon=0} \sqrt{(x+h(\epsilon))^{\top}(x+h(\epsilon))} = \frac{<x+h(0), \frac{dh(0)}{d\epsilon}>}{|x+h(0)|}.$$

Furthermore, from

$$(B\bar{q})^{\top} B\hat{u}\bar{q} = \bar{q}^{\top}\hat{u}\bar{q} = 0,$$
$$r^{\top} B\hat{u}\bar{q} = -r^{\top} B\hat{\bar{q}}u = (\hat{\bar{q}}B^{\top}r)^{\top}u = (-B^{\top}r \times \bar{q})^{\top}u,$$

we can simplify (5) as

$$a \cdot u = \int_{\mathcal{B}} \frac{-GM(B^{\top}r \times \bar{q})^{\top}u}{|r+B\bar{q}|^3} dm(\bar{q}),$$

which then leads to

$$D_B V(B) = B \int_{\mathcal{B}} \frac{-GM(\widehat{B^{\top}r \times \bar{q}})}{|r+B\bar{q}|^3} dm(\bar{q}).$$

□

The global representation (3) of the second tangent bundle and the dual of the second tangent bundle on $SO(3)$ also prove to be useful in finding the derivation or variations of a function (e.g. Lagrangian) on $TSO(3)$. In the following, we state the Lagrange-d'Alembert Principle in terms of these representations.

Theorem 1 *[18, 19] On $TSO(3)$, let a system be described by a Lagrangian L. The Lagrange-d'Alembert Principle in the invariant form [17] applied to the motions on $SO(3)$ gives us the Euler-Lagrange equation,*

$$< \frac{d}{dt}D_2L(A, A\hat{\Omega}), A\hat{u} > = < D_1L(A, A\hat{\Omega}), A\hat{u} > + < \alpha, A\hat{u} >, \quad \forall A\hat{u} \in T_A SO(3), \tag{6}$$

where α is the external force (note that D_1, D_2 denote the Fréchet differential with respect to A, $A\hat{\Omega}$, respectively). □

Now we consider the Hamiltonian structure of rigid body dynamics in terms of these global representations. Let (M, ω) be a symplectic manifold, i.e., M is a smooth manifold of dimension $2n$, and ω is a closed, nondegenerate 2-form on M, cf. [1]. Let $\mathcal{X}(M)$ be the set of all vector fields on M. We have that ω is a bilinear skew-symmetric map which maps the vector field in $\mathcal{X}(M) \times \mathcal{X}(M)$ to a smooth real valued functions on M. Suppose $M = T^*Q$ and $p \in M$, then $T_pM \cong Q \times Q^*$. It is natural to equip T_pM with the pairing $< \cdot, \cdot >$, a natural pairing on $Q \times Q^*$. Therefore, within a symplectic chart, for every

$$X(x, \alpha) = (u, a), \quad Y(x, \alpha) = (v, b) \in \mathcal{X}(M),$$

one can explicitly define

$$\omega(x, \alpha)(X, Y) =< b, u > - < a, v >, \quad (x, \alpha) \in M$$

as a symplectic 2-form on M. For a Hamiltonian H, the corresponding Hamiltonian vector field X_H is defined by requiring that the relation

$$\omega(X_H, Y) = dH \cdot Y \tag{7}$$

holds for all $Y \in \mathcal{X}(M)$.

Now we restrict our attention to $SO(3)$. For $M = T^*SO(3)$, every vector field w on M can be denoted by $\left(A\hat{u}, A(\hat{u}\hat{\Pi} + \hat{v})\right) \in T_{(A,A\hat{\Pi})}T^*SO(3)$. Let $H(A, A\hat{\Pi}) = \bar{H}(A, \Pi)$, then

$$dH(A, A\hat{\Pi}) \cdot w = \left.\frac{d}{dt}\right|_{t=0} H\left(Ae^{t\hat{u}}, Ae^{t\hat{u}}(\hat{\Pi} + t\hat{v})\right) = \left.\frac{d}{dt}\right|_{t=0} \bar{H}\left(Ae^{t\hat{u}}, \Pi + tv\right) = (D_A\bar{H}, \frac{\partial \bar{H}}{\partial \Pi}) \cdot (A\hat{u}, v).$$

As has been summarized in Proposition 1, the canonical representation of elements in $T^*_{(A,A\hat{\Pi})}T^*SO(3)$ is $\left(A(-\hat{\Pi}\hat{b} + \hat{a}), A\hat{b}\right)$. Let $D_A\bar{H} = A\hat{\alpha}$, then

$$dH(A, A\hat{\Pi}) = (D_1H, D_2H) = \left(A(-\hat{\Pi}\widehat{\frac{\partial \bar{H}}{\partial \Pi}} + \hat{\alpha}), A\widehat{\frac{\partial \bar{H}}{\partial \Pi}}\right).$$

Now, the left-hand side of equation (7) becomes

$$\omega\left((\dot{A}, \dot{A\hat{\Pi}}), (v, b)\right) =< b, \dot{A} > - < \dot{A\hat{\Pi}}, v >,$$

whereas the right-hand side of equation (7) satisfies

$$\left(A(-\hat{\Pi}\widehat{\frac{\partial \bar{H}}{\partial \Pi}} + \hat{\alpha}), A\widehat{\frac{\partial \bar{H}}{\partial \Pi}}\right) \cdot (v, b) =< A(-\hat{\Pi}\widehat{\frac{\partial \bar{H}}{\partial \Pi}} + \hat{\alpha}), v > + < b, A\widehat{\frac{\partial \bar{H}}{\partial \Pi}} >.$$

As a consequence, we obtain the follow canonical equations,

$$\begin{aligned} \dot{A} &= A\widehat{\frac{\partial \bar{H}}{\partial \Pi}} \\ \dot{A\hat{\Pi}} &= A\left(\hat{\Pi}\widehat{\frac{\partial \bar{H}}{\partial \Pi}} - \hat{\alpha}\right) = A\left(\widehat{\frac{\partial \bar{H}}{\partial \Pi}}\hat{\Pi} + \widehat{\Pi \times \frac{\partial \bar{H}}{\partial \Pi}} - \hat{\alpha}\right). \end{aligned} \tag{8}$$

This is exactly the Hamilton's equation on $T^*SO(3)$ corresponding to the Hamiltonian H. Moreover, equations (8) can be also expressed as

$$\begin{aligned} \dot{A} &= A\widehat{\frac{\partial \bar{H}}{\partial \Pi}} \\ \dot{\Pi} &= \Pi \times \frac{\partial \bar{H}}{\partial \Pi} - \alpha. \end{aligned} \tag{9}$$

These are the Hamilton's equations expresses on $T^*SO(3) \cong SO(3) \times \mathcal{R}^3$.

Theorem 2 *Let $M = T^*SO(3)$ and let (M, ω) be a symplectic manifold with $\omega(X, Y) =< b, u > - < a, v >$, $\forall X = (u, v)$ and $Y = (v, b) \in \mathcal{X}(M)$. Furthermore, let H be a Hamiltonian function on $T^*SO(3)$. The Hamiltonian vector field is $X_H = (\dot{A}, \dot{A\hat{\Pi}}) \in T_{(A,A\hat{\Pi})}T^*SO(3)$. Then, the Hamilton's equation can be written as*

$$\omega(X_H, \cdot) = \left(A(-\hat{\Pi}\widehat{\frac{\partial \bar{H}}{\partial \Pi}} + \hat{\alpha}), A\widehat{\frac{\partial \bar{H}}{\partial \Pi}}\right)$$

where $\bar{H}(A, \Pi) \equiv H(A, A\hat{\Pi})$ and $D_A\bar{H} = A\hat{\alpha}$. □

5 Lie Bracket in Second Tangent bundle

Newton's principle of determinacy says [3]: *The initial state of a mechanical system (the totality of position and velocity of its points at some moment of time) uniquely determines all of its motion.* This principle implies the real word we live in is a second-order system. For this reason, a closer investigation on the second tangent bundle (or cotangent bundle) and its duality is necessary. In section 3, the representations of such second bundle on $SO(3)$ have been obtained with some related properties. As frequently seen in nonlinear control theory, the Lie bracket computation for two vector fields plays an important role. Indeed, as we know, in addition to the involution conditions in Frobenius theorem and Chow's theorem, there are still many important results or principles in control literature described in terms of Lie brackets, for instance: accessibility property, controllability property, equivalence theorem, Bang-Bang theorem, and optimality conditions, (cf. [15] and the references therein). Therefore, this section addresses the issue of how to compute the Lie bracket based on the rotation matrix representation of $SO(3)$. We start from the original definition, e.g. see [21], and equivalent expressions:

Proposition 2 *Let X, $Y \in \mathcal{X}(M)$, with flows ϕ^x_t, ϕ^y_t, respectively. Then*

$$[X, Y](p) \equiv \lim_{t\to 0} \frac{((\phi^x_{-t})_* Y)(p) - Y(p)}{t} = \left.\frac{d}{dt}\right|_{t=0} ((\phi^x_{-t})_* Y)(p) = \left.\frac{d}{dt}\right|_{t=0} \left.\frac{d}{d\lambda}\right|_{\lambda=o} \phi^x_{-t} \circ \phi^y_\lambda \circ \phi^x_t(p).$$

□

Now we consider the general product space of $SO(3)$ and $\mathcal{R}^n$. Let Q be the configuration manifold $(SO(3))^m \times \mathcal{R}^n$ and $M = TQ$. We shall derive the representation of the Lie bracket on T_pM with the base point p in M which can be parameterized as:

$$p = (A_1, A_1\hat{\Omega}_1, \dots, A_m, A_m\hat{\Omega}_m, r),$$

where $A_1, \dots, A_m \in SO(3)$, $\Omega_1, \dots, \Omega_m \in \mathcal{R}^3$, and $r \in \mathcal{R}^n$. Let vector fields X, $Y \in \mathcal{X}(M)$ at point p be denoted as (cf. 3),

$$X(p) = \left(A_1\widehat{u_1(q)}, A_1\left(\widehat{u_1(q)}\hat{\Omega}_1 + \widehat{v_1(q)}\right), \dots,\right.$$

$$A_m \widehat{u_m(q)}, A_m \left(\widehat{u_m(q)}\Omega_m + \widehat{v_m(q)}\right), w(q)\Big), \tag{10}$$

$$\begin{aligned} Y(p) &= \Big(A_1 \widehat{a_1(q)}, A_1 \left(\widehat{a_1(q)}\Omega_1 + \widehat{b_1(q)}\right), \ldots, \\ &\quad A_m \widehat{a_m(q)}, A_m \left(\widehat{a_m(q)}\Omega_m + \widehat{b_m(q)}\right), c(q)\Big), \end{aligned} \tag{11}$$

with $q = (A_1, \Omega_1, \ldots, A_m, \Omega_m, r)$. The flows of X, Y can be found to be, respectively:

$$\begin{aligned} \phi_t^x(p) &= \Big(A_1 e^{t\widehat{u_1(q)}}, A_1 e^{t\widehat{u_1(q)}} \left(\hat{\Omega}_1 + t\widehat{v_1(q)}\right), \ldots, \\ &\quad A_m e^{t\widehat{u_m(q)}}, A_m e^{t\widehat{u_m(q)}} \left(\hat{\Omega}_m + t\widehat{v_m(q)}\right), r + tw(q)\Big), \\ \phi_t^y(p) &= \Big(A_1 e^{t\widehat{a_1(q)}}, A_1 e^{t\widehat{a_1(q)}} \left(\hat{\Omega}_1 + t\widehat{b_1(q)}\right), \ldots, \\ &\quad A_m e^{t\widehat{a_m(q)}}, A_m e^{t\widehat{a_m(q)}} \left(\hat{\Omega}_m + t\widehat{b_m(q)}\right), r + tc(q)\Big). \end{aligned}$$

For compactness, define $\Phi_t^x(q), \Phi_t^y(q)$ as:

$$\Phi_t^x(q) = \left(A_1 e^{t\widehat{u_1(q)}}, \Omega_1 + tv_1(q), \ldots, A_m e^{t\widehat{u_m(q)}}, \Omega_m + tv_m(q), r + tw(q)\right) \tag{12}$$

$$\Phi_t^y(q) = \left(A_1 e^{t\widehat{a_1(q)}}, \Omega_1 + tb_1(q), \ldots, A_m e^{t\widehat{a_m(q)}}, \Omega_m + tb_m(q), r + tc(q)\right). \tag{13}$$

Now, the composition of flows $\phi_\lambda^y \circ \phi_t^x(p)$ is:

$$\begin{aligned} &\phi_\lambda^y \circ \phi_t^x(p) \\ = &\Bigg(\underbrace{A_1 e^{t\hat{u}_1(q)} e^{\lambda a_1(\widehat{\Phi_t^x(q)})}}_{\tilde{A}_1}, A_1 e^{t\hat{u}_1(q)} e^{\lambda a_1(\widehat{\Phi_t^x(q)})} \underbrace{\left(\hat{\Omega}_1 + t\widehat{v_1(q)} + \lambda b_1(\widehat{\Phi_t^x}(q))\right)}_{\hat{\tilde{\Omega}}_1}, \\ &\ldots, \underbrace{A_m e^{t\hat{u}_m(q)} e^{\lambda a_m(\widehat{\Phi_t^x(q)})}}_{\tilde{A}_m}, \\ &A_m e^{t\hat{u}_m(q)} e^{\lambda a_m(\widehat{\Phi_t^x(q)})} \underbrace{\left(\hat{\Omega}_m + t\widehat{v_m(q)} + \lambda b_m(\widehat{\Phi_t^x}(q))\right)}_{\hat{\tilde{\Omega}}_m}, \underbrace{r + tw(q) + \lambda c(q)}_{\tilde{r}}\Bigg) \end{aligned}$$

Let $\Psi(q) \equiv \Phi_\lambda^y \circ \Phi_t^x(q)$. We have

$$\Psi(q) = (\tilde{A}_1, \tilde{\Omega}_1, \ldots, \tilde{A}_m, \tilde{\Omega}_m, \tilde{r}).$$

Now we compute the composition of flows needed in Proposition 2. The composition of flows $\phi_{-t}^x \circ \phi_\lambda^y \circ \phi_t^x(p)$ needed in can be found to be

$$\begin{aligned} &\phi_{-t}^x \circ \phi_\lambda^y \circ \phi_t^x(p) \\ = &\phi_{-t}^x(\tilde{A}_1, \tilde{A}_1 \hat{\tilde{\Omega}}_1, \ldots, \tilde{A}_m, \tilde{A}_m \hat{\tilde{\Omega}}_m, \tilde{r}) \\ = &\Big(\tilde{A}_1 e^{-tu_1(\widehat{\Psi(q)})}, \tilde{A}_1 e^{-tu_1(\widehat{\Psi(q)})}(\tilde{\Omega}_1 - tv_1(\widehat{\Psi(q)})), \ldots, \\ &\tilde{A}_m e^{-tu_m(\widehat{\Psi(q)})}, \tilde{A}_m e^{-tu_m(\widehat{\Psi(q)})}(\tilde{\Omega}_m - tv_m(\widehat{\Psi(q)})), \tilde{r} - tw(\Psi(q))\Big). \end{aligned}$$

According to Proposition 2, we take the derivative with respect to λ first:

$$\begin{aligned} &\left.\frac{d}{d\lambda}\right|_{\lambda=o} \phi_{-t}^x \circ \phi_\lambda^y \circ \phi_t^x(p) \\ = &\Bigg(A_1 e^{t\widehat{u_1(q)}} \widehat{a_1(\Phi_t^x)} e^{-tu_1(\widehat{\Phi_t^x})} + A_1 e^{t\widehat{u_1(q)}} \left.\frac{d}{d\lambda}\right|_{\lambda=0} e^{-tu_1(\widehat{\Psi(q)})}, \\ &\left(A_1 e^{t\widehat{u_1(q)}} \widehat{a_1(\Phi_t^x)} e^{-tu_1(\widehat{\Phi_t^x(q)})} + A_1 e^{t\widehat{u_1(q)}} \left.\frac{d}{d\lambda}\right|_{\lambda=0} e^{-tu_1(\widehat{\Psi(q)})}\right) \cdot \\ &\left(\hat{\Omega}_1 + t\widehat{v_1(q)} - tv_1(\widehat{\Phi_t^x}(q))\right) \\ &+ A_1 e^{t\widehat{u_1(q)}} e^{-tu_1(\widehat{\Phi_t^x(q)})} \left(b_1(\widehat{\Phi_t^x}(q)) - \left.\frac{d}{d\lambda}\right|_{\lambda=0} tv_1(\widehat{\Psi(q)})\right), \ldots, \\ &A_m e^{t\widehat{u_m(q)}} a_m(\widehat{\Phi_t^x}(q)) e^{-tu_m(\widehat{\Phi_t^x(q)})} + A_m e^{t\widehat{u_m(q)}} \left.\frac{d}{d\lambda}\right|_{\lambda=0} e^{-tu_m(\widehat{\Psi(q)})}, \\ &\left(A_m e^{t\widehat{u_m(q)}} a_m(\widehat{\Phi_t^x}(q)) e^{-tu_m(\widehat{\Phi_t^x(q)})} + A_m e^{t\widehat{u_m(q)}} \left.\frac{d}{d\lambda}\right|_{\lambda=0} e^{-tu_m(\widehat{\Psi(q)})}\right) \cdot \\ &\left(\hat{\Omega}_m + t\widehat{v_m(q)} - tv_m(\widehat{\Phi_t^x}(q))\right) \\ &+ A_m e^{t\widehat{u_m(q)}} e^{-tu_m(\widehat{\Phi_t^x(q)})} \left(b_m(\widehat{\Phi_t^x}(q)) - \left.\frac{d}{d\lambda}\right|_{\lambda=0} tv_m(\widehat{\Psi}(q))\right) \\ &c(\Phi_t^x(q)) - \left.\frac{d}{d\lambda}\right|_{\lambda=0} tw(\Psi(q))\Bigg) \end{aligned}$$

The property $\Psi(q)|_{\lambda=0} = \Phi_t^x(q)$ has been used in above calculation. Taking the derivative with respect to t once more, we could get the Lie bracket of X and Y. For simplicity, the derivative with respect to t and λ at $t = 0$, $\lambda = 0$, will be abbreviated as: $\frac{d}{dt|_o}$, $\frac{d}{d\lambda|_o}$, repetitively, so that we now have

$$\begin{aligned} &[X, Y](p) \\ = &\frac{d}{dt|_o} \frac{d}{d\lambda|_o} X_1^{-t} \circ X_2^\lambda \circ X_1^t(p) \\ = &\Bigg(A_1 \widehat{u_1(q)} \widehat{a_1(q)} + A_1 \frac{d}{dt|_o} a_1(\widehat{\Phi_t^x}(q)) - A_1 \widehat{a_1(q)} \widehat{u_1(q)} - A_1 \frac{d}{d\lambda|_o} u_1(\widehat{\Phi_\lambda^y}(q)), \\ &\Big(A_1 \widehat{u_1(q)} \widehat{a_1(q)} + A_1 \frac{d}{dt|_o} a_1(\widehat{\Phi_t^x}(q)) - A_1 \widehat{a_1(q)} \widehat{u_1(q)} - \\ &A_1 \frac{d}{d\lambda|_o} u_1(\widehat{\Phi_\lambda^y}(q))\Big) \hat{\Omega}_1 + A_1 \frac{d}{dt|_o} b_1(\widehat{\Phi_t^x}(q)) - A_1 \frac{d}{d\lambda|_o} v_1(\widehat{\Phi_\lambda^y}(q)), \ldots, \\ &A_m \widehat{u_m(q)} \widehat{a_m(q)} + A_m \frac{d}{dt|_o} a_m(\widehat{\Phi_t^x}(q)) - \\ &\qquad A_m \widehat{a_m(q)} \widehat{u_m(q)} - A_m \frac{d}{d\lambda|_o} u_m(\widehat{\Phi_\lambda^y}(q)), \\ &\Big(A_m \widehat{u_m(q)} \widehat{a_m(q)} + A_m \frac{d}{dt|_o} a_m(\widehat{\Phi_t^x}(q)) - A_m \widehat{a_m(q)} \widehat{u_m(q)} - \\ &A_m \frac{d}{d\lambda|_o} u_m(\widehat{\Phi_\lambda^y}(q))\Big) \hat{\Omega}_m + A_m \frac{d}{dt|_o} b_m(\widehat{\Phi_t^x}(q)) - A_m \frac{d}{d\lambda|_o} v_m(\widehat{\Phi_\lambda^y}(q)), \\ &\frac{d}{dt|_o} c(\Phi_t^x(q)) - \frac{d}{d\lambda|_o} w(\Phi_\lambda^y(q))\Bigg). \end{aligned}$$

Therefore, the following proposition is obtained.

Proposition 3 *Let $Q = (SO(3))^m \times \mathcal{R}^n$. Let*

$$p = (A_1, A_1\hat{\Omega}_1, \ldots, A_m, A_m\hat{\Omega}_m, r) \in Q.$$

Every vector field X, $Y \in \mathcal{X}(TQ)$ can be expressed at p as (10), (11), respectively. Let $\Phi_t^x(q), \Phi_t^y(q)$ be defined as in (12), (13), respectively. Then the Lie bracket of X, Y at p can be computed as

$$\begin{aligned} &[X, Y](p) \\ = &\Bigg(A_1(\widehat{u_1 \times a_1} + \frac{d}{dt|_o} \widehat{a_1 \circ \Phi_t^x} - \frac{d}{dt|_o} \widehat{u_1 \circ \Phi_t^y}), \\ &A_1((\widehat{u_1 \times a_1} + \frac{d}{dt|_o} \widehat{a_1 \circ \Phi_t^x} - \frac{d}{dt|_o} \widehat{u_1 \circ \Phi_t^y})\Omega_1 + \frac{d}{dt|_o} \widehat{b_1 \circ \Phi_t^x} - \frac{d}{dt|_o} \widehat{v_1 \circ \Phi_t^y}), \\ &\ldots, A_m(\widehat{u_m \times a_m} + \frac{d}{dt|_o} \widehat{a_m \circ \Phi_t^x} - \frac{d}{dt|_o} \widehat{u_m \circ \Phi_t^y}), \\ &A_m((\widehat{u_m \times a_m} + \frac{d}{dt|_o} \widehat{a_m \circ \Phi_t^x} - \frac{d}{dt|_o} \widehat{u_m \circ \Phi_t^y})\hat{\Omega}_m + \\ &\qquad \frac{d}{dt|_o} \widehat{b_m \circ \Phi_t^x} - \frac{d}{dt|_o} \widehat{v_m \circ \Phi_t^y}), \\ &\frac{d}{dt|_o} c \circ \Phi_t^x - \frac{d}{dt|_o} w \circ \Phi_t^y\Bigg)(q). \end{aligned}$$

□

By the analogy of the vector fields between $T_{(A,A\hat{\Omega})}TSO(3)$ and $T_{(A,A\hat{\Pi})}T^*SO(3)$, we have similar results for X, $Y \in \mathcal{X}(T^*Q)$, where $Q = (SO(3))^m \times \mathcal{R}^n$.

6 An Application: Controllability of Spacecraft System

Consider the control system of a spacecraft with three gas jets. Let J be the moment of inertia matrix of the spacecraft and b_i, $i = 1, 2, 3$, be the axes about which the corresponding control torques u_i, $i = 1, 2, 3$, are applied respectively with opposing pairs of gas jets.

The dynamics of a spacecraft moving in a central gravitational field should consist of both translational and rotational motion. However, in order to demonstrate the techniques described in this paper, we consider only the rotational motion. More complete discussion on the problem of a spacecraft will appear in a up-coming paper [11]. For the simple case, the configuration space is simply $SO(3)$. Let $(A, A\hat{\Omega})$ be an element in $TSO(3)$ with the physical interpretation that A represents the attitude of the spacecraft and Ω be the instantaneous angular velocity in spacecraft frame. The Lagrange of the system can be written as

$$L(A, A\Omega) = \frac{1}{2} < \Omega, J\Omega > .$$

As shown in [18, 19], by Theorem 1 and some derivation we get the equations of motion:

$$\begin{aligned} \dot{A} &= A\Omega \\ J\dot{\Omega} &= -\Omega \times J\Omega + \sum_{i=1}^{3} b_i u_i. \end{aligned}$$

On the other hand, letting the angular momentum Π defined as $J\Omega$, the Hamiltonian is

$$H(A, A\hat{\Pi}) = \frac{1}{2} < \Pi, J^{-1}\Pi > .$$

With the help of (8), we get

$$\begin{aligned} \dot{A} &= A\widehat{J^{-1}\Pi} \\ A\dot{\hat{\Pi}} &= A(\hat{\Pi}\widehat{J^{-1}\Pi} + \sum_{i=1}^{3} b_i u_i). \end{aligned}$$

For a nonlinear control system

$$\dot{x} = f(x) + \sum_{i=1}^{m} g_i(x) u_i, \tag{14}$$

recall that one of the necessary conditions for the controllability of a spacecraft system is

$$span(\mathcal{L}(f,\ g)) = T_x M, \quad \forall\ x \in M, \tag{15}$$

where $\mathcal{L}(f,\ g)$ denotes the Lie algebra generated by $\{f, g_1, \cdots, g_m\}$. For our problem,

$$\begin{aligned} f(A, A\hat{\Pi}) &= \begin{bmatrix} A\widehat{J^{-1}\Pi} \\ A(\widehat{J^{-1}\Pi}\hat{\Pi} + \widehat{\Pi \times J^{-1}\Pi}) \end{bmatrix}, \\ g_i(A, A\hat{\Pi}) &= \begin{bmatrix} 0 \\ A\hat{b}_i \end{bmatrix}, \quad \forall\ i = 1, 2, 3. \end{aligned}$$

According to the formula in Proposition 3, we obtain

$$\begin{aligned} [f,\ g_i](A, A\hat{\Pi}) &= -\begin{bmatrix} A\frac{d}{dt}\widehat{J^{-1}(\Pi + tb_i)} \\ A\left(\frac{d}{dt}\widehat{J^{-1}(\Pi + tb_i)}\hat{\Pi} + \frac{d}{dt}\widehat{(\Pi + tb_i) \times J^{-1}(\Pi + tb_i)}\right) \end{bmatrix} \\ &= -\begin{bmatrix} A\widehat{J^{-1}b_i} \\ A\widehat{J^{-1}b_i}\hat{\Pi} + \widehat{b_i \times J^{-1}\Pi + \Pi \times J^{-1}b_i} \end{bmatrix} \end{aligned}$$

Since b_1, b_2, b_3 are linearly independent, the vector fields g_i, $[f, g_i]$, $\forall\ i = 1, 2, 3$, span the tangent space $T_{(A, A\hat{\Pi})}T^*SO(3)$ everywhere. This implies the condition (15) is satisfied. In fact, some strong conclusion can also be made. Since the system $\frac{d}{dt}(A, A\hat{\Pi}) = f(A, A\hat{\Pi})$ is a Hamiltonian system envolving on a bounded manifold, and this implies it is a Poisson stable system directly by the Poincaré recurrence theorem [4, 16]. The controllability theorem [5, 12] says that:

> If $\dot{x} = f(x)$ is Poisson stable. Then the system (14) is controllable if and only if the condition (15) is satisfied.

Hence, the controllability of the spacecraft system is guaranteed.

7 Conclusions

As a global representation of the rigid body attitude, some mathematical structures of $SO(3)$ have been investigated. After the representations of the second tangent (cotangent) bundle of $SO(3)$ and its duality are formally given, the Hamilton's equation envolving on the $T^*SO(3)$ are derived. For its important role in nonlinear control theory, the Lie bracket computation on the tangent bundle of $SO(3)$ is the main subject in section IV. Starting from the invariant definition and running through a series of calculation, the elegant formula for the computation of the Lie bracket on $T((SO(3))^m \times \mathcal{R}^n)$ was obtained.

Once the representation and Lie bracket on $SO(3)$ have been well established, there are many applications, as indicated in Introduction, which will become available. As a demonstration, the controllability property of a spacecraft with three gas jets was reconstructed.

References

[1] R. Abraham and J. E. Marsdon. *Foundations of Mechanics.* Benjamin/Cummings, 2nd edition, 1978.

[2] J. Angeles. *Rational Kinematics.* Springer-Verlag, New York, 1988.

[3] V. I. Arnold. *Mathematical Method of Classical Mechanics.* Springer-Verlag, 2nd edition, 1988.

[4] V. I. Arnold, V. V. Kozlov, and A. I. Neihstadt. *Dynamical Systems III.* Encyclopaedia of Math. Sciences. Springer-Verlag, Berlin Heidelberg, 1988.

[5] B. Bonnard. Contrôlabilité des systèmes nonlinéaires. *C. R. Acad, Sci, Paris*, 292:535–537, 1981.

[6] B. Bonnard. Contrôle de l'attitude d'un satellite rigide. *RAIRO Automatique*, 16:85–93, 1982.

[7] J. C. K. Chou. Quaternion kinematic and dynamic differential equations. *IEEE Tran. Robotics Automat.*, 8(1):53–64, 1992.

[8] P. E. Crouch. Spacecraft attitude control and stabilization. *IEEE A.C.*, 29(4):321–331, 1984.

[9] A. Karger and J. Novak. *Space Kinematics and Lie Groups.* Gordon and Breach Science Publishers S.A., 1985.

[10] P. S. Krishnaprasad, R. Yang, and W. P. Dayawansa. Control problems on principal bundles and nonholonomic mechanics. *Proceedings of 30th IEEE conference on Decision and Control*, pages 1133–1138, 1991.

[11] K.-Y. Lian, L.-S. Wang, and L.-C. Fu. Controllability of spacecraft system in a central gravitational field. *in preparing.*

[12] C. Lobry. Controllability of nonlinear systems on compact manifolds. *SIAM J. Control*, 12(1):1–4, 1974.

[13] M. D. Shuster. A survey of attitude representations. *to appear in the Journal of the Astronautical Sciences.*

[14] K. W. Spring. Euler parameters and the use of quaternion algebra in the manipulation of finite rotations: A review. *Mechanism Machine Theory*, 21(5):365–373, 1986.

[15] H. J. Sussmann. Lie brackets. In *Systems and Control Encyclopedia*, pages 2754–2756. Pergamon Press, 1989.

[16] F. Verhulst. *Nonlinear Differential Equations and Dynamical Systems.* Springer-Verlag, 1990.

[17] A. M. Vershik and L. D. Faddeev. Lagrangian mechanics in invariant form. *Sel. Math. Sov.*, 4:339–350, 1981.

[18] L.-S. Wang. *Geometry, Dynamics and Control of Coupled Systems.* PhD thesis, University of Maryland, 1990.

[19] L.-S. Wang and P. S. Krishnaprasad. A multibody analog of the dual-spin problem. In *Proc. of the 29th IEEE Conference on Decision and Control*, pages 1294–1299, 1990.

[20] L.-S. Wang, P. S. Krishnaprasad, and J. H. Maddocks. Hamiltonian dynamics of a rigid body in a central gravitational field. *Celestial Mechanics and Dynamical Astronomy*, 50:349–386, 1991.

[21] F. W. Warner. *Foundations of Differentiable Manifolds and Lie Groups.* Springer-Verlag, New York, 1983.

[22] J. T.-Y. Wen and K. Kreutz-Delgado. The attitude control problem. *IEEE A.C*, 36(10):1148–1162, 1991.

Proceedings of the
American Control Conference
San Francisco, California • June 1993

Model Conversion and Digital Redesign for Singular Systems

Jason S. H. Tsai[1], Chu T. Wang[2], Leang S. Shieh[3]

[1]*Control System Laboratory*
Department of Electrical Engineering
National Cheng-Kung University
Tainan 70101, Taiwan, R.O.C.

[2]*Department of Electrical Engineering*
Fortune Junior College of Technology
Chishan, Kaohsiung, Taiwan, R.O.C.

[3]*Department of Electrical Engineering,*
University of Houston
Houston, TX 77204-4793, U.S.A.

Abstract — In this paper, we propose the design procedures for model conversion and digital redesign of a singular system, which is controllable at finite and impulsive modes. In order to attain a standard regular problem, we use some techniques to decompose the singular system into a reduced-order regular and nondynamic subsystem. As a result, some well-known design methodologies for a regular system can be applied to the reduced-order regular subsystem. Finally, we transform the results obtained back to those of the original coordinate system.

1 Introduction

A large number of control systems are characterized by continuous-time dynamic equations. Also many theories and practical methods have been developed for continuous-time models. However, it is well-known that since the digital computers and the digital processors are not only greatly advanced in technology, but also possess many advantages such as improved sensitivity, better reliability, no drift, less effect due to noise as well as disturbance, lower cost, etc., so it is often desirable to refit these systems with digital transducers and digital controllers. In order to match the states of the equivalent discrete-time system to those of the continuous-time system as closely as possible, the sampling period must be sufficiently small. Unfortunatly, the resulting discrete-time system may be unstable even if the original continuous-time system is stable. Thus, we apply the so-called digital redesign technique [1-2] to arrive at an approximated digital system which closely matches the response of the continuous-time system with the same inputs and initial conditions, rather than designing a new system using digital control theory.

In this paper, we extend the model conversion and digital redesign problems to singular systems, also called descriptor systems, characterized by

$$E_r\dot{x}(t) = A_rx(t) + B_ru(t) \tag{1}$$

where $x(t) \in R^n$, $u(t) \in R^m$, and E_r is a singular matrix. The constant matrices E_r, A_r, as well as, B_r are all have appropriate dimensions. It should be noted that we assume the pencil $(sE_r - A_r)$ to be regular, i.e., $det(sE_r - A_r) \neq 0$ and that the singular system has a unique solution if the singular system considerd in (1) is controllable at finite and impulsive modes in the sense of Cobb [4].

Definition 1 [4]: The singular system is referred to as controllable at finite modes iff $rank[sE_r - A_r,\ B_r] = n$, for all finite $s \in C$.

Definition 2 [4]: If $rank[E_r,\ B_r] = n$, then the singular system is referred to as controllable at impulsive modes.

It is also noted that even if $rank[E_r,\ B_r] \neq n$, there may still exists a dynamic feedback control law such that impulsive modes can be moved to finite locations. In addition, if $rank(E_r) - deg\{det(sE_r - A_r)\} \triangleq q$, where $rank(E_r) \triangleq g$ is called the generalized order of the singular system, and $deg\{det(sE_r - A_r)\} \triangleq k$ is said to be the order of the slow subsystem, then the singular system has q impulsive modes, which occur in the fast subsystem and created by either inconsistent initial conditions or discontinuous control input [5-6].

Cobb [7] and Tsai et al. [8] used preliminary linear feedback controlers to make the singular system (1) causal (i.e., to remove impulsive modes from the system response by moving the associated poles from infinity to some finite locations). Tsai's work is more comparable to the elegant and technical paper proposed by Cobb [7], because Cobb's approach needs to solve complex and difficult eigenvalue-eigenvector problems, in particular, when the singular system has a large order and is in the deflective Jordan form. Also, it is not easy to determine a preliminary feedback control law such that the impulsive modes can be moved to finite locations. Although sometimes Tsai's method requires to solve the eigenvector problem, it is not complicated for processing a low-order submatrix with all zero eigenvalues.

2 Preliminaries

2.1 Introduction to the Matrix Sign Function

The matrix sign function of a square matrix $A \in C^{n\times n}$ with $Re(\sigma(A)) \neq 0$ is defined by [11]

$$sign(A) = 2sign^+(A) - I_n \tag{2}$$

where I_n is an $n \times n$ identity matrix and

$$sign^+(A) = \frac{1}{2\pi i}\oint_{c_+}(\lambda I_n - A)^{-1}d\lambda. \tag{3}$$

c_+ is a simple closed contour in right-half plane of λ and encloses all the right-half-plane eigenvalues of A. On the other hand, the matrix sign function [11] is also defined as

$$sign(A) = A(\sqrt{A^2})^{-1} = A^{-1}(\sqrt{A^2}) \tag{4}$$

where the matrix $\sqrt{A^2}$ denotes the principal square root of A^2. Some fast and numerically stable algorithms with $r \geq 2$ can be found in Tsai et al. [10].

One main feature of the matrix sign function is that it preserves the eigenvectors of the original matrix. A singular matrix A can be modified using the bilinear transformation,

$$\tilde{A} = (A - \rho I_n)(A + \rho I_n)^{-1} \tag{5}$$

where ρ is a radius of a circle with the center at the origin such that the circle contains only those zero eigenvalues, and no eigenvalue of A is located on the circle. Therefore, the eigenvalues within the circle will be mapped into the left-half plane of the complex s-plane, and those outside the circle will be mapped into the right-half plane of the complex s-plane. Note that the bilinear transformation preserves the eigenvectors of the original system.

2.2 Introduction to the Regular Pencil and the Standard one

Definition 3: The regular pencil [9]
Let E_r and A_r be two square constant matrices. If $det(sE_r - A_r) \neq 0$, for all s, then $(sE_r - A_r)$ is called a regular pencil.

Definition 4: The standard pencil [9]
Let $(sE_n - A_n)$ be a regular pencil. If there exist scalars α and β such that $\alpha E_n + \beta A_n = I_n$, then $(sE_n - A_n)$ is called a standard pencil.

Note that any regular pencil, $(sE_r - A_r)$, can be easily transformed into a standard one by premultiplying $(\alpha E_r + \beta A_r)^{-1}$ to E_r and A_r, respectively, where α and β are scalars such that $det(\alpha E_r + \beta A_r) \neq 0$. Hence, the matrix coefficients of a standard pencil, $(sE_n - A_n)$, become

$$E_n \triangleq (\alpha E_r + \beta A_r)^{-1}E_r \tag{6}$$

$$A_n \triangleq (\alpha E_r + \beta A_r)^{-1}A_r. \tag{7}$$

The modified system retains its state vector $x(t)$ and the matrices E_n and A_n have the following nice properties.

Lemma 1: [3]
(L1) $E_nA_n = A_nE_n$, that is, E_n and A_n commute.
(L2) E_n and A_n have the same eigenspaces.

3 The Optimal Regional-Pole-Placement Design Method for Singular Systems [8]

Consider a linear continuous-time singular system, which is controllable at finite and impulsive modes, characterized by (1). As we have discussed in Sec. 2, the regular pencil $(sE_r - A_r)$ can easily be transformed into a standard one, says $(sE_n - A_n)$. Note that since E_n is a singular matrix, which has at least one zero eigenvalue, β can not equal zero. Hence, we have

$$E_n\dot{x}(t) = A_nx(t) + B_nu(t) \tag{8}$$

where $E_n = (\alpha E_r + \beta A_r)^{-1}E_r$, $A_n = (\alpha E_r + \beta A_r)^{-1}A_r$ and $B_n = (\alpha E_r + \beta A_r)^{-1}B_r$. Due to $\alpha E_n + \beta A_n = I_n$, so the pencil $(sE_n - A_n)$ is a standard one. Now, let

$$x(t) = M\bar{x}(t) \tag{9}$$

where the constant matrix M is a block modal matrix of E_n and determined by means of the extended matrix sign function shown below:

Step 1. Find $sign(\tilde{E}_n)$ via the extended matrix sign function with an adequate ρ, where $\tilde{E}_n = (E_n - \rho I_n)(E_n + \rho I_n)^{-1}$.

Step 2. Find $sign^+(\tilde{E}_n) = \frac{1}{2}[I_n + sign(\tilde{E}_n)]$ and $sign^-(\tilde{E}_n) = \frac{1}{2}[I_n - sign(\tilde{E}_n)]$.

Step 3. Construct $M = \left[ind(sign^+(\tilde{E}_n))\ \ ind(sign^-(\tilde{E}_n))\right]$, where $ind(\cdot)$ represents the collection of the linearly independent column vectors of $(\cdot)$.

Substituting (9) back to (8), and multiplying M^{-1} on the left of the equality, one has $M^{-1}E_nM\dot{\bar{x}}(t) = M^{-1}A_nM\bar{x}(t) + M^{-1}B_nu(t)$
$= M^{-1}\frac{1}{\beta}(I_n - \alpha E_n)M\bar{x}(t) + M^{-1}B_nu(t)$

$$\Rightarrow \begin{bmatrix} \bar{E}_1 & O \\ O & \bar{E}_2 \end{bmatrix}\dot{\bar{x}}(t) = \begin{bmatrix} \frac{1}{\beta}(I_k - \alpha\bar{E}_1) & O \\ O & \frac{1}{\beta}(I_{n-k} - \alpha\bar{E}_2) \end{bmatrix}\bar{x}(t) + \begin{bmatrix} \bar{B}_1 \\ \bar{B}_2 \end{bmatrix}u(t) \tag{10}$$

where $\bar{x}(t) = [\bar{x}_s^t(t), \bar{x}_f^t(t)]^t$. $M^{-1}E_nM = block\ diagonal\{\bar{E}_1, \bar{E}_2\}$. $\bar{E}_1$ is invertible with $rank(\bar{E}_1) = deg\{det(sE_r - A_r)\} \triangleq k$. $\bar{E}_2$ is a nilpotent matrix with dimension $(n-k) \times (n-k)$, and $[\bar{B}_1^t, \bar{B}_2^t]^t = M^{-1}B_n$. Notice that since $det(I_{n-k} - \alpha\bar{E}_2) = 1$, it is invertible. Simplifying (10) by premultiplying the *block diagonal*$\{\bar{E}_1^{-1},\ \beta(I_{n-k} - \alpha\bar{E}_2)^{-1}\}$ on both sides of equality, one obtains

$$\begin{bmatrix} I_k & O \\ O & \bar{E}_f \end{bmatrix}\dot{\bar{x}}(t) = \begin{bmatrix} \bar{A}_s & O \\ O & I_{n-k} \end{bmatrix}\bar{x}(t) + \begin{bmatrix} \bar{B}_s \\ \bar{B}_f \end{bmatrix}u(t) \tag{11}$$

where $\bar{E}_f = \beta(I_{n-k} - \alpha\bar{E}_2)^{-1}\bar{E}_2$, $\bar{A}_s = \frac{1}{\beta}(\bar{E}_1^{-1} - \alpha I_k)$, $\bar{B}_s = \bar{E}_1^{-1}\bar{B}_1$ and $\bar{B}_f =$

$\beta(I_{n-k} - \alpha\bar{E}_2)^{-1}\bar{B}_2$. It is remarkable to note that since

$$rank(E_r) - deg\{det(sE_r - A_r)\} = rank(\bar{E}_f), \quad (12)$$

it is much easier to determine the number of the impulsive mode via the above equation relating to (11).

In order to avoid the complexity of statement, we discuss only those kind of singular systems which include at least one impulsive mode. First, assume that the singular system (11) has q impulsive modes, then $rank(\bar{E}_f) = q$. It should be emphasized that since the nilpotent matrix $\bar{E}_f$, in general, is not in the Jordan block form, it is necessary to solve the eigenvector problem for $\bar{E}_f$. The following proposed method is more convenient to find the preliminary feedback gain K_f and to prove the K_f can eliminate the impulsive modes.

Let

$$\bar{x}(t) = V\hat{x}(t) \quad (13)$$

where $\hat{x}(t) = [\bar{x}_s^t(t), \hat{x}_f(t)^t]^t = [\bar{x}_s^t(t), (U^{-1}\bar{x}_f(t))^t]^t$, and $V = block\ diagonal\{I_k, U\}$. U is a modal matrix of $\bar{E}_f$ with dimension $(n-k)\times(n-k)$ such that $U^{-1}\bar{E}_fU$ is in the Jordan block form. Substituting (13) into (11) and premultiplying it by V^{-1}, we obtain

$$\begin{bmatrix} I_k & O \\ O & \hat{E}_f \end{bmatrix}\dot{\hat{x}}(t) = \begin{bmatrix} \hat{A}_s & O \\ O & I_{n-k} \end{bmatrix}\hat{x}(t) + \begin{bmatrix} \hat{B}_s \\ \hat{B}_f \end{bmatrix}u(t) \quad (14)$$

where $\hat{E}_f = U^{-1}\bar{E}_fU$, $\hat{A}_s = \bar{A}_s$, $\hat{B}_s = \bar{B}_s$ and $\hat{B}_f = U^{-1}\bar{B}_f$. Notice that $\hat{E}_f$ is in the Jordan block form with d blocks of sizes $\mu_1, \mu_2, \cdots, \mu_d$, where $\sum_{i=1}^{d}\mu_i$ =column (row) number of $\hat{E}_f$. Taking the Laplace transformation of the fast subsystem $\hat{E}_f\dot{\hat{x}}_f(t) = \hat{x}_f(t) + \hat{B}_fu(t)$ in (14), one obtains

$$\hat{X}_f(s) = -\sum_{i=0}^{l-1} s^i\hat{E}_f^i(\hat{E}_f\hat{x}_f(0) + \hat{B}_fU(s)) \quad (15)$$

where $\hat{X}_f(s)$ and $U(s)$ denote the Laplace transformations of $\hat{x}_f(t)$ and $u(t)$, respectively. $\hat{x}_f(0)$ denotes the initial value of $\hat{x}_f(t)$, and l is said to be the nilpotency index of $\hat{E}_f$. Taking the inverse Laplace transformation of the above equation, we have the well-known result [6]

$$\hat{x}_f(t) = -\sum_{i=1}^{l-1}\hat{E}_f^i\hat{x}_f(0)\delta^{(i-1)}(t) - \sum_{i=0}^{l-1}\hat{E}_f^i\hat{B}_fu^{(i)}(t) \quad (16)$$

where $\delta(t)$ and $\delta^{(i)}(t)$ denote the delta function and the ith derivative of the delta function, respectively. Apparently, it shows that the impulsive modes of the fast state result from inconsistent initial conditions of the fast state or discontinuous control input (or its derivatives).

Here, we propose a preliminary feedback design method to eliminate the impulsive modes, which is simpler than Cobb's [7]. The method for determining the preliminary feedback gain $K_f = [k_1, k_2, \cdots, k_{n-k}]_{m\times(n-k)}$, where k_j is of dimension $m\times 1$ for $j = 1, 2, \cdots, (n-k)$, is summarized as follows:

1. If $\mu_i \geq 1$, where $1 \leq i \leq d$, and its corresponding Jordan block is a null matrix, then

$$\begin{aligned} k_{\mu_1+\mu_2+\cdots+\mu_{i-1}+1} = O_{m\times1}; k_{\mu_1+\mu_2+\cdots+\mu_{i-1}+2} &= O_{m\times1}; \\ \cdots; k_{\mu_1+\mu_2+\cdots+\mu_i} &= O_{m\times1}. \end{aligned}$$

2. If $\mu_i > 1$, where $1 \leq i \leq d$, and its corresponding Jordan block is not a null matrix, then

$$\begin{aligned} k_{\mu_1+\mu_2+\cdots+\mu_{i-1}+1} &= \begin{bmatrix} \delta(\hat{b}_{(\mu_1+\mu_2+\cdots+\mu_i)1}) \\ \delta(\hat{b}_{(\mu_1+\mu_2+\cdots+\mu_i)2}) \\ \vdots \\ \delta(\hat{b}_{(\mu_1+\mu_2+\cdots+\mu_i)m}) \end{bmatrix} \\ k_{\mu_1+\mu_2+\cdots+\mu_{i-1}+2} &= O_{m\times1}; \cdots; k_{\mu_1+\mu_2+\cdots+\mu_i} = O_{m\times1} \end{aligned}$$

where

$$\hat{B}_f \triangleq \begin{bmatrix} \hat{b}_{k+1} \\ \hat{b}_{k+2} \\ \vdots \\ \hat{b}_n \end{bmatrix}_{(n-k)\times m}, \quad \hat{b}_i \triangleq \begin{bmatrix} \hat{b}_{i1} & \hat{b}_{i2} & \cdots & \hat{b}_{im} \end{bmatrix}_{1\times m}$$

$$\delta(\hat{b}_{ij}) \triangleq \begin{cases} 0 & \text{if } \hat{b}_{ij} = 0 \\ 1 & \text{if } \hat{b}_{ij} > 0 \\ -1 & \text{if } \hat{b}_{ij} < 0 \end{cases} \quad j = 1, 2, \cdots, m.$$

Let

$$u(t) = -K_f\hat{x}_f(t) + v(t) = -[\,O_{m\times k},\ K_f\,]\hat{x}(t) + v(t). \quad (17)$$

Substituting (17) back to (14) yields

$$E_k\dot{\hat{x}}(t) = A_k\hat{x}(t) + B_kv(t) \quad (18)$$

where

$$E_k = \begin{bmatrix} I_k & O \\ O & \hat{E}_f \end{bmatrix}, \ A_k = \begin{bmatrix} \hat{A}_s & -\hat{B}_sK_f \\ O & I_{n-k} - \hat{B}_fK_f \end{bmatrix}, \ B_k = \begin{bmatrix} \hat{B}_s \\ \hat{B}_f \end{bmatrix}.$$

Lemma 2:

The singular system in (18) has the original k finite modes and another $q(= rank(\bar{E}_f) = rank(\hat{E}_f))$ finite modes that were induced by applying a linear preliminary feedback control law $u(t)$ in (17) to the system in (14). All these finite modes are guaranteed to be controllable.

Here, we have to emphasize that Cobb's method for determining the preliminary feedback control law in (17), we may need to find an invertible matrix and execute the operations of elementary row and column interchange. Our method, however, is very easy and efficient requiring no computation.

Now, we want to decompose the singular system into a reduced-order regular system with $k+q$ controllable finite modes and a nondynamic equation with $n-k-q$ infinite nondynamic ones. It can be accomplished by using previously outlined steps once again. First, we transform the regular form into a standard one by premultiplying (18) by $(\gamma E_k + \eta A_k)^{-1}$, where γ and η are arbitrary scalars such that $(\gamma E_k + \eta A_k)$ is invertible. Therefore, we obtain

$$(\gamma E_k + \eta A_k)^{-1}E_k\dot{\hat{x}}(t) = (\gamma E_k + \eta A_k)^{-1}A_k\hat{x}(t) + (\gamma E_k + \eta A_k)^{-1}B_kv(t). \quad (19)$$

Let

$$\hat{x}(t) = \tilde{M}\tilde{x}(t) \quad (20)$$

where the constant matrix $\tilde{M}$ is determined using the extended matrix sign function. The procedure is the same as in the previous illustration for finding M, expect that it operates on $(\gamma E_k + \eta A_k)^{-1}E_k$. Substituting (20) into (19), and premultiplying it by $\tilde{M}^{-1}$, one gets

$$\begin{aligned} \tilde{M}^{-1}(\gamma E_k + \eta A_k)^{-1}E_k\tilde{M}\dot{\tilde{x}}(t) &= \frac{1}{\eta}[I_n - \gamma\tilde{M}^{-1}(\gamma E_k + \eta A_k)^{-1}E_k\tilde{M}]\tilde{x}(t) \\ &\quad + \tilde{M}^{-1}(\gamma E_k + \eta A_k)^{-1}B_kv(t) \\ \Rightarrow \begin{bmatrix} \bar{E}_{sk} & O \\ O & \bar{E}_{fk} \end{bmatrix}\dot{\tilde{x}}(t) &= \begin{bmatrix} \frac{1}{\eta}(I_{k+q} - \gamma\bar{E}_{sk}) & O \\ O & \frac{1}{\eta}(I_{n-k-q} - \gamma\bar{E}_{fk}) \end{bmatrix} \\ &\quad \tilde{x}(t) + \begin{bmatrix} \bar{B}_{sk} \\ \bar{B}_{fk} \end{bmatrix}v(t) \\ \Rightarrow \begin{bmatrix} \bar{E}_{sk} & O \\ O & O_{(n-q-k)} \end{bmatrix}\dot{\tilde{x}}(t) &= \begin{bmatrix} \frac{1}{\eta}(I_{k+q} - \gamma\bar{E}_{sk}) & O \\ O & \frac{1}{\eta}I_{n-k-q} \end{bmatrix}\tilde{x}(t) \\ &\quad + \begin{bmatrix} \bar{B}_{sk} \\ \bar{B}_{fk} \end{bmatrix}v(t) \end{aligned} \quad (21)$$

where $\tilde{x}(t) = [\tilde{x}_s^t(t), \tilde{x}_f^t(t)]^t$. $\tilde{M}^{-1}(\gamma E_k + \eta A_k)^{-1}E_k\tilde{M} = block\ diagonal\{\bar{E}_{sk}, \bar{E}_{fk}\} = block\ diagonal\{\bar{E}_{sk}, O_{(n-k-q)}\}$. $\bar{E}_{sk}$ is invertible with $rank(\bar{E}_{sk}) = deg\{det(sE_k - A_k)\} = (q+k)$. $\bar{E}_{fk}$ is a null matrix with dimension $(n-k-q)\times(n-k-q)$, and $[\bar{B}_{sk}^t, \bar{B}_{fk}^t]^t = \tilde{M}^{-1}(\gamma E_k + \eta A_k)^{-1}B_k$.

4 Model Conversion

It is clear to see that the above equation in (21) can be decomposed into a reduced-order regular system and a nondynamic equation as follows:

$$\begin{aligned} \dot{\tilde{x}}_s(t) &= \frac{1}{\eta}(\bar{E}_{sk}^{-1} - \gamma I_{k+q})\tilde{x}_s(t) + \bar{E}_{sk}^{-1}\bar{B}_{sk}v(t) \triangleq \tilde{A}_{sk}\tilde{x}_s(t) + \tilde{B}_{sk}v(t) \quad (22) \\ \tilde{x}_f(t) &= -\eta\bar{B}_{fk}v(t). \quad (23) \end{aligned}$$

If $v(t)$ is a piecewise-constant input, i.e., $v(t) = v(kT)$ for $kT \leq t < kT+T$, where T is a sampling period, then we have the discrete-time system corresponding to (22) and (23) in the following:

$$\begin{aligned} \tilde{x}_{ds}(kT+T) &= \tilde{G}_s\tilde{x}_{ds}(kT) + \tilde{H}_sv(kT) \quad (24) \\ \tilde{x}_{df}(kT) &= -\tilde{H}_fv(kT) \quad (25) \end{aligned}$$

where $\tilde{G}_s = exp(\tilde{A}_{sk}T)$, $\tilde{H}_s = (\tilde{G}_s - I_{q+k})\tilde{A}_{sk}^{-1}\tilde{B}_{sk}$ and $\tilde{H}_f = \eta\bar{B}_{fk}$.

In general, the matrices $\tilde{G}_s$ and $\tilde{H}_s$ can be determined exactly using the eigenvalue-eigenvector approach. However, approximations are required for obtaining $\tilde{G}_s$ and $\tilde{H}_s$ matrices when matrix $\tilde{A}_{sk}$ is singular. There are many methods avaliable to evaluate approximately $\tilde{G}_s$ and $\tilde{H}_s$; specially, using Pade's approximation method [2], which is more popular. Some of the approximations obtained using the Pade's approximation method are listed below:

$$\begin{aligned} \tilde{G}_s &\approx (I_{q+k} - \frac{1}{2}\tilde{A}_{sk}T)^{-1}(I_{q+k} + \frac{1}{2}\tilde{A}_{sk}T) \quad (26) \\ &\approx [I_{q+k} - \frac{1}{2}\tilde{A}_{sk}T + \frac{1}{12}(\tilde{A}_{sk}T)^2]^{-1}[I_{q+k} + \frac{1}{2}\tilde{A}_{sk}T + \frac{1}{12}(\tilde{A}_{sk}T)^2] \quad (27) \\ \tilde{H}_s &\approx T(I_{q+k} - \frac{1}{2}\tilde{A}_{sk}T)^{-1}\tilde{B}_{sk} \quad (28) \\ &\approx T[I_{q+k} - \frac{1}{2}\tilde{A}_{sk}T + \frac{1}{12}(\tilde{A}_{sk}T)^2]^{-1}\tilde{B}_{sk}. \quad (29) \end{aligned}$$

Combining (24) with (25) yields

$$\begin{aligned} \begin{bmatrix} I_{q+k} & O \\ O & O_{n-q-k} \end{bmatrix}\begin{bmatrix} \tilde{x}_{ds}(kT+T) \\ \tilde{x}_{df}(kT+T) \end{bmatrix} &= \begin{bmatrix} \tilde{G}_s & O \\ O & I_{n-q-k} \end{bmatrix} \\ &\quad \times \begin{bmatrix} \tilde{x}_{ds}(kT) \\ \tilde{x}_{df}(kT) \end{bmatrix} + \begin{bmatrix} \tilde{H}_s \\ \tilde{H}_f \end{bmatrix}v(kT). \end{aligned} \quad (30)$$

We transform (30) back to that of the appropriate discrete-time system coordinate, which is corresponding to case of the continuous-time system $E_r\dot{x}_d(t) = (A_r - B_rK_p)x_d(t) + B_rv(t)$ where $K_p = [O_{m\times k}, K_f](MV)^{-1}$, as follows:

$$(MV\tilde{M})\left[\begin{array}{c|c} I_{q+k} & O \\ \hline O & O_{n-q-k}\end{array}\right](MV\tilde{M})^{-1}x_d(kT+T)$$

$$= (MV\tilde{M})\left[\begin{array}{c|c} \tilde{G}_s & O \\ \hline O & I_{n-q-k}\end{array}\right](MV\tilde{M})^{-1}x_d(kT) + (MV\tilde{M})\left[\begin{array}{c} \tilde{H}_s \\ \hline \tilde{H}_f\end{array}\right]v(kT). \quad (31)$$

5 Digital Redesign

Consider the slow subsystem and the fast subsystem described by (22) and (23), respectively. Also, let the optimal control law obtained by using the method of Shieh et al. [12] for the slow subsystem be

$$v(t) = -K_{cs}\bar{x}_s(t) + E_{cs}r(t). \quad (32)$$

Thus the closed-loop system becomes

$$\dot{\bar{x}}_s(t) = (\tilde{A}_{sk} - \tilde{B}_{sk}K_{cs})\bar{x}_s(t) + \tilde{B}_{sk}E_{cs}r(t) \quad (33)$$

$$\bar{x}_f(t) = \eta\bar{B}_{fk}K_{cs}\bar{x}_s(t) - \eta\bar{B}_{fk}E_{cs}r(t) \quad (34)$$

and its eigenvalues locate on or within the hatched region of Fig. 1.

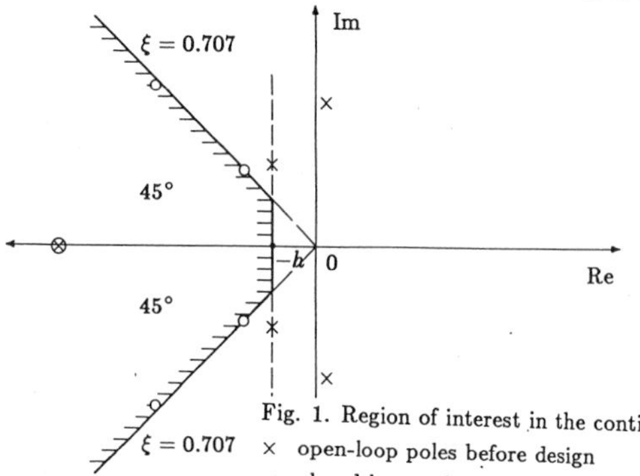

Fig. 1. Region of interest in the continuous-time s-plane.
× open-loop poles before design
o closed-loop poles after design

Assuming $r(t) = r(kT)$ for $kT \le t < kT + T$, we have the respective discrete-time models of (33) and (34) as follows:

$$\bar{x}_{ds}(kT+T) = G_s\bar{x}_{ds}(kT) + H_sr(kT) \quad (35)$$

$$\bar{x}_{df}(kT) = \eta\bar{B}_{fk}K_{cs}\bar{x}_{ds}(kT) - \eta\bar{B}_{fk}E_{cs}r(kT) \quad (36)$$

where $G_s = exp((\tilde{A}_{sk} - \tilde{B}_{sk}K_{cs})T)$, $H_s = (G_s - I_{q+k})(\tilde{A}_{sk} - \tilde{B}_{sk}K_{cs})^{-1}\tilde{B}_{sk}E_{cs}$. Its eigenvalues are located on or within the hatched region of Fig. 2.

Suppose a digital model which approximates the slow subsystem in (22) is represented by

$$\dot{\bar{x}}_d(t) = \tilde{A}_{sk}\bar{x}_d(t) + \tilde{B}_{sk}v(kT). \quad (37)$$

Then the equivalent discrete-time model can be written as

$$\bar{x}_d(kT+T) = \tilde{G}_d\bar{x}_d(kT) + \tilde{H}_dv(kT) \quad (38)$$

where $\tilde{G}_d = exp(\tilde{A}_{sk}T)$, $\tilde{H}_d = (\tilde{G}_d - I_{q+k})\tilde{A}_{sk}^{-1}\tilde{B}_{sk}$. Let the digital control law for the discrete-time model in (38) be

$$v(kT) = -K_d\bar{x}_d(kT) + E_dr(kT). \quad (39)$$

Then we have the designed closed-loop subsystem as

$$\bar{x}_d(kT+T) = (\tilde{G}_d - \tilde{H}_dK_d)\bar{x}_d(kT) + \tilde{H}_dE_dr(kT). \quad (40)$$

To match $\bar{x}_{ds}(kT) \approx \bar{x}_d(kT)$ with a sufficiently small sampling period T and the same inputs, as well as, the initial conditions, the explicit feedback gain K_d and forward gain E_d have already been solved by Tsai et al. [2] as follows:

First, G_s can be approximated by using the Pade approximation method as

$$G_s = exp((\tilde{A}_{sk} - \tilde{B}_{sk}K_{cs})T)$$

$$\approx [I_{q+k} - \frac{1}{2}(\tilde{A}_{sk} - \tilde{B}_{sk}K_{cs})T]^{-1}[I_{q+k} + \frac{1}{2}(\tilde{A}_{sk} - \tilde{B}_{sk}K_{cs})T]. \quad (41)$$

Next, based on the fact that

$$(A + BCD)^{-1} = A^{-1} - A^{-1}B(C^{-1} + DA^{-1}B)^{-1}DA^{-1}. \quad (42)$$

Thus we can find the important results from the following derivations:

$$G_s \approx \tilde{G}_d - \tilde{H}_d[\frac{1}{2}(I_m + \frac{1}{2}K_{cs}\tilde{H}_d)^{-1}K_{cs}(I_{q+k} + \tilde{G}_d)]$$

$$= \tilde{G}_d - \tilde{H}_dK_d \quad (43)$$

$$H_s = (G_s - I_{q+k})(\tilde{A}_{sk} - \tilde{B}_{sk}K_{cs})^{-1}\tilde{B}_{sk}E_{cs}$$

$$\approx \tilde{H}_d(I_m + \frac{1}{2}K_{cs}\tilde{H}_d)^{-1}E_{cs} = \tilde{H}_dE_d. \quad (44)$$

Hence

$$K_d = \frac{1}{2}(I_m + \frac{1}{2}K_{cs}\tilde{H}_d)^{-1}K_{cs}(I_{q+k} + \tilde{G}_d) \quad (45)$$

$$E_d = (I_m + \frac{1}{2}K_{cs}\tilde{H}_d)^{-1}E_{cs}. \quad (46)$$

Finally, the state feedback control law $u(kT)$ can be derived through some adequate coordinate transformation and the necessary definition.

$$x_d(kT) \triangleq M\begin{bmatrix}\tilde{x}_d(kT) \\ \tilde{x}_f(kT)\end{bmatrix} \triangleq MV\begin{bmatrix}\hat{x}_d(kT) \\ \hat{x}_f(kT)\end{bmatrix} \triangleq MV\tilde{M}\begin{bmatrix}\bar{x}_d(kT) \\ \bar{x}_f(kT)\end{bmatrix}$$

$$\approx MV\tilde{M}\begin{bmatrix}\bar{x}_{ds}(kT) \\ \bar{x}_{df}(kT)\end{bmatrix} = x(kT). \quad (47)$$

By the above definitions, one gets

$$u(t) = -K_f\hat{x}_f(t) + v(t) = -[\ O_{m\times k},\ K_f\ ]\begin{bmatrix}\hat{x}_s(t) \\ \hat{x}_f(t)\end{bmatrix} + v(t)$$

$$= -[\ O_{m\times k},\ K_f\ ](MV)^{-1}x(t) + v(t) \triangleq -K_px(t) + v(t) \quad (48)$$

$$v(kT) = -K_d\bar{x}_d(kT) + E_dr(kT)$$

$$= -[\ K_d,\ O_{m\times(n-q-k)}\ ]\begin{bmatrix}\bar{x}_d(kT) \\ \bar{x}_f(kT)\end{bmatrix} + E_dr(kT)$$

$$= -[\ K_d,\ O_{m\times(n-q-k)}\ ](MV\tilde{M})^{-1}x_d(kT) + E_dr(kT)$$

$$\triangleq -Kx_d(kT) + E_dr(kT) \quad (49)$$

where $K_p = [\ O_{m\times k}, K_f\ ](MV)^{-1}$, $K = [\ K_d, O_{m\times(n-q-k)}\ ](MV\tilde{M})^{-1}$. The redesigned digital system is shown in Fig. 3. It is noted that when the discrete-time state $x_d(kT)$ is not accessible, the ideal state reconstructor methods [13-14] can be applied to reconstruct the exact discrete-time state $x_d(kT)$ using the input data and fast-rate output data of the original continuous-time system without establishing an observer.

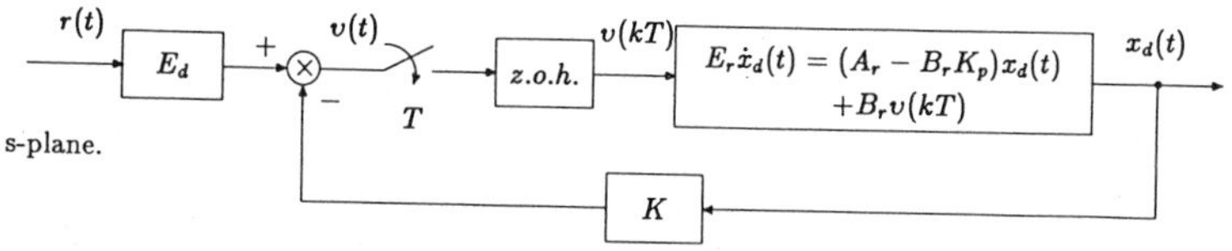

Fig. 3. Digital redesign system

6 Illustrative Example

Consider a linear continuous-time singular system described in (1) with

$$E_r = \begin{bmatrix} 1 & 2 & 1 & 1 & -3 & -2 \\ 0 & 2 & 2 & 1 & -3 & -3 \\ 1 & 2 & 1 & 1 & -3 & -2 \\ 1 & 2 & 1 & 3 & -5 & -4 \\ 0 & 2 & 1 & 1 & -2 & -2 \\ 1 & 0 & 0 & 0 & -1 & 0 \end{bmatrix}, \quad A_r = I_6, \quad B_r^t = \begin{bmatrix} 1 & 0 & 0 & 0 & 0 & -1 \\ 0 & 0 & -1 & 1 & 0 & 0 \end{bmatrix}.$$

Since $0E_r + A_r = A_r = I_6$, by definition of the standard form, $\{E_r, A_r\}$ is in standard form. In other words, if we take $\alpha = 0$ and $\beta = 1$, then $E_n = E_r$, $A_n = A_r$ and $B_n = B_r$. Because E_n is singular, i.e., E_n includes some zero eigenvalues, utilizing the bilinear transform to find the similarity transformation matrix M of E_n is necessary. Taking $\rho = 0.5$ and using the algorithm described in Sec. 3, one has

$$\tilde{E} = (E_n - \rho I_6)(E_n + \rho I_6)^{-1} = \begin{bmatrix} 0.3333 & 1.6 & -2.4 & 0.16 & 0.9067 & 2.24 \\ 0 & 0.6 & 1.6 & 0.16 & -1.76 & -1.76 \\ 1.3333 & 1.6 & -3.4 & 0.16 & 0.9067 & 2.24 \\ 1.3333 & 1.6 & -2.4 & 0.76 & -0.6933 & 0.64 \\ 0 & 1.6 & -2.4 & 0.16 & 1.24 & 2.24 \\ 1.3333 & 0 & 0 & 0 & -1.3333 & -1 \end{bmatrix}$$

$$M = [ind(sign^+(\tilde{E}))\ ind(sign^-(\tilde{E}))] = \begin{bmatrix} 1 & 1 & 0 & 0 & -1 & -1 \\ 0 & 1 & 0 & 0 & 0 & -1 \\ 1 & 1 & 0 & -1 & -1 & 0 \\ 1 & 1 & 1 & -1 & -1 & -1 \\ 0 & 1 & 0 & 0 & -1 & -1 \\ 1 & 0 & 0 & -1 & 0 & 0 \end{bmatrix}$$

From (10), we obtain

$$M^{-1}E_nM = \left[\begin{array}{c|c} \bar{E}_1 & O \\ \hline O & \bar{E}_2 \end{array}\right] = \left[\begin{array}{ccc|ccc} 1 & 0 & 0 & 0 & 0 & 0 \\ 0 & 2 & 1 & 0 & 0 & 0 \\ 0 & 0 & 2 & 0 & 0 & 0 \\ \hline 0 & 0 & 0 & 0 & 0 & 0 \\ 0 & 0 & 0 & 0 & 0 & 1 \\ 0 & 0 & 0 & 0 & 0 & 0 \end{array}\right]$$

$$M^{-1}A_nM = \left[\begin{array}{c|c} I_3 & O \\ \hline O & I_3 \end{array}\right]$$

$$M^{-1}B_n = [\ \bar{B}_1^t\ \mid\ \bar{B}_2^t\ ]^t = \left[\begin{array}{ccc|ccc} 1 & 1 & 1 & 2 & 0 & 1 \\ 0 & -1 & 1 & 0 & 0 & -1 \end{array}\right]^t.$$

Based on (11) and the fact that $\bar{E}_f$ is in the Jordan form, one has

$$V = I_6, \quad \hat{E}_f = \bar{E}_f\bar{E}_1 = \begin{bmatrix} 0 & 0 & 0 \\ 0 & 0 & 1 \\ 0 & 0 & 0 \end{bmatrix}, \quad \hat{A}_s = \bar{A}_s = \frac{1}{\beta}\bar{E}_1^{-1} = \begin{bmatrix} 1 & 0 & 0 \\ 0 & 0.5 & -0.25 \\ 0 & 0 & 0.5 \end{bmatrix}$$

$$\hat{B}_s = \bar{B}_s = \bar{E}_1^{-1}\bar{B}_1 = \begin{bmatrix} 1 & 0 \\ 0.25 & -0.75 \\ 0.5 & 0.5 \end{bmatrix}, \quad \hat{B}_f = \bar{B}_f = \bar{B}_2 = \begin{bmatrix} 2 & 0 \\ 0 & 0 \\ 1 & -1 \end{bmatrix}.$$

Since $rank(\bar{E}_f) = q = 1$, the singular system has one impulsive mode by means of (12) associated with (11).

Now, we compute the preliminary feedback gain K_f for eliminating the impulsive mode of the singular system. As $\mu_1 = 1$, $k_1 = O_{2\times1}$. In addition, since $u_2 = 2$ and its corresponding Jordan block is not a null matrix, one has

$$k_{\mu_1+1} = k_2 = \begin{bmatrix} \delta(b_{(\mu_1+\mu_2)1}) \\ \delta(b_{(\mu_1+\mu_2)2}) \end{bmatrix} = \begin{bmatrix} \delta(b_{31}) \\ \delta(b_{32}) \end{bmatrix} = \begin{bmatrix} 1 \\ -1 \end{bmatrix}, \; k_{\mu_1+\mu_2} = k_3 = O_{2\times1}.$$

Thus we get the preliminary feedback gain

$$K_f = \begin{bmatrix} 0 & 1 & 0 \\ 0 & -1 & 0 \end{bmatrix}$$

and the control law

$$u(t) = -[\; O_{2\times3}\;,\; K_f \;]\hat{x}(t) + v(t) = -\begin{bmatrix} 0 & 0 & 0 & 0 & 1 & 0 \\ 0 & 0 & 0 & 0 & -1 & 0 \end{bmatrix}\hat{x}(t) + v(t).$$

Computing the closed-loop singular system with respect to the preliminary feedback gain yields

$$E_k = \left[\begin{array}{c|c} I_3 & O \\ \hline O & \hat{E}_f \end{array}\right] = \left[\begin{array}{ccc|ccc} 1 & 0 & 0 & 0 & 0 & 0 \\ 0 & 1 & 0 & 0 & 0 & 0 \\ 0 & 0 & 1 & 0 & 0 & 0 \\ \hline 0 & 0 & 0 & 0 & 0 & 0 \\ 0 & 0 & 0 & 0 & 0 & 1 \\ 0 & 0 & 0 & 0 & 0 & 0 \end{array}\right]$$

$$A_k = \left[\begin{array}{c|c} \hat{A}_s & -\hat{B}_s K_f \\ \hline O & I_3 - \hat{B}_f K_f \end{array}\right] = \left[\begin{array}{ccc|ccc} 1 & 0 & 0 & 0 & -1 & 0 \\ 0 & 0.5 & -0.25 & 0 & -1 & 0 \\ 0 & 0 & 0.5 & 0 & 0 & 0 \\ \hline 0 & 0 & 0 & 1 & -2 & 0 \\ 0 & 0 & 0 & 0 & 1 & 0 \\ 0 & 0 & 0 & 0 & -2 & 1 \end{array}\right]$$

$$B_k = \left[\begin{array}{c} \hat{B}_s \\ \hline \hat{B}_f \end{array}\right] = \left[\begin{array}{cc} 1 & 0 \\ 0.25 & -0.75 \\ 0.5 & 0.5 \\ \hline 2 & 0 \\ 0 & 0 \\ 1 & -1 \end{array}\right].$$

We transform the regular form $\{E_k, A_k\}$ into a standard one once again with $\gamma = 2$ and $\eta = -1$, and use the extended matrix sign function to find a similarity transformation matrix $\tilde{M}$ of E_k

$$\tilde{M} = \begin{bmatrix} 1 & 0 & 0 & 0 & 0 & 0 \\ 0 & 1 & 0 & 0 & 0 & 0 \\ 0 & 0 & 1 & 0 & 0 & 0 \\ 0 & 0 & 0 & 1 & 1 & 0 \\ 0 & 0 & 0 & 0.5 & 0 & 1 \\ 0 & 0 & 0 & 1 & 0 & 0 \end{bmatrix}.$$

Let $\hat{x}(t) = \tilde{M}\tilde{x}(t)$ and compute (21), then one has $\tilde{M}^{-1}(\gamma E_k + \eta A_k)^{-1}E_k\tilde{M} = block\ diagonal\{\bar{E}_{sk},\ O_2\}$, where

$$\bar{E}_{sk} = \begin{bmatrix} 1 & 0 & 0 & -0.3333 \\ 0 & 0.6667 & -0.1111 & -0.2222 \\ 0 & 0 & 0.6667 & 0 \\ 0 & 0 & 0 & 0.6667 \end{bmatrix}$$

$$\frac{1}{\eta}[I_6 - \gamma\tilde{M}^{-1}(\gamma E_k + \eta A_k)^{-1}E_k\tilde{M}] = \left[\begin{array}{c|c} \frac{1}{\eta}(I_4 - \gamma\bar{E}_{sk}) & O \\ \hline O & \frac{1}{\eta}I_2 \end{array}\right]$$

where

$$\frac{1}{\eta}(I_4 - \gamma\bar{E}_{sk}) = \begin{bmatrix} 1 & 0 & 0 & -0.6667 \\ 0 & 0.3333 & -0.2222 & -0.4444 \\ 0 & 0 & 0.3333 & 0 \\ 0 & 0 & 0 & 0.3333 \end{bmatrix}$$

and

$$\frac{1}{\eta}I_2 = \begin{bmatrix} -1 & 0 \\ 0 & -1 \end{bmatrix}$$

$$\tilde{M}^{-1}(\gamma E_k + \eta A_k)^{-1}B_k = \left[\begin{array}{c} \bar{B}_{sk} \\ \hline \bar{B}_{fk} \end{array}\right] = \left[\begin{array}{cc} 0.3333 & 0.6667 \\ -0.3333 & -0.1111 \\ 0.3333 & 0.3333 \\ 0.3333 & -0.3333 \\ \hline -1 & -1 \\ 0.5 & -0.5 \end{array}\right].$$

Therefore we get the reduced-order regular subsystem and the nondynamic subsystem in (22) and (23), respectively,

$$\begin{aligned} \dot{\tilde{x}}_s(t) &= \frac{1}{\eta}(\bar{E}_{sk}^{-1} - \gamma I_4)\tilde{x}_s(t) + \bar{E}_{sk}^{-1}\bar{B}_{sk}v(t) \\ &= \tilde{A}_{sk}\tilde{x}_s(t) + \tilde{B}_{sk}v(t) \\ &= \begin{bmatrix} 1 & 0 & 0 & -0.5 \\ 0 & 0.5 & -0.25 & -0.5 \\ 0 & 0 & 0.5 & 0 \\ 0 & 0 & 0 & 0.5 \end{bmatrix}\tilde{x}_s(t) + \begin{bmatrix} 0.5 & 0.5 \\ -0.25 & -0.25 \\ 0.5 & 0.5 \\ 0.5 & -0.5 \end{bmatrix}v(t) \end{aligned}$$

and

$$\tilde{x}_f(t) = -\eta\bar{B}_{fk}v(t) = \begin{bmatrix} -1 & -1 \\ 0.5 & -0.5 \end{bmatrix}v(t).$$

(1). Model Conversion

The discrete-time model corresponding to (22) and (23) is in (24) and (25), respectively, where $T = 0.1$ second,

$$\tilde{G}_s = exp(\tilde{A}_{sk}T) = \begin{bmatrix} 1.1052 & 0 & 0 & -0.0539 \\ 0 & 1.0513 & -0.0263 & -0.0526 \\ 0 & 0 & 1.0513 & 0 \\ 0 & 0 & 0 & 1.0513 \end{bmatrix}$$

$$\tilde{H}_s = (\tilde{G}_s - I_4)\tilde{A}_{sk}^{-1}\tilde{B}_{sk} = \begin{bmatrix} 0.0513 & 0.0539 \\ -0.0276 & -0.0250 \\ 0.0513 & 0.0513 \\ 0.0513 & -0.0513 \end{bmatrix}, \; \tilde{H}_f = \eta\bar{B}_{fk} = \begin{bmatrix} 1 & 1 \\ -0.5 & 0.5 \end{bmatrix}.$$

Thus we find the discrete-time singular system corresponding to the continuous-time singular system $E_r\dot{x}_d(t) = (A_r - B_rK_p)x_d(t) + B_rv(kT)$ by computing (31), and the result is as follows:

$$(MV\tilde{M})\left[\begin{array}{c|c} I_4 & O \\ \hline O & O_2 \end{array}\right](MV\tilde{M})^{-1} = \begin{bmatrix} 1 & 1 & -0.5 & 0 & -0.5 & 0.5 \\ 0 & 1 & 0 & 0 & 0 & 0 \\ 1 & 1 & -0.5 & 0 & -0.5 & 0.5 \\ 1 & 1 & -1.5 & 1 & -0.5 & 0.5 \\ 0 & 1 & -0.5 & 0 & 0.5 & 0.5 \\ 1 & 0 & -1 & 0 & 0 & 1 \end{bmatrix}$$

$$\begin{aligned} &(MV\tilde{M})\left[\begin{array}{c|c} \tilde{G}_s & O \\ \hline O & I_2 \end{array}\right](MV\tilde{M})^{-1} \\ &= \begin{bmatrix} 1.1052 & 0.0513 & -0.1321 & -0.0263 & 0.0532 & 0.1584 \\ 0 & 1.0513 & -0.0526 & -0.0263 & 0.0788 & 0.0788 \\ 0.1052 & 0.0513 & 0.8679 & -0.0263 & 0.0532 & 0.1584 \\ 0.1052 & 0.0513 & -0.1834 & 1.0250 & 0.0532 & 0.1584 \\ 0 & 0.0513 & -0.0782 & -0.0263 & 1.1045 & 0.1045 \\ 0.1052 & 0 & -0.1052 & 0 & 0 & 1.1052 \end{bmatrix} \end{aligned}$$

$$(MV\tilde{M})\begin{bmatrix} \tilde{H}_s \\ \tilde{H}_f \end{bmatrix} = \begin{bmatrix} 0.4468 & -0.3942 \\ -0.0788 & 0.0263 \\ -0.5532 & -1.3942 \\ -0.5532 & -1.2916 \\ 0.3955 & -0.4481 \\ -1 & -0.8948 \end{bmatrix}$$

The continuous-time singular system are with 4 finite eigenvalues, $\{1, 0.5, 0.5, 0.5\}$, and 2 infinite nondynamic eigenvalues. Its corresponding discrete-time model has 4 finite eigenvalues, $\{1.1052, 1.0513, 1.0513, 1.0513\}$, and 2 infinite nondynamic eigenvalues.

(2). Digital Redesign

Set the desired control law for the slow subsystem be described by (32) where

$$K_{cs} = \begin{bmatrix} 7.9819 & -23.9457 & -13.8190 & 5.8507 \\ 28.3801 & -1.1403 & -21.8009 & -6.8643 \end{bmatrix}, \; E_{cs} = I_4.$$

The eigenvalues of the closed-loop continuous-time singular system $E_r\dot{x}(t) = (A_r - B_rK)x(t) + B_rr(t)$, denoted by $\sigma(sE_r - A_r + B_rK)$ where $K = \{[O_{2\times3}, K_f] + [K_{cs}, O_{2\times2}]\tilde{M}^{-1}\}(MV)^{-1}$, include 2 infinite nondynamic eigenvalues and 4 finite eigenvalues $\{-3, -2.5, -2.5, -2.5\}$ which lie within the specified region with $h = 1$ in Fig. 1. Therefore one has the equivalent discrete-time model in (38) with

$$\tilde{G}_d = exp(\tilde{A}_{sk}T) = \begin{bmatrix} 1.1052 & 0 & 0 & -0.0539 \\ 0 & 1.0513 & -0.0263 & -0.0526 \\ 0 & 0 & 1.0513 & 0 \\ 0 & 0 & 0 & 1.0513 \end{bmatrix}$$

$$\tilde{H}_d = (\tilde{G}_d - I_4)\tilde{A}_{sk}^{-1}\tilde{B}_{sk} = \begin{bmatrix} 0.0513 & 0.0539 \\ -0.0276 & -0.0250 \\ 0.0513 & 0.0513 \\ 0.0513 & -0.0513 \end{bmatrix}.$$

Hence K_d and E_d concerning the digital control law in (39) are

$$\begin{aligned} K_d &= \frac{1}{2}(I_2 + \frac{1}{2}K_{cs}\tilde{H}_d)^{-1}K_{cs}(I_4 + \tilde{G}_d) \\ &= \begin{bmatrix} 6.1532 & -18.4535 & -10.2956 & 4.8638 \\ 21.3588 & -0.7265 & -15.9422 & -5.5982 \end{bmatrix} \end{aligned}$$

$$E_d = (I_2 + \frac{1}{2}K_{cs}\tilde{H}_d)^{-1}E_{cs} = \begin{bmatrix} 0.7516 & -0.0054 \\ -0.0045 & -0.7163 \end{bmatrix}.$$

Thus the state feedback gains K_p and K for continuous-time singular system and the redesigned sampled-data system, respectively, are

$$K_p = [\; O_{2\times3}\;,\; K_f \;](MV)^{-1} = \begin{bmatrix} 0 & 1 & 0 & 0 & -1 & 0 \\ 0 & -1 & 0 & 0 & 1 & 0 \end{bmatrix}$$

$$\begin{aligned} K &= [\; K_d,\; O_{2\times2} \;](MV\tilde{M})^{-1} \\ &= \begin{bmatrix} 6.1532 & -18.4535 & -13.5897 & -10.2956 & 17.7322 & 23.8853 \\ 21.3588 & -0.7265 & -6.3246 & -15.9422 & 0.9081 & 22.2668 \end{bmatrix}. \end{aligned}$$

The eigenvalues of the equivalent discrete-time singular system

$$\begin{aligned} &(MV\tilde{M})\left[\begin{array}{c|c} I_4 & O \\ \hline O & O_2 \end{array}\right](MV\tilde{M})^{-1}x_d(kT + T) \\ &= (MV\tilde{M})\left\{\left[\begin{array}{c|c} \tilde{G}_s & O \\ \hline O & I_2 \end{array}\right](MV\tilde{M})^{-1} - \left[\begin{array}{c} \tilde{H}_s \\ \hline \tilde{H}_f \end{array}\right]K\right\}x_d(kT) \\ &+ (MV\tilde{M})\left[\begin{array}{c} \tilde{H}_s \\ \hline \tilde{H}_f \end{array}\right]E_dr(kT) \end{aligned}$$

include 2 infinite nondynamic eigenvalues and 4 finite eigenvalues $\{0.7408, 0.7788, 0.7788, 0.7788\}$ which lie within the specified region with $h = 1$ in Fig. 2. The simulation results with respect to controls are shown in Fig. 4. and Fig. 5, respectively.

7 Conclusions

The model conversion and digital redesign problems for regular system have been extended to the case of a singular system which is controllable at finite and impulsive modes. If the singular system doesn't have any impulsive mode, then we can easily utilize the good characteristics of the standard pair and apply the extended matrix sign function to decompose the singular system into a reduced-order regular subsystem and a nondynamic subsystem. Otherwise, we must apply a preliminary feedback control law, which is simpler and more efficient than that of Cobb's, to the singular system in order to eliminate all impulsive modes. Finally, we apply the given results to the reduced-order regular subsystem and then the relating the reduced-order regular subsystem are transformed back to those of the original coordinates.

Acknowledgment

This work was supported by the National Science Council of the Republic of China under contract NSC-81-0404-E-006-572, the NASA-Johnson Space Center under grant NAG-9-380, and the U.S. Army Research Office under grant DAAL-03-91-G0106.

References

[1] B. C. Kuo, *Digital Control Systems*. N. Y.: Holt, Rinehart and Winston, 1980.

[2] J. S. H. Tsai, L. S. Shieh, J. L. Zhang and N. P. Coleman, "Digital redesign of pseudo-continuous-time suboptimal regulators for large-scale discrete systems," *Control-Theory and Advanced Technology,* vol. 5, no. 1, pp. 37-65, 1989.

[3] S. L. Campbell, *Singular Systems of Differential Equations. II.* N.Y.: Pitman, 1982.

[4] D. Cobb, "Controllability, observability, and duality in singular system," *IEEE Trans. Automat. Contr.,* vol. AC-29, no. 12, pp. 1076-1082, 1984.

[5] G. C. Verghese, B. C. Levy and T. Kailath, "A Generalized State-Space for Singular Systems," *IEEE Trans. Automa. Contr.,* vol. AC-26, no. 4, pp. 811-831, 1981.

[6] L. Dai, "Impulsive modes and causality in singular systems," *Int. J. Control,* vol. 50, no. 4, pp. 1267-1281, 1989.

[7] D. Cobb, "Descriptor variable systems and optimal state regulation," *IEEE Trans. Automat. Contr.,* vol. AC-28, no. 5, pp. 601-611, 1983.

[8] J. S. H. Tsai, C. T. Wang and L. S. Shieh, "The optimal regional-pole-placement design method for singular systems," *Journal of Control Systems and Technology,* vol. 1, no. 1 (to appear in March 1993).

[9] R. Nikoukhah, A. S. Willsky and B. C. Levy, "Boundary-value descriptor systems: well-posedness, reachability and observability," *Int. J. Control,* vol. 46, no. 5, pp. 1715-1737, 1987.

[10] J. S. H. Tsai, L. S. Shieh and R. E. Yates, "Fast and stable algorithms for computing the principal nth root of a complex matrix and the matrix-sector function," *Int. J. Comput. & Appl. Math.,* vol. 15, no. 11, pp. 903-913, 1988.

[11] L. S. Shieh, Y. T. Tsay, S. W. Lin and N. P. Coleman, "Block-diagonalization and block-triangularization of a matrix via the matrix-sign function," *Int. J. Systems Science,* vol. 15, no. 11, pp. 1203-1213, 1984.

[12] L. S. Shieh, H. M. Dib and S. Ganesan, "Continuous-time quadratic regulators and pseudo-continuous-time quadratic regulators with pole placement in a specific region," *IEE Proceedings, Part D,* vol. 134, no. 5, pp. 338-346, 1987.

[13] M. E. Polites, "Ideal state reconstructor for deterministic digital control systems," *Int. J. Control,* vol. 49, no. 6, pp. 2001-2011, 1989.

[14] J. S. H. Tsai, C. M. Chen and L. S. Shieh, "Digital redesign of the cascaded continuous-time controller: time-domain approach," *Control-Theory Adv. Tech.,* vol. 7, no. 4, pp. 643-661, 1991.

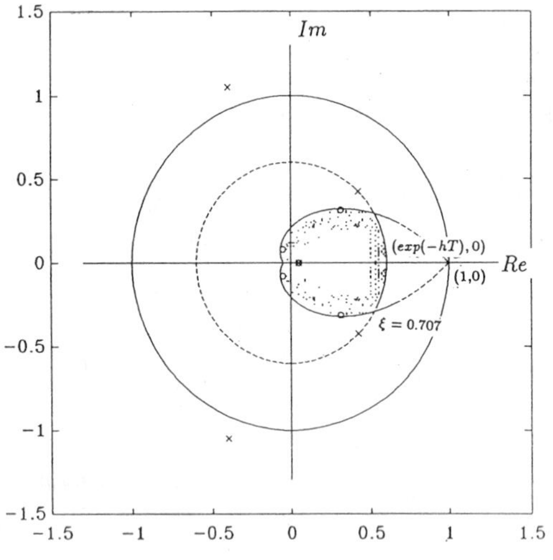

Fig. 2. Region of interest in the z-plane

x poles before design

o poles after design

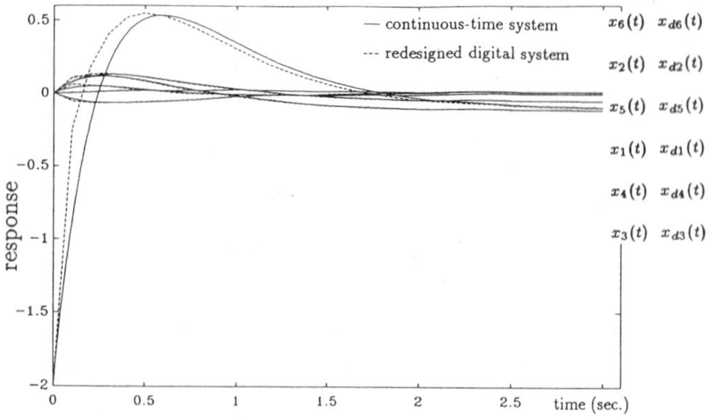

Fig. (4a). Simulation results

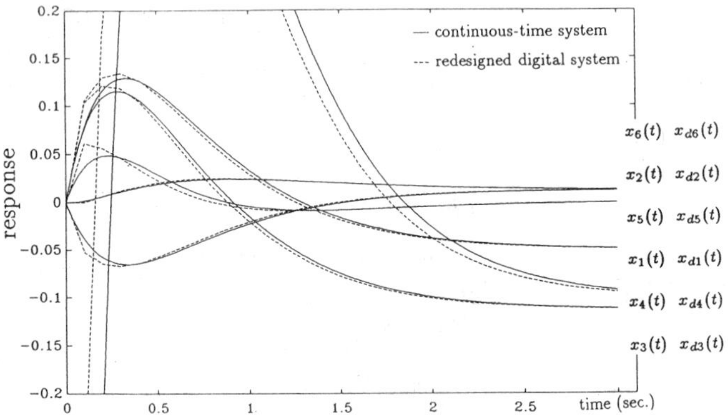

Fig. (4b). A part of Fig. (4a)

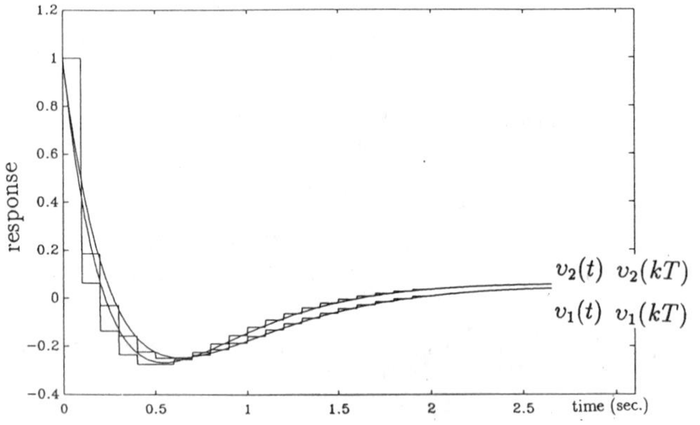

Fig. 5. Control signals

Proceedings of the
American Control Conference
San Francisco, California • June 1993

$\mathcal{H}_2$ and $\mathcal{H}_\infty$ Designs of Multirate Sampled-Data Systems[1]

Li Qiu
Inst. of Math. & Its Appl.
University of Minnesota
Minneapolis, MN
USA 55455

Tongwen Chen
Dept. of Elect. & Comp. Engg.
University of Calgary
Calgary, Alberta
Canada T2N 1N4

Abstract

Treating causality constraints, this paper studies the optimal syntheses of multirate sampled-data systems with $\mathcal{H}_2$ and $\mathcal{H}_\infty$ performance criteria. Explicit solutions to both the $\mathcal{H}_2$ and $\mathcal{H}_\infty$ problems are obtained by input-output space extensions (lifting) and frequency-domain techniques.

1 Introduction

Designing digital controllers directly using continuous-time performance measures is receiving considerable attention recently; this is evidenced by work in the $\mathcal{H}_2$ framework [6, 17, 3] and $\mathcal{H}_\infty$ framework [14, 28, 2, 25, 27, 15]. A general mathematical tool, the lifting technique, has been developed [28, 31, 2, 4] for attacking problems in single-rate sampled-data systems.

All work mentioned above is in the single-rate setting. However, multirate sampled-data systems arise in a more natural way. In general, faster A/D and D/A conversions lead to better performance in digital control systems but also mean higher cost in implementation. Allowing different speeds for A/D and D/A conversions results in better trade-offs between performance and implementation cost.

The concept of multirate sampling was pioneered by Kranc [18]. Recent interests in multirate systems are reflected in the LQG/LQR designs [5, 1, 19, 7], the parametrization of stabilizing controllers [20, 23], and among others. While the research on single-rate direct digital design has been active, little work has been done on multirate systems using the direct design approach. The main obstacle is perhaps the so-called causality constraint [20, 23], which presents a unique difficulty for synthesizing the feedthrough term in lifted controllers. A similar constraint also arises in discrete-time periodic control; interesting solutions were obtained for the $\mathcal{H}_\infty$ problem [10, 11, 30] and the $\mathcal{H}_2$ problem [30]. In this paper we treat multirate designs directly from a sampled-data point of view and use matrix factorization theory to tackle causality constraints.

The organization of this paper is as follows. Section 2 presents the multirate setup for our study and discusses desirable properties of multirate controllers. Section 3 extends the lifting idea in [4] to the multirate case. Section 4 formulates and solves explicitly the multirate $\mathcal{H}_2$-optimal control problem using the lifting presented in Section 3. Section 5 is devoted to the multirate $\mathcal{H}_\infty$ control problem. We show how to reduce the multirate sampled-data problem to a discrete-time $\mathcal{H}_\infty$ problem with causality constraint. The latter problem is then solved explicitly using frequency-domain methods. We refer to [22] for proofs and details.

The notation is quite standard. We use ℓ to denote the space of sequences, perhaps vector-valued, defined on the time set $\{0, 1, 2, \cdots\}$. The external direct sum of n copies of ℓ is denoted ℓ^n. The space ℓ_2 is a subspace of ℓ of square-summable sequences. Similarly for the external direct sum ℓ_2^n. If G is a linear time-invariant (LTI) system, we shall not distinguish G from its transfer function. Finally, for an operator K and an operator matrix

$$P = \begin{bmatrix} P_{11} & P_{12} \\ P_{21} & P_{22} \end{bmatrix},$$

the associated linear fractional transformation is denoted

$$\mathcal{F}(P, K) = P_{11} + P_{12}K(I - P_{22}K)^{-1}P_{21}.$$

Of course, the domains and co-domains of the operators must be compatible and the inverse must exist.

2 Setup

The setup of the paper is shown in Figure 1, where G is an analog plant, S_{mh} an ideal sampler with period mh, H_{nh} a zero-order hold

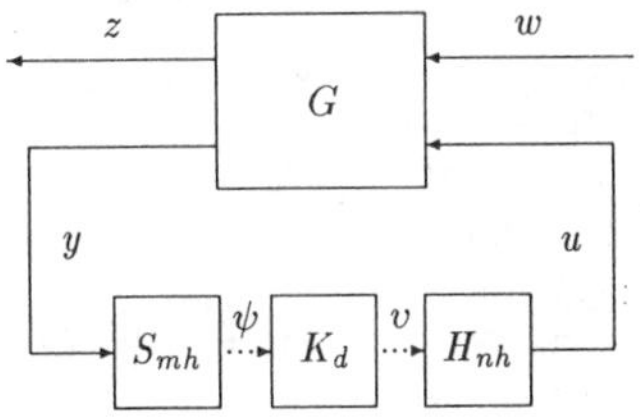

Figure 1: A multirate control system

with period nh, and K_d a multirate digital controller which is synchronized with S_{mh} and H_{nh} by a clock in the sense that K_d takes in a value of the sampled measurement ψ at times $t = k(mh)$, $k \geq 0$, and outputs a value of the control sequence v to the hold device at $t = k(nh)$, $k \geq 0$. We shall assume throughout the paper that m and n are coprime integers.

This setup is not the most general one as in [20, 23]; in fact, it has a uniform sampling rate and a uniform hold rate. But since the ratio of the two rates can be any positive rational number, this setup captures all the essential features in multirate systems while maintains some clarity in the exposition. Extensions to more general setup are possible [8].

We shall consider only the analog G which are LTI, causal, and finite-dimensional. What are the corresponding concepts for the multirate controller K_d? Throughout K_d is regarded as a linear map from ℓ to ℓ. Since the input and output time scales are not compatible, the single-rate definitions must be modified.

The sampled-data controller $H_{nh}K_dS_{mh}$ as a continuous-time operator is in general time-varying. However, note that both S_{mh} and H_{nh} are periodic elements, their least common period being $T = mnh$; so, by proper choice of K_d it is possible that $H_{nh}K_dS_{mh}$ is T-periodic in continuous time. Now let U be the unit time delay on ℓ and U^* the unit time advance. We define K_d to be (m, n)-*periodic* if

$$(U^*)^m K_d U^n = K_d.$$

Then it is not hard to see that $H_{nh}K_dS_{mh}$ is T-periodic iff K_d is (m, n)-periodic.

[1]The first author carried out part of this research at the Fields Institute for Mathematical Sciences, 185 Columbia St. W., Waterloo, Ont., Canada and was supported by the Ministry of Colleges and Universities of Ontario and the Natural Sciences and Engineering Research Council of Canada. The second author was supported by the Natural Sciences and Engineering Research Council of Canada.

This periodicity implies a deeper fact if we lift K_d properly. Define the discrete lifting operator $L_m : \ell \to \ell^m$ via $\underline{v} = L_m v$:

$$\{v(0), v(1), \cdots\} \mapsto \left\{ \begin{bmatrix} v(0) \\ \vdots \\ v(m-1) \end{bmatrix}, \begin{bmatrix} v(m) \\ \vdots \\ v(2m-1) \end{bmatrix}, \cdots \right\}.$$

Similarly for L_n. Now define the lifted controller

$$\underline{K_d} := L_m K_d L_n^{-1}. \tag{1}$$

This is now single-rate with the underlying period being T. Then $\underline{K_d}$ is time-invariant iff K_d is (m,n)-periodic.

Next is causality. Again we require that $H_{nh} K_d S_{mh}$ be causal in continuous time. This condition translates to an interesting constraint on K_d. To see this more clearly, we look at the lifted controller $\underline{K_d}$. The feedthrough term $\underline{D}$ in $\underline{K_d}$ is an $m \times n$ block matrix, namely,

$$\underline{D} = \begin{bmatrix} D_{00} & \cdots & D_{0,n-1} \\ \vdots & & \vdots \\ D_{m-1,0} & \cdots & D_{m-1,n-1} \end{bmatrix}.$$

Now the causality of $H_{nh} K_d S_{mh}$ translates exactly to the causality of $\underline{K_d}$ and a constraint on $\underline{D}$, namely,

$$D_{ij} = 0, \qquad \text{whenever } jm > in.$$

This condition on $\underline{D}$ will be called the *(m,n)-causality constraint.* For ease of reference, the set of all $\underline{D}$ satisfying the (m,n)-causality constraint is denoted by $\Omega(m,n)$.

We say K_d is *(m,n)-causal* if the single-rate $\underline{K_d}$ is causal and $\underline{D}$ satisfies the (m,n)-causality constraint. It follows then that the sampled-data controller $H_{nh} K_d S_{mh}$ is causal in continuous time iff K_d is (m,n)-causal. More general treatment of these concepts can be found in, e.g., [20, 23].

A similar notion is that of strict causality. We say $\underline{D}$ satisfies the *strict (m,n)-causality constraint* if

$$D_{ij} = 0, \qquad \text{whenever } jm \geq in.$$

The set of all such $\underline{D}$ is $\Omega_s(m,n)$. It follows that $H_{nh} K_d S_{mh}$ is strictly causal in continuous time iff $\underline{K_d}$ is causal and $\underline{D} \in \Omega_s(m,n)$.

Finally, we turn to finite dimensionality of the controller K_d. This is again best explained in terms of $\underline{K_d}$. Assume K_d is (m,n)-periodic and (m,n)-causal. Then from the previous discussion $\underline{K_d}$ is LTI and causal. We furthermore assume $\underline{K_d}$ is finite-dimensional. Thus $\underline{K_d}$ has a state model

$$\underline{K_d} = \left[\begin{array}{c|ccc} A & B_0 & \cdots & B_{n-1} \\ \hline C_0 & D_{00} & \cdots & D_{0,n-1} \\ \vdots & \vdots & & \vdots \\ C_{m-1} & D_{m-1,0} & \cdots & D_{m-1,n-1} \end{array} \right].$$

The corresponding difference equations for K_d ($v = K_d \psi$) are

$$\eta(k+1) = A\eta(k) + \sum_{j=0}^{n-1} B_j \psi(nk+j), \tag{2}$$

$$v(mk+i) = C_i \eta(k) + \sum_{j=0}^{n-1} D_{ij} \psi(nk+j), \; i = 0, 1, \cdots m-1. \tag{3}$$

Here η, the state for $\underline{K_d}$, is updated every $T = mnh$ seconds and v every nh seconds. Such difference equations can be implemented on microprocessors with only finite memory because the vector η is finite-dimensional.

In summary, in this paper we are interested in the class of multirate controllers K_d which are (m,n)-periodic, (m,n)-causal, and finite-dimensional; this class is called the *admissible* class of K_d and can be modeled by the difference equations (2) and (3) with $D_{ij} = 0$ when $jm > in$. The corresponding admissible class of $\underline{K_d}$ is characterized by LTI, causal, and finite-dimensional $\underline{K_d}$ with the same constraint on $\underline{D}$.

3 Multirate Lifting

The single-rate lifting technique [28, 31, 2, 4] is very powerful in sampled-data control because it converts a periodic sampled-data system into an LTI discrete system with infinite-dimensional input and output spaces. In this section we shall extend this technique to the multirate case.

In Figure 1, partition G according to its inputs and outputs and bring in a state model:

$$G = \begin{bmatrix} G_{11} & G_{12} \\ G_{21} & G_{22} \end{bmatrix} = \left[\begin{array}{c|cc} A & B_1 & B_2 \\ \hline C_1 & 0 & D_{12} \\ C_2 & 0 & D_{22} \end{array} \right]. \tag{4}$$

Now move S_{mh} and H_{nh} into the plant to get $\mathcal{F}(G, H_{nh} K_d S_{mh}) = \mathcal{F}(G_{sd}, K_d)$, where

$$G_{sd} = \begin{bmatrix} G_{11} & G_{12} H_{nh} \\ S_{mh} G_{21} & S_{mh} G_{22} H_{nh} \end{bmatrix}.$$

With our assumptions on K_d, $\mathcal{F}(G_{sd}, K_d)$ is T-periodic in continuous time. So the idea of lifting can be used.

Following [4], let $\mathcal{E}$ be any finite-dimensional Euclidean space, $\mathcal{E}^n$ be the external direct sum of n copies of $\mathcal{E}$, $\mathcal{K}$ be $\mathcal{L}_2[0,T)$, and $\ell_2(\mathcal{K})$ be the function-valued sequence space [4]. To handle unbounded signals, we bring in the two extended spaces $\mathcal{L}_{2e}[0,\infty)$ and $\ell_{2e}(\mathcal{K})$ defined in the obvious way. The lifting operator L_T, mapping $\mathcal{L}_{2e}[0,\infty)$ to $\ell_{2e}(\mathcal{K})$ is defined by

$$\psi = L_T y \Leftrightarrow \psi_k(t) = y(t+kT), \quad 0 \leq t < T.$$

Now we lift the system $\mathcal{F}(G_{sd}, K_d)$ with respect to the period T. Define

$$\underline{G_{sd}} = \begin{bmatrix} L_T G_{11} L_T^{-1} & L_T G_{12} H_{nh} L_m^{-1} \\ L_n S_{mh} G_{21} L_T^{-1} & L_n S_{mh} G_{22} H_{nh} L_m^{-1} \end{bmatrix}. \tag{5}$$

and $\underline{K_d}$ again as in (1) to get the lifted system $\mathcal{F}(\underline{G_{sd}}, \underline{K_d})$. We saw in Section 2 that $\underline{K_d}$ is LTI; it is not hard to see that $\underline{G_{sd}}$ too is LTI. So $\mathcal{F}(\underline{G_{sd}}, \underline{K_d})$ represents a discrete LTI system. It is easily verified that $\mathcal{F}(\underline{G_{sd}}, \underline{K_d}) = L_T \mathcal{F}(G, H_{nh} K_d S_{mh}) L_T^{-1}$. The usefulness of this relationship is due to the fact that the operators L_T and L_T^{-1} preserve norms.

Now with a state model for G in (4), we can derive a state-space representation for $\underline{G_{sd}}$ which maps $\ell_{2e}(\mathcal{K}) \oplus \ell^m$ to $\ell_{2e}(\mathcal{K}) \oplus \ell^n$:

$$\underline{G_{sd}} = \left[\begin{array}{c|cc} A_d & \underline{B_1} & B_{2d} \\ \hline \underline{C_1} & \underline{D_{11}} & \underline{D_{12}} \\ C_{2d} & \underline{D_{21}} & D_{22d} \end{array} \right].$$

Here A_d, B_{2d}, C_{2d}, D_{22d} are matrices and the rest are operators as follows:

$$\underline{B_1} : \mathcal{K} \to \mathcal{E}, \qquad \underline{C_1} : \mathcal{E} \to \mathcal{K},$$
$$\underline{D_{11}} : \mathcal{K} \to \mathcal{K}, \qquad \underline{D_{12}} : \mathcal{E}^m \to \mathcal{K},$$
$$\underline{D_{21}} : \mathcal{K} \to \mathcal{E}^n.$$

The explicit expressions in terms of the realization of G are given in [22] and are omitted here for space consideration. Note that $D_{22d} \in \Omega(n,m)$. Furthermore, $D_{22d} \in \Omega_s(n,m)$ if G_{22} is strictly causal ($D_{22} = 0$).

4 $\mathcal{H}_2$-Optimal Control

This section treats the first synthesis problem: Design an admissible K_d to achieve internal stability and minimize some generalized $\mathcal{H}_2$ performance measure.

First of all, let us look at the performance measure. Recall that for an admissible K_d, the closed-loop system $\mathcal{F}(G, H_{nh}K_dS_{mh})$ in Figure 1 is T-periodic. Thus we adopt the generalized $\mathcal{H}_2$ measure proposed for periodic systems in [17, 3].

Let F be a continuous-time, T-periodic, causal system described by the following integral operator

$$(Fu)(t) = \int_0^t f(t,\tau)u(\tau)\,d\tau.$$

We assume that f, the matrix-valued impulse response of F, is locally square-integrable. The periodicity of F implies $f(t+T, \tau+T) = f(t,\tau)$, and the causality implies that $f(t,\tau) = 0$ if $\tau > t$. If f is square-integrable on $[0,\infty) \times [0,T)$, we can define a norm for F as follows [17, 3]:

$$\|F\|_{per} = \left\{ \frac{1}{T}\int_0^T \int_0^\infty \text{trace}\,[f'(t,\tau)f(t,\tau)]\,dt\,d\tau \right\}^{1/2}$$

Now we lift F to get $\underline{F} := L_T F L_T^{-1}$. The lifted system $\underline{F} : \ell_{2e}(\mathcal{K}) \mapsto \ell_{2e}(\mathcal{K})$ can be described by ($\underline{y} = \underline{F}\,\underline{u}$)

$$\underline{y}_k = \sum_{j=0}^{k} \underline{f}_{k-j}\underline{u}_j, \quad k \geq 0,$$

where $\underline{f}_i$, $i \geq 0$, map $\mathcal{K}$ to $\mathcal{K}$ via

$$(\underline{f}_i u)(t) = \int_0^T f(t+iT, \tau)u(\tau)\,d\tau, \quad 0 \leq t < T.$$

$\underline{F}$ is LTI in discrete time; its transfer function is defined as

$$\underline{F}(\lambda) = \sum_{i=0}^{\infty} \underline{f}_i \lambda^i.$$

The local square-integrability of $f(t,\tau)$ implies that the operators $\underline{f}_i$, $i \geq 0$, are Hilbert-Schmidt operators [32]. Moreover, the set of Hilbert-Schmidt operators equipped with the Hilbert-Schmidt norm, $\|\cdot\|_{HS}$, is a Hilbert space [13]. Thus the transfer function $\underline{F}$ is a Hilbert-space vector-valued function on some subset of $\mathcal{C}$. We say the function $\underline{F}$ belongs to $\mathcal{H}_2$ if

$$\left(\sum_{i=0}^{\infty} \|\underline{f}_i\|_{HS}^2 \right)^{1/2} < \infty,$$

and the left-hand side is defined to be its $\mathcal{H}_2$ norm, denoted $\|\underline{F}\|_2$ [26]. It follows from [3] that $\underline{F}$ is in $\mathcal{H}_2$ iff every element of f is square-integrable on $[0,\infty) \times [0,T)$; in this case, $\frac{1}{\sqrt{T}}\|\underline{F}\|_2 = \|F\|_{per}$.

For internal stability of Figure 1, let the plant state be x and the controller state be η. Define the continuous-time vector

$$x_{sd}(t) := \begin{bmatrix} x(t) \\ \eta(k) \end{bmatrix}, \quad kT \leq t < (k+1)T.$$

The (autonomous) multirate sampled-data system is *internally stable*, or K_d *internally stabilizes* G, if for any initial value $x_{sd}(t_0)$, $0 \leq t_0 < T$, $x_{sd} \to 0$ as $t \to \infty$.

We need a few standing assumptions in this section about the plant G in (4):

1. (A, B_2) is stabilizable and (C_2, A) is detectable;
2. the period T is non-pathological with respect to G [16, 6];
3. $D_{22} = 0$.

Assumptions 1 and 2 are mild and standard. Assumption 3 is for the well-posedness of the closed-loop system. It follows that K_d internally stabilizes G iff $\underline{K_d}$ internally stabilizes $\underline{G_{22}}$ in discrete time, where $\underline{G_{22}}$ is a standard discrete system.

We can now state the $\mathcal{H}_2$-optimal control problem precisely: Given G, m, n, and h, design an admissible K_d to provide internal stability and minimize $\|\mathcal{F}(G, H_{nh}K_dS_{mh})\|_{per}$. By the above discussion, we can recast the problem exactly in the lifted spaces: Design an admissible $\underline{K_d}$ to internally stabilize $\underline{G_{22}}$ and minimize the $\mathcal{H}_2$ norm of $\mathcal{F}(\underline{G_{sd}}, \underline{K_d})$. This $\mathcal{H}_2$ problem will be solved using a frequency-domain approach. The problem is harder than the single-rate one [17, 3] due to the facts that $\underline{D_{21}}$ is nonzero and that $\underline{K_d}$ must satisfy the causality constraint.

Now bring in a doubly-coprime factorization for the real rational transfer matrix $\underline{G_{22}}$:

$$\underline{G_{22}} = NM^{-1} = \tilde{M}^{-1}\tilde{N},$$

$$\begin{bmatrix} \tilde{X} & -\tilde{Y} \\ -\tilde{N} & \tilde{M} \end{bmatrix} \begin{bmatrix} M & Y \\ N & X \end{bmatrix} = I,$$

with $M(0) = I$ and $\tilde{M}(0) = I$. It follows from [20, 23] that the set of admissible K_d which internally stabilize G is parametrized by

$$\underline{K_d} = (Y - MQ)(X - NQ)^{-1}, \quad Q \in \mathcal{RH}_\infty, \quad Q(0) \in \Omega(m,n).$$

With this controller applied, the closed-loop map is

$$\mathcal{F}(\underline{G_{sd}}, \underline{K_d}) = T_1 - T_2QT_3,$$

where T_1, T_2, T_3 are given by

$$\begin{aligned} T_1 &= \underline{G_{11}} + \underline{G_{12}}M\tilde{Y}\underline{G_{21}}, \\ T_2 &= \underline{G_{12}}M, \\ T_3 &= \tilde{M}\underline{G_{21}}. \end{aligned}$$

Therefore, the multirate $\mathcal{H}_2$ problem is equivalent to the following constrained $\mathcal{H}_2$ model-matching problem

$$\inf_{Q \in \mathcal{RH}_\infty, Q(0) \in \Omega} \|T_1 - T_2QT_3\|_2. \tag{6}$$

Here we used Ω for $\Omega(m,n)$ to simplify notation. Note that T_1, T_2, T_3 are all operator-valued. For an operator-valued transfer function $T(\lambda)$, denote the transfer function of the adjoint system by $T^{\sim}(\lambda) := T^*(1/\lambda)$. To proceed further, we need one additional assumption:

4. For every λ on the unit circle, $T_2(\lambda)$ and $T_3^{\sim}(\lambda)$ are both injective.

Note that $T_2^{\sim}T_2$ and $T_3T_3^{\sim}$ are both matrix-valued. It follows that $T_2^{\sim}T_2$ and $T_3T_3^{\sim}$ are both para-symmetric real-rational matrices and have full ranks on the unit circle (Assumption 4). So we can perform spectral factorizations $T_2^{\sim}T_2 = T_{2o}^{\sim}T_{2o}$ and $T_3T_3^{\sim} = T_{3co}T_{3co}^{\sim}$ with T_{2o}, T_{2o}^{-1}, T_{3co}, $T_{3co}^{-1} \in \mathcal{RH}_\infty$. An inner-outer factorization $T_2 = T_{2i}T_{2o}$ and a co-inner-outer factorization $T_3 = T_{3co}T_{3ci}$ can be obtained by defining

$$T_{2i} = T_2T_{2o}^{-1}, \quad T_{3ci} = T_{3co}^{-1}T_3.$$

Define the real-rational matrix in $\mathcal{L}_2$

$$R_{11} = T_{2i}^{\sim}T_1T_{3ci}^{\sim}$$

and denote the constant term of R_{11} by R_{110}. Let $\Pi_{\mathcal{H}_2} : \mathcal{L}_2 \to \mathcal{H}_2$ and $\Pi_{\mathcal{H}_2^\perp} : \mathcal{L}_2 \to \mathcal{H}_2^\perp$ be the orthogonal projections. We are now set up to state the main result of this section.

Theorem 1 *The optimal Q in (6) is given by*

$$Q_{opt} = Q_0 + \lambda T_{2o}^{-1}\left\{\Pi_{\mathcal{H}_2}\left[\lambda^{-1}(R_{11} - T_{2o}Q_0T_{3co})\right]\right\}T_{3co}^{-1},$$

where the constant matrix Q_0 is the optimal $Q(0)$ solving

$$\min_{Q(0)\in\Omega} \|R_{110} - T_{2o}(0)Q(0)T_{3co}(0)\|_2. \quad (7)$$

Now we look at how to use matrix factorization theory to find Q_0 solving (7). For square and nonsingular matrices $T_{2o}(0)$ and $T_{3co}(0)$, bring in factorizations

$$T_{2o}(0) = U_2R_2, \quad T_{3co}(0) = R_3U_3,$$

where U_2, R_2, U_3, R_3 are all square, U_2, U_3 are orthogonal ($U_2'U_2 = I$, $U_3'U_3 = I$), and R_2, R_3 are lower-triangular. The existence and computation of such factorizations follow analogously from those of the well-known QR factorization. Recall that the 2-norm for matrices is induced by the inner product:

$$\langle A, B\rangle := \text{trace}\,(A'B).$$

Thus the subspace Ω has its orthogonal complement $\Omega^\perp$ in the space of matrices of appropriate dimensions. Let Π_Ω and $\Pi_{\Omega^\perp}$ be the orthogonal projections to Ω and $\Omega^\perp$ respectively. It follows then that Π_Ω amounts to simply retaining the blocks corresponding to the unconstrained blocks in Ω and zeroing the other blocks.

Lemma 1 *The optimal $Q(0)$ solving (7) is*

$$Q_0 = R_2^{-1}\Pi_\Omega[U_2'R_{110}U_3']R_3^{-1}.$$

Finally, we refer to [22] for the proofs of the results and for an explicit and detailed procedure for computation.

5 $\mathcal{H}_\infty$-Optimal Control

In this section we shall study the multirate $\mathcal{H}_\infty$ control problem: Design an admissible K_d to provide internal stability and achieve a pre-specified level of $\mathcal{H}_\infty$ performance, i.e., $\|\mathcal{F}(G, H_{nh}K_dS_{nh})\| < \gamma$, where γ is positive and the norm is $\mathcal{L}_2$-induced. By proper scaling, we can always take $\gamma = 1$.

In principle, the multirate lifting procedure in Section 3 could be employed to reduce the problem to a discrete-time $\mathcal{H}_\infty$ problem with causality constraint. However, in this section we shall present a simpler reduction process which is based on recent single-rate results [2, 15] and the discrete lifting. Then the constrained discrete $\mathcal{H}_\infty$ problem is solved explicitly.

With the state model of G in (4), Assumptions 1-3 made in Section 4 are in force in this section. Let $\underline{D}_{11h} : \mathcal{L}_2[0,h) \to \mathcal{L}_2[0,h)$ be defined by

$$(\underline{D}_{11h}w)(t) = C_1\int_0^t e^{(t-\tau)A}B_1w(\tau)\,d\tau.$$

An additional assumption is needed:

4'. $\|\underline{D}_{11h}\| < 1$.

This is a necessary condition for $\|\mathcal{F}(G, H_{nh}K_dS_{mh})\| < 1$; its computation was studied in [2].

Corresponding to the two integers m and n, introduce the discrete sampling operator $S_m : \ell \to \ell$ defined via

$$\psi = S_m\phi \Leftrightarrow \psi(k) = \phi(mk)$$

and the discrete hold operator $H_n : \ell \to \ell$ via

$$\psi = H_n\phi \Leftrightarrow \psi(kn+j) = \phi(k), \quad j = 0, 1, \cdots, n-1.$$

Now we bring in a discrete LTI system

$$G_d := \left[\begin{array}{c|cc} A_d & B_{1d} & B_{2d} \\ \hline C_{1d} & D_{11d} & D_{12d} \\ C_{2d} & 0 & 0 \end{array}\right]. \quad (8)$$

Here G_d is an equivalent system for the single-rate $\mathcal{H}_\infty$ sampled-data problem with sampling period h; several sets of realization matrices were given in several recent papers, e.g., [2, 15]. Define the lifted discrete system $\underline{K_d}$ as in Section 2 and

$$\underline{G_d} = \begin{bmatrix} L_{mn} & 0 \\ 0 & L_nS_m \end{bmatrix} G_d \begin{bmatrix} L_{mn}^{-1} & 0 \\ 0 & H_nL_m^{-1} \end{bmatrix}.$$

It is not hard to check that $\underline{G_d}$ is LTI, causal, and finite-dimensional. The following result establishes the connection between the multirate $\mathcal{H}_\infty$ problem and a discrete $\mathcal{H}_\infty$ problem.

Theorem 2 *Under Assumptions 1-3 and 4', we have*

(i) K_d internally stabilizes G iff $\underline{K_d}$ internally stabilizes $\underline{G_d}$;

(ii) $\|\mathcal{F}(G, H_{nh}K_dS_{mh})\| < 1$ iff $\|\mathcal{F}(\underline{G_d}, \underline{K_d})\|_\infty < 1$.

A different reduction process was recently reported in [29]. This theorem also implies that the multirate $\mathcal{H}_\infty$ problem can be recast as a constrained $\mathcal{H}_\infty$ model-matching problem. To see this, we note that the (2,2) block in $\underline{G_d}$, $\underline{G_{22d}}$, is (n,m)-strictly causal. Parametrize all the stabilizing and admissible controllers $\underline{K_d}$ for $\underline{G_{22d}}$ as in Section 4 to get

$$\mathcal{F}(\underline{G_d}, \underline{K_d}) = T_1 - T_2QT_3,$$

where T_1, T_2, T_3 are real-rational matrices in $\mathcal{H}_\infty$ and can be found from $\underline{G_d}$. Then the multirate $\mathcal{H}_\infty$ problem is equivalent to the discrete $\mathcal{H}_\infty$ model-matching problem of finding a $Q \in \mathcal{RH}_\infty$ with the constraint $Q(0) \in \Omega(m,n)$ such that

$$\|T_1 - T_2QT_3\|_\infty < 1. \quad (9)$$

If such a Q exists, we say the multirate $\mathcal{H}_\infty$ problem is *solvable*.

From now on we shall focus on this constrained $\mathcal{H}_\infty$ problem. For regularity, we need an assumption similar to Assumption 4 in Section 4:

5'. For every λ on the unit circle, $T_2(\lambda)$ and $T_3^\sim(\lambda)$ are both injective.

Under this assumption, perform an inner-outer factorization $T_2 = T_{2i}T_{2o}$ and an co-inner-outer factorization $T_3 = T_{3co}T_{3ci}$, where T_{2o} and T_{3co} are both invertible over $\mathcal{RH}_\infty$. Apply unitary transformations to $T_1 - T_2QT_3$ and define

$$R = \begin{bmatrix} T_{2i}^\sim \\ I - T_{2i}T_{2i}^\sim \end{bmatrix} T_1 \begin{bmatrix} T_{3ci}^\sim & I - T_{3ci}^\sim T_{3ci} \end{bmatrix}.$$

We shall consider the causality constraint at a later stage; let us now drop this constraint on $Q(0)$ and look at the unconstrained problem. This allows us to use the powerful result in [12] to parametrize all Q in $\mathcal{RH}_\infty$ achieving (9). The unconstrained problem in (9) is solvable iff

$$\left\|\begin{bmatrix} \Pi_{\mathcal{H}_2^\perp} & 0 \\ 0 & I \end{bmatrix} R|_{\mathcal{H}_2\oplus\mathcal{L}_2}\right\| < 1. \quad (10)$$

Moreover, if (10) is satisfied, then there exists an $\mathcal{RH}_\infty$ matrix

$$K = \begin{bmatrix} K_{11} & K_{12} \\ K_{21} & K_{22} \end{bmatrix}$$

with $K_{12}^{-1}, K_{21}^{-1} \in \mathcal{RH}_\infty$ and $\|K_{22}\|_\infty < 1$ such that all $Q \in \mathcal{RH}_\infty$ satisfying (9) are characterized by

$$Q = \mathcal{F}(K, Q_1), \quad Q_1 \in \mathcal{RH}_\infty, \quad \|Q_1\|_\infty < 1. \quad (11)$$

We refer to [12] for the details of checking inequality (10) and the expression of K. Hereafter, we shall assume that (10) is true.

By (11), $Q(0)$ depends on $Q_1(0)$ in a linear fractional manner. To simplify this, introduce another linear fractional transformation $Q_1 = \mathcal{F}(V, Q_2)$, where V, partitioned as usual, is a constant unitary matrix:

$$V = \begin{bmatrix} K_{22}'(0) & [I - K_{22}'(0)K_{22}(0)]^{1/2} \\ [I - K_{22}(0)K_{22}'(0)]^{1/2} & -K_{22}(0) \end{bmatrix}.$$

It follows that the mapping $Q_2 \mapsto Q_1$ is bijective from the open unit ball of $\mathcal{RH}_\infty$ onto itself [24]. Thus all Q satisfying (9) can be re-parametrized by

$$\begin{aligned} Q &= \mathcal{F}[K, \mathcal{F}(V, Q_2)] \\ &= \mathcal{F}(L, Q_2), \quad Q_2 \in \mathcal{RH}_\infty, \quad \|Q_2\|_\infty < 1. \end{aligned}$$

It can be checked that $L_{22}(0) = 0$ and $L_{12}(0)$, $L_{21}(0)$ are still nonsingular. Thus

$$Q(0) = L_{11}(0) + L_{12}(0)Q_2(0)L_{21}(0). \tag{12}$$

Now we bring in the causality constraint on $Q(0)$. Our goal is to find the necessary and sufficient condition for the existence of a $Q_2 \in \mathcal{RH}_\infty$ with $\|Q_2\|_\infty < 1$ such that $Q(0)$ in (12) lies in $\Omega(m,n)$. Since $Q(0)$ depends only on $Q_2(0)$ and in general $\|Q_2\|_\infty \geq \|Q_2(0)\|$, the problem is the same as searching a constant matrix $Q_2(0)$ with $\|Q_2(0)\| < 1$ such that $Q(0) \in \Omega(m,n)$, the norm being the largest singular value of $Q_2(0)$.

As in Section 4, introduce matrix factorizations

$$L_{12}(0) = R_1U_1, \quad L_{21}(0) = -U_2R_2,$$

where R_1, R_2, U_1, U_2 are all square, R_1, R_2 are lower-triangular, and U_1, U_2 are orthogonal. Substitute the factorizations into (12) and pre- and post-multiply by R_1^{-1} and R_2^{-1} respectively to get

$$R_1^{-1}Q(0)R_2^{-1} = R_1^{-1}L_{11}(0)R_2^{-1} - U_1Q_2(0)U_2.$$

Define

$$W := R_1^{-1}L_{11}(0)R_2^{-1}, \quad P := U_1Q_2(0)U_2.$$

It follows that $\|Q_2(0)\| < 1$ iff $\|P\| < 1$ and $Q(0) \in \Omega(m,n)$ iff $R_1^{-1}Q(0)R_2^{-1} \in \Omega(m,n)$ [20]. Therefore, we arrive at the following equivalent matrix problem: Given W, find P with $\|P\| < 1$ such that $W - P \in \Omega(m,n)$.

Partition W and P as required in $\Omega(m,n)$. Apparently, P must cancel the $\Omega^\perp$-part of W. The solution is somewhat complicated. First, let us distinguish two cases: The fixed blocks in P, or the zero blocks in $\Omega(m,n)$, take the (block) row-echelon form if $m < n$ and the (block) column-echelon form if $n < m$. Next, we need to locate all the *maximum fixed submatrices* of P, namely, the submatrices which consist of only the fixed blocks and have maximum sizes. To do this, denote the integer part of a positive real number x by $\lfloor x \rfloor$. If $m < n$, let $l = m$ and for $k = 0, 1, \ldots, l-1$, define

$$\begin{aligned} M_k &= \underbrace{\left.\begin{bmatrix} I & & \\ & \ddots & 0 \\ & I & \end{bmatrix}\right\}}_{m \text{ blocks}} k+1 \text{ blocks} \\ N_k &= \underbrace{\left.\begin{bmatrix} & 0 & \\ I & & \\ & \ddots & \\ & & I \end{bmatrix}\right\}}_{n-1-\lfloor \frac{kn}{m} \rfloor \text{ blocks}} n \text{ blocks} \end{aligned}$$

If $n < m$, define $l = n - 1$ and for $k = 0, 1, \ldots, l-1$, define

$$\begin{aligned} M_k &= \underbrace{\left.\begin{bmatrix} I & & \\ & \ddots & 0 \\ & I & \end{bmatrix}\right\}}_{m \text{ blocks}} 1 + \lfloor \tfrac{(k+1)m}{n} \rfloor \text{ blocks} \\ N_k &= \underbrace{\left.\begin{bmatrix} & 0 & \\ I & & \\ & \ddots & \\ & & I \end{bmatrix}\right\}}_{n-1-k \text{ blocks}} n \text{ blocks} \end{aligned}$$

Then it can be checked that $M_kWN_k, k = 0, 1, \ldots, l-1$, are exactly those maximum fixed submatrices of P. Define

$$\mu := \max\{\|M_kWN_k\| : \ k = 0, 1, \ldots, l-1\}.$$

Theorem 3 *Under Assumptions 1-3 and 4'-5', the multirate $\mathcal{H}_\infty$ problem is solvable, i.e., there exists a matrix P with $\|P\| < 1$ such that $W - P \in \Omega(m,n)$, iff $\mu < 1$.*

The proof is based on a result on norm preserving dilations from operator theory [21, 9], which also provides a constructive procedure to determine the free blocks in P to get $\|P\| = \mu$; for details, see [22].

To summarize, let us list the solvability conditions for the multirate $\mathcal{H}_\infty$ control problem $\|\mathcal{F}(G, H_{nh}K_dS_{mh})\| < 1$:

(a) $\|\underline{D}_{11h}\| < 1$;

(b) $\left\| \begin{bmatrix} P_{\mathcal{H}_2^\perp} & 0 \\ 0 & I \end{bmatrix} R|_{\mathcal{H}_2 \oplus \mathcal{L}_2} \right\| < 1$;

(c) $\mu < 1$.

Condition (a) was studied in detail in [2]. Condition (b) is the solvability condition for a standard $\mathcal{H}_\infty$ problem. When conditions (a-b) hold, a necessary and sufficient test for condition (c) is given in Theorem 3; it amounts to computing the norms of several constant matrices.

6 Concluding Remarks

In this paper we have addressed causality constraints in direct designs of multirate sampled-data control systems using $\mathcal{H}_2$ and $\mathcal{H}_\infty$ performance measures. Explicit solutions are given for the $\mathcal{H}_2$-optimal controller and the $\mathcal{H}_\infty$-suboptimal controllers which achieve the performance requirement $\|\mathcal{F}(G, H_{nh}K_dS_{mh})\| < 1$. $\mathcal{H}_\infty$ controllers which are arbitrarily close to optimality can be computed based on the solvability conditions (a-c) (with proper scaling) and a standard bisection search. Finally, we mention that extensions to the more general setup have been made using operators between appropriate nests [8].

References

[1] H. Al-Rahmani and G. F. Franklin, "A new optimal multirate control of linear periodic and time-varying systems," *IEEE Trans. Automat. Control*, vol. 35, pp. 406-415, 1990.

[2] B. Bamieh and J. B. Pearson, "A general framework for linear periodic systems with application to $\mathcal{H}_\infty$ sampled-data control," *IEEE Trans. Automat. Control*, vol. 37, pp. 418-435, 1992.

[3] B. Bamieh and J. B. Pearson, "The $\mathcal{H}_2$ problem for sampled-data systems," *Systems and Control Letters*, vol. 19, pp. 1-12, 1992.

[4] B. Bamieh, J. B. Pearson, B. A. Francis, and A. Tannenbaum, "A lifting technique for linear periodic systems with applications to sampled-data control," *Systems and Control Letters*, vol. 17, pp. 79-88, 1991.

[5] M. C. Berg, N. Amit, and J. Powell, "Multirate digital control system design," *IEEE Trans. Automat. Control*, vol. 33, pp. 1139-1150, 1988.

[6] T. Chen and B. A. Francis, "$\mathcal{H}_2$-optimal sampled-data control," *IEEE Trans. Automat. Control*, vol. 36, pp. 387-397, 1991.

[7] T. Chen and B. A. Francis, "Linear time-varying $\mathcal{H}_2$-optimal control of sampled-data systems," *Automatica*, vol. 27, No. 6, pp. 963-974, 1991.

[8] T. Chen and L. Qiu, "$\mathcal{H}_\infty$ design of general multirate sampled-data control systems," IMA Preprint Series # 1090, University of Minnesota, December 1992.

[9] C. Davis, M. M. Kahan, and H. F. Weinsberger, "Norm-preserving dilations and their applications to optimal error bounds," *SIAM J. Numer. Anal.*, vol. 19, pp. 445-469, 1982.

[10] A. Feintuch, P. P. Khargonekar, and A. Tannenbaum, "On the sensitivity minimization problem for linear time-varying periodic systems," *SIAM J. Control and Optimization*, vol. 24, pp. 1076-1085, 1986.

[11] T. T. Georgiou and P. P. Khargonekar, "A constructive algorithm for sensitivity optimization of periodic systems," *SIAM J. Control and Optimization*, vol. 25, pp. 334-340, 1987.

[12] K. Glover, D. J. N. Limebeer, J. C. Doyle, E. M. Kasenally, and M. G. Safonov, "A characterization of all solution to the four block general distance problem," *SIAM J. Control and Optimization*, vol. 29, pp. 283-324, 1991.

[13] I. C. Gohberg and M. G. Kreĭn, *Introduction to the Theory of Linear Nonselfadjoint Operators*, American Mathematical Society, Providence, Rhode Island, 1969.

[14] S. Hara and P. T. Kabamba, "Worst case analysis and design of sampled-data control systems," *Proc. CDC*, 1990.

[15] Y. Hayakawa, Y. Yamamoto, and S. Hara, "$\mathcal{H}_\infty$ type problem for sampled-data control system — a solution via minimum energy characterization," *Proc. CDC*, 1992.

[16] R. Kalman, Y. C. Ho, and K. Narendra, "Controllability of linear dynamical systems," in *Contributions to Differential Equations*, vol. 1, Interscience, New York, 1963.

[17] P. P. Khargonekar and N. Sivashankar, "$\mathcal{H}_2$ optimal control for sampled-data systems," *Systems and Control Letters*, vol. 18, No. 3, pp. 627-631, 1992.

[18] G. M. Kranc, "Input-output analysis of multirate feedback systems," *IRE Trans. Automat. Control*, vol. 3, pp. 21-28, 1957.

[19] D. G. Meyer, "A theorem on translating the general multi-rate LQG problem to a standard LQG problem via lifts," *Proc. ACC*, 1991.

[20] D. G. Meyer, "A parametrization of stabilizing controllers for multirate sampled-data systems," *IEEE Trans. Automat. Control*, vol. 35, pp. 233-236, 1990.

[21] S. Parrott, "On a quotient norm and the Sz.-Nagy-Foias lifting theorem", *J. Funct. Anal.*, vol. 30, pp. 311-328, 1978.

[22] L. Qiu and T. Chen, "$\mathcal{H}_2$ and $\mathcal{H}_\infty$ designs of multirate sampled-data systems," IMA Preprint Series # 1062, University of Minnesota, November 1992.

[23] R. Ravi, P. P. Khargonekar, K. D. Minto, and C. N. Nett, "Controller parametrization for time-varying multirate plants," *IEEE Trans. Automat. Control*, vol. 35, pp. 1259-1262, 1990.

[24] R. M. Redheffer, "On a certain linear fractional transformation," *J. Math. Phys.*, vol. 39, pp. 269-286, 1960.

[25] W. Sun, P. P. Khargonekar, K. M. Nagpal, and K. Poolla, "Digital control systems: $\mathcal{H}_\infty$ controller design with a zero-order hold function," *Proc. CDC*, 1992.

[26] B. Sz.-Nagy and C. Foiaş, *Harmonic Analysis of Operators on Hilbert Space*, North-Holland Publishing Company, Amsterdam, 1970.

[27] G. Tadmor, "Optimal $\mathcal{H}_\infty$ sampled-data control in continuous time systems," *Proc. ACC*, 1991.

[28] H. T. Toivonen, "Sampled-data control of continuous-time systems with an $\mathcal{H}_\infty$ optimality criterion," *Automatica*, vol. 28, No. 1, pp. 45-54, 1992.

[29] P. G. Voulgaris and B. Bamieh, "Optimal $\mathcal{H}_\infty$ control of hybrid multirate systems," *Proc. CDC*, 1992.

[30] P. G. Voulgaris, M. A. Dahleh, and L. S. Valavani, "$\mathcal{H}_\infty$ and $\mathcal{H}_2$ optimal controllers for periodic and multi-rate systems," *Proc. CDC*, 1991.

[31] Y. Yamamoto, "A new approach to sampled-data control systems: a function space method," *Proc. CDC*, 1990.

[32] N. Young, *An Introduction to Hilbert Spaces*, Cambridge University Press, Cambridge, UK, 1988.

Proceedings of the
American Control Conference
San Francisco, California • June 1993

A TIME DOMAIN APPROACH TO ROBUSTNESS OF MULTI-RATE DELTA OPERATOR SYSTEMS

Jean E. Piou and Kenneth M. Sobel
Dept. of Electrical Engineering
The City College of New York
New York, NY 10031

E. Y. Shapiro
HR Textron
25200 W. Rye Canyon Rd.
Valencia, CA 91355

INTRODUCTION

Yu et. al. [1] have proposed a new sufficient condition for the robust stability of a linear time invariant system subject to linear time varying structured state space uncertainty. This robustness conditionis a sum of terms each of which involves the i-th right eigenvector, the i-th left eigenvector, and the real part of the i-th eigenvalue. Thus, this method is called the modal decomposition approach to time domain robustness.

Piou and Sobel [2] extended the result of [1] to systems which are represented by Goodwin and Middleton's [3] unified delta model which is valid both for continuous time and sampled data operation of the plant. An important property of the delta model is that the discrete time eigenvalues approach the continuous time eigenvalues as the sampling period approaches zero. This result is valid for time invariant structured state space uncertainty.

An alternative approach to stability robustness of a linear time invariant system was proposed by Yedavalli [4] who uses a Lyapunov approach. Piou et. al. [5] extended the work of [4] to the unified delta representation of a linear time invariant plant which is subject to time invariant structured state space uncertainty.

Araki and Hagiwara [6] have proposed a model for a class of multi-rate sampled data systems. This class consists of systems with multiple input rate sampling and fixed output rate sampling (MIFO). In this paper, we extend the results of [6] to obtain a delta operator representation for a MIFO system. Then, we extend the robustness results of [2] and [5] to MIFO delta operator systems.

PROBLEM FORMULATION

Consider a nominal linear time-invariant multi-input multi-outputsystem described by

$$\dot{x}(t) = Ax(t) + Bu(t) \tag{1}$$

$$y(t) = Cx(t) \tag{2}$$

where $x \in \mathbb{R}^n$ is the state vector, $u \in \mathbb{R}^m$ is the input vector, $y \in \mathbb{R}^r$ is the output vector, and A, B, C, are constant matrices.

The constant gain output feedback control law is described by

$$u(t) = Fy(t) \tag{3}$$

The nominal closed loop system is given by

$$\dot{x}(t) = (A + BFC)x(t) \tag{4}$$

The continuous plant is sampled such that the m inputs change from one constant value to another at m successive uniformly spaced time instants $t=k\Delta_i$. The sampling periods Δ_i's have a rational ratio. The Δ_i's are given by

$$\Delta_i = (\Delta_o/n_i)i = 1, 2, \ldots, m \tag{4a}$$

where n_i's are positive integers

$$n = \mathrm{LCM}\ (n_1, n_2, \ldots, n_m) \tag{4b}$$

$$\bar{n} = n_1 + n_2 + \ldots + n_m \tag{4c}$$

$$\tau_o = (\Delta_o/n) \tag{4d}$$

$$l_i = n/n_i \qquad i = 1, 2, \ldots, m \tag{4e}$$

Insert Eq.(3d) into Eq.(3a) to obtain

$$\Delta_i = \tau_o n/n_i \tag{5a}$$

$$\Delta_i = l_i \tau_o \tag{5b}$$

where Δ_o is the least common multiple (LCM) of the sample periods and is referred to the main sampling interval. The quantity τ_o defines the base sample period. The corresponding closed loop multirate sampled data system, which is obtained by using Middleton and Goodwin's [3] delta operator, is shown below

$$\delta x = (A_\delta + \bar{B}_\delta \bar{F}_\delta C)x \tag{6}$$

$$y = Cx \tag{7}$$

where

$$A_\delta = \Omega A \tag{8a}$$

$$\Omega = \frac{1}{\Delta_o}\int_0^{\Delta_o} e^{A\tau}d\tau \tag{8b}$$

$$\bar{B}_\delta = [\ \bar{B}_1\ \bar{B}_2 \ldots \bar{B}_m\ ] \tag{10a}$$

Each $\bar{B}_i$ is a $n \times n_i$ matrix defined by

$$\bar{B}_i = [\ b_{\delta i}\ \exp(A\Delta_i)\cdot b_{\delta i} \ldots \exp(A(n_i-1)\Delta_i)\cdot b_{\delta i}\ ] \tag{10b}$$

where

$$b_{\delta i} = \frac{1}{\Delta_o}\int_0^{\Delta_i} e^{A\tau}d\tau\ b_i \tag{10c}$$

and where b_i is the i-th column of the matrix B.

The gain matrix is given by

$$\bar{F}_\delta = [\ \bar{F}_1\ \bar{F}_2 \ldots \bar{F}_m\ ] \tag{11}$$

where each $\bar{F}_i$ is a n_i dimensional column vector.

$$\delta = \frac{q-1}{\Delta_o} \tag{12}$$

and where the shift operator q is defined by

$$qx_k = x_{k+1} \tag{13}$$

The nominal unified closed loop multirate state space model can be described by

$$\rho x(t) = (A_\rho + \bar{B}_\rho \bar{F}_\rho C)x(t) \tag{14}$$

where

$$A_\rho = \begin{cases} A & \text{in continuous time} \\ A_\delta & \text{in discrete time} \end{cases} \tag{15}$$

$$\bar{B}_\rho = \begin{cases} B & \text{in continuous time} \\ \bar{B}_\delta & \text{in discrete time} \end{cases} \tag{16}$$

$$\bar{F}_\rho = \begin{cases} F & \text{in continuous time} \\ \bar{F}_\delta & \text{in discrete time} \end{cases} \tag{17}$$

and where

$$\rho = \begin{cases} \frac{d}{dt} & \text{in continuous time} \\ \delta & \text{in discrete time} \end{cases} \tag{18}$$

Suppose that the nominal delta system is subject to linear time-invariant uncertainties in the entries of A_ρ, $\bar{B}_\rho$ described by dA_ρ and $d\bar{B}_\rho$, respectively, where

$$dA_\rho = \begin{cases} dA & \text{in continuous time} \\ dA_\delta & \text{in discrete time} \end{cases} \tag{19}$$

$$d\bar{B}_\rho = \begin{cases} dB & \text{in continuous time} \\ d\bar{B}_\delta & \text{in discrete time} \end{cases} \tag{20}$$

and where

$$dA_\delta = \frac{1}{\Delta_o}\left[\exp\{(A+dA)\Delta_o\} - \exp(A\Delta_o)\right] \tag{21}$$

$$d\bar{B}_\delta = [\ (d\bar{B}_1-\bar{B}_1)\ (d\bar{B}_2-\bar{B}_2) \ldots (d\bar{B}_m-\bar{B}_m)\ ] \tag{22a}$$

Each $d\bar{B}_i$ is a $n \times n_i$ matrix defined by

$$d\bar{B}_i = [db_{\delta i} \;\; \exp((A+dA)\Delta_i)\cdot db_{\delta i} \;\ldots\; \exp\{(A+dA)(n_i-1)\}\cdot db_{\delta i}\,] \tag{22b}$$

where

$$db_{\delta i} = \frac{1}{\Delta_o}\int_0^{\Delta_i} e^{(A+dA)\tau}\, d\tau\,(b_i + db_i) \tag{22c}$$

and where db_i is the i-th column of the matrix dB.

The unified closed loop system with uncertainty is given by

$$\rho x(t) = (A_\rho + \bar{B}_\rho \bar{F}_\rho C)x(t) + (dA_\rho + d\bar{B}_\rho \bar{F}_\rho C)x(t) \tag{23}$$

Further, suppose that bounds are available on the maximum absolute values of the elements of dA and dB. That is,

$$|da_{ij}| \le (a_{ij})_{max};\; i=1,\ldots,n;\; j=1,\ldots,n \tag{24}$$

$$|db_{ij}| \le (b_{ij})_{max};\; i=1,\ldots,n;\; j=1,\ldots,m \tag{25}$$

Then, the corresponding bounds on the δ system, through Eqs. (21) and (22a), are

$$|da_\delta(i,j)| \le [da_\delta(i,j)]_{max};\; i=1,\ldots,n;\; j=1,\ldots,n \tag{26}$$

$$|d\bar{b}_\delta(i,j)| \le [d\bar{b}_\delta(i,j)]_{max}\;;i=1,\ldots,n;j=1,\ldots,m \tag{27}$$

Define dA_ρ^+ and $d\bar{B}_\rho^+$ as the matrices obtained by replacing the entries of dA_ρ and $d\bar{B}_\rho$ by their absolute values. Also, define $A_{\rho max}$ and $\bar{B}_{\rho max}$ as the matrices with entries $(a_{ij})_{max}$ and $(b_{ij})_{max}$, respectively in continuous time or with entries $[da_\delta(i,j)]_{max}$ and $[d\bar{b}_\delta(i,j)]_{max}$, respectively in discrete time.

Then,

$$\{dA_\rho :\; dA_\rho^+ \le A_{\rho max}\} \tag{28}$$

and

$$\{d\bar{B}_\rho :\; d\bar{B}_\rho^+ \le \bar{B}_{\rho max}\} \tag{29}$$

where

$$A_{\rho max} = \begin{cases} A_{max} & \text{in continuous time} \\ A_{\delta max} & \text{in discrete time} \end{cases} \tag{30}$$

$$B_{\rho max} = \begin{cases} B_{max} & \text{in continuous time} \\ \bar{B}_{\delta max} & \text{in discrete time} \end{cases} \tag{31}$$

and where

$$A_{\delta max} = \frac{1}{\Delta_o}\left[\exp\{(A^+ + A_{max})\Delta_o\} - \exp(A^+\Delta_o)\right] \tag{32}$$

$$\bar{B}_{\delta max} = [(\bar{B}_{1max} - \bar{B}_1^+)\;\; (\bar{B}_{2max} - \bar{B}_2^+)\;\; \ldots\;\; (\bar{B}_{mmax} - \bar{B}_m^+)] \tag{33a}$$

Each $\bar{B}_i^+$ is a $n \times n_i$ matrix defined by

$$\bar{B}_i^+ = [\, b_{\delta i}^+ \;\exp(A^+\Delta_i)\cdot b_{\delta i}^+ \;\ldots\; \exp(A^+(n_i-1)\Delta_i)\cdot b_{\delta i}^+\,] \tag{33b}$$

and

$$b_{\delta i}^+ = \frac{1}{\Delta_o}\int_0^{\Delta_i} e^{A^+\tau} d\tau\; b_i^+ \tag{33c}$$

where b_i^+ is the i-th column of the matrix B^+. Each $\bar{B}_{imax}$ is an $n \times n_i$ matrix which is defined by

$$\bar{B}_{imax} = [b_{\delta imax}\;\; \exp((A^+ + A_{max})\Delta_i)\cdot b_{\delta imax} \;\ldots\; \exp\{(A^+ + A_{max})(n_i-1)\Delta_i\}\cdot b_{\delta imax}] \tag{33d}$$

$$b_{\delta imax} = \frac{1}{\Delta_o}\int_0^{\Delta_i} e^{(A^+ + A_{max})\tau} d\tau\,(b_i^+ + b_{imax}) \tag{33e}$$

where b_{imax} is the i-th column of the matrix B_{max}.

Finally, the stability robustness problem can be stated as follows: Given a block feedback gain matrix $\bar{F}_\rho \in \mathbb{R}^{m \times r}$ such that the nominal closed loop multirate delta system exhibits desirable performance, determine if the uncertain closed loop multirate delta system is asymptotically stable for all time-invariant dA_ρ and $d\bar{B}_\rho$ described by Eqs. (28) and (29), respectively.

ROBUSTNESS RESULTS

Theorem 1: (Modal Decomposition Approach)

Suppose that $\bar{F}_\rho$ is such that the nominal closed loop system described by Eq. (14) is asymptotically stable with $(A_\rho + \bar{B}_\rho \bar{F}_\rho C)$ non-defective . Then, the uncertain closed loop system given by Eq. (23) is asymptotically stable for dA_ρ and $d\bar{B}_\rho$ described by Eqs. (28) and (29), respectively if

$$\lambda_{max}\left\{ \sum_{i=1}^{n} \frac{(v_i w_i^*)^+}{f(\gamma_i)} A_{\rho cmax} \right\} < 1 \tag{34}$$

where

$$f(\gamma_i) = \begin{cases} -\mathrm{Re}(\gamma_i) & \text{continuous time} \\ \frac{1}{\Delta_o}\left[1 - (1 + \Delta_o\gamma_i)^+\right] & \text{discrete time} \end{cases} \tag{35}$$

$$A_{\rho cmax} = \begin{cases} A_{max} + B_{max}(FC)^+ & \text{continuous time} \\ A_{\delta max} + \bar{B}_{\delta max}(\bar{F}_\delta C)^+ & \text{discrete time} \end{cases} \tag{36}$$

where $A_{\delta max}$, $\bar{B}_{\delta max}$ and $\bar{F}_\delta$ are given by Eqs. (32), (33a), and (11), respectively and where γ_i is the i-th eigenvalue of $(A_\rho + \bar{B}_\rho \bar{F}_\rho C)$ with v_i and w_i^* the corresponding right and left eigenvectors, respectively; and where $(\cdot)^*$ denotes the complex conjugate transpose.

Theorem 2: (Lyapunov Approach)

Suppose the nominal closed multirate system described by Eq. (14) is asymptotically stable with $(A_\rho + \bar{B}_\rho \bar{F}_\rho C)$ non-defective. Then, the uncertain closed loop system given by Eq. (23) is asymptotically stable for all dA_ρ and dB_ρ described by Eqs. (28) and (29) if

$$\sigma_{max}(E_{2max}^T\, P_\rho^+\, E_{1max})_s < 1 \tag{37}$$

where

$$E_{1max} = A_{\rho max} + \bar{B}_{\rho max}(\bar{F}_\rho C)^+ \tag{38}$$

$$E_{2max} = \{I_n + \Delta_o[A_\rho + \bar{B}_\rho(\bar{F}_\rho C)]\}^+ + (\Delta_o/2)E_{1max} \tag{39}$$

and where P_ρ satisfies the Lyapuonv equation given by

$$A_{\rho c}^T P_\rho + P_\rho A_{\rho c} + \Delta_o A_{\rho c}^T P_\rho A_{\rho c} = -2I_n \tag{40}$$

where

$$A_{\rho c} = \begin{cases} A + BFC & \text{in continuous time} \\ A_\delta + \bar{B}_\delta \bar{F}_\delta C & \text{in discrete time} \end{cases} \tag{41}$$

and where P_ρ^+ is the matrix formed by the modulus of the entries of the matrix P_ρ and $(\cdot)_s$ denotes the symmetric part of a matrix.

REFERENCES

1. Yu, W., Piou, J.E. and Sobel, K.M., "Robust Eigenstructure Assignment for the Extended Medium Range Air to Air Missile",Proceedings of the 30th IEEE Conference on Decision and Control, Brighton, United Kingdom, December 1991.
2. Piou, J.E. and Sobel, K.M., "Robust Sampled Data Eigenstructure Assignment Using the Delta Operator", Proceedings of the 1992 AIAA Conference on Guidance, Navigation, and Control, Hilton Head, SC, August 1992.
3. Middleton, R.H. and Goodwin, G.C., Digital Control and Estimation: A Unified Approach , 1990, Prentice Hall Inc., Englewood Cliffs NJ.
4. Yedavalli, R.K., "Perturbation Bounds for Robust Stability in Linear State Space Models", International Journal of Control, Vol. 42, No. 6, 1985, 1507-1517.
5. Piou, J.E., Sobel, K.M., and Shapiro, E.Y., "Robust Lyapunov Constrained Sampled Data Eigenstructure Assignment Using the Delta Operator with Application to Missile Flight Control", Proceedings of the 1st IEEE Conference On Control Applications, Dayton, OH, September 1992.
6. Araki, M. and Hagiwara, T., "Pole Assignment by Multirate Sampled Data Output Feedback", Int. J. Control, 1986, Vol. 44, No. 6, 1661-1673.

Proceedings of the
American Control Conference
San Francisco, California • June 1993

Preservations of Positive Realness under Discretizations

Jin Jiang
Department of Electrical Engineering
The University of Western Ontario
London, Ontario, N6A 5B9
CANADA

Abstract

Positive Realness preservation properties of five commonly used discretization methods have been examined in this paper.

Introduction

The concept of Positive Realness has appeared in many areas of dynamic system analysis. The first application of such an important concept is in network synthesis where it was found that any network with positive real driving-point impedance can be realized by a collection of passive elements only,[1]. Dynamic systems with positive real transfer functions have become a very important part of control system analysis when Popov developed the stability criterion for feedback systems with a single memoryless nonlinearity (absolute stability) and Hyperstability theory,[2,3]. Recently, the concept of positive real systems has been extensively used in the design and analysis of the stability and the convergence of most popular adaptive systems. In fact, many adaptive algorithms are developed based on the assumption that a certain part of the system (or underlying signal model in adaptive signal processing) be positive real,[4,5].

The properties of dynamic systems with positive real transfer functions have been studied extensively in many different frameworks: time domain, frequency domain, and state space representations,[6-9]. The definitions and test procedures for positive real transfer functions in continuous and discrete domains, respectively, are straightforward and well known. However, the following question still remains unanswered: when we discretize a positive real **continuous** system, does the resulting **discrete** system remain positive real? There is no simple 'yes/no' answer to this question. The answer really relies on what type of discretization methods have been utilized in deriving the discrete equivalence of the original continuous system. The objective of this paper is to try to answer this question for five discretization techniques: (1) Forward difference; (2) Backward difference; (3) Bilinear transformations; (4) Impulse-invariant; and (5) Zero-order hold. Due to the space limitations, only major conclusions are presented here.

These five conditions for discrete systems have the same implications as their continuous time counterparts in Definition I except that the imaginary axis in s-domain has now been mapped onto the unit circle in z-domain. As it is stated, both condition (3) in Definitions I & II are for special cases where one or more poles are on the system stability boundary. For the sake of easy presentation, we will exclude these situations for now. However, all the results of the paper are still applicable to general situations where continuous system poles can be on the imaginary axis and discrete systems can have poles on the unit circle because any poles of g(s) satisfying condition (3) in Definition I will automatically satisfy the corresponding condition in Definition II under all five discretization techniques considered in this paper.

At this point, it is worthwhile to mention that positive real systems are passive in nature. In order words, a system with a positive real transfer function does not generate energy. It only dissipates energy, or transforms it from one form to another.

It should be realized that **Strictly Positive Real (SPR)** systems can easily be defined by replacing the argument of g(s) by $(s-\varepsilon)\ \ \forall\ \ \varepsilon>0$ and the argument of h(z) by $(\gamma z)\ \ \ \forall\ \ \ 0<\gamma<1$ within the above Definitions. It should also noted that in **SPR** systems, no poles on the imaginary axis in the continuous domain or unit circle in the discrete domain are permitted. Hence, for **SPR** systems, the condition (3) in both Definitions I and II should be removed. Although this paper deals mainly with positive real systems, however, most of the results can readily be extended to strictly positive real situations as well.

Main Results

Theorem 1

If the transfer function of a continuous system is $g^+(s)$, and its discrete equivalence h(z), is obtained by the forward difference discretization method, then

$$g^+(s) \qquad \text{Forward} \Rightarrow h(z) \not\Rightarrow \qquad h^+(z) \tag{1}$$

Theorem 2

If the transfer function of a continuous system is $g^+(s)$, and its discrete equivalence h(z), is obtained by the backward difference discretization method, then

$$g^+(s) \qquad \text{Backward} \Rightarrow h(z) \Rightarrow \qquad h^+(z) \in H^+(z) \tag{2}$$

One interesting feature associated with the backward difference operator is that it is capable of transforming a non-positive real continuous system to a positive real discrete one. The following example illustrates this very special case.

Example 1:
The transfer function of a non-positive real continuous system is:

$$g(s) = \frac{2-s}{s} \tag{3}$$

Its discrete equivalent can be found as:

$$h(z) = \frac{(2T-1)z+1}{z-1} \tag{4}$$

A simple calculation shows that when the sampling period $T \geq 1$, h(z) is always positive real.

Theorem 3

If the transfer function of a continuous system is $g^+(s)$, and its discrete equivalence h(z), is obtained by the bilinear transformation method, then

$$g^+(s) \qquad \text{Bilinear} \Rightarrow h(z) \Rightarrow \qquad h^+(z) \in H^+(z) \tag{5}$$

Unlike the forward and backward difference operators, the bilinear transformation provides a **bijective** mapping between $G^+(s)$ and $H^+(z)$.

Discretization by the impulse-invariant method constitutes no simple maps between continuous and discrete transfer functions, even though the pole of the discrete system transfer function, z_i is related to that of the continuous system, p_i, by the nonlinear relationship: $z_i = e^{p_i T}$. The underlying philosophy of the impulse-invariant discretization technique is to convert a continuous system to a discrete one such that the unit pules response of the discrete system matches the impulse of the continuous system at the sampling points. Before we present the results on impulse-invariant discretization method, let's take a look of the following lemma:

Lemma 1

Given a rational continuous transfer function, g(s), if one can decompose it into the summation of the following terms:

$$g(s) = K_{-1}s + K_{\infty} + \frac{K_1}{s+p_1} + \sum_{i=1}^{M} \frac{c_i s + d_i}{s^2 + a_i s + b_i} \tag{6}$$

where $K_i \geq 0 \quad \forall \quad i$, and $a_i \geq 0$, $\quad b_i \geq 0$, $\quad a_i \cdot c_i \geq d_i \geq 0$, then

$$g(s) \quad \in \quad G^+(s) \tag{7}$$

Remarks:

(1) If the order of the numerator is equal to that of the denominator, constant K_{-1} will be zero. If the order of the numerator is lower than that of the denominator, then $K_{\infty} = 0$.

(2) If the order of g(s) happens to be an even number, then $K_1 = 0$.

(3) The second order terms can be used to represent both complex and double real modes in a given system.

(4) The condition given in Lemma 1 is only sufficient for positive realness. The process of partial fraction is non-unique. If one can not get the similar form as in Eqn. (21), it does not necessarily mean that the system is not positive real. Fortunately, one does not have to test positive realness in this way. In fact, this lemma will only be used to establish Theorem 4.

Example 2

Suppose the transfer function of a continuous system is:

$$g(s) = \frac{2s^2 + 10s + 8}{(s+1)(s+2)(s+3)} \tag{8}$$

Clearly, both K_{-1} and K_{∞} will be absent. The g(s) can be decomposed into first order and second order terms. However, such decomposition is non-unique, i.e.

$$g(s) = \frac{1}{s+1} + \frac{s+4}{s^2 + 5s + 6} \tag{9}$$

which is obviously positive real. But g(s) can also be decomposed as a second form:

$$g(s) = \frac{2}{s+2} + \frac{2}{s^2 + 4s + 3} \tag{10}$$

which does not satisfy the condition in Lemma 1.

Theorem 4

If the transfer function of a continuous system is $g^+(s)$ which satisfies all the conditions in Lemma 1, and its discrete equivalence, h(z) is obtained by the impulse-invariant method, then

$$g^+(s) \text{ Impulse} \Rightarrow h(z) \Rightarrow h^+(z) \in H^+(z) \tag{11}$$

The above result comes as no surprise; because from energy-conservation point of view by matching the unit response of a discrete system at sampling points to the impulse response of a continuous system, no additional energy has been introduced (or dissipated). Therefore, if the original continuous system is positive real, there is no reason why its discrete counterpart be non-positive real under an impulse-invariant discretization. Along the same line of reasoning, one may ask the following question: Does zero-order hold discretization preserve positive realness? Well, the first reaction is that it may not, simply because when we use a zero-order hold to hold the signal between two samples, we do introduce additional energy into the discrete system. An extreme example is that by applying a series of unit impulses at the input of a zero-order hold (synchronized with the sampling period), its output would be a unit step function, which is definitely not energy preservative. The detailed analysis will be presented next in Theorem 5.

Theorem 5

If the transfer function of a continuous strictly proper system is $g^+(s)$, and its discrete equivalence, h(z) is obtained by the zero-order hold discretization methods, then

$$g^+(s) \quad \text{Zero-Order} \Rightarrow h(z) \not\Rightarrow \quad h^+(z) \in H^+(z) \tag{12}$$

In summary, the zero-order hold discrete equivalent of a strictly proper positive real continuous system will turn out to be non-positive real unless the sampling period approaches to zero. Besides the interpretation from the energy preservation points of view as we did previously, we can also think of zero-order hold as some kind of time delay operator which introduces additional phase lag into the system. Hence, the condition (5) in Definition II is violated.

Conclusion

Preservation of positive realness properties of five commonly used discretization techniques have been examined in this paper. It concludes that backward difference, bilinear transformation, and impulse-invariant discretizations will preserve the positive realness of the original continuous system. However, in the cases of forward difference and zero-order hold discretizations, positive realness of the original continuous systems will not be guaranteed. The consequences of loss of positive realness under discretizations have been briefly discussed in the framework of hyperstability of nonlinear feedback systems in general and Model Reference Adaptive System in particular.

References

[1] Baher, H., Synthesis of Electrical Networks, John Wiley & Sons, Toronto, 1984.

[2] Popov, V. M., Hyperstability of Control Systems, Springer-Verlag, New York, 1973.

[3] Popov, V. M., "Absolute Stability of Nonlinear Control Systems of Automatic Control," Automation and Remote control, Vol. 22, pp. 857-875, 1962.

[4] Sastry, S., and Bodson, M., Adaptive Control: Stability, Convergence, and Robustness, Prentice-Hall, 1989

[5] Ljung, L., "On Positive Real Transfer Functions and the Convergence of Some Recursion," IEEE Trans. on Automatic Control, Vol. AC-22, pp. 539-551, 1977.

[6] Bar-Kana, I. "Positive-realness in Multivariable Stationary Linear Systems," Journal of Franklin Institute, Vol. 328, No. 4, pp. 403-417, 1991.

[7] Hill, D. J., and Moylan, P. J. "Dissipative Dynamical Systems: Basic Input-Output and State Properties," Journal of Franklin Institute, Vol. 309, No. 5, pp. 327-357, 1980.

[8] Hitz, B. E., and Anderson, B. D. O. "Discrete Positive-real Functions and Their Application to System Stability," Proc. IEE, Vol. 116, No. 1, pp. 153-155, 1969.

[9] Wen, J. T., "Time Domain and Frequency Domain Conditions for Strict Positive Realness," IEEE Trans. on Automatic Control, Vol, AC-33, No. 10, pp.988-992, 1988.

Proceedings of the
American Control Conference
San Francisco, California • June 1993

Boundedness of the $\mathcal{L}_2$-Induced Norm Implies Quadratic Stability for Uncertain Sampled-Data Control Systems

H. Hu and C. V. Hollot

Department of Electrical and Computer Engineering
University of Massachusetts, Amherst, MA 01003

ABSTRACT

In this paper, we consider an uncertain continuous-time linear system with sampled-data feedback control. For a particular structure of uncertainty we show that if the $\mathcal{L}_2$-induced norm of a specific operator is bounded, then the uncertain continuous-time linear system with sampled-data feedback control is quadratically stable.

I. INTRODUCTION

The renewed attention to sampled-data control; e.g., see [1 – 8], has focussed on extending the H_∞ design methodology. A distinguished feature of sampled-data control systems is that they contain both continuous and discrete-time signals and recently developed techniques successfully deal with this hybridness. For example, Bamieh and Pearson [1] consider the sampled-data control system in Figure 1 where u, y, w and z are continuous time signals and u_k and y_k are discrete-time signals. The objective is to ensure stability and to make the $\mathcal{L}_2$ -induced norm of the sampled-data operator T_{wz} sufficiently small. In [1] it is shown that this task is equivalent to a solvable H_∞ optimal control problem for a finite-dimensional, linear shift-invariant system. Consequently, performance and robustness problems that manifest themselves as bounds on sampled-data operators can now be recast as discrete-time H_∞ optimal control problems. Indeed the robust stability of the robust sampled-data control shown in Figure 1 where Δ is an unknown stable transfer function having $\|\Delta\|_\infty \leq 1$ is equivalent to making the H_∞ norm of the associated discrete-time system less than 1.

In this paper, we continue with the robust stability analysis of the uncertain sampled-data control system in Figure 1 and seek a connection between these new robustness results and quadratic stability. Recall that such a link exists in the continuous-time framework where quadratic stabilization for the uncertainty class

$$\{\Delta \in R^{q\times p}: \ \Delta'\Delta \leq 1\}$$

is equivalent to $\|T_{zw}\|_\infty < 1$. The question now is whether this is true in a sampled-data setting. This paper gives half an answer: *If the $\mathcal{L}_2$ -induced norm of the sampled-data operator T_{zw} is less than 1, then the sampled-data control system is quadratically stabilizable against the above uncertainty class.*

In establishing this connection, two things are needed:

1. That the boundedness of the sampled-data operator T_{zw} implies that a discrete-time Ricatti equation (DARE) has a positive-definite solution.
2. That the solution to this DARE serves as a quadratic Lyapunov function for the uncertain sampled-data control system.

The first of these results is an immediate consequence of the previously discussed work of Bamieh and Pearson [1] and the relationship between the discrete-time

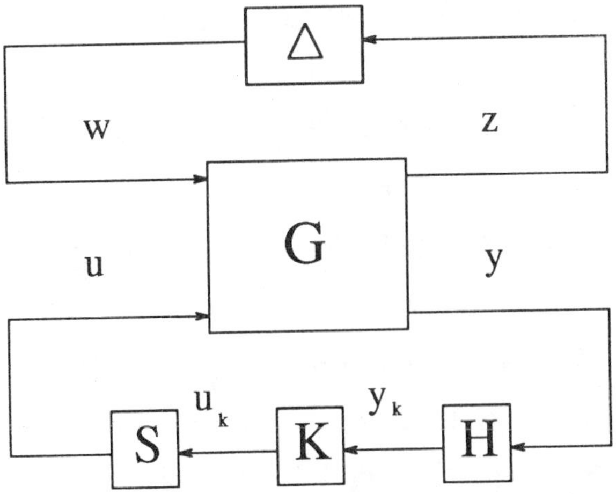

Figure 1: Typical sampled-data control system

H_∞problem and a DARE; see Furuta and Phoojaruenchanachai [2]. The second result is the technical novelty of this paper.

The paper is arranged as follows: In the next section we formulate the robust control problem and state some necessary mathematical facts. Section 3 contains a key lemma and in Section 4 we state and prove the main result. Section 5 contains some proofs.

II. PROBLEM FORMULATION AND PRELIMINARIES

Consider the uncertain continuous-time linear system described by

$$\dot{x} = (A + E\Delta F)x + Bu; \ \Delta \in R^{q\times p}, \ \Delta'\Delta \leq I \quad (1)$$

where A, E and F are matrices of dimensions $R^{n\times n}$, $R^{n\times q}$ and $R^{p\times n}$ and Δ is the uncertainty. Assume a sampled-data feedback control

$$u(t) = Kx(k\tau), \ k\tau \leq t < (k+1)\tau, \ \tau > 0. \quad (2)$$

The block diagram for this sampled-data control systems is depicted in Figure 1 where S is the sampler with period τ and H is the zero-order hold. This system can be represented by the state equations

$$\begin{aligned} \dot{x} &= Ax + Ew + Bu \\ z &= Fx \\ w &= \Delta z; \ \Delta \in R^{q\times p}, \ \Delta'\Delta \leq I \\ u(t) &= Kx(k\tau), \ k\tau \leq t < (k+1)\tau, \ \tau > 0. \quad (3) \end{aligned}$$

An equivalent representation, developed by Bamieh and Pearson [1], has state space description

$$x_{k+1} = \tilde{A}x_k + \tilde{E}\tilde{w}_k + \tilde{B}u_k$$

$$\tilde{z}_k = \tilde{F}x_k + \tilde{D}_0\tilde{w}_k + \tilde{D}u_k$$
$$\tilde{w}_k = \tilde{\Delta}\tilde{z}_k$$
$$u_k = Kx_k \quad (4)$$

where

$$\tilde{z}_k(t) = z(k\tau + t),\ t \in [0,\tau], \quad (5)$$
$$\tilde{w}_k(t) = w(k\tau + t),\ t \in [0,\tau], \quad (6)$$

and

$$\tilde{A} \doteq e^{A\tau},\ \tilde{B} \doteq \Psi(\tau)B,\ \Psi(\tau) \doteq \int_0^\tau e^{As}ds,$$
$$\tilde{D} : R^n \rightarrow \mathcal{L}_2\,[0,\tau],\ \tilde{D}u_k \doteq F\Psi(t)Bu_k,$$
$$\tilde{E} : \mathcal{L}_2\,[0,\tau] \rightarrow R^n,\ \tilde{E}\tilde{w}_k \doteq \int_0^\tau e^{A(\tau-s)}E\tilde{w}_k(s)ds,$$
$$\tilde{F} : R^n \rightarrow \mathcal{L}_2\,[0,\tau],\ \tilde{F}x_k \doteq Fe^{At}x_k,$$
$$\tilde{D}_0 : \mathcal{L}_2\,[0,\tau] \rightarrow \mathcal{L}_2\,[0,\tau],\ \tilde{D}_0\tilde{w}_k \doteq \int_0^t Fe^{A(t-s)}E\tilde{w}_k(s)ds,$$
$$\tilde{\Delta} : \mathcal{L}_2\,[0,\tau] \rightarrow \mathcal{L}_2\,[0,\tau],\ \tilde{\Delta}\tilde{z}_k \doteq \Delta\tilde{z}_k;\ \Delta'\Delta \leq I \quad (7)$$

where $\mathcal{L}_2\,[0,\tau]$ denotes the Lebesgue space of real measurable functions on $[0,\tau]$. Under a condition for well-posedness; e.g., $(I-\tilde{D}_0\tilde{\Delta})^{-1}$ exists, the closed loop system is described by

$$x_{k+1} = [\tilde{A} + \tilde{B}K + \tilde{E}\tilde{\Delta}(I - \tilde{D}_0\tilde{\Delta})^{-1}(\tilde{F} + \tilde{D}K)]x_k. \quad (8)$$

Define $\bar{A}(\tilde{\Delta}) \doteq \tilde{A} + \tilde{B}K + \tilde{E}\tilde{\Delta}(I - \tilde{D}_0\tilde{\Delta})^{-1}(\tilde{F} + \tilde{D}K)$ and notice that $\bar{A}(\tilde{\Delta}) \in R^{n\times n}$. In fact, $\bar{A}(\tilde{\Delta}) \in R^{n\times n}$ is the state matrix associated with conventional discretization; i.e.,

$$\bar{A}(\tilde{\Delta}) = e^{(A+E\Delta F)\tau} + \int_0^\tau e^{(A+E\Delta F)(\tau-s)}BKds. \quad (9)$$

Thus, the uncertain sampled-data control system (1) is equivalently described by (8) with $\tilde{\Delta}$ given by (7).

We now define the notion of quadratic stability for the uncertain sampled-data control system (1).

Definition: The uncertain sampled-data control system (1) is *quadratically stable* if there exists positive definite symmetric matrix P such that

$$\bar{A}(\tilde{\Delta})'P\bar{A}(\tilde{\Delta}) - P < 0 \quad (10)$$

for all $\tilde{\Delta}$ satisfying (7).

Our present goal is to establish a relationship between quadratic stability and the induced norm of T_{wz}. In the remainder of this section, we collect some mathematical facts whose proofs are deferred in Section 5. First, we introduce basic definitions for operators on a Hilbert space.

With the inner product

$$<x,y> = \int_0^\tau x'ydt,\quad x,y \in \mathcal{L}_2\,[0,\tau], \quad (11)$$

$\mathcal{L}_2\,[0,\tau]$ becomes a Hilbert space. The norm induced by this inner product is

$$\|x\| = <x,x>^{1/2}. \quad (12)$$

Let H be an operator from H_1 to H_2. Its adjoint operator, $H^* : H_2 \rightarrow H_1$, satisfies

$$<H^*y,x> = <x,Hy> \quad (13)$$

for any $x \in H_1$ and $y \in H_2$. An operator H is self-adjoint if $H^* = H$. We write $H > 0$ if $<x,Hx>$ is positive for all $x \neq 0$. Assume that $B : \mathcal{L}_2\,[0,\tau] \rightarrow R^n$ is a linear bounded operator. The following facts are established in Section 5.

Fact 1: *If $I - BB^* > 0$, then $I - B^*B > 0$.*

Fact 2: *Let P be positive definite matrix and $\bar{B} = (BB^*)^{1/2}$. If $I - \bar{B}'P\bar{B} > 0$, then $I - B^*PB > 0$. Moreover,*

$$B(I - B^*PB)^{-1}B^* = \bar{B}'(I - \bar{B}'P\bar{B})^{-1}\bar{B}. \quad (14)$$

III. Key Lemma

In this section. we establish a link between the quadratic stability of the uncertain sampled-data control system (1) and the solution of a DARE associated with a particular discrete-time system. To begin, let

$$\tilde{A}_0 : R^n \rightarrow R^n$$
$$\tilde{B}_0 : \mathcal{L}_2\,[0,\tau] \rightarrow R^n$$
$$\tilde{C}_0 : R^n \rightarrow \mathcal{L}_2\,[0,\tau]$$

be bounded linear operators. The associated Riccati equation is defined by

$$\tilde{A}_0'P\tilde{A}_0 - P + \tilde{C}_0^*\tilde{C}_0 + \tilde{A}_0'P\bar{B}(I - \bar{B}'P\bar{B})^{-1}\bar{B}'P\tilde{A}_0 + Q = 0;$$
$$I - \bar{B}'P\bar{B} > 0 \quad (1$$

where $\bar{B} \doteq (\tilde{B}_0\tilde{B}_0^*)^{1/2}$ and $P,\ Q \in R^{n\times n}$. Now, consider a linear discrete-time system described by

$$x_{k+1} = (\tilde{A}_0 + \tilde{B}_0\tilde{\Delta}_0\tilde{C}_0)x_k \quad (16)$$

where

$$\tilde{\Delta}_0 : \mathcal{L}_2\,[0,\tau] \rightarrow \mathcal{L}_2\,[0,\tau],\ \tilde{\Delta}_0^*\tilde{\Delta}_0 - I \leq 0.$$

Remark: The system described by (16) is a non-standard discrete-time dynamical system since $\tilde{B}_0$, $\tilde{C}_0$ and $\tilde{\Delta}_0$ are maps with either domain or range in $\mathcal{L}_2\,[0,\tau]$.

We now give our key lemma.

Lemma 1: *Consider the linear discrete-time dynamical system (16). If the Riccati equation (15) is satisfied for some positive definite matrices P and Q, then the system (16) is quadratically stable.*

Proof: Choose the Lyapunov function

$$V(x_k) = x_k'Px_k.$$

The Lyapunov difference is then

$$\begin{aligned}\delta V_k &= V(x_{k+1}) - V(x_k)\\ &= x_{k+1}'Px_{k+1} - x_k'Px_k\\ &= x_k'(\tilde{A}_0 + \tilde{B}_0\tilde{\Delta}_0\tilde{C}_0)'P(\tilde{A}_0 + \tilde{B}_0\tilde{\Delta}_0\tilde{C}_0) - x_k'Px_k\\ &= x_k'(\tilde{A}_0'P\tilde{A}_0 - P)x_k + 2x_k'\tilde{A}_0'P\tilde{B}_0\tilde{\Delta}_0\tilde{C}_0x_k\\ &\quad +x_k'\tilde{C}_0^*\tilde{\Delta}_0^*\tilde{B}_0^*P\tilde{B}_0\tilde{\Delta}_0\tilde{C}_0x_k.\end{aligned}$$

Since $I - \bar{B}'P\bar{B} > 0$, it follows from Fact 2 in Section 2 that $I - \tilde{B}_0^*P\tilde{B}_0 > 0$. Hence $(I - \tilde{B}_0^*P\tilde{B}_0)^{-1/2}$ exists. Therefore,

$$\begin{aligned}\delta V_k &= x_k'(\tilde{A}_0'P\tilde{A}_0 - P)x_k + x_k'\tilde{C}_0^*\tilde{\Delta}_0^*\tilde{B}_0^*P\tilde{B}_0\tilde{\Delta}_0\tilde{C}_0x_k\\ &\quad 2x_k'\tilde{A}_0'P\tilde{B}_0(I - \tilde{B}_0^*P\tilde{B}_0)^{-1/2}\\ &\quad (I - \tilde{B}_0^*P\tilde{B}_0)^{1/2}\tilde{\Delta}_0\tilde{C}_0x_k.\end{aligned}$$

Since $2|<x,y>| \le <x,x> + <y,y>$, we have

$$\begin{aligned}\delta V_k &\le x_k'(\tilde{A}_0'P\tilde{A}_0 - P)x_k + x_k'\tilde{C}_0^*\tilde{\Delta}_0^*\tilde{B}_0^*P\tilde{B}_0\tilde{\Delta}_0\tilde{C}_0x_k\\ &\quad +x_k'\tilde{A}_0'P\tilde{B}_0(I - \tilde{B}_0^*P\tilde{B}_0)^{-1}\tilde{B}_0^*P\tilde{A}_0x_k\\ &\quad +x_k'\tilde{C}_0^*\tilde{\Delta}_0^*(I - \tilde{B}_0^*P\tilde{B}_0)\tilde{\Delta}_0\tilde{C}_0x_k\\ &= x_k'(\tilde{A}_0'P\tilde{A}_0 - P)x_k + x_k'\tilde{C}_0^*\tilde{\Delta}_0^*\tilde{\Delta}_0\tilde{C}_0x_k\\ &\quad +x_k'\tilde{A}_0'P\tilde{B}_0(I - \tilde{B}_0^*P\tilde{B}_0)^{-1}\tilde{B}_0^*P\tilde{A}_0x_k\end{aligned}$$

and by (16),

$$\begin{aligned}\delta V_k &\le x_k'(\tilde{A}_0'P\tilde{A}_0 - P)x_k + x_k'\tilde{C}_0^*\tilde{C}_0x_k\\ &\quad +x_k'\tilde{A}_0'P\tilde{B}_0(I - \tilde{B}_0^*P\tilde{B}_0)^{-1}\tilde{B}_0^*P\tilde{A}_0x_k.\end{aligned}$$

Finally, by Fact 2

$$\begin{aligned}\delta V_k &= x_k'(\tilde{A}_0'P\tilde{A}_0 - P)x_k + x_k'\tilde{C}_0^*\tilde{C}_0x_k\\ &\quad +x_k'\tilde{A}_0'P\bar{B}(I - \bar{B}'P\bar{B})^{-1}\bar{B}'P\tilde{A}_0x_k\\ &< -x_k'Qx_k.\end{aligned}$$

Hence, system (16) is quadratically stable. □

This key lemma establishes a link between the Riccati equation (15) and the quadratic stability of the linear system (16). Later on, we will show that the sampled-data control system (8) can be transformed to the form of (16). To this end, the following two lemmas are needed.

Lemma 2: (see Theorem 6 in [1] for proof) *Consider the sampled-data control system*

$$\begin{aligned}x_{k+1} &= \tilde{A}x_k + \tilde{E}\tilde{w}_k + \tilde{B}u_k\\ \tilde{z}_k &= \tilde{F}x_k + \tilde{D}_0\tilde{w}_k + \tilde{D}u_k\\ u_k &= Kx_k\end{aligned} \tag{17}$$

with $\|\tilde{D}_0\| < 1$. *Let* $\tilde{T}_{\tilde{w}\tilde{z}}$ *be the operator from* $\tilde{w}$ *to* $\tilde{z}$. *Form matrices* T_b, T_{cd}, Σ_b *and* Σ_{cd} *from the following symmetric decompositions:*

$$\tilde{E}(I - \tilde{D}_0^*\tilde{D}_0)^{-1}\tilde{E}^* = T_b^*\begin{pmatrix}\Sigma_b & 0\\ 0 & 0\end{pmatrix}T_b;$$

$$\begin{pmatrix}\tilde{F}^*\\ \tilde{D}^*\end{pmatrix}(I - \tilde{D}_0^*\tilde{D}_0)^{-1}[\tilde{F}\ \tilde{D}] = \tilde{T}_{cd}^*\begin{pmatrix}\Sigma_{cd} & 0\\ 0 & 0\end{pmatrix}T_{cd}.$$

Additionally, consider the discrete-time system

$$\begin{aligned}x_{k+1} &= \hat{A}x_k + \hat{B}_0\hat{w}_k + \hat{B}u_k\\ \hat{z}_k &= \hat{C}_0x_k\\ u_k &= Kx_k\end{aligned} \tag{18}$$

where

$$\hat{A} = \tilde{A} + \tilde{E}\tilde{D}_0^*(I - \tilde{D}_0\tilde{D}_0^*)^{-1}\tilde{F},\quad \hat{B} = \tilde{E}\tilde{D}_0^*(I - \tilde{D}_0\tilde{D}_0^*)^{-1}\tilde{D} + \tilde{B}$$

and

$$\hat{B}_0 = \tilde{T}_b^*\begin{pmatrix}\Sigma_b^{1/2}\\ 0\end{pmatrix},\quad [\hat{C}_0\ \hat{D}] = [\Sigma_{cd}^{1/2}\ 0]T_{cd}.$$

Let $\hat{T}_{\hat{w}\hat{z}}$ *be the transfer function from* $\hat{w}$ *to* $\hat{z}$. *Then, the following are equivalent:*

(i) The sampled-data control system (17) is internally stable and has

$$\|\tilde{T}_{\tilde{w}\tilde{z}}\| < 1.$$

(ii) The discrete-time control system (18) is internally stable and has

$$\|\hat{T}_{\hat{w}\hat{z}}\| < 1.$$

The next lemma is due to Furuta and Phojaruenchanachai [2].

Lemma 3: (see Theorem 4.1 in [2] for proof) *Consider the transfer function* $T(z) = H(zI - F)^{-1}G$ *where* F, G *and* H *are matrices of compatible dimensions. Then,* $\|T(z)\|_\infty < 1$ *if and only if there exist positive definite matrices* P *and* Q *such that the following Riccati equation holds:*

$$\begin{aligned}F'PF - F + H'H + F'PG(I - G'PG)^{-1}G'PF + Q = 0;\\ I - G'PG > 0\end{aligned} \tag{19}$$

IV. Main Result

Recall the uncertain sampled-data control system

$$\begin{aligned}\dot{x} &= (A + E\Delta F)x + Bu;\ \Delta'\Delta \le I,\\ u &= Kx,\ k\tau \le t < (k+1)\tau,\ \tau > 0\end{aligned} \tag{20}$$

and equivalent representation

$$x_{k+1} = \bar{A}(\tilde{\Delta})x_k;\ \tilde{\Delta} : \mathcal{L}_2\,[0,\tau] \to \mathcal{L}_2\,[0,\tau]\ \tilde{\Delta}^*\tilde{\Delta} - I \le 0 \tag{21}$$

where

$$\bar{A}(\tilde{\Delta}) = \tilde{A} + \tilde{B}K + \tilde{E}\tilde{\Delta}(I - \tilde{D}_0\tilde{\Delta})^{-1}(\tilde{F} + \tilde{D}K).$$

To apply Lemma 1 to this system we first put (21) into the form of (16). To this end, assume that $\|\tilde{D}_0\| < 1$; hence, $(I - \tilde{D}_0\tilde{\Delta})^{-1}$ exists for all admissible $\tilde{\Delta}$. Now,

$$\begin{aligned}\bar{A}(\tilde{\Delta}) &= \tilde{A} + \tilde{B}K + \tilde{E}\tilde{\Delta}(I - \tilde{D}_0\tilde{\Delta})^{-1}(\tilde{F} + \tilde{D}K)\\ &= \tilde{A} + \tilde{B}K + \tilde{E}\tilde{D}_0^*(I - \tilde{D}_0\tilde{D}_0^*)^{-1}(\tilde{F} + \tilde{D}K)\\ &\quad +\tilde{E}\tilde{\Delta}(I - \tilde{D}_0\tilde{\Delta})^{-1}(\tilde{F} + \tilde{D}K)\\ &\quad -\tilde{E}\tilde{D}_0^*(I - \tilde{D}_0\tilde{D}_0^*)^{-1}(\tilde{F} + \tilde{D}K).\end{aligned}$$

and combining the last two terms gives

$$\begin{aligned}\bar{A}(\tilde{\Delta}) &= \tilde{A}+\tilde{B}K+\tilde{E}\tilde{D}_0^*(I-\tilde{D}_0\tilde{D}_0^*)^{-1}(\tilde{F}+\tilde{D}K)\\ &+\tilde{E}(I-\tilde{D}_0^*\tilde{D}_0)^{-1}(\tilde{\Delta}-\tilde{D}_0^*)(\bar{I}-\tilde{D}_0\tilde{\Delta})^{-1}(\tilde{F}+\tilde{D}K).\end{aligned}$$

Define

$$\tilde{\Delta}_0 \doteq (I-\tilde{D}_0^*\tilde{D}_0)^{-1/2}(\tilde{\Delta}-\tilde{D}_0^*)(\bar{I}-\tilde{D}_0\tilde{\Delta})^{-1}(I-\tilde{D}_0\tilde{D}_0^*)^{1/2} \quad (22)$$

so that

$$\begin{aligned}\bar{A}(\tilde{\Delta}) &= \tilde{A}+\tilde{B}K+\tilde{E}\tilde{D}_0^*(I-\tilde{D}_0\tilde{D}_0^*)^{-1}(\tilde{F}+\tilde{D}K)\\ &+\tilde{E}(I-\tilde{D}_0^*\tilde{D}_0)^{-1/2}\tilde{\Delta}_0(I-\tilde{D}_0\tilde{D}_0^*)^{-1/2}\\ &(\tilde{F}+\tilde{D}K). \quad (23)\end{aligned}$$

The matrix $\bar{A}(\tilde{\Delta})$ has the form of the state matrix in the linear discrete-time dynamical system (16). The next lemma verifies that the newly defined uncertainty $\tilde{\Delta}_0$ satisfies (16).

Lemma 4: (see Section 5 for proof) *If $\tilde{\Delta}^*\tilde{\Delta}-I\le 0$, then $\tilde{\Delta}_0^*\tilde{\Delta}_0-I\le 0$.*

The next lemma is obvious.

Lemma 5: *Suppose $\|\tilde{D}_0\|<1$. The uncertain sampled-data control system (21), equivalently system (1), is quadratically stable if the following system is quadratically stable:*

$$\begin{aligned}x_{k+1} &= [\tilde{A}+\tilde{B}K+\tilde{E}\tilde{D}_0^*(I-\tilde{D}_0\tilde{D}_0^*)^{-1}(\tilde{F}+\tilde{D}K)\\ &\tilde{E}(I-\tilde{D}_0^*\tilde{D}_0)^{-1/2}\tilde{\Delta}_0(I-\tilde{D}_0\tilde{D}_0^*)^{-1/2}\\ &(\tilde{F}+\tilde{D}K)]x_k. \quad (24)\end{aligned}$$

where $\tilde{\Delta}_0 : \mathcal{L}_2\,[0,\tau]\to\mathcal{L}_2\,[0,\tau];\ \tilde{\Delta}_0^*\tilde{\Delta}_0-I\le 0.$

We now present the main result.

Theorem 1: *Consider the uncertain sampled-data control system (1) and its equivalent description*

$$\begin{aligned}\dot{x} &= Ax+Ew+Bu\\ z &= Fx\\ w &= \Delta z;\ \Delta\in R^{q\times p},\ \Delta'\Delta\le I\\ u(t) &= Kx(k\tau),\ k\tau\le t<(k+1)\tau,\ \tau>0. \quad (25)\end{aligned}$$

Recall that T_{wz} is the operator from w to z. System (1) is quadratically stable if the nominal system ($\Delta=0$) is internally stable and the induced norm of the sampled-data operator T_{wz} is less than 1.

Proof: From [1], the uncertain system (17) is internally stable and $\|\tilde{T}_{\tilde{w}\tilde{z}}\|=\|T_{wz}\|$. Therefore, $\|\tilde{T}_{\tilde{w}\tilde{z}}\|<1$ and $\|\tilde{D}_0\|<1$. By Lemma 5, it suffices to show that the uncertain system (24) is quadratically stable. By Lemma 2, we have that the system (18) is internally stable and $\|\hat{T}_{\tilde{w}\tilde{z}}\|<1$. That is, $\hat{A}+\hat{B}K$ is asymptotically stable and

$$\|(\hat{C}_0+\hat{D}K)(zI-\hat{A}-\hat{B}K)^{-1}\hat{B}_0\|_\infty<1.$$

Moreover,

$$\begin{aligned}\hat{A}+\hat{B}K &= \tilde{A}+\tilde{E}\tilde{D}_0^*(I-\tilde{D}_0\tilde{D}_0^*)^{-1}\tilde{F}\\ &+(\tilde{E}\tilde{D}_0^*(I-\tilde{D}_0\tilde{D}_0^*)^{-1}\tilde{D}+\tilde{B})K\\ &= \tilde{A}+\tilde{B}K+\tilde{E}\tilde{D}_0^*(I-\tilde{D}_0\tilde{D}_0^*)^{-1}(\tilde{F}+\tilde{D}K),\\ \hat{B}_0\hat{B}_0' &= \tilde{E}(I-\tilde{D}_0^*\tilde{D}_0)^{-1}\tilde{E}^*\end{aligned}$$

and

$$\begin{pmatrix}\hat{C}_0'\\ \hat{D}'\end{pmatrix}[\hat{C}_0\ \ \hat{D}]=\begin{pmatrix}\tilde{F}^*\\ \tilde{D}^*\end{pmatrix}(I-\tilde{D}_0\tilde{D}_0^*)^{-1}[\tilde{F}\ \ \tilde{D}].$$

By Lemma 3, there exists positive definite matrices P and Q such that

$$\begin{aligned}&(\hat{A}+\hat{B}K)'P(\hat{A}+\hat{B}K)+(\hat{C}_0+\hat{D}K)'(\hat{C}_0+\hat{D}K)\\ &+(\hat{A}+\hat{B}K)'P\hat{B}_0(I-\hat{B}_0'P\hat{B}_0)^{-1}\hat{B}_0'P(\hat{A}+\hat{B}K)+Q=0\end{aligned}$$

and

$$I-\hat{B}_0'P\hat{B}_0>0.$$

Now, Lemma 1 guarantees the following system is quadratically stable:

$$x_{k+1}=(\hat{A}+\hat{B}K+\bar{B}_0\tilde{\Delta}_0\bar{C}_0)x_k;\quad \tilde{\Delta}_0^*\tilde{\Delta}_0-I\le 0 \quad (26)$$

where

$$\begin{aligned}\bar{B}_0 &= \tilde{E}(I-\tilde{D}_0^*\tilde{D}_0)^{-1/2}\\ \bar{C}_0 &= (I-\tilde{D}_0\tilde{D}_0^*)^{-1/2}(\tilde{F}+\tilde{D}K).\end{aligned}$$

System (26) is precisely (24). Hence, the uncertain sampled-data control system (1) is quadratically stable. □

V. Proofs

In this section, we prove Fact 1 and Fact 2 stated in Section 2 and Lemma 4. Assume that B is a linear bounded operator on Hilbert spaces.

Fact 1: *If $I-BB^*>0$, then $I-B^*B>0$.*

Proof: Since $I-BB^*>0$, we have $<x,(I-BB^*)x>\ >0$. On the other hand,

$$\begin{aligned}<x,(I-BB^*)x> &= <x,x> - <x,BB^*x>\\ &= <x,x> - <B^*x,B^*)x> > 0.\end{aligned}$$

Therefore, $\|B^*\|<1$. This implies that $\|B\|<1$. Equivalently,

$$<u,u>\ >\ <Bu,Bu>, \text{for any } u\in\mathcal{L}_2\,[0,\tau].$$

It follows that

$$\begin{aligned}<u,(I-B^*B)u> &= <u,u> - <uB^*Bu>\\ &= <u,u> - <Bu,Bu>> 0.\end{aligned}$$

Hence, $I-B^*B>0$. □

Fact 2: *Let P be positive definite matrix and $\bar{B}=(BB^*)^{1/2}$. If $I-\bar{B}'P\bar{B}>0$, then $I-B^*PB>0$. Moreover,*

$$B(I-B^*PB)^{-1}B^*=\bar{B}(I-\bar{B}'P\bar{B})^{-1}\bar{B}.$$

Proof: Since $I - \bar{B}\bar{B}^* = I - (BB^*)^{1/2}P(BB^*)^{1/2} > 0$, it follows from Fact 1, $I - \bar{B}^*\bar{B} = I - P^{1/2}BB^*P^{1/2} > 0$. Furthermore, let $\hat{B} = P^{1/2}B$. Hence, $I - \hat{B}\hat{B}^* = I - P^{1/2}BB^*P^{1/2} > 0$. Again by Fact 1, we have

$$I - \hat{B}^*\hat{B} = I - B^*PB > 0.$$

Consequently, $(I - B^*PB)^{-1}$ exists. Moreover, we can show that $(I - BB^*P)^{-1}$ exists. In fact, if $I - BB^*P$ is singular, then there exists a nonzero $y(\neq 0)$ such that

$$y'(I - BB^*P) = 0.$$

Therefore,

$$\begin{aligned} 0 &= y'(I - BB^*P)BB^*y \\ &= y'(BB^*)^{1/2}(I - (BB^*)^{1/2}P(BB^*)^{1/2})(BB^*)^{1/2}y. \end{aligned}$$

This implies that

$$y'(BB^*)^{1/2} = 0.$$

On the other hand,

$$y'(I - BB^*P) = y' - y'(BB^*)^{1/2}(BB^*)^{1/2}P = y' \neq 0.$$

This is a contradiction. Hence, $(I - BB^*P)$ is nonsingular; i.e., $(I - BB^*P)^{-1}$ exists. With all the inverses well defined, we have

$$\begin{aligned} B(I - B^*PB)^{-1}B^* &= ((I - BB^*P)^{-1}BB^* \\ &= (I - BB^*P)^{-1}(BB^*)^{1/2}(BB^*)^{1/2} \\ &= \bar{B}(I - \bar{B}'P\bar{B})^{-1}\bar{B}. \end{aligned}$$

This concludes the proof. □

In the next we prove Lemma 4. Recall

$$\tilde{\Delta}_0 \doteq (I - \tilde{D}_0^*\tilde{D}_0)^{-1/2}(\tilde{\Delta} - \tilde{D}_0^*)(\bar{I} - \tilde{D}_0\tilde{\Delta})^{-1}(I - \tilde{D}_0\tilde{D}_0^*)^{1/2}.$$

Lemma 4: *If* $\tilde{\Delta}^*\tilde{\Delta} - I \leq 0$, *then* $\tilde{\Delta}_0^*\tilde{\Delta}_0 - I \leq 0$.

Proof: Clearly,

$$\begin{aligned} \tilde{\Delta}_0^*\tilde{\Delta}_0 &= (I - \tilde{D}_0\tilde{D}_0^*)^{1/2}(\bar{I} - \tilde{\Delta}^*\tilde{D}_0^*)^{-1}(\tilde{\Delta}^* - \tilde{D}_0)(\bar{I} - \tilde{D}_0^*\tilde{D}_0)^{-1} \\ &\quad (\tilde{\Delta} - \tilde{D}_0^*)(\bar{I} - \tilde{D}_0\tilde{\Delta})^{-1}(I - \tilde{D}_0\tilde{D}_0^*)^{1/2} \\ &= (I - \tilde{D}_0\tilde{D}_0^*)^{-1/2}(\bar{I} - \tilde{\Delta}^*\tilde{D}_0^*)^{-1}(\tilde{\Delta}^* - \tilde{D}_0) \\ &\quad (\tilde{\Delta}(I - \tilde{D}_0\tilde{\Delta})^{-1} - \tilde{D}_0^*(I - \tilde{D}_0\tilde{D}_0^*)^{-1})(I - \tilde{D}_0\tilde{D}_0^*)^{1/2}. \end{aligned}$$

Since

$$\begin{aligned} &(\tilde{\Delta}^* - \tilde{D}_0)(\tilde{\Delta}(I - \tilde{D}_0\tilde{\Delta})^{-1} - \tilde{D}_0^*(I - \tilde{D}_0\tilde{D}_0^*)^{-1}) \\ =\; &\tilde{\Delta}^*\tilde{\Delta}(I - \tilde{D}_0\tilde{\Delta})^{-1} - \tilde{D}_0\tilde{\Delta}(I - \tilde{D}_0\tilde{\Delta})^{-1} \\ &-\tilde{\Delta}^*\tilde{D}_0^*(I - \tilde{D}_0\tilde{D}_0^*)^{-1} + \tilde{D}_0\tilde{D}_0^*(I - \tilde{D}_0\tilde{D}_0^*)^{-1} \\ =\; &\tilde{\Delta}^*\tilde{\Delta}(I - \tilde{D}_0\tilde{\Delta})^{-1} - (I - \tilde{D}_0\tilde{\Delta})^{-1} \\ &-\tilde{\Delta}^*\tilde{D}_0^*(I - \tilde{D}_0\tilde{D}_0^*)^{-1} + (I - \tilde{D}_0\tilde{D}_0^*)^{-1}, \end{aligned}$$

we have

$$\begin{aligned} \tilde{\Delta}_0^*\tilde{\Delta}_0 &= (I - \tilde{D}_0\tilde{D}_0^*)^{1/2}(I - \tilde{\Delta}^*\tilde{D}_0^*)^{-1}(\tilde{\Delta}^*\tilde{\Delta} - I) \\ &\quad (I - \tilde{D}_0\tilde{\Delta})^{-1}(I - \tilde{D}_0\tilde{D}_0^*)^{1/2} + (I - \tilde{D}_0\tilde{D}_0^*)^{1/2} \\ &\quad (I - \tilde{\Delta}^*\tilde{D}_0^*)^{-1}(I - \tilde{\Delta}^*\tilde{D}_0^*)(I - \tilde{D}_0\tilde{D}_0^*)^{-1/2} \\ &= (I - \tilde{D}_0\tilde{D}_0^*)^{1/2}(I - \tilde{\Delta}^*\tilde{D}_0^*)^{-1}(\tilde{\Delta}^*\tilde{\Delta} - I)(I - \tilde{D}_0\tilde{\Delta})^{-1} \\ &\quad (I - \tilde{D}_0\tilde{D}_0^*)^{1/2} + I. \end{aligned}$$

Therefore,

$$\begin{aligned} &\tilde{\Delta}_0^*\tilde{\Delta}_0 - I = (I - \tilde{D}_0\tilde{D}_0^*)^{1/2}(I - \tilde{\Delta}^*\tilde{D}_0^*)^{-1} \\ &(\tilde{\Delta}^*\tilde{\Delta} - I)((I - \tilde{D}_0\tilde{\Delta})^{-1}(I - \tilde{D}_0\tilde{D}_0^*)^{1/2}. \end{aligned}$$

Hence,

$$\tilde{\Delta}_0^*\tilde{\Delta}_0 - I \leq 0.$$

□

ACKNOWLEDGEMENT

This research was supported in part by National Science Foundation under grant NSF-8858366.

References

[1] B. Bamieh and J. B. Pearson,"A General Framework for Linear Periodic Systems with Applications to $\mathcal{H}_\infty$ Sampled-Data Control", *IEEE Transactions on Automatic Control*, pp. 418–435, Vol. 37, 1992.

[2] K. Furuta and S. Phoojaruenchanachai,"An Algebraic Approach to Discrete-Time H_∞ Control Problems", *Proceedings of the 29th Conference on Decision and Control*, pp. 3067–3073, 1990.

[3] B. Bamieh and J. B. Pearson, "The $\mathcal{H}_2$ Problem for Sampled-Data System", *Systems & Control Letters*, 19, pp. 1-12, 1992.

[4] B. Bamieh, M. Dahleh and J. B. Pearson, "Minimization of the $\mathcal{L}_\infty$-Induced Norm for Sampled-Data Systems", Report no. 9109, Department of Electrical and Computer Engineering, Rice University, TX, June 1991.

[5] B. Bamieh, J. B. Pearson, B. A. Francis, A. Tannenbaum, "A Lifting Technique for Linear Periodic Systems with Applications to Sampled-Data Control", *Systems & Control Letters*, 17, pp. 79–88, 1991.

[6] T. Chen and B. A. Francis, "On the $\mathcal{L}_2$-Induced Norm of a Sampled-Data System", *Systems & Control Letters*, 15, pp. 211–219, 1990.

[7] N. Sivashankar and P. P. Khargonekar,"Induced Norms for Sampled-Data Systems", To appear in Automatica, a preliminary version appeared in *Proceedings of the American Control Conference*, pp. 167–172, 1991.

[8] N. Sivashankar and P. P. Khargonekar, "Characterization of the $\mathcal{L}_2$-Induced Norm for Linear Systems with Jumps with Applications to Sampled-Data Systems", Internal Report, University of Michigan, Ann Arbor.

Proceedings of the
American Control Conference
San Francisco, California • June 1993

CIRCULAR POLE ASSIGNMENT FOR DISCRETE–TIME SINGULAR SYSTEMS

Guojun Shi
On leave from the Eighth Department
East China Institute of Technology
Nanjing 210014, P. R. China

Xiang Liu
510 Research Group, The Fifth Department
East China Institute of Technology
Nanjing 210014, P. R. China

ABSTRACT

The problem of circular pole assignment for discrete–time singular systems is considered. The goal of the problem is to assign the maximum number of finite eigenvalues in a prespecified circle and guarantee the closed–loop regularity. A simple, effective generalized Riccati equation approach is developed to solve the addressed problem. It is shown that a desired state feedback law is determined by using the solution of a standard discrete Riccati equation which can be computed directly.

1. INTRODUCTION

One of the fundamental problems in singular system theory is the design of feedback laws that places the finite closed–loop poles at desired locations and satisfies some necessary contraints. Much of the pole assignment literature focuses on the problem of *exact* pole placement [1–4]. However, in practice, it is sufficient that closed–loop finite poles be placed in a suitable region of the complex z–plane instead of placing them at respective exact positions. Also, the pole region placement technique is well suited for the requirements of robustness against large parameter variations, sensor failures, implementation accuracies and gain reduction *etc.*.

In this paper, the problem of circular pole assignment for discrete–time singular systems is considered. It is shown that the desired state feedback control law is determined by using the solution of a generlized discrete Riccati equation which can be converted into a standard discrete Riccati equation (SDARE).

2. PROBLEM FORMULATION

Consider the following discrete time–invariant linear singular system

$$E\dot{x}(k) = Ax(k) + Bu(k) \tag{2.1}$$

where $x(k) \in \mathbf{R}^n$ is the descriptor–variable vector, $u(k) \in \mathbf{R}^m$ is the control–variable vector, and E, A, B are real constant coefficient matrices with appropriate dimensions. The matrix E is singular with

$$\mathrm{rank}(E) = p < n \tag{2.2}$$

When a descriptor–variable control law

$$u(k) = Kx(k) \tag{2.3}$$

is applied to system (2.1), we have a closed–loop system

$$E\dot{x}(k) = A_C x(k), \quad A_C = A + BK \tag{2.4}$$

Define

$$deg|zE - A_C| = q \leqslant p \tag{2.5}$$

and $\sigma(E\ A_C)$ denotes the set of the q finite closed–loop eigenvalues.

For the closed–loop system (2.4) we consider a circular region $\Omega(\alpha, r)$ with center at $\alpha + j0$ and radius $r \leqslant \alpha$(Fig. 1) and address the following problem:

Fig.1

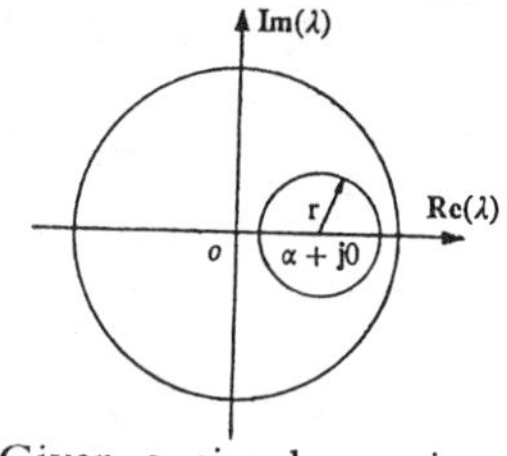

Problem CPA: Given a circular region $\Omega(\alpha, r)$, determine a descriptor–variable control law (2.3) such that the following requirements are simultaneously met:

(a) There are p finite eigenvalues constrained to lie within the circle $\Omega(\alpha, r)$, *i.e.* $\sigma(E\ A_C) \subset \Omega(\alpha, r)$ and $q = p$;

(b) Closed–loop system regularity is guaranteed, *i.e.*, the matrix pencil $(zE - A_C)$ is regular.

We conclude this section by presenting the following notation. Perform a singular value decomposition (SVD) of E as follows:

$$MEN = \begin{bmatrix} \Sigma & 0 \\ 0 & 0 \end{bmatrix} \tag{2.6}$$

where $\Sigma = diag\ (\sigma_1, \sigma_2, \cdots, \sigma_p)$ and the σ_i, $i = 1, 2, \cdots, p$ are the non–zero singular valuess of E. $M$and N are orthogonal matrices. Furthermore, partition $n \times n$ matrix MA_CN into $p \times p$, $p \times (n-p)$, $(n-p) \times p$ and $(n-p) \times (n-p)$ subblocks as

$$MA_cN = \begin{bmatrix} A_{V11} & A_{V12} \\ A_{V21} & A_{V22} \end{bmatrix} \quad (2.7)$$

where M and N are the matrices in the SVD(2.6).

In the next section the problem of circular pole assignment (refered to as CPA) will be solved.

3. CIRCULAR POLE ASSIGNMENT

The enforcement of the requirement (a) and (b) in the problem (CPA) is relate to a matrix equation and two constrains. The proofs of all the following results will be omitted due to space limitations.

Theorem 3.1: Given a circular region $\Omega(\alpha, r)$. Then a descriptor–variable control law (2.3) is the solution to the problem if the following matrix equation

$$-\alpha A_C^T PE - \alpha E^T PA_C + A_C^T PA_C + (\alpha^2 - r^2)E^T PE + Q = 0 \quad (3.1)$$

where Q is a positive definite symmetric matrix and $(\cdot)^T$ denotes the transpose of a matrix, has a positive definite solution P and the following two constraints are met

$$|A_{V22}| \neq 0, \text{ and } |A_C| \neq 0 \quad (3.2)$$

we shall make the following assumption.

Assumption I: $\det(A - \alpha E) \neq 0$

Remark 3.1: It should be noted that Assumption I causes no loss of generality.

In connection with the system (2.1) satisfying Assumption I, we now introduce a standard discrete algebraic Riccati equation (SDARE).

$$S = \hat{A}^T S\hat{A} - \hat{A}^T SB(R + B^T SB)^{-1}B^T S\hat{A} + \hat{Q} \quad (3.3)$$

where

$$\hat{A} := EA_O^{-1}, \quad \hat{Q} = A_O^{-T}QA_O^{-1}$$
$$A_O = (A - \alpha E)/r \quad (3.4)$$

As a method to choose a descriptor–variable control law that solves our problem (CPA), we present the following theorem by using a discrete Riccati equation.

Theorem 3.2: Given (E, A, B) and $\Omega(\alpha, r)$ satisfying Assumption I. Suppose that $(\hat{A}, B)$ is controllable. Then, the descriptor–variable control law

$$u(k) = -(r^2R + B^T PB)^{-1}B^T P(A - \alpha E)x(k) \quad (3.5)$$

satisfying the constraints

$$|A_{V22}| \neq 0, \text{ and } |A_C| \neq 0 \quad (3.6)$$

is a solution of the Problem (CPA), where R and $\hat{Q}$ are arbitrarily positive definite matrices and P is given by

$$P = -(S^{-1} + BR^{-1}B^T)^{-1} \quad (3.7)$$

and S is negative definite solution to the SDARE (3.3) satisfying

$$S^{-1} + BR^{-1}B^T < 0 \quad (3.8)$$

REFERENCES

[1] G. R. Duan, "Solution to matrix equation $AV + BW = EVF$ and eigenstructure assignment for descriptor systems," *Automatica*, Vol. 28, No. 3, 1992, to appear.

[2] M. M. Fahmy and J. O'Reilly, " Parametric eigenstructure assignment for continuous–time descriptor systems," *Int. J. Control*, Vol. 49, No. 1, pp. 129–143, 1989.

[3] L. R. Fletcher, "Eigenstructure assignment by output feedback in descriptor systems," *IEE Proc.–D*, Vol. 135, No. pp. 302–308, 1988.

[4] L. R. Fletcher, J. Kautsky and N. K. Nichols, "Eigenstructure assignment in descriptor systems ," *IEEE Trans. Automat. Control*, Vol. AC–31, No. pp. 1138–1141, 1986.

[5] K. Furuta and S. B. Kim, "Pole assignment in a specified disk," *IEEE Trans. Automat. Control*, Vol. AC–32, No. 5, pp. 423–427, 1987.

Proceedings of the
American Control Conference
San Francisco, California • June 1993

STABILITY OF COUPLED STRINGS VIBRATION SYSTEM DUE TO DIFFERENT BOUNDARY CONDITIONS

G.R. Sarhangi, M. Najafi and H. Wang
Department of Mathematics and Statistics
The Wichita State University, Wichita, KS 67260-0033

Abstract

We study the rate of convergence of a coupled wave systems under two different boundary conditions, energy absorbing in two ends for one and free or fixed boundary controls in two ends for the other one. We will observe the theoretical results by numerical computations as well.

1. Introduction.

We study the rate of convergence of the solution of the system:

$$u_{tt} - c^2 u_{xx} = \alpha\,(v-u), \tag{1.1. a}$$

$$v_{tt} - c^2 v_{xx} = \alpha\,(u-v). \qquad x \in (0,1) \tag{1.1. b}$$

Where $\alpha \in \mathbb{R}^+$, and $c \in \mathbb{R}^+$. The initial and boundry conditions are:

$$u(x,0) = u_0, \quad u_t(x,0) = u_1, \tag{1.2. a}$$

$$v(x,0) = v_0, \quad v_t(x,0) = v_1, \quad x \in [0,1], \tag{1.2. b}$$

$$u_x(0,\ t) = u_x(1,t) = 0, \quad \text{(two sides are free)} \tag{1.3. a}$$

$$v_x(0,t) = \beta v_t(0,t), \quad v_x(1,t) = -\beta v_t(1,t), \quad t \geq 0, \text{ and} \tag{1.3. b}$$

$$u(0,\ t) = u(1,t) = 0, \qquad \text{(two sides are fixed)} \tag{1.4. a}$$

$$v_x(0,t) = \beta v_t(0,\ t), \quad v_x(1,t) = -\beta v_t(1,t), \quad t \geq 0. \tag{1.4. b}$$

Here t and x are the time and space variable, respectively, u and v are the deflections of the strings from the equilibrium lines. The wave speed c and α (spring constant) are the system parameters and the damping coefficient $\beta>0$ is boundary control parameter. The boundary controls (1.3.b) correspond to a control mechanism which monitor v_t at $x=0$ and $x=1$ and transform them into the vertical force which transfers through the spring to the upper string (1.1.a).

2. Well-Posedness And Some Properties

Our proper function space $H = H_0^1 \times L^2 \times H_0^1 \times L^2$ is the set of all quadruplets $U = (u,z,v,w)^{\mathrm{T}}$ equipped with the norm

$$\|U\|_H^2 = \int_0^1 \{c^2 u_x^2 + z^2 + c^2 v_x^2 + w^2 + \alpha(u-v)^2\}dx. \tag{2.1}$$

in the class of functions $[f] = \{g | g = f + \text{constant}\}$. The system operator is

$$A = \begin{bmatrix} 0 & 1 & 0 & 0 \\ c^2\partial_x^2 - \alpha & 0 & \alpha & 0 \\ 0 & 0 & 0 & 1 \\ \alpha & 0 & c^2\partial_x^2 - \alpha & 0 \end{bmatrix}. \tag{2.2}$$

The domain is defined with respect to each boundary condition as follows:

$$\mathfrak{D}_1(A) = \left\{ U \in \tilde{H} \,\middle|\, \begin{matrix} u_x(0) = 0, & u_x(1) = 0 \\ v_x(0) = \beta w(0), & v_x(1) = -\beta w(1) \end{matrix} \right\},$$

$$\mathfrak{D}_2(A) = \left\{ U \in \tilde{H} \,\middle|\, \begin{matrix} u(0) = 0, & u(1) = 0 \\ v_x(0) = \beta w(0), & v_x(1) = -\beta w(1) \end{matrix} \right\},$$

where $\tilde{H} = H_0^2 \times H^1 \times H_0^2 \times H^1$ is dense in H. In order to show the well-posedness of the problem, we utilize the following Lemma

Lemma 2.1 *The system operator A acting on each domain $\mathfrak{D}_1(A)$, and $\mathfrak{D}_2(A)$ generates a C_0-semigroup of contractions.*

Proof. Clearly the domain of A is dense in H. Moreover, A is a dissipative [3] closed [4] operatore. To show A is maximal, let $F = \big(f_1(x), g_1(x), f_2(x), g_2(x)\big)^{\mathrm{T}} \in H$, then the resolvent equation will be

$$(A - \lambda I)(u,z,v,w)^{\mathrm{T}} = \big(f_1(x), g_1(x), f_2(x), g_2(x)\big)^{\mathrm{T}}, \tag{2.3}$$

which yields to

$$\underline{\overline{X}}' = \hat{A}_\lambda\, \underline{\overline{X}} + \hat{B}_\lambda, \tag{2.4}$$

where

$$\underline{\overline{X}} = \begin{pmatrix} u \\ u' \\ v \\ v' \end{pmatrix}, \quad \hat{A}_\lambda = \begin{bmatrix} 0 & 1 & 0 & 0 \\ \frac{\lambda^2+\alpha}{c^2} & 0 & \frac{-\alpha}{c^2} & 0 \\ 0 & 0 & 0 & 1 \\ \frac{-\alpha}{c^2} & 0 & \frac{\lambda^2+\alpha}{c^2} & 0 \end{bmatrix}, \text{and } \hat{B}_\lambda = \begin{pmatrix} 0 \\ \frac{g_1(x)+\lambda f_1(x)}{c^2} \\ 0 \\ \frac{g_2(x)+\lambda f_2(x)}{c^2} \end{pmatrix},$$

The solutions of the system are:

$$u_c = k_1(\cosh ax + \cosh bx) + k_2\Big(\frac{\sinh ax}{a} + \frac{\sinh bx}{b}\Big) + k_3(\cosh ax - \cosh bx) + k_4\Big(\frac{\sinh ax}{a} - \frac{\sinh bx}{b}\Big),$$

$$u_p = \frac{1}{2}\int_0^x \Big\{ a^{-1}\big(g(\theta) + i\zeta f(\theta)\big)\sinh a(x-\theta) + b^{-1}\big(\hat{g}(\theta) + i\zeta\hat{f}(\theta)\big)\sinh b(x-\theta)\Big\}d\theta,$$

$$v_c = k_1(\cosh ax - \cosh bx) + k_2\Big(\frac{\sinh ax}{a} - \frac{\sinh bx}{b}\Big) + k_3(\cosh ax + \cosh bx) + k_4\Big(\frac{\sinh ax}{a} + \frac{\sinh bx}{b}\Big),$$

$$v_p = \frac{1}{2}\int_0^x \Big\{ a^{-1}\big(g(\theta) + i\zeta f(\theta)\big)\sinh a(x-\theta) - b^{-1}\big(\hat{g}(\theta) + i\zeta\hat{f}(\theta)\big)\sinh b(x-\theta)\Big\}d\theta,$$

where c, and p correspond to complementary and particular solution, and

$$f = \frac{f_1+f_2}{c^2}, \quad \hat{f} = \frac{f_1-f_2}{c^2}, \quad g = \frac{g_1+g_2}{c^2}, \quad \hat{g} = \frac{g_1-g_2}{c^2}.$$

Applying the boundary conditions (1.3-1.4), we can obtain the exact values of coefficients K_i, $i=1,\ldots,4$. Hence, A is maximal and proof of lemma follows from the Lummer-Phillips theorem [4]. □

In order to prove the theorem 3.1 of the next section , we need the following lemma which has been shown in [3].

Lemma 2.2. *For every eigenvalue $\lambda \in \sigma(A)$, $Re\lambda < 0$.*

3. Study of The Decay Rate

Theorem 3.1. *The system* (1.1) *along with boundary conditions* (1.3) *or* (1.4) *are strongly convergent. However, it does not decay exponentially.*

To furnish the proof of the theorem, we need to study the following results obtained in [2] and [1] .

Theorem 3.2. *Let $S(t)$ be a uniform bounded C_0-semigroup on Banach space, and let $Re\lambda<0$ for all $\lambda \in \sigma(A)$, then $S(t)$ is strongly asymptotically stable; Conversely, let $S(t)$ be strongly asymptotically stable, then $S(t)$ is uniform bounded, $Re\lambda \le 0$ for all $\lambda \in \sigma(A)$, and there is on imaginary axis neither point nor residual spectrum of A.*

Theorem 3.3. *Let Γ be homologous to zero in Ω and such that $n(\Gamma, z)$ is either 0 or 1 for any point z not on Γ. Suppose that $\Psi(z)$ and $\Phi(z)$ are analytic in Ω and satisfy the inequality $|\Psi(z)-\Phi(z)|<|\Phi(z)|$ on Γ.* Then $\Psi(z)$ and $\Phi(z)$ have the same number of zeros enclosed by Γ.

Proof of Theorem 3.1. In section 2 we already verified all conditions of the theorem 3.2. Therefore the energy of the system approaches zero strongly. To show this decay is not exponential, we find a sequence of eigenvalues of the system which approaches the imaginary axis and as a result, the system is not uniformly stable. For this, we utilize Theorem 3.3. Since we are interested in this sequence close to the imaginary axis, we only consider the strip $S=\{\, z=x+iy \mid -1<x<1\}$ in our discussion. Consequently we obtain this fact that sinh z and cosh z are bounded in this strip. To find the eigenvalues we solve the following equation

$$(A-\lambda I)(u,z,v,w)^{T}=0. \tag{3.1}$$

After solving the equation similar to (2.4) we obtain

$$u=k_1(\cosh ax+\cosh bx)+k_2\Big(\frac{\sinh ax}{a}+\frac{\sinh bx}{b}\Big) +k_3(\cosh ax-\cosh bx)+k_4\Big(\frac{\sinh ax}{a}-\frac{\sinh bx}{b}\Big), \tag{3.2}$$

$$v=k_1(\cosh ax-\cosh bx)+k_2\Big(\frac{\sinh ax}{a}-\frac{\sinh bx}{b}\Big) + k_3(\cosh ax+\cosh bx)+k_4\Big(\frac{\sinh ax}{a}+\frac{\sinh bx}{b}\Big), \tag{3.3}$$

$$\text{where } a=\frac{\omega}{c} \text{ and } b=\frac{\sqrt{\omega^2+2\alpha}}{c}. \tag{3.4}$$

Applying boundary conditions (1.3), one can get the following determinant for which we can compute the eigenvalues of the system

$$detQ=a^2[4h^{-1}\sinh a \sinh b+4\beta c(\sinh a \cosh b+h^{-1}\cosh a \sinh b)-2\beta^2c^2 +\beta^2c^2(h+h^{-1})\sinh a \sinh b+2\beta^2c^2\cosh a \cosh b].$$

From which we obtain the following two functions:

$$\Psi(a)=\frac{detQ}{a^2},\quad \Phi(a)=4\beta c \sinh(a+b)+2\beta^2c^2(\cosh(a+b)-1). \tag{3.6}$$

consider the sequence of numbers a_n such that

$$a_n+b_n=i\,2n\pi. \qquad n=1,2,3,\ldots \tag{3.7}$$

then we observe that $\Phi(a_n)=0$. Now, define the domain Γ_n as follows

$$\Gamma_n=\Big\{\, z \mid z=a_n+\frac{1}{n}e^{i\theta},\quad 0\le\theta<2\pi \Big\}, \text{ for } n \text{ large such that } \Gamma_n\subset S. \tag{3.8}$$

We stimate $|\Psi-\Phi|$ and $|\Phi|$ as in[3] for large n and obtain the inequality

$$|\Phi(a)|>|\Psi(a)-\Phi(a)|, \qquad a\in\Gamma_n,\ n \text{ large}.$$

Hence, by Rouche's Theorem, $\Phi(z)$ and $\Psi(z)$ have the same number of zeros inside the disk Γ_n and the theorem follows for (1.3). A similar work is true for (1.4).□

4. Numerical Computation

In Fig. 4.1, the previous work [3] is illustrated. There we proved that the energy absorbing boundary control in both right ends for u and v make the system decays exponentially. In Fig. 4.2.a and 4.2.b we observe our present work.

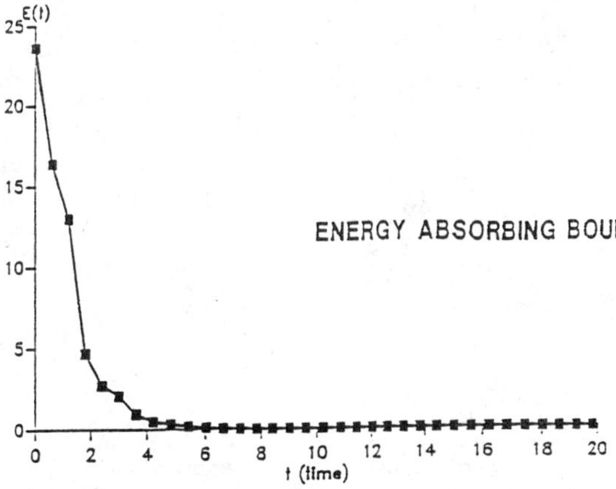

Fig. 4.1

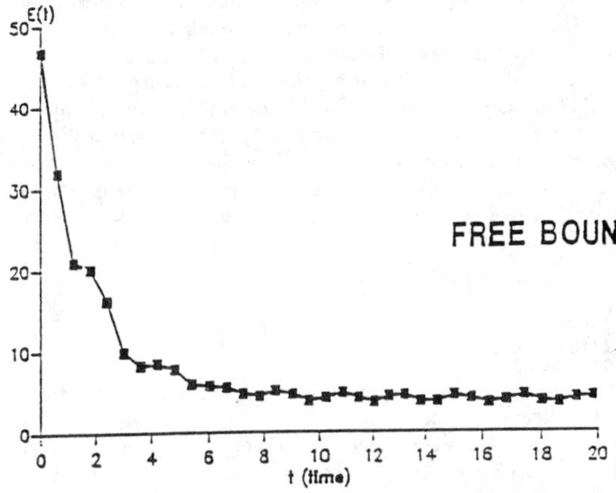

Fig. 4.2.a

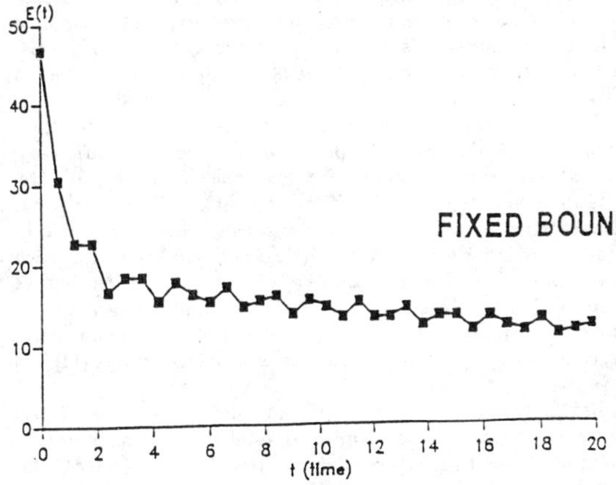

4.2.b

References

[1] L. V. Ahlfors, *Complex Analysis*, McGraw-Hill , New York, 1979.

[2] F. L. Huang, *Asymptotic stability theory for linear dynamical systems in Banach spaces* (in Chinese) KEXUE TONGBAO, 10(1983), 584-586.

[3] M. Najafi, G.R. Sarhangi and H. Wang, *The study of stabilizability of the coupled wave equations under various end conditions*, The 31st IEEE Conference on Decision and Control, Tucson, Arizona, December 1992.

[4] A. Pazy, *Semigroups of linear operators and applications to partial differential equations*, Springer-Verlag, New York, 1983.

Proceedings of the
American Control Conference
San Francisco, California • June 1993

On the Persistence of Excitation in the Adaptive Estimation of Distributed Parameter Systems *

M. A. Demetriou[†‡] and I. G. Rosen[†]
University of Southern California,
Los Angeles, California 90089

Abstract

Persistence of excitation is a sufficient condition for parameter convergence in a class of adaptive, or on-line, identification schemes for dynamical systems. In the case of abstract linear parabolic and hyperbolic distributed parameter systems, this condition requires that a family of bounded linear functionals be norm bounded away from zero. In general, this condition on the plant is difficult to verify. The level of persistence of excitation of the plant and its implications are considered for a simple parabolic and hyperbolic system for the purpose of gaining insight into its effect in the more general case. Its effect on the qualitative and quantitative behavior of the estimators is investigated. Numerical studies illustrating the results of the analysis are discussed.

1 Introduction

In this short note we consider the persistence of excitation condition in the adaptive, or on-line, identification of abstract distributed parameter systems. For a certain class of schemes which we have studied in depth in [5] (see also [4]), the persistence of excitation of the plant is a sufficient condition for parameter convergence. The condition requires that a certain infinite family (parameterized by time) of bounded linear functionals be norm bounded away from zero. Persistence of excitation is, in general, difficult or impossible to check. It is also not immediately obvious as to how its being satisfied leads to parameter convergence. It would be useful therefore to understand how the level, or absense, of the plant's persistence of excitation, together with the choice of values for the scheme's *tuning* parameters, affects the qualitative behavior of the estimator and, in particular, the rate and nature of convergence. The schemes that we looked at in [4] and [5] are infinite dimensional analogs of a well-known approach in finite dimensions. The persistence of excitation condition that we have defined in [5] is the natural extension to infinite dimensions, or infinite dimensional analog, of the persistence of excitation, or richness, condition specified in the finite dimensional treatments [11] and [12].

In [7], [8] and [9] Hong and Bentsman define the notion of persistence of excitation for the purpose of establishing parameter convergence for a model reference adaptive control scheme (MRAC) for parabolic partial differential equations. Their approach in [7], [8], and [9] and ours here and in [5] have a number of significant differences and some similarities. First they consider the MRAC problem, while we are interested strictly in on-line identification. Our approach is more general (in fact we develop an abstract framework) and functional analytic in nature, while their treatment is restricted to parabolic partial differential equations and is more classical in spirit. Their effort is fundamentally nonlinear while our treatment is entirely linear. On the other hand, both schemes lead to what are essentially the same set of error equations, and the two notions of persistence of excitation appear to be in some sense related. For a parabolic partial differential equation in one space dimension, their definition of persistence of excitation is a richness condition on the first spatial derivative of the plant. When our approach is applied to the same problem, our definition of persistence of excitation is also, in some sense a richness condition on the first spatial derivative of the plant. But in fact, the two conditions are quite different. Because of the very fundamental differences which exist between the two treatments (some of which are outlined above) it is not immediately clear how to completely and rigorously reconcile the two definitions.

Other related efforts in the area of adaptive identification of distributed parameter systems are detailed in [1], [2], and [6]. A more complete survey of the relevant literature can be found in [4] or [5].

We consider here two simple examples, one parabolic and the other hyperbolic, for which the persistence of excitation conditions are readily checked. In particular, we consider one dimensional heat and wave equations with what we shall refer to as mono-chromatic, or modal, input. In this way both the plant and the estimator become finite dimensional. It then becomes readily apparent how the level of excitation and the other tuning parameters qualitatively affect the behavior of the estimator. In fact, we found that choosing the tuning parameters and the level of excitation amounts to tuning the damping and stiffness in a damped linear harmonic oscillator. Too much dissipation, or the level of excitation too low, results in overdamping. Parameter convergence will be slow. Too little dissipation, or too high a level of excitation, and the estimator becomes stiff and underdamped. In this case undesirable oscillations result. We also studied how the relative level of excitation with respect to two unknown parameters affects the relative performance of their respective estimators. We were, for the most part, able to observe the results predicted by our theoretical treatment in [5].

We note that while the two examples we consider here are relatively simple, and are effectively finite dimensional, they are significant in that they provide valuable insight which can then be applied in the context of more complex estimation problems. This would include, for example, the identification of functional (i.e. spatially varying) parameters as was done in the examples presented in [4] and [5]. In particular, the study detailed here has served in a number of instances, as a guide for the authors in interpreting the behavior of an estimator, and in determining optimal values for a scheme's tuning parameters.

In Section 2, we briefly outline the theory developed in [5]. In Section 3 an example involving the identification of a one dimensional heat equation is discussed, while in Section 4 we treat a hyperbolic system. A fifth section contains a brief summary and discussion.

2 The Plant, the Estimator, and Convergence

In this section we briefly outline the theory and results developed in [5]. Let H be a real Hilbert space with inner product $\langle\cdot,\cdot\rangle$ and corresponding induced norm $|\cdot|$, and let V be a real reflexive Banach space with norm denoted by $\|\cdot\|$. We assume that V is embedded densely and continuously in H. It then follows that $V \hookrightarrow H \hookrightarrow V^*$, where V^* denotes the dual of V, and that all of the embeddings are dense and continuous. We denote the usual operator norm on V^* by $\|\cdot\|_*$.

Let Q be a real Hilbert space with inner product $\langle\cdot,\cdot\rangle_Q$ and corresponding induced norm $|\cdot|_Q$, and for each $q \in Q$ let $a(q,\cdot,\cdot) : V \times V \to R^1$ be a bilinear form on V satisfying

*This research was supported in part by the Air Force Office of Scientific Research under grant AFOSR 91-0076.

†Center for Applied Mathematical Sciences, Department of Mathematics.
‡Department of Electrical Engineering - Systems.

$(A1)$ (Boundedness) $|a(q^*;\varphi,\psi)| \le \alpha^0(q^*)\|\varphi\|\|\psi\|, \qquad \varphi,\psi \in V,$

$(A2)$ (Coercivity) $a(q^*;\varphi,\varphi) + \lambda(q^*)|\varphi|^2 \ge \alpha_0(q^*)\|\varphi\|^2, \qquad \varphi \in V,$

for at least one $q^* \in Q$, where $\lambda(q^*) \in R^1$ and $\alpha^0(q^*)$, $\alpha_0(q^*) > 0$. Note that the above assumptions imply that the bilinear form $a(q^*;\cdot,\cdot)+\lambda(q^*)\langle\cdot,\cdot\rangle$ is bounded and coercive. In addition, we assume that the map $q \to a(q;\cdot,\cdot)$ is affine. That is, it can be represented in the form $a(q;\varphi,\psi) = a_1(q;\varphi,\psi) + a_2(\varphi,\psi)$, $q \in Q$, $\varphi,\psi \in V$, where $a_1(\cdot;\cdot,\cdot)$ is a trilinear form on $Q \times V \times V$ and $a_2(\cdot,\cdot)$ is a bilinear form on $V \times V$.

For $q \in Q$ we consider the first order, linear, abstract parabolic initial value problem given by

$$\langle D_t u(t),\varphi\rangle + a(q;u(t),\varphi) = \langle f(t),\varphi\rangle, \qquad \varphi \in V, t > 0, \tag{2.1}$$

$$u(0) = u_0, \tag{2.2}$$

where $u_0 \in H$, and $f \in L_2^{loc}(0,\infty;V^*)$. When, for $\overline{q} \in Q$, the bilinear form on V, $a(\overline{q};\cdot,\cdot)$, is bounded and coercive, it is not difficult to argue that the initial value problem (2.1), (2.2) with $q = \overline{q}$ is well posed. In particular, this can be established via either linear semigroup theory or variational techniques (see, for example, [10]). Under the assumptions that $a(\overline{q};\cdot,\cdot)+\lambda(\overline{q})\langle\cdot,\cdot\rangle$ is bounded and coercive on V, the system (2.1), (2.2) with $q = \overline{q}$ admits a unique solution $\overline{u} \in L_2(0,T;V) \cap C([0,T];H)$ with $D_t\overline{u} \in L_2(0,T;V^*)$.

For $q \in Q$ let $A_1(q)$ be the linear operator from V into V', the algebraic dual of V, determined by the bilinear form $a_1(q;\cdot,\cdot)$ via

$$\langle A_1(q)\varphi,\psi\rangle = a_1(q;\varphi,\psi), \qquad \varphi,\psi \in V. \tag{2.3}$$

Definition 2.1 A *plant* is a pair $(\overline{q},\overline{u})$ with $\overline{q} \in Q$ and $\overline{u} : [0,\infty) \to V$, for which there exists a constant $\overline{\alpha} > 0$ such that $|\langle A_1(p)\overline{u}(t),\varphi\rangle| \le \overline{\alpha}|p|_Q\|\varphi\|$, $p \in Q, \varphi \in V$, and almost all $t > 0$, and $\bar{u}$ satisfies the initial value problem (2.1), (2.2) with $q = \overline{q}$.

It is possible to specify sufficient conditions for a solution $\overline{u}$ to the initial value problem (2.1),(2.2) with $q = \overline{q}$ to have the necessary regularity for $(\overline{q},\overline{u})$ to be a plant (see [5]).

Given a plant $(\overline{q},\overline{u})$, we define an estimator for $\overline{q}$ and $\overline{u}$ in the form of the initial value problem

$$\begin{aligned}\langle D_t u(t),\varphi\rangle + a(q^*;u(t),\varphi) + \lambda(q^*)\langle u(t),\varphi\rangle + a_1(q(t);\overline{u}(t),\varphi) \quad (2.4)\\ = \langle f(t),\varphi\rangle + a_1(q^*;\overline{u}(t),\varphi) + \lambda(q^*)\langle\overline{u}(t),\varphi\rangle, \qquad \varphi \in V, t > 0,\end{aligned}$$

$$\langle D_t q(t),p\rangle_Q + a_1(p;\overline{u}(t),\overline{u}(t) - u(t)) = 0, \qquad p \in Q, t > 0, \tag{2.5}$$

$$u(0) \in H, \qquad q(0) \in Q. \tag{2.6}$$

The parameters q^* and $\lambda(q^*)$ are chosen so that Assumptions $(A1)$ and $(A2)$ are satisfied. They can be thought of as a means to "tune" the estimator. Weighting the Q-inner product can also serve to enhance the performance (i.e. convergence rate) of the estimator. It is not difficult to demonstrate the existence of a unique solution to the initial value problem (2.4)-(2.6) (see [5]).

Setting $e(t) = u(t) - \overline{u}(t)$ and $r(t) = q(t) - \overline{q}$, it is desired that $\lim_{t\to\infty}|e(t)| = 0$ and $\lim_{t\to\infty}|r(t)|_Q = 0$. The convergence of the state estimator can be established directly. However, in order to establish parameter convergence, we must extend the finite dimensional notion of *persistence of excitation.*

Definition 2.2 A plant $(\overline{q},\overline{u})$ is said to be *persistently excited,* or an input f is called *persistently exciting* for the plant $(\overline{q},\overline{u})$, if there exists $T_0,\delta_0,\epsilon_0 > 0$ such that for each $p \in Q$ with $|p|_Q = 1$ and each $t_1 > 0$ sufficiently large, there exists a $\bar{t} \in [t_1,t_1+T_0]$ such that

$$\left\|\int_{\bar{t}}^{\bar{t}+\delta_0} A_1(p)\overline{u}(\tau)d\tau\right\|_* \ge \epsilon_0. \tag{2.7}$$

Definition 2.2 is the natural extension to infinite dimensions, or infinite dimensional analog, of the definition of persistence of excitation, or the richness condition, in the finite dimensional case as it is given in, for example, [11] and [12]. The following theorem is proven in [5].

Theorem 2.3 *If $(\overline{q},\overline{u})$ is a plant, then $\lim_{t\to\infty}|e(t)| = 0$. If, in addition, $(\overline{q},\overline{u})$ is persistently excited, then $\lim_{t\to\infty}|r(t)|_Q = 0$.*

Moreover, it is argued in [5] that the convergence of the combined state and parameter estimator error to zero is enhanced when the parameters δ_0 and ϵ_0 in the definition of persistence of excitation, decrease and increase respectively.

In the absence of persistence of excitation and with some minor additional assumptions on the regularity of $\overline{u}$ (see [5]), it is possible to prove a somewhat weaker convergence result. Let

$$\hat{Q} = \left\{q \in Q : \lim_{t\to\infty}\left|\int_t^{t+L}\langle A_1(q)\overline{u}(\tau),\varphi\rangle d\tau\right| = 0, \varphi \in V, L > 0\right\}, \tag{2.8}$$

and set $B_\xi = \{q \in Q : |q|_Q \le \sqrt{\xi}\}$. Note that $(\overline{q},\overline{u})$ a plant implies that $\hat{Q}$ is a closed linear subspace of Q. Letting $P_{\hat{Q}}$ denote the orthogonal projection of Q onto $\hat{Q}$, we obtain the following theorem.

Theorem 2.4 *Let $(\overline{q},\overline{u})$ be a plant and let (u,q) be the solution to the initial value problem (2.4)-(2.6). Then $\lim_{t\to\infty}|e(t)| = 0$ and $\lim_{t\to\infty} dist\,(r(t),\hat{Q}\cap B_\xi) = 0$, where the distance function is with respect to to the weak topology on Q. Moreover, $w-\lim_{t\to\infty}q(t) = \overline{q}+P_{\hat{Q}}(q(0)-\overline{q})$.*

Of course when Q is finite dimensional the weak convergence becomes strong convergence in Q. Note that if $Q = Q_1 \oplus Q_1^\perp$ with $Q_1 \subset \hat{Q}^\perp$ (i.e. the ordered pair $(Q_1,\hat{Q}^\perp)$ is compatible), the conclusion of Theorem 2.4 implies that $w-\lim_{t\to\infty}P_1q(t) = P_1\overline{q}$, where P_1 denotes the orthogonal projection of Q onto Q_1. That is, if the plant is persistently excited with respect to certain components of the parameter space, those components will converge (weakly) to the corresponding components of the plant parameters.

3 Example I: Parabolic System

In this section we illustrate how the level of persistence of excitation (as determined by the parameters δ_0 and ϵ_0 in Definition 2.2) affects the rate of convergence and qualitative behavior of the parameter estimator. To do this, we consider a one dimensional heat equation with a time invariant mono-chromatic (i.e. modal) input. While this effectively finite dimensionalizes the plant and the estimator, the underlying simplicity of this test problem provides valuable insight into how the level of persistence of excitation ultimately affects parameter convergence. Moreover, since a large class of systems decouple when expressed in modal coordinates, the experience gained with this example, to a large extent, carries over to more complex systems. In particular, we found that the insight gained from the study we present here significantly aided us in determining input signals and tuning parameter values which enhanced both state and parameter convergence in a number of estimation problems that we have considered.

We consider the one dimensional heat equation

$$\frac{\partial u}{\partial t}(t,x) - q\frac{\partial^2 u}{\partial x^2}(t,x) = \alpha\sqrt{2}\sin(n\pi x), \qquad t > 0, \qquad 0 < x < 1,$$

where n is a positive integer, together with the Dirichlet boundary conditions

$$u(t,0) = 0 = u(t,1), \qquad t > 0.$$

In this case we take $H = L_2(0,1)$ and $V = H_0^1(0,1)$ endowed with the usual inner products and corresponding induced norms. We take $Q = R^1$ endowed with the weighted Euclidean inner product $\langle q,p\rangle_Q = \gamma qp$, $q,p \in Q$, where $\gamma > 0$. For each $q \in Q$, the form $a(q;\cdot,\cdot) : V \times V \to R$ is given by

$$a(q;\varphi,\psi) = a_1(q;\varphi,\psi) = q\int_0^1 D\varphi(x)D\psi(x)dx, \qquad \varphi,\psi \in H_0^1(0,1).$$

For the plant, we assume that $\overline{q} > 0$ and that the system is initially at rest. Then for $t > 0$ and $0 < x < 1$ we have

$$\begin{aligned}\overline{u}(t,x) &= \alpha\int_0^t e^{-\overline{q}n^2\pi^2(t-s)}ds\sqrt{2}\sin(n\pi x)\\ &= \frac{\alpha}{\overline{q}n^2\pi^2}(1-e^{-\overline{q}n^2\pi^2 t})\sqrt{2}\sin(n\pi x)\overline{U}(t)\sqrt{2}\sin(n\pi x),\end{aligned}$$

where $\overline{U}(t) = \frac{\alpha}{\overline{q}n^2\pi^2}(1-e^{-\overline{q}n^2\pi^2 t})$. In the estimator (2.4)-(2.6) we take $\lambda(q^*) = 0$ and zero initial conditions, and obtain

$$\dot{U}(t) + q^*n^2\pi^2U(t) + q(t)n^2\pi^2\overline{U}(t) = \alpha + q^*n^2\pi^2\overline{U}(t), \qquad t > 0,$$

$$\dot{q}(t) - \frac{n^2\pi^2}{\gamma}\overline{U}(t)U(t) = -\frac{n^2\pi^2}{\gamma}\overline{U}^2(t), \qquad t > 0,$$

$$U(0) = 0 \qquad q(0) = 0,$$

where $u(t,x) = U(t)\sqrt{2}\sin(n\pi x)$, $t \ge 0$, $0 \le x \le 1$. The state and parameter error, e and r, satisfy the error equations given by

$$\begin{bmatrix} e(t) \\ r(t)\end{bmatrix} = \Lambda(t)\begin{bmatrix} e(t) \\ r(t)\end{bmatrix}, \qquad t \ge 0, \tag{3.1}$$

where

$$\Lambda(t) = \begin{bmatrix} -q^*n^2\pi^2 & -\frac{\alpha}{\overline{q}}(1-e^{-\overline{q}n^2\pi^2 t}) \\ \frac{\alpha}{\overline{q}\gamma}(1-e^{-\overline{q}n^2\pi^2 t}) & 0\end{bmatrix}. \tag{3.2}$$

For $t_1 > 0$, $\bar{t} \ge t_1$, $\delta_0 > 0$, and $|p| = 1$, the persistence of excitation condition (2.7) takes the form

$$\left\| \int_{\bar{t}}^{\bar{t}+\delta_0} A_1(p)\overline{u}(\tau)d\tau \right\|_* = \sup_{\|\varphi\|_{H_0^1(0,1)} \le 1} \left| \int_{\bar{t}}^{\bar{t}+\delta_0} a_1(p; \overline{u}(\tau), \varphi)d\tau \right|$$

$$\ge \frac{|\alpha|}{\overline{q}} \int_{\bar{t}}^{\bar{t}+\delta_0} \left(1 - e^{-\overline{q}n^2\pi^2\tau}\right) d\tau$$

$$= \frac{|\alpha|}{\overline{q}} \left\{ \delta_0 - \frac{e^{-\overline{q}n^2\pi^2\bar{t}}}{\overline{q}n^2\pi^2} \left(1 - e^{-\overline{q}n^2\pi^2\delta_0}\right) \right\}.$$

Thus for t_1 sufficiently large, we have $\epsilon_0 \approx \frac{|\alpha|}{\overline{q}}\delta_0$. Recalling the remark following Theorem 2.3, we would expect to see convergence enhanced with increasing $|\alpha|$. Exactly how increasing $|\alpha|$ (as well as varying the other "tuning" parameters, q^* and γ) affects convergence can be seen by analyzing the linear system (3.1).

The matrix $\Lambda(t)$ given by (3.2) can be written as $\Lambda(t) = \Lambda_0 + \Lambda_1(t)$ where

$$\Lambda_0 = \begin{bmatrix} -q^*n^2\pi^2 & -\frac{\alpha}{\overline{q}} \\ \frac{\alpha}{\overline{q}\gamma} & 0 \end{bmatrix} \text{ and } \Lambda_1(t) = e^{-\overline{q}n^2\pi^2 t} \begin{bmatrix} 0 & \frac{\alpha}{\overline{q}} \\ -\frac{\alpha}{\overline{q}\gamma} & 0 \end{bmatrix}. \tag{3.3}$$

Clearly $\lim_{t\to\infty} \Lambda(t) = \Lambda_0$. Moreover, as a result of the negative exponential, we have $\int_0^\infty |\Lambda_1(t)|dt < \infty$ and $\int_0^\infty t|\Lambda_1(t)|dt < \infty$. It follows (see [3], Theorem 8.1) that for t large or n chosen of moderate size, it is reasonable to analyze the qualitative behavior of solutions to the nonautonomous linear system (3.1) by considering the solutions to the constant coefficient system

$$\begin{bmatrix} \dot{e}_0(t) \\ \dot{r}_0(t) \end{bmatrix} = \Lambda_0 \begin{bmatrix} e_0(t) \\ r_0(t) \end{bmatrix}. \tag{3.4}$$

Indeed, it is shown in [3] that if λ_+ and λ_- are the (assumed to be distinct) eigenvalues of the matrix Λ_0 with the corresponding eigenvectors v_+ and v_-, then there exist solutions φ_+ and φ_- to the nonautonomous system (3.1) for which

$$\lim_{t\to\infty} |\varphi_\pm(t) - e^{\lambda_\pm t}v_\pm| = 0.$$

It is not difficult to argue that the larger n is chosen, the better the approximation will be for a given value of t.

Inspection of the matrix Λ_0 in (3.3) reveals that the system (3.4) behaves like a damped linear harmonic oscillator. The characteristic equation associated with the matrix Λ_0 is given by

$$\lambda^2 + q^*n^2\pi^2\lambda + \frac{\alpha^2}{\overline{q}^2\gamma} = 0,$$

with roots

$$\lambda_\pm = -\frac{q^*n^2\pi^2}{2} \pm \sqrt{\left(\frac{q^*n^2\pi^2}{2}\right)^2 - \frac{\alpha^2}{\overline{q}^2\gamma}}.$$

Critical damping occurs when $\frac{\alpha^2}{\gamma} = \overline{q}^2\left(\frac{q^*n^2\pi^2}{2}\right)^2$. The system is overdamped when $\frac{\alpha^2}{\gamma} < \overline{q}^2\left(\frac{q^*n^2\pi^2}{2}\right)^2$ and underdamped when $\frac{\alpha^2}{\gamma} > \overline{q}^2\left(\frac{q^*n^2\pi^2}{2}\right)^2$. The level of damping increases with increasing q^*. The stiffness increases with increasing $|\alpha|$ and decreases with increasing γ. In the underdamped case, the quasi-frequency of the oscillation also increases with increasing $|\alpha|$ and decreasing γ.

To illustrate, we set $\overline{q} = .1$, $n = 4$, $q^* = 1.0 \times 10^{-3}$ and $\gamma = 1$, and used our scheme to estimate $\overline{q}$. In Figure 3.1 we plot the parameter error, $r(t)$, on the interval $0 \le t \le 100$, for various values of α. The analysis above predicts that critical damping occurs when $\alpha \approx \pm.008$. When the system is severely overdamped (i.e. α small) convergence is slow. When it is severely underdamped, or too stiff, (i.e. α large), oscillations result. Of course similar results could be obtained by varying γ. Both the extreme overdamped and underdamped cases are undesirable and should be avoided. Indeed, in the overdamped case parameter convergence is sluggish, and if this on-line identification scheme is to be used as a part of an indirect adaptive control algorithm, the oscillations which result in the underdamped case could lead to instability.

In Figure 3.2 we plot the effects of varying the damping level, q^*, in the underdamped case. Of course too large of a variation in q^* could shift the system from the underdamped case to either the critically damped or the overdamped case.

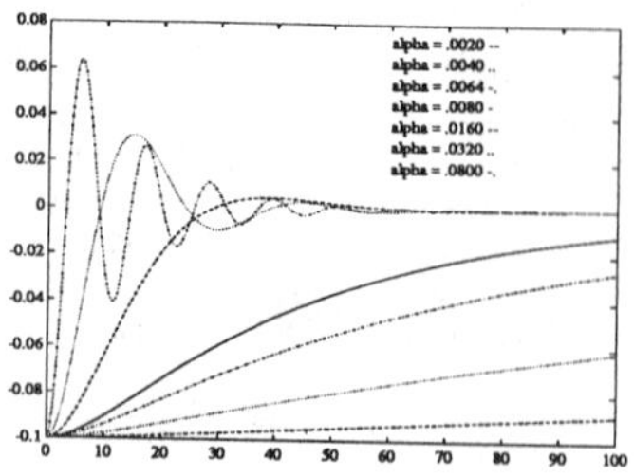

Figure 3.1: Parameter error, r, in parabolic case.

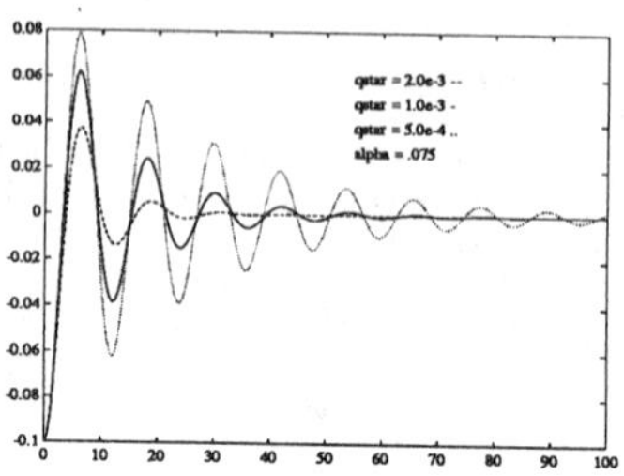

Figure 3.2: Parameter error, r, in underdamped case.

4 Example II: A Hyperbolic System

In this example we consider the result given in Theorem 2.4. We observe the convergence to the plant parameters of the estimators with respect to which the plant is persistently excited, and the non-, or slower, convergence of those parameters with respect to which the plant is either not, or is to a lesser extent, persistently excited.

We consider the identification of the one dimensional wave equation with Kelvin - Voigt viscoelastic damping given by

$$\frac{\partial^2 w}{\partial t^2}(t,x) - q_2\frac{\partial^2}{\partial x^2}\frac{\partial w}{\partial t}(t,x) - q_1\frac{\partial^2 w}{\partial x^2}(t,x) = g(t,x), \tag{4.1}$$

for $t > 0$ and $0 < x < 1$, together with the Dirichlet boundary conditions

$$w(t,0) = 0 = w(t,1), \qquad t > 0, \tag{4.2}$$

and the initial data

$$w(0,x) = w_0(x) \text{ and } \frac{\partial w}{\partial t}(0,x) = w_1(x), \quad 0 < x < 1. \tag{4.3}$$

Let $H_0 = L_2(0,1)$ and $V_0 = H_0^1(0,1)$, both endowed with the usual inner products and corresponding induced norms. Denote the inner product on H_0 by $\langle\cdot,\cdot\rangle_0$ and the corresponding induced norm by $|\cdot|_0$. Let $\|\cdot\|_0$ denote the norm on V_0. Let $Q = R^2$, and let it be endowed with the inner product $\langle q,p\rangle_Q = q^T\Gamma p$, $q,p \in Q$, where $\Gamma = diag\,(\gamma_1,\gamma_2)$, $\gamma_i > 0$, $i = 1,2$. For each $q = (q_1,q_2)^T \in Q$, define the forms $a^i(q;\cdot,\cdot) : V_0 \times V_0 \to R$, $i = 1,2$, by

$$a^1(q,\varphi,\psi) = q_1 \int_0^1 D\varphi(x)D\psi(x)dx, \qquad \varphi,\psi \in H_0^1(0,1), \tag{4.4}$$

and

$$a^2(q;\varphi,\psi) = q_2 \int_0^1 D\varphi(x)D\psi(x)dx, \qquad \varphi,\psi \in H_0^1(0,1), \tag{4.5}$$

respectively.

We rewrite the initial-boundary value problem (4.1)-(4.3) in weak or variational form as

$$\langle D_t^2 w(t),\varphi\rangle_0 + a^2(q;D_t w(t),\varphi) + a^1(q;w(t),\varphi) = \langle g(t),\varphi\rangle_0, \tag{4.6}$$

$$w(0) = w_0, \qquad D_t w(0) = w_1 \tag{4.7}$$

for $\varphi \in V_0$, where for $t \ge 0$, $g(t) = g(t,\cdot)$. We assume that $g \in L_2^{loc}(0,\infty;V_0^*)$, $w_0 \in V_0$ and $w_1 \in H_0$. In [5] it is shown how the theory for first order systems outlined in Section 2 can be applied to second order systems. To do this, one must rewrite the second order initial value problem (4.6), (4.7) as an equivalent first order system of the form given in (2.1), (2.2). Let $q^* = (q_1^*, q_2^*)$ be a fixed but arbitrary element in the positive orthant of R^2 and let H be the Hilbert space defined by $H = V_0 \times V_0$ with inner product

$$\langle\varphi,\psi\rangle = a^1(q^*;\varphi_1,\psi_1) + \langle\varphi_2,\psi_2\rangle_0, \tag{4.8}$$

for $\varphi = (\varphi_1, \varphi_2), \psi = (\psi_1, \psi_2) \in H$. Let V be the reflexive Banach space defined by $V = V_0 \times V_0$ with norm given by

$$\|\varphi\| = (\|\varphi_1\|_0^2 + \|\varphi_2\|_0^2)^{\frac{1}{2}}, \quad \text{for} \quad \varphi = (\varphi_1, \varphi_2) \in V.$$

It follows that $V \hookrightarrow H \hookrightarrow V^*$ with the embeddings dense and continuous. Define the form $a(\cdot;\cdot,\cdot) : Q \times V \times V \to R$ by

$$a(q;\varphi,\psi) = a^1(q^*;\varphi_2,\psi_1) + a^1(q;\varphi_1,\psi_2) + a^2(q;\varphi_2,\psi_2), \qquad (4.9)$$

for $q \in Q$, $\varphi = (\varphi_1, \varphi_2)$, $\psi = (\psi_1, \psi_2) \in V$. Since $q^* > 0$, the expression given in (4.8) clearly defines an inner product on H. It is also easily verified that the form $a(\cdot;\cdot,\cdot)$ defined in (4.9) above satisfies Assumptions $(A1)$ and $(A2)$ given in Section 2. It is clear that the map $q \to a(q;\cdot,\cdot)$ is affine. Finally, for $t \geq 0$, we set $f(t) = (0, g(t))$, and in the usual manner (see, for example, [13]) consider the second order initial value problem (4.6), (4.7) to be equivalent to the first order system (2.1), (2.2) with $u \sim (w, D_t w)$. In terms of the forms $a^1(\cdot;\cdot,\cdot)$ and $a^2(\cdot;\cdot,\cdot)$ specified in (4.4) and (4.5) above, for $q \in Q$ the operator $A_1(q) : V \to V'$ defined in (2.3) is given by

$$\langle A_1(q)\varphi, \psi\rangle_{V',V} = a^1(q;\varphi_1,\psi_2) + a^2(q;\varphi_2,\psi_2),$$

for $\varphi = (\varphi_1, \varphi_2)$, $\psi = (\psi_1, \psi_2) \in V$. The persistence of excitation condition (2.7) takes the form

$$\left\| \int_{\bar{t}}^{\bar{t}+\delta_0} a^1(p;\overline{w}(\tau),\cdot) + a^2(p;D_\tau\overline{w}(\tau),\cdot)d\tau \right\|_{V_0^*} \geq \epsilon_0, \qquad (4.10)$$

and the set $\hat{Q}$ defined by (2.8) is given by

$$\hat{Q} = \{q \in Q : \lim_{t\to\infty} \left| \int_t^{t+L} a^1(q;\overline{w}(\tau),\varphi) + a^2(q;D_\tau\overline{w}(\tau),\varphi)d\tau \right| = 0, \quad \varphi \in V,\ L > 0\},$$

where $\overline{w}$ is assumed to be the state of a plant corresponding to (4.6), (4.7) in the sense of Definition 2.1 with $\overline{u} = (\overline{w}, D_t\overline{w})$. In order to illustrate the result given in Theorem 2.4, we set

$$\overline{w}(t,x) = \alpha\cos(\beta t)\sin(n\pi x), \qquad t > 0, \qquad 0 < x < 1,$$

where n is a positive integer. Let $\overline{q}_1, \overline{q}_2 > 0$ and set $\overline{q} = (\overline{q}_1, \overline{q}_2)^T$. We want the plant corresponding to (4.6), (4.7) to be given by the pair $(\overline{q}, \overline{w})$. Consequently for $t > 0$ and $0 < x < 1$ we set

$$\begin{aligned} f(t,x) &= \frac{\partial^2\overline{w}}{\partial t^2}(t,x) - \overline{q}_2\frac{\partial^2}{\partial x^2}\frac{\partial\overline{w}}{\partial t}(t,x) - \overline{q}_1\frac{\partial^2\overline{w}}{\partial x^2}(t,x) \\ &= \alpha\left\{\left(\overline{q}_1 n^2\pi^2 - \beta^2\right)\cos(\beta t) - \overline{q}_2\beta n^2\pi^2\sin(\beta t)\right\}\sin(n\pi x), \end{aligned}$$

$$w_0(x) = \overline{w}(0,x) = \alpha\sin(n\pi x), \qquad 0 < x < 1,$$

and

$$w_1(x) = \frac{\partial\overline{w}}{\partial t}(0,x) = 0, \qquad 0 < x < 1.$$

In this case the persistence of excitation condition (4.10) is given by

$$\left\| \int_{\bar{t}}^{\bar{t}+\delta_0} a^1(p;\overline{u}(\tau),\cdot) + a^2(p;D_\tau\overline{u}(\tau),\cdot)d\tau \right\|_{V_0^*} \qquad (4.11)$$

$$\geq \left| \int_{\bar{t}}^{\bar{t}+\delta_0} \frac{\alpha n^2\pi^2}{2}\{p_1\cos(\beta\tau) - p_2\beta\sin(\beta\tau)\}\,d\tau \right|$$

$$\approx \frac{|\alpha|n^2\pi^2}{2}\delta_0\left|p_1\cos(\beta\tilde{t}) - p_2\beta\sin(\beta\tilde{t})\right| = \frac{|\alpha|n^2\pi^2}{2}\delta_0|\mathbf{p}\cdot\mathbf{v}_\beta|,$$

where $\mathbf{p} = (p_1, p_2) \in R^2$ and $\mathbf{v}_\beta = (\cos(\beta\tilde{t}), -\beta\sin(\beta\tilde{t})) \in R^2$. Inspection of the final expression in (4.11) reveals that if $\beta \neq 0$, increasing $|\alpha|$ will increase the overall level of persistence of excitation (i.e. ϵ_0). Thus, we expect that by choosing $|\alpha|$ sufficiently large, both estimators, the stiffness, $q_1(t)$, and the damping, $q_2(t)$, will converge to the respective plant parameters, $\overline{q}_1$ and $\overline{q}_2$, as $t \to \infty$. This is similar to what was observed in the parabolic case treated in Section 3 above.

From (4.11), when $\beta = 0$ (i.e. a time invariant input and plant) the plant is persistently excited with respect to q_1 and is not persistently excited with respect to q_2 (see the remark following Theorem 2.4). In this case we have $\hat{Q} = R^1$ and $P_{\hat{Q}}q = P_{\hat{Q}}(q_1, q_2)^T = (0, q_2)$. Consequently, Theorem 2.4 predicts that if $|\alpha|$ is sufficiently large, $\lim_{t\to\infty} q_1(t) = \overline{q}_1$ and $\lim_{t\to\infty} q_2(t) = q_2(0)$.

Now as β increases from zero, the plant becomes persistently excited with respect to both q_1 and q_2. However, for $0 < \beta < 1$, the level of persistence of excitation is greater with respect to q_1 than it is with respect to q_2. That is, in (4.11) the component of $\mathbf{v}_\beta$ in the q_1 direction tends to dominate the component in the q_2 direction. Consequently, more of the excitation is directed towards the estimation of q_1 than it is towards the estimation of q_2. Thus in this case, Theorem 2.4 and the remark following it suggest that if $|\alpha|$ is sufficiently large, both estimates should converge to the plant parameters, but the stiffness parameter, q_1, should do so somewhat more rapidly. When β is somewhat larger, i.e. $\beta > 1$, we would expect the situation to be reversed.

To test these observations, we set $n = 4$, $\overline{q}_1 = .0308$, $\overline{q}_2 = .01$, $q_1^* = 2.0\times10^{-4}$, $q_2^* = .5$, and $\gamma_1 = \gamma_2 = 5.33\times10^1$. We took the initial condition for the estimator (2.4), (2.5) to be $u(0) = (\overline{w}(0,\cdot), \frac{\partial\overline{w}}{\partial t}(0,\cdot))$, and $q(0) = (0,0)^T$. We first set $\beta = 5.0$ and varied α. In Figure 4.1 we plot $q_1(t)$, and in Figure 4.2 we plot $q_2(t)$ on the interval $[0, 100]$, for various values of α. The observed behavior is analogous to that which was observed in the parabolic case. In the remaining plots, we hold α fixed at $\alpha = .25$ and vary β. We plot the absolute error for each parameter. That is, we plot $|r_1(t)| = |q_1(t) - \overline{q}_1|$ and $|r_2(t)| = |q_2(t) - \overline{q}_2|$. It is clear that if α is too small, neither estimator converges. As β increases, q_1 is favored when $0 < \beta < 1$ and the q_2 estimator is favored when $\beta > 1$. From Figure 4.6 we see that when $\beta = 1$, the *rate* of convergence is approximately the same for both q_1 and q_2. This observed behavior agrees with the theoretical predictions given above. We do note however, that in the case where $\beta = 0$ (i.e. Figure 4.4) we do not see $\lim_{t\to\infty} q_2(t) = q_2(0) = 0$ (or equivalently, $\lim_{t\to\infty} |r_2(t)| = \lim_{t\to\infty} |q_2(t) - \overline{q}_2| = |q_2(0) - \overline{q}_2| = .01$) as was predicted above. Instead we observe $|r_2(t)| \approx .012$ for all $t > 6$. We believe that this small discrepancy is an artifact of the numerical integration of the estimator equations, (2.4), (2.5).

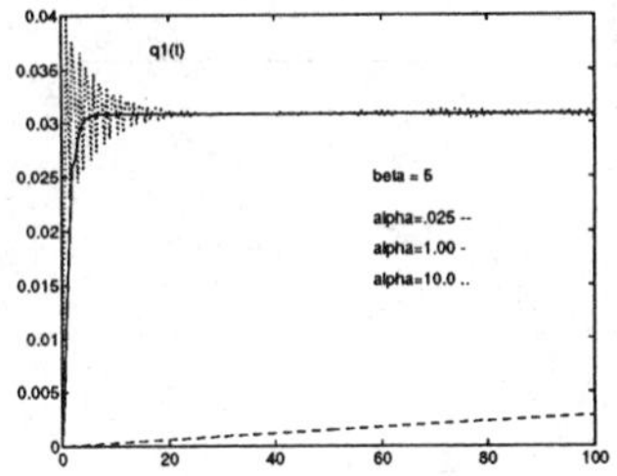

Figure 4.1: Stiffness parameter convergence.

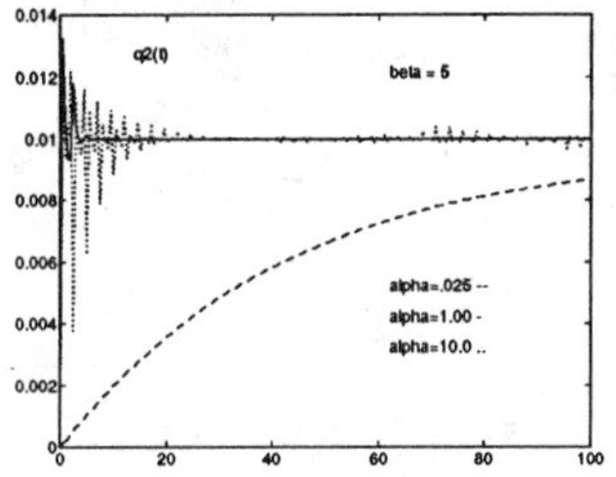

Figure 4.2: Damping parameter convergence.

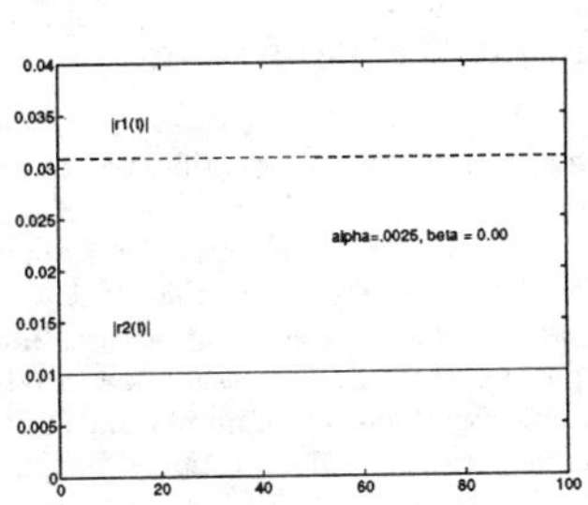

Figure 4.3: Absolute parameter error.

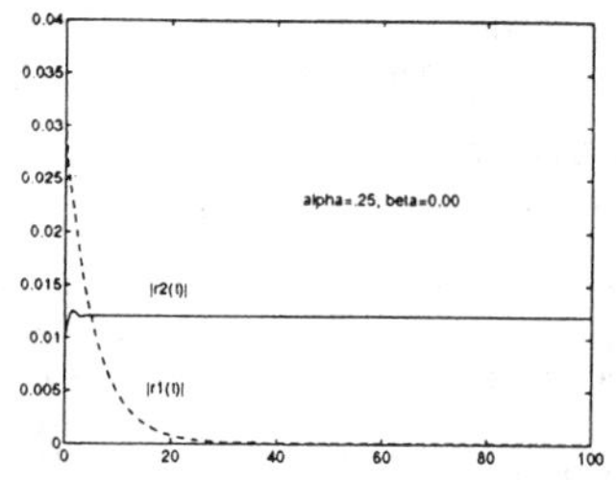

Figure 4.4: Absolute parameter error.

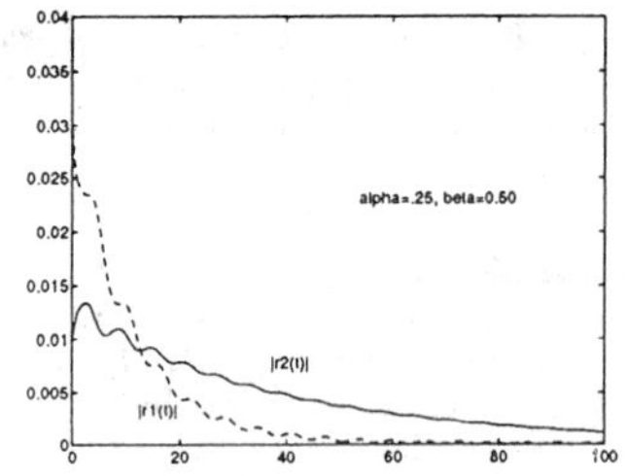

Figure 4.5: Absolute parameter error.

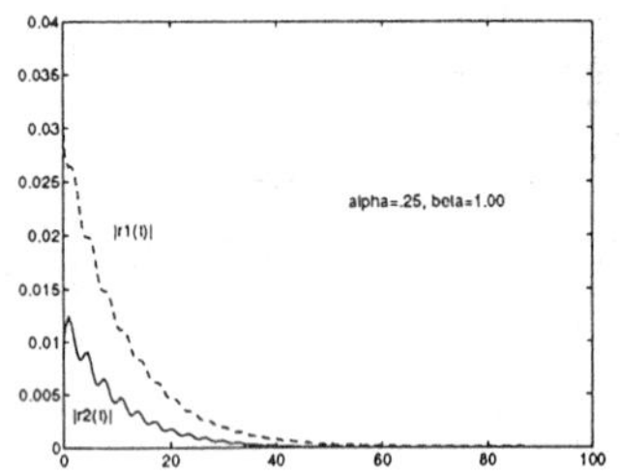

Figure 4.6: Absolute parameter error.

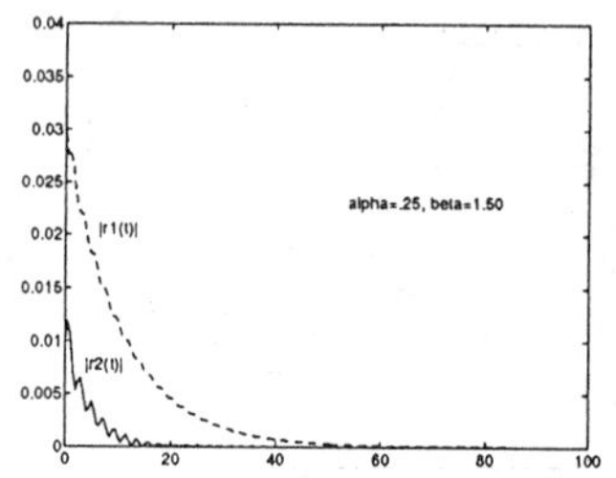

Figure 4.7: Absolute parameter error.

5 Summary and Discussion

In this short note we have considered the persistence of excitation condition for the adaptive, or on-line, identification of abstract distributed parameter systems. The effect of the level of persistence of excitation on the qualitative and quantitative behavior of the estimator (in particular, their convergence to the plant parameters as $t \to \infty$) for a one dimensional heat equation with a time invariant mono-chromatic input was studied. The resulting estimator behaved like a damped harmonic oscillator. The damping and stiffness are determined by the level of persistence of excitation of the plant together with the scheme's tuning parameters. If the estimator is overdamped, convergence is slow. If it is underdamped, oscillations result. For a hyperbolic system, we investigated how the relative level of persistence of excitation with respect to different parameters affects the relative rates of convergence of their corresponding estimators. We considered a one dimensional wave equation with Kelvin-Voigt viscoelastic damping and a time varying (sinusoidal) monochromatic input. We observed that the relative performance (i.e. rate of convergence) of the stiffness and damping parameter estimators is determined by their respective contributions to the level of persistence of excitation of the plant. In particular, we were able to illustrate both *partial* and *non-* parameter convergence in the absence of persistence of excitation.

In practice, systems of interest are likely to be far more complex than the examples we have considered here. It is also unreasonable to expect available actuator hardware to permit single mode input and in general, it is unreasonable or impossible to check the level of persistence of excitation. However, we have found that the simple examples that were studied here have provided valuable insight into the relative effects of the scheme's various tuning parameters (one of which is the plant's level of excitation). In particular, they have helped us to better understand the behavior of the estimator in the far more complex (and analytically intractable) situation of estimating functional, or spatially varying parameters (i.e. $q = q(x)$), and they significantly aided us in determining appropriate choices for the tuning parameter q^*, the weighting of the Q inner product (i.e. γ in the parabolic case and γ_1 and γ_2 in the hyperbolic case), and the level and structure of the input.

References

[1] H. T. Banks and K. Kunisch, *Estimation Techniques for Distributed Parameter Systems*, Birkhauser, Boston, 1989.

[2] J. Baumeister and W. Scondo, *Asymptotic embedding methods for parameter estimation*, in Proceedings of the 26th IEEE Conference on Decision and Control, Los Angeles, CA, December, 9-11 1987, pp. 170–174.

[3] E. A. Coddington and N. Levinson, *Theory of Ordinary Differential Equations*, McGraw Hill, New York, 1955.

[4] M. A. Demetriou and I. G. Rosen, *Adaptive identification of second order distributed parameter systems*, CAMS Report 93-3, Center of Applied Mathematical Sciences, Department of Mathematics, University of Southern California, Los Angeles, CA 90089-1113, March, 1993, also submitted to *Inverse Problems*, 1992.

[5] ——, *On-line estimation for infinite dimensional dynamical systems*, CAMS Report 93-2, Center for Applied Mathematical Sciences, Department of Mathematics, University of Southern California, Los Angeles, CA 90089-1113, February 1993, also submitted to *SIAM J. Control and Optimization*, 1993.

[6] K. H. Hoffmann and J. Sprekels, *On the identification of parameters in general variational inequalities by asymptotic regularization*, SIAM J. Math. Anal., 17 (1986), pp. 1198–1217.

[7] K. Hong and J. Bentsman, *Nonlinear control of diffusion processes with uncertain parameters using MRAC approach*, in Proceedings of the 1992 American Control Conference, Chicago, Illinois, June 24-26 1992, pp. 1343–1347.

[8] ——, *Direct adaptive control of parabolic systems: Algorithm synthesis, and convergence and stability analysis*, Technical Report, Department of Mechanical and Industrial Engineering, University of Illinois, Urbana, also submitted to *IEEE Trans. Automatic Control*, 1992.

[9] K. S. Hong, *Vibrational and Adaptive Control of a Class of Distributed Parameter Systems Described by Parabolic Partial Differential Equations*, PhD thesis, Department of Mechanical and Industrial Engineering, University of Illinois, Urbana, 1991.

[10] J. L. Lions, *Optimal Control of Systems Governed by Partial Differential Equations*, Springer-Verlag, New York, 1971.

[11] A. P. Morgan and K. S. Narendra, *On the stability of nonautonomous differential equations $\dot{x} = [A+B(t)]x$, with skew symmetric matrix $B(t)^*$*, SIAM J. Control and Optimization, 15 (1977), pp. 163–176.

[12] K. S. Narendra and A. M. Annaswamy, *Stable Adaptive Systems*, Prentice Hall, Englewood Cliffs, NJ, 1989.

[13] R. E. Showalter, *Hilbert Space Methods for Partial Differential Equations*, Pitman, London, 1977.

Proceedings of the
American Control Conference
San Francisco, California • June 1993

SLIDING MODE CONTROL OF CHEMICAL PROCESS SYSTEMS DESCRIBED BY PARTIAL DIFFERENTIAL EQUATIONS

Eric M. Hanczyc and Ahmet Palazoglu

Department of Chemical Engineering
University of California
Davis, CA 95616

ABSTRACT

This paper focuses on the application of sliding mode control theory to distributed parameter chemical process systems. For a class of partial differential equations, the method of characteristics is used to exactly transform the distributed parameter system to a finite set of ordinary differential equations, allowing for the implementation of geometric methods to extend sliding mode concepts. Through simulations the method is shown to be effective in controlling a steam heater.

INTRODUCTION

Many processes in chemical engineering are modeled as distributed parameter systems (DPS) when more than one independent variable exists. Under such circumstances, the governing equations of heat, mass, and momentum transport will contain temporally dependent terms as well as spatial gradients. Analytical solution of these (possibly nonlinear) partial differential equations (PDEs) is generally nontrivial.

Models of plug flow reactors, steam heaters, and crystallizers are processes typically modeled by single hyperbolic PDEs. A double-pipe heat exchanger can be described by two hyperbolic PDEs. The governing equations for a nonisothermal plug flow reactor are parabolic. The Method of Characteristics is applicable to all of these sets of equations.

In process control literature, the modeling and control of DPS have been addressed by various researchers (Ray, 1981; Foss et al., 1980; Bonvin et al., 1983). The most common approach to modeling and subsequent control design is based on lumping procedures using orthogonal collocation. The set of PDEs is transformed into a set of ODEs by collocation, and typically the resulting lumped model is of very high order. Thus, necessitating further order reduction (Bonvin and Mellichamp, 1982) to use available control design methodologies. This process naturally leads to a mismatch between the simple, low order lumped model and the original distributed system. Despite its importance for feedback control, however, the issue of robustness is seldom addressed, for DPS (Palazoglu and Owens, 1987; Hanczyc and Palazoglu, 1992).

An alternative approach is to utilize the method of characteristics and develop controller designs for DPS described by nonlinear first order partial differential equations (NFOPDEs). The DPS is transformed into a finite set of characteristic ODEs (Arnold, 1988). These characteristic ODEs along with their Cauchy data (initial conditions) *exactly* describe the original DPS. Thus control design may be performed on a set of ODEs in place of the NFOPDE without approximation. For example, sliding mode control may be designed for a DPS based on the characteristic equations (Sira-Ramirez, 1990).

In this paper, we shall present the method of characteristics for a NFOPDE and the subsequent implementation of sliding mode control to a steam heater.

METHOD OF CHARACTERISTICS

Consider the following NFOPDE:

$$\frac{\partial v}{\partial t} + \Phi\left(v, \mathbf{x}, t, \frac{\partial v}{\partial \mathbf{x}}\right) = 0 \qquad (1)$$

where v is state of the system, t denotes time, $\mathbf{x}$ is the vector of n local spatial coordinate functions x_i (i = 1, ... n), $\mathbf{p}$ is the n-dimensional vector of components p_i (i = 1, ... n) denoting the spatial partial derivatives of the state, $\partial v/\partial x_i$, and Φ is a smooth function of its arguments. Also q will denote the temporal partial derivative of the state, $\partial v/\partial t$.

Eq. (1) can be interpreted as a 2n+2 dimensional hypersurface in the 1-jet space, $\mathbf{J}^1$, which is the extension of the space $\chi = (\mathbf{x}, t)$ in $\mathbf{R}^{(n+1)}$ to the space with coordinates $\mathbf{z} = (v, \mathbf{x}, t, \mathbf{p}, q)$ in $\mathbf{R}^{(2n+3)}$. Recall that $\mathbf{p}$ and q are simply the first derivatives of v, the state of the system. Thus $\mathbf{J}^1$ is the space which has as coordinate functions the state of the system, v, time, t, spatial coordinates, $\mathbf{x}$, and all first derivatives of the state, $\mathbf{p}$ and q. The 2n+2 hypersurface is denoted by $\mathbf{E}$ and defined as

$$\mathbf{E} = \phi^{-1}(0) \equiv \{\mathbf{z} \in \mathbf{J}^1 : \phi(\mathbf{z})$$

$$= q + \Phi(v, \mathbf{x}, t, \mathbf{p}) = 0\}. \qquad (2)$$

It can be shown (Arnold, 1988) that, assuming $\mathbf{E}$ is noncharacteristic at all points z of the space $\mathbf{J}^1$, the set of ODEs which generate the jet-characteristics for Eq. (1) can be computed. A surface is noncharacteristic if its tangent planes and contact planes are transversal; i.e. these planes do not coincide everywhere. Typically, if the problem is well-posed, the surface is noncharacteristic. The assumption that $\mathbf{E}$ is noncharacteristic simply requires $\phi(z)$ to be smooth and the initial conditions for the system to be consistent.

The jet characteristics of a PDE are the set of integral curves that are determined from the set of characteristic ODEs. The following expression is obtained for the components of the jet-characteristic vector ξ (for the details of this procedure, one is referred to Arnold (1988)):

$$\dot{v} = p\,\phi_p + q = p\Phi_p + q$$
$$\dot{x} = \phi_p = \Phi_p \quad \dot{t} = 1 \qquad (3)$$
$$\dot{p} = -\phi_v p - \phi_x = -\Phi_v p - \Phi_x$$
$$\dot{q} = -\phi_v q - \phi_t = -\Phi_v q - \Phi_t$$

or more concisely, in terms of the local coordinates,

$$\dot{z} = \xi(z) \qquad (4)$$

To completely define the problem, the initial condition for the equation $\phi = 0$ is needed. The state v must be assigned some particular value on the points of an n-dimensional hypersurface (on the x coordinates) defined in the n+1 dimensional space of coordinates $\chi = (x, t)$. This is commonly known as the Cauchy data. The initial jet-manifold (i.e. the initial conditions for (v, x, t, p, q)) is constructed in a straightforward manner from the Cauchy data.

DISTRIBUTED SLIDING MODE CONTROL OF NFOPDE

Sliding mode control is a method of discontinuous control for non-linear systems (Utkin, 1978). The main idea is to define a surface on which the system has some desirable behavior. A Lyapunov-like stability condition guarantees that the distance to the surface decreases along all system trajectories and constrains the trajectories to point towards the sliding surface. Once on the surface, the trajectories remain there. The following extends this idea to distributed systems described by a first order PDE,

$$\frac{\partial v}{\partial t} + \Phi(v, x, t, u, p) = 0 \qquad (5)$$

$$y = h(v, x, t) \qquad (6)$$

where v, t, x, p, q, Φ are defined as in the previous section, y is the system output defined by the smooth scalar function h, and $u = u(v, x, t)$ is a distributed, smooth, time-varying feedback control law.

A Lyapunov-like stability condition that drives the system trajectories to the sliding surface (defined below) is a switching law (Sira-Ramirez, 1990). The following feedback switching law determines the control action:

$$u = \begin{cases} u^+(v,x,t) \text{ for } y>0 \\ \text{or} \\ u^-(v,x,t) \text{ for } y<0 \end{cases} \qquad (7)$$

with $u^+(v, x, t) > u^-(v, x, t)$. Defining a distributed switch function ν :

$$\nu = \begin{cases} 1 \text{ for } y>0 \\ \text{or} \\ 0 \text{ for } y<0 \end{cases} \qquad (8)$$

allows the control law to be expressed as

$$u = u^- + \nu\,(u^+ - u^-) \qquad (9)$$

The control objective is to drive the output y to 0 (i. e. $h(v, x, t) = 0$). This defines locally a solution $v = \sigma(x, t)$. This solution set is the sliding manifold or sliding surface and is defined as

$$S \equiv \{\, \eta = (v, x, t) \text{ in } \mathbf{R}^{(n+2)}:\ v = \sigma(x, t) \,\} \qquad (10)$$

It is onto this surface that the distributed sliding control drives the system.

Substituting the control law given by Eq. (9) into Eq. (5) yields the following equations describing the controlled system:

$$\frac{\partial v}{\partial t} + F(v, x, t, p) + \nu\, G(v, x, t, p) = 0 \qquad (17)$$
$$y = h(v, x, t) \qquad (12)$$

where $F(v, x, t, p) = \Phi(v, x, t, u^-(v, x, t), p)$

and $G(v, x, t, p) = \Phi(v, x, t, u^+(v, x, t), p) - \Phi(v, x, t, u^-(v, x, t), p)$

The components for the discontinuously controlled jet-characteristic vector are obtained as:

$$\dot{v} = p\,(F_p + \nu\, G_p) + q$$
$$\dot{x} = F_p + \nu\, G_p \ ; \ \dot{t} = 1 \qquad (13)$$
$$\dot{q} = -(F_v + \nu\, G_v)\, q - (F_t + \nu\, G_t)$$
$$\dot{p} = -(F_v + \nu\, G_v)\, p - (F_x + \nu\, G_x)$$

or

$$\dot{z} = \xi^-(z) + \nu(\xi^+(z) - \xi^-(z)) \qquad (14)$$

As before, noncharacteristic initial Cauchy data is necessary to complete the problem description. Eq. (8) represents the controlled characteristic ODEs describing the original first order PDE. If a single PDE models the physical system and the spatial coordinate is scalar (as it is for a steam heater - see the example) then Eq. (8) is comprised of five ODEs.

The existence of sliding regimes in the 1-jet space and in the space with $\eta = (v, x, t)$ as coordinates has been shown by Sira-Ramirez (1990) and Utkin (1978). If the problem is well-posed with consistent boundary and initial conditions, the sliding regime will exist for the PDE. Then, it is possible to replace the distributed switch position function ν with an equivalent, smooth, distributed control law represented by,

$$\nu^{EQ} = -\frac{\left[\frac{\partial h}{\partial x} F_p + \frac{\partial h}{\partial t} + \frac{1}{2}\lambda h\right]}{\frac{\partial h}{\partial x} G_p} \qquad (15)$$

where $0 < \nu^{EQ} < 1$. The application of the equivalent smooth control law is necessary to reduce chattering in the control action and in the controlled output. Switching between discrete control actions will cause oscillations within the controlled system since infinitely fast control actuation is impossible and complete knowledge of the state is often unavailable.

PRACTICAL IMPLICATIONS

Before illustrating the methodology with an example, some important practical implications must be addressed. Consider the denominator of Eq. (15). The output of the system, h, is driven to zero by the application of the control law. If this takes place smoothly, the spatial derivative of the output will also be driven to zero as the desired state is approached. This poses a computational problem that can be alleviated with some algebra. For example, consider the output of a system to be the difference between the state and its set point: $v - v_{sp}$. Thus, one has

$$v^{EQ} = -\frac{\left(\frac{\partial v}{\partial x} - \frac{dv_{sp}}{dx}\right)F_p + \frac{\partial v}{\partial t} + \frac{\lambda}{2}(v - v_{sp})}{\left(\frac{\partial v}{\partial x} - \frac{dv_{sp}}{dx}\right)G_p}$$

$$= -\frac{\left(p - \frac{dv_{sp}}{dx}\right)F_p + q + \frac{\lambda}{2}\left(v - v_{sp}\right)}{\left(p - \frac{dv_{sp}}{dx}\right)G_p} \quad (16)$$

Rearranging this equation and using the first relationship in Eq. (13) yields

$$v^{EQ} = -\frac{\dot{v} - \frac{dv_{sp}}{dx}F_p + \frac{\lambda}{2}(v - v_{sp})}{\frac{dv_{sp}}{dx}G_p} \quad (17)$$

If G_p equals zero, there are two possible explanations. If F_p is also zero, then no spatial derivatives exist; i. e. the equations are ordinary differential equations. If F_p is non-zero, then u^+ and u^- are improperly set, implying that the Lyapunov-like stability condition is violated.

The second consideration for the practical implementation of this algorithm concerns system inputs that may not vary spatially. In many chemical engineering examples, this is often the case. Adjusting the flowrate of an incompressible fluid through a plug flow reactor to control the outlet concentration or temperature is an example. The distributed sliding mode control algorithm determines a spatially-dependent input. For implementation, this function, weighted or unweighted, may be integrated over the spatial domain to obtain an input that is only temporally dependent. In the following example, such an integration is demonstrated.

EXAMPLE

Consider the model for a flow-forced steam-heated heat exchanger (Friedly, 1972). For simplicity, the steam temperature is considered uniform and the thermal capacity of the walls is taken to be zero. Under these conditions, the double pipe heat exchanger is described in deviation variables by

$$\frac{\partial T}{\partial t} + (u+1)\frac{\partial T}{\partial x} + H(T - T_s) = 0 \quad (18)$$

The initial condition is $T = T_0(x)$ at $t = 0$; the boundary condition is $T = T_{in}(t)$ at $x = 0$. For control purposes, the output is described by

$$y(x,t) = T(x,t) - T_{sp}(x) \quad (19)$$

The temperature, T, is the state of the system, t denotes time, x is the spatial coordinate, u is the flowrate through the heater and the system input, and H is the heat transfer coefficient. T_s is the steam temperature and T_{sp} is the set point. Rewriting Eq. (10) in new variables yields

$$q + (u+1)p + H(T - T_s) = 0 \quad (20)$$

where p is the spatial partial derivative of the state, $\partial T/\partial x$, and q is the temporal partial derivative of the state, $\partial T/\partial t$.

The flow through the heater is assumed to be incompressible. This implies that u does not vary spatially. Thus, a change in the flowrate would instantaneously affect the entire domain. The control action is determined by a feedback switching law,

$$u = u^- + v\,(u^+ - u^-) \quad (21)$$

where v is determined by Eq. (14) and u^+ and u^- are selected as constants for simplicity. The sliding manifold is chosen to be the surface determined by

$$y(x,t) = 0 \quad \text{or} \quad T(x,t) - T_{sp}(x) = 0 \quad (22)$$

Applying the method of characteristics, the following ODEs are obtained:

$$\dot{T} = q + p(u+1) = -H(T - T_s) \quad (23)$$

$$\dot{x} = (u+1)\,;\ \dot{t} = 1\,;\ \dot{p} = -pH\,;\ \dot{q} = -qH$$

Remark: Since the system input multiplies the spatial temperature derivative and p and q appear linearly in Eq. (20), Eq. (18) is classified as a *quasilinear* first order partial differential equation. The generalized characteristics reduce to the usual characteristic equations. Distributed sliding mode control of quasilinear FOPDEs was studied by Sira-Ramirez (1989). Nevertheless, the development of the method of characteristics for *general* NFOPDEs is still necessary to determine the equivalent smooth sliding mode control law.

Figure 1 shows the temperature profiles as a function of time for a step change in the desired outlet temperature. Using the switching law, the response is underdamped, settling to the new set point in 3 time units. The control action, however, is not acceptable as shown in Figure 2. The input switches rapidly between u^+ and u^- to maintain the proper average flow through the heater to keep the temperature at the desired value. The desirable constant flowrate at steady state lies between u^+ or u^-.

The input applied to the system is computed by a summation of the state error at several discrete points along the heater. This sum, weighted or unweighted, determines whether u^+ or u^- is to be applied. Identical results to those in Figure 1 are obtained if the desired set point profile is known exactly.

If the set point profile is estimated, a weighted summation with a heavier penalty on the outlet temperature delivers desirable set point tracking. Using only the information at the outlet in the calculation is equivalent to infinite weighting of the outlet temperature. Weighting the output, however, may cause internal oscillations despite maintaining the desired outlet temperature.

In this simulation, the control action is assumed to be instantaneous. Such a response is physically unrealistic. This switching would be slowed by the response time of the actuators. To alleviate any chattering that may occur in the output due to the physical limitations of the system, and to remedy the excessive control action, a smooth control law may be developed from Eq. (15):

$$v^{EQ} = -\frac{\left\{\left(\frac{\partial T}{\partial x} - \frac{dT_{sp}}{dx}\right)(u^- + 1) + \frac{\partial T}{\partial t} + \frac{\lambda}{2}(T - T_{sp})\right\}}{\left(\frac{\partial T}{\partial x} - \frac{dT_{sp}}{dx}\right)(u^+ - u^-)} \quad (24)$$

Rearranging this equation and using Eqs. (20) and (21), one obtains

$$\frac{dT_{sp}}{dx}(1 + u(t)) = q + p(1 + u(t)) + \frac{\lambda}{2}(T - T_{sp})$$

$$= -H(T - T_s) + \frac{\lambda}{2}(T - T_{sp}) \quad (25)$$

Since the flowrate is temporally but not spatially dependent, Eq. (25) is integrated with respect to x to eliminate the necessity for the slope of the temperature profile set point along the heater. An expression for the equivalent switching function can also be determined using Eq. (21):

$$v^{EQ} = -\frac{\left\{(T_{sp}[x=1] - T_{sp}[x=0])(1+u^-) + \frac{\lambda}{2}(<T> - <T_{sp}>) - H(<T> - T_s)\right\}}{(u^+ - u^-)(T_{sp}[x=1] - T_{sp}[x=0])} \quad (26)$$

Figure 3 shows the temperature profiles as a function of time for the same step change in the desired outlet temperature using a smooth control law with $\lambda=5$. The response is more damped than the discontinuous control law. The desired outlet temperature is attained quickly and smoothly without the undesirable control action when a switching law is used. Figure 4 depicts the significant improvement of the input action under the smooth control law. The input moves to a constant value between the upper and lower limits, u^+ and u^- in four time units.

The smooth control law derived above performs well for set point changes. However, disturbances to the system may cause steady-state offset. Among the remedies, one can cite weighting the output in the algorithm, adding an integrator to the controller, or, if possible, measuring the disturbance (e.g. steam temperature/pressure changes, inlet temperature changes, etc.) and adjusting the control law correspondingly.

Figure 5 shows the effect of a disturbance in the inlet temperature on the temperature profiles using the smooth control law. Steady-state offset is observed due to this unmeasured disturbance. For this case, the steady state offset is reduced by employing a weighted control law (Figure 6).

The weighted control law is determined as follows. Both sides of Eq. (25) is multiplied by a normalized weighting function w(x) and integrated over the spatial domain. This yields the following equation:

$$\int_{x=0}^{x=1} \frac{dT_{sp}}{dx}(1 + u(t))\, w(x)\, dx$$

$$= -H(<wT> - T_s) + \frac{\lambda}{2}(<wT> - <wT_{sp}>) \quad (27)$$

Integration by parts and rearranging yields

$$1+u(t) = -\frac{\frac{\lambda}{2}(<wT> - <wT_{sp}>) - H(<wT> - T_s)}{\left\{(wT_{sp})_{[x=1]} - (wT_{sp})_{[x=0]} - \int_{x=0}^{x=1} T_{sp}\frac{dw}{dx}dx\right\}} \quad (28)$$

Substituting for u using Eq. (21) determines an expression for the equivalent switching function.

CONCLUSIONS

The combination of the method of characteristics and sliding mode control is a methodology useful in designing controllers for a class of nonlinear systems described by first order partial differential equations. We have shown that a steam heater described by a single PDE, and classified as a hyperbolic system can be effectively controlled using this methodology.

REFERENCES

Arnold, V. I., *Geometric Methods in the Theory of Ordinary Differential Equations*, Springer Verlag, New York (1988).

Bonvin, D., R.G. Rinker, and D.A. Mellichamp, "On Controlling an Autothermal Fixed-bed Reactor at an Unstable Steady State," *Chem. Eng. Sci.* **38**, 233 (1983).

Bonvin, D., and D.A. Mellichamp, "A Unified Derivation and Critical Review of Modal Approaches to Model Reduction," *Int. J. Con.*, **35**, 829 (1982).

Foss, A.S., J.M. Edmunds, and B. Kouvaritakis, "Multivariable Control System for Two-bed Reactors by the Characteristic Loci Method," *Ind. Eng. Chem. Fundam.* ,**19**, 109 (1980).

Friedly, J. C., *Dynamic Behavior of Processes*, Prentice-Hall, New Jersey (1972).

Hanczyc, E. M., and A. Palazoglu, "Eigenvalue Inclusion for Model Approximations to Distributed Parameter Systems," *Ind. & Eng. Chem., Res.*, **31**, 2538 (1992).

Olver, P. J., *Applications of Lie Groups to Differential Equations*, Springer Verlag, New York (1986).

Palazoglu, A., and S. E. Owens, "Robustness Analysis of a Fixed-bed Tubular Reactor: Impact of Modeling Decisions," *Chem. Eng. Comm.*, **59**, 213 (1987).

Ray, W. H., *Advanced Process Control*, McGraw-Hill, New York, (1981).

Sira-Ramirez, H., "Distributed Sliding Regimes in Systems Described by Quasilinear Partial Differential Equations," *Sys. & Cont. Lett.*, **13**, 177 (1989).

Sira-Ramirez, H., "Distributed Sliding Regimes in Systems Described by Nonlinear First Order Partial Differential Equations," Fourth Latin American Congress of Automatic Control, Puebla, Mexico (1990).

Utkin, V. I., *Sliding Modes and Their Application in Variable Structure Systems*, MIR Publishers, Moscow (1978).

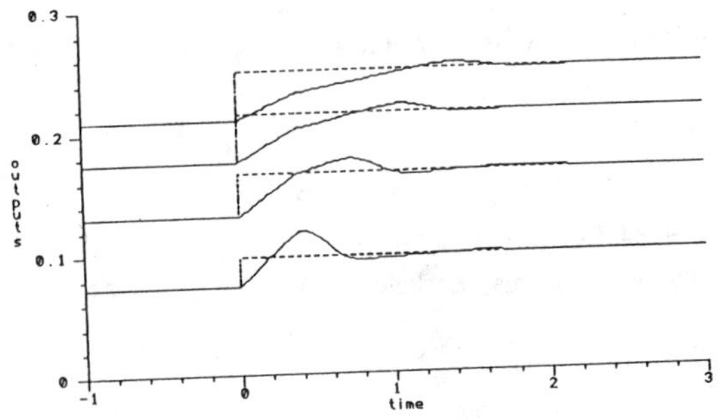

Figure 1. Set point response of temperatures at x = 0.25, 0.50, 0.75, and 1.0, under sliding mode control with the switching feedback control law.

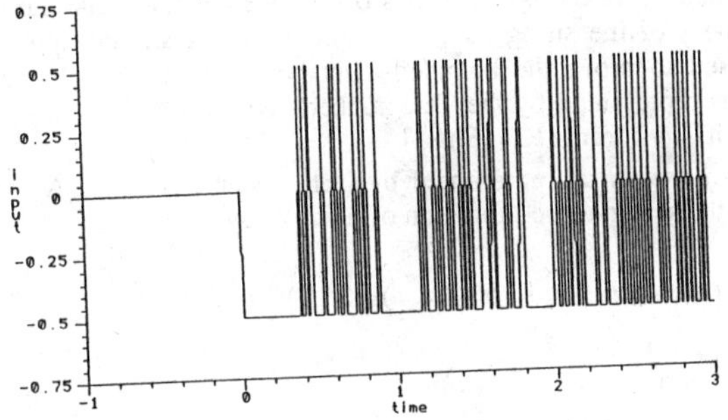

Figure 2. Input response to a set point change with the switching feedback control law.

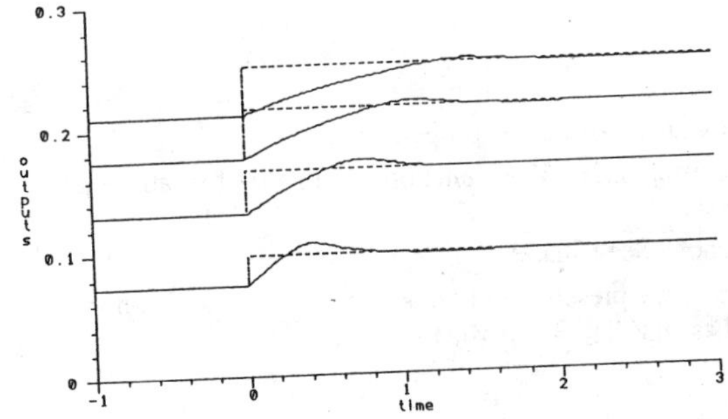

Figure 3. Set point response of temperatures at x = 0.25, 0.50, 0.75, and 1.0, under sliding mode control with the continuous feedback control law.

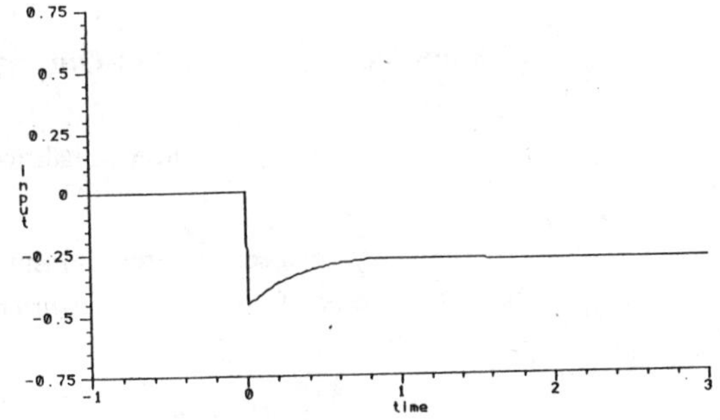

Figure 4. Input response to a set point change with the continuous feedback control law.

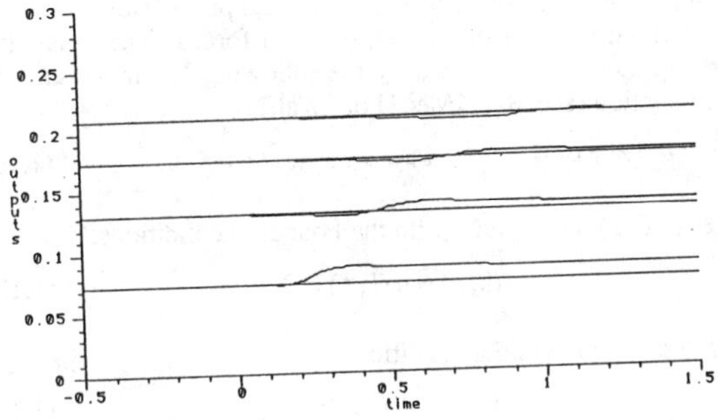

Figure 5. Temperature responses to a disturbance at the inlet with the continuous feedback control law.

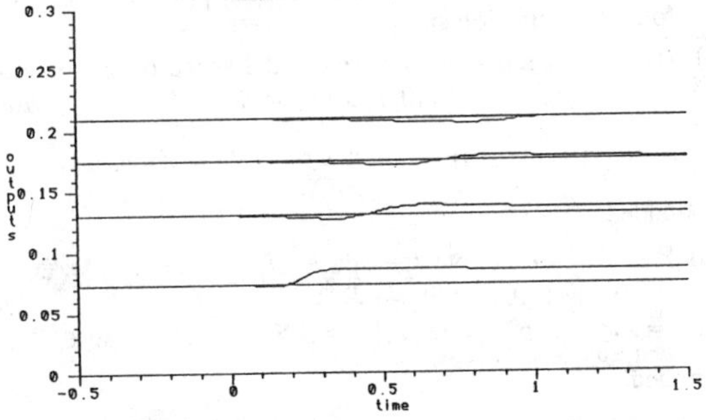

Figure 6. Temperature responses to a disturbance at the inlet with the weighted, continuous feedback control law.

Proceedings of the
American Control Conference
San Francisco, California • June 1993

Bounded-Input Bounded-Output Stability of Damped Linear Strings

S. M. Shahruz* and A. Imam+

* Berkeley Engineering Research Institute, P. O. Box 9984, Berkeley, CA 94709

+ Department of Mechanical Engineering, University of California, Berkeley, CA 94720

Abstract

In this note, we prove that the displacement of a linearly damped string under bounded distributed forces is bounded. The proof is achieved by showing that an energy-like (Lyapunov) function of the string is bounded.

1. Introduction

In this note, we consider a linearly damped elastic string of length l which is under distributed external forces. The dynamics of the string can be represented by the following linear partial differential equation (see, e.g., [Mei.1] or [Wal.1]):

$$u_{tt}(x,t) + 2\,\delta\, u_t(x,t) = a\, u_{xx}(x,t) + f(x,t)\,, \quad (1.1a)$$

for all $x \in (0, l)$ and $t \geq 0$, with the boundary conditions:

$$u(0,t) = u(l,t) = 0\,, \quad (1.1b)$$

for all $t \geq 0$, and the initial conditions:

$$u(x,0) = u_t(x,0) = 0\,, \quad (1.1c)$$

for all $x \in (0, l)$, where $u(\cdot,\cdot) \in \mathbb{R}$ denotes the transversal displacement of the string due to the distributed external force $f(\cdot,\cdot) \in \mathbb{R}$, the constant $\delta > 0$ represents the damping in the string, $a > 0$ is a constant, and $u_t := \partial u/\partial t$, $u_{tt} := \partial^2 u/\partial t^2$, and $u_{xx} := \partial^2 u/\partial x^2$.

In this note, we establish the boundedness of u when f is bounded. In order to define the boundedness precisely, we introduce the following function spaces:

(i) By X_p, $1 \leq p < \infty$, we denote the space of all functions $v(x,t)$, where $v : (0,l) \times \mathbb{R}_+ \to \mathbb{R}$, for which $\| v \|_{X_p} := \sup_{t \geq 0} \left[\int_0^l | v(x,t) |^p \, dx \right]^{1/p} < \infty$. We say that a $v \in X_p$ is X_p-bounded.

(ii) By X_∞ we denote the space of all functions $w(x,t)$, where $w : (0,l) \times \mathbb{R}_+ \to \mathbb{R}$, for which $\| w \|_{X_\infty} := \sup_{t \geq 0} \sup_{x \in (0,l)} | w(x,t) | < \infty$. We say that a $w \in X_\infty$ is X_∞-bounded.

Note that $X_\infty \subset X_2$ because $L_\infty(0,l) \subset L_2(0,l)$. Thus, if a function is X_∞-bounded, then it is X_2-bounded, however, the converse may not be true; for instance $v(x,t) = x^{-1/3} \sin t$, where $x \in (0,l)$ and $t \geq 0$, is in X_2 but not in X_∞.

We now make assumptions on the boundedness of the force f and the solution of the system u. We assume that:

(A1) the force f is X_∞-bounded, i.e., $\| f \|_{X_\infty} < \infty$;

(A2) the system (1.1) with f satisfying (A1) has a solution u, where $u(\cdot,t)$, $u(\cdot,t)\, u_x(\cdot,t)$, and $u_x(\cdot,t)\, u_t(\cdot,t)$ are absolutely continuous functions of x on $[0, l]$ for all $t \geq 0$.

In this note, our goal is to provide a *simple* proof for the X_∞-boundedness of u. That is, to show that the system (1.1) is bounded-input bounded-output stable - an intuitively obvious result for a damped linear second-order system.

2. Boundedness of the Displacement of the String

It is perhaps possible to use the results from the theory of semi-groups generated by operators, and in particular, those in [Cur.1] and the references therein, to prove the boundedness of the displacement of the string. However, we take a different and simpler approach: We define an energy-like (Lyapunov) function of time for the system (1.1), and denote it by V. We prove that V is a bounded function of time due to the X_∞-boundedness of the force f. Then, from the boundedness of V, we conclude that the displacement of the string, u, is X_∞-bounded. A similar approach was used to prove the bounded-input bounded-output stability of systems represented by the Telegrapher's equation, which is somewhat different from (1.1) [Sha.1].

For the string represented by (1.1) under (A1) and (A2), we define the scalar-valued function of time V by

$$V(t) := E(t) + \int_0^l [\,\delta\, u_t(x,t)\, u(x,t) + \delta^2 u^2(x,t)\,]\, dx\,, \quad (2.1)$$

for all $t \geq 0$, where

$$E(t) := \frac{1}{2} \int_0^l [\, u_t^2(x,t) + a\, u_x^2(x,t)\,]\, dx\,. \quad (2.2)$$

We can rewrite V as

$$V(t) = \frac{1}{2} \int_0^l [\, (u_t(x,t) + \delta\, u(x,t))^2 + \delta^2 u^2(x,t) + a\, u_x^2(x,t)\,]\, dx\,, \quad (2.3)$$

for all $t \geq 0$.

Now, we prove some properties of V.

Lemma 2.1: The function $V(t) \geq 0$ for all $t \geq 0$, and $V(0) = 0$.

Proof: See [Sha.2]. □

Next, we present conditions under which the L_∞-norm of V, defined as $\| V \|_\infty := \sup_{t \geq 0} V(t)$, is finite.

Lemma 2.2: The norm $\| V \|_\infty < \infty$, if and only if u, u_x and u_t are X_2-bounded.

Proof: See [Sha.2]. □

Now, we show that V can be bounded by E defined in (2.2).

Lemma 2.3: The function V satisfy

$$V(t) \leq K(\delta)\, E(t)\,, \quad (2.4)$$

for all $t \geq 0$, where $K(\delta) > 0$ is a constant depending on δ.

Proof: See [Sha.2]. □

Now, we show that the function V is a bounded function of time due to the X_∞-boundedness of the force f.

Lemma 2.4: The function V in (2.3) is a bounded function of time.

Proof: From (2.3) we obtain (the argument (x, t) of the functions is deleted.)

$$\dot{V}(t) = \int_0^l [\, (u_{tt} + \delta\, u_t)(u_t + \delta\, u) + \delta^2\, u_t\, u + a\, u_{xt}\, u_x \,]\, dx \,, \quad (2.5)$$

for all $t \geq 0$. Substituting u_{tt} from (1.1a) into (2.5), we obtain

$$\dot{V}(t) = -\,\delta \int_0^l u_t^2\, dx + \delta\, a \int_0^l u_{xx}\, u\, dx + a \int_0^l (u_{xx}\, u_t + u_{xt}\, u_x)\, dx$$

$$+ \int_0^l (u_t + \delta\, u)\, f\, dx \,, \quad (2.6)$$

for all $t \geq 0$.

By (A2), $u\, u_x$ and $u_x\, u_t$ are absolutely continuous functions of x; using this fact and the boundary conditions $u(0, t) = u(l, t) = 0$ and $u_t(0, t) = u_t(l, t) = 0$ for all $t \geq 0$, we obtain (see, e.g., [Tit.1, p. 364] or [Roy.1, p. 110])

$$\int_0^l u_{xx}\, u\, dx = \int_0^l (u\, u_x)_x\, dx - \int_0^l u_x^2\, dx = -\int_0^l u_x^2\, dx \,, \quad (2.7a)$$

$$\int_0^l (u_{xx}\, u_t + u_{xt}\, u_x)\, dx = \int_0^l (u_x\, u_t)_x\, dx = 0 \,. \quad (2.7b)$$

Furthermore, we have the inequality

$$\int_0^l (u_t + \delta\, u)\, f\, dx \leq \frac{\gamma}{2} \int_0^l (u_t + \delta\, u)^2\, dx + \frac{1}{2\gamma} \int_0^l f^2\, dx$$

$$\leq \gamma\, V(t) + \frac{1}{2\gamma} \int_0^l f^2\, dx \,, \quad (2.8)$$

for all $t \geq 0$ and an arbitrary γ. We choose $0 < \gamma < 2\,\delta/K(\delta)$.

Using (2.7) and (2.8) in (2.6), we obtain the differential inequality

$$\dot{V}(t) \leq -\,(2\,\delta/K(\delta) - \gamma)\, V(t) + \frac{1}{2\gamma}\, \phi(t) \,, \quad (2.9)$$

for all $t \geq 0$ with $V(0) = 0$, where $\phi(t) := \int_0^l f^2(x, t)\, dx$, for all $t \geq 0$. By (A1), f is X_∞-bounded; hence it is X_2-bounded, and $0 < \phi(t) \leq \| f \|_{X_2}^2 < \infty$ for all $t \geq 0$.

By a comparison theorem given in ([Bir.1, p. 29] or [Lak.1, p. 30]), we conclude that the function V in (2.9) satisfies

$$V(t) \leq \frac{1}{2\gamma} \int_0^t e^{-(2\,\delta/K(\delta) - \gamma)(t - \tau)}\, \phi(\tau)\, d\tau \,, \quad (2.10)$$

for all $t \geq 0$. Therefore,

$$V(t) \leq \frac{\| f \|_{X_2}^2}{2\gamma} \int_0^t e^{-(2\,\delta/K(\delta) - \gamma)(t - \tau)}\, d\tau \,, \quad (2.11)$$

for all $t \geq 0$. Making the change of variable $t - \tau = \theta$ in (2.11), we obtain

$$V(t) \leq \frac{\| f \|_{X_2}^2}{2\gamma} \int_0^t e^{-(2\,\delta/K(\delta) - \gamma)\,\theta}\, d\theta$$

$$\leq \frac{\| f \|_{X_2}^2}{2\gamma} \int_0^\infty e^{-(2\,\delta/K(\delta) - \gamma)\,\theta}\, d\theta \,, \quad (2.12)$$

for all $t \geq 0$. Therefore,

$$V(t) \leq \frac{\| f \|_{X_2}^2}{2\gamma\,(2\,\delta/K(\delta) - \gamma)} < \infty \,, \quad (2.13)$$

for all $t \geq 0$ and $\| V \|_\infty < \infty$, i.e., V is a bounded function of time. □

Having proved that V is a bounded function of time, we prove that the displacement of the string, u , is X_∞-bounded.

Theorem 2.5: Consider the string represented by (1.1) for which (A1) and (A2) hold. The displacement of the string, u , is X_∞-bounded.

Proof: By Lemma 2.4, $\| V \|_\infty < \infty$. Thus, by Lemma 2.2, the function u_x is X_2-bounded, i.e., $\| u_x \|_{X_2} < \infty$. By (A1), $u(\cdot, t)$ is an absolutely continuous function of x on $[0, l]$ for all $t \geq 0$; using this fact and the boundary condition $u(0, t) = 0$ for all $t \geq 0$, we obtain (see, [Tit.1, p. 364] or [Roy.1, p. 110])

$$| u(x, t) | = | \int_0^x u_\xi(\xi, t)\, d\xi | \leq \int_0^x | u_\xi(\xi, t) |\, d\xi \leq \int_0^l | u_x(x, t) |\, dx \,, \quad (2.14)$$

for all $x \in (0, l)$ and $t \geq 0$. By squaring both sides of (2.14) and using Jensen's inequality (see, e.g., [Roy.1, p. 115]), we obtain

$$u^2(x, t) = | u(x, t) |^2 \leq (\int_0^l | u_x(x, t) |\, dx)^2 \leq l \int_0^l u_x^2(x, t)\, dx \,, \quad (2.15)$$

for all $x \in (0, l)$ and $t \geq 0$. From (2.15) we have

$$| u(x, t) | \leq l^{1/2}\, [\, \int_0^l u_x^2(x, t)\, dx \,]^{1/2} \leq l^{1/2}\, \| u_x \|_{X_2} < \infty \,, \quad (2.16)$$

for all $x \in (0, l)$ and $t \geq 0$. Therefore, $\| u \|_{X_\infty} \leq l^{1/2}\, \| u_x \|_{X_2} < \infty$. □

3. Conclusion

In this note, we proved that if the force applied to a linearly damped elastic string is X_∞-bounded, then the displacement of the string is X_∞-bounded, that is, the string has bounded displacement for all instances of time.

References

[Bir.1] Birkhoff, G., and Rota, G.-C., 1989, *Ordinary Differential Equations*, 4th edition, John Wiley & Sons, New York.

[Cur.1] Curtain, R. F., 1988, "Equivalence of input-output stability and exponential stability of infinite-dimensional systems," *Mathematical Systems Theory*, Vol. 21, pp. 19-48.

[Lak.1] Lakshmikantham, V., Leela, S., and Martynyuk, A. A., 1989, *Stability Analysis of Nonlinear Systems*, Marcel Dekker, New York.

[Mei.1] Meirovitch, L., 1967, *Analytical Methods in Vibrations*, Macmillan, New York.

[Roy.1] Royden, H. L., 1988, *Real Analysis*, 3rd edition, Macmillan, New York.

[Sha.1] Shahruz, S. M., and Imam, A., December 1992, "Bounded-Input Bounded-Output Stability of Systems Represented by the Telegrapher's Equation," *Proceedings of the 31th IEEE Conference on Decision and Control*, pp. 3111-3112.

[Sha.2] Shahruz, S. M., and Imam, A., February 1992, "Bounded Displacement of Damped Linear Strings Under Bounded External Forces," *ESRC Technical Report*, No. ESRC 92-5, Engineering Systems Research Center, University of California, Berkeley.

[Tit.1] Titchmarsh, E. C., 1939, *The Theory of Functions*, 2nd edition, Oxford University Press, Oxford.

[Wal.1] Walker, J. A., 1980, *Dynamical Systems and Evolution Equations*, Plenum Press, New York.

Proceedings of the
American Control Conference
San Francisco, California • June 1993

Robust optimal control for a class of distributed parameter system

Boris Mordukhovich and Kaixia Zhang
Department of Mathematics
Wayne State University
Detroit, MI 48202

In this paper, we study some optimal control and stabilization problems for N dimensional linear heat-diffusion equations with state constraints. The originial motivation for considering such problems came from the development of automatic control systems in irrigation networks which ensure an optimal groundwater regime under uncertain external perturbations; see Skaggs [8] and Mordukhovich [4] for more details. A core problem arising in these considerations is robust stabilization of the system dynamics by state-feedback controls. We study a class of distributed parameter systems where control appear in boundary conditions and have a bounded amplitude. The later creates essential difficulties in employing H_∞-optimal control theory based on Riccati equations; see, e.g., Khargonekar et al. [3], Curtain et al. [2] and references therein.

Here we develop another approach to a minimax design of distributed parameter systems under consideration initiated in [6] for the one dimensional heat equation. This approach is based on multi-step approximations of the initial problem by taking into account its special characteristics. In this way, we justify an optimal three positional structure of the feedback boundary controller and compute its parameters. Moreover, we obtain the effectively sufficient conditions for the robust stability of the closed-loop nonlinear control system considered in the presence of uncertain perturbations.

Let Ω be a bounded set of R^N, and let $\partial\Omega$ be the boundary of Ω. We consider the system

$$\begin{cases} \frac{\partial H}{\partial t} = \Sigma_{i,j=1}^{N} a_{ij} \frac{\partial^2 H}{\partial x_i \partial x_j} + cH + \beta(t), \\ H(x,0) = 0,\ x \in \Omega, \\ H(x,t) = u(t),\ x \in \partial\Omega,\ t \in [0,T], \end{cases} \tag{1}$$

where a_{ij}, $c \leq 0$ are dynamic characteristic parameters, $\beta(t)$ is a perturbation depending on time t, and $u(t)$ is a control function. We require the system to be stable in a given state H_0 (assume 0) within the accuracy $\pm\eta$ under the action of uncertain perturbations $\beta(t)$ in the given region. This means that

$$\mid H(x_0,t) \mid \leq \eta,\ t \in [0,T] \tag{2}$$

for any $\beta(t)$ satisfying

$$-\beta_2 \leq \beta(t) \leq \beta_1,\ \beta_i \geq 0,\ i = 1,2,\ t \geq 0. \tag{3}$$

We also assume that controls are bounded, i.e.

$$-H_2 \leq u(t) \leq H_1,\ H_i \geq 0,\ i = 1,2,\ t \geq 0. \tag{4}$$

The optimization problem can be described as follows: find the feedback control

$$u(t) = u(H(x_0,t)),\ t \geq 0 \tag{5}$$

according to (1) − (4) such that minimizing

$$J(u) = \max_{\beta(\cdot)} \int_0^T \mid u(H(x_0,t)) \mid dt. \tag{6}$$

We depart the problem into two symmetric cases. One is

$$-H_2 \leq u(t) \leq 0,\ \mid H(x_0,t) \mid \leq \eta,\ t \in [0,T]. \tag{7}$$

The other is reversed. It can be shown that the maximum perturbations will occur on the boundary of $\beta(t)$. For $\beta(t) = \beta_1$, we will solve the problem described by (1), (5) − (7).

Under the standard assumption, equation (1) has the unique solution $H \in L_2(0,T;\ H_0^1(\Omega) \cap H^2(\Omega))$.

We treat the worst case that is $\beta(t) \equiv \beta_1$. For definiteness, here we only consider the case $\alpha = \Sigma_{k=1}^{\infty} \frac{c_k}{\lambda_k} > 0$. The other case is symmetric.

Using series representation of the solution $H(x_0,t)$, we consider the following sequence of approximate optimal control problems for ODE's:

$$H_K(t) = \alpha\beta_1 - \eta + x_1(t) + \cdots + x_K(t) \tag{8}$$

where $K = 1, 2, \cdots$, and $x_k(t)$ satisfy

$$\begin{cases} \frac{dx_k}{dt} = -\lambda_k x_k + (c + \lambda_k) c_k u(t), \\ x_k(0) = -\frac{\beta_1 c_k}{\lambda_k}, \end{cases} \tag{9}$$

$k = 1, 2, \cdots, K$. Based on the approximation schemes in [5], We find a suboptimal control for the original problem subject to minimizing the following relaxed cost functional

$$J_\epsilon(u) = \int_0^T [-u(t) + \frac{1}{\epsilon}(\max\{0, H_K(t)\})^2] dt. \tag{10}$$

By using the Pontryaqin's maximum principle on sequence (9) for $k = 1$, a suboptimal control $\bar{u}_{1\epsilon}(t)$ can be expressed in the form

$$\bar{u}_{1\epsilon}(t) = \begin{cases} 0 & t \in [0,t_1) \cup (t_2,T] \\ u_1 & t \in [t_1,t_2] \end{cases} \tag{11}$$

where $u_1 = \frac{\lambda_1}{c_1(c+\lambda_1)}[\frac{\lambda_1 \epsilon}{2c_1(c+\lambda_1)} + \eta - \alpha\beta_1]$, $t_1 \approx -\frac{1}{\lambda_1} ln[(\alpha\beta_1 - \eta - \frac{\lambda_1 \epsilon}{2c_1(c+\lambda_1)})\lambda_1/\beta_1 c_1]$, and t_2 satisfies a specical equation with $t_2 \to T$ as $\epsilon \to 0$.

When $K \geq 2$, we consider

$$P_K(t) = 1 - \frac{2}{\epsilon}\sum_{i=1}^{K} c_i(c+\lambda_i)\int_t^T \max\{0, H_K(s)\}e^{-\lambda_i(s-t)}ds \quad (12)$$

and determine an approximating suboptimal control as

$$\bar{u}_{K\epsilon}(t) = \begin{cases} \bar{u}_0(t), & P_K(t) = 0 \\ 0, & P_K(t) > 0 \\ -H_2, & P_K(t) < 0. \end{cases} \quad (13)$$

To compute the singular control $\bar{u}_0(t)$, we get that $\bar{u}_0(t)$ should satisfy a suitable differential equation of higher orders. Taking $\epsilon \to 0$, as $K = 1$, we obtain

$$\bar{u}(t) = \begin{cases} 0 & t \in [0, t_1^0) \\ -\max\{0, \frac{\alpha\beta_1 - \eta}{1+c\alpha}\} & t \in [t_1^0, T], \end{cases} \quad (14)$$

where $t_1^0 = \frac{1}{\lambda_1} ln \frac{\beta_1(1+c\alpha)}{(c+\lambda_1)(\alpha\beta_1-\eta)}$.

Symmetrically when $\beta(t) = -\beta_2$, we get the first order approximating optimal control

$$\bar{u}(t) = \begin{cases} 0 & t \in [0, t_2^0) \\ \max\{0, \frac{\alpha\beta_2 + \eta}{1+c\alpha}\} & t \in [t_2^0, T], \end{cases} \quad (15)$$

where $t_2^0 = \frac{1}{\lambda_1} ln \frac{\beta_2(1+c\alpha)}{(c+\lambda_1)(\alpha\beta_2+\eta)}$.

Combining the results above for the closed-loop control system, we obtain a three-position controller

$$\bar{u}(H) = \begin{cases} -u_1^0 & \text{if } H \geq \sigma \\ 0 & \text{if } -\bar{\sigma} < H < \sigma \\ u_2^0 & \text{if } H \leq -\bar{\sigma}, \end{cases} \quad (16)$$

Here $(-\bar{\sigma}, \sigma)$ is the dead region ($0 \leq \sigma \leq \eta$ and $0 \leq \bar{\sigma} \leq \eta$, $i = 1, 2$), u_i^0 and $\bar{u}_i^0$, $i = 1, 2$, are chosen to ensure the robust stabilization of the system as $t \to \infty$ within accuracy $\pm\eta$ for any perturbations considered. It is well known that if we do not select the dead region good enough, the considered nonlinear system will lose robustness. This means that the interval $[-\bar{\sigma}, \sigma]$ can not be very small. It can be shown that if

$$\sigma^0(T) = \beta_1[\alpha - \frac{c_1(c+\lambda_1)(\alpha\beta_1 - \eta)}{\lambda_1\beta_1(1+c\alpha)}], \quad (17)$$

$$\bar{\sigma}^0(T) = -\beta_2[-\alpha + \frac{c_1(c+\lambda_1)(\alpha\beta_2 + \eta)}{\lambda_1\beta_2(1+c\alpha)}], \quad (18)$$

the closed-loop system $(1), (5)-(7)$ enjoys the robust stability for any dead region $(-\bar{\sigma}, \sigma)$ with $\bar{\sigma} + \sigma \geq \bar{\sigma}^0 + \sigma^0$, where $0 < \sigma, \bar{\sigma} \leq \eta$.

References

[1] W. H. Fleming and R. W. Rishel, *Deterministic and Stochastic Optimal Control*, Springer-Verlag, New York, 1975.

[2] B. Keulen, M. Peter, and R. Curtain, *H_∞ -control with state feedback: the infinite dimensional case*, Dept. of Math., Univ. of Groningen, W-9015, 1991.

[3] P. P. Khargonekar, I. R. Petersen and K. Zhou, *Robust stabilization and H_∞-optimal control*, IEEE Trans. Autom. Control, **AC-35**(3), 356-361, 1990.

[4] B. Mordukhovich, *Optimal control of ground water regime on two-way engineering reclamation systems*, Water Resources, **12**(3), 1986, 244-253.

[5] B. Mordukhovich, *Approximation Methods in Problems of Optimilization and Control*, Nauka, Moscow, 1988 (in Russian. English translation to appear in Wiley-Interscience.)

[6] B. Mordukhovich, *Minimax design of a class of distributed control system*, Autom. and Remote Control, **50**(10), 1333-1340, Oct. 1989.

[7] A. Pazy, *Semigroups of Linear Operators and Applications to Partial Differential Equations*, Springer-Verlag, 1983.

[8] R. Skaggs, *Water movement factors important to design and operation of subirrigation systems*, Trans. ASAE St. Joseph, Mich., **24**(6), 1551-1561,1981.

Proceedings of the
American Control Conference
San Francisco, California • June 1993

CONTROL OF A VIBRATING STRING USING IMPEDANCE MATCHING

Dr. Jacob S. Glower, Dept. of Electrical Engineering, North Dakota State University, Fargo, North Dakota 58105 glower@vm1.nodak.edu

1 Abstract

The problem of adding damping to a vibrating string considered. An approach novel to the control community is used to define the time optimal control for this system. This approach treats the string as a waveguide and oscillations as a result of reflections at discontinuities -- namely the end points. Through the appropriate choice of the controller, the energy in the string can be completely absorbed by the control, eliminating reflections and likewise oscillations.

In this paper, the characteristic impedance of a string is defined. It is shown that by choosing the control to be a damper of like impedance, all oscillations decay as quickly as possible. A finite element model of a string is used to verify the results.

2 Notation

ρ density of the sting, (kg/m)

c wave speed on the string, (m/s) $c = \sqrt{T/\rho}$

T the tension of the string, (N)

B the damping force applied to the end of the string, (kg/s)

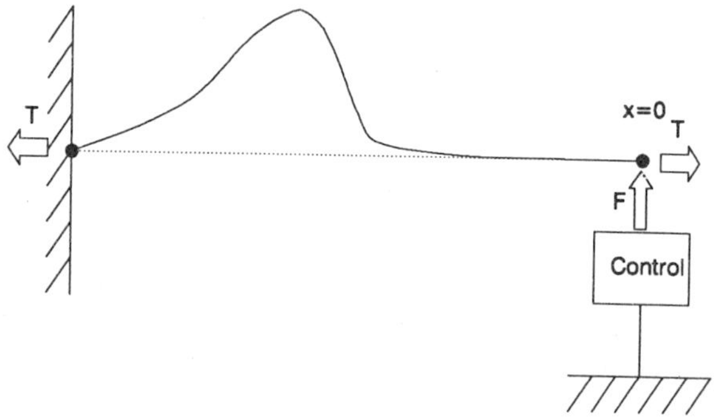

Figure 1: A String Under Tension with Control

3 Introduction

Consider the problem of trying to dampen the oscillations in a vibrating string as presented in Figure 1. Here, a string is held under constant tension with one end firmly anchored to a wall and the other to a control actuator. The problem to be addressed is "What force should the control apply to the string and what control law achieves this?"

The problem of damping a vibrating string is important since it is a relatively simple system that is similar to some real systems that have come under study recently, such as the damping of vibrations in buildings during earthquakes. Such problems are fairly common in the control literature and have been approached from several directions. First, a state space model of the system is defined. Since flexible structures, such as strings, have an infinite number of modes, they also have an infinite number of states. To make the problem manageable, the second step is to reduce the order of the model down to the N most significant states. Typically, these will be the N lowest-frequency modes of the system. Third, sensors and actuators are placed to sense and excite these N modes respectively. This results in an Nth order multi-input multi-output model of the system. Fourth, a control that defines the actuator forces given the sensor information is defined using H-infinity, KQ, LQR, or other design techniques.

This approach works fairly well but has limitations. First, order reduction requires some approximations to be made when designing the controller. The stability of actual system thus becomes as issue. By keeping this gains low, however, this issue can be pretty much avoided. Secondly, the resulting controller is generally of high order and/or requires a large number of sensors and actuators. Third, the resulting design generally has relatively poor performance due to problems with stabilizing lightly damped modes without using high gains.

Consider instead the problem familiar to anyone who has been placed on hold while making a phone call: that of trying to excite and then dampen oscillations in a stretched phone cord. For this system, only a single actuator is used: the hand holding the phone. In addition, only one or two sensors are used: one's eyes and possibly the force applied to the hand. Given this limited set of inputs and outputs, it is quite easy to dampen the oscillations. The ease of this suggests that there must be a simpler approach for controlling this system.

One approach that eliminates oscillations without resorting to high-order models is one familiar to electrical engineers in the area of field-theory and waveguides [Krause, 1973]. There, transmission lines are used to transfer signals (energy) from one point to another. To prevent standing waves from appearing on these lines, it is desired to keep the energy flowing in one direction i.e. to keep reflections down to a minimum. Reflections appear where ever discontinuities exists, such at the terminal end. To reduce this reflection, the end is often terminated with a resistor. When a signal hits this resistor, part of the energy is absorbed and part is reflected back. The size of the reflection is given by the reflection coefficient, Γ, where

$$\Gamma = \frac{R - \sqrt{L/C}}{R + \sqrt{L/C}}, \tag{1}$$

R is the terminal resistance, and L and C are the line inductance and capacitance respectively. Note that by making R equal to $\sqrt{L/C}$, the reflection will disappear and all energy in the signal will be absorbed by the resistor. $\sqrt{L/C}$ Is thus called the "characteristic impedance" of the transmission line and the "ideal" loading of the end point is a pure resistor equal to this value.

A string under tension follows similar equations as a transmission line and behaves in a similar fashion. For transmission lines, a device that dissipates energy is used to terminate the line -- namely a resistor. For a string, a device that dissipates energy would be used -- namely a damper. If R=∞ in (1), Γ=-1 and the reflected wave is the mirror image of the incident wave, only inverted. The same is true for a string with the end point clamped ($B \to \infty$). If R=0, Γ=1 and the reflected wave is equal to the mirror image of the incident wave. Again, this is precisely what happens with a string when the end point is free or B=0. As R varies from ∞ to 0, the reflection drops in amplitude to the point where the reflection is zero at R=$\sqrt{L/C}$. It is reasonable to speculate that for some value of B, the reflection in a string must also be zero. This value of B would likewise be termed the "characteristic impedance" of the string.

4 Derivation

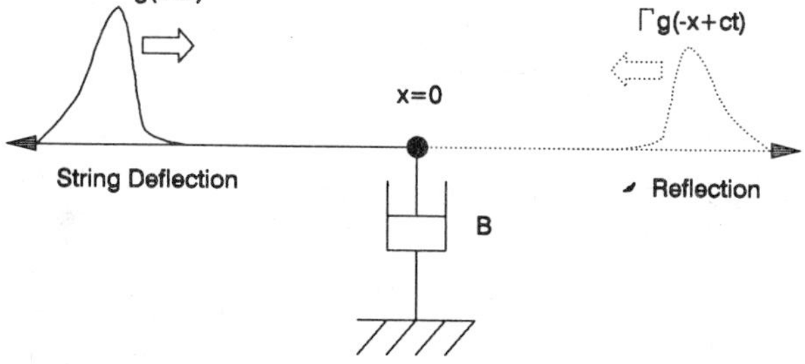

Figure 2: The Incident Wave and its Reflection

The method used to determine the reflection coefficient of a string is based upon an energy balance. Consider an infinite string terminated at x=0 as presented in Figure 2. To the left of x=0, the string is given some initial displacement, g(x-ct), traveling to the right. When g(x-ct) hits the discontinuity at x=0, it will be reflected and start traveling left. Equivalently, this reflection can be thought of as resulting from an extension of the string past x=0 with some initial displacement $\Gamma g(-x+ct)$ traveling to the left. At any time, the total displacement of the string will be the sum of these two signals.

From conservation of energy, the difference in energy between g and its reflection must be equal to the energy dissipated in the damper. By setting these two quantities equal to each other, the relationship between B and Γ can be determined.

The stored in a string with initial displacement g(x-ct) is given by [1]

$$E(g) = \rho c^2 \int_{-\infty}^{0} \left(\frac{dg}{dx}\right)^2 dx. \tag{2}$$

The energy in its reflection will be identical to the energy in g, only scaled down by Γ^2, resulting in the difference in energy being

$$E(g - \Gamma g) = (1 - \Gamma^2)\rho c^2 \int_{-\infty}^{0} \left(\frac{dg}{dx}\right)^2 dx. \tag{3}$$

This must equal the energy dissipated in the damper. To determine this energy, the position of the damper at a given time is used:

$$\begin{aligned} Y(x=0) &= g(ct) + \Gamma g(-ct) \\ &= (1+\Gamma) g(ct) \end{aligned} \tag{4}$$

The force applied by the damper is proportional to the velocity in the y direction

$$\begin{aligned} F &= B\dot{y} \\ &= B(1+\Gamma)\frac{dg}{dt} \end{aligned} \tag{5}$$

Noting that

$$\begin{aligned} \frac{dg}{dt} &= \frac{dg}{dx}\frac{dx}{dt} \\ &= \frac{dg}{dx} \cdot c \end{aligned} \tag{6}$$

allows (5) to be rewritten as

$$F = (1+\Gamma) B c \frac{dg}{dx}. \tag{7}$$

The incremental energy dissipated in the damper is force times distance, or

$$\begin{aligned} dE_{damper} &= F \cdot dy \\ &= \left((1+\Gamma) \cdot B \cdot c \cdot \frac{dg}{dx}\right) \cdot \frac{d(1+\Gamma)g}{dx} dx \end{aligned} \tag{8}$$

with the total energy being

$$E_{damper} = \int_{-\infty}^{0} (1+\Gamma)\cdot B \cdot c \cdot \frac{d(1+\Gamma)g}{dx}\,dx \qquad (10)$$

$$= (1+\Gamma)^2 Bc \int_{-\infty}^{0} \left(\frac{dg}{dx}\right)^2 dx$$

Setting (3) equal to (10) results in

$$(1-\Gamma^2)\rho c^2 \int_{-\infty}^{0} \left(\frac{dg}{dx}\right)^2 dx = (1+\Gamma)^2 Bc \int_{-\infty}^{0} \left(\frac{dg}{dx}\right)^2 dx \qquad (11)$$

or

$$(1-\Gamma^2)\rho c = (1+\Gamma)^2 B \qquad (12)$$

Solving for Γ results in

$$\Gamma = \frac{\rho c - B}{\rho c + B} \qquad (13)$$

From (13), the relationship between the damper and the reflection can be seen. For B=0, Γ=1 implying that the reflection is the mirror image of the incident wave. For $B \to \infty$, Γ=-1 implying that the reflection is equal to the incident wave, only inverted. As B increases from 0, the reflection drops in amplitude until at $B = \rho c$ where the reflection disappears. By analogy to waveguides, it would be reasonable to call this quality the string's characteristic impedance:

Characteristic Impedance of a String (14)
$\equiv \rho c$

5 Optimality of the Solution

From (13), no reflections will result from choosing $B = \rho c$. This implies that all of the energy in g will be dissipated when it encounters the controller at x=0. The best that any controller can do is absorb all the energy, thus this control is optimal in time. The maximum time that it will take to reduce the energy in the system to zero is equal to the maximum time it takes a wave to encounter the controller. This is equal to the distance such a signal would travel (twice the length of the string for traveling left, bouncing off the left wall, and then traveling back to the controller) divided by the wave's speed, or

$$t(settle) = 2L/c$$

In order for this solution not to be optimal in time, some other control must exist that affects a wave packet before it encounters the control at x=0 or else reduces the time required for a signal to encounter the control at x=0.

First, consider trying to add more controllers so that the wave encounters some controller sooner. Adding a control in the middle of the string will change the dynamics at that point. This change will act as a discontinuity and therefore produce reflections. Some of these reflections will send energy away from the control at x=0, and thus increase the settling time. If the discontinuity at x=-L were replaced with another controller set to the string's characteristic impedance, this discontinuity would effectively be eliminated and the settling time could be reduced by half. This violates the assumption of fixing this end point, however. If a distributed controller were placed along the length of the string, reflections would be avoided by not having any discontinuities. This could speed up the response, but would require a controller which is not practical to build. This is partially why the assumption was made that the control only affects a distinct point: the end of the string.

Second, consider trying to reduce the time required for a wave to encounter the control at x=0. In order for this to happen, the control must either increase the effective tension in the string or else decrease the string's mass - either increasing $c = \sqrt{T/\rho}$. A distributed controller could accomplish this, but as mentioned before, would be impractical.

From this, it is clear that the time-optimal solution is to place a pure damper at end of the string set to the string's characteristic impedance.

6 Example

To illustrate the optimality of using a pure damper at one end point, a string similar to Figure 3 was simulated using a finite element model with the following specifications:

Length: L=5m
Density: ρ=0.314kg/m (Aluminum, 6mm diameter cable)
Tension: T=50 Newtons
Wave Velocity: c=12.61m/s=$\sqrt{T/\rho}$
Finite Elements: 250

Two separate simulation runs were made for this system: First, the controller was assumed to be a pure damper varying from 0 to 20 N/m/s. The initial conditions were then set so that a wave packet was traveling towards the controller. The amplitude and phase of the reflected signal was then noted as depicted in Table 1 and Figure 4. Note that the expected amplitude of the reflection is nearly equal to the expected value predicted by (13) and that negligible reflections occur at $B = \rho c = 3.9623$ as expected.

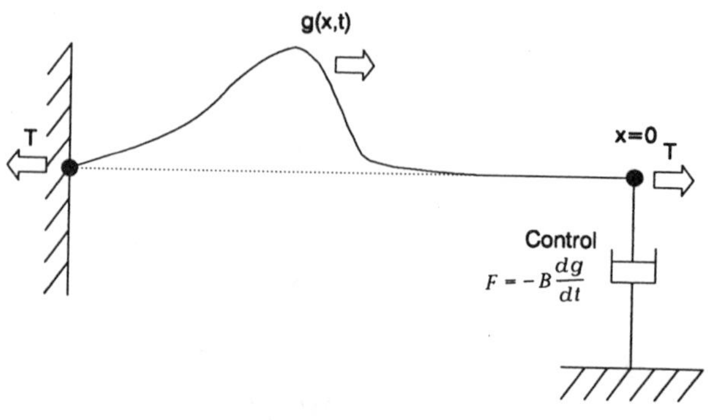

Figure 3: Set-Up Used for Simulation Studies

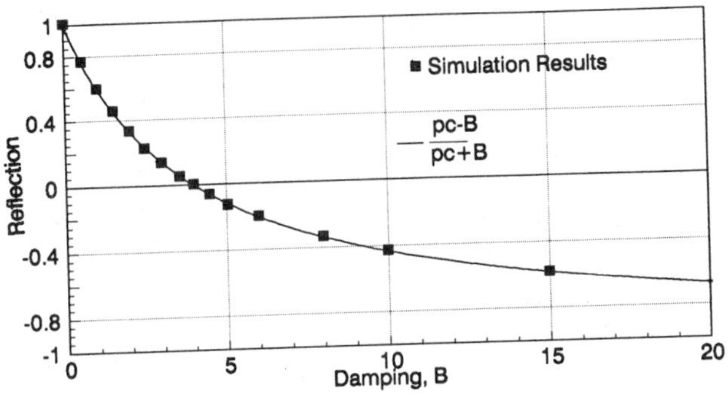

Figure 4: Theoretical & Simulated Reflection Coefficient vs. Damper Force

Table 1: Simulated vs. Theoretical Reflection		
B	Reflection / Incident Wave (Simulated)	Γ (Eq 13)
0	0.99408	1.00000
2	0.32907	0.32912
3.9623 (ρc)	0.00630	0.00000
8	-0.33749	-0.33753
20	-0.66893	-0.66929

Second, the damper was set to 3.9623 and the string was displaced in the middle by one meter and released. The position of the actuator at x=L and the control force was then plotted in Figure with the energy contained in the system plotted in Figure 6. Here, the force should be a square wave, but due to slight errors incurred by using a finite element model, a small amount of noise is observed in the velocity measurement and likewise appears in the control force.

Note that at T=0.8s the displacement of the string at x=L and the energy contained in the system becomes zero. This results from the longest distance a wave packet can travel before encountering the controller being 10m. With a wave velocity of 12.618m/s, this results in a delay of 0.7925s or roughly the 0.8s observed in the simulation. This can also be seen in Figure 5 where the potential energy, kinetic energy, and total energy of the string is plotted vs time. Due to the initial conditions chosen, the damper bleeds off energy at a fixed rate until T=0.8s, where the remaining energy in the system is theoretically zero. Due to the presence of noise created by the finite element approximations and imperfect integration, the energy remains finite, though, as can be seen, remains quite small.

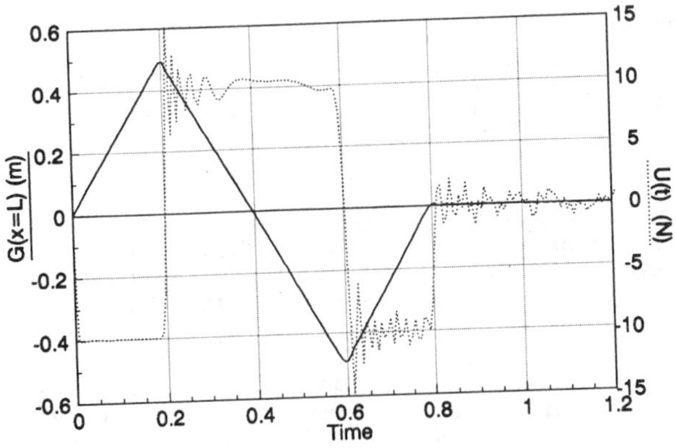

Figure 5: Displacement of the Endpoint and the Applied Force

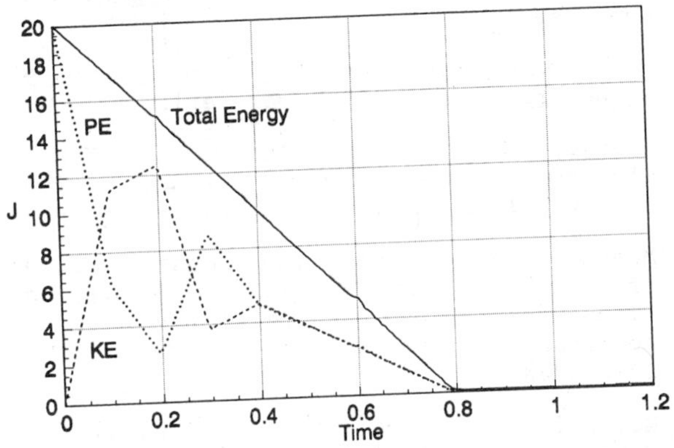

Figure 6: Energy Contained in the String vs. Time

7 Results & Conclusions

The results presented in this paper demonstrate a connection between damping vibrations in a flexible string and preventing reflections in a waveguide. This connection suggests that vibrations in strings result from reflections off of discontinuities. By choosing the control at one end point to be a damper equal to the string's "characteristic impedance," the discontinuity at one end can be eliminated, eliminating reflections and likewise vibrations.

While a vibrating string is an interesting problem to study, the more complex problems dealing with oscillating beams, plates, and three-dimensional structures is of more practical use. Since the application of field-theory results to the simple problem of a string proved useful in simplifying the problem, giving good insight as to what the control is doing, and in obtaining a highly robust, simple, and time optimal control, it appears reasonable to conjecture that gains could be made by applying similar results to these problems as well.

8 References

Balas, M. J., "Modal Control of Certain Flexible Dymanic Systems," SIAM Journal of Control and Optimization, Vol 16, No. 3, pp. 450-462, 1978.

Ferri, A.A., Bindmann, A.C., " Damping and Vibration of Beams with Various Types of Frictional Support Conditions," Journal of Vibrations and Acoustics, pp. 289-296, July 1992.

Gibson, J. S., "A Note on Stabillization of Finite Dimensional Linear Oscillators by Compact Linear Feedback," SIMA Journal of Control and Optimization, pp. 311-316, May 1980.

Joshi, S. M., Moghami, P. G., "Dissipative Compensators for Flexible Spacecraft Control," 1990 American Controls Conference.

Joshi, S.M., Control of Large Flexible Space Structures, Berlin-Springer Verlag, 1989.

Krause, J.D., Carver, K.R., Electromagnetics, Chapters 12 & 13, The McGraw Hill Book Company, 1973.

Maghami, P.G., S. Gupta, S.M. Joshi, "Design of Low-Authority Controllers Using an Eigensystem Assignment Technique," 1992 American Controls Conference, pp. 2780-2783.

Meirovitch, L, Analytical Methods in Vibrations, The MacMillan Company, New York, 1967.

Yang, B., "Noncolocated Control of a Damped String Using Time Delay," 1992 American Controls Conference, pp. 2445-2488.

Young, B., Mote, C.D., "Active Vibration Control of the Axially Moving String in the s-Domain," Journal of Applied Mechanics (in press)

Watkins, J., Yurkovich. S.,, "Vibration Control for Slewing Flexible Structures," 1992 American Controls Conference, pp. 2525-2529.

Proceedings of the
American Control Conference
San Francisco, California • June 1993

FORMULATION OF A ONE-STEP DISCRETE STOCHASTIC CONTROLLER WITH APPLICATION TO ADAPTIVE CONTROL

Mike Knowles* and David Hullender **

Abstract

This paper pertains to the formulation and evaluation of a discrete time control algorithm that takes into consideration current state estimates and an uncertain model with stochastic inputs. The algorithm represents a single or one-step formulation of a linear system quadratic performance index solution but introduces the flexibility of a changing weighting parameter in the performance index based on current estimates and on the control saturation limits. The algorithm represents a simple adaptive technique for real time implementation. Application of the algorithm to the inertial stabilization of a line-of-sight system with coulomb friction disturbances is presented.

Introduction

Attempts to design robust controllers for dynamic systems has been and will continue to be a top priority for control engineers in the years to come. Conventional or optical controllers based on an assumed model have proven to be inferior in cases where the model and/or its inputs are uncertain to begin with or change over time. This paper introduces an application of the very familiar linear system quadratic performance index control formulation. The method utilizes current estimates of the system parameters and states along with control saturation limits to establish the ideal weighting parameter in the performance index for the next single time step. Thus, the performance index essentially changes with each time step so as to provide to best possible control during that step considering estimates of the states and the model. By including estimates of the system model in the formulation, the problem becomes a nonlinear adaptive control algorithm for real time implementation.

Adaptive control techniques can be described as having two basic objectives. First, for the system to be controlled, the best estimate of its current status must be determined, and second, given this estimate, the best control to apply at that instant in time must be ascertained [1]. The need for a simple, real-time adaptive control algorithm which addresses these two objectives commonly arises in systems with time varying nonlinear models that are subjected to stochastic inputs. Ideally, the algorithm should perform in real-time in order to adapt to rapidly changing conditions, and, thus, to provide efficient, effective control.

To perform the two objectives mentioned above, much research has been undertaken in the area of adaptive control techniques. A brief, and by no means complete, discussion of control techniques currently in the literature is presented here to recognize the variety of design methodologies which have been investigated. For example, Bigley and Schupan [2] after studying a conventional design for controlling and stabilizing a high precision mobile platform, suggested that three additional inertial rate sensors strategically placed and filtered could provide a better estimate of the system, and hence, provide improved performance. They referred to this technique as the strong stabilization technique. Another control method actively being investigated is referred to as Time Delay Control (TDC). Its approach is to observe the system's responses and the control inputs at time t-Dt to directly alter the applied control at time t [3, 4]. Still another control method is Predictive Adaptive Control (PAC) which attempts to preview the effect of control application and to modify the current control policy before it is applied in order to achieve better performance [5]. While preview control is conceptually superior to conventional control due to the emphasis on the future impact and appropriate correction of control application, predicting future behavior and computing the corresponding correction can be very burdensome. This led to the study of Rapid Advancement Preview Tracking (RAPT) which generally follows the same preview control philosophy as the PAC, but reportedly is approaching the required computational simplicity to be implemented in real-time [6]. Dissimilar to preview controllers, learning control is based on trial and error, so it is dependent on repeating the same task in order to make adjustments based on previous results and achieve the desired performance enhancement. Closely related to learning controllers, repetitive controllers are designed for the special purpose of handling periodic reference inputs and disturbances [7]. Other techniques mentioned in the literature include Model Reference Adaptive Control (MRAC) which uses a reference model to design an adaptive controller that adjusts the control parameters to minimize the error between the output of the model and the actual system [8]. And finally, briefly discussed by Hilkert and Hullender [1] and Youcef-Toumi and Ito [4] as another technique currently being investigated, sliding mode control is characterized by a discontinuous function with high frequency chattering which has the potential of producing undesirable nonlinear system behavior. The following paragraph expands in detail on the control methodology that is the focus of the rest of this paper.

The Linear Quadratic Gaussian (Linear system, Quadratic performance index, Gaussian disturbance, LQG) theory is a commonly employed control technique. As stated previously, adaptive controllers are called on to accomplish two tasks, estimate the system and then, using that estimate, derive the best control. Due to the certainty equivalence property, the LQG technique is quite applicable to the basic adaptive control problem. The certainty equivalence property, as it applies to the LQG method, allows the estimation task and the control task to be treated independently, thus creating a "...tractable problem, yielding a readily synthesized, efficiently implemented, linear feedback control law..." [9]. By separating the total control design into the combination of two independent components, the design process is substantially simplified compared to attempting the filter and controller design all at once which generally is unsolvable. The resulting feedback control gains are independent of all uncertainty, so the control design is simplified by assuming a deterministic model. The estimation filter is independent of the performance index, so it can be designed ignoring the control problem. This systematic design capability makes the LQG formulation very attractive. In fact, it is common for nonlinear systems to utilize a local or statistical linearization technique in order to take advantage of the LQG synthesis [10, 11, 12]. Utilizing the LQG control technique, the focus of this paper is on the control design aspect with the estimation process being beyond the scope of this study.

This paper pertains to the formulation and evaluation of a discrete time control algorithm that takes into consideration current estimates of a rapidly changing system model that is subjected to stochastic inputs. It is important that the formulation be simple and practical for real-time implementation. The specific contribution of this paper is the formulation and evaluation of this algorithm. The algorithm represents a single or one-step formulation of a discrete LQG controller. The merits of the controller are demonstrated by means of application to three inertial stabilization examples

One-step controller derivation

In order to formulate the one-step controller, it is important to be familiar with the LQG controller formulation because the thought process and logical development of the one-step controller ascends from this algorithm. Consistent with the LQG assumptions, a standard approach for deriving the controller begins with expressing the system as a linear differential equation

$$\dot{x}(t) = F(t)x(t) + G(t)u(t) + L(t)v \tag{1}$$

where x is the state vector, u is the control vector, and w is the input process noise vector modeled as a Gaussian white noise with

* Flour Daniel, Inc., Houston,TX
** Professor, Department of Mechanical Engineering, The University of Texas at Arlington

$$E[w(t)] = 0 \quad (2)$$

$$E\left[w(t)\, w^T(\tau)\right] = Q\, \delta(t-\tau) \quad (3)$$

Next a quadratic performance index is written as

$$J = x^T(t_f)S(t_f)x(t_f) + \int_{t_0}^{t_f}\left(x^T(t)A(t)x(t) + u^T(t)B(t)u(t)\right)dt \quad (4)$$

where $S(t_f)$ is the weight on the final value of the state vector, A(t) is the weight on the state vector at all other times, and B(t) is the weight on the control vector. The selection of these weight terms is obviously a large part of the control solution, and can be simplified by the normalization of the performance index which reduces the number of weight terms to be selected. Although the algorithm is generally applicable to any number of controls or states in the performance index, the following discussion is based on a scalar control u, and a single state x_1 in the performance index. Thus, the first two weighting matrices become

$$S(t_f) = \begin{bmatrix} S_{11} & 0 & \cdots & 0 \\ 0 & 0 & \cdots & 0 \\ \vdots & \vdots & \ddots & \vdots \\ 0 & 0 & \cdots & 0 \end{bmatrix} \quad (5)$$

$$A(t) = \begin{bmatrix} A_{11} & 0 & \cdots & 0 \\ 0 & 0 & \cdots & 0 \\ \vdots & \vdots & \ddots & \vdots \\ 0 & 0 & \cdots & 0 \end{bmatrix} \quad (6)$$

Returning to the normalization process, the weighting terms from the performance index can initially be selected as the inverse of the maximum allowable value squared as suggested by Bryson and Ho [14]. This selection yields

$$S_{11} = \frac{1}{x_{1\,max}^2} \quad (7)$$

$$A_{11} = \frac{1}{x_{1\,max}^2} \quad (8)$$

$$B = \frac{1}{u_{1\,max}^2} \quad (9)$$

Assuming a second order system for demonstration purposes, the performance index becomes

$$J = x^T(t_f)\begin{bmatrix} \frac{1}{x_{1\,max}^2} & 0 \\ 0 & 0 \end{bmatrix} x(t_f) + \int_{t_0}^{t_f}\left(x^T(t)\begin{bmatrix} \frac{1}{x_{1\,max}^2} & 0 \\ 0 & 0 \end{bmatrix} x(t) + \frac{1}{u_{max}^2}u^2(t)\right)dt \quad (10)$$

And multiplying both sides by the constant $x_{1\,max}^2$, the result is the normalized performance index J'

$$J' = x^T(t_f)\begin{bmatrix} 1 & 0 \\ 0 & 0 \end{bmatrix} x(t_f) + \int_{t_0}^{t_f}\left(x^T(t)\begin{bmatrix} 1 & 0 \\ 0 & 0 \end{bmatrix} x(t) + \frac{x_{1\,max}^2}{u_{max}^2}u^2(t)\right)dt \quad (11)$$

or

$$J' = x^T(t_f)\begin{bmatrix} 1 & 0 \\ 0 & 0 \end{bmatrix} x(t_f) + \int_{t_0}^{t_f}\left(x^T(t)\begin{bmatrix} 1 & 0 \\ 0 & 0 \end{bmatrix} x(t) + Bu^2(t)\right)dt \quad (12)$$

Notice the weighting terms are constant and are expressed as

$$S(t_f) = \begin{bmatrix} 1 & 0 \\ 0 & 0 \end{bmatrix} \quad (13)$$

$$A = \begin{bmatrix} 1 & 0 \\ 0 & 0 \end{bmatrix} \quad (14)$$

$$B = \frac{x_{1\,max}^2}{u_{max}^2} \quad (15)$$

Now only one weighting term, B, is unknown, and its value is determined iteratively starting with the above value based on the physical constraints (e.g. stability, structural integrity, etc.) and the desired output of the system. By adjusting B, the amount of applied control and the minimization of x_1 can be adjusted.

The control, u, that minimizes the above performance index is a function of the state vector, x, and can be written as

$$u(t) = -\,C(t)x(t) \quad (16)$$

where the control gain C(t) is expressed as

$$C(t) = \frac{G^T(t)S(t)}{B} \quad (17)$$

with G(t) and B known from the system model equation and the performance index, respectively. The S(t) matrix is calculated by solving the matrix Riccati equation below backwards through time

$$\dot{S} = -SF - F^TS + SG^TB^{-1}GS - A \quad (18)$$

where $S(t_f)$ is known from the performance index [9, 14, 15].

Solving this equation backward in time and storing the solution in order to calculate the control gains as the process propagates forward, is only possible if the coefficients of the model are constant and the inputs are stationary. A very common way to eliminate this problem is to solve the $\dot{S}$ equation backward to steady state ($\dot{S} = 0$) and use this value of S, S_{ss}, for all time, thus assuming that only the stationary portion of the solution is of interest.

Given that the G and B matrices are time invariant, the result of using S_{ss} is a constant control gain, C_{ss},

$$C_{ss} = \frac{G^TS_{ss}}{B} \quad (19)$$

The advantages of the stationary technique include solving the matrix Riccati equation only once, and utilizing the constant control gain. This is very desirable from an application point of view because the constant control gain is simple, easy to implement, and can be derived ahead of time by solving the Riccati equation to steady state. Of course, this is not possible if the inputs are not stationary and/or the system model is time varying.

When considering a time variant plant, a constant control gain seems illogical and solving for a steady state solution to the Riccati equation is not applicable. These drawbacks are the reason for this study. The desired controller is one that efficiently derives the amount of control to apply at discrete time intervals based on the current state and plant values. The technique derived to achieve these objectives is labeled the one-step controller and will be discussed in a discrete context instead of the continuous format used for the stationary controller.

The discretization of the original system model equation 1 results in the difference equation

$$x_{k+1} = \Phi_k x_k + \Gamma_k u_k + \Lambda_k w_k \tag{20}$$

However, for only one-step,

$$x_N = \Phi_{N-1} x_{N-1} + \Gamma_{N-1} u_{N-1} + \Lambda_{N-1} w_{N-1} \tag{21}$$

Now the general discrete performance index is written as

$$J = x_N^T S_N x_N + \sum_{k=1}^{N-1} x_k^T A_k x_k + u_k^T B_k u_k \tag{22}$$

which, in one-step form becomes

$$J = x_N^T S_N x_N + x_{N-1}^T A_{N-1} x_{N-1} + u_{N-1}^T B_{N-1} u_{N-1} \tag{23}$$

where S_N, A_{N-1}, and B_{N-1} are analogous to the continuous weight terms $S(t_f)$, $A(t)$, and $B(t)$ in equation 4. The discrete control equation in one-step notation is

$$u_{N-1} = - C_{N-1} x_{N-1} \tag{24}$$

Since u is a scalar, the discrete control gain is [14]

$$C_{N-1} = \frac{\Gamma_{N-1}^T S_N \Phi_{N-1}}{\Gamma_{N-1}^T S_N \Gamma_{N-1} + B_{N-1}} \tag{25}$$

Substituting 25 into 24 produces

$$u_{N-1} = - \frac{\Gamma_{N-1}^T S_N \Phi_{N-1} x_{N-1}}{\Gamma_{N-1}^T S_N \Gamma_{N-1} + B_{N-1}} \tag{26}$$

To calculate the control to be applied at this step, Φ_{N-1}, Γ_{N-1}, B_{N-1} and S_N are required. The current values for Φ_{N-1} and Γ_{N-1} are known or estimated at every step, and the normalized performance index provides S_N. By writing an individual performance index at each step, the weight on the state vector at the end of the current interval, S_N, is known from the normalized performance index. Knowing S_N eliminates the need to solve for the steady state solution of the Riccati equation, and this computation reduction provides the desired simplification that allows the control gain to be calculated at every step. The only remaining variable required to compute the control (equation 26) is the weight term, B_{N-1}.

When selecting B_{N-1}, it is beneficial to consider the physical capabilities of the controller itself. For example, consider the output of a torque motor with the maximum output being the available amount of control, $\pm u_{avail}$.

The problem is to choose a value for B_{N-1} at each step. By definition, B_{N-1} is greater than or equal to 0. A value of $B_{N-1} = 0$ gives the largest (absolute) value for u_{N-1}. If the magnitude u_{N-1}, with $B_{N-1} = 0$, exceeds u_{avail}, then u_{avail} should be used for u_{N-1}, i.e.

$$u_{N-1} = \pm u_{avail} \tag{27}$$

The sign in equation 27 is determined by the sign of the quantity "$- \Gamma_{N-1}^T S_N \Phi_{N-1} x_{N-1}$" (the numerator of equation 26). However, should the magnitude of the right side of equation 26 be less than u_{avail}, then the maximum level of control is not desired. In this case,

$$u_{N-1} = - \frac{\Gamma_{N-1}^T S_N \Phi_{N-1} x_{N-1}}{\Gamma_{N-1}^T S_N \Gamma_{N-1} + 0} < u_{avail} \tag{28}$$

To summarize, the advantage of the one-step formulation is the incorporation of the current plant conditions into a simple control calculation designed to be computable in real-time. Performing this control calculation at every step provides the desired sensitivity to changing parameters and eliminates the computational burden associated with the steady state solution of the Riccati equation.

APPLICATION OF A ONE-STEP CONTROLLER TO AN INERTIAL STABILIZATION SYSTEM

Line-of-sight (LOS) stabilization/tracking systems are implemented in order to establish and maintain objects at prescribed angular orientations in inertial space. Conventional inertial stabilization designs can be separated into a tracking system and a stabilization system. The tracking system is responsible for the overall orientation of the controlled object, and the stabilization routine is charged with reducing or optimally negating "jitter" by insulating the controlled object from the operating environment. If both systems are successful in their tasks, the object is positioned and preserved at the desired inertial orientation. For the stabilization system to realize its performance objective, it must reject the disturbances present in the operating environment which are predominantly a function of the host vehicle motion [2, 13]. Masten and Zak [13] list aircraft, missiles, ships, spacecraft, and land vehicles as potential host vehicles.

The block diagram for the inertial stabilization system investigated in this paper is shown in figure 1. This control loop is one part of the overall line-of-sight (LOS) stabilization/tracking system, and its purpose is to maintain the LOS rate, $\dot{\theta}$, as close to zero as possible in the presence of torque disturbance T_d. This goal is pursued by estimating the current LOS rate and attempting to correct it to zero by applying control, u. Note that the control and the input rate command, $\dot{\theta}_c$, are the input to the torque motor. For stabilization system analysis, the input rate command is often assumed to be zero. Given this assumption, the ideal controller would be one that produces the torque motor output, T_m, that exactly cancels the torque disturbance, T_d.

Throughout this paper, the following assumptions have been made to simplify the investigation of this stabilization system. First, the gyro bandwidth is assumed to be infinite. Second, the input rate command is assumed to be zero. Third, the transfer function for the torque motor is assumed to be unity. And finally, since pure coulomb friction is discontinuous and many estimation filters as well as linearization techniques require taking partial derivatives, a continuous differentiable function is introduced for the friction model. For this study, the continuous and differentiable arctangent function is selected as a nonlinear friction model [1]. Investigation into the accuracy of the arctangent friction model as a representation of coulomb friction is beyond the scope of this study. The arctangent function is simply employed as a means of simulating nonlinear friction. Figure 2 depicts the block diagram with these assumptions incorporated.

Performing a controller study on the system in figure 2 is complicated by the presence of a nonlinear friction model, an incomplete or unknown structure model, and noise-corrupted measurements. Through the use of simplifying assumptions, it is possible to reduce the system down to a more basic level, thus minimizing the confounds and focusing on the control aspect. The knowledge and insight gained from the more simple system can be built upon by adding complexities, one at a time, and observing the effect of each added complexity. At this point, it is important to reiterate that investigation of the one-step control technique emanates from the desire to develop a real-time control algorithm that accounts for changing plant parameters. For the stabilization system currently being discussed, changing plant parameters arise from the linearization of a nonlinearity and/or from on-line estimation of plant parameters. The examples in this paper are constructed to examine the one-step controller's performance in the following systems: 1) systems with varying plant parameters that result from the linearization of a nonlinearity, and 2) systems where the assumed structure model is incomplete. The evaluation of on-line estimation algorithms is not included in the scope of this study, so, by assuming the system is known and constant, on-line estimation is not required. Furthermore, the ability of an estimation algorithm to deliver accurate state variable estimates while receiving noise-corrupted measurements is beyond the scope of this study. In this paper, noise-corrupted measurements are avoided by assuming that perfect state knowledge is available at all times. This assumption is recognized as unrealistic, but is utilized to focus on the control aspect of the stabilization system.

In the following examples, the key component models are the structure model and the arctangent friction model. Prior to the examples being presented, a brief description of these models is included. There are two structure models utilized in the following examples. The rigid body structure model is a very simple representation of the real structure, and it is used when the most basic structure model is desired in order to simplify the system under investigation as much as possible. The more complex structure model includes the first resonant frequency in an attempt to more fully describe the real structure. In reality, even this model is fairly simple.

As mentioned earlier, the arctangent function is used to represent nonlinear friction. The section of the arctangent function in the vicinity of the origin exhibits linear behavior, and is, therefore, referred to as the linear region. Also, as the slope through the origin increases to infinity, the arctangent function becomes increasingly more nonlinear. For the following examples, the slope of the linear region is selected based on the statistics of the input relative velocity, $\dot{\delta}$, so that the input corresponds to the linear region approximately 16% of the time. Therefore, the produced friction level is at or near the saturation level, f, about 84% of the time. This manipulation of the arctangent function is used to represent nonlinear friction in the simulations. Further details of this statistical procedure can be found in reference [20].

In addition to the percent linear manipulation discussed in the above paragraph, it is important to realize that the arctangent function requires linearization to be consistent with the LQG formulation. The linearization technique used in this study involves a first order approximation of the arctangent function using the Taylor's series expansion which yields a slope and an intercept. The slope naturally becomes part of the Φ matrix ($x_{k+1} = \Phi x_k$), and the question becomes how to account for the intercept. Obviously, the intercept is necessary in order to identify and utilize the proper line for the friction model. For the examples in this paper, the intercept is considered to be constant over the time interval, and it is assigned to be a state variable with its derivative being zero. Now the proper line is used for the linearization of the arctangent function, and the controller can account for the total input (slope and intercept) since the friction level is incorporated into the Φ matrix and x vector. It is important to note that the slope and intercept are functions of the current states, and for every time interval a new slope and intercept are calculated. Thus, the linearization process creates a time variant plant. A detailed derivation of the linearization process outlined above can be found in reference [20].

For each of the examples, a series of simulations are presented and interpretations of the results are offered. Each individual simulation assumes a maximum available control amount in order to emulate the physical capability of the hardware that is present in a given control system. By assuming a different maximum allowable control amount for each simulation and performing multiple simulations, the effect of different torque motor capabilities can be examined. A number of simulations are performed starting with u_{avail} at zero (no control) and increasing until the corresponding root mean square (rms) value of the LOS rate no longer appreciably changes.

Example 1

Now that the structure and friction models have been discussed, and the overall simulation procedure has been outlined, the first example can be presented. The block diagram for example 1 (shown in figure 2) includes the nonlinear friction model, a rigid body structure model, and the assumption that perfect state knowledge is available. The purpose of this example is to study the performance of the one-step controller when applied to a simple time varying system. The one-step control of equation 28 is used. As previously mentioned, the 16% linear arctangent friction model is utilized to represent coulomb friction.

For this first example, a brief demonstration of the formulation utilized for the linearization of the arctangent function is included. This linearization procedure is described in detail in reference [20], but it is discussed here, as well. As discussed throughout this paper, the presence of unmodeled structural dynamics should be considered in the design and implementation of stabilization systems, and example 3 illustrates a situation wherein such model insufficiencies cause performance degradation for particular available control ranges. In the first two examples, the rms LOS rate decreases as the available control amount increases. From the block diagram in figure 2, the system equations can be written as

$$\dot{x}_1 = \frac{T_d + u}{J} \tag{29}$$

$$\dot{x}_2 = -\frac{1}{\tau} x_2 + \frac{1}{\tau} w \tag{30}$$

where the state variables are defined as

$$x_1 = \dot{\theta} \quad \text{(LOS rate)} \tag{31}$$

$$x_2 = \dot{\theta}_b \quad \text{(base motion)} \tag{32}$$

The difference between the state variables is defined to be the relative input velocities of the friction model

$$\dot{\delta} = x_2 - x_1 \tag{33}$$

The normalized torque disturbance, $\overline{T}_d$, is derived and the pertinent variables are defined in reference [20]. The result of the derivation in [20] can be expressed as

$$\overline{T}_d = C_f \operatorname{atan}\left(\frac{s}{C_f}\dot{\delta}\right) \tag{34}$$

The next step is to expand the torque disturbance equation about the reference point $\dot{\delta}_o$ using the Taylor series. Dropping the higher order terms, the result is simplified to be the following linear equation

$$\overline{T}_d = m\dot{\delta} + K_{lin} \tag{35}$$

where
m = slope
K_{lin} = intercept

The K_{lin} term represents a deterministic input. Since K_{lin} is assumed to be constant over the time interval, it can be formulated as an additional state variable with a derivative of zero.

$$x_3 = K_{lin}$$

$$\dot{x}_3 = 0$$

Now the system equations can be written as

$$\dot{x}_1 = -mx_1 + mx_2 + x_3 + \frac{u}{J} \tag{36}$$

$$\dot{x}_2 = -\frac{1}{\tau} x_2 + \frac{1}{\tau} w \tag{37}$$

$$\dot{x}_3 = 0 \tag{38}$$

By following the discretization method outlined in [20], this formulation can be discretized to become the difference equation

$$x_{k+1} = \Phi_k x_k + \Gamma_k u_k + \Lambda_k w_k \tag{39}$$

The corresponding control equation for this third order system is

$$u_k = -C_{1k} x_{1k} - C_{2k} x_{2k} - C_{3k} x_{3k} \tag{40}$$

Notice the control equation accounts for the deterministic input, K_{lin}.

The above discussion briefly summarizes the linearization of the arctangent function and the formulation technique utilized in all of the examples.

The results of example 1 are presented in figure 3. The selection of a variety of available control amounts results in a range of rms LOS rates. Notice that as u_{avail} increases the rms LOS rate decreases, as expected. Also note that all cases with control produce more favorable results than the no control case. Obviously, it is very important for performance to be enhanced by the addition of control.

Figure 4 is a plot of the LOS rate and the applied control versus time for the u_{avail} equal to 0.3 case. Notice the applied control is constantly positive or negative 0.3, the maximum amount. This pattern is exhibited because the amount of control required to bring the LOS rate to zero is more than the amount of control that is available. In this situation, the controller applies all the control at its disposal, so the maximum value (positive or negative) is applied at every step. Also note that the applied control is opposite in sign of the LOS rate, as expected. Figure 5 is similar to figure 4, but it corresponds to the u_{avail} equal to 1.0 case. Comparing figures 4 and 5, obviously, the u_{avail} equal to 1.0 case (figure 5) relates to a larger applied control and a LOS rate that is maintained closer to zero. For the u_{avail} equal to 1.0 case, the maximum available control is applied less frequently than in the $u_{avail} = 0.3$ case because the LOS is closer to zero more frequently. Figure 6 shows the LOS rate time histories with and without control. These plots are included to illustrate the increase in performance as a result of adding the one-step controller.

To conclude example 1, this simple, time variant system is controlled and performance improvement is realized with the application of the one-step controller. The control gains are derived at every step based upon the available control and the local conditions.

Example 2

The assumed rigid body structure model in example 1 is a very simple representation of the real structure, and it is used to simplify the system investigated in example 1 as much as possible. For example 2, the slightly more complex structure model that includes the first resonant frequency (derived in reference [20]) replaces the rigid body model. The purpose of example 2 is to study the effect of the more complex structure model on the performance of the one-step controller. The block diagram for this system is displayed in figure 7.

The difference between examples 1 and 2 is the structure model, and, by comparing the results of these examples, the effect of the more complex structure model can be explored. Figure 8 plots the results for examples 1 and 2. Notice that example 2, which includes the first resonant frequency model, demonstrates a higher LOS rate for all available control amounts.

The structural dynamics present in the structure model used in example 2 cause the system to be more difficult to control. However, improvement is still observed by the application of the one-step controller to the more complex system. The resulting rms LOS rate for a given available control amount is higher than the corresponding value in example 1.

Example 3

In the first two examples, the structure is assumed to be completely described by the model utilized in the example; i.e., it is assumed that there are no unknown structural dynamics. In reality, there can be an infinite number of structural modes, making it impossible to completely describe the structure with a finite model. Example 3 investigates the performance of the one-step controller when unknown/unmodeled structural dynamics are present. In example 3, the controller will be designed assuming the rigid body model, but the actual simulation will be performed with the first resonant frequency model. This simulation strategy emulates the situation where unknown structural dynamics are present [16].

The results for this example are presented in figure 9. Similar to the first two examples, as the available control is increased, the corresponding rms LOS rate decreases. Unique to this example, however, the rms LOS rate eventually starts to increase with increasing available control amounts. These findings are assumed to be due to the unmodeled dynamics. As the controller is not designed to account for these dynamics (they are theoretically unknown), at some point, performance actually degrades as the available control increases. The point at which performance degrades varies with the system being examined.

As discussed throughout this paper, the presence of unmodeled structural dynamics should be considered in the design and implementation of stabilization systems, and example 3 illustrates a situation wherein such model insufficiencies cause performance degradation for particular available control ranges. In the first two examples, the rms LOS rate decreases as the available control amount increases. The rms LOS rate asymptotically approaches alminimum value as the available control increases. In other words, the larger the controller the lower the rms LOS rate. However, in example 3, it is demonstrated that, for systems with incomplete structure models, the control issue is not resolved by installing the largest possible controller. In this example, the minimum achievable rms LOS rate is determined iteratively by simulating various available control amounts. This iterative process indicates that larger controllers can actually deliver less desirable performance than observed for smaller controllers.

CONCLUSIONS

Control schemes designed for LOS stabilization systems have to perform in operating environments that include time varying plant parameters. The one-step controller derived and examined in this paper represents an attempt to construct a control scheme that responds to quickly changing plant conditions. This desired adaptability requires calculations that are simple enough to be applied in real-time. Utilizing the LQG formulation, the one-step controller derives the control to be applied over each step in time based on a performance index written for that individual time interval, the current plant conditions, and the amount of available control. This step-by-step assessment of the performance index is designed to adapt to local conditions and to be computable in real-time.

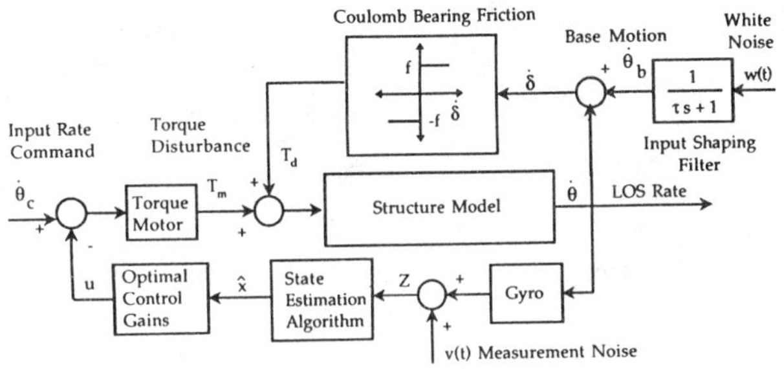

Fig. 1. Stabilization system block diagram

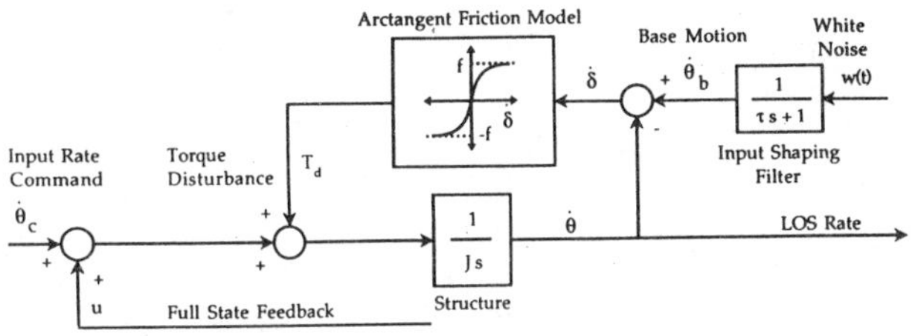

Fig. 2. Simplified stabilization system block diagram

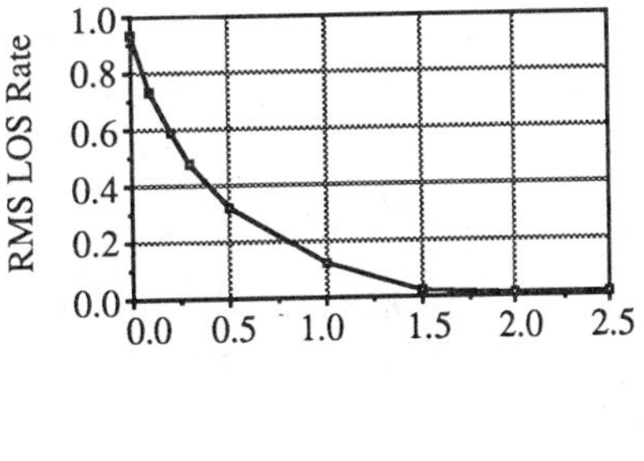

Fig. 3. RMS LOS rate versus available control for example

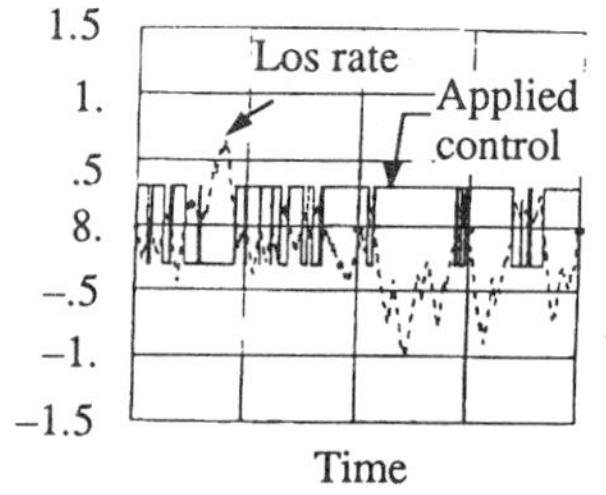

Fig. 4. LOS rate and applied control versus time for available control equal to 0.3 (20 seconds shown from 160 second simulation)

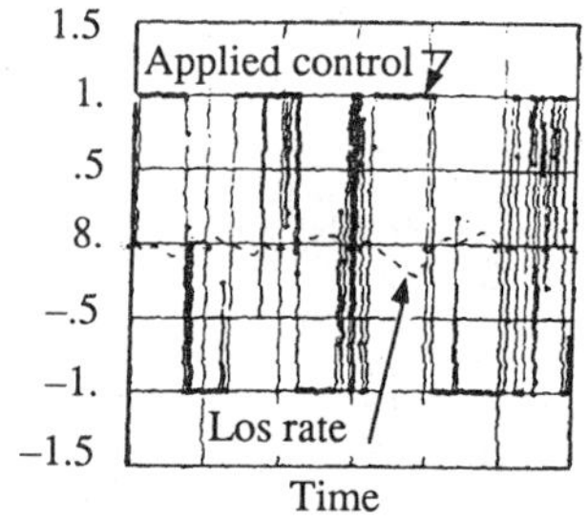

Fig. 5. LOS rate and applied control versus time for available control equal to 1.0 (3 seconds shown from 160 second simulation)

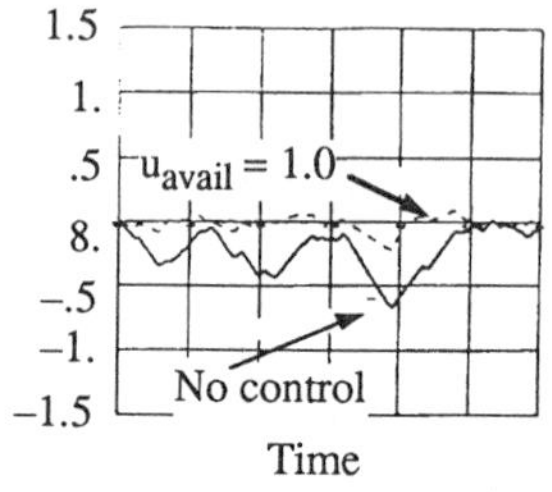

Fig. 6. LOS rate time histories for available control equals to 1.0 and no control (3 seconds shown from 160 second simulation)

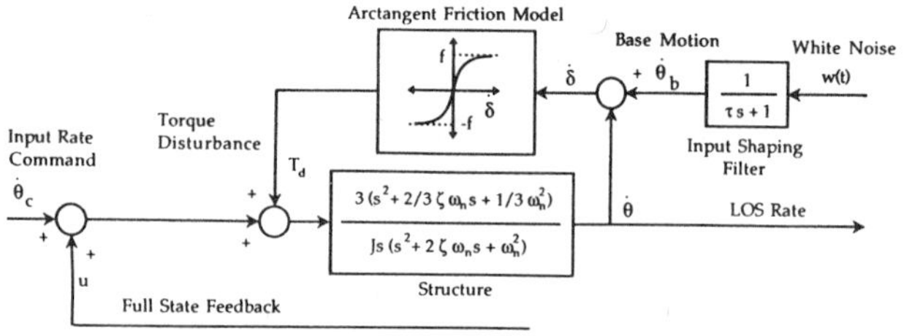

Fig. 7. System block diagram for example 2

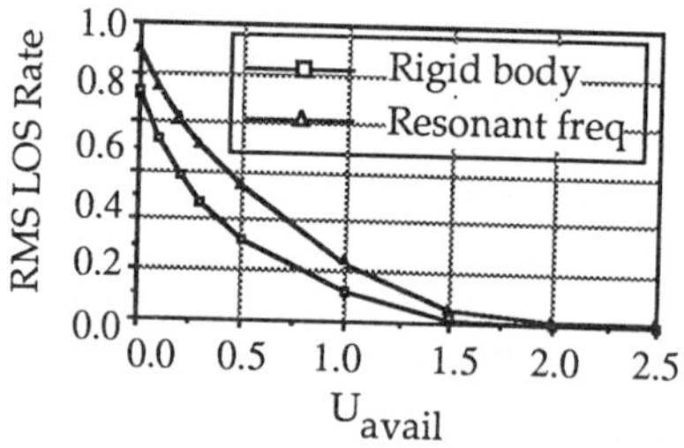

Fig. 8. RMS LOS rate versus available control for examples 1 and 2

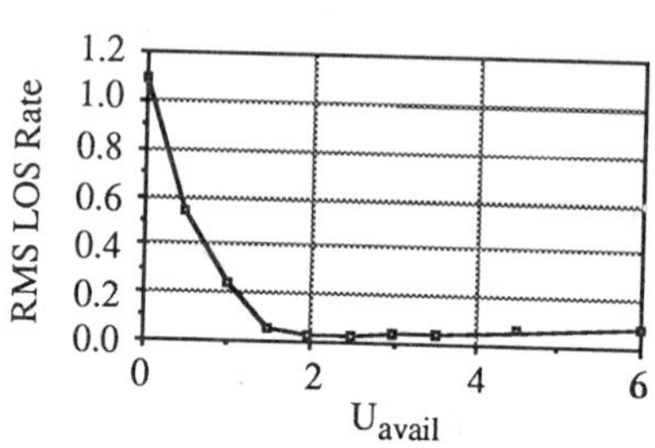

Fig. 9. RMS LOS rate versus available control for example 3

References

1. Hilkert, J.M. and D.A. Hullender, 1990. Adaptive control techniques applied to inertial stabilization systems, *Society of Photo-Optical Instrumentation Engineers Proce.*1304-21 (April), 190-206.
2. Bigley, William J. and Fred Schupan, 1987. Wideband based motion isolation control for a mobile platform. *Proceedings of the 1987 American Control Conference in Minneapolis, MN, June 10-12, 1987*, by the American Automatic Control Conference, Green Valley, AZ, IEEE, 2 1483-1490.
3. Youncef-Toumi, K. and J. Bobbett, 1991. Stability of uncertain linear systems with time delay. *Journal of Dynamic Systems, Measurement, and Control* 113 (December) 558-567.
4. Youncef-Toumi, Kamal, and Osamu Ito, 1988. A time delay controller for systems with unknown dynamics. *Proceedings of the 1988 American Control Conference in Atlanta, June 15-17, 1988*, by the American Control Conference, Green Valley, AZ, IEEE, 2 904-911.
5. Centinkunt, Sabri and Sijun Wu, 1991. Output predictive adaptive control of a single link flexible arm. In *DSC-Vol. 33, Control of Systems with Inexact Dynamic Models*, by the American Society of Mechanical Engineers, 125-132.
6. Long, T.W. and C.K. Carrington, 1991. The RAPT control method for nonlinear systems, *Journal of Dynamic Systems, Measurement, and Control*, 113 (December), 736-741.
7. Tomizuka, Masayoshi, Tsu-Chin Tsao, and Kok-Kia Chew, 1989. Analysis and synthesis of discrete-time repetitive controllers, *Journal of Dynamic Systems, Measurement, and Control* 111 (September), 353-358.
8. Yang, Sangsik and Masayoshi Tomizuka, 1988. Adaptive pulse width control for precise positioning under the influence of stiction and coulomb friction, *Journal of Dynamic Systems, Measurement, and Control* 110 (September), 221-227.
9. Maybeck, Peter S., 1982. *Stochastic Models, Estimation, and Control*, Vol. 3, New York: Academic Press.
10. Chang, R.J., 1991. Optimal linear feedback control for a class of nonlinear nonquadratic non-Gaussian problems, J. of Dynamic Systems, Measurement, and Control 113 (Dec.), 568-574.
11. Horowitz, Isaac, 1988. Quantitative feedback theory (QFT), *Proceedings of the 1988 American Control Conference in Atlanta, June 15-17, 1988*, by the American Control Conference, Green Valley, AZ, IEEE, 3, 2032-2935.
12. Walcott, Bruce L. and Henry R. Sebesta, 1987. Combined observer-controller synthesis for nonlinear/uncertain dynamical systems. *Proceedings of the 1987 American Control Conference in Minneapolis, MN, June 10-12, 1987*, by the American Control Conference, Green Valley, AZ, IEEE, 2, 868-873.
13. Mastin, Michael K. and Stanislaw H. Zak, 1987. Line-of-sight stabilization/tracking systems: An overview. *Proceedings of the 1987American Control Conference in Minneapolis, MN, June 10-12, 1987*, by the American Control Conference, Green Valley, AZ, IEEE, 2, 1477-1482.
14. Bryson, Arthur E. and Yu-Chi Ho, 1969. *Applied Optimal Control: Optimization, Estimation, and Control*, Waltham, MA: Ginn and Company.
15. Lewis, Frank L., 1986. *Optimal Estimation*, New York: John Wiley & Sons.
16. Bar-Kana, Izhak, 1991. Rohrs examples and robustness of simple adaptive control, *Journal of Dynamic Systems, Measurement, and Control* 113, (December), 721-728.
17. Gelb, Arthur and Wallace E. Vander Velde, 1968, *Multiple-Input Describing Functions and Nonlinear System Design*, New York: McGraw-Hill.
18. D'Azzo, John J. and Constantine H. Houpis, 1988. *Linear Control System Analysis and Design: Conventional and Modern*, New York: McGraw Hill.
19. Hullender, David, Paul Arrendell, Bo Li, Mike Knowles, Traci Riess, and Mazen Skaf, 1991. Applications of Adaptive Control Techniques to Inertial Stabilization and Sightline Control/Tracking Systems. Arlington,TX: The University of Texas at Arlington, Mechanical Engineering Department.
20. Knowles, Michael, 1992. "Formulation of a One-Step Discrete Stochastic Controller with Application to the Adaptive Control of An Inertial Stabilization System," Masters Thesis, The University of Texas at Arlington.

Proceedings of the
American Control Conference
San Francisco, California • June 1993

ROBUST DESIGN OF STOCHASTIC CONTROLLER FOR A GUIDANCE SYSTEM OF COMMAND GUIDED MISSILE

M. ABDEL-RAHIM, M. EL-GENEIDY, M. RIZK
Department of Electrical Engineering, Alexandria University,
Alexandria, Egypt.

Abstract

In this work, we use the previous results on the stabilizing property of a control scheme designed for a class of continuous time linear system with additive noise. The existing controller will be made more robust with a prescribed degree of stability by proper modifications. A state feedback controller is used in order to minimize the error between a reference states, which are the states of the system when there is no noise, and the system states which are affected by the noise. this noise is represented by a white noise with zero mean and unit variance.

1. Introduction

A command guidance system is defined as one wherein intelligence is transmitted to the missile from an outside source causes the missile to transverse a directed path in space, this path depends on the used guidance method. There are four guidance methods which are used in the command surface-to-air missile [1], these methods are the three points, the half lead angle, the full lead angle, and the C. There are several works which are applied to the guided missile systems. In the majority of the literatures [2]-[6] the guidance law is derived based on the equation of motion, analytical expressions for the capture area, missile command acceleration, homing time duration for an air-air missile. The influence of autopilot dynamics, maneuvering targets acceleration saturation, measurements bias, and missile slowdown following thrust cutoff on the miss distance is investigated. An optimal guidance law is derived to minimize a certain performance index. The robustness is discussed due to a certain parameter variations in [2], and not due to the all parameter variations. In this work the controller is derived using the equation that produces the controlling signals and the robustness of this controller is discussed due to the effect of a several factors which are considered as an additive noise.

2. The Problem of the Guidance of Command Guided Missile

In spite of the efficiency of the used guidance methods, it was found that the probability of destroying the target by one missile is law, because it is affected by several factors. These factors are related to the target, the missile, and the guidance station. To increase the probability of destruction, more than one missile, are launched at one target. To decrease the number of missiles which are launched at one target, we must increase the probability of destruction of the target by one missile, this will be done by applying a robust feedback controller to the computer so that the produced controlling commands will not be affected by the factors which decrease the probability of destruction, and the guidance process will be more efficient. In this method we consider that the factors which affect the probability of destroying the target by one missile are represented by an additive noise. We assume that this noise affect the computation of the controlling commands. Therefore the missile angles will be different from the reference values which correspond to the ideal bond values. Thus the missile will not realign with the ideal bond and the target will be missed.

3. Mathematical Model of the Problem

In the following equations the relations between the controlling commands and the error signals are given. Only the half lead angle method is presented here. As given in [1] the equations are as follows

$$K_1 = \lambda_\varepsilon \sin(45-\gamma) + \lambda_\beta \cos(45-\gamma) \quad (3\text{-}1)$$

$$K_2 = \lambda_\varepsilon \cos(45-\gamma) - \lambda_\beta \sin(45-\gamma) \quad (3\text{-}2)$$

$$\gamma = \int_0^t \dot{\beta}_t \sin \varepsilon_t \, dt \quad (3\text{-}3)$$

$$\lambda_\varepsilon = [h_\varepsilon + h_\varepsilon \frac{sT_1}{1+sT_2} + h_{d\varepsilon} + h_\omega] \frac{1+sT_3}{1+sT_4} \quad (3\text{-}4)$$

$$\lambda_\beta = [h_\beta + h_\beta \frac{sT_1}{1+sT_2} + h_{d\beta}] \frac{1+sT_3}{1+sT_4} \quad (3\text{-}5)$$

$$h_\varepsilon = h_{\delta\varepsilon} + h_{r\varepsilon} + h_{cr} \quad (3\text{-}6)$$

$$h_\beta = h_{\delta\beta} + h_{r\beta} + h_{cr} \quad (3\text{-}7)$$

$$h_{\delta\varepsilon} = r_r . \delta\varepsilon \quad (3\text{-}8)$$

$$h_{\delta\beta} = r_r . \delta\beta \quad (3\text{-}9)$$

$$h_{r\varepsilon} = - r_r \frac{\dot{\varepsilon}_t}{2 \dot{\delta r}} \delta r \quad (3\text{-}10)$$

$$h_{r\beta} = - r_r \frac{\dot{\beta}_t \cos \varepsilon_t}{2 \dot{\delta r}} . \delta r \quad (3\text{-}11)$$

$$h_{cr} = \delta\phi . r_t \quad (3\text{-}12)$$

$$\delta\phi = \omega \frac{r_t}{C} \qquad \omega = 2 \Pi f \qquad f = 16 \text{ c/sec}$$

The equation of the ideal bond of the half lead angle method are given as [1]

$$\left.\begin{aligned} \varepsilon_r &= \varepsilon_t - \frac{\dot{\varepsilon}_t}{2 \dot{\delta r}} \delta r \\ \beta_r &= \beta_t - \frac{\dot{\beta}_t \cos \varepsilon_t}{2 \dot{\delta r}} \delta r \end{aligned}\right\} \quad (3\text{-}13)$$

Where :

f : frequency of the scanning beam.

$C = 3\times10^8$ m/sec velocity of electro-magnetic waves.

k_1, k_2: the controlling command in the elevation and azimuth planes respectively.

$\lambda_\varepsilon, \lambda_\beta$: the control signal in the elevation and azimuth planes respectively.

γ : the twist angle of the ground coordinate system around the axis X.

h_ε, h_β : error signal in the elevation and azimuth planes respetively.

$h_{d\varepsilon}, h_{d\beta}$: dynamic error signal in the elevation and azimuth planes respectively.

h_w : component of weighting error.

T_1, T_2, T_3, and T_4 are time constants.

$h_{\delta\varepsilon}, h_{\delta\beta}$: error signal in the elevation and azimuth planes respectively.

$h_{r\varepsilon}, h_{r\beta}$: deviation error.

h_{cr} : angular error signal with respect to distance.

$\delta\phi$: angular error.

r_r, r_t : missil and target distances.

ε_t, β_t: target elevation and horizontal angles.

ε_r, β_r: missile elevation and horizontal angles.

$\dot{\varepsilon}_t, \dot{\beta}_t$: the target angular velocities.

$\delta\varepsilon$: the difference between the target and the missile elevation angles.
$\delta\beta$: the difference between the target and the missile azimuth angles.
δr : the difference between the target and the missile distances.

$\delta\dot{r}$: the rate of change of the difference between the target and the missile distances.

The system equations (3-1)-(3-12) can be divided into three parts. The first one is concerned with the calculation of the error signals. this part is represented by the equations (3-6)-(3-12). Since the calculation of these error signals depend on the used guidance method, then the contents of the first part will change according to the used guidance method. The second part is related to the calculation of the control signals, it is represented by the equations (3-4)&(3-5), this is the linear part of the system. The third part is related to the calculation of the controlling commands according to the controlling signals, it is represented by the equations (3-1)&(3-2). These commands are produced as a projection of the controlling signals because the missile has an x-shape [1]. We note that if one can control the linear part of the system we can adjust the controlling commands. Thus we conclude that equation (3-4)&(3-5) are our system equations to be considered. It is clear from these equations that the elevation and azimuth planes are decoupled. These equations can be rewritten as

$$\lambda_\varepsilon(s) = \frac{[1+s(T_1+T_2)](1+sT_3)}{(1+sT_2)(1+sT_4)} h_\varepsilon(s) + \frac{1+sT_3}{1+sT_4}[h_{d\varepsilon}(s)+h_w(s)] \qquad (3\text{-}14)$$

$$\lambda_\beta(s) = \frac{[1+s(T_1+T_2)](1+sT_3)}{(1+sT_2)(1+sT_4)} h_\beta(s) + \frac{1+sT_3}{1+sT_4} h_{d\beta}(s) \qquad (3\text{-}15)$$

Since $h_w(t)$ is constant [1], then after substituting the typical values for T_1, T_2, T_3, and T_4 in the previous equations, [1]. The system equations can be written in the matrix form. Since the operation of the radar tracking system depends on a train of transmitted and received pulses, and since the control signals to the missile are transmitted in the form of pulses, then the system is in fact discrete time system. If an additive noise is included to the discretized equations, it will be

$$x_{k+1} = A_d\, x_k + B_d\, u_k + f(x_k, u_k, W_k) \qquad (3\text{-}16)$$
$$y_k = C_d\, x_k + D_d\, u_k \qquad (3\text{-}17)$$

Where $f(x_k, u_k, W_k)$ represents the additive noise which is assumed to have the properties given in [12], and

$$A_d = \text{diag}(.994,\ .895,\ .994,\ .895)$$

$$B_d = \begin{bmatrix} .0023 & .0044 & .0057 & 0 & 0 \\ -.166 & 0 & 0 & 0 & 0 \\ 0 & 0 & 0 & .0023 & .0044 \\ 0 & 0 & 0 & -.166 & 0 \end{bmatrix}$$

$$C_d = \begin{bmatrix} .994 & .895 & 0 & 0 \\ 0 & 0 & .994 & .895 \end{bmatrix}$$

$$D_d = \begin{bmatrix} 2.01 & .2274 & .0057 & 0 & 0 \\ 0 & 0 & 0 & 2.01 & .227 \end{bmatrix}$$

Here we assume that the sampling period is .02 seconds. We can assume that the function

$$f(x_k, u_k, W_k) = G\, W_k \qquad (3\text{-}18)$$

with the following statistics

$$E\{f_k\} = E\{G\, W_k\} = G\, E\{W_k\} = 0 \qquad (3\text{-}19)$$

and

$$E\{f_k f_k^T\} = E\{G W_k\, W_k^T\, G^T\} = G\, E\{W_k\, W_k^T\} G^T \qquad (3\text{-}20)$$

Equations (3-16)&(3-18) have one of the forms represented by Yaz in [7]. Thus we can apply the robust stochastic controller proposed in [8]. Thus the feedback controller will be

$$u_k = -c(R + B^T P_{N-1} B)^{-1} B^T P_{N-1} A\, e_k$$
$$\simeq k(P_{N-1})\, e_k \qquad (3\text{-}21)$$

Where P_{N-1} is found from

$$P_{j+1} = A^T P_j A - A^T P_j B(R + B^T P_j B)^{-1} B^T P_j A + Q = \phi(P_j) \qquad (3\text{-}22)$$

The iteration starts with $P_o = F = F^T > 0$

Where e_k is the error in the states, i.e.,

$$e_k = x_k - x_{k\,ref} \qquad (3\text{-}23)$$

Where x_k the states under the effect of noise, x_{kref} the referece states, i.e., the states without the effect of noise.

Since the system is decoupled, (the matrix A_d is diagonal), then we can apply the state feedback controller to the vertical plane and to the horizontal one separately. Fig(3-1) illustrates the block diagram of the system with the state feedback controller for the vertical plane only. The horizontal plane has a similar block diagram except that $x_1(t)$, $x_2(t)$, $h_\varepsilon(t)$, $h_{d\varepsilon}(t)$, λ_ε, u_{1k}, $x_{1\,ref}$, and $x_{2\,ref}$ are replaced by $x_3(t)$, $x_4(t)$, $h_\beta(t)$, $h_{d\beta}(t)$, λ_β, u_{2k}, $x_{3\,ref}$, x_{4ref} respectively. Also $h_w(t)$ is equal zero for the horizontal plane.

4. Numerical Example

In this example we shall consider a target which is assumed to be flying at a constant altitude and with a constant velocity. We will show that, the missile will destroy the taget if the system is not affected by the noise. If the system is affected by the noise the missile will miss the target. Finally, the missile will destroy the target if the controller is applied to the system under the effect of noise. Since the system is discussed kinematically, then this controller is applied to the system under the effect of noise at three separate instants of time.

In the first case the controller is applied at one discretizing time before the impact point. In the second case the controller is applied after 14 sec from the beginning of the guidance process. In the third case the controller is applied from the beginning of the guidance process. In the three separate cases the target is destroyed. Consequently, it is proved that the controller is efficient.

The condition of destruction is fulfilled when the miss distance is less than 70 meters [1]. The following values are given as the launch and initial conditions for the target.

Velocity = 400 m/sec. Altitude= 10 km
Initial distance= 25 km

The initial elevation angle= 23.58°

The initial horizontal angle= 60°

The results of the above cases at the impact point are summarized in the following tables. Let the interception time to be denoted by t_f, and the miss distance to be denoted by z.

Table 4-1 " Results without the effect of noise, and with the effect of noise "

item	result without noise	result with noise
t_f	29.48 sec	29.48 sec
z	59.63 meter	240.97 meter
r_t	16.668 km	16.668 km
ε_t	36.88°	36.88°
β_t	37.3°	37.3°
r_r	16.61 km	16.61 km
ε_r	36.9°	37.53°
β_r	37.3°	37.94°

Table 4-2 " Results after controller applications "

item	t_f (sec)	z (meter)	r_t (km)	ε_t (°)
result	29.48	59.65	16.668	36.88
item	β_t (°)	r_r (km)	ε_r (°)	β_r (°)
result	37.3	16.61	36.9	37.3

The figures (4-1)&(4-2) show the target and the missile trajectories for the different cases.

5.Conclusion

In this paper the application of robust stochastic controller to the guidance system is studied. It is shown that the system consists of three parts, and the control of the linear part of the system, which is the second part, can adjust the whole system performance. The suggested controller is applied to the system under the effect of noise. The application of the controller is studied in three separate cases. It is proved that in the three cases the target is destroyed due to the controller application. The application of the controller is discussed in three different and separate cases because our system is discussed kinematically. From the dynamic point of view it is better to apply the controller from the beginning of the guidance process.

Reference

[1] J. slavicek, " Lecture Notes "; M.T.C Cairo 1968.

[2] S.D. Brierly and R. Longchamp,"Application of Sliding-Mode control to Air-Air Interception Problem " IEEE Trans. on Aerospace and Electronic Systems, Vol. 26, No. 2, pp. 306-325, March 1990.

[3] Ciann-Dong Yang & Fei-Bin Hsiao and Fang-Bo Yeh, " Generalized Guidance Law for Homing Missiles " IEEE Trans. on Aerospace and Electronic System, Vol. AES-25, No. 2 pp. 197-211, March 1989.

[4] Ilan Rusnak and Levi Meir, " Optimal guidance for accelerating constrained Missile and Maneuvering Target "IEEE Trans. on Aerospace and Electronic Systems, Vol. 26, No. 4,pp. 618-624,JULY 1990.

[5] Ilan Rusnak, " Discrete Optimal Guidance for High-Order Missile and Maneuvering Target " IEEE Trans. on Aerospace and Electronic Systems, Vol. 27, No. 6, pp. 870-872, NOV. 1991.

[6] J. Shinar and I. Forte, " On the Optimal Pure Strategy Sets for a Mixed Missile Guidance Law Synthesis " IEEE Trans. on Autom. Cont. Vol. 36, No. 11, pp. 1296-1300, NOV. 1991.

[7] E. Yaz, " A Controller Scheme for a Class of Discrete Nonlinear Stochastic Systems "; IEEE Trans. Automat. Cont., Vol.AC-32 No. 1, pp. 77-80, JAN. 1987.

[8] E.Yaz, " Robust Design of Stochastic Controller for Nonlinearsystem "; IEEE Trans. Automat. Cont., Vol. 34, No.3 pp. 349-352 MARCH. 1989.

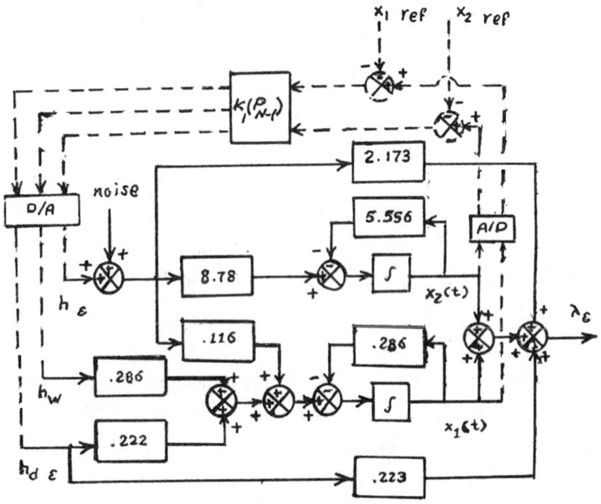

Fig(3-1) block diagram of the system with the controller for the vertical plane

Fig(4-1) the trajectories for the half lead angle method

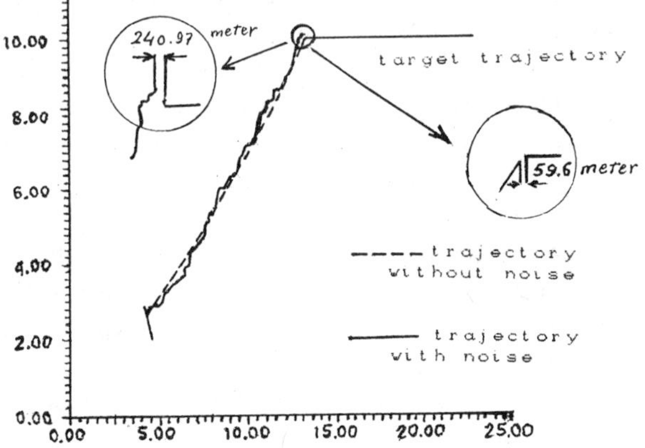

Fig(4-2) the trajectories after the controller applications

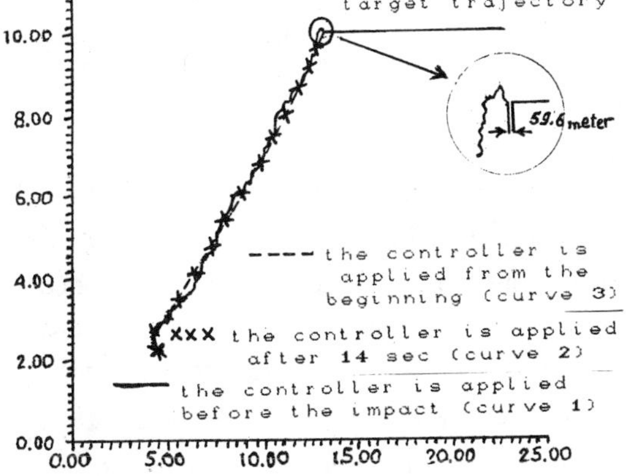

Proceedings of the
American Control Conference
San Francisco, California • June 1993

On the Stability of Stochastic Hereditary Systems with Uncertain Elements

Engin Yaz
Electrical Engineering Dept.
University of Arkansas
Fayetteville, AR 72701

Ilke Yaz
Mathematics Dept.
Centenary College
Shreveport, LA 71115

Summary. Conditions are presented for mean square asymptotic stability of systems described by nonlinear stochastic differential equations with multiple delays and uncertain terms. Stochastic Lyapunov method is used in the analysis which furnishes delay-independent stability results.

MAIN RESULTS

This paper is on delay-independent mean square asymptotic stability of uncertain nonlinear stochastic differential systems with multiple delays. The motivation for this work comes from the numerous application possibilities of stochastic models with delays, some of which are given in [1]. The stability properties of such systems are considered in [1]-[5]. We will be interested in the mean square asymptotic stability property whose definition is given in [1] and [3]. Moreover, we will consider delay-independent stability which means that the required stability property is preserved irrespective of the values of delay times. First, the system with associated assumptions and the physical reasoning behind those assumptions will be introduced. Then, sufficient conditions will be given for the stability of such systems in the mean square asymptotic sense. The stability results will be true for a whole class of nonlinear systems with a possible application to stability robustness of delay differential systems in the presence of deterministic (but unknown) and random parameter perturbations. Simple examples are included to illustrate the main result.

Let us consider the nonlinear stochastic functional differential equation

$$dx_t = \left[f_o(x_t) + \sum_{j=1}^{J} f_j(x_{t-\tau_j})\right]dt + \sum_{k=1}^{K} g_{ok}(x_t)v_k + \sum_{l=1}^{K} g_{1l}(x_{t-\theta_l})dw_l \qquad (1)$$

where $x, f_o, f_j, g_{ok}, g_l \in R^n$ for all $1 \le j \le J, 1 \le k \le K, 1, 1, \le l \le L$. $v_k, 1 \le k \le K$, and $w_l, 1 \le l \le L$ are scalar standard Wiener processes which are mutually uncorrelated and also independent of the initial conditions. We assume that the unknown nonlinear functions f_o, f_j, g_{ok} and g_{1l} together with the initial conditions are such that there exists a solution x_t of (1) which is sample continuous and strictly stationary [3]. Let us now specify the degree of uncertainty we have on the nonlinear functions.

Assumption 1. There exist positive scalars $\alpha_o, \alpha_j, 1 \le j \le J, \beta_{ok}, 1, = k \le K$, $\beta_{1l}, 1 \le l \le L$ and constant matrices A, $B_k \in R^{nxn}$, $1 \le k \le K$ such that

$$\|f_o(x) - Ax\| \le \alpha_o \|x\| \qquad (2a)$$

$$\|f_j(x)\| \le \alpha_j \|x\|, \; 1 \le j \le J \qquad (2b)$$

$$\|g_{ok}(x) - B_k x\| \le \beta_{ok}\|x\|, \; 1 \le k \le K \qquad (2c)$$

$$\|g_{1l}(x)\| \le \beta_{1l}\|x\|, 1 \le l \le L \qquad (2d)$$

for all $x \in R^n$ where $\|x\|$ is the Euclidean vector norm.

The above assumption shows that the nonlinearities we will be interested in are of sector-like nonlinearities which pass through the origin $x = \mathbf{0}$. In (2a) and (2c), α_o and β_{ok} represent the maximum deviation of the nonlinear functions from linearity described by Ax and $B_k x$, respectively. Our results, therefore, will be true for a fairly large class of systems (see [6] for models which include sinusoidal, saturation, deadzone, etc., type nonlinearities that fit this description). It is also possible to treat linear unstructured parameter perturbation problem for delay differential systems in this framework by just letting $f_o(x) = (A + \Delta_o)x$ and $f_j = \Delta_j x_{t-\tau_j}$ where Δ_o, Δ_j represent the parameter perturbations. There is another potential use for these results. One can model structured random parameter perturbations of a delay differential system by using (2c) and (2d) which results in the bounds on maximum perturbations for maintaining stability.

Assumption 2. Let there be two positive scalars γ and δ and two matrices P, $Q \in R^{nxn}$ both symmetric and positive definite such that the following are true

$$A^TP + PA + \gamma \sum_{k=1}^{K} B_k^T P B_k + \left(2\alpha_o + \delta + \gamma^{-1}\sum_{k=1}^{K}\beta_{ok}^2\right)\bar{\lambda}(P)I = -Q \qquad (3a)$$

and

where $\bar{\lambda}(P)$ $(\underline{\lambda}(P))$ are the maximum (minimum) eigenvalue of the P matrix.

Main Result. Suppose assumptions 1 and 2 are satisfied by the system (1), then it is mean square asymptotically stable for all

$$\frac{\underline{\lambda}(P)}{\bar{\lambda}^2(P)} > \frac{\delta^{-1} J \sum_{j=1}^{J} \alpha_j^2 + \sum_{l=1}^{L} \beta_{1l}^2}{\underline{\lambda}(Q)} \tag{3b}$$

nonlinearities in the class given by (2a)-(2d), and delay times given by (1).

Sketch of Proof. The proof is done in three steps:

1. The stochastic Lyapunov analysis using a quadratic function $V(x) = x^T P x > 0$ and the differential operator [1]:

$$\mathcal{L} V_t := 2x^T P \left[f_o + \sum_{j=1}^{J} f_j \right] + \sum_{k=1}^{K} g_{ok}^T P g_{ok} + \sum_{l=1}^{L} g_{1l}^T P g_{1l} \tag{4}$$

which, after a few algebraic manipulations, yields

$$\mathcal{L} V_t \le - a_o V_t + \sum_{j=1}^{J} a_j V_{t-\tau_j} + \sum_{l=1}^{L} b_l V_{t-\theta_l} \tag{5}$$

where

$$a_o = \underline{\lambda}(Q) / \bar{\lambda}(P) \tag{6a}$$

$$a_j = \delta^{-1} J \frac{\bar{\lambda}(P)}{\underline{\lambda}(P)} \alpha_j^2 \tag{6b}$$

$$b_l = \frac{\bar{\lambda}(P)}{\underline{\lambda}(P)} \beta_{1l}^2 \tag{6c}$$

2. Comparison result of [3] which allows one to infer stochastic stability results from deterministic differential inequalities.
3. A deterministic stability result in [7] for the scalar delay differential system

$$\dot{x}_t = -c_o x_t + \sum_{i=1}^{q} c_i x_{t-r_i} \tag{7}$$

which states that delay-independent asymptotic stability can be guaranteed if $c_o > 0$, $c_i \ge 0$, $1 \le i \le q$ and $c_o > \sum_{i=1}^{q} c_i$.

Examples

1. Consider the scalar stochastic delay differential system

$$dx_t = f_o(x_t)dt + g_{01}(x_t)dv_1 + g_{11}(x_{t-\theta_1})dw_1 \tag{8}$$

with

$$|f_o(x) - Ax| \le \alpha_o |x|, \ |g_{01}(x) - B_1 x| \le \beta_{01} |x|, \ |g_{11}(x)| \le \beta_{11} |x| \tag{9}$$

Since $\beta_j = 0$ for all $1 \le j \le J$, we can drop δ and using (3a) and (3b) find the conditions for stability directly in terms of system parameters (by eliminating P and Q) as

$$2(A + \alpha_o) + \beta_{11}^2 + \gamma B_1^2 + \gamma^{-1} \beta_{01}^2 < 0 \tag{10}$$

One can see that inequality (10) allows optimization of the value of $\gamma > 0$ if $2(A + \alpha_o) + \beta_{11}^2 < 0$ and $[2(A + \alpha_o) + \beta_{11}^2]^2 > 4B_1^2 \beta_{01}^2$ which yields the minimum value of the left hand side

$$2(A + \alpha_o) + \beta_{11}^2 + 2|B_1| \beta_{01} < 0 \tag{11}$$

that guarantees mean square asymptotic stability for all nonlinear functions satisfying (9).

2. This time consider

$$dx_t = f_0(x_t)dt + f_1(x_{t-\tau_1}) + g_{11}(x_{t-\theta_1})dw_1 \tag{12}$$

where $|f_1(x)| \le \alpha_1 |x|$. Now, γ can be taken as zero to yield the stability condition

$$2(A + \alpha_0) + \beta_{11}^2 + \delta + \delta^{-1} \alpha_1^2 < 0 \tag{13}$$

which upon optimization over $\delta > 0$ yields the minimum of the left hand side of (13) as

$$2(A + \alpha_o + \alpha_1) + \beta_{11}^2 < 0 \tag{14}$$

provided that $2(A + \alpha_0) + \beta_{11}^2 < 0$ and $[2(A + \alpha_0) + \beta_{11}^2]^2 > 4\alpha_1^2$.

REFERENCES

[1] V.B. Kolmanovskii and V. R. Nosov, Stability of Functional Differential Equations, Academic Press, London, 1986.

[2] H. J. Kushner, On the stability of processes defined by stochastic difference differential equations, J. Diff. Eqns., v. 4, pp. 424-443, 1968.

[3] G. S. Gadde, Differential inequalities and stochastic functional differential equations, J. Math. Phys., v. 15, pp. 738-743, 1974.

[4] T. Sasagawa, Mean-square asymptotic stability of linear heredity systems, Int. J. Systems Sci., v. 19, pp. 935-944, 1988.

[5] Z. S. Feng, Y. Q. Liu, and F. W. Guo, Multidelay linear stochastic systems: Mean square stability independent of delay, Proc. of ACC, Chicago IL, pp. 1089-1090, 1992.

[6] J.J.E. Slotine and W. Li, Applied Nonlinear Control, Prentice Hall, 1991.

[7] Z. S. Feng, Y. Q. Liu, and H. Z. Zhao, Necessary and sufficient conditions for delay-independent stability of multidelay linear systems, Appl. Math Comput., v. 46, pp. 23-32, 1991.

Proceedings of the
American Control Conference
San Francisco, California • June 1993

Second Order Interacting Multiple Model Algorithm for Systems With Markovian Switching Coefficients*

W.D. Blair

Research and Technology Department
Naval Surface Warfare Center
Dahlgren, Virginia 22448-5000

D. Kazakos

Dept. of Electrical Engineering
University of Virginia
Charlottesville, Virginia 22908

Abstract

An important problem is the estimation of the state of a linear system with Markovian switching coefficients. In this problem, the dynamics of the system is represented by multiple models which are hypothesized to be correct. The Interacting Multiple Model (IMM) algorithm is a novel approach to merging the different model hypotheses. In the IMM algorithm, the state estimate is computed under each possible model hypothesis over the most recent sampling period with each model using a different combination of previous model-conditioned estimates. In this paper, the second order Interacting Multiple Model (IMM2) algorithm is developed for estimating the state of a linear system with Markovian switching coefficients. In the IMM2 algorithm, the state estimate is computed under each possible model hypothesis over the two most recent sampling periods with each model hypothesis using a different combination of the previous model-conditioned estimates. Simulation results are given for a target tracking example to demonstrate the performance of the IMM2 algorithm relative to that of the IMM and second order Generalized Pseudo-Bayesian algorithms.

1. Introduction

An important problem is the estimation of the state of a linear system with Markovian switching coefficients. In this problem, the dynamics of the system is represented by multiple models which are hypothesized to be correct. Such a linear system with Markovian switching coefficients can be represented as

$$X_{k+1} = F_k(\theta_{k+1})X_k + G_k(\theta_{k+1})W_k \tag{1.1}$$

with observations

$$Z_k = H_k(\theta_{k+1})X_k + v_k \tag{1.2}$$

where X_k is the system state, and θ_{k+1} is a finite state Markov chain taking values in $\{1, ..., N\}$ according to the transition probability p_{ij} of switching from model i to model j. The W_k are white Gaussian errors for the system state process, and v_k are the white Gaussian errors in the observations and independent of W_k.

The optimal approach to estimating the state of the system in Eqs. (1.1) and (1.2) requires that every possible sequence of models from the initial observation through the most recent measurement be considered. Thus, for r models, the optimal approach requires r^k filters for processing the kth observation. Since this optimal approach is not practical, efficient management of the multiple hypotheses is critical to limiting the computational requirements, while maintaining the performance capability of the algorithm. One approach to managing these hypotheses is the Generalized Pseudo-Bayesian (GPB) algorithms.

In the GPB algorithms, the hypotheses that differ only in the "older" models are combined. The first order GPB algorithm, denoted as GPB1 and developed by Ackerson and Fu [1], considers only the possible models over the most recent sample period. In the GPB1 algorithm for r models, r filters with a common state estimate are used to generate the r different hypotheses. The r hypotheses are then merged to compute the state estimate and associated error covariance for output and the next filtering cycle. The second order GPB algorithm, denoted as GPB2 and developed by Chang and Athans [2], considers only the possible models over the two most recent sample periods. In the GPB2 algorithm for r models, r^2 filters are used to generate the r^2 different hypotheses. The r^2 hypotheses are then merged to produce r hypotheses that provide the input to the next filtering cycle. The r hypotheses are further merged to compute the output state estimate and associated error covariance. The means and error covariances of the r hypotheses are then input into the r different filters to produce the next r^2 hypotheses. The GPB algorithms of order greater than two are rarely used because of their computational requirements and complexity. Furthermore, the performance of the GPB1 algorithm is rather poor when tracking maneuvering targets because the hypothesized models usually differ only in the acceleration.

The Interacting Multiple Model (IMM) algorithm developed by Blom [3,4,5] is a novel approach to merging the different model hypotheses. In the IMM algorithm, the state estimate is computed under each possible model hypothesis for the most recent sampling period with each model using a different combination of previous model-conditioned estimates. The r hypotheses are then merged to compute the output state estimate and associated error covariance. The means and error covariances of the r hypotheses are then mixed to produce r model-conditioned estimates for the r filters to produce the next r hypotheses. The performance of the IMM algorithm closely approximates that of the GPB2 algorithm, while requiring slightly more computations than the GPB1 algorithm. Previous investigations documented in the literature indicate that the IMM algorithm is the superior technique when the computational requirements of the different techniques are considered [6].

In this paper, the second order Interacting Multiple Model (IMM2) algorithm is developed for estimating the state of a linear system with Markovian switching coefficients. In the IMM2 algorithm, the state estimate is computed under each possible model hypothesis over the two most recent sampling periods with each model combination using different previous model-conditioned estimates. The r^2 hypotheses are then merged to produce r hypotheses that are further merged to compute the output state estimate and associated error covariance. The means and error covariances of the r^2 hypotheses are then mixed to produce r^2 model-conditioned estimates for the r^2 filters to produce the next r^2 hypotheses. The performance of the IMM2 algorithm should closely approximate that of the third order GPB algorithm, while requiring approximately the computations of the GPB2 algorithm. Thus, the performance of IMM2 algorithm should be better than that of the IMM and GPB2 algorithms.

* This work was supported in part by the NSWCDD Independent Exploratory Development Program, Naval Surface Warfare Center Dahlgren Division, Dahlgren Virginia.

This paper is organized as follows. The IMM algorithm is presented in Section 2, while the IMM2 algorithm is developed in Section 3. In Section 4, the performances of the GPB2, IMM, and IMM2 algorithms are compared through a target tracking example. In Section 5, a summary and conclusions are given.

2. IMM Algorithm

In the IMM algorithm, the output state estimate and error covariance is computed under each possible model hypothesis during the previous sample period. For r models, a total of r hypotheses are considered through r filters operating in parallel with each filter using a different combination of the previous model-conditioned estimates. The probability density of the state at time k given measurements $Z^k = \{Z_k, Z_{k-1}...Z_1\}$ is approximated by

$$f[X_k|Z^k] = \sum_{i=1}^{r} f[X_k|M_k^i, Z^k]P\{M_k^i|Z^k\} \tag{2.1}$$

where $P\{A|B\}$ denotes the probability of event A given event B, and M_k^i denotes model i at time k. Since each filter uses a mixed estimate, consider the model-conditioned posterior density of the state given by

$$f[X_k|M_k^i, Z_k, Z^{k-1}] = \frac{f[Z_k|M_k^i, X_k, Z^{k-1}]}{f[Z_k|M_k^i, Z^{k-1}]} f[X_k|M_k^i, Z^{k-1}] \tag{2.2}$$

which reflects one cycle of the state estimation matched to model M_k^i. Using the principle of total probability over the models at time $k-1$ gives

$$f[X_k|M_k^i, Z^{k-1}] = \sum_{j=1}^{r} f[X_k|M_{k|k-1}^{i|j}, Z^{k-1}]\mu_{k-1|k-1}^{j|i} \tag{2.3}$$

$$\approx \sum_{j=1}^{r} f[X_k|M_k^i, X_{k-1|k-1}^j, P_{k-1|k-1}^j]\mu_{k-1|k-1}^{j|i} \tag{2.4}$$

where

$$\mu_{k-1|k-1}^{j|i} = P\{M_{k-1}^j|M_k^i, Z^{k-1}\} \tag{2.5}$$

and $M_{k|k-1}^{i|j}$ denotes model i at time k and model j at time $k-1$. As indicated by Eq. (2.4), the filter cycle matched to model M_k^i uses a probability density that is a mixture of the previous densities. Since the error processes are assumed Gaussian and the time or model update is linear, the probability density function for X_k in Eq. (2.4) is a mixed Gaussian density that can be approximated as a Gaussian density at $k-1$ with the estimates $X_{k-1|k-1}^j$ and associated error covariances $P_{k-1|k-1}^j$.

The IMM algorithm consists of a filter for each model, a model probability evaluator, an estimate mixer at the input of the filters, and an estimate combiner at the output of the filters. The flow diagram of an IMM algorithm with two models is given in Fig. 1, where $X_{k|k}$ is the state estimate based on both models, $X_{k|k}^j$ is the state estimate for time k based on model j, Λ_k is the vector of model likelihoods at time k, and μ_k is the vector of model probabilities at time k when all the likelihoods have been considered. With the assumption that the model switching is governed by an underlying Markov chain, the mixer uses the model probabilities and the model switching probabilities to compute a mixed estimate for each filter. At the beginning of a filtering cycle, each filter uses a mixed estimate and a measurement to compute a new estimate and a likelihood for the model within the filter. The likelihoods, prior model probabilities, and the model switching probabilities are then used to compute new model probabilities. The overall state estimate is then computed with the new state estimates and their model probabilities. A derivation and detailed explanation of the IMM algorithm are given in [4,5,7].

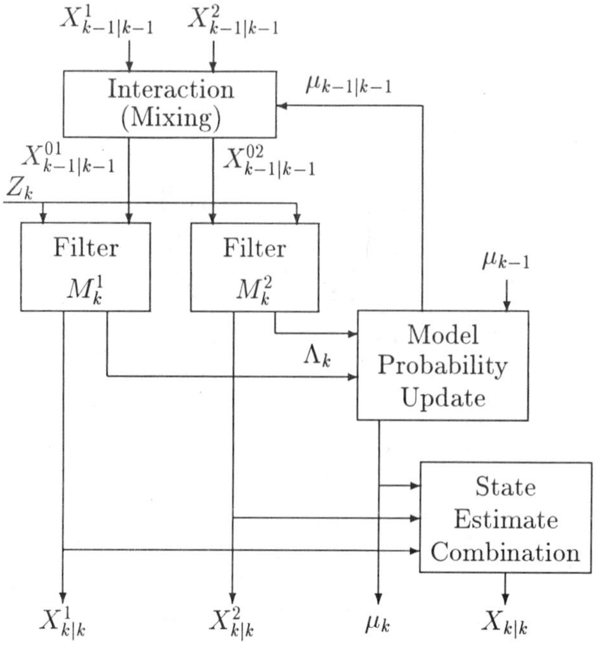

Fig. 1. The IMM Algorithm

3. IMM2 Algorithm

In the IMM2 algorithm, the state estimate at time k is computed under each possible model hypothesis over the two most recent sampling periods with each model hypothesis using a different combination of the previous model-conditioned estimates. For r models, a total of r^2 hypotheses are considered through r^2 filters operating in parallel with each filter using a different combination of the previous model-conditioned estimates. Using the principle of total probability for the r^2 model hypotheses, the density function for the state X_k given measurements Z^k is approximated by

$$f[X_k|Z^k] = \sum_{j=1}^{r}\sum_{i=1}^{r} f[X_k|M_{k|k-1}^{j|i}, Z^k]P\{M_{k|k-1}^{j|i}, |Z^k\}$$

$$= \sum_{j=1}^{r}\sum_{i=1}^{r} f[X_k|M_{k|k-1}^{j|i}, Z^k]P\{M_{k-1}^i|M_k^j, Z^k\}P\{M_k^j|Z^k\}$$

$$= \sum_{j=1}^{r}\sum_{i=1}^{r} f[X_k|M_k^j, M_{k-1}^i, Z^k]\ \mu_{k-1|k}^{i|j}\ \mu_k^j \tag{3.1}$$

The model-conditioned posterior probability density of the state is given by

$$f[X_k|M_{k|k-1}^{j|i}, Z^k] = \frac{f[Z_k|M_{k|k-1}^{j|i}, X_k, Z^{k-1}]}{f[Z_k|M_{k|k-1}^{j|i}, Z^{k-1}]} f[X_k|M_{k|k-1}^{j|i}, Z^{k-1}] \tag{3.2}$$

which reflects one cycle of the state estimation matched to models M_k^j and M_{k-1}^i. Thus, using the principle of total probability over the models M_{k-2}^l gives

$$f[X_k|M_{k|k-1}^{j|i}, Z^{k-1}]$$

$$= \sum_{l=1}^{r} f[X_k|M_{k|k-1|k-2}^{j|i|l}, Z^{k-1}]P\{M_{k-2}^l|M_{k|k-1}^{j|i}, Z^{k-1}\}$$

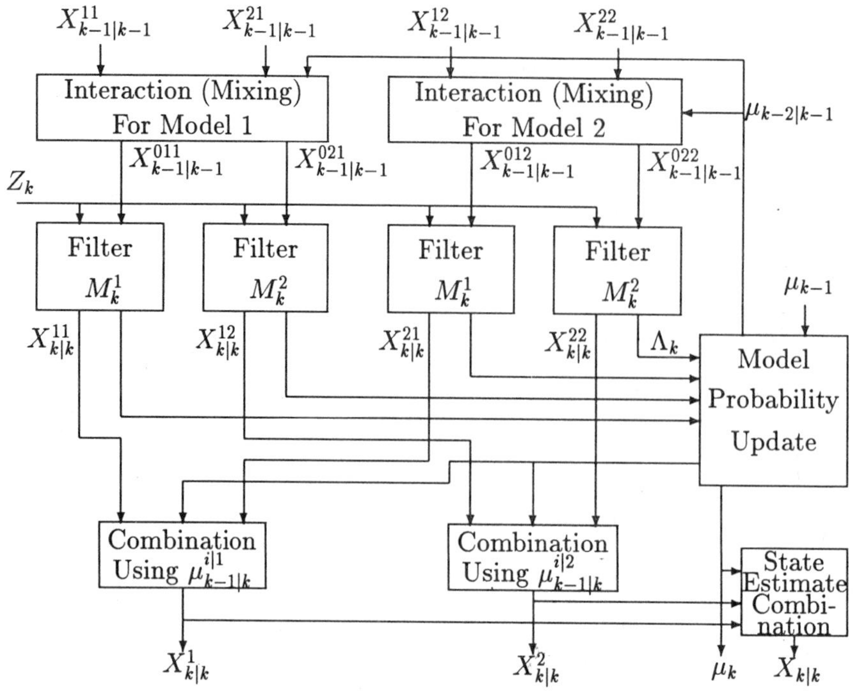

Fig. 2. The IMM2 Algorithm

$$\approx \sum_{l=1}^{r} f[X_k|M_k^j, X^{li}_{k-1|k-1}, P^{li}_{k-1|k-1}]\mu^{l|ij}_{k-1|k-1} \qquad (3.3)$$

where

$$\begin{aligned}\mu^{l|ij}_{k-1|k-1} &= P\{M^l_{k-2}|M^{j|i}_{k|k-1}, Z^{k-1}\}\\ &= \frac{1}{\bar{c}_{ij}}P\{M_k^j|M^{i|l}_{k-1|k-2}, Z^{k-1}\}P\{M^l_{k-2}|M^i_{k-1}, Z^{k-1}\}\\ &= \frac{1}{\bar{c}_{ij}}P\{M_k^j|M^i_{k-1}, Z^{k-1}\}\mu^{l|i}_{k-2|k-1}\\ &= \frac{1}{\bar{c}_{ij}}p_{ij}\ \mu^{l|i}_{k-2|k-1} \qquad (3.4)\end{aligned}$$

$$\bar{c}_{ij} = \sum_{l=1}^{r} p_{ij}\ \mu^{l|i}_{k-2|k-1} \qquad (3.5)$$

and $X^{li}_{k-1|k-1}$ is the state estimate for time $k-1$ with measurements through time $k-1$ that is based on model l at time $k-2$ and model i at time $k-1$, and $P^{li}_{k-1|k-1}$ is the associated error covariance. The probability $\mu^{l|ij}_{k-2|k-1}$ is computed as part of the model probabilities update on the previous filter cycle as given in Step 4 of the algorithm outline in this section. Eq. (3.3) is an approximation because the past through $k-1$ is summarized by r^2 model-conditioned estimates and covariances.

Since the error processes are assumed Gaussian and the time or model update is linear, the probability density function for X_k in Eq. (3.3) is a mixed Gaussian density that can be approximated as a Gaussian density at $k-1$ with the estimates $X^{li}_{k-1|k-1}$ and associated error covariances. With the Gaussian density for X_k with measurements through n denoted as $N[X_k; X_{k|n}, P_{k|n}]$,

$$\begin{aligned}&f[X_k|M^{j|i}_{k|k-1}, Z^{k-1}]\\ &= \sum_{l=1}^{r} N\Big[X_k; E[X_k|M^{j|i|l}_{k|k-1|k-2}, X^{li}_{k-1|k-1}], \mathrm{cov}[\cdot]\Big]\mu^{l|ij}_{k-1|k-1}\\ &= N\Big[X_k; \sum_{l=1}^{r} E[X_k|M^{j|i|l}_{k|k-1|k-2}, X^{li}_{k-1|k-1}]\mu^{l|ij}_{k-1|k-1}, \mathrm{cov}[\cdot]\Big]\\ &= N\Big[X_k; E[x_k|, \sum_{l=1}^{r} X^{li}_{k-1|k-1}\mu^{l|ij}_{k-1|k-1}], \mathrm{cov}[\cdot]\Big] \qquad (3.6)\end{aligned}$$

The IMM2 algorithm consists of r filters for each model, a model probability evaluator, r estimate mixers at the input of the filters, and an estimate combiner at the output of the filters. The flow diagram of an IMM2 algorithm with two models is given in Fig. 2, where $X_{k|k}$ is the state estimate based on both models, $X^j_{k|k}$ is the state estimate for time k based on model j, $X^{ij}_{k|k}$ is the state estimate for time k based on model j at time k and model i at time $k-1$, Λ_k is the vector of model likelihoods at time k, and μ_k is the vector of model probabilities at time k when all the likelihoods have been considered. The $\mu^{i|j}_{k-1|k}$ is the probability of model j at time k and model i at time $k-1$ given data through k. The $\mu_{k-2|k-1}$ is the matrix containing all of the $\mu^{i|j}_{k-2|k-1}$. With the assumption that the model switching is governed by an underlying Markov chain, the mixer for model i uses the model probabilities conditioned on model i at time $k-1$ and the model switching probabilities to compute a mixed estimate for r of the r^2 filters. At the beginning of a filtering cycle, each filter uses a mixed estimate and a measurement to compute a new estimate and a likelihood for the model within the filter. The likelihoods, prior model probabilities, and the model switching probabilities are then used to compute new model probabilities. The overall state estimate is then computed with the new state estimates and their model probabilities.

One cycle of the IMM2 algorithm for r models is summarized in the following five steps.

1. Mixing of the State Estimates

Starting with $X^{li}_{k-1|k-1}$, one computes the mixed estimate for the filter matched to M_{k-1}^i and M_k^j according to Eq. (3.6) as

$$X_{k-1|k-1}^{0ij} = \sum_{l=1}^{r} X_{k-1|k-1}^{li} \mu_{k-1|k-1}^{l|ij} \quad (3.7)$$

where $\mu_{k-1|k-1}^{l|ij}$ is given by Eq. (3.4). The covariance corresponding to Eq. (3.7) is given by

$$P_{k-1|k-1}^{0ij} = \sum_{l=1}^{r} \mu_{k-1|k-1}^{l|ij} \Big[P_{k-1|k-1}^{li} + (X_{k-1|k-1}^{li} - X_{k-1|k-1}^{0ij}) \cdot (X_{k-1|k-1}^{li} - X_{k-1|k-1}^{0ij})^T \Big] \quad (3.8)$$

Step 2: Model Conditioned Updates

The r^2 filters implementing the Kalman filtering equations are used to perform the time or model updates for the r models. For M_k^j with input $X_{k-1|k-1}^{0ij}$ and $P_{k-1|k-1}^{0ij}$,

$$X_{k|k-1}^{ij} = F_{k-1}^j X_{k-1|k-1}^{0ij} \quad (3.9)$$

$$P_{k|k-1}^{ij} = F_{k-1}^j P_{k-1|k-1}^{0ij} (F_{k-1}^j)^T + G_{k-1}^j Q_{k-1}^j (G_{k-1}^j)^T \quad (3.10)$$

$$T_k^{ij} = H_k^j P_{k|k-1}^{ij} (H_k^j)^T + R_k \quad (3.11)$$

$$K_k^{ij} = P_{k|k-1}^{ij} (H_k^j)^T (T_k^{ij})^{-1} \quad (3.12)$$

$$\widetilde{Z}_k^{ij} = Z_k^j - H_k^j X_{k|k-1}^{ij} \quad (3.13)$$

$$X_{k|k}^{ij} = X_{k|k-1}^{ij} + K_k^{ij} [\widetilde{Z}_k^{ij}] \quad (3.14)$$

$$P_{k|k}^{ij} = [I - K_k^{ij} H_k^j] P_{k|k-1}^{ij} \quad (3.15)$$

Step 3: Model Likelihood Computations

The likelihood functions corresponding to the r^2 filters are computed as

$$\Lambda_k^{ij} = f[Z_k | M_k^j, M_{k-1}^i, Z^{k-1}] = f[Z_k | M_k^j, X_{k-1|k-1}^{0ij}, P_{k-1|k-1}^{0ij}] \quad (3.16)$$

The likelihood of M_k^j and M_{k-1}^i is computed with the filter residuals $\widetilde{Z}_k^{ij}$, the covariance of the filter residuals T_k^{ij}, and the assumption of Gaussian statistics. The likelihood of M_k^j and M_{k-1}^i is given by

$$\Lambda_k^{ij} = \frac{1}{\sqrt{|2\pi T_k^{ij}|}} \exp[-0.5 (\widetilde{Z}_k^{ij})^T (T_k^{ij})^{-1} \widetilde{Z}_k^{ij}] \quad (3.17)$$

Step 4: Model Probabilities Update

The model probabilities for mixing on the next filter cycle are updated as follows

$$\mu_{k-1|k}^{i|j} = P\{M_{k-1}^i | M_k^j, Z_k, Z^{k-1}\} = \frac{1}{c_j} f[Z_k | M_{k|k-1}^{j|i}, Z^{k-1}] P\{M_k^j | M_{k-1}^i, Z^{k-1}\} \mu_{k-1}^i = \frac{1}{c_{li}} \Lambda_k^{ij} \, p_{ij} \, \mu_{k-1}^i \quad (3.18)$$

where

$$c_j = \sum_{i=1}^{r} \Lambda_k^{ij} \, p_{ij} \, \mu_{k-1}^i \quad (3.19)$$

The model probabilities for output and Eq. (3.19) are computed as follows

$$\mu_k^j = P\{M_k^j | Z_k, Z^{k-1}\} = \frac{1}{c} \sum_{i=1}^{r} f[Z_k | M_{k|k-1}^{j|i}, Z^{k-1}] P\{M_k^j | M_{k-1}^i, Z^{k-1}\} \mu_{k-1}^i = \frac{1}{c} \sum_{i=1}^{r} \Lambda_k^{ij} \, p_{ij} \, \mu_{k-1}^i = \frac{c_j}{c} \quad (3.20)$$

where $c = \sum_{i=1}^{r} c_j$.

Step 5: Combination of State Estimates

For output only, the state estimate for M_k^j is computed according to inner summation of Eq. (3.1) as follows

$$X_{k|k}^j = \sum_{i=1}^{r} X_{k|k}^{ij} \mu_{k-1|k}^{i|j} \quad (3.21)$$

where $\mu_{k-1|k}^{i|j}$ is given by Eq. (3.18). The covariance corresponding to Eq. (3.21) is given by

$$P_{k|k}^j = \sum_{i=1}^{r} \mu_{k-1|k}^{i|j} \Big[P_{k|k}^{ij} + (X_{k|k}^{ij} - X_{k|k}^j)(X_{k|k}^{ij} - X_{k|k}^j)^T \Big] \quad (3.22)$$

The output state estimate is computed according to the outer summation of Eq. (3.1) as

$$X_{k|k} = \sum_{j=1}^{r} X_{k|k}^j \mu_k^j \quad (3.23)$$

where μ_k^j is given by Eq. (3.20). The covariance corresponding to Eq. (3.23) is given by

$$P_{k|k} = \sum_{j=1}^{r} \mu_k^j \Big[P_{k|k}^j + (X_{k|k}^j - X_{k|k})(X_{k|k}^j - X_{k|k})^T \Big] \quad (3.24)$$

4. Target Tracking Example

To demonstrate the performance of the IMM2 algorithm, the IMM, GPB2, and IMM2 algorithms were simulated for a radar tracking system with measurements that are zero-mean Gaussian with standard deviations of 110 meters in range and 3.5 mrad or 0.2 degree in bearing. The radar measures the target position with period $T = 4$ s. Targets performing multiple g maneuvers are expected. For comparing the tracking performance of the proposed IMM2 algorithm with that of the IMM and GPB2 algorithms, the same models and parameters are utilized in the all three algorithms.

For all three algorithms, the models were chosen as (1) the Constant Velocity (CV) model, and (2) Constant Acceleration (CA) model with constant jerk process noise and the kinematic constraint for constant speed motion [8]. The IMM algorithm was tuned with a target trajectory that moves with a constant speed of 310 m/s and maneuvers with 3 g's of acceleration from 124 s to 140 s. The target began at a range of about 120 km and moves directly for the radar until a range of about 90 km where it makes the 3 g maneuver to turn about 90 degrees. The parameters for the IMM algorithm are also used in the IMM2 and GPB2 algorithms.

For all three algorithms, the process noise covariances were $Q_k^1 = 1.0 I_3$ m^2/s^4 and $Q_k^2 = 36.0 I_3$ m^2/s^6, where I_3 is the 3×3 identity matrix. The kinematic constraint variance for model 2 is given by $(100(0.75)^k + 174)$ m^2/s^4. The initial model probabilities were $\mu_0 = [\,0.8 \quad 0.2\,]$ and the model switching probability matrix is given by

$$\Pi = \begin{bmatrix} 0.9 & 0.1 \\ 0.3 & 0.7 \end{bmatrix} \quad (4.1)$$

Simulation results are given for the constant speed target in Figs. 3 and 4. The results are the average of 200 experiments. The Root-Mean Square Errors (RMSE) in the estimated position and velocity for all three algorithms are shown in Fig. 3. The IMM2 algorithm provides significantly better tracking performance than the IMM and GPB2 algorithms when the target is not maneuvering, while maintaining performance similar to that of the IMM and GPB2 algorithms during the maneuver. The

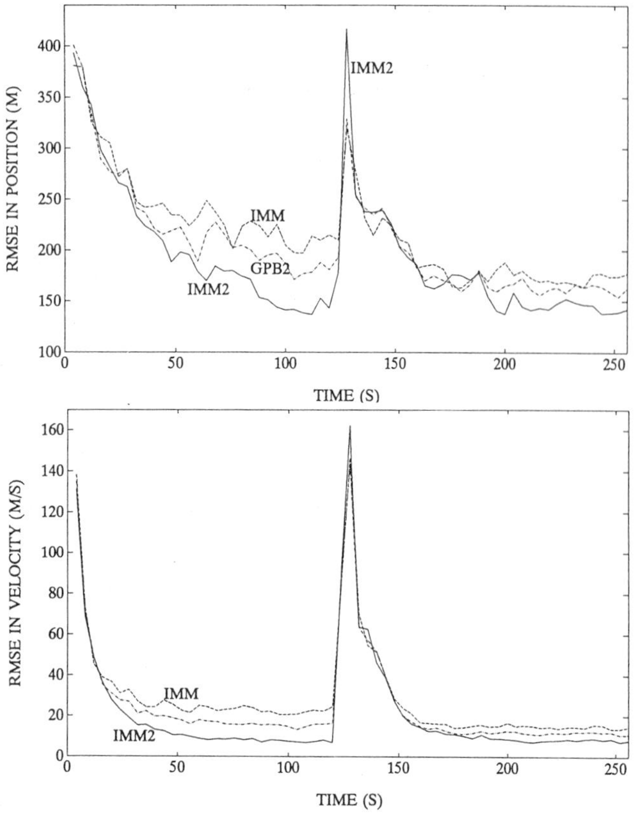

Fig. 3. RMSE in the State Estimates

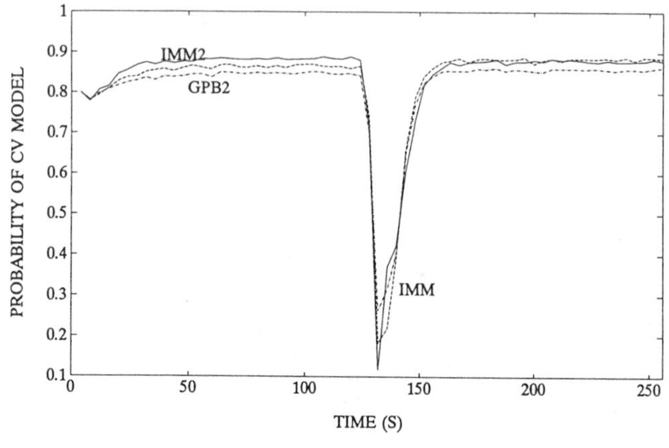

Fig. 4. Probabilities of CV Model

large peak error of the IMM2 algorithm corresponds to one time point. At the time points before and after the peak error, the IMM2 algorithm has errors that are smaller than the IMM or GPB2 algorithms. The average model probabilities of the IMM2, IMM, and GPB2 algorithms for the CV model are given in Fig. 4.

5. Summary and Conclusions

An extension of the IMM algorithm to second order has been presented for estimation of the state of a linear system with Markovian switching coefficients. This IMM2 algorithm is implemented for r models with r^2 filters that operate in parallel with each filter using a different combination of the previous model-conditioned estimates. While the computational cost of the IMM2 algorithm is significantly larger than that of the IMM algorithm, the additional computational cost may be very easily justified for systems with extremely demanding performance specifications. Also, when applications such as air traffic control have a very low data rate, the computations required by the IMM2 algorithm will be more easily justified. By utilizing the concepts used to developed the Interacting Multiple Acceleration Model (IMAM) algorithm [9], the computations required to implement the IMM2 algorithm may be reduced significantly. The IMM2 algorithm has a potential application in robust estimation for observations that have (heavy-tailed) non-Gaussian errors [10]. Furthermore, since the IMM2 algorithm maintains model hypotheses over the two most recent sampling periods, it may provide a technique for tracking maneuvering targets with observations that have (heavy-tailed) non-Gaussian errors.

Acknowledgements

The authors are grateful to Mr. R.T. Lee of the Naval Surface Warfare Center Dahlgren Division, for encouraging them to develop the IMM2 algorithm through stressing performance rather than computational cost.

References

1. G.A. Ackerson, and K.S. Fu., "On State Estimation in Switching Enviroments," *IEEE Trans. Auto. Cont.*, 1970, pp. 10-17.
2. C.B. Chang, and M. Athans, "State Estimation for Discrete Systems with Switching Parameters," *IEEE Trans. Aero. Elect. Sys.*, 1978, pp. 418-425.
3. H.A.P. Blom, "An Efficient Filter for Abruptly Changing Systems," *Proc. of 23rd IEEE Conf. Decision and Control*, Las Vegas, Dec. 1984.
4. H.A.P. Blom, and Y. Bar-Shalom, "The Interacting Multiple Model Algorithm for Systems with Markovian Switching Coefficients," *IEEE Trans. Auto. Cont.*, 1988, pp. 780-783.
5. Y. Bar-Shalom, *Estimation and Multitarget-Multisensor Tracking: Princples and Techniques*, UCLA Extension short course notes, 1993.
6. J.K. Tugniat, "Detection and Estimation for Abruptly Changing Systems," *Automatica*, 1982, pp. 607-615.
7. Y. Bar-Shalom, C.Y. Chang, and H.A.P. Blom, "Tracking a Maneuvering Target Using Input Estimation Versus The Interacting Multiple Model Algorithm," *IEEE Trans. Aero. Elect. Syst.*, 1989, pp. 296-300.
8. G.A. Watson and W.D. Blair, "IMM Algorithm for Tracking Targets Maneuvering Through Coordinated Turns," *Proc. of Signal and Data Processing for Small Targets 1992*, SPIE Orlando'92, Orlando, FL, April 1992.
9. W.D. Blair and G.A. Watson, "Interacting Multiple Bias Model Algorithm With Application To Tracking Maneuvering Targets," *Proc. of 31st IEEE Conf. on Dec. and Cont.*, Tucson, AZ, Dec. 1992.
10. C.J. Masreliez, and R.D. Martin, "Robust Bayesian Estimation for the Linear Model and Robustifying the Kalman Filter," *IEEE Trans. Auto. Cont.*, 1977, pp. 361-371.

Proceedings of the
American Control Conference
San Francisco, California • June 1993

STOCHASTIC ADAPTIVE CONTROL OF MULTIVARIABLE SYSTEMS WITH DEAD-ZONE NONLINEARITIES

Y.F. Xiong and S. LeQuoc

École de Technologie Supérieure
Université du Québec
Montreal, Quebec, Canada, H2T 2C8

R.M.H. Cheng

Centre for Industrial Control
Mechanical Engineering Department
Concordia University
Montreal, Quebec, Canada, H3G 1M8

Abstract

This paper presents a novel scheme for the direct stochastic adaptive control of a class of nonlinear dynamic systems. This class is characterized by a cascade of dead-zone nonlinearities and a linear multivariable system with a general interactor matrix. A piece-wise linear preload vector is introduced to invert the dead zone nonlinearity vector. An optimal adaptive control law is derived using a cost function in which the nonlinear parameter vector of the model is included. A switching gain sequence vector is employed in order to overcome problems of parameter estimation. This scheme is applicable even to systems whose linear parts are open-loop unstable and/or non-minimum phase processes. The algorithm ensures global stability and convergence.

1. Introduction

Many nonlinear dynamic systems may be modeled as a cascade connection of a static nonlinear element followed by a dynamic linear plant, where the nonlinear component may be a dead-zone, a saturation, some hysteretic phenomenon such as friction, and so on. In a real system, the parameters of these are often not known precisely, nor are they necessarily constant in value. The full potential of these dynamic systems will not be realized unless these static nonlinearities are properly taken care of by such well-established methodologies as system identification and adaptive control.

Several adaptive controllers have been proposed for SISO-systems with static nonlinearities, notably represented in [1]-[5]. To deal with the dead-zone nonlinearity effectively, a model reference adaptive control [6] was proposed for systems with a dead-zone with known parameters. For systems with unknown parameters, a stochastic adaptive control scheme [7] has been developed. An adaptive control was proposed for a cascade of a preload nonlinearity with dead-zone followed by a linear system in [8]. Furthermore, a tight control of the dynamic and stead-state performances of a nonlinear hydraulic systems was achieved in [9], where the important nonlinearity is a dead-zone element.

Compared with the research of adaptive controllers for SISO-systems with static nonlinearities, only very few have been reported for multivariable cases, e.g., a recent contribution in [10], where an adaptive control is proposed for multivariable systems with amplitude-dependent nonlinearities. This paper is an attempt to address the stochastic adaptive control of this class of nonlinear multivariable systems with a general interactor matrix. The nonlinear system is modelled by a cascade connection of a dead-zone vector followed by a linear multivariable system. In order to estimate the nonlinear parameters which appear to the identification algorithm as a rapidly varying system gain vector, we introduce a switching-gain sequence vector. This approach results in treating the nonlinear parameters to be estimated as time-invariant. By introducing a piece-wise linear preload vector to invert the dead-zone nonlinearity vector, an optimal adaptive control law is derived for the nonlinear multivariable system from a special cost function in which the nonlinear parameter vector of the discussed model is included. This scheme is applicable even to systems whose linear parts are open-loop unstable and/or non-minimum phase processes. Under certain conditions, the algorithm ensures global stability and convergence.

2. Design of Controller

2.1 Problem statement

Consider the nonlinear multivariable system described by

$$A(q^{-1})y(k) = B(q^{-1})\bar{u}(k) + C(q^{-1})\varepsilon(k) \tag{1}$$

where $y(k)$, $\bar{u}(k)$ and $\varepsilon(k) \in R^n$ are the output, input and disturbance vectors respectively. $A(q^{-1})$, $B(q^{-1})$ and $C(q^{-1})$ are $n \times n$ polynomial matrices in the unit delay backward shift operator q^{-1} with orders n_a, n_b and n_c, respectively. Note that $C(0) = I$, and

$$\bar{u}(k) = u(k) + m' \tag{2}$$

where m' is a time-varying parameter vector defined as follows,

$$m' = [m_1', m_2', \cdots m_n']^T, \tag{3}$$

with

$$m_i' = \begin{cases} -\mu_i', & \text{if } u_i(k) > \mu_i' \\ -u_i(k), & \text{if } |u_i(k)| \le \mu_i' \\ \mu_i', & \text{if } u_i(k) < -\mu_i' \end{cases} \tag{4}$$

where $0 < \mu_i' < \infty$, $i = 1 \cdots n$. The disturbance sequence $\{\varepsilon(k)\}$ is assumed to be white Gaussian noise with

$$E\{\varepsilon(k/k-1)\} = 0, \qquad \text{a.s.} \tag{5}$$

where $\varepsilon(k/k\text{-}1)$ is the prediction of $\varepsilon(k)$ based on all values up to and including time k-1,

$$E\{\varepsilon(k)\varepsilon^T(k)/k\text{-}1\} = \Lambda\ , \quad \text{a.s.} \tag{6}$$

with trace $\Lambda < \infty$,

$$\lim_{N\to\infty} \frac{1}{N}\sum_{k=1}^{N} \|\varepsilon(k)\|^2 < \infty \tag{7}$$

The model (1) and (2) can be written into its transfer function matrix form as

$$y(k) = T(q^{-1})[u(k) + m'] + N(q^{-1})\varepsilon(k), \tag{8}$$

where

$$T(q^{-1}) = A(q^{-1})^{-1}B(q^{-1}), \tag{9}$$

$$N(q^{-1}) = A(q^{-1})^{-1}C(q^{-1}). \tag{10}$$

Fig. 1 depicts such a nonlinear system with two variables.

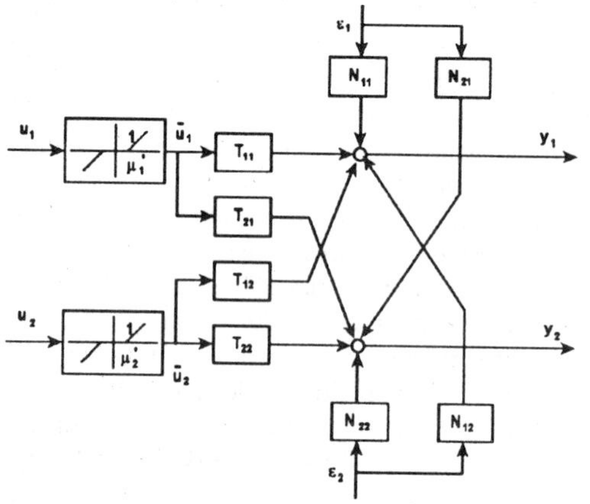

Figure 1. Model of the nonlinear system with disturbance

In (8), the transfer function matrix $T(z)$ between $\{\bar{u}(k)\}$ and $\{y(k)\}$ is supposed to be full rank almost everywhere in the complex variable z. From this assumption it then follows that [11,12]:

$$\lim_{z\to\infty} S(z)T(z) = K \tag{11}$$

where $K < \infty$ and nonsingular, the matrix $S(z)$ with $S(0)=0$ is called the interactor matrix [13].

For the system in (1) we make the following assumptions:

A1. The upper bounds for n_a, n_b and n_c are known.

A2. The interactor matrix $S(z)$ is known.

A3. det $C(z)$ has all its roots strictly inside the unit circle of the z plane, i.e. in $|z| < 1$.

A4. The reference sequence $\{y^*(k)\}$ is bounded.

2.2 The control law for a known system.

For the system described by (1), the measurable signals are $u(k)$ and $y(k)$. The signal $\bar{u}(k)$ is not possibly measurable. In order to design a control law, let us make a further assumption, that there exist limiting positive numbers μ_i'' that satisfy the following relations:

$$\mu_i' < \mu_i'' < \infty\ , \qquad i = 1 \cdots n\ . \tag{12}$$

Eq. (12) is not restrictive, since we do expect a real system to behave as such. For example, the ramp function can be used to determine approximately the value of μ_i'' [6]. Let us introduce a preload to be connected with the system shown in Fig. 1.

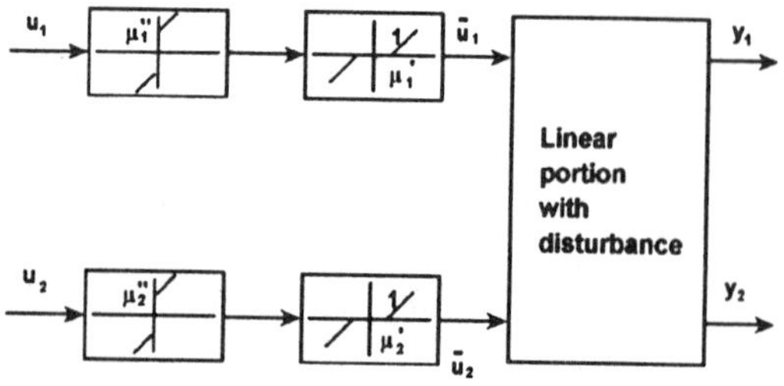

Figure 2. The equivalent nonlinear model

Because this preload nonlinearity inverts the dead zone (see Fig. 2), the equivalent model can be written as:

$$A(q^{-1})y(k) = B(q^{-1})[u(k) + m] + C(q^{-1})\varepsilon(k) \tag{13}$$

where

$$m = [m_1\ , m_2\ ,\cdots\ m_n]^T, \tag{14}$$

$$m_i = \begin{cases} \mu_i\ , & if\ u_i(k)>0 \\ 0\ , & if\ u_i(k)=0 \\ -\mu_i\ , & if\ u_i(k)<0 \end{cases} \tag{15}$$

with

$$\mu_i = \mu_i'' - \mu_i' \tag{16}$$

The objective is to find a control law which stabilizes the system, in the sense that all signals are sample mean-square bounded, and minimizes the cost function:

$$J=E\{(\|P(q^{-1})S(q)y(k)\text{-}R(q^{-1})y^*(k)\|^2+\|Q'(q^{-1})(u(k)+m)\|^2)/k\}, \tag{17}$$

where $P(q^{-1})$ with $detP(0)=detP_0\neq 0$, $R(q^{-1})$ and $Q'(q^{-1})$ are weighting polynomials in q^{-1} and m is as defined in (14).

Define

$$\Phi(k+d) = P(q^{-1})S(q)y(k), \tag{18}$$

where d is the maximum forward shift in $S(q)$. The optimal control law which minimizes (17) is deduced by using the optimal predictor

$$\hat{\Phi}(k+d) = E\{\Phi(k+d\ /k)\}, \tag{19}$$

which is given by the following Lemma.

Lemma 1

The optimal predictor $\hat{\Phi}(k+d)$ for $\Phi(k+d)$ satisfies,

$$G(q^{-1})\hat{\Phi}(k+d) = \alpha(q^{-1})y(k) + \beta(q^{-1})(u(k) + m), \tag{20}$$

where

$$\hat{\Phi}(k+d) = \Phi(k+d) - F(q)\varepsilon(k), \tag{21}$$

and

$$\alpha(q^{-1}) = \alpha_0 + \alpha_1 q^{-1} +\cdots + \alpha_{n1}q^{-n1}, \tag{22}$$

$$\beta(q^{-1}) = \beta_0 + \beta_1 q^{-1} +\cdots +\beta_{n2}q^{-n2}, \tag{23}$$

$$G(q^{-1}) = I + G_1 q^{-1} +\cdots + G_{n3}q^{-n3}, \tag{24}$$

$$F(q) = F_1 q + F_2 q^2 +\cdots + F_d q^d. \tag{25}$$

where $\beta_0 = P_0 K$ is finite and nonsingular. The proof for Lemma 1 is a straightforward extension of the linear case [11].

Theorem 1

(a) The optimal control law which minimizes (17) is given by

$$\hat{\Phi}(k+d) = R(q^{-1})y^*(k) - Q(q^{-1})[u(k) + m] \tag{26}$$

where

$$Q(q^{-1})=\beta_0^{T\text{-}1}\ Q'(0)^T Q'(q^{-1}) \tag{27}$$

(b) The resulting closed-loop system is given by

$$\begin{bmatrix} A(q^{-1}) & -B(q^{-1}) \\ P(q^{-1})S(q) & Q(q^{-1}) \end{bmatrix} \begin{bmatrix} y \\ u+m \end{bmatrix} = \begin{bmatrix} 0 \\ R(q^{-1}) \end{bmatrix} y^* + \begin{bmatrix} C(q^{-1}) \\ F(q) \end{bmatrix} \varepsilon \tag{28}$$

Proof.
Substituting (21) into (17) and equating $\partial J/\partial u$ to zero give

$$\partial J/\partial u = 2[\partial\hat{\Phi}(k+d)/\partial u(k)]^T E\{[\hat{\Phi}(k+d)+F(q)\varepsilon(k)-R(q^{-1})y^*(k)]/k\}$$
$$+ 2Q'(0)^T Q'(q^{-1})[u(k) + m]$$
$$= 2[\partial\hat{\Phi}(k+d)/\partial u(k)]^T(\hat{\Phi}(k+d)-R(q^{-1})y^*(k))$$
$$+ 2Q'(0)^T Q'(q^{-1})[u(k) + m] = 0. \tag{29}$$

From (20) we obtain $[\partial\hat{\Phi}(k+d)/\partial u(k)]^T = \beta_0^T$. (30)

From (29) and (30) we obtain (26). Using (13), (18), (21) and (26) implies the closed-loop equation (28).
Define

$$T_1(z) = \det\begin{bmatrix} A(z) & -B(z) \\ P(z)S(z) & Q(z) \end{bmatrix} \tag{31}$$

If we choose $P(z)$ and $Q(z)$ such that $T_1(z) \neq 0$ in $|z| \geq 1$, the closed-loop system will be stable. Substituting (26) into (21) and introducing this result into (17) yields,

$$E\{\|P(q^{-1})S(q)y(k)-R(q^{-1})y^*(k)+Q(q^{-1})[u(k)+m]\|^2 / k\}=L, \tag{32}$$

where $L = E\{\|F(q)\varepsilon(k)\|^2 / k\}$. (33)

3. A Direct Adaptive Control Algorithm

In this section, we derive a direct adaptive control algorithm for the nonlinear system described by (13). The parameter matrices of the controller are to be estimated recursively. First we have to determine the estimation equation of the parameters of the controller and the control law equation. The optimal predictor (20) can be written as

$$\hat{\Phi}(k+d) = \alpha(q^{-1})y(k) + \beta(q^{-1})[u(k) + m] + q(I-G(q^{-1}))\hat{\Phi}(k+d-1)$$
$$= \theta^T x(k) \tag{34}$$

where $\theta = [\alpha_0 \cdots \alpha_{n1}, \beta_0 \cdots \beta_{n2}, -G_1 \cdots -G_{n3}]^T,$ (35)

$$x(k) = [y^T(k) \cdots y^T(k-n_1), u^T(k)+m^T \cdots u^T(k-n_2)$$
$$+m^T, \hat{\Phi}^T(k+d-1) \cdots \hat{\Phi}^T(k+d-n_3)]^T. \tag{36}$$

In the linear case, i.e. $m = 0$, we identify recursively in time the parameters of (35) and compute the optimal control law according to (26) and (34) as,

$$\hat{\theta}^T x(k) - R(q^{-1})y^*(k) + Q(q^{-1})u(k) = 0. \tag{37}$$

In the nonlinear case, since m as defined by (14) is unknown, it is impossible to identify θ directly. However, an extension of the method that is developed in [7] for SISO models is applicable to the multivariable case.

Define $H(k) = [h_1(k), h_2(k), \cdots h_3(k)]^T, \quad i = 1 \cdots n,$ (38)
where

$$h_i(k) = \begin{cases} 1, & \text{if } u_i(k)>0 \\ 0, & \text{if } u_i(k)=0 \\ -1, & \text{if } u_i(k)<0 \end{cases} \tag{39}$$

$H(k)$ is called as a switching-gain sequence vector.

Define $M = diag\ (\mu_i), \quad i = 1 \cdots n,$ (40)

We rewrite (35) and (36) as,

$$\theta = [\alpha_0 \cdots \alpha_{n1}, \beta_0 \cdots \beta_{n2}, \beta_0^* \cdots \beta_{n2}^*, -G_1 \cdots -G_{n3}]^T \tag{41}$$

$$x(k) = [y^T(k) \cdots y^T(k-n_1), u^T(k) \cdots u^T(k-n_2), H^T(k) \cdots H^T(k-n_2),$$
$$\hat{\Phi}^T(k+d-1) \cdots \hat{\Phi}^T(k+d-n_3)]^T. \tag{42}$$

where $\beta_i^* = \beta_i M$, $i = 0 \cdots n_2$. By making use of the switching-gain sequence vector $H(k)$, the parameters in matrix θ can be estimated. The optimal predictor $\hat{\Phi}(k+d)$ is a function of θ, which contains the coefficients of the polynomial matrices $\alpha(q^{-1})$, $\beta(q^{-1})$, and $G(q^{-1})$. In the recursive algorithm, θ is replaced by its estimate $\hat{\theta}(k)$. Also, in the special form that we have developed, the optimal predictor $\hat{\Phi}(k+d)$ depends on $\hat{\Phi}(k+d-1), \cdots \hat{\Phi}(k+d-n_3)$. In the recursive prediction, these values are replaced by estimates depending on $\hat{\theta}(k-1), \cdots \hat{\theta}(k-n_3)$. This motivates the following modified recursive least-squares algorithm for $k \geq d$:

$$\hat{\theta}(k) = \hat{\theta}(k-d) + a(k-d)P(k-d)\hat{x}(k-d)e(k), \tag{43}$$

with any deterministic initial values $\theta(j)$ for $j = 0 \cdots d-1$, where

$$e(k) = \Phi(k) - \hat{\theta}^T(k-d)\hat{x}(k-d), \tag{44}$$

$$\hat{x}(k) = [y^T(k) \cdots y^T(k-n_1), u^T(k) \cdots u^T(k-n_2), H^T(k) \cdots H^T(k-n_2),$$
$$\overline{\Phi}^T(k+d-1) \cdots \overline{\Phi}^T(k+d-n_3)]^T, \tag{45}$$

and $\overline{\Phi}(k+d)$ is the a posteriori prediction given by

$$\overline{\Phi}(k+d) = \theta^T(k)\hat{x}(k-d), \text{ with } \overline{\Phi}(j) = 0 \text{ for } j \leq 2d-1. \tag{46}$$

Define $r(k-d)$ recursively by

$$r(k-d) = r(k-d-1) + \|\hat{x}(k-d)\|^2, \text{ with } r(-d) = \cdots = r(-1)=1 \tag{47}$$

and $P(-d) = \cdots = P(-1) = n(n_1 + 2\cdot n_2 + n_3)I.$ (48)

Calculate the matrix $P'(k)$ as

$$P'(k-d) = P(k-2d) - \frac{P(k-2d)\hat{x}(k-d)\hat{x}^T(k-d)P(k-2d)}{1 + \hat{x}^T(k-d)P(k-2d)\hat{x}(k-d)} \tag{49}$$

and its maximum and minimum eigenvalues λ_{max} and λ_{min}. If

$$\lambda_{max}(k-d)/\lambda_{min}(k-d) \leq k_1 < \infty, \tag{50}$$

and $\hat{x}^T(k-d)P'(k-d)\hat{x}(k-d) \leq k_2 < 1,$ (51)

then $P(k-d) = P'(k-d),$ (52)

and $a(k-d) = 1.$ (53)

If neither (50) nor (51) is satisfied, then

$$P(k-d) = r(k-2d)P(k-2d)/r(k-d) \tag{54}$$

and $a(k-d) = 1/(1+\hat{x}^T(k-d)P(k-d)\hat{x}(k-d)).$ (55)

The modified least squares algorithm (43)-(55) is a straight-forward extension of the algorithm [14] for the case $d = 1$ and the SISO-algorithm [15]. Some useful properties of the algorithm (43)-(55) are summarized in the following.

Lemma 2

$$e(k) = \sigma(k)/(1-a(k-d)\hat{x}^T(k-d)P(k-d)\hat{x}(k-d)) \tag{56}$$

and $0 < (1-a(k)\hat{x}^T(k)P(k)\hat{x}(k)) \leq 1, \quad$ for all k (57)

where $\sigma(k) = \Phi(k+d) - \overline{\Phi}(k+d).$ (58)

Lemma 3

$$\lim_{N\to\infty} \frac{1}{r(N)} \sum_{k=1}^{N} \|\sigma(k)-v(k)\|^2 = 0, \qquad a.s. \tag{59}$$

where $$v(k) = F(q)\varepsilon(k-d). \tag{60}$$

Lemmas 2 and 3 are evident from using a similar argument applied in [14]. With $\hat{\theta}^T(k)$, the optimal control law can be written according to (26) and (34) as,

$$\hat{\theta}^T(k)\hat{x}(k) - R(q^{-1})y^*(k) + Q(q^{-1})[u(k) + m] = 0, \tag{61}$$

where $$\hat{\theta}^T(k)\hat{x}(k) = \hat{\alpha}(q^{-1})y(k) + \hat{\beta}(q^{-1})u(k) + \hat{\beta}^*(q^{-1})H(k) + q(I-\hat{G}(q^{-1}))\overline{\Phi}(k+d-1), \tag{62}$$

$$Q(q^{-1})[u(k) + m] = Q(q^{-1})u(k) + Q^*(q^{-1})H(k), \tag{63}$$

and where $\beta^*(q^{-1}) = \beta(q^{-1})M$ and $Q^*(q^{-1}) = Q(q^{-1})M$. Because $\hat{\beta}(q^{-1})$ and $\hat{\beta}^*(q^{-1})$ are obtained from $\hat{\theta}(k)$, M and $Q^*(q^{-1})$ can be calculated. Because $H(k)$ and $u(k)$ are mutually inter-dependent, we cannot directly calculate $u(k)$ from (62). *Thus*, $P(z)$ and $Q(z)$ are chosen off-line similar to (31) such that

$$T_1(z) = \det\begin{bmatrix} A(z) & -B(z) \\ P(z)S(z) & Q(z) \end{bmatrix} \neq 0, \qquad in\ |z| \geq 1. \tag{64}$$

We know that $H(k)$ is only related to the sign of $u(k)$. From this point of view, we try to determine the sign of $u(k)$ first. Define

$$V_1 = R(q^{-1})y^*(k) - \hat{\alpha}(q^{-1})y(k) - q(I-\hat{G}(q^{-1}))\overline{\Phi}(k+d-1). \tag{65}$$

By using (61), (62), and (65), the optimal control law is as

$$[\hat{\beta}(q^{-1}) + Q(q^{-1})]u(k) + [\hat{\beta}^*(q^{-1}) + Q^*(q^{-1})]H(k) = V_1. \tag{66}$$

Define $$V_2 = [\hat{\beta}(q^{-1}) - \hat{\beta}_0 + Q(q^{-1}) - Q_0]u(k) + [\hat{\beta}^*(q^{-1}) - \hat{\beta}_0^* + Q^*(q^{-1}) - Q_0^*]H(k) \tag{67}$$

$$V = V_1 - V_2. \tag{68}$$

Equation (66) can be rewritten as

$$(\hat{\beta}_0^* + Q_0^*)u(k) + (\hat{\beta}_0^* + Q_0^*)H(k) = V. \tag{69}$$

We know that V is not related to $H(k)$ and $u(k)$, while $H(k)$ on the left side of (69) depends on the sign of u(k), which can be determined according to (69). Thus calculating $u(k)$ is a straightforward extension of [7] for the single variable case.

4. Global Stability and Convergence Analysis

A stability analysis of this adaptive algorithm is performed. Proof of the stability and convergence is based on the elementary properties of the parameter estimation algorithm in (43)-(55), which are already summarized in *Lemma 2* and *3*.

The following assumption is useful.

A5. $[c(z) - I/2]$ is strictly positive and real.

Theorem 2 (on global stability and convergence)

Let equations (5)-(7) and (64) and assumptions *A1-A5* hold for the nonlinear system described in (13). If the adaptive algorithm in section 3 is used to system (13), it is globally stable and convergent in the sense that with probability one,

$$\lim_{N\to\infty} sup \frac{1}{N} \sum_{k=1}^{N} \|y(k)\|^2 < \infty \tag{70}$$

$$\lim_{N\to\infty} sup \frac{1}{N} \sum_{k=1}^{N} \|u(k)\|^2 < \infty \tag{71}$$

$$\lim_{N\to\infty} sup \frac{1}{N} \sum_{k=1}^{N} \|\bar{u}(k)\|^2 < \infty \tag{72}$$

$$\lim_{N\to\infty} \frac{1}{N} \sum_{k=1}^{N} E\{\|PSy(k) - Ry^*(k) + Q[u(k)+m]\|^2/k\} = L \tag{73}$$

where L is defined in (33).

Proof.

Define $$\delta(k) = 1 - a(k)\hat{x}^T(k)P(k)\hat{x}(k) \tag{74}$$

From Lemma 2 we have, $$e(k) = \sigma(k)/\delta(k-d) \tag{75}$$

and $$0 < \delta(k) \leq 1, \quad \text{for all } k \tag{76}$$

Using (44) and (61),

$$e(k+d) = P(q^{-1})S(q)y(k) + Q(q^{-1})[u(k) + m] - R(q^{-1})y^*(k) \tag{77}$$

By using the adaptive control to system (13), the closed-loop system is described by,

$$\begin{bmatrix} A & -B \\ PS & Q \end{bmatrix}\begin{bmatrix} y(k) \\ u(k)+m \end{bmatrix} = \begin{bmatrix} 0 \\ R \end{bmatrix} y^*(k) + \begin{bmatrix} C \\ \delta(k)^{-1}F \end{bmatrix}\varepsilon(k) + \begin{bmatrix} 0 \\ \delta(k)^{-1}I \end{bmatrix}[\sigma(k+d)-v(k+d)] \tag{78}$$

Because $T_1(z)$ is stable and $\delta(k)^{-1}$, $\varepsilon(k)$ and $y^*(k)$ are bounded according to (64), (76), (7) and A4, $y(k)$ and $u(k)$ in (78) can be considered as the outputs of an asymptotically stable linear system with inputs $y^*(k)$, $\varepsilon(k)$ and $[\sigma(k+d)-v(k+d)]$. By applying *Lemma A.1* [16] to (78), there exist constants K_i, $i = 1 \cdots 6$, which are independent of N such that,

$$\frac{1}{N}\sum_{k=1}^{N} \|y(k)\|^2 \leq K_1 + \frac{K_2}{N}\sum_{k=1}^{N} \|\sigma(k+d)-v(k+d)\|^2, \qquad a.s. \tag{79}$$

$$\frac{1}{N}\sum_{k=1}^{N} \|u(k)\|^2 \leq K_3 + \frac{K_4}{N}\sum_{k=1}^{N} \|\sigma(k+d)-v(k+d)\|^2, \qquad a.s. \tag{80}$$

$$\frac{1}{N}\sum_{k=1}^{N} \|\bar{u}(k)\|^2 \leq K_5 + \frac{K_6}{N}\sum_{k=1}^{N} \|\sigma(k+d)-v(k+d)\|^2, \qquad a.s. \tag{81}$$

where $0 \leq K_1, K_3, K_5 < \infty$ and $0 < K_2, K_4, K_6 < \infty$. Substituting (18) into (58) yields,

$$\overline{\Phi}(k+d) = P(q^{-1})S(q)y(k) - v(k) - [\sigma(k)-v(k)]. \tag{82}$$

Using the Schwarz inequality to (82), we have

$$\|\overline{\Phi}(k+d)\|^2 \leq 3\|PSy(k)\|^2 + 3\|v(k)\|^2 + 3\|\sigma(k)-v(k)\|^2. \tag{83}$$

From (7) and (79), (83) implies

$$\frac{1}{N}\sum_{k=1}^{N} \|\overline{\Phi}(k+d)\|^2 \leq K_7 + \frac{K_8}{N}\sum_{k=1}^{N} \|\sigma(k+d)-v(k+d)\|^2, \qquad a.s. \tag{84}$$

where $0 \leq K_7 < \infty$ and $0 < K_8 < \infty$. From (47) we obtain

$$\frac{r(N)}{N} = \frac{1}{N}\sum_{k=1}^{N} \|\hat{x}(k)\|^2 \qquad (85)$$

According to the definition of $\hat{x}(k)$ in (45) and from (79), (80) and (84), (85) means by using the Schwarz inequality:

$$\frac{r(N)}{N} \le K_9 + \frac{K_{10}}{N}\sum_{k=1}^{N} \|\sigma(k+d)-v(k+d)\|^2, \quad a.s. \qquad (86)$$

where $0 \le K_9 < \infty$ and $0 < K_{10} < \infty$. From (59) we have

$$\lim_{N\to\infty} \frac{1}{r(N)}\sum_{k=1}^{N} \|\sigma(k+d)-v(k+d)\|^2 = 0, \quad a.s. \qquad (87)$$

From (86) and (87) we obtain

$$\lim_{N\to\infty} \frac{1}{N}\sum_{k=1}^{N} \|\sigma(k+d)-v(k+d)\|^2 = 0, \quad a.s. \qquad (88)$$

Equations (70)-(72) now follow from (88). Using above results and similar methods to those used in the proof of Theorem 4.1 [15] or Lemma 8.5.3 [17] we immediately obtain (73).

5. Conclusion

Mechanical systems are often characterized by static amplitude-dependent nonlinearities, and combinations thereof. For example, the hydraulic press of a cold rolling mill is a multivariable system with dead-zone nonlinearity. Presently, no control schemes are available for these systems unless the parameters of the nonlinear characteristics are known.

As a contribution towards the adaptive control, this paper has developed a new direct adaptive control algorithm for an important class of nonlinear multivariable system as defined by (1). In order to design the controller, a piecewise pre-load nonlinearity vector is introduced to invert the dead-zone vector. An optimal adaptive control law is then derived from a special cost function in which the nonlinear parameter vector of the model is included. These nonlinear parameters appear to the identification algorithm as a rapidly varying system gain vector. Their estimation rely on a switching-gain sequence vector, thus making the nonlinear parameters time-invariant. The power of the algorithm lies in the fact that the scheme can deal with unstable and/or nonminimum phase processes. Under suitable conditions, the algorithm is globally stable and convergent.

Acknowledgment

This work is supported by the Natural Sciences and Engineering Research Council of Canada (NSERC), under grant No. A1718.

References

[1] M.C. Kung and B.F. Womack, "Discrete time adaptive control of linear dynamic systems with a two-segment piecewise linear asymmetric nonlinearity," *IEEE Trans. on Automatic Control*, 29, pp. 170-172, 1984.

[2] M.C. Kung, and B.F. Womack, "Discrete time adaptive control of linear systems with preload nonlinearity," *Automatica*, vol. 20, pp. 477-479, 1984.

[3] D.Y. Abramovitch and G.F. Franklin, "On the stability of adaptive pole-placement controllers with a saturating actuator," *IEEE Trans. on Automatic Control*, 35, pp. 303-306, 1990.

[4] Y.F. Xiong and H. Unbehauen, "Adaptive control of systems with a class of direction-dependent non-linearities," *Preprints of 9th IFAC Symp. on Identification and System Parameter Estimation*, Budapest, Hungary, vol. 2, pp. 1008-1012, 1991.

[5] Y.F. Xiong and H. Unbehauen, "Explicit adaptive control of nonminimum phase systems with a class of preload nonlinearities", *Proceedings of IEE Int. Conf. on Control*, Edinburgh, U.K., vol. 2, pp. 1079-1083, 1991.

[6] P. Du, Realisierung eines neuen adaptiven Konzepts Für hydraulich Vorschubantriebe mittels Mikroprozessor. Dissertation, Reihe 8: Mess-, Steuerungs- und Regelungs-technik, VDI Verlag Düsseldorf, Germany, 1990.

[7] Y.F. Xiong and H. Unbehauen, "Adaptive Control of Systems with Unknown Dead Zone Nonlinearies", *in Book 'Mathematics of the Analysis and Design of Process Control'*, eds. P. Borne, S.G. Tzafestas and N.-E. Radhy, North-Holland Press, pp. 455-464, 1992.

[8] S. LeQuoc, Y.F. Xiong and R.H.M. Cheng, "Adaptive control of systems with multiple amplitude-dependent nonlinearities," Submitted to *Trans. ASME, Journal of Dynamic Systems, Measurement and Control*, 1992.

[9] S. LeQuoc, Y.F. Xiong and R.M.H. Cheng, "Identification and control of nonlinear hydraulic system", *SAE Int. Off-Highway & Powerplant Congress*, Paper Series 921622, Milwaukee, 1992.

[10] Y.F. Xiong and H. Unbehauen, "Stochastic adaptive control of multivariable systems with a class of amplitude-dependent nonlinearities," *Journal of Optimal Control Applications & Methods*, to appear, 1993.

[11] L. Dugard, G.C. Goodwin and X. Xianya, "The role of the interactor matrix in multivariable stochastic adaptive control", *Automatica*, 20, pp. 701-709, 1984.

[12] R. Scattolini, "A multivariable self-tuning controller with integral action", *Automatica*, 22, pp. 619-627, 1986.

[13] W.A. Wolovich and P.L. Falb, "Invariants and canonical forms under dynamic compensation", *SIAM Journal of Control and Optimization*, 14, pp. 996-1008, 1974.

[14] H.F. Chen, "Recursive system identification and adaptive control by use of the modified least squares algorithm", *SIAM Journal of Control and Optimization*, 22, pp. 758-776, 1984.

[15] Y.H. Zhang, 1981, "Stochastic adaptive control and prediction based on a modified least squares--The general delay-colored noise case", *IEEE Trans. on Automatic Control*, 27, pp. 1257-1260, 1981.

[16] G.C. Goodwin, P.J. Ramadge and P.E. Caines, "Discrete time stochastic adaptive control", *SIAM Journal of Control and Optimization*, 19, pp. 829-853, 1981.

[17] G.C. Goodwin and K.S. Sin, Adaptive Filtering Prediction and Control, Prentice-Hall, Englewood Cliffs, 1984.

Proceedings of the
American Control Conference
San Francisco, California • June 1993

DECENTRALIZED ROBUST STABILIZATION INDEPENDENT OF DELAY FOR MULTIDELAY STOCHASTIC LARGE SCALE SYSTEMS*

Zhao-Shu Feng and Yong-Qing Liu

Department of Automation, South China University of Technology
Guangzhou 510641, P. R. China

ABSTRACT

In this paper, by using the various types of Lyapunov functionals and the property of Lyapunov matrix equation as well as the property of Riccati matrix equation, criteria are established for decentralized stabilization of multidelay stochastic large scale systems using local state feedback. The stability of the closed-loop stochastic large scale systems is independent of delay and robust for the uncertain coefficient matrices and the uncertain strength of stochastic disturbance which vary in a bounded range. Two of the theorems obtained in this paper (Theorem 1 and 2) possess the following character: under some reasonable and simple conditions, the asymptotic stability of the closed-loop stochastic large scale systems is guaranteed, without solving Lyapunov matrix equation and Riccati matrix equation.

1. INTRODUCTION

There have been a number of research works on decentralized stabilization for delay deterministic large scale systems, for example, [1]-[8]. The paper of Socha and Willems [9] may be the first research works reported in the literature on decentralized stabilization of stochastic large scale systems. Recently, the authors also give some discussion on the this problem (refer to [10] and [11]). However, up to date, the problem of decentralized stabilization of delay stochastic large scale systems had not been considered.

In this paper, by applying Lyapunov functionals and the property of Lyapunov matrix equation as well as the property of Riccati matrix equation, we establish criteria for decentralized stabilization of multidelay stochastic large scale systems by local state feedback. Several of these criteria make it possible that multidelay stochastic large scale systems can be robust stabilized independent of delay in the sense of mean-square asymptoticstability without solving the Lyapunov matrix equation and Riccati matrix equation.

This paper is organized as follows. In Section 2 we describe the multidelay stochastic large scale systems and formulate the main problem, and then we review briefly some preliminary results. In Section 3 we establish several criteria for decentralized robust stabilization of multidelay stochastic large scale systems by two kinds of Lyapunov functionals. In Section 4 we give a conclusion.

2. SYSTEM DESCRIPTION AND LEMMAS

Consider the multidelay stochastic large scale systems consisting of the following N interconnected subsystems

$$dx_i(t)=[(A_i+\Delta A_i)x_i(t)+B_iu_i(t)]dt+\sum_{j=1}^{r_i}F_{ij}x_i(t)dW_{ij}(t)+\sum_{k=1}^{N}A_{ik}x_k(t-\tau_{ik})dt,\quad i=1,\dots,N \tag{1}$$

where $x_i(t)\in\mathbb{R}^{n_i}$ and $u_i(t)\in\mathbb{R}^{m_i}$ are the state vector and input vector of the ith subsystem respectively; A_i is an $n_i\times n_i$ constant matrix, ΔA_i is an $n_i\times n_i$ bounded uncertain matrix; $W_i=(W_{i1},\dots,W_{ir_i})^T$ is an m_i-dimensional zero-mean standard Wiener process with independent components; F_{ij} is an $n_i\times n_i$ bounded uncertain matrix which denotes the strength of stochastic disturbance W_{ij}; A_{ik} is an $n_i\times n_k$ interconnecting constant matrix, and for $i=1,\dots, N$, $\sum_{k=1}^{N}A_{ik}A_{ik}^T\neq 0$; τ_{ik} is a nonnegative real constant. Where $j=1,\dots,r_i$; $i=1,\dots,N$; $k=1,\dots,N$.

The stochastic large scale system (1) can be considered as a linear interconnection of the following N isolated stochastic subsystems

$$dx_i(t)=[(A_i+\Delta A_i)x_i(t)+B_iu_i(t)]dt+\sum_{j=1}^{r_i}F_{ij}x_i(t)dW_{ij}(t),\qquad i=1,\dots,N \tag{2}$$

The main objective of this paper, is to make the multidelay stochastic large scale systems decentralized stabilization which is independent of delay and robust for uncertain parameters, by using the local state feedback control law in the form of

$$u_i(t)=K_ix_i(t),\qquad i=1,\dots,N \tag{3}$$

By using the above control law, the closed-loop systems of (1) and (2) are given respectively by

$$dx_i(t)=(A_i+B_iK_i+\Delta A_i)x_i(t)dt+\sum_{j=1}^{r_i}F_{ij}x_i(t)dW_{ij}(t)+\sum_{k=1}^{N}A_{ik}x_k(t-\tau_{ik})dt,\quad i=1,\dots,N \tag{4}$$

and

$$dx_i(t)=(A_i+B_iK_i+\Delta A_i)x_i(t)dt+\sum_{j=1}^{r_i}F_{ij}x_i(t)dW_{ij}(t),\qquad i=1,\dots,N \tag{5}$$

Let

$$n=\sum_{i=1}^{N}n_i,\quad m=\sum_{i=1}^{N}m_i,\quad x=(x_1^T,\dots,x_N^T)^T,\quad u=(u_1^T,\dots,u_N^T)^T,$$

$$A=\text{block-diag}\{A_1,\dots,A_N\},\quad \Delta A=\text{block-diag}\{\Delta A_1,\dots,\Delta A_N\},$$

$$B=\text{block-diag}\{B_1,\dots,B_N\},$$

$$H(x_t)=\left(\left(\sum_{k=1}^{N}A_{1k}x_k(t-\tau_{1k})\right)^T,\dots,\left(\sum_{k=1}^{N}A_{Nk}x_k(t-\tau_{Nk})\right)^T\right)^T,$$

and let $\mathcal{F}_{ij}$ be an $n\times n$ matrix consisting block matrices in which the block matrix on the ith row and jth cloumn is F_{ij} and all other block matrices are zero-matrices with proper dimension.

By introducing the above notations, the multidelay stochastic large scale system (1) can be represented by the following equivalent form

$$dx(t)=[(A+\Delta A)x(t)+Bu(t)]dt+\sum_{i=1}^{N}\sum_{j=1}^{r_i}\mathcal{F}_{ij}x(t)dW_{ij}(t)+H(x_t)dt \tag{6}$$

Let $K=\text{block-diag}\{K_1,\dots,K_N\}$. The closed-loop system (4) can be rewritten by

$$dx(t)=(A+BK+\Delta A)x(t)dt+\sum_{i=1}^{N}\sum_{j=1}^{r_i}\mathcal{F}_{ij}x(t)dW_{ij}(t)+H(x_t)dt \tag{7}$$

Definition 1. The closed-loop stochastic large scale system (7) is said to be mean-square asymptotically stable independent of delay, if for any nonnegative real number τ_{ik} $(i,\ k=1,\dots,N)$, the equilibrium $x(t)\equiv 0$ of (7) is mean-square asymptotically stable (refer to [12]-[16]).

Definition 2. The stochastic large scale system (1) is said to be robust stabilized by local state feedback control law (3), if for uncertain coefficient matrix ΔA_{ik} and stochastic disturbance matrix F_{ij} which vary in a bounded range, the closed system (7) is mean-square asymptotically stable independent of delay.

Definition 3. Given $n\times n$ system matrix A and $n\times m$ input matrix B. (A,B)

* This work was supported by the National Natural Science Foundation of China under grant No. 69104001.

is said to be stablizable, if there exists a $m\times n$ matrix K such that all eigenvalues of $A+BK$ possess negative real parts, i.e.

$$\mathrm{Re}\lambda_i(A+BK)<0, \quad i=1,\dots,n. \tag{8}$$

Lemma 1[17]. For any $n\times n$ matrices X and Y, for any positive number r, the following inequality holds

$$X^TY+YX\le rX^TX+\frac{1}{r}Y^TY \tag{9}$$

Lemma 2[18]. Assume that A is a $n\times n$ stable constant matrix, i.e., all the eigenvalues of A possess negative real parts. Then, for any given $n\times n$ symmetric and positive definite matrix Q, the Lyapunov matrix equation

$$A^TP+PA=-Q \tag{10}$$

has a unique $n\times n$ symmetric and positive solution matrix P and P satisfies the following inequality holds

$$|P|\le\frac{|Q|}{-2\mu(A)} \tag{11}$$

where $\mu(A)<0$, $|\cdot|$ is the matrix norm induced by Euclidean norm.

Lemma 3. Given an $n\times n$ constant matrix A, for the matrix norm $|A|$ induced by Euclidean norm and the corresponding measure $\mu(A)$, the following inequality holds

$$\mathrm{Re}\lambda_i(A_i)\le\mu(A), \quad i=1,\dots,N \tag{12}$$

Lemma 4. For the $n\times n$ constant matrix A and the $n\times m$ constant matrix B, if there exists an $m\times n$ constant matrix K such that

$$\mu(A+BK)<0 \tag{13}$$

Then (A,B) is stabilizable.

Proof: The result follows from Lemma 1 and Definition 3.

In this paper, for simplifying notation, $x_i(t)$ and $x(t)$ are written as x_i and $x(t)$ if there is no confusion.

3. DECENTRALIZED ROBUST STABILIZATION OF MULTIDELAY STOCHASTIC LARGE SCALE SYSTEMS

For each fixed i, let M_i be the number of non-zero matrices among $A_{i1},\dots,A_{iN}$, and let $J_i=\{k\,|\,A_{ik}\neq 0\}$, where $i=1,\dots,N$.

Theroem 1. For the stochastic large scale system (1), if $\sum_{k=1}^{n} A_{ik}A_{ik}^T\neq 0$, and there exists an $m_i\times n_i$ constant matrix K_i, $i=1,\dots,N$, such that

$$\mu(A_i+B_iK_i)+2|\Delta A_i|+\sum_{j=1}^{r_i}|F_{ij}|^2+|M_i\sum_{k=1}^{N}A_{ik}A_{ik}^T|^{1/2}<0, \quad i=1,\dots,N \tag{14}$$

Then the local state feedback control law (3) determined by K_i makes the multidelay stochastic large scale system (1) decentralized robust stabilization.

Proof: By condition (14), and applying Lemma 3 and 4, we get that (A_i,B_i) is stablizable, $i=1,\dots,N$. Hence, for

$$q_i=-\mu(A_i+B_iK_i)|M_i\sum_{k=1}^{N}A_{ik}A_{ik}^T|^{-1/2}, \quad i=1,\dots,N \tag{15}$$

by Lemma 2, the Lyapunov matrix equation

$$(A_i+B_iK_i)^TP_i+P_i(A_i+B_iK_i)=-2q_iM_iI_i, \quad i=1,\dots,N \tag{16}$$

has a unique symmetric and positive definite solution matrix P_i, and P_i satisfies the following inequality

$$|P_i|\le\frac{2q_iM_i}{-2\mu(A_i+B_iK_i)}=\frac{q_iM_i}{-\mu(A_i+B_iK_i)}, \quad i=1,\dots,N \tag{17}$$

For the closed-loop multidelay stochastic large scale system (4), we construct the following Lyapunov functional

$$V(x_t)=\sum_{i=1}^{N}\left[x_i^TP_ix_i+\sum_{k\in J_i}\int_{-\tau_{ik}}^{0}x_k^T(t+s)x_k(t+s)ds\right] \tag{18}$$

Let $\mathcal{L}$ be the differential operator generated by (4) (refer to (3.2) in [12]). We have

$$\begin{aligned}\mathcal{L}V(x_t)=\sum_{i=1}^{N}\Big\{&x_i^T\Big[(A_i+B_iK_i)^TP_i+P_i(A_i+B_iK_i)+\Delta A_i^TP_i+P_i\Delta A_i+\sum_{j=1}^{r_i}F_{ij}^TP_iF_{ij}+M_iI_i\Big]x_i\\&+\sum_{k=1}^{N}\Big[x_i^TP_iA_{ik}x_k(t-\tau_{ik})+x_k^T(t-\tau_{ik})A_{ik}^TP_ix_i\Big]-\sum_{k=1}^{N}x_k^T(t-\tau_{ik})x_k(t-\tau_{ik})\Big\}\end{aligned} \tag{19}$$

By using (17) and Lemma 1, we obtain

$$\begin{aligned}\mathcal{L}V(x_t)\le&\sum_{i=1}^{N}\Big\{x_i^T\Big[-2q_iM_iI_i+\Delta A_i^TP_i+P_i\Delta A_i^T+\sum_{j=1}^{r_i}F_{ij}^TP_iF_{ij}+M_iI_i\Big]x_i\\&+x_i^TP_i\sum_{k=1}^{N}A_{ik}A_{ik}^TP_ix_i\\\le&\sum_{i=1}^{N}\Big\{[-(q_i-1)]+\Big[-(q_i-1)M_i+|P_i|(2|\Delta A_i|+\sum_{j=1}^{r_i}|F_{ij}|^2)\Big]\\&+\Big[-M_i+|P_i|^2|\sum_{k=1}^{N}A_{ik}A_{ik}^T|\Big]\Big\}|x_i|^2\end{aligned} \tag{20}$$

By the results given in [19] and [20], the closed-loop stochastic large scale system (4) is mean-square asymptotically stable independent of delay, if the following inequalities (19)-(21) are satisfied

$$-(q_i-1)<0, \quad i=1,\dots,N \tag{21}$$

$$-(q_i-1)M_i+|P_i|(2|\Delta A_i|+\sum_{j=1}^{r_i}|F_{ij}|^2)\le 0, \quad i=1,\dots,N \tag{22}$$

$$-M_i+|P_i|^2|\sum_{k=1}^{N}A_{ik}A_{ik}^T|\le 0, \quad i=1,\dots,N \tag{23}$$

It is easy to verify (21) from (14) and (15). By (14), (15) and (17), we have

$$\begin{aligned}&-(q_i-1)M_i+|P_i|(2|\Delta A_i|+\sum_{j=1}^{r_i}|F_{ij}|^2)\\&\le-(q_i-1)M_i+\frac{M_i}{-\mu(A_i+B_iK_i)}\Big[-\mu(A_i+B_iK_i)-|M_i\sum_{k=1}^{N}A_{ik}A_{ik}^T|^{1/2}\Big]\\&=M_i+q_i\cdot\frac{M_i}{\mu(A_i+B_iK_i)}|M_i\sum_{k=1}^{N}A_{ik}A_{ik}^T|^{1/2}\\&=0, \qquad i=1,\dots,N\end{aligned} \tag{24}$$

and

$$-M_i+|P_i|^2|\sum_{k=1}^{N}A_{ik}A_{ik}^T|\le-M_i+q_i^2\cdot\frac{M_i^2}{\mu^2(A_i+B_iK_i)}|\sum_{k=1}^{N}A_{ik}A_{ik}^T|=0, \quad i=1,\dots,N \tag{25}$$

By (24) and (25), we get that (22) and (23) are satisfied. Hence, the closed-loop stochastic large scale system (4) is mean-square asymptotically stable independent of delay. That is, the local state feedback control law (3) determined by K_i makes the stochastic large scale system (1) decentralized robust stabilization. This completes the proof.

Theorem 2. For the stochastic large scale system (1), assume that the following conditions are satisfied:

(i) there exists constant matrix K_i such that

$$\mu(A_i+B_iK_i)+|M_i\sum_{k=1}^{N}A_{ki}^TA_{ki}|^{1/2}<0, \quad i=1,\dots,N; \tag{26}$$

(ii) for q_i satisfying

$$|\sum_{k=1}^{N}A_{ki}^TA_{ki}|<q_i<\frac{1}{M_i}\mu^2(A_i+B_iK_i), \quad i=1,\dots,N \tag{27}$$

the following inequality holds

$$2|\Delta A_i|+\sum_{j=1}^{r_i}|F_{ij}|^2<-\mu(A_i+B_iK_i)+\frac{q_iM_i}{\mu(A_i+B_iK_i)}-\varepsilon_i, \quad i=1,\dots,N \tag{28}$$

where ε_i is a sufficiently small positive number satisfying

$$0<\varepsilon_i<-\mu(A_i+B_iK_i)+\frac{q_iM_i}{\mu(A_i+B_iK_i)}, \quad i=1,\dots,N \tag{29}$$

Then, the local state feedback control law (3) determined by K_i in condition (i) makes the multidelay stochastic large scale system (1) decentralized robust stabilization.

Proof: By (26) and applying Lemma 3 and 4, we get that (A_i,B_i) is stabilizable. Hence, for q_i satisfying (27), analogously to the proof of Theorem 1, the Lyapunov matrix equation

$$(A_i+B_iK_i)^TP_i+(A_i+B_iK_i)P_i=-2q_iI_i, \quad i=1,\dots,N \tag{30}$$

has a unique symmetric and positive definite $n_i\times n_i$ solution matrix P_i. And P_i satisfies the following inequality

$$|P_i|\le\frac{2q_i}{-2\mu(A_i+B_iK_i)}=\frac{q_i}{-\mu(A_i+B_iK_i)}, \quad i=1,\dots,N \tag{31}$$

For the closed-loop multidelay stochastic large scale system (4), we choose the following Lyapunov functional

$$V(x_t)=\sum_{i=1}^{N}\left[x_i^T P_i x_i+\sum_{k\in J_i}\int_{-\tau_{ik}}^{0} x_k^T(t+s)A_{ik}^T A_{ik} x_k(t+s)ds\right] \tag{32}$$

Let $\mathcal{L}$ be the differential operator generated by the closed-loop multidelay stochastic large scale system (4) (refer to [12]). We have

$$\begin{aligned}\mathcal{L}V(x_t)=\sum_{i=1}^{N}\Big\{&x_i^T\Big[(A_i+B_iK_i)^T P_i+P_i(A_i+B_iK_i)+\Delta A_i^T P_i+P_i\Delta A_i+\sum_{j=1}^{r_i}F_{ij}^T P_i F_{ij}\\ &+\sum_{k=1}^{N}A_{ki}^T A_{ki}\Big]x_i+\sum_{k\in J_i}\left[x_k^T(t-\tau_{ik})A_{ik}^T P_i x_i+x_i^T P_i A_{ik} x_k(t-\tau_{ik})\right]\\ &-\sum_{k=1}^{N}x_k^T(t-\tau_{ik})A_{ki}^T A_{ki} x_k(t-\tau_{ik})\Big\}\end{aligned} \tag{33}$$

Applying (27), (30), and Lemma 1, we obtain

$$\begin{aligned}\mathcal{L}V(x_t)&=\sum_{i=1}^{N}\left\{x_i^T\left[-q_iI_i+\Delta A_i^T P_i+P_i\Delta A_i+\sum_{j=1}^{r_i}F_{ij}^T P_i F_{ij}\right]x_i+\sum_{k\in J_i}x_i^T P_i^2 x_i\right\}\\ &\le\sum_{k=1}^{N}\left\{-q_i-|P_i|\left(2|\Delta A_i|+\sum_{j=1}^{r_i}|F_{ij}|^2\right)+M_i|P_i|^2\right\}|x_i|^2\end{aligned} \tag{34}$$

By (28) and (31), we get that

$$\begin{aligned}&-q_i+|P_i|\left(2|\Delta A_i|+\sum_{j=1}^{r_i}|F_{ij}|^2\right)+M_i|P_i|^2\\ &\le -q_i+\frac{q_i}{-\mu(A_i+B_iK_i)}\left[-\mu(A_i+B_iK_i)+\frac{q_iM_i}{\mu(A_i+B_iK_i)}-\varepsilon_i\right]+\frac{q_i^2M_i}{\mu^2(A_i+B_iK_i)}\\ &\le\frac{q_i\varepsilon_i}{\mu(A_i+B_iK_i)}\end{aligned} \tag{35}$$

From (34) and (35), we have

$$\mathcal{L}V(x_t)\le\sum_{i=1}^{N}\frac{q_i\varepsilon_i}{\mu(A_i+B_iK_i)}|x_i|^2 \tag{36}$$

and thus there exists a positive number γ_1 such that

$$\mathcal{L}V(x_t)\le-\gamma_1|x|^2 \tag{37}$$

Hence, by the results given in [19] or [20], we get that the closed-loop stochastic large scale system (4) is mean-square asymptotically stable independent of delay. That is, the local state feedback control law (3) makes the multidelay stochastic large scale system (1) decentralized robust stabilization. This completes the proof.

Remark 1. Now we compare the conditions of Theorem 1 and 2. Let

$$G=\begin{bmatrix}A_{11} & \cdots & A_{1N}\\ \cdots & \cdots & \cdots\\ A_{N1} & \cdots & A_{NN}\end{bmatrix} \tag{38}$$

where A_{ik} is the coefficient matrix of delay interconnection term $x_k(t-\tau_{ik})$ of stochastic large scale system (1), $i=1,\ldots,N$.

The condition involving interconnecting matrix in Theroem 1 implies

$$\mu(A_i+B_iK_i)+|M_i\sum_{k=1}^{N}A_{ki}A_{ki}^T|^{1/2}<0,\quad i=1,\ldots,N \tag{39}$$

while the condition involving interconnecting matrix in Theorem 2 requires

$$\mu(A_i+B_iK_i)+|M_i\sum_{k=1}^{N}A_{ki}^T A_{ki}|^{1/2}<0,\quad i=1,\ldots,N \tag{40}$$

We note that, inequality (39) is given by the sum of product of block matrices on each row of G and their transpose, while (40) is given by the sum of product of block matrices on each column of G and their transpose. The difference between them comes from the different usage of the different Lyapunov functional (18) and (32) in Theorem 1 and Theorem 2, respectively. But we also note that (37) and (40) have rather analogous form.

Theroem 3. For the multidelay stochastic large scale system (1), assume that the following conditions are satisfied:

(i) (A_i,B_i) is stabilizable, and for some positive number $q_i>1$, the Riccati matrix equation

$$A_i^T P_i+P_iA_i-P_iB_iB_i^T P_i=-2q_iM_iI_i \tag{41}$$

has a unique symmetric and positive definite $n_i\times n_i$ solution matrix P_i, $i=1,\ldots,N$;

(ii) the following inequalities hold

$$2|\Delta A_i|+\sum_{j=1}^{r_i}|F_{ij}|^2<\frac{(q_i-1)M_i}{|P_i|},\quad i=1,\ldots,N \tag{42}$$

$$|\sum_{k=1}^{N}A_{ki}A_{ki}^T|<\frac{M_i}{|P_i|^2},\quad i=1,\ldots,M \tag{43}$$

Then, the local state feedback control law (3) determined by

$$K_i=-\frac{1}{2}B_i^T P_i,\quad i=1,\ldots,N \tag{44}$$

makes the multidelay stochastic large scale system (1) decentralized robust stabilization.

Proof: For the closed-loop stochastic large scale system (4), by the matrix P_i in condition (i), we construct the Lyapunov functional in the form of (18). Let $\mathcal{L}$ be the differential operator generated by (4) (refer to [12]). We have

$$\begin{aligned}\mathcal{L}V(x_t)=\sum_{i=1}^{N}\Big\{&x_i^T\Big[A_i^T P_i+P_iA_i-P_iB_iB_i^T P_i+\Delta A_i^T P_i+P_i\Delta A_i+\sum_{j=1}^{r_i}F_{ij}^T P_i F_{ij}+M_iI_i\Big]x_i\\ &+\sum_{k=1}^{N}\left[x_i^T P_i A_{ik} x_k(t-\tau_{ik})+x_k^T(t-\tau_{ik})A_{ik}^T P_i x_i\right]-\sum_{k=1}^{N}x_k^T(t-\tau_{ik})x_k(t-\tau_{ik})\Big\}\end{aligned} \tag{45}$$

By applying (41), (42), (43) and Lemma 1 to (45), analogously to proof of Theorem 1, we have

$$\begin{aligned}\mathcal{L}V(x_t)&\le\sum_{i=1}^{N}\Big\{[-(q_i-1)]+\Big[-(q_i-1)M_i+|P_i|(2|\Delta A_i|+\sum_{j=1}^{r_i}|F_{ij}|^2)\Big]\\ &\qquad+\Big[-M_i+|P_i|^2|\sum_{k=1}^{N}A_{ik}A_{ik}^T|\Big]\Big\}|x_i|^2\\ &\le\sum_{i=1}^{N}[-(q_i-1)]|x_i|^2\\ &\le-\gamma_2|x|^2\end{aligned} \tag{46}$$

where

$$\gamma_2=\min_{1\le i\le N}\{q_i-1\} \tag{47}$$

Hence, the local state feedback control law (3) determined by (44) makes the multidelay stochastic large scale system (1) decentralized robust stabilization. This completes the proof.

Theorem 4. For the multidelay stochastic large scale system (1), assume that the following conditions are satisfied:

(i) there exists matrix H_{ij} with appropriate dimension such that

$$A_{ij}=B_{ij}H_{ij},\quad i=1,\ldots,N; \tag{48}$$

(ii) (A_i,B_i) is stabilizable, and for some $q_i>1$, the following Riccati matrix algebraic equation

$$A_i^T P_i+P_iA_i-P_iB_iB_i^T P_i=-2q_iM_iI_i \tag{49}$$

has a unique symmetric and positive definite matrix P_i, $i=1,\ldots,N$;

(iii) the following inequalities hold

$$|\sum_{k=1}^{N}H_{ik}H_{ik}^T|\le\rho_i-1,\quad i=1,\ldots,N \tag{50}$$

$$2|\Delta A_i|^2+\sum_{j=1}^{r_i}|F_{ij}|^2<\frac{M_i}{|P_i|},\quad i=1,\ldots,N \tag{51}$$

where $\rho_i>1$ is a positive constant.

Then, the local state feedback control law (3) determined by

$$K_i=-\frac{1}{2}\rho_iB_i^T P_i,\quad i=1,\ldots,N \tag{52}$$

makes the multidelay stochastic large scale system (1) decentralized robust stabilization.

Proof: For the closed-loop stochastic large scale system (4) by local state feedback (3) with (52), by the matrix P_i in condition (ii), construct the Lyapunov functional in the form of (18). Analogously to the proof of Theorem 3, we have

$$\begin{aligned}\mathcal{L}V(x_t)=\sum_{i=1}^{N}\Big\{&x_i^T\Big[A_i^T P_i+P_iA_i-\rho_iP_iB_iB_i^T P_i+\Delta A_i^T P_i+P_i\Delta A_i+\sum_{j=1}^{r_i}F_{ij}^T P_i F_{ij}+M_iI_i\Big]x_i\\ &+\sum_{k=1}^{N}\left[x_i^T P_i A_{ik} x_k(t-\tau_{ik})+x_k^T(t-\tau_{ik})A_{ik}^T P_i x_i\right]-\sum_{k=1}^{N}x_k^T(t-\tau_{ik})x_k(t-\tau_{ik})\Big\}\end{aligned} \tag{53}$$

By applying Lemma 1 and the conditions of the theorem, we have

$$\mathcal{L}V(x_t)\le \sum_{i=1}^{N}\Big\{x_i^T P_i B_i\Big[(1-\rho_i)I_i+\sum_{k=1}^{N} H_{ik}H_{ik}^T\Big]B_i^T P_i x_i + x_i^T\Big[-M_i I_i+\Delta A_i^T P_i+P_i\Delta A_i$$
$$+\sum_{j=1}^{r_i} F_{ij}^T P_i F_{ij}\Big]x_i + x_i^T\Big[-2(q_i-1)M_i I_i\Big]x_i\Big\}$$
$$\le \sum_{k=1}^{N}\Big\{\Big[-2(q_i-1)M_i\Big]+\Big[-M_i+|P_i|(2|\Delta A_i|+\sum_{j=1}^{r_i}|F_{ij}|^2)\Big]\Big\}|x_i|^2$$
$$\le -\gamma_3|x|^2 \tag{54}$$

where

$$\gamma_3=\min_{1\le i\le N}\{2(q_i-1)\} \tag{55}$$

Hence, the local state feedback control law (3) determined by (52) makes the multidelay stochastic large scale system (1) decentralized robust stabilization. This completes the proof.

Theorem 5. For the multidelay stochastic large scale system (1), assume that the following conditions are satisfied:

(i) there exist matrices H_{ik} and D_{ik} with appropriate dimension, such that

$$A_{ik}=B_i H_{ik}+D_{ik},\qquad i,k=1,\dots,N \tag{56}$$

$$\sum_{k=1}^{N} D_{ik}D_{ik}^T\ne 0,\qquad i=1,\dots,N \tag{57}$$

(ii) (A_i,B_i) is stabilizable, and there exist $m_i\times n_i$ constant matrix K_i^0 and positive number $\delta_i>0$, such that

$$\mu(A_i+B_iK_i^0)+|M_i\sum_{k=1}^{N} D_{ik}D_{ik}^T|^{1/2}+2|\Delta A_i|+\sum_{j=1}^{r_i}|F_{ij}|^2<-\delta_i,\qquad i=1,\dots,N \tag{58}$$

(iii) for

$$q_i=-\mu(A_i+B_iK_i^0)|M_i\sum_{k=1}^{N} D_{ik}D_{ik}^T|^{-1/2} \tag{59}$$

the Lyapunov matrix equation

$$(A_i+B_iK_i^0)^T P_i+P_i(A_i+B_iK_i^0)=-2q_iM_iI_i \tag{60}$$

has a unique $n_i\times n_i$ symmetric and positive definite solution matrix P_i, $i=1,\dots,N$.

Then, the local state feedback control law (3) determined by

$$K_i=K_i^0-\frac{1}{2(q_i-1)}\sum_{k=1}^{N} H_{ik}H_{ik}^T B_i^T P_i,\qquad i=1,\dots,N \tag{61}$$

makes the multidelay stochastic large scale system (1) decentralized robust stabilization.

Proof: For the closed-loop stochastic large scale system (4) with (61), by q_i and P_i in the conditions of Theorem 5, construct the following Lyapunov functional

$$V(x_t)=\sum_{i=1}^{N}\Big[x_i^T P_i x_i+q_i\sum_{k\in J_i}\int_{-\tau_{ik}}^{0} x_k^T(t+s)x_k(t+s)ds\Big] \tag{62}$$

Analogously to the proof of Theorem 3, we have

$$\mathcal{L}V(x_t)=\sum_{i=1}^{N}\Big\{x_i^T\Big[(A_i+B_iK_i^0)^T P_i+P_i(A_i+B_iK_i^0)-\frac{1}{q_i-1}\sum_{k=1}^{N} P_iB_iH_{ik}H_{ik}^T B_i^T P_i$$
$$+\Delta A_i^T P_i+P_i\Delta A_i+\sum_{j=1}^{r_i} F_{ij}^T P_i F_{ij}+q_iM_iI_i\Big]x_i+\sum_{k=1}^{N}\Big[x_i^T P_i(B_iH_{ik}+D_{ik})x_k(t-\tau_{ik})$$
$$+x_k^T(t-\tau_{ik})(B_iH_{ik}+D_{ik})^T P_i x_i\Big]-\sum_{k=1}^{N} q_i x_k^T(t-\tau_{ik})x_k(t-\tau_{ik})\Big\} \tag{63}$$

By applying (60) and Lemma 1 to the above inequality, we get that

$$\mathcal{L}V(x_t)\le \sum_{i=1}^{N}\Big\{x_i^T\Big[-2q_iM_iI_i+\Delta A_i^T P_i+P_i\Delta A_i^T+\sum_{j=1}^{r_i} F_{ij}^T P_i F_{ij}+q_iM_iI_i$$
$$-\sum_{k=1}^{N}\frac{1}{q_i-1}P_iB_iH_{ik}H_{ik}^T B_i^T P_i\Big]x_i+\sum_{k=1}^{N}\Big[\frac{1}{q_i-1}x_i^T P_iB_iH_{ik}H_{ik}^T B_i^T P_i x_i$$
$$+(q_i-1)x_k^T(t-\tau_{ik})x_k(t-\tau_{ik})\Big]+\sum_{k=1}^{N}\Big[x_i^T P_i D_{ik}D_{ik}^T P_i x_i$$
$$+x_k^T(t-\tau_{ik})x_k(t-\tau_{ik})\Big]-\sum_{k=1}^{N} q_i x_k^T(t-\tau_{ik})x_k(t-\tau_{ik})\Big\}$$
$$\le \sum_{i=1}^{N}\Big\{\Big[-(q_i-1)M_i+|P_i|\Big(2|\Delta A_i|+\sum_{j=1}^{r_i}|F_{ij}|^2\Big)\Big]$$
$$+\Big[-M_i+|P_i|^2|\sum_{k=1}^{N} D_{ik}D_{ik}^T|\Big]\Big\}|x_i|^2 \tag{64}$$

For q_i defined by (59), by Lemma 2, we obtain

$$|P_i|\le\frac{2q_iM_i}{-2\mu(A_i+B_iK_i^0)}=\frac{q_iM_i}{-\mu(A_i+B_iK_i^0)},\qquad i=1,\dots,N \tag{65}$$

By (58), (59), (65) and condition (ii), we have

$$-(q_i-1)M_i+|P_i|\Big(2|\Delta A_i|+\sum_{j=1}^{r_i}|F_{ij}|^2\Big)$$
$$\le-(q_i-1)M_i+\frac{q_iM_i}{-\mu(A_i+B_iK_i^0)}\Big[-\mu(A_i+B_iK_i^0)-|M_i\sum_{k=1}^{N} A_{ik}A_{ik}^T|^{1/2}-\delta_i\Big]$$
$$\le-\frac{q_iM_i\delta_i}{\mu(A_i+B_iK_i^0)},\qquad i=1,\dots,N \tag{66}$$

and

$$-M_i+|P_i|^2|\sum_{k=1}^{N} D_{ik}D_{ik}^T|\le-M_i+\frac{q_i^2M_i^2}{\mu^2(A_i+B_iK_i^0)}|\sum_{k=1}^{N} D_{ik}D_{ik}^T|\le 0,\qquad i=1,\dots,N \tag{67}$$

By (64), (66) and (67), we get that

$$\mathcal{L}V(x_t)\le-\gamma_4|x|^2 \tag{68}$$

where

$$\gamma_4=\min_{1\le i\le N}\Big\{-\frac{q_iM_i\delta_i}{\mu(A_i+B_iK_i^0)}\Big\} \tag{69}$$

Hence, by (68) and the theroems given in [19] and [20], we get that the closed-loop stochastic large scale system (4) is mean-square asymptotically stable independent of delay. That is, the local state feedback control law (3) with (61) makes the multidelay stochastic large scale system (1) decentralized robust stabilization. This completes the proof.

Remark 2. It should be noted that the conditions of Theorem 1 and 2 do not require sloving Riccati matrix equation or Lyapunov matrix equation because of using Lemma 4, while the conditions of Theorem 3 and 4 require solving Riccati matrix equation and the conditions of Theorem 5 require solving Lyapunov matrix equation.

4. CONCLUSION

In this paper, the problem of decentralized stabilization of Ito-type stochastic large scale system is discussed. By using various types of Lyapunov functionals and applying the properties of Lyapunov matrix equation and Riccati matrix equation, criteria are established for decentralized robust stabilization of multidelay stochastic large scale system by local state feedback. Some criteria (Theorem 1 and 2) possess a very good property. That is, by choosing appropriate local state feedback gain matrix, such that: (a) measure of the system matrix of closed-loop isolated subsystem is appropriate negative, and (b) the uncertain coefficient matrices and the strength of stochastic disturbance satisfy proper requirement for boundedness, then the closed-loop stochastic large scale system is mean-square asymptotically stable independent of delay, without solving Lyapunov matrix equation or Riccati matrix equation.

REFERENCES

[1] B. D. O. Anderson, "Time delays in large-scale systems," in: *Proc. 18th IEEE Conference on Decision and Control*, Fort Lauderdale, Florida, U.S.A., 1979, pp.655-660.

[2] M. Ikeda and D. D. Siljak, "Decentralized stabilization of large scale systems with time delay," *Large Scale Systems*, Vol.1, pp.273-279, 1980.

[3] I. H. Suh and Z. Bien, "On stabilization by local state feedback for discrete-time large-scale systems with delays in interconnection," *IEEE Trans. Autom. Control*, Vol.27, pp.744-746, 1982.

[4] M. Jamshidi and C. M. Wang, "A computational algorithm for large scale nonlinear time-delay systems," in: *Proc. IEEE Symposium on Large Scale Systems*, Virginia Beach, U.S.A., 1982, pp.258-262.

[5] A. El-Kashlam, M. El-Geneidy, O. A. Sebakhy, and A. I. Salama, "Eigenvalue assignments for large-scale discrete systems containing delayed interconnections: a two-level control," *IEEE Control Systems*, Vol.4, pp.2-5, 1984.

[6] T. N. Lee and U. L. Radovic, "General decentralized stabilization of large-scale linear continuous and discrete time-delay systems," *Int. J. Control*, Vol.46, pp.2127-2140, 1987.

[7] T. N. Lee and U. L. Radovic, "Decentralized stabiliztion of linear continuous and discrete-time systems with delays in interconnection," *IEEE Trans. Autom. Control*, Vol.33, pp.767-761, 1988.

[8] A. S. C. Sinha, "Stabilization of large-scale non-linear infinite delay systems," *Int. J. Systems Sci.*, Vol. 21, pp. 2679-2648, 1990.

[9] L. Socha and J. L. Willems, "Decentralized stabilization of stochastic composite systems," *Int. J. Systems Sci.*, Vol.16, pp.1003-1013, 1986.

[10] Zhao-Shu Feng, Yong-Qing Liu and Gong-Yong Tang, "Decentralized exponential stabilization of deterministic and stochastic large scale systems: a unified approach," in: *Proceedings of the 30th IEEE Conference on Decision and Control*, pp.333-338, 1991.

[11] Zhao-Shu Feng, Yong-Qing Liu, and Gong-You Tang, "Linear and nonlinear local state feedback for decentralized stabilization of stochastic large scale systems," in: *Proceedings of IFAC Symposium on Large Scale Systems: Theory and Applications*, Beijing, China, Aug. 24-26, 1992.

[12] G. S. Ladde, "Differential inequalities and stochastic functional differential equations," *J. Math. Phys.*, Vol.15, pp.738-743, 1974.

[13] Zhao-Shu Feng and Feng-Wei Guo, "Functional differential inequalities and time-delay stochastic systems (I): comparison principle," in: *A Special Collection of Young Papers on Ordinary Differential Equations* (in Chinese), Beijing: Science Press, 1991, 193-197.

[14] Zhao-Shu Feng, Yong-Qing Liu, and Feng-Wei Guo, "Multidelay linear stochastic systems: mean-square stability independent of delay," in: *Proceedings of 1992 American Control Conference*, pp.1089-1090, 1992.

[15] T. Sasagawa, "Mean-square asymptotic stability of linear hereditary systems," *Int. J. Systems Sci.*, Vol.19, pp.935-944, 1988.

[16] Zhao-Shu Feng, Yong-Qing Liu, and Feng-Wei Guo, "Mean-square uniform asymptotic stability of time-delay stochastiic systems," *Chinese Science Bulletin* (in English), Vol.37, 1982.

[17] K. Zhou and P. P. Khargonekar, "Robust stabilization of linear systems with norm-bounded time-varying uncertainty," *Systems & Control Letters*, Vol.10, pp.17-20, 1988.

[18] T. Mori, "Another bounds for the solution to the Lyapunov matrix equation," *Trans. IECE* (in Japanese), Vol.63-A, No.1, 38-40, 1980.

[19] T. Sasagawa, On the stability of stochastic systems dependent on the past history, in: *VII Internationale Konferenz uber nichtlineare Schwigungen*, Band II, 2, Berlin: Akademie-Verlag, Berlin, 1977, 319-325.

[20] V. B. Kolmanovskii and V. R. Nosov, *Stability of Functional Differential Equations*, New York: Academic Press, 1986, Chapter 4.

Proceedings of the
American Control Conference
San Francisco, California • June 1993

The Reducing Transformation and Smith Predictor Methods for Stabilizing Plants with Transport Lag

A. Anthony Pandiscio Jr. * A. E. Pearson †

Division of Engineering
Brown University
Providence, RI 02912 USA

Abstract

The reducing transformation and Smith Predictor methods facilitate finite dimensional controller design techniques for stabilizing plants with transport lag. This paper begins by deriving nominal stability results confirming the fact that for unstable plants, controllers which use the Smith Predictor compensator cannot stabilize the closed loop system. By contrast, it is verified that the reducing transformation can be applied in these unstable plant cases. After developing the nominal stability results, the structured singular value is used to define conditions for robust stability of an entire parameter family of plants. An example, using the reducing transformation, is given at the end of the paper.

I Introduction

The reducing transformation (RT) and Smith Predictor (SP) methods employ specialized compensators which can be used to simplify the controller design for plants with a transport lag [1]. The compensators are applied to the plant input signal, u in Figure 1, and the resulting output, y_{sp} or y_{rt}, is then added to the augmented plant output, y, forming a new signal, z. This new signal z is then used for feedback instead of using the original augmented plant output. The advantage of using z as the feedback signal is that the resulting dynamics between (u, r) and z are delay-free. Finite dimensional (FD) controller design techniques can then be applied to stabilize this delay-free system which, under suitable conditions, will imply the closed loop stability of the original system with the transport lag.

The SP was first proposed by Smith in 1957, see [11], for use with single-input single-output (SISO) plants having a single time delay. Alevisakis and Seborg [1] generalized it to a special class of multi-input multi-output (MIMO) plants with both input and output delays. Many authors have considered stability and performance issues related to the SP including: Furukawa and Shimemura [4] where the stability of the SP is investigated from the state space point of view and an alternative predictive scheme which is closely related to the RT is proposed; Marshall [8] where the SP tracking and disturbance rejection properties are examined; and Palmor and Halevi [9] where the stability theory of dead time compensators is developed including the SP as an example.

*Author is on a Raytheon Company Fellowship pursuing a Ph.D. at Brown University.

†Author for correspondence. tel. (401) 863-2602, Fax. (401) 863-1157, E-mail: aep@lems.brown.edu. The research of this author has been supported in part by NASA grant NAG-1-1065 and in part by the National Science Foundation under grant ECS-8713771.

[1]The RT can also be applied to plants with multiple input, state and output delays, see for instance [10].

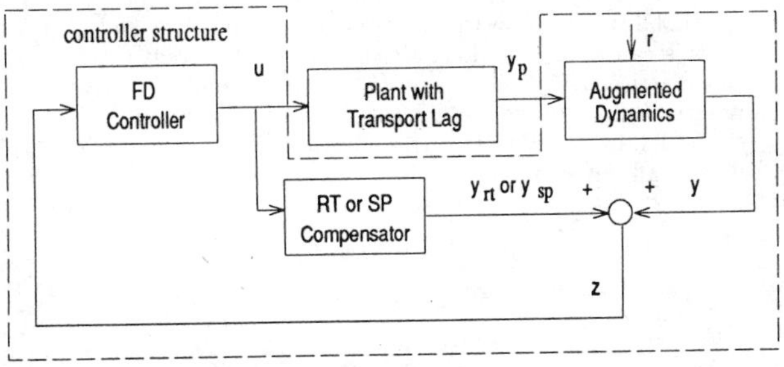

Figure 1: RT and SP Block Diagram

The RT terminology was first introduced by Pearson and Fiagbedzi in [10] to denote the set of finite duration integrals which "reduce" a large class of retarded and input delay differential equations to systems of ordinary differential equations. The use of these finite duration integrals can be seen in earlier papers such as Manitius and Olbrot [7] where the existence and uniqueness of the resulting closed loop solutions is discussed as well as some sensitivity results, Kwon and Pearson [6] where the technique is used to stabilize a MIMO input-delayed plant, Watanabe and Ito [12] where a predictive control framework is used to propose a command following controller design for input delayed plants, and Artstein [2] which gives a particularly rigorous examination of the general methodology for the input-delayed case.

This paper focuses on the control of a MIMO plant with a single delay on the input. Nominal stability results of the above mentioned papers are generalized by considering an arbitrary FD linear time invariant (LTI) model for both the FD controller and the augmented dynamics. The level of generality encompasses a majority of control schemes such as those resulting from tracking and disturbance attenuation problems, and thus the stability results are not limited to a particular controller methodology. After developing the nominal stability results, the structured singular value is used to develop conditions for robust stability of an entire parameter family of plants. These results are then used to evaluate the robust stability of a double integrator plant with a transport lag.

II System Description

This paper examines the use of the RT and SP in controlling the family of MIMO LTI input-delayed plants described by the state equations:

$$\begin{aligned}
\dot{x}_p(t) &= [\,A_p + \sum_{k=1}^{k^a} \delta_k^a \, v_k^a \, r_k^{a'}\,]\, x_p(t) + \\
&\qquad [\,B_p + \sum_{k=1}^{k^b} \delta_k^b \, v_k^b \, r_k^{b'}]\, u(t - d_0 - d_\delta) \qquad (1)\\
y_p(t) &= [\,C_p + \sum_{k=1}^{k^c} \delta_k^c \, v_k^c \, r_k^{c'}\,]\, x_p(t) \\
x_p(0) &= x_{p0} \text{ and } u(t) \in c([-(d_0 + d_{max}), 0], \mathcal{R}^m) \text{ given}
\end{aligned}$$

where $x_p \in \mathcal{R}^{n_p}$, $u \in \mathcal{R}^m$, $y_p \in \mathcal{R}^{p_p}$, $d_0 \geq 0$, $d_\delta \in [d_{min}, d_{max}]$ with $-d_0 \leq d_{min} \leq d_{max}$, and $\delta_k^\alpha \in [-1, 1]$ $\forall\, k = 1, \cdots, k^\alpha$ and $\alpha = a, b, c$. Additionally, v_k^a, v_k^b, v_k^c, r_k^a, r_k^b, r_k^c are n_p, n_p, p_p, n_p, m, n_p dimensional column vectors, and $c([a, b], \mathcal{R}^m)$ is the Banach space of real m dimensional continuous functions on the interval $[a, b]$. The vectors (v_k^α, r_k^α) are employed to facilitate scaling for the various perturbed entries. It is assumed that they are specified by the user so that $\delta_k^\alpha \in [-1, 1]$ allows for all possible perturbations in the model.

The augmented dynamics shown in Figure 1 are used primarily when a tracking controller is desired. The output vector y typically contains the integrals of the errors between a set of reference inputs r and the plant outputs y_p. These integral output errors are then used for feedback such that at steady state, the plant outputs equal the reference values. For this paper, the augmented dynamics are modeled as a general FDLTI system, where $x_a(t) \in \mathcal{R}^{n_a}$, $y(t) \in \mathcal{R}^p$ and $r(t) \in \mathcal{R}^w$:

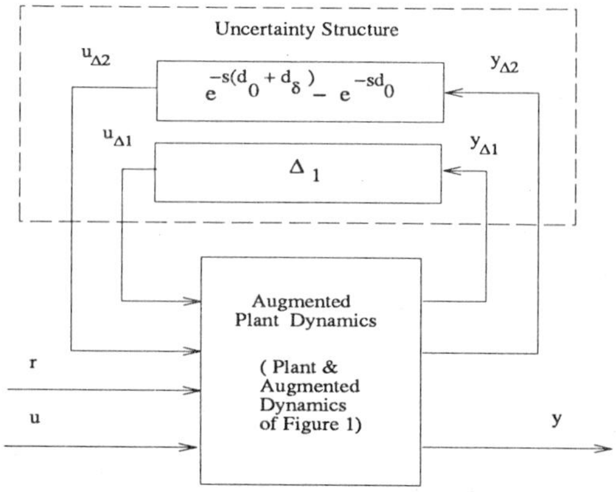

Figure 2: Block Diagonal Form

$$\begin{aligned} \dot{x}_a(t) &= A_a\, x_a(t) + B_a\, y_p(t) + B_a^{ref}\, r(t) \\ y(t) &= C_a\, x_a(t) + D_a\, y_p(t) + D_a^{ref}\, r(t) \\ x_a(0) &= x_{a0} \end{aligned} \quad (2)$$

The plant and augmented dynamics models are now manipulated and combined into a more useful form. First, the plant model is put into an equivalent form where the perturbations are combined into a block diagonal structure. This form closely resembles the standard block diagonal system representation used in deriving FD robust stability results. However, because of the inclusion of a delay perturbation d_δ, the standard FD form has to be extended by including an additional input/output pair, $(u_{\Delta 2}, y_{\Delta 2})$, so that after taking Laplace transforms, all perturbations, including d_δ, will be isolated into a block diagonal matrix. This new plant model is then combined with the augmented dynamics in (2) yielding the augmented plant model below, where $n = n_p + n_a$, $x(t) \stackrel{\text{def}}{=} [\, x_p(t)'\ x_a(t)'\,]'$, I_m is the $m \times m$ identity matrix and $0_{n\times m}$ is the $n \times m$ null matrix. This combined form, see Figure 2, will be used to derive the stability results in Section III.

$$\begin{aligned} \dot{x}(t) &= A\, x(t) + B\, u(t-d_0) + B^{ref}\, r(t) + \\ &\qquad\qquad B_\Delta\, u_{\Delta 1}(t) + B\, u_{\Delta 2}(t) \\ y(t) &= C\, x(t) + D^{ref}\, r(t) + D_\Delta\, u_{\Delta 1}(t) \\ &\text{and} \\ y_{\Delta 1}(t) &= C_\Delta\, x(t) + E_\Delta\, u(t-d_0) + E_\Delta\, u_{\Delta 2}(t) \\ u_{\Delta 1}(t) &= \Delta_1\, y_{\Delta 1}(t) \\ \Delta_1 &= \text{diag}\{\delta_1^{\text{a}}, \cdots, \delta_{k^{\text{a}}}^{\text{a}}, \delta_1^{\text{b}}, \cdots, \delta_{k^{\text{b}}}^{\text{b}}, \delta_1^{\text{c}}, \cdots, \delta_{k^{\text{c}}}^{\text{c}}\} \\ y_{\Delta 2}(t) &\doteq u(t) \\ u_{\Delta 2}(t) &= y_{\Delta 2}(t-d_0-d_\delta) - y_{\Delta 2}(t-d_0) \end{aligned} \quad (3)$$

$$\begin{aligned} A &= \begin{bmatrix} A_p & 0_{n_p\times n_a} \\ B_a C_p & A_a \end{bmatrix} \quad ; \quad B = \begin{bmatrix} B_p \\ 0_{n_a\times m} \end{bmatrix} \\ B^{ref} &= \begin{bmatrix} 0_{n_p\times m} \\ B_a^{ref} \end{bmatrix} \quad ; \quad C = [\, D_a C_p \quad C_a \,] \\ D^{ref} &= D_a^{ref} \quad ; \quad B_\Delta = \begin{bmatrix} B_\Delta^p \\ B_a D_\Delta^p \end{bmatrix} \\ C_\Delta &= [\, C_\Delta^p \quad 0_{k^t\times n_a} \,] \quad ; \quad D_\Delta = D_a D_\Delta^p \\ E_\Delta &= E_\Delta^p \end{aligned}$$

$$\begin{aligned} B_\Delta^p &= [\, v_1^a \cdots v_{k^a}^a\ v_1^b \cdots v_{k^b}^b\ 0_{n\times k^c} \,] \\ C_\Delta^p &= [\, r_1^a \cdots r_{k^a}^a\ 0_{n\times k^b}\ r_1^c \cdots r_{k^c}^c \,]' \\ D_\Delta^p &= [\, 0_{p\times k^a}\ 0_{p\times k^b}\ v_1^c \cdots v_{k^c}^c \,] \\ E_\Delta^p &= [\, 0_{m\times k^a}\ r_1^b \cdots r_{k^b}^b\ 0_{m\times k^c} \,]' \\ k^t &= k^a + k^b + k^c \end{aligned}$$

The nominal augmented plant will be defined by: $\Delta_1 \equiv 0$ and $d_\delta = 0$. This nominal model will be used to define the RT and SP, since both compensators require knowledge of the nominal augmented plant dynamics. Additionally, it is assumed that $[A, B]$ is controllable and $[A, C]$ is observable. As will be seen later, these assumptions ensure that there exists a FD controller which will stabilize the nominal augmented plant dynamics in (3).

The RT and SP compensators do not require any special form for the FD controller. Hence, to keep the results independent of the particular controller structure or design methodology, the same general FDLTI model that was used for the augmented dynamics is used for the FD controller, where $x_c \in \mathcal{R}^q$:

$$\begin{aligned} \dot{x}_c(t) &= A_c\, x_c(t) - B_c\, z(t) \\ u(t) &= C_c\, x_c(t) - D_c\, z(t) \\ x_c(0) &= x_{c0}. \end{aligned} \quad (4)$$

The SP is now defined by the state model:

$$\begin{aligned} \dot{x}_{sp}(t) &= A\, x_{sp}(t) + B\, u(t) - B\, u(t-d_0) \\ y_{sp}(t) &= C\, x_{sp}(t) \\ x_{sp}(0) &= x_{sp0} \text{ and } u(t) \in c([-d_0, 0], \mathcal{R}^m) \text{ given} \end{aligned} \quad (5)$$

By adding the nominal augmented plant output $y(t)$ to $y_{sp}(t)$ the signal $z(t)$ is formed as shown in Figure 1; thus,

$$\begin{aligned} z(t) &= y_{sp}(t) + y(t) = C[x_{sp}(t) + x(t)] + D^{ref} r(t) \\ &\stackrel{\text{def}}{=} C\, e_{sp}(t) + D^{ref}\, r(t). \end{aligned} \quad (6)$$

Differentiation and substitutions from (3) and (5) gives:

$$\begin{aligned} \dot{e}_{sp}(t) &= \dot{x}_{sp}(t) + \dot{x}(t) \\ &= A\, e_{sp}(t) + B\, u(t) + B^{ref}\, r(t) \end{aligned} \quad (7)$$

and the dynamics between (u, r) and z, i.e., $(6-7)$, are delay-free as desired. Section III gives conditions under which a FD controller which stabilizes $(6-7)$ will also stabilize the original delayed plant when used in conjunction with the SP. Assuming these conditions are met, what remains to be done is to find matrices A_c, B_c, C_c and D_c such that the resulting controller in (4) stabilizes $(6-7)$. Equivalently, this amounts to choosing controller matrices such that the eigenvalues of $Q(B)$ defined by:

$$Q(B) = \begin{bmatrix} A - BD_cC & BC_c \\ -B_cC & A_c \end{bmatrix} \quad (8)$$

are all in the open left half of the complex plane, i.e., $\mathcal{C}_-$. The controllability and observability assumptions on A, B and C ensure that this can always be done. It should be noted that the reference input matrices B^{ref} and D^{ref} in $(6-7)$ have no affect on closed loop stability and, therefore, do not enter into the condition.

The RT for the MIMO single input delay augmented plant (3) is defined and implemented by:

$$\begin{aligned} x_{rt}(t) &= \textstyle\int_{t-d_0}^{t} e^{A(t-d_0-\tau)} Bu(\tau)\, d\tau \\ y_{rt}(t) &= C\, x_{rt}(t). \end{aligned} \quad (9)$$

It can also be represented by the state model:

$$\begin{aligned} \dot{x}_{rt}(t) &= A\,x_{rt}(t) + e^{-Ad_0} B\,u(t) - B\,u(t-d_0) \\ y_{rt}(t) &= C\,x_{rt}(t) \\ x_{rt}(0) &= \textstyle\int_{-d_0}^{0} e^{A(-d_0-\tau)} Bu(\tau)\,d\tau \\ u(t) &\in c([-d_0,0],\mathcal{R}^m) \text{ given} \end{aligned} \quad (10)$$

It is important to note that although the state model representation (10) is input/output equivalent to (9), its Laplace transform contains removable singularities at the eigenvalues of A which are not actually present in the RT transfer function, see [7] and Lemma 1 ii). This fact is important in order to correctly ascertain closed loop stability.

As in the SP case, the RT also allows FD design techniques to be employed as can be seen by determining the dynamics between (u,r) and z using the RT:

$$\begin{aligned} z(t) &= y_{rt}(t) + y(t) = C[x_{rt}(t) + x(t)] + D^{ref} r(t) \\ &\stackrel{\text{def}}{=} C\,e_{rt}(t) + D^{ref}\,r(t). \end{aligned} \quad (11)$$

Again by differentiation and substitutions from (3) and (10):

$$\begin{aligned} \dot{e}_{rt}(t) &= \dot{x}_{rt}(t) + \dot{x}(t) \\ &= A\,e_{rt}(t) + e^{-Ad_0} B\,u(t) + B^{ref}\,r(t). \end{aligned} \quad (12)$$

The delay-free dynamics of (11 – 12) are the same as for the SP case except that B is replaced by $e^{-Ad_0}B$. Since e^{-Ad_0} commutes with A it is straightforward to show that $[A, e^{-Ad_0}B]$ is controllable when $[A,B]$ is controllable and, therefore, as in the SP case the poles of the FD system resulting from the RT, i.e., the eigenvalues of $Q(e^{-Ad_0}B)$, can always be made stable.

III Closed Loop Stability

In line with standard definitions of exponential asymptotic stability, we define the system in Figure 1 as being closed loop stable, for a given specified plant, if and only if for arbitrary initial conditions and $r \equiv 0$, the composite state vector $[\ x_c(t)'\ x(t)'\ x_*(t)'\ ]'$, $*$ = rt or sp, converges exponentially to zero. Specifically, if the closed loop system is stable for the nominal plant defined in Section II, we say the system is nominally stable. The system is robustly stable if it is stable for all allowed perturbations in the plant model (1). A necessary and sufficient condition to imply stability is that the composite row vector $\bar{x}_*(t) \stackrel{\text{def}}{=} [\ y_{\Delta 1}(t)'\ y_{\Delta 2}(t)'\ x_c(t)'\ x(t)'\ x_*(t)'\ ]'$ converges exponentially to zero for arbitrary initial conditions and $r \equiv 0$. This is equivalent to showing that the characteristic equation of the Laplace transformed system between $\bar{x}_*(t)$ and the initial conditions has all its zeros in $\mathcal{C}_-$, see [5, 7]. This section derives these characteristic equations, using the $*$ notation to delineate the RT and SP equations. They are then used to determine conditions for nominal and robust stability.

Denote $\mathcal{L}$ as the Laplace transform operator and $\bar{x}_*(s) = \mathcal{L}[\bar{x}_*(t)]$. Further, make the following definitions with $det[\ ]$ standing for the determinant, $i = \sqrt{-1}$, and $\mathcal{C} = \mathcal{C}_- \cup \mathcal{C}_+$.

Definition 1

$$\Delta(s) = \text{diag}\{\Delta_1, (1-e^{-sd_\delta})I_m\}$$

$$N_{sp}(s) = (I_n - e^{-sd_\delta} I_n)B$$

$$N_{rt}(s) = \left(\int_{-d_0}^{0} e^{\gamma(A-sI_n)}\,d\gamma\right)Be^{-sd_0}$$

$$L_{sp}(s) = (sI_n - A)$$

$$L_{rt} = I_n$$

$$\Upsilon = \begin{bmatrix} I_{k^t} & 0_{k^t\times m} & 0_{k^t\times q} & 0_{k^t\times n} & 0_{k^t\times n} \\ 0_{m\times k^t} & I_m & 0_{m\times q} & 0_{m\times n} & 0_{m\times n} \end{bmatrix}$$

$$\Phi_*(s) = \begin{bmatrix} e^{-sd_0}E_\Delta D_c D_\Delta & e^{-sd_0}E_\Delta \\ D_c D_\Delta & 0_{m\times m} \\ B_c D_\Delta & 0_{q\times m} \\ (e^{-sd_0}BD_cD_\Delta - B_\Delta) & e^{-sd_0}B \\ N_* D_c D_\Delta & 0_{n\times m} \end{bmatrix}$$

$$\Psi_*(s) =$$

$$\begin{bmatrix} I_{k^t} & 0_{k^t\times m} & -e^{-sd_0}E_\Delta C_c & (e^{-sd_0}E_\Delta D_c C - C_\Delta) & e^{-sd_0}E_\Delta D_c C \\ 0_{m\times k^t} & I_m & -C_c & D_c C & D_c C \\ 0_{q\times k^t} & 0_{q\times m} & (sI_q - A_c) & B_c C & B_c C \\ 0_{n\times k^t} & 0_{n\times m} & -e^{-sd_0}BC_c & (sI_n - A + e^{-sd_0}BD_cC) & e^{-sd_0}BD_cC \\ 0_{n\times k^t} & 0_{n\times m} & -N_*C_c & N_*D_cC & (L_* + N_*D_cC) \end{bmatrix}$$

$$M_*(s) = \Upsilon\Psi_*^{-1}(s)\Phi_*(s).$$

The two main theorems are now stated below.

Theorem 1 *The system in Figure 1, using the SP and with perturbation $\Delta(s)$, is nominally stable iff the zeroes of:*

$$\eta_{sp}(s) = det[sI_{n+q} - Q(B)]det[sI_n - A]det[I_{k^t+m} + M_{sp}(s)\Delta(s)]$$

are all in $\mathcal{C}_-$.

Theorem 2 *The system in Figure 1, using the RT and with perturbation $\Delta(s)$, is nominally stable iff the zeroes of:*

$$\eta_{rt}(s) = det[sI_{n+q} - Q(e^{-Ad_0}B)]det[I_{k^t+m} + M_{rt}(s)\Delta(s)]$$

are all in $\mathcal{C}_-$.

To prove these Theorems, we need some preliminary results which are given in Lemma 1.

Lemma 1

i) $\mathcal{L}[x_{rt}(t)] = N_{rt}(s)\,u(s) + \int_{-d_0}^{0} e^{A\gamma} B\left(\int_{-(d_0+\gamma)}^{0} e^{-s(d_0+\gamma+\tau)}u(\tau)d\tau\right)d\gamma$

ii) $N_{rt}(s)$ *is entire and* $N_{rt}(s) = \left(\sum_{k=0}^{\infty} \frac{(sI_n - A)^k\, d_0^{k+1}}{(k+1)!}\right)Be^{-sd_0}$

iii) $(sI_n - A)N_{rt}(s) = (e^{-Ad_0} - e^{-sd_0}I_n)B$

iv) $det\begin{bmatrix} A & B \\ C & D \end{bmatrix} \begin{aligned} &= det[A]det[D - CA^{-1}B];\ if\ A^{-1}\ exists \\ &= det[A - BD^{-1}C]det[D];\ if\ D^{-1}\ exists \end{aligned}$

v) $det[I + MN] = det[I + NM]$

vi) There exists D_{R_*}, a Nyquist contour of radius R_*, such that all the zeros of $\eta_*(s)$ which lie in $\mathcal{C}_+$ lie either inside the region bounded by D_{R_*} or on the imaginary axis portion of D_{R_*}.

Proofs of Theorems 1 and 2: Take the Laplace Transforms of (3), (4), (5) and (9) with $r \equiv 0$. Then using the properties *i*) and *ii*) in Lemma 1, we get $[\Psi_* + \Phi_*\Delta\Upsilon]\bar{x}_*(s) = I.C.$ where $I.C.$ indicates a vector function of the initial conditions. The characteristic equation is then defined as $\eta_*(s) = det[\Psi_* + \Phi_*\Delta\Upsilon]$ and its zeros determine the system poles. Defining $g_c(s) = C_c(sI_q - A_c)^{-1}B_c + D_c$ and using *iv*) - *vi*) in Lemma 1 to manipulate $\eta_*(s)$:

$$\eta_*(s) = det[I_{k^t+m} + M_*\Delta]det[\Psi_*]$$
$$= det[I_{k^t+m} + M_*\Delta]det[sI_q - A_c]$$
$$det\begin{bmatrix} (sI_n - A + e^{-sd_o}Bg_cC) & e^{-sd_o}Bg_cC \\ N_*g_cC & (L_* + N_*g_cC) \end{bmatrix}$$
$$= det[I_{k^t+m} + M_*\Delta]det[sI_q - A_c]det[L_* + N_*g_cC]$$
$$det[sI_n - A + e^{-sd_o}Bg_cC - e^{-sd_o}g_cC(L_* + N_*g_cC)N_*g_cC]$$
$$= det[I_{k^t+m} + M_*\Delta]det[L_*]det[sI_q - A_c]$$
$$det[sI_n - A + (sI_n - A)L_*^{-1}N_*g_cC + e^{-sd_o}Bg_cC]$$
$\Longrightarrow$ for the SP case
$$= det[I_{k^t+m} + M_{sp}\Delta]det[sI_q - A_c]det[sI_n - A + Bg_cC]$$
$$det[sI_n - A]$$
$$= det[I_{k^t+m} + M_{sp}\Delta]det[sI_{n+q} - Q(B)]det[sI_n - A]$$
$\Longrightarrow$ for the RT case using Lemma 1 *iv*)
$$= det[I_{k^t+m} + M_{rt}\Delta]det[sI_q - A_c]$$
$$det[sI_n - A + e^{-Ad_o}Bg_cC]$$
$$= det[I_{k^t+m} + M_{rt}\Delta]det[sI_{n+q} - Q(e^{-Ad_o}B)]$$

This proves the Theorems.

The remaining results are given as corollaries to the above theorems. The detailed proofs of Lemma 1 and the robust stability result, Corollary 3, have been omitted due to space limitations, but are available upon request.

Corollary 1 (to Theorem 1) *The closed loop system using the SP is nominally unstable when the nominal augmented plant is unstable.*

Proof: This follows directly from the fact that when using the SP the open loop augmented plant poles always appear as zeros of the characteristic equation.

Corollary 2 (to Theorem 2) *The closed loop system using the RT is nominally stable independent of whether the augmented nominal plant is stable or unstable assuming the FD controller in* (4) *stabilizes* (11 – 12), *i.e., the eigenvalues of* $Q(e^{-Ad_o}B)$ *are all in* $\mathcal{C}_-$.

Proof: This follows from the fact that when $\Delta(s) \equiv 0$ the zeros of the characteristic equation are the finite number of zeros of $det[sI_{n+q} - Q(e^{-Ad_o}B)] = 0$ which, by assumption, are in $\mathcal{C}_-$.

Corollary 3 gives necessary and sufficient conditions for the robust stability of the family of plants in (1). The conditions involve the calculation of the real structured singular value, μ, defined below. The calculation of μ as well as upper and lower bounds for it have been addressed in many papers, see for example [3], and will not be considered further in this paper.

To cast the problem into the structured singular value framework, the complex exponential in the perturbation matrix $\Delta(s)$, which results from the delay, is replaced by a linear fractional transform (LFT) which is equivalent to the exponential function along the imaginary axis, see [13]. Once the proper terms are defined and the LFT is made, the Corollary follows directly.

Definition 2 *For a given* $\omega \in [0, R_*]$ *and* $\sigma \in \mathcal{R}$ *define:*

$$\theta_\delta = \min\{\frac{\pi}{2}, \frac{\omega}{4}(d_{max} - d_{min})\}$$
$$\theta_\pm = [-\frac{\omega}{2}(d_{max} + d_{min}) \pm \theta_\delta] \bmod[2\pi]$$
$$l_\delta = \tan(\frac{\theta_\delta}{2})$$
$$\Omega = \mathrm{diag}\{0_{k^t \times k^t}, I_m\}$$
$$\mathcal{H} = \mathrm{diag}\{I_{k^t}, 0_{m\times m}\}$$
$$\mathcal{G}_*^\pm = [I_{k^t+m} + (1 - e^{i\theta_\pm})M_*(i\omega)\Omega]$$
$$P_*^\pm = (\mathcal{G}_*^\pm)^{-1}[M_*(i\omega)(\mathcal{H} - (1 + e^{i\theta_\pm})l_\delta i\Omega) - l_\delta i\Omega]$$
$$\Delta_r = \mathrm{diag}\{\Delta_1, \sigma I_m\}$$
$$\mu(P) = \begin{cases} 0 & ; \det[I + P\Delta_r] \neq 0 \; \forall \, \Delta_r \\ (\inf\{|\Delta_r| \mid det[I + P\Delta_r] = 0\})^{-1} & ; \text{otherwise} \end{cases}$$

Corollary 3 *Assuming the nominal closed loop system is stable, in either the RT or SP case, the family of plants defined in* (1) *is robustly stable iff* $det[\mathcal{G}_*^\pm] \neq 0$ *and* $\mu(P_*^\pm) < 1 \; \forall \omega \in [0, R_*]$.

Sketch of Proof: First, the argument principle is used to show that a perturbation $\Delta(s)$ destabilizes the system if and only if there is a positive number of clockwise encirclements of the origin by the map $det[I_{k^t+m} + M_*\Delta(s)]$ as s traces D_{R_*}. The encirclement condition is then shown to be equivalent to the condition that $det[I_{k^t+m} + M_*\Delta(i\omega)] \neq 0$ for all possible perturbations and $\omega \in [0, R_*]$. This follows from the definition of R_*, the fact that the perturbed encirclement plot is homotopic to 1, and the fact that the perturbation set is convex.

Next, following steps similar to those in [13] and using the definitions of $\theta_\pm$ and l_δ, the set of allowable delay perturbations can be expressed as the union of two sets of LFT's:

$$\{e^{-i\omega d_\delta} \mid d_\delta \in [d_{min}, d_{max}]\} = \cup_{\theta=\theta_+,\theta_-}\{e^{i\theta}(\tfrac{1+\sigma l_\delta i}{1-\sigma l_\delta i}) \mid \sigma \in [-1,1]\} \quad (13)$$

By substituting these LFT's for e^{-sd_δ} in the $det[I_{k^t+m} + M_*\Delta(i\omega)]$ condition and manipulating the resulting matrix expression, we arrive at the the conditions of Corollary 3. Note that as part of these manipulations $(\mathcal{G}_*^\pm)^{-1}$ is assumed to exist, and this results in the $det[\mathcal{G}_*^\pm] \neq 0$ condition.

IV Double Integrator Plant Example

This example focuses on the stabilization of the input-delayed double integrator plant defined below. This type of model can result from considering the rigid body dynamics of a spacecraft or large antenna, where the plant is located a large distance from the controller, e.g., on another planet.

$$\begin{bmatrix} \dot{x}_{1p}(t) \\ \dot{x}_{2p}(t) \end{bmatrix} = \begin{bmatrix} 0 & 1 \\ 0 & 0 \end{bmatrix}\begin{bmatrix} x_{1p}(t) \\ x_{2p}(t) \end{bmatrix} + \begin{bmatrix} 0 \\ .001 \end{bmatrix} u(t - .1)$$
$$y_p(t) = \begin{bmatrix} 1 & 0 \end{bmatrix}\begin{bmatrix} x_{1p}(t) \\ x_{2p}(t) \end{bmatrix}. \quad (14)$$

Since the open loop plant is unstable, the SP should not be used, and therefore we focus on the RT method. No augmented dynamics are used for this example except to define the output $y(t)$ as the error between a command input $r(t)$ and the plant output $y_p(t)$, i.e., $y(t) = r(t) - y_p(t)$. By applying the RT, the stabilization of the original plant is reduced to the stabilization of the simpler delay-free plant below:

$$\begin{bmatrix} \dot{e}_{1rt}(t) \\ \dot{e}_{2rt}(t) \end{bmatrix} = \begin{bmatrix} 0 & 1 \\ 0 & 0 \end{bmatrix}\begin{bmatrix} e_{1rt}(t) \\ e_{2rt}(t) \end{bmatrix} + \begin{bmatrix} -.0001 \\ .001 \end{bmatrix} u(t)$$
$$z(t) = \begin{bmatrix} -1 & 0 \end{bmatrix}\begin{bmatrix} e_{1rt}(t) \\ e_{2rt}(t) \end{bmatrix} + r(t) \quad (15)$$

The delay-free plant has the same poles as the original plant, and a non-minimum phase zero at $\frac{1}{d_o} = 10$ rad/sec.

The H^∞ mixed sensitivity design methodology was used to define a FD controller which stabilizes (15) and results in a command following step response possessing a .5 second rise time and a 20 % overshoot. The resulting controller is fourth order and is defined by the block partitioned matrix below.

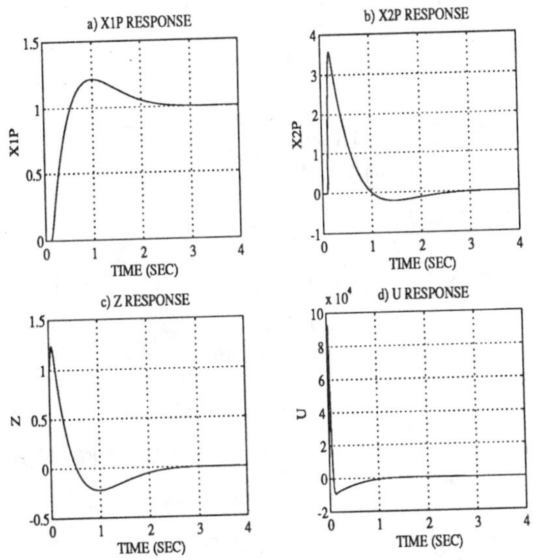

Figure 3: Nominal Step Response

$$\begin{bmatrix} A_c & B_c \\ C_c & D_c \end{bmatrix} = \begin{bmatrix} -27.6 & 28.6 & -59.6 & 641. & -.0064 \\ 5.65 & -8.05 & 15.8 & -171. & .5503 \\ -3.95 & 5.38 & -13.4 & 138. & 2.147 \\ -5.91 & -7.36 & 2.35 & -54.1 & -16.00 \\ & & & & \\ -3.5e4 & 3.7e4 & -7.7e4 & 8.3e5 & 0.0 \end{bmatrix} \quad (16)$$

Step response results of the combined system are shown in Figure 3. The "wrong way" effect in the $z(t)$ response results from the non-minimum phase zero in the delay-free dynamics. This phenomena causes a .1 second delay in the $z(t)$ error decay, which coincides with the time delay of the plant output response $y_p(t)$.

The robust stability of this closed loop system was evaluated for simultaneous variations of ±80% in the plant DC gain and ±100% in the time delay, i.e., the family of plants (1) defined by: $k^a = 0$, $k^b = 1, k^c = 0$, $v_b^1 = [\,0\ .001\,]'$, $r_c^1 = .8$, and $d_{min} = -.1$, $d_{max} = .1$. The two real structured singular values, one for θ_+ and one for θ_- as described in Corollary 3, were calculated for a set of frequencies, and the maximum of the two values plotted, see Figure 4a). The set of selected frequencies consisted of a logarithmically spaced 200 point grid over the interval $[.001, 100]$. Since both $\mu < 1$ and the nonzero determinant condition of Corollary 3 was met for all w on the grid, it was concluded that the system is robustly stable. In fact, since the peak value of μ was .8, we can infer that the system will remain robustly stable for simultaneous variations of ±99% in the DC gain and $(-100\%, +110\%)$ in the time delay.

As a test, two specific plant perturbations were chosen to see if the resulting closed loop system remained stable. The first perturbation increased the nominal plant DC gain by 80 % and increased the delay to .2 seconds. Since this particular perturbed plant is within the robustly stable family of plants defined above, the closed loop system should be stable. The dashed step response curve in Figure 4b) shows that there is some performance degradation from the nominal (solid curve), but that the system remains stable.

The second perturbation increased the nominal DC gain by 110 % and increased the delay to .23 seconds. This particular perturbation is beyond even the inferred robust stability limits and therefore the closed loop system is expected to be unstable. The dash-dot step response in Figure 4b) shows the unstable oscillations resulting from this overly perturbed plant.

V Conclusion

This paper considered the use of the RT and SP compensators for stabilizing plants with a transport lag and verified that both methods allow FD controller design techniques to be applied. Nominal

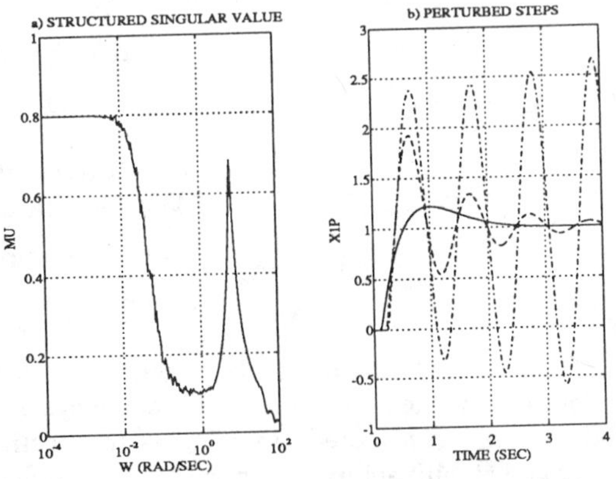

Figure 4: Robustness Results

and robust stability results were presented, the latter involving the simultaneous stabilization of an entire family of plants. These techniques were used to evaluate the nominal and robust stability of a double integrator plant; the results verify the tightness of the robust stability bounds.

References

[1] G. Alevisakis and D. E. Seborg. An extension of the smith predictor method to multivariable linear systems containing time delays. *International Journal of Control*, 3:541–551, 1973.

[2] Zvi Artstein. Linear systems with delayed controls: A reduction. *IEEE Transactions on Automatic Control*, 27:869–879, 1982.

[3] Michael K. H. Fan, Andre' L. Tits, and John C. Doyle. Robustness in the presence of mixed parametric uncertainty and unmodeled dynamics. *IEEE Transactions on Automatic Control*, 36:25–38, 1991.

[4] Toshio Furukawa and Etsujiro Shimemura. Predictive control for systems with time delay. *International Journal of Control*, 37:399–412, 1983.

[5] J. Hale. *Theory of Functional Differential Equations*. Springer Verlag, 1977.

[6] W. H. Kwon and A. E. Pearson. Feedback stabilization of linear systems with delayed control. *IEEE Transactions on Automatic Control*, AC-25(2):266–269, April 1980.

[7] Andrzej Z. Manitius and Andrzej Z. Olbrot. Finite spectrum assignment problem for systems with delays. *IEEE Transactions on Automatic Control*, 24:541–553, 1979.

[8] J. E. Marshall. *Control of time-delay systems*. Peter Peregrinus Ltd., 1979.

[9] Z. J. Palmor and Y. Halevi. On the design and properties of multivariable dead time compensators. *Automatica*, 19:255–264, 1983.

[10] A. E. Pearson and Y. A. Fiagbedzi. Controller design for time lag systems via the reducing transformation method. *Recent Advances in Control of Nonlinear and Distributed Parameter Systems, Robust Control, and Aerospace Control Applications*, 10:39–44, 1988.

[11] O. J. M. Smith. Closer control of loops with dead time. *Chemical Engineering Progress*, 53(5):217–219, 1957.

[12] Keiji Watanabe and Masami Ito. A process-model control for linear systems with delay. *IEEE Transactions on Automatic Control*, 26:1261–1269, 1981.

[13] D. N. Zhang, M. Saeki, and K. Ando. Stability margin calculation of systems with structured time-delay uncertainties. *IEEE Transactions on Automatic Control*, 37:865–868, 1992.

Proceedings of the
American Control Conference
San Francisco, California • June 1993

Approximate Controllability and Stabilizability of Time Delay Systems: Functional Analytic and Algebraic Results

Andrzej W. Olbrot
Department of Electrical and Computer Engg.
Wayne State University, Detroit, Mi 48202
aolbrot@ece.eng.wayne.edu

Abstract
Approximate versions of controllability, reachability, and null controllability for linear functional-differential systems of retarded type are considered in relation to spectral controllability and stabilizability in general function spaces not necessarily generating a C_0 - semigroup in the state space. It is shown that spectral controllability is necessary for approximate controllability and reachability in a large variety of state spaces. Spectral controllability is also necessary for approximate null controllability on a fixed time interval. On the other hand, if the space of control functions is closed under right shifts, uniform approximate controllability implies spectral controllability. Also, open loop stabilizability is necessary for approximate null controllability. We show that three large families of concrete function spaces, $C^{(k)}$, M^p, and $W^{(k,p)}$, satisfy all our general assumptions. We generalize the notions of a dual transposed system and dual observability concepts, developed in [1], corresponding to approximate controllability concepts. This enables completion of our general results by proving that spectral controllability is sufficient for approximate null controllability and by deriving testable criteria from the dual problems. Such criteria assume an especially simple form when the final time T is greater than nh and also in case of discrete delays where connections to controllability over the ring of polynomials in a delay operator are established

1. INTRODUCTION

Our aim is to examine various approximate controllability and related stabilizability properties of linear systems with time delays described by functional-differential equations of the form

$$(1) \qquad d/dt\, x(t) = A x_t + B u(t)$$

with an initial condition

$$(2) \qquad x_0 = f$$

where the state x_t is a piece of past trajectory of the solution vector, $x_t(r) = x(t + r) \in \mathbb{R}^n$, $r \in [-h, 0]$, B is a real matrix, and A is a linear convolution operator, $A x_t = (a_* x)(t)$, where the matrix a(.) has support in [0, h] and its atomic part is finite. More specifically, we assume the following representation for A

$$A\varphi = \sum_{i=0}^{N} A_i \varphi(-h_i) + \int_{-h}^{0} \alpha(r)\varphi(r)dr$$

where $0 = h_0 < h_1 < \dots < h_N = h$, the matrices A_i are real and a(.) is a real matrix valued function assumed to be Lebesgue integrable in [-h,0].

The literature on controllability of delay systems is quite rich; the reader is referred to [1] and [2] for basic references. In early works the research concentrated mainly on two problems: the reachability of the trajectory endpoint x(T) for some final time T where various forms of complete solutions were obtained [3], [4], and the controllability to equilibrium (to the zero final state $x_T = 0$) where the first complete solution was obtained in [5] in 1973 by reducing the problem to geometric problems of minimal and maximal controllability subspaces in finite dimension and later algebraic solutions over specific subrings of entire functions as Laplace transforms were obtained, [6], [7]. Next, some authors tried to examine reachability of arbitrary final states x_T in some function spaces. It soon appeared that this concept is much too strong to be useful in control theory since it typically required rank B = n, thus excluding systems with a single control and more than one state variable. It occurs that the concept of approximate controllability is much less restrictive, still appealing from the application point of view, and strongly related to other fundamental concepts like stabilizability and spectral controllability.

First complete results on approximate controllability were derived in [1] in 1977 where, for the state spaces L^p, M^p, C, and $W^{(1,p)}$, this property was characterized by dual observability problems for a dual (transposed) system. It was also shown that multipoint controllability and spectral controllability are necessary for approximate controllability in all these spaces except L^p. For the case of commensurable delays, the complete set of necessary and sufficient conditions for approximate controllability on a fixed time interval was derived. A sequence of other results followed, [8], [9], [10], [2]. Manitius and Triggiani, [8], examined the case with one delay and the state spaces L^2

and M^2. Marchenko, [9], proved that approximate null controllability, with finite time dependent on an initial state, is equivalent to feedback stabilizability. Manitius, [10], proved that approximate controllability in the space M^2 is equivalent to spectral controllability and complettability where the latter condition means the existence of a linear feedback which transforms the original system into a system with a complete set of generalized eigenfunctions. The rank condition equivalent to complettability appeared earlier in [1]. Salamon, [2], demonstrated that approximate null controllability on a sufficiently long time interval is equivalent to spectral controllability. For systems with neutral terms, criteria for approximate controllability in $W^{(1,p)}$ were given in [11] (see also [2] for more results and references on neutral systems).

Summarizing this short overview of literature, we note that the results were obtained for very specific function spaces (mostly M^2 and $W^{(1,p)}$) using the methods of the C_0 - semigroup theory and, typically, for systems with one or several discrete time delays.

In this paper, we extend the above mentioned results in several ways. We will consider systems with both discrete and distributed delays. The main feature of our approach is that we are not restricted to a specific function space as opposed to most previous papers and we do not need the C_0 - semigroup properties.

In Section 2, we recall definitions of various approximate controllability notions and show basic interrelationships between them due to system linearity and time invariance. In Section 3, we prove that spectral controllability is necessary for approximate controllability on both fixed and state dependent intervals, as well as for approximate null controllability on a fixed interval, and this holds in general function spaces satisfying some natural mild axioms. Next result is that the open loop stabilizability is necessary for approximate null controllability (on intervals dependent on initial states). Finally, we show that three large families of concrete function spaces, $X = C^{(k)}$, M^p, and $W^{(k,p)}$ satisfy all our general assumptions.

Essential tools in our theory are the notion of a dual transposed system and dual observability concepts corresponding to approximate controllability concepts which contribute to the general duality theory of controllability and observability. In Section 4, we generalize the notions of a dual transposed system and dual observability concepts, developed in [1], corresponding to approximate controllability concepts. This enables completion of our general results by proving that spectral controllability is sufficient for approximate null controllability and by deriving testable criteria from the dual problems. Such criteria assume an especially simple form when the final time T is greater than nh (Section 5) and also in case of discrete delays where connections to controllability over the ring of polynomials in a delay operator can be established (Section 6).

2. CONTROLLABILITY DEFINITIONS

Consider a control interval [0, T], some linear function space X of states with a topology, and some space U of control functions on [0, T]. We assume that the pair (U,X) is compatible in the sense that U is a subset of integrable functions, X is a subset of essentially bounded functions, and for any initial condition f in X and any control u in U the corresponding states x_t are in X for all $t \in [0, T]$. The solution to the system equations (1),(2) can be represented as

$$(3) \quad x_t = S(t)f + C(t)u$$

where S(t) and C(t) are linear operators defined by the variation of constants formula with the fundamental matrix solution X(t) (see Hale, [12])

(4)

$$x(t) - \Xi(t)\varphi(0)$$

$$+ \int_0^h \Xi(t-\tau)\{\sum_{i=0}^{N} A_i \Phi(\tau - h_i) + \int_{-h}^{0} \alpha(r)\Phi(\tau + r)dr\}d\tau$$

$$+ \int_0^t \Xi(t-\tau)Bu(\tau)d\tau$$

where F(t) = f(t) for $t \in [-h,0]$ and F(t) = 0 otherwise. The closure of the reachable subspace $R(t)$ = cl C(t)U will play an essential role in our considerations. The following are basic definitions of controllability for system (1),(2).

Definition 2.1 (Approximate controllability) System (1),(2) is approximately controllable if for any initial condition in X, any y in X, and any neighborhood Ny of y there is a final time T and a control u in U such that the final state x_T of the corresponding solution x(.) to (1),(2) belongs to Ny. This system is approximately controllable on an interval [0, T] if the above property holds with a fixed value of T and it is uniformly approximately controllable if there is a T such that it is approximately controllable on the interval [0, T].

Definition 2.2 (Approximate null controllability) System (1),(2) is approximately null controllable if for any initial condition in X, and any neighborhood N of zero there is a final time T and a control u in U such that the final state x_T of the corresponding solution x(.) to (1),(2) belongs to N. This system is approximately null controllable on the interval [0, T] if the above property holds with the fixed value of T and it is uniformly approximately null controllable if there is a T such that it is approximately null controllable on the interval [0, T].

Definition 2.3 (Approximate reachability) If system (1),(2) satisfies the properties of Definition 1, except that spaces X. In [14], we show that three large family of concrete function spaces satisfy the assumptions of Theorems 3.2 and 3.4. These are, with norms suitably defined [14],

(a) The space $X = C^{(k)}$ of R^n - valued functions on [-h,0] with continuous k-th derivative.

(b) The space $X = M^p$ of R^n - valued p-integrable functions on [-h,0].

(c) The space $X = W^{(k,p)}$ of R^n - valued functions on [-h,0] with p-integrable k-th derivative.

4. DUAL OBSERVABILITY PROBLEMS

We introduce the following dual (transposed) system with an output y(t)

(8) $\quad d/dt\ \xi(t) = A'\ \xi_t$

(9) $\quad y(t) = B'\ \xi(t)$

where B' is the transpose of the matrix B and A' is the formal transpose of A, that is, the operator of same form as A but with all its matrices replaced by their transposes. We define two notions of observability.

Definition 4.1 (Observability and Final Observability) Let Γ denote a subspace of integrable functions on [-h, 0]. System (8), (9) is called Γ- observable on [0, T] if $\xi_0 \in \Gamma$ and $y(t) = 0$ for all t in [0, T] imply $\xi_0 = 0$, and it is called finally Γ- observable on [0, T] if $\xi_0 \in \Gamma$ and $y(t) = 0$ for all t in [0, T] imply $\xi(t) = 0$ for $t > T$.

Theorem 4.2 Assume that the following hypotheses hold
(H1) The space of controls contains $C(0, \infty ; R^m)$
(H2) The functionals $f \in X^*$ can be represented as

$$f(x) = \int_{-h}^{0} \langle dg(r), x(r) \rangle$$

where g is of bounded variation with g(0) =0.
Then
(i) System (1),(2) is approximately controllable on an interval [0, T] iff the dual system (8),(9) is Γ_B - observable on [0, T-h] with Γ_B given by all initial functions of form $\xi_0(t) = \int_0^h \Xi'(t+h-r)dg(-r)$ where g(.) is determined by all functionals $f \in X^*$ such that $\xi_0(t) \in \ker B'$
(i) System (1),(2) is approximately null controllable on [0, T] iff the dual system (8),(9) is finally Γ_B - observable on [0, T-h] with Γ_B given as above.
Proof: To be published

5. THE CASE OF FINAL TIME $T > nh$

We know from Section 3 that spectral controlllability is necesssary for uniform approximate null controllability. Now, we will show that it is also sufficient and, moreover, the time interval [0, T] on which this holds can be estimated by $T > nh$.

Theorem 5.1 Assume the hypotheses (H1) and (H2) hold. Then the following statements are equivalent.
(I) The sytem is spectrally controllable
(II) The sytem is uniformly approximately null controllable
(III) The sytem is approximately null controllable on any interval [0,T] where $T > nh$.
Proof: To be published

Completing the characterization of approximate null controllability are the following

Theorem 5.2 Suppose that the set U of controls is such that, for some t_o, all functions of form $u(t) = 0$ for $t \in [0, t_o]$ and, for $t > t_o$, $u(t) = K_o x(t) + \int_0^h K_1(r)x(t-r)dr$, with $K_1(.)$ of class L^1, belong to U for all initial conditions $x_o(.)$. Assume that the state space X is such that the conditions $\exp(\alpha t)x(t) \rightarrow 0$ as $t \rightarrow \infty$ and $\alpha > 0$ imply $\| x_t \| \rightarrow 0$ as $t \rightarrow \infty$. Then system (1),(2) is approximately null controllable iff it is stabilizable, i.e., condition (5) holds for $Re(s) \geq 0$.
Proof: To be published

Corollary 5.3 System (1),(2) is approximately null controllable on [0,T], where $T > nh$, iff the only solution to (8), corresponding to an integrable initial function, such that the output (9) vanishes on $[0, \infty)$ is a small solution, i.e., vanishing after a finite time.
Proof: To be published

Corollary 5.4 System (1),(2) is approximately null controllable on [0,T], $T \leq nh$, iff the only solution to (8), corresponding to an initial function $\xi_0(.) \in \Gamma_B$, such that the output (9) vanishes on [0,T] is a small solution vanishing after $T - h$.
Proof: To be published

Corollary 5.5 System (1),(2) is approximately controllable on [0,T], $T \leq nh$, if it is spectrally controllable and rank $[A_N, B] = n$. The latter condition is also necessary if we assume that the distributed delays are bounded away from -h, i.e., $\alpha(r) = 0$ for all $r \in [-h, -h + \varepsilon]$ for some $\varepsilon > 0$.
Proof: To be published

6. ALGEBRAIC CONDITIONS

a fixed zero initial state (2) is assumed, then it is, respectively, approximately reachable, approximately reachable on [0, T], and uniformly approximately reachable.

Clearly, our definitions make sense only if $T > h$. Some of the above properties are obviously interrelated by definition, others are related thanks to the linearity and time invariance of eq. (1). To the latter category we include

Proposition 2.4 The following implications hold:
(i) Approximate controllability on [0,T] implies approximate null controllability on [0,T].
(ii) Uniform approximate controllability implies uniform approximate null controllability.
(iii) If U is closed under right shifts in time then approximate (null) controllability on $[0,T_1]$ implies approximate (null) controllability on $[0,T_2]$ for $T_2 > T_1 > 0$. A similar implication holds for reachability.
Proof: See [14].

3. CONNECTIONS WITH SPECTRAL CONTROLLABILITY AND STABILIZABILITY

In this section we will examine necessary conditions for approximate controllability in terms of stabilizability and spectral controllability which are known to be algebraic properties in the sense that they do not depend on the state space, they are rather characterized by algebraic rank conditions involving system matrices, [13]. We will show that spectral controllability is necessary for both approximate controllability and uniform approximate null controllability and stabilizability is necessary for approximate null controllability and these facts hold true independent of the set of controls and, under some mild assumptions, independent of the state space X.
Let us recall the definitions of spectral controllability and stabilizability. Note that we use "open loop" definitions, no feedback control is involved contrary to most literature. Although the feedback versions are fully equivalent, under some restrictions on feedback, as demonstrated by the theory developed in [13], we find the open loop versions more natural and easier to apply in considerations concerning controllability properties.

Definition 3.1 (Stabilizability and spectral controllability) System (1),(2) is g-stabilizable, for a given real number g, if for any x_o in X there exists a control u in $L^1{}_{loc}(0,\infty)$ such that both u and the corresponding solution x behaves asymptotically as $o(e^{-\gamma t})$. The system is called stabilizable if it is γ-stabilizable with $\gamma = 0$, and it is spectrally controllable if it is g-stabilizable for any g.

It follows from [13] that γ-stabilizability is equivalent to

$$(5) \qquad \text{rank}\ [sI - \mathbb{A}(s),\ B] = n$$

for any complex s with $re(s) \geq \gamma$ and spectral controllability holds if and only if (5) holds for any complex s where

$$(6) \qquad \mathbb{A}(s) = \sum_{i=0}^{N} e^{-sh_i} A_i + \int_{-h}^{0} e^{sr} \alpha(r) dr$$

Now, we are in a position to show

Theorem 3.2 Assume that X is a normed state space such that all functionals F of the form

$$(7) \qquad F(\phi) = \langle q, \phi(0) \rangle + \int_{-h}^{0} \langle f(r), \phi(r) \rangle\, dr$$

where $q \in R^n$, f is a sum of a piecewise analytic and a $W^{(1,\infty)}$ function, are continuous and F is nontrivial if q is nonzero. Then spectral controllability is necessary for approximate reachability (and therefore approximate controllability). If, additionally, the function space of control inputs is closed under right shifts and, for some T, all final states x_T generated by zero controls, zero initial functions, and nonzero x(0) belong to the state space X then uniform approximate null controllability implies spectral controllability.
Proof: See [14].

Remark 3.3 By Proposition 2.1 and definitions, spectral controllability is also necessary for approximate controllability and approximate null controllability on a given interval as well as for uniform approximate controllability but not for approximate null controllability. The latter is obvious since some systems without control, like $d/dt\ x(t) = -x(t)$, are formally approximately null controllable according to Definition 2.2. However, in general, we have

Theorem 3.4 Let all assumptions of Theorem 3.2 be satisfied. Then approximate null controllability implies stabilizability.
Proof: See [14].

Remark 3.5 The results of Theorems 3.2 and 3.4 can be strengthen by weakening the topology in X. In fact, it follows from the proofs that, in the weak topology in X, spectral controllability is necessary for approximate controllability and uniform approximate null controllability while stabilizability is necessary for approximate null controllability. Moreover, even a weaker topology generated by all functionals of type (7) can be taken without losing validity of Theorems 3.2 and 3.4.

Remark 3.6 In the theory of delay systems it is customary to work with specific function spaces as state

For the case of discrete commensurate delays we can obtain elegant algebraic criteria. Consider system (1), (2) without distributed delays (i.e., $\alpha(r) = 0$) and with commensurable delays $h_i = ih$. Denoting by d the delay operator, $(dx)(t) = x(t-h)$, we can write system equations in a compact form

$$(10) \quad d/dt\, x = A(d)x + Bu$$

where $A(d)$ is the polynomial matrix in the delay operator corresponding to system (1),

$$A(d) = A_o + dA_1 + \ldots + d^N A_N.$$

The following results utilize a corresponding polynomial controllability matrix.

Theorem 6.1 Suppose the assumptions of Theorem 3.2 concerning the approximate controllability (resp., uniform approximate null controllability) hold. Then a necessary condition for the approximate controllability (resp., uniform approximate null controllability) of system (10) is that the rank of the following polynomial controllability matrix

$$\text{rank } [B, A(z)B, \ldots, A(z)^{n-1}B] = n$$

be equal n for at least one real z (equivalently, its rank over the field of real rational functions (in z) equals n).

Theorem 6.2 Assume (H1) and (H2) stated in Theorem 4.2 hold true. If

$$\text{rank } [B, A(z)B, \ldots, A(z)^{n-1}B] = n$$

for all nonzero complex z and

$$\text{rank } [B, A^N] = n$$

where A^N is the highest order matrix coefficient of $A(z)$ then the system is approximately controllable on $[0,T]$ with $T > nh$.

REFERENCES

[1]. A. W. Olbrot, Control of retarded systems with function space constraints. Part 2: Approximate controllability, Control & Cybernetics, Vol. 6, No. 2, pp. 17-69, 1977

[2]. D. Salamon, Control and Observation of Neutral Systems, Pitman, 1984

[3]. R. V. Gabasov and F. M. Kirillova, Qualitative Theory of Optimal Processes, Nauka, Moscow, 1971

[4]. A. Manitius and A. W. Olbrot, Controllability conditions for linear systems with delayed state and control, Archiv. Autom. Telemech., Vol. 17, pp. 119-131, 1972.

[5]. A. W. Olbrot, Algebraic criteria of controllability to zero function for linear constant time-lag systems, Control & Cybernetics, Vol. 2, No. 1/2, pp. 59-77, 1973

[6]. A. W. Olbrot, Control to equilibrium of linear delay-diffeential systems, IEEE Trans. Autom. Control, Vol. AC-28, No. 4, pp. 521-523, 1983

[7] A. W. Olbrot and L. Pandolfi, Null controllability of a class of functional differential systems, Int. J. Control, Vol. 43, No. 1, pp. 193-208, 1988

[8]. A. Manitius and R. Triggiani, Function space controllability of linear retarded systems: A derivation from abstract operator conditions, SIAM J. Control & Optim., Vol. 16, pp. 599-645, 1978

[9]. V. M. Marchenko, Quasicontrollability of linear systems with aftereffect (in Russian), Avtomatika Telemech., Vol. 18, No. 3, pp. 18-22, 1979 (English transl. in Automat. Remote Control, Vol. 40, No. 3, part 1, pp. 335-339, 1979

[10]. A. Manitius, Necessary and sufficient conditions of approximate controllability for general linear retarded systems, SIAM J. Control & Optim., Vol. 19, pp. 516-632, 1981

[11]. D. A. O'Connor and T. J. Tarn, On the function space controllability of linear neutral systems, SIAM J. Control & Optim., Vol. 21, pp. 306-329, 1983

[12]. J. Hale, Theory of Functional Differential Equations, Springer-Verlag, 1977

[13]. A. W. Olbrot, Stabilizability, detectability, and spectrum assignment for linear systems with general time delays, IEEE Trans. Autom. Control, Vol. AC-23, No. 5, pp. 887-890, 1978

[14]. A. W. Olbrot, Approximate controllability of linear functional-differential systems: A state space independent approach, to appear in Control and Geometry of Dynamics (a volume devoted to the 70th birthday of Larry Markus), Marcel Dekker, 1993

Proceedings of the
American Control Conference
San Francisco, California • June 1993

THE LQR PROBLEM FOR FUNCTIONAL DIFFERENTIAL EQUATIONS

Richard Datko

Department of Mathematics
Georgetown University, Washington, DC 20057-0001

Introduction. We present a special version of a more general result which appears in [1]. Our aim is to demystify certain LQR problems for autonomous linear functional differential equations. These problems have a natural infinite-dimensional setting and are direct extrapolations of the original Kalman LQR-Problems [3] in finite dimensions. The major triumphs of the Kalman problem were that its solution was computable and lead to a stabilizing feedback controller via the so-called Riccati operator. In almost any infinite-dimensional version of the Kalman problem the optimal controller also generate a feedback which makes the system uniformly exponentially stable. But the computability of the feedback operator is difficult. In our view this invalidates the practicality of this approach to the stabilization of most infinite-dimensional control systems, at least if computability of the Riccati feedback operator is the goal. However it is sometimes possible to "find" the point spectra and the corresponding eigenvectors for LQR problems without too much difficulty. By "find" we of course mean the ability to express solutions in a form which is amenable to the computation. In this paper we present one such approach for a simple class of LQR problems governed by a linear functional differential with one delay. The method however is quite general and may be applied to complex neutral functional differential equations set in an infinite-dimensional Hilbert space (see e.g. [2]).

1. The Basic Method.

Let $h \geq 0$ be fixed and consider the functional differential equation described by

$$(1) \qquad \dot{x}(t) = A_0 x(t) + A_1 x(t-h) + B\mu(t), \text{ if } t > 0,$$

and by

$$(2) \qquad x(t) = \phi(t) \text{ if } t \in [-h, 0].$$

In equation (1) A_0 and A_1 are real $n \times n$ matrices and B is a real $m \times n$ matrix, $m \leq n$, which represents a one-to-one mapping from the complex m-space, $\mathcal{C}^m$, into the complex n-space, $\mathcal{C}^n$. The complex inner product on $\mathcal{C}^m$ or C^n is represented by $(\cdot,\cdot)$ and the adjoint of any matrix Q by Q^*. In (2) ϕ is a continuous linear mapping from $[-h, 0]$ into $\mathcal{C}^n$. We shall denote the space of all such mapping furnished with the usual supremum norm by $C([-h,0],\mathcal{C}^n)$. The mapping μ in (1) is assumed to be a mapping from $[0,\infty)$ into $\mathcal{C}^m$ which is L_2-integrable in the usual sense. The space of all L_2-integrable mappings from $[0,\infty)$ into the complex k space, $\mathcal{C}^k$, will be denoted by $L^2(R^+,\mathcal{C}^k)$.

The LQR problem we are concerned with is the following. Let W be a real positive semidefinite symmetric $n \times n$ matrix. We wish to optimize the functional

$$(3) \qquad C(\mu,\phi) = \int_0^\infty [(Wx(t,\phi,\mu), x(t,\phi,\mu)) + (\mu(t),\mu(t))]dt,$$

where $x(t,\phi,\mu)$ satisfies (1)-(2) and ϕ is fixed.

Conditions for $C(\cdot,\phi)$ to possess a finite minimum value for all $\phi \in C([-h,0],\mathcal{C}^n]$ may be found in [3]. We shall take it for granted that suitable ones exist. It is well known that if $C(\cdot,\phi)$ is optimizable for all ϕ, then the optimal solutions generate a linear feedback operator on $C([-h,0],\mathcal{C}^n)$ and that the resulting system is a C_0-semigroup on $C([-h,0],\mathcal{C}^n)$ (see e.g. [1]). Let us assume this semigroup is exponential stable (it is guaranteed to be if W in (3) is positive definite). Then the eigenvalues of the feedback system have real parts negative.

Let λ be such an eigenvalue and $x_0 \neq 0$ a corresponding eigenvector. Since the control is a feedback, the optimal trajectory and the optimal control must respectively be of the form

$$(4) \qquad x(t,\phi,\mu) = x_0 e^{\lambda t}, \text{ and}$$

$$(5) \qquad \mu(t) = \mu_0 e^{\lambda t}.$$

But (4) and (5) also must satisfy equation (1). Hence the relationship between λ_0 and μ_0 is

$$(6) \qquad x_0 = (\lambda I - A_0 - A_1 e^{\lambda h})^{-1} B\mu_0$$

if $\mu_0 \neq 0$, or

$$(7) \qquad (\lambda I - A_0 - A_1 e^{-\lambda h})x_0 = 0$$

if $\mu_0 = 0$. Since B is one-to-one mapping the above relationship is unique.

Now let

$$\hat{S}(\mu) = (\mu I - A_0 - A_0 - A_1 e^{\mu h})^{-1}$$

and let $S(t)$ denote the inverse Laplace transform of (7), i.e.

$$(8) \qquad S(t) = \frac{1}{2\pi i}\int_{\sigma_1 - i\infty}^{\sigma_1 + i\infty} e^{\mu t}\hat{S}(\mu)d\mu,$$

where $\sigma_1 > 0$ is sufficiently large. It is shown in [2] that $x(\cdot,\phi,\mu)$ and $\mu(\cdot)$ are respectively an optimal trajectory and an optimal control for (3) if and only if for all $h \in L^2(R^+, C^m)$, for which the function

(9) $$y(t,h) = \int_0^t S(t-\sigma)Bh(\sigma)d\sigma$$

is in $L^2(R^+, C^n)$, the condition

(10) $$Re[\int_0^\infty [(Wx(t,\phi,\mu), y(t,h) + (\mu(t), h(t))]dt] = 0$$

is satisfied.

Thus if

$$x(t,\phi,\mu) = x_0 e^{\lambda t}, \mu(t) = \mu_0 e^{\lambda t}$$

equation (10) reduces to

$$Re[\int_0^\infty [(Wx_0 e^{\lambda t}, y(t,h) + \mu_0 e^{\lambda t}, h(t))]dt]$$

(11)

$$= Re[(Wx_0, \hat{S}(-\bar{\lambda})B\hat{h}(-\bar{\lambda})) + (\mu_0, \hat{h}(-\bar{\lambda}))] = 0,$$

where $\hat{h}(\mu)$ denotes the Laplace transform of h.

Hence a sufficient condition for λ to be an eigenvalue of the feedback system and for x_0 to be a corresponding eigenvector is that λ, x_0 and μ_0 satisfy

(12) $$B^*[\hat{S}(-\bar{\lambda})]^* W x_0 + \mu_0 = 0.$$

Equations (6) and (12) then lead to sufficient conditions for λ to be an eigenvalue of the LQR problem. Namely that there exist $x_0 \neq 0$ or $\mu_0 \neq 0$ such that either

(13) $$x_0 = -\hat{S}(\lambda)BB^*[\hat{S}(-\bar{\lambda})]^* W x_0, Re\lambda < 0$$

or

(14) $$\mu_0 = -B^*[\hat{S}(-\bar{\lambda})]^* W\hat{S}(\lambda)B\mu_0, Re\lambda < 0.$$

Are conditions (13) or (14) also necessary for λ to be an eigenvalue of the LQR problem? The answer is "almost " yes. It is based on the following lemma whose proof is given in [2].

<u>Lemma</u>. There exists an L_2-integrable scalar function $r(t)$ such that (i) the Laplace transform, $\hat{r}(\lambda)$, of r is an entire function all of whose zeros lie in $Re\lambda > 0$ and (ii) given any $h_0 \in C^m$ the function

(15) $$y(t, r(t)h_0) = \int_0^t S(t-\sigma)B(r(\sigma)h_0)d\sigma$$

is in $L^2(R^+, C^n)$.

Thus suppose λ is an eigenvalue of the feedback system such that

$$(\lambda I - A_0 - A_1 e^{-\lambda h})^{-1}$$

exists. Then there is a corresponding $x_0 \neq 0$ in C^n and $\mu_0 \neq 0$ in C^m such that (6) and (11) are satisfied. If

$$\mu_0 \neq -B^*[\hat{S}(-\bar{\lambda})]^* W x_0$$

the vector

(16) $$h_0 = (B^*[\hat{S}(-\bar{\lambda})]^* W x_0 + \mu_0)\overline{\hat{r}(-\bar{\lambda})} \neq 0$$

in C^n. Hence by the lemma the function

(17) $$h(t) = r(t)h_0$$

is in $L^2(R^+, C^m)$ and $y(t, h(t)) \in L^2(R^+, C^n)$. For this function (11) reduces to

(18) $$\|B^*[\hat{S}(-\bar{\lambda})]^* W x_0 + \mu_0\|^2 |\hat{r}(-\lambda)|^2 = 0$$

($\|\cdot\|$ denotes the norm in C^m). Since $(\hat{r} - (\bar{\lambda})) \neq 0$ this leads to a contradiction. Hence

(19) $$\mu_0 = -B^*[\hat{S}(-\bar{\lambda})]^* W x_0.$$

We now state the following theorem.

<u>Theorem</u>. If the LQR problem is uniformly exponentially stable. Then the eigenvalues of the feedback systems satisfy either equation (13) or (14) if

(20) $$(\lambda I - A_0 - A_1 e^{\lambda h})^{-1} B$$

exits. If (20) does not exist and λ is an eigenvalue of the system, then the relationship is given by

$$(\lambda I - A_0 - A_1 e^{-\lambda h})x_0 = 0$$

and

$$(Wx_0, (-\bar{\lambda} I - A_0 - A_1 e^{-\bar{\lambda} h})^{-1} B h_0) = 0$$

for all $h_0 \in C^m$ and some $x_0 \neq 0$.

<u>Example</u>

Consider the system in 2-space given by

(21) $$\begin{bmatrix} \dot{x}(t) = y(t) \\ \dot{y}(t) = -x(t-h) + \mu(t) \end{bmatrix}$$

(22) $$C(\mu,\phi) = \int_0^\infty [|x(t,\phi,\mu)|^2 + |\mu(t)|^2]dt.$$

Here

$$A_0 = \begin{pmatrix} 0 & , & 1 \\ 0 & , & 0 \end{pmatrix}, A_1 = \begin{pmatrix} 0 & , & 0 \\ -1 & , & 0 \end{pmatrix}, B = \begin{pmatrix} 0 \\ 1 \end{pmatrix}$$

and

$$W = \begin{pmatrix} 1 & 0 \\ 0 & 0 \end{pmatrix}.$$

$$\hat{S}(\lambda) = \frac{\begin{pmatrix} \lambda & , & 1 \\ -e^{-\lambda h} & , & \lambda \end{pmatrix}}{\lambda^2 + e^{-\lambda h}}$$

and

$$[\hat{S}(-\bar{\lambda})]^* = \frac{\begin{pmatrix} -\lambda & , & -e^{\lambda h} \\ 1 & , & -\lambda \end{pmatrix}}{\lambda^2 + e^{\lambda h}}.$$

The equivalent of equation (14) for this system is

$$1 = -(0,1)\frac{\begin{pmatrix} -\lambda, & -e^{\lambda h} \\ 1, & -\lambda \end{pmatrix}}{\lambda^2 + e^{\lambda h}} \begin{pmatrix} 1,0 \\ 0,0 \end{pmatrix} \frac{\begin{pmatrix} \lambda, 1 \\ -e^{-\lambda h}, & \lambda \end{pmatrix}}{\lambda^2 + e^{-\lambda h}} \begin{pmatrix} 0 \\ 1 \end{pmatrix}.$$

Thus reduces to

$$\lambda^4 + 2\lambda^2 \cosh \lambda h + 2 = 0, \quad Re\lambda < 0. \tag{23}$$

Notice that as $h \to 0$ (23) tends to

$$\lambda^4 + 2\lambda^2 + 2 = 0, \quad Re\lambda < 0, \tag{24}$$

which is the equation for the solution of (21)-(22) when $h = 0$.

References

1. R. Datko, Neutral autonomous functional equations with quadratic cost, SIAM J. Control Opt. **11** (1974), 70-82.
2. R. Datko, The point spectra of some LQR problems, to appear.
3. R.E. Kalman, Contributions to the theory of optimal control, Bol. Soc. Mat. Mexicana, **5** (1960), 102-119.

Proceedings of the
American Control Conference
San Francisco, California • June 1993

TRACKING CONTROLLER FOR OUTPUT FEEDBACK LINEAR TIME DELAY SYSTEMS

Dong H. Chyung

Department of Electrical and Computer Engineering
University of Iowa
Iowa City, Iowa 52242

ABSTRACT

Some preliminary results are presented on a tracking controller design for observable vector feedback linear time delay systems. The design is carried out in two steps. The first is to find the output feedback controller which stabilizes the given system and also satisfies the transient requirements. This is accomplished by finding a control which minimizes a cost function for a particular initial condition. Then a feedforward controller is derived for tracking a polynomial reference input. An example is given to illustrate the proposed controller.

I. INTRODUCTION

In this paper, preliminary results are presented on a tracking controller design for observable vector feedback linear time delay systems. The design is carried out in two steps. The first is to find the output feedback controller which stabilizes the given system and also satisfies the transient requirements. This is accomplished by finding a control which minimizes a cost function for a particular initial condition. Then a feedforward controller is derived for tracking a polynomial reference input.

The problem of stabilizing a delay system has been studied extensively. When only a partial state vector is observable for feedback, one may implement an observer or reconstruct the complete state vector[1]. This, however, often introduces its own difficulties. On the other hand, in many cases, a perfectly satisfactory controller can be designed by feeding back only the observable state variables. In fact, even in nondelay systems, the majority of controllers in real systems are based on partial state feedback such as PD and PID. The problem of finding a feedback control for locating some of the closed loop characteristic roots in preassigned locations has also been studied by many investigators. The outstanding problem is, however, where to locate the closed loop characteristic roots so that the transient response requirements are satisfied and the roots can indeed be located at the locations with observable vector feedback only. In this paper, a method is presented for finding an observable vector feedback controller. It is based on minimizing a quadratic cost function with respect to the feedback gain vector for a specific initial function.

Tacking controller for linear delay systems, too, has been investigated by many authors. Basically there are two different methods. The first is to augment the given system with additional error integrators and then to design a stabilizing controller[2]. The major problem with this methods is that the resulting system is soft and thus is very susceptible to external disturbances. This is the main reason why many practical control systems do not employ this method. The other method is to design a feedforward controller for tracking[3]. Although this scheme has the drawback of being sensitive to parameter variations, this is the method preferred in the majority of real systems. Currently there are no systematic ways to derive the feedforward tracking controller for partial state feedback delay systems. In this paper, a method is presented for finding the feedforward tracking controller for polynomial reference inputs.

In order not to be side tracked by peripheral issues and also for the sake of simplicity, we consider only step or ramp reference inputs. In real control system designs, one rarely, if at all, considers a reference input which is more than a ramp function. It is also assumed that the given system is stabilizable by the observable vector feedback and a tracking controller exists.

II. PROBLEM STATEMENT

Consider the linear time-invariant control system with N time delays

$$\dot{x}(t) = \sum_{i=0}^{N} A_i x(t-ih) + Bu(t) \tag{S}$$
$$y(t) = Cx(t)$$
$$z(t) = Dy(t) = DCx(t)$$

where $x=(x_1,x_2,\dots,x_n)^T$ is the (nx1) state vector, $u=(u_1,u_2,\dots,u_m)^T$ is the (mx1) control vector, $y=(y_1,y_2,\dots,y_q)^T$ is the (qx1) observable vector, $z=(z_1,z_2,\dots,z_r)^T$ is the (rx1) output vector, B, C, D and A_i, i=0,1, ... ,N, are constant matrices with compatible dimensions, and $h > 0$ is the basic time delay. The reference input vector z^* is given by

$$z^*(t) = a_o + a_1 t \tag{1}$$

where a_o and a_1 are (rx1) constant vectors. The problem is to design a controller u as a constant feedback of the observable vector y such that the corresponding response z(t) follows the reference input vector $z^*(t)$ in steady state without error, that is, $z(t)\to z^*(t)$ as $t\to\infty$. It is assumed that the system is stabilizable, that is, there exists a linear feedback control which stabilizes the system (S) and a tracking controller exists.

III. FEEDFORWARD CONTROLLER

In this section, we derive a feedforward tracking controller.

Suppose the observable vector feedback control

$$u(t) = -Ky(t) = -KCx(t) \tag{2}$$

stabilizes the given system (S). Here, K is the feedback gain matrix. Let x^* and u^* satisfy the equations

$$\dot{x}^*(t) = \sum_{i=0}^{N} A_i x^*(t-ih) + Bu^*(t)$$
$$z^*(t) = DCx^*(t)$$

If such x^* and u^* do not exist, then it is not possible for the output to follow the reference input z^*. Let

$$\Delta x = x - x^*, \qquad \Delta y = y - y^*, \qquad \Delta u = u - u^*,$$

where $y^*=Cx^*$. Then,

$$\Delta\dot{x}(t) = \sum_{i=0}^{N} A_i \Delta x(t-ih) + B\Delta u(t) \tag{3}$$

Let

$$\Delta u(t) = -K\Delta y(t) = -KC\Delta x(t)$$

Since $u=-Ky$ stabilizes system(S), Δu stabilizes system (3), that is, $\Delta x(t)\to 0$ as $t\to\infty$. Then, $x(t)\to x^*(t)$ as $t\to\infty$, and so $z(t)\to z^*(t)$ as

$t \to \infty$. Thus,

$$u(t) = u^*(t) + \Delta u(t) = u^*(t) - K\{y(t) - y^*(t)\} \quad (4)$$

is a desired tracking controller.

It is now necessary to find $x^*(t)$ and $u^*(t)$ as linear functions of the reference input function $z^*(t)$. Because $z^*(t)$ is a ramp function, $z^{*(i)}(t)=0$ for all $i \geq 2$. Suppose $x^*(t)$ and $u^*(t)$ are given by

$$x^*(t) = F_0\, z^*(t) + F_1\dot{z}^*(t)$$
$$u^*(t) = G_0\, z^*(t) + G_1\dot{z}^*(t) \quad (5)$$

for some constant matrices F_0, F_1, G_0 and G_1. Then $\ddot{x}^*(t)=0$, and

$$x^*(t-ih) = x^*(t) - i\,h\,\dot{x}^*(t)$$
$$\dot{x}^*(t-ih) = \dot{x}^*(t)$$

Substituting the above to the original system (S),

$$\dot{x}^*(t) = \sum_{i=0}^{N} A_i\, x^*(t-ih)+Bu^*(t) = \sum_{i=0}^{N} A_i\, x^*(t) - \sum_{i=0}^{N} ih\, A_i\, \dot{x}^*(t)+Bu^*(t)$$
$$z^*(t) = DCx^*(t),$$

Differentiating the above,

$$\ddot{x}^*(t) = \sum_{i=0}^{N} A_i\dot{x}^*(t-ih) + B\dot{u}^*(t) = \sum_{i=0}^{N} A_i\dot{x}^*(t) + B\dot{u}^*(t) = 0$$

$$\dot{z}^*(t) = DC\dot{x}^*(t)$$

Combining the above two sets of equations, one can write in matrix form,

$$\begin{bmatrix} \sum_{i=0}^{N} A_i & -(I+\sum_{i=0}^{N} ihA_i) & B & 0 \\ 0 & \sum_{i=0}^{N} A_i & 0 & B \\ DC & 0 & 0 & 0 \\ 0 & DC & 0 & 0 \end{bmatrix} \begin{bmatrix} x^* \\ \dot{x}^* \\ u^* \\ \dot{u}^* \end{bmatrix} = \begin{bmatrix} 0 \\ 0 \\ z^* \\ \dot{z}^* \end{bmatrix} \quad (6)$$

By solving the above simultaneous linear algebraic equations, x^* and u^* are obtained in terms of z^* and $\dot{z}^*$. A unique solution exists if and only if the rank of the above coefficient matrix has the full rank $2(n+r)$. Thus, this is a necessary and sufficient condition for the existence of linear feedforward tracking controller for ramp reference input. If z^* is a step function, then $\dot{z}^*(t)=0$, $\dot{x}^*(t)=0$ and $x^*(t-ih)=x^*(t)$. Thus, x^* and u^* are found by solving the equation

$$\begin{bmatrix} \sum_{i=0}^{N} A_i & B \\ DC & 0 \end{bmatrix} \begin{bmatrix} x^* \\ u^* \end{bmatrix} = \begin{bmatrix} 0 \\ z^* \end{bmatrix} \quad (6)'$$

A unique solution exists, that is, a step function tracking controller exists, if and only if the above coefficient matrix has the full rank $n+r$. The solution of eq.(6) is in the form

$$x^*(t) = F_0\, z^*(t) + F_1\dot{z}^*(t)$$
$$u^*(t) = G_0\, z^*(t) + G_1\dot{z}^*(t)$$

where F_0, F_1, G_0 and G_1 constant matrices. Note that x^* and u^* are indeed in the form assumed in eq.(5).

Since $y^* = Cx^*$ and $\dot{z}^*(t) = \frac{1}{h}\{z^*(t)-z^*(t-h)\}$,

$$y^*(t) = C\{F_0\, z^*(t) + F_1\dot{z}^*(t)\} = C\{F_0+\tfrac{1}{h}F_1\}z^*(t) - \tfrac{1}{h}C\, F_1 z^*(t-h)$$

The tracking controller is now given by

$$u(t) = G_0\, z^*(t) + G_1\dot{z}^*(t) - K[y(t) - \{CF_0\, z^*(t) + CF_1\dot{z}^*(t)\}] \quad (7)$$

or, in delayed feedforward form without derivatives,

$$u(t) = (G_0+\tfrac{1}{h}G_1)z^*(t) - \tfrac{1}{h}G_1 z^*(t-h) - K[y(t)-C\{F_0+\tfrac{1}{h}F_1\}z^*(t) - \tfrac{1}{h}z^*(t-h)] \quad (7)'$$

In the above, if z^* is a step function, then $\dot{z}^*=0$, and so one can let $F_1=G_1=0$.

IV OBSERVABLE VECTOR FEEDBACK CONTROL

A tracking controller is derived in the previous section, provided a stabilizing controller $u=-Ky=-KCx$ is available. In this section, a method is presented for finding a observable vector feedback control which stabilizes the closed loop system and also satisfies the required transient response conditions. The results are tentative and require further investigation. However, numerous simulations indicate that they are basically correct.

For the system (S)

$$\dot{x}(t) = \sum_{i=0}^{N} A_i x(t-ih) + Bu(t) \quad (S)$$
$$y(t) = Cx(t)$$
$$z(t) = Dy(t) = DCx(t),$$

let

$$u(t) = -Ky(t) = -KCx(t) \quad (8)$$

where K is the constant observable vector feedback gain matrix, and define the cost function J(K) as

$$J(K) = \int_0^\infty (x^T(t)\, Q\, x(t) + u^T(t)\, R\, u(t))\, dt \quad (9)$$

where R is a positive definite matrix and Q is a positive semi-definite matrix. Choose a nonzero constant output vector z_o such that there exist constant vectors x_o and u_o which satisfy the equations

$$\sum_{i=0}^{N} A_i\, x_o + Bu_o = 0, \qquad z_o = CDx_o$$

The feedback gain matrix K is now found by minimizing the cost function J(K) subject to the system equation (S) with the initial condition

$$x(t)=x_o, \quad -Nh \leq t \leq 0. \quad (10)$$

As in the LQ optimal controller design for linear systems without delays, the required transient requirements are satisfied by choosing appropriate Q and R matrices in the cost function as well as the initial function x_o. Unlike nondelay systems, the cost is minimized for a particular initial function x_o, and so the stability of the closed loop is not automatically guaranteed. It is thus necessary to check the stability of the resulting system by examining the closed loop characteristic roots.It seems that the closed loop system is stable for most of none zero initial functions x_o. However, exactly what conditions must be satisfied by the initial function to guarantee the closed loop system stability is one of the open questions.The minimizing feedback gain is obtained by a numerical method.

V EXAMPLE

Consider the system

$$\dot{x}(t) = \begin{bmatrix} -10 & 2 & 0 & 0 & 0 \\ 0 & -1 & 1 & 0 & 0 \\ -24 & -6 & -39 & 3 & 22 \\ -1 & 0 & 0 & -10 & 2 \\ 2 & -2 & 8 & -3 & -7 \end{bmatrix} x(t) + \begin{bmatrix} 20 & -1 & 0 & 0 & 0 \\ 0 & 1 & 0 & 0 & 0 \\ 30 & 1 & 0 & 1 & 0 \\ 1 & 0 & 0 & 10 & 0 \\ 10 & 2 & 0 & 1 & 0 \end{bmatrix} x(t-0.1) + \begin{bmatrix} -10 & 0 & 0 & 0 & 0 \\ 0 & 0 & 0 & 0 & 0 \\ -10 & 0 & 0 & 0 & 0 \\ 0 & 0 & 0 & 0 & 0 \\ -10 & 0 & 0 & 0 & 0 \end{bmatrix} x(t-0.2) + \begin{bmatrix} 0 & 0 \\ 0 & 0 \\ 1 & -4 \\ 0 & 0 \\ 0 & 1 \end{bmatrix} u(t)$$

$$y = \begin{bmatrix} 1 & 0 & 0 & 0 & 0 \\ 0 & 1 & 0 & 0 & 0 \\ 0 & 0 & 0 & 1 & 0 \end{bmatrix} x$$

$$z = \begin{bmatrix} 1 & 0 & 0 \\ 0 & 0 & 1 \end{bmatrix} y = \begin{bmatrix} 1 & 0 & 0 & 0 & 0 \\ 0 & 0 & 0 & 1 & 0 \end{bmatrix} x$$

Suppose the reference input z* is a step function. It is desired that step responses have minimum amount of overshoot and settling time is as short as possible. Because only a partial state is available for feedback, the overshoot and the settling time cannot be made arbitrarily small and, in addition, they cannot be controlled independently.

Choose

$$x_o = \begin{bmatrix} 1 \\ 0 \\ 0 \\ -1 \\ 0 \end{bmatrix}, \quad Q = \begin{bmatrix} 4000 & 0 & 0 & 0 & 0 \\ 0 & 400 & 0 & 0 & 0 \\ 0 & 0 & 0 & 0 & 0 \\ 0 & 0 & 0 & 4000 & 0 \\ 0 & 0 & 0 & 0 & 700 \end{bmatrix}, \quad R = \begin{bmatrix} 1 & 0 \\ 0 & 1 \end{bmatrix}$$

Then,

$$K = \begin{bmatrix} 27 & 19 & -1 \\ -44 & -36 & 25 \end{bmatrix}, \quad x^* = \begin{bmatrix} 1 & 0 \\ 0 & 0 \\ 0 & 0 \\ 0 & 1 \\ 0 & 0 \end{bmatrix} z^*, \quad y^* = \begin{bmatrix} 1 & 0 \\ 0 & 0 \\ 0 & 1 \end{bmatrix} z^*, \quad u^* = \begin{bmatrix} -4 & 4 \\ -2 & 2 \end{bmatrix} z^*$$

and the tracking control is given by

$$u(t) = u^*(t) - K\{y(t) - y^*(t)\}$$
$$= \begin{bmatrix} 23 & 3 \\ -46 & 27 \end{bmatrix} z^*(t) - \begin{bmatrix} 27 & 19 & -1 \\ -44 & -36 & 25 \end{bmatrix} y(t).$$

Various step responses as well as the closed loop characteristics roots(with nonnegative imaginary parts only) are shown in the figures given below.

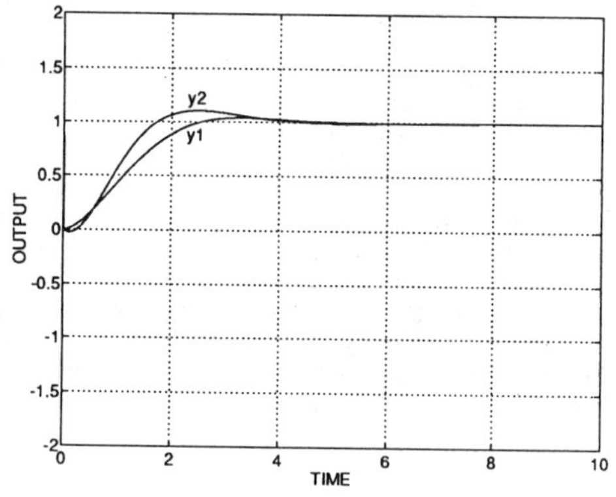

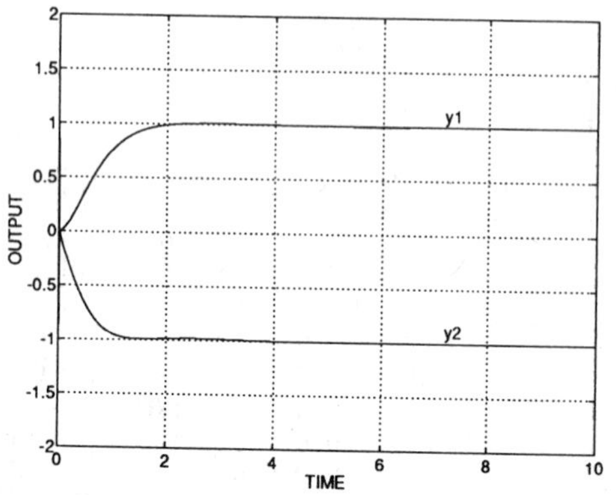

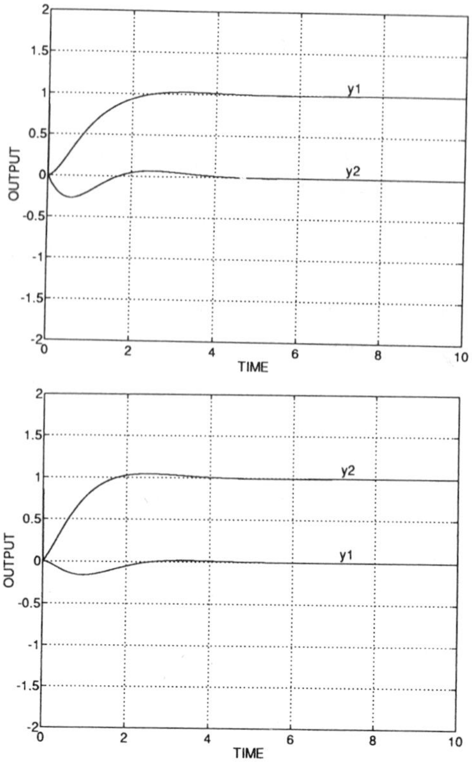

Fig.1 Step Responses

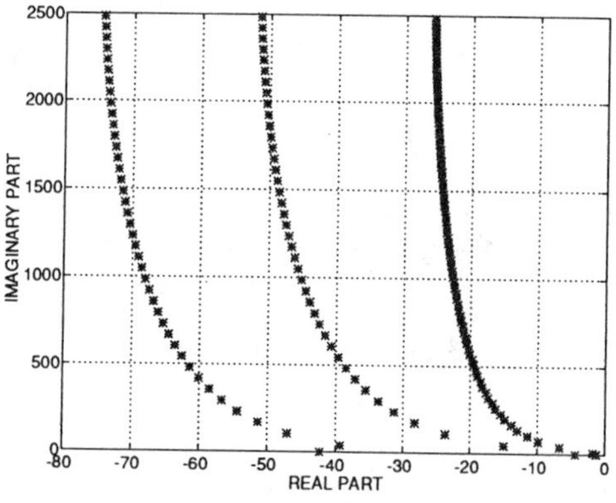

(a) General Distribution

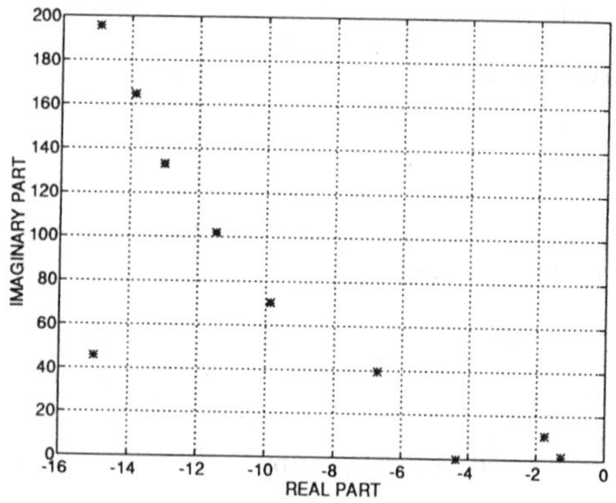

(b) Dominant Roots

Fig. 2 Closed Loop Characteristic Roots

VI. CONCLUSIONS

The problem of designing an observable vector feedback tracking controller for linear time invariant control systems with time delays is investigated. It is assumed that the reference input is a ramp function. The results can be easily extended to general polynomial reference input functions. It can also be extended to systems which contain time delays in the control as well. Some of the results, however, require further study.

REFERENCES

1. Pourboghrat, F and Chyung, D. H., Exact State Variable Reconstruction of Delay Systems, Int. J. of Control, Vol.144, No.3, 1986

2. Chyung, D. H., Robust Tracking Controller for Time Delay Systems, 28th CDC, Tampa, Florida, December 1989.

3. Chyung, D. H., Feedforward Tracking Controller for Systems Containing Time Delays, 1990 ACCC, San Diego, CA, May 1990.

WM12 - 12:20

Proceedings of the American Control Conference
San Francisco, California • June 1993

A new approach to stabilize time delay systems

M. Wang † *E. B. Lee* † *D. Boley* ‡

Control Science and Dynamical Systems Center
University of Minnesota
200 Union Street
Minneapolis, MN 55455
e-mail: mwang@cs35d.cs.umn.edu eblee@ee.umn.edu boley@cs.umn.edu

ABSTRACT

The use of periodic sampled output feedback control for linear time delay systems is considered. The suggested design procedure contains two steps: one for eigenvalue assignment, the other for final status control. Some examples are given.

1. Introduction

Many techniques have been suggested for stability analysis and stabilization of time delay systems. For example, a class of Lyapunov functions, one is the so called Lyapunov-Krasovskii function, has been applied to analyze the stability of time delay systems [Kr-N], [Wa-W], [Sk-V] [Wa-M] and [Fe-E]. In [Wa-M] we applied this function to stabilize a delay system by a constant feedback controller, i.e. by a simple finite dimensional controller. The feedback gain can be computed by solving a parametric Riccati equation. To do so, first we need to search for parameters to make the Riccati equation solvable and then to stabilize the system. Generally, this is not a easy task and sometimes we cannot find any suitable solution.

There are some other approaches to design finite dimensional controllers, for example, rational approximation technique, coprime factorization technique and spectrum assignment over algebraic ring and finite spectrum assignment. The rational approximation technique often increases the degree of the dynamic controllers. The coprime factorization technique usually is not easy to realize numerically. Algebraic ring method might suffer numerical computation difficulty.

Considering the fact that modern control is extensively applied digital control, we find that such computer technique has enriched our tools and strategies. For example, by digital control we can easily compute a time varying feedback gain and simply realize this control by our program. We do not have to be restricted by time invariant controls. This is our motivation to study some new techniques in a wider class of control strategies.

Recently deadbeat-type control has been of interest and has been applied to various periodic control problems. For example, for infinite dimensional systems[Ta-T], for uncertain system control[Ol-A-2] and multi system simultaneous control[Kh-P]. The simple theoretic background, the linear structure, the easy computation and the potential for optimizing the performance might be the main attraction of the deadbeat-type control. Here in this paper we develop time varying periodic control for time delay systems and discuss the reality and the robustness of the algorithm.

† : supported by Grants DMS9002019
‡ : supported by Grant CDA 9222922

2. Periodic sampled output control

We start our discussion by considering delay systems with only one input delay, namely, consider the model with input (or output) delay

$$\dot{x}(t) = A_0 x(t) + Bu(t-h) \tag{1.1}$$

$$y = Cx(t) \tag{1.2}$$

The existence of input/output delay is a common situation. Usually the output delay can be ignored. But there are some cases where we have to take the delay into account. Many efforts have been given to this kind of systems for finite spectrum assignment. For example [Ol-A], [Ma-A] and [Pa-L].

We can see that this system is not spectrum controllable due to the input delays, even if (A, B) is a controllable pair. However the system can be stabilized by a periodic sampled output control as long as (A, B) is a controllable pair and (A, C) is a observable pair.

Theorem 1 System (1) is periodic sampled output stabilizable if and only if (A, B) is controllable and (A, C) is observable.

Proof: This actually is a corollary of the theorem 1 from [Ta-T]. Let $\Phi(t, \tau) = e^{A(t-\tau)}$ be the fundamental matrix which solves the homogeneous system. Integrate system (1):

$$x(t) = \Phi(t)x(0) + \int_0^t \Phi(t-\tau)Bu(\tau-h)\, d\tau$$

Set $u(t) = Ky(0) = KCx(0)$ when $T > t > h$ and $u(t) = 0$ when $t < h$. Then

$$x(T) = [\Phi(T) + \int_h^T \Phi(T-\tau)BKC d\tau]\, x(0)$$

$$= [\Phi(T) + GC + \int_h^T (\Phi(T-\tau)BK - G)\, d\tau C]\, x(0)$$

so

$$x(NT) = [\Phi(T) + \int_h^T \Phi(T-\tau)BKC d\tau]^N\, x(0)$$

From the observability of (A, C) and the controllability of (A, B), G can be chosen such that the spectral radius of $\Phi(T)+GC$ is much smaller than 1, and K can be chosen properly such that for some period $T > h$, $\int_h^T [\Phi(T-\tau)BK - G]\, d\tau$ is sufficient small. For example K can be chosen as a deadbeat-type control to follow the 'target' G,

$$K(t) = B'\Phi(-\tau)'W_c^{-1}G$$

where W_c is a Gramian matrix: $W_c = \int_h^T \Phi(-\tau)BB'\Phi(-\tau)'$ then $\int_h^T [\Phi(T-\tau)BK-G]\, d\tau < \varepsilon$, for a sufficiently small $\varepsilon > 0$. For the frozen time t=NT, simple arithmetic leads to the result that

$$\|[\Phi(T)+GC+\int_h^T(\Phi(T-\tau)BK-G)\, d\tau C]^N\| \tag{2}$$

will be sufficiently small for a finite large number N. When N tends to ∞, the terms in (2) will vanishes. So the system is stabilized. Furthermore, the feedback system will have form

$$x(t) = [\Phi(t)+\int_h^t \Phi(t-\tau)BKCd\tau]\, x(t-T)$$

where the periodic gain $K(t) = K(t+MT)$ for all integer numbers M. □

Let us take a scalar system as a simple example.

Example 1: Consider model

$$\dot{x}(t) = x(t)+u(t-h)$$

$$y = x(t)$$

where $x(t)$ is a scalar variable. Obviously this system is not spectrally controllable. It has been pointed out that when $h \geq 1$, no simple control $u(t) = kx(t)$ is available[Ol-A-2]. However we can easily find a period $T > h = 1$ such that there exists a periodic control gain $k(t)$ to guarantee that $\Phi(T)+\int_h^T \Phi(T-\tau)kd\tau$ is a contraction. For example, set $T = 2$ and choose $G = e^T - \frac{1}{4}$, then $\Phi(T) - GC = \frac{1}{4}$. Compute a deadbeat-type control

$$k(t) = -e^{-t}[\int_1^2 e^{-2\tau}d\tau]^{-1}G = -17.0911e^{-t}G$$

$$\text{when } t\in((M-1)T-h,\, MT]$$

$$k(t) = 0 \text{ when } t\in((M-1)T,\ (M-1)T-h]$$

where M is an integer. After N periods elapse,

$$[\Phi(T)+\int_1^2 \Phi(T-\tau)K(t)d\tau G]^N = 4^{-N}$$

The eigenvalue $\frac{1}{4}$ shows the speed of decay of the state to zero.

Now we consider the systems with multi input delays:

$$\dot{x}(t) = A_0x(t)+\sum_{i=0}^{r} B_k u(t-h_i) \tag{4.1}$$

$$y = Cx(t) \tag{4.2}$$

Corollary 2 Let **B** be the set of possible combinations of $\{B_i,\ i = 0, \ldots, r\}$. Let $\bar{B}$ be a member of **B**. The system in (4) is stabilizable by periodic sampled output feedback if and only if (A, C) is observable and there is at least one $\bar{B}$, such that $(A, \bar{B})$ is controllable.

Proof: The solution of (4.1) has form:

$$x(t) = \Phi(t)x(0)+\sum_{i=0}^{r}\int_0^t \Phi(t-\tau)B_iu(\tau-h_i)d\tau \tag{5}$$

Let $T > h_r$ and $u(t) = K(t)y(k)$, where $K(t) = K_i(t)$ for $t\in(h_i, h_{i+1}],\ i = 0, \ldots, r-1$, $K(t) = K_r(t)$ for $t\in(h_r, T]$, and $K(t) = K(t+MT)$ for any integer M. Then for $t = T$, the solution (5) can be represented as below:

$$x(T) = \left[\Phi(T)+\left[\int_0^{h_1}\Phi(T-\tau)B_0K_0+\int_{h_1}^{h_2}\Phi(T-\tau)B_1K_1+\ldots+\int_{h_{r-1}}^{h_r}\Phi(T-\tau)B_rK_r\right]C\right]y(0)$$

In a similar way to prove theorem 1,

$$\left[\Phi(T)+\left[\int_0^{h_1}\Phi(T-\tau)B_0K_0+\int_{h_1}^{h_2}\Phi(T-\tau)\sum_{i=0}^{1}B_iK_1+\ldots+\int_{h_{r-1}}^{h_r}\Phi(T-\tau)\sum_{i=0}^{r}B_iK_r\right]C\right]$$

$$= \left[\Phi(T)+GC+\left[\int_0^{h_1}\Phi(T-\tau)B_0K_0+\int_{h_1}^{h_2}\Phi(T-\tau)\sum_{i=0}^{1}B_iK_1+\ldots+\int_{h_{r-1}}^{h_r}\Phi(T-\tau)\sum_{i=0}^{r}B_iK_r-G\right]C\right]$$

The observability condition enables us to find a suitable G to assign the spectral radius of $\Phi(T)+GC$ arbitrarily, meanwhile the controllability condition ensures the existence of $K(t)$ such that the norm in (6) is sufficiently small:

$$\left[\int_0^{h_1}\Phi(T-\tau)B_0K_0+\int_{h_1}^{h_2}\Phi(T-\tau)\sum_{i=0}^{1}B_iK_1+\ldots+\int_{h_{r-1}}^{h_r}\Phi(T-\tau)\sum_{i=0}^{r}B_iK_r-G\right]C \tag{6}$$

So there exists a finite number N such that

$$\left\|\left[\Phi(T)+GC+\left[\int_0^{h_1}\Phi(T-\tau)B_0K_0+\int_{h_1}^{h_2}\Phi(T-\tau)\sum_{i=0}^{1}B_iK_1+\ldots+\int_{h_{r-1}}^{h_r}\Phi(T-\tau)\sum_{i=0}^{r}B_iK_r-G\right]C\right]^N\right\|$$

is sufficiently small, and the system (4) is stabilized. □

Multi input delays offer more choices for the feedback gain. By periodic sampled output feedback, this delay system can treaded like an ordinary finite dimensional system.

From above statement we can see that the procedure to design a periodic sampled output control can be decomposed into two steps:

Step 1: For a fixed time $t = T$, search for G, working for a spectrum assignment.

Step 2: Taking G as a given final status, search for $K(t)$ to provide a minimum of the above norm.

Multi-input delays do not increase the complexity for the theory although the computation increases. There is no difference in the problem solution for commensurate delays or independent delays.

3. Robustness and uncertainty tolerance

This periodic control technique actually is also an eigenvalue assignment technique. The difference is that here we consider the problem in the time domain and assign eigenvalues for a frozen time. First we choose the frozen time T as our period and then to search matrix G to do eigenvalue assignment of $\Phi(T)+GC$. After that we compute $K(t)$ to match G. In this way

$$\Phi(T)+\left[\int_0^{h_1}\Phi(T-\tau)B_0K_0+\int_{h_1}^{h_2}\Phi(T-\tau)\sum_{i=0}^{1}B_iK_1+\ldots+\int_{h_{r-1}}^{h_r}\Phi(T-\tau)\sum_{i=0}^{r}B_iK_r\right]$$

becomes a contraction.

It is well know that the value of $\Phi(t)$ increases exponentially for an unstable system. When T is large, we will encounter a numerical precision limit. So we need to analyze the robustness and the tolerance of the algorithm to the model uncertainty and to the computation precision. For simplicity in remaining part we will use system model (1) and omit the multi-input delay case. Stabilizing system (1) is to choose G and the gain $K(t)$ such that the spectral radius of

$$[\Phi(T)+GC+\int_h^T(\Phi(T-\tau)BK-G)\,d\tau C] \tag{7}$$

is small enough. The smaller it is, the faster the system goes to the equilibrium. Next we will analyze the uncertainty tolerance. Assume that $\int_h^T(\Phi(T-\tau)BK-G)\,d\tau C \neq 0$, then what is the effect of this difference?

Corollary 3 Let

$$\Delta = |\int_h^T(\Phi(T-\tau)BK-G)\,d\tau C|$$

and let P be the solution of discrete time Lyapunov equation

$$P-[\Phi(T)+GC]'P[\Phi(T)+GC]=I \tag{8}$$

where I is an identity matrix. Define

$$\beta := \sqrt{\frac{1}{\|P\|}+\|\Phi(T)+GC\|^2} - \|\Phi(T)+GC\| \tag{9}$$

then (7) is a contraction if $\Delta < \beta$.

Proof: See [Wa-M-2].

β can be obtained from solving Lyapunov equation (8). Formula (9) can be explained as the error bound for the control in one period. The error is based on the integral value in one period time, which implies that $K(t)$ is very flexible. The longer the period T is, the more robustness $K(t)$ has. We have freedom to choose the function structure for $K(t)$. This naturally leads to an optimal control problem.

Let us see example 1 again. In this scalar system, $\Phi(t)=e^t$, $GC=G$. The eigenvalue of e^T-G is equal to the norm of e^T-G. Assume we choose $T=2$ and $G=e^T-\frac{1}{4}$, i.e. the spectral radius $\rho(e^T-G)=\frac{1}{4}$. The deadbeat-type control law gives gain $k(t)=-122.0134e^{-t}$ for $t\in[(M-1)T-h, MT]$. If we use $\hat{k}(t)=k(t)+\Delta$ instead of $k(t)$, and we seek eigenvalue of $e^T+\int_1^T e^{T-\tau}\hat{k}(\tau)d\tau$ to be less than or equal to $\frac{1}{2}$. Then simple computation gives that the tolerance Δ is 0.2910, i.e. as long as $|\Delta| < 0.2910$, the system vanishes at least at the rate of 2^{-N}.

It has been mentioned that for this scalar system no simple feedback $u=kx$ available. However by this periodic sampled output control method, we have shown a time varying periodic control $k(t)=-122.0134e^{-t}$ for $t\in[(M-1)T+h, MT]$ and $k(t)=0$ for $t\in[MT, MT+h]$. The delay duration $h=1$. The control is very simple.

Something even more interesting is if we apply mean value theorem, we can even choose a periodic control with constant gain, $k(t)=-1.5820$, for $t\in[(M-1)T+h, MT]$ and $k(t)=0$ for $t\in[MT, MT+h]$. The gain is constant, but this is still periodic. Figure 1 gives the state response for a sinusoidal input and figure 2 is the sampled output for system in formula (1).

We use the following algorithm to summarize this section.

Algorithm: Compute a periodic sampled output control.

(1) Choose period $T > h$, then find G such that spectral radius $\rho(\Phi(t)+GC)$ is as desired, i.e. is small enough for good convergence.

(2) Solve Lyapunov equation (8) for P.

(3) Compute the error bound β according to formula (9).

(4) Choose a sufficiently small ε, with $0<\varepsilon<\beta$ and search for $K(t)$ such that

$$\|(\int_h^T\Phi(T-\tau)BK(t)d\tau - G)C\| < \varepsilon.$$

Figure 1: Continuous output, sinusoidal response

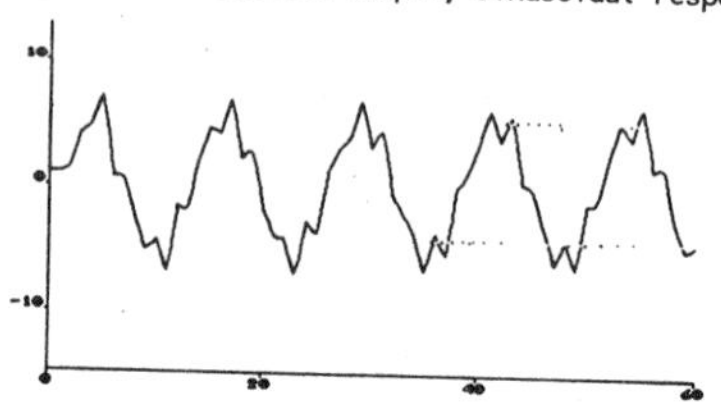

Figure 2: Sampled output, sinusoidal response

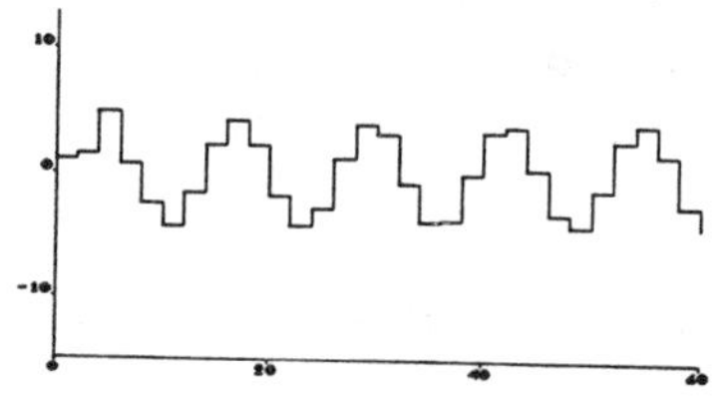

4. Periodic control and the high frequency 'pollution'

The periodic sampled output control is robust. This can be seen from an error bound analysis. The bound is restricted by the integral over the whole period, so the error caused by some unpredicted disturbance can be easily adjusted. However the main shortage of this method is the discontinuity. The periodic 'turn-down and shut-off' produces a periodic oscillation. Przyluski[Pr-K] and Goodwin[Go-G] have studied the theoretic reason for the periodic oscillation. They found that the periodic control adds high frequency poles to the system. The next example shows this oscillation inside of the system.

Example 2 [Ma-A]

$$\dot{x}_1(t)=u(t-h)$$

$$\dot{x}_2(t)=x_1(t)+x_2(t)$$

$$y(t)=x_2(t)$$

Figure 3 and figure 4 show the step responses for continuous output and sampled output respectly. From these results we can see that the error between continuous data and sampled data is periodic.

One approach to reduce this oscillation is to set an optimal performance to restrict the bias of the error perturbation. But the price is that we have to solve a time varying Riccati differential equation.

Figure 3 Continuous output, step response

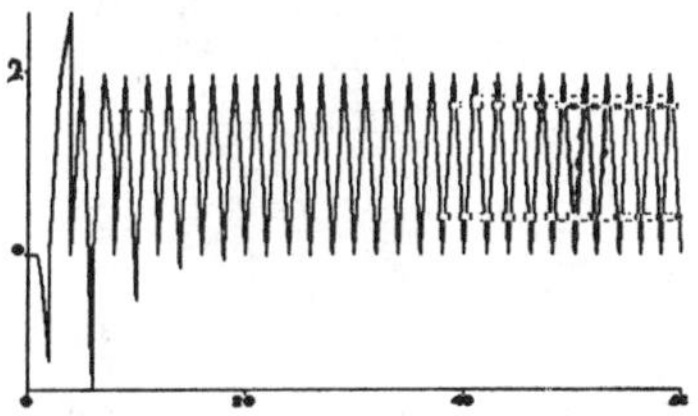

Figure 4 Sample output, step response

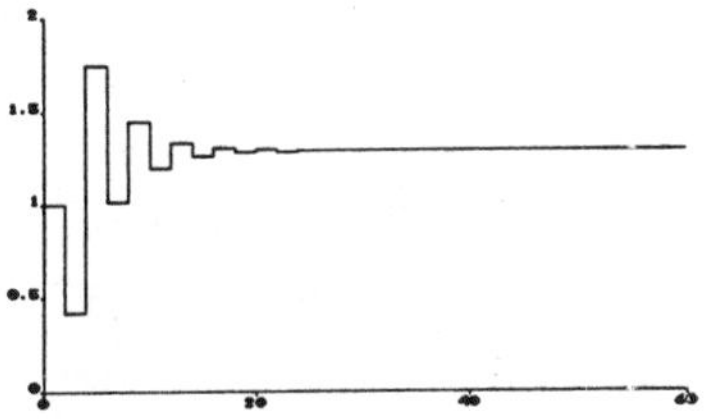

We can choose a weighting function for a better smoothness of function $K(t)$. We can slice the time interval T into several pieces and search $K_i(t_i)$ over each of these sub-intervals with the constraint that the jump of $K_i(t_i)$ at an adjacent point is as small as possible.

5. Periodic control for system with state delays

The main difficulty in applying a periodic control for systems with state delay is the computation of the state transit matrix. A delay system has at most a finite number of unstable poles. For any real number α, the transit matrix can be decomposed into two parts: One which has all of the poles to the left side of $s = \alpha$, the other has all of the poles to the right side of $s = \alpha$. The virtue of a delay system in applying the periodic sampled output control is that the second part is always finite dimensional. As shown in the literature, for the stabilization problem, we can work with an approximate finite dimensional system. If $\alpha < 0$ with large enough norm, then the first part can always be ignored. This fact leads us to stabilize an approximate finite dimensional system instead of working with an infinite dimensional system.

The existence of this kind of controllers has been given by Tarn [Ta-Z]. The concrete task is to find a feasible algorithm to choose a suitable α then to compute the second part transit matrix. We need to know the error bound between the original system and the approximate model under which the controller designed upon for the model is sufficient for the original system.

Consider the system below:

$$\dot{x}(t) = A_0x(t)+A_1x(t-h)+B_0u(t)+B_1u(t-h) \quad (10.1)$$

$$y = Cx(t) \quad (10.2)$$

Assume that for a given period T, $\Phi(t,\tau)$ is the fundamental matrix of this system and $\hat{\Phi}(t,\tau)$ is a finite dimensional approximation. Let

$$\Delta := \Phi(T,0) - \hat{\Phi}(T) + \int_h^T \left[[\Phi(T,\tau) - \hat{\Phi}(T-\tau)]BK(t)d\tau\right] C$$

Then we have following result.

Theorem 4 Assume a periodic sampled output control stabilizes an finite dimensional approximation of the system (10) and contains all the unstable modes of system (10). Then This control also stabilizes the system (10) if the perturbation error bound of the stabilized approximate system

$$\beta > \|\Delta\|. \quad (11)$$

Proof: Let

$$\dot{x}(t = \hat{A}x(t)+\hat{B}_0u(t)+\hat{B}_1u(t-h) \quad (12.1)$$

$$y = \hat{C}x(t) \quad (12.2)$$

be the finite dimensional approximation for the system in (10). Assume that $K(t)$ is the periodic control to stabilize (12) with error bound β. Then there exist $P > 0$, such that

$$P - [\hat{\Phi}(T)+\int_h^T \hat{\Phi}(T-\tau)BKCd\tau]'P[\Phi(T)+\int_h^T \Phi(T-\tau)BKCd\tau] = -I$$

Since $\|\Delta\| < \beta$, from theorem 3, in one period, the spectral radius of

$$[\Phi(T,0)+\int_h^T \Phi(T,\tau)BKCd\tau]$$

is smaller then 1 and

$$[\Phi(T,0)+\int_h^T \Phi(T,\tau)BKCd\tau]^N$$

which goes to 0 when N goes to ∞. □

This theorem also suggests an algorithm to search for the control gain, $K(t)$. We can use iteration method:

(1) Choose an approximation, then try to find K;

(2) Check condition (11). If this holds then we are done; otherwise increase the degree and repeat the procedure.

We can combine the approximation and the control design together. To find Δ, we can use an impulse response method, which is easy to do.

6. Conclusion:

We have shown that how to find a periodic sampled output feedback control for time delay system stabilization. This method is easy to use via a digital computer. However this simplicity has it's price: the periodic control will bring in an oscillation. We also explained how an iterative algorithm can be applied to search a gain function $K(t)$ for time delay systems with state delays. The iterative method implies that we can combine the approximation and controller designs together. The model error can be tested by the impulse response method.

References:

[Fe-E] E. Feron, V. Balaskrishnan and S. Boyd, Design of stabilization state feedback for delay systems via convex optimization, 31st IEEE Conf. Dec. Contr. 1992.

[Kh-P] P.P. Khargonekar, K. Poolla and A. Tannebaum, Robust control of linear time-invariant plants using periodic compensation, IEEE. Trans. Automat. Control, AC-30, pp1088-1096, 1985.

[Kr-N] N.N. Krasovskii, Application of Lyapunov's second method for equations with time delay, PMM, 20(3):315-327, 1956.

[Ma-A] A. Manitius and A. Olbrot, Finite spectrum assignment problem for systems with delay, IEEE. Trans. Automat. Control, AC-24, n0.4, pp541-553, 1979.

[Go-G] Graham C. Goodwin, Linear periodic control: a frequency domain viewpoint, System & Control Letters,vol.19, pp379-390, 1992.

[Ol-A] A. Olbrot, Stabilizability, detectability, and spectrum assignment for linear autonomous systems with general time delays, IEEE. Trans. Automat. Control, AC-23, no.5, 887-890, 1978.

[Ol-A-2] A. Olbrot, Robust stabilization of uncertain systems by periodic feedback, Int. J. Control, vol.45, no.3, pp747-758, 1987.

[Pa-L] L. Pandolfi, Dynamic stabilization of systems with input delays, Automatica, vol.27, no.6, pp1047-1050, 1991.

[Pr-K] K. Maciej Przyluski, Stabilization of the system $\dot{x}(t) = Fx(t)+Gu(t-h)$. by a discrete feedback control, IEEE. Trans. Automat. Control, PP269-270, 1977.

[Sk-V] V.I. Skorodinskii, Iterational method of construction of Lyapunov-Krasovskii functionals for linear systems with delay, Automation and remote control, 51(9):1205-1212, 1990.

[Ta-T] T. Tarn, J. R. Zavgren, Jr., and X. Zeng, Stabilization of infinite-dimensional systems with periodic feedback gains and sampled output, Automatica, vol.24, no.1, pp95-99, 1988.

[Wa-W] W. Wang, C. Song and C. Kao, Robustness bounds for large-scale time-delay systems with structured and unstructured uncertainties, Int. J. Sys. Sci., vol.22, no.1, pp209-216, 1991.

[Wa-M] M. Wang, D. Boley and E. B. Lee, "Robust Stability And Stabilization of Time Delay System In Real Parameter Space", Proceedings of 1992 American Control Conference, pp85-86, Chicago, June, 1992.

[Wa-M-2] M. Wang, E. B. Lee and D. Boley, "Matrix Pencil and Matrix Measure Methods For Robust Stability in Real Parameter Space", Proceedings of the 29th Conf. on Decision and Contr. pp411-415, Brighton, England, Dec. 1991.

Proceedings of the
American Control Conference
San Francisco, California • June 1993

ROBUST STABILITY OF TIME VARYING FUNCTIONAL DIFFERENTIAL EQUATIONS

Brad Lehman and Khalil Shujaee
Department of Electrical and Computer Engineering
Mississippi State University
Mississippi State, MS 39762

Abstract: This paper presents sufficient delay independent conditions that guarantee stability of nonlinear time varying functional differential equations (FDE). Assuming that the FDE takes the form of $x'(t) = A(t)\, x(t) + f(t, x(t-g_1(t)), \ldots, x(t-g_m(t)))$, stability conditions are derived in terms of the matrix measure (logarithmic norm) of A(t) and in terms of bounds on function f.

I. INTRODUCTION

There has been a great amount of literature over the past thirty years discussing delay independent stability conditions for functional differential equations (FDE) [1–14]. Much of this literature focuses on linear time invariant point delay systems [1–8]. There are several different approaches to developing stability conditions of such types of systems. Two of the most common techniques are to either use Lyapunov functions [1–4] or to analyze the FDE from a completely algebraic point of view [4,5]. While both techniques provide a powerful theoretical framework for stability analysis, there are several associated disadvantages: (1) the results are generally valid for linear time invariant (LTI) point delay systems only and/or (2) the results are often difficult to verify.

Recently, [6,7] derived delay independent stability conditions for LTI point delay systems in terms of a matrix measure (logarithmic norm). Furthermore, [8] calculated estimates on the decay rate of these systems, and therefore, information about both stability properties and transient responses of special classes of FDE's could be obtained.

The use of matrix measures in the analysis of delay equations has the benefits of being both an algorithmic procedure and being simple computationally. The work of [9] generalizes [6–8] by presenting delay independent stability conditions of point delay systems where the nominal plant is LTI but the perturbations are special classes of nonlinear, time varying, bounded globally Lipschitz functions with point delay only. Presenting an algorithmic approach, [9] extends the work of [6–8] and the older works of [10–12] (which provide highly theoretical and computationally difficult to apply delay independent stability conditions for FDE's).

One drawback with [6–9] is that the nominal plant is assumed time invariant. Some work has been performed on linear time varying point delay systems [10–16]; however, once again, the conditions derived are either computationally difficult to verify [10–14] or there are strong restrictions on the time varying part of the system [15, 16].

The work presented in this paper is an extension of [6–14]; however, in particular we have been greatly influenced by [10–12]. The results of this paper provide:. (1) sufficient delay independent stability conditions for general classes of nonlinear time varying systems which are computationally simple to verify and (2) give estimates on the decay rate of stable solutions of such systems. It is, in fact, these estimates which turn out to be the most difficult to prove.

Chapter II discusses the mathematical preliminaries necessary to present the main results of this work, which are found in Chapter III. Chapter III also provides examples which demonstrate the theory, and Chapter IV summarizes the results.

II. PRELIMINARIES AND PROBLEM FORMULATION

This paper considers the stability properties of functional differential equations in the form

$$x'(t) = A(t)x(t) + f(t, x(t-g_1(t)), \ldots, x(t-g_m(t))) \tag{2.1}$$

where $x \in \mathfrak{R}^n$, $A(t) \in \mathfrak{R}^{n \times n}$, $A(\cdot)$ is continuous on $t \geq t_0$, the function $f\colon (t_0 - r, a) \times \Omega \times \Omega \times \ldots \times \Omega \to \mathfrak{R}^n, \Omega \subset \mathfrak{R}^n$, is continuous in time, and $'$ denotes the right hand derivative. It will always be assumed that $0 \leq g_i(t) \leq r$ for $t \geq t_0$, i=1, . . ., m and some $0 \leq r < \infty$. Assume that the continuous initial condition of (2.1) takes the form $x(t) = \psi(t)$ for $t_0 - r \leq t \leq t_0$.

For simplicity, we will define the function $\chi_t = \chi_t(\sigma) \equiv \chi(t+\sigma)$ for $-r \leq \sigma \leq 0$. Then it is known [12] that (2.1) can be rewritten as

$$x'(t) = A(t)\, x(t) + F(t, x_t) \tag{2.2}$$

$$x_{t_0} = \psi_{t_0} .$$

Let $C([-r,0]; \Omega)$ be the space of all continuous functions mapping $[-r,0] \to \Omega$, and define $J = [t_0 - r, \infty)$. Then $F\colon J \times C([-r,0]; \Omega) \to \mathfrak{R}^n$, and F is continuous in time.

For a function $\psi \in C([-r,0]; \Omega)$ define

$$\|\psi\|_r = \sup_{-r \leq \sigma \leq 0} \|\psi(\sigma)\| . \tag{2.3}$$

System (2.2) can be viewed as an ordinary differential equation with perturbation (possibly unknown) $F(t,x_t)$. In this case, [9] discusses the following definition. Assume $x=0$ is an equilibrium of (2.2).

<u>Definition:</u> The trivial solution of system (2.2) is said to be robustly stable if there exist bounds on perturbation $F(t, .)$ such that $x=0$ of (2.2) is uniformly asymptotically stable. (Note that $x=0$ may not be the only equilibrium point of (2.2).)

It is the purpose of this paper to discuss conditions in which (2.2) is robustly stable. In order to do this, it is necessary to introduce the following notations.

The norm of a real vector x, denoted by $\|x\|_k$, is defined as

$$\|x\|_k = \begin{cases} \max_i |x_i| & k = \infty \\ \sum_i |x_i| & k = 1 \\ \left(\sum_i |x_i|^2\right)^{1/2} & k = 2 \end{cases} \tag{2.5}$$

Then the corresponding induced matrix norm is given as

$$\|A\|_k = \begin{cases} \max_i \sum_j |a_{ij}| & k = \infty \\ \max_j \sum_i |a_{ij}| & k = 1 \\ [\lambda_{max}(A^* A)]^{1/2} & k = 2 \end{cases} \tag{2.6}$$

Here x_i denotes the elements of vector x, $A = [a_{ij}]$, $\lambda_{max}(\cdot)$ is the maximum eigenvalue of matrix $(\cdot)$, and * denotes the conjugate transpose.

The matrix measure, sometimes referred to as the logarithmic norm, is defined by

$$\mu_k(A) = \lim_{\delta \to 0^+} \frac{\|I + \delta A\|_k - 1}{\delta} \quad (2.7)$$

The matrix measure has the property that it can have both negative and positive values. Further, it is specifically induced by the corresponding norm $\|\cdot\|_k$. We have

$$\mu_k(A) = \begin{cases} \max_i \left\{ a_{ii} + \sum_{j \neq i} |a_{ij}| \right\} & k = \infty \\ \max_j \left\{ a_{jj} + \sum_{i \neq j} |a_{ij}| \right\} & k = 1 \\ \lambda_{max}[A^* + A]/2 & k = 2 \end{cases} \quad (2.8)$$

III. ROBUST STABILITY

It is the purpose of this chapter to determine conditions in which (2.2) is robustly stable. The results presented are more general than those presented in [6–9] because (1) A(t) is time varying, and (2) the assumptions on perturbation $F(t,x_t)$ are less restrictive. In particular, [9] considers (2.1) when $A(t) = A =$ constant and

$$F(t, x_t) = f_0(t, x(t)) + \sum_{i=1}^{m} f_i(t, x(t - r_i)) .$$

In addition, the results of this chapter generalize the classical works of [10–12] which also give sufficient conditions for robust stability of (2.2); however, these papers do not give easily calculable results such as given in this chapter. In these older works, sufficient conditions are given in terms of properties of a fundamental solution of a linear time varying delay differential equation. It is the purpose of this chapter to provide similar sufficient conditions in terms of $\mu_k(A(t))$. Furthermore, this chapter derives upper bounds on solutions to (2.2) which provide estimates on the transient response. This upper bound, however, is dependent on the delay, and therefore, gives a formula which suggests the effect of the delay on the transient response. In particular, the larger the delay, the slower the upper bound decays.

In the course of stability analysis of (2.2), it will be necessary to use the following lemma, which is a generalization of [11, 10 (page 389)].

Lemma: Let v(t) and f(t) be continuous real valued non-negative functions on $[t_0 - r, \beta)$ and $[t_0, \beta)$, respectively. Assume that f(t) is positive and non-decreasing for all $t \in [t_0, \beta)$. Assume further that for all $t \in [t_0, \beta)$

$$v'(t) \le -f(t)\, v(t) + b\|v_t\|_r , \quad (3.1)$$

where b is some positive constant satisfying $0 < b < f(t)$ on $t \in [t_0, \beta)$.

Then

$$v(t) \le \|v_{t_0}\|_r \, e^{-\int_{t_0}^{t} \gamma(s)ds} , \qquad t_0 - r \le t < \beta \quad (3.2)$$

where $\gamma(t)$ is the non-decreasing unique continuous solution to

$$\gamma(t) = \begin{cases} f(t_0) - be^{\gamma(t)r} & t < t_0 \\ f(t) - be^{\gamma(t)r} & t \in [t_0, \beta) \end{cases} . \quad (3.3)$$

Furthermore, $\gamma(t)$ satisfies the inequality $0 < \gamma(t) < f(t)$ on $t \in [t_0, \beta)$.

Proof: Let $\Delta(\gamma, t) = \gamma(t) - f(t) + be^{\gamma(t)r}$. Fix $t = t_1 \ge t_0$. Let $\gamma_1 = \gamma(t_1) =$ constant and let $\alpha_1 = f(t_1) =$ constant > 0. Then

$$\Delta(\gamma_1, t_1) = \Delta(\gamma_1) = \gamma_1 - \alpha_1 + b\, e^{\gamma_1 r} \quad (3.4)$$

Equation (3.4) is not time varying, and therefore the techniques of [10, 11] can be applied: Since

$$\Delta(0) = -\alpha_1 + b < 0, \quad \Delta(\alpha_1) = b\, e^{\alpha_1 r} > 0$$

and $\frac{\partial \Delta}{\partial \gamma} = 1 + \gamma\, b\, e^{\gamma r} > 0$ for all $\gamma \ge 0$, it follows that there exists a unique γ_1, $0 < \gamma_1 < \alpha_1$, for which $\Delta(\gamma_1) = 0$. Since t_1 is arbitrary, it also follows that $\Delta(\gamma(t)) = 0$ uniquely defines a function $\gamma(t)$. Further, $\gamma(t)$ is continuous since $\Delta(\cdot)$ depends continuously on $\gamma(\cdot)$ and $f(\cdot)$, where $f(\cdot)$ has been assumed continuous. This also implies that $0 < \gamma(t) < f(t)$ on $t \in [t_0, \beta)$.

Define $w(t) = \|v_{t_0}\|_r \exp\left\{-\int_{t_0}^{t} \gamma(s)\, ds\right\}$ for $t_0 - r \le t < \beta$. Then on $t_0 - r \le t \le t_0$, $v(t) \le w(t)$ since on this interval $\left[-\int_{t_0}^{t} \gamma(t_0)\, ds\right] > 0$.

Suppose there exists some $t_2 > t_0$ such that $v(t) \le w(t)$ for $t_0 - r \le t \le t_2$, $v(t_2) = w(t_2)$ and $v(t) > w(t)$ on $t \in (t_2, t_2 + \tau)$, for some $\tau > 0$. Then it must be that $v'(t_2) > w'(t_2)$.

By definition

$$v'(t_2) \le -f(t_2)\, v(t_2) + b\|v_{t_2}\|_r \quad (3.5)$$

Since $v(t_2) = w(t_2)$, (3.5) can be rewritten as

$$v'(t_2) \le -f(t_2)\, \|v_{t_0}\|_r \exp\left\{-\int_{t_0}^{t_2} \gamma(s)\, ds\right\}$$

$$+ b\, \|v_{t_0}\|_r \sup_{t \in [t_2 - r,\, t_2]} \exp\left\{-\int_{t_0}^{t} \gamma(s)\, ds\right\} \quad (3.6)$$

Noting that $\gamma(t)$ is positive for all $t > t_0$,

$$\sup_{t \in [t_2 - r,\, t_2]} \exp\left\{-\int_{t_0}^{t} \gamma(s)\, ds\right\} = \exp\left\{-\int_{t_0}^{t_2 - r} \gamma(s)\, ds\right\} \quad (3.7)$$

and therefore, under our assumptions, (3.5) becomes

$$v'(t_2) \le -f(t_2)\, w(t_2) + bw(t_2 - r) . \quad (3.8)$$

Taking the derivative of the definition of w(t), it is easy to show that

$$w'(t_2) = w(t_2)\left[-f(t_2) + be^{\gamma(t_2)r}\right] . \quad (3.9)$$

By assumption, $v'(t_2) > w'(t_2)$. Using (3.8) and (3.9), this implies that

$$w(t_2)\, e^{\gamma(t_2)r} < w(t_2 - r) . \quad (3.10)$$

Using the definition of w(t), this gives

$$e^{\gamma(t_2)r} < e^{\int_{t_2 - r}^{t_2} \gamma(s)\, ds} . \quad (3.11)$$

Since $\gamma'(t) = \frac{f'(t)}{1 + be^{\gamma(t)}}$ and $f(t)$ has been assumed non-decreasing, this implies that $\gamma(t)$ is non-decreasing also. Therefore,

$\|\gamma_{t_2}\|_r = \gamma(t_2)$, and hence (3.11) yields equivalently

$$e^{\int_{t_2-r}^{t_2} \sup_{-r \le \sigma \le 0} \|\gamma(t_2+\sigma)\|_r \, ds} < e^{\int_{t_2-r}^{t_2} \gamma(s)\, ds} \quad , \qquad (3.12)$$

which is never true. Contradiction. **Q.E.D.**

Using the lemma, it is possible to determine conditions in which $x=0$ of (2.2) is robustly stable. For a function $\psi \in C([-r, 0]; \Omega)$, let

$$\|\psi\|_{kr} = \sup_{-r \le \sigma \le 0} \|\psi(\sigma)\|_k \quad , \qquad (3.13)$$

where $\|\psi(\sigma)\|_k$ is defined in (2.5).

Theorem: Assume in system (2.2) that $A(\cdot)$ is continuous and that there exists a constant $M > 0$ with an open neighborhood Ω ($0 \in \Omega$) such that $\|F(t, \xi)\|_k \le M \|\xi\|_{kr}$ for all $(t, \xi) \in (t_0, \infty) \times C([-r,0]; \Omega)$. Suppose, further, that for all $t \ge t_0$,

$$\mu_k(A(t)) < -M < 0 \quad , \qquad (3.14)$$

and $\mu_k(A(t))$ is non-increasing.

Then (i) the trivial solution of system (2.2) is robustly stable independent of r. (ii) Furthermore, if $\psi \in C([-r,0]; \Omega)$, an estimate on the transient response is given by

$$\|x(t)\|_k \le \|\psi\|_{kr} \exp\left\{ - \int_{t_0}^{t} \gamma_k(s)\, ds \right\} \quad , \qquad (3.15)$$

where $0 < \gamma_k(t) < -\mu_k(A(t))$ and $\gamma_k(t)$ is the solution to

$$\gamma_k(t) = -\mu_k(A(t)) - M e^{\gamma_k(t) r} \qquad t \ge t_0 \quad . \qquad (3.16)$$

Proof: Since x(t) is right differential for $t \ge t_0$, (2.2) is equivalent to

$$\frac{x(t+\delta) - x(t)}{\delta} = A(t)\, x(t) + F(t, x_t) + O(\delta) \quad , \qquad x_{t_0} = \psi_{t_0} , \qquad (3.17)$$

where $\delta > 0$ and $O(\delta) \to 0$ as $\delta \to 0^+$. This implies that for $t \ge t_0$

$$\|x(t+\delta)\|_k \le \|I + \delta A(t)\|_k \cdot \|x(t)\|_k + \delta \|F(t, x_t)\|_k + \delta O(\delta) \quad . \qquad (3.18)$$

Therefore,

$$\lim_{\delta \to 0^+} \frac{\|x(t+\delta)\|_k - \|x(t)\|_k}{\delta} \le \lim_{\delta \to 0^+} \frac{(\|I + \delta A(t)\| - 1)\, \|x(t)\|_k}{\delta} + M\|x_t\|_{kr} + O(\delta) \quad . \qquad (3.19)$$

The left-hand side of (3.19) is the right-hand derivative of $\|x(t)\|_k$. So we have

$$\frac{d^+}{dt} \|x(t)\|_k \le \mu_k(A(t))\, \|x(t)\|_k + M\|x_t\|_{kr} \quad , \qquad (3.20)$$

where $\frac{d^+}{dt}$ denotes the right-hand derivative. Letting $v(t) = \|x(t)\|_k$ for $t > t_0$, $v(t) = \psi(t)$ for $t \in [t_0 - r, t_0]$, and defining $f(t) = -\mu_k(A(t))$, the lemma can be directly applied (as long as $\psi \in C([-r,0]; \Omega)$), since it has been assumed that for $t \ge t_0$, $0 < M < -\mu_k(A(t))$. This proves (ii) of the theorem which, in turn, immediately implies (i). **Q.E.D.**

Remark 1: The sufficient conditions of the theorem are dependent on the choice of norm and the corresponding matrix measure. It is possible that robust stability conditions will be valid for one norm, but not another. Since there are explicit formulas to compute matrix measures (see (2.8)), the above theorem provides a constructive means for determining robust stability independent of delay.

Remark 2: The above theorem provides robust stability conditions which are independent of delay. Often times exact knowledge of delays are not known or perhaps the delays drift between values. In these cases, the theorem becomes quite useful. Additionally, the theorem provides an estimate on the exponential decay of solutions to (2.2). These estimates of decay are, however, delay dependent. The function $\gamma(t)$ actually decreases as r increases, as can be seen by (3.16).

Remark 3: In the proof of the lemma, it is shown that if $\mu_k(A(t))$ decreases, $\gamma_k(t)$ will increase. Therefore, in this case, the transient response could decay extremely quick (certainly faster than $\exp\left[-(t-t_0)\,\gamma(t_0)\right]$, where $\gamma(t_0)$ = constant). In the special case when $A(t) = A$ = constant and $F(t, x_t) = \sum_{i=1}^{m} f(t, x(t - r_i))$, and $\Omega = \Re^n$, then $\gamma_k(t) = \gamma_k$ = constant, and the results of [6–9] are obtained.

Corollary: Assume in system (2.2) that $A(\cdot)$ is continuous and that there exists a neighborhood Ω $(0 \in \Omega)$ such that $\| F(t,\xi) \|_k \le M \| \xi \|_{kr}$ for all $(t,\xi) \in (t_0, \infty) \times C([-r,0]; \Omega)$. Suppose that $\sup_{t \ge t_0} [\mu_k(A(t))] < -M < 0$, but $\mu_k(A(t))$ is not non-increasing (as assumed in the theorem).

Then (i) the trivial solution of system (2.2) is robustly stable independent of r. (ii) Furthermore, if $\psi \in C([-r,0];\Omega)$, then an estimate of the transient response is given by

$$\|x(t)\|_k \le \|\psi\|_{kr} \exp\left\{-(t - t_0)\,\gamma\right\} \qquad (3.22)$$

where $0 < \gamma < |\mu_k(A(t))|$ for all $t \ge t_0$ and γ is the constant solution to

$$\gamma = \inf_{t \ge t_0} \left[-\mu_k(A(t))\right] - M e^{\gamma r} \quad . \qquad (3.23)$$

Proof: Almost immediate from the proof of the theorem. Clearly (3.20) implies that

$$\frac{d^+}{dt}\|x(t)\| \le \sup_{t \ge t_0} \left[\mu_k(A(t))\right] \|x(t)\|_k + M \|x_{t_0}\|_{kr} \quad . \qquad (3.24)$$

Defining v(t) as before and defining

$$f(t) = -\sup_{t \ge t_0} \left[\mu_k(A(t))\right] = \inf_{t \ge t_0} \left[-\mu_k(A(t))\right] \quad ,$$

the lemma can be directly applied to obtain (i) and (ii). **Q.E.D.**

Remark 4: In the special case when r = 0, it is known [17] that a non-trivial ($\neq$ 0) lower bound on the transient response can always be obtained. However, for $r \neq 0$, arbitrarily small, in general this is not the case. For non-zero delays, "small solutions" can exist, i.e., solutions which reach zero in finite time. Therefore, the best lower bound on $\|x(t)\|$ one can, in general, expect is zero (which is trivial to obtain since $\|\cdot\|$ is non-negative). The reader is referred to the upcoming book by Verduyn-Lunel et. al. [18] for further discussion on the complicated topic of small solutions.

Remark 5: The above theorem can be applied to systems not exactly written in the form of (2.1) or (2.2). Consider the delay differential equation

$$x'(t) = f\big(t,\ x(t),\ x(t - g_1(t)), \ldots,\ x(t - g_m(t))\big), \qquad (3.25)$$

where x, f, and g_i are previously defined in (2.1). Clearly, if f is continuously Frechet differentiable with respect to its second argument, then (3.25) can be rewritten as

$$x'(t) = A(t)\, x(t) + [f(t, x(t), x(t-g_1(t)), \dots, x(t-g_m(t))) - A(t)\, x(t)] , \quad (3.26)$$

where $A(t) = \dfrac{\partial f(t,0,0,\dots,0)}{\partial x(t)}$. By defining $F(t,x_t)$ as the term in the square brackets, system (3.26) is in the form such that the conditions of the theorem may be applied for some sufficiently small neighborhood of the origin where the above linearization is valid.

Remark 6: Suppose that there exists some $t_1 > t_0$ such that $\mu_k(A(t)) < -M < 0$ for all $t > t_1$ but not for all $t > t_0$. Then, as long as $\sup_{t \in [t_0, t_1]} \|A(t)\|_k < \infty$, the trivial solution of system (2.2) is still robustly stable. This is immediate from the proof of Theorem 1 and upon noting that under these assumptions, $\|x(t)\|_{kr}$ can always be bounded by a sufficiently large constant on any finite time interval, $t_0 \le t \le t_1$.

Example 1

Consider the linear delay differential system given by

$$x'(t) = A_0(t)\, x(t) + \sum_{i=1}^{m} A_i(t)\, x(t - g_i(t)) , \quad (3.27)$$

where $A_i(t)$ are continuous matrix functions, $0 \le g_i(t) \le r < \infty$ for all $t \ge 0$ and $x(t) = \psi(t)$ for $t \in [-r, 0]$. By the corollary, if

$$\mu_k(A_0(t)) < -\sum_{i=1}^{m} \|A_i(t)\|_k \quad \text{for} \quad t \ge t_0 , \quad (3.28)$$

then $x=0$ (3.27) is robustly stable independent of delay. Furthermore, if $\mu_k(A(t))$ is non-increasing, then an estimate on the transient response is given by (3.15) with $M = \sum_{i=1}^{m} \|A_i(t)\|_k$.

Example 2

Consider (2.1) with $x(t) = [x_1(t), x_2(t)]$,

$$A(t) = \begin{bmatrix} -t-3 & e^t \\ -e^t & -t-4 \end{bmatrix} \quad (3.29)$$

$$f(t, x(t), x(t-g_1(t))) = \begin{bmatrix} \sin^2(t)\, x_1^2\,(t - \sin(t) - 1) \\ x_2^3(t) \end{bmatrix} \quad (3.30)$$

Let $x_1(t) = c \cos t$ on $t \in [-2, 0]$, where c = constant, and let $x_2(0) = 0$. Using the notation of the theorem, define $\Omega \subset \Re^n$ as $\{x \in \Omega: \|x\|_k < 1\}$, and let $F(t,\xi) = f(t,\xi(t), \xi(t - \sin(t) - 1))$. Since $0 < \sin(t) + 1 \le 2$, we can define the constant r to be 2.

Using (2.8) we have

$$\mu_1(A(t)) = \mu_\infty(A(t)) = -t - 3 + e^t$$

$$\mu_2(A(t)) = -t - 3 . \quad (3.31)$$

For sufficiently large t, $\mu_1 = \mu_\infty$ are positive functions and, therefore to apply the theorem, we must use $\mu_2(A(t))$ which is a non-increasing function. Using $\|\cdot\|_2$, the condition of the theorem that $\|F(t,\xi)\|_2 < M\|\xi\|_{2r}$, for all $\xi \in \Omega$ is satisfied for $M = 1$. Since (3.14) is satisfied for all $t > 0$, i.e.,

$$-t - 3 < -1 < 0, \quad t > 0 , \quad (3.32)$$

the trivial solution of this system is indeed robustly stable independent of delay.

Furthermore, in (3.15),

$$\|\psi\|_{2r} = \sup_{-2 \le \sigma \le 0} \|[c \cos\sigma, 0]^T\|_2 = c .$$

Hence, if $c < 1$, then an estimate on the transient decay is given by

$$\|x(t)\|_2 \le c \exp\left\{ -\int_0^t \gamma_1(s)\, ds \right\} , \quad (3.33)$$

where $0 < \gamma_2(t) < t + 3$ and $\gamma_2(t)$ is the solution to

$$\gamma(t) = t + 3 - e^{2\gamma_2(t)} , \quad t \ge 0 . \quad (3.34)$$

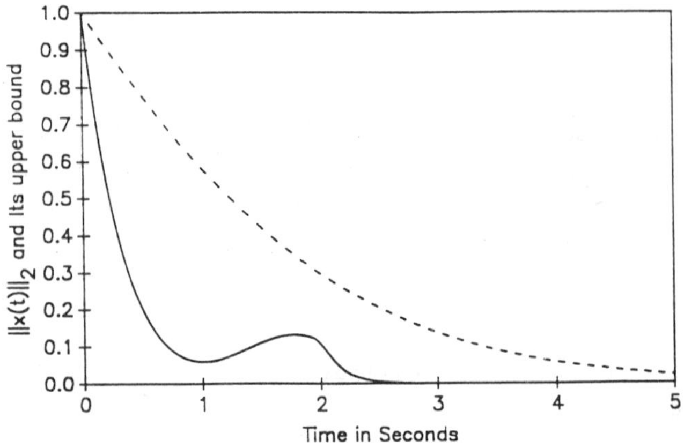

Fig. 1: $\|x(t)\|_2$ (solid curve) and its upper bound (dashed curve) versus time for example 2.

Figure 1 plots both the left-hand side of (3.34), (solid curve) and the right-hand side of (3.34), (dashed curve) versus time for c = 0.99. From this figure, it is verified that the right-hand side of (3.34) is an upper bound on $\|x(t)\|_2$ for all $t \ge 0$.

IV. CONCLUSION

This paper presents sufficient, easily calculable, delay independent stability conditions for time varying functional differential equations. An estimate on the bound of transient decay is also presented. It is shown that this bound depends exponentially on the area underneath the curve of the time varying function $\gamma_k(t)$. This function is found by solving a time varying nonlinear algebraic equation.

REFERENCES

[1] A. Thowsen, "Further Comments on "Stability of time–delay systems," *IEEE Trans. Automat. Control*, Vol. AC–28, p. 935, 1983.

[2] T. N. Lee and S. Diant, "Stability of time–delay systems," *IEEE Trans. Automat. Control*, Vol. AC–26, pp. 951–953, 1982.

[3] M. Malek–Zavarei and M. Jamshidi, *Time Delay Systems: Analysis, Optimization and Applications*, Elsevier Science, NY, 1987.

[4] E. B. Lee, W. S. Lee and N. E. Wu, A Lyapunov theory for linear time–delay systems, *IEEE Trans. Automat. Control*, Vol. AC–31, pp. 259–261, 1986.

[5] E. Kamen, "Linear systems with commensurate time delays: stability and stabilization independent of delay," *IEEE Trans. Automat. Control*, Vol. AC–27, pp. 367–375, 1982.

[6] T. Mori and H. Kokame, "Stability of $\dot{x}(t) = Ax(t) + Bx(t-r)$," *IEEE Trans. Automat. Control*, Vol. AC–34, pp. 460–462, 1989.

[7] T. Mori, "Criteria for asymptotic stability of linear time–delay systems,"*IEEE Trans. Automat. Control*, Vol. AC–30, pp. 158–161, 1985.

[8] T. Mori, N. Fukuma and M. Kuwahara, "On an estimate of the decay rate for stable linear systems," *Int. J. Control*, Vol. 36, pp. 95–97, 1982.

[9] S. Wang, B. Chen and T. Lin, "Robust stability of uncertain time delay systems," *Int. J. Control*, Vol. 46, pp. 963–976, 1987.

[10] J. Repin, "On the stability of solutions of equations with retarded arguments (Russian)," *Prikl. Mat. Meh*, Vol. 21, pp. 253–261, 1957.

[11] A. Halanay, *Differential Equations: Stability, Oscillations, Time Lags*, Academic Press, NY, 1966.

[12] R. Driver, *Ordinary and Delay Differential Equations*, Springer–Verlag, NY, 1977.

[13] E. Cheres, S. Gutman and Z. Palmer, "Stabilization of uncertain dynamic systems including state delay," *IEEE Trans. Automat. Control*, Vol. AC–34, pp. 1199–1203, 1989.

[14] G. Shanholt, "Slowly varying linear functional differential equations," *IEEE Trans. Automat. Control*, pp. 166–167, 1972.

[15] J. Bentsman, J. Fakhfakh, H. Hvostov and B. Lehman, "Stability of fast periodic systems with time lags," *IEEE Trans. Automat. Control*, Vol. AC–34, pp. 462–465, 1989.

[16] B. Lehman and J. Bentsman, "Vibrational control of linear time lag systems with arbitrarily large but bounded delays," *IEEE Trans. Automat. Control*, Vol. AC–10, pp. 1576–1582, 1992.

[17] M. Vidyasagar, *Nonlinear System Analysis*, Prentice–Hall, NJ, 1978.

[18] O. Diekman, S. A. van Gils, H. O. Walther, and S. M. Verduyn Lunel, *Delay Equations: Functional Complex and Nonlinear Analysis*, Springer Verlag, NY, to appear.

Proceedings of the
American Control Conference
San Francisco, California • June 1993

A Nonlinear Flexible Pointing System for Digital Control Research

Michael S. Mattice

Automation and Robotics Team, Building 95 North
U.S. Army Armament Research, Development and Engineering Center
Picatinny Arsenal, NJ 07806-5000

Introduction

The purpose of this paper is to introduce the nonlinear flexible pointing system's hardware, models, microprocessor-based control implementation environment and the baseline performance objectives upon which the papers in sessions WM13 and TM13 are based. The primary objective of the sessions was to gain an understanding of the following:

1. How an expert in the "x" control field, given a real-life control problem, does a complete control design using their particular methodology.
2. The engineering/theoretical "insights" utilized by the expert throughout the design process, i.e. did the model raise any specific issues related to the methodology, or if weighting filters were necessary, how were the values determined, etc.
3. What problems or tuning issues arose when the controller was actually implemented on the real-system.
4. What (if any) refinements or modifications to the design methods are needed to improve their performance on this plant.

Many issues may surface as a result of this work, such as the effects of modelling error, the "best" way to model structural flexibility, inherent limitations imposed by backlash and friction, what does "slowly varying parameter" mean on a real system and how to improve endpoint control of flexible beams with limited and/or fixed sensors. Other issues may arise such as the potential limitations of the models provided to the authors, performance degradations due to sensor noise or even a need for faster, more powerful microprocessor implementation environments.

The Hardware

The nonlinear flexible pointing system is a U.S. Army test fixture used to simulate the types of nonlinearities and disturbances that are present in typical flexible beam stabilization problems. It is located in the U.S. Army's Automation and Robotics Lab, Picatinny Arsenal, NJ. The fixture, formally known as the ATB1000, is an electro-mechanical pointing system with flexible modes, variable backlash, variable friction, variable transmission compliance, base motion disturbances and impulsive disturbances entering at the load. The fixture's main body is an aluminum wheel free to rotate in the horizontal plane. Affixed to the edge of the wheel is an interchangeable steel beam 1 meter in length. The actuator used to control the angular motion of the wheel is a brushless DC motor which transmits it's torque through the on-line variable backlash and the variable compliance. An on-line variable friction force is applied to the edge of the wheel. The entire system described to this point, is mounted on a base actuated by 4 motor driven slides, which can introduce base motion disturbances in x, y and rotation. A solenoid mounted on the wheel is intended to introduce disturbances which affect the position of the beam tip. A laser-based system mounted on a rotating platform measures the beam tip position with respect to ground. See figure 8 for a schematic of the ATB1000. Listed below are the sensors available on the ATB1000, some of which are not to be used for feedback:

- DC motor encoder
- DC motor tachometer
- encoder after the backlash
- encoder on the wheel
- strain gage pair 1/4 distance to beam tip
- strain gage pair 1/2 distance to beam tip
- accelerometer on the beam tip
- 3 accelerometers on the base
- 4 slide motor encoders
- encoder on the laser platform
- beam tip position from the laser detector
- voltage applied to the disturbance solenoid

The Models

Two models were provided to the session authors for design purposes, a linear model and a nonlinear model. The original versions of these models were done by Integrated Systems, Inc. (ISI), Santa Clara, CA. Both the linear and nonlinear models share the same wheel/beam state space model and include encoder scale factors, bearing damping, variable compliance and the amplifier gains on the analog signals. ISI chose to model the beam dynamics using a finite element method with four identical beam elements [1]. The state space form of the equations were transformed into modal coordinates where a damping of 0.005 was introduced. The result is an 8th order state space model which includes the first three flexible modes of the beam. The nonlinear model accounts for the nominal and variable friction and the variable backlash.

Figures 1-7 show the results of a recent model validation effort. The bode plots were computed from time response data generated by inputting single-tone sinusoids into the DC motor of the real system, nonlinear model and the linear model. The experiments were done at amplitudes of 0.75 and 1.0 volts. Sixty eight frequency points between 0.2 and 25 Hz were acquired for the 0.75 volt case and sixty four points between 0.5 and 25 Hz for the 1.0 volt case. The data was acquired at 500 Hz and the length of the experiments varied with respect to the input frequency. The Correlation Method [2] was used to calculate the gain and phase. In terms of data preprocessing, only the biases were removed from the real data because the data was acquired at steady state and the first 2 seconds of the simulation data was ignored due to transients and the biases were also removed.

One very interesting phenomena that appeared during the validation effort shows up on the bode plots for the wheel encoder, strain gages and the beam tip accelerometer between 15 and 20 Hz. This mode which gradually gains amplitude as the measurement moves farther out towards the beam tip, is an unmodelled mode of the structure which holds the DC motor in place above the rotating wheel. This inverted pendulum-like mode of the structure is dependent on the position of the flexible beam and it overshadows the second bending mode of the beam even when the single tone input is exactly at the second mode frequency. This effect was not intentionally designed into the ATB1000, however, it is desirable from an experimental point of view because it is a structural phenomena that occurs in many Army stabilization problems.

The models can be obtained by writing to the author or sending an email to mmattice@pica.army.mil.

The Microprocessor-based Implementation Environment

The real-time environment used to implement the controllers is an AC100 model 3/i860 from ISI. The AC100 has three Intel i860, 64 bit RISC processors running at 40 MHz, encoder inputs, analog I/O and digital I/O. The controllers are implemented by representing them as a block (or blocks) in MATRIXx's graphic interface SystemBuild. From the SystemBuild diagrams, AutoCode generates optimized C language source code which is compiled, linked and downloaded to the AC100. An Interactive Animation Module allows the designer to use a SUN SPARCstation 2 to monitor the controller by viewing signal values or changing control variables on-line by using the mouse. This is how the backlash and friction in the AC100 is varied during an experiment. The AC100 also allows the control designer to run the i860's at separate rates and to acquire data on any of the I/O channels or internal variables of the controller.

Baseline Performance Objectives

The baseline performance objective was to make the beam tip of the nominal plant track a class of reference commands "as best you can" in the face of the nominal disturbances. Once a designer has accomplished this goal, they were free to address the issues related to their area of expertise, i.e. robustness to parameter variations and/or mismodelled dynamics, nonlinear control, friction compensation, fault tolerance, etc. The nominal system was defined as the ATB1000 configured as linear as possible with no backlash and no additional friction beyond the nominal motor and bearing frictions. The variable compliance was set in it's most flexible configuration and no base motion was introduced. Sinusoidal input disturbances would be applied to the motor input with amplitudes between 0.5-10.0 volts and frequencies between 3.5-4 Hz and/or 21-23 Hz. The impulsive disturbance from the solenoid would also be introduced between 3.5-4 Hz and/or 21-23 Hz with a given torque profile. The reference commands for the beam tip position shall consist of the following:

1. Steps, from 0 to a maximum of 1.396 radians. (The maximum range of motion of the fixture is +/- 1.396 radians.)

2. Ramps or a series of ramps, with slopes no greater than 1.396 radians/second.

References

[1] Zinkiewicz, O.C., 1967. *The Finite Element Method.* McGraw Hill.

[2] Ljung, L., 1987. *System Identification: Theory for the User.* Prentice-Hall, Princeton, NJ.

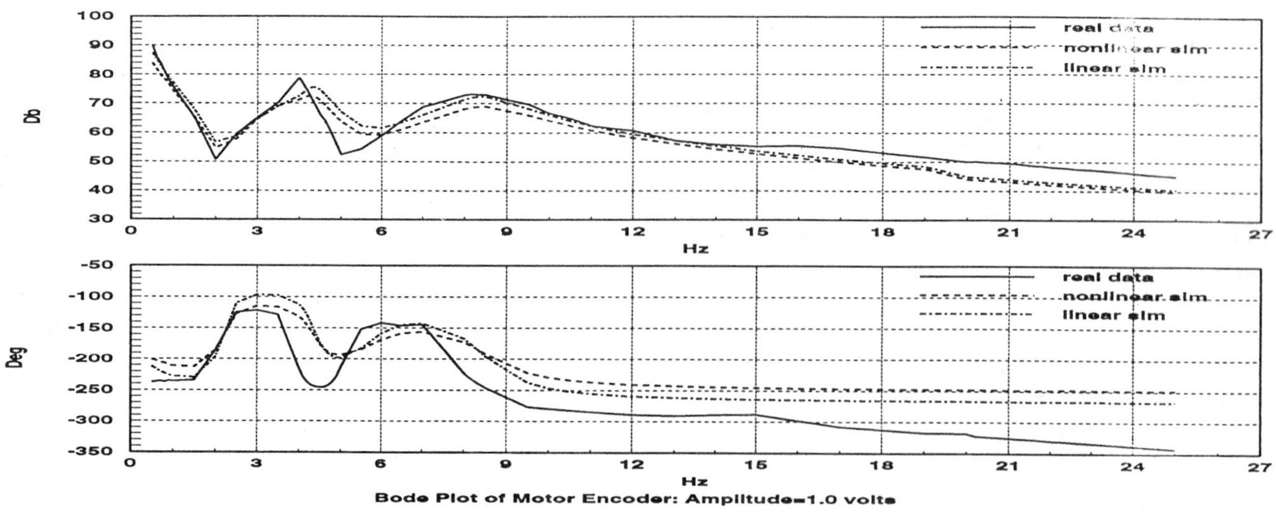

Figure 1

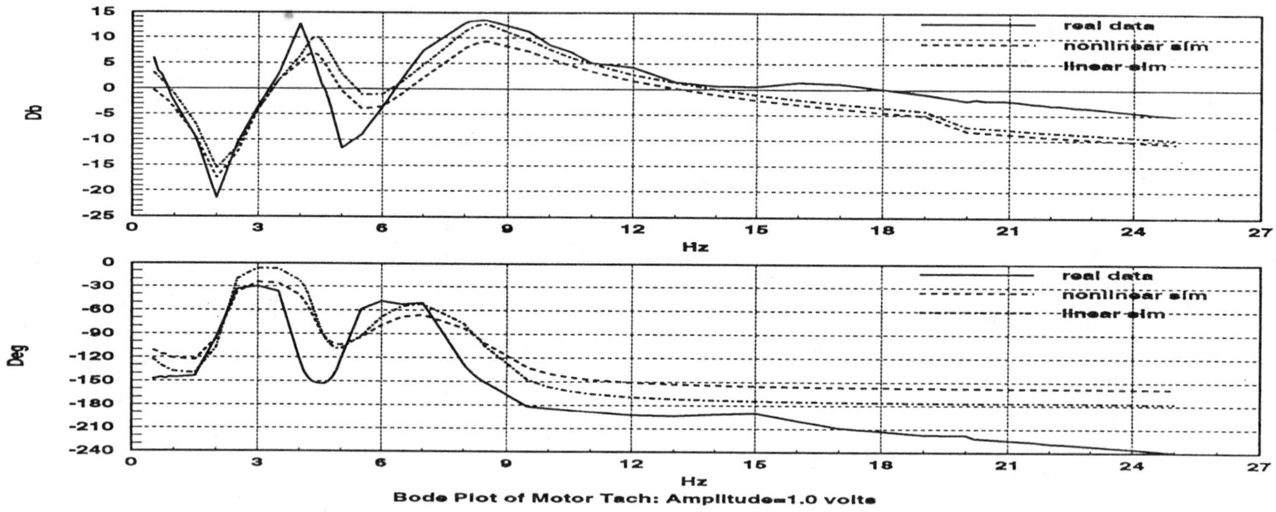

Figure 2

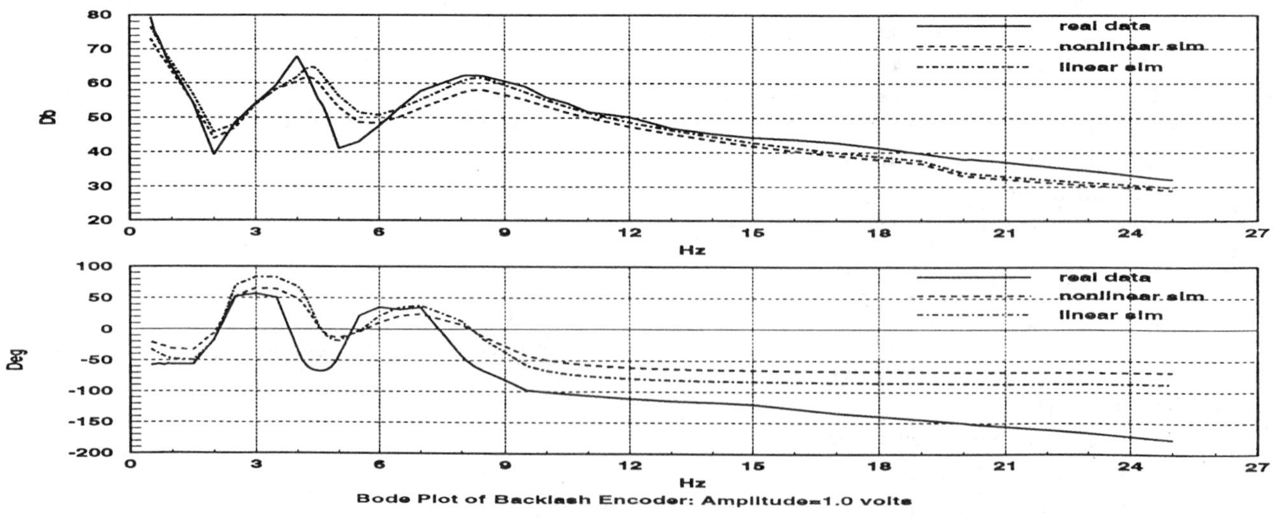

Figure 3

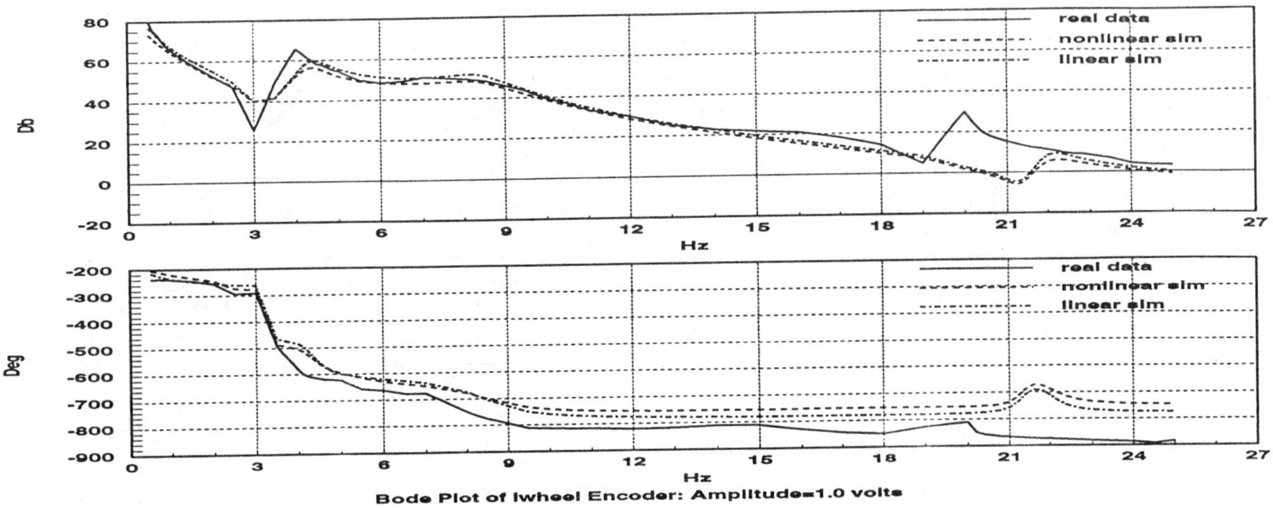

Figure 4

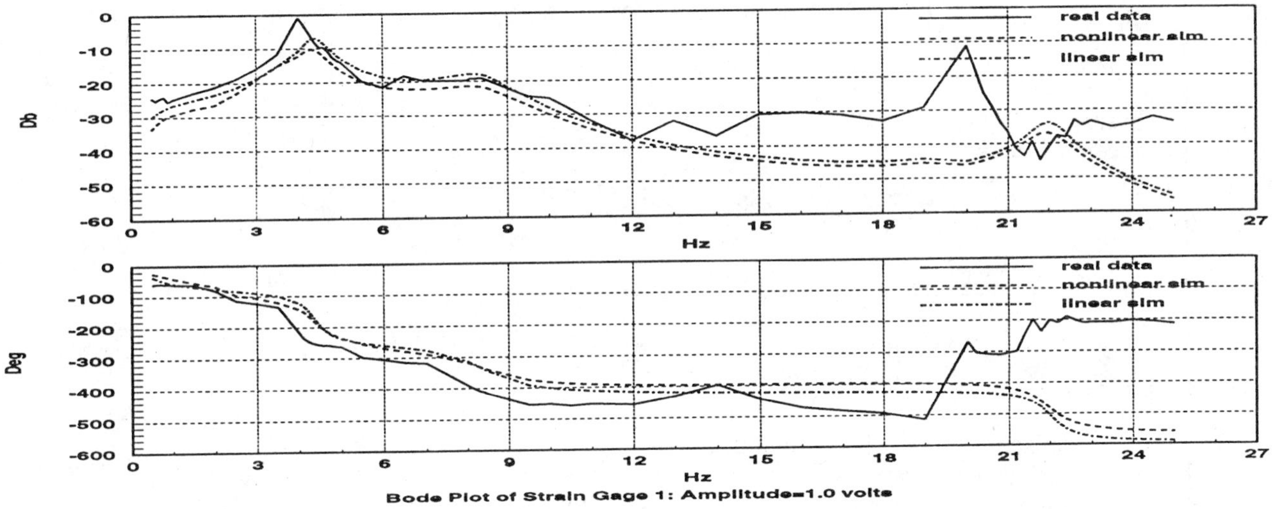

Figure 5

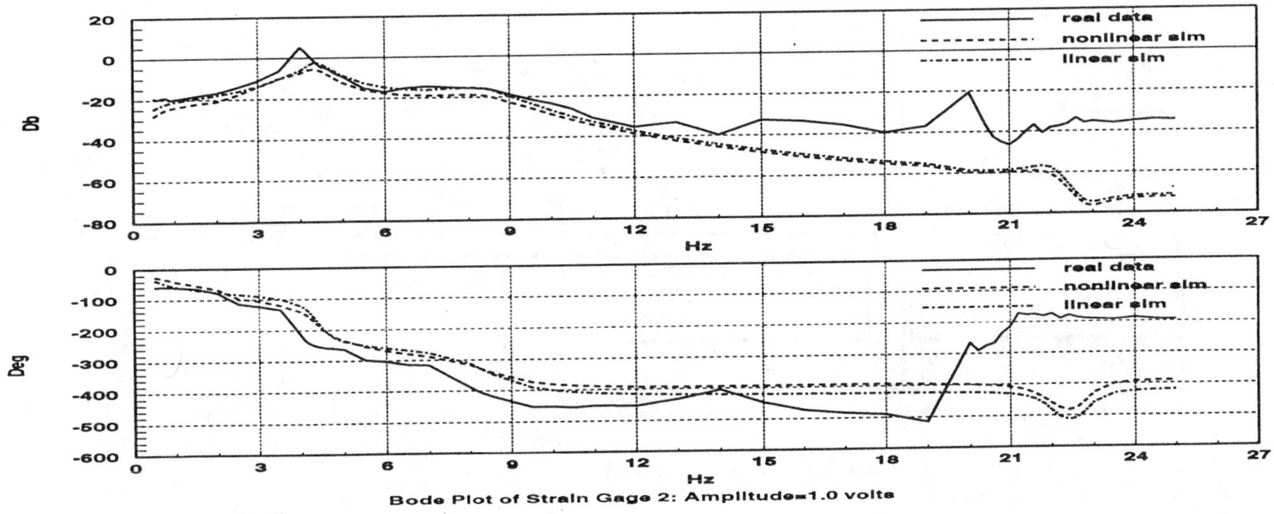

Figure 6

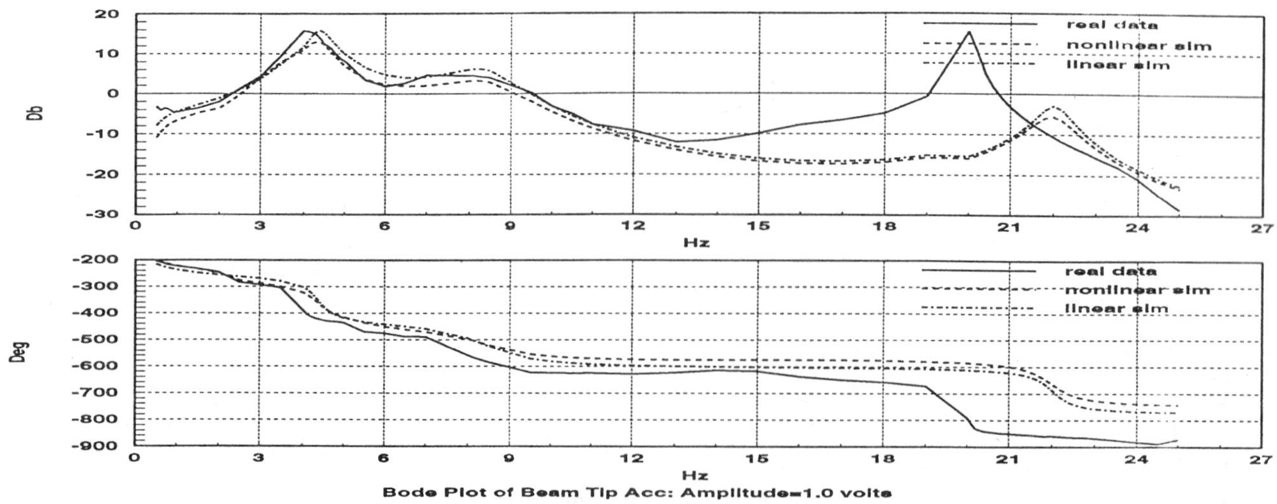
real data
nonlinear sim
linear sim
Db
Deg
Hz
Bode Plot of Beam Tip Acc: Amplitude=1.0 volts

Figure 7

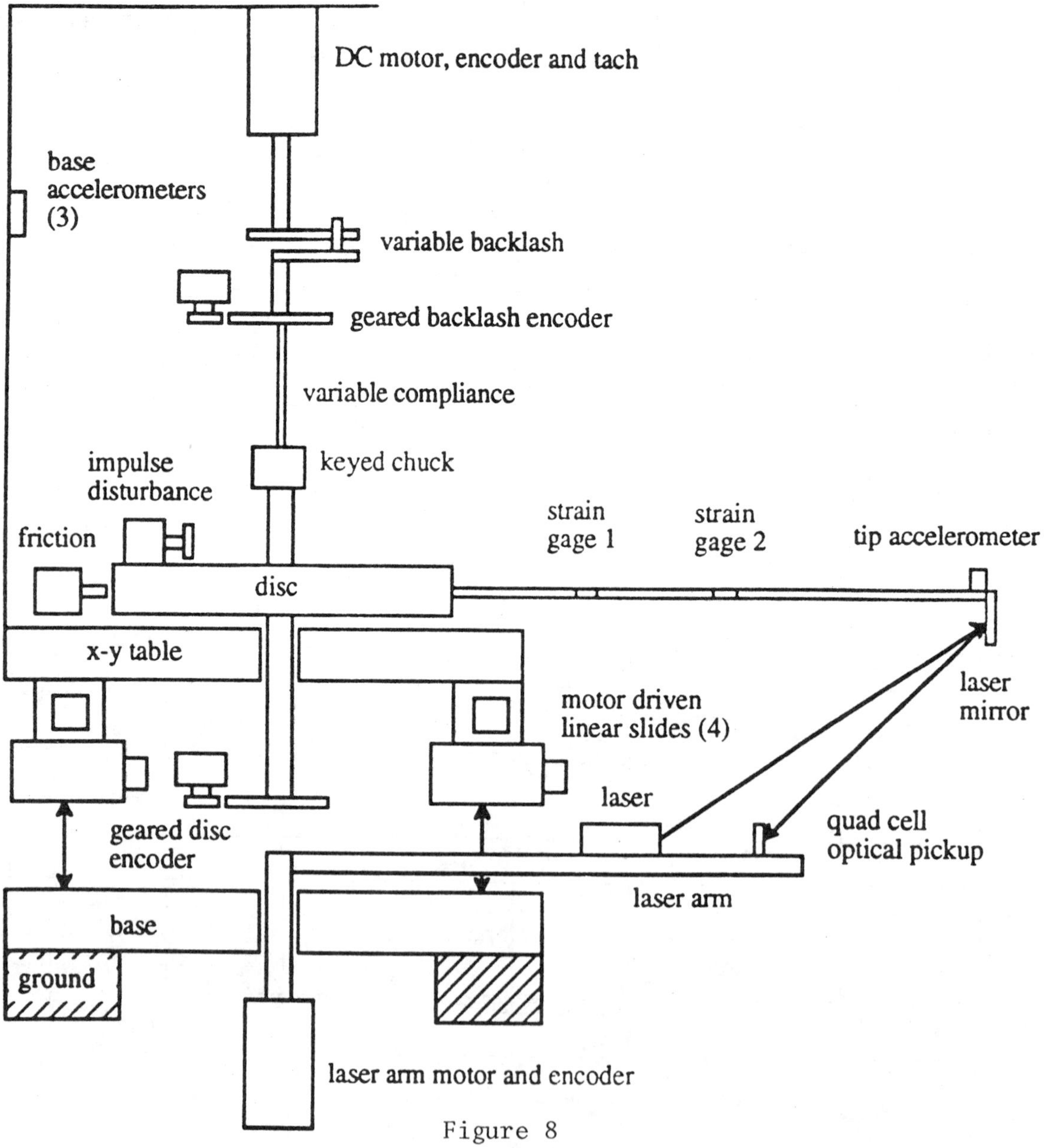
DC motor, encoder and tach
base accelerometers (3)
variable backlash
geared backlash encoder
variable compliance
keyed chuck
impulse disturbance
friction
disc
strain gage 1
strain gage 2
tip accelerometer
x-y table
laser mirror
motor driven linear slides (4)
laser
quad cell optical pickup
geared disc encoder
laser arm
base
ground
laser arm motor and encoder

Figure 8

Proceedings of the
American Control Conference
San Francisco, California • June 1993

Synthesis Methods for Robust Nonlinear Control

Daniel Bugajski
Systems and Research Center
Honeywell Inc.
3660 Technology Drive
Minneapolis, MN 55418

Dale Enns
Systems and Research Center
Honeywell Inc.
3660 Technology Drive
Minneapolis, MN 55418
and
Aerospace Engineering
University of Minnesota

Allen Tannenbaum
Department of Electrical Engineering
University of Minnesota
Minneapolis, MN 55455

Abstract

In this paper, we will discuss the application of robust control techniques and especially μ-synthesis to the Army's ATB-1000 test fixture. For comparison, two SISO controller designs are also described. The test fixture is pattered after the Apache helicopter's 30 mm gun and has tunable nonlinearities which may be representative not only of the nonlinearities of the gun, but of other mechanical systems as well. The models of the test fixture which were available at the time of the work are also described. The goal in pointing the gun is to reduce dispersions of fired gun rounds on targets. The resulting μ-synthesis design, when connected with a nonlinear simulation, exhibited limit-cycle behavior of unacceptable amplitude. The unacceptable performance is due to the nonlinearities and, in future work, would be improved upon by frequency domain trade-offs during the synthesis step. In particular, we will sketch the use of advanced nonlinear H^∞ techniques for such problems.

1 Introduction

In this paper, we will consider some novel robust control synthesis procedures for nonlinear systems. We will focus our attention on the ATB1000 test fixture at the Picatinny Arsenal in New Jersey which is patterned after the Apache's 30 mm gun.

For proper overall functioning of most of the Army's weapons systems, specific subsystems demand high precision control. For example, a guided munition system may be fitted with laser systems for ranging and/or targeting. Both of the laser subsystems call for accurate pointing control systems. These are in addition to the high performance guidance and control of the munition itself. Tank and gun systems require stabilized platforms from which rapid firing and re-targeting occur. Stabilized platforms are also necessary for antenna systems and video camera systems which are envisioned in future battlefield scenarios. Oftentimes, the accuracy of these control laws is limited by the mechanical system itself, for example, dead zones in gear drives, or friction in bearings.

The Army Research Office has built a laboratory fixture to study control laws for problems that are dominated by "hard" nonlinearities. Example nonlinearities in this group are saturations, static friction effects, and gear backlash. The fixture, the ATB-1000, is patterned after the Apache helicopter gun, and has built-in tunable nonlinearities. It is ideal for studying problems in application of linear and nonlinear control law designs.

This paper offers three potential linear control designs for the ATB-1000. Section 2 briefly discusses the objectives for the design, and Section 3 describes the models available for design and analysis. Section 4 discusses the three different designs, and Section 5 contains some nonlinear simulation and linear analyses for one of the designs. Finally in Section 6, we outline an advanced design technique that we plan to apply in the future.

2 System Requirements

The ATB-1000 is a test fixture patterned after the Apache's 30 mm gun. The basic goal for this weapon is to reduce dispersion of its rounds on targets. So the objective for the ATB-1000 is to minimize the barrel pointing angle deviation from a commanded value in the presence of platform motion (simulated with disk motion), gun firing-induced transients (simulated with a solenoid), and mechanism nonlinearities (simulated with adjustable backlash and friction). The laboratory fixture (see Figure 1) is outfitted with a laser arm to accurately measure the barrel tip position and hence experimentally determine performance. There are also disturbance levels and ranges of parametric nonlinearity adjustments that are part of the requirements.

3 Models

In practice, the development of a successful control system design is highly dependent on obtaining representative models of the system to be controlled. The models are a direct input to the control law synthesis and analysis steps in the development process. Models and modeling data come in many different forms, and different types of models are used for different purposes. Two distinct models of ATB-1000 test fixture were examined as part of this preliminary control design effort. These two models will be described and compared in this section. Some discrepancies between these two models have been identified and it will be necessary to resolve them for future studies.

During the summer of 1991, modeling data was received and analyzed from the Army Research Office. The modeling material consisted of MatrixX block diagrams, tables containing definitions, scale factors, sign conventions, units, signal size information, and linear models for the truncated finite element model of the barrel (with 8 states) and a 27th order identification model. This section will refer to an analytical model and an identification model. The analytical model is based on the block diagrams, tabular data, first principles of dynamics, and includes four relay-type nonlinearities and two deadband-type nonlinearities. The identification model is a linear model whose inputs and outputs are a subset of those in the analytical model.

The MatrixX block diagrams and the tabular data were used to generate a linear model and a nonlinear simulation using Honeywell computer tools. The linear model treats the deadband as a unity operator which neglects backlash, and the relay as a zero operator which neglects friction. The linear model was then examined in terms of its poles, transfer function zeros for certain inputs and outputs, and time and frequency responses. There are degrees-of-freedom for the disk translation and rotation in a plane, motor rotation, inertia wheel rotation, laser arm motor rotation, laser arm rotation, and three elastic degrees of freedom for the gun barrel (simulated with a rod attached to the inertia wheel).

The linear open loop model consists of two physical systems: the disk, inertia wheel, and rod system, and the laser arm system. There is a motor associated with each system. There are five pairs of open loop poles at the origin (because friction is neglected) associated with the rigid body degrees-of-freedom. There are two pairs of complex poles associated with the compliances in both systems, and there are three pairs of complex poles associated with the gun barrel resonances with small damping ratios.

The plant transfer function between the control motor torque and the barrel pointing angle can be regarded as a double integrator (at frequencies below 10 rad/sec) with disturbances (from disk motion) and some high frequency elastic modes. The nonlinear simulation was executed with different test inputs to assess its behavior. An identification (ID) model was obtained in a state space format with seven outputs, one input, and 27 states. The outputs are torque motor resolver, backlash resolver, disk velocity, quadcell output, strain gauge #1, strain gauge #2, and torque motor tachometer, the input is the control motor torque, and the 27 states are not physically defined but the linear ID model fits the data from the identification experiments. This model was compared to the analytical model in terms of poles, frequency response, and time histories.

The ID model shows more open loop damping e.g. ζ_{ID}=0.07 versus $\zeta_{analytic}$=0.01 for the first elastic mode (near 31 rad/sec) and ζ_{ID}=0.15 versus $\zeta_{analytic}$=0.084 for the shaft compliance mode (near 55 rad/sec) between torque motor and inertia wheel. The low frequency behavior of the ID model shows a slope of -1 on a Bode gain plot versus the slope of -2 in the analytical model, because friction is present in the identification experiment, but neglected in analytical model. In addition, the low frequency accuracy of the ID model is limited by the length of time used for the identification experiment. Thus the ID model is not close to the analytical model for frequencies below 10 rad/sec. Except for the poles and low frequency asymptote, the ID and analytical models agree for torque motor resolver, backlash resolver, and torque motor tachometer outputs. On the other hand, the ID and analytical models for strain gauge #2 show 180 deg phase discrepancies, and the the quadcell output does not show close agreement at any frequency.

For future design work, it will be necessary to resolve these discrepancies before closed loop testing can be performed. The ID model was utilized (despite these discrepancies) for demonstration of the μ-synthesis design methodology. Actually a balanced realization of the ID model was truncated to twelve states for the μ-synthesis design. The analytical model was utilized to develop alternate control laws with classical approaches. One of these classical alternates uses motor tachometer feedback, and the other has lead and notch compensation of the inertia wheel position. The next section discusses each of these three designs.

4 Control Law Design

In this section a preliminary design effort for the ATB-1000 test fixture will be described in detail. The design is incomplete, but adequately serves as a starting point for future work. To limit the scope of the preliminary effort, the "hard" nonlinearities were neglected for the control synthesis. However closed loop simulations were carried out where the nonlinearities were included. These preliminary simulations showed that the nonlinearities are significant and it will be necessary to include them in future designs. In this preliminary look at control law design, three design approaches were considered. Two approaches were SISO and one was multivariable μ-synthesis. The SISO designs are of interest because they correspond to minimal sensor requirements. The μ-synthesis approach is of interest because the nonlinearities are accounted for by treating them as bounded operators.

The control problem is to point the gun barrel in the face of disturbances. For the demonstration design presented here, the pointing was quantified in terms of the quadcell output and only the solenoid disturbance was included in the design objective. Model uncertainty was incorporated with a multiplicative perturbation at the torque motor location. Sensor noise was also included in the formal μ-synthesis problem statement. More detailed designs would incorporate frequency domain weighting transfer functions, which act as linear bounds for the effects of the six system nonlinearities. Requirements would also be defined and incorporated for actuator activity and physical limitations.

It was necessary to append a solenoid disturbance input (which simulates gun firing) to the ID model. This was done by selecting a constant gain matrix from the frequency response of the analytical model near the first elastic mode frequency. This is an approximation used for expediency during this preliminary design. In a more detailed design effort, the effect of the disturbance input on the equations of motion would be included more carefully into the state-space matrices for the interconnection structure used for μ-synthesis.

It is worth noting that the gun stabilization fixture is similar to a particular elastic structure control problem which has received a large amount of attention in the control and modeling literature. In addition, experimental studies have been performed at various laboratories [7, 4]. The problem is that of rotating disks (at least two) that are connected with rods that are elastic in torsion. These studies motivated the first design.

Colocated SISO Design One of the SISO designs was for colocated feedback between the torque motor resolver and the motor torque. This choice was motivated by the knowledge that under certain assumptions regarding a lower bound for inherent structural damping, and sufficiently high bandwidth sensors, computers, and actuators, such a mechanical system can be robustly stabilized with colocated sensors and actuators even in the presence of some significant nonlinearities. When the sensor and actuator are not colocated, robust stabilization is, in general, more difficult to achieve due to limitations imposed by non-minimum phase aspects. [11, 12, 1]

The reduced order ID model was utilized to determine the feedback compensation. Recall that the transfer function has a $1/s$ shape below 10 rad/sec in the case of the ID model. Thus a pure gain can be selected to set the unit loop gain crossover at 10 rad/sec as a preliminary design choice. Higher frequency resonances are stabilized because of the colocation and the assumptions about inherent damping, sensors, and actuators. A higher crossover could be considered but this would require more accurate modeling of even higher frequency elastic behavior and tighter requirements on sensors and actuators. A pure gain feedback between motor position and motor torque would not be stabilizing if connected to the analytical model because it has a $1/s^2$ shape below 10 rad/sec as discussed above.

Noncolocated SISO Design The other SISO design was developed with the analytical model for noncolocated feedback between the inertia wheel encoder and motor torque. In this case a lead compensation element was employed to create a unit loop gain crossover at 10 rad/sec. In this case, some of the higher frequency resonances are destabilized by the noncolocated feedback. To prevent this destabilization, notch filters were included for the first elastic mode and the compliant mode between the motor and inertia wheel. This design approach is of interest (as compared to the colocated design) because the colocated motor position is not as closely related to the pointing angle as is the inertia wheel. This design also has value as a further comparison against the μ-synthesis design.

Mu-Synthesis Design The μ-synthesis design approach is multivariable and is cast in terms of the interconnection structure shown in Figure 1. There is a multiplicative perturbation at the torque motor location represented by Δ and the input v_1 and output z_1. There is a performance output called e_{quad} which is the quadcell output passed through a weighting function. The external inputs are sensor noise and the solenoid disturbance. There is also the torque motor input and the seven sensors to close the feedback loop with the compensator K.

The interconnection structure includes weighting transfer functions for uncertainty bounds, performance requirements, and disturbances. The uncertainty was modeled as a multiplicative perturbation and was bounded with a third order Butterworth filter having break frequencies at 20 and 300 rad/sec and a high frequency gain of 675. This can be interpreted as 20% model error below 20 rad/sec and 67,500% model error above 300 rad/sec. The pointing requirement is included by weighting the quadcell output with a low pass transfer function $360(s+10)/(s^2+84s+60^2)$. This has unit steady-state gain, so outputs of less than 1 volt would be acceptable. The seven sensor noises are weighted with the constant value of 0.01, so this corresponds to either volts or counts depending on the sensor. Finally, the solenoid disturbance is weighted with a low pass transfer function $0.3/(s+10)$, so inputs of 0.03 volts are expected. The weightings were not carefully related to the hardware in this preliminary design demonstration. This relationship should be more carefully addressed to better account for known hardware characteristics. In particular a weighting for the disturbance would take into account the duty cycle of the solenoid. Additional inputs and outputs as well as weightings could be utilized to represent the nonlinearities which have not been accounted for in the preliminary design.

The state space solution to the H^∞ control synthesis problem was used to find a feedback compensator K. This compensator has as many states (18) as the interconnection structure and it was possible to reduce the compensator order by residualization to 16 states. The closed loop transfer function is denoted by M and connects the inputs: v_1, solenoid, and sensor noise to the outputs: z_1, and quadcell.

The next step in the μ-synthesis design was to introduce D-scales to properly account for the model uncertainty and performance variable response to external inputs. A constant D-scale=3 was employed because a dynamic D-scale was not deemed necessary in this preliminary design. The D-scale was incorporated by multiplying z_1 by 3 and dividing v_1 by 3 (i.e., DMD^{-1}) and a new interconnection structure P was established. The H^∞ problem was then re-solved for the compensator K and the iterations were terminated. Detailed analyses of this compensator appear in the following section.

5 Analyses

The μ-synthesis results are graphed in Figure 2. There are five plots of Bode magnitude versus frequency. The top curve is relatively flat because it is the maximum singular value of the closed loop interconnection structure ($\bar{\sigma}[M]$), and H^∞ optimization makes its peak value as small as possible. The next curve down is the structured singular value, $\mu[M]$, and is necessarily less than or equal to the upper curve, since $\bar{\sigma}[M]$ is a theoretical upper bound for $\mu[M]$. There is a low frequency difference between the structured and maximum singular values, which indicates that performance improvements are possible by further D-K iteration and frequency dependent D-scales.

The next two curves in Figure 2 correspond to robust stability and nominal performance. Theoretically these curves are less than or equal to the structured singular value and this is consistent with the numerical results. The robust stability curve is relative to to the defined multiplicative perturbation, and dominates $\mu[M]$ at higher frequencies. The robust stability curve can be further interpreted as the weighted complementary sensitivity, where the weighting is the bound for the multiplicative perturbation. The nominal performance curve is the maximum singular value of the transfer function matrix between the weighted quadcell and the external inputs including the weighted solenoid disturbance and sensor noise. This curve dominates $\mu[M]$ at low frequencies and can be further interpreted as the weighted sensitivity. The lowest curve in the figure corresponds to the weighted quadcell response due to sensor noise. This is more than an order of magnitude less than $\mu[M]$, so the quadcell/sensor noise path does not have much influence on the optimal design.

Further analyses of the μ-synthesis design were carried out to assess closed loop poles, input and output loop properties, and time response to solenoid disturbances. The closed loop poles indicated closed loop stability and damping improvements for the first elastic mode ($\zeta_{CL}=0.12$ versus $\zeta_{OL}=0.08$) and compliant mode ($\zeta_{CL}=0.21$ versus $\zeta_{OL}=0.14$). Gain and phase margins for the SISO loop transfer function at the torque motor actuator location were evaluated. The lowest frequency unit gain crossover occurs at 5.8 rad/sec with a phase margin of 81 degrees. The phase margins surrounding the first elastic mode frequency are larger than 43 degrees. All gain margins are larger than 7 db. These are considered good margins with respect to model uncertainty at the actuator location.

The linear closed loop system was simulated with the disturbance model used for the μ-synthesis design. This disturbance model is a constant gain matrix between the solenoid and the measurements including the quadcell output. Thus this model is only accurate near the first elastic mode frequency and is not accurate at low or high frequencies. The disturbance input was a 10 Hz sequence of 10 msec, 1 volt pulses. (See Figure 3a.) The quadcell output response is dominated by the the compliant mode because the pulse frequency is close in proximity to the compliant mode frequency. The quadcell output during the 10 msec solenoid firing is not accurate, so disregarding these portions of the response, the quadcell output shows a residual oscillation near the compliant mode frequency with less than 3 volts peak-to-peak. (See Figure 3b.) This is not considered satisfactory performance and the interconnection structure should be further refined to improve the performance by making better tradeoffs with the weighting functions.

6 Nonlinear H^∞

In this section, we will consider new approaches to design using nonlinear generalizations of H^∞ theory which should give bounds for control limitations in the presence of noninvertible nonlinearities such as those present in the ATB-1000. To fix ideas about how such a procedure would go, let us consider the simple sensitivity minimization problem form a nonlinear SISO plant P and weighting filter W. (See [10] for all the necessary assumptions and the precise definitions.)

We consider the problem of finding

$$\mu_\delta := \inf_C \sup_{\|v\|\leq\delta} \|[(I + P \circ C)^{-1} \circ W]v\|,$$

where we assume all the operators involved are admissible [10]. Thus we are looking at a worst case disturbance attenuation problem where the energy of the signals v is required to be bounded by some pre-specified level δ. (In the linear case, since everything scales, we can always without loss of generality take $\delta = 1$. For nonlinear systems, we must specify the energy bound *a priori*.) Under the proper assumptions [8, 9, 10], one sees that this problem is equivalent to the problem of finding

$$\mu_\delta = \inf_{q\in C_l} \sup_{\|v\|\leq\delta} \|(W - P \circ q)v\|,$$

where C_l denotes the space of causal, analytic operators (see the above references). (All the input/output operators we consider here will be time-invariant as well.)

One can give an iterative procedure for approximating a solution to such a problem. Briefly, the idea is that we write

$$\begin{aligned} W &= W_1 + W_2 + \cdots, \\ P &= P_1 + P_2 + \cdots, \\ q &= q_1 + q_2 + \cdots, \end{aligned}$$

where W_j, P_j, q_j are homogeneous polynomials of degree j. Notice that

$$\mu_\delta = \delta \inf_{q_1\in H^\infty} \|W_1 - P_1 q_1\| + O(\delta^2),$$

where the latter norm is the operator norm (i.e., H^∞ norm). From H^∞ theory, we can find an optimal (linear, causal, time-invariant) $q_{1,opt} \in H^\infty$ such that

$$\mu_\delta = \delta\|W_1 - P_1 q_{1,opt}\| + O(\delta^2).$$

Now the iterative procedure of [10] gives a way of giving higher order corrections to this linearization. Let us illustrate this now with the second order correction. Indeed, having fixed now the linear part $q_{1,opt}$ of q in the last equation, we note that

$$W(v) - P(q(v)) - (W_1 - P_1 q_{1,opt})(v) =$$

$$W_2(v) - P_2(q_{1,opt}(v)) - P_1 q_2(v) + \text{higher order terms.}$$

Regarding W_2, P_2, q_2 as linear operators on $H^2 \otimes H^2 \cong H^2(D^2, \mathbf{C})$, we see that

$$\sup_{\|v\|\leq\delta} \|(W - P\circ q)(v) - (W_1 - P_1 q_{1,opt})v\| \leq \delta^2\|\hat{W}_2 - P_1 q_2\| + O(\delta^3),$$

where the "weight"

$$\hat{W}_2 := W_2 - P_2(q_1 \otimes q_1).$$

We can now use the methods of [10] to pick an optimal admissible $q_{2,opt}$, and so on.

In short, instead of simply designing a linear compensator for a linearization of the given nonlinear system, this methodology allows one to explicitly take into account the higher order terms of the nonlinear plant, and therefore increase the ball of operation for the nonlinear controller. Of course, for a realistic design for the ATB-1000 such a procedure would nave to be applied to the full standard H^∞ problem.

Acnowledgement: This work was supported in part by grants from the National Science Foundation DMS-8811084 and ECS-9122106, by the Air Force Office of Scientific Research AFOSR-90-0024, and by the Army Research Office DAAL03-91-G-0019.

References

[1] G.J. Balas, "Robust Control of Flexible Structures: Theory and Experiments," Ph. D. Dissertation, California Institute of Technonlogy, 1990.

[2] J. Ball and J. W. Helton, "H^∞ control for nonlinear plants: connections with differential games," Proc. of the 28-th CDC, Tampa, Florida, December 1989, pp. 956–962.

[3] J. Ball and J. W. Helton, "Nonlinear H^∞ control theory for stable plants," Technical Report, Department of Mathematics, University of California at San Diego, 1990.

[4] R.H. Cannon and D.E. Rosenthal, "Experiments in control of flexible structures with noncolocated sensors and actuators," *Journal of Guidance Control and Dynamics* **7**, No. 5, p. 546, Sept.-Oct., 1984.

[5] J. C. Doyle, "Analysis of feedback systems with structured uncertainties," *IEE Proc.* **129** (1982), pp. 242–250.

[6] J. C. Doyle, B. Francis, and A. Tannenbaum, *Feedback Control Theory*, McMillan, New York, 1991.

[7] D. Enns, "Model reduction for control system design", Ph. D. Dissertation, Dept. of Aeronautics and Astronautics, Stanford University, 1984.

[8] D. Enns, C. Foias, T. Georgiou, M. Jackson, B. Schipper, and A. Tannenbaum, "On the nonlinear mixed sensitivity problem," Proc. of 28-th IEEE Conference on Decision and Control, Tampa, Florida, December 1989, pp. 2673–2678.

[9] C. Foias and A. Tannenbaum, "Weighted optimization theory for nonlinear systems," *SIAM J. on Control and Optimization* **27** (1989), pp. 842–860.

[10] C. Foias, C. Gu, and A. Tannenbaum, "Nonlinear H^∞ optimization: a causal power series approach," submitted for publication to *SIAM J. on Control and Opt.*

[11] C.S. Greene and G. Stein, "Inherent damping, solvability conditions, and solutions for structural vibration control," Proc. of 1979 IEEE Conference on Decision and Control, December 1979.

[12] D.E. Rosenthal, "Experiments in control of flexible structure with uncertain parameters," Ph. D. Dissertation, Dept. of Aeronautics and Astronautics, Stanford University, 1984.

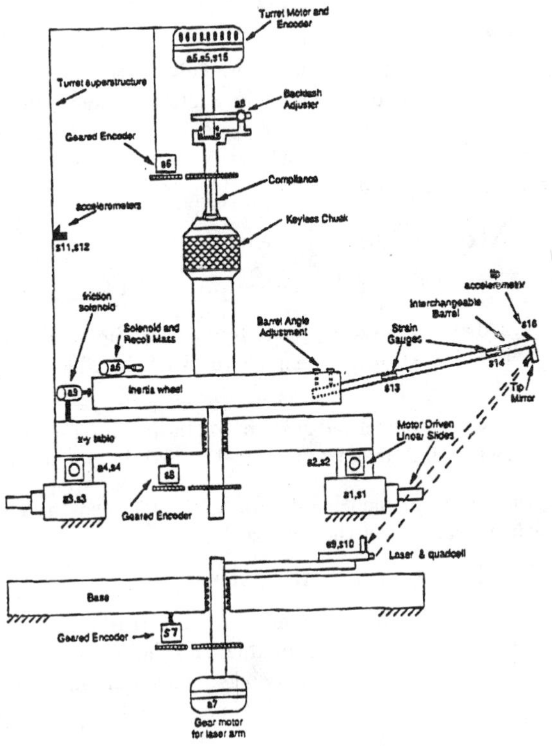

Schematic of ATB-1000 test fixture.

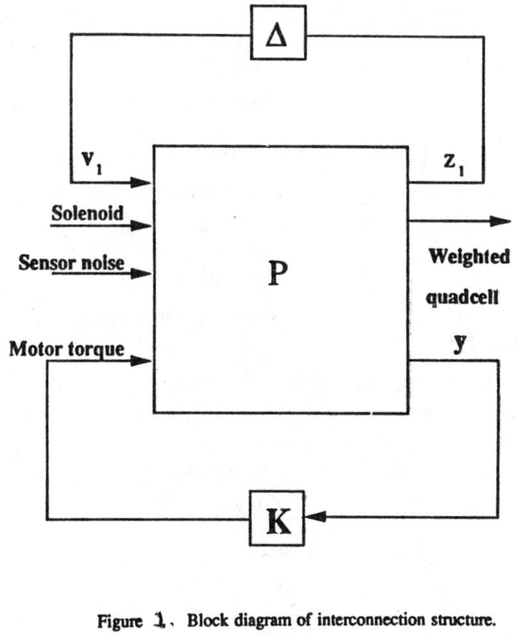

Figure 1. Block diagram of interconnection structure.

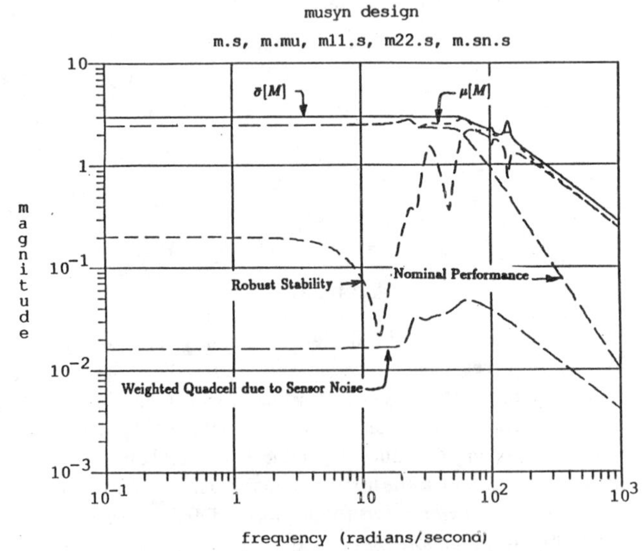

Figure 2. Graphical summary of mu-synthesis design.

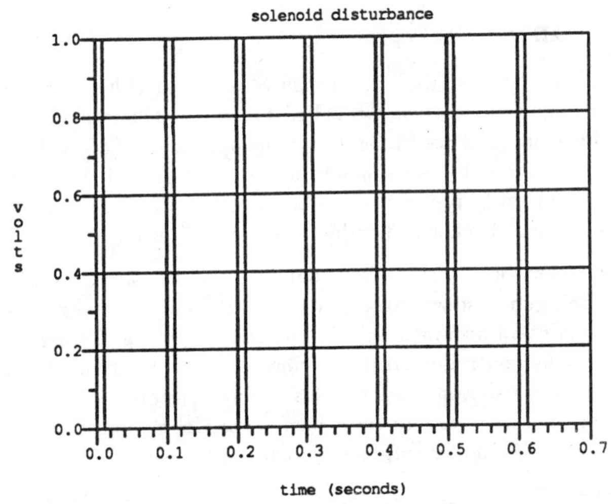

a)

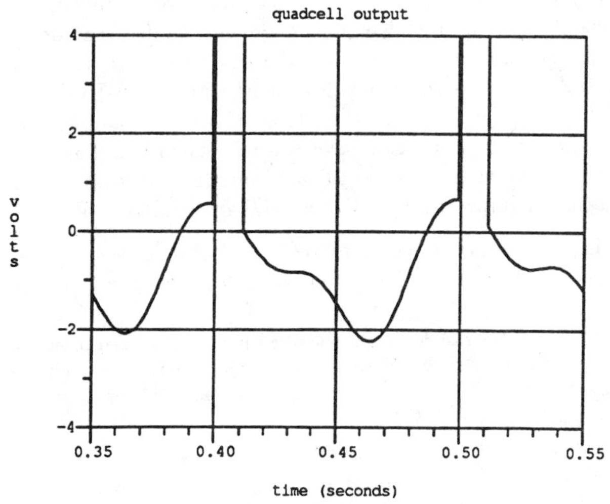

b)

Figure 3. Time histories using mu-synthesis design.

Proceedings of the
American Control Conference
San Francisco, California • June 1993

Robust Nonlinear Control System Synthesis Method for Electro-Mechanical Pointing Systems with Flexible Modes

James H. Taylor and Jin Lu
Odyssey Research Associates
Ithaca, New York 14850-1326
email: jim@oracorp.com

Abstract [1]

This paper describes the design of a robust control system for a gun turret testbed called the ATB1000. The control system incorporates a control scheme based on sinusoidal-input describing function (SIDF) models of the testbed's drive subsystem to reduce the effects of backlash and nonlinear friction, and a dissipative control scheme to make the control system insensitive to the unmodeled dynamics and parameter imprecision associated with the flexible modes of the wheel/barrel subsystem.

1 Introduction

This paper describes the design of a robust control system for a gun turret testbed called the ATB1000 (see Fig. 1). This testbed is used to simulate the dynamics of a gun-firing platform and to test schemes for controlling and stabilizing the gun-firing process in the presence of uncertainties such as friction, backlash, flexible modes and gun recoil.

Our control objective is to obtain good transient response as the gun is slewed towards a specified reference angle and to maintain accurate pointing during gun firing. To achieve this, the controller must overcome the effects of gun recoil, nonlinear friction, and backlash. Furthermore, the control system is required to be robust to modeling uncertainties, such as parameter imprecision and unmodeled dynamics.

The testbed system can be decomposed into two subsystems which pose different control problems. The drive subsystem has limitations due to Coulomb friction and backlash, and the wheel/barrel subsystem has the "spill-over" problem associated with unmodeled high-frequency modes that occur in characterizing the motion of the flexible gun barrel. The control system described below incorporates a SIDF-based control scheme to reduce the effects of backlash and nonlinear friction, and a dissipative control scheme to make the control system insensitive to the unmodeled dynamics and parameter imprecision of the wheel/barrel subsystem.

This paper is organized as follows: In Section 2, we describe the testbed model and highlight some of the features of the system that make its control difficult; in Section 3, we formulate the control problem; in Sections 4 and 5 we detail the design of a robust control system for the testbed; finally, in Section 6, we verify the control system by simulating it on the testbed model.

[1] Support for the research described herein has been provided by the Defense Advanced Research Project Agency through the U.S. Army AMCCOM at Picatinny Arsenal, NJ by Contract Number DAAA21-92-C-0013.

2 Model Description

As shown in Fig. 1, the testbed consists of two subsystems:

- a drive subsystem, including a DC motor (with nonlinear friction), a gear chain (with backlash), and an elastic shaft;
- a wheel/barrel subsystem, including an inertia wheel (with nonlinear friction) and a flexible gun barrel.

In the work outlined below, we have neglected the effect of platform motion on the testbed.

2.1 The Drive Subsystem

The drive subsystem dynamics are governed by two sets of differential equations, depending on whether the gears are engaged on not. When the two gears are not engaged, there is no interaction between the DC motor and the elastic shaft:

$$J_m\ddot{\theta}_m = T_m - T_{mf} \quad (1)$$
$$J_b\ddot{\theta}_b = -T_s \quad (2)$$

where θ_m and θ_b are the angles of driving gear and driven gear, respectively. J_m, J_b are the inertia constants of the motor and elastic shaft assemblies, T_m is the torque of the motor, T_{mf} is the Coulomb friction torque on the motor

$$T_{mf} = b_m \operatorname{sgn}(\dot{\theta}_m)$$

where b_m is the magnitude of the friction torque and T_s is the reactive torque of the elastic shaft,

$$T_s = k_s(\theta_b - \theta_i) + b_s(\dot{\theta}_b - \dot{\theta}_i), \quad (3)$$

where k_s, b_s are spring and viscous friction constants respectively, and θ_i is the inertia wheel yaw angle.

When the two gears are engaged, the subsystem can be treated as if there were no gears. In this case, $\dot{\theta}_m = \dot{\theta}_b$ and $\theta_m = \theta_b + x_b$ (positive engagement) or $\theta_m = \theta_b$ (negative engagement), where x_b is the backlash gap. The differential equation governing the dynamics of θ_b is

$$(J_m + J_b)\ddot{\theta}_b = T_m - T_s - T_{mf} \quad (4)$$

We note that there is a "jump" in the states $\dot{\theta}_m$ and $\dot{\theta}_b$ at the moment the two gears become engaged. Let the moment of engagement be t_e, $\dot{\theta}_m(t_e^-)$ and $\dot{\theta}_b(t_e^-)$ the gear speeds before collision, $\dot{\theta}_m(t_e^+)$ and $\dot{\theta}_b(t_e^+)$ the gear speeds after collision. If we neglect the elasticity of the gear material, then by conservation of momentum we have:

$$\dot{\theta}_m(t_e^+) = \dot{\theta}_b(t_e^+) = \frac{J_m}{J_m + J_b}\dot{\theta}_m(t_e^-) + \frac{J_b}{J_m + J_b}\dot{\theta}_b(t_e^-) \quad (5)$$

The conditions for the gears to become engaged are:

1. (positive engagement)

$$\theta_m - \theta_b = x_b \text{ and } \dot{\theta}_m - \dot{\theta}_b > 0; \quad (6)$$

or

$$\theta_m - \theta_b = x_b \text{ and } \ddot{\theta}_m - \ddot{\theta}_b > 0; \quad (7)$$

2. (negative engagement)

$$\theta_m - \theta_b = 0 \text{ and } \dot{\theta}_m - \dot{\theta}_b < 0; \quad (8)$$

or

$$\theta_m - \theta_b = 0 \text{ and } \ddot{\theta}_m - \ddot{\theta}_b < 0; \quad (9)$$

We note that in the above conditions, the dynamics of θ_m and θ_b are governed by differential equations (1) and (2).

2.2 The Wheel/Barrel Subsystem

The gun barrel is a distributed parameter system which can be approximated by a lumped parameter system using the finite element method. After this approximation, the wheel/barrel subsystem is described by a state-space model of the following form:

$$\ddot{x} + D\dot{x} + Kx = B(T_s - T_g + T_{f_1} + T_{f_2}) \quad (10)$$
$$y = Cx \quad (11)$$

where $x \in \mathcal{R}^n$ is the subsystem state vector (vector of modal coordinates) and $y^T = [\theta_i \ \theta_{tip}]$ is the output vector; θ_i is the inertia wheel angle, and θ_{tip} is the gun barrel tip angle; matrices D, K, C and B are of appropriate dimensions. The arrays D and K are diagonal matrices with non-negative elements. T_g is the disturbance torque introduced by gun firing (recoil), and T_{f_1} and T_{f_2} are torques introduced by viscous and Coulomb friction between the inertia wheel and the supporting platform under it,

$$T_{f_1} = b_1\dot{\theta}_i \quad (12)$$
$$T_{f_2} = b_2 \,\text{sgn}(\dot{\theta}_i) \quad (13)$$

where b_1 and b_2 are the friction coefficients.

The dimension of a flexible structure model are usually very high. From a numerical standpoint, we usually base the design of a controller for a flexible structure on a reduced-order model that contains the critical modes of the structure. In our case, we only consider four low-frequency modes of the wheel/barrel structure ($n = 4$ in (10)). One important issue is how to design a control based on the reduced-order model that does not destabilize the unmodeled modes when applied to the actual system.

3 Control Problem Statement

The objective of the control system is to smoothly slew and accurately point the gun barrel tip angle θ_{tip} with respect to a reference angle in the presence of gun firing, backlash, friction and unmodeled dynamics. To be specific, we want to find a control law $T_m = T_m(t)$ such that θ_{tip} will gracefully slew to θ_{ref} within some acceptable tolerance in reasonable time. To achieve this control objective, the control system must overcome the effect of backlash (the DC motor has no control over the wheel/barrel subsystem during disengagement) and Coulomb friction. In addition, the control system is required to be insensitive to modeling uncertainty, such as unmodeled high-frequency modes and system parameter imprecision of the flexible gun barrel.

Substituting (3) and (12) into (10) we can write the model of the wheel/barrel subsystem as

$$\ddot{x} + (D + (b_s + b_1)BC_1)\dot{x} + (K + k_sBC_1)x = Bu + Bw \quad (14)$$

where $\theta_i = C_1x$, $u = b_s\dot{\theta}_b + k_s\theta_b$ and $w = T_g + T_{f_2}$.

The variable $u = b_s\dot{\theta}_b + k_s\theta_b$ can be considered as the input to system (14) and an output of the drive subsystem. Our approach to control design consists of two step: (1) find a control law u^d for the input u to system (14) such that the resulting θ_{tip} has the desired properties outlined above; (2) find a control law for T_m so that u as an output of the drive tracks the desired control law u^d found in step (1). This design approach is illustrated in Fig. 2, where controller $C_2(s)$ is designed in step (1) and controller C_{nl} is designed in step (2). In step (1), we will use a robust control scheme that does not destabilize unmodeled high-frequency modes and is insensitive to parameter uncertainty. In step (2), we will use a control scheme based on sinusoidal-input describing function (SIDF) models of the testbed's drive subsystem to deal with backlash and frictions. The SIDF models are used because we believe they provide the best characterization of the major nonlinear effects of the drive subsystem with which we are concerned: the sensitivity of the drive subsystem's input/output (I/O) behavior to the amplitude of the input signal due to backlash and friction.

4 Robust Control of the Wheel/Barrel Subsystem

Consider a constant feedback control law for system (14)

$$u = -F_1\dot{x} - F_2x \quad (15)$$

where F_1 and F_2 are two feedback gains.

Substituting (15) into (14) gives

$$\ddot{x} + (D + (b_s + b_1)BC_1 + BF_1)\dot{x} + (K + k_sBC_1 + BF_2)x = Bw \quad (16)$$

We note that $C_1 = [c_{11} \cdots c_{1i}]$ $(\theta_i = C_1x)$ and $B = [b_1 \cdots b_n]^T$ in model (16) has the relation $c_{1i}b_i > 0, i = 1, \cdots, n$. In fact, the viscous bearing torque $T_{f_1} = b_1\dot{\theta}_i = b_1C_1\dot{x}$. If we assume that the wheel/barrel subsystem is only subject to the viscous bearing torque and has natural damping $D = 0$, then we have from (10),

$$\ddot{x} + Kx = -BT_{f_1} = -BC_1\dot{x} \quad (17)$$

We know that a system with only viscous bearing force (torque) is always energy dissipative. For system (17), this is true if and only if $c_{1i}b_i > 0, i = 1, \cdots, n$.

The following results give sufficient conditions for system (16) to be stable; refer to [1] for proofs:

Proposition 1: Assume diagonal matrices D and K satisfy $\dim(D) \geq n-1$ and $\dim(K) \geq (n-1)$. Then system (14) with control law (15) is asymptotically stable if $F_1 = f_1C_1$ and $F_2 = f_2C_1$ with $f_1 \geq 0$ and $f_2 \geq 0$ (namely, $u = f_1\dot{\theta}_i + f_2\theta_i$) •

In the following result, we neglect the damping in system (14), since a control law that stabilizes system (14) with zero natural damping is likely to stabilize the system with added non-zero natural damping.

Proposition 2: Let the damping matrix D in system (14) be zero, and the diagonal matrix K satisfy $\dim(K) \geq (n-1)$. System (14) with control law (15) is asymptotically stable if $F_1 = f_1C_1 + f_3[1\ 0\ \cdots\ 0]$ and $F_2 = f_2C_1$ with $f_1 \geq 0$, $f_2 \geq 0$ and $f_3 \geq 0$ (namely, $u = f_1\dot{\theta}_i + f_3\dot{x}_1 + f_2\theta_i$) •

Propositions 1 and 2 define control schemes that are robust with respect to system modeling errors and structural perturbations, because the control schemes do not depend on system parameters.

In the sequel, we will only consider the control scheme

$$u = f_1\dot{\theta}_i + f_3\dot{x}_1 + f_2\theta_i \qquad (18)$$

where $f_i \geq 0, i = 1, 2, 3$. The freedom in choosing f_i's in the control scheme allows us to achieve other performance requirements such as desirable pole assignment while ensuring the stability of the system.

5 SIDF Control of the Drive Subsystem

Assume that we have found the control law for $u = b_s\dot{\theta}_b + k_s\theta_b$ for the wheel/barrel subsystem (14) which guarantees the required behavior of θ_{tip}. Now, we will design a nonlinear control based on sinusoidal-input describing function (SIDF) models of the drive subsystem such that $u = b_s\dot{\theta}_b + k_s\theta_b$ as an output of the drive subsystem matches this desired form (see Fig. 2). To generate a SIDF between input T_m and output $u = b_s\dot{\theta}_b + k_s\theta_b$, a sinusoidal function $T_m = a\sin(\omega t)$ is used as input to the drive subsystem. The corresponding output of the drive subsystem $u = b_s\dot{\theta}_b + k_s\theta_b$ is treated via Fourier analysis [3] to obtain the SIDF model $G(j\omega, a)$. For linear systems, such a model is independent of input amplitudes; in fact, it is the transfer function $G(j\omega)$. For nonlinear systems, however, SIDF models generally depend on the amplitude of the system input.

The procedure for designing a nonlinear controller using SIDF models for a number of input amplitudes is described in some detail in our companion paper [4], or in more depth in [3]. The end result of following that synthesis approach is a nonlinear control law in the following form:

$$T_m = f_P(e) + \int_0^t f_I(e)\,dt + \frac{d}{dt}f_D(e) \qquad (19)$$

where T_m (the motor input) is the output of the controller, $e = \theta_{ref} - u$ with θ_{ref} an external input (see Fig. 2), and $f_P(\cdot)$, $f_P(\cdot)$ and $f_P(\cdot)$ are nonlinear functions obtained by an amplitude-desensitization process involving SIDF inversion. Again, for a detailed description of the SIDF-based control design method, see [3, 4].

6 Design and Simulation Study

The parameters of the testbed system are listed in Table 1. The dynamic response of θ_{tip} of the open-loop testbed system in the presence of initial non-zero condition ($\theta_{tip} \neq 0$), friction, backlash and gun-firing disturbance is shown in Fig. 3. From Fig. 3, we see that the modes of the barrel are quite lightly damped. We found that the damping ratio of the lowest-frequency mode is about 10%, and the damping ratios of other modes are less then 10%. Therefore, we use the degrees of freedon in (18) to increase the damping of the two lowest-frequency modes. Using any existing pole assignment methods (for example, see [2]) we find that when $u = -3.5\dot{x}_1 - 10\theta_i$, the damping factors of the first and second lowest-frequency modes are 40% and 20% respectively. By Proposition 2, the control scheme guarantees the stability of the system.

The SIDF-based control nonlinearities for the drive subsystem (19) is shown in Fig. 4. Figure 5 shows the uniformly fast response of $u = b_s\dot{\theta}_b + k_s\theta_b$ of the drive subsystem controlled by the nonlinear control to a step input v with different amplitudes. For comparison, Fig. 6 shows the response of $u = b_s\dot{\theta}_b + k_s\theta_b$ of the drive subsystem controlled by a linear control system (designed based on a linearized model of the testbed) to the step input v with different amplitudes. Fig. 6 also includes the response of $u = b_s\dot{\theta}_b + k_s\theta_b$ of the *linearized* model controlled by the linear control system. As mentioned earlier, the dynamic response of the SIDF-based nonlinear control system is insensitive to the amplitudes of input signal.

To summarize, the final composite nonlinear control law for the motor torque T_m is given by Eqn. (19) where $e = u^d - u = -3.5\dot{x}_1 - 10\theta_i - (b_s\dot{\theta}_b + k_s\theta_b)$ and $f_P(e), f_I(e), f_D(e)$ are the nonlinear functions shown in Fig. 4. The dynamic responses of θ_{tip} controlled by the nonlinear control law (19) is shown in Fig. 7, along with analogous results for inner-loop linear control. The closed-loop system is subject to several slew-angle commands (θ_{ref} values), as indicated; the responses are normalized by dividing by θ_{ref} so the amplitude sensitivity of the responses can be compared conveniently. The same levels of friction, backlash and gun-firing disturbance are used as in the open-loop case shown in Fig. 3. The closed-loop behavior of θ_{tip} has been improved greatly over the open-loop behavior.

A more detailed view of gun pointing accuracy is provided in Fig. 8, where the responses with linear and nonlinear control are shown for the smallest command $\theta_{ref} = 0.05$; note that the slowly decaying transients in the linear case completely dominate the response while the (much smaller) effect of gun-firing disturbance is seen in the nonlinear control case as being the dominant source of pointing error.

To test the robustness of this control scheme, we randomly

change the values of the components of vectors D, K, B and C_1 in system (14) without changing their signs. The closed-loop testbed system with control scheme (19) was always stable with such parameter changes and in most cases the dynamic response did not change noticeably.

7 Conclusion

We have developed a control system for the ATB1000 testbed model. The control system fulfilled our performance specification – it worked well in the presence of backlash, nonlinear friction, and gun-firing disturbances. The control system is robust with respect to both input amplitude and modeling uncertainties such as parameter imprecision and unmodeled dynamics of the flexible element.

References

[1] Jin Lu, "Robust Control of Semi-Rigid/Flexible Structures," *Proc. American Control Conference*, San Francisco, CA, 1993.

[2] G. Roppenecker and J. O'Reilly, "Parametric Output Feedback Controller Design," *Automatica, Vol. 25*, No. 2, pp. 259-265, 1989.

[3] Taylor, J. H., and K. L. Strobel, "Nonlinear Compensator Synthesis via Sinusoidal-Input Describing Functions," *Proc. American Control Conference*, Boston MA, pp. 1242-1247, 1985.

[4] Taylor, J. H., and J. Lu, "Computer-Aided Control Engineering Environment for the Synthesis of Nonlinear Control Systems," *Proc. American Control Conference*, San Francisco, CA, 1993.

notation	description	value	unit
x_b	backlash clearance	0-0.05	rad
b_s	spring viscosity	0.1	$Nm/rad\ sec^{-1}$
k_s	spring constant	34.3	Nm/rad
b_m	motor friction magnitude	0.5	1
J_m	motor and driving gear inertia	0.006	$Kg\ m^2$
J_b	driven gear and shaft inertia	0.01	$Kg\ m^2$
b_1	bearing viscosity	0.67	$Nm/rad\ sec^{-1}$
b_2	inertia wheel friction magnitude	0.1	1
D	damping matrix	diag([0 0.891 4.08 11.35])	$Nm/rad\ sec^{-1}$
K	stiffness matrix	diag([0 912.5 19124 148155])	Nm/rad
B^T	input gain vector	[5.7 27.6 -17.1 -14.9]	
C	output matrix	$\begin{bmatrix} 1.28 & 0.316 & -0.063 & -0.015 \\ 1.28 & -0.798 & -1.45 & 1.23 \end{bmatrix}$	

Table 1: Parameters of the ATB1000

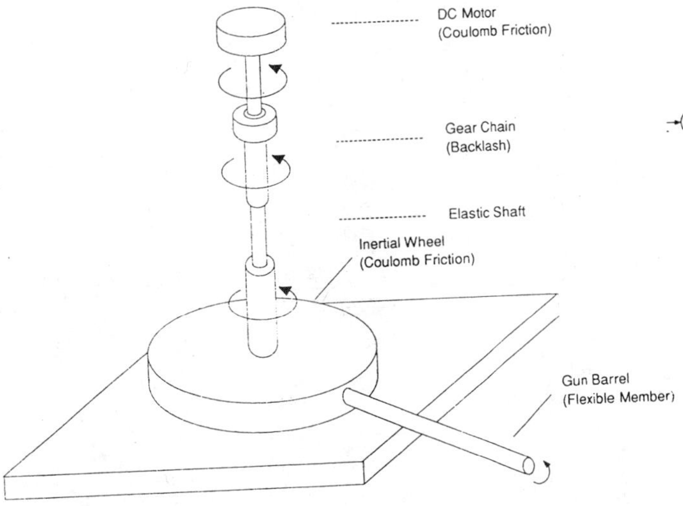

Fig. 1: A Schematic of a Tank Turret System

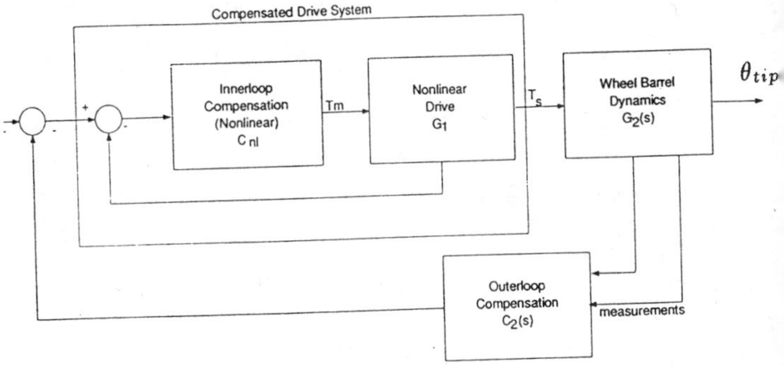

Fig. 2: Diagram of a Nonlinear Control System

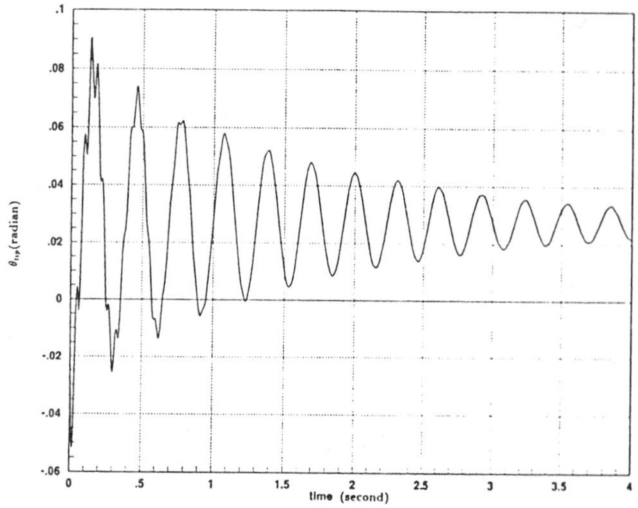

Fig. 3: Open-Loop Dynamic Response of θ_{tip}

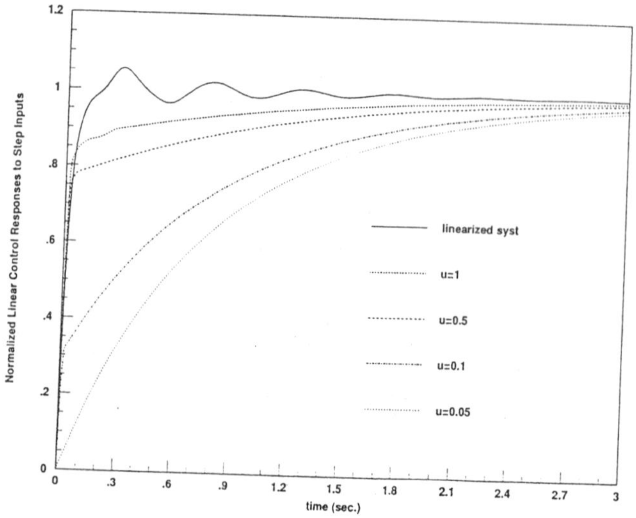

Fig. 6: Normalized Linear Control Responses to Step Inputs u

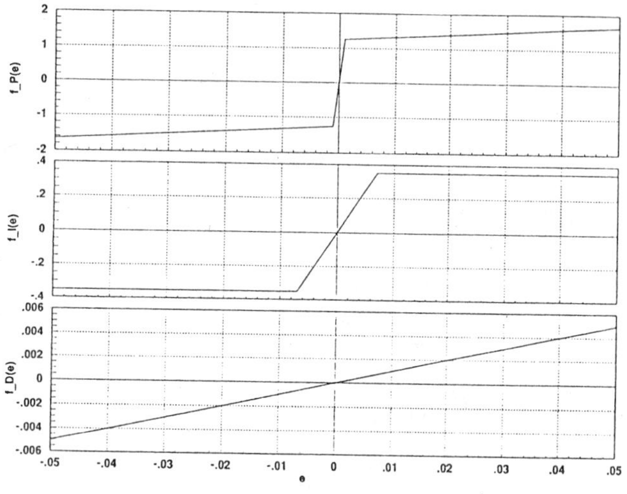

Fig. 4: Results of SIDF Inversion

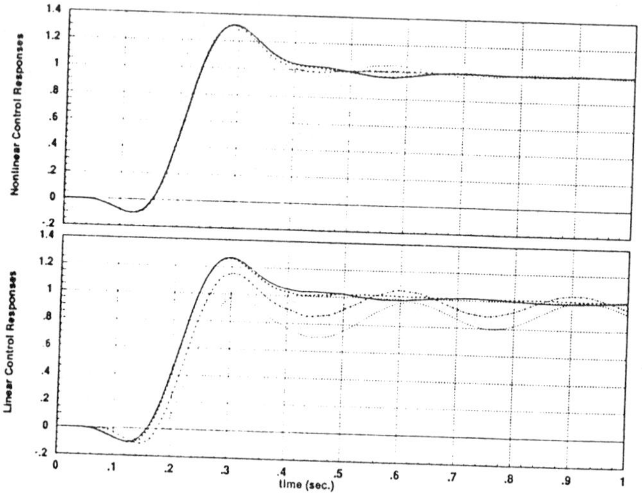

Fig. 7: Normalized Closed-Loop Responses of θ_{tip}

—: $\theta_{tip}^{ref} = 1(rad.)$, - - - : $\theta_{tip}^{ref} = .5(rad.)$,
- · - : $\theta_{tip}^{ref} = .1(rad.)$, · · · : $\theta_{tip}^{ref} = .05(rad.)$,

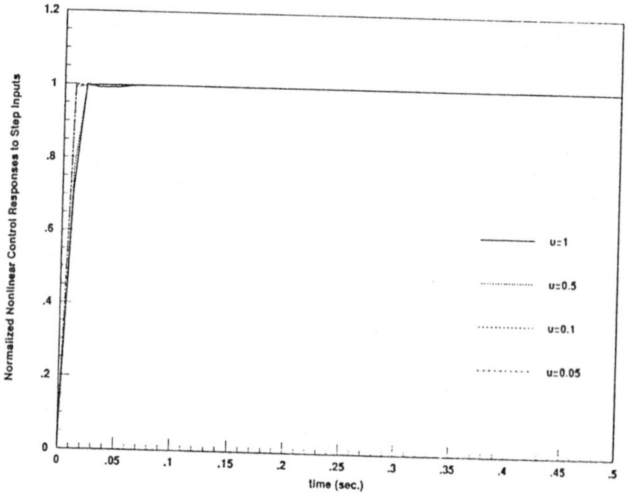

Fig. 5: Normalized Nonlinear Control Responses to Step Inputs u

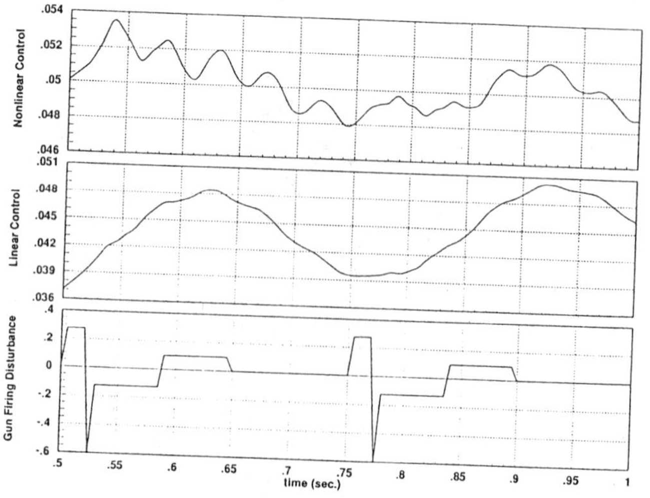

Fig. 8: Responses of θ_{tip} to Gun Firing Disturbance

Proceedings of the
American Control Conference
San Francisco, California • June 1993

Hybrid Optimal Control of Turret-Gun System†

J. L. Zhang and L. S. Shieh
Electrical Engineering Department
University of Houston
4800 Calhoun
Houston, TX 77204-4793

Abstract

This paper presents a hybrid technique for optimal discrete-time control of a continuous-time nonlinear Turret-gun system. For effective design of this nonlinear Turret-gun system with multi-flexible modes, the linearized state-space representation of the nonlinear system is block-decoupled into a multi-time scale structure using the fast and stable matrix sign algorithm. Then, to enhance the robust stability and robust performance of the linearized system, an optimal regional-pole placement technique is applied to design a continuous-time optimal state-feedback control law with regional-pole constraints for individual block-decoupled subsystems. For digital control of the continuous-time Turret-gun system, the designed continuous-time state-feedback control law need to be converted into an equivalent discrete-time state-feedback control law, using the recently developed digital redesign technique. Since the states of the nonlinear Turret-gun system are inaccessible, a digital observer needs to be constructed for practical digital implementation of the digitally redesigned discrete-time state-feedback control law. In this paper, a reduced-order robust observer is established to reconstruct the true state of the nonlinear system. The designed results are demonstrated by the digital simulation of the controlled nonlinear model and the practical real-time control of the ATB-1000 testbed.

1. Introduction

The Turret-gun system has inherent hard nonlinearities such as Coulomb friction, backlash, and saturation, and it is subjected to external disturbances such as the firing disturbances and base motion, as well as, to parameter variations caused by thermal effects on gun barrel and torsional stiffness. The primary objective of the Turret-gun servo control system is to rapidly stabilize and accurately point the gun at a target in the presence of the above-mentioned nonlinearities, disturbances, and model uncertainties. This requires that the designed servo control system to have the properties of robustness, rapid and accurate tracking, and disturbance and noise rejection. To develop, demonstrate, and validate the advanced algorithms for the Turret-gun control system, the advanced weapon tracking testbed (ATB-1000) was developed at the Army Research Development Engineering Center to facilitate a realistic simulation of Turret-gun system (which has a prescribed sampling period) in laboratory environment [1]. The detailed linear and nonlinear models, developed by Integrated System Inc. (ISI), are used as the basis for this study.

The primary objective of this paper is to develop a digitally implementable optimal controller for the continuous-time nonlinear Turret-gun system so that the responses of the system converge at an appropriate speed and whether vibrating modes if any, are well damped.

† supported by the U.S. Army Research Office under contract DAAL-03-91-G0106 and the NASA-Johnson Space Center under grant NAG-9-380

The hybrid controller design methodology developed in this paper can be briefly described as follows.

A cascaded internal model (which contains an integrator) and a feedback integrator are inserted into the continuous-time linearized model to attenuate nonlinear effects and firing disturbances. For effective design of the above integrated large-scale linear model, the augmented state-space representation is block-decoupled into a multi-time scale structure using the fast and stable matrix sign algorithm [2,3]. Then, the linear quadratic regulator (LQR) approach [4] is utilized to design a robust optimal state-feedback control law. The LQR approach [4] does not involve a time-consuming trial and error procedure to determine the weighting matrices associated with a quadratic cost function. The obtained control law can optimally place the closed-loop poles of the above integrated linear model within the common region of an open sector and to the left hand side of a line parallel to the imaginary axis in the complex s-plane. Thus, the designed system provides a prescribed degree of stability, while its responses converge with an appropriate speed and if any vibrating modes are present, will be well damped. Moreover, for digital control of the continuous-time Turret-gun system, the recently developed digital redesign techniques [5,6] are applied for digital redesign of the inserted continuous-time internal models and the developed continuous-time optimal state-feedback control law. The obtained digitally redesigned state-feedback controller enables to closely match the states of the digitally controlled closed-loop system with those of the original continuous-time closed-loop system for a relatively large sampling period. During the digital simulation of the designed closed-loop nonlinear model, we observe that the designed optimal state-feedback control law is able to preserve the inherent robustness in the presence of the aforementioned hard nonlinearities if the state-feedback controller is implemented on the true state. This observation will be verified by the digital simulation of the designed closed-loop nonlinear system in which the state-feedback controller is implemented on the true state of the nonlinear system. Unfortunately, the nonlinear system state is not accessible for the purpose of the real-time state-feedback control. In order to estimate the true state and preserve the robustness of the designed closed-loop linear system, a reduced-order observer with the property of complete loop transfer recovery [7] is established.

2. Design formulation

A linear model obtained from the given nonlinear model of the ATB-1000 test fixture is described by the following state-space equations:

$$\begin{aligned}\dot{x}_o &= A_o x_o + B_o u_o \\ y_o &= C_o x_o\end{aligned} \tag{1}$$

where $x_o \in \mathcal{R}^{10\times 1}$, $u_o \in \mathcal{R}$, $y_o \in \mathcal{R}^{6\times 1}$, and

$$A_o = \begin{bmatrix} 0 & 58.553 & 0 & 0 & 0 & 0 & 0 & 0 & 0 & 0 \\ -5.758 & -5.776 & -11.356 & -7.651 & 0.138 & 0.212 & 0.003 & 0.017 & 11.885 & 1.221 \\ 0 & 0 & 0 & 39.323 & 0 & 0 & 0 & 0 & 0 & 0 \\ -5.138 & -5.154 & -33.338 & -7.718 & 0.123 & 0.189 & 0.002 & 0.015 & 10.606 & 1.090 \\ 0 & 0 & 0 & 0 & 0 & 89.357 & 0 & 0 & 0 & 0 \\ 22.962 & 23.034 & 45.288 & 30.510 & -214.569 & -4.923 & -0.010 & -0.066 & -47.399 & -4.871 \\ 0 & 0 & 0 & 0 & 0 & 0 & 0 & 371.373 & 0 & 0 \\ 60.981 & 61.174 & 120.275 & 81.030 & -1.464 & -2.241 & -398.966 & -11.531 & -125.882 & -12.936 \\ 0 & 0 & 0 & 0 & 0 & 0 & 0 & 0 & 0 & 41.096 \\ 33.735 & 4.939 & 66.537 & 6.543 & -0.810 & -0.181 & -0.015 & -0.014 & -69.638 & -7.156 \end{bmatrix}$$

$$B_o = [0 \;\; 0 \;\; 0 \;\; 0 \;\; 0 \;\; 0 \;\; 0 \;\; 0 \;\; 0 \;\; 5.000]^T,$$

$$C_o = \begin{bmatrix} 0 & 0 & 0 & 0 & 0 & 0 & 0 & 0 & 5.888 & 0 \\ 0 & 0 & 0 & 0 & 0 & 0 & 0 & 0 & 0 & 15.597 \\ 2.709 & 0 & 5.344 & 0 & -0.065 & 0 & -0.001 & 0 & 0 & 0 \\ 0.003 & 0.003 & 21.178 & 0.004 & 5.519 & -0.000 & 0.149 & 0 & -0.006 & -0.001 \\ 0.001 & 0.001 & 35.183 & 0.001 & 0.324 & 0 & 0.540 & 0 & -0.002 & -0.000 \\ 0.008 & 0.008 & -63.487 & 0.010 & -41.737 & -0.000 & 10.677 & 0 & -0.016 & -0.002 \end{bmatrix}.$$

The effect of nonlinearities is simply ignored in this model, but it will be considered during the formulation of the controller structure. The six outputs of the system which are considered are turret motor yaw, turret motor rate, inertial wheel yaw, strain gauge 1, strain gauge 2, and tip acceleration. Although there exist other measurable outputs on the ATB-1000 test fixture, they are not practically accessible for measurements in a real Turret-gun system. It can be noticed that the elements of the system matrices in (1) are obtained from the given nonlinear model (NL_ATB4) using the MATRIXx *lin* function, with all its nonlinear components removed. The system matrices are scaled to avoid numerical computation complications due to the iterative nature of the design method employed in this paper. The objective of scaling is to minimize the spread of the singular values of the system matrix A_o. The outputs of the system are also scaled to appropriate ranges.

In order to reduce the effect of nonlinearities and to increase the robustness of the designed control system, an internal model which contains an integrator is inserted before the system. The steady-state error of the barrel tip position caused by nonlinearities is eliminated by an additional integrator appended to the third output of y_o, i.e., the inertia wheel yaw. Here the inertia wheel yaw is used instead of barrel tip position due to the non-availability of the tip sensor. With these two integrators, the overall augmented system becomes a 12th order system as shown in Fig. 1. The augmented state-space equations are given as

$$\begin{aligned} \dot{x} &= Ax + Bu \\ y &= Cx \end{aligned} \tag{2}$$

where

$$x = \begin{bmatrix} x_{i1} \\ x_o \\ x_{i2} \end{bmatrix} \in \mathcal{R}^{12\times 1}, \; u \in \mathcal{R}, \; y \in \mathcal{R}$$

$x_{i1} \triangleq$ output of the first integrator

$x_{i2} \triangleq$ output of the second integrator

$$A = \begin{bmatrix} 0 & 0_{1\times 10} & 0 \\ B_o & A_o & 0_{10\times 1} \\ 0 & -C_{o3} & 0 \end{bmatrix} \in \mathcal{R}^{12\times 12}$$

$$B = \begin{bmatrix} 1 \\ 0_{10\times 1} \\ 0 \end{bmatrix} \in \mathcal{R}^{12\times 1}, \; C = [0 \;\; 0_{1\times 10} \;\; 1] \in \mathcal{R}^{1\times 12}$$

The "r" in Fig. 1 is the reference input or the command input for the inertia wheel yaw (which is identical to the tip position at the steady state). Since "r" is considered as an external disturbance in the design of the optimal state feedback control law, it does not appear in (2)

The eigenvalues of the system in (2) are $\{0.0, 0.0, -4.50, -2.11 \pm j27.57, -5.76 \pm j59.61, -2.52 \pm j138.43, -5.77 \pm j384.88\}$. It can be observed that the eigenvalues have large spread. Although the optimal regional-pole placement method [4] can be directly used to optimally place the closed-loop poles in the previously mentioned region, a rather large feedback gain would be obtained as a result of the large eigenvalue spread. This is undesirable due to the presence of nonlinearities and unmodelled dynamics. Since the state-feedback gain is to be connected to the observed or reconstructed states, any deviation of the observed or reconstructed state from the true state will significantly affect the control effort. For example, the controller may saturate the actuator, even worsen, or destabilize the closed-loop system. Therefore, it is advantageous to decompose this large-scale and stiff system into a completely decoupled multi-time scale structure so that each subsystem has distinct characteristics and it can be designed accordingly.

The multi-stage design algorithm developed by Tsai, *et al.* [5] is modified and utilized here to design the system in (2). The design procedures can be described as follows:

Step 1. The eigenvalues of the augmented system in (2) are divided into four groups that are located in four circular rings, $[0, r_1], [r_1, r_2], [r_2, r_3]$, and $[r_3, r_4]$, as shown in Fig. 2, where $r_1 = 15$, $r_2 = 100$, $r_3 = 200$, and $r_4 = 400$. The first circular ring contains the eigenvalues $\{0, 0, 0, -4.5\}$; the second circular ring $\{-2.11 \pm j27.57, -5.76 \pm j59.61\}$; the third circular ring $\{-2.52 \pm j138.43\}$; and the fourth circular ring $\{-5.77 \pm j384.88\}$. A block modal matrix [2] is constructed by using the fast and stable matrix sign algorithm [3], which decomposes the original system into four decoupled subsystems corresponding to the four groups of eigenvalues. The modal matrix [2] is given as

$$M_s = [S_4 \; S_3 \; S_2 \; S_1] \tag{3}$$

where

$$S_i \triangleq \text{ind}[\text{sign}^+_{(r_{i-1}, r_i)}(h(A))] \in \mathcal{R}^{12\times n_i}, \; 1 \le i \le 4$$

$$\text{and} \quad n_1 = 4, n_2 = 4, n_3 = 2, n_4 = 2$$

$$\text{sign}^+_{(r_{i-1}, r_i)}(h(A)) \triangleq \frac{1}{2}[\text{sign}_{(r_{i-1}}(h(A)) - \text{sign}_{(r_i)}(h(A))]$$

$$h(A) = (A - r_i I_n)(A + r_i I_n)^{-1}$$

In the above definitions, ind$(\cdot)$ represents the collection of the linearly independent column vectors of $(\cdot)$ and $r_0 = 0$, $\text{sign}_{(0)}(h(A)) = I_n$.

Then

$$A_d = M_s^{-1}AM_s = \text{block diag}(A_{d4}, A_{d3}, A_{d2}, A_{d1})$$
$$B_d = M_s^{-1}B = \begin{bmatrix} B_{d4} \\ B_{d3} \\ B_{d2} \\ B_{d1} \end{bmatrix} \quad (4)$$

where $A_{di} \in \mathcal{R}^{n_i \times n_i}$, $B_{di} \in \mathcal{R}^{n_i \times 1}$.
Step 2: Set $i = 1$, $\bar{A} = A_d =$ block diag$[\bar{A}_4\bar{A}_3, \bar{A}_2, \bar{A}_1]$, $\bar{B} = B_d =$ block diag$[B_4^T, B_3^T, B_2^T, B_1^T]^T$, $M_1 = I_n$, and the feedback gain $\bar{K}_c = 0_{m\times n}$.
Step 3: The subsystem considered for design at this stage is $(\bar{A}_i, \bar{B}_i)$. Design this subsystem by using the optimal regional-pole placement method [4]. Let the immediate optimal feedback gain be $\bar{K}_i$ and the corresponding continuous-time closed-loop system be $(\bar{A}_{c_i}, \bar{B}_i)$.
Step 4: Update

$$\bar{K}_c := \bar{K}_c + [0_{m\times(n-n_i)}, \bar{K}_i]M_1^{-1} \quad (5a)$$

$$\bar{A} := \bar{A} - \bar{B}[0_{m\times(n-n_i)}, \bar{K}_i] = \begin{bmatrix} \tilde{A}_i & W_i \\ 0_{n_i\times(n-n_i)} & \bar{A}_{c_i} \end{bmatrix} \quad (5b)$$

where $\tilde{A}_i =$ block diag $[\hat{A}_{ci}, \hat{A}_i]$, $W_i = -[\bar{B}_i^T, \hat{B}_i^T]^T\bar{K}_i$. The n_i is the order of the subsystem that is being designed at this stage. The dimensions of the matrices $\tilde{A}_i$ and W_i are $(n-n_i)\times(n-n_i)$, $(n-n_i)\times n_i$, respectively.
Step 5: Block-diagonalize the partially designed system $\bar{A}$ and move the last block of $\bar{A}$ in (5b) (viz., $\bar{A}_{c_i}$) to the first block, via a transformation matrix M_2 which is given as

$$M_2 = \begin{bmatrix} L_i & I_{n-n_i} \\ I_{n_i} & 0_{n_i\times(n-n_i)} \end{bmatrix}, \quad M_2^{-1} = \begin{bmatrix} 0_{n_i\times(n-n_i)} & I_{n_i} \\ I_{n-n_i} & -L_i \end{bmatrix} \quad (6a)$$

The matrix L_i $(\in \mathcal{R}^{(n-n_i)\times n_i})$ can be solved from the following Lyapunov equation,

$$\tilde{A}_i L_i - L_i\bar{A}_{c_i} + W_i = 0_{(n-n_i)\times n_i} \quad (6b)$$

The transformed system is

$$\bar{A} := M_2^{-1}\bar{A}M_2 = \begin{bmatrix} \bar{A}_{c_i} & 0_{n_i\times(n-n_i)} \\ 0_{(n-n_i)\times n_i} & \tilde{A}_i \end{bmatrix} \quad (6c)$$

$$\bar{B} := M_2^{-1}\bar{B} = [\bar{B}_i^T, (\tilde{B}_i - L_i\bar{B}_i)^T]^T \quad (6d)$$

where $\tilde{B}_i = [B_c^T, \hat{B}_i^T]^T$. Accumulate the transformations in $M_1 := M_1M_2$.
Step 6: Set $i := i+1$. If $i > k$ (k is the number of time-scales. In this specific case, it is 4), then proceed to Step 7; else, go to Step 3.
Step 7: The state-feedback gain for the original system is obtained as $K_c = \bar{K}_cM_s^{-1}$.
Note that the above described design procedure has been utilized in MATRIXx as user defined functions by the authors. The Lyapunov equations and Riccati equations are solved by using the matrix sign algorithm [3,6].

For the use of the optimal regional-pole placement technique [4] to design individual block-decoupled subsystems, we choose the prescribed degree of stability for each subsystem as $h_1 = 15, h_2 = 20, h_3 = 15$, and $h_4 = 0$ (since the fourth subsystem in (4) is not being designed for the reason explained later). The state-feedback gain is computed as

$$K_c = [356.0 \;\; 11959.0 \;\; 64562.0 \;\; 18317.0 \;\; -11018.0 \;\; 24168.0 \;\; 4919.0 \;\; -1.0 \;\; -1.0 \;\; 18289.0 \;\; 11197.0 \;\; -40977.0] \quad (7)$$

The obtained closed-loop eigenvalues are $\{-25.48, -29.99, -30.00, -30.00, -37.85 \pm 27.65j, -67.85 \pm 67.81j, -27.48 \pm 138.43j, -5.77 \pm 384.88j\}$. The last two closed-loop eigenvalues remain the same as the open-loop eigenvalues since the corresponding 4th subsystem in (4) (i.e., the 4th block) has not being designed. The reason for not designing the 4th subsystem is that the eigenvalues of this subsystem are closely associated with the 3rd flexible mode of the gun-barrel subsystem, whose operating frequency falls within the the noise signal spectrum of the ATB-1000 testbed. Any attempt to control this mode will inevitably introduce predominant noise signals into the control signal which may destabilize the controlled system. This phenomenon was observed while implementing a controller with designed 4th subsystem (here the degree of stability h_4 has chosen as 10) for the real-time control of the ATB-1000 testbed. Though the digital simulation of the designed nonlinear closed-loop model was quite satisfactory, the real-time control of the ATB-1000 testbed resulted in unstable response from the system. Analysis of frequency response of the observer/state-feedback gain subsystem revealed that there exists a relatively large gain in the frequency region where the sensor noise is predominant, lead to this problem. This problem was tackled by redesigning the controller by choosing $h_4 = 0$ (omitting the 4th subsystem from design) and also by narrowing the bandwidth of the observer make it immune to noise. As a result, the controlled closed-loop system became stable when this modified controller was implemented for real-time control of the ATB-1000 testbed, even the undesired large loop gain was eliminated.

3. Digital implementation

3.1. Digital redesign

In order to implement the designed continuous-time state-feedback control law in the sampled-data environment of the ATB-1000 test fixture which has a prescribed sampling period $T = 0.0025$ sec, the digital redesign technique [5,6] is used to convert the continuous-time control gain K_c in (7) to an equivalent discrete-time control gain K_d. The state-feedback gain K_d is represented as

$$K_d = \frac{1}{2}(I_m + \frac{1}{2}K_cH)^{-1}K_c(I_n + G) \quad (8)$$

where K_c is given in (7), $G = e^{AT}$, $H = \int_0^T e^{A\tau}\,d\tau$, and $T = 0.0025$ sec. The K_d is computed as

$$K_d = [K_{d1}, K_{do}, K_{d2}] \quad (9)$$

where

$$K_{d1} = 276.0$$
$$K_{do} = [7768.0 \;\; 40783.0 \;\; 12262.0 \;\; -6293.0 \;\; 13711.0 \;\; 4934.0 \;\; 0 \;\; -1.0 \;\; 10949.0 \;\; 7608.0]$$
$$K_{d2} = -25528.0$$

The digital control law is then written as:

$$\begin{aligned} u_d(kT) &= -K_dx_d(kT) \\ &= -K_{d1}x_{di1}(kT) - K_{do}x_{do}(kT) - K_{d2}x_{di2}(kT) \end{aligned} \quad (10)$$

Furthermore, the inserted integrators can be discretized by using the Tustin approximation: $\frac{1}{s} \to \frac{2}{T}\frac{(1+z^{-1})}{(1-z^{-1})}$.

To demonstrate the robustness of this designed optimal state-feedback control law in the presence of the aforementioned hard nonlinearities, digital simulation of the designed closed-loop nonlinear system is carried out using the true state. The simulation results are shown in Fig. 4-5 and are quite satisfactory.

3.2. Reduced-order digital observer with complete loop transfer recovery

For the implementation of the digital controller in (10), an observer is required to reconstruct the inaccessible state. Although a full-order observer can be designed for the linear system in (1), the estimated state has significant deviation from the true state when the hard nonlinearities are present in the system. As a result, the closed-loop nonlinear system no longer preserves the robustness and performance of the designed closed-loop linear system. In this paper, a reduced-order robust observer with complete loop transfer recovery [7] is established to reconstruct the true state. The estimated state using this robust observer is very close to the true state of the nonlinear system; thus, the robustness of the optimal state-feedback controlled linear system is preserved.

The robust observer design problem [7] is briefly described as follows.

Consider a designed closed-loop system given by

$$\begin{aligned} \dot{x}(t) &= Ax(t) + Bu(t) \\ y(t) &= Cx(t) \\ u(t) &= Kx(t) \end{aligned} \tag{11}$$

where $x(t) \in \mathcal{R}^{n\times 1}$, $u(t) \in \mathcal{R}^{m\times 1}$, $y(t) \in \mathcal{R}^{p\times 1}$, and $p \geq m$. The corresponding reduce-order observer is given as

$$\dot{z}(t) = Fz(t) + Ly(t) + TBu(t), z(t) \in \mathcal{R}^{(n-p)\times 1} \tag{12a}$$

$$\hat{x}(t) = \begin{bmatrix} C \\ T \end{bmatrix}^{-1} \begin{bmatrix} y(t) \\ z(t) \end{bmatrix} \tag{12b}$$

$$K\hat{X}(t) = Nz(t) + My(t) \tag{12c}$$

where $F \in \mathcal{R}^{(n-p)\times(n-p)}$ is an arbitrarily assigned stable matrix. For the existence of the reduced-order observer in (12), the necessary and sufficient conditions are

$$TA - FT = LC \tag{13a}$$

and

$$K = NT + MC \tag{13b}$$

The loop transfer function of this observer system, measured at the break point $u(t)$ is

$$L_o(s) = [I_n - N(sI_n - F)^{-1}TB]^{-1}[M + N(sI_n - F)^{-1}L]G(s), \tag{14a}$$

where $G(s) = C(sI_n - A)^{-1}B$ and I_n is an $n \times n$ identity matrix. Also, the loop transfer function, measured at the break point $K\hat{x}(t)$ is

$$L(s) = MG(s) + N(sI_n - F)^{-1}[TB + LG(s)], \tag{14b}$$

and the loop transfer function of the direct state-feedback system is

$$L_s(s) = K(sI_n - A)^{-1}B. \tag{14c}$$

It has been shown in [7] that $L(s) = L_s(s)$. The condition for the complete loop transfer recovery can be stated as $L_o(s) = L_s(s) = L(s)$. To satisfy this condition, we need $TB = 0$ or $N(sI_n - F)^{-1}TB = 0$.

Note that $TB = 0$ implies that the observer in (12) is not directly related to the control input $u(t)$. That is, the estimated state $\hat{x}(t)$ is computed only from the output measurements. For the nonlinear system under investigation, all the nonlinearities (i.e., motor friction, inertial wheel friction, and backlash) can be viewed as certain additive signals to the inputs of the corresponding linear system. For instance, if only the motor friction is considered, the nonlinear system reduces to the linear system in (1) with the control input $u(t)$ chosen as

$$u(t) = \bar{u}(t) - f_c * \text{sign}(x_2(t)) \tag{15}$$

where $\bar{u}(t)$ is the linear control input, f_c is the friction coefficient, and $x_2(t)$ is the motor velocity. The significance of this observation is that the performance of the reduced-order observer with complete loop transfer recovery will not be affected by the nonlinear term in (15). Thus, the robustness of the optimal state-feedback controlled linear system is preserved.

The algorithm proposed in [8] is utilized in this paper to design the reduced-order observer in (13) with $TB = 0$. The design procedure is described as follows.

Step 1. Let the QR factorization of B be computed as

$$B = [W_1 \; W_2] \begin{bmatrix} S \\ 0 \end{bmatrix}, \tag{16a}$$

where $S \in \mathcal{R}^{m\times m}$, $W_1 \in \mathcal{R}^{m\times m}$, and $W_2 \in \mathcal{R}^{m\times(n-m)}$.

Step 2. Set $A_1 = W_2^T A W_1 \in \mathcal{R}^{(n-m)\times m}$, $A_2 = W_2^T A W_2 \in \mathcal{R}^{(n-m)\times(n-m)}$, $C_1 = CW_1 \in \mathcal{R}^{p\times m}$, and $C_2 = CW_2 \in \mathcal{R}^{p\times(n-m)}$.

Step 3. Let the QR factorization of C_1 be computed as

$$C_1 = Q \begin{bmatrix} \hat{R} \\ 0 \end{bmatrix}, \tag{16b}$$

where $Q \in \mathcal{R}^{p\times p}$, and $\hat{R} \in \mathcal{R}^{m\times m}$.

Step 4. Set

$$Q^T C_2 = \begin{bmatrix} E_1 \\ E_2 \end{bmatrix}, \tag{16c}$$

where $E_1 \in \mathcal{R}^{m\times(n-m)}$, and $E_2 \in \mathcal{R}^{(p-m)\times(n-m)}$.

Step 5. Solve the following Sylvester matrix equation:

$$Z(A_2 - A_1\hat{R}^{-1}E_1) - FZ = L_2E_2, \tag{16d}$$

where $Z \in \mathcal{R}^{(n-p)\times(n-m)}$, and $L_2 \in \mathcal{R}^{(n-p)\times(p-m)}$ is arbitrarily chosen.

Step 6. Set $L_1 = ZA_1\hat{R}^{-1}$ and $L = [L_1 \; L_2]Q^T$

Step 7. Set $T = ZW_2^T$.

Step 8. If $[C^T \; T^T]^T$ is singular or ill-conditioned, change the entries of L_2 and/or F, and go to step 5; otherwise proceed to next step.

Step 9. Set $[M, N] = K \begin{bmatrix} C \\ T \end{bmatrix}^{-1}$.

The parameters of designed reduced-order robust observer for the system in (1) and the state-feedback gain in (7) are

$$F = \begin{bmatrix} -40 & 0 & 0 & 0 \\ 0 & -50 & 0 & 0 \\ 0 & 0 & -60 & 0 \\ 0 & 0 & 0 & -90 \end{bmatrix} \tag{17a}$$

$$L = \begin{bmatrix} -9.990 & -14.987 & 0 & 67.001 & 0.000 & 67.603 \\ 0 & 4.259 & 67.000 & 0.000 & 0 & 0.000 \\ 0.006 & 4.500 & 0 & 135.000 & 0 & -0.001 \\ 0.008 & 5.221 & 0 & -0.000 & 135.200 & 67.600 \end{bmatrix} \tag{17b}$$

$$\begin{aligned} M = [&17987.416 \quad -5344.457 \quad 1083192.343 \\ &-490257.142 \quad -324160.594 \quad 49353.949] \end{aligned} \tag{17c}$$

$$N = [68560.462 - 22188.684 \quad 135745.660 \quad 1006980.333] \tag{17d}$$

with the design parameters chosen as

$$L_2 = \begin{bmatrix} 10 & 0 & 67 & 0 & 67.6 \\ 0 & 67 & 0 & 0 & 0 \\ 0 & 0 & 135 & 0 & 0 \\ 0 & 0 & 0 & 135.2 & 67.6 \end{bmatrix} \quad (17e)$$

The discretized version of the observer is given as

$$F_d = \begin{bmatrix} 0.905 & 0 & 0 & 0 \\ 0 & 0.883 & 0 & 0 \\ 0 & 0 & 0.861 & 0 \\ 0 & 0 & 0 & 0.799 \end{bmatrix} \quad (18a)$$

$$L_d = \begin{bmatrix} -0.024 & -0.036 & 0 & 0.159 & 0 & 0.161 \\ 0 & 0.010 & 0.158 & 0 & 0 & 0 \\ 0 & 0.010 & 0 & 0.313 & 0 & 0 \\ 0 & 0.012 & 0 & 0 & 0.303 & 0.151 \end{bmatrix} \quad (18b)$$

$$M_d = [13175.913 \quad -3578.112 \quad 510706.489 \quad -295773.175 \quad -283747.930 \quad 37917.663] \quad (18c)$$

$$N_d = [62281.426 \quad -15004.876 \quad 87126.347 \quad 636093.747] \quad (18d)$$

where $T_s = 0.0025$ sec, $F_d = e^{FT_s}$, $L_d = \int_0^{T_s} e^{F(T_s-\tau)} L \, d\tau$, and $[M_d, N_d] = K_{d2} \begin{bmatrix} C \\ T \end{bmatrix}^{-1}$

Note that it is very important to check the singularity or the condition number of the matrix $[C^T \; T^T]^T$. Although the entries of the matrix L_2 can be chosen arbitrarily, it is advantageous to choose L_2 such that the condition number of the matrix $[C^T \; T^T]^T$ is minimized. It has been observed that the magnitudes of the designed feedback gain matrices M and N tend to be small if the condition number of the matrix $[C^T \; T^T]^T$ is small.

4. Simulation results

The digitally controlled ATB-1000 test fixture with a prescribed sampling period $T = 0.0025$ is shown in Fig. 3. Nonlinear simulations are carried out using the MATRIXx simulation tools and the results are shown in Figs. 4-5. Nonlinear simulations of the closed-loop systems which use the state-feedback controller implemented on the true state, and the state-feedback controller implemented on the estimated state are shown in the same figures for comparison. The simulation results are quite satisfactory.

5. Conclusions

A hybrid technique for optimal discrete-time control of a continuous-time nonlinear Turret-gun system has been proposed in this paper. A continuous-time linear state-feedback control law has been designed using the optimal regional-pole placement technique. This continuous-time control law is then converted to an equivalent discrete-time control law for digital implementation aided by a digital redesign technique. A reduced-order robust observer which provides complete recovery of the loop transfer function and the robustness of state-feedback controlled systems has been established to reconstruct the true state of the nonlinear system. Finally, the optimal digital state-feedback controller and the reduced-order robust observer is integrated into an implementable digital controller for real-time control of the ATB-1000 test fixture. The digital simulation of the designed nonlinear Turret-gun system is quite satisfactory.

References

[1] M. Mattice, N. Coleman, S. Banks, J. C. Juang, and C. F. Lin, "Robust weapon control systems design", *Proc. of American Control Conference*, pp.429–433, 1992

[2] L. S. Shieh, H. M. Dib, and R.E. Yates, "Separation of matrix eigenvalues and structural decomposition of large-scale systems," *IEE Proc. Pt. D*, 133(2):90–96, 1986.

[3] L. S. Shieh, S.R.Lian, and B.C. Mcinnis, "Fast and stable algorithm for computing the principal square root of a complex matrix," *IEEE Trans. Automatic Control*, AC-32(9):820–822,1987.

[4] L. S. Shieh, H. M. Dib, and S. Ganesan, "Continuous-time quadratic regulators and pseudo-continuous-time quadratic regulators with pole placement in a specific region," *IEE Proc. Pt. D*, 134(5):338–346, 1987.

[5] J. S. H. Tsai, L. S. Shieh, J. L. Zhang, and P. C. Coleman, "Digital redesign of pseudo-continuous-time suboptimal regulators for large-scale discrete systems", *Control-Theory and Advanced Technology*,5(1):37–65,1989.

[6] L. S. Shieh, X. M. Zhao, and J. W. Sunkel, "Hybrid state-space self-tuning control using dual-rate sampling," *IEE Proc. Pt. D*, 138(1):50–58, 1991.

[7] C. Tsui, "New approach to robust observer design," *Int J. Control*, 47(3):745–751, 1988.

[8] J. B. Barlow, M. M. Monahemi, and D. P. O'Leary, " Constrained matrix Sylvester Equations," *SIAM J. Matrix Anal. Appl.*, 13(1):1–9, 1992.

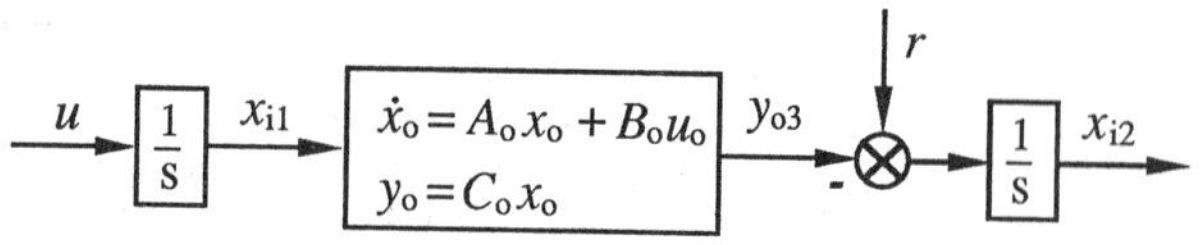

Fig. 1 Augmented system

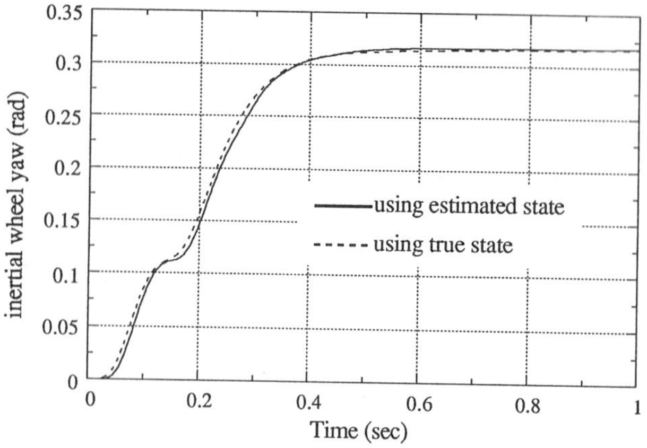

Fig. 4 Step response of digitally controlled nonlinear closed-loop system.

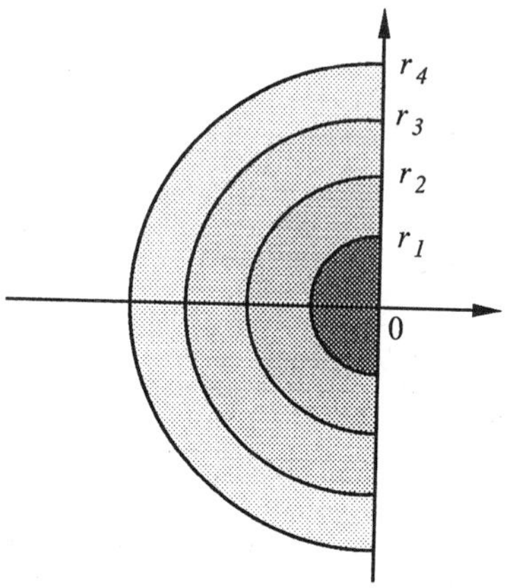

Fig. 2 The four circular rings of interest

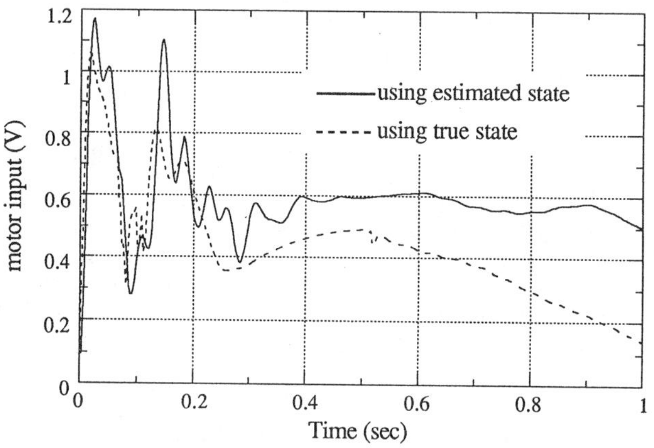

Fig. 5 Control signal (u_d)

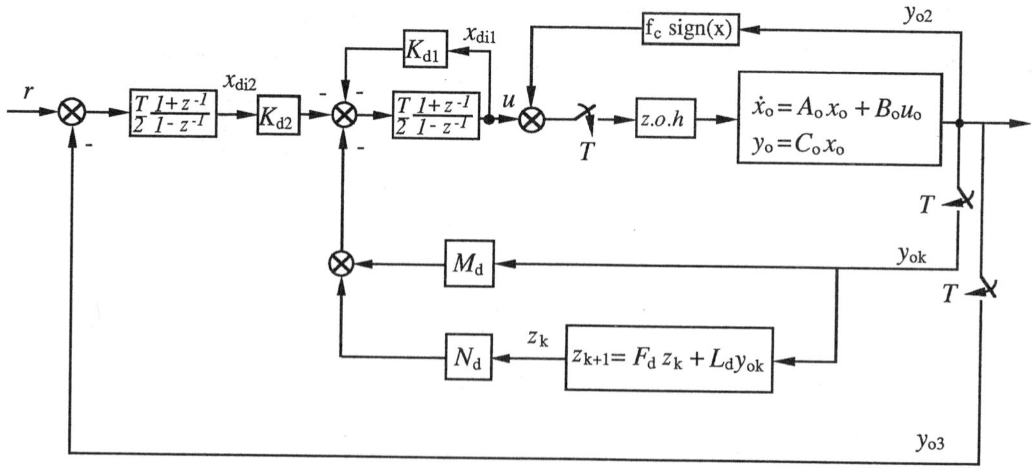

Fig. 3 Designed digitally controlled system

Proceedings of the
American Control Conference
San Francisco, California • June 1993

Real-Time Implementation Issues in Nonlinear Model Inversion

M. Güntekin Kabuli   Sudarshan P. Bhat   Robert L. Kosut *

Integrated Systems Inc., 3260 Jay Street, Santa Clara, CA 95054-3309

Abstract

A real-time control problem associated with a flexible testbed fixture is considered. The regulated variable is the deflection at the tip of a flexible beam attached to an inertia wheel base which is subject to a disturbance torque. The control torque affects the base wheel through a coupling which has both compliance and variable backlash. The performance specifications include disturbance attenuation and rapid slewing at the tip. The designs are based on an analytically derived continuous-time model which is tuned in accordance with the measured data. The model consists of an interconnection of a linear time-invariant part and piecewise-linear algebraic nonlinearities modeling friction and backlash. The candidate designs must be based on available measurements only; moreover, the final discrete-time control law must be executable with the real-time controller hardware limitations at hand.

Introduction

The first design approach is based on the linear model where the nonlinearities due to friction and backlash are set to zero. A single tone additive actuation disturbance is attenuated at the regulated output by incorporating the disturbance model in the feedback loop. Designs are based on a discretized plant model and implemented on an Integrated Systems AC-100 real-time control processor.

The second approach is a case study based on feedback linearization where a single parametric nonlinearity is included in the design model. Due to the nonminimum-phase zero dynamics characteristics from the actuation to the tip of the flexible beam, the study focuses on the base wheel position and slewing performance. We study the sensitivity of two certainty equivalence based control laws for the frozen parameter case. Based on the least sensitive non-adaptive design, an adaptive slewing controller is designed. This approach for slewing design is later modified to obtain a *baseline* design for attenuating a measured multi-tone disturbance. The disturbance model is based on a periodic torque waveform affecting the wheel base after the coupling driven by the actuator motor. The resulting continuous time control law was simulated to verify the performance enhancement due to the signal generator in the proposed feedforward/feedback scheme. One of the major tasks for real-time implementability was to obtain a discrete-time approximation to the continuous-time simulations of the nonlinear control law subject to the sampling rate and computational load limitations imposed by the real-time controller hardware. The approximate discretization was downloaded to the real-time controller processor and the continuous-time versus discrete-time simulation comparison proved to be satisfactory. The disturbance rejection part is a baseline design which is currently unimplementable unless the disturbance can be measured; however, the current discrete-time control law is an implementable candidate for real-time slewing tests.

Design Approach 1

An adaptive controller was designed for rejecting single tone sinusoidal disturbance in a prespecified frequency range. The controller consists of an inner-loop, robustly stabilizing component and an outer-loop, adaptive error rejection component. The control design was accomplished in three steps (see Figure 1) .

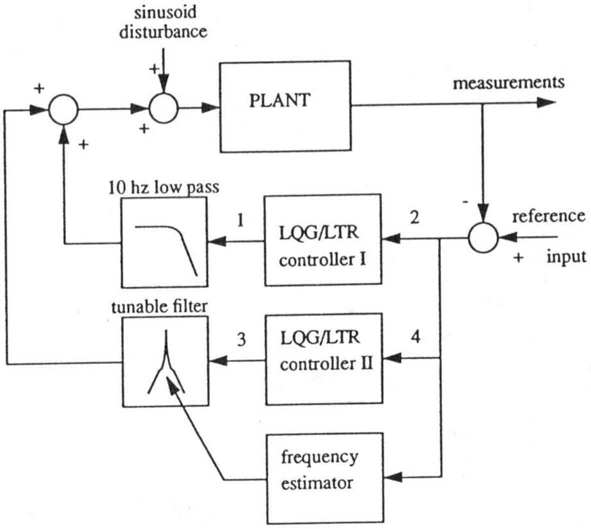

Figure 1:

The first step was the design of the inner loop controller. A 10 hz low pass filter was included in the loop to avoid any destabilizing loopgain in excess of 10 hz. This underscores the objective of actively controlling the rigid body slew mode and the first flexible mode (around 4.7 hz frequency range). This will also result in the flexible modes in excess of 10 hz to be unregulated. The stabilizing 'LQG/LTR controller I' in the innerloop was designed using the LQG/LTR design approach based on the input/output relation from '1' to '2' (see Figure 1) in the inner-loop in the absence of the outer loop; note that this requires an LQG/LTR design for an augmented plant which includes the actual plant cascaded by the 10 hz low pass filter at the input.

*Research supported by ARO, Engineering Sciences Division under contract DAAL03-91-C-0011 and AFOSR, Directorate of Aerospace Sciences under contract F49620-90-C-0064.

The second step was the design of the outer loop controller for rejection of a nominal single tone sinusoid disturbance frequency of 4 hz on plant. The outer error rejection loop contains a frequency shaping block that contains an undamped pole at 4 hz. This undamped pole provides an infinite gain at 4 hz which in a stabilizing loop assures perfect rejection of a single tone, 4 hz, sinusoid disturbance on the plant. A 20 dB attenuation on both directions from the 4 hz frequency assures the retaining of inner-loop characteristics outside the 4 hz range. The stabilizing 'LQG/LTR controller II' in the outerloop was designed using the LQG/LTR design approach, just like in the inner-loop, based on the input/output relation from '3' to '4' (see Figure 1) in the presence of the inner-loop. Figure 2 shows the LQG/LTR loop gain through the plant with the two stages of control (solid line) and with only the inner stage of control (dotted line). The corresponding sensitivities are shown in Figure 3 .

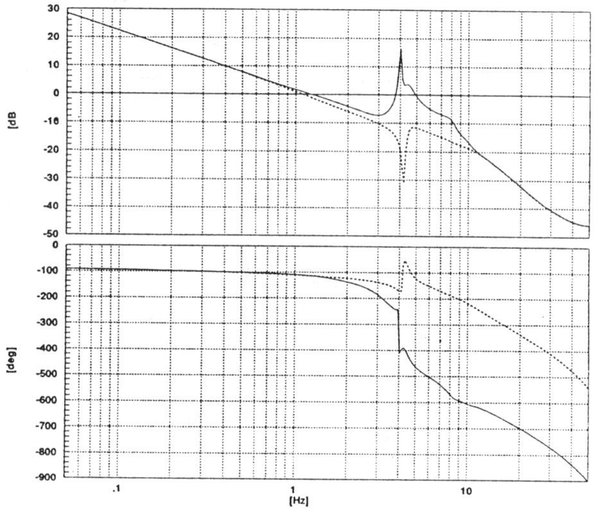

Figure 2:

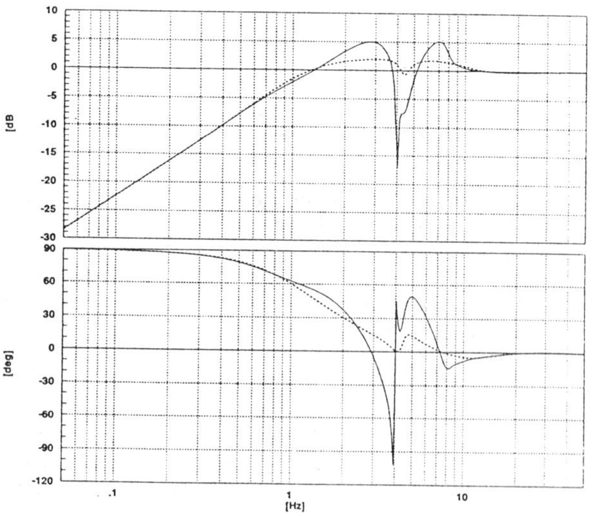

Figure 3:

The third step was the adaptive relocation of the undamped pole in the outer-loop shaping filter to the estimated frequency of disturbance. When the estimated frequency is equal to the actual frequency of a sinusoid disturbance and the resulting outer-loop is stable, a perfect disturbance rejection is guaranteed. The frequency of disturbance was estimated using an extended Kalman filter based on a notch filter. It is emphasized again that the only change from the two stage controller designed above is the adaptive tuning of the shaping filter in the outer loop. The entire inner loop and the 'LQG/LTR controller II' in the outer loop remain unchanged. Such an adaptive tuning was facilitated by the fact that the two stage loop was found analytically stable for the filter peak placed anywhere in the range 2 to 7 hz.

Figures 4 and 5 are plots generated from the data captured during a real-time implementation of the adaptive controller on the testbed fixture. A step response of the adaptive controller is shown in Figure 4 . The top seven strip charts plot the sensor measurement data from motor encoder, backlash encoder, iwheel encoder, strain gage 1, strain gage 2, motor velocity and tip accelerometer respectively. The bottom strip chart refers to the actuation voltage data to the motor. Figure 5 shows the same sensor measurements (top seven strip charts) for a steady 0.6 V sinusoid disturbance at the actuator with the disturbance frequency undergoing step changes (in hz) from from 4 to 3.75, 4 and 4.25 (8th strip). The 9th strip shows the real time estimate of the disturbance frequency. The strip data shows a disturbance buildup immediately following the step change in the disturbance frequency. This is followed by disturbance attenuation which occurs as the frequency of disturbance estimator locks on to the true frequency of the sinusoid disturbance. Adaptation and complete disturbance rejection is accomplished within 5 to 10 seconds following a step change in the disturbance frequency.

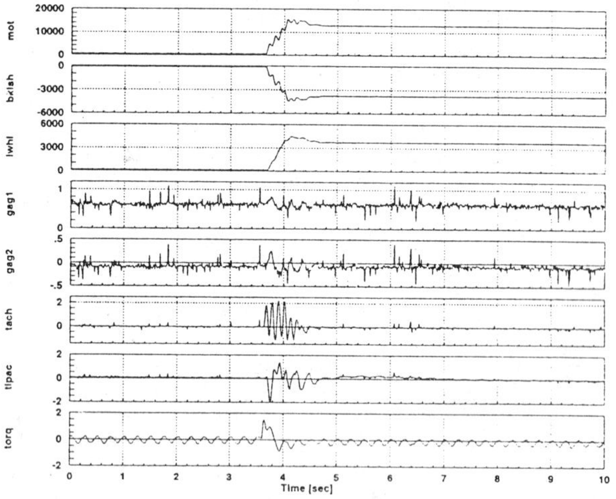

Figure 4:

The adaptive controller presented here was not able to handle disturbance rejection on the testbed fixture in the range 4.6 to 4.8 hz (also confirmed from analytical simulations). This behavior can be attributed to the presence of a lightly damped flexible mode around 4.7 hz. The adaptation mechanism could lock on the disturbance frequency only if the sensor measurements were dominated by the single tone of the disturbance. With the disturbance frequency in the 4.6 to 4.8 hz range, the sensor measurements also contained a significant contribution from the lightly damped mode.

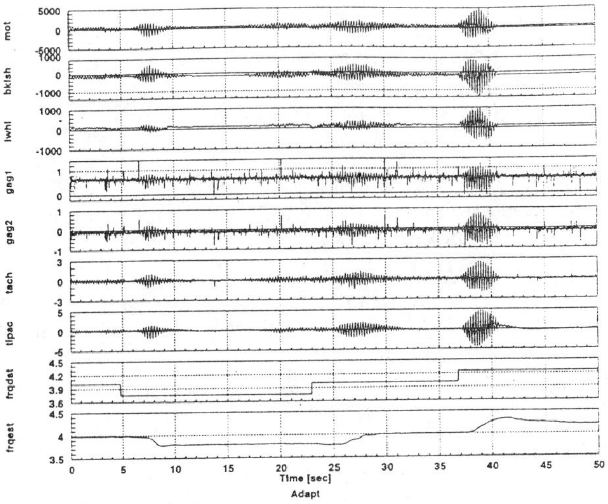

Figure 5:

This situation resulted in the frequency estimator flip-flop-ing between the two dominant frequencies, resulting in ringing.

Design Approach 2

Consider the nonlinear plant model shown in Figure 6 , where G denotes the *known* linear part and $\mathcal{F}$ denotes the algebraic nonlinearity (e.g., friction, saturation) which depends on an *unknown* parameter θ . The signals v_i and v_o at the input and output of the nonlinearity are *unavailable* as measurements. The disturbances and regulated variables are denoted by w and z , respectively. The goal is to determine a control input u such that using only the measurement at y, the output y asymptotically tracks a desired reference signal.

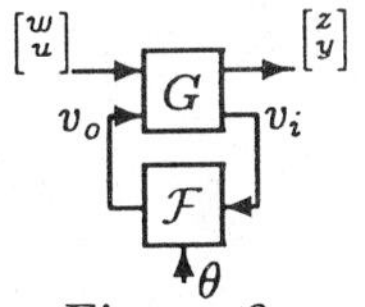

Figure 6:

The adaptive scheme we are investigating is based on a feedforward-feedback configuration (see Figure 7). This configuration gives rise to two nontrivial subproblems: 1) Sensitivity of the non-adaptive design, i.e., the stability and tracking robustness of the closed-loop subject to perturbations of $\hat{\theta}$ about the nominal θ and 2) Parameter estimation. Without closing the loop via the parameter estimator in Figure 7, we first design a tracking controller based on a known signal $\hat{\theta}$. The motivation behind the sensitivity study is that for sufficiently slow adaptation, one recovers the performance of the inherent tracking design. Hence, the goal is to determine the least-sensitive non-adaptive design. So far, our studies have shown that among other tracking designs based on the certainty-equivalence principle (use the parameter estimate *as if* it were correct), the underlying design in Figure 7 is consistently the least sensitive. For a known parameter estimate $\hat{\theta}$, a candidate input-output pair $(\hat{u}, \hat{y})$ is generated using the model in Figure 6 with θ replaced by $\hat{\theta}$. The tracking controller $\mathcal{C}_T$ achieves the desired tracking of the reference signal r in the loop with the model $\widehat{\mathcal{P}}$. This input-output pair $(\hat{u}, \hat{y})$ is injected to a feedback system where $\mathcal{C}_R$ stabilizes the actual plant; $\mathcal{C}_R$ alone need not be a tracking compensator. This approach improves the "performance bandwidth" without increasing the "control bandwidth" of the feedback system. Hence it has the potential of improving existing controller performance without a total redesign.

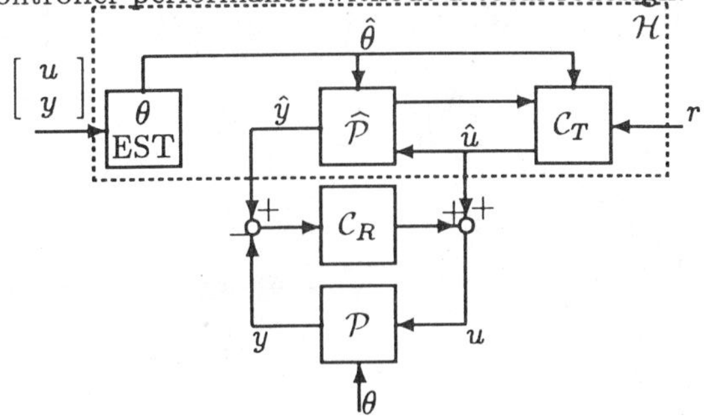

$\mathcal{H}$: adaptive feedforward signal generator (high performance)
$\mathcal{C}_R$: inner loop stabilizing controller (low performance)
$\widehat{\mathcal{P}}$: plant model
$\mathcal{P}$: actual plant

Figure 7:

The plant model is of the form

$$\dot{x} = Ax + b_u u + b_w(w - \theta f(\dot{y}))$$
$$y = c_y x$$

where the 10 state, relative degree 3 SISO system (c_y, A, b_u) is minimum-phase with a lightly damped zero at 3.25 Hz . The algebraic nonlinearity $f(\cdot) = \mathrm{sat}_1(40\cdot)$, where sat_1 is the odd symmetric piecewise-linear saturation function with unity slope and ± 1 saturation limits. In the rest of this study $\hat{f}(\cdot) = \tanh(40\cdot)$ will denote the smooth approximation to f . The periodic disturbance torque is denoted by w . Using $y, \dot{y}, y^{(2)}$, the control u determined by

$$\beta_2 u = u_l - \alpha_2 x - \beta_3(w - \theta f(\dot{y}))$$
$$+\beta_1(\dot{\theta} f(\dot{y}) + \theta f^{(1)}(\dot{y}) y^{(2)} - \dot{w}) ,$$

for appropriate coefficients α and β , renders $y^{(3)} = u_l$. Let $\mathcal{L}$ denote the associated map (i.e., from x, w, $\dot{w}$, θ, f to u_l) . Note that $\mathcal{L}$ can only be realized in the ideal case where x, w, $\dot{w}$, θ and f are all known. Although such is not the case, it still is interesting to note that the steady-state actuation demand to decouple y from w is given by $\frac{1}{\beta_2}(\beta_3 w + \beta_1 \dot{w})$. For the particular periodic w and actuation limits at hand, this translates into disturbance rejection of up to 7 harmonics of w . Similarly let $\widehat{\mathcal{L}}$ denote the map depending on the available signals $\hat{x}$, $\hat{w}$, $\dot{\hat{w}}$, $\hat{\theta}$ and the smooth approximation $\hat{f}$.

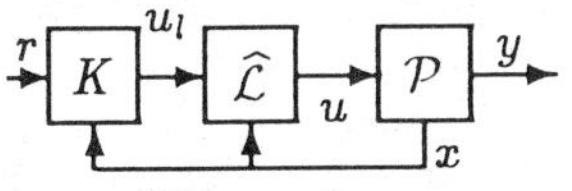

Figure 8:

Sensitivity of the nominal design

Consider the interconnection in Figure 8 , and a 10 mrad slew with the desired tracking performance for $\widehat{\mathcal{L}} = \mathcal{L}$ as shown in Figure 9 (lower curves) . The solid and dashed lines denote the base and tip positions, respectively. The periodic disturbances w and $\dot{w}$ are exactly canceled. Note that the feedback linearization results in the inversion which causes the lightly damped 3.25 Hz mode. In the upper curves the mismatch is *only* f vs $\hat{f}$; i.e, x, w, $\dot{w}$, θ are exactly used in the feedback linearizer except that the algebraic nonlinearities are not identical. Performance degradation is self-explanatory.

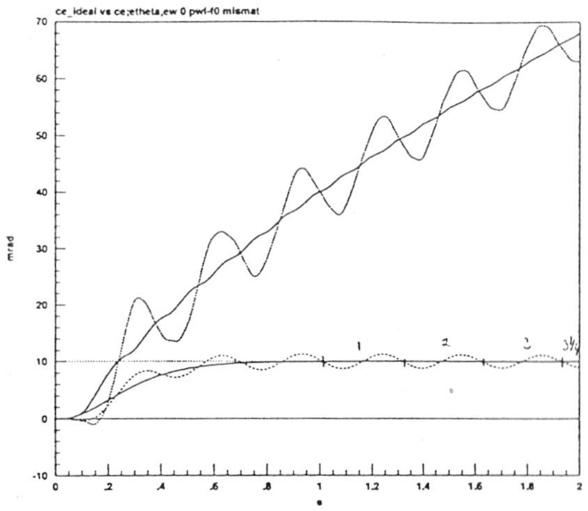

Figure 9:

Due to the sensitivity of the one-loop implementation of the certainty-equivalence principle in Figure 8 , we resorted to the certainty-equivalence based control scheme as shown in Figure 10 (redrawn from Figure 7 for ease of comparison with Figure 8) . A simple controller $C = 10$ stabilized the inner loop. The performance, on the other hand, depends on the generated signals $(\hat{u}, \hat{y})$. Our design studies have shown that the model-follower scheme in Figure 10 consistently proves to be the least sensitive to mismatches. These observations are mainly due to the fact that the inner-loop is inherently stable and the performance depends on the *cascade* structure. However, in Figure 8 , *both* stability and tracking performance have to be achieved in one loop.

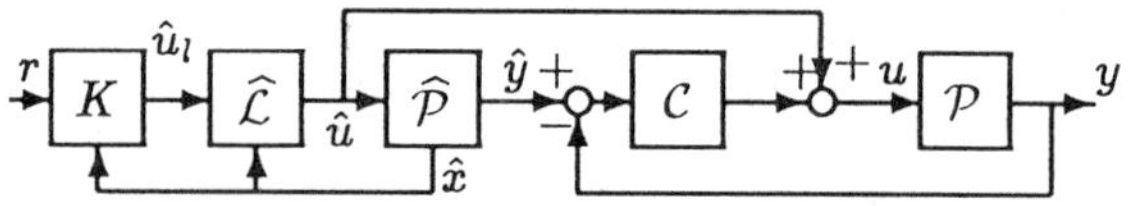

Figure 10:

Adaptive Slewing with $w = 0$

A parameter estimation block is introduced in the certainty-equivalence based tracking control design scheme in Figure 10 , to complete the interconnection as shown in Figure 7 . The disturbance w and the initial conditions $x(0) = \hat{x}(0)$ are assumed to be zero ; however, $\theta \neq \hat{\theta}$ and $f \neq \hat{f}$. Moreover, the state x is not being used in the control law and the parameter estimator solely depends on available signals u and y . In other words, for the disturbance free case, the interconnections in Figure 10 and Figure 7 are candidates for *implementable* designs since they depend on available signals only. However, real-time implementation requires the extra step of control law discretization, which proves to be a nontrivial task as it will be emphasized later on.

Consider Figure 11 . The dashed line denotes the the signal generator output trajectory (i.e., $\hat{y}$) and the solid line denotes the basewheel yaw (i.e., y) . The reference signal r is a smooth ± 20 mrad periodic waveform which $\hat{y}$ tracks after 4 seconds. Note that the output y tracks r within 1 mrad after approximately 6 seconds. There are two important points to be made about these responses: 1) the signal generator depends on $\hat{\theta}$ which is not constant (depends on the parameter estimator output waveform). Moreover, unlike the case in Figure 10 , when the parameter estimator loop is closed, $\hat{\theta}$ is no longer an exogenous signal for the signal generator, hence for slow adaptation (over the 6 second window), $\hat{y}$ also exhibits transient response (see dashed lines over the first 4 seconds in Figure 11) . When $\hat{\theta}$ is an exogenous signal, the signal generator is designed so that $\hat{y}$ tracks r in less than a second. 2) due to f and $\hat{f}$ mismatch, even with $\theta = \hat{\theta}$, the ideal tracking performance in the lower solid line in Figure 8 degrades to 1 mrad off at 2 seconds ; hence the offset emphasized by parallel lines in Figure 11 . The parameter estimator output (i.e., $\hat{\theta}$) is shown in Figure 12 .

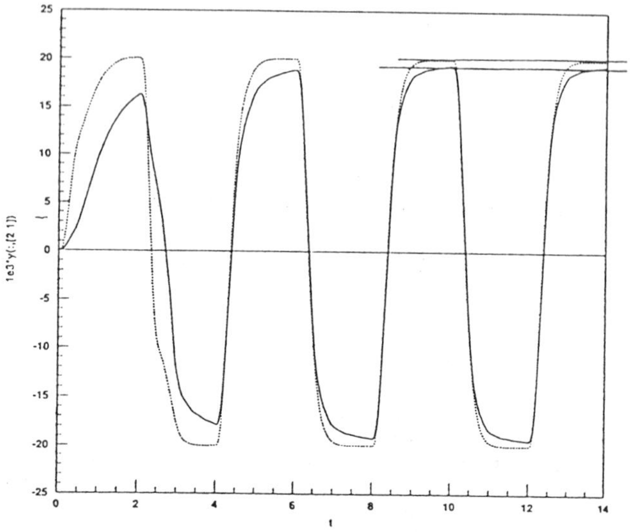

Figure 11:

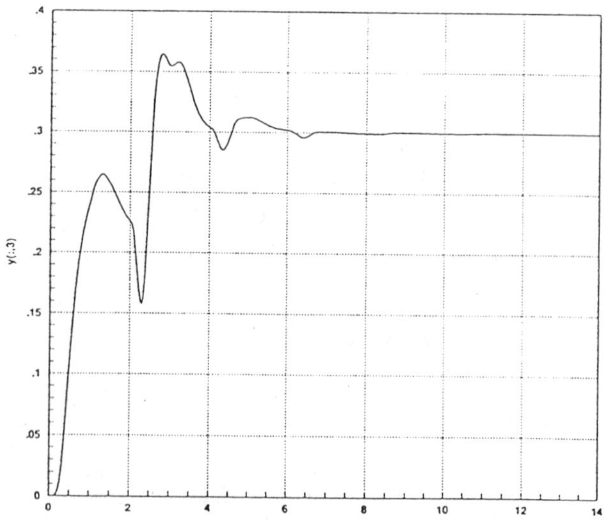

Figure 12:

Baseline disturbance rejection design and discretization issues

In order to illustrate the approach, consider the case where the interconnection in Figure 10 is LTI and modified to incorporate the disturbance w ; the disturbance estimate used in the signal generator will be denoted by $\hat{w}$. The LTI plant from (w, u) to y is denoted by $[P_{yw}\ ,\ P_{yu}]$ and C denotes an LTI stabilizing compensator. Let

$$\begin{aligned} y &= P_{yu}(\hat{u} + C(\hat{y} - y)) + P_{yw}w \\ \hat{y} &= P_{yu}\hat{u} + P_{yw}\hat{w} \quad , \end{aligned}$$

where $\hat{y}$ denotes the desired plant output. Let e_y and e_w denote the errors $(y - \hat{y})$ and $(w - \hat{w})$, respectively. Then

$$e_y = (I + P_{yu}C)^{-1}P_{yw}e_w \quad .$$

Clearly, there are two options: 1) relying on the poles of $P_{yu}C$ at the disturbance poles or 2) choosing C to be any stabilizing controller and trying to set $e_w \to 0$. In the following baseline design, we will make the assumption that the disturbance w is periodic with a known period and can be *measured* . Even with these stringent assumptions, deriving a *discrete-time* implementation of the feedback linearization based model-follower scheme turned out to be a nontrivial task. In fact, even if w is assumed to be measured, the disturbance does not come in additive at the plant input; canceling the effect of w at y requires higher order derivatives of w . Since the performance depends on the success of cancellation, the derivatives are not constructed by filtered/delayed versions of w ; instead, an identifier is built to determine the Fourier coefficients of the harmonics of interest and the signal generator outputs $(\hat{u}, \hat{y})$ are derived accordingly. Throughout this process, the inner-loop controller is chosen as a simple gain $C = 10$; the inner-loop is inherently stable, and the w identifier generates the $\hat{w}$ information used in the signal generator. Throughout the following, there is a nonlinearity mismatch ; the plant model in the inner-loop uses f , whereas the signal generator uses the smooth version $\hat{f}$. The parameters satisfy $\theta = \hat{\theta} = 0.3$. A continuous-time design was completed ; the next step was to recover the continuous-time simulation results using a discrete-time controller. A maximum sampling rate of 400 Hz is dictated by hardware limitations. The minimum step-size of 2.5 ms was not small enough to reasonable replicate the nonlinear ordinary differential equation solution with *any* fixed step-size integration algorithm. The final successful discretization was based on the 4th order Runge-Kutta algorithm, which requires intersample point evaluation. In order to avoid oversampling, the controller was decomposed into an LTI system in feedback with algebraic nonlinearities and the LTI subsystem was discretized using the 4th order Runge-Kutta algorithm, introducing additional states as many as the inputs, to avoid intersampling. Using this particular discretization at 400 Hz, the continuous-time performance was sufficiently reproduced (see Figures 13 and 14) .

The two strip plots in Figure 13 correspond to the tip position before and after the model-follower is included ; the base is commanded a -3 mrad slew. The top strip is the tip position for the inner-loop controller $C = 10$, $\hat{u} = 0$, $\hat{y} = -3$ mrad (see Figure 10) . The disturbance w is periodic. The lower strip corresponds to the case where $\hat{w}$ is identified up to the first 7 harmonics and the $\hat{w}$ information is used in the signal generator to command the basewheel a -3 mrad slew and to cancel the effect of the 7 harmonics . Initially, the identifier coefficients are all zero ; it takes approximately 1 second for the parameters to converge. After

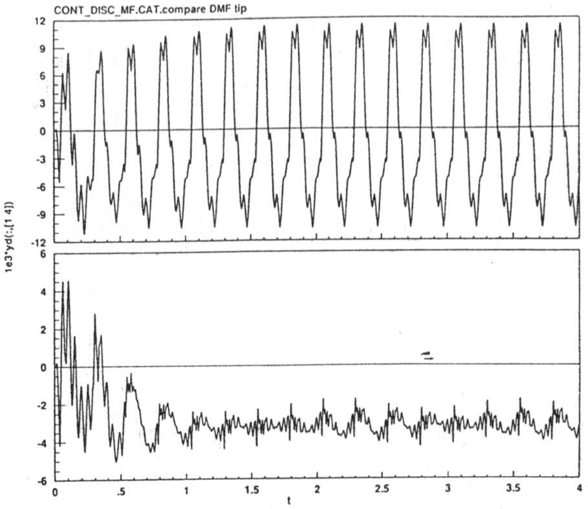

Figure 13:

1 second, the base is at -3 mrad and the tip has approximately ± 1 mrad deviation (see lower strip, Figure 13) .

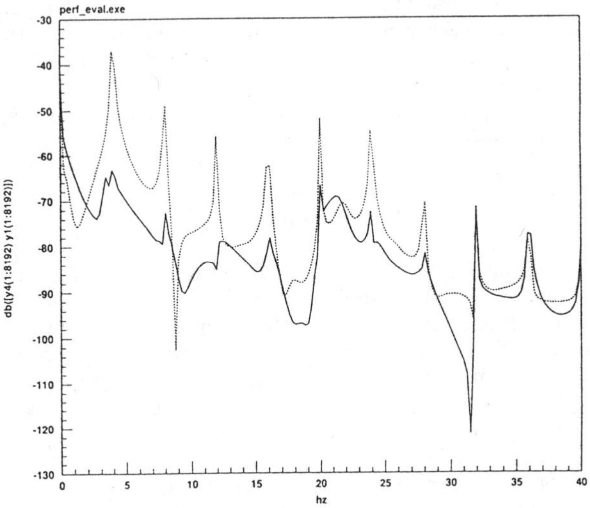

Figure 14:

Since the performance plots in Figure 13 do not correspond to an LTI system, one cannot represent the reduction of the harmonic term contributions directly. Although a transfer function description does not exist, we can still compare the frequency contents of each signal to substantiate the reduction of the harmonics at the tip. Using the discrete Fourier transforms of the two signals in Figure 13 , we obtain Figure 14 . The dashed and solid lines, respectively denote before and after the model-follower is introduced. The disturbance is 4 Hz periodic, and the identifier was built for the first seven harmonics. Hence the improvements are apparent up to 28 Hz , with reductions 26, 26, 26, 16, 16, 16 and 10 dB at 4, 8, 12, 16, 20, 24 and 28 Hz, respectively.

Proceedings of the
American Control Conference
San Francisco, California • June 1993

NON-COLLOCATED FLEXIBLE BEAM MOTION CONTROL BASED ON A DELAYED ADAPTIVE INVERSE METHOD[1]

David S. Wang, Guo-Ben Yang, and Max Donath

Department of Mechanical Engineering
University of Minnesota, Minneapolis, Minnesota 55455

Abstract

The viability of a delayed adaptive inverse method for motion control of the tip of a flexible beam is demonstrated in this paper. This method is based on an adaptive linear FIR filter which provides a stable and close approximation to the inverse plant dynamics. Such FIR filters can be used to control non-minimum phase systems, certain nonlinear systems, or plants of unknown dynamics and can be implemented using real-time interrupt driven high performance computational devices such as digital signal processing (DSP) based hardware. The effects of varying parameters of the delayed adaptive inverse controller (such as the values of the initial weights, the gain constants, and the length of delay) on the system performance are presented. Since the method is computationally efficient, it can be used in high bandwidth applications for control of complex plants given only the desired and the actual measured outputs for the plant. A feedback controller is used in conjunction with the delayed adaptive inverse controller to eliminate the residual errors that would occur if only feedforward control were used.

This delayed adaptive inverse method is then compared to an H_∞-based loopshaping controller.

1. Introduction

Motion control of mechanical systems with inherent structural and joint flexibility represents a class of nonlinear systems found in many important applications such as manufacturing, medicine, mining and construction. In most such systems, the primary subsystem involves the positioning of a structural element (which may incorporate optics, lasers, X-rays, radioactive sources, etc.) via an actuator. Such subsystems often include structural components or transmissions which exhibit compliance. Even when the subsystems are designed to be stiff or massive, inertial loading can cause significant deformation at higher speeds. Robot manipulators are but one example of such a system. Each robot's actuated link can be considered as a motor driven beam in which the beam's tip motion must be controlled. It is the control of the tip motion in an inertial coordinate frame that is of interest in most applications. As such, one needs to compute and control the torque applied at the actuator so that the measured motion of the tip will match the prescribed motion.

Two problems arise in such cases. One, sensors for measuring tip motion have, to date, been severely limited in bandwidth; and two, given the non-minimum phase nature of such non-collocated systems, the use of traditional inverse dynamics based control will lead to instabilities. The problem in many applications is further exacerbated by the nonlinear nature of the plant to be controlled. Nonlinearities include the inherent geometric/continuous nonlinearities and discontinuity effects such as backlash, stiction and friction. An exact Fourier series-based inverse method was developed [1], in which good agreement was achieved between the desired and computed motion. However, the use of such exact inverse dynamics based formulations for the control of non-minimum phase systems requires prior knowledge regarding the desired motion/path boundary conditions and can lead to instabilities due to the generation of unstable poles in the controller.

In order to address the first problem above, we have developed a sensor that can be used for tracking the six degrees of freedom motion of an end effector. In Sorensen et al. [2], we described an early prototype which is capable of high bandwidth (480 Hz) measurement of the XYZ coordinates of moving points on rigid or deformable bodies. The system, based on a laser scanning approach, is designed in a pipeline configuration such that each sensed point's coordinates are immediately available in registers and memory mapped into the data acquisition CPU. Three planes of laser scan through the measurement field at constant angular velocity. By measuring the elapsed time of movement from fixed locations at the boundaries of the field to each of the moving point targets, one can derive the swept angles to each of the targets and consequently their XYZ coordinates. In addition to being able to track each point target's motion, each target has its own path into the CPU thus facilitating the accurate computation of (i) the six degrees of freedom of any number of bodies each carrying at least three targets and (ii) the relative motion of the instantaneous axis of rotation between bodies. Significant improvements have been implemented as a follow-up to the experiments described in Sorensen et al. [2]. As a result, such sensors can now be used to characterize the relative motion of joints (e.g. transmissions) and structural elements even when compliance is a major factor. This advance in technology makes it possible to consider multi-degree of freedom end point control.

In this paper, we will focus on a method to handle the second problem mentioned earlier, that of controlling a nonlinear non-minimum phase system. We will present a method for controlling the tip motion of a flexible beam. In contrast to most inverse dynamics methods, the delayed adaptive inverse method that we propose attempts to address the problems associated with the non-minimum phase behavior of the flexible system and provides a stable and close approximation to the inverse dynamics. Furthermore, the approach is conducive to the use of high speed Digital Signal Processing (DSP) hardware. There has been considerable research on the control of compliant links and

[1] Work was partially supported by the Army High Performance Computing Research Center (U.S. Army Grant #DAAL03-89-C-0038) and the Productivity Center at the University of Minnesota.

joints used in robot manipulators based on collocated sensor feedback methods.

Book et al. [3] implemented a flexible feedback control scheme (FFC) based on a pole shifting algorithm. Siciliano and Book [4] applied the singular perturbation and integral manifold approaches to control a single link flexible arm. To overcome the sensitivity of these methods to plant parameter variations, adaptive methods were investigated. Nelson and Mitra [5] used on-line load mass estimation and load-adaptive optimal control for varying load conditions. Other adaptive control methods were also proposed by Meldrum and Balas [6]. However all these adaptive control designs involve a significant computational component thereby limiting their application to real time control. Again these papers are limited to cases of collocated feedback.

To obtain better performance for very flexible manipulators, Cannon and his research group ([7] and [8]) experimentally investigated end-point control techniques for flexible link systems in planar motion. This was the first attempt at non-collocated control for a flexible beam model of a manipulator using traditional control design methodologies.

Research on the control of systems with joint flexibility was first initiated in the 1980s. Under the assumption of weak elasticity at the joint, Ficola et al. [9] used the singular perturbation approach to design a feedback controller. Khorasani and Spong [10] extended this work by using the invariant and integral manifold approach. A pseudo-linearization technique was proposed by Nicosia et al. [11] while adaptive control approaches were investigated by Tomei et al. [12]. All these studies ignored structural compliance and cannot be readily modified to incorporate such compliance.

Furthermore, the control methods in most of the literature mentioned above was based on an analysis of the forward dynamics, in which the flexible link (or joint) displacements, velocities and accelerations are determined by the specified joint torque. An inverse dynamics type of control law based on the concept of "Computed Torque" was first applied to a cylindrical coordinate arm with drive train compliance by Forrest-Barlach and Babcock [13]. Other such feedforward methods followed. Asada and Ma [14] presented a recursive inverse dynamics analysis based on a virtual rigid link coordinate system. None of this latter group of inverse based methods was adaptive and as such was sensitive to parameter uncertainty. Furthermore, none took advantage of tip feedback and suffered from the limitations inherent to systems in which direct measurement of the parameter under control is not available.

An approach that explicitly deals with the non-minimum component of a plant was described by Tomizuka [15] who proposed a zero phase error tracking controller (ZPETC) to solve the problem. This approach used a feedforward controller to cancel all closed-loop poles and cancelable closed-loop zeros (zeros on the left-half of the s-plane). For uncancelable zeros (zeros on the right-half of the s-plane), the feedforward controller cancels the phase shift induced by them. Since ZPETC is based on pole/zero cancellation and phase cancellation, the tracking performance using ZPETC is sensitive to modeling errors and plant parameter variations. To solve the problem of unknown plant parameters and parameter variations, Tsao and Tomizuka [16] developed an adaptive ZPETC. The plant is separated into a known part (with cancelable poles and zeros) and an unknown part. A normalized least square parameter adaptation algorithm (PAA) was used to adjust the unknown parameters used in the feedforward controller. However, in both cases, the results were dependent on having a good model of the system.

Another approach for designing robust controllers of non-minimum phase, linear systems is H_∞ based loopshaping [17]. The objective is to shape the complementary sensitivity transfer function, the transfer function from the reference signal to the output of the plant, in order to obtain the desired system performance. The ideal loopshape of the complementary sensitivity transfer function is represented by a second order system with desired response characteristics such as the amount of damping and natural frequency. This transfer function is then incorporated, as a weighting function, into the system model for a controller design that minimizes the induced two norm between the reference signal and the output of the weighting function.

In this paper we examine a method based on a delayed adaptive inverse filter which eliminates the non-minimum problem associated with inverse methods by using an FIR filter for feedforward control. The method is based on the on-line characterization of the inverse dynamics based on an adaptation algorithm in which a delay must be injected to ensure causality. We will demonstrate the viability of the delayed adaptive inverse method for motion control of flexible beams. An adaptive linear function whose weighting is adapted by the LMS algorithm was used to replace the unstable exact inverse model. By using a FIR filter to represent the inverse dynamics, we avoid the instabilities associated with pole/zero cancellation (only zeros are present in FIR filters) when controlling non-minimum phase systems. Furthermore, we may be able to control complex plants given only the desired and actual output values for the plant, provided that the control inputs are accessible. Since the method is computationally efficient, it can be incorporated into closed-loop controllers for position or trajectory control so that the residual errors can be eliminated (see discussion later).

This paper significantly expands on an earlier preliminary presentation describing the method [18]. A general description of the delayed adaptive inverse model is provided in section 2. The weight vector used in this model is updated using the LMS algorithm, which is discussed in section 3. The contents of sections 2 and 3 were presented in Yang and Donath [18], but they are included here for completeness. A control strategy based on the adaptive inverse model is described in section 4. The approach, as applied to a model of the flexible beam located at the Armament Research, Development and Engineering Center, is described in section 5. The adaptive inverse controller is then compared with an H_∞ based loopshaping controller.

2. A Delayed Adaptive Inverse Model

The application of adaptive filters to control design can be categorized into two groups: (i) the adaptive model control (AMC) method; and (ii) the adaptive inverse control (AIC) method. It is difficult to control a non-minimum phase system by using the AMC method, since the control signal will have a transform with poles outside the unit circle and will thus be unstable. However, a delayed AIC method can form stable approximate inverse models without knowing a priori whether or not the plant is minimum phase.

In this paper, we will apply the delayed AIC method to the tip control of flexible beams, a non-minimum phase system. An adaptive linear combiner, or non-recursive adaptive filter, is used to compute the applied joint torque, which, in turn, generates a desired motion. One advantage, among many, of the adaptive linear combiner is that it is relatively straightforward to analyze and implement. A schematic diagram of a delayed adaptive inverse model used in the AIC method is shown in Figure 1, where the terms, u_k, d_k, n_k, y_k, V_k, and ε_k are respectively the command input, the command after a delay of Δ sample periods, the noise input, the plant output, the output of the inverse plant model, and the error between d_k and V_k. P(z) and H(z) are z transfer functions of the plant and of the adaptive inverse model.

The delay of Δ samples in Figure 1 is to allow for the delay, or propagation time, through the plant and the adaptation associated with the inverse modeling. Including such a delay generally results in a much lower value for the minimum mean-square-error and causes the output of the converged adaptive system, y_k, to approximate the input, u_k, with a delay of Δ.

The mathematical description for this model can be expressed in discrete system form as follows. The input vector of the inverse model, Y, which represents a window of L values associated with the kth sample, is the input to the delayed inverse model (assuming n_k is zero). It can be expressed as:

$$\text{(single input)} \quad Y_k = [y_k \; y_{k-1} \ldots y_{k-L+1}]^T ,$$
$$\text{(multiple inputs)} \quad Y_k = [y_{1k} \; y_{2k} \ldots y_{Lk}]^T \tag{1}$$

for the single input case or for multiple inputs, respectively, and the weight vector, W_k, associated with the kth sample can be expressed as $W_k = [w_{1k}.w_{2k} \ldots w_{Lk}]^T$. The expression for w_{ik} (i = 1, ..., L) will depend on the approach used. The elements of the input vector for the inverse model, Y_k, are considered to be L sequential sample inputs from a single input source, or L simultaneous inputs from L different input sources in the multiple inputs case. The elements, y_j (where j = k, k-1, ... k-L+1), of the single input vector Y, are set to zero if subscript j is equal to or less than zero (i.e., when k < L).

The output of the inverse model, V, for a linear combination of the input vector, Y_k, and weight vector, W_k, is written as

$$V_k = Y_k^T W_k = W_k^T Y_k , \tag{2}$$

where, again, the subscript k is used as a time or sample number index. This function is the linear combiner or weighting function.

Thus the error associated with sample k from Figure 1 is

$$\varepsilon_k = d_k - V_k = d_k - Y_k^T W_k = d_k - W_k^T Y_k , \tag{3}$$

and the mean-square error is

$$\xi = E[\varepsilon_k^2] = E[d_k^2] + W_k^T E[Y_k Y_k^T] W_k - 2E[d_k Y_k^T] W_k$$
$$= E[d_k^2] + W_k^T R W_k - 2PW_k , \tag{4}$$

where the input correlation matrix is $R = E[Y_k Y_k^T]$, and the cross correlation column vector is $P = E[d_k Y_k^T]$.

Our goal is to find the minimum mean-square error for the inverse model. Several adaptive methods, such as Newton's method and the steepest descent method, can be applied to adjust the weight vector in order to obtain the minimum mean-square-error. The disadvantage of these two methods is that they usually require off-line gradient estimation or repetition of data in order to compute ξ in equation (4) and its gradient, which reduces the computation speed for real time applications. By contrast, the LMS algorithm does not require an estimate of all the above terms, and computes the weighting function based only on instantaneous error. The details of the LMS algorithm are described in the next section.

3. The LMS Algorithm

In Newton's method or in the steepest descent method, the gradient of $\xi = E[\varepsilon_k^2]$ is estimated by taking differences between short-term averages of ε_k^2. However, for the LMS algorithm, ε_k^2 itself is used as an estimate of ξ_k without averaging.

The error in equation (3) is

$$\varepsilon_k = d_k - Y_k^T W_k \tag{5}$$

and the estimated gradient of the mean-square-error can be obtained by differentiating equation (5)

$$\nabla_k = \frac{\partial \varepsilon_k^2}{\partial w} = \begin{bmatrix} \frac{\partial \varepsilon_k^2}{\partial w_1} \\ \cdot \\ \cdot \\ \cdot \\ \frac{\partial \varepsilon_k^2}{\partial w_L} \end{bmatrix} = 2\varepsilon_k \begin{bmatrix} \frac{\partial \varepsilon_k}{\partial w_1} \\ \cdot \\ \cdot \\ \cdot \\ \frac{\delta \varepsilon_k}{\partial w_L} \end{bmatrix} = -2\varepsilon_k Y_k \tag{6}$$

For many practical adaptive system applications, the system transfer function is not fully determined and needs to be measured or estimated based on the sensed data. The slow adaptation (compared with Newton's method) used in the steepest descent method provides a filter process which reduces the effects of gradient measurement noise. Using the same slow adaptation as in the steepest descent method, the LMS algorithm's weighting update function is expressed as

$$w_{i,k+1} = w_{i,k} - \mu \nabla_k = w_{i,k} + 2\mu \varepsilon_k Y_k \quad (i = 1, \ldots L) \tag{7}$$

where μ is the gain constant that regulates the speed and stability of the adaptation and has dimensions of reciprocal input power. Equations (5) and (7) are a form of the adaptive LMS algorithm proposed by Widrow et al. [19]. It has been pointed out by Widrow and Stearns [20] that for the LMS algorithm, the mean of ε converges to zero as k approaches infinity provided that the following condition is satisfied: $0 < \mu < 1/\lambda_{max}$, where λ_{max} is the largest element in the diagonal eigenvalue matrix of R. Increasing the gain constant, μ, tends to reduce the number of iterations required for the LMS algorithm to reach its steady-state value, but also causes a corresponding increase in the average square error.

Only simple numerical operations (no squaring, averaging or differentiation) are performed in the LMS algorithm, making this approach computationally more efficient than Newton's method or the steepest descent method. Since the change in the weight vector at each iteration is based on imperfect estimates, ε_k^2, without averaging, the results obtained from the LMS algorithm may include higher frequency components (i.e., noise) and will not be a perfect match with the optimal (i.e., the case when $\varepsilon = 0$). Usually, the more one wants to attenuate the noise, the longer the computation time, but given the nature of the LMS algorithm, this does not appear to be a significant factor. The expected residual error can be reduced by using closed loop control.

4. Control Based On An Adaptive Inverse Model

Based on the inverse model described in section 2 with weights adapted by the LMS algorithm, we developed a delayed adaptive inverse model controller. The controller is designed to generate the approximate inverse of the plant given the desired and actual outputs. For a non-minimum phase system, some of the plant transfer function zeros are located in the right half of the s-plane or outside the unit circle in the z-plane for the discrete (or digital) case. In such cases, the exact inverse model (or the reciprocal transfer function) of the plant will have poles in the right half of the s-plane or poles outside the unit circle in the z-plane. Thus, the control input of a plant computed by using an exact inverse model will always continue to increase in magnitude with time and be unbounded. Including a delay lets the adaptive inverse model have a two-sided impulse response, thus resolving the instability problem. A delayed adaptive inverse model [20] which can be used for control of a non- or unknown minimum phase plant, as shown in Figure 2, will give an approximated but stable system. This means that the stability of the controller can be assured regardless of whether or not the plant is minimum phase.

The delayed adaptive inverse model in the right half of Figure 2 is essentially the same as that shown earlier in Figure 1. The controller version on the left is a copy of the delayed adaptive inverse model. The weights are computed and updated on-line for real-time implementation of the delayed adaptive inverse control algorithm. Although the plant transfer function in Figure 2 may be entirely unknown, certain information regarding the plant characteristics would be useful for selecting the number of weights and the length of delay. The number of weights should be proportional to the complexity of the plant; the higher the order of the plant, the larger the number of weights should be. The delay should approximate the propagation time from the input of the plant to the output of the delayed adaptive inverse model. A general rule of thumb is to set the delay, Δ, to be half of the number of weights. Once a convergent set of weights is obtained, the delay is increased or decreased for an optimal solution.

5. Control of a Flexible Beam Unit: Simulation Results

The application of the delayed adaptive inverse method to a flexible beam unit with both joint and structural flexibility was reported in Yang [1]. It was demonstrated that the delayed adaptive inverse method works for controlling systems with differentiable nonlinearities. In this paper, more recent results for the delayed adaptive inverse control of a flexible beam system will be presented. The system that we will consider here is a testbed located at the Armament Research, Development and Engineering Center (ARDEC) to simulate the motion control problems found on typical Army systems. A simplified schematic of the testbed is shown in Figure 3; the support and bearing structures are not shown for clarity. A linear model of the testbed developed by Integrated Systems Inc. [21] is provided in Figure 4. Elements of the block diagram model shown in this figure are described from left to right. The first block is the torque constant of the actuating motor with

$$Kt = 0.89 \text{ N-m/volt}. \tag{8}$$

The second block represents the motor dynamics described by

$$\frac{62.5}{s^2} \text{ radians/N-m}, \tag{9}$$

where s is the Laplace variable. The third block represents the compliance and damping of the shaft; it has the form $Bs+K$, where B is the damping term and K is the spring constant of the shaft. They are

$$B = 0.1 \text{ N-m/rad-sec}^{-1}, \text{ and } K = 34.3 \text{ N-m/radians} \tag{10}$$

The next block represents a state space model of the inertia wheel and the associated flexible beam dynamics. Three outputs of this block are the inertia wheel angular position and angular velocity, and the beam's tip acceleration. The input to this block is the effective torque applied to the inertia wheel. The block below the inertia wheel and beam dynamics is the inertia wheel bearing viscous friction term with a viscous friction coefficient of 0.67 N-m/rad-sec^{-1}. The last block is a double integrator which will provide the tip displacement in radians needed for the H_∞ controller which will be tested for comparison purposes. The state space model for the inertia wheel and the flexible beam was developed using finite element methods by modeling the beam as four identical beam elements [22]. The beam element's mass and stiffness matrices are given by

$$K_{el} = \frac{EI}{l^3}\begin{bmatrix} 12 & 6l & -12 & 6l \\ 6l & 4l^2 & -6l & 2l^2 \\ -12 & -6l & 12 & -6l \\ 6l & 2l^2 & -6l & 4l^2 \end{bmatrix} \tag{11}$$

$$M_{el} = \frac{\rho A l}{420}\begin{bmatrix} 156 & 22l & 54 & -13l \\ 22l & 4l^2 & 13l & -3l^2 \\ 54 & 13l & 156 & -22l \\ -13l & -3l^2 & -22l & 4l^2 \end{bmatrix} \tag{12}$$

where E, ρ, A, I, l are the Young's modulus, the density, the cross sectional area, the moment of inertia, and the element length of the beam, respectively. Each finite element beam segment satisfies the equations of motion for that element and is modeled based on Euler-Bernoulli theory.

The root locus of this inertia wheel and beam model, shown in Figure 5, indicates that there are three right half plane zeros in the Laplace domain; this information confirms that the system is indeed non-minimum phase due to the non-collocatedness of actuation and sensing locations. A comparison of the frequency responses of the linear model of the flexible beam from motor torque input to beam tip acceleration with the experimental test results is shown in Figure 6. For the analysis proposed in this paper, reasonable agreement was observed over a range of frequencies. The performance objective is to get the tip of the beam to accurately track a desired path with specified boundary conditions on the motion. In this study, we will focus on the use of the accelerometer as the tip motion sensor in order to explore the limit of this readily available sensor. The desired acceleration profile will be used as the input command, r(t), (i.e., the desired motion) of the controller in Figure 2. Since the output of the controller is a control torque, the adaptive inverse model is generating a characterization of the plant that can be described as an inertial effect, i.e., $\tau = I\ddot{\theta}$.

The desired displacement, velocity, and acceleration trajectories were generated by a fifth order Hermite polynomial [13] to ensure that the desired motion of the tip satisfies the initial and final conditions as given in equation (13).

$$\begin{aligned} &y_d(0) = \dot{y}_d(0) = \ddot{y}_d(0) = 0 \\ &y_d(t_f) = y_{dt} \\ &\dot{y}_d(t_f) = \ddot{y}_d(t_f) = 0 \end{aligned} \qquad (13)$$

For the set of tests we considered, we arbitrarily picked a motion involving a 45 degree swing in one second followed by a one second hold. Therefore, in the above equation (15), t_f was set to 1.0 second, and $y_d(t_f)$ was set at 0.785 radians. The sampling period, t_s, is 2.5 msec corresponding to a sampling frequency of 400 Hz. The desired beam tip motion, r(t), entering the controller of Figure 2 was set equal to $\ddot{y}_d(t_f)$, i.e., the acceleration profile was used. The number of weights used in the adaptive inverse model was 64, and the delay, Δ, was 32 sampling periods. A controller design and analysis software package, MatrixX[2], is used for the simulation of the adaptive inverse controller.

The position response of the flexible beam for the specified acceleration profile is given in Figure 7 along with the desired position response. A initial delay is visible. Both the commanded and the controlled tip motion are completed in less than one second as desired. The difference between the desired and actual displacement is shown in Figure 8. The parameters of the delayed adaptive inverse controller are obtained via an iterative manual optimization process: the values were determined to work best with initial weights set at 0.12, μ set at 1.64e-5, and with 20 adaptive iterations between each sampling period.

Although the parameters of the delayed adaptive inverse model are obtained via a manually derived iteration approach, the parameters have predictable effects on the system response. The gain constant, μ, determines the rate and stability of the adaptation. A large value of μ will shorten the time for convergence but may also cause instability of the controlled system. Effects of μ on the system response are shown for three values of μ in Figure 9. It is seen from this figure that when μ is smaller or greater than the optimal value of 1.64e-5 a steady state error will appear in the system response.

In Figure 10, three responses are plotted for various values of the initial weights. The steady state error increased for smaller values of the initial weights. The initial weights should be chosen iteratively to optimize the system response so that the control error, ε_k, (see Figure 1) is minimized within the iterations performed during each sampling time periods.

As discussed earlier, the number of the delay periods used in the delayed adaptive inverse method reflects the propagation time through the plant and the adaptation associated with the inverse modeling. A general rule of thumb is to set the number of delay periods to be half of the number of weights. After iterative simulations, a delay of 32 sampling periods (in our case, the delay equals to 32x0.0025 seconds or 0.08 seconds) was found to be optimal for our 64 weight FIR based controller. As shown in Figure 11, the smaller the delay, the larger the steady state error of the system response.

A residual "ripple" error remains after the one second settling time (see Figure 8). A feedback control loop can be incorporated into the delayed adaptive inverse approach as shown in Figure 12 in order to remove the residual error in the system response. A linear controller can be used for this purpose since the amount of residual error is small in magnitude. To verify this, a simple proportional gain was successfully used as a feedback controller to entirely eliminate the residual error.

We designed an H_∞ based loopshaping controller using the methodology described in Doyle et al. [17] for controlling the tip motion of our flexible beam (i.e., the plant described by Figure 5 and equations (8) through (13)). We used the Robust Controller Toolbox in MatrixX for the controller design. For comparison purposes, no uncertainty was considered in designing the controller, i.e., only the nominal performance was considered. In an attempt to obtain the desired position response shown in Figure 7, an initial design specification for determining the ideal complementary sensitivity transfer function for loopshaping was formulated as a settling time of one second with critical damping for a step input. The double integrated accelerometer signal (or beam tip position) was used for feedback. However, an optimal controller was not obtained since this specification was too stringent and not achievable. Therefore, the design specification was relaxed to a settling time of one second with an overshoot of less than 20% of the steady state value for a step input. The successful H_∞ based loopshaping controller is thirteenth order, as a result of the order of the system (which is tenth order) and the order of the weighting function (which is third order). The motion response of the flexible beam tip using this H_∞ based loopshaping controller with the desired displacement profile of equation (13) is shown in Figure 13. Comparison of this response with the response of the system based on the adaptive inverse feedforward combined with the linear feedback controller shows that the settling time for the H_∞ controller is 0.5 seconds slower. It would seem that the adaptive inverse controller with a proportional controller results in better performance. However, it is important to note that the improvement achieved by the delayed adaptive inverse controllers over H_∞ based loopshaping controllers is only demonstrated for nominal performance and not for robust performance.

Conclusion

The work described here presents the development of a delayed adaptive inverse method which may facilitate the closed-loop control of a flexible beam. An adaptation of a linear combiner was achieved by using the LMS algorithm to find a best fit to the reciprocal of a given plant transfer function. A copy of this delayed adaptive inverse model was used to compute the necessary torques required to control the non-minimum phase system as shown in Figure 2.

[2] Available from Integrated Systems, Inc., Santa Clara, CA.

The simulation results for the system show that the applied torque is bounded. Comparison of the two system responses, one with adaptive inverse feedforward and linear feedback controllers, and one with H_∞ based loopshaping controller, shows that the first system has better response characteristics. Although the delayed adaptive inverse method works for differentiable nonlinear systems, in this preliminary study, a linear system was used to demonstrate the performance of the delayed adaptive inverse controller so that the result could be compared with that of an H_∞ based loopshaping controller (applicable to linear systems only). Both the delayed adaptive inverse controllers and the H_∞ based loopshaping controllers ought to be able to handle model uncertainty. This will be a subject for future investigation.

The delayed adaptive inverse method uses only knowledge of the desired values for the output (specified as an input r(t) in Figure 2) and the actual plant output measurements in order to determine the control input, u(t), to the plant. This method can be applied equally well to linear systems, systems with differentiable nonlinearities, or even unknown plants as long as a control input can be applied and the plant output can be measured. The question of handling systems with non-differentiable nonlinearities such as backlash, hysteresis, friction, etc. is still an open one and needs to be addressed further.

References

[1] Yang, G.B., "A Delayed Adaptive Inverse Method for End Point Motion Control of Flexible Beams" Ph.D. Thesis, Department of Mechanical Engineering, University of Minnesota, 1991.

[2] Sorensen, B., Donath, M., Yang G., and Starr, R., "The Minnesota Scanner: A Prototype Sensor for 3D Tracking of Moving Body Segments" *IEEE Journal of Robotics and Automation*, vol. 5, no. 4, pp. 499-509, 1989.

[3] Book, W.J., Maizza-Neto, O., and Whitney, D. E., "Feedback Control of Two Beam, Two Joint Systems with Distributed Flexibility" *Journal of Dynamic Systems, Measurement, and Control*, vol. 97, no. 4, pp. 424-431, 1975.

[4] Siciliano, B. and Book, W.J., "A Singular Perturbation Approach to Control of Lightweight Flexible Manipulators" *International Journal of Robotics Research*, vol. 7, no. 4, pp. 79-90, 1988.

[5] Nelson, W.L. and Mitra, D., "Load Estimation and Load-Adaptive Optimal Control for a Flexible Robot Arm" Proceedings of the IEEE International Conference on Robotics and Automation, pp. 206-211, 1986

[6] Meldrum, D.R. and Balas, M.J., "Direct Adaptive Control of Flexible Remote Manipulator Arm" ASME 1985 Winter Annual Meeting, PED, vol. 15, pp. 115-119, 1985.

[7] Cannon, R.H. and Schmitz, E., "Initial Experiments on the End-Point Control of a Flexible One-Link Robot" *International Journal of Robotics Research*, vol. 3, no. 3, pp. 62-75, 1984.

[8] Schmitz, E., "Modeling and Control of a Planar Manipulator with an Elastic Forearm" Proceedings of the IEEE International Conference on Robotics and Automation, pp. 894-899, 1989.

[9] Ficola, A., Marino, R., and Nicosia, S., "A Singular Perturbation Approach to the Dynamic Control of Elastic Robots" Proceedings of the 21st Allerton Conference on Communication, Control, and Computing, 1983.

[10] Khorasani, K.M. and Spong. M.W., "Invariant Manifolds and Their Application to Robot Manipulators with Flexible Joints" Proceedings of the IEEE International Conference on Robotics and Automation, pp. 978-983, 1985.

[11] Nicosia, S., Tomei, P., and Tornambe, A., "Feedback Control of Elastic Robots by Pseudo-Linearization Techniques" Proceedings of the Conference on Decision and Control, pp. 397-402, 1986.

[12] Tomei, P., Nicosia, S., and Ficola, A., "An Approach to the Adaptive Control of Elastic at Joint Robots" Proceedings of the IEEE International Conference on Robotics and Automation, pp. 552-558, 1986.

[13] Forrest-Barlach, M.G. and Babcock, S.M., "Inverse Dynamics Position Control of a Compliant Manipulator" Proceedings of the IEEE International Conference on Robotics and Automation, pp. 196-205, 1986.

[14] Asada, H. and Ma, Z.-D., "Inverse Dynamics of Flexible Robots: Modeling and Recursive Computation Using Virtual Link Coordinate Systems" Proceedings of the American Control Conference, pp. 2352-2359, 1989.

[15] Tomizuka, M., "Zero Phase Error Tracking Algorithm for Digital Control" *Journal of Dynamic System, Measurement, and Control*, ASME, vol. 109, pp. 65-68, 1987.

[16] Tsao, T.-C. and Tomizuka, M. "Adaptive Zero Phase Error Tracking Algorithm for Digital Control," Journal of Dynamic Systems Measurement and Control, vol. 109, pp. 349-354, 1987.

[17] Doyle, J.C., Francis, B.A., and Tannenbaum A. R., *Feedback Control Theory*, Macmillan Publishing Company, New York, 1992.

[18] Yang, G.B. and Donath, M., "A Delayed Adaptive Inverse Method for Position Control of a Flexible Robot Manipulator" Proceedings of the Japan-U.S.A. Symposium on Flexible Automation, ISCIE, Kyoto, Japan, July, pp. 949-956, 1990.

[19] Widrow, B., et al., "Adaptive Noise Canceling: Principles and Applications" Proceedings of IEEE, vol. 63, no. 12, pp. 1692-1716, 1975.

[20] Widrow, B. and Stearns, S.D., *Adaptive Signal Processing* Prentice-Hall, Inc., New Jersey, 1985.

[21] Mattice, M., "Advanced Testbed 1000 (ATB1000) Model: nl_atb4" Automation and Robotics Team, U.S. Army Armament Research, Development and Engineering Center, Picatinny Arsenal, NJ, June, 1992.

[22] Bhat, S.P., "Technical Report for the Advanced Weapons Test Bed" ISI report no. 7834-003, Integrated Systems Inc., June, 1991.

Figures

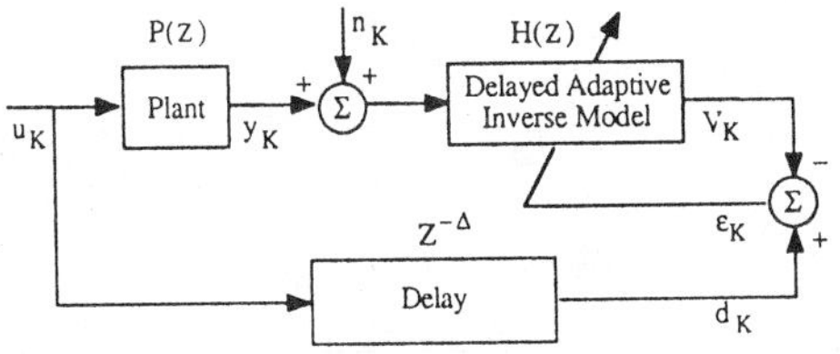

Figure 1. A delayed adaptive inverse model

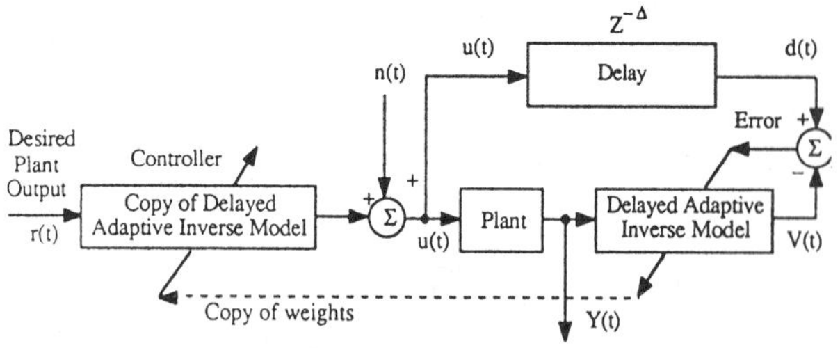

Figure 2. An adaptive inverse model based controller

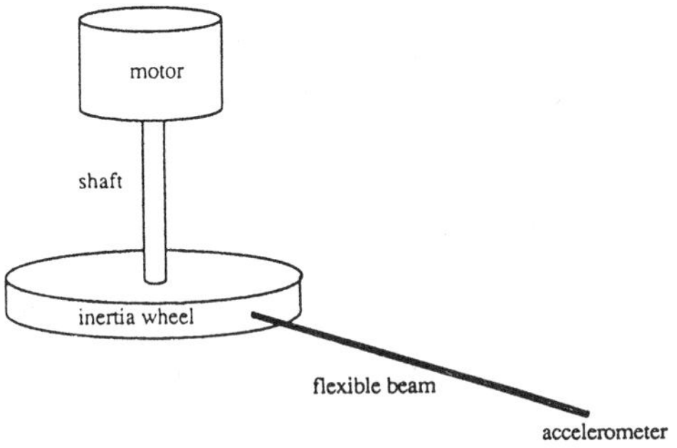

Figure 3. Schematic of the ARDEC flexible beam testbed

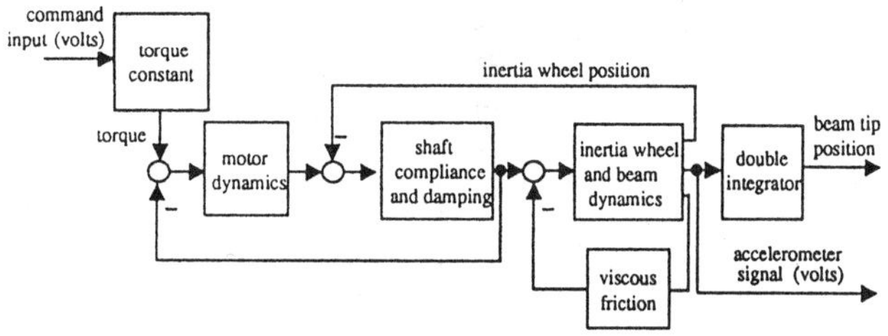

Figure 4. Linear model of the ARDEC flexible beam testbed

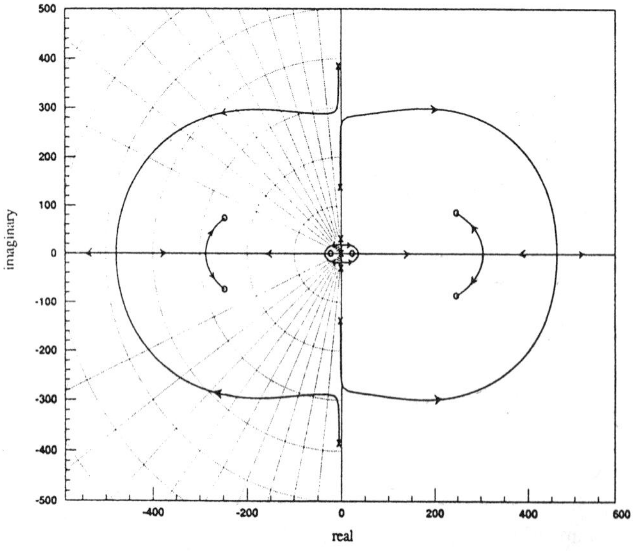

Figure 5. Root locus of the inertia wheel and beam model

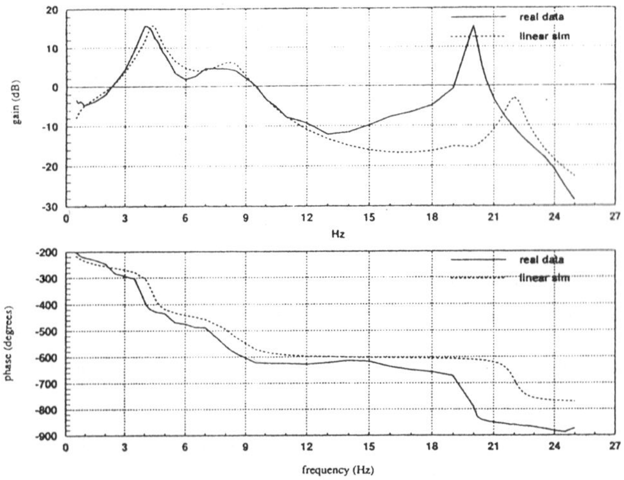

Figure 6. Analytical *vs.* measured frequency responses: torque to tip acceleration (from Mattice, 1992)

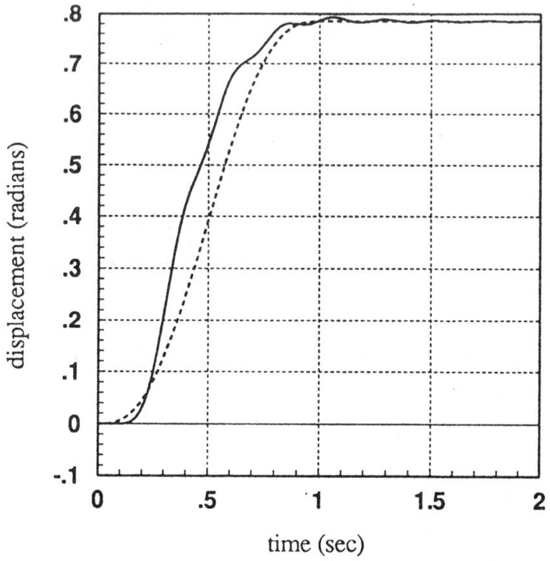

Figure 7. Simulated response of the flexible beam (solid) and desired response (dash)

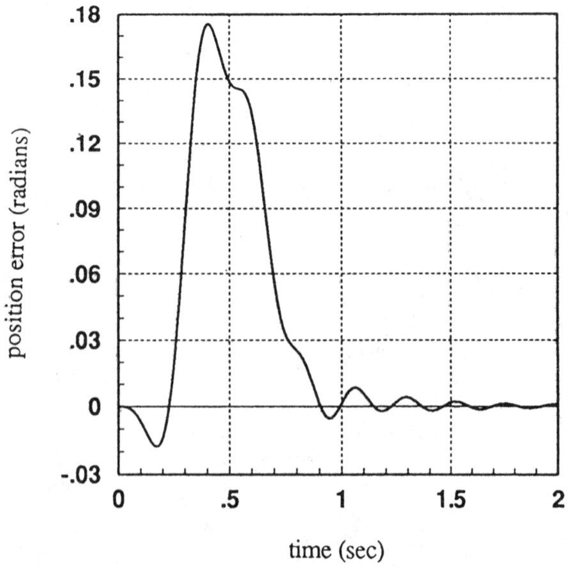

Figure 8. Tip position error for the delayed adaptive inverse method

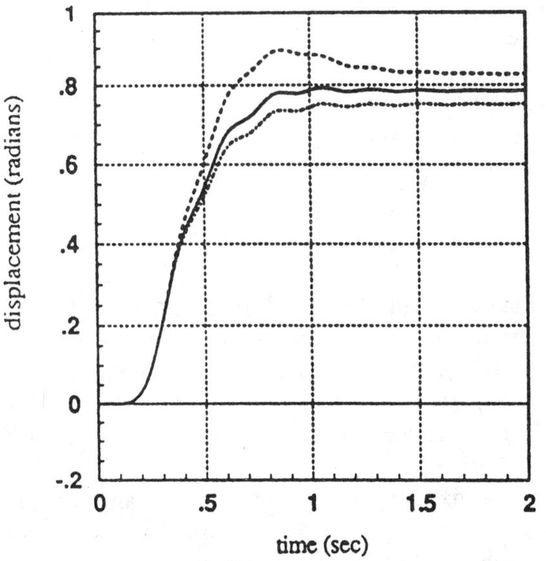

Figure 9. Effects of gain factor μ on the system response 1.64e-5 (solid), 1.0e-5 (dash), 2.0e-5 (dot-dash)

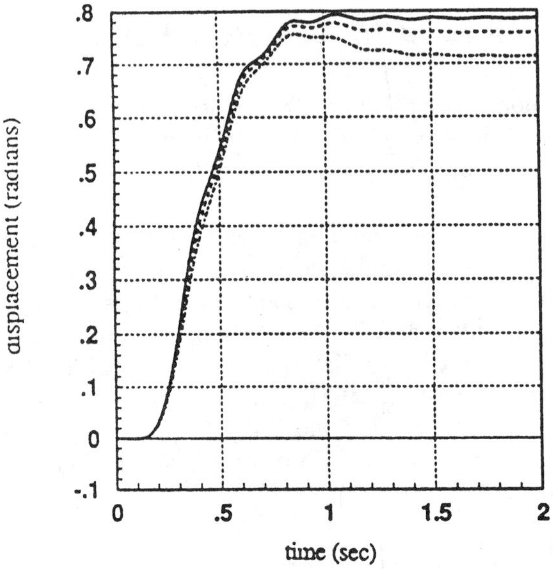

Figure 10. System responses for various values of the initial weights 0.12 (solid), 0.11 (dash), 0.10 (dot-dash)

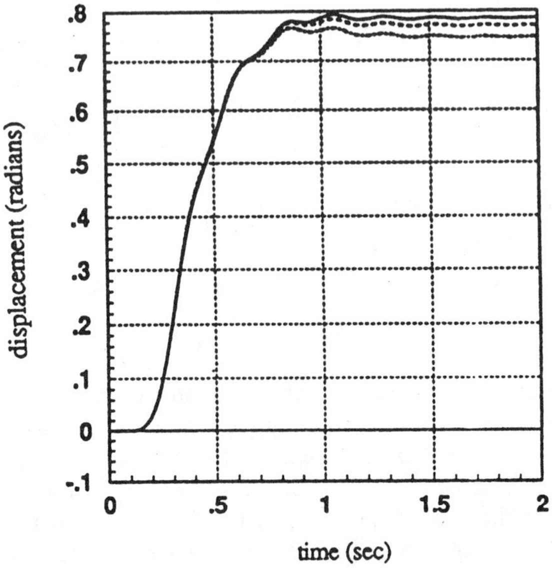

Figure 11. System responses for various number of delays 32 (solid), 26 (dash), 20 (dot-dash)

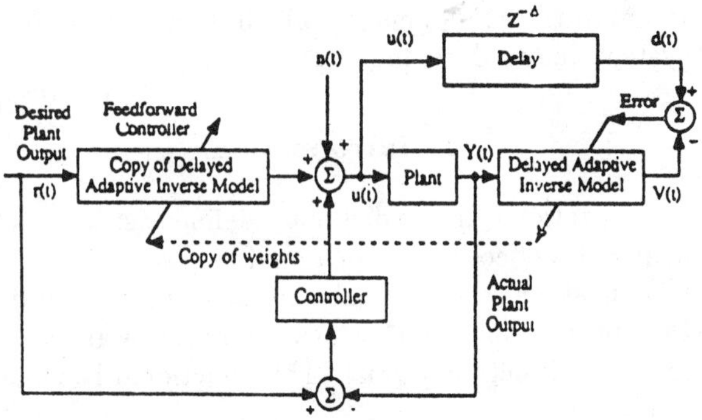

Figure 12. A closed loop control scheme based on the adaptive inverse method

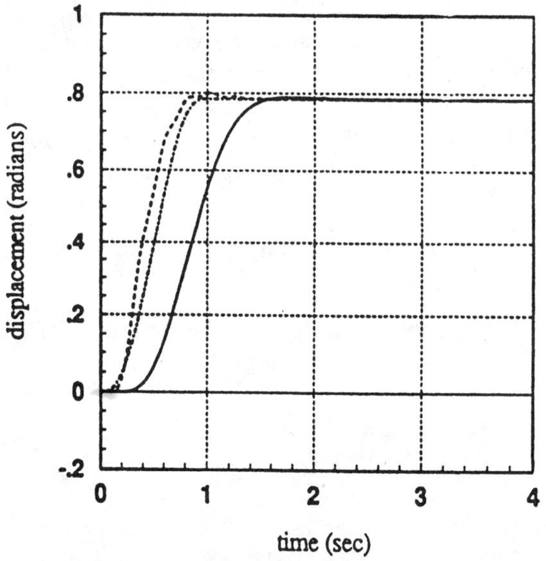

Figure 13. Response of tip position with an H_∞ based loopshaping controller for an input shown in Figure 7, actual response (solid), response of delayed inverse adaptive FIR method as in Figure 7 (dash), desired response (dot-dash)

Proceedings of the
American Control Conference
San Francisco, California • June 1993

OPTIMAL AND ADAPTIVE CONTROL OF UNDERWATER VEHICLES

Dr.ing. Svein I. Sagatun
ABB Industry AS. - Department of Marine Automation
N0501 Oslo, NORWAY - e-mail sis@itk.unit.no

Abstract

This article contains a continuous-time optimal and adaptive control scheme for underwater vehicles moving in six degrees of freedom. The control scheme is an extension of the algorithm of [4] and a modification of the algorithm found in [6]. The algorithm is optimal in the sense that it minimizes the state errors and the forces which contribute to the vehicle's kinetic energy that is spend to correct these errors. The performance measure does also contain a term which penalizes the quadratic tracking errors proportional to the rate of energy which dissipates from the system due to damping.

1 Introduction.

Optimization is in the dictonary defined as: "To make as perfect, effective or functional as possible". Formally speaking, the optimal-control problem is to find the optimal control $\boldsymbol{u}^*$ which minimizes a given performance functional $J(\boldsymbol{u})$. This functional is usually written as:

$$J(\tilde{\boldsymbol{z}}, \boldsymbol{u}) = S(\boldsymbol{z}(t_f)) + \int_{t_0}^{t_f} L(\tilde{\boldsymbol{z}}(\tau), \boldsymbol{u}(\tau))\, d\tau \qquad (1)$$

where $\tilde{\boldsymbol{z}}$ is the system state we wish to control. It is well known from the literature, e.g. [1], that the optimal control $\boldsymbol{u}_x^*(t)$ for the state space we want to control with the performance measure in (1) is found by solving the following equation for all t:

$$\frac{\partial J^*(\tilde{\boldsymbol{z}},t)}{\partial t} + \min_{\boldsymbol{u}_x(t)} \left\{ L(\tilde{\boldsymbol{z}}(t), \boldsymbol{u}_x(t)) + \frac{\partial J^*(\tilde{\boldsymbol{z}},t)^T}{\partial \tilde{\boldsymbol{z}}} \dot{\tilde{\boldsymbol{z}}} \right\} = 0 \qquad (2)$$

Hence, the problem is to find the function $J^*(\tilde{\boldsymbol{z}}, t)$ which is called the Hamilton principle function of optimization.

2 Kinematics.

This article uses an earth-fixed coordinate system sometimes denoted the inertial frame and a vehicle fixed system. We will use the SNAME convention, [8] for the placement of the coordinate systems. Position and orientation will be represented by Euler angles and inertial-fixed coordinates $\boldsymbol{x} = [x, y, z, \phi, \theta, \psi]^T \in \Re^6$ while we will only deal with vehicle-fixed velocities and accelerations denoted $\boldsymbol{v} = [u, v, w, p, q, r]^T \in \Re^6$ and $\dot{\boldsymbol{v}} \in \Re^6$.
The earth-fixed velocities and rate of change of Euler angles $\dot{\boldsymbol{x}} = [\dot{x}, \dot{y}, \dot{z}, \dot{\phi}, \dot{\theta}, \dot{\psi}]^T$ can be transformed to a vehicle-fixed velocity vector $\boldsymbol{v}$ by using the transformation matrix $\boldsymbol{J}(\boldsymbol{x})$, the so called Jacobian matrix. Hence, the transformation from the vehicle-fixed frame to the inertial frame can be performed by employing the following relations:

$$\begin{aligned} \boldsymbol{v} &= \boldsymbol{J}^{-1}(\boldsymbol{x})\dot{\boldsymbol{x}} \\ \dot{\boldsymbol{v}} &= \boldsymbol{J}^{-1}(\boldsymbol{x})\left(\ddot{\boldsymbol{x}} - \dot{\boldsymbol{J}}(\boldsymbol{x})\boldsymbol{J}^{-1}(\boldsymbol{x})\dot{\boldsymbol{x}}\right) \end{aligned} \qquad (3)$$

for a nonsingular $\boldsymbol{J}(\boldsymbol{x})$ matrix. Notice that the vector $\boldsymbol{v}$ is not generalized coordinates, while the vector $\boldsymbol{x}$ represents proper generalized coordinates.

While it is most common to express the equations of motion in the vehicle-fixed frame, the formulation in the inertial frame has some advantages. One is that the differentiation of position, with respect to time, yields velocity directly without going through the Jacobian matrix $\boldsymbol{J}(\boldsymbol{x})$. This property is necessary if we want to employ the Euler-Lagrange equation and is of great advantage in proofs of stability and optimality.

3 The Vehicle Model.

The kinetic energy for the vehicle and its ambient water is in the inertial-fixed frame formulation given by:

$$T_x = \frac{1}{2}\dot{\boldsymbol{x}}^T \boldsymbol{M}(\boldsymbol{x})\dot{\boldsymbol{x}}$$

where $\boldsymbol{M}(\boldsymbol{x}) = \boldsymbol{J}^{-T}(\boldsymbol{x})\boldsymbol{M}_q\boldsymbol{J}^{-1}(\boldsymbol{x})$ and $\boldsymbol{x}$ is a generalized coodinate vector. $\boldsymbol{M}_q$ is the mass of the vessel and its added inertia formulated in the vehicle-fixed frame. We can formulate the Euler-Lagrange equations for the "rigid body-ambient water" system in the vehicle-fixed frame:

$$\tau_{x_i} = \frac{d}{dt}\left(\frac{\partial T_x}{\partial \dot{x}_i}\right) - \frac{\partial T_x}{\partial x_i} + \frac{\partial \mathcal{F}_d}{\partial \dot{x}_i} \qquad ; i = 1..n \quad (4)$$

which yields

$$\boldsymbol{\tau} = \boldsymbol{M}(\boldsymbol{x})\ddot{\boldsymbol{x}} + \dot{\boldsymbol{M}}(\boldsymbol{x},\dot{\boldsymbol{x}})\dot{\boldsymbol{x}} - \frac{1}{2}\frac{\partial}{\partial \boldsymbol{x}}(\dot{\boldsymbol{x}}^T\boldsymbol{M}(\boldsymbol{x})\dot{\boldsymbol{x}}) + \boldsymbol{D}(\boldsymbol{x},\dot{\boldsymbol{x}})\dot{\boldsymbol{x}}$$

or

$$\boldsymbol{\tau} = \boldsymbol{M}(\boldsymbol{x})\ddot{\boldsymbol{x}} + \boldsymbol{C}(\boldsymbol{x},\dot{\boldsymbol{x}})\dot{\boldsymbol{x}} + \boldsymbol{D}(\boldsymbol{x},\dot{\boldsymbol{x}})\dot{\boldsymbol{x}} \qquad (5)$$

where $\boldsymbol{D}$ is the vehicle's damping matrix formulated in the vehicle-fixed frame. Recall that $\dot{\boldsymbol{M}}$ equals to 0. It is useful to define the matrix $\boldsymbol{C}(\boldsymbol{x},\dot{\boldsymbol{x}})$ as:

$$\boldsymbol{C}(\boldsymbol{x},\dot{\boldsymbol{x}}) = \frac{1}{2}\dot{\boldsymbol{M}}(\boldsymbol{x}) + \boldsymbol{N}(\boldsymbol{x},\dot{\boldsymbol{x}}) \qquad (6)$$

where $\boldsymbol{N}(\boldsymbol{x},\dot{\boldsymbol{x}})$ is defined such that

$$\boldsymbol{N}(\boldsymbol{x},\dot{\boldsymbol{x}})\dot{\boldsymbol{x}} = \frac{1}{2}\dot{\boldsymbol{M}}(\boldsymbol{x})\dot{\boldsymbol{x}} - \frac{1}{2}\frac{\partial}{\partial \boldsymbol{x}}(\dot{\boldsymbol{x}}^T\boldsymbol{M}(\boldsymbol{x})\dot{\boldsymbol{x}}) \qquad (7)$$

It is easy to prove that $\boldsymbol{N}(\boldsymbol{x},\dot{\boldsymbol{x}})$ is such that $\dot{\boldsymbol{x}}^T\boldsymbol{N}(\boldsymbol{x},\dot{\boldsymbol{x}})\dot{\boldsymbol{x}} = 0 \quad \forall \dot{\boldsymbol{x}}(t)$. The physical interpretation of this is that the $\boldsymbol{N}_x(\boldsymbol{x},\dot{\boldsymbol{x}})$ matrix represents the workless forces of the vehicle, [7] and [6] .

We will, in the rest of this article, assume that potential energy, i.e. the effect of gravity, is included in the $\boldsymbol{\tau}$ vector such that $\boldsymbol{\tau} = \boldsymbol{\tau}_{ox} - \boldsymbol{g}(\boldsymbol{x})$ is the vector representing forces and moments acting on the vehicle due to gravity.

4 Optimal Criteria.

[4] presents an adaptive and optimal controller for a mechanical manipulator which minimizes the tracking errors and the forces which are needed to correct these errors. Only the forces which contribute to the manipulator's kinetic energy are minimized. There is no point in optimizing the forces that contributes to the potential energy since the potential energy is end-point dependent only. This article presents several modifications of the control scheme introduced in [4]. We employ a performance measure which, in addition to the kinetic energy also includes the energy which dissipate away from the vehicle due to damping effects from the water, e.g. viscous friction. The work done by the system when subtracting potential energy becomes:

$$W = \int_{t_o}^{t_f} \dot{\boldsymbol{x}}^T\left(\boldsymbol{M}\ddot{\boldsymbol{x}} + \frac{1}{2}\dot{\boldsymbol{M}}\dot{\boldsymbol{x}} + \boldsymbol{N}\dot{\boldsymbol{x}} + \boldsymbol{D}\dot{\boldsymbol{x}}\right) dt$$

The term $\dot{\boldsymbol{x}}^T\boldsymbol{N}_x\dot{\boldsymbol{x}}$ is evaluated to zero. A natural extension of the control variabel foun in [4] is therefore for underwater robots:

$$\boldsymbol{u} = \boldsymbol{M}_x\boldsymbol{T}_1\dot{\tilde{\boldsymbol{z}}} + (\boldsymbol{D}_x + \frac{1}{2}\dot{\boldsymbol{M}}_x)\boldsymbol{T}_1\tilde{\boldsymbol{z}} \qquad (8)$$

since the dissipative effect (i.e. viscous damping) is very important for marine vehicles. The vector $\tilde{\boldsymbol{z}}$ is defined as $\tilde{\boldsymbol{z}} = [(\dot{\boldsymbol{x}} - \dot{\boldsymbol{x}}_r)^T, (\boldsymbol{x} - \boldsymbol{x}_r)^T]^T$ and the matrix $\boldsymbol{T}_1$ is the upper $n \times 2n$ matrix of $\boldsymbol{T}_o$ defined as

$$\boldsymbol{T}_o = \begin{bmatrix} \boldsymbol{T}_1 \\ \boldsymbol{T}_2 \end{bmatrix} = \begin{bmatrix} \boldsymbol{T}_{11} & \boldsymbol{T}_{12} \\ 0_{n\times n} & \boldsymbol{I}_{n\times n} \end{bmatrix}$$

The introduction of the $\boldsymbol{T}_o$ matrix results in a non-physical interpretation of the $\boldsymbol{u}$ vector since the matrices are multiplied with a linear combination of acceleration and velocity, and velocity and position respectively. An advantage with the use of the $\boldsymbol{T}_o$ matrix is that the new control variable also becomes a function of the position errors.

5 Basic Assumptions.

The following assumptions are made in the derivation of the control schemes in this article. Assumption A8 is relaxed when the adaptive controller is derived.

A1: The motion is in the inertial reference frame governed by the equation (5).

A2: The reference trajectory is smooth, bounded and within kinematic and physical limits. This can be achieved by assuming that the desired reference trajectory is generated by the strictly stable reference model

$$\ddot{\boldsymbol{x}}_r + \boldsymbol{K}_d\dot{\boldsymbol{x}}_r + \boldsymbol{K}_p\boldsymbol{x}_r = \boldsymbol{K}_p\boldsymbol{x}_d \qquad (9)$$

The $n \times n$ matrices $\boldsymbol{K}_d$ and $\boldsymbol{K}_p$ are define such that $\ddot{\boldsymbol{x}}_r$, $\dot{\boldsymbol{x}}_r$ and $\boldsymbol{x}_r$ are within the physical limits of the vehicle. Physical limited accelerations and velocities imply that $\ddot{\boldsymbol{x}}_r$, $\dot{\boldsymbol{x}}_r$ and $\boldsymbol{x}_r$ are $\in L^\infty$ and $\boldsymbol{x}_r \in C^1$.

A3: The state variables we use in the presented control algorithm are defined by the vector $\boldsymbol{z} = [\dot{\boldsymbol{x}}^T, \boldsymbol{x}^T]^T$ and the tracking error vector $\tilde{\boldsymbol{z}} = [(\dot{\boldsymbol{x}} - \dot{\boldsymbol{x}}_r)^T, (\boldsymbol{x} - \boldsymbol{x}_r)^T]^T$, $\tilde{\boldsymbol{z}} \in \Re^{2n}$. It will also be useful to define the vector $\boldsymbol{z}_r = [\dot{\boldsymbol{x}}_r^T, \boldsymbol{x}_r^T]^T$.

A4: The control variable to be minimized is given by (8).

A5: All states are measured, that is vehicle fixed velocities $\boldsymbol{v}$ and inertial positions and orientations $\boldsymbol{x}$.

A6: In the discussion of the controller, the $\boldsymbol{y}$ vector is referred to as the measurement vector, see also A5. A useful transformation in the coming discussion is $\boldsymbol{z} = \boldsymbol{T}\boldsymbol{y}$ where the transformation matrix $\boldsymbol{T}$ is given as $\boldsymbol{T} = diag(\boldsymbol{J}(\boldsymbol{x}), \boldsymbol{I}_{n\times n})$.

A7: The structure of the equations of motion are completely known and linear in its parameters.

A8: The parameters in the equations of motion are completely known.

A9: We will use the term global stability when we use Jacobian matrices, even though, it is not mathematically correct from a rigorous point of view, since the Jacobian matrices may become singular.

6 The Optimal Control Algorithm.

This section presents extensions of the algorithm presented in [4]. Global uniformly asymptotic stability is proven for the case of a perfectly known vehicle model. However, this is rarely the case for underwater vehicles, so an adaptive version of the algorithm is also presented. Global asymptotic stability is proven for the tracking errors and a bounded parameter estimate is guaranteed in the adaptive case.

State-space representation

A state-space description of (5) combined with the control variable in (8) expressed in the $\tilde{z}$ space can be found according to:

$$\begin{aligned} \dot{\tilde{z}} &= T_o^{-1} \begin{bmatrix} -M^{-1}(C+D) & 0_{n\times n} \\ T_{11}^{-1} & -T_{11}^{-1}T_{12} \end{bmatrix} T_o \tilde{z} \\ &+ T_o^{-1} \begin{bmatrix} M^{-1} \\ 0_{n\times n} \end{bmatrix} u \end{aligned} \tag{10}$$

The control objective

The control objective is to minimize the quadratic performance index given by (1) with the Lagrangian:

$$L(\tilde{z}, u) = \frac{1}{2}\tilde{z}^T \left(Q + T_o^T E D(z) E^T T_o \right) \tilde{z} + \frac{1}{2} u^T R u \tag{11}$$

where $R = r_1 \cdot I_{m\times m} = R^T > 0$, $E = [I_{n\times n}, 0_{n\times n}]^T$, $Q = Q^T > 0$, and t_f is not fixed. A diagonal structure of the matrix R given above is assumed since energy spent to correct tracking errors in one direction is as valuable as in another one. The weighting of the distribution of energy to each of the vehicle's thrusters is taken care of in (22). It is important to realize that we minimize the velocity and thrust in the inertial coordinate system.

Optimality and stability

It is well known from the literature, e.g. [1], that the optimal control $u_x^*(t)$ for the state equation in (10) with the performance measure in (1) can be found by solving the Hamilton-Jacobi equation given by (2).

Lemma 1

The following function J^* satisfies the Hamilton-Jacobi equation and constitutes a Hamilton's principal function for the optimization problem formed by (2) and (11) under the assumptions made above:

$$J^*(\tilde{z}) = \frac{1}{2}\tilde{z}^T(t) T_o^T \begin{bmatrix} M(x) & 0_{n\times n} \\ 0_{n\times n} & K \end{bmatrix} T_o \tilde{z}(t) \tag{12}$$

where K is a positive definite symmetric matrix $K \in \Re^{n\times n}$ and for K and T_o solving the matrix equation

$$\begin{pmatrix} 0_{n\times n} & K \\ K & 0_{n\times n} \end{pmatrix} + Q - T_o^T E R^{-1} E^T T_o = 0 \tag{13}$$

The optimal feedback law u^* that minimizes (1) with the Lagrangian in (11) is

$$u^*(t) = -R^{-1} E^T T_o \tilde{z}(t) \tag{14}$$

Proof: The proof is rather lenghty. A complete proof is found in [6].
□

Theorem 1

The system described by (10) and controlled by (14) always globally uniformly asymptotically stable with the choice of the weighting matrices T_o and K given in [4] and the above assumptions.

Proof: The theorem is proved if we can find a suitable Lyapunov function candidate $V(\tilde{z}, t)$ for the nonautonomous system described by (10) satisfying, [5]:
i) $V(\tilde{z}, t)$ is continuous at $\tilde{z} = 0$ $\forall t$,
ii) $V(\tilde{z}, t)$ is positive radially growing with $||\tilde{z}||$,
iii) $V(\tilde{z}, t)$ has a unique minimum at the origin of the error space and
iv) $\dot{V}(\tilde{z}, t)$ is negative definite along $\tilde{z}$ and t.
It is straightforward to show that $V(\tilde{z}, t) = J^*(\tilde{z}, t)$ satisfies the three first requirements. The last requirement is also easily proven since (2) states that

$$\begin{aligned} \frac{dV}{dt} &= \frac{\partial J^*(\tilde{z}, t)}{\partial t} + \frac{\partial J^*(\tilde{z}, t)^T}{\partial \tilde{z}} \dot{\tilde{z}} = -L(\tilde{z}(t), u(t)) \\ &\Downarrow \\ \frac{dV}{dt} &\le 0 \quad \forall \tilde{z}(t) \neq 0 \end{aligned}$$

Hence we have shown that the system described by (10) and controlled by (14) is always globally uniformly asymptotically stable. This concludes the proof.
□

Comment 1. The dissipative forces in (11), represented by the $D(z)$ matrix, increase the stability of the system. This can also be seen when we look on the mapping from the vehicle's thrust τ to velocity $\dot{x}$ written as $\tau \mapsto \dot{x}$ which is dissipative since $\dot{V} = \tau^T \dot{x} - \dot{x}^T D(z)\dot{x}$, [7]. We observe from the expression of $\dot{V}$ that the gradient of V becomes more negative, that is V converges faster to zero, with increased damping. This is, of course expected compared to the corresponding linear case where the phase margin increases with increased damping. The positive term $\tilde{z}(t)^T T_o^T E D(z) E^T T_o \tilde{z}(t)$ with $T_{12} = 0$ $T_{11} = I_{n\times n}$ corresponds to the rate the energy dissipates from the vehicle.

□

The control law

A combination of the control variable in (8) with the state-space representation in (10) yields the following expression for the resulting thruster forces:

$$\begin{aligned}\tau^* &= C\dot{x} + D\dot{x} + M\Big[\ddot{x}_r - T_{11}^{-1}T_{12}\dot{\tilde{x}} - \\ &\quad T_{11}^{-1}M^{-1}\Big(\left(C + D\right)E^T T_o \tilde{z} - u^*(t)\Big)\Big]\end{aligned}$$

where u_x^* is given by (14). This expression is considerably simplified if we also assume that the Q matrix can be written on the form $Q = diag[q_1 \cdot I_{n\times n},\ q_2 \cdot I_{n\times n}]$. T_{11} and T_{12} will then become diagonal matrices such that $T_{11} = t_{11} \cdot I_{n\times n}$ and $T_{12} = t_{12} \cdot I_{n\times n}$. The new control law then becomes

$$\tau^* = M\left(\ddot{x}_r - \frac{t_{12}}{t_{11}}\dot{\tilde{x}}\right) + (C + D)\left(\dot{x}_r - \frac{t_{12}}{t_{11}}\tilde{x}\right) + \frac{u^*}{t_{11}} \tag{15}$$

This expression can be simplified even more by defining the signals

$$\begin{aligned} s(t) &= t_{11}\dot{x}_r - t_{12}\tilde{x} \\ \dot{s}(t) &= t_{11}\ddot{x}_r - t_{12}\dot{\tilde{x}} \end{aligned} \tag{16}$$

and performing the parameterization:

$$\psi(\dot{s}, s, \dot{x}, x)\theta = \frac{1}{t_{11}}\left(M\dot{s} + Cs + Ds\right)$$

and $u_{t_{11}}^*(t) = \frac{1}{t_{11}}u(t)$ such that

$$\tau^* = \psi(\dot{s}, s, \dot{x}, x)\theta + u_{t_{11}}^*(t) \tag{17}$$

Notice the similarity between the error signal $s(t)$ and the one employed by [3]. The control law in (17) is of no practical use, since the resulting thrust forces are calculated in an inertial reference frame. Eq. (17) is also impractical in the sense that they use velocities decomposed in an inertial reference frame while we measure the vehicle-fixed velocities. A last drawback with (17) is that it is much more complicated in the inertial-frame than in the vehicle-fixed frame. It is, however, possible to transform equation (17) to the vehicle-fixed frame by using the following lemma.

Lemma 2.

The equation described by (17) can be transformed to a vehicle-fixed coordinate system by employing the following transformation:

$$J^T(x)\psi(\dot{s}, s, \dot{x}, x)\theta = \psi_q(\dot{s}_q, s_q, v)\theta_q$$

where the regressor matrix ψ_q is found from

$$\psi_q(\dot{s}_q, s_q, v)\theta_q = \frac{1}{t_{11}}\left(M_q\dot{s}_q + C_q(v)s_q + D_q(v)s_q\right) \tag{18}$$

where $\dot{s}_q$ and s_q is defined in (21). The resulting control law formulated in the vehicle fixed coordinate system then becomes:

$$\tau_q^* = \psi_q(\dot{s}_q, s_q, v)\theta_q + u_q^* \tag{19}$$

The feedback control law formulated in the vehicle-fixed frame $u_q^*(t)$ is found from

$$u_q^*(t) = -\frac{1}{t_{11}}J^T(x)R^{-1}E^T T_o T\tilde{y} \tag{20}$$

Proof: The new signals $\dot{s}_q$ and s_q are found by using (3) on each term in (16) such that:

$$\begin{aligned} s_q(t) &= t_{11}v_r - t_{12}J^{-1}(x)\tilde{x} \\ \dot{s}_q(t) &= t_{11}\dot{v}_r - t_{12}\left(\dot{J}^{-1}(x)\tilde{x} + \tilde{v}\right) \end{aligned} \tag{21}$$

The rest of the proof is straightforward.

□

Note that the first term in $\dot{s}_q$ and s_q are feed-forward terms while the latter are feedback terms. The reparameterization, by using a virtual vector in (18), is similar to the one employed in [3]. Notice also that all signals in (21) are measurable or preprogrammed. The form of the ψ_q vector is also much simpler than the ψ vector.

The corresponding commanded angular velocities n_d to each thruster can be computed from:

$$n_d = B_t^\dagger(v)\tau_q^* \tag{22}$$

where $B_t^\dagger(v) = W^{-1}B_t^T(B_t^T W^{-1}B_t)^{-1}$ for $m > n$ and $B_t^\dagger = B_t^{-1}(v)$ when $B_t^\dagger(v)$ is non-singular. We have used a positive and diagonal W which distributes energy between the different thrusters after a quadratic cost criterion.

7 The Adaptive Control Algorithm.

Many of the parameters in the M, $D(v)$ and $C(v)$ matrices are unknown and time-varying for marine vehicles and especially for small underwater vehicles. This motivates to use an adaptive version of (19).

Rewrite (19) such that it is expressed as a function of the current estimate of the parameters

$$\boldsymbol{\tau}_q = \boldsymbol{\psi}_q(\dot{\boldsymbol{s}}_q, \boldsymbol{s}_q, \boldsymbol{v})\hat{\boldsymbol{\theta}}_q + \boldsymbol{\psi}_{q_o}(\dot{\boldsymbol{s}}_q, \boldsymbol{s}_q, \boldsymbol{v}) + \boldsymbol{u}_q^*(t) \quad (23)$$

where $\hat{(\cdot)}$ denotes the estimated value of $(\cdot)$ and $\boldsymbol{\psi}_o$ represents the part of the model which is completely known. The effective control variable $\boldsymbol{u}_q$ is found by comparing (23) and (19) to be:

$$\boldsymbol{u}_q = \boldsymbol{u}_q^* + \boldsymbol{\psi}_q(\dot{\boldsymbol{s}}_q, \boldsymbol{s}_q, \boldsymbol{v})\tilde{\boldsymbol{\theta}}_q \quad (24)$$

where $\boldsymbol{\psi}_q \in \Re^{n \times p}$ and $\tilde{\boldsymbol{\theta}}_q \in \Re^p$, p is the number of parameters we want to adapt. The corresponding new feedback law formulated in the inertial frame becomes

$$\boldsymbol{u}_{t_1}(t) = \boldsymbol{u}_{t_1}^*(t) + \boldsymbol{\psi}(\dot{\boldsymbol{s}}, \boldsymbol{s}, \dot{\boldsymbol{x}}, \boldsymbol{x})\tilde{\boldsymbol{\theta}} \quad (25)$$

We define the augmented error vector $\boldsymbol{e} \in \Re^{2n+p}$ such that $\boldsymbol{e} = [\tilde{\boldsymbol{z}}^T, \tilde{\boldsymbol{\theta}}^T]^T$ and introduce the new Lyapunov function candidate, [4]:

$$V_e(\boldsymbol{e}, t) = V(\tilde{\boldsymbol{z}}, t) + V_{\theta_q}(\tilde{\boldsymbol{\theta}}_q) \quad (26)$$

where $V_{\theta_q}(\tilde{\boldsymbol{\theta}}_q) = \tilde{\boldsymbol{\theta}}_q^T \boldsymbol{K}_\theta \tilde{\boldsymbol{\theta}}_q$ and $\boldsymbol{K}_\theta = \boldsymbol{K}_\theta^T > 0$ and $V(\tilde{\boldsymbol{z}}, t)$ is found in Theorem 1. We are now ready to formulate the following theorem:

Theorem 2.

The system described by (23) with unknown parameters and controlled by (24) is always globally asymptotically stable with respect to $\tilde{\boldsymbol{y}}$ with the following adaption law:

$$\dot{\hat{\boldsymbol{\theta}}}_q = -\boldsymbol{K}_\theta^{-1}\boldsymbol{\psi}_q^T \boldsymbol{J}^{-1}(\boldsymbol{x})\boldsymbol{E}^T \boldsymbol{T}_o \boldsymbol{T}\tilde{\boldsymbol{y}} \quad (27)$$

Furthermore, the adaptive control law in (27) is stable in the sense that all parameters remain bounded for all t. The adaptive controller will be an optimal adaptive control system for constant parameters when $\tilde{\boldsymbol{\theta}}_q = 0$ and under the assumptions made in the previous section.

Proof: If we differentiate (26) with respect to time we get:

$$\dot{V}_e(\boldsymbol{e}, t) = \dot{V}(\tilde{\boldsymbol{z}}, t) + \dot{V}_{\theta_q}(\tilde{\boldsymbol{\theta}}_q) \quad (28)$$

A combination of (28) with the control law in (25) and the results from [4] and [6] yield:

$$\dot{V}_e(\boldsymbol{e}, t) \leq 0$$

Notice that we assume constant parameters, i.e. $\dot{\boldsymbol{\theta}} = 0$. We use the adaption law in (27) to eliminate terms containing $\boldsymbol{\theta}$ and $\dot{\boldsymbol{\theta}}$. Hence we have proved that $\dot{V}(\boldsymbol{e}, t) \leq 0$. This implies that $V(t) \leq V(0)$ which, in turn, implies that $\tilde{\boldsymbol{z}} = \boldsymbol{T}\tilde{\boldsymbol{y}}$ is bounded. Bounded reference trajectories and the fact that $\boldsymbol{\psi}_q$, $\boldsymbol{\theta}$ and $\boldsymbol{J}(\boldsymbol{x})$ are continuous bounded functions ensure that $\ddot{V}(\boldsymbol{e}, t)$ is bounded, consequently $\dot{V}(\boldsymbol{e}, t)$ is uniformly continuous in time. Finally, application of Barbălat's lemma [2] shows that $\dot{V}(\boldsymbol{e}, t) \to 0$ implying that $\tilde{\boldsymbol{z}} = \boldsymbol{T}\tilde{\boldsymbol{y}}$ converges to zero and that $\hat{\boldsymbol{\theta}}_q$ remains bounded for all t. We have $\boldsymbol{u}_q = \boldsymbol{u}_q^*$ in the case of no parameter errors and, hence, we have an optimal controller with respect to the performance criterion in (1).
□

8 Acknowledgments

The author wish to express its gratitude to Dr. Rolf Johansson and Dr. Thor I. Fossen for helpful discussions. Parts of this research has been funded by an Underwater Technology Grant from BP Exploration Norway AS.

References

[1] M. Athans and P. L. Falb, editors. *Optimal Control.* McGraw-Hill Book Company, New York, 1966.

[2] Barbălat. Systèmes d'Èquations Diffèrentielles d'Oscillations Non Linèaires. *Revue de Mathèmatiques Pures et Appliquèes*, Vol. 4(2):267–270, 1959. Acadèmie de la Rèpublique Populaire Roumaine (in French).

[3] T. I. Fossen and S. I. Sagatun. Adaptive Control of Nonlinear Underwater Robotic Systems. In *Proceedings of the IEEE Conference on Robotics and Automation*, pages 1687–1695, Sacramento, California, April 1991. 1991a.

[4] R. Johansson. Quadratic Optimization of Motion Coordination and Control. *IEEE TAC*, RAC-35(11):1197–1208, 1990.

[5] E. B. Lee and L. Markus. *Foundation of Optimal Control Theory.* John Wiley and Sons, Inc, New York, NY, 1967.

[6] S. I. Sagatun. *Modelling and Control of Underwater Vehicles: a Lagrangian approach* Dr. thesis ITK report 1992:28-W NTH, Trondheim, NORWAY. June 1992.

[7] S. I. Sagatun and T.I. Fossen. Lagrangian Formulation of Underwater Vehicles' Dynamics. In *Proceedings of the IEEE IC SMC*, pages 1029–1034, Charlottesville, VA, October 13-16, 1991.

[8] SNAME. The Society of Naval Architects and Marine Engineers. Nomenclature for Treating the Motion of a Submerged Body Through a Fluid. In *Technical and Research Bulletin 1-5*, 1950.

Proceedings of the
American Control Conference
San Francisco, California • June 1993

A Learning Control of Underwater Robotic Vehicles with Thruster Dynamics†

J. Yuh

Department of Mechanical Engineering
Oregon State University
Corvallis, Oregon 97331, USA

Abstract
Most vehicle control systems based on the simplified vehicle model often result in poor performance because of the nonlinear and time-varying vehicle dynamics as well as thruster dynamics. It is desired to have an advanced control system with capability of learning and adapting to changes in the vehicle dynamics and parameters. This paper describes a learning control system using neural networks for under-water robotic vehicles having a velocity-controlled thruster system. Its effectiveness was investigated by simulation with a single thruster system.

1. Introduction

Underwater robotic vehicles (URVs) are used in unstructured and hazardous environment such as undersea and nuclear plant. In the undersea environment, URVs are used for various work assignments. Among them are: pipe-lining, inspection, data collection, drill support, hydrography mapping, construction, maintenance and repairing undersea equipment etc. URVs for nuclear plants can also provide us with a precision tool to inspect high radiation areas, helping improve our knowledge of the condition of reactors and their internals and our ability to plan maintenace and repair tasks. The vehicles can perform visual inspection to the relevant safety codes in reactor vessels, spent fuel storage pools, suppression pools and other storage tank environments.

† *Funding for this research was provided in part by (R/OE-13) the UH Sea Grant College Program under Institutional Grant No. NA89AA-D-SG063 from the NOAA Office of Sea Grant, Department of Commerce, and in part by the National Science Foundation Grant No. BCS91-57896. This is Sea Grant Publication UNIHI-SEAGRANT-CP-93-06.*

As the use of such vehicles is increased, and operator training and reliability have become important elements in the economic equation, the development of vehicles having greater autonomy becomes highly desired. Engineering problems associated with the high density, non-uniform and unpredictable environment, and the nonlinear response of the vehicle, make a high degree of autonomy difficult to achieve. High technology developed for on-land systems cannot be directly adapted to underwater vehicle systems since such vehicles have different dynamic characteristics from on-land vehicles and their operating environment is unstructured. The control system is one of the most critical subsystems to increase autonomy of the vehicle. It is difficult to obtain high performance by using the conventional control algorithm because of nonlinear vehicle dynamics, unknown hydrodynamic coefficients, unpredictable disturbance. The control system should be able to learn and adapt to the changes in the dynamics of the vehicle and its environment. Most control techniques [1-5] for underwater vehicles in the literature have addressed the control problem of the vehicle without considering the effect of thruster dynamics. There are two types of thruster systems commonly used in the vehicle system: torque-controlled thruster and velocity-controlled thruster. The torque-controlled thruster has the linear steady-state relationship between torque and thruster force but its time constant depends on the propeller angular velocity. At low velocity, the effect of thruster dynamics on the overall vehicle dynamics becomes significant. Effects of a torque-controlled thruster system were investigated in refs. 6 and 7. In this paper, we consider a velocity-controlled thruster system that our research vehicle has, and design a learning control system using a neural network. We also investigate the effect of different number of neurons and hidden layers of the neural network for the learning control application. The contribution of this paper would be a learning vehicle control approach using neural network, which would be justified by extensive simulation study and attract further theoretical investigation.

2. Vehicle Dynamics

In the Autonomous Systems Laboratory of the University of Hawaii, an autonomous underwater robotic vehicle was designed and its first model was built as a part of our research in developing a low-cost test platform for advanced vehicle technologies [8]. This vehicle was designed to have the omni-directional motion with four vertical and four horizontal thrusters. In this section, we discuss vehicle dynamics based our vehicle model.

There are various external forces and torques due to hydrodynamic forces, gravitational forces, buoyant forces, etc. Additional inertia terms to rigid body inertia terms must be introduced to account for the effective mass of surrounding fluid that must be accelerated with the vehicle, so called added mass. The resultant force and moment of a thruster configuration can be expressed as the vector sum of the force and moment from each individual thruster. We assume that the moment of each thruster is negligible compared to the resulting moment of thruster forces. All external forces and torques can be consolidated into the rigid body equations of motion, and then the vehicle dynamic model can be described by:

$$M\dot{V} + C(V,V_f)V + G(X) = F \quad (1)$$

$$\dot{X} = J(X)\, V \quad (2)$$

$$F = RF_T \quad (3)$$

where $V = [u\ v\ w\ p\ q\ r]^T$ is linear and angular velocities in the vehicle coordinates, X is the position and orientation in global coordinates, J is a 6 x 6 transformation matrix, V_f is a fluid velocity vector, the 6x6 inertia matrix $M = M_r$ (rigid body inertia)+M_a(added mass), C is a 6x6 matrix including all the nonlinear dynamic terms with inertia velocity terms, terms associated with the forces and torques exerted on the vehicle by fluid motion, drag forces and torques, G is a vector of gravity and buoyancy and a 6-dimensional vector F represents the forces and torques generated by the thruster forces F_T with a matrix R that is given by the thrusters and the control surface configuration. The detailed description of Eq. 1 can be found in ref. 4.

3. Thruster Dynamics

In this section, we briefly discuss the thruster dynamics. The major problem that is encountered in thruster modeling is that they behave as highly nonlinear actuators. The velocity-controlled thruster has a servo velocity feedback loop, resulting in Eq. 4:

$$T_{ai}\dot{\Omega}_i + \Omega_i = U_{si} \quad (4)$$

where the subscript i indicates the i-th thruster, U_s is the servo velocity control input, and T_a represents a time constant. The servo velocity loop is usually designed to have a much smaller time constant than overall system's time constant, and consequently its dynamics could be ignored. Thrust force F_{Ti} of the i-th thruster is proportional to the absolute square of angular velocity:

$$F_{Ti} = C_{ti}U_i \quad (5)$$

where $U_i = \Omega_i|\Omega_i|$, C_{ti} is a constant and Ω_i is the propeller angular velocity. The constant C_t is often unknown or changes for forward and backward motions due to thruster's configuration. We tested the thruster system mounted on our research vehicle. The experimental results of F_T vs. Ω indicate C_t=5.44E-5 for the forward and 1.79E-5 for the backward thrusts. The effect of motor saturation is introduced by thruster force limits F_{Tmin} and F_{Tmax}.

4. A Learning Control System

A neural net controller considered here is shown in Fig. 1. The neural network has one input layer, one output layer, and multiple hidden layers. Each layer has multiple neurons. Inputs to neurons of the input layer are position errors, velocity errors, and arbitrary constants. One neuron of each hidden layer has also arbitrary constant input signal. Neurons of the output-layer output the control input signals to the vehicle. During the feedforward process, the input signals propagate from the input layer to the output layer, being multiplied by weights between neurons of two layers in sequel and being modified at each neuron by activation functions. We consider a sigmoid activation function $f(x) = (1 - e^{-x})/(1+e^{-x})$ for neurons in the hidden layers and a linear activation function $f(x) = x$ for neurons in the input and output layers. During the learning process, the control error signals are estimated by the critic equation and then used in the learning algorithm to adjust the weights of the network. Each process is described in the following.

4.1 Feedforward Process

The output of the i-th neuron in the m-th layer is computed by

$$q_i^m(t) = f(W_i^m(t)^T q^{m-1}(t)) \quad (6)$$

where W_i^m is a weight vector between the i-th neuron of the m-th layer and the neurons of the (m-1)-th layer, q^{m-1} is an output vector of neurons in the (m-1)-th layer, and the superscript T implies the transpose of the matrix. The output vector of the input layer is

$$q^{input}(t) = [e^T(t) \;\; d]^T \quad (7)$$

where d is arbitrary constant and error vector e includes the position error and velocity error. The output vector of the output layer is the thruster control input U:

$$q^{output}(t) = U(t) \quad (8)$$

From Eqs. 4 & 5, the servo control input to the i-th thruster motor, U_{si} is computed by

$$U_{si}(k) = (|U_i|)^{1/2} \; sgn(U_i) \quad (9)$$

where U_i is the i-th component of U.

4.2 Learning Algorithm

A general form of the error back-propagation can be described by a recursive algorithm Eqs. 10-12:

$$W_i(t) = W_i(t-1) + \rho F_i(t)\Psi_i(t)\,\epsilon(t) \quad (10)$$

where W_i is a weight vector associated with the i-th neuron in the network, ρ is a positive constant known as a learning rate. $\Psi_i(t,W)$ is the gradient of U(t,W) with respect to W_i, and ϵ is the network output error vector. $F_i(t)$ is updated using the following equation based on constant trace method:

$$\bar{F}_i(t+1) = F_i(t) - \frac{F_i(t)\Psi_i(t+1)\Psi_i^T(t+1)\,F_i(t)}{[\,\lambda I + \Psi_i^T(t+1)\,F_i(t)\,\Psi_i(t+1)\,]} \quad (11)$$

$$F_i(t+1) = \frac{\alpha\,\bar{F}_i\,(t+1)}{trace[\bar{F}_i(t+1)]} \quad (12)$$

where α is a positive constant trace of F_i and $0 < \lambda \leq 1$. The learning algorithm (Eqs. 10-12) has been studied in ref. [8]. For simplicity, in this paper, we use $F_i(t)=1$ that results in the classical error back-propagation approach.

4.3 Critic Equation

Unlike the classic backpropagation algorithm [9], the desired mapping of inputs to outputs of the network is unknown a priori. (i.e. the desired values of its outputs are not known a priori.) Therefore, the network must be trained indirectly. We chose a critic function approach [10]. The error signal ϵ is estimated at each time step by the following critic equation:

$$\epsilon(t) = C_e\,[e_v(t) + \beta e_x(t)] \quad (13)$$

where $e_v(t)=V_d(t)-V(t)$, $e_x(t)=X_d(t)-X(t)$, V and X are the actual velocity and position vectors, V_d and X_d are the desired velocity and position vectors, constant β is chosen for a reasonable compensation of position errors, and C_e is a positive constant matrix with appropriate dimension. A network is trained by the critic signal based on the system performance.

5. Simulation

We implement the presented control system for a single thruster system. We consider the same thruster model as the one attached to our underwater vehicle. Thruster force is saturated at -3.5N and 11N. The vehicle is tested with the repeated motion in x-axis. Each cycle of the repeated motion has the same motion. The first cycle, $2t_1$ sec. of the desired motion of the vehicle in x-axis is generated by the following equation and it is repeated for the following cycles:

$$x(t) = f(t) \qquad 2(n-1)t_1 \le t < (2n-1)t_1$$

$$= d_2 - f(t-t_1) \qquad (2n-1)t_1 \le t < 2nt_1$$

where $f(t)=d_1 + (d_2/t_1)[\tau-(t_1/2\pi)\sin(2\pi\tau/t_1)]$

$\tau=t-2(n-1)t_1$, n is a number of cycle, initial position $d_1=0$, final position $d_2=0.5$m, $t_1=2.5$ sec.

We used different neural networks having different number of neurons each layer and differnt number of hidden layers. For simplicity, we use a notation (n_0-n_1- ... -n_k-n_{k+1}) indicating a network having k hidden layers with n_0 input layer neurons; n_1 neurons in the first hidden layer; n_k neurons in the k-th hidden layer; n_{k+1} output layer neurons. Fig. 2 shows mean square errors (MSE) in position with neural networks having different number of hidden layers: (3-4-1), (3-4-4-1), (3-4-4-4-1), and (3-4-4-4-4-1). As time goes by, MSE is getting smaller and networks having two and more hidden layers provide the almost same performance. Fig. 3 shows MSE with a network (3-1) that has no hidden layer and is like a conventional adaptive control system based on PD controller. It shows poor performance with no hidden layer. Fig. 4 shows MSEs with neural networks having different number of hidden neurons in 2 hidden layered network structure: (3-2-2-1), (3-4-4-1), (3-6-6-1), and (3-8-8-1). The more hidden neurons are in the network, the better its performance is. However, after a certain number of neurons, (in our case, 5 neurons in each hidden layer) the performance improvement is not significant. We also tested the effect of number of neurons with 1 hidden layered network structure: (3-4-1), (3-6-1), and (3-8-1). We can have the same remark from the results shown in Fig. 5 as one with 2 hidden layered network case. From these results shown in Figs. 4 & 5, we can also observe that performance of (3-4-1) is not as good as (3-4-4-1). It leads one to say that more hidden neurons are needed for less hidden layered networks to achieve desired performance. However, we would not like to mislead that the number of hidden neurons are more important than the number of hidden layers. Recent studies [11] have shown that multilayered feedback networks with as few as a single hidden layer ad arbitary sigmoid hidden layer activation fuction are capable of arbitrarily accurate approximation to an arbitrary mapping, providing sufficiently many hidden neurons are available. Figs. 2, 4 and 5 show MSE is getting smaller as time goes by even though no information about the controlled system was used to design the control system, except numbers of inputs and outputs. It quantatively proves that the neural network control approach presented here has learning capability.

6. Conclusions

In this paper, thruster dynamics and its nonlinearity between thruster force and angular velocity were discussed with experimental data. We presented a learning controller using neural network for underwater robotic vehicles including the effect of thruster dynamics and its saturation. We also investigated the effect of different number of neurons and layers of the neural network.

We are currently constructing experiment set-up to verify the learning control concept using neural networks. The set-up consists of single thruster, water tank, AD/DA, Intel Neural Network chips (80170NX), Intel iNNTS, encoder, and linear mechanism. We plan to initially implement the off-line approach.

References

[1] H. Kazerooni, and T.B. Sheridan, "Computer Simulation and Control of Underwater Vehicles," MIT Sea Grant College Program, Report No. MITSG 82-19, Oct., 1982

[2] D.N. Yoerger, and J.E. Slotine, "Robust Trajectory Control of Underwater Vehicles," IEEE J. of Oceanic Engineering, Vol. OE-10, No. 4, pp. 462-470, (1985)

[3] K.R. Goheen, and E.R. Jefferys, "Multivariable Self-tuning Autopilots for Autonomous and Remotely Operated Underwater Vehicles," IEEE J. of Oceanic Engr., Vol. 15, No. 3, pp. 144-151, (1990)

[4] J. Yuh, "Modeling and Control of Underwater Robotic Vehicles," IEEE Trans. Sys., Man and Cyber., Vol. 20, No. 6, (1990)

[5] J. Yuh, "A Neural Net Controller for Underwater Robotic Vehicles," IEEE J. Oceanic Engineering, Vol. 15, No. 3, pp. 161-166 (1990)

[6] Yoerger, D.N., J.G. Cooke, and J.E. Slotine 1990. The Influence of Thruster Dynamics on Underwater Vehicle Behavior and

Their Incorporation Into Control System Design, IEEE J. of Oceanic Engr., Vol. OE-15, No. 3, pp. 167-178.
[7] J. Yuh and K.V. Gonugunta, "A Learning Control of Underwater Robotic Vehicles with Thruster Dynamics," submitted for publication in IEEE J. of Oceanic Engineering, 1992
[8] S. Choi and J. Yuh, "Design of an Omni-directional Underwater Robotic Vehicle and its Coordinated Motion Control," ACC, 1993
[9] Yuh, J. 1992. A Multilayered Neural Net Controller using Direct Learning Algorithm, Int'l J. of Computers & Elec. Engr., In press.
[10] Widrow, B., N.K. Gupta, and S. Maitra 1987, "Punish/Reward: Learning with a Critic in Adaptive Threshold Systems", IEEE Trans. Systems, Man and Cyber., Vol. SMC 3, No. 5, pp. 455-465
[11] M. Stinchcombe and H. White, "Universal Approximation using Feedforward Networks with Non-Sigmoid Hidden Layer Activation Functions," Proc. International Joint Conference on Neural Networks, Washington, D.C., pp. I613-I617, 1989

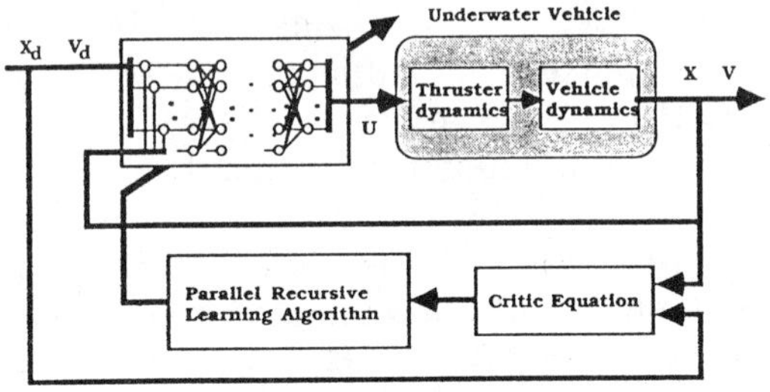

Fig. 1: A Neural Net Control System

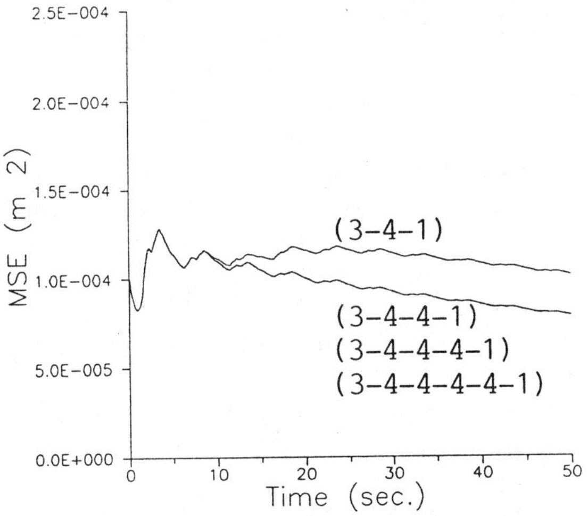

Fig. 2: MSE w/ networks having different number of hidden layers

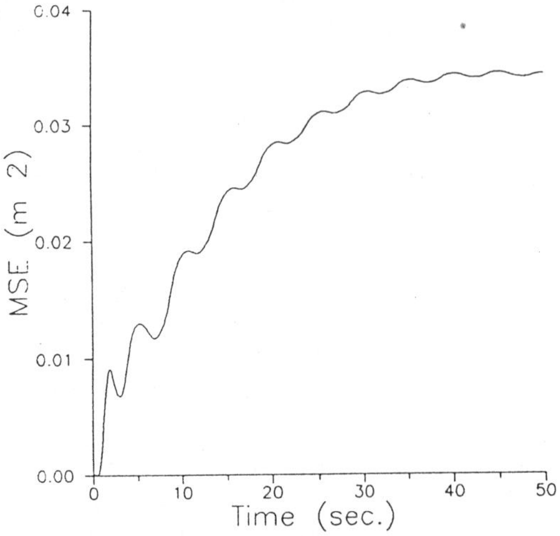

Fig. 3: MSE w/ a network (3-1)

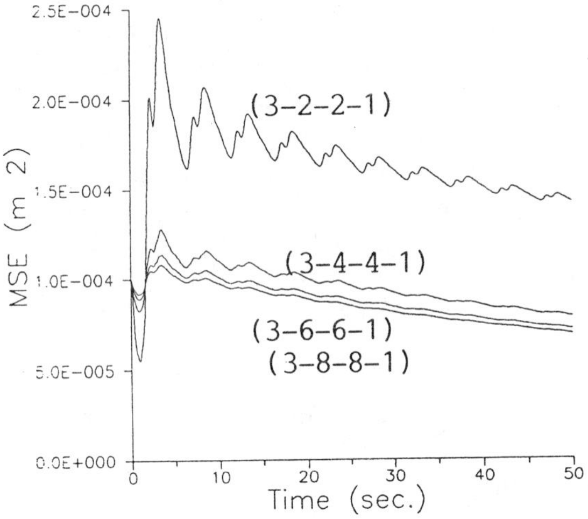

Fig. 4: MSE w/ 2 hidden layered networks having different numbers of neurons

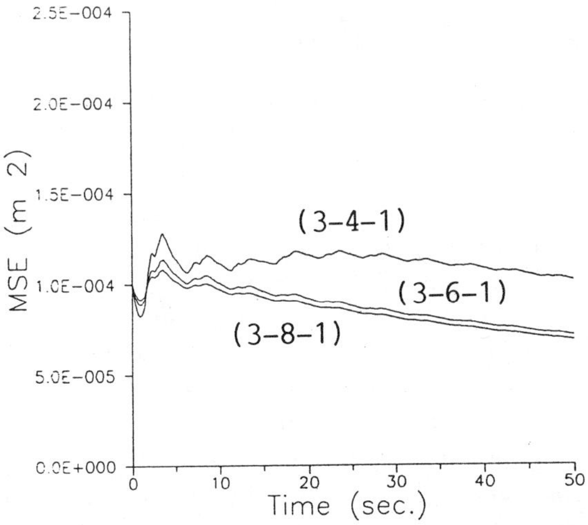

Fig. 4: MSE w/ 1 hidden layered networks having different numbers of neurons

Proceedings of the
American Control Conference
San Francisco, California • June 1993

Design of An Omni-Directional Underwater Robotic Vehicle and Its Coordinated Motion Control

J. Yuh and S. K. Choi

Autonomous Systems Laboratory
Department of Mechanical Engineering
University of Hawaii
Honolulu, Hawaii 96822, USA

Abstract

Underwater robotic vehicles (URVs) have been very attractive for scientific survey, construction, and maintenance in hazardous environments such as ocean and nuclear plant. The development of advanced vehicle technologies is accelerated by the demand for an underwater robotic vehicle with high performance and efficient operation in terms of time and cost. In the Autonomous Systems Laboratory, an autonomous URV was designed and its first model was built as a part of our research in developing a low-cost test platform for advanced vehicle technologies. This paper describes two controllers: nonlinear controller and adaptive controller for the coordinated motion of the vehicle and manipulator, considering the effect of thruster dynamics.

1. Introduction

During the last few years, the use of URVs has rapidly increased since such a vehicle can be operated in the deeper and riskier areas that divers cannot reach. Such vehicles are used in unstructured and hazardous environment such as undersea and nuclear plant. As the use of such vehicles is increased, and operator training and reliability have become important elements in the economic equation, the development of vehicles having greater autonomy becomes highly desired. Engineering problems associated with the high density, non-uniform and unpredictable environment, and the nonlinear response of the vehicle, make a high degree of autonomy difficult to achieve. High technology developed for on-land systems cannot be directly adapted to underwater vehicle systems since such vehicles have different dynamic characteristics from on-land vehicles and their operating environment is unstructured.

URVs perform several challenging functions. During the working mode, the vehicle maintains a steady position to perform a particular task (stationkeeping); during the navigation mode, the vehicle follows a prescribed trajectory in search of an object whose location has already been determined (tracking). The control system is one of the most critical subsystems to increase autonomy of the vehicle. The followings are the major facts that make up a difficult control problem of the URV: The dynamic behavior of the vehicle and manipulator is highly nonlinear; Hydrodynamic coefficients cannot be easily known; The vehicle motion is also disturbed by unpredictable, multidirectional currents. Therefore, it is difficult to obtain high performance by using the conventional control algorithm.

Most control techniques for underwater vehicles in the literature have addressed the control problem. Kazerooni and Sheridan[1] have developed the control system based on the Clayton-Bishop model by using the pole placement and observer method. Their system can be used when all states of the system are not available. However, robustness of the control system with respect to parameter uncertainties cannot be guaranteed. Yoerger and Slotine[2] have proposed a series of single-input and single-output continuous-time controllers by using the sliding control technique. Robustness of their control system with respect to parameter uncertainties was demonstrated by computer simulation using a planar model of the University of New Hampshire Experimental Autonomous Vehicle (EAVE). In their simulation, the effect of pitch, roll and vertical movement were not considered, inertia terms were simplified by placing the moving coordinate system at the center of mass, and the effect of a single thruster on more than one velocity was ignored. Goheen and Jefferys[3] have designed multivariable self-tuning autopilots for underwater vehicles. Yuh[4] presented a dynamic model of URVs and an adaptive vehicle control system. Yuh[5] proposed a neural network control system for URVs. Mahesh, Yuh & Lakshmi [6] proposed a coordinated motion control of an underwater vehicle and manipulator. Yoerger et al. [7] explored the effect of torque-controlled thruster dynamics whose time constant varies with propeller speed. They tested two conventional linear controllers (the lead compensator and the controller by pole cancellation technique) and adaptive sliding controller by computer simulation for the single d.o.f. vehicle model. Results show that the conventional controllers provide poor performance for the low velocity case where the effect of thruster dynamics is significant while the adaptive sliding controller provides better performance for the low velocity. Yuh and Gonugunta [8] designed a neural net based learning controller for the vehicle with the torque-controlled thruster system. Results shows that their control system can provide good performance in spite of changes in the order of overall system dynamics and their parameters. In this paper, we briefly describe our new research test vehicle designed in the Autonomous Systems Laboratory and discuss nonlinear control systems for the coordinated motion of the vehicle and manipulator including the thruster dynamics and saturation.

2. Vehicle Description

We designed an omni-directional, autonomous vehicle in the closed frame. The vehicle's mechanical & electrical architectures were designed to be easily expanded for additional components. The configuration of the vehicle is a closed-framed sphere with eight thruster assemblies and a manipulator. The simplicity of the shape provides rather simple modifications to the shape in testing new experimental vehicles. The eight thrusters provide instantaneous, omni-directional (6 d.o.f.) prowess. Four vertical thrusters and four horizontal thrusters are used for the omni-directional motion. One vertical thruster and one horizontal thruster are paired and four pairs are positioned 90 degree apart along the equator of the spherical vehicle. Fig. 1 shows a picture of the vehicle before attaching four horizontal thrusters. The pitch and altitude control experiments are being conducted with the four vertical thrusters. The manipulator is positioned 45 degrees between the two thrusters. The manipulator is only capable of 1 d.o.f. motion; however, this is sufficient for most tasks due to the omni-directional capabilities of the vehicle and the coordinated motion control of the vehicle and manipulator, which will be further discussed later in this paper. The vehicle can be controlled by either an on-board computer in autonomous mode or a ground computer in remote control mode. The computer makes adjustments to the position and velocity through the integration of various sensors as feedback sources. The vehicle specifications are summarized in Table 1.

2. Control System

There are various external forces and torques due to hydrodynamic forces, gravitational forces, buoyant forces, etc. Additional inertia terms to rigid body inertia terms must be introduced to account for the effective mass of surrounding fluid that must be accelerated with the vehicle, so called added mass. These added mass coefficients are defined as the proportionality constants which relate each of the linear and angular accelerations with each of the hydrodynamic forces and moments they

Table 1: Summary of Vehicle Specifications

Motion	omni-directional
Control mode	remote/autonomous
Speed	max. 1 knot
Accuracy	max. 0.2 m in position
Depth	max. 30 m
Duration	max. 5 hrs w/ battery
Frame material	Aluminum
Frame shape	sphere, closed frame
Frame diameter	0.63 m
Weight in air	150 kg
On-board	Motorola68030-32 CPU
Ground	PC-AT and SGI
Elec. structure	3U VME

generate. For a vehicle moving in a low density fluid, such as an airplane, the forces and moments exerted on the vehicle by fluid motion can be neglected. However, for an URV traveling at low speeds in the ocean, these effects are significant and must be included in the dynamic model. The drag is usually described as a force proportional to the square of the corresponding relative motion of the vehicle. In general, the gravitational force and buoyant forces are defined in terms of the global coordinate system. They must be transformed to the local coordinate systems.

All external forces and torques can be consolidated into the rigid body equations of motion, and then the vehicle dynamic model can be described by:

$$M\dot{V} + C(V,V_f)V + G(X) = F \qquad (1)$$

$$\dot{X} = J(X)\,V \qquad (2)$$

$$F^* = RF_T \qquad (3)$$

where $V = [V^{*T}\ \omega]^T$, $V^* = [u\ v\ w\ p\ q\ r]^T$ is linear and angular velocities in the vehicle coordinates, ω is angular velocity of the manipulator joint, X is the position and orientation in global coordinates, J is a 7x7 matrix including a 6 x 6 transformation matrix, V_f is a fluid velocity vector, the 7x7 inertia matrix $M = M_r$ (rigid body inertia) + M_a (added mass), C is a 7x7 matrix including all the nonlinear dynamic terms with inertia velocity terms, terms associated with the forces and torques exerted on the vehicle by fluid motion, drag forces and torques, G is a vector of gravity and buoyancy and a 7-dimensional vector $F=[F^{*T}\ T_\theta]$, T_θ is a joint torque, F^* represents the forces and torques generated by the thruster forces F_T with a matrix R that is given by the thrusters and the control surface configuration. The detailed description of Eq. 1 can be found in ref. 4 & 6.

In this paper, we consider the velocity-controlled thruster system that our research vehicle has. The velocity-controlled thruster has a servo velocity feedback loop, resulting in Eq. 4:

$$T_{ai}\dot{\Omega}_i + \Omega_i = U_{si} \qquad (4)$$

where the subscript i indicates the i-th thruster, U_s is the servo velocity control input, and T_a represents a time constant. The servo velocity loop is usually designed to have a much smaller time constant than overall system's time constant, and consequently its dynamics could be ignored.

Thrust force F_{Ti} of the i-th thruster is proportional to the absolute square of angular velocity:

$$F_{Ti} = C_{ti}U_i \qquad (5)$$

where $U_i = \Omega_i|\Omega_i|$, C_{ti} is a constant and Ω_i is the propeller angular velocity. The effect of motor saturation is introduced by thruster force limits F_{Tmin} and F_{Tmax}.

Assuming that we have information about the exact model of the vehicle and values of its system parameters, we design a nonlinear controller for the vehicle as follows.

The vehicle system equations 1, 3 and 5 can be rewritten by:

$$M\dot{V} + C(V,V_f)V + G(X) = RC_tU \qquad (6)$$

The objective of the control system here is to control the vehicle to follow a linear reference model that can be chosen as

$$\dot{V}_m = A_mV_m + B_mU_m \qquad (7)$$

where V_m is the output velocity of the reference model, A_m is a stable 7x7 matrix, B_m is a 7x7 matrix, and U_m is the desired input vector.

The control objective can be achieved by

$$U = C_t^{-1}R^{-1}\{C\,V + G + M[A_mV + B_mU_m]\} \qquad (8)$$

From Eqs. 4 & 5, the servo control input to the i-th thruster motor, U_{si} is computed by

$$U_{si}(k) = (|U_i|)^{1/2}\ \mathrm{sgn}(U_i) \qquad (9)$$

where U_i is the i-th component of U.

This nonlinear controller can provide the

desired performance when we have information about the exact values of the system parameters and nonlinear expression of the system dynamics. However, as discussed earlier, hydrodynamic parameters of the vehicle system such as added mass, drag coefficients, and thruster constant C_t are poorly known and varying.

The control system is determined using a discrete-time approximation of the URV dynamic model (Eqs. 1, 3 & 5) which can be expressed by the following vector equation:

$$V(k+1) = A1*V(k) + A0 + B1*U(k) \tag{10}$$

where k is the k-th sampling time step, and V is the 7-dimensional velocity vector of the URV. If the parameters in the discrete-time model were known exactly, a conventional digital control law could be determined using classical methods. However, since the poorly known hydrodynamic coefficients are included among the parameters of the dynamic model, a conventional control scheme cannot guarantee high performance in URV motion control. Therefore, a Parameter Adaptation Algorithm (PAA) is introduced to solve this problem. The PAA estimates the parameters in the discrete-time model at each sampling time step using input-output measurements from the URV. These estimates are then used to adjust the controller gains to provide the required control signals. In this section, a discrete-time adaptive velocity controller for URVs is designed.

The basis of this control algorithm is a linear predictor that is designed with the aim that the prediction error vanishes according to

$$\lim_{k\to\infty} \{\epsilon(k+1)=C_R(q^{-1})[V(k+1)-\hat{V}(k+1)]\}=0 \tag{11}$$

where $\hat{V}(k+1)$ is the predicted value of $V(k+1)$, $C_R(q^{-1}) = I + q^{-1}C_R{}^*$ defines the regulation dynamics, I is the identity matrix and q^{-1} is the unit delay operator. Defining $R = C_R{}^* + A1$ and $A0 = Wd$ where W and a constant d are arbitrary factors of A0, Eq. (11) will be satisfied if the predictor equation is

$$C_R(q^{-1})\hat{V}(k+1)=\hat{R}(k)V(k)+\hat{W}(k)d+\hat{B}1(k)U(k) \tag{12}$$

with the following PAA:

$$\hat{\Theta}(k+1) = \hat{\Theta}(k) + F(k+1)\Phi(k)\epsilon(k+1)^T \tag{13}$$

$$F(k+1) = \left(\frac{1}{\lambda_1(k)}\right)\left\{F(k) - \frac{F(k)\Phi(k)\Phi^T(k)F(k)}{\alpha + \Phi^T(k)F(k)\Phi(k)}\right\} \tag{14}$$

where ˆ is used to denote an estimated value, $\alpha = \lambda_1(k)/\lambda_2(k)$, $0 < \lambda_1(k) \le 1$, $0 \le \lambda_2(k) < 2$,

$F(0) > 0$, $\hat{\Theta}^T(k) = [\hat{B}1(k)\ \hat{R}(k)\ \hat{W}(k)]$ and

$\Phi^T(k) = [U^T(k)\ V^T(k)\ d^T]$.

The parameter adaptation algorithm (Eqs. 13 & 14) and the effect of $\lambda_1(k)$ and $\lambda_2(k)$ were originally discussed for single-input single-output system by Landau and Lozano[9]. The parameter values estimated by the predictor are then used at each time step to compute a control signal such that the output of the predictor follows the desired trajectory:

$$C_R(q^{-1})\hat{V}(k+1)=C_R(q^{-1})V^d(k+1) \tag{15}$$

Substituting Eq. 15 into Eq. 12 and solving for U(k):

$$U(k)=\hat{B}1^{-1}(k)[C_R(q^{-1})V^d(k+1)-\hat{R}(k)V(k)-\hat{W}(k)d] \tag{16}$$

From Eqs. 4 & 5, the servo control input to the i-th thruster motor, U_{si} is computed by

$$U_{si}(k) = (|U_i|)^{1/2}\ \mathrm{sgn}(U_i) \tag{17}$$

where U_i is the i-th component of U.

To summarize, in the proposed control algorithm the parameters of the predictor are estimated at each time step using Eqs. 13 and 14 then the values of these estimated parameters are used to compute the control signal in Eqs. 16 and 17.

6. Conclusions

In this paper, we have presented a continuous-time nonlinear controller and the discrete-time adaptive controller for the underwater robotic vehicle including the effect of thruster dynamics and its saturation. Experimental study for these controllers are being conducted. Experimental results will be shown in the near future.

References

[1] H. Kazerooni, and T.B. Sheridan, "Computer Simulation and Control of Underwater Vehicles," MIT Sea Grant College Program, Report No. MITSG 82-19, Oct., 1982

[2] D.N. Yoerger, and J.E. Slotine, "Robust Trajectory Control of Underwater Vehicles," IEEE J. of Oceanic Engineering, Vol. OE-10, No. 4, pp. 462-470, 1985

[3] K.R. Goheen, and E.R. Jefferys, "Multivariable Self-tuning Autopilots for Autonomous and Remotely Operated Underwater Vehicles," IEEE J. of Oceanic Engr., Vol. 15, No. 3, pp. 144-151, 1990

[4] J. Yuh, "Modeling and Control of Underwater Robotic Vehicles," IEEE Trans. Sys., Man and Cyber., Vol. 20, No. 6, 1990

[5] J. Yuh, "A Neural Net Controller for Underwater Robotic Vehicles," IEEE J. Oceanic Engr., Vol. 15, No.3, pp.161-166, 1990

[6] Mahesh, H., J. Yuh, R. Lakshmi, "A Coordinated Control of an Underwater Vehicle and Robotic Manipulator," J. of Robotic Systems, 8(3), pp. 339-370

[7] Yoerger, D.N., J.G. Cooke, and J.E. Slotine, "The Influence of Thruster Dynamics on Underwater Vehicle Behavior and Their Incorporation Into Control System Design," IEEE J. of Oceanic Engr., 15(3), pp. 167-178.

[8] J. Yuh and K.V. Gonugunta, "A Learning Control of Underwater Robotic Vehicles with Thruster Dynamics," submitted for publication in IEEE J. of Oceanic Engineering, 1992

[9] I.D. Landau and R. Lozano, "Unification of Discrete-time Explicit Model Reference Adaptive Control Designs," Automatica, Vol. 17, No. 4, pp. 593-611, (1981)

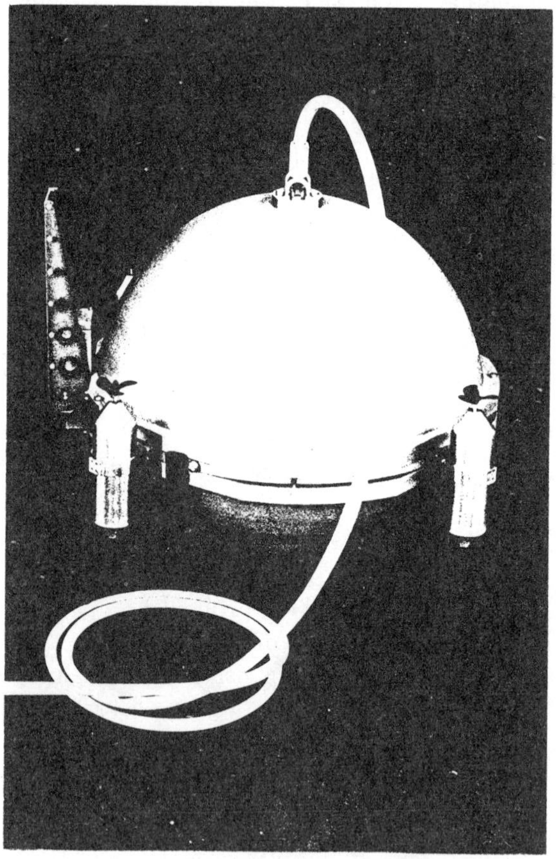

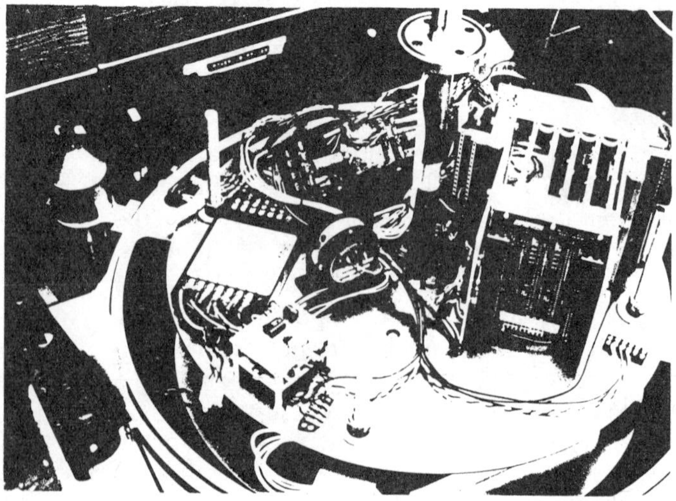

Figure 1: An omni-directional underwater robotic vehicle (Inside & Outside - Pictures were taken before attaching 4 horizontal thrusters.)

Proceedings of the
American Control Conference
San Francisco, California • June 1993

Practical Experiments in ROV System Identification

Linton Clark Kevin R. Goheen Dana R. Yoerger

Dept. of Mechanical & Aerospace Engineering
Carleton University
Ottawa, Ontario
Canada K1S 5B6

Dept. of Ocean Engineering
Woods Hole Oceanographic
Institution, Woods Hole, Massachusetts
USA 02543

Abstract

This paper presents research-in-progress from a joint project between the Department of Mechanical and Aerospace Engineering, Carleton University and the Ocean Engineering Department at the Woods Hole Oceanographic Institute (WHOI). The initial stage of the project is concerned with the application of System Identification (SI) to Remotely Operated Vehicle (ROV) modelling.

Models for ROVs are difficult to derive because their dynamics are strongly coupled, highly nonlinear and vary according to the vehicle's operating configuration. In addition, conventional modelling techniques require the use of expensive, specialised testing equipment. An alternative procedure using SI to process data gathered during simple free-running trials can generate fast, inexpensive and accurate ROV models. A preliminary set of vehicle trials is described. These trials took place in September 1991 at the WHOI's small indoor ROV test tank, using a modified RCV 225. Three SI algorithms are tested on the ROV data and compared for accuracy.

1. Introduction

In the increased depths where offshore oil exploration and production are now taking place, manned intervention techniques, including even saturation diving, are no longer possible. These roles have fallen to ROVs, and possibly, in the future, to AUVs.

The designers of ROVs have traditionally sacrificed the considerations of good hydrodynamic design and controllability for flexibility and reliability. This has lead to vehicles which have been very difficult to pilot and even more complex to model. Accurate dynamic models are crucial if ROV pilot simulators and enhanced autopilots are ever to be realized. Given the expense of offshore operations, it is obvious that a desirable goal would be a pilot with increased skills who has previously attempted a task through simulation and who is now operating a vehicle with greater controllability.

In spite of their usefulness, it is not common for a mathematical model of a new ROV to be derived. Conventional methods involve long and expensive tank testing, followed by substantial engineering effort to derive a model from the experimental results. This will lead to a prohibitively expensive model which will be incorrect as soon as vehicle configuration is changed by the addition of different equipment.

Recent approaches to model derivation have used a numerical technique known as Parameter Estimation (PE). PE has been used a great deal in the aerospace industry to measure the stability and control derivatives of fixed- and rotary-winged aircraft. A typical PE programme is MMLE3, a large, NASA-developed computer program which implements Maximum Likelihood Estimation. MMLE3 suffers from the disadvantage of large memory and time resource requirements on a mainframe computer. This paper will describe the use of System Identification (SI) techniques as both an alternative to PE and its new application to underwater vehicle dynamics. SI algorithms are related to PE methods, but since they are usually formulated in a recursive manner, their computer hardware requirements are much less. In addition, the experiments required for SI model derivation should be much less expensive than conventional trials.

A multi-input/multi-output (MIMO) SI program, written by the one of the authors and running on an inexpensive personal computer, is capable of estimating discrete-time equivalents of the PE model. Alternatively, if only input-output information is required, then the SI model can be used directly for pilot training simulators or autopilot design. This is projected to be a major application of SI models of underwater vehicles.

The framework of these algorithms is described, along with their extension to multi-input/multi-output (MIMO) estimation. A preliminary set of vehicle trials is described. These trials took place in September 1990 at the WHOI's small indoor ROV test tank, using a modified RCV 430. A SHARPS ultrashort baseline sonar system was used to measure accurately the global displacement at two points on the ROV. As well, the instrumentation fit employed roll, pitch and yaw rate sensors. PRBS (pseudo-random binary sequences) were sent to the vehicle's thrusters and simultaneously logged.

The SI method used here requires measurements of the ROV's thruster commands, its local velocities in surge, sway and heave and the roll, pitch and yaw rates. The geometric transformations from trials measurements into these quantities is described. The derived measurements are then fed through a similar SI exercise as took place at the simulation stage. The results of the SI analysis are compared to observed vehicle behaviour; SI is shown to produce models with similar accuracy.

2. Problems with Conventional Modelling Techniques

The ROV model has many similarities with the more familiar models of conventional submarines and aircraft though there are important differences arising from the ROV's creeping motion through the water, often along all three axes simultaneously.

This behaviour manifests itself in the expressions for the mass matrix and the vector of hydrodynamic forces. All the forces and moments caused by the relative motion between the water and the vehicle are included in these two components and are conveniently expressed in terms of hydrodynamic derivatives. Conventional tank trials and subsequent analysis usually leads to very complicated expressions. In a previous study, the equations of motion for the UMEL 'Seapup' ROV were used [2]. The expression for the surge force illustrates the complexity:

$$X = 1/2 \rho L_c^2 U_0^2 [X_u U' + X_u U u' U' + X_{uu} U'^2 + X_{wU} W' U' + X_{uw} U' W' + X_\beta sgn(\pi - \beta) u' U' + X_{ru} r' U' + X_{rrv} r'^2 v' / U' + X_{qq} q'^2 + X_{wwq} W'^2 q' / U' + X_{pv} p' v' + X_{ppw} p'^2 v' / U' + X_{pq} p' q' + X_{rq} r' q'] + X_{\dot{u}} \dot{U} + X_{\dot{r}} \dot{r} \tag{1}$$

where:

$$U' = (u^2 + v^2 + w^2) / U_o \tag{2}$$

Here, L_c is a characteristic length, U_0 is a reference velocity, ρ is the density of sea water, U' is the total speed of the vehicle and the coefficients of the residual force terms are the hydrodynamic derivatives e.g.

$$X_{pv} = \delta^2 X / \delta p \delta v \tag{3}$$

Experience has shown that substantial effort must go into the derivation of these terms and the subsequent model validation [2]. Because of the model's complexity, it is easy to derive equations which will not produce accurate results.

Figure 1 shows a typical ROV and the axis set which is used to describe it. The conventional equations which describe this motion are:

$$M\dot{Q} = \boldsymbol{F}_d(Q) + \boldsymbol{H}(u_r, v_r, w_r, p, q, r) + \boldsymbol{G}(\Phi, \theta, \psi) + \boldsymbol{U} + \boldsymbol{T} \tag{4}$$

where

- M = mass matrix including hydrodynamic added mass
- Q = $\{u\ v\ w\ p\ q\ r\}^T$, the surge, sway, heave, roll, pitch and yaw rates
- F_d = vector of rigid-body kinetic forces
- H = vector of hydrodynamic forces
- G = vector of hydrostatic forces
- U = vector of forces due to umbilical cable
- T = vector of forces due to thrusters
- Φ, Θ, Ψ = orientation (Euler) angles, roll, pitch and yaw

A discussion of the nature of these equations is given in by Lewis, et al [1] and Goheen, et al [2]. This coordinate system will be used in later sections to describe the SI results.

During digital simulation of hydrodynamic-based models, sums of large numbers of terms are made and divided by other long sums to yield output values. SI techniques, on the other hand, would directly identify the quotient of the two sums i.e. state-space models such as:

$$\dot{x} = Ax + Bu \tag{5}$$

This possibly will be more accurate and definitely will require less effort at the experimental stage. For conventional hydrodynamic modelling, a scale model of the marine vehicle, or in the case of the ROV, the vehicle itself, is mounted in a Planar Motion Mechanism (PMM). This device oscillates the model in a prescribed manner, usually so that it moves purely in one degree of freedom only. The PMM itself is attached to the towing tank's carriage. A series of tests with each oscillatory mode and varying PMM frequency and carriage speed yields a pair of hydrodynamic coefficients related to the in-phase and in-quadrature forces and their speed and frequency dependence.

Clearly such a method is very time consuming and hence, expensive. Previous work indicates that it is also of limited worth [3]. A SI modelling trial would dispense with the need for a towing tank and PMM. Instead, the vehicle is run in a protected body of water, ideally a manoeuvring tank. The ROV is equipped with a navigational system for measuring positions and velocities and its control system is modified to accept thruster commands from a computer. This computer also logs the navigational data.

Multivariable SI methods operate on a series of data points and simultaneously estimate the ARMAX (autoregressive, moving-average with exogenous inputs) models which the data best fits. Hence, one experiment which excites all thrusters and degrees of freedom and is of sufficient duration to yield a few hundred input and output data samples could determine the entire model. This was first tested by using raw data produced by a comprehensive nonlinear simulation of an ROV [3].

3. System Identification Background

Ljung and Soderstrom show that models can be derived by two methods [4]. The first, called appropriately, "modelling", determines the parameter values of the physical mechanisms which all together make up the system. Examples would be finding the values of mass, damping and stiffness in a second order system or conventional hydrodynamic modelling of a marine vehicle. An alternative is "identification" where measured signals produced by the system are used to construct the model. If a mass/spring/ dashpot system is set oscillating and the frequency and log decrement of the vibrations noted from the output, then the model has been derived by identification. This section describes in general terms the SI processses used in this study; it is derived primarily from an original section in [3].

If the underlying system changes over time, then the identification must take place continuously. Batch algorithms which operate on the entire set of measured data would be inappropriate since computer memory and processing time would increase with the length of the data set, *Z(t)*:

$$Z(t) = [y(t), y(t-1), \ldots, u(t), u(t-1), \ldots] \tag{6}$$

The "identification problem" is to map the record *Z(t)* to an estimate of the model parameters θ:

$$Z(t) \rightarrow \theta'(t; Z(t)) \tag{7}$$

where ′ denotes an estimate of the true value. The model of the system generates the next output from the parameter values and the previous inputs and responses *Z(t):*

$$y(t+1) = M(\theta(t), Z(t)) \tag{8}$$

The solution is to condense *Z(t)* into an auxiliary memory quantity *S(t)* of fixed dimensions. Recursive SI algorithms are of the form:

$$\begin{aligned} \theta'(t) &= F(\theta'(t-1), S(t), z(t)) \\ S(t) &= H(S(t-1), \theta'(t-1), z(t)) \end{aligned} \tag{9}$$

Since the current parameter estimate θ'(t) is found from the previous estimates, the current auxiliary variable and current measurement, there is only the need to store θ'(t) and S(t), arrays that do not increase in size over time. The recursive SI problem is simply to choose i) the model M (8), ii) the experimental conditions, including the input signal and iii) the functions F and H (9).

The first choice that has to be made is the model set which will represent the true system. If the data is sampled in discrete time, a natural selection would be a linear difference equation or ARMAX model:

$$A(z^{-1})y(t) = B(z^{-1})u(t) + C(z^{-1})e(t) \tag{10}$$

Here, y is the value of the output variable (or vector of variables if a MIMO system), u, the control variable, e, uncorrelated or "white" noise, and z is the backward shift operator. The *z* matrix polynomials in equation (10) are:

$$\begin{aligned} A(z^{-1}) &= I + A_1 z^{-1} + \ldots + A_n z^{-n} \\ B(z^{-1}) &= B_1 z^{-1} + \ldots + B_m z^{-m} \\ C(z^{-1}) &= I + C_1 z^{-1} + \ldots + A_r z^{-r} \end{aligned} \tag{11}$$

where the elements of A_i, B_i and C_i make up the parameter vector θ. With the chosen model set, there are different ways of calculating the 'best' estimate of θ. Least Squares (LS) strives to minimize the equation error:

$$V(\theta) = 1/N \sum_{\alpha_t}^{N} [y(t) - y'(t|\theta)]^2 \tag{12}$$

Here, $C(z^{-1})$ is chosen to be unity and a_t is a factor which changes the weights given to different measurements. If the actual noise model is not unity then LS can give biased estimates of the parameters. This method has a criterion function which is quadratic in θ and so, can be minimized analytically. In general, this is not the case with other Recursive Prediction Error Methods (RPEM) and so approximations must be made in minimizing the equation error. The approximations are dependent on the choice of model. An example is Extended Least Squares (ELS) where the noise model is estimated along with $A(z^{-1})$ and $B(z^{-1})$.

The type of SI algorithm is only one decision that needs to be made. Two other choices of particular interest are the experimental conditions and the model order. Issues to consider with the former includes the sampling rate, what exactly to measure and how to prefilter the raw data. These considerations will be discussed in sections 4 and 5.

Another factor in the experiment is the choice of the input signal. A poor choice can lead to numerical difficulties or even more dangerous, poor estimates without any indication of numerical difficulty. The input must be 'persistently exciting', so that over the course of the experiments, all modes of the system and all combinations of parameters must be perturbed. Since the tests are often driven by computer, a good choice for the inputs is a Pseudo Random Binary Sequence (PRBS), where the signal randomly switches between two levels.

Model order is a compromise between a good description of the data and complexity. Soderstrom reviews many model order determination techniques, two which will be discussed here [5].

The loss function $V_n(\theta)$ (12) decreases as the model order increases. Statistical tests can be used to determine whether this loss is significant. If $V_n(\theta)$ is achieved for a model with n parameters and $V_m(\theta)$ by a model whose number of parameters has been increased to m, then the statistic:

$$F_{n \to m} = \frac{(V_n - V_m)(N - m)}{V_m(m - n)} \tag{13}$$

is F(m-n, N-m: α) distributed, where N is the number of sampling points and α is the risk of error, typically chosen to be between 0.005 and 0.1.

Various figures of merit or "criterion functions" have been proposed for choosing model order, the most widely used being Akaike's Information Criteria (AIC), given by [6]:

$$AIC = -2 \log L + 2v \tag{14}$$

This represents a compromise between the maximum of the likelihood function, L, and the number of model parameters, v, and should be minimum for a correct model. The likelihood function is given by:

$$L = -\exp\left(\frac{N}{2} \log 2\pi + \frac{N}{2} \log R_v + \frac{1}{2} R_v N e^2(k)\right) \tag{15}$$

where $R_v = 1/n \, \Sigma \, e^2(k)$ is the variance of the equation error. By substituting (15) into (14), the expression for AIC becomes:

$$AIC = N(\log 2\pi + 1 + \log R_v) + 2v \tag{16}$$

4. Sensors and Trials Procedure

A collaborative program of work by the Department of Mechanical and Aerospace Engineering, Carleton University and the Deep Submergence Laboratory, Woods Hole Oceanographic Institution was conducted in September 1990 using a modified Benthos RCV 430 ROV in a small testing tank at WHOI. The RCV 430 is an eyeball-type vehicle, shaped approximately like a 1-m-high cylinder of diameter 1 m. It has five fixed-pitch, variable speed thrusters. Four are arranged in a symmetric pattern in the vehicle's x-y plane, at right angles to each other. When used in the appropriate combinations, these will yield longitudinal, lateral and yaw motions. They will also excite the vehicle's pitch and roll dynamics. The fifth thruster is mounted vertically in a tunnel through the vehicle's centreline. It is used primarily to move the ROV in the heave direction.

The instrumentation used consisted of two SHARPS ultra-short baseline pingers mounted on the ROV, on the port and starboard ends of the vehicle's y-axis and roll, pitch and yaw rate gyros. The SHARPS system yields very accurate (~mm) over short distances, such as found in the test tank. The signals were not conditioned by any filters before being sampled. The signals were then converted to digital form and logged by an AT-type microcomputer. The normal joystick control of the ROV was modified to accept the addition of thruster signals from the computer, though manual override by the joystick was always available in order to keep the ROV from striking the tank walls.

5. Results

The input series considered is a PRBS of with varying sample clock cycles and magnitude to the fixed-pitch propellers. The two pingers (hereafter denoted D and E) were sampled asynchronously at 2.27 Hz, the three rate gyros at 25 Hz and the thruster commands at 25 Hz. The computer's clock was used to time-stamp each datum. After carefully ballasting the ROV to make it neutrally buoyant, the first runs were done with the vehicle suspended on a rope in order to get a feel for the allowable magnitude of the PRBS input to the thrusters. A total of 12 trials were attempted; in seven of them, the ROV hit either the tank bottom or side. In an effort to eliminate this problem, the last trials consisted of flying the ROV manually in a "random" fashion; this technique is the method of choice in aircraft and helicopter parameter estimation studies because of the danger of moving too far away from trim conditions.

Coordinate Transformations and Data Filtering

SI takes place with $\{u \; v \; w \; \Phi \; \Theta \; r\}^T$ as the output vector and the five thruster levels (measured in volts) as the input vector. The first step necessary, therefore, is to transform the raw measurements into the output quantities. The voltage inputs to the thrusters were derived from the sampled measurements by scaling the seven-bit signal into the equivalent +/- 10 volts after subtracting the zero-level of the AD convertor. The output transformations were more complicated [7].

The raw data contains the global positions at two points on the ROV, sampled asynchronously. The position data is first synchronized with respect to sensor D. The global position of the centre of the vehicle C is then taken as the average of pingers D and E:

$$\begin{aligned} X_C &= (X_D + X_E)/2 \\ Y_C &= (Y_D + Y_E)/2 \\ Z_C &= (Z_D + Z_E)/2 \end{aligned} \qquad (17)$$

where X, Y, and Z are the global positions of the ROV, which correspond to the u, v and w directions when the three Euler angles are zero. The global speeds dX/dt, dY/dt and dZ/dt are then determined numerically from the changing global positions.

The Euler angles at each time are required in order to convert the global velocities into local velocities. Note that with only two global positions on the ROV recorded that it is impossible to determine unique roll, pitch and yaw angles. In this case, we calculated the Euler angle time series from the local attitude rate measurements. The calculations required were:

$$\begin{pmatrix} \phi(t+1) \\ \theta(t+1) \\ \psi(t+1) \end{pmatrix} = \int_t^{t+1} \begin{pmatrix} \dot\phi(t) \\ \dot\theta(t) \\ \dot\psi(t) \end{pmatrix} dt + \begin{pmatrix} \phi(t) \\ \theta(t) \\ \psi(t) \end{pmatrix} \qquad (18)$$

The initial conditions for roll and pitch were assumed to be zero degrees and the yaw attitude was derived from the X coordinate of the two pingers. In addition, it was necessary, before carrying out (18), to convert the local attitude rates into global rates:

$$\begin{pmatrix} \dot\phi \\ \dot\theta \\ \dot\psi \end{pmatrix} = \begin{bmatrix} 1 & \sin(\phi)\tan(\theta) & \cos(\phi)\tan(\theta) \\ 0 & \cos(\phi) & -\sin(\phi) \\ 0 & \dfrac{\sin(\phi)}{\tan(\theta)} & \dfrac{\cos(\phi)}{\cos(\theta)} \end{bmatrix} \begin{pmatrix} p \\ q \\ r \end{pmatrix} \qquad (19)$$

Applying equations (18) and (19) to the entire set of data will yield the Euler angles at each time which will then allow us to derive local velocities:

$$\begin{pmatrix} u(t) \\ v(t) \\ w(t) \end{pmatrix} = \begin{bmatrix} \cos(\psi)\cos(\theta) & \cos(\psi)\sin(\theta)\sin(\phi) - \sin(\psi)\cos(\phi).. \\ \sin(\psi)\cos(\theta) & \sin(\psi)\sin(\theta)\sin(\phi) + \cos(\psi)\cos(\phi).. \\ -\sin(\theta) & \cos(\theta)\sin(\phi).. \end{bmatrix}$$

$$\begin{matrix} ..\cos(\psi)\sin(\theta)\cos(\phi) + \sin(\psi)\sin(\phi) \\ ..\sin(\psi)\sin(\theta)\cos(\phi) - \cos(\psi)\sin(\phi) \\ ..\cos(\theta)\cos(\phi) \end{matrix} \Bigg]^{-1} \begin{pmatrix} \dot X(t) \\ \dot Y(t) \\ \dot Z(t) \end{pmatrix} \qquad (20)$$

These transformations were relatively easily implemented in MATLAB.

Determination of Model Order

Initially, the simple LS algorithm was used on a record of 300 data points. The orders of $A(z^{-1})$ and $B(z_{-1})$ were increased together starting from 1 until the optimal order is determined. Table 1 lists the values of the loss function $Vn(\theta)$ (12) and AIC_n (16) for n = 1, 2 and 3.

The minimum value of the criterion function shows that while a first order model is adequate to represent surge, second order descriptions are required for the other five degrees of freedom. Therefore, second order matrix polynomials must be used throughout; the F statistics also show these orders are best.

Table 1: Model Order Determination

DOF	Order n	V(θ)	AIC
u	1	$.101 \times 10^{-3}$	-3148
	2	$.174 \times 10^{-3}$	-2851
	3	$.224 \times 10^{-3}$	-2698
v	1	$.118 \times 10^{-3}$	-3075
	2	$.123 \times 10^{-3}$	-3023
	3	$.157 \times 10^{-3}$	-2875
w	1	$.229 \times 10^{-4}$	-3891
	2	$.685 \times 10^{-6}$	-5576
	3	$.666 \times 10^{-6}$	-5704
Φ	1	$.922 \times 10^{-2}$	-898
	2	$.868 \times 10^{-3}$	-2051
	3	$.139 \times 10^{-2}$	-1791
Θ	1	$.236 \times 10^{-1}$	-428
	2	$.103 \times 10^{-1}$	-1968
	3	$.218 \times 10^{-2}$	-1567
r	1	1.088	1482
	2	1.010	1465
	3	0.988	1651

Least Squares, Extended Least Squares and Recursive Prediction Error Methods

The LS algorithm used in the previous section produces a model whose performance is compared to the raw data in figure 2. It is obvious that the vehicle dynamics are characterized very well. In some conditions however, other algorithms might prove to be more suitable. ELS estimates the noise model as well as $A(z^{-1})$ and $B(z^{-1})$; this is important in situations where the noise affecting the system is not white since it prevents biased parameter estimates. The RPEM algorithm uses a more complex gradient approximation than LS or ELS, allowing RPEM to converge in more general conditions than LS or ELS, leading to better accuracy for very long data series from linear systems. However, for systems such as the nonlinear ROV, with unmodelled dynamics, the accuracy of RPEM may not be as good as LS or ELS.

The values of AIC produced by the three different methods operating on the same data series were compared. LS and ELS produce models with nearly identical AIC values. This indicates that modelling $C(z^{-1})$ is really not essential for this data, but it is of some slight value. RPEM had worse performance relative to the more simple algorithms, especially for the shorter data series; this supports the arguments about strong convergence on linear systems.

6. Conclusions

It has been shown that MIMO SI methods can be applied advantageously to the problem of modelling ROV dynamics. All of the nonlinear dynamics which are thought to be essential in modelling a ROV are conveniently lumped into low order linear models. If only am ARMAX model is required, modelling ROVs by SI methods compared with the conventional hydrodynamic approach can result in great savings, both in time and cost. These savings occur because specialized testing equipment such as Planar Motion Mechanisms are no longer required while the velocity and position measuring equipment that is needed for SI is more commonly available.

Once a reliable and efficient method for ROV model derivation by SI is established, it is planned to use the model for control system experimentation and design. One potential area will be a proposed ROV autopilot competition, where different research groups will receive the parameters of the RCV 225 and use it as a benchmark design problem. Final autopilots will be tested during a contest at WHOI.

Successful recursive SI in real-time is a prerequisite for adaptive control, where the dynamics of the ROV are estimated continuously and the controller adjusted accordingly [3,8].

Acknowledgements

The work described here was supported partially by the Natural Sciences and Engineering Research Council of Canada. WHOI provided support for the manoeuvring tank trials.

References

[1] Lewis D.J., Lipscombe J.M and Thomasson P.G. "The Simulation of Remotely Operated Underwater Vehicles.", Proc. ROV '84, The Marine Technology Society, San Diego, 1984, pp 245-252.

[2] Goheen K.R., Jefferys E.R and Broome D.R. "Robust Self-Designing Controllers for Underwater Vehicles.", Proc. ASME Journal of Offshore Mechanics and Arctic Engineering, Vol.109, 1987, pp 170-178.

[3] Goheen K.R. and Jefferys E.R. "System Identification of Remotely Operated Vehicle Dynamics." ASME Journal of Offshore Mechanics and Arctic Engineering, Vol.112, pp 230-236, 1990.

[4] Ljung L. and Soderstrom T. "Theory and Practice of Recursive Identification." MIT Press, Cambridge, Mass., 1983.

[5] Soderstrom T. "On Model Order Testing in System Identification." International Journal of Control, Vol.26, pp 1-18, 1977.

[6] Akaike, H. "Use of an Information Theoertic Quantity for Statistical Model Identification." Proc. 5th Hawaii International Conference on System Science, pp 249-250, 1972.

[7] Clayton B. and Bishop R.E.D., Mechanics of Marine Vehicles, E.& F.N. Spon, London, 1981.

[8] Goheen K.R. and Jefferys E.R. "Multivariable Self-Tuning Autopilots for Autonomous and Remotely Operated Underwater Vehicles." IEEE Journal of Oceanic Engineering, Vol.15, no.3, 1990, pp 144-150.

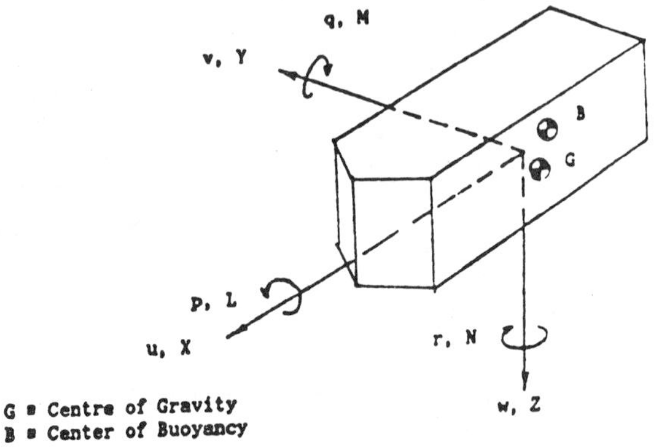

Figure 1: ROV Axis Set (from [2])

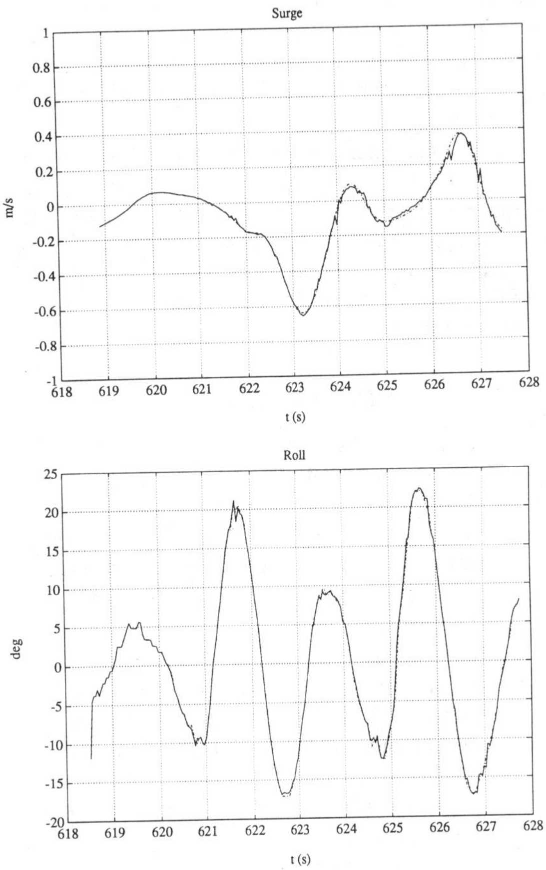

Figure 2: Representative Fit Between the SI Model and Measurements (----: Measurements; - - -: SI Fit)

Proceedings of the
American Control Conference
San Francisco, California • June 1993

A Fuzzy Rule Based Docking Procedure for Two Moving Autonomous Underwater Vehicles

G.J.S. Rae, S.M. Smith, D.T. Anderson, A.M. Shein
Advanced Marine Systems Group
Department of Ocean Engineering
Florida Atlantic University
Boca Raton
Fl 33431
(407) 367-3804
e-mail : graeme@transquest.oe.fau.edu

Abstract – A fuzzy logic control system is described which allows an Autonomous Underwater Vehicle (AUV) to safely dock with another moving underwater vehicle. The fuzzy logic controller's rulebase recursively drives the docking vehicle towards intermediate fuzzy targets that will put the vehicle in an increasingly better position from which docking is more achievable .

A six degree of freedom non-linear model of the Ocean Voyager dynamics is used to test the performance of an AUV under fuzzy control. The imaginary docking collar is fixed to a simple, moving model of a 688 Los Angeles Class submarine. Docking is then attempted from any position around the submarine. Models of uncertainties in vehicle position sensing, turbulence and hull suction effects are also included.

INTRODUCTION

The increasing interest in AUVs with longer mission durations makes appealing the concept of covertly deploying and recovering an AUV from a mother submarine. In this manner, the AUV can be carried to site inside the submarine, launched to carry out a mission, and unlike a regular torpedo (the original AUV), return to its launch tube for further missions. The availability of torpedos that can return home after an unsuccessful mission would also mean a significant increase in the effective payload (i.e. the payload that is successfully used) carried by the submarine. The problem to be addressed here is the algorithm required to autonomously dock an underwater vehicle with a moving mother submarine. It is assumed that the vehicle has an accurate position sensing ability relative to the docking ring. In a previous paper [7] we described an algorithm for docking with a stationary target, however as most underwater vehicles require forward motion in order to maintain control, the ability to dock with a moving target is both more challenging and more likely to be implemented. In other similar problems, path planners have computed the entire trajectory for the docking maneuver. This would require very accurate information about the dynamics of the AUV, and the present environment – information that is largely unavailable. The approach to be used is a goal based fuzzy algorithm. This method allows the vehicle to recursively aim for a target closer and closer to the final docking ring. This fuzzy goal approach does not rely on specific waypoints, or high accuracy maneuvers. Instead, overlapping fuzzy goals are continually evaluated as the vehicle moves to produce a virtual docking funnel. Accuracy increases as the vehicle approaches the target and the funnel constricts. At long ranges the vehicle can be way off course, but as long as it remains within the predetermined funnel it will dock, . Theoretically, once the vehicle has found its way to its first goal it should always manage to dock. However, the presence of uncertainties in position sensing and a current, mean this may not always be the case. We have also simulated a simple model of hull suction to mimic the effects of a very small AUV coming alongside a very large moving submarine. The fact that the algorithm is recursive should deal with these problems as the goals are constantly redefined and the ability of the vehicle to successfully complete docking is re-assessed as it moves toward the target

The algorithm was tested by attempting to dock a highly accurate graphical simulation of the FAU AUV, the 'Ocean Voyager', with a simple linear simulation of a 688 Los Angeles Class Submarine. Docking is attempted at several speeds and from several positions around the mother submarine. The only assumptions made about the mother submarine are that it is unaffected by the hull suction effects and is travelling slowly enough that the AUV is able to catch up with it. A layout of the problem is shown in Figure 1.

SIMULATION AND CONTROLLER

The simulation is a full six degree of freedom model based on the David Taylor Standard Submarine Equations of motion. The simulation also models actuator dynamics, sensor responses and vehicle-surface interaction effects. A full description of the simulation can be found in [8] and [11]. The Flight Control System (FCS) is a rule-based fuzzy controller that is described in [1] and [10].

SUCTION FORCES

In order to model the force acting on a small torpedo-like body moving alongside a much larger underwater body a method of sources, sinks and images was used. Some assumptions were made :

The larger body can be modelled as a flat plate.
The larger body is unaffected by the force.
The AUV can be modelled by a rankine ovoid.
The AUV is moving parallel to the larger body
Seawater is an ideal fluid.

The overall concept was to generate a 2-D 'lookup table' for the suction force indexed by distance from the 688 and speed of the

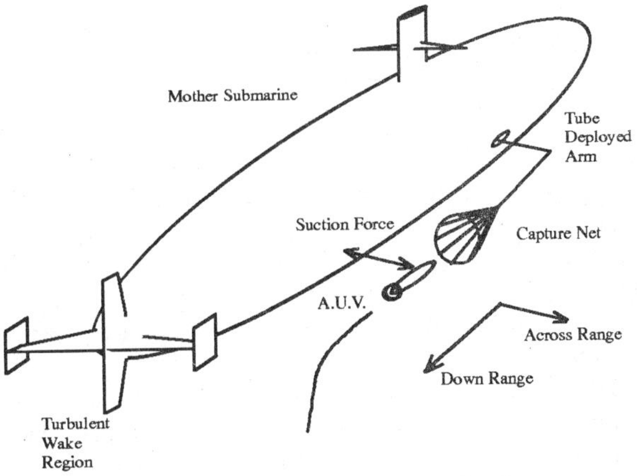

Figure 1 : General Layout of Problem

AUV to immediately indicate a suction force, rather than calculate the velocity and potential fields around the AUV at every time step. This has the added benefit of the generation of a set of non-dimensional curves that provide the force on any size body moving at varying speeds and distances from a flat plate or other non-pliant surfaces.

The velocity potential for the flow past a source-sink pair, giving rise to a single rankine ovoid is given by :

$$\phi = Ux - \frac{m}{4\pi}\left[(x+a)^2 + y^2 + z^2\right]^{-\frac{1}{2}} + \frac{m}{4\pi}\left[(x-a)^2 + y^2 + z^2\right]^{-\frac{1}{2}}$$

Where :

U	=	speed of AUV
m	=	source strength
a	=	offset of source and sink from $x=0$

The stagnation points (and hence the length of the body) are at:

$$x = \pm\frac{l}{2} \quad \text{where} \quad \left(\frac{l^2}{4} - a^2\right)^2 = 2al\left(\frac{m}{4\pi U}\right)$$

Where :

l	=	body length
b	=	body diameter

The value for the source strength is given by

$$m = \pi U b^2\left(1 + \frac{b^2}{a^2}\right)^{\frac{1}{2}}$$

Unfortunately, given the values for l and b we can only solve for m and a numerically.

To evaluate the force acting on the AUV we model the situation as a pair of rankine bodies moving side by side. This produces a flow field that is symmetrical about the center line giving the same effect as a solid boundary between them. By evaluating the potential field around this pair of bodies we can determine the velocity field. Using Bernoulli's equation we can directly relate this velocity field to a pressure distribution on the dividing wall. By summing this pressure distribution we can determine the total force mutually exerted on the mother ship and the AUV.

The potential flow around a pair of rankine bodies at a distance d from the center line is:

$$\phi = Ux - \frac{m}{4\pi}\Bigg[\left[(x+a)^2 + (y+d)^2 + z^2\right]^{-\frac{1}{2}} + \left[(x-a)^2 + (y+d)^2 + z^2\right]^{-\frac{1}{2}} + \left[(x+a)^2 + (y-d)^2 + z^2\right]^{-\frac{1}{2}} + \left[(x+a)^2 + (y-d)^2 + z^2\right]^{-\frac{1}{2}}\Bigg]$$

Where x,y,z are the distances from the center of the dividing wall and d is the distance between the centerline of the AUV and the wall. The velocity of the flow at any point is given by :

$$V^2 = \left(\frac{\partial\phi}{\partial x}\right)^2 + \left(\frac{\partial\phi}{\partial y}\right)^2 + \left(\frac{\partial\phi}{\partial z}\right)^2$$

An example of the velocity profile around a body travelling at 2 kts is shown in Figure 2 below. It can be seen that the distribution is non symmetrical, giving rise to a non-symmetrical pressure distribution around the AUV.

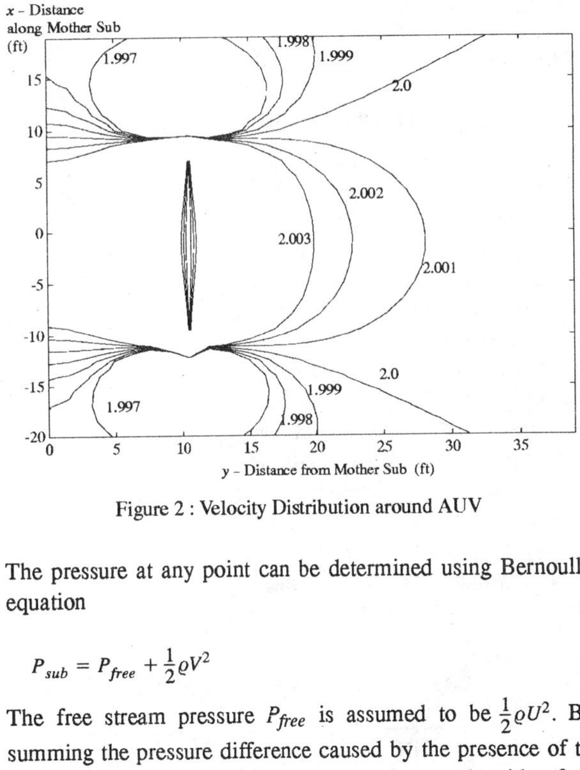

Figure 2 : Velocity Distribution around AUV

The pressure at any point can be determined using Bernoullis equation

$$P_{sub} = P_{free} + \frac{1}{2}\varrho V^2$$

The free stream pressure P_{free} is assumed to be $\frac{1}{2}\varrho U^2$. By summing the pressure difference caused by the presence of the AUV over a large flat plane that approximates the side of the mother submarine we can estimate the force caused the interaction of two bodies. This allowed the production of the set of non-dimensional curves shown in figure 3.

WAKE TURBULENCE

A simple model of wake turbulence is also included, in order to model the effects of a torpedo trying to dock through the wake of a moving submarine. The effect of the turbulence is to push the AUV off track or off course, with increasing force as the AUV enters the wake zone. As information concerning the properties

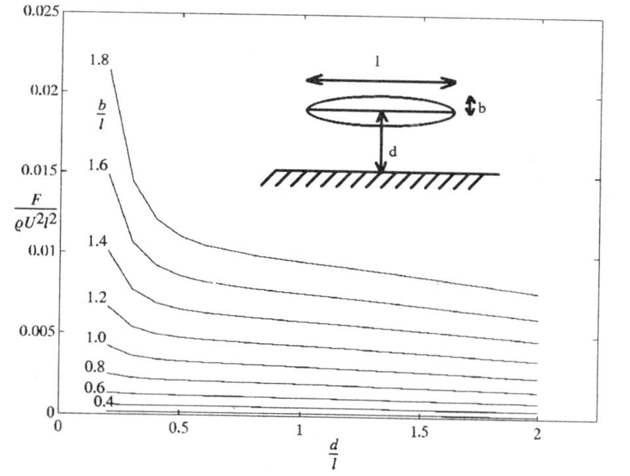

Figure 3 : Non-Dimensional Suction Force Curves

of Submarine wakes is fairly scarce, the size and strength of the wake forces was determined from photographs of slow moving submarines. The wake was estimated to be about 800 feet long, and 400 feet wide at the end. The power of the wake is also unknown. It is assumed that right at the propeller of the target sub, the wake can push the AUV anywhere up to 5 feet off track. This decreases exponentially down range from the propeller and to either side of the center line.

THE FUZZY APPROACH

The method used by the docking algorithm is a recursive goal based system, that repeatedly drives the AUV towards goals that are both easier to achieve, and closer to the final goal as the vehicle moves forward. All the rules are summarized in two diagrams shown in Figures 5 and 6. These diagrams only show the support of each fuzzy term, in actual fact, more than one rule will fire at a time, generating intermediate goal positions. For example, consider the cases shown in Figure 4 below. The vehicle starts at 'o'. In the non fuzzy case, the only cell that is active is 'A', this directs the AUV to 'x', clearly still on the line to the goal 'g', but the AUV will have to turn hard one it reaches 'x' and rule 'C' fires. In the fuzzy case, the vehicle again starts at 'o', but in this case, Cell 'A' is the main rule to fire, but 'o' is within the domain of the other three rules also. The resulting position will be a weighted average of all four rules, based on the distance of 'o' from the center of each cell, The weighting is

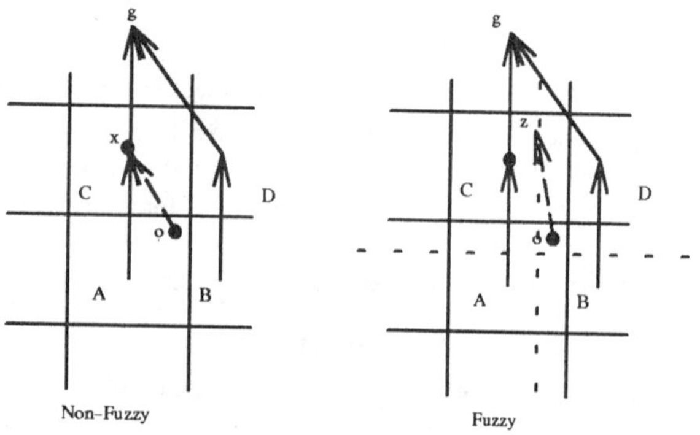

Figure 4 : Fuzzy vs Non-Fuzzy Goal Seeking

determined by the membership function of each rule that fired. This would produce a new goal 'z'. Obviously this is a much better situation than in the non-fuzzy case.

CELL GENERATION

The initial sizes of the goal cells for docking the AUV were estimated using the simulation under human control, and from knowledge of the close-in maneuvering abilities of the AUV (Which was designed for long range cruising). These are known to be fairly poor, due to the length of the vehicle and the small size of its control surfaces, for example, the AUVs minimum turning circle is approximately 150 feet in diameter, and thus the location of target cells must be carefully chosen to allow the AUV to be able to maneuver from one cell to the next.

Fortunately, as the AUV moves from cell to cell, the vehicle heading is implicitly being driven towards the target heading. This has the effect of making it much easier to for the AUV to achieve its goals as it closes with the target, as each subsequent goal lies almost directly ahead of the vehicle.

POSITION CONTROL

A set of goals for each of the position cells is shown in Figure 5. Once the AUV is in one of these cells and in an orientation where it can reach the next cell, docking should be completed. The only case where docking may fail is if the AUV is pushed into one the cells too close to the mother submarine. Here the goal is either the Backout Cell (BO), or another cell which has the Backout Cell as its goal. This second case is to ensure the AUV is in a suitable orientation from which to reach the Backout Cell. The backout cell is defined as (across range = very big, down range = very big).

Table 1 : Fuzzy Definitions

Fuzzy Variable	Depth Error	Azimuth Range	Across Range	Down Range
Negative	–	–	–	< 0 ft
Neg Big	< –15 ft	–	–30 → –15 ft	–
Neg Medium	–25 → –12 ft	–	–22 → –7 ft	–
Neg Small	–15 → 0 ft	–	–15 → 0 ft	–
Zero	–5 → + 5 ft	–	–7 → + 7 ft	< ±400 ft
Very Small	–	< 250 ft	–	< 400 ft
Pos Small	0 → +15 ft	0 → 500 ft	0 → + 90 ft	200 → 600 ft
Pos Medium	+12 → +25 ft	250 → 1000 ft	40 → 160 ft	200 → 1000 ft
Pos Big	> +15 ft	500 → 1500 ft	> 120 ft	900 → 1600 ft
Very Big	–	> 1000 ft	–	> 1200 ft

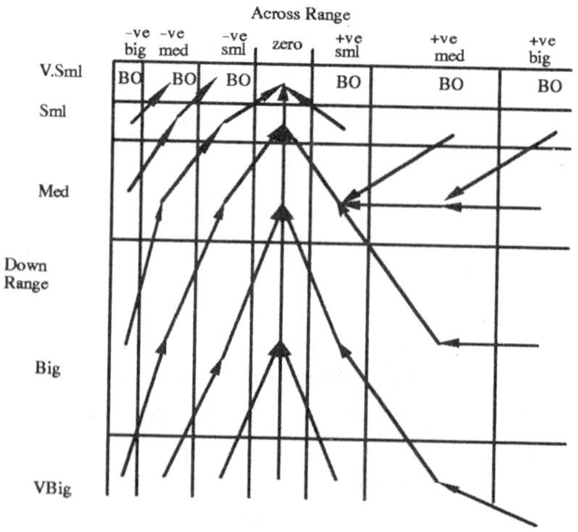

Figure 5 : Goal Cells for Position Control

SPEED CONTROL

The speed of the AUV as it approaches the dock is based on the azimuthal distance to the target and the horizontal distance to the wall of the mother submarine. Simply, speed decreases with distance to the target and distance to the wall.

DEPTH CONTROL

The AUVs ability to control depth is very good [1], and hence the definitions for the goal cells on depth approach can be a lot smaller and a lot closer to the target. A layout of the depth cells is shown in Figure 6. Unlike our previous attempts at docking with a stationary submarine resting on the seafloor [7][10], the submarine is assumed to be moving in clear water with no danger area below it, this allows for a simpler, symmetric cell map for depth goal cells. These fuzzy depth definitions are given in Table 1.

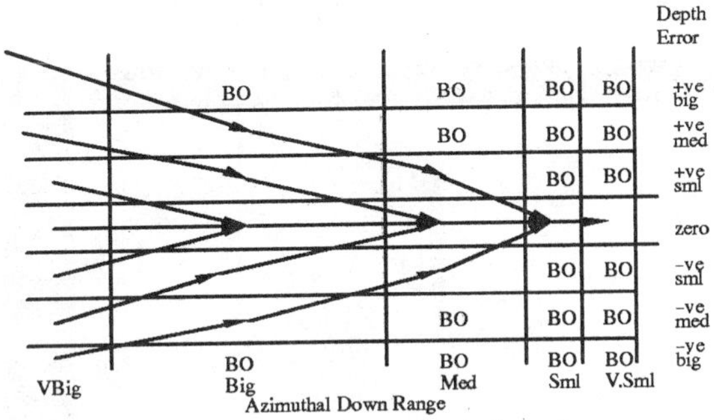

Figure 6 : Goal Cells for Depth Control

RESULTS

The results of a sample run are presented in Figures 7 through 12. The actual path of the vehicle is overlaid with the *estimated* position passed to the docking controller. The AUV manages to dock even in the presence of these uncertainties. The AUV quickly reaches and holds the target depth. (In this example the mother sub is maintaining a constant depth). Heading is presented to show the effect of the suction force on the AUVs motion. For most of the run, the AUVs heading is less than the target heading, as it moves in towards the mother submarine. However, in the final approach the AUV is *heading* in the opposite direction, while *moving* along the correct heading. This crabbing is caused by the balancing of the fin forces with the suction force, resulting in a yaw angle. This yaw angle then reduces as the speed reduces towards final docking. The AUVs speed as it docks is rather confused. This is largely due to the uncoupled nature of the speed controller and the slow response time of the speed system. The sudden drop in speed at around 100 seconds is due to activity by the planes and rudder, which dramatically increase the drag on the AUV. The suction force is related to the square of the velocity and is inversely proportional to the distance. The force only acts when the AUV is alongside the mother submarine.

CONCLUSIONS

We have presented a method whereby an Autonomous Underwater Vehicle is able to successfully dock with a moving target. Obstacle avoidance and heading control are implicitly controlled by the layout of the maneuvering cells. Improvements over the original research into this area include the addition of a moving target, positional uncertainty, turbulence and suction effects, all of which are easily overcome by the docking controller. Eventually this algorithm will be tested in at sea experiments using the Florida Atlantic University AUV, the 'Ocean Voyager' which will attempt to dock with underwater structures and a surface support ship.

REFERENCES

[1] **D.T. Anderson, S. Smith,** "Use of Fuzzy Logic in an UUV Flight Control System," To be published in *Proc. FT&T (1992)*

[2] **H. Farreny, H. Prade,** "Uncertainty Handling and Fuzzy Logic Control in Navigation Problems," *Intl. Auton. Systems. Conf. 1986 pp218-225, (1987)*

[3] **B.R. Gaines,** "Foundations of Fuzzy Reasoning," *Int. Jnl Man-Machine Studies No. 8 pp 623-668 (1976)*

[4] **J. Goguen,** "On Fuzzy Robot Planning, Fuzzy Sets and Their Application to Cognitive and Decision Processes," *eds. L.A. Zadeh et al, pp 429-447, (1974)*

[5] **C.C. Lee,** "Fuzzy Logic in Control Systems: Fuzzy Logic Controller,Part I," *IEEE Trans. of Systems, Man and Cybernetics. Vol 20. No. 2 (1990)*

[6] **C.C. Lee,** "Fuzzy Logic in Control Systems: Fuzzy Logic Controller,Part II," *IEEE Trans. of Systems, Man and Cybernetics. Vol 20. No. 2 (1990)*

[7] **G.J.S. Rae, S.M. Smith,** "A Fuzzy Rule Based Docking Procedure for Autonomous Underwater Vehicles", *Proc. Oceans '92, Rhode Island (1992)*

[8] **A. Shein, J. Kloske,** "Development of Simulation Facilities at Florida Atlantic University for AUV Research," *Proc. S.C.C.S. Baltimore (1991)*

[9] **S.M. Smith,** "Robotics Applications of Fuzzy Decision Making Techniques for Simultaneous Multiple Elastic Constraint Resolution," *Proc. 5th Annual Conf. on recent Advances in Robotics. FAU. Boca Raton Fl. (1992)*

[10] **S.M. Smith, G.J.S. Rae, D.T. Anderson,** "Applications of Fuzzy Logic to the Control of an Autonomous Underwater Vehicle", *Proc. Fuzzy Theory and Technology Conf. Durham, NC, (1992)*

[11] **S.M. Smith, B. Steer, A. Shein, D. Anderson, G. Rae,** "The Design and Implementation of a Real-Time UUV Control System Using Fuzzy Logic, Hardware-in-the-Loop-Simulation, and Sensor Based Navigation." Submitted for publication in *Proc. IARP-92 Italy (1992)*

[12] **M. Sugeno, M. Nishida,** "Fuzzy Control of Model Car," *Fuzzy Sets and Systems, Vol 16 pp103-113, (1985)*

[13] **D.R. Yoerger, A.M. Bradley, B.B. Walden,** "A Deep Ocean AUV for Scientific Survey- The Autonomous Benthic Explorer," *Unmanned Systems, Vol 9, No. 2, pp 17-23 (1991).*

[14] **L.A. Zadeh,** *Fuzzy Algorithms Information and Control, vol 122 pp94-102, (1968).*

[15] Anon. *Unmanned Vehicle Systems: Weapons Systems for the 1990s, (1986)*

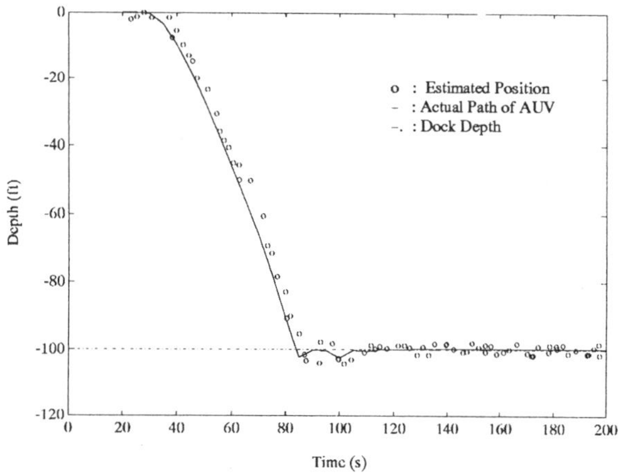

Figure 7 : AUV Depth

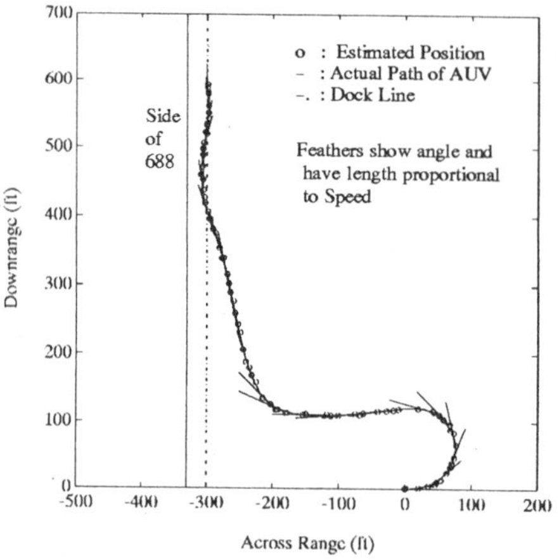

Figure 8 : Path of AUV

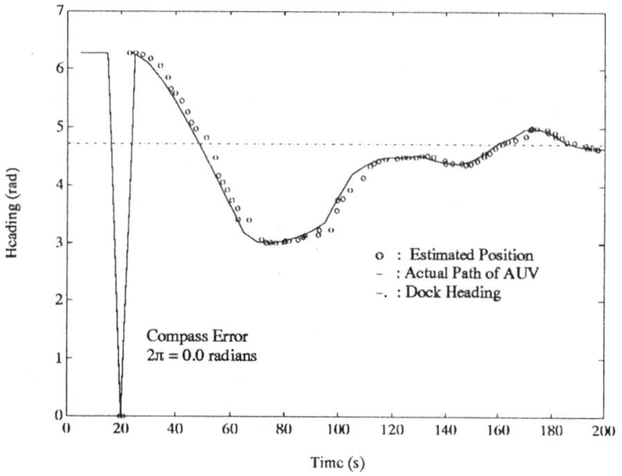

Figure 9 : AUV Heading

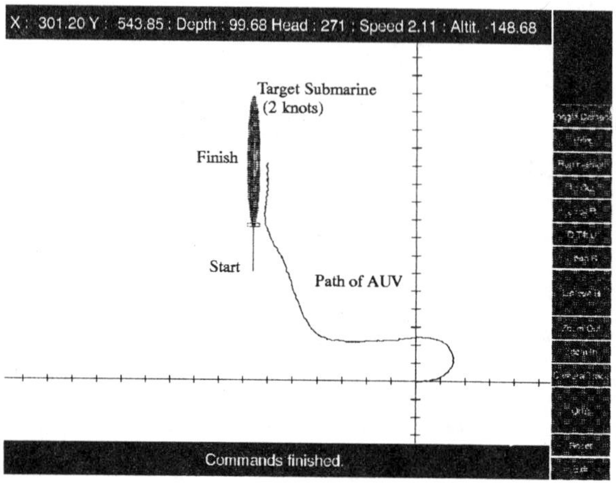

Figure 10 : Snapshot of Simulator

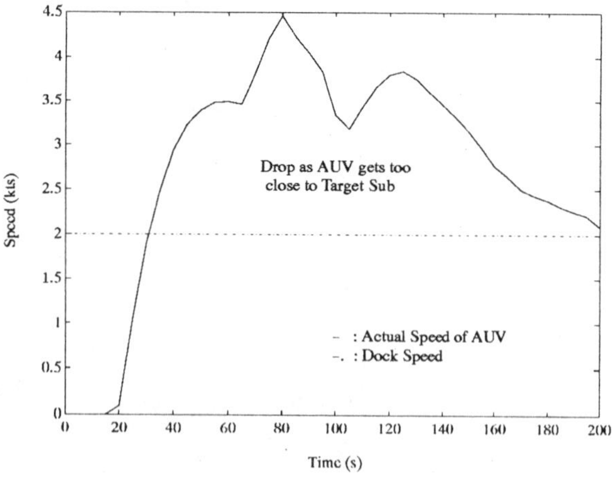

Figure 11 : AUV Speed

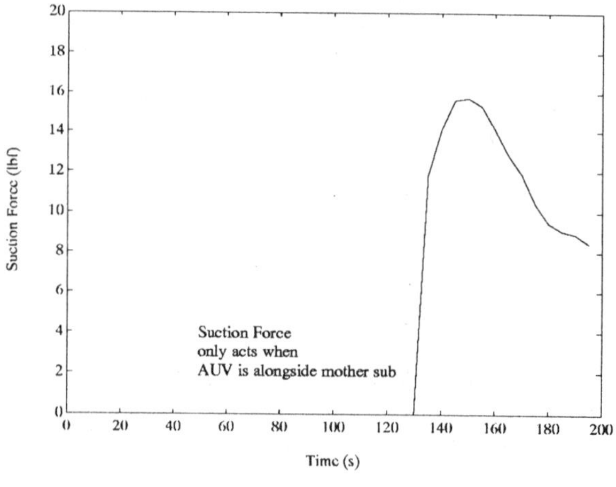

Figure 12 : Suction Force

Proceedings of the
American Control Conference
San Francisco, California • June 1993

TOWARDS AN AUTOMATIC HEALTH MONITOR FOR AUTONOMOUS UNDERWATER VEHICLES USING PARAMETER IDENTIFICATION

A. J. Healey
Naval Postgraduate School
Monterey, Calif. 93943
(408)-656-3462 (Phone)
(408)-656-2238 (Fax)
healey@lex.me.nps.navy.mil

Abstract

In the last few years, interest has grown in the use of autonomous underwater vehicles for commercial, scientific and military missions. Reliability is critical and autonomous fault detection with programmed recovery procedures have to be built into their control logic. It is important that the mission controller have information concerning the current status of the maneuverability subsystems of the vehicle to perform requested motions. The normal techniques of servo error monitors, limit and trend checks, and Kalman filter state estimators with innovations checks go a long way to providing sensor fault detection. However, the inherent capability of a vehicle to determine the state of health of its steering, diving, and speed subsystems (including fin jams) is not easily discovered by these methods.

This paper discusses the use of both batch least squares and Kalman Filters for system parameter identification as a means to detect a change in performance. Applied to the experimental maneuvering responses of the NPS AUV II autonomous underwater vehicle we wish to determine the range of variability of key steering system response parameters that would form the basis of a health monitor. In this application we are not seeking parameter values for the purpose of adaptive control. Instead, we wish to determine if key parameters such as input gain have changed or are out of range.

Background and Context

It is in context of providing an on line autonomous fault detection capability to an autonomous underwater vehicle that this paper is written. We wish to design real time software that will process data from sensory returns including gyro rates and positions and control surface inputs and determine the present operational status of each of the vehicles major subsystems. Operational performance classification would possibly done by neural network elements (Healey et. al., 1992) but the basis of the network inputs would be sensory data preprocessed by a system parameter identifier based on one of several parameter identification schemes currently available. Figure 1 gives an outline of the concept. Figure 2 shows a sketch of the NPS AUV II vehicle currently running as a real time intelligent control systems testbed vehicle at the Naval Postgraduate School. It is a fully autonomous mobile robot submarine that has been designed as a testbed for the development of real time intelligent control concepts. Its capabilities have been outlined recently (Healey and Good, 1992). It can hover and perform dynamic positioning as well as cruise at slow speed to a maximum of about 1 m/s. Recently, motion control experiments have been conducted in the NPS swimming pool (Healey and Marco, 1992) for oval track, figure eight, and waypoint acquisition runs.

Vehicle Modeling

The subsystems that provide the vehicle with its operational mobility capabilities are the steering, diving, propulsion, and hovering control systems, each of which is stabilized by commands from a GESPAC 68030 processor that go to control surfaces, propulsion and thruster motors, and receive input from rate gyros, heading and vertical gyros, and paddle wheel and shaft speed sensors. Vehicle motion response is modeled considering the vehicle as a rigid body in three dimensional motion with forces arising from gravity, hydrostatics, and hydrodynamics [Yuh, 1990].

In this paper we simplify consideration to the horizontal plane steering performance where the control input is a deflection command equally taken by bow and stern rudders and the response is the yaw rate of turn, while speed is assumed to be constant. In marine vehicle maneuvering large body forces generated from side slip support the centripetal accelerations so that the yaw rate (r) and side slip velocity (v) equations are coupled.

The equations of motion for the vehicle may be expressed as

$$m(\dot{v} + ur) = 0.5\rho L^4[Y_{\dot{r}}\dot{r}] + 0.5\rho L^3[Y_{\dot{v}}\dot{v} + Y_r ur] + 0.5\rho L^2[Y_v uv + Y_{\delta b}u^2\delta_b + Y_{\delta s}u^2\delta_s]$$

$$I_{zz}\dot{r} = 0.5\rho L^5[N_{\dot{r}}\dot{r}] + 0.5\rho L^4[N_{\dot{v}}\dot{v} + N_r ur] + 0.5\rho L^3[N_v uv + N_{\delta b}u^2\delta_b + N_{\delta s}u^2\delta_s]$$

where $Y_{\dot{r}}$, $Y_{\dot{v}}$ and $N_{\dot{r}}$, $N_{\dot{v}}$ are the hydrodynamic added mass coefficients for the vehicle in the sway and yaw modes respectively (by convention, negative), and Y_r, Y_v and N_r, N_v are the hydrodynamic force derivatives relating sway and yaw forces and moments to the individual motion components taken as local slopes

Parameter Estimate Prediction: $\hat{\theta}_{k+1|k} = \hat{\theta}_{k|k}$

Error covariance Prediction: $P_{k+1|k} = P_{k|k} + Q$

New Measurement Error:

$$e_{k+1} = r_{k+1} - \Phi_{k+1}\hat{\theta}_{k+1}$$

Gain Update:

$$K_{k+1} = P_{k+1|k}\Phi'_{k+1}[\Phi_{k+1}P_{k+1|k}\Phi'_{k+1} + \rho]^{-1}$$

Parameter Correction: $\hat{\theta}_{k+1|k+1} = \hat{\theta}_{k+1|k} + K_{k+1}e_{k+1}$

Error Covariance Correction:

$$P_{k+1|k+1} = [I - K_{k+1}\Phi_{k+1}]P_{k+1|k}$$

In this work ρ was held at 1.0 and Q was diagonal with equal elements.

EWLS for Parameter Identification

The exponentially weigthed least squares technique produces a recursive parameter estimation without the matrix inversion of the KF and may be expressed as the algorithm used for the KF with ,

$$K_{k+1} = P_{k+1}\Phi'_{k+1}$$

where

$$P_{k+1} = [P_k - (P_k\Phi'_{k+1}\Phi_{k+1}P_k) / (\lambda + \Phi_{k+1}P_k\Phi'_{k+1})] / \lambda$$

and λ is the forgetting factor (Ljung and Soderstrom, 1983)

Experimental Results

Experimental results from maneuvering tests with the NPS AUV II vehicle during the last year have provided numerous data runs that are being analysed. In particular experiments that feature sinusoidal additive steering signals for the purpose of enhancing the parameter identification have been performed. Also, experiments that feature waypoint following in steering the vehicle around the test area of the swimming pool have given data that can also be used for identification purposes. Concentrating on the steering system dynamics, the series of Figures 3-5 illustrate the steering responses with a PD controller tuned to provide rapid steering behavior with some ringing of the control where an additive sinusoidal test signal has been inserted in the loop for identification purposes.

Figure 3 shows the path of the vehicle as a plot of global position Y versus X. Figure 4 shows the measured response of vehicle yaw rate plotted together with steering control surface deflection. The first 40 seconds from the start are characterized by the vehicle accelerating to speed and depth, executing sinusoidal steering motions. The region from 40 to 60 seconds is where the vehicle goes into a turn through 180 degrees, is controlled as it regains the new heading, and from 60 seconds on, continues to execute sinusoidal steering maneuvers until again it is required to turn back to a zero degree heading. During these maneuvers, the vehicle depth was controlled to be effectively constant. Several such experiments were conducted with the vehicle.

It is of interest that the yaw rate response to fully saturated actuation is different from than when the actuator returns the vehicle to its commanded heading and the controller is fully active.

One of the expected results is that at slow speed during the start of the run, the steering strength is low and, on full saturation of the rudder, the planes stall and the effective input gain loses strength dynamically. The parameter identification scheme should detect the loss of gain, and we should focus on the ability of the identification technique to detect input gain changes as a measure of the strength of the control. We know that the gain will be time varying and a function of the maneuver because the time dependent behavior of hydrodynamic pressure distributions on the vehicle make a constant parameter model only a gross simplification of the real world.

Parameter Identification Results

Performing a BLS analysis on the entire oval track record the averaged parameters for the first and second order models are found to be

θ = [1.3413, -0.3642, -0.0021, -0.0058]; with a zero at z_1=-2.7403, and poles λ_1, λ_2 = 0.9632, 0.3781 for the second order model and θ = [0.9674, -0.0119] for the first order model with a pole λ_1= 0.9674

The measure of how an unbiased, constant parameter model will predict the response data is given in Figure 6 and shows that a favorable comparison partially exists but that in several regions there are discrepancies where time variation of parameters is particularly noticeable; in the turn (40 - 60 sec.), and at the start. The straight line in Figure 5 represents the input gain parameter. The second order model identifies the expected non-minimum phase nature of the vehicle steering behavior by the unstable zero.

The analysis with the KF identifier requires the initialization of the parameter vector and the error covariance matrix must be chosen appropriately. The major design variable is the estimation of the parameter noise Q and the measurement noise ν. In view of the fact that the rate gyro signal is clean, the filter tuning is done by adjustment of the parameter noise strength, **Q**. Figure 6 shows the results for the estimation of θ versus time with **Q** = diag(0.01). Notice that the second order denominator coefficients vary little and that the gain terms are small as the vehicle accelerates to speed, build up at speed as they are identified, are reduced as the vehicle goes into a turn at 40 - 60 sec. and finally regain their nominal values.

Figure 7 shows a comparison of the variability of the second order model gain measure ($\theta_3+\theta_4$) for (**Q** = 0.001, about a null motion point at nominal forward speed. $Y_{\delta b}$, $Y_{\delta s}$ and $N_{\delta b}$, $N_{\delta s}$ are the local slopes of the actuation forces and moments from control fin deflection.

The hydrodynamic derivatives may be estimated from wing theory (Lewis,1988) but are usually considered to highly uncertain, only valid for small angles of side slip ($\tan(\beta) = -v/u$) and are expected to be time dependent. In spite of this, symmetry of this particular vehicle is such that we would not expect the cross coupled hydrodynamic added mass terms to be significant and could assume that the excitation of the sway mode (v) by the combined bow and stern rudders to be self cancelling. It follows that a first order approximation to the yaw response may be sufficient to identify key parameters for the purpose of a diagnostic system identification, thus assuming

$$\delta = \delta_b = -\delta_s; \quad N_{\delta b} = -N_{\delta s} = N_\delta; \quad N_v = 0;$$

$$\dot{r} = a_1 r + b_1 \delta; \quad H(s) = \frac{K}{(s+\tau)}$$

$$a_1 = \frac{0.5\rho L^3 (N_v u)}{[I_{zz} - 0.5\rho L^5 N_{\dot{r}}]}; \quad b_1 = \frac{\rho L^3 N_\delta u^2}{[I_{zz} - 0.5\rho L^5 N_{\dot{r}}]}$$

Alternatively, as a second order model including the influence of side slip, we can define a sideslip angle β and the model is expressed by

$$\dot{r} = a_1 r + a_2 \beta + b_1 \delta$$
$$\dot{\beta} = a_3 \beta + a_4 r + b_2 \delta$$

with

$$H(s) = \frac{K(s+\tau_0)}{(s+\tau_1)(s+\tau_2)}$$

Parameter Identification Method

Many parameter identification methods have been developed with most involving the minimization of a measure of the mean square prediction error between model and data.

Three popular methods that are commonly in use include a batch least squares (BLS) where parameters are constant and the recursive least squares using kalman filters (KF) and the exponentially weighted least squares (EWLS) technique for tracking time varying parameters, although a new approach using Hopfield networks shows promise for this application (Chu, et. al., 1992). If the parameters are constant, or an averaged estimate of parameter values over the time of the data batch is needed, BLS is acceptable and straight forward. If the system uncertainty is such that the parameters vary with time then a recursive technique is needed and the use of the EWLS or KF technique is required. In these cases it is not necessarily easy to determine the bandwidth of the identifier filter to provide the best trade-off between noise in the estimate and tracking of the time varying parameter. Each application is unique and this work is aimed at a study of the situation for the case at hand.

Batch

Writing the yaw rate equation in ARMA form we get

$$r_i = p_1 r_{i-1} + q_1 \delta_{i-1} + \mu_i$$

where the coefficients p_1 and q_1 have their usual meaning and μ_i is a white noise sequence.

For the first order representation of the model, the prediction based on regression of prior data would be

$$\hat{r}_i = \Phi'_i \hat{\Theta}_i \text{ with } \Phi'_i = [r_{i-1}, \delta_{i-1}] \text{ and}$$
$$\hat{\Theta}'_i = [\hat{p}_1(i), \hat{q}_1(i)]$$

and a minimization of the squared error J(k-p,k) over a batch of p prior points with even weighting

$$J(k-p,k) = \sum_{i=k-p}^{i=k} \left\| (r_i - \Phi'_i \hat{\Theta}_i) \right\|$$

gives

$$\hat{\boldsymbol{\Theta}} = [\boldsymbol{\Phi}\boldsymbol{\Phi}']^{-1}\boldsymbol{\Phi}\mathbf{R}$$

where

$$\boldsymbol{\Phi}' = \begin{bmatrix} [r_{k-p}, \delta_{k-p}] \\ \cdot \\ [r_i, \delta_i] \\ \cdot \\ [r_k, \delta_k] \end{bmatrix} \quad \mathbf{R} = \begin{bmatrix} r_{k-p+1} \\ \cdot \\ r_{i+1} \\ \cdot \\ r_{k+1} \end{bmatrix}$$

A similar form for the second order system model has been employed as in

$$r_i = p_1 r_{i-1} + p_2 r_{i-2} + q_1 \delta_{i-1} + q_2 \delta_{i-2}$$

This calculation provides the batch least squares fit to data over the interval k-p to k, where the block size p may be chosen based on an estimate of the time dependency of the parameters. For instance, the entire maneuver could be used, or the last few seconds of data could be used as appropriate. A sufficient record length however is required to capture 'persistency of excitation' otherwise the data matrix will not have strong enough singular values. We have found that a block of 50 data points at 10 Hz. is sufficient to provide an identification.

Kalman Filter for Parameter Identification

The use of the Kalman filter is standard for the nominally constant parameter model given by,

Parameter model: $\boldsymbol{\theta}_{k+1} = \boldsymbol{\theta}_k + \mathbf{w}_k$

$$E\{\mathbf{w}_k \mathbf{w}'_k\} = \mathbf{Q}$$

Measurement Model: $r_k = \boldsymbol{\Phi}_k \boldsymbol{\theta}_k + v_k$

$$E\{v^2_k\} = \rho$$

0.100) while Figure 6 had **Q**=0.01. Figure 8 shows the comparison of the predicted yaw rate (**Q**=0.01) with the measured record, indicating good agreement. Even the slow filter is able to detect that the initial acceleration phase of the vehicle motion has a low steering capability and the period around 45 -50 seconds is characterized by a slight loss of input strength - but not enough to cause a problem.

Comment on first order vs second order models

First order and second order results for the gain identification are essentially the same and it appears that only a slight difference can be detected. Which system to use could be argued. We prefer to use the second order filter because it is more representative of the physical modeling, including side slip as well as yaw.

Comment on the EWLS

Results for the EWLS identification are so similar to those of the KF that they are not presented here.

Conclusions

Underwater vehicle steering parameters are time variable, but can be well identified by the Kalman parameter filter. A second order modeling is proposed and the identification of the steering gain together with suitable limits, will be a reliable way to determine if operational degradation of the rudder system occurs.

References

Chu, S. R., Shoureshi, R., Healey, A. J., "A Hopfield-Based Neuro-Diagnostic System" Proceedings of the American Control Conference, Chicago, Illinois, June 24-26, 1992.

Healey, A.J., Good, M., "The NPS AUV II Autonomous Underwater Vehicle Testbed: Design and Experimental Verification" Naval Engineers Journal, ASNE, May 1992. pp.191-202

Healey, A.J., Marco, D. B., " Experimental Verification of Mission Planning by Autonomous Mission Execution and Data Visualization using the NPS AUV II " Proceedings of IEEE Oceanic Engineering Society Symposium on Autonomous Underwater Vehicles, AUV-92 Washington D.C., June 2-3, 1992, pp.65-73

Healey, A.J., "A Neural Network Approach to Failure Diagnostics for Underwater Vehicles" Proceedings of IEEE Oceanic Engineering Society Symposium on Autonomous Underwater Vehicles, AUV-92 Washington D.C., June 2-3, 1992, pp.131-135

Lewis, E. V. (Ed) *Principles of Naval Architecture - Vol III* The Society of Naval Architects and Marine Engineers, 1988

Ljung, L., Soderstrom, T., 1985*Theory and Practice of Recursive Identification* Cambridge, Mass. MIT Press

Yuh, J., "Modeling and Control of Underwater Vehicles" IEEE Transactions on Systems, Man, and Cybernetics, Vol. 20, No. 6, 1990, pp 1475-1483

Acknowledgements

The author recognizes the financial assistance of the Naval Postgraduate School Direct Research Fund and technical sponsorship of the Office of Naval Technology in support of the AUV project at NPS.

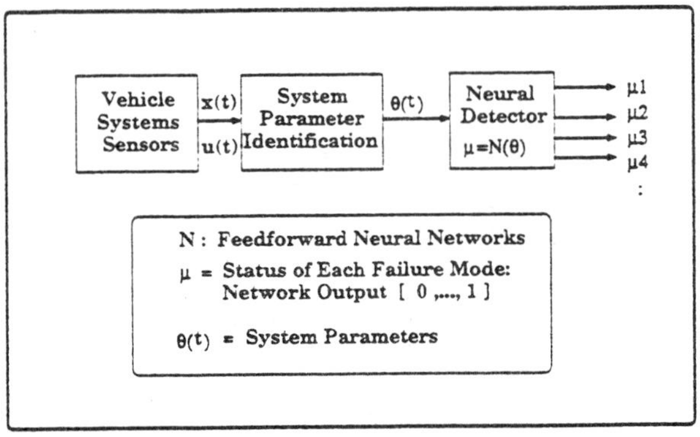

Figure 1 Schematic of the Fault Detection and Classification System

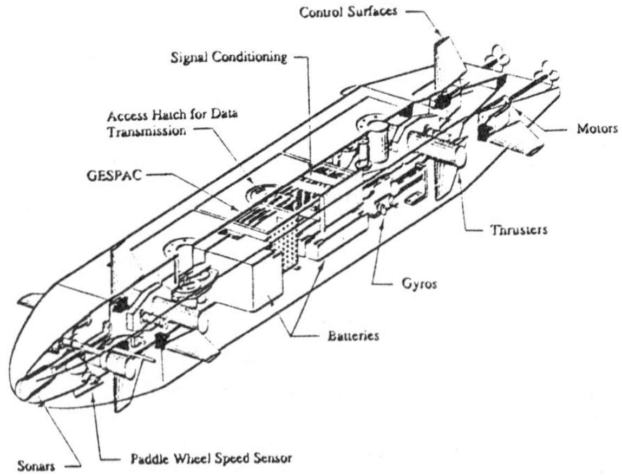

Figure 2 Sketch of the NPS AUV II Vehicle

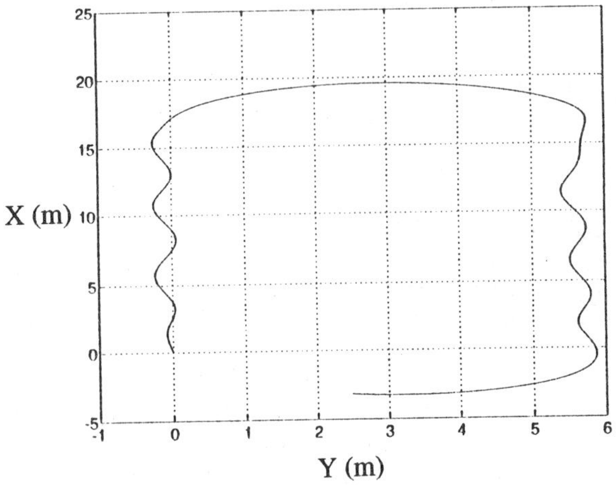

Figure 3 Oval Track Path Response with Sinusoidal Steering Maneuvers

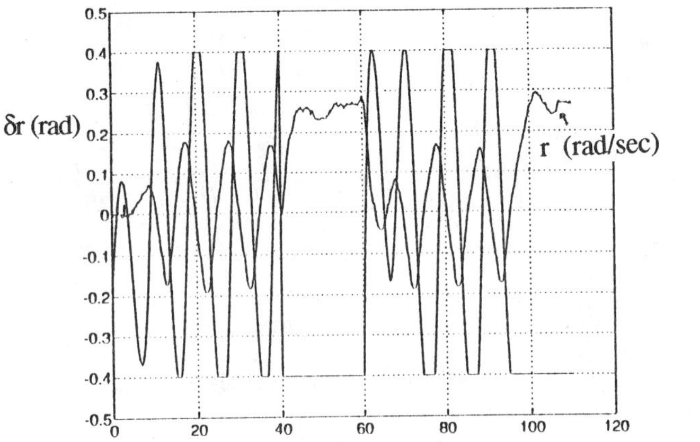

Figure 4 Yaw Rate (r) and Rudder Input (δr) versus Time

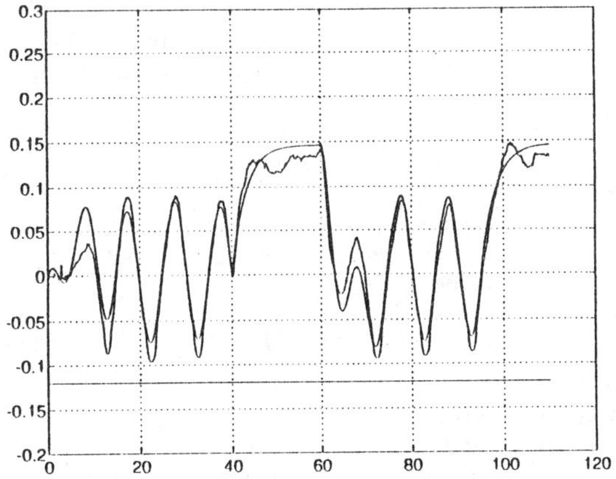

Figure 5 Measured and Predicted Yaw Rate - Batch Processed - First Order Model with the Identified Gain

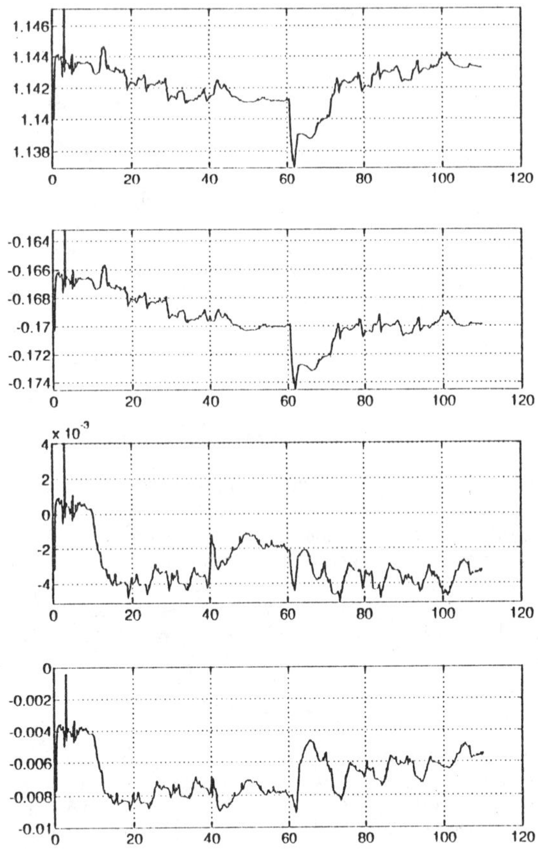

Figure 6 Second Order Model Parameters as Identified Top to Bottom θ_1 θ_2 θ_3 θ_4

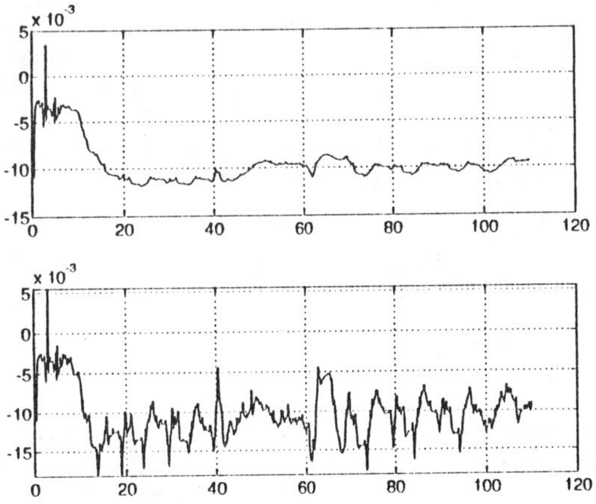

Figure 7 Slow (Upper) and Fast (Lower) Gain Identification (θ_3+θ_4)

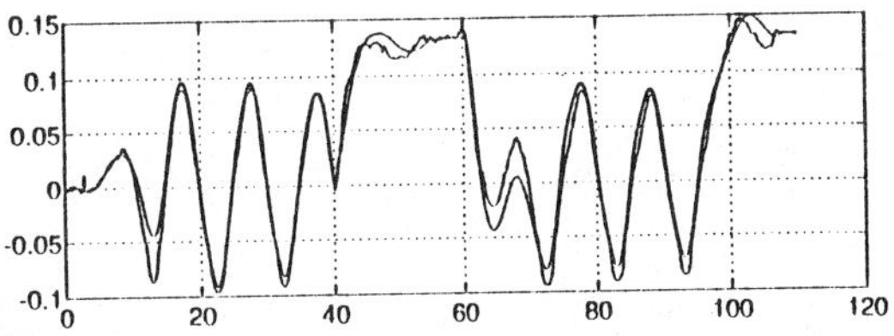

Figure 8 Second Order Model Comparison with Measured Yaw Rate versus Time

Proceedings of the
American Control Conference
San Francisco, California • June 1993

An Extension of A-A-K Hankel Approximation Theory Using State-Space Formulation

Ciann-Dong Yang

Institute of Aeronautics and Astronautics
National Cheng Kung university
Tainan, Taiwan, Republic of China

Fang-Bo Yeh

Institute of Applied Mathematics
Tunghai University
Taichung, Taiwan, Republic of China

Abstract

The optimal Hankel-norm approximation problem studied in [1] is reformulated in a state-space setting. It is shown that the A-A-K Hankel approximation theory can be generalized to optimal multivariable case. The optimal Hankel approximants obtained in this way are identical to those obtained by Glover [2], however, the present approach provides a deep insight into the A-A-K approximation theory and throws a new lignt on its future applications

1. Introduction

Concerning the Hankel approximation problems, the work of Adamjan, Arov and Krein [3] is limited to scalar systems except for a multivarible extension problem [4] where the zero-order approximation is considered. Kung and Lin [5,6] generalized the result of A-A-K to multivarible case for minimal-degree (sub-optimal) approximation (MDA) problems. The objective of this paper is to show that A-A-K theory can be generalized to both MDA and minimal-norm (optimal) approximation (MNA) problems. State-space characterization of all optimal Hankel approximants is derived. Although the result is identical to the celebrated results of Glover [2], the present approach provides a deep insight into the A-A-K approximation theory. Before we proceed further it is better to review some preliminary results of Hankel approximation problem.

(A) Operations on linear systems

A state-space realization of a continuous linear time-invariant system is represented by

$$G(s) = C(sI - A)^{-1}B + D = \{A,\ B,\ C,\ D\} = \left[\begin{array}{c|c} A & B \\ \hline C & D \end{array}\right] \quad (1)$$

The following operations are helpful to our later derivation.

- Cascade connection :

$$G_1(s)G_2(s) = \left[\begin{array}{c|c} A_1 & B_1 \\ \hline C_1 & D_1 \end{array}\right]\left[\begin{array}{c|c} A_2 & B_2 \\ \hline C_2 & D_2 \end{array}\right] = \left[\begin{array}{cc|c} A_1 & B_1C_2 & B_1D_2 \\ 0 & A_2 & B_2 \\ \hline C_1 & D_1C_2 & D_1D_2 \end{array}\right] \quad (2)$$

- Inverse system :

$$G(s)^{-1} = \left[\begin{array}{c|c} A - BD^{-1}C & -BD^{-1} \\ \hline D^{-1}C & D^{-1} \end{array}\right] \quad (3)$$

- Similarity transformation :

$$T^{-1}G(s)T = \left[\begin{array}{c|c} T^{-1}AT & T^{-1}B \\ \hline CT & D \end{array}\right] \quad (4)$$

- Transformed cascaded system :
  Consider the following transformation

$$T = \begin{bmatrix} I & X \\ 0 & I \end{bmatrix}, \qquad T^{-1} = \begin{bmatrix} I & -X \\ 0 & I \end{bmatrix}$$

Then the transformed cascaded system becomes

$$T^{-1}G_1(s)G_2(s)T$$

$$= \left[\begin{array}{cc|c} A_1 & A_1X + B_1C_2 - XA_2 & B_1D_2 - XB_2 \\ 0 & A_2 & B_2 \\ \hline C_1 & C_1X + D_1C_2 & D_1D_2 \end{array}\right]$$

$$= \left[\begin{array}{c|c} A_1 & B_1D_2 - XB_2 \\ \hline C_1 & D_3 \end{array}\right] + \left[\begin{array}{c|c} A_2 & B_2 \\ \hline C_1X + D_1C_2 & D_1D_2 - D_3 \end{array}\right] \quad (5)$$

where D_3 is an arbitrary constant matrix and X satisfies $A_1X - XA_2 + B_1C_2 = 0$.

(B) Gramians and Lyapunov equations

Let P and Q be, respectively, the observability and controllability gramians associated with the state-space realization (1), i.e.,

$$P = \int_0^\infty e^{At}BB^Te^{A^Tt}\,dt \quad (6a)$$

$$Q = \int_0^\infty e^{A^Tt}C^TCe^{At}\,dt \quad (6b)$$

By considering the corresponding matrix differential equations it is easily verified that P and Q satisfy the following Lyapunov equations.

$$AP + PA^T + BB^T = 0 \quad (7a)$$

$$A^TQ + QA + C^TC = 0 \quad (7b)$$

There is an important connection between the inertias of A and P satisfying the Liapunov equation (7a). It is proved in [2] that If (A, B) is controllable, then

$$In(A) = In(-P) \quad (8)$$

(C) Hankel operator

The Hankel operator H_G induced by an $m \times m$ stable function matrix $G(s)$ with McMillan degree n can be defined via the following mapping.

$$(H_Gu)(s) = (G(s)u(s))_+ \quad (9)$$

where u is an $m \times 1$ anti-stable function vector and $(\cdot)_+$ denotes the projection into stable part. Let σ_i be the ith singular value of H_G and x_i and y_i be the corresponding left and right singular vectors , then

$$H_Gx_i = \sigma_iy_i \quad (10)$$

Using the manipulation defined in Eq.(9), we can derive a functional representation of Eq.(10) as

$$(G(s)x_i(-s))_+ = \sigma_i y_i(s), \quad i = 1, \cdots, n \tag{11a}$$

or

$$(G^T(s)y_i(-s))_+ = \sigma_i x_i(s), \quad i = 1, \cdots, n \tag{11b}$$

where $x_i(s)$ and $y_i(s)$ are stable functions. The Hankel singular value is related to the controllability and the observability gramians via

$$\sigma_i(H_G) = \sigma_i(PQ) \tag{12}$$

(D) Balanced Realization

Consider a stable, rational, $m \times m$ transfer function $G(s)$ with Hankel singular values $\sigma_1 \geq \sigma_2 \cdots \geq \sigma_k > \sigma = \sigma_{k+1} = \sigma_{k+2} \cdots = \sigma_{k+r} > \sigma_{k+r+1} \geq \cdots \geq \sigma_n > 0$. Let $(A,\ B,\ C,\ D)$ be a balanced realization of $G(s)$. Then,

$$A\Sigma + \Sigma A^T + BB^T = 0 \tag{13a}$$

$$A^T\Sigma + \Sigma A + C^T C = 0 \tag{13b}$$

where $\Sigma = \text{diag}(\sigma_1, \sigma_2, \cdots, \sigma_k, \sigma_{k+r+1}, \cdots, \sigma_n, \sigma_{k+1}, \cdots, \sigma_{k+r}) = \text{diag}(\Sigma_1,\ \sigma I_r)$ is the Hankel singular values of $G(s)$. Partition $(A,\ B,\ C)$ conformally with Σ, and rewrite Eq.(13) as

$$\begin{bmatrix} A_{11} & A_{12} \\ A_{21} & A_{22} \end{bmatrix}\begin{bmatrix} \Sigma_1 & 0 \\ 0 & \sigma I_r \end{bmatrix} + \begin{bmatrix} \Sigma_1 & 0 \\ 0 & \sigma I_r \end{bmatrix}\begin{bmatrix} A_{11}^T & A_{21}^T \\ A_{12}^T & A_{22}^T \end{bmatrix} + \begin{bmatrix} B_1B_1^T & B_1B_2^T \\ B_2B_1^T & B_2B_2^T \end{bmatrix} = 0 \tag{14a}$$

$$\begin{bmatrix} A_{11}^T & A_{21}^T \\ A_{12}^T & A_{22}^T \end{bmatrix}\begin{bmatrix} \Sigma_1 & 0 \\ 0 & \sigma I_r \end{bmatrix} + \begin{bmatrix} \Sigma_1 & 0 \\ 0 & \sigma I_r \end{bmatrix}\begin{bmatrix} A_{11} & A_{12} \\ A_{21} & A_{22} \end{bmatrix} + \begin{bmatrix} C_1^TC_1 & C_1^TC_2 \\ C_2^TC_1 & C_2^TC_2 \end{bmatrix} = 0 \tag{14b}$$

(E) Minimal-degree approximation problem

Let $\sigma \in (\sigma_{k+1},\ \sigma_k)$. The MDA problem is to find $\hat{G}(s)$ of lowest possible order such that

$$\|G(s) - \hat{G}(s)\|_H \leq \sigma \tag{15}$$

It has been shown by Kung and Lin [5] that the lowest possible degree that can be attained is k and the corresponding k^{th}-order approximant can be expressed by

$$\hat{G}^k(s) = G(s) - \sigma\left[Y(s)X(-s)^{-1}\right]_+ \tag{16}$$

where $X(s)$ and $Y(s)$ are stable, invertible, $m \times m$ function matrices satisfying

$$G(s)X(-s) - \sigma Y(s) = K(s) \tag{17a}$$

$$G^T(s)Y(-s) - \sigma X(s) = L(s) \tag{17b}$$

where $K(s)$ and $L(s)$ are anti-stable. Eq.(16) is a generalization of A-A-K result to MDA problem. Note that σ can not equal any Hankel singular values of $G(s)$ in this case. The present results will further generalize A-A-K's work to MNA problems, allowing $\sigma = \sigma_{k+1}$.

2. Extension of A-A-K approximation theory

The main result is summarized in the following theorem.

Theorem 1 :

Let σ=σ_{k+1} be the $(k+1)^{th}$ Hankel singular value of G and let $X(s)$ and $Y(s)$ satisfy Eq.(17). Assume that $\hat{G}$ and $\hat{F}$ are the stable and unstable part of $G(s) - \sigma Y(s)X(-s)^{-1}$, respectively, i.e.,

$$\hat{G}(s) + \hat{F}(s) = G(s) - \sigma Y(s)X(-s)^{-1} \tag{18}$$

Then,

(i)

$$\min_{G^k, F} \|G(s) - G^k(s) - F(s)\|_\infty = \|G(s) - \hat{G}(s) - \hat{F}(s)\|_\infty = \sigma \tag{19}$$

(ii) $\hat{G}(s)$ is of McMillan degree k, satisfying

$$\min_{G^k} \|G(s) - G^k(s)\|_H = \|G(s) - \hat{G}(s)\|_H = \sigma \tag{20}$$

where $G^k(s)$ is any stable function matrix with McMillan degree k and F is any anti-stable function matrix.

Theorem 1 will be proved throughout this paper. The key issue of MDA and MNA problem following A-A-K concept relies on the construction of $X(s)$ and $Y(s)$. Comparing Eq.(17) with Eq.(11), we can observe that the condition having invertible $m \times m$ $X(s)$ and $Y(s)$ satisfying Eq.(17a) and Eq.(17b) is equivalent to requiring the existence of m independent singular vector pairs $(x_i(s),\ y_i(s))$, $i = 1, \cdots, m$, satisfying

$$(G(s)x_i(-s))_+ = \sigma_{k+1}y_i(s)$$
$$(G^T(s)y_i(-s))_+ = \sigma_{k+1}x_i(s), \ i = 1, \cdots, m$$

$X(s)$ and $Y(s)$ are composed of $x_i(s)$ and $y_i(s)$ via the relations

$$X(s) = [x_1(s)\ x_2(s)\ \cdots\ x_n(s)]$$
$$Y(s) = [y_1(s)\ y_2(s)\ \cdots\ y_n(s)]$$

In the following we will derive a state-space representation of all $X(s)$ and $Y(s)$ satisfying Eq.(17).

Consider stable $G(s)$ and $X(s)$ having the state-space expressions

$$G(s) = \left[\begin{array}{c|c} A & B \\ \hline C & D \end{array}\right], \qquad X(s) = \left[\begin{array}{c|c} A_x & B_x \\ \hline C_x & D_x \end{array}\right] \tag{21}$$

where matrices A_x, B_x, C_x, and D_x are to be determined to satisfy Eq.(17). We starts with the product of $G(s)$ and $X(-s)$.

$$G(s)X(-s) = \left[\begin{array}{c|c} A & B \\ \hline C & D \end{array}\right]\left[\begin{array}{c|c} -A_x & B_x \\ \hline -C_x & D_x \end{array}\right] = \left[\begin{array}{cc|c} A & -BC_x & BD_x \\ 0 & -A_x & B_x \\ \hline C & -DC_x & DD_x \end{array}\right] \tag{22}$$

Applying the similarity transformation $\begin{bmatrix} I & X_1 \\ 0 & I \end{bmatrix}$ where X_1 satisfying

$$AX_1 + X_1A_x - BC_x = 0 \tag{23}$$

yields

$$G(s)X(-s) = \left[\begin{array}{c|c} A & BD_x - X_1B_x \\ \hline C & D_{gx} \end{array}\right] + \left[\begin{array}{c|c} -A_x & B_x \\ \hline CX_1 - DC_x & DD_x - D_{gx} \end{array}\right] \tag{24}$$

From Eq.(17a) we observe that $\sigma Y(s)$ is the stable part of $G(s)X(-s)$, while $K(s)$ is the anti-stable part of $G(s)X(-s)$. It turns out that

$$Y(s) = \left[\begin{array}{c|c} A & \sigma^{-1}(BD_x - X_1B_x) \\ \hline C & \sigma^{-1}D_{gx} \end{array}\right] \tag{25}$$

$$K(s) = \left[\begin{array}{c|c} -A_x & B_x \\ \hline CX_1 - DC_x & DD_x - D_{gx} \end{array}\right] \tag{26}$$

, where D_{gx} is an invertible constant matrix to be determined. In the next step we use this $Y(s)$ to form the product of $G^T(s)Y(-s)$.

$$G^T(s)Y(-s)$$

$$= \left[\begin{array}{c|c} A^T & C^T \\ \hline B^T & D^T \end{array}\right] \left[\begin{array}{c|c} -A & \sigma^{-1}(BD_x - X_1B_x) \\ \hline -C & \sigma^{-1}D_{gx} \end{array}\right]$$

$$= \left[\begin{array}{cc|c} A^T & 0 & \sigma^{-1}C^TD_{gx} - \sigma^{-1}X_2(BD_x - X_1B_x) \\ 0 & -A & \sigma^{-1}(BD_x - X_1B_x) \\ \hline B^T & B^TX_2 - D^TC & \sigma^{-1}D^TD_{gx} \end{array}\right] \quad (27)$$

In the last equation the similarity transformation $\begin{bmatrix} I & X_2 \\ 0 & I \end{bmatrix}$ has been used, where X_2 satisfies

$$A^TX_2 + X_2A - C^TC = 0 \quad (28)$$

As compared with Eq.(13b), X_2 is found to be $-\Sigma$. $\sigma X(s)$ and $L(s)$ are identified as the stable and anti-stable parts of $G^T(s)Y(-s)$, respectively, as can be seen from Eq.(17b). Therefore,

$$X(s) = \left[\begin{array}{c|c} A^T & \sigma^{-2}(C^TD_{gx} + \Sigma(BD_x - X_1B_x)) \\ \hline B^T & \sigma^{-1}D_{gy} \end{array}\right] \quad (29)$$

$$L(s) = \left[\begin{array}{c|c} -A & \sigma^{-1}(BD_x - X_1B_x) \\ \hline -B^T\Sigma - D^TC & \sigma^{-1}D^TD_{gx} - D_{gy} \end{array}\right] \quad (30)$$

where D_{gy} is an invertible constant matrix to be determined. The two expressions for $X(s)$ in Eq.(21) and Eq.(29) must be equal. Hence,

$$\left[\begin{array}{c|c} A^T & \sigma^{-2}(C^TD_{gx} + \Sigma(BD_x - X_1B_x)) \\ \hline B^T & \sigma^{-1}D_{gy} \end{array}\right] = \left[\begin{array}{c|c} A_x & B_x \\ \hline C_x & D_x \end{array}\right]$$

Solving for A_x, B_x, C_x, and D_x, we have

$$A_x = A^T \quad (31a)$$

$$B_x = \sigma^{-2}\left[C^TD_{gx} + \Sigma(BD_x - X_1B_x)\right] \quad (31b)$$

$$C_x = B^T \quad (31c)$$

$$D_x = \sigma^{-1}D_{gy} \quad (31d)$$

Substituting $A_x = A^T$ and $C_x = B^T$ into Eq.(23), and comparing the resultant with Eq.(13a), we see that X_1 is equal to $-\Sigma$. The solution for B_x needs some attentions. Partitioning $B_x = [B_{x_1}^T \ B_{x_2}^T]^T$ and using the partitioned form of B, C, and Σ in Eq.(14), we obtain

$$\begin{bmatrix} \sigma^2I - \Sigma_1^2 & 0 \\ 0 & 0 \end{bmatrix} \begin{bmatrix} B_{x_1} \\ B_{x_2} \end{bmatrix} = \begin{bmatrix} C_1^TD_{gx} + \Sigma_1B_1D_x \\ C_2^TD_{gx} + \sigma B_2D_x \end{bmatrix} \quad (32)$$

It is noted from (2,2) blocks of Eq.(14a) and Eq.(14b) that $B_2B_2^T = C_2^TC_2$. Hence, there exists an unitary matrix U such that

$$B_2 = -C_2^TU \quad (33)$$

Using this relation in the second row of Eq.(32), we have

$$C_2^T(D_{gx} - \sigma UD_x) = 0 \quad (34)$$

Now we can determine D_{gx} as

$$D_{gx} = \sigma UD_x \quad (35)$$

and the first row of Eq.(32) gives the desired solution for B_{x_1} :

$$B_{x_1} = -\Gamma_1^{-1}(\sigma C_1^TU + \Sigma_1B_1)D_x \quad (36)$$

, where $\Gamma_1 = \Sigma_1^2 - \sigma^2I$. Now the Hankel singular vectors $X(s)$ and $Y(s)$ can be determined as

$$X(s) = \left[\begin{array}{c|c} A^T & \sigma^{-2}(C^TD_{gx} + \Sigma(BD_x + \Sigma B_x)) \\ \hline B^T & D_x \end{array}\right] \quad (37)$$

$$Y(s) = \left[\begin{array}{c|c} A & \sigma^{-1}(BD_x + \Sigma_1B_x) \\ \hline C & UD_x \end{array}\right] \quad (38)$$

In the above process of finding A_x, B_x, C_x, and D_x to satisfy Eq.(17), we can see that two parameters B_{x_2} and D_x can be chosen arbitrarily without violating Eq.(17). If D_x is chosen to be invertible, then $X(s)$ and $Y(s)$ are also invertible, and this, in turn, implies that the m left and right singular vectors contained in $X(s)$ and $Y(s)$ are linear independent.

Up to this stage we have derived the n independent Hankel singular-vector pairs $X(s)$ and $Y(s)$ of $G(s)$. We now ready to show part (i) of theorem 1. From Eq.(18) we have

$$G(s) - \hat{G}(s) - \hat{F}(s) = \sigma Y(s)X(-s)^{-1}$$

We must show that $\|\sigma Y(s)X(-s)^{-1}\|_\infty = \sigma$. Indeed, it can be shown that $Y(s)X(-s)^{-1}$ is an all-pass function. First we note that the condition

$$(Y(s)X(-s)^{-1})^*(Y(s)X(-s)^{-1}) = I$$

can be rewritten in an equivalent form

$$Y^T(s)Y(-s) = X^T(-s)X(s) \quad (39)$$

Substituting into the expressions for $X(s)$ and $Y(s)$ and applying the decomposition formula of Eq.(5), we can show that Eq.(39) is satisfied. It is this property from that we get a clue to the optimal Hankel approximation problem. Let $\hat{G}(s)$ be a stable function with McMillan degree k and $F(s)$ be a anti-stable function. The follwing result has been derived by Glover [2].

$$\sigma_{k+1} = \min_{G^k,F} \|G(s) - G^k(s) - F(s)\|_{L^\infty}$$

$$= \min_{G^k} \|G(s) - G^k(s)\|_H \quad (40)$$

In the above derivation we already show that if we choose $G^k(s) + F(s) = G(s) - \sigma Y(s)X(-s)^{-1}$, then the minimum will be attained. From Eq.(17a) we have

$$G(s) - \sigma Y(s)X(-s)^{-1} = K(s)X(-s)^{-1} \quad (41)$$

Hence, it remains to show that the stable part of $K(s)X(-s)^{-1}$ is of McMillan k, and this together with the all-pass property of $Y(s)X(-s)^{-1}$ justify $K(s)X(-s)^{-1}$ as the optimal function $\hat{G}(s) + \hat{F}(s)$ satisfying Eq.(19) and Eq.(20).

3. Construction of optimal Hankel approximants HANKEL APPROXIMANTS

(A) Minimal-norm approximation

In this section $K(s)X(-s)^{-1}$ is shown to be the optimal k^{th} order Hankel approximant of $G(s)$ and its state-space realization will be characterized explicitly. Using the state-space expressions of $K(s)$ and $X(s)$ from Eq.(26) and Eq.(29), yields

$$K(s)X(-s)^{-1}$$

$$= \left[\begin{array}{cc|c} -A_x & B_xD_x^{-1}C_x & B_xD_x^{-1} \\ 0 & -A_x + B_xD_x^{-1}C_x & B_xD_x^{-1} \\ \hline CX_1 - DC_x & DC_x - D_{gx}D_x^{-1}C_x & D - D_{gx}D_x^{-1} \end{array}\right]$$

The above expression can be further simplified by applying similarity transformation $T = \begin{bmatrix} I & I \\ 0 & I \end{bmatrix}$ and by using the relations $A_x = A^T$, $C_x = B^T$, $D_{gx} = \sigma UD_x$, and $X_1 = -\Sigma$.

$$K(s)X(-s)^{-1} = \left[\begin{array}{c|c} -A^T + B_xD_x^{-1}B^T & B_xD_x^{-1} \\ \hline -C\Sigma - \sigma UB^T & D - \sigma U \end{array}\right] \quad (42)$$

The terms involving B_x need some more manipulations. Recall the expression of B_{x_1} in Eq.(36). Substituting B_x into the B-matrix of $K(s)X(-s)^{-1}$ yields

$$B_x D_x^{-1} = \begin{bmatrix} -\Gamma_1^{-1}(\sigma C_1^T U + \Sigma_1 B_1) \\ B_{x_2} D_x^{-1} \end{bmatrix}$$

The C-matrix of $K(s)X(-s)^{-1}$ becomes

$$-C\Sigma - \sigma U B^T = [-C_1\Sigma_1 - \sigma U B_1^T \;\; 0]$$

The A-matrix of $K(s)X(s)^{-1}$ can be expanded as

$$-A^T + B_x D_x^{-1} B^T$$

$$= \begin{bmatrix} -A_{11}^T + B_{x_1} D_x^{-1} B_1^T & -A_{21}^T + B_{x_1} D_x^{-1} B_2^T \\ -A_{12}^T + B_{x_2} D_x^{-1} B_1^T & -A_{22}^T + B_{x_2} D_x^{-1} B_2^T \end{bmatrix}$$

Next we consider the A-matrix of $K(s)X(-s)^{-1}$ term by term.

(1,1) block :

$$\begin{aligned} & -A_{11}^T + B_{x_1} D_x^{-1} B_1^T \\ &= -A_{11}^T + (\sigma^2 I - \Sigma_1^2)^{-1}(\sigma C_1^T U + \Sigma_1 B_1) B_1^T \\ &= (\Sigma_1^2 - \sigma^2 I)^{-1}(\sigma^2 A_{11}^T + \Sigma_1 A_{11} \Sigma_1 - \sigma C_1^T U B_1^T) \end{aligned}$$

where the relation in the (1,1) block of Eq.(14a) has been used.

(1,2) block :

$$\begin{aligned} & -A_{21}^T + B_{x_1} D_x^{-1} B_2^T \\ &= -A_{21}^T + (\sigma^2 I - \Sigma_1^2)^{-1}(-\sigma C_1^T C_2 + \Sigma_1 B_1 B_2^T) \\ &= \sigma(\Sigma_1^2 - \sigma^2 I)^{-1}(\sigma A_{21}^T + \Sigma_1 A_{12} + C_1^T C_2) = 0 \end{aligned}$$

where the relations in the (1,2) blocks of Eq.(14a) and Eq.(14b) have been used. Using these results in $K(s)X(-s)^{-1}$ and removing the unobservable mode, yields

$$K(s)X(-s)^{-1} = \begin{bmatrix} \hat{A}_{11} & \hat{B}_1 \\ \hat{C}_1 & \hat{D} \end{bmatrix} =$$

$$\begin{bmatrix} \Gamma_1^{-1}(\sigma^2 A_{11}^T + \Sigma_1 A_{11}\Sigma_1 - \sigma C_1^T U B_1^T) & \Gamma_1^{-1}(\sigma C_1^T U + \Sigma_1 B_1) \\ C_1\Sigma_1 + \sigma U B_1^T & D - \sigma U \end{bmatrix} \tag{43}$$

Next we proceed to verify that there are exactly k stable poles in $K(s)X(-s)^{-1}$. We start with the all-pass property of $\sigma Y(s)X(-s)^{-1}$. Note that

$$\sigma Y(s)X(-s)^{-1} = G(s) - K(s)X(-s)^{-1}$$

$$= \left[\begin{array}{cc|c} A & 0 & B \\ 0 & \hat{A}_{11} & \hat{B}_1 \\ \hline C & -\hat{C}_1 & D - \hat{D} \end{array}\right] = \begin{bmatrix} A_e & B_e \\ C_e & D_e \end{bmatrix} \tag{44}$$

Let P_e and Q_e be the corresponding controllability and observability gramians of $(A_e,\, B_e,\, C_e,\, D_e)$. P_e and Q_e are the solutions of the following Lyapunov's equations

$$A_e P_e + P_e A_e^T + B_e B_e^T = 0 \tag{45a}$$

$$A_e^T Q_e + Q_e A_e + C_e^T C_e = 0 \tag{45b}$$

Since $\sigma Y(x)X(-s)^{-1}$ is all-pass, P_e and Q_e must also satisfy

$$P_e Q_e = \sigma^2 I \tag{46}$$

Solving Eq.(45) and Eq.(46) for P_e and Q_e, we obtain

$$P_e = \begin{bmatrix} \Sigma_1 & 0 & I \\ 0 & \sigma I & 0 \\ I & 0 & \Sigma_1\Gamma_1^{-1} \end{bmatrix}, \quad Q_e = \begin{bmatrix} \Sigma_1 & 0 & -\Gamma_1 \\ 0 & \sigma I & 0 \\ -\Gamma_1 & 0 & \Sigma_1\Gamma_1 \end{bmatrix} \tag{47}$$

With this result, the (1,1) block of Eq.(45a) is reduced to

$$\hat{A}_{11}\Sigma_1\Gamma_1^{-1} + \Sigma_1\Gamma_1^{-1}\hat{A}_{11}^T + \hat{B}_1\hat{B}_1^T = 0$$

Using the connection between the inertias of two matrices satisfying Lyapunov's equation as stated in section II, yields

$$In(\hat{A}_{11}) = In(-\Sigma_1\Gamma_1^{-1}) \tag{48}$$

Recall the definition of $\Gamma_1 = \Sigma_1 - \sigma I$, we have

$$\pi(\hat{A}_{11}) = \pi(-\Sigma_1\Gamma_1^{-1}) = n - r - k \tag{49a}$$

$$\nu(\hat{A}_{11}) = \nu(-\Sigma_1\Gamma_1^{-1}) = k \tag{49b}$$

This shows that there are exactly k stable poles in $G(s) - \sigma Y(s)X(\,-s)^{-1}$. We thus complete the proof of theorem 1.

(B) Minimal-degree approximation

Let $\rho \in (\sigma_{k+1},\, \sigma_k)$. The MDA problem in Eq.(15) is to find a $\hat{G}$ with degree k such that

$$\|G(s) - \hat{G}(s)\|_H = \rho \tag{50}$$

This is a special case of theorem 1 with $\sigma = \rho \neq \sigma_{k+1}$, and the desired $\hat{G}$ is given by Eq.(16). The state-space characterization of $X(s)$ and $Y(s)$ is similar to the MNA problem, leading to the same form of Eq.(31). But there are two different points between MNA and MDA problems.

(i) U can be an arbitrary $m \times m$ unitary matrix and the constraint imposed by Eq.(33) is no longer necessary in the MDA case.

(ii) Since ρ is not equal to any of the singular value σ_i, $\Gamma = \Sigma^2 - \rho^2 I$ is invertible. Hence B_x can be obtained directly from Eq.(31b) as

$$B_x = -\Gamma^{-1}(\rho C^T U + \Sigma B) D_x \tag{51}$$

Using this B_x in Eq.(44) yields

$$G(s) - \rho Y(s)X(-s)^{-1}$$

$$= \left[\begin{array}{c|c} \Gamma^{-1}(\rho^2 A^T + \Sigma A \Sigma - \rho C^T U B^T) & \Gamma^{-1}(\rho C^T U + \Sigma B) \\ \hline C\Sigma + \rho U B^T & D - \rho U \end{array}\right]$$

$$= \left[\begin{array}{c|c} \hat{A} & \hat{B} \\ \hline \hat{C} & \hat{D} \end{array}\right] \tag{52}$$

From the above equation $\rho Y(s)X(-s)^{-1}$ can be expressed as

$$\rho Y(s)X(-s)^{-1} = G(s) - K(s)X(-s)^{-1}$$

$$= \left[\begin{array}{cc|c} A & 0 & B \\ 0 & \hat{A} & \hat{B} \\ \hline C & -\hat{C} & D - \hat{D} \end{array}\right] = \left[\begin{array}{c|c} A_e & B_e \\ \hline C_e & D_e \end{array}\right]$$

It is not hard to verify that $\rho Y(s)X(-s)^{-1}$ is all-pass and the controllability and observability gramians for $(A_e,\, B_e,\, C_e,\, D_e)$ can be shown as following.

$$P_e = \begin{bmatrix} \Sigma & 0 & I \\ 0 & \rho I & 0 \\ I & 0 & \Sigma\Gamma^{-1} \end{bmatrix}, \quad Q_e = \begin{bmatrix} \Sigma & 0 & -\Gamma \\ 0 & \rho I & 0 \\ -\Gamma & 0 & \Sigma\Gamma \end{bmatrix} \tag{53}$$

The Lyapunov's equation for P_e becomes

$$\hat{A}\Sigma\Gamma^{-1} + \Sigma\Gamma^{-1}\hat{A}^T + \hat{B}\hat{B}^T = 0$$

Therefore, we have

$$In(\hat{A}) = In(-\Sigma\Gamma^{-1}) = In(\Sigma(\rho^2 I - \Sigma^2)^{-1}) = (n-k, k, 0)$$

It turns out that $\hat{G}(s) = G(s) - \rho(Y(s)X(-s)^{-1})_-$ has exactly k poles, and the all-pass property of $Y(s)X(-s)^{-1}$ implies that $\|G(s) - \hat{G}(s)\|_H = \rho$.

4. Parametrization of all optimal Hankel approximants

In the previous section we have characterized the state-space expression for the kth order Hankel approximant $\hat{G}(s) + \hat{F}(s) = K(s)X(-s)^{-1}$. This result can be further simplified in terms of linear fraction transformation. Let x, w, and z be, respectively, the state, input, and output variables of $K(s)X(-s)^{-1}$. From Eq.(45) the state equation of $K(s)X(-s)^{-1}$ for MNA problem can be expressed as

$$\dot{x} = \Gamma_1^{-1}(\sigma^2 A_{11}^T + \Sigma_1 A_{11}\Sigma_1 - \sigma C_1^T U B_1^T)x + \Gamma_1^{-1}(\sigma C_1^T U + \Sigma_1 B_1)w \quad (54a)$$

$$z = (C_1\Sigma_1 + \sigma U B_1^T)x - \sigma U w \quad (54b)$$

In order to isolate the free parameter U from the state equation, new input variable u and output variable y are introduced below.

$$u = \sigma U(B_1^T x - w) \quad (55a)$$

$$y = \sigma(B_1^T x - w) \quad (55b)$$

In terms of the two inputs w and u and the two outputs z and y, the state equation can be rewritten as

$$\dot{x} = \Gamma_1^{-1}(\sigma^2 A_{11}^T + \Sigma_1 A_{11}\Sigma_1)x + \Gamma_1^{-1}\Sigma_1 B_1 w - \Gamma_1^{-1}C_1^T w \quad (56a)$$

$$z = C_1\Sigma_1 x + u \quad (56b)$$

$$y = \sigma B_1^T x - \sigma w \quad (56c)$$

$$u = Uy \quad (56d)$$

In this expression the free parameter U only appears in the output feeedback loop $u = Uy$ (see Fig.1). The transfer function matrix $P(s)$ betweem inputs $\begin{bmatrix} w \\ u \end{bmatrix}$ and outputs $\begin{bmatrix} z \\ y \end{bmatrix}$ is directly obtained from Eq.(56) as

$$P(s) = \begin{bmatrix} P_{11}(s) & P_{12}(s) \\ P_{21}(s) & P_{22}(s) \end{bmatrix}$$

$$= \left[\begin{array}{c|cc} \Gamma_1^{-1}(\sigma^2 A_{11}^T + \Sigma_1 A_{11}\Sigma_1) & \Gamma_1^{-1}\Sigma_1 B_1 & -\Gamma_1^{-1}C_1^T \\ \hline C_1\Sigma_1 & 0 & I \\ \sigma B_1^T & -\sigma I & 0 \end{array}\right] \quad (57)$$

The optimal approximation function $\hat{G}(s) + \hat{F}(s)$ is just the transfer function between w and z, i.e.,

$$z = (\hat{G}(s) + \hat{F}(s))w \quad (58)$$

The above equation can be expressed in terms of $P_{ij}(s)$ as

$$\hat{G}(s) + \hat{F}(s) = F_l\left(\begin{bmatrix} P_{11} & P_{12} \\ P_{21} & P_{22} \end{bmatrix}, U\right) \quad (59)$$

where $F_l\left(\begin{bmatrix} P_{11} & P_{12} \\ P_{21} & P_{22} \end{bmatrix}, U\right)$ is the lower linear fraction transformation defined as

$$F_l\left(\begin{bmatrix} P_{11} & P_{12} \\ P_{21} & P_{22} \end{bmatrix}, U\right) = P_{11}(s) + P_{12}(s)U(I - P_{22}(s)U)^{-1}P_{21}(s)$$

This result is identical to that of Glover [2] (Corollary 8.6). Note that the free parameter U is an unitary matrix satisfying $B_2 = -C_2^T U$. It can be shown [2] that the Hankel norm remains the same if U is changed from an unitary matrix to an all-pass function $U(s)$ satisfying $B_2 = -C_2^T U(s)$. The parametrization of optimal approximation functions for MDA problem exhibits the same form as that of MNA problem except that the augmented plant is now modified to

$$P(s) = \left[\begin{array}{c|cc} \Gamma^{-1}(\rho^2 A^T + \Sigma A \Sigma) & \Gamma^{-1}\Sigma B & -\Gamma^{-1}C^T \\ \hline C\Sigma & 0 & I \\ \rho B^T & -\rho I & 0 \end{array}\right] \quad (60)$$

The free parameter $U(s)$ is all-pass and the constraint $B_2 = -C_2^T U(s)$ is not necessary in this case.

5. Conclusion

By exploiting state-space formulation, this paper generalizes the A-A-K extension concept from sub-optimal case (minimal degree approximation) to optimal case (minimal-norm approximation) for multivariable systems. It is found that the state-space interpretation of this generalized A-A-K extension approach is identical to the calebrated results of Glover [2]. This result hopefully provides a deep insight into the A-A-K approximation theorem and throws a new light on its its future applications.

Reference

[1] C.D. Yang, and F.B. Yeh, "One-Step Extension Approach to Optimal Hankel-Norm Approximation and H^∞ Optimization Problems," Proceedings of The 29th IEEE Conference on Decision and Control, Honolulu, 1990, also IEEE AC, May, 1993.

[2] K. Glover, "All Optimal Hankel-Norm Approximation of Linear Multivariable Systems an Their L^∞-Error Bounds," Int. J. Control, Vol.39, No.6, pp.1115-1193, 1984.

[3] V.M. Adamjan, D.Z. Arov, and M.G. Krein, "Analytic Property of Schmidt Pairs for a Hankel Operator and the Generalized Schmidt-Takagi Problem," Math. USSR Sbornik, Vol.15, pp.31-73, 1971.

[4] V.M. Adamjan, D.Z. Arov, and M.G. Krein, "Infinite Hankel Block Matrices and Related Extension Problems," American Mathematical Translations, Series 2, No.111, pp.113-156, 1978.

[5] S.Y. Kung, and D.W. Lin, "Optimal Hankel-Norm Model Reduction : Multivariable Systems," IEEE Trans. Automatic Control Vol.AC-26, pp.832-852, Aug. 1981.

[6] S.Y. Kung, and D.W. Lin, "A State-Space Formulation for Optimal Hankel-Norm Approximations," IEEE Trans. Automatic Control, Vol.AC-26, pp.942-946, 1981.

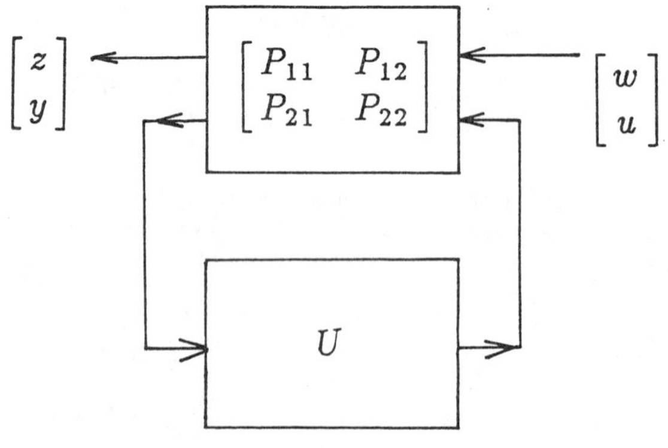

$$\hat{G}(s) + \hat{F}(s) = F_l\left(\begin{bmatrix} P_{11} & P_{12} \\ P_{21} & P_{22} \end{bmatrix}, U\right)$$

Fig.1 lower linear fraction transformation

Proceedings of the
American Control Conference
San Francisco, California • June 1993

Minimum Control Effort State–Feedback $\mathcal{H}_\infty$-Control

Ewald Schömig[1]
Department of
Electrical Engineering, FT-10
University of Washington
Seattle, Washington 98195

Mario Sznaier[2]
Electrical Engineering
Department
University of Central Florida
Orlando, FL 32816-0450

Uy-Loi Ly[3]
Department of
Aero- and Astronautics, FS-10
University of Washington
Seattle, Washington 98195

Abstract

Optimal $\mathcal{H}_\infty$-controllers may exhibit large gains, resulting in large control efforts. In this paper we consider the problem of designing a *minimum gain* static full state-feedback controller such that the closed-loop transfer function satisfies a $\mathcal{H}_\infty$-constraint. The main result of the paper shows that, by minimizing an upper bound for the Frobenius-norm of the feedback-gain matrix and using a parametrization as in [6], the problem can be cast into a finite-dimensional, convex optimization problem. Scalar cost-functions for the $\mathcal{H}_\infty$-bound and various other constraints allow the application of gradient-based software packages to these problems. Finally, we illustrate how to apply this theory to the mixed $\mathcal{H}_2/\mathcal{H}_\infty$-control problem with minimum control effort.

1. Introduction

Consider the following linear time-invariant system:

$$\Sigma : \begin{cases} \dot{x} &= Ax + B_1 w + B_2 u \\ z_2 &= C_0 x + D_0 u \\ z_\infty &= C_1 x + D_1 u \\ y &= x \\ u &= Ky \end{cases} \tag{1}$$

where (A, B_2) is controllable. $x \in R^n$ represents the states, $u \in R^m$ represents the control action, $z_2 \in R^p$ represents variables subject to possible $\mathcal{H}_2$-performance specifications, $w \in R^r$ represents an exogenous disturbance and the transfer function from w to $z_\infty \in R^q$ is subject to the $\mathcal{H}_\infty$-bound. Note that a non-zero direct feedthrough matrix from w to z_∞ can be incorporated into this framework as well. However, without loss of generality we assume this feedthrough matrix to be zero. Given a state-feedback matrix $K \in R^{m \times n}$, the closed-loop system can be expressed as follows:

$$\Sigma_{cl} : \begin{cases} \dot{x}_{cl} &= A_{cl} x_{cl} + B_1 w \\ &= (A + B_2 K) x_{cl} + B_1 w \\ z_2 &= (C_0 + D_0 K) x_{cl} = C_{cl0} x_{cl} \\ z_\infty &= (C_1 + D_1 K) x_{cl} = C_{cl1} x_{cl} \end{cases} \tag{2}$$

Let $T_2(s)$ denote the closed-loop transfer function from $w(s)$ to $z_2(s)$ and $T_\infty(s)$ the closed-loop transfer function from $w(s)$ to $z_\infty(s)$. Let $Tr(.)$ represent the trace operator, then we can state the design objective of a *minimum control effort* $\mathcal{H}_\infty$-problem as follows:

P1. Find a stabilizing state-feedback gain matrix K such that $\|T_\infty(s)\|_\infty < \gamma$ and (an upper bound for) $\|K\|_F = Tr\{KK^T\}$ is minimized.
We also address the problem where $\|K\|_F$ is not actually minimized but bounded from above by a certain prespecified value b_K. Hence we can define an alternate criterion as follows:
P1'. Find a stabilizing state-feedback gain matrix K such that $\|T_\infty(s)\|_\infty < \gamma$ and $\|K\|_F < b_K$.

The mixed $\mathcal{H}_2/\mathcal{H}_\infty$-control problem with minimum control effort can be put into the following form:
P2. Find a stabilizing state-feedback gain matrix K such that $\|T_\infty(s)\|_\infty < \gamma$ and an upper bound for the weighted sum of $\|T_2(s)\|_2$ and $\|K\|_F$ is minimized.

Similar to objective P1' we can also define design objectives where bounds are imposed on $\|T_2(s)\|_2$ and/or $\|K\|_F$ if so desired. These cases will be outlined later. Note that all problems involving an $\mathcal{H}_\infty$-bound have a solution if and only if the associated pure $\mathcal{H}_\infty$-problem has a solution as shown in [14]. Also, design strategies that include a bound either on $\|K\|_F$ as in P1' or a bound on $\|T_2(s)\|_2$ such that $\|T_2(s)\|_2 < b_2$ may not have a solution even if the corresponding pure $\mathcal{H}_\infty$-bound problem has a solution.
In general all the above objectives will reduce the control effort according to $\|u\|_2 \leq \|K\|_F \|x\|_2$. Without proof we state the following results.

Lemma 1 ([6], [7]) *For a stable system Σ_{cl} the following statements are equivalent:*

[1, 3] This work was supported in part by NASA Ames DFRF under grant NAG-2-629.
[2] This work was supported in part by NSF under grant ECS-9211169.

1. $\|T_\infty(s)\|_\infty < \gamma$

2. *ARI: There exists a symmetric positive-definite matrix Y such that*

$$YA_{cl}^T + A_{cl}Y + \gamma^{-2}YC_{cl1}^TC_{cl1}Y + B_1B_1^T < 0 \quad (3)$$

For future reference we define the convex sets

$$\begin{aligned} \Theta &:= \{X \in R^{n\times n} : X = X^T > 0\} \\ \Upsilon &:= \{(X,W) \in \Theta \times R^{m\times n}\} \\ \Omega &:= \{(\tau, X) \in R \times \Theta : \tau > 0\} \\ \Psi &:= \{(\tau, X, W) \in \Omega \times R^{m\times n}\} \end{aligned}$$

Lemma 2 **([6])** *Consider the system defined in Lemma 1 and let $K = WX^{-1}$ with $(X,W) \in \Upsilon$, then the following holds:*
1. The matrix function $Q(X,W) : \Upsilon \to R^{n\times n}$

$$\begin{aligned} Q(X,W) &:= X[A + B_2WX^{-1}]^T + [A + B_2WX^{-1}]X \\ &+ \gamma^{-2}X[C_1 + D_1WX^{-1}]^T[C_1 + D_1WX^{-1}]X \\ &+ B_1B_1^T \end{aligned} \quad (4)$$

is convex on Υ. Furthermore, there exists a static state-feedback $K = WX^{-1}$ such that $\|T_\infty(s)\|_\infty < \gamma$ if and only if there is a $(X,W) \in \Upsilon$ such that $Q(X,W) < 0$.
Convexity is defined in terms of the usual ordering of symmetric matrices:

$$\begin{aligned} &Q[\alpha(W_1,X_1) + (1-\alpha)(W_2,X_2)] \quad (5) \\ \le\ &\alpha Q(W_1,X_1) + (1-\alpha)Q(W_2,X_2). \end{aligned}$$

for two pairs of matrices $(W_1,X_1) \in \Upsilon$ and $(W_2,X_2) \in \Upsilon$.
2. The scalar quantity

$$R(X,W) = Tr\{[C_0 + D_0WX^{-1}]X[C_0 + D_0WX^{-1}]^T\}$$

is convex on Υ. Furthermore, if $(X,W) \in \Upsilon$ satisfies $Q(X,W) < 0$, then $R(X,W) > \|T_2(s)\|_2^2$.

Obviously $Q(X,W)$ represents the left-side argument of inequality (3) with a state feedback $K = WX^{-1}$ in place and $Y = X \in \Theta$. Hence the parametrization $K = WX^{-1}$ allows the formulation of the mixed $\mathcal{H}_2/\mathcal{H}_\infty$-problem in a convex setting. It should be noted that a pair $(X,W) \in \Upsilon$ that satisfies $Q(X,W) < 0$ implies that $\|T_\infty(s)\|_\infty < \gamma$. However, $Q(\tilde{X},\tilde{W}) \in \Psi$ and $K = \tilde{W}\tilde{X}^{-1}$ that satisfies the $\mathcal{H}_\infty$-bound $\|T_\infty(s)\|_\infty < \gamma$ does not necessarily imply $Q(\tilde{X},\tilde{W}) < 0$. In this case Lemma 1 states that there is a matrix Y such that (3) is satisfied. In order to have $Q(\tilde{X},\tilde{W}) < 0$ satisfied, we have to require additionally that $Y = \tilde{X}$. Hence $Q(X,W) < 0$ is only a sufficient condition for $\|T_\infty(s)\|_\infty < \gamma$, not a necessary one. Note that Lemma 2 only refers to the existence of a static state-feedback matrix (that satisfies the $\mathcal{H}_\infty$-bound) in terms of $Q(X,W)$. In the next section we will give a convex upper bound for $\|WX^{-1}\|_F$ that allows us to formulate the overall problem P1 as a convex optimization problem.

2. Convex Upper Bounds for $\|WX^{-1}\|_F$

Theorem 1 *Consider the Frobenius norm of the state-feedback gain matrix $\|K\|_F = \|WX^{-1}\|_F$, then*

$$\begin{aligned} J_{B1}(\tau,X,W) &= \frac{1}{2}\tau^2\lambda_{max}(X^{-1}) + \frac{1}{2}Tr(W^TW) \\ J_{B2}(\tau,X,W) &= \frac{1}{2}Tr(\tau^2X^{-1}) + \frac{1}{2}Tr(W^TW) \end{aligned}$$

with $\tau^2X \ge I$ represent upper bounds for $\|WX^{-1}\|_F$ such that

$$\|WX^{-1}\|_F \le J_{B1}(\tau,X,W) \le J_{B2}(\tau,X,W).$$

Furthermore, $J_{B1}(\tau,X,W)$ and $J_{B2}(\tau,X,W)$ are convex on Ψ and

$$\tfrac{1}{\tau^2}I - X \le 0 \ (\Longleftrightarrow \tau^2X \ge I)$$

is a convex constraint on Ψ.

Proof: The following chain of inequalities proofs that $J_{B1}(\tau,X,W)$ and $J_{B2}(\tau,X,W)$ represent upper bounds for $\|WX^{-1}\|_F$.

$$\begin{aligned} \|WX^{-1}\|_F &= \sqrt{Tr(WX^{-1}X^{-1}W^T)} && (6) \\ &\le \sqrt{Tr(\tau^2X^{-1}W^TW)} && (7) \\ &\qquad s.\ t.\ \frac{1}{\tau^2}I - X \le 0 \\ &\le \sqrt{\tau^2\lambda_{max}(X^{-1})Tr(W^TW)} && (8) \\ &\le \frac{1}{2}\tau^2\lambda_{max}(X^{-1}) + \frac{1}{2}Tr(W^TW) && (9) \\ &\le \frac{1}{2}Tr(\tau^2X^{-1}) + \frac{1}{2}Tr(W^TW) && (10) \end{aligned}$$

provided that $\frac{1}{\tau^2}I - X \le 0$. Obviously equation (9) is equivalent to $J_{B1}(\tau,X,W)$ and equation (10) represents $J_{B2}(\tau,X,W)$. Equation (7) follows from (6) by the scaling of $\|K\|_F$ with $\tau^2X \ge I$. (8) follows from (7) using Lemma 3 in the Appendix. (9) follows from (8) using the arithmetic-geometric mean inequality with $\alpha = \frac{1}{2}$ and the facts that $\lambda_{max}(\tau^2X^{-1}) \ge 0$ and $Tr(W^TW) \ge 0$ (see Appendix). $J_{B1}(\tau,X,W) \le J_{B2}(\tau,X,W)$ finally follows from $\lambda_{max}(Z) \le Tr(Z)$ for any $Z \in \Theta$. Convexity of $Tr(W^TW)$ is shown in [4] (p. 556, problem 33) and the remaining convexity proofs are provided in the Appendix (see Theorems 4 and 5). As the sum of convex mappings is convex, overall convexity follows. Note that $\frac{1}{\tau^2}I - X \le 0$ is equivalent to $\tau^2X \ge I$. $\frac{1}{\tau^2}I - X \le 0$, however, is a convex constraint on Ω as shown in Theorem 6.

Both bounds are continuous on Ψ and $J_{B1}(\tau,X,W)$ is obviously a tighter bound than $J_{B2}(\tau,X,W)$. However, $J_{B2}(\tau,X,W)$ is differentiable on Ψ while $J_{B1}(\tau,X,W)$ is not differentiable at points where $\lambda_{max}(X^{-1}) = \lambda_i(X^{-1}) = \lambda_j(X^{-1})$, $i \ne j$. This property is important in the numerical solution of the minimization problem. Design problems corresponding to these objectives can now be stated as follows.

P1: Minimum effort control with an $\mathcal{H}_\infty$-bound:

$$\begin{aligned}
&\min_{(\tau,X,W)\in\Psi} J_{P1}(\tau,X,W)\\
&J_{P1}(\tau,X,W) = J_{Bi}(\tau,X,W), \quad i=1 \ or \ i=2\\
&s.\ t.\ \ Q(X,W)<0\\
&\qquad \frac{1}{\tau^2}I - X \leq 0
\end{aligned}$$

P2: Minimum effort mixed $\mathcal{H}_2/\mathcal{H}_\infty$-control:

$$\begin{aligned}
&\min_{(\tau,X,W)\in\Psi} J_{P2}(\tau,X,W)\\
&J_{P2}(\tau,X,W) = \beta J_{Bi}(\tau,X,W) + (1-\beta)R(X,W),\\
&i=1 \ or \ i=2\\
&s.\ t.\ \ Q(X,W)<0\\
&\qquad \frac{1}{\tau^2}I - X \leq 0
\end{aligned}$$

where $\beta \in [0,1]$ is a weighting factor. For $\beta = 0$ only the $\mathcal{H}_2$-performance measure is taken into consideration, with $\beta = 1$ the minimum effort control problem is addressed. Both minimization problems are continuous in all involved parameters and convex on Ψ.

3. A Gradient-Based Formulation

Ellipsoid or Cutting-Plane methods are applicable to this type of problem. For a review of the advantages and disadvantages of these methods and descent methods see [2] and references therein. In many cases, however, descent-methods provide faster convergence rates. In this section, we will show how to characterize the above constraints in terms of differentiable functions that maintain the convexity properties of the original constraints. Hence we arrive at unconstrained optimization problems.

Theorem 2 *Let $(X,W) \in \Upsilon$. We define a scalar measure for the $\mathcal{H}_\infty$-bound as*

$$J_I(X,W,t_f) = Tr\{e^{Q(X,W)t_f}\} \qquad (11)$$

where the scaling factor t_f is introduced for algorithmic reasons (see section 4). $J_I(X,W,t_f)$ has the following properties:

1. *$J_I(X,W,t_f)$ is non-negative.*
   Given a t_f, $J_I(X,W,t_f)$ is continuous, differentiable and convex on Υ.
2. $\lim_{t_f\to\infty} \min_{X,W} J_I(X,W,t_f) = 0 \Leftrightarrow Q(X,W) < 0$

Proof: Convexity follows from (6), Weyl's Theorem and Lemma 5 (see Appendix). The latter property of $J_I(X,W,t_f)$ follows from the fact that $Q(X,W)<0$ is equivalent to $Q(X,W)$ being stable as $Q(X,W)$ is Hermitian. As $Tr\{e^{Q(X,W)t_f}\}$ is the sum of the exponential of the eigenvalues of $Q(X,W)t_f$, property *2.* follows directly.

It can be shown that first-order gradients of $J_I(X,W,t_f)$ can be found using the matrix series expansion of the involved matrix exponential and Kleinman's Lemma (see e.g. [13], p.263). After some matrix algebra, the gradient expressions are as follows.

$$\begin{aligned}
\frac{\delta J_I(X,W,t_f)}{\delta W} &= 2t_f[B_2^T + D_1^T U]e^{Q(X,W)t_f}\\
\frac{\delta J_I(X,W,t_f)}{\delta X} &= t_f[Te^{Q(X,W)t_f} + e^{Q(X,W)t_f}T^T]
\end{aligned}$$

where

$$\begin{aligned}
T &= A^T + C_1^T U\\
U &= \gamma^{-2}(C_1X + D_1W)
\end{aligned}$$

Other constraints such as $\frac{1}{\tau^2}I - X \leq 0$ can be converted to convex scalar functions as well. Also, at this point we want to emphasize, that suboptimal design objectives such as in P1' can be accommodated in the same way by forming a scalar penalty function. As long as the constraint is in the form of a Hermitian matrix inequality or a scalar inequality such as $J_{B1}(\tau,X,W) < b_K$ or $R(X,W) < b_2$, this method will result in a penalty function with the same property as in Theorem 2 retaining the convexity properties of the original constraint.

4. Proposed Algorithm

The problem formulation combines all the peformance costs and the constraint penalty functions into single cost function $J_O(X,W,t_f)$.

$$J_O(X,W,t_f) = J_P(\tau,X,W) + J_C(\tau,X,W,t_f) \qquad (12)$$

where $J_P(\tau,X,W)$ is either $J_{P1}(\tau,X,W)$ or $J_{P2}(\tau,X,W)$ and represents the performance objective. $J_C(\tau,X,Wt_f)$ is the sum of all penalty function terms corresponding to constraints including the $\mathcal{H}_\infty$-penalty function $J_I(X,W,t_f)$. The proposed algorithm starts at a small t_{fs} so that initial guesses W, X and τ that do not satisfy the constraints will not result in numerical overflow problems. In a feasibility stage we optimize on $J_C(\tau,X,W,t_{fs})$ only, trying to find a feasible solution $\bar{W}$, $\bar{X}$ and $\bar{\tau}$ satisfying the relevant constraints. Once a feasible solution is found, the performance part of the overall cost function is optimized. t_f is increased to a large value t_{fl} such that the $J_C(\bar{\tau},\bar{X},W,t_{fl}) << J_P(\bar{\tau},\bar{X},\bar{W},t_{fl})$ (note, that in the limit as $t_f \to \infty$ all exponential terms in $J_C(W,X,\tau,t_f)$ will go to zero if the according constraints are satisfied). In fact, for large but finite t_f, $J_C(\tau,X,W,t_f)$ acts as a barrier function in the optimization process.

5. Example

To illustrate our approach, consider a 4th-order system used in [11]. It represents the scaled subsystem of the lateral dynamics of a BOEING 767 aircraft:

$$A = \begin{pmatrix} -0.0168 & 0.1121 & 0.0003 & -0.5608 \\ -0.0164 & -0.7771 & 0.9945 & 0.0015 \\ -0.0417 & -3.6595 & -0.9544 & 0 \\ 0 & 0 & 1 & 0 \end{pmatrix},$$

$$B_1 = \begin{pmatrix} 1 \\ 0 \\ 0 \\ 1 \end{pmatrix}, \quad B_2 = \begin{pmatrix} -0.0243 \\ -0.0634 \\ -3.6942 \\ 0 \end{pmatrix},$$

$$C_0 = \begin{pmatrix} 0 & 0 & 1 & 0 \end{pmatrix}, \quad D_0 = 1,$$

$$C_1 = \begin{pmatrix} 0.01 & 0 & 0.01 & 0 \end{pmatrix}, \quad D_1 = 0.01.$$

The open-loop system is stable, the subsystem $T_\infty(s)$ is non-minimum phase. The minimally achievable $\|T_\infty(s)\|_\infty$ is approximately 0.007. In the following picture we plot 2 curves. Each $\diamond$ represents a point design solving the convex optimization problem P1 (see (11) with $J_{B1}(\tau, X, W)$ as performance index subject to $Q(X, W) < 0$ with γ_{spec} being the specified $\mathcal{H}_\infty$-bound. Each o represents a point design that solves the following (non-convex) optimization problem.

$$\min_{(\tau,X,W)\in\Psi} J_{B1}(\tau, X, W)$$

subject to $\|T_\infty(s)\|_\infty < \gamma_{spec}$. Both curves show a typical

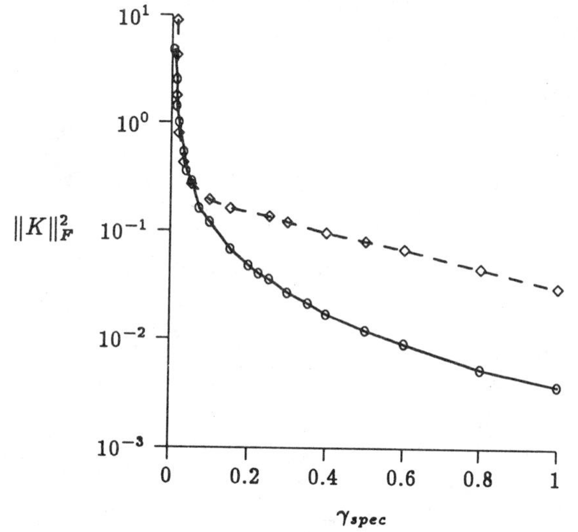

behaviour for mixed performance/robustness design objectives. For large γ_{spec}, $\|K\|_F$ is very small. If the overall problem becomes unconstrained in terms of the $\mathcal{H}_\infty$-constraint, that is if γ_{spec} is chosen large enough, $\|K\|_F$ will converge to zero (if the open-loop plant is stable). For small γ_{spec} on the other hand a dramatic increase in the controller gain can be observed for both design curves. The constraint $Q(X, W) < 0$ – as pointed out earlier – is conservative in terms of the $\mathcal{H}_\infty$-bound as it only represents a sufficient condition for $\|T_\infty(s)\|_\infty < \gamma_{spec}$. This fact is reflected in the difference between the two curves. The constraint $\|T_\infty(s)\|_\infty < \gamma_{spec}$ yields better performance than the constraint $Q(X, W) < 0$ for a given γ_{spec}. However, the latter constraint is convex while $\|T_\infty(s)\|_\infty < \gamma_{spec}$ is not.

6. Conclusions

During the last decade a powerful $\mathcal{H}_\infty$-framework has been developed, addressing the issue of robust stability in the presence of norm-bounded plant perturbations. In general, suboptimal controllers are preferred, since optimal $\mathcal{H}_\infty$-controllers may exhibit some undesirable properties, such as very large gains. Since suboptimal controllers are seldom unique, the extra degrees of freedom available can be used to solve a problem of the form *nominal performance with robust stability.* Nominal performance in this paper is characterized by *minimum control effort.* First we have shown that, by using a controller characterization as in [6], this problem can be cast into a finite-dimensional convex constrained optimization form. In the second part transformed this optimization problem into a unconstrained differentiable optimization problem, amenable to solution by gradient-based methods.

References

[1] E.F. Beckenbach, R. Bellman, "Inequalities," Fourth Printing, Springer Verlag, 1983.

[2] S.P. Boyd, C.H. Barratt, "Linear Controller Design, Limits of Performance," Prentice Hall, 1991.

[3] R.Y. Chiang, M.G. Safonov, "Design of an $\mathcal{H}_\infty$ controller for a Lightly Damped System using a Bilinear Pole Shifting Transform," ACC 1991, pp. 1927–1928.

[4] R. Horn, C.R. Johnson, "Matrix Analysis," Cambridge University Press, 1985.

[5] R. Horn, C.R. Johnson, "Topics in Matrix Analysis," Cambridge University Press, 1991.

[6] P.P. Khargonekar, M.A. Rotea, "Mixed H_2/H_∞ Control: A Convex Optimization Approach," *IEEE Trans. AC-36,* No. 7, 1991, pp. 824–837.

[7] P.P. Khargonekar, K. Zhou, "An Algebraic Riccati Equation Approach to H^∞ Optimization," *Systems and Control Letters 11,* 1988, pp. 85–91.

[8] J.R. Magnus, H. Neudecker, "Matrix Differential Calculus With Applications In Statistics And Econometrics," Wiley Series in Probability and Mathematical Statistics, John Wiley and Sons, 1988.

[9] M.A. Rotea, P.P. Khargonekar, "H^2-Control with an H_∞-Constraint: The State Feedback Case," *Automatica,* Vol. 27, No. 2, 1991, pp. 307–316.

[10] M.A. Rotea, P.P. Khargonekar, "Simultaneous H^2/H^∞ Optimal Control with State Feedback," ACC 1990, pp. 2380–2384.

[11] E. Schömig, U. Ly, "Mixed H_2/H_∞-Control With An Output–Feedback Compensator Using Parameter Optimization," ACC 1992, pp. 733–737.

[12] E. Schömig, "Mixed H_2/H_∞-Control with General Output–Feedback Using Parameter Optimization Methods," Ph.D. Dissertation, Electrical Engineering Department, University of Washington, 1993.

[13] A. Weinmann, "Uncertain Models and Robust Control," Springer-Verlag, Wien New York, 1991.

[14] K. Zhou, J. Doyle, K. Glover, B. Bodenheimer, "Mixed H_2 and H_∞ Control," ACC 1990, pp. 2502–2507.

Appendix

Theorem 3 (Weyl's Theorem, [4], p.181)
Let $G,\ H \in R^{n\times n}$ be Hermitian matrices, let the eigenvalues of G, H and $G+H$ be arranged in the following order
$\lambda_1(G) \le \lambda_2(G) \le ... \le \lambda_n(G) = \lambda_{max}(G)$
$\lambda_1(H) \le \lambda_2(H) \le ... \le \lambda_n(H) = \lambda_{max}(H)$
$\lambda_1(G{+}H) \le \lambda_2(G{+}H) \le ... \le \lambda_n(G{+}H) = \lambda_{max}(G{+}H)$,
then

$$\lambda_i(G+H) \le \lambda_i(G) + \lambda_{max}(H) \qquad (13)$$

for all $i = 1, 2, ...n$.
In particular we have

$$\lambda_{max}(G+H) \le \lambda_{max}(G) + \lambda_{max}(H). \qquad (14)$$

and, for $H \le 0$,

$$\begin{aligned} \lambda_i(G+H) &\le \lambda_i(G) \\ \lambda_{max}(G+H) &\le \lambda_{max}(G). \end{aligned}$$

Lemma 3 ([13], p.630)
Let $G,\ H \in R^{n\times n}$ be Hermitian matrices such that $G \ge 0$ and $H \ge 0$, then

$$Tr(GH) \le \lambda_{max}(G)Tr(H). \qquad (15)$$

Lemma 4 ([1])
(Arithmetic–Geometric Mean Inequality)
Let x and y be two non-negative scalars, then

$$x^\alpha y^{(1-\alpha)} \le \alpha x + (1-\alpha)y \qquad (16)$$

for every $\alpha \in (0,1)$.

Lemma 5 ([5])
Let Z_1 and Z_2 be Hermitian matrices and $\alpha \in (0,1)$, then

$$\begin{aligned} Tr\{e^{[\alpha Z_1+(1-\alpha)Z_2]t_f}\} &\le [Tr(e^{Z_1 t_f})]^\alpha [Tr(e^{Z_2 t_f})]^{(1-\alpha)} \\ &\le \alpha Tr(e^{Z_1 t_f}) + (1-\alpha)Tr(e^{Z_2 t_f}). \end{aligned}$$

Theorem 4
The function

$$J(\tau, X) = \tau^2 \lambda_{max}(X^{-1}) \qquad (17)$$

is convex on Ω.

Proof: The proof utilizes results in [6] and is very similar to that. As $J(\alpha\tau, \alpha X) = \alpha J(\tau, X)$ we only have to show that

$$J(\tau_1+\tau_2, X_1+X_2) \le J(\tau_1, X_1) + J(\tau_2, X_2). \qquad (18)$$

Let S be a nonsingular matrix such that

$$\begin{aligned} S^T X_1 S &= \Lambda_1 = diag(\lambda_{1,i}),\ \ i = 1,2,...,n \\ S^T X_2 S &= \Lambda_2 = diag(\lambda_{2,i}),\ \ i = 1,2,...,n \end{aligned}$$

Such a matrix exists for positive–definite matrices X_1 and X_2 (see [6]).

$$\begin{aligned} & J(\tau_1+\tau_2, X_1+X_2) \\ =\ & \lambda_{max}[(\tau_1+\tau_2)^2(X_1+X_2)^{-1}] \\ =\ & \lambda_{max}[S^{-1}\{diag(\frac{(\tau_1+\tau_2)^2}{\lambda_{1,i}+\lambda_{2,i}})\}S^{-T}] \\ =\ & \lambda_{max}[S^{-1}\{diag(\frac{\tau_1^2}{\lambda_{1,i}} + \frac{\tau_2^2}{\lambda_{2,i}} + \psi_i)\}S^{-T}] \\ =\ & \lambda_{max}[\tau_1^2 S^{-1}\Lambda_1^{-1}S^{-T} + \tau_2^2 S^{-1}\Lambda_2^{-1}S^{-T} \\ & + S^{-1}diag(\psi_i)S^{-T}] \end{aligned}$$

where $\psi_i = -\frac{(\tau_1\lambda_{2,i}-\tau_2\lambda_{1,i})^2}{(\lambda_{1,i}\lambda_{2,i})\lambda_{1,i}\lambda_{2,i}}$, $i = 1,2,...,n$.
Thus

$$J(\tau_1+\tau_2, X_1+X_2) = \lambda_{max}[\tau_1^2 X_1^{-1} + \tau_2^2 X^{-1} + Q] \qquad (19)$$

for $Q = S^{-1}diag(\psi_i)S^{-T} \le 0$ and hence

$$\begin{aligned} J(\tau_1+\tau_2, X_1+X_2) &\le \lambda_{max}(\tau_1^2 X_1^{-1} + \tau_2^2 X_2^{-1}) \\ &\le \lambda_{max}(\tau_1^2 X_1^{-1}) + \lambda_{max}(\tau_2^2 X_2^{-1}) \\ &= J(\tau_1, X_1) + J(\tau_2, X_2) \end{aligned}$$

The inequalities follow immediately from the above Lemmas and Weyl's Theorem. An alternative proof can be constructed using Fischer's min-max theorem (see [8]).

Theorem 5
The function

$$J(\tau, X) = Tr(\tau^2 X^{-1}) \qquad (20)$$

is convex on Ω.

Proof: A proof can be constructed using the same tools as above. It is essentially equivalent to the proof of Lemma 4.4 in [6] and is omitted here.

Theorem 6
Consider a mapping $f : \Omega \to R^{n\times n}$ and f given by

$$f(\tau, X) = \frac{1}{\tau^2}I - X. \qquad (21)$$

Then $f(\tau, X)$ is a real–analytic convex mapping on Ω.

Proof: $f(\tau, X)$ is affine in X. $\frac{1}{\tau^2}$ is a strictly monotonically decreasing function for all $\tau > 0$. Convexity on Ω follows immediately.

Proceedings of the
American Control Conference
San Francisco, California • June 1993

The General $\mathcal{H}_\infty$ Problem with Static Output Feedback

J. Stoustrup H. H. Niemann

Mathematical Institute, Technical University of Denmark, DK-2800, Lyngby, Denmark

Abstract

In this paper we shall consider the $\mathcal{H}_\infty$ control problem using static output feedback. Recently, this problem was solved in the regular case. We shall extend this result such that no assumption concerning the direct feedthrough term in the $\mathcal{H}_\infty$ problem is made. The main result states that the $\mathcal{H}_\infty$ static output feedback control problem is solvable if and only if the general $\mathcal{H}_\infty$ static state feedback problem is solvable and, further, that a certain 'geometric Riccati type' side constraint is satisfied.

1 Introduction

Frequently, static output feedback controllers are desired in miscellaneous control engineering problems and are sometimes implemented, mostly in ad hoc design schemes. Whereas static state feedback controllers and dynamic output feedback controllers are quite well understood from a theoretical point of view and have systematic design algorithms which are easy to implement, nothing similar is true for static output feedback controllers and there is a great lack of feasible design algorithms for such controllers.

It is not clear what characterizes the closed loop systems which can be obtained by zeroth order controllers. Recently [1], the static output feedback problem has been considered in an eigenstructure assignment approach, where some important properties of static output feedback controllers has been recorded.

Under 'generic' conditions, a static output feedback controller can assign at most r closed loop poles where r is the smaller of (1) no. of states (2) no. of inputs + no. of outputs - 1, and the paper provides an algorithm for assigning these poles, whenever it is possible. There is no guarantee, however, that the unstable poles are among the assignable ones, and henceforth pole assignment strategies do not provide sufficiently general, systematic design techniques.

It has not been clear at all how to generalize the popular $\mathcal{H}_2$ and $\mathcal{H}_\infty$ control design techniques to static output feedback systems.

Recently, however, a solution to the regular static output feedback $\mathcal{H}_\infty$ problem has been given [8], in terms of simultaneous solvability of a Riccati inequality and a partial Riccati inequality (see below). The approach in [8] was based on methods from the covariance control literature [5, 6, 4].

The main restriction in this approach, besides computational aspects, is the technical assumption that the direct feedthrough term from controllers to output should have full (column) rank. In the present paper we shall try to overcome this difficulty.

2 Preliminaries

In the sequel we shall consider systems of the following form:

$$\begin{array}{rclcl} \dot{x} & = & Ax & + & B_1 w & + & B_2 u \\ z & = & C_1 x & & & + & D_{12} u \\ y & = & C_2 x & & & & \end{array} \qquad (1)$$

for which we shall study control laws of the form $u = Ky$ for constant K which solve the $\mathcal{H}_\infty$ standard problem [3].

For technical reasons we shall assume that this system has no invariant zeros on the imaginary axis, i.e. the matrix $\begin{pmatrix} A - i\omega I & B_2 \\ C_1 & D_{12} \end{pmatrix}$ has constant rank for all ω, but we shall make no assumptions on the rank of D_{12}.

We need to introduce the kernel of C_2 in terms of the matrix V_2 given by the singular value decomposition of C_2.

$$C_2 = \begin{pmatrix} U_1 & U_2 \end{pmatrix} \begin{pmatrix} \tilde{\Sigma} & 0 \\ 0 & 0 \end{pmatrix} \begin{pmatrix} V_1 & V_2 \end{pmatrix}' \qquad (2)$$

The main result of [8] provides the solution to the static output feedback $\mathcal{H}_\infty$ problem for the special case where D_{12} has full column rank:

Theorem 1 *Consider the system (1). The following two statements are equivalent.*

(i) There exists a matrix $K \in \mathcal{R}^{m\times p}$, such that when applying the static output feedback law $u = Ky$, the resulting closed loop system is internally stable, and the $\mathcal{H}_\infty$ norm from w to z is smaller than γ.

(ii) There exists a positive definite solution P to the following two inequalities.

$$\begin{array}{c} A'P + PA + C_1'C_1 + \gamma^{-2}PB_1B_1'P \\ -(PB_2 + C_1'D_{12})R^{-1}(PB_2 + C_1'D_{12})' < 0 \end{array} \quad (3)$$

$$V_2'(A'P+PA+C_1'C_1+\gamma^{-2}PB_1B_1'P)V_2 < 0 \quad (4)$$

where $R := D_{12}'D_{12}$ and V_2 is given by (2).

In this paper we shall extend Theorem 1 to the general case where no assumptions are made on the rank of D_{12}. To that end, we shall need the solution to the so called singular $\mathcal{H}_\infty$ state feedback problem which can be found in [9].

Consider the following state feedback system:

$$\begin{array}{rcllll} \dot{x} &=& Ax &+ B_1w &+ & B_2u \\ z &=& C_1x & &+& D_{12}u \\ y &=& x & & & \end{array} \quad (5)$$

The existence of state feedback laws for (5) is characterized by the following result.

Theorem 2 *The following two are equivalent.*

1. *There exists a state feedback gain F such that $A + B_2F$ is stable and such that*

$$\left\|(C_1 + D_{12}F)(sI - A - B_2F)^{-1}B_1\right\|_\infty < \gamma$$

2. *There exists $P \geq 0$ such that the following three hold*

(a) $$F(P) = \begin{pmatrix} F_{11}(P) & F_{12}(P) \\ F_{21}(P) & F_{22}(P) \end{pmatrix} =: \begin{pmatrix} C_P' \\ D_P' \end{pmatrix}\begin{pmatrix} C_P & D_P \end{pmatrix} \geq 0$$

where

$$\begin{array}{rcl} F_{11}(P) &=& A'P + PA + C_1'C_1 \\ && +\gamma^{-2}PB_1B_1'P \\ F_{12}(P) &=& PB_2 + C_1'D_{12} \\ F_{21}(P) &=& B_{12}'P + D_{12}'C_1 \\ F_{22}(P) &=& D_{12}'D_{12} \end{array}$$

(b) $$m_{nr} := \operatorname{rank}\begin{pmatrix} C_P & D_P \end{pmatrix} = \max_{s\in C}\operatorname{rank}\,(C_1(sI - A)^{-1}B_2 + D_{12})$$

(c) $$\operatorname{rank}\begin{pmatrix} sI - A - \gamma^{-2}B_1B_1'P & -B_2 \\ C_P & D_P \end{pmatrix} = n + m_{nr}\ , \ \forall s \in \bar{C}^+$$

Whenever $P \geq 0$ exists satisfying the three conditions (2a-2c) of Theorem 2 such P can be found by solving a reduced order Riccati equation. Moreover, it can be shown that P is unique (see [9]).

3 Main Results

In this section, we shall derive necessary and sufficient conditions for solvability of the general $\mathcal{H}_\infty$ problem by static output feedback control.

First, however, we need the following preliminary result.

Lemma 1 *Consider the system*

$$\begin{array}{rcllll} \dot{x} &=& Ax &+ B_1w &+& B_2u \\ z &=& C_{1,\varepsilon}x & &+& D_{12,\varepsilon}u \\ y &=& x & & & \end{array} \quad (6)$$

where $C_{1,\varepsilon} = \begin{pmatrix} C_1 \\ \varepsilon I \\ 0 \end{pmatrix}$ *and* $D_{12,\varepsilon} = \begin{pmatrix} D_{12} \\ 0 \\ \varepsilon I \end{pmatrix}$

Then the following three statements are equivalent.

1. *There exists a static state feedback F for the system (5) such that $A + B_2F$ is stable and such that $\left\|(C_1 + D_{12}F)(sI - A - B_2F)^{-1}B_1\right\|_\infty < \gamma$*

2. *There exists ε_1 such that for all $\varepsilon \in (0;\varepsilon_1]$ there exists a static state feedback F_ε such that $A + B_2F_\varepsilon$ is stable and such that*

$$\left\|(C_{1,\varepsilon} + D_{12,\varepsilon}F_\varepsilon)(sI - A - B_2F_\varepsilon)^{-1}B_1\right\|_\infty < \gamma$$

3. *There exists ε_1 such that for all $\varepsilon \in (0;\varepsilon_1]$ there exists $P_\varepsilon > 0$ such that*

$$\begin{array}{c} \varepsilon^2 I + A'P_\varepsilon + P_\varepsilon A + C_1'C_1 + \gamma^{-2}P_\varepsilon B_1B_1'P_\varepsilon \\ -(P_\varepsilon B_2 + C_1'D_{12})R^{-1}(P_\varepsilon B_2 + C_1'D_{12})' < 0 \end{array}$$

where $R := D_{12}'D_{12} + \varepsilon^2 I$

Moreover, the sequence P_ε is convergent, $P_\varepsilon \to P$, and the limit P satisfies conditions (2a-2c) of Theorem 2.

Proof. The equivalence of Lemma 1(2) and Lemma 1(3) is the well known regular state feedback result. The equivalence of Lemma 1(1) and Lemma 1(2) is a general $\mathcal{H}_\infty$ cheap control result. The proof of the regular case carries through to the general case without any basic changes. Finally, that $P_\varepsilon \to P$, where P satisfies Theorem 2(2a-2c) is proved in [7]. □

Lemma 1 states that in the general case, the well known regular case Riccati equation [2] has to be substituted with the three conditions in Theorem 2(2a-2c) as $\varepsilon \to 0$. Our main result states that solvability of the general $\mathcal{H}_\infty$ control problem is equivalent to solvability of a generalization of the three conditions in Theorem 2(2a-2c) along with a 'geometric' condition of the same type as Theorem 1(4).

Theorem 3 *The following two are equivalent.*

1. *There exists a static output feedback gain K such that $A+B_2KC_2$ is stable and such that*

$$\|(C_1+D_{12}KC_2)\Phi B_1\|_\infty < \gamma \ ,$$
$$\Phi(s) := (sI - A - B_2KC_2)^{-1}$$

2. *There exists $P \geq 0$ and $W > 0$ such that the following four hold*

(a) $F_W(P) = \begin{pmatrix} F_{11W}(P) & F_{12W}(P) \\ F_{21W}(P) & F_{22W}(P) \end{pmatrix}$

$$=: \begin{pmatrix} C_P' \\ D_P' \end{pmatrix} \begin{pmatrix} C_P & D_P \end{pmatrix} \geq 0$$

where

$$\begin{aligned} F_{11W}(P) &= A'P + PA + C_{1W}'C_{1W} \\ &\quad + \gamma^{-2}PB_1B_1'P \\ F_{12W}(P) &= PB_2 + C_{1W}'D_{12W} \\ F_{21W}(P) &= B_2'P + D_{12W}'C_{1W} \\ F_{22W}(P) &= D_{12W}'D_{12W} \end{aligned}$$

(b) $m_{nr} := \operatorname{rank}\begin{pmatrix} C_P & D_P \end{pmatrix}$

$$= \max_{s\in\mathcal{C}} \operatorname{rank}\,(C_{1W}(sI-A)^{-1}B_2 + D_{12W})$$

(c) $\operatorname{rank}\begin{pmatrix} sI - A - \gamma^{-2}B_1B_1'P & -B_2 \\ C_P & D_P \end{pmatrix}$

$$= n + m_{nr} \ , \ \forall s \in \bar{\mathcal{C}}^+$$

(d) $V_2'(A'P+PA+C_1'C_1+\gamma^{-2}PB_1B_1'P)V_2 < 0$

where $\begin{pmatrix} C_{1W}' \\ D_{12W}' \end{pmatrix}\begin{pmatrix} C_{1W} & D_{12W} \end{pmatrix}$

$$:= \begin{pmatrix} C_1'C_1 + W & C_1'D_{12} \\ D_{12}'C_1 & D_{12}'D_{12} \end{pmatrix}$$

and V_2 is given by (2).

Proof. First, we note that the existence of a K satisfying Theorem 3(1) is equivalent to the existence of K_ε such that $A + B_2K_\varepsilon C_2$ is stable and such that

$$\|(C_{1,\varepsilon} + D_{12,\varepsilon}K_\varepsilon C_2)\Phi_\varepsilon B_1\|_\infty < \gamma \qquad (7)$$
$$\Phi_\varepsilon := (sI - A - B_2K_\varepsilon C_2)^{-1}$$

where $C_{1,\varepsilon}$ and $D_{12,\varepsilon}$ are defined as in Lemma 1. This is seen by a cheap control argument. Define $C_{1,0} := \begin{pmatrix} C_1 \\ 0 \\ 0 \end{pmatrix}$ and $D_{12,0} := \begin{pmatrix} D_{12} \\ 0 \\ 0 \end{pmatrix}$. Then,

$$\|(C_{1,0} + D_{12,0}KC_2)(sI - A - B_2KC_2)^{-1}B_1\|_\infty$$
$$= \|(C_1 + D_{12}KC_2)(sI - A - B_2KC_2)^{-1}B_1\|_\infty$$

Also, it is easy to see that

$$\|(C_{1,0} + D_{12,0}KC_2)(sI - A - B_2KC_2)^{-1}B_1\|_\infty$$
$$\leq \|(C_{1,\varepsilon} + D_{12,\varepsilon}KC_2)(sI - A - B_2KC_2)^{-1}B_1\|_\infty$$

for all ε proving that (7) implies Theorem (3)(1). Conversely, assume that

$$\|(C_{1,0} + D_{12,0}KC_2)(sI - A - B_2KC_2)^{-1}B_1\|_\infty$$
$$= \gamma - \delta \ , \ \delta > 0$$

Stability of $A + B_2KC_2$ implies boundedness of $\|(sI - A - B_2KC_2)^{-1}B_1\|_\infty =: M$. Obviously, ε_1 can be chosen such that

$$\|(C_{1,\varepsilon} + D_{12,\varepsilon}KC_2) - (C_{1,0} + D_{12,0}KC_2)\| < \frac{\delta}{2M}$$

for all $\varepsilon \in (0;\varepsilon_1]$. Hence, for all $\varepsilon \in (0;\varepsilon_1]$,

$$\|(C_1 + D_{12}KC_2)(sI - A - B_2KC_2)^{-1}B_1\|_\infty$$
$$= \|(C_{1,0} + D_{12,0}KC_2)(sI - A - B_2KC_2)^{-1}B_1\|_\infty$$
$$= \|(C_{1,\varepsilon} + D_{12,\varepsilon}KC_2)(sI - A - B_2KC_2)^{-1}B_1$$
$$-((C_{1,0} + D_{12,0}KC_2) - (C_{1,\varepsilon} + D_{12,\varepsilon}KC_2))$$
$$\times(sI - A - B_2KC_2)^{-1}B_1\|_\infty \leq \gamma - \delta + \frac{\delta}{2M}M < \gamma$$

Thus, applying Theorem 1 we obtain that Theorem 3(1) is equivalent to the existence of ε_1, $P_\varepsilon \geq 0$, $W_\varepsilon > 0$ and K such that

$$\varepsilon^2 I + A'P_\varepsilon + P_\varepsilon A + C_1'C_1 + \gamma^{-2}P_\varepsilon B_1B_1'P_\varepsilon$$
$$-(P_\varepsilon B_2 + C_1'D_{12})R_\varepsilon^{-1}(P_\varepsilon B_2 + C_1'D_{12})' = -W_\varepsilon \quad (8)$$
$$V_2'(A'P_\varepsilon + P_\varepsilon A + C_1'C_1 + \gamma^{-2}P_\varepsilon B_1B_1'P_\varepsilon)V_2 < 0 \quad (9)$$

where $R_\varepsilon := D_{12}'D_{12} + \varepsilon^2 I$ and V_2 is given by (2), for all $\varepsilon \in (0;\varepsilon_1]$.

In (8) W_ε is bounded from below by 0, but from standard Riccati theory W_ε is also bounded from above. In fact (8) is solvable for all $\varepsilon \in (0;\varepsilon_1]$ if and only if it is solvable also with the right hand side substituted with W, $W_\varepsilon \geq W \geq 0$, $\forall \varepsilon \in (0;\varepsilon_1]$. Now, rewriting (8) as

$$\varepsilon^2 I + A'P_\varepsilon + P_\varepsilon A + C'_{1W}C_{1W} + \gamma^{-2}P_\varepsilon B_1 B'_1 P_\varepsilon$$

$$-(P_\varepsilon B_2 + C'_{1W}D_{12W})R_\varepsilon^{-1}(P_\varepsilon B_2 + C'_{1W}D_{12})' = 0$$

where C_{1W} and D_{12W} are defined by

$$\begin{pmatrix} C'_{1W} \\ D'_{12W} \end{pmatrix} \begin{pmatrix} C_{1W} & D_{12W} \end{pmatrix} := \begin{pmatrix} C'_1C_1 + W & C'_1D_{12} \\ D'_{12}C_1 & D'_{12}D_{12} \end{pmatrix}$$

We are now in position to apply Lemma 1 with $F = KC_2$ to obtain that $\lim_{\varepsilon\to 0} P_\varepsilon = P$, where $P \geq 0$ satisfies Theorem 3(2a-2c). Finally, Theorem 3(2d) follows from (9) as ε tends to zero from continuity of the eigenvalues of a matrix as functions of the entries, and sufficiency follows from uniqueness of P. (Actually, the proof given here does not give *strict* inequality, but this can again easily be obtained by perturbation techniques as above.) □

To obtain $W > 0$ and $P \geq 0$ satisfying Theorem 3(2a-2d) one has to iterate on W and γ. For γ sufficiently large and for W sufficiently small there exist a unique $P \geq 0$ satisfying 2a-2c which can be found by solving a reduced order Riccati equation (see [9]). Once such P has been obtained, condition 2d has to be checked. If 2d fails, one has to decrease W and/or decrease γ. This scheme will converge if and only if there exists any stabilizing static controllers at all, which might not be the case even if the system is stabilizable and detectable in the usual sense.

Given such P a static output feedback gain can easily be determined, either through a cheap control method using the approach in [8] or by finding an appropriate state feedback gain and solving a number of linear equations.

Finally, consider instead the system

$$\begin{aligned} \dot{x} &= Ax + B_1 w + B_2 u \\ z &= C_1 x \\ y &= C_2 x + D_{21} w \end{aligned} \qquad (10)$$

By dualizing Theorem 3 we get the following result

Theorem 4 *The following two are equivalent.*

1. *There exists a static output feedback gain K such that $A + B_2KC_2$ is stable and such that*

$$\|C_1\Phi(B_1 + B_2KD_{21})\|_\infty < \gamma$$

$$\Phi = (sI - A - B_2KC_2)^{-1}$$

2. *There exists $P \geq 0$ and $W > 0$ such that the following four hold*

(a) $$F_W(P) = \begin{pmatrix} F_{11W}(P) & F_{12W}(P) \\ F_{21W}(P) & F_{22W}(P) \end{pmatrix} =: \begin{pmatrix} B_P \\ D_P \end{pmatrix} \begin{pmatrix} B'_P & D'_P \end{pmatrix} \geq 0$$

where

$$\begin{aligned} F_{11W}(P) &= PA' + AP + B_{1W}B'_{1W} \\ &\quad + \gamma^{-2}PC'_1C_1P \\ F_{12W}(P) &= PC'_2 + B_{1W}D'_{21W} \\ F_{21W}(P) &= C_2P + D_{21W}B'_{1W} \\ F_{22W}(P) &= D_{21W}D'_{21W} \end{aligned}$$

(b) $$m_{nr} := \text{rank} \begin{pmatrix} B_P & D_P \end{pmatrix} = \max_{s\in C} \text{rank } (C_2(sI - A)^{-1}B_{1W} + D_{21W})$$

(c) $$\text{rank} \begin{pmatrix} sI - A - \gamma^{-2}PC'_1C_1 & B_P \\ -C_2 & D_P \end{pmatrix} = n + m_{nr} \ , \ \forall s \in \bar{C}^+$$

(d) $\hat{U}'_2(AP + PA' + B_1B'_1 + \gamma^{-2}PC'_1C_1P)\hat{U}_2 < 0$

where

$$\begin{pmatrix} B_{1W} \\ D_{12W} \end{pmatrix} \begin{pmatrix} B_{1W} \\ D_{12W} \end{pmatrix} \begin{pmatrix} B'_{1W} & D'_{21W} \end{pmatrix} := \begin{pmatrix} B_1B'_1 + W & B_1D'_{21} \\ D_{21}B'_1 & D_{21}D'_{21} \end{pmatrix}$$

and U_2 is given by

$$C_2 = \begin{pmatrix} \hat{U}_1 & \hat{U}_2 \end{pmatrix} \begin{pmatrix} \hat{\Sigma} & 0 \\ 0 & 0 \end{pmatrix} \begin{pmatrix} \hat{V}_1 & \hat{V}_2 \end{pmatrix}'$$

4 Closing Remarks

Above we have provided necessary and sufficient conditions for the existence of zeroth order $\mathcal{H}_\infty$ controllers. The result was given as simultaneous solvability of a quadratic matrix inequality, two associated rank conditions and a 'geometric' side constraint.

The conditions are constructive in the sense, that the corresponding static output gains are calculated directly in terms of the matrix P found in the necessary and sufficient conditions. The actual algorithms to determine P depend upon solutions to reduced order Riccati equations as described in [9] in combination with an optimization approach.

The main drawback of the suggested approach is probably the involved computational aspects. It is the authors belief, however, that the algorithmic complexity associated with checking the given conditions relate to the complexity of the problem itself rather than to the specific approach taken.

The advantages of the present approach in comparison to a perturbation method based on [8] are improved numerical aspects along with the more direct approach from a theoretical point of view.

Finally, the methods used above and in [8] are conjectured to apply equally well for $\mathcal{H}_2$ or LQG problems and the like, which is a subject for further research.

References

[1] P.G. Maghami, J.-N. Juang, K.B. Lim, "Eigensystem Assignment with Output Feedback", *Journal of Guidance, Control, and Dynamics* , vol. 15, no. 2, pp. 531-535, 1992.

[2] J. C. Doyle, K. Glover, P.P. Khargonekar, and B.A. Francis, " State-space solutions to standard $\mathcal{H}_2$ and $\mathcal{H}_\infty$ control problems," *IEEE Transactions on Automatic Control,* vol. 34, no. 8, pp.831-847, August 1989.

[3] B. A. Francis, "A Course in $\mathcal{H}_\infty$ Control Theory." Springer Verlag, 1988.

[4] A. Hotz and R.E. Skelton, "Covariance Control Theory", Int. J. Control, 46(1), pp. 13-32, 1987.

[5] R.E. Skelton and M. Ikeda, "Covariance controllers for linear continous time systems," Int. J. Control, 49(5), pp. 1773-1785, 1989.

[6] R.E. Skelton and T. Iwasaki, "Liapunov and covariance controllers," Proc. American Control Conference, Chicago, pp. 2861-2865, 1992.

[7] C. Scherer, "The Riccati Inequality And State-Space $\mathcal{H}_\infty$-Optimal Control", Ph.D. dissertation, Würzburg University, Germany, 1990.

[8] R.E. Skelton, J. Stoustrup, T. Iwasaki, "The $\mathcal{H}_\infty$ Control Problem using Static Output Feedback", submitted for publication.

[9] A. A. Stoorvogel, "The $\mathcal{H}_\infty$ Control Problem - A State Space Approach", Prentice Hall, 1992.

Proceedings of the
American Control Conference
San Francisco, California • June 1993

A Complete Solution to the General H_∞ Control Problem: LMI Existence Conditions and State Space Formulas

T. Iwasaki and R. E. Skelton
Space Systems Control Laboratory
Purdue University
West Lafayette, IN 47907

Abstract

This paper presents all controllers for the general $\mathcal{H}_\infty$ control problem (with no assumptions on the plant matrices). Necessary and sufficient conditions for the existence of an $\mathcal{H}_\infty$ suboptimal controller of any order are given in terms of three Linear Matrix Inequalities (LMIs). Furthermore, we provide the set of all $\mathcal{H}_\infty$ suboptimal controllers explicitly parametrized in the state space using the positive definite solutions to the LMIs. The inequality formulation converts the existence conditions to a convex feasibility problem, and also a free matrix parameter in the controller formula defines a *finite* dimensional design space, as opposed to the infinite dimensional space associated with the Q-parametrization.

1 Introduction

Consider the n_p^{th} order linear time-invariant plant (Σ_p)

$$\begin{aligned} \dot{x} &= Ax + B_1 w + B_2 u \\ z &= C_1 x + D_{11} w + D_{12} u \\ y &= C_2 x + D_{21} w + D_{22} u \end{aligned} \tag{1.1}$$

where $x \in \Re^{n_p}$ is the plant state, $w \in \Re^{n_w}$ is any exogenous input, including plant disturbances, measurement noise, etc., $u \in \Re^{n_u}$ is the control input, $z \in \Re^{n_z}$ is the regulated output and $y \in \Re^{n_y}$ is the measured output. Recall that most of the existing $\mathcal{H}_\infty$ control theory (see [13, 11, 20, 19, 18, 14, 15] for a few exceptions) imposes the following "standard" assumptions : $D_{12}^T D_{12} > 0$ and $D_{21} D_{21}^T > 0$ and there are no invariant zeros on the $j\omega$-axis.

This paper considers a general $\mathcal{H}_\infty$ control problem without any assumptions on the plant matrices (A, B_1, B_2, C_1, C_2, D_{11}, D_{12}, D_{21}). Without loss of generality, we can let $D_{22} = 0$ provided the feedback connection is well-posed. Consider the n_c^{th} order linear time-invariant controller (Σ_c)

$$\dot{x}_c = A_c x_c + B_c y$$

$$u = C_c x_c + D_c y \tag{1.2}$$

where $x_c \in \Re^{n_c}$ is the controller state. We consider the design of a stabilizing controller (Σ_c) which yields the closed loop transfer matrix with $\mathcal{H}_\infty$ norm bounded above by a specified number. Such a controller is said to be an $\mathcal{H}_\infty$ suboptimal controller. Necessary and sufficient conditions for the existence of an $\mathcal{H}_\infty$ suboptimal controller of some (unspecified) order are given in terms of three Linear Matrix Inequalities (LMIs). Positive definite solutions to the LMIs form a convex set. The controller order can be fixed by imposing an additional rank condition (at the expense of convexity) on the solutions to the LMIs. Moreover, the set of all $\mathcal{H}_\infty$ suboptimal controllers is characterized explicitly in the state space. Of course, the results can be specialized to the standard case. In this event, there is a strong similarity to the Q-parametrization [8, 4]; except that our existence conditions involve two Riccati inequalities instead of two Riccati equations, and the set of all $\mathcal{H}_\infty$ controllers is parametrized by *a constant matrix of fixed dimension with a norm bound* (this is a finite dimensional parametrization) instead of the freedom in the Q-parametrization by *any real-rational stable transfer matrix Q(s) with an $\mathcal{H}_\infty$ norm bound* (hence this is an *infinite dimensional* parametrization). Another difference is that positive definite solutions to Riccati inequalities are not unique and this nonuniqueness also provides freedom in the parametrization of all $\mathcal{H}_\infty$ suboptimal controllers.

Our approach is purely algebraic. We will show that the general $\mathcal{H}_\infty$ control problem can be reduced to the problem of solving an LMI for controller parameters. Similar types of linear algebra problems have been studied in the covariance control literature (see [16] and the references therein) where linear matrix *equalities* (Lyapunov equations) are considered. See [6, 9] for the equality counterpart of the present paper (but with the standard assumptions).

The main advantage of our LMI formulation lies in the computational aspects. Convexity of the set of all positive definite solutions to the LMIs implies the existence of powerful numerical algorithms to solve certain optimization or feasibility problems over the set [1, 3, 7, 12]. Finiteness of the dimension of the norm bounded design space means that a search for a particular value of the free parameters to give the desired closed loop properties is much easier than a search in the infinite dimensional space of real-rational stable transfer matrices.

Another advantage of our LMI approach includes the fact that the controller order can be fixed by imposing a rank condition on the positive definite solutions to the LMI existence conditions. Of course, this additional rank condition would destroy convexity of the controller design problem, making the problem much harder. Nevertheless, our result parametrizes all low order controllers. If the order is not specified a priori the computational problems are convex and the resulting controller will be of order equal to or less than the plant.

We will use the following notation. An $n \times m$ matrix with real elements is denoted by $A \in \Re^{n\times m}$. A^T denotes the transpose of A. A^{-T} means $(A^T)^{-1}$. A^+ is the unique Moore Penrose inverse of A. $\mathcal{N}(A)$ and $\mathcal{R}(A)$ denote the nullspace and the range space of A, respectively. $A^\perp$ denotes a matrix with the following properties; $\mathcal{N}(A^\perp) = \mathcal{R}(A)$ and $A^\perp A^{\perp T} > 0$. Note that $A^\perp$ exists iff A has linearly dependent rows. Also note that, for a given A, $A^\perp$ is not unique, but throughout the paper, any choice is acceptable. The norm of a matrix $\|A\|$ is the largest singular value of A. For a symmetric matrix A, $\lambda_{max}(A)$ denotes the largest eigenvalue. For a nonnegative definite matrix A, $A^{\frac{1}{2}}$ denotes the unique nonnegative definite square root of A. I_n is the $n \times n$ identity matrix. SVD stands for the singular value decomposition.

2 The General $\mathcal{H}_\infty$ Control Problem

2.1 Problem Formulation

Consider the linear time-invariant controller (Σ_c) and generalized plant (Σ_p) where $D_{22} = 0$. Combining the plant (Σ_p) and the controller (Σ_c), the closed loop system (Σ_{cl}) can be described by

$$\dot{x}_{cl} = A_{cl}x_{cl} + B_{cl}w$$

$$z = C_{cl}x_{cl} + D_{cl}w \quad (2.1)$$

where

$$A_{cl} := \hat{A} + \hat{B}_2G\hat{C}_2, \quad B_{cl} := \hat{B}_1 + \hat{B}_2G\hat{D}_{21} \quad (2.2)$$

$$C_{cl} := \hat{C}_1 + \hat{D}_{12}G\hat{C}_2 \quad D_{cl} := D_{11} + \hat{D}_{12}G\hat{D}_{21} \quad (2.3)$$

and for the dynamic output feedback case ($n_c > 0$),

$$x_{cl} := \begin{bmatrix} x \\ x_c \end{bmatrix}, \quad \hat{A} := \begin{bmatrix} A & 0 \\ 0 & 0 \end{bmatrix}, \quad \hat{B}_2 := \begin{bmatrix} B_2 & 0 \\ 0 & I_{n_c} \end{bmatrix},$$

$$\hat{B}_1 := \begin{bmatrix} B_1 \\ 0 \end{bmatrix}, \quad \hat{C}_2 := \begin{bmatrix} C_2 & 0 \\ 0 & I_{n_c} \end{bmatrix}, \quad \hat{D}_{21} := \begin{bmatrix} D_{21} \\ 0 \end{bmatrix},$$

$$\hat{C}_1 := \begin{bmatrix} C_1 & 0 \end{bmatrix}, \quad \hat{D}_{12} := \begin{bmatrix} D_{12} & 0 \end{bmatrix},$$

and for the static output feedback case ($n_c = 0$),

$$x_{cl} := x, \quad \hat{A} := A, \quad \hat{B}_1 := B_1, \quad \hat{B}_2 := B_2,$$

$$\hat{C}_1 := C_1, \quad \hat{C}_2 := C_2, \quad \hat{D}_{12} := D_{12}, \quad \hat{D}_{21} := D_{21}.$$

and the controller matrices are described by matrix parameter G as follows.

$$G = \begin{bmatrix} D_c & C_c \\ B_c & A_c \end{bmatrix} \quad (\text{ if } n_c > 0 \text{ }), \quad G = D_c \quad (\text{ if } n_c = 0 \text{ }). \quad (2.4)$$

We denote the closed loop transfer matrix from w to z by T_{zw}. To state the $\mathcal{H}_\infty$ control problem, we need the following definition.

Definition 1 :

Given a positive scalar γ. The controller (Σ_c) is said to be an "*$\mathcal{H}_\infty$ suboptimal controller*" if the following two conditions hold.

1) A_{cl} is asymptotically stable.

2) $\|T_{zw}\|_\infty < \gamma$

Note that the internal stability is included as a property of $\mathcal{H}_\infty$ suboptimal controllers. Without loss of generality, we shall set the $\mathcal{H}_\infty$ norm bound γ to 1 to simplify the presentation for the rest of our discussion. Our objectives are :

Find the necessary and sufficient conditions for the existence of an $\mathcal{H}_\infty$ suboptimal controller. If one exists, obtain an explicit formula for all such controllers.

2.2 LMI Approach

In this subsection, we will convert the $\mathcal{H}_\infty$ control problem to a problem of solving LMIs for the controller parameter G defined in (2.4). The following well known lemma gives a characterization of all $\mathcal{H}_\infty$ suboptimal controllers.

Lemma 2.1 *Suppose a generalized plant (Σ_p) and a controller (Σ_c) are given. Define*

$$Q := A_{cl}X_{cl} + X_{cl}A_{cl}^T + B_{cl}B_{cl}^T \quad (2.5)$$

$$+(X_{cl}C_{cl}^T + B_{cl}D_{cl}^T)R^{-1}(X_{cl}C_{cl}^T + B_{cl}D_{cl}^T)^T \quad (2.6)$$

$$R := I - D_{cl}D_{cl}^T \quad (2.7)$$

The following statements are equivalent.

1) (Σ_c) is an $\mathcal{H}_\infty$ suboptimal controller.

2) $R > 0$ and there exists an $X_{cl} > 0$ satisfying $Q < 0$.

Recall that each closed loop matrix (A_{cl}, B_{cl}, etc.) is a linear function of the controller parameter G. Hence, the conditions $Q < 0$ and $R > 0$ can be considered as QMIs in G. Our approach for solving the $\mathcal{H}_\infty$ control problem is the following. Find the necessary and sufficient conditions for the existence of a matrix G which satisfies the inequalities $Q < 0$ and $R > 0$ simultaneously, and give an explicit parametrization of all such G when one exists. With such an approach, in general, existence conditions are obtained as inequalities with unknown matrix X_{cl}. Thus the existence conditions for an $\mathcal{H}_\infty$ suboptimal controller can be equivalently written in terms of the existence of a positive definite matrix X_{cl} satisfying certain matrix inequalities. The matrix X_{cl} will also be used to parametrize the set of all $\mathcal{H}_\infty$ suboptimal controllers. Of course, the dimension of the matrix X_{cl} fixes the order of the controller.

The following lemma converts the two QMIs ($Q < 0$ and $R > 0$) into just *one linear* matrix inequality (LMI).

Lemma 2.2 *Consider a generalized plant (Σ_p) and a controller (Σ_c). The following statements are equivalent.*

1) The controller (Σ_c) is an $\mathcal{H}_\infty$ suboptimal controller.

2) There exists a symmetric matrix $X_{cl} > 0$ satisfying

$$\bar{B}G\bar{C}\bar{X} + (\bar{B}G\bar{C}\bar{X})^T + \bar{Q} < 0 \quad (2.8)$$

where

$$\bar{Q} := \begin{bmatrix} \hat{A}X_{cl} + X_{cl}\hat{A}^T & X_{cl}\hat{C}_1^T & \hat{B}_1 \\ \hat{C}_1X_{cl} & -I_{n_z} & D_{11} \\ \hat{B}_1^T & D_{11}^T & -I_{n_w} \end{bmatrix},$$

$$\bar{X} := \begin{bmatrix} X_{cl} & 0 & 0 \\ 0 & I_{n_z} & 0 \\ 0 & 0 & I_{n_w} \end{bmatrix}, \quad \bar{B} := \begin{bmatrix} \hat{B}_2 \\ \hat{D}_{12} \\ 0 \end{bmatrix}, \quad \bar{C} := \begin{bmatrix} \hat{C}_2 & 0 & \hat{D}_{21} \end{bmatrix}.$$

Lemma 2.2 reduced the general $\mathcal{H}_\infty$ control problem to a linear algebra problem of finding a matrix G satisfying (2.8). The following lemma solves the problem.

Lemma 2.3 *Let matrices $B \in \Re^{n\times m}$, $M \in \Re^{k\times n}$, $X \in \Re^{n\times n}$ and $Q \in \Re^{n\times n}$ be given where $X = X^T$, $Q = Q^T$ and X is invertible. Let r_B and r_M denote the ranks of B and M, respectively and suppose $r_B < n$, $r_M < n$. Then there exists a matrix $G \in \Re^{m\times k}$ satisfying*

$$BGMX + (BGMX)^T + Q < 0 \quad (2.9)$$

iff

$$Q_B := -B^\perp QB^{\perp T} > 0, \quad Q_M := -M^{T\perp}X^{-1}QX^{-1}M^{T\perp T} > 0 \quad (2.10)$$

hold, in which case, all such G are given by

$$G = -B^+(XM^T + QB^{\perp T}Q_B^{-1}\Gamma^T)R + B^+BL + (I - B^+B)Z \quad (2.11)$$

where $Z \in \Re^{m\times k}$ is arbitrary and $L \in \Re^{m\times k}$ is any matrix such that

$$\|P^{-\frac{1}{2}}BLR^{-\frac{1}{2}}\| < 1 \quad (2.12)$$

where

$$P := \frac{1}{\epsilon^2}XM^TMX - Q > 0, \; R := (\epsilon^2 I + \Gamma Q_B^{-1}\Gamma^T)^{-1}, \; \Gamma := MXB^{\perp T}$$

and $\epsilon \in \Re$ is an arbitrary scalar such that

$$0 < \epsilon \quad \text{if} \quad Q \leq 0$$
$$0 < \epsilon < \frac{1}{\sqrt{\mu}} \quad \text{if} \quad \lambda_{max}(Q) > 0$$

where, using the SVD of M,

$$\mu := \lambda_{max}[M_R X^{-1}(Q + QX^{-1}M^{T\perp T}Q_M^{-1}M^{T\perp}X^{-1}Q)X^{-1}M_R^T]$$

$$M = \begin{bmatrix} U_{M1} & U_{M2} \end{bmatrix} \begin{bmatrix} \Sigma_{M1} & 0 \\ 0 & 0 \end{bmatrix} \begin{bmatrix} V_{M1}^T \\ V_{M2}^T \end{bmatrix}, \quad M_R := \Sigma_{M1}^{-1}V_{M1}^T.$$

3 All $\mathcal{H}_\infty$ Controllers

Necessary and sufficient conditions for the existence of an $\mathcal{H}_\infty$ suboptimal controller and explicit state space formulas are obtained by directly applying Lemma 2.3 to the general $\mathcal{H}_\infty$ control problem.

3.1 General Case

First, we present the most general result in the sense that there is no assumption on the plant (Σ_p).

Theorem 3.1 *Let n_c be a given integer such that $0 \leq n_c$. Then the following statements are equivalent.*
1) There exists an $\mathcal{H}_\infty$ suboptimal controller of order n_c.
2) There exist symmetric matrices X and Y such that

$$B^\perp \begin{bmatrix} AX + XA^T + B_1B_1^T & XC_1^T + B_1D_{11}^T \\ C_1X + D_{11}B_1^T & D_{11}D_{11}^T - I_{n_z} \end{bmatrix} B^{\perp T} < 0, \quad (3.1)$$

$$C^{T\perp} \begin{bmatrix} YA + A^TY + C_1^TC_1 & YB_1 + C_1^TD_{11} \\ B_1^TY + D_{11}^TC_1 & D_{11}^TD_{11} - I_{n_w} \end{bmatrix} C^{T\perp T} < 0, \quad (3.2)$$

$$\begin{bmatrix} X & I_{n_p} \\ I_{n_p} & Y \end{bmatrix} \geq 0, \quad (3.3)$$

$$n_c \geq rank(I_{n_p} - XY). \quad (3.4)$$

where

$$B := \begin{bmatrix} B_2 \\ D_{12} \end{bmatrix}, \quad C := \begin{bmatrix} C_2 & D_{21} \end{bmatrix},$$

If $B^\perp$ does not exist, the condition (3.1) is considered to be satisfied for any X. Similarly for the condition (3.2) when $C^{T\perp}$ does not exist.

Clearly, the set of matrix pairs (X,Y) satisfying (3.1)-(3.3) is convex. Hence, if we let the controller order be arbitrary, the existence of an $\mathcal{H}_\infty$ suboptimal controller can be checked via finite dimensional convex feasibility program. Moreover, the $\mathcal{H}_2$ performance measure [2, 12] can easily be incorporated for the mixed $\mathcal{H}_2/\mathcal{H}_\infty$ control problem without destroying the convexity since the above matrix X is indeed an upper bound for the plant state covariance [10]. Parametrization of all general $\mathcal{H}_\infty$ controllers follows.

Theorem 3.2 *Suppose there exists an $\mathcal{H}_\infty$ suboptimal controller of order n_c ($0 \leq n_c$). Then the existence conditions (3.1)- (3.4) are satisfied for some X and Y. The set of all $\mathcal{H}_\infty$ suboptimal controllers associated with the matrices X and Y is given by*

$$G = -\bar{B}^+(\bar{X}\bar{C}^T + \bar{Q}\bar{B}^{\perp T}\bar{Q}_B^{-1}\Gamma^T)\bar{R} + \bar{B}^+\bar{B}L + (I - \bar{B}^+\bar{B})Z \quad (3.5)$$

where $Z \in \Re^{(n_u+n_c)\times(n_y+n_c)}$ is arbitrary and $L \in \Re^{(n_u+n_c)\times(n_y+n_c)}$ is any matrix such that

$$\|P^{-\frac{1}{2}}\bar{B}L\bar{R}^{-\frac{1}{2}}\| < 1 \quad (3.6)$$

where

$$P := \frac{1}{\epsilon^2}\bar{X}\bar{C}^T\bar{C}\bar{X} - \bar{Q} > 0, \; \bar{R} := (\epsilon^2 I + \Gamma\bar{Q}_B^{-1}\Gamma^T)^{-1}, \; \Gamma := \bar{C}\bar{X}\bar{B}^{\perp T},$$

$$\bar{Q}_B := -\bar{B}^\perp\bar{Q}\bar{B}^{\perp T} > 0, \quad \bar{Q}_C := -\bar{C}^{T\perp}\bar{X}^{-1}\bar{Q}\bar{X}^{-1}\bar{C}^{T\perp T} > 0 \ .$$

and $\epsilon \in \Re$ is an arbitrary scalar such that

$$0 < \epsilon \quad \text{if} \quad \bar{Q} \leq 0$$
$$0 < \epsilon < \frac{1}{\sqrt{\mu}} \quad \text{if} \quad \lambda_{max}(\bar{Q}) > 0$$

where, using the SVD of $\bar{C}$,

$$\mu := \lambda_{max}[C_R\bar{X}^{-1}(\bar{Q} + \bar{Q}\bar{X}^{-1}\bar{C}^{T\perp T}\bar{Q}_C^{-1}\bar{C}^{T\perp}\bar{X}^{-1}\bar{Q})\bar{X}^{-1}C_R^T]$$

$$\bar{C} = \begin{bmatrix} U_{C1} & U_{C2} \end{bmatrix} \begin{bmatrix} \Sigma_{C1} & 0 \\ 0 & 0 \end{bmatrix} \begin{bmatrix} V_{C1}^T \\ V_{C2}^T \end{bmatrix}, \quad C_R := \Sigma_{C1}^{-1}V_{C1}^T.$$

The only unknown matrix X_{cl}, which appears as an element of $\bar{X}$, is constructed as follows. If $n_c = 0$, let $X_{cl} := X$. If $n_c > 0$, then let $L_x \in \Re^{n_p \times n_c}$ be any matrix factor

$$L_xL_x^T = X - Y^{-1}, \quad (3.7)$$

and let $R_x \in \Re^{n_c\times n_c}$ be any positive definite matrix. Then let

$$X_{cl} := \begin{bmatrix} X & L_xR_x \\ R_xL_x^T & R_x^2 \end{bmatrix}. \quad (3.8)$$

Theorem 3.2 gives an explicit state space parametrization of the set of all $\mathcal{H}_\infty$ suboptimal controllers using the (nonunique) positive definite solutions X and Y to the LMIs (3.1)-(3.3). Note that for each pair of X and Y, there corresponds a set of matrices X_{cl} which satisfy $Q < 0$. The freedom in the choices of L_x and R_x contributes only to the controller coordinate transformation. The freedom due to Z disappears if there are no redundant actuators, i.e., $B_2^TB_2 > 0$ which implies $\bar{B}^+\bar{B} = I$. Thus, all the essential controller design freedom is parametrized by L, which is a matrix of *fixed dimension with the norm bound* (3.6). Clearly, the set of all such matrices L is convex. Since the controller order is determined by the dimension of X_{cl}, we see from (3.8) that the controller order is minimal for a given pair of X and Y if the matrix factor L_x in (3.7) is chosen to be full column rank. Hence, we call a controller (Σ_c) a *minimal order $\mathcal{H}_\infty$ suboptimal controller* if it satisfies $Q < 0$ and $R > 0$ as in Lemma 2.1 with some positive definite matrix $X_{cl} > 0$ whose 12-block (X_{pc}) has linearly independent columns. As we shall see in the following subsection, such a minimality assumption on the controller together with the standard assumption on the plant matrices greatly simplifies the controller formula; specifically, the ϵ-dependence can be eliminated. It is worth noting that for any $\mathcal{H}_\infty$ suboptimal controller of order $n_c > n_p$, one can always construct a controller of order $n_c = n_p$ which achieves the same $\mathcal{H}_\infty$ norm bound. This known fact (see for example [4]) can easily be verified by noting that the rank of $(X - Y^{-1})$ in (3.7) can never exceed n_p due to the dimension constraint.

3.2 Standard Case

In this subsection, we specialize the general results of the previous section to the standard case where

$$D_{11} = 0,\ D_{12}^T\,[\,C_1\ D_{12}\,] = [\,I\ 0\,],\ D_{21}\,[\,B_1^T\ D_{21}^T\,] = [\,I\ 0\,]. \tag{3.9}$$

The above assumptions are enforced throughout this subsection. As mentioned in the previous subsection, we shall assume $X_{pc}^T X_{pc} > 0$ for minimality of the controller.

Theorem 3.3 *Let n_c be a given integer such that $0 \le n_c$. Suppose the assumption (3.9) holds. Then the following statements are equivalent.*

1) There exists an $\mathcal{H}_\infty$ suboptimal controller of order n_c.

2) There exist symmetric matrices X and Y such that

$$AX + XA^T + XC_1^T C_1 X + B_1 B_1^T - B_2 B_2^T < 0, \tag{3.10}$$

$$YA + A^T Y + YB_1 B_1^T Y + C_1^T C_1 - C_2^T C_2 < 0, \tag{3.11}$$

$$\begin{bmatrix} X & I_{n_p} \\ I_{n_p} & Y \end{bmatrix} \ge 0, \tag{3.12}$$

$$n_c \ge rank(I_{n_p} - XY). \tag{3.13}$$

In this case, all such controllers G with minimal order are given by

$$G = G_1 + G_2 L G_3 \tag{3.14}$$

where $L \in \Re^{(n_u+n_c)\times(n_y+n_c)}$ is any matrix such that $\|L\| < 1$ and

$$G_1 := (M_1^T - Q_{12}Q_{22}^{-1}M_2^T)(M_2 Q_{22}^{-1} M_2^T)^{-1},$$

$$G_2 := (-Q_{11} + Q_{12}Q_{22}^{-1}Q_{12}^T - G_1 G_3^2 G_1^T)^{\frac{1}{2}},\quad G_3 := (-M_2 Q_{22}^{-1} M_2^T)^{\frac{1}{2}},$$

$$\begin{bmatrix} Q_{11} & Q_{12} \\ Q_{12}^T & Q_{22} \end{bmatrix} := \begin{bmatrix} T_{B1} \\ T_{B2} \end{bmatrix} \bar{Q} \begin{bmatrix} T_{B1}^T & T_{B2}^T \end{bmatrix}$$

where for the dynamic output feedback case ($n_c > 0$),

$$T_{B1} := \begin{bmatrix} 0 & 0 & D_{12}^+ & 0 \\ 0 & I_{n_c} & 0 & 0 \end{bmatrix},\quad T_{B2} := \begin{bmatrix} I_{n_p} & 0 & -B_2 D_{12}^+ & 0 \\ 0 & 0 & D_{12}^\perp & 0 \\ 0 & 0 & 0 & I_{n_w} \end{bmatrix},$$

$$M_1 := \begin{bmatrix} 0 & C_2 X_{pc} \\ 0 & X_c \end{bmatrix},\quad M_2 := \begin{bmatrix} C_2 X_p & 0 & D_{21} \\ X_{pc}^T & 0 & 0 \end{bmatrix},$$

and for the static output feedback case ($n_c = 0$),

$$T_{B1} := \begin{bmatrix} 0 & D_{12}^+ & 0 \end{bmatrix},\quad T_{B2} := \begin{bmatrix} I_{n_p} & -B_2 D_{12}^+ & 0 \\ 0 & D_{12}^\perp & 0 \\ 0 & 0 & I_{n_w} \end{bmatrix},$$

$$M_1 := \begin{bmatrix} 0 \end{bmatrix},\quad M_2 := \begin{bmatrix} C_2 X_p & 0 & D_{21} \end{bmatrix}.$$

If D_{12} is square and invertible, $D_{12}^\perp$ does not exist. In this case, $D_{12}^+ = D_{12}^{-1}$ and the second row block of T_{B2} and the second column block of M_2 should be removed. Finally, the unknown matrix X_{cl} can be constructed in exactly the same way as in Theorem 3.2.

Gahinet [5] has obtained the existence conditions (3.10)-(3.13) assuming $X_{pc}^T X_{pc} > 0$. However, our existence conditions in Theorem 3.3 have been derived by specializing Theorem 3.1 *without* assuming $X_{pc}^T X_{pc} > 0$. Moreover, Theorem 3.3 provides an explicit controller formula which captures all minimal order $\mathcal{H}_\infty$ controllers. The formulas can be obtained by specializing Theorem 3.2 to the standard case. However, we can eliminate the ϵ-dependence from the controller formula if we directly consider the standard case. Notice that our parametrization of all $\mathcal{H}_\infty$ suboptimal controllers has similarity to the well-known state space formula for the standard $\mathcal{H}_\infty$ control problem [4, 8] in the following sense. Recall that in the Q-parametrization, the free parameter is a real-rational stable transfer matrix with its $\mathcal{H}_\infty$ norm less than a specified number. In our parametrization, (3.14), the freedom is a matrix L of fixed dimension with a norm bound.

3.3 Singular Case

In this subsection, we consider the singular $\mathcal{H}_\infty$ control problem where the following assumptions are made on the plant matrices.

$$D_{11} = 0,\quad D_{12} = 0,\quad D_{21} = 0. \tag{3.15}$$

The results are obtained by specializing the general result presented in section 3.1. We will state the necessary and sufficient conditions for the existence of an $\mathcal{H}_\infty$ suboptimal controller. A state space formula for all such controllers are given by Theorem 3.2.

Theorem 3.4 *Let n_c be a given integer such that $0 \le n_c$. Suppose the assumption (3.15) holds. Then the following statements are equivalent.*

1) There exists an $\mathcal{H}_\infty$ suboptimal controller of order n_c.

2) There exist symmetric matrices X and Y such that

$$B_2^\perp(AX + XA^T + XC_1^T C_1 X + B_1 B_1^T)B_2^{\perp T} < 0, \tag{3.16}$$

$$C_2^{T\perp}(YA + A^T Y + YB_1 B_1^T Y + C_1^T C_1)C_2^{T\perp T} < 0, \tag{3.17}$$

$$\begin{bmatrix} X & I_{n_p} \\ I_{n_p} & Y \end{bmatrix} \ge 0, \tag{3.18}$$

$$n_c \ge rank(I_{n_p} - XY). \tag{3.19}$$

If $B_2^\perp$ ($C_2^\perp$) does not exist, then the first (second) condition is considered to be satisfied for any X (Y).

In this subsection, we have considered the "totally singular case" where both D_{12} and D_{21} are zero matrices. We can also specialize the general result (Theorems 3.1 and 3.2) for other cases such as $D_{12}^T D_{12} > 0$ and $D_{21} = 0$. In this case, we have the existence conditions (3.10), (3.17), (3.18) and (3.19), which agree with the previous result in [17] for the static output feedback case. If all the states are available for feedback ($C_2 = I$), then (3.17) becomes redundant and hence, we can always choose Y to be X^{-1} to obtain a *constant gain* state feedback controller. Thus Theorem 3.4 provides another proof for the known fact first proved by Khargonekar et al. [11]. It can be easily verified using the Finsler's lemma that (3.16) is equivalent to Petersen's ϵ-Riccati equation [13].

4 Conclusion

The solution to the general $\mathcal{H}_\infty$ control problem is presented. Existence conditions are given in terms of three linear matrix inequalities. The set of all $\mathcal{H}_\infty$ suboptimal controllers is parametrized using positive definite solutions to the LMIs, which form a convex set. For each pair of the positive definite matrices, there corresponds a set of $\mathcal{H}_\infty$ suboptimal controllers. A state space formula parametrizing all such controllers is obtained, where free parameters are *constant matrices* with fixed dimensions and a real number ϵ within a known interval.

If we specialize our result to the standard case where D_{12} and D_{21} are full rank, the general LMI existence conditions reduce to Riccati inequalities which are identical to the familiar $\mathcal{H}_\infty$ Riccati equations with minor modifications (such as dualization and replacement of inequalities by equalities). The set of all controllers associated with given positive definite matrices satisfying the Riccati inequalities is parametrized by an arbitrary matrix of fixed dimension with bounded norm.

The main advantages of our results over the existing $\mathcal{H}_\infty$ control theory are the following. We do not require any assumptions on the generalized plant matrices (except for the well-posedness of the feedback connection). Our parametrization has computational advantages due to the free design parameters L and (X,Y), each of which forms a finite dimensional convex set (note that the Q-parametrization is not finite dimensional). Furthermore, the controller order can be fixed if desired, at the expense of convexity.

References

[1] C. Beck. Computational issues in solving LMIs. *Proc. IEEE Conf. Decision and Contr.*, pages 1259–1260, 1991.

[2] D. S. Bernstein and W. M. Haddad. LQG control with an H_∞ performance bound: a Riccati equation approach. *IEEE Trans. Automat. Contr.*, AC-34(3):293–305, March 1989.

[3] S. P. Boyd and C. H. Barratt. *Linear Controller Design: Limits of Performance.* Prentice Hall, Englewood Cliffs, 1991.

[4] J. C. Doyle, K. Glover, P. P. Khargonekar, and B. A. Francis. State-space solutions to standard H_2 and H_∞ control problems. *IEEE Trans. Automat. Contr.*, AC-34(8):831–847, August 1989.

[5] P. Gahinet. A convex parametrization of suboptimal H_∞ controllers. *Int'l J. Contr.* To appear.

[6] P. M. Gahinet. A new representation of H_∞ suboptimal controllers. *Proc. American Contr. Conf.*, pages 2240–2244, 1992.

[7] J. C. Geromel, P. L. D. Peres, and J. Bernussou. On a convex parameter space method for linear control design of uncertain systems. *SIAM J. Contr. Opt.*, 29(2):381–402, March 1991.

[8] K. Glover and J. Doyle. State-space formulae for all stabilizing controllers that satisfy an H_∞ norm bound and relations to risk sensitivity. *Syst. Contr. Lett.*, 11:167–172, 1988.

[9] T. Iwasaki and R. E. Skelton. All low order H_∞ controllers with covariance upper bound. *American Contr. Conf.*, 1993.

[10] T. Iwasaki, R. E. Skelton, and M. J. Corless. A computational algorithm for covariance control: Discrete-time case. *American Contr. Conf.*, 1993.

[11] P. P. Khargonekar, I. R. Petersen, and M. A. Rotea. H_∞ optimal control with state feedback. *IEEE Trans. Automat. Contr.*, AC-333(8):786–788, 1988.

[12] P. P. Khargonekar and M. A. Rotea. Mixed H_2/H_∞ control: A convex optimization approach. *IEEE Trans. Automat. Contr.*, AC-36(7):824–837, July 1991.

[13] I. R. Petersen. Disturbance attenuation and H_∞ optimization: A design method based on the algebraic Riccati equation. *IEEE Trans. Automat. Contr.*, AC-32(5):427–429, May 1987.

[14] C. Scherer. H_∞-control by state feedback for plants with zeros on the imaginary axis. *SIAM J. Contr. Opt.*, 30(1):123–142, 1992.

[15] C. Scherer. H_∞-optimization without assumptions on finite or infinite zeros. *SIAM J. Contr. Opt.*, 30(1):143–166, 1992.

[16] R. E. Skelton and T. Iwasaki. Liapunov and covariance controllers. *Proc. American Contr. Conf.*, 1992. Also to appear *Int'l J. Contr.*

[17] R. E. Skelton, J. Stoustrup, and T. Iwasaki. The H_∞ control problem using static output feedback. *Syst. Contr. Lett.* submitted for publication.

[18] A. A. Stoorvogel. The singular H_∞ control problem with dynamic measurement feedback. *SIAM J. Contr. Opt.*, 29(1):160–184, 1991.

[19] A. A. Stoorvogel and H. L. Trentelman. The quadratic matrix inequality in singular H_∞ control with state feedback. *SIAM J. Contr. Opt.*, 28(5):1190–1208, 1990.

[20] K. Zhou and P. P. Khargonekar. An algebraic Riccati equation approach to H_∞ optimization. *Syst. Contr. Lett.*, 11:85–92, 1988.

Proceedings of the
American Control Conference
San Francisco, California • June 1993

On the design of H_∞ controllers when standard assumptions are not satisfied

Ramine Nikoukhah, François Delebecque
INRIA, Rocquencourt, BP 105, 78153 Le Chesnay Cedex, France

Abstract

In this paper, a method is presented for obtaining the H_∞ controller in a number of situations where the standard assumptions needed for the application of the Riccati-based solution method fail. The situations considered are encountered frequently in practical applications due to the requirements to have integral action in the controller, large roll-off at high frequencies, etc...

1 Introduction

The "standard problem" formulation of the mixed-sensitivity problem is a general framework for solving many controller design problems using the H_∞ method. In practice, however, most resulting standard problems do not satisfy the usual assumptions needed for the Riccati based computation of the solution [3]. In order to get around this problem, the designer has to perturb certain design parameters in order to obtain a standard problem meeting the necessary assumptions (perturbing poles on the $j\omega$-axis, introducing poles near infinity, etc...). This method however has many drawbacks: numerical problems (even though the perturbed problem meets the required assumptions, it is numerically ill-posed), construction not systematic (perturbations must be small enough compared to the modes of the system yet large enough to avoid numerical ill-posedness) and loss of optimality with no a priori measure of discrepancy.

Practical considerations that lead to the violation of the standard assumptions are: the requirement that the controller contains an integrator action (e.g. using the internal model principle), the requirements on the high frequency roll-off of the open-loop gain, wanting to impose a zero on the $j\omega$-axis in the closed-loop system, etc... To transform these ill-posed problems into problems satisfying the needed assumptions, we use an idea introduced in [2] which is a methodology based on pre- and post-filtering the standard plant in such a way as to remove the problem causing zero and infinity poles, and, to recover the required full-rankedness conditions.

Our approach is based on two main ideas. The first is the use of improper systems as construction blocks in the formulation of the standard problem, and the second, shifting, by means of pre- and post-filtering, the problem causing poles. To implement the first idea, we need to use a state-space formulation of improper systems to avoid multiplying unnecessarily the number of poles during system integration which may lead to standard problems violating the stabilizability or detectability assumptions. There are two ways of representing improper systems in state-space form: one is using descriptor systems, i.e., coding the improper transfer function $H(s)$ into (E, A, B, C) such that $H(s) = C(sE - A)^{-1}B$, and second, using the standard state-space formulation (A, B, C, D) but allowing D to be a polynomial matrix, i.e., $H(s) = C(sI - A)^{-1}B + D(s)$. We refer to this as the polynomial state-space description.

In the polynomial state-space formulation, the polynomial part of the system is coded into the D matrix. Converting a rational matrix into this form is trivial. In addition, the infinite modes can be handled much easier since they remain separate from the other modes. The only difficulty with this formulation is the series cascading (system multiplication). This problem is considered in the next section. In the rest of this paper, we shall only use the polynomial state-space formulation.

The second idea is that of shifting the problem causing poles on the $j\omega$-axis and at infinity using pre- and post filters and not perturbing them as is usually done[1]. The advantage of our approach is that we can shift the poles on the $j\omega$-axis and at infinity to any desired location without loss of optimality since these artificial modes are a posteriori cancelled out exactly in the construction of the controller.

2 Improper systems

Consider the mixed-sensitivity standard problem [1]

$$P(s) = \begin{bmatrix} W_1(s) & -W_1(s)G(s) \\ 0 & W_2(s) \\ 0 & W_3(s)G(s) \\ I & -G(s) \end{bmatrix}.$$

[1] for example a pure integrator $1/s$ in the plant is usually perturbed and replaced by $1/(s+\epsilon)$ for a small ϵ and the difficulty is the choice of this ϵ; too large it would interfere with small modes of the system and too small, it would yield a numerically ill-posed standard problem

In most applications the weighting matrices and the nominal plant G are given in transfer function form but clearly, to apply the Riccati equation based solutions [3], we need to convert $P(s)$ into state-space form. It is a well known fact that trying to convert directly $P(s)$ into state-space form may lead to a generically non-minimal realization. To avoid this problem, one can either construct the state-space form using the state space realizations of $W_1(s)$, $W_2(s)$, $W_3(s)$ and $G(s)$ using the formulae given for example in [1], or, one can use the fact that

$$P(s) = \begin{bmatrix} W_1(s) & 0 & 0 \\ 0 & W_2(s) & 0 \\ 0 & 0 & W_3(s) \\ I & 0 & 0 \end{bmatrix} \begin{bmatrix} I & 0 & 0 \\ 0 & I & 0 \\ -I & 0 & I \end{bmatrix} \begin{bmatrix} I & -G \\ 0 & I \\ I & 0 \end{bmatrix}.$$

Since $W_1(s)$, $W_2(s)$, $W_3(s)$ and $G(s)$ each appear only once in this expression, if each of the three matrix factors is converted into state-space form separately and the multiplications are carried out in state-space domain, no duplication of modes will occur and we will end up with a generically minimal realization. The key idea here is that we should write the system as an expression in which each subsystem appears only once.

In many applications, either directly from the mixed-sensitivity formulation of the H_∞ problem or simply to insure that the full-rankedness assumption on D_{12} for the resulting standard problem is satisfied, we need to use improper W_i's [4, 1]. In that case, it is clear that if we restrict ourselves to standard state-space formulations, neither of the two methods mentioned above for the state-space construction of $P(s)$ can be applied. This problem is a motivation, but not the only motivation as we shall see in the next section, for introducing polynomial state-space description. This description allows us to construct, without introducing artificial modes, standard problems even if W_i's are not proper.

A polynomial state-space description is a generalization of the standard state-space description in which we allow the D matrix to be a polynomial matrix. The usual operations on standard state-space descriptions generalize trivially to the polynomial state-space case, all except system multiplication. We shall now present a method for performing this operation in polynomial state-space case.

Theorem 2.1 *Let $\Sigma = \Sigma_1 \star \Sigma_2$. Then a PSSD of $\Sigma = (A, B, C, D(s))$ can be constructed as follows:*

$$A = \begin{bmatrix} A_1 & B_1C_2 \\ 0 & A_2 \end{bmatrix}, \quad B = Y, \quad C = T,$$

and

$$D(s) = \begin{bmatrix} C_1 & D_1(s)C_2 \end{bmatrix} X(s) + Z(s)Y + D_1(s)D_2(s)$$

where the polynomial matrix $X(s)$ and the constant matrix Y satisfy

$$\begin{bmatrix} B_1D_2(s) \\ B_2 \end{bmatrix} = (sI - A)X(s) + Y$$

and where the polynomial matrix $Z(s)$ and the constant matrix T satisfy

$$\begin{bmatrix} C_1 & D_1(s)C_2 \end{bmatrix} = Z(s)(sI - A) + T.$$

Matrices $X(s)$, $Z(s)$, Y and T can be constructed using the Euclidian division algorithm.

In this section, we have provided a method for constructing the standard problem from proper and improper systems.

3 Main results

For simplicity, we shall consider only the case where the nominal plant is scalar. The generalization to the multivariable case can be found in [5].

Theorem 3.1 *Consider the standard problem:*

$$P = \begin{pmatrix} P_{11} & P_{12} \\ P_{21} & P_{22} \end{pmatrix}$$

where we search for a controller K which internally stabilizes P_{22_m}, a minimal realization of P_{22}, i.e. the physical part of the system, and minimizes *the L_∞ norm (thus not requiring internal stability) of $F_l(P, K)$. Let L and R be two stable systems having stable inverses. Then if K_{aug} is a (sub-) optimal solution to the standard problem*

$$P_{aug} = \begin{pmatrix} I & 0 \\ 0 & R \end{pmatrix} P \begin{pmatrix} I & 0 \\ 0 & L \end{pmatrix}$$

then $K = LK_{aug}R$ is a (sub-) optimal solution to the standard problem P.

Moreover, L and R may contain poles on the $j\omega$-axis and at infinity as long as these poles are not cancelled out by the zeros of P_{22m} (i.e. P_{22m} does not contain zeros at these pole locations).

Thanks to this theorem, we can try to normalize standard problems not satisfying the assumptions and solve them using the Riccati based solutions. Instead of presenting the systematic approach for constructing the pre-filter L and the post-filter R, we shall present two cases that come up frequently in practical design problems and show how they can be handled using this technique. A systematic approach can be found in [5].

3.1 Integrator in the controller

To force a $1/s$ (or powers of it) into the controller in the mixed-sensitivity framework, we need to include a $1/s$ in the W_1 weighting matrix. The problem however is that, as mentioned earlier, the resulting standard problem is not normalized. To see this let $W_1(s) = \bar{W}_1(s)/s$, then the mixed-sensitivity standard problem can be expressed as follows

$$P(s) = \begin{bmatrix} \bar{W}_1(s)/s & -\bar{W}_1(s)G(s)/s \\ 0 & W_2(s) \\ 0 & W_3(s)G(s) \\ I & -G(s) \end{bmatrix}.$$

It is clear that (assuming for simplicity that G(s) has no poles at zero) the pole at zero of $P(s)$ is not observable by y because it is not present in P_{22}. It is possible however to normalize this problem by taking $R = (s+\alpha)/s$ where α is any positive real number. The normalized plant then would be

$$P_{aug}(s) = \begin{bmatrix} \bar{W}_1(s)/s & -\bar{W}_1(s)G(s)/s \\ 0 & W_2(s) \\ 0 & W_3(s)G(s) \\ (s+\alpha)/s & -(s+\alpha)G(s)/s \end{bmatrix}.$$

Note that the McMillan degree for the pole at zero of P_{aug} is one, equal to that of the minimal realization of its $(2,2)$-block: $-(s+\alpha)G(s)/s$. The solution to this problem can thus be computed. Finally the optimal controller to the original problem can be constructed as $K = K_{aug}(s+\alpha)/s$ where K_{aug} is the solution to the normalized standard problem P_{aug}. As expected, K contains $1/s$.

3.2 Controller with arbitrary roll-off

It is a well-known fact that optimal solutions to H_∞ normalized problems are proper but not strictly proper controllers. In practice however, to impose required high frequency roll-off we need that the degree of the denominator of the controller exceeds that of its numerator by a given number. In the mixed-sensitivity formulation, this can be done either by chosing the W_2 weighting matrix improper (the degree of its numerator exceeding that of its numerator by this given number) or/and using an improper W_3.

Let us suppose that we require the degree of the denominator of the controller to be equal to that of its numerator plus n and suppose that for this purpose, we have chosen an improper W_2 (degree of numerator of W_2 – degree of denominator of $W_2 = n$). Clearly, the resulting problem P is not normalized (because it is not proper); it can however be normalized by using the pre-filter $L = 1/(s+\alpha)^n$.

4 Example

In this section we illustrate our approach through of an example which has been presented in [4] where a number of the difficulties discussed earlier is encountered. The solution to this problem in [4] is obtained by some hand calculations and by introducing a clever modification to the Riccati-based solution of the H_∞ problem. Using our methodology, we show that there is a systematic way of constructing a normalized standard problem (to which Riccati-based solutions can be applied without modification).

The problem considered is the mixed-sensitivity problem:

$$\left\| \begin{matrix} W_1(I-GK)^{-1} \\ W_3GK(I-GK)^{-1} \end{matrix} \right\|_\infty < 1$$

where

$$G(s) = \frac{-4.444e^5 + 4.007e^2 s + 5.498 s^2}{1.214e^5 + 9.520e^3 s + 93.72 s^2 + s^3},$$

$$W_1(s) = \frac{20\rho}{s(s+20)}, \quad W_3(s) = \frac{(s+30)(s+60)}{18000}.$$

Note that in this problem one integrator is needed in the controller; this is indicated by the pole at zero of W_1. Moreover, a difference of one is needed between the degrees of the numerator and denominator of the controller (this can be seen by examining W_3 or more specifically W_3G).

The standard problem associated with this mixed sensitivity formulation is the following:

$$P(s) = \begin{bmatrix} W_1(s) & -W_1(s)G(s) \\ 0 & W_3(s)G(s) \\ I & -G(s) \end{bmatrix}.$$

It is not difficult to see that this plant is not normalized ($W_3(s)G(s)$ is not proper and the pole at zero is not detectable). Here we solve this problem by showing that the associated standard problem can be normalized, allowing the use of the usual formulae [3].

To normalize this plant, we use pre- and post-filters as follows: $L = 1/(s+1)$,$R = (s+1)/s$, which yields the standard problem:

$$P_{aug}(s) = \begin{bmatrix} W_1 & -W_1G/(s+1) \\ 0 & W_3G/(s+1) \\ (s+1)/s & -G/s \end{bmatrix}.$$

Of course, we cannot construct the state-space realization of $P_{aug}(s)$ directly because, as mentioned earlier, we will end up with a non minimal realization. In particular, we can end up with a realization in which the pole at zero has multiplicity larger than one. This would be a disaster since in that case the realization would not be either detectable or stabilizable.

Fortunately, there is a way to avoid multiplying unnecessarily the poles of the system (introduced earlier); we should express the system as a product where each subsystems appears only once. The particular twist of this problem is that the pole at zero of R and that of W_1 can be realized as a pole at zero with multiplicity one. Even though the solution that we present here to avoid multiplying the pole at zero may seem tricky, and does not follow a systematic approach, it can be coded once and for all and applied to every problem of this type. The trick is to express P_{aug} as follows:

$$\begin{bmatrix} sW_1 & 0 & 0 \\ 0 & W_3 & 0 \\ 0 & 0 & s+1 \end{bmatrix} \begin{bmatrix} 1 & 0 \\ -s & 1 \\ 1 & 0 \end{bmatrix} \begin{bmatrix} \frac{1}{s} & 0 \\ 0 & 1 \end{bmatrix} \begin{bmatrix} 1 & -G \\ 1 & 0 \end{bmatrix} \begin{bmatrix} 1 & 0 \\ 0 & \frac{1}{s+1} \end{bmatrix}$$

It is straightforward to see that the P_{aug} constructed by putting each matrix in the state-space form individually and carrying out the multiplications in the state-space domain as well, we end up with a normalized problem to which we can apply the Riccati-based solution method and obtain the optimal (central) H_∞ controller K_{aug}. The optimal controller K is then obtained as $K = K_{aug}/s$. As expected, K contains an integrator and is strictly proper.

References

[1] Chiang R., Safonov M.G., (1988), Robust Control Toolbox User's Guide, Mathworks, Sherborn, MA.

[2] Copeland, B. R. and Safonov, M. G., (1992), Zero cancelling compensators for singular control problems and their application to the inner-outer factorization problem, Int. J. Robust and Nonlinear Control, 2.

[3] Doyle J. C. , Glover K., Khargonekar P., Francis B.A., (1989), State-Space Solutions to Standard H_2 and H_∞ Control Problems, IEEE Trans. Auto. Contr., 34.

[4] Kuraoka H., Ohka N., Hosoe S., Zhang F., (1990), Application of H_∞ Design to Automative Fuel Design, IEEE Control System Magazine.

[5] Nikoukhah, R. and Delebecque, F., (1992), Normalizing compensators for general H_∞ standard problems, INRIA report 1803, (also submitted for publication).

[6] Safonov M. G., Limebeer D. J., Chiang R. Y., (1989) : Simplifying the H_∞ theory via loop-shifting, matrix pencil and descriptor concepts, Int. Journal of Control, 50.

Proceedings of the
American Control Conference
San Francisco, California • June 1993

Existence Conditions for a Nonstandard H_∞ Problem [1]

Jeremy B. Matson† Tsutomu Mita‡ Brian D.O. Anderson†

† Department of Systems Engineering,
Research School of Physical Sciences and Engineering,
Australian National University,
GPO Box 4,
Canberra ACT 0200, AUSTRALIA

‡ Department of Electrical and Electronic Engineering,
Chiba University,
1-33 Yayoi-cho, Inage-ku,
Chiba 263, JAPAN

Abstract

Necessary and sufficient conditions are derived for the existence of H_∞ controllers for a class of linear, time-invariant generalized plants which is excluded by the assumptions generally made in the solution of H_∞ problems. The assumptions relaxed in this work concern the comparative dimensions of the plant's input and output spaces.

1 INTRODUCTION

In much of the H_∞ literature (e.g. [1]-[5]), a standard assumption made is that the generalised plant has at least as many controlled outputs as inputs and no more measurements than disturbances. These assumptions can certainly be violated in applications. In such circumstances, control inputs may outnumber controlled outputs and/or the number of disturbances associated with the infinity-norm objective may be less than the number of measurable outputs. Such situations provide greater opportunity for multi-objective controller design.

This standard assumption has been relaxed in a number of recent papers [7]-[11]. In [7]-[9], conditions for the existence of output feedback suboptimal H_∞ controllers are established using a pair of quadratic matrix inequalities, the solutions of which allow state-space construction of controllers. No assumptions are made in these papers concerning the rank of the direct feedthrough matrices from controlled inputs to outputs or from disturbances to measurement outputs. In the present work, as in [10] and [11], an H_∞ problem is treated in which these rank conditions are maintained and for which questions of controller existence and construction can be answered in terms of the solution of a pair of algebraic Riccati equations, rather than inequalities.

In [10] stable, minimum-phase squaring-down compensators allow transformation of the original non-standard H_∞ design problem into one where the standard techniques of [2]-[5] are applicable. The paper [10] also contains a helpful discussion of why techniques employed in the solution of the standard problem are inapplicable in the nonstandard case. Most recently the nonstandard problem has been addressed in [11] where conditions for the existence of compensators are developed in terms of a pair of algebraic Riccati equations and a coupling condition involving their solutions. A full parametrisation of suboptimal H_∞ controllers is then constructed based upon these solutions.

The present work focuses on the question of controller existence only. The necessary and sufficient conditions presented in [11] are derived here via different means. The technique employed in obtaining these conditions elucidates the connection with the standard problem. In the next section, the nonstandard H_∞ problem is defined and results from the standard theory briefly reviewed. The nonstandard problem is reformulated in the subsequent section by augmenting the original plant to produce a family of plants to which the results of the standard problem are applicable. The existence of nonnegative definite stabilizing solutions to two algebraic Riccati equations and satisfaction of an associated coupling condition are shown to be necessary and sufficient conditions for the existence of controllers.

Before proceeding, we introduce some notational conventions: Given a matrix M, M' denotes its transpose, $M^\dagger$ its Moore-Penrose inverse, $M^\perp$ its orthogonal complement, $\lambda_i(M)$ its ith eigenvalue, $\bar{\sigma}(M)$ its maximum singular value and $\rho(M) \triangleq \max_i |\lambda_i(M)|$, its spectral radius. $\Re\{z\}$ denotes the real part of a complex number z. The infinity norm $\|G\|_\infty$ is the supremum of $\bar{\sigma}(G(j\omega))$ over $0 \le \omega < \infty$. $\left(\begin{array}{c|c} A & B \\ \hline C & D \end{array}\right) \triangleq C(sI-A)^{-1}B+D$.

[1] The authors wish to acknowledge the funding of the activities of the Cooperative Research Centre for Robust and Adaptive Systems by the Australian Commonwealth Government under the Cooperative Research Centres Program.

2 PRELIMINARIES

2.1 Problem formulation.

In this paper, we seek existence conditions for H_∞ controllers of linear, time-invariant generalized plants described by an operator G:

$$\begin{pmatrix} z(t) \\ y(t) \end{pmatrix} = \begin{pmatrix} G_{11} & G_{12} \\ G_{21} & G_{22} \end{pmatrix} \begin{pmatrix} w(t) \\ u(t) \end{pmatrix} \tag{1}$$

The operator has been partitioned according to the following interpretation: G describes the behaviour of an *objective signal* $z(t)$ in response to an exogenous *disturbance* $w(t)$ and *control signal* $u(t)$. Our objective is to design *internally stabilizing control laws* of the form $u(t) = Ky(t)$ where K is a causal linear operator with its input being the *observed output* $y(t)$. When implemented, such a controller produces a closed-loop transfer function $T_{zw} \triangleq G_{11} + G_{12}K(I - G_{22}K)^{-1}G_{21}$, the infinity norm of which we seek to bound by a specified constant $\gamma > 0$.

We assume that G, when realized in the Laplace domain, has the following structure:

$$G(s) \triangleq \left(\begin{array}{c|cc} A & B_1 & B_2 \\ \hline C_1 & 0 & D_{12} \\ C_2 & D_{21} & 0 \end{array}\right) \tag{2}$$

No loss of generality is made in assuming that D_{11} and D_{22} are zero-matrices [1]. The following assumptions are made concerning $G(s)$ throughout this paper.

Assumptions on $G(s)$:

A.1 D_{12} and D_{21} are of full rank.

A.2 Neither $G_{12}(s)$ nor $G_{21}(s)$, as described by the above state space realization, have imaginary axis zeros.

A.3 (A, B_2) is stabilizable and (C_2, A) is detectable.

The papers [2]-[5] address what we refer to here as the *standard H_∞* problem in which the following assumption is invoked in addition to those above.

Standard Assumption on $G(s)$:

A.4 D_{12} is of full column rank and tall and D_{21} is of full row rank and fat.

In this work, we relax this assumption, referring to this case as the *nonstandard H_∞* problem. Our search is for conditions which ensure the existence of *γ-admissible* controllers for $G(s)$. Such controllers are defined by the following problem statement.

The nonstandard H_∞ control problem:

Given a plant $G(s)$ satisfying A.1 , A.2 and A.3 , and a constant $\gamma > 0$, find (if they exist) linear, time-invariant, causal controllers which produce an internally stable closed loop system T_{zw} for which $\|T_{zw}\|_\infty < \gamma$.

In the next section, we summarize results for the well-known special case of the above problem in which the standard assumption A.4 holds. In the remainder of the paper, our interest of course is in the case when this is violated.

2.2 Standard H_∞ Results.

In this section, we review the H_∞ design results obtained in [3] for the standard problem which are important in the development of this paper.

Lemma 2.1 *Given a plant $G(s)$ with the realization in (2), satisfying assumption A.4 in addition to assumptions A.1 ,A.2 and A.3 , a necessary and sufficient condition for the existence of γ-admissible controllers is that the following conditions hold:*

1. The following Riccati equation has a nonnegative definite stabilizing solution X:

$$0 = X(A - B_2E_{12}^{-1}D_{12}'C_1) + (A - B_2E_{12}^{-1}D_{12}'C_1)'X + X(\gamma^{-2}B_1B_1' - B_2E_{12}^{-1}B_2')X + C_1'(I - D_{12}E_{12}^{-1}D_{12}')C_1 \quad (3)$$

2. The following Riccati equation has a nonnegative definite stabilizing solution Y:

$$0 = Y(A - B_1D_{21}'E_{21}^{-1}C_2)' + (A - B_1D_{21}'E_{21}^{-1}C_2)Y + Y(\gamma^{-2}C_1'C_1 - C_2'E_{21}^{-1}C_2)Y + B_1(I - D_{21}'E_{21}^{-1}D_{21})B_1' \quad (4)$$

3. $\rho(XY) < \gamma^2$

where $E_{12} \triangleq D_{12}'D_{12}$ and $E_{21} \triangleq D_{21}D_{21}'$.

Proof: This result is stated in a slightly different form as part of Theorem 1 in [3]. □

3 EXISTENCE CONDITIONS.

It is shown in this section that existence results for the standard H_∞ problem lead to similar results for the nonstandard case. This connection is made via a family of augmented plants to which the standard results can be applied. Subsequently, a limiting process establishes existence conditions for the nonstandard problem.

In the general nonstandard problem, each of D_{12} and D_{21} may or may not be of nonstandard form. For the sake of brevity, we restrict our discussion to the case where both D_{12} and D_{21} are of nonstandard form. We shall refer to such plants in the subsequent discussion as being *doubly-nonstandard*. The *singly-nonstandard* case (ie where only one of D_{12} and D_{21} are nonstandard) can be treated in a very similar manner.

3.1 The ϵ-Augmented Problem.

In order to study the doubly nonstandard system $G(s)$, we introduce the following system, parametrised by a real number $\epsilon \geq 0$.

$$\begin{pmatrix} z^\epsilon(t) \\ y(t) \end{pmatrix} = G^\epsilon(s)\begin{pmatrix} w^\epsilon(t) \\ u(t) \end{pmatrix} \quad (5)$$

The state space structure of the operator G^ϵ is described as follows.

The ϵ-Augmented Plant.

$$G^\epsilon(s) \triangleq \left(\begin{array}{c|ccc} A & B_1 & \epsilon\bar{B}_1 & B_2 \\ \hline C_1 & 0 & 0 & D_{12} \\ \epsilon\bar{C}_1 & 0 & 0 & \epsilon({D_{12}}^\perp)' \\ C_2 & D_{21} & \epsilon({D_{21}}^\perp)' & 0 \end{array}\right) \quad (6)$$

The matrices ${D_{12}}^\dagger, {D_{12}}^\perp, {D_{21}}^\dagger$ and ${D_{21}}^\perp$ are defined by the following relations

$$\begin{pmatrix} D_{12} \\ ({D_{12}}^\perp)' \end{pmatrix}\begin{pmatrix} {D_{12}}^\dagger & {D_{12}}^\perp \end{pmatrix} = \begin{pmatrix} I & 0 \\ 0 & I \end{pmatrix}$$

$$\begin{pmatrix} {D_{21}}^\dagger \\ {D_{21}}^\perp \end{pmatrix}\begin{pmatrix} D_{21} & ({D_{21}}^\perp)' \end{pmatrix} = \begin{pmatrix} I & 0 \\ 0 & I \end{pmatrix} \quad (7)$$

The matrices ${D_{12}}^\dagger$ and ${D_{12}}^\perp$ (${D_{21}}^\dagger$ and ${D_{21}}^\perp$) can be calculated in a straightforward manner from a QR factorisation of D_{12}' (D_{21}). Appropriate choices for the matrices $\bar{B}_1, \bar{C}_1$ will become clear in the ensuing analysis.

The augmented feedthrough matrices are square, of full rank and have inverses as follows:

$$\begin{pmatrix} D_{12} \\ \epsilon({D_{12}}^\perp)' \end{pmatrix}^{-1} = \begin{pmatrix} {D_{12}}^\dagger & \frac{1}{\epsilon}{D_{12}}^\perp \end{pmatrix} \quad (8)$$

$$\begin{pmatrix} D_{21} & \epsilon({D_{21}}^\perp)' \end{pmatrix}^{-1} = \begin{pmatrix} {D_{21}}^\dagger \\ \frac{1}{\epsilon}{D_{21}}^\perp \end{pmatrix} \quad (9)$$

For any nonzero ϵ, H_∞ theory with standard assumptions can be directly applied to $G^\epsilon(s)$. This fact, in conjuction with the following lemma, allows the deduction of conditions on the existence of controllers for the nonstandard system.

Lemma 3.1 *Given a plant $G(s)$ and a controller $K(s)$, $\exists\ \epsilon^* > 0$ such that $\forall\ \epsilon \in [0, \epsilon^*)$, $K(s)$ is γ-admissible for $G(s)$ if and only if it is γ-admissible for $G^\epsilon(s)$.*

Proof:

1. *Internal stability.* The augmentation does not affect the control inputs or measured outputs. This means that $G_{22}^\epsilon(s) = G_{22}(s)$. If $K(s)$ internally stabilizes $G_{22}(s)$, then by [6] (Ch.4 Thm.1), it will internally stabilize both $G^\epsilon(s)$ and $G(s)$.

2. *The H_∞ -bound* result is based on the following connection between the augmented and original closed-loop transfer matrices

$$T_{z^\epsilon w^\epsilon}(s) = \begin{pmatrix} T_{zw}(s) & T_{z\bar{w}}(s) \\ T_{\bar{z}w}(s) & T_{\bar{z}\bar{w}}(s) \end{pmatrix} \quad (10)$$

and the fact that $T_{z\bar{w}}(s)$ and $T_{\bar{z}w}(s)$ are both of order ϵ and that $T_{\bar{z}\bar{w}}(s)$ is of order ϵ^2.

$\Rightarrow$ Suppose a controller has been implemented which ensures $\|T_{zw}\|_\infty < \gamma$. Clearly, if $\epsilon = 0$, the same controller ensures the H_∞ constraint is satisfied for the augmented system. Since the singular values of $T_{z^\epsilon w^\epsilon}(j\omega)$ vary continuously with ϵ, there will be some $\epsilon^* > 0$ such that $\epsilon \in [0, \epsilon^*)$ implies $\|T_{z^\epsilon w^\epsilon}\|_\infty < \gamma$.

$\Leftarrow$ Suppose a controller has been implemented which ensures $\|T_{z^\epsilon w^\epsilon}\|_\infty < \gamma$. Since $T_{zw}(s)$ is a submatrix of $T_{z^\epsilon w^\epsilon}(s)$, $\|T_{zw}\|_\infty \leq \|T_{z^\epsilon w^\epsilon}\|_\infty < \gamma$.

□

3.2 ϵ-Dependent Conditions for Existence

Having established a connection between the infinity-norm properties of the original and the ϵ -augmented system, we now utilize this connection to make statements about the existence of γ-admissible controllers for the original system.

Lemma 3.2 *A necessary and sufficient condition for the existence of a γ-admissible controller of a doubly-nonstandard plant $G(s)$ realized as in (2) and satisfying A.1 ,A.2 and A.3 is that $\exists\ \epsilon^* > 0$ such that the following conditions hold for any $\epsilon \in (0, \epsilon^*)$*

1. The following algebraic Riccati equation has a nonnegative definite stabilizing solution

$$0 = X_\epsilon A_X + A_X'X_\epsilon + X_\epsilon Q(\epsilon)X_\epsilon \quad (11)$$

$$A_X \triangleq (A - B_2{D_{12}}^\dagger C_1 - B_2{D_{12}}^\perp\bar{C}_1)$$

$$Q(\epsilon) \triangleq \gamma^{-2}B_1B_1' + \gamma^{-2}\epsilon^2\bar{B}_1\bar{B}_1' - B_2{D_{12}}^\dagger({D_{12}}^\dagger)'B_2' - \frac{1}{\epsilon^2}B_2{D_{12}}^\perp({D_{12}}^\perp)'B_2' \quad (12)$$

2. The following algebraic Riccati equation has a nonnegative definite stabilizing solution

$$0 = Y_\epsilon A_Y' + A_Y Y_\epsilon + Y_\epsilon P(\epsilon)Y_\epsilon \quad (13)$$

$$A_Y \triangleq (A - B_1{D_{21}}^\dagger C_2 - \bar{B}_1{D_{21}}^\perp C_2)$$

$$P(\epsilon) \triangleq \gamma^{-2}C_1'C_1 + \gamma^{-2}\epsilon^2\bar{C}_1'\bar{C}_1 - C_2'({D_{21}}^\dagger)'{D_{21}}^\dagger C_2 - \frac{1}{\epsilon^2}C_2'({D_{21}}^\perp)'{D_{21}}^\perp C_2 \quad (14)$$

3. $$\rho(X_\epsilon Y_\epsilon) < \gamma^2 \quad (15)$$

Proof: Say a γ-admissible controller exists for $G(s)$. By Lemma 3.1 we know that their exists an $\epsilon^* > 0$ such that the same controller is admissible for $G^\epsilon(s)$ when $\epsilon \in (0, \epsilon^*)$. Since $G^\epsilon(s)$ is of standard form, we can apply Lemma (2.1) to the ϵ -augmented system, thus obtaining equivalent conditions in terms of the solutions to two Riccati equations (3) and (4). The above Riccati equations and coupling condition are obtained by direct application of this result to the realisation of G^ϵ in (6), incorporating the formulae for $D_{12}^\epsilon, D_{21}^\epsilon$ and their inverses. □

Whilst Lemma 3.2 does give necessary and sufficient conditions for the existence of nonstandard γ-admissible controllers, it is of limited use. The dependence in these equations on ϵ needs to be eliminated since we have no knowledge in general of the size of ϵ^*. Direct implementation of an ϵ-augmented controller is likely to be subject to numerical difficulties if ϵ^* is very small. At this stage, one cannot eliminate the ϵ-dependence of the Riccati equation by the limiting process $\epsilon \to 0$ since the term $-\frac{1}{\epsilon^2} B_2 D_{12}{}^{\perp}(D_{12}{}^{\perp})' B_2'$ in the Riccati equation (11) diverges. One can, however show the following:

Theorem 3.1 *Given that the Riccati equations for X_ϵ and Y_ϵ in Lemma 3.2 have nonnegative definite stabilizing solutions and satisfy (15) $\forall \epsilon \in (0, \epsilon^*)$, limiting solutions to the equations exist with the following properties:*

1 a) $\lim_{\epsilon \to 0} X_\epsilon = X_0 \geq 0$

b) $\lim_{\epsilon \to 0}(A_X + Q(\epsilon)X_\epsilon)$ *exists and has all eigenvalues in the open left half-plane.*

2 a) $\lim_{\epsilon \to 0} Y_\epsilon = Y_0 \geq 0$

b) $\lim_{\epsilon \to 0}(A_Y + P(\epsilon)Y_\epsilon)$ *exists and has all eigenvalues in the open left half-plane.*

3 $\rho(X_0 Y_0) < \gamma^2$

Proof:

1. a) First differentiate the ARE (11) for X_ϵ with respect to ϵ to get

$$\frac{dX_\epsilon}{d\epsilon}(A_X + Q(\epsilon)X_\epsilon) + (A_X + Q(\epsilon))'\frac{dX_\epsilon}{d\epsilon} + X_\epsilon \frac{dQ(\epsilon)}{d\epsilon} X_\epsilon = 0$$

It is straightforward to show from (12) that $\frac{dQ(\epsilon)}{d\epsilon} \geq 0$. By hypothesis, X_ϵ is a stabilizing solution for any $\epsilon \in (0, \epsilon^*)$. This means that $A_X + Q(\epsilon)X_\epsilon$ is a stability matrix. These two facts, and application of Lyapunov's stability lemma to the above equation allow us to conclude that $\frac{dX_\epsilon}{d\epsilon} \geq 0$ Thus, X_ϵ is monotonically increasing with ϵ and always nonegative definite for $\epsilon \in (0, \epsilon^*)$. Hence as $\epsilon \to 0$, X_ϵ must converge to some finite nonnegative symmetric matrix X_0.

b) X_ϵ is by hypothesis a strictly stabilizing solution of (11) $\forall \epsilon \in (0, \epsilon^*)$. In fact, it is shown in Appendix A that A_X has no imaginary axis eigenvalues and also that

$$\lambda_i(A_X + Q(\epsilon)X_\epsilon) = \left\{ \begin{array}{ll} \lambda_i(A_X) & \text{if } \Re\{\lambda_i(A_X)\} < 0 \\ -\lambda_i(A_X) & \text{otherwise} \end{array} \right\} \quad (16)$$

Now since $Q(\epsilon)$ and X_ϵ vary continuously with ϵ, the eigenvalues $\lambda_i(A_X + Q(\epsilon)X_\epsilon)$ will also. Since they are always in the finite set $\{\pm\lambda_i(A_X)\}$, they are unchanged as $\epsilon \to 0$. Hence in the limit as $\epsilon \to 0$, the eigenvalues of $(A_X + Q(\epsilon)X_\epsilon)$ are all in the open left half-plane.

2. This result follows via arguments identical to those for X_ϵ.

3. This result is shown via a chain of inequalities and employs the fact that $X_\epsilon \geq X_0$ and $Y_\epsilon \geq Y_0$ for any $\epsilon \in (0, \epsilon^*)$. These inequalities follow from the arguments used in the proof of *1. a)* above. $\gamma^2 > \rho(X_\epsilon Y_\epsilon) = \rho(Y_\epsilon^{\frac{1}{2}} X_\epsilon Y_\epsilon^{\frac{1}{2}}) \geq \rho(Y_\epsilon^{\frac{1}{2}} X_0 Y_\epsilon^{\frac{1}{2}}) = \rho(X_0^{\frac{1}{2}} Y_\epsilon X_0^{\frac{1}{2}}) \geq \rho(X_0^{\frac{1}{2}} Y_0 X_0^{\frac{1}{2}}) = \rho(X_0 Y_0)$ □

We now set about connecting the existence of γ-admissible controllers with X_0 and Y_0. In addition, we seek ϵ-independent Riccati equations for X_0 and Y_0. The next section contains important observations on the structure of nonstandard systems which enable such equations to be found.

3.3 Eliminating ϵ-Dependence.

In the case of nonstandard feedthrough matrices, the zeros of $G_{12}(s)$ and/or $G_{21}(s)$ play an important role in simplifying the structure of the two ϵ-dependent Riccati equations (11) and (13). These zeros can be found using the following lemma.

Lemma 3.3 *Given a realization of $G(s)$ as in equation (2) which satisfies assumptions* A.1 ,A.2 *and* A.3 ,

1. *If D_{12} violates assumption* A.4, *the zeros of $G_{12}(s)$ are given by the uncontrollable modes of* $(A - B_2 D_{12}{}^{\dagger} C_1, B_2 D_{12}{}^{\perp})$.
2. *If D_{21} violates assumption* A.4, *the zeros of $G_{21}(s)$ are given by the unobservable modes of* $(D_{21}{}^{\perp} C_2, A - B_1 D_{21}{}^{\dagger} C_2)$.

Proof: See [11]. □

It is a standard result of linear systems theory that a state similarity transformation T can be found which produces a controllability canonical form for the pair $(A - B_2 D_{12}{}^{\dagger} C_1, B_2 D_{12}{}^{\perp})$:

$$T^{-1}(A - B_2 D_{12}{}^{\dagger} C_1)T = \begin{pmatrix} A_0 & 0 \\ A_{01} & A_1 \end{pmatrix} \quad (17)$$

$$T^{-1} B_2 D_{12}{}^{\perp} = \begin{pmatrix} 0 \\ \beta \end{pmatrix} \quad (18)$$

such that the pair (A_1, β) is controllable. A similarity transformation can also be found which produces an observability canonical form for $(D_{21}{}^{\perp} C_2, A - B_1 D_{21}{}^{\dagger} C_2)$.

$$U(A - B_1 D_{21}{}^{\dagger} C_2)U^{-1} = \begin{pmatrix} \alpha_0 & \alpha_{10} \\ 0 & \alpha_1 \end{pmatrix} \quad (19)$$

$$D_{21}{}^{\perp} C_2 U^{-1} = \begin{pmatrix} 0 & \phi \end{pmatrix} \quad (20)$$

such that the pair (ϕ, α_1) is observable.

From Lemma (3.3), we see that the zeros of $G_{12}(s)$ are the eigenvalues of A_0 and that the zeros of $G_{21}(s)$ are those of α_0.

Lemma 3.4 *With the following choice of augmentation, the structure of the ϵ-dependent Riccati equation is simplified:*

1. *With $\tilde{C}_1 = -\begin{pmatrix} L_1 & L_2 \end{pmatrix} T^{-1}$ chosen such that $A_1 + \beta L_2$ is stable, a nonnegative definite stabilizing solution to the ϵ-dependent Riccati equation (11), when it exists, is independent of the particular choice of stabilizing $\tilde{C}_1$ and has the following form:*

$$X_\epsilon = (T')^{-1} \begin{pmatrix} \Psi_\epsilon & 0 \\ 0 & 0 \end{pmatrix} T^{-1} \quad (21)$$

In addition it satisfies the following equality:

$$X_\epsilon B_2 D_{12}{}^{\perp} = 0 \quad (22)$$

2. *With $\tilde{B}_1 = -U^{-1} \begin{pmatrix} M_1 \\ M_2 \end{pmatrix}$ chosen such that $\alpha_1 + M_2 \phi$ is stable, a nonnegative definite stabilizing solution to the ϵ-dependent Riccati equation (13), when it exists, is independent of the particular choice of stabilizing $\tilde{B}_1$ and has the following form:*

$$Y_\epsilon = U^{-1} \begin{pmatrix} \Theta_\epsilon & 0 \\ 0 & 0 \end{pmatrix} (U')^{-1} \quad (23)$$

In addition it satisfies the following equality:

$$D_{21}{}^{\perp} C_2 Y_\epsilon = 0 \quad (24)$$

Proof: We concentrate, without loss of generality, on one Riccati equation only. With definitions $\tilde{X}_\epsilon \triangleq T' X_\epsilon T$ and $\tilde{Q}(\epsilon) \triangleq T^{-1} Q(\epsilon)(T^{-1})'$, we return to the Riccati equation (11), expressed in the basis corresponding to the transformation T.

$$0 = \tilde{X}_\epsilon \left(\begin{pmatrix} A_0 & 0 \\ A_{01} & A_1 \end{pmatrix} - \begin{pmatrix} 0 \\ \beta \end{pmatrix} \tilde{C}_1 T \right) + \left(\begin{pmatrix} A_0 & 0 \\ A_{01} & A_1 \end{pmatrix} - \begin{pmatrix} 0 \\ \beta \end{pmatrix} \tilde{C}_1 T \right)' \tilde{X}_\epsilon + \tilde{X}_\epsilon \tilde{Q}(\epsilon) \tilde{X}_\epsilon \quad (25)$$

Simplification of the Riccati equation is possible if we choose a matrix $\bar{C}_1$ which stabilizes the controllable modes corresponding to A_1. Since the pair (A_1, β) is controllable, it is possible to find an L_2 with $(A_1 + \beta L_2)$ stable and hence such a $\bar{C}_1$ exists. With the above choice of $\bar{C}_1$, the Riccati equation, transformed as in equation (25) is expressed thus:

$$0 = \tilde{X}_\epsilon \begin{pmatrix} A_0 & 0 \\ A_{01} + \beta L_1 & A_1 + \beta L_2 \end{pmatrix} + \left(\begin{pmatrix} A_0 & 0 \\ A_{01} + \beta L_1 & A_1 + \beta L_2 \end{pmatrix} + \tilde{Q}(\epsilon)\tilde{X}_\epsilon \right)' \tilde{X}_\epsilon \quad (26)$$

If one right-multiplies this equation by the matrix $\begin{pmatrix} 0 \\ I \end{pmatrix}$, one obtains:

$$\begin{pmatrix} 0 \\ 0 \end{pmatrix} = \tilde{X}_\epsilon \begin{pmatrix} 0 \\ I \end{pmatrix} (A_1 + \beta L_2) + \left(\begin{pmatrix} A_0 & 0 \\ A_{01} + \beta L_1 & A_1 + \beta L_2 \end{pmatrix} + \tilde{Q}(\epsilon)\tilde{X}_\epsilon \right)' \tilde{X}_\epsilon \begin{pmatrix} 0 \\ I \end{pmatrix} (27)$$

Note first that $(A_1 + \beta L_2)$ has been designed stable and that $\left(\begin{pmatrix} A_0 & 0 \\ A_{01} + \beta L_1 & A_1 + \beta L_2 \end{pmatrix} + \tilde{Q}(\epsilon)\tilde{X}_\epsilon \right)$ is stable since X_ϵ is by hypothesis a nonnegative definite stabilizing solution to (11). The stability of these two matrices allows us to deduce from (27) that $\tilde{X}_\epsilon \begin{pmatrix} 0 \\ I \end{pmatrix} = \begin{pmatrix} 0 \\ 0 \end{pmatrix}$. Since $\tilde{X}_\epsilon$ is symmetric, its (1,2),(2,1) and (2,2) blocks are zero matrices. This yields the structure of X_ϵ shown in equation (21).

Let the nonzero (1,1) partition of $\tilde{X}_\epsilon$ be Ψ_ϵ. From examination of the equation (26), we see that Ψ_ϵ satisfies

$$\Psi_\epsilon A_0 + A_0'\Psi_\epsilon + \Psi_\epsilon \begin{pmatrix} I & 0 \end{pmatrix} \tilde{Q}(\epsilon) \begin{pmatrix} I & 0 \end{pmatrix}' \Psi_\epsilon = 0 \quad (28)$$

from which it is clear that Ψ_ϵ is independent of $\bar{C}_1$. Note that it is still dependent on $\bar{B}_1$ which is present in $Q(\epsilon)$, however this dependence disappears in the limit as $\epsilon \to 0$. Since T is also independent of $\bar{C}_1$, we deduce from (21) that X_ϵ is also.

The identity (22) follows after application of the transformation T to the easily established identity: $\tilde{X}_\epsilon \begin{pmatrix} 0 \\ \beta \end{pmatrix} = \begin{pmatrix} 0 \\ 0 \end{pmatrix}$.

□

The above result can be used to eliminate the divergent term in the ϵ-dependent Riccati equations. This allows application of a simple limiting process to produce a Riccati equation for X_0 and Y_0.

Lemma 3.5 *A necessary and sufficient condition for the existence of a γ-admissible controller of the doubly-nonstandard plant $G(s)$ as realized in (2), satisfying A.1 ,A.2 and A.3 is that $\exists\ \epsilon^* > 0$ such that the following conditions hold for any $\epsilon \in (0, \epsilon^*)$ with $\bar{B}_1$ and $\bar{C}_1$ chosen according to Lemma (3.4):*

1. The following algebraic Riccati equation has a stabilizing solution $X_\epsilon \geq 0$

$$X_\epsilon A_X + A_X' X_\epsilon + X_\epsilon \mathcal{Q}(\epsilon) X_\epsilon = 0 \quad (29)$$

$$\mathcal{Q}(\epsilon) \triangleq \gamma^{-2} B_1 B_1' + \gamma^{-2}\epsilon^2 \bar{B}_1 \bar{B}_1' - B_2 D_{12}{}^{\dagger} (D_{12}{}^{\dagger})' B_2' \quad (30)$$

2. The following algebraic Riccati equation has a stabilizing solution $Y_\epsilon \geq 0$

$$Y_\epsilon A_Y' + A_Y Y_\epsilon + Y_\epsilon \mathcal{P}(\epsilon) Y_\epsilon = 0 \quad (31)$$

$$\mathcal{P}(\epsilon) \triangleq \gamma^{-2} C_1' C_1 + \gamma^{-2}\epsilon^2 \bar{C}_1' \bar{C}_1 - C_2' (D_{21}{}^{\dagger})' D_{21}{}^{\dagger} C_2 \quad (32)$$

3.

$$\rho(X_\epsilon Y_\epsilon) < \gamma^2 \quad (33)$$

Proof: From Lemma (3.2), we have existence conditions in terms of the solutions to two Riccati equations. Our aim here is to show that the equations in the statement of the present lemma have exactly the same solutions as those in Lemma (3.2).

⇒ From (11) and (13) and with the special choice of $\bar{B}_1$ and $\bar{C}_1$ in Lemma (3.4), one can use the identities (22) and (24) to eliminate the divergent terms $-\frac{1}{\epsilon^2} B_2 D_{12}{}^{\perp} (D_{12}{}^{\perp})' B_2'$ in (11) and $-\frac{1}{\epsilon^2} C_2' (D_{21}{}^{\perp})' D_{21}{}^{\perp} C_2$ in (13).

⇐ If we now assume nonnegative definite stabilizing solutions to (29) and (31), we can show by an identical argument to that in Lemma (3.4) that X_ϵ has a structure identical with that in (21) and Y_ϵ identical with that in (23). The identities (22) and (24) also hold for solutions to (29) and (31). Since positive definite stabilizing solutions of such equations are unique, the solutions to (29) and (31) are those of (11) and (13) respectively.
□

The next lemma is needed to prove the ϵ-independent existence result in Theorem (3.2).

Lemma 3.6 *Suppose that the equation $XA + A'X + XQX = 0$ has a nonnegative definite stabilizing solution X. For any nonnegative definite matrix S, $\exists\ \eta^* > 0$ such that for $\eta \in [0, \eta^*)$, the equation*

$$X_\eta A + A' X_\eta + X_\eta (Q + \eta S) X_\eta = 0$$

also has a nonnegative definite stabilizing solution X_η.

Proof: See Appendix B. □

The following theorem is the main result of this paper. It provides necessary and sufficient conditions under which γ-admissible controllers for the nonstandard system exist. As is shown in [11], once the conditions of the following theorem are satisfied, it is possible to construct all possible nonstandard H_∞ controllers. The full connection between state-space controller construction and the ϵ-augmentation approach is a topic currently under investigation.

Note the absence of the constant terms in these AREs. An equation of similar form appears in [12] where a state-feedback H_∞ control problem is addressed with $D_{12} = I$. It is shown how the simple structure of the ARE leads to its being solvable by direct calculation of the solution of two associated Lyapunov equations. A similar idea is presented in [13] where the Lyapunov equation solutions lead to a method by which the optimal H_∞ disturbance attenuation can be directly calculated for an output feedback H_∞ problem.

Theorem 3.2 *A necessary and sufficient condition for the existence of a γ-admissible controller for the doubly-nonstandard plant $G(s)$ as realized in (2) and satisfying A.1 ,A.2 and A.3 is that the following ϵ-independent conditions hold with $\bar{B}_1$ and $\bar{C}_1$ chosen according to Lemma (3.4):*

1. The following algebraic Riccati equation has a stabilizing solution $X_0 \geq 0$

$$X_0 A_X + A_X' X_0 + X_0 (\gamma^{-2} B_1 B_1' - B_2 D_{12}{}^{\dagger} (D_{12}{}^{\dagger})' B_2') X_0 = 0 \quad (34)$$

2. The following algebraic Riccati equation has a stabilizing solution $Y_0 \geq 0$

$$Y_0 A_Y' + A_Y Y_0 + Y_0 (\gamma^{-2} C_1' C_1 - C_2' (D_{21}{}^{\dagger})' D_{21}{}^{\dagger} C_2) Y_0 = 0 \quad (35)$$

3.

$$\rho(X_0 Y_0) < \gamma^2 \quad (36)$$

In fact, when such X_0 and Y_0 exist, they are independent of the choice of $\bar{B}_1$ and $\bar{C}_1$ satisfying Lemma (3.4)

Proof:
Necessity: Assume a γ-admissible control law for $G(s)$ has been found and implemented. By Lemma (3.5), the Riccati equation (29) has a nonnegative definite stabilizing solution for some finite ϵ-interval $(0, \epsilon^*)$. The limiting process $\epsilon \to 0$ establishes the X_0 equation (34). Note the existence of X_0, its nonnegativity and the fact that it is a stabilizing solution to (34) is secured by Theorem (3.1). An analogous argument establishes the Y_0 equation from the Y_ϵ equation. The coupling condition $\rho(X_0 Y_0) < \gamma^2$ has been established in Theorem (3.1).
Sufficiency: Suppose one has nonnegative definite stabilizing solutions to both (34) and (35) which satisfy (36). We now aim

to prove the existence of a γ-optimal controller by establishing conditions *1*, *2* and *3* of Lemma (3.5).

Let X_0 be a nonnegative definite stabilizing solution to (34). By comparing the quadratic term of this equation with that of (29), one can apply Lemma (3.6) to conclude that $\exists\ \hat{\epsilon} > 0$ such that $\epsilon \in (0, \hat{\epsilon}) \Rightarrow \exists X_\epsilon$ which is a nonnegative stabilizing solution of (29). Similar arguments establish the existence of $\bar{\epsilon} > 0$ such that $\epsilon \in (0, \bar{\epsilon}) \Rightarrow Y_\epsilon$ is a nonnegative stabilizing solution of (31).

By hypothesis, $\rho(X_0 Y_0) < \gamma^2$. Since X_ϵ and Y_ϵ depend continuously on ϵ so will the singular values and thus the spectral radius of their product. Hence $\exists\ \epsilon_\rho > 0$ such that $\epsilon \in (0, \epsilon_\rho)$ guarantees that $\rho(X_\epsilon Y_\epsilon) < \gamma^2$.

One can then apply Lemma (3.2) with $\epsilon^* = \min(\hat{\epsilon}, \bar{\epsilon}, \epsilon_\rho)$ to establish existence of the γ-admissible controller.

An argument similar to that used in the proof of Lemma 3.4 in conjunction with the Riccati equations (34) and (35) with basis transformations T and U respectively, reveal that both X_0 and Y_0 are independent of $\bar{B}_1$ and $\bar{C}_1$. □

4 CONCLUSIONS

This paper presents necessary and sufficient conditions for the existence of H_∞ controllers of a plant which violates the assumptions normally made in H_∞ design on the comparative dimensions of its input and output spaces. The approach developed to solve this problem relies on a parametrized augmentation of the nonstandard plant, application of standard H_∞ results and a limiting argument. The resulting existence conditions depend on the solution of two algebraic Riccati equations of particulary simple structure and the satisfaction of a coupling condition on their solutions. As is shown in [11], solutions to these equations lead directly to the construction of all γ-admissible controllers.

5 APPENDICES

5.1 Appendix A - Proof of eigenvalue reflection property in Theorem 3.1.

Suppose we have a nonnegative definite stabilizing solution to the equation $X_\epsilon(A_X + Q(\epsilon)X_\epsilon) + A_X^{'} X_\epsilon = 0$. Let λ be any eigenvalue of $(A_X + Q(\epsilon)X_\epsilon)$ with corresponding eigenvector w: $(A_X + Q(\epsilon)X_\epsilon)w = \lambda w$ and $\Re\{\lambda\} < 0$. Right multiplying the Riccati equation for X_ϵ by w, we deduce that $\lambda X_\epsilon w + A_X^{'} X_\epsilon w = 0$. For this equation to hold, it is required that either $X_\epsilon w = 0$ or that $-\lambda$ be an eigenvalue of A_X. (Note that A_X has no imaginary axis eigenvalues since these actually correspond with the zeros of $G_{12}(s)$ which, by assumption A.2 are never on the imaginary axis). If $X_\epsilon w = 0$, it is easily seen that $A_X w = \lambda w$ and thus that λ is also a stable eigenvalue of A_X. If $X_\epsilon w \neq 0$, then λ is the reflection of some unstable eigenvalue of A_X. □

5.2 Appendix B - Proof of Lemma (3.6)

Nonnegative definiteness: First differentiate (3.6) to obtain

$$\frac{dX_\eta}{d\eta}(A + (Q + \eta S)X_\eta) + (A + (Q + \eta S)X_\eta)' \frac{dX_\eta}{d\eta} + X_\eta S X_\eta = 0 \quad (37)$$

If one sets $\eta = 0$, the above equation reads

$$\left.\frac{dX_\eta}{d\eta}\right|_{\eta=0} (A + QX) + (A + QX)' \left.\frac{dX_\eta}{d\eta}\right|_{\eta=0} + XSX = 0 \quad (38)$$

By hypothesis, $A + QX$ is a stability matrix and $S \geq 0$. These two facts, by Lyapunov's stability lemma imply that $\left.\frac{dX_\eta}{d\eta}\right|_{\eta=0} \geq 0$. This allows deduction of the local properties of X_η. In particular, $\exists\ \hat{\eta} > 0$ such that $\eta \in [0, \hat{\eta}) \Rightarrow X_\eta \geq X \geq 0$.
Stability: Since X_η is a continuous function of η, it is true that the real part of the eigenvalues, $\Re\{\lambda_i(A + (Q + \eta S)X_\eta)\}$ also vary continuously with η. By hypothesis, at $\eta = 0$, all of these eigenvalues have negative real parts. By continuity, $\exists\ \bar{\eta} > 0$ such that this will also be true for $\eta \in [0, \bar{\eta})$.
Choice of interval: Choosing $\eta^* = \min(\hat{\eta}, \bar{\eta})$ completes the proof. □

References

[1] M.G.Safonov, D.J.N.Limebeer, *Simplifying the H_∞ Theory via Loop Shifting*, Proc. 27th Conf.Decision & Control, Austin Texas Dec. 1988.

[2] J.C.Doyle, K. Glover, P.P. Khargonekar, B.A. Francis. *State-Space Solutions to Standard H_2 and H_∞ Control Problems*, IEEE Trans.Automat.Contr., **AC-34**, August 1989, pp. 831-847.

[3] K. Glover, J.C. Doyle, *State-space formulae for all stabilizing controllers that satisfy an H_∞-norm bound and relations to risk sensitivity*, Syst. and Control Letters, **11**, 1988, pp. 167-172.

[4] D.J.N. Limebeer, B.D.O. Anderson, P.P. Khargonekar, M. Green, *A Game Theoretic Approach to H_∞ Control for Time-Varying Systems*, SIAM J. Control Optim., **30**, March 1992 , pp. 262-283.

[5] I.R. Petersen, B.D.O. Anderson, E. Jonckheere, *A First Principles Solution to the Non-Singular H_∞ Control Problem*, International Journal of Robust and Nonlinear Control, Vol. 1, 1991, pp. 171-185.

[6] B.A. Francis, *A Course in H_∞ Control Theory*, Lecture Notes in Control and Information Sciences, Springer Verlag 1987.

[7] M. Sampei, T. Mita, M. Nakamichi, *An algebraic approach to H_∞ output feedback control problems*, Syst. and Control Letters, **14**, 1990, pp. 13-24.

[8] A.A. Stoorvogel, *The Singular H_∞ Control Problem with Dynamic Measurement Feedback*, SIAM J. Control Optim., **29**, January 1991, pp. 160-184.

[9] C. Scherer, *H_∞ -Optimization without Assumptions on Finite or Infinite Zeros*, SIAM J. Control Optim., **30**, January 1992, pp. 143-166.

[10] V.X. Le, M.G. Safonov, *Rational Matrix GCD's and the Design of Squaring-Down Compensators - A State-Space Theory*, IEEE Trans.Automat.Contr., **AC-37**, March 1992, pp. 384-392.

[11] T. Mita, J.B. Matson, *A Singular H_∞ Control Problem*, Submitted to the 12th IFAC World Congress, Sydney, Australia 1993.

[12] I.R. Petersen, *Complete Results for a Class of State Feedback Disturbance Attenuation Problems*, IEEE Trans.Automat.Contr., **AC-34** , November 1989 , pp. 1196-1199 .

[13] B.M. Chen, A. Saberi, U. Ly, *Exact Computation of the Infimum in H_∞ -Optimization Via Output Feedback* , IEEE Trans.Automat.Contr., **AC-37**, January 1992 , pp.70-78.

Proceedings of the
American Control Conference
San Francisco, California • June 1993

H_∞ Performance of Weighted Interval Plants: Complete Characterization of Vertex Results

C. V. Hollot

Department of Electrical and
Computer Engineering
University of Massachusetts
Amherst, Massachusetts 01003

R. Tempo

CENS-CNR
Politecnico di Torino
Corso Duca degli Abruzzi 24
10129 Torino (Italy)

Abstract

Recently, it has been shown in [1] that the worst-case H_∞ norm of an interval plant weighted by the transfer function

$$\frac{p(s)}{s^\ell(s+\alpha)}$$

is achieved at one of the so-called weighted Kharitonov plants. In this paper, we show that this class of weights is maximal in the sense that more complex weights do *not* generally lead to such extremality properties.

I. Motivations and Preliminaries

In this paper, we consider an uncertain, proper, stable transfer function modelled by a so-called *interval plant* structure. An interval plant is described by

$$P(s,q,r) = \frac{N(s,q)}{D(s,r)} = \frac{q_0 + q_1 s + q_2 s^2 + \ldots + q_m s^m}{r_0 + r_1 s + r_2 s^2 + \ldots + s^n} \tag{1}$$

where the coefficient vectors q and r vary in the rectangles

$$Q \doteq \left\{ q : q_i^- \le q_i \le q_i^+ : i = 0, 1, \ldots, m \right\}$$

and

$$R \doteq \left\{ r : r_i^- \le r_i \le r_i^+ : i = 0, 1, \ldots, n-1 \right\}.$$

In [3] and [4], it is shown that the worst-case H_∞ norm of such interval plants enjoy the extremality property

$$\max_{q\in Q, r\in R} \|P(s,q,r)\|_\infty = \max_{i,k=1,2,3,4} \|P_{ik}(s)\|_\infty \tag{2}$$

where $P_{ik}(s)$ for $i,k = 1,2,3,4$ are the so-called *Kharitonov plants* defined by

$$P_{ik}(s) = \frac{N_i(s)}{D_k(s)}$$

and where $N_i(s)$ for $i = 1,2,3,4$ and $D_k(s)$ for $k = 1,2,3,4$ are the *Kharitonov polynomials* associated with $N(s,q)$ and $D(s,r)$; see [5]. Namely, for the numerator polynomial $N(s,q)$,

$$\begin{aligned}
N_1(s) &\doteq q_0^+ + q_1^+ s + q_2^- s^2 + q_3^- s^3 + q_4^+ s^4 + q_5^+ s^5 + \cdots;\\
N_2(s) &\doteq q_0^- + q_1^- s + q_2^+ s^2 + q_3^+ s^3 + q_4^- s^4 + q_5^- s^5 + \cdots;\\
N_3(s) &\doteq q_0^- + q_1^+ s + q_2^+ s^2 + q_3^- s^3 + q_4^- s^4 + q_5^+ s^5 + \cdots;\\
N_4(s) &\doteq q_0^+ + q_1^- s + q_2^- s^2 + q_3^+ s^3 + q_4^+ s^4 + q_5^- s^5 + \cdots;
\end{aligned}$$

and for the denominator polynomial $D(s,r)$,

$$\begin{aligned}
D_1(s) &\doteq r_0^+ + r_1^+ s + r_2^- s^2 + r_3^- s^3 + r_4^+ s^4 + r_5^+ s^5 + \cdots;\\
D_2(s) &\doteq r_0^- + r_1^- s + r_2^+ s^2 + r_3^+ s^3 + r_4^- s^4 + r_5^- s^5 + \cdots;\\
D_3(s) &\doteq r_0^- + r_1^+ s + r_2^+ s^2 + r_3^- s^3 + r_4^- s^4 + r_5^+ s^5 + \cdots;\\
D_4(s) &\doteq r_0^+ + r_1^- s + r_2^- s^2 + r_3^+ s^3 + r_4^+ s^4 + r_5^- s^5 + \cdots.
\end{aligned}$$

In [1] (see also [2]), it has been shown that

$$\max_{q\in Q, r\in R} \left\| \frac{p(s)}{s^\ell(s+\alpha)} P(s,q,r) \right\|_\infty = \max_{i,k=1,2,3,4} \left\| \frac{p(s)}{s^\ell(s+\alpha)} P_{ik}(s) \right\|_\infty \tag{3}$$

where $p(s)$ is an arbitrary polynomial and $\alpha > 0$. In this work, we prove that this restriction to weighted transfer functions having denominator of the form $s^\ell(s+\alpha)$ is actually a *hard constraint* imposed by the nature of interval plants. That is, given the weight

$$\frac{p(s)}{p_1(s)}$$

where $p_1(s)$ is a stable polynomial of degree greater than one, there exists an interval plant $P(s,q,r)$ such that

$$\max_{q\in Q, r\in R} \left\| \frac{p(s)}{p_1(s)} P(s,q,r) \right\|_\infty > \max_{i,k=1,2,3,4} \left\| \frac{p(s)}{p_1(s)} P_{ik}(s) \right\|_\infty . \tag{4}$$

Thus, in general, (3) is the best possible result.

II. Extremality Properties of the H_∞ Norm of Weighted Interval Plants

We are now ready to state the main result of the paper.

Theorem 1: (See Appendix for proof) *Let a polynomial $p(s)$ and a Hurwitz polynomial $p_1(s)$ with degree greater than one be given. Then, there exists a proper, stable interval plant* (1) *such that*

$$\max_{q\in Q, r\in R} \left\| \frac{p(s)}{p_1(s)} P(s,q,r) \right\|_\infty > \max_{i,k=1,2,3,4} \left\| \frac{p(s)}{p_1(s)} P_{ik}(s) \right\|_\infty . \tag{5}$$

□

III. Conclusion

In this paper, together with the results in [1], we completely characterize the vertex results for H_∞ performance of interval plants.

Appendix—Proof of Theorem 1

The proof of Theorem 1 is constructive and proceeds in two steps. First, under the assumption that $p_1(s)$ is a stable polynomial of degree greater than one, we construct a stable plant $N(s)/D(s)$ and identify a number $\epsilon > 0$ such that

$$\max_{\lambda\in[-\epsilon,\epsilon]}\left\|\frac{N(s)}{D(s)+\lambda p_1(s)}\right\|_\infty > \max_{\lambda=\pm\epsilon}\left\|\frac{N(s)}{D(s)+\lambda p_1(s)}\right\|_\infty. \quad (6)$$

The polynomials $N(s)$ and $D(s)$ form the basis for the next step in which we construct a Hurwitz polynomial $p_2(s)$ and another number $\delta > 0$ such that

$$\max_{\lambda\in[-\delta,\delta]}\left\|\frac{p(-s)}{p_1(s)}\frac{N(s)p_1(-s)p_2(-s)}{D(s)p(s)p_2(s)+\lambda}\right\|_\infty >$$

$$\max_{\lambda=\pm\delta}\left\|\frac{p(-s)}{p_1(s)}\frac{N(s)p_1(-s)p_2(-s)}{D(s)p(s)p_2(s)+\lambda}\right\|_\infty \quad (7)$$

The proof of Theorem 1 is completed by taking $R = [-\delta, \delta]$ and

$$P(s,q,r) = \frac{N(s)p_1(-s)p_2(-s)}{D(s)p(s)p_2(s)+r}.$$

We proceed with the first step.

Lemma 1: *If $p_1(s)$ is a stable polynomial of degree greater than one, then there exist a numerator polynomial $N(s)$, a denominator Hurwitz polynomial $D(s)$ and a real $\epsilon > 0$ such that (6) holds.*

Proof of Lemma 1: Since $p_1(s)$ is a Hurwitz polynomial of degree greater than one, then $p_1(s)$ is not a real convex direction; see [6]. Using the techniques in [6], it is possible to identify a frequency $\omega^* > 0$, a number $\tilde{\epsilon} > 0$ and a Hurwitz polynomial $q(s)$ such that:
(i)

$$\arg q(j\omega^*) = \arg p_1(j\omega^*); \quad (8)$$

(ii) the polynomial

$$\tilde{p}(s,\lambda) \doteq (s^2+\omega^{*2})q(s) + \lambda p_1(s)$$

is Hurwitz for all $\lambda \in [-\tilde{\epsilon}, \tilde{\epsilon}]\backslash 0$. By construction, $\tilde{p}(j\omega^*, 0) = 0$. Letting

$$\begin{aligned} D(s) &= (s+\omega^*)^2 q(s); \\ N(s) &= (s^2+\omega^{*2})q(s) - (s+\omega^*)^2 q(s) \end{aligned} \quad (9)$$

it follows that

$$\left|\frac{N(j\omega)}{D(j\omega)}\right| < 1 \quad (10)$$

for all $\omega \neq \omega^*$ and

$$\left|\frac{N(j\omega^*)}{D(j\omega^*)}\right| = 1. \quad (11)$$

A straightforward computation gives

$$\frac{\partial}{\partial\lambda}|P(s,\lambda)|^2\bigg|_{\substack{\lambda=0\\ s=j\omega^*}} =$$

$$\frac{4\omega^{*2}|N(j\omega^*)|^2(Im(q)\ Re(p_1) - Re(q)Im(p_1))}{|D_0(j\omega^*)|^4} \stackrel{(8)}{=} 0. \quad (12)$$

Likewise, another application of (8) gives

$$\frac{\partial^2}{\partial\lambda^2}|P(s,\lambda)|^2\bigg|_{\substack{\lambda=0\\ s=j\omega^*}} =$$

$$\frac{-2|N(j\omega^*)|^2(Re(p_1)^2 + Im(p_1)^2)}{|D_0(j\omega^*)|^4} > 0. \quad (13)$$

Since

$$\left|\frac{N(s)}{D(s)+\lambda p_1(s)}\right|$$

is a continuous function of λ, it follows from (10)—(13) that there exists a sufficiently small $\epsilon > 0$ such that

$$\left\|\frac{N(s)}{D(s)+\lambda p_1(s)}\right\|_\infty < 1 \quad (14)$$

for all $\lambda \in [-\tilde{\epsilon}, \tilde{\epsilon}]\backslash 0$. This proves Lemma 1. □

Now that (6) has been shown, we proceed to the second step and prove that (7) holds. First, define

$$\begin{aligned} f(s,\lambda) &\doteq 1 + \frac{N(s)}{D(s)+\lambda p_1(s)}; \\ \tilde{f}(s,\lambda) &\doteq 1 + \frac{N(s)p(s)p_1(-s)p_2(-s)}{D(s)p(s)p_1(s)p_2(s)+\lambda p_1(s)} \end{aligned} \quad (15)$$

where $p_2(s)$ is a Hurwitz polynomial to be determined. From (10), (11) and (14), it follows that

$$f(s,\lambda) = 0 \quad (16)$$

has only stable solutions for all $\lambda \in [-\epsilon, \epsilon]\backslash 0$. For $\lambda = 0$, (16) has only stable solutions except for a pair of $j\omega$-axis roots $s = \pm j\omega^*$. Our objective is to select $p_2(s)$ Hurwitz so that $\tilde{f}(s,\lambda) = 0$ enjoys the same solution properties as (16). First, notice that

$$\left|\frac{N(j\omega)p(-j\omega)p_1(-j\omega)p_2(-j\omega)}{D(j\omega)p(j\omega)p_1(j\omega)p_2(j\omega)}\right| = \left|\frac{N(j\omega)}{D(j\omega)}\right| \stackrel{(10)}{<} 1. \quad (17)$$

for all $\omega \neq \omega^*$. Now, if

$$\frac{p(-j\omega^*)p_1(-j\omega^*)p_2(-j\omega^*)}{p(j\omega^*)p_1(j\omega^*)p_2(j\omega^*)} = 1 \quad (18)$$

then, together with (17), we can conclude that $\tilde{f}(s,0)$ has only stable solutions except for a pair at $s = \pm j\omega^*$.

Next, we evaluate

$$\begin{aligned} s'(\lambda) &= -\frac{\partial f}{\partial\lambda}\left(\frac{\partial f}{\partial s}\right)^{-1}; \\ \tilde{s}'(\lambda) &= -\frac{\partial\tilde{f}}{\partial\lambda}\left(\frac{\partial f}{\partial\tilde{s}}\right)^{-1} \end{aligned} \quad (19)$$

and

$$\begin{aligned} s''(\lambda) &= -\frac{\partial^2 f}{\partial\lambda^2}\left(\frac{\partial f}{\partial s}\right)^{-1} + \frac{\partial f}{\partial\lambda}\frac{\partial^2 f}{\partial s^2}\left(\frac{\partial f}{\partial s}\right)^{-2}; \\ \tilde{s}''(\lambda) &= -\frac{\partial^2\tilde{f}}{\partial\lambda^2}\left(\frac{\partial\tilde{f}}{\partial\tilde{s}}\right)^{-1} + \frac{\partial\tilde{f}}{\partial\lambda}\frac{\partial^2\tilde{f}}{\partial\tilde{s}^2}\left(\frac{\partial\tilde{f}}{\partial\tilde{s}}\right)^{-2} \end{aligned} \quad (20)$$

where $s(\lambda)$ and $\tilde{s}(\lambda)$, respectively, denote the root functions of $f(s,\lambda)$ and $\tilde{f}(s,\lambda)$ for which $s(0) = \tilde{s}(0) = j\omega^*$.

To force $\tilde{f}(s,\lambda)$ to have only stable zeroes for all λ in some punctured neighborhood of the origin, we require

$$\begin{aligned}
\left.\frac{\partial f}{\partial \lambda}\right|_{\substack{\lambda=0\\ s=j\omega^*}} &= \left.\frac{\partial \tilde{f}}{\partial \lambda}\right|_{\substack{\lambda=0\\ s=j\omega^*}};\\
\left.\frac{\partial^2 f}{\partial \lambda^2}\right|_{\substack{\lambda=0\\ s=j\omega^*}} &= \left.\frac{\partial^2 \tilde{f}}{\partial \lambda^2}\right|_{\substack{\lambda=0\\ s=j\omega^*}};\\
\left.\frac{\partial f}{\partial s}\right|_{\substack{\lambda=0\\ s=j\omega^*}} &= \left.\frac{\partial \tilde{f}}{\partial \tilde{s}}\right|_{\substack{\lambda=0\\ s=j\omega^*}};\\
\left.\frac{\partial^2 f}{\partial s^2}\right|_{\substack{\lambda=0\\ s=j\omega^*}} &= \left.\frac{\partial^2 \tilde{f}}{\partial \tilde{s}^2}\right|_{\substack{\lambda=0\\ s=j\omega^*}}.
\end{aligned} \tag{21}$$

From (19) and (20), we see that $\tilde{s}'(0) = s'(0)$ and $\tilde{s}''(0) = s''(0)$ if (21) holds. A tedious but straightforward computation shows that condition (21) is satisfied if

$$\begin{aligned}
\left.\frac{p(-s)p_1(-s)p_2(-s)}{p(s)p_1^2(s)p_2^2(s)}\right|_{s=j\omega^*} &= p_1(j\omega^*);\\
\left.\frac{p(-s)p_1(-s)p_2(-s)}{p(s)p_1^3(s)p_2^3(s)}\right|_{s=j\omega^*} &= p_1(j\omega^*)^2;\\
\left.\left(\frac{p(-s)p_1(-s)p_2(-s)}{p(s)p_1(s)p_2(s)}\right)'\right|_{s=j\omega^*} &= 0;\\
\left.\left(\frac{p(-s)p_1(-s)p_2(-s)}{p(s)p_1(s)p_2(s)}\right)''\right|_{s=j\omega^*} &= 0.
\end{aligned} \tag{22}$$

Equivalently, relation (22) holds if there exists a Hurwitz polynomial $p_2(s)$ such that

$$p(j\omega^*)p_1(j\omega^*)p_2(j\omega^*) = 1 \tag{23}$$

and

$$\begin{aligned}
\left.\frac{p(-s)p_1(-s)p_2(-s)}{p(s)p_1(s)p_2(s)}\right|_{s=j\omega^*} &= 1;\\
\left.\left(\frac{p(-s)p_1(-s)p_2(-s)}{p(s)p_1(s)p_2(s)}\right)'\right|_{s=j\omega^*} &= 0;\\
\left.\left(\frac{p(-s)p_1(-s)p_2(-s)}{p(s)p_1(s)p_2(s)}\right)''\right|_{s=j\omega^*} &= 0.
\end{aligned} \tag{24}$$

Notice that (24) includes (18) and that (24) is satisfied for some $p_2(-s)/p_2(s)$ if there exists a stable all-pass function

$$a(s) = \frac{n_a(s)}{n_d(s)}$$

such that

$$\begin{aligned}
a(s)|_{s=j\omega^*} &= b(j\omega^*)^{-1};\\
a(s)'|_{s=j\omega^*} &= -b(j\omega^*)^{-2}b(j\omega^*)';\\
a(s)''|_{s=j\omega^*} &= -b(j\omega^*)''b(j\omega^*)^{-2} + 2(b(j\omega^*)')^2 b(j\omega^*)^{-3}
\end{aligned}$$

where

$$b(s) = \frac{p(-s)p_1(-s)}{p(s)p_1(s)}.$$

Such a stable all-pass function always exists. Now, take

$$p_2(s) = \frac{n_d(s)}{p(j\omega^*)p_1(j\omega^*)n_d(j\omega^*)}. \tag{25}$$

For this $p_2(s)$, (23) and (24) are met; therefore (22) is satisfied. Hence, there exists a number $\tilde{\delta} > 0$ such that $\tilde{f}(s,\lambda)$ has only left half plane zeroes for all $\lambda \in [-\tilde{\delta},\tilde{\delta}]\backslash 0$; likewise, $\tilde{f}(s,0)$ has only left half plane zeroes except for a pair of $j\omega$-axis roots at $\omega = \omega^*$. This implies, together with (6) and (15), that there exists a $\delta > 0$ such that (7) holds. This proves Theorem 1.

Acknowledgements

This work was partially supported by the U.S. National Science Foundation under Grant NSF-8858366 and by CENS-CNR of Italy. C. V. Hollot conducted part of the research while visiting the Laboratory of Automatic Control at the University of Louvain, Louvain-La-Neuve (Belgium), the Institute for Automatic Control, Swiss Federal Institute of Technology, Zurich (Switzerland) and CENS-CNR, Politecnico di Torino, Torino (Italy). He is grateful for their support.

References

[1] C. V. Hollot and R. Tempo, "New Vertex Results on H_∞ Performance of Interval Plants and Interval Feedback Systems," *Proceedings of the IEEE Conference on Decision and Control*, Tucson, AZ, December 1992.

[2] C. V. Hollot, R. Tempo and V. Blondel, "H_∞ Performance of Interval Plants and Interval Feedback Systems," in "Robustness of Dynamic Systems with Parameter Uncertainties," M. Mansour, S. Balemi and W. Truöl (Editors), pp. 201-209, *Birkhäuser*, Basel, 1992.

[3] T. Mori and S. Barnett, "On Stability Tests for Some Classes of Dynamical Systems with Perturbed Coefficients," *IMA Journal of Mathematical Control and Information*, Vol. 5, pp. 117-123, 1988.

[4] H. Chapellat, M. Dahleh and S. P. Bhattacharyya, "Robust Stability Under Structured and Unstructured Perturbations," *IEEE Transactions on Automatic Control*, Vol. AC-35, pp. 1100-1108, 1990.

[5] V. L. Kharitonov, "Asymptotic Stability of an Equilibrium Position of a Family of Systems of Linear Differential Equations," *Differentsial'nye Uravneniya*, Vol. 14, pp. 2086-2088, 1978.

[6] A. Rantzer, "Stability Conditions for a Polytope of Polynomials," *IEEE Transactions on Automatic Control*, Vol. AC-37, pp. 79-89, 1992.

Proceedings of the
American Control Conference
San Francisco, California • June 1993

$\mathcal{H}_\infty$ ROBUST CONTROL BY STATIC OUTPUT FEEDBACK *

P. L. D. Peres J. C. Geromel S. R. Souza†
LAC/DT-FEE UNICAMP, CP 6101, 13081-970, Campinas, SP, Brazil,
e-mail: peres@dt.fee.unicamp.br Fax: (55) 192 39 13 95

Abstract

This paper addresses the problem of robust output feedback stabilization under prespecified $\mathcal{H}_\infty$ attenuation level. Linear uncertain systems in convex bounded domains are considered, with no need of matching conditions. The necessary and sufficient condition for quadratic stabilizability with prescribed $\mathcal{H}_\infty$ attenuation level via linear output feedback provided, is based on the existence of an appropriate similarity transformation.

1. Introduction

In the last decade, the linear systems control theory has incorporated parameter uncertainty to the design specifications, as an *a priori* information which, associated with $\mathcal{H}_2/\mathcal{H}_\infty$ performance measures, has allowed a strong development of the so called Robust Control [3]. As a matter of fact, the $\mathcal{H}_2/\mathcal{H}_\infty$ optimization design has produced fundamental results in control theory, mainly in the very recent years. Concerning precisely known systems, the paper of Doyle et al. [2] has deeply discussed standard $\mathcal{H}_2$ and $\mathcal{H}_\infty$ control problems, using a state-space framework. Several papers have extended those results to the uncertain case, providing robust state feedback control concerning both quadratic stabilization and $\mathcal{H}_\infty$ limiting bounds, as [6], or $\mathcal{H}_\infty$ guaranteed cost control for uncertain systems in convex bounded domains [5]. However, in the majority, the proposed methods suppose full state availability or reconstruction throughout linear observers. A few papers have dealt with static output feedback stabilization of uncertain systems, but with very restrictive assumptions.

This paper focuses on quadratic stabilizability by linear output feedback (see also [1]) with γ disturbance attenuation. We provide necessary and sufficient conditions for the existence of a static stabilizing output feedback gain which guarantees a prespecified $\mathcal{H}_\infty$ level for all uncertain plants considered. This is done by defining adequately a similarity transformation, leading the problem of robust output stabilization to a convex equivalent problem. The set of static output feedback gains assuring the prescribed $\mathcal{H}_\infty$ bound for the closed-loop uncertain transfer function in consideration is thus mapped into a convex one, throughout a non-linear relationship. Standard mathematical programming tools can be used to calculate the desired robust $\mathcal{H}_\infty$ feedback control.

2. Preliminaries

Consider the linear continuous-time system described by the state space equation (1), where $x \in \Re^n$ is the state vector, $u \in \Re^m$ is the control vector, $w \in \Re^l$ is the disturbance vector, $y \in \Re^r$ is the controlled output vector and $z \in \Re^q$ is the measured output vector.

$$\left\{ \begin{array}{rcl} \dot{x} & = & Ax + B_1 w + B_2 u \\ u & = & -Ly \\ y & = & C_2 x \\ z & = & C_1 x + D_1 u \end{array} \right. \tag{1}$$

All matrices are assumed to be of appropriate and known dimensions and $C_1' D_1 = 0$, $D_1' D_1 > 0$. The matrix pair (A, B_2) is supposed to be uncertain, that is, defining the augmented matrix $F \in \Re^{p \times p}$ as

$$F = \begin{bmatrix} A & -B_2 \\ \mathbf{0} & \mathbf{0} \end{bmatrix}$$

where $p \triangleq n + m$, we assume that F belongs to the uncertain domain $\mathcal{D}$ given by

$$\mathcal{D} \triangleq \left\{ F \ : \ F = \sum_{i=1}^N \xi_i F_i \ , \ \xi_i \geq 0 \ , \ \sum_{i=1}^N \xi_i = 1 \right\}$$

Notice that any feasible F can be expressed as an unknown convex combination of the N "extreme matrices" $F_i \leadsto (A_i, B_{2i})$, $i = 1 \cdots N$. Clearly, $N = 1$ represents a precisely known plant. The output matrix C_2 is supposed precisely known (representing only the state availability). The problem to be addressed here is the one of finding a linear robust output feedback gain $L \in \Re^{m \times r}$ such that the closed-loop system

$$A_{cl} = A - B_2 L C_2 \tag{2}$$

is asymptotically stable for all $F \in \mathcal{D}$ and the closed-loop transfer function from w to z

$$H(s) \triangleq C_{cl}[s\mathbf{I} - A_{cl}]^{-1} B_1$$

with $C_{cl} \triangleq C_1 - D_1 L C_2$ satisfies a prespecified $\gamma > 0$ attenuation level, i.e., $\|H(s)\|_\infty \leq \gamma$, $\forall\ F \in \mathcal{D}$.

Before stating the main results of this paper, let us define the following extended matrices: $G \in \Re^{p \times m}$, $Q \in \Re^{p \times p}$ and $R \in \Re^{p \times p}$,

$$G = \begin{bmatrix} \mathbf{0} \\ \mathbf{I} \end{bmatrix} \quad Q = \begin{bmatrix} B_1 B_1' & \mathbf{0} \\ \mathbf{0} & \mathbf{0} \end{bmatrix} \quad R = \begin{bmatrix} C_1' C_1 & \mathbf{0} \\ \mathbf{0} & D_1' D_1 \end{bmatrix}$$

Notice that the open-loop model (1) is completely defined by matrices F, Q and R. On the contrary, matrix G is always constant and presents an important property to be used in the sequel: $\forall\ v \in \mathcal{N}(G')$ is written as $v' = [x' \ \ \mathbf{0}]$, where $\mathcal{N}(\cdot)$ denotes the null space of $(\cdot)$ and $x \in \Re^n$.

3. Main Results

Define the convex matricial function

$$\Theta_{\infty i}(\mathcal{W}) \triangleq F_i \mathcal{W} + \mathcal{W} F_i' + \gamma^{-2} \mathcal{W} R \mathcal{W} + Q \tag{3}$$

and the convex set $\mathcal{C}_\infty \triangleq \cap_{i=1}^N \mathcal{C}_{\infty i}$, where

$$\mathcal{C}_{\infty i} \triangleq \left\{ \mathcal{W} = \mathcal{W}' \geq 0 \ : \ v' \Theta_{\infty i}(\mathcal{W}) v \leq 0 \ : \ \forall\ v \in \mathcal{N}(G') \right\}$$

where the symmetric matrix $\mathcal{W} \in \Re^{p \times p}$ is partitioned as

$$\mathcal{W} = \begin{bmatrix} W_1 & W_2 \\ W_2' & W_3 \end{bmatrix}, \ W_1 > 0 \tag{4}$$

*Grants by FAPESP, CNPq and CAPES - Brazil
†On leave from DES, EE, UFG, Goiânia, Brazil

with $W_1 \in \Re^{n\times n}$, $W_2 \in \Re^{n\times m}$ and $W_3 \in \Re^{m\times m}$. Following the results of [5], the problem is to select from the elements $\mathcal{W} \in \mathcal{C}_\infty$, the ones satisfying the projection condition $KY_2 = W_2'W_1^{-1}Y_2 = \mathbf{0}$, where $Y_2 = \mathcal{N}(C_2)$. This condition assures the existence of an output feedback gain with the desired properties.

Theorem 1: The uncertain system given by (1) is quadratically stabilizable by output feedback with γ disturbance attenuation if and only if there exists $E \in \Re^{n\times(n-r)}$ such that

a) $T \triangleq \begin{bmatrix} C_2 \\ E' \end{bmatrix} \in \Re^{n\times n}$ is full rank.

b) $\mathcal{C}_\infty(E) \triangleq \mathcal{C}_\infty \bigcap \left\{ \mathcal{W} : \begin{bmatrix} C_2 & \mathbf{0} \\ \mathbf{0} & \mathbf{I} \end{bmatrix} \mathcal{W} \begin{bmatrix} E \\ \mathbf{0} \end{bmatrix} = \mathbf{0} \right\} \neq \emptyset$

In the affirmative case, $L = W_2'C_2'\left(C_2W_1C_2'\right)^{-1}$ is a robust output feedback gain.

The above result follow from the fact (for details, see [5]) that $\forall\ \mathcal{W} \in \mathcal{C}_\infty$, $K = W_2'W_1^{-1}$ is a quadratic stabilizing state feedback gain assuring γ disturbance attenuation. Furthermore, if there exists E such that $\mathcal{W} \in \mathcal{C}_\infty(E)$, using matrix T defined in a) we have

$$\begin{aligned} K &= W_2'T'\left(TW_1T'\right)^{-1}T \\ &= \begin{bmatrix} W_2'C_2' & W_2'E \end{bmatrix} \begin{bmatrix} C_2W_1C_2' & C_2W_1E \\ E'W_1C_2' & E'W_1E \end{bmatrix}^{-1} \begin{bmatrix} C_2 \\ E' \end{bmatrix} \end{aligned}$$

and with the additional linear constraints b) we get

$$\begin{aligned} K &= \begin{bmatrix} W_2'C_2' & 0 \end{bmatrix} \begin{bmatrix} C_2W_1C_2' & 0 \\ 0 & E'W_1E \end{bmatrix}^{-1} \begin{bmatrix} C_2 \\ E' \end{bmatrix} \\ &= W_2'C_2'\left(C_2W_1C_2'\right)^{-1}C_2 = LC_2 \end{aligned}$$

That is, the state feedback gain can be factorized as an output feedback gain.

It is simple to see that the determination of matrix E, which assures the necessary and sufficient condition, may be a difficult task. A preliminary result concerning this point will be addressed in the sequel. For the moment, let us mention that, for E fixed, $\mathcal{C}_\infty(E)$ is a convex set. In this case, the numerical determination of $\mathcal{W} \in \mathcal{C}_\infty(E)$ can be easily done, by using the similarity transformation $\tilde{x} = Tx$, which leads to

$$\mathcal{W} \in \mathcal{C}_\infty(E) \iff \mathcal{W}_o \in \mathcal{C}_\infty \qquad (5)$$

where $\mathcal{W}_o \in \Re^{p\times p}$ is constrained to have the following structure

$$\mathcal{W}_o = \underbrace{\begin{bmatrix} W_{11} & \mathbf{0} & W_{21} \\ \mathbf{0} & W_{22} & \mathbf{0} \\ W_{21}' & \mathbf{0} & W_3 \end{bmatrix}}_{r \quad n-r \quad m} \begin{matrix} \}\ r \\ \}\ n-r \\ \}\ m \end{matrix} \qquad (6)$$

In this new system of coordinates, an output feedback gain is readily given by $L = W_{21}'W_{11}^{-1}$. This result is summarized in the following Corollary.

Corollary 2: If there exists $\mathcal{W}_o \in \mathcal{C}_\infty$, then the uncertain system (1) is quadratically stabilizable by linear output feedback with γ disturbance attenuation. In the affirmative case, $L = W_{21}'W_{11}^{-1}$ is a robust output feedback gain.

Let us now consider the problem concerning the determination of matrix E, which is crucial for our approach. Using Theorem 1, we realize that a necessary condition (unfortunately, not sufficient) to have E such that $\mathcal{C}_\infty(E) \neq \emptyset$ whenever an output feedback gain exists is $\forall i$, $i = 1 \cdots N$

$$A_iW_1 - B_{2i}W_2' + W_1A_i' - W_2B_{2i}' + B_1B_1' \leq 0 \qquad (7)$$

$$C_2W_1E = 0 \quad , \quad W_2'E = 0 \qquad (8)$$

which can be rewritten, with $E = W_1^{-1}Y_2$, only in terms of matrix W_1 as

$$W_1 \in \mathcal{C}_Z \quad \text{and} \quad W_1^{-1} \in \mathcal{C}_Y \qquad (9)$$

where $\mathcal{C}_Z$ and $\mathcal{C}_Y$ are convex sets given by $(Z_{2i} = \mathcal{N}(B_{2i}'))$

$$\mathcal{C}_Z = \bigcap_{i=1}^{N} \left\{ W > 0 : Z_{2i}'\left(A_iW + WA_i' + B_1B_1'\right)Z_{2i} \leq 0 \right\}$$

$$\mathcal{C}_Y = \bigcap_{i=1}^{N} \left\{ V > 0 : Y_2'\left(A_i'V + VA_i + VB_1B_1'V\right)Y_2 \leq 0 \right\}$$

We have reduced the problem to the determination of matrix W_1 satisfying (9) which can be achieved by the following min-max procedure. Set $\ell \leftarrow 0$, $V_\ell = \mathbf{I}$ and iterate until convergence:

$$\begin{aligned} W_\ell &= \arg\min\left\{\alpha \ :\ W \in \mathcal{C}_Z \ :\ V_\ell^{-1} \leq W \leq \alpha V_\ell^{-1}\right\} \\ V_{\ell+1} &= \arg\max\left\{\beta \ :\ V \in \mathcal{C}_Y \ :\ \beta W_\ell^{-1} \leq V \leq W_\ell^{-1}\right\} \end{aligned}$$

Clearly, we have to solve only convex problems at each iteration and at the convergence $\alpha = \beta = 1$ and $W = V^{-1}$ yielding $E = VY_2$.

4. Conclusion

This paper addresses the problem of quadratic stabilizability of uncertain systems with prescribed $\mathcal{H}_\infty$ norm bound by linear static output feedback. The necessary and sufficient condition depends on a certain matrix E which, in some instances, can be determined by a min-max procedure. Although the convergence has not been proved, it has been verified in many numerical examples solved. Table 1 shows the behavior of α_ℓ and β_ℓ for the example proposed in [4] with uncertainties 20 times bigger, which provides E such that $\mathcal{C}_\infty(E) \neq \emptyset$.

ℓ	0	1	2	3	4	5
α_ℓ	1.89	1.44	7.10	1.13	1.01	
β_ℓ		0.39	0.11	0.88	0.99	1.00

Table 1: min-max procedure

References

[1] D. S. Bernstein and W. M. Haddad, "Robust Decentralized Static Output Feedback", *Syst. & Cont. Letters*, Vol. 12, pp. 309-318, 1989.

[2] J. C. Doyle, K. Glover, P. P. Khargonekar and B. Francis, "State-Space Solutions to the Standard H^2 and H^∞ Control Problems", *IEEE Trans. Aut. Control*, Vol. 34, pp. 831-847, 1989.

[3] J. C. Geromel, P. L. D. Peres and J. Bernussou, "On a Convex Parameter Space Method for Linear Control Design of Uncertain Systems", *SIAM J. Control and Opt.*, vol. 29, N. 2, pp. 381-402, March 1991.

[4] L. Keel, S. P. Bhattacharyya and J. W. Howze, "Robust Control with Structured Perturbations", *IEEE Trans. Aut. Control*, Vol. 33, No. 1, pp. 68-78, 1988.

[5] P. L. D. Peres, J. C. Geromel and S. R. Souza, "$\mathcal{H}_\infty$ guaranteed cost control for uncertain continuous-time systems", *Syst. Cont. Letters*, to appear.

[6] P. P. Khargonekar, I. R. Petersen and K. Zhou, "Robust Stabilization of Uncertain Linear Systems: Quadratic Stabilizability and H^∞ Control Theory", *IEEE Trans. Aut. Control*, Vol. 35, No. 3, pp. 356-361, 1990.

Proceedings of the
American Control Conference
San Francisco, California • June 1993

Robust Control of a Flexible System - Covering Parametric Uncertainty with a Non-Parametric Model

Syed K. Ahmed and C. V. Hollot

Department of Electrical and Computer Engineering
University of Massachusetts, Amherst, MA 01003

ABSTRACT

In this paper we consider the robust control of a free-free Euler-Bernoulli beam model having 20% uncertainty in the modal frequencies. Using the H_∞ design framework and non-parametric uncertainty models, we design for robust performance. The novelty of this work rests on the fact that we try to reduce the conservatism in using disks to cover the parametric uncertainty.

I. Research Goal

In this paper we consider the control of a flexible mechanical system having parametrically defined uncertainty in the modal frequencies. The goal is to develop techniques for modelling the parametric uncertainty so that:

- The H_∞ design technique can be used.
- The level of robust performance is maximized.

Employing H_∞ techniques necessarily requires the parametric uncertainty to be *covered* by a *non-parametric* uncertainty model [2, 4, 5, 8]. The main objective of this research is to design covers which lead to good robust performance. We choose the H_∞ design procedure and non-parametric uncertainty models because:

1. The H_∞ design procedure is automatic and easy to use [1, 3].
2. By modelling the parametric uncertainty with a single non-parametric block, we retain the simplicity and intuition of single-loop control. Such intuition can be lost in a *structured* uncertainty approach [1, 7].
3. The H_∞ design procedure generalizes to the multivariable plant case.

It is well-known that the H_∞ design methodology is tailor-made for handling ignored *high frequency* dynamics and thus is ideally suited for the control of flexible structures. However, this does not automatically guarantee robustness to *parametric* uncertainty. In the next section, we give an example to illustrate this very point. The remainder of this paper then describes one method for explicitly incorporating parametric uncertainty into an H_∞ design. Most importantly, we attempt to achieve this with minimal performance degradation.

II. Motivating Example

Consider the transfer function of a free-free Euler-Bernoulli beam model [1]

$$P(s) \doteq \frac{y_p(s)}{u(s)} = \sum_{k=0}^{\infty} \frac{1}{s^2 + 2\zeta_k(q\omega_k)s + (q\omega_k)^2} \quad (1)$$

[1]The free-free Euler-Bernoulli beam has modal frequencies $\approx ((k+\frac{1}{2})\rho)^2$, $k = 1, 2, 3, \ldots$ where ρ is a beam constant. In this paper we consider modal frequencies $(k\rho)^2$, $k = 1, 2, 3, \ldots$ with normalized $\rho = 1$.

where y_p and u represent a beam displacement and applied force respectively and where $\omega_k = k^2$, $\zeta_k = .01$ and parameter q has nominal value .5. The control objective is to keep the disturbed output $y(s) = y_p(s) + d(s)$ small; i.e.,

$$|y(j\omega)| \leq .1, \quad \forall \omega \geq 0 \quad (2)$$

in the face of all output disturbances $d(s)$ satisfying

$$|d(j\omega)| \leq 1, \quad \forall \omega \leq \omega_0. \quad (3)$$

This objective translates into the closed loop specification

$$|W_1^\alpha S(j\omega)| \leq 1, \quad \forall \omega \geq 0 \quad (4)$$

where $S(s) \doteq (1 + PC(s))^{-1}$ is the *sensitivity* function, $C(s)$ the compensator and where

$$W_1^\alpha(s) = \frac{10}{(\frac{s}{\alpha}+1)^2}$$

models the desired disturbance attenuation described in (2) and (3). The parameter α affects the band of frequencies over which attenuation is achieved. To design a finite-dimensional compensator we require a finite-dimensional approximation to $P(s)$. This is where the so-called ignored high-frequency dynamics enter the picture. Take

$$\tilde{P}(s) = \sum_{k=0}^{4} \frac{1}{s^2 + 2\zeta_k(q\omega_k)s + (q\omega_k)^2} \quad (5)$$

as an approximation to $P(s)$ where the number of retained modes, 4, is chosen based on acceptable compensator order and desired bandwidth. The error between $P(s)$ and $\tilde{P}(s)$ is modelled by an additive non-parametric uncertainty structure

$$\tilde{P}(s) + \Delta_a(s)$$

where $\Delta_a(s)$ varies over the set of stable transfer functions satisfying

$$|\Delta_a(j\omega)| \leq \ell_a(\omega), \quad \forall \omega \geq 0$$

where $\ell_a(\omega)$ verifies

$$\ell_a(\omega) \geq |P(j\omega) - \tilde{P}(j\omega)|, \quad \forall \omega \geq 0. \quad (6)$$

Such an ℓ_a is shown in Figure 1. Robust performance is met if there exists a compensator $C(s)$ and a number α such that

$$\left[|W_1^\alpha S(j\omega)|^2 + |W_2 T(j\omega)|^2\right]^{\frac{1}{2}} < \frac{1}{2}, \quad \forall \omega \geq 0 \quad (7)$$

where $T(s) \doteq 1 - S(s)$ and $W_2(s)$ is a stable transfer function for which

$$|W_2(j\omega)| \approx \ell_a(\omega)|\tilde{P}^{-1}(j\omega)|, \quad \forall \omega \geq 0.$$

In this example, we take

$$W_2(s) = .02\frac{(\frac{s}{.8}+1)(s+1)}{(\frac{s}{5}+1)(\frac{s}{10}+1)}\tilde{P}^{-1}(s).$$

Inequality (7) is a standard *mixed sensitivity* H_∞ problem. For our data, this problem is solvable with $\alpha = .3$ giving a robust performance bandwidth of 1 rad/sec. The magnitude frequency plots of S and T are given in Figure 2.

Even though designs meeting (7) are guaranteed to be robust to the ignored high-frequency dynamics, they are not automatically guaranteed to be robust to parametric uncertainty in the low frequency dynamics $\tilde{P}(s)$. The previous design is a case in point. The nominally stable loop ($q = .5$) becomes unstable for small variations ($\pm 4\%$) in q. This loss of stability is even more surprising when we recognize that flexible systems as in (5) are easy to robustly stabilize against variations in q. To see this, consider the pole-zero plot for the uncompensated beam dynamics as shown in Figure 3 for the nominal value $q = .5$. The alternating pole-zero pattern, which holds for any value of $q \geq 0$, guarantees, in the absence of unmodeled dynamics, robust closed loop stability for any range of positive q when using a simple lead compensator [6][2]. However, the H_∞ compensator adversely affects this pole-zero pattern and renders the design sensitive to q variations. More precisely, the H_∞ design *cancels* all the stable plant poles, see Figure 4, upsetting the alternating pole-zero pattern. Generally speaking, the resulting pole-zero configuration is sensitive to loop gain variations and in particular, sensitive to variations in parameter q. Hence, robustness of an H_∞ design to ignored high frequency dynamics is not an immediate guarantee of robustness to low frequency parametric uncertainty. In the next section, we show how one can take this source of uncertainty into account.

III. A Cover for Parametric Uncertainty

Let the parametrically defined uncertainty in the modal frequencies be described by

$$\tilde{P}(s,q) = \sum_{k=0}^{4} \frac{1}{s^2 + 2\zeta_k(q\omega_k)s + (q\omega_k)^2} \qquad (8)$$

where q is the uncertain parameter assumed to take value in $[.4, .6]$

Remark 1: This uncertainty model is simplistic – it assumes that the modal frequencies vary dependently on the single parameter q. However, this dependency was chosen only for expediency. The foregoing techniques hold equally well for more realistic uncertainty models.

We now give the uncertain plant $\tilde{P}(s,q)$ a multiplicative non-parametric cover

$$P_0(s)[1 + \Delta_m(s)]$$

[2] This can also be explained by passivity-multiplier theory using a multiplier s and noting that both $s\tilde{P}(s)$ and $\frac{1}{s}C_{lead}(s)$ are both positive real.

where $P_0(s)$ is some *nominal* plant and $\Delta_m(s)$ is any stable transfer function satisfying $|\Delta_m(j\omega)| \leq \ell_m(\omega)$ where

$$\ell_m(\omega) \geq \max_{q\in[.4,.6]} \left|\frac{\tilde{P}(j\omega,q)}{P_0(j\omega)} - 1\right|. \qquad (9)$$

With this multiplicative model in hand, we now use H_∞ techniques to achieve performance which is robust to both the ignored high-frequency dynamics and the lower frequency parametric uncertainty. We combine the additive and multiplicative uncertainty into a single multiplicative model

$$P_0(s)[1 + \Delta_{total}(s)]$$

where

$$|\Delta_{total}(j\omega)| \leq \ell_{total}(\omega), \;\; ; \;\; \forall\omega \geq 0$$

and

$$\ell_{total}(\omega) \doteq \ell_a(\omega)|\tilde{P}_0^{-1}(j\omega)| + \ell_m(\omega), \quad \forall\omega \geq 0. \qquad (10)$$

Choose $P_0(s) = \tilde{P}(s,.5)$. The resulting error bound ℓ_{total} is shown in Figure 5 together with the frequency response of a stable transfer function approximation

$$W_3(s) = .001\frac{(\frac{s}{.01}+1)^2(\frac{s}{.02}+1)(\frac{s}{.05}+1)(\frac{s}{10}+1)(\frac{s}{200}+1)}{(\frac{s}{.5}+1)(\frac{s}{.7}+1)(s+1)^2}.$$

We now seek a compensator $C(s)$ and the largest α for which

$$\left[|W_1^\alpha S(j\omega)|^2 + |W_3 T(j\omega)|^2\right]^{\frac{1}{2}} < \frac{1}{2}, \quad \forall\omega \geq 0 \qquad (11)$$

holds. This robust performance can be achieved when $\alpha = .008$, resulting in a performance bandwidth of .022 rad/sec. The magnitude frequency plots of solutions S and T are given in Figure 6. Root locus plots for variations $q \in [.4, .6]$ are shown in Figure 7 to verify the parametric robustness of the design.

Remark 2: In achieving robustness against parametric uncertainty, the *level* of performance was sacrificed. Notice that the performance bandwidth decreased from 1 rad/sec in Figure 2 to .022 rad/sec in Figure 6. It is reasonable to expect a decrease in performance in trade for robustness to parametric uncertainty, but, ***is it reasonable to expect such a large decrease?*** In the next section, we show that the level of robust performance can indeed be increased by selecting a *better* non-parametric cover for the parametric uncertainty.

IV. Increasing the Level of Robust Performance

Our philosophy in designing a better non-parametric cover for parametric uncertainty is simply to make $|W_3(j\omega)|$ smaller at each frequency. Doing so allows (11) to be solvable for larger values of α which translates into higher bandwidth designs. We can make $|W_3(j\omega)|$ smaller by requiring smaller $\ell_m(\omega)$; see (10). This in turn can be reduced by selecting the complex number $P_0(j\omega)$ to minimize the right-hand-side of (9); i.e.,

$$\min_{P_0(j\omega)} \max_{q\in[.4,.6]} \left|\frac{\tilde{P}(j\omega,q)}{P_0(j\omega)} - 1\right|.$$

Remark 3: In the preceding, we suggest minimizing over the complex numbers $P_0(j\omega)$ – this means that we treat the nominal plant $P_0(s)$ as a *free* modelling parameter. Crucial to the success of this approach is the fact that we ultimately achieve ***robust performance***. That is, we guarantee performance for ***all members*** of the non-parametric family, not just the nominal plant $P_0(s)$.

Our objective now is to find a rational function $P_0^*(s)$ such that

$$P_0^*(j\omega) \approx Z^*(\omega), \quad \forall\omega \geq 0 \tag{12}$$

where

$$Z^*(\omega) \doteq \arg\min_{z\in P_\omega} \max_{q\in[.4,.6]} \left|\frac{\tilde{P}(j\omega,q)}{z} - 1\right|, \quad \forall\omega \geq 0 \tag{13}$$

and

$$P_\omega = \left\{\tilde{P}(j\omega,q) : q \in [.4,.6]\right\}.$$

The resulting optimal ℓ_m is then

$$\ell_m^*(\omega) = \max_{q\in[.4,.6]} \left|\frac{\tilde{P}(j\omega,q)}{P_0^*(j\omega)} - 1\right|, \quad \forall\omega \geq 0. \tag{14}$$

Remark 4: Solving (12) and (13) is non-trivial. First, for more complex parametric descriptions, solving the maximization problem in (13) over q may be intractable. Presently, we sidestep this issue and use brute force gridding to compute the maximum. Secondly, it is not at all clear how to solve (12) - what measure do we use? We do not pursue this important issue here. In the following we proceed naively – the immediate objective is to show the payoff of this thinking.

Return to our specific example. Given the problem data, we determine $Z^*(\omega)$ as in (13) and plot its magnitude frequency response in Figure 8. Heuristically, we select $P_0^*(s)$ to be a stable transfer function which reasonably approximates $|Z^*(j\omega)|$ over $\omega \in [0,.6]$ and a reasonable fit is made by taking

$$P_0^*(s) = \tilde{P}(s,.4)$$

which is also plotted in Figure 8 for comparison. The resulting ℓ_{total}^* and W_3^* are shown in Figure 9; compare this with ℓ_m in Figure 5. Finally, we solve the robust performance problem

$$\left[|W_1^\alpha S(j\omega)|^2 + |W_3^* T(j\omega)|^2\right]^{\frac{1}{2}} < \frac{1}{2}, \quad \forall\omega \geq 0 \tag{15}$$

where

$$W_3^*(s) = .01\frac{(\frac{s}{.01}+1)(\frac{s}{.04}+1)(\frac{s}{.1}+1)(\frac{s}{10}+1)^2}{(\frac{s}{.5}+1)(\frac{s}{.7}+1)(s+1)}.$$

is a stable rational function having magnitude approximating ℓ_{total}^*. Inequality (15) is solvable when $\alpha = .014$. The frequency responses of solutions S and T are shown in Figure 10. Notice that the guaranteed bandwidth for this design is $\approx .04$ which is a 100% increase over the previous design. Again, a root locus plot (see Figure 11) verifies the parametric robustness of the design.

V. Conclusion

In this paper we demonstrate one method for handling parametric uncertainty within the H_∞ design framework. We also consider an approach for reducing the conservatism in using a non-parametric cover for the parametric uncertainty. This method was applied to a free-free Euler-Bernoulli beam model having 20% uncertainty in the modal frequencies and a two-to-one increase in robust performance level was achieved.

Acknowledgements

This research was supported by Martin Marietta Civil Space and Communications Company, Denver, CO 80201 under NASA's CSI Guest Investigator Program.

References

[1] G. J. Balas, J. C. Doyle, K. Glover, A. Packard and R. Smith, *μ-Analysis and Synthesis Toolbox: User's Guide*, MUSYN, Inc. and The MathWorks, Inc., 1991.

[2] J. C. Doyle, B. A. Francis and A. R. Tannenbaum, *Feedback Control Theory*, Macmillan Publishing Company, New York, 1992.

[3] J. C. Doyle, K. Glover, P. Khargonekar and B. A. Francis, "State-Space Solutions to Standard H_2 and H_∞ Control Problems," *IEEE Transactions on Automatic Control*, Vol. AC-34, pp. 831-847, 1989.

[4] D. P. Lawrence, *Issues in Using Non-Parametric Models to Represent Parametric Uncertainty*, Master's Thesis, University of Massachusetts at Amherst, September 1991.

[5] M. Morari and E. Zafiriou, *Robust Process Control*, Englewood Cliffs, N.J., Prentice Hall, 1989.

[6] G. D. Martin, *On The Control of Flexible Mechanical Systems*, Doctoral Dissertation, Stanford University, May 1978.

[7] A. Packard and J. Doyle, "The Complex Structured Singular Value," *Automatica*, Vol. 29, No.1, pp. 71-109, 1993.

[8] S. Skogestad, M. Morari and J. C. Doyle, "Robust Control of Ill-Conditioned Plants: High-Purity Distillation," *IEEE Transactions on Automatic Control*, Vol. AC-33, pp. 1092-1105, 1988.

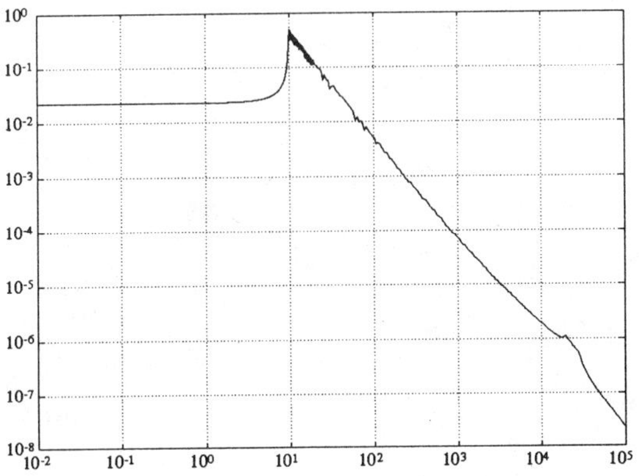

Figure 1: Bound on Additive Non-Parametric Error Due to Ignored High Frequency Dynamics.

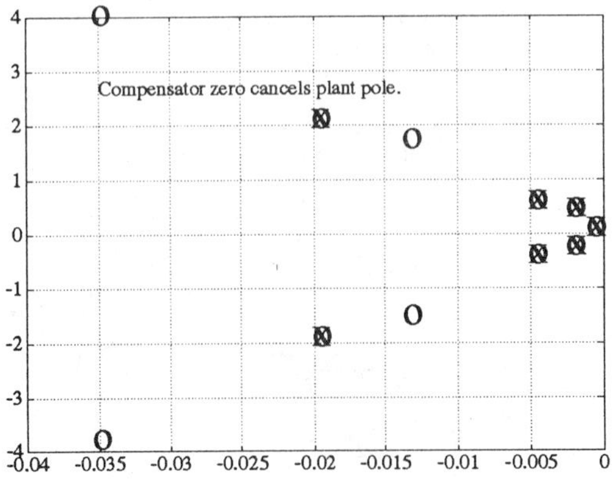

Figure 4: A Partial View of Pole-Zero Locations of Compensated Loop - H_∞ Design.

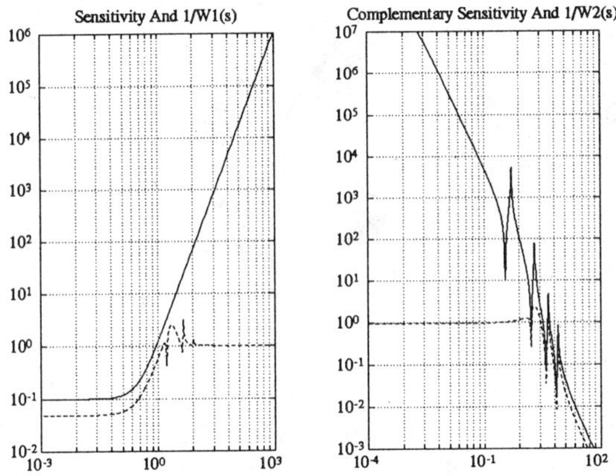

Figure 2: H_∞ Design - No Parametric Uncertainty.

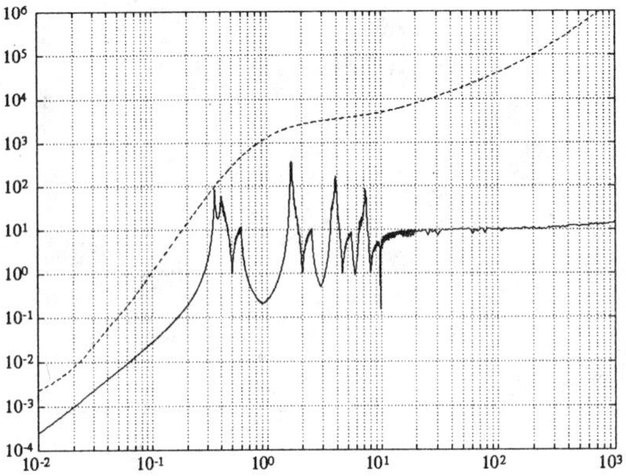

Figure 5: Non-Optimal Parametric Cover: Total Multiplicative Error Bound and an Approximation.

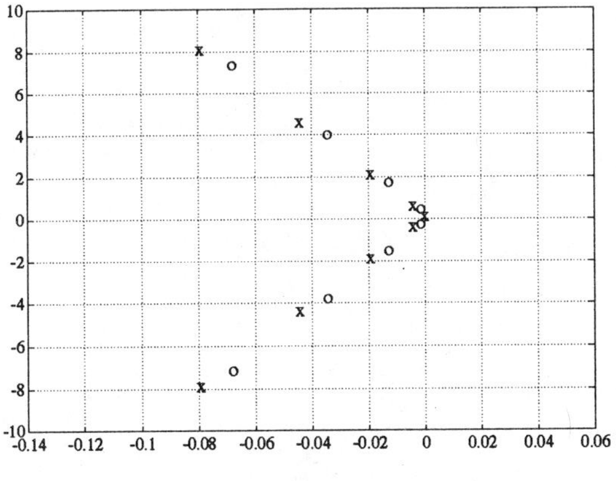

Figure 3: Pole-Zero Locations of Uncompensated Plant.

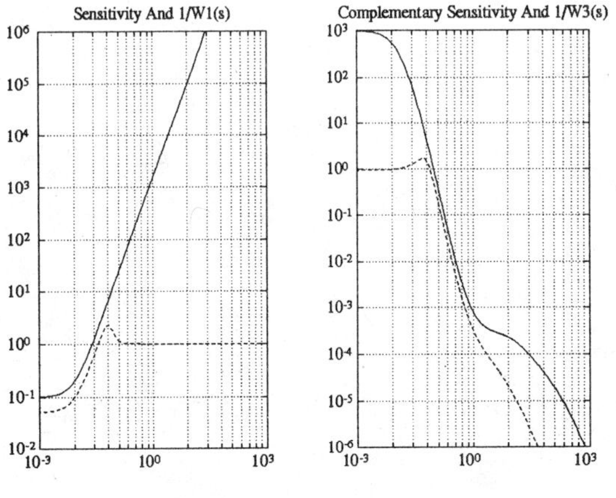

Figure 6: Design Using Non-Optimal Parametric Cover.

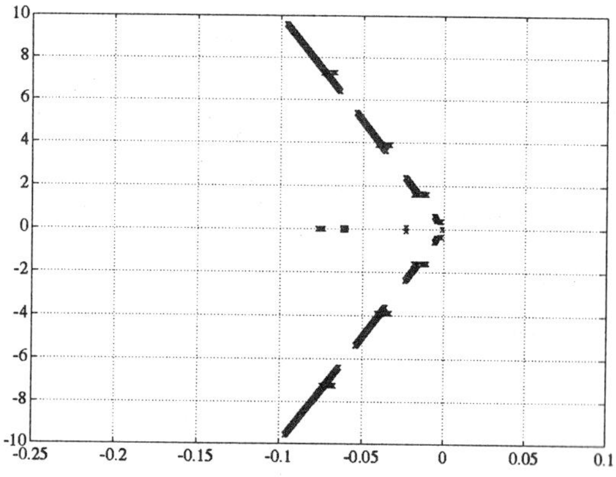

Figure 7: Root Locus For Non-Optimal Cover.

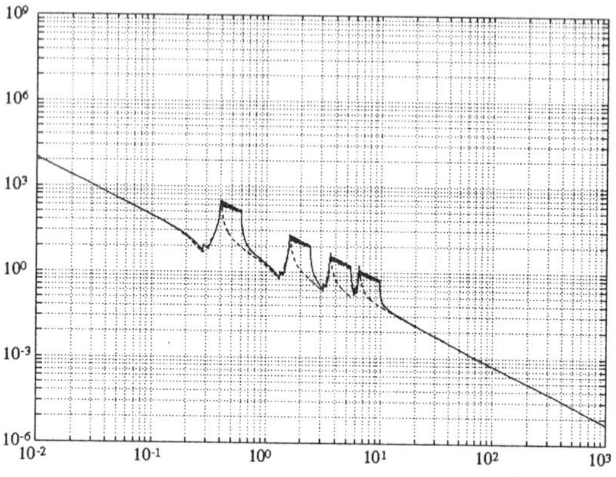

Figure 8: Nominal Plant (solid) corresponding to Optimal Cover and an Approximation (dashed).

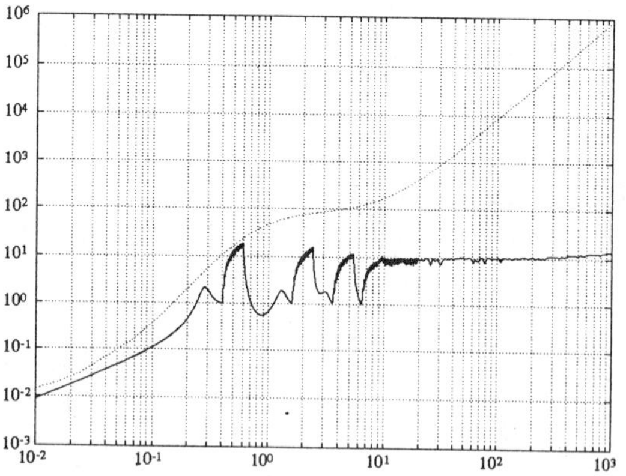

Figure 9: Optimal Parametric Cover: Total Multiplicative Error Bound and an Approximation (Compare to Figure 5).

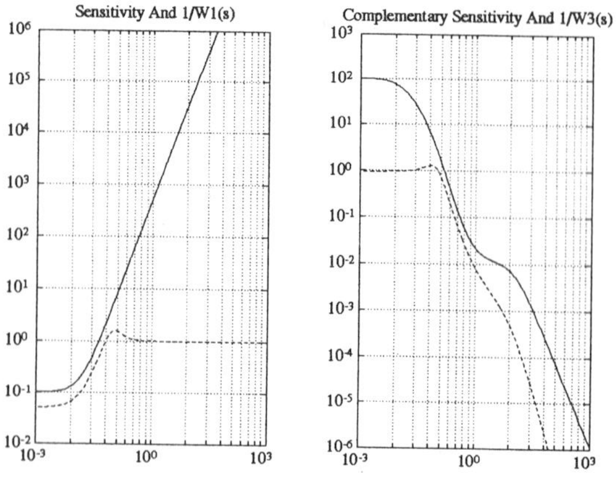

Figure 10: Design Using Optimal Parametric Cover.

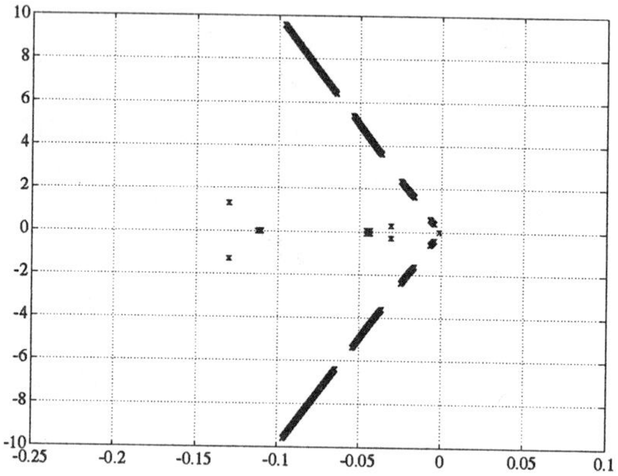

Figure 11: Root Locus For Optimal Cover.

Proceedings of the
American Control Conference
San Francisco, California • June 1993

Geometric Aspects of the Covariance Partial Realization Problem

Chin Chang and Tryphon T. Georgiou

Abstract

In this paper, both Euclidean geometric and non-Euclidean geometric descriptions for the regions of the solution set to the covariance partial realization problem are discussed. In particular, it is shown that all the solution functions are located inside a Euclidean disk – the Weyl disk, and a non-Euclidean disk – the Apollonian disk. The radius of each disk depends on the norm of the parameterizing Schur functions. Moreover, it is pointed out that the well known maximum entropy solution is exactly the hyperbolic center of the Apollonian disk; while, the associated power spectral density function is the geometric mean center of the real region where the Weyl disk is projected to along the imaginary axis. Sensitivity analysis of the Weyl disk radius and Apollonian disk center due to the perturbation of the given finite covariance data is presented. [1]

1 Introduction

Consider a zero mean, wide sense stationary process y_t, $t \in Z$. The computed autocorrelation (covariance) lag $c_k := \mathbf{E}\{y_t y_{t-k}^*\}$ with $c_{-k} = c_k^*$ is related to the spectral distribution function $d\sigma(\theta)(\geq 0)$ of the process y_t via

$$c_k = \frac{1}{2\pi}\int_{-\pi}^{\pi} e^{-ik\theta} d\sigma(\theta) \qquad k = 0, \pm 1, \pm 2, \ldots. \quad (1)$$

For the given covariance sequence $\mathbf{c} := \{c_0, c_1, c_2, \ldots\}$, one can associate a function in $\mathbf{D}$

$$F(z) = c_0 + 2c_1 z + 2c_2 z^2 + \ldots + 2c_n z^n + \ldots. \quad (2)$$

It is well known ([1], p.178) that the function $F(z)$ in (2) belongs to $\mathcal{C}$ [2] if and only if the associated Toeplitz matrices $T_n := [c_{l-m}]_{l,m=0}^n$ are nonnegative definite. Moreover, if $T_n > 0$ for all $n > 0$, the associated distribution function $\sigma(\theta)$ is unique [13], has an infinite set of points of increase in $[-\pi, \pi]$, and

$$d\sigma(\theta) = \Re e F(\theta) d\theta. \quad (3)$$

Where, $\Re e F(\theta)$ is called the spectral density function of y_t. For the case $T_n > 0$, the sequence $\mathbf{c}$ is deemed to be a positive sequence. Without loss of generality, c_0 can be normalized to be unity.

The standard covariance partial realization problem [3] [14] [17] may be stated as: given *finite length* of covariance lags (second order statistics) $\mathbf{c}_n := \{c_0, c_1, c_2, \ldots, c_n\}$ of the process y_t, find all of the spectral distribution functions $d\sigma_n(\theta) = \Re e F_n(\theta) d\theta$ which satisfy the interpolation condition (1) for $k = 0, \pm 1, \pm 2, \ldots, \pm n$. It is a classical result that if $T_k > 0$ for $k = 0, 1, \ldots, n$, the set of Caratheodory functions $F_n(z)$ which satisfy (2) can be algebraically parametrized via a linear fractional transformation (LFT) on $\mathcal{S}$ or $\mathcal{C}$ [1] [16]. Geometrically, the region of the function set $F_n(z)$ are confined in the so called *Weyl disks* [2] and the *Apollonian disks* [9]; these two kinds of disks are the same but are interpreted in different metric spaces. Based on the classic work of Geronimus [9] [10] and Krein [15], further discussions of the geometry of the solution sets to the covariance partial realization problem are made in this paper. More specifically, we show that, in terms of the Euclidean metric, all the solutions $\Re e F_n(\theta)$ are located in a positive real interval with the real part of the maximum entropy solution being its geometric mean center. While in terms of the non-Euclidean metric, all the functions $F_n(z)$ are inside a hyperbolic disk with maximum entropy solution being the center. The radii of these disks are monotonic increasing functions of the H_∞ norm of the free parameterizing $\mathcal{S}$ functions. Then, we discuss the drift of the Weyl disk radius and Apollonian disk center in the plane under the deviation of the given covariance data $\mathbf{c}_n$. Some explicit perturbation bounds will be provided to clarify the continuous behavior of the relation. For the proofs of the results of the paper, the connections with the linear prediction and inverse scattering problems along with some historic remarks, see [4].

2 Background

From the orthogonal system $\{e^{ik\theta}; k = 0, \pm 1, \pm 2, \ldots,\}$ in $L_2(-\pi, \pi)$, one can use the Gram–Schmidt procedure to recursively construct an orthogonal polynomial system $\phi_n(z)$

[1]This work was supported in part by the National Science Foundation and the Air Force Office for Scientific Research, U.S.A.

Department of Electrical Engineering, University of Minnesota, Minneapolis, MN 55455.

[2]$\mathcal{C} := \{F(z) \in \mathcal{H}(\mathbf{D}) : \Re e(F(z)) \geq 0$ for $\forall z \in \mathbf{D}\}$ is called the Caratheodory function set and $\mathcal{S} := \{f(z) \in \mathcal{H}(\mathbf{D}) : |f(z)| \leq 1$ for $\forall z \in \mathbf{D}\}$ is called the Schur function set.

with respect to the positive measure $d\sigma(\theta)$ in (1). Here, the associated Gram's matrices are the Toeplitz matrices $T_n(>0)$, and the inner product

$$< \phi_n(z), \phi_m(z) >:= \frac{1}{2\pi}\int_{-\pi}^{\pi} \phi_n(e^{i\theta})\phi_m(e^{i\theta})^* d\sigma(\theta) = \delta_{n,m}$$

with $\delta_{n,m}$ being the Kronecker function. These so called Szegö (first kind) orthogonal polynomials $\phi_n(z)$ can also be generated via the Szegö–Levinson recursion ([9], p.5) [11]

$$\frac{\phi_{n+1}(z)}{\alpha_{n+1}} = z\frac{\phi_n(z)}{\alpha_n} - \gamma_n^* \frac{\phi_n(z)_*}{\alpha_n^*} \quad (4)$$

for $n = 0, 1, 2, \ldots$, where $\phi_n(z)_* := z^n\phi_n^*(z^{-1}) := z^n\phi_n(z^{-*})^*$,

$$\alpha_n := (\det T_{n-1}/\det T_n)^{\frac{1}{2}}, \quad (5)$$

$$\gamma_n := \frac{(-1)^n}{\det T_n}\det\begin{bmatrix} c_1 & c_0 & c_{-1} & \cdots & c_{-n+1} \\ c_2 & c_1 & & & \vdots \\ \vdots & & \ddots & & \vdots \\ c_{n+1} & & \cdots & & c_1 \end{bmatrix} \quad (6)$$

$\phi_0(z) := 1$, and $\det T_{-1} := 1$. Moreover, from ([10], (8.6), (8.9') and the second line on p.161) we have the inequalities

$$\prod_{k=0}^{n-1}\{\frac{1-|\gamma_k|}{1+|\gamma_k|}\}^{1/2} \le |\phi_n(z)_*| \le \prod_{k=0}^{n-1}\{\frac{1+|\gamma_k|}{1-|\gamma_k|}\}^{1/2} \quad (7)$$

$\forall z \in \mathbf{D} \cup \partial\mathbf{D}$. Corresponding to the positive sequence $\mathbf{c}$ with $c_0 = 1$, there exists an *inverse* positive sequence [8] $\mathbf{c}' := \{1, c_1', c_2', \ldots,\}$ defined by

$$F'(z) := 1 + 2c_1'z + 2c_2'z^2 + \ldots + 2c_n'z^n + \ldots = F(z)^{-1}.$$

This $\mathbf{c}'$ also defines a positive measure $d\sigma(\theta)'$ on $[-\pi, \pi]$ via the infinite interpolation constraints (1). Following a similar procedure as above, one can define an orthogonal polynomial system $\psi_n(z)$ respect to the positive measure $d\sigma(\theta)'$. These so called second kind orthogonal polynomials ([9], p.7), [10] [11] also satisfy a recurrence relation

$$\frac{\psi_{n+1}(z)}{\alpha_{n+1}'} = z\frac{\psi_n(z)}{\alpha_n'} - \gamma_n'^* \frac{\psi_n(z)_*}{\alpha_n'^*}, \quad (8)$$

for $n = 0, 1, 2, \ldots$, where $T_n' := [c_{l-m}']_{l,m=0}^n > 0$,

$$\alpha_n' := (\det T_{n-1}'/\det T_n')^{\frac{1}{2}},$$

$$\gamma_n' := \frac{(-1)^n}{\det T_n'}\det\begin{bmatrix} c_1' & c_0' & c_{-1}' & \cdots & c_{-n+1}' \\ c_2' & c_1' & & & \vdots \\ \vdots & & \ddots & & \vdots \\ c_{n+1}' & & \cdots & & c_1' \end{bmatrix},$$

$\psi_0(z) := 1$, and $\det T_{-1}' := 1$. Furthermore, it is a classical result [9], [10] that

$$\gamma_n = -\gamma_n', \quad \text{and} \quad \alpha_n = \alpha_n', \quad (9)$$

for $n = 0, 1, 2, \ldots$. Here the γ_n's are known as *Schur parameters* and have modulus less than 1 for $T_n > 0$. Also, one has the following relation ([9], p.6)

$$\alpha_n = \prod_{k=0}^{n-1}\frac{1}{\sqrt{1-|\gamma_k|^2}}.$$

From (4) and (8), one can show the equality [10]

$$\phi_n(z)_*\psi_n(z) + \phi_n(z)\psi_n(z)_* = 2z^n \quad \text{for} \quad z \in \mathbf{D} \cup \partial\mathbf{D}, \quad (10)$$

for $n = 0, 1, 2, \ldots$. Moreover, by combining the equations (4) and (8), using the relations in (9), one obtains a compact form

$$\begin{bmatrix} \phi_{n+1}(z)_* & -\phi_{n+1}(z) \\ \psi_{n+1}(z)_* & \psi_{n+1}(z) \end{bmatrix}\begin{bmatrix} \frac{1}{\alpha_{n+1}^*} & 0 \\ 0 & \frac{1}{\alpha_{n+1}} \end{bmatrix} =$$

$$\begin{bmatrix} \phi_n(z)_* & -\phi_n(z) \\ \psi_n(z)_* & \psi_n(z) \end{bmatrix}\begin{bmatrix} \frac{1}{\alpha_n^*} & 0 \\ 0 & \frac{1}{\alpha_n} \end{bmatrix}\begin{bmatrix} 1 & 0 \\ 0 & z \end{bmatrix}\begin{bmatrix} 1 & \gamma_n^* \\ \gamma_n & 1 \end{bmatrix},$$

for $n = 0, 1, 2, \ldots$.

3 Geometric regions of the solution set

Weyl disks and Euclidean geometry

Let $\phi_n(z)$ and $\psi_n(z)$ be the first and second kind orthogonal polynomials, respectively, as defined in section 2. When the given data $\mathbf{c}_n$ are such that $T_n > 0$, the indeterminate solution set $F_n(z)$ to the covariance partial realization problem can be expressed as

$$F_n(z) = \frac{\psi_n(z)_* + zf(z)\psi_n(z)}{\phi_n(z)_* - zf(z)\phi_n(z)}, \quad (11)$$

for arbitrary $f(z) \in \mathcal{S}$ (see [1], [7] and [9] for example). If one uses the graph symbols

$$\begin{bmatrix} D_{F_n}(z) \\ N_{F_n}(z) \end{bmatrix} \quad \text{and} \quad \begin{bmatrix} D_f(z) \\ N_f(z) \end{bmatrix},$$

all in $\mathcal{H}_\infty$, to describe the functions $F_n(z) = N_{F_n}(z)D_{F_n}(z)^{-1}$ and $f(z) = N_f(z)D_f(z)^{-1}$ respectively, and define

$$\Theta_k := \frac{1}{\sqrt{1-|\gamma_k|^2}}\begin{bmatrix} 1 & 0 \\ 0 & z \end{bmatrix}\begin{bmatrix} 1 & \gamma_k^* \\ \gamma_k & 1 \end{bmatrix}$$

for $k = 0, 1, 2, \ldots$, then (11) is readily expressed as

$$\begin{bmatrix} D_{F_n}(z) \\ N_{F_n}(z) \end{bmatrix} = \begin{bmatrix} 1 & -1 \\ 1 & 1 \end{bmatrix}\Theta_0\Theta_1\cdots\Theta_n\begin{bmatrix} D_f(z) \\ zN_f(z) \end{bmatrix}. \quad (12)$$

In network theory, (12) has a simple cascade realization ([6] Sec.5, [17]) with the function $zf(z)$ being interpreted as the scattering function of a "free" end load. It is considered that $||f(z)||_\infty = 1$ corresponds to a lossless load and $f(z) = 0$ corresponds to a unit loss load. Therefore, the assumption $||f(z)||_\infty \le r_f \le 1$ reflects the loss level of the end load.

Because the function $F_n(z)$ is in $\mathcal{C}$, the range of the mapping in (11) is in the right half plane $RHP := \{z : \Re ez \ge 0\}$ for $z \in \mathbf{D}$. By invoking the equality in (10), it is clear that the determinant of the coefficient function matrix

$$\begin{bmatrix} \psi_n(z)_* & z\psi_n(z) \\ \phi_n(z)_* & -z\phi_n(z) \end{bmatrix}$$

for the transformation $f(z) \Rightarrow F_n(z)$ in (11) is $-2z^{n+1}$, which is nonzero in $\mathbf{D} \cup \partial\mathbf{D}$ except for $z = 0$. Therefore, when $||f(z)||_\infty \le r_f < 1$, the image of $F_n(z)$ will be portrayed inside some disks in RHP as shown below.

Lemma 1 . *If $T_n > 0$, then the free Schur function $f(z)$ has $|f(z)| \le r_f \le 1$ if, and only if all the corresponding Caratheodory functions $F_n(z)$ lie in the Weyl disks*

$$|F_n(z) - \mathcal{O}_n(z)| \le \mathcal{R}_{n,1}(z), \tag{13}$$

where

$$\mathcal{O}_n(z) := \frac{\phi_n(z)_*^*\psi_n(z)_* + |r_f z|^2\phi_n(z)^*\psi_n(z)}{|\phi_n(z)_*|^2 - |r_f z\phi_n(z)|^2}, \tag{14}$$

$$\mathcal{R}_{n,1}(z) := \frac{2r_f|z|^{n+1}}{|\phi_n(z)_*|^2 - |r_f z\phi_n(z)|^2}, \tag{15}$$

for $\forall z \in \mathbf{D}$. □

In view of the definition of $\phi_n(z)_*$, $|\phi_n(e^{i\theta})_*| = |\phi_n(e^{i\theta})|$ for $\theta \in [-\pi, \pi]$. Because $\phi_n(z)_* \ne 0 \quad \forall z \in \mathbf{D} \cup \partial\mathbf{D}$ [10], by using the maximum modulus principle, one has

$$\left|\frac{\phi_n(z)}{\phi_n(z)_*}\right| \le 1 \qquad \forall z \in \mathbf{D}. \tag{16}$$

Hence, from (15), the radii $\mathcal{R}_{n,1}(z) \ge 0$ and have a simple upper bound

$$\mathcal{R}_{n,2}(z) := \frac{2r_f|z|^{n+1}}{(1 - |r_f z|^2)|\phi_n(z)_*|^2}.$$

Therefore, the Weyl disks in (13) are covered by the disks

$$|F_n(z) - \mathcal{O}_n(z)| \le \mathcal{R}_{n,2}(z), \tag{17}$$

for $\forall z \in \mathbf{D}$.

The disks in (13), usually called the Weyl disks, were originally introduced to describe the solutions for Sturm–Liouville type equations [2], [5]. Geometrically, the Weyl disk provides an Euclidean picture for the region of the solution sets $F_n(z)$. For each $z_i \in \mathbf{D}$, $F_n(z_i)$ is inside a disk centered at $\mathcal{O}_n(z_i)$ with radius $\mathcal{R}_{n,1}(z_i)$. As $n \to \infty$, $\mathcal{R}_{n,2}(z) \to 0$, $\mathcal{R}_{n,1}(z) \to 0$, and therefore $F_n(z) \to \mathcal{O}_n(z)$ uniformly in $\mathbf{D}$. Recall that the real part of $F_n(z)$ is obtained by projecting the Weyl disk to the real axis in parallel with the imaginary axis. The following inequalities can then be acquired from Lemma 1 and the simple Euclidean geometry:

$$\Re e\mathcal{O}_n(z) - \mathcal{R}_{n,1}(z) \le \Re eF_n(z) \le \Re e\mathcal{O}_n(z) + \mathcal{R}_{n,1}(z)$$

for $\forall z \in \mathbf{D}$. Furthermore, the harmonic function $\Re eF_n(z)$ has the following boundary property.

Theorem 1 . *If $T_n > 0$ and $||f(z)||_\infty \le r_f < 1$, then*

$$\left(\frac{1-r_f}{1+r_f}\right)\frac{1}{|\phi_n(e^{i\theta})_*|^2} \le \Re eF_n(e^{i\theta}) \le \left(\frac{1+r_f}{1-r_f}\right)\frac{1}{|\phi_n(e^{i\theta})_*|^2} \tag{18}$$

a.e., for $\theta \in [-\pi, \pi]$. □

While the reverse direction of Theorem 1 does not always hold, we have the following.

Proposition 1 . *If $T_n > 0$ and a constant $r_f \in [0, 1)$ such that*

$$\left(\frac{1-r_f}{1+r_f}\right)\frac{1}{|\phi_n(e^{i\theta})_*|^2} \le \Re eF_n(e^{i\theta}) \le \left(\frac{1+r_f}{1-r_f}\right)\frac{1}{|\phi_n(e^{i\theta})_*|^2} \tag{19}$$

a.e., for $\theta \in [-\pi, \pi]$, then $||f(z)||_\infty \le r_f$ provided the parametric Schur function is of the finite Blaschke product form

$$f(z) = \kappa \prod_{k=1}^{N} \frac{z - z_k}{1 - z_k^* z} \tag{20}$$

with a constant $\kappa \in \mathbf{R}$, appropriate chosen integer N and $z_k \in \mathbf{D}$. □

Remark. In his pioneer works, Youla proved the Theorem 1 under the assumption that the free Schur function $f(z)$ is chosen to be a finite Blaschke product as in (20) ([17], p.21). If one restricts the $\mathcal{S}$ function to be Blaschke products, Proposition 1 indicates that Theorem 1 holds in both directions for some appropriate chosen integer N. □

From (7) and (18), we obtain Schur parameter related upper and lower bounds on $\Re eF_n(e^{i\theta})$ as

$$\frac{1-r_f}{1+r_f}\prod_{k=0}^{n-1}\left\{\frac{1-|\gamma_k|}{1+|\gamma_k|}\right\} \le \Re eF_n(e^{i\theta}) \le \frac{1+r_f}{1-r_f}\prod_{k=0}^{n-1}\left\{\frac{1+|\gamma_k|}{1-|\gamma_k|}\right\} \tag{21}$$

a.e., with $\theta \in [-\pi, \pi]$. As matter of fact, (18) and (21) provide bounds on the absolutely continuous part of the distribution function $\sigma_n(\theta)$ which then provides the solution to the covariance partial realization problem via (3). If $r_f = 0$, the inequalities of (21) reduces to the Burg's autoregressive spectral estimator bounds ([3], II-69).

In order to visualize the geometric regions for the center functions $\mathcal{O}_n(z)$, the disks in (13) and the bounds in (18), we present a simple example.

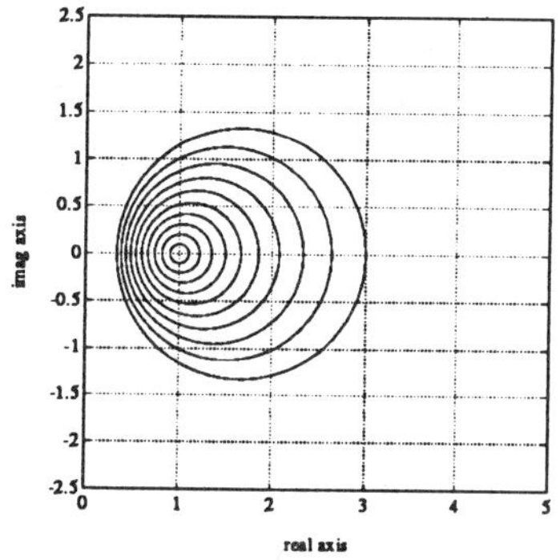

Figure 1: The region of the center function $\mathcal{O}_1(z)$ with $r_f = 0$. The radius increasing circles are the image of $\mathcal{O}_1(z)$ when $|z| = 0.1r$ for $r = 1, 2, \ldots, 10$.

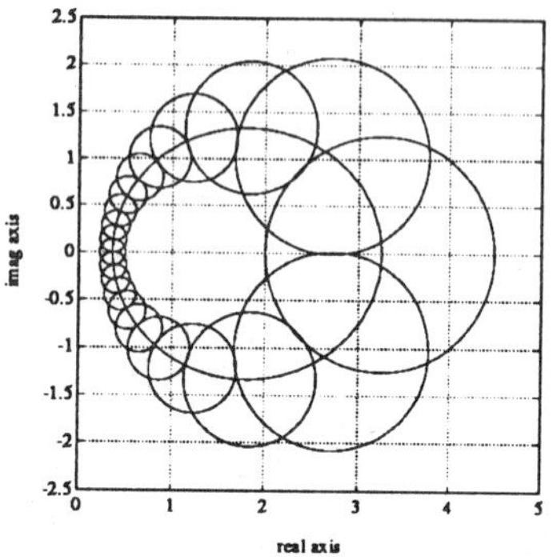

Figure 2: The region of $F_1(e^{i\theta})$ with $r_f = 0.2$. The center circle is $\mathcal{O}_1(e^{i\theta})$. The radius of each circular template centered at each point of $\mathcal{O}_1(e^{i\theta})$ is determined by $\mathcal{R}_{1,1}(e^{i\theta})$

Example. Let the given data $\mathbf{c}_2 := \{1, 1/2, 0\}$. It is routine to check that $T_k > 0$ for $k = 0, 1, 2$. By definitions (5) and (6) and the relations in (9), we compute the associated parameters $(\gamma_0, \gamma_1) = (1/2, -1/3)$, $(\alpha_0, \alpha_1) = (1, 2/\sqrt{3})$, $(\gamma_0', \gamma_1') = (-1/2, 1/3)$, and $(\alpha_0', \alpha_1') = (1, 2/\sqrt{3})$. The recursions in (4) and (8) yield the first and the second kind orthogonal polynomials

$$\phi_1(z) = \frac{2}{\sqrt{3}}(z - \frac{1}{2}), \qquad \phi_1(z)_* = \frac{2}{\sqrt{3}}(1 - \frac{1}{2}z),$$

$$\psi_1(z) = \frac{2}{\sqrt{3}}(z + \frac{1}{2}), \qquad \psi_1(z)_* = \frac{2}{\sqrt{3}}(1 + \frac{1}{2}z).$$

Substituting these polynomials into (14) and (15), the center function $\mathcal{O}_1(z)$ and the radius function $\mathcal{R}_{1,1}(z)$ for $z \in \mathbf{D}$ are defined by the free parameter $0 \le r_f \le 1$. If $r_f = 0$, it returns that $\mathcal{R}_{1,1}(z) = 0$ for $\forall z \in \mathbf{D}$, and therefore $\mathcal{O}_1(z) = F_1(z) = \frac{1+0.5z}{1-0.5z}$. The image of $\mathcal{O}_1(z)$ for $r_f = 0$ when $z \in \mathbf{D} \cup \partial\mathbf{D}$ is shown in Figure 1. The graph in Figure 2 shows the Weyl disks $|F_1(z) - \mathcal{O}_1(z)| \le \mathcal{R}_{1,1}(z)$ with $z \in \partial\mathbf{D}$ for $r_f = 0.2$, and Figure 3 exhibits the associated upper and lower bounds (18) of the real part of all the function set $F_1(e^{i\theta})$. □

Apollonian disks and non–Euclidean metrics

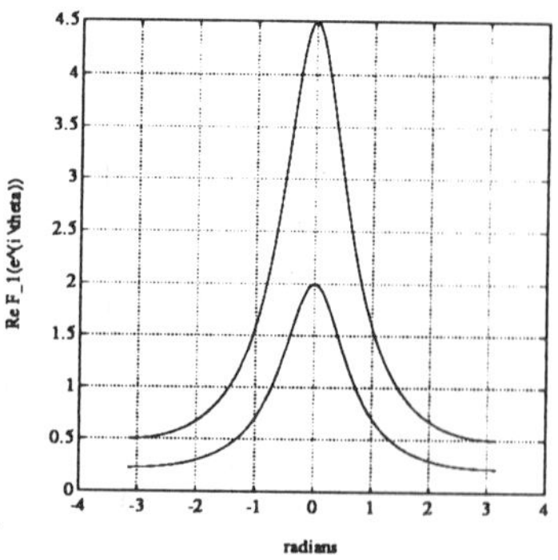

Figure 3: The upper and lower bounds for the real part of $F_1(e^{i\theta})$ with $r_f = 0.2$

In this part, we show that it is more succinct to describe the range of the mapping (11) by using a natural generalization of the non–Euclidean model RHP and the associated hyperbolic metric.

Let z_1 and z_2 be in RHP. Define the *pseudo-chordal distance* between z_1 and z_2 as

$$\zeta(z_1, z_2) := \left| \frac{z_1 - z_2}{z_1 + z_2^*} \right|.$$

It is easy to check that $\zeta(z_1, z_2) < 1$. The *hyperbolic metric* in RHP is then obtained as $ds = \frac{|dz|}{\Re e z}$, which indicates the infinitesimal of the hyperbolic length. Therefore, under this metric the *hyperbolic distance* between z_1 and z_2 in RHP is

$$\eta(z_1, z_2) = \ln \frac{1 + \zeta(z_1, z_2)}{1 - \zeta(z_1, z_2)}.$$

In view of the hyperbolic distance, the inequality

$$\eta(z, z_0) < r_0 \qquad (\eta(z, z_0) \le r_0) \tag{22}$$

describes an open (closed) *hyperbolic disk* in RHP with the hyperbolic center z_0 and the hyperbolic radius r_0. Elementary algebra yields that the hyperbolic disk in (22) coincides with a Euclidean disk

$$\left| z - \frac{z_0 + q z_0^*}{1 - q} \right| \le \frac{\sqrt{q}}{1 - q}(z_0 + z_0^*), \tag{23}$$

where $q := \frac{e^{r_0} - 1}{e^{r_0} + 1}$. Conversely, the Euclidean disk $|z - z_e| \le r_e$ in the RHP corresponds to the non–Euclidean disk in (22) with

$$\begin{aligned} z_0 &= \frac{1}{2}(z_e - z_e^* + \sqrt{(z_e + z_e^*)^2 - 4r_e^2}), \\ q &= \frac{1}{4r_e^2}(z_e + z_e^* - \sqrt{(z_e + z_e^*)^2 - 4r_e^2}), \\ r_0 &= 2\tanh^{-1}(q). \end{aligned}$$

As a natural generalization of the non–Euclidean geometry in the RHP, one can define the quantity

$$\vartheta(g_1(z), g_2(z)) := \sup_\theta \tanh^{-1} \left| \frac{g_1(e^{i\theta}) - g_2(e^{i\theta})}{g_1(e^{i\theta}) + g_2(e^{i\theta})^*} \right| \tag{24}$$

and further show that (24) quantifies as a hyperbolic distance in the function space $\mathcal{C}$. Under this metric, the solution set (11) to the covariance partial realization problem can be described with the following.

Theorem 2 *If $T_n > 0$ and $\|f(z)\|_\infty \le r_f < 1$, then all the Caratheodory functions $F_n(z)$ lie in the Apollonian disks*

$$\vartheta(F_n(z), \frac{\psi_n(z)_*}{\phi_n(z)_*}) \le \frac{1}{2}\ln\frac{1+r_f}{1-r_f} = \tanh^{-1}(r_f) \qquad (25)$$

for $\forall z \in \mathbf{D} \cup \partial\mathbf{D}$. □

Comparing with the center of the Weyl disks in (13), it is interesting to observe that the hyperbolic center of the Apollonian disks in (25) is independent of r_f, while their radius are monotonic increasing functions of r_f. Then, the norm of the free $\mathcal{S}$ function $f(z)$ reflects the geometric range of the solution set. When $r_f = 0$, the Weyl disks in (13) shrinks to the point $\frac{\psi_n(z)_*}{\phi_n(z)_*}$ because $\mathcal{R}_{n,1}(z)|_{r_f=0} = 0$. In this case, the hyperbolic center

$$\mathcal{O}_{n,i}(z) = \frac{\psi_n(z)_*}{\phi_n(z)_*}$$

coincides with the Weyl disk center $\mathcal{O}_n(z)$, and such a point is exactly the maximum entropy $\mathcal{C}$ function [3]. Meanwhile, the real part of $\frac{\psi_n(e^{i\theta})_*}{\phi_n(e^{i\theta})_*}$, which equals the maximum entropy spectral density function $\Phi_{ME}(\theta) := \frac{1}{|\phi_n(e^{i\theta})_*|^2}$ in the associated positive measure $d\sigma(\theta)$, is exactly the geometric mean center of the real interval (18).

4 Perturbation analysis

In this section, we shall consider the problem: if the given covariance sequence $\mathbf{c}_n$ is perturbed to $\hat{\mathbf{c}}_n$, what is the associated deviation of the Weyl disk radius and the Apollonian disk center? We first address the admissibility and a quantitative measure of the covariance perturbations.

If considering a finite length covariance sequence $\mathbf{c}_n := \{c_0, c_1, c_2, \ldots, c_n\}$ as a row vector in $\mathbf{C}^{n+1}$, one can define the functional

$$\|\mathbf{c}_n\|_T := \|T_n\|_2,$$

where T_n is the associated Toeplitz matrix. It can be shown that $\|\cdot\|_T$ defines a norm on $\mathbf{C}^{n+1}$ and is called the *vector Toeplitz norm*.

Under the vector Toeplitz norm, the distance between two sequences $\{c_0, c_1, \ldots, c_n\}$ and $\{\hat{c}_0, \hat{c}_1, \ldots, \hat{c}_n\}$ is defined as $\|\Delta\mathbf{c}_n\|_T$, where $\Delta\mathbf{c}_n := [\Delta c_0, \Delta c_1, \ldots, \Delta c_n]$ with $\Delta c_k := c_k - \hat{c}_k$. In this paper, we use the Toeplitz norm to measure the distance between two sets of finite covariance data.

It is well known that, the positivity of the given finite covariance sequence $\mathbf{c}_n$, which is equivalent to the positive definiteness of the associated Toeplitz matrices, is a necessary and sufficient condition for the associated partial realization problem being solvable. Therefore, for a given positive sequence $\{c_0, c_1, \ldots, c_n\}$, the allowable perturbations should be restricted such that the perturbed sequence $\{\hat{c}_0, \hat{c}_1, \ldots, \hat{c}_n\}$ is also positive. Let $\Delta T_n := [\Delta c_{i-j}]_{i,j=0}^n$ and $\lambda_{\min}(A)$ be the minimal eigenvalue (with possible multiplicities) of a matrix A. Then, we have the following.

Corollary 1 *All the admissible perturbation of the positive sequence $\{c_0, c_1, \ldots, c_n\}$ is*

$$\Delta\mathbf{C}_n := \{\Delta c_0, \Delta c_1, \ldots, \Delta c_n | \quad \lambda_{\min}(T_n^{-1}\Delta T_n) > -1\}. \square$$

According to the bijective mapping (6) between the Schur parameter sequence $\{\gamma_k, \text{ for } k = 0, 1, \ldots, n\}$ and the positive sequence $\{c_k, \text{ for } k = 1, 2, \ldots, n+1\}$, the above admissible perturbation set in covariance corresponds to the allowable perturbation set in Schur parameter γ_i which then is described as

$$\Delta\Gamma_n := \{\Delta\gamma_0, \Delta\gamma_1, \ldots, \Delta\gamma_n; \quad s.t., \quad |\gamma_k + \Delta\gamma_k| < 1\}$$

for $k = 1, 2, \ldots, n$. While the Schur parameter perturbation set $\Delta\Gamma_n$ is in a hypercube, the covariance perturbation set $\Delta\mathbf{C}_n$ is in a hypercone of the Euclidean space $\mathbf{C}^{n+1}$.

Assume that the given finite covariance sequence $\mathbf{c}_n$ with $c_0 = 1$ is perturbed by $\Delta\mathbf{c}_n \in \Delta\mathbf{C}_n$ to $\hat{\mathbf{c}}_n$ with $\hat{c}_0 = 1$. The quantities associated with $\hat{\mathbf{c}}_n$ are the Toeplitz matrix $\hat{T}_n$, the first kind orthogonal polynominal $\hat{\phi}_n(z)$, the Apollonian disk inner center $\hat{\mathcal{O}}_{n,i}(z)$ and the Weyl disk radius $\hat{\mathcal{R}}_{n,1}(z)$.

Proposition 2 *Let $\rho := \|T_n^{-1}\|_2$ and $\beta := \prod_{k=0}^{n-1}\{\frac{1+|\gamma_k|}{1-|\gamma_k|}\}^{1/2}$. If the perturbation $\Delta\mathbf{c}_n$ to the covariance sequence $\mathbf{c}_n$ is allowable (i.e. $\in \Delta\mathbf{C}_n$) and*

$$\|\Delta\mathbf{c}_n\|_T \le \delta \quad \text{with} \quad \delta < \frac{1}{\rho(\sqrt{n+1}\beta\rho + 1)},$$

then

$$\|\phi_n(z)_*^{-1} - \hat{\phi}_n(z)_*^{-1}\|_\infty \le \frac{\sqrt{n+1}\beta^2\rho^2\delta}{1 - \delta\rho(1 + \sqrt{n+1}\beta\rho)} =: \epsilon. \square$$

Theorem 3 *If $\mathbf{c}_n$ and $\Delta\mathbf{c}_n$ are in $\mathbf{R}^{n+1}$ and if $\|f(z)\|_\infty \le r_f \le 1$, then under the same conditions as in Proposition 2,*

$$|\mathcal{R}_{n,1}(z) - \hat{\mathcal{R}}_{n,1}(z)|$$
$$\le \frac{2|z|^{n+1}r_f}{(1-|z|^2r_f^2)^2}\epsilon\{\epsilon + 2\beta + r_f^2|z|^2[\epsilon + 2\beta^2(\epsilon + \beta)]\},$$

nd

$$|\mathcal{O}_{n,i}(z) - \hat{\mathcal{O}}_{n,i}(z)| \le (8n+1)\epsilon(\epsilon + 2\beta).$$

for $\forall z \in \mathbf{D}$. □

Corollary 2 *The mapping from the covariance data* $\mathbf{c}_n$ *to the maximum entropy spectral density function* $\Phi_{ME}(\theta)$ *is a continuous mapping, and vice versa.* □

5 Concluding Remarks

We conclude the paper with an interesting comparison. Consider the classic one step extension problem: Given a positive covariance sequence $\mathbf{c}_n$, find the geometric region of all the possible c_{n+1} such that the sequence $\mathbf{c}_{n+1}$ is still positive. The solution to this problem ([12], p.31), ([15], p.155) and ([17], p.5). reads that all the c_{n+1} which completes the positivity of $\mathbf{c}_{n+1}$ should be inside a disk in **C** with center

$$o_{c,n+1} := \frac{(-1)^{n-1}}{\det T_{n-1}} \det \begin{bmatrix} c_1 & c_0 & c_{-1} & \cdots & c_{-n+1} \\ c_2 & c_1 & & & \vdots \\ \vdots & & \ddots & & \vdots \\ 0 & & \cdots & & c_1 \end{bmatrix}$$

and radius

$$r_{c,n+1} := \frac{\det T_n}{\det T_{n-1}} = \frac{1}{\alpha_n^2}.$$

If one keeps choosing $c_k = o_{c,k}$ for $k = n+1, n+2, \ldots$, then Theorem 2 in [17] shows that the completed infinite length sequence c_k uniquely determines a power spectral density function $\Phi_n(\theta)$ via the relation in (1). Such a $\Phi_n(\theta)$ is exactly the so called maximum entropy solution $\Phi_{ME}(\theta)$ defined in [3], [17]. As has been shown in Theorem 1, this $\Phi_{ME}(\theta)$ is the geometric mean center function of the possible region of the positive function family $\mathcal{F}_n$ whose first $n+1$ Laurent coefficients match the given covariance sequence $\mathbf{c}_n$. Also, the corresponding $\mathcal{C}$ function $\frac{\psi_n(z)_*}{\phi_n(z)_*}$ is the center function of a non-Euclidean disk as described in Theorem 2. On the other hand, if one selects the geometric mean center function $\Phi_{ME}(\theta)$ as the power spectral density function of the stochastic process y_t, then the associated infinite length covariance sequence is the center sequence $o_{c,k}$ for $k = 0, 1, 2, \ldots$. Therefore, the center sequence in the covariance domain corresponds to the geometric mean center function in the spectral function domain.

References

[1] N.I. Akhiezer, **The Classical Moment Problem and Some Related Questions in Analysis.** Oliver and Boyd Ltd., London, 1965.

[2] F.V. Atkinson, **Discrete and Continuous Boundary Problems.** Academic press, New York, 1964.

[3] J.P. Burg, **Maximum Entropy Spectral Analysis,** Ph.D. dissertation, Stanford University, 1975.

[4] C. Chang and T.T. Georgiou, "Geometric aspects of the Caratheodory extension problem," Preprint, (1991).

[5] Ph. Delsarte, Y. Genin and Y. Kamp, "The Nevanlinna-Pick problem for matrix-valued functions," *SIAM J. Appl.Math.* 36(1):47-61 (1979).

[6] Ph. Delsarte, Y. Genin, Y. Kamp and P. Van Dooren, "Speech modelling and the trigonometric moment problem," *Philips J. Res.*, 37:277-292 (1982).

[7] T.T. Georgiou, **Partial Realization of Covariance Sequences**, Ph.D. dissertation, University of Florida, 1983.

[8] T.T. Georgiou and P.P. Khargonekar, "Linear fractional transformation and spectral factorization," *IEEE Trans. Automatic control* AC-31(4): 345-347 (1986).

[9] Ya.L. Geronimus, "Polynomials orthogonal on a circle and its applications," *Amer. Math. Soci. Transl.* No.104, 1-79 (1954). (Russian original 1948).

[10] Ya.L. Geronimus, **Orthogonal Polynomials**, Consultants Bureau, New York, 1961. (Russian original 1958).

[11] U. Grenander and G. Szegö, **Toeplitz Forms and Their Applications,** University of California Press, Berkeley CA. 1958.

[12] S. Haykin, ed. **Nonlinear Methods of Spectral Analysis.** Springer-Verlag, New York, 1979.

[13] K. Hoffman, **Banach Spaces of Analytic Functions**, Dover Public. Inc., New York, 1962.

[14] R.E. Kalman, "On partial realizations, transfer functions and canonical forms," *Acta Polytechnica Scandinavica,* Vol.31:9-32, (1979).

[15] M.G. Krein and A.A. Nudelman, **The Markov Moment Problem and Extremal Problems,** *Transl. Math. Monographs,* Vol.50, Amer. Math. Soc., Providence, Rhode Island, 1977.

[16] J.L. Walsh, **Interpolation and Approximation by Rational Functions in the Complex Domain,** Amer. Math. Soc. Colloquium Publications, Providence, RI., 1956.

[17] D.C.Youla, "The FEE: A new tunable high resolution spectral estimator," Polytechnic Tech. Note No.3, (1978).

Proceedings of the
American Control Conference
San Francisco, California • June 1993

Reduced-order Multimodel Control using Linear Matrix Inequalities: Sufficient Conditions

Laurent El Ghaoui
Ecole Nationale Supérieure de Techniques Avancées
32, Bd. Victor, 75015 Paris, France
e-mail: elghaoui@ensta.fr

Keywords: Reduced-order output feeedback, multimodel control, Linear Matrix Inequalities.

1 Introduction

For controlling an uncertain LTI system, one approach is to design a single controller for a finite number of plant configurations, each representing a particular operating point. In the state-space domain, authors concentrated mainly on quadratically stabilizable uncertain systems, *i.e.* for which there exists a single quadratic Lyapunov function establishing stability of all closed-loop models [Bar83, Pet87, ZK88, PGA91, BGFB93]. Moreover, most results pertain to the case when the full state is available for feedback. In this paper, we obtain a sufficient condition which guarantees the existence of a single controller *of a given order* which stabilizes a number of LTI systems. This condition does not require quadratic stabilizability. This condition is written in terms of Linear Matrix Inequalities (LMIs), and is therefore readily checked using now standard convex optimization algorithms (see *e.g.*, [BG93] and references therein). If the condition is satisfied, the method also provides the controller gains. Finally, several constraints on the closed-loop system, such as $\mathbf{H}_2$-, $\mathbf{H}_\infty$- or scaled $\mathbf{H}_\infty$-norm constraints, linear constraints on the controller gains, etc ..., are easily incorporated in the design process.

2 Multimodel stabilization

Consider an LTI system $\dot{x} = A_x + B_u u$, with (A, B_u) is stabilizable. It is easy to show the following result [VMP90]:

Lemma 1 *Let $Q = Q^T \geq 0$. For any pair (X, K) such that $X = X^T > 0$ and*

$$(A+B_uK)^TX+X(A+B_uK)+K^TK+Q<0, \quad (1)$$

the control law $u = Fx$, with $F = -B_u^TX$, is also stabilizing and

$$(A+B_uF)^TX+X(A+B_uF)+F^TF+Q<0.$$

Consider a set of L n-th order LTI systems $\dot{x} = A_ix + B_{u,i}u$, $y = C_{y,i}x$, $i = 1, \dots, L$. We now seek a *single* dynamic control law of order $r \leq n$ which stabilizes every system.

The closed-loop systems are described by the dynamics $\dot{\tilde{x}} = (\tilde{A}_i + \tilde{B}_{u,i}K\tilde{C}_{y,i})\tilde{x}$, where

$$\tilde{A}_i = \begin{bmatrix} A_i & 0 \\ 0 & 0 \end{bmatrix}, \; \tilde{B}_{u,i} = \begin{bmatrix} 0 & B_{u,i} \\ I & 0 \end{bmatrix},$$

$$\tilde{C}_{y,i} = \begin{bmatrix} 0 & I \\ C_{y,i} & 0 \end{bmatrix}, \; K = \begin{bmatrix} A_K & B_K \\ C_K & D_K \end{bmatrix}.$$

With this augmented system, the problem becomes a static one. We now seek a single matrix K such that $\tilde{A}_i + \tilde{B}_{u,i}K\tilde{C}_{y,i}$ is stable for all i, $i = 1, \dots, L$. We assume that for each i, there exist a matrix K_i such that $\tilde{A}_i + \tilde{B}_{u,i}K_i$ is stable (this is the same as requiring stabilizability of $(A_i, B_{u,i})$), and that a stabilizing state-feedback gain K_i has been found. Now solve the following problem.

Problem 1 Find *matrices $X_1, \dots, X_p$ and K such that, for all i, $i = 1, \dots, L$,*

$$\begin{array}{l} X_i = X_i^T > 0, \\ (\tilde{A}_i + \tilde{B}_{u,i}K_i)^TX_i + X_i(\tilde{A}_i + \tilde{B}_{u,i}K_i) + K_i^TK_i < 0, \\ K\tilde{C}_{y,i} = -\tilde{B}_{u,i}^TX_i. \end{array} \quad (2)$$

Lemma (1) implies that, for any solution $(X_1, \dots, X_L, K)$ to this problem, the matrix K is such that $\tilde{A}_i + \tilde{B}_{u,i}K\tilde{C}_{y,i}$ is stable for all i. In turn, this implies that the corresponding dynamic control law stabilizes each plant model.

In problem (1), equality constraints are used to eliminate redundant variables. The inequality constraints are linear matrix inequalities in the remaining variables. There are quite efficient methods to date for solving these LMIs, which can reliably check wether a given set of LMIs are feasible, even with large number of variables. We refer the reader to [NN90, BG93] and references therein. Note that the approach does not require quadratic stabilizability (the matrices X_i may be all *different*).

A drawback of the method is that it relies on an arbitrary choice of the state-feedback gain matrices K_i designed for each plant. Program (1) being infeasible does not imply that it would be so for another choice of the K_i's. Note that the success of the method outlined in [PGA91] also relies on the choice of an arbitrary matrix.

3 Performance specifications

We can impose several constraints on the closed-loop system, in addition to mere stabilization. These constraints include $\mathbf{H}_2$-norm constraints, $\mathbf{H}_\infty$-norm and scaled $\mathbf{H}_\infty$-norm constraints, and linear constraints on the matrices A_K,B_K,C_K,D_K themselves.

To illustrate this extension, consider the problem of minimizing the maximum of the scaled $\mathbf{H}_\infty$-norms of the square transfer matrices $T_{zw,i}(K) = C_{z,i}(sI - A - B_{u,i}KC_{y,i})^{-1}B_{w,i}$ by proper choice of the static output feedback gain matrix K. (Just as before, the approach easily generalizes to dynamic feedback.)

Precisely, we seek a control law $u = Ky$ which minimizes $\mu(K) = \max_i \mu_i(K)$, where $\mu_i(K)$ is a measure of robustness against nonlinear structured perturbations (see [BY89] for details):

$$\mu_i(K) \stackrel{\Delta}{=} \inf_{P\in\mathcal{P}} \|P^{1/2}T_{zw,i}P^{-1/2}\|_\infty .$$

Here, $\mathcal{P}$ is a set of positive-definite block-diagonal matrices, which defines the structure of the perturbations.

To adress this situation, Problem (1) should be modified as follows.

Problem 2 Find *matrices* $X_1, \ldots, X_p$, $P \in \mathcal{P}$ *and* F *such that, for all* i, $i = 1, \ldots, L$,

$$\begin{array}{l} X_i = X_i^T > 0, \\ (\tilde{A}_i + \tilde{B}_{u,i}K_i)^T X_i + X_i(\tilde{A}_i + \tilde{B}_{u,i}K_i) \\ +\frac{1}{\gamma^2}X_iB_{w,i}P^{-1}B_{w,i}^TX_i \\ +\tilde{C}_{z,i}^TPC_{z,i} + K_i^TPK_i < 0, \\ F\tilde{C}_{y,i} = -\tilde{B}_{u,i}^TX_i. \end{array} \qquad (3)$$

To a solution of this problem, if any, corresponds a static output matrix $K = -P^{-1}F$ which stabilizes the system while ensuring $\mu(K) < \gamma$. We note that the constraints above are readily transformed into LMIs. Minimizing γ subject to the constraints of Problem (2) is a "generalized eigenvalue minimization problem". This problem can be reliably solved (and its global minimum found) using for instance the algorithms of [NN93, BG93].

4 Concluding Remarks

The approach taken here provides a sufficient condition for a given set of plants to be stabilizable with a single reduced-order feedback controller, in terms of a set of LMIs. Quadratic stability is not required, at the expense of a large number of variables in the optimization program. Note there are now very efficient (polynomial-time) algorithms to solve LMIs. An attractive feature of this method is that $\mathbf{H}_2$-, $\mathbf{H}_\infty$-norm and structured singular value constraints can be included in the design, as well as decentralized control requirements and bounds on the gain matrix itself.

References

[Bar83] B. R. Barmish. Stabilization of uncertain systems via linear control. *IEEE Trans. Aut. Control*, AC-28(8):848–850, August 1983.

[BG93] S. Boyd and L. El Ghaoui. Method of centers for minimizing generalized eigenvalues. *Linear Algebra and Applications, special issue on Numerical Linear Algebra Methods in Control, Signals and Systems*, 188, July 1993.

[BGFB93] S. Boyd, L. El Ghaoui, E. Feron, and V. Balakrishnan. Linear matrix inequalities in systems and control theory, 1993. Monograph in preparation.

[BY89] S. Boyd and Q. Yang. Structured and simultaneous Lyapunov functions for system stability problems. *Int. J. Control*, 49(6):2215–2240, 1989.

[NN90] Yu. Nesterov and A. Nemirovsky. Self-concordant functions and polynomial time methods in convex programming. Technical report, Centr. Econ. & Math. Inst., USSR Acad. Sci., Moscow, USSR, April 1990.

[NN93] Yu. Nesterov and A. Nemirovsky. *Interior point polynomial methods in convex programming: Theory and applications.* SIAM, 1993.

[Pet87] I. R. Petersen. Disturbance attenuation and $\mathbf{H}_\infty$ optimization: A design method based on the algebraic Riccati equation. *IEEE Trans. Aut. Control*, AC-32(5):427–429, May 1987.

[PGA91] P. L .D. Peres, J. C. Geromel, and A. M .K Almuga. Quadratic stabilizability of uncertain systems by linear output feedback. In *European Control Conference*, pages 2262–2265, July 1991.

[VMP90] R.J. Veillette, J.V Medanic, and W.R Perkins. Computation of families of $\mathbf{H}_\infty$ control laws. In *Proc. IEEE Conf. on Decision and Control*, pages 00–00, December 1990.

[ZK88] K. Zhou and P. P. Khargonekar. Robust stabilization of linear systems with norm-bounded time-varying uncertainty. *Syst. Control Letters*, 10:17–20, 1988.

Proceedings of the
American Control Conference
San Francisco, California • June 1993

Rational $\mathcal{L}^1$ Suboptimal Compensators for Continuous–Time Systems

Franco Blanchini† and Mario Sznaier‡

Abstract

The persistent disturbance rejection problem ($\mathcal{L}^1$ Optimal Control) for continuous time–systems leads to non–rational compensators, even for SISO systems [1–3]. As noted in [2], the difficulty of physically implementing these controllers suggest that the most significant applications of the continuous time $\mathcal{L}^1$ theory is to furnish bounds for the achievable performance of discrete–time controllers. However, at the present time, there are no theoretical results relating the optimal l^1 norm of the discrete time system with the actual performance obtained when the controller is used in the continuous–time system. In this paper we use the theory of positively invariant sets to provide a design procedure, based upon the use of the discrete Euler approximating system, for suboptimal rational $\mathcal{L}^1$ controllers. The main results of the paper show that i) the $\mathcal{L}^1$ norm of the resulting continuous–time system is bounded above by the l^1 norm of the discrete–time counterpart and ii) the proposed rational compensators yield $\mathcal{L}^1$ cost arbitrarily close to the optimum, even in cases where the design procedure proposed in [2] fails due to the existence of plant zeros on the stability boundary.

1. Introduction

A large number of control problems involve designing a controller capable of stabilizing a given linear time invariant system while minimizing the worst case response to some exogenous disturbances. This problem is relevant for instance for disturbance rejection, tracking and robustness to model uncertainty (see [2] and references therein). When the exogenous disturbances are modeled as bounded energy signals and performance is measured in terms of the energy of the output, this problem leads to the well known $\mathcal{H}_\infty$ theory. The case where the signals involved are persistent bounded signals leads to the $\mathcal{L}^1$ optimal control theory, formulated and further explored by Vidyasagar [1, 3] and solved by Dahleh and Pearson both in the discrete [4] and continuous time [2] cases.

The $\mathcal{L}^1$ theory is appealing because it directly incorporates time–domain specifications. Moreover, it furnishes a complete solution to the robust performance problem [5]. However, in contrast with the discrete time l^1 theory, the solution to the continuous–time $\mathcal{L}^1$ optimal control problem leads to non–rational compensators, even for SISO systems. As noted in [2], the difficulty of physically implementing these controllers suggest that the most significant applications of the continuous time $\mathcal{L}^1$ theory is to provide bounds for the achievable performance of discrete–time controllers. In [6] a controller for a constrained continuous–time system was designed by first discretizing the system and then using l^1 techniques. However, at the present time, there is no theory relating the optimal value of the l^1 norm of the discretized system with the actual performance obtained when the discrete–time controller is implemented in the original continuous–time system.

In this paper we use the theory of positively invariant sets to provide a design procedure, based upon the use of the discrete Euler approximating system (EAS), for suboptimal rational $\mathcal{L}^1$ controllers. The main results of the paper show that i) the $\mathcal{L}^1$ norm of the resulting continuous–time system is bounded above by the l^1 norm of the discrete–time counterpart and ii) the optimal $\mathcal{L}^1$ system can be approximated arbitrarily close by a rational compensator related to the optimal l^1 compensator for the EAS.

† Dipartamento di Matematica e Informatica, Universita degli studi di Udine, Via Zannon 6, 33100, Udine, Italy.

‡ Electrical Engineering, University of Central Florida, Orlando, FL, 32816–2450. Author to whom all correspondence should be addressed.

Supported in part by NSF under grant ECS–9211169 and Florida Space Grant Consortium.

The paper is organized as follows: In section II we introduce the notation to be used and we restate the main results concerning the $\mathcal{L}^1$ problem. In section III we introduce the discrete time Euler approximating system and we propose a method for designing suboptimal rational controllers, yielding cost arbitrarily close to the optimal $\mathcal{L}^1$ cost, based upon the use of the optimal l^1 theory for the EAS. In section IV we present a simple design example and we compare our controller to the optimal $\mathcal{L}^1$ controller. Finally, in section V, we summarize our results.

2. Preliminaries

2.1 Notation

By $\mathcal{L}_\infty$ we denote the Lebesgue space of complex valued transfer matrices which are essentially bounded on the imaginary axis with norm $\|T(z)\|_\infty \stackrel{\Delta}{=} \sigma_{\max}(T(jw)).\mathcal{H}_\infty$ denotes the set of stable complex matrices $G(s) \in \mathcal{L}_\infty$, i.e analytic in $\Re(s) \geq 0$. $\mathcal{RH}_\infty$ denotes the subset of $\mathcal{H}_\infty$formed by real rational transfer matrices. l_∞ denotes the space of bounded real sequences $\{e_k\}$ equipped with the norm $\|e\|_\infty \stackrel{\Delta}{=} \sup_k |e_k|$. l^1 denotes the space of real sequences, equipped with the norm $\|q\|_1 = \sum_{k=0}^{\infty} |q_k| < \infty$. $\mathcal{L}^p(R_+)$ denotes the space of measurable functions $f(t)$ equipped with the norm: $\|f\|_p = \left(\int_0^\infty |f(t)|^p dt\right)^{\frac{1}{p}} < \infty$. $\mathcal{RL}^1$ denotes the subset of $\mathcal{L}^1$ formed by matrices with real rational Laplace Transform. Given a function $q(t) \in \mathcal{L}^1$ we will denote its Laplace transform by $Q(s) \in \mathcal{L}_\infty$. Throughout the paper we will use packed notation to represent state–space realizations, i.e.

$$G(s) = C(sI-A)^{-1}B + D \stackrel{\Delta}{=} \left(\begin{array}{c|c} A & B \\ \hline C & D \end{array}\right)$$

Finally, given two transfer matrices $T = \begin{pmatrix} T_{11} & T_{12} \\ T_{21} & T_{22} \end{pmatrix}$ and Q with appropriate dimensions, the lower *linear fractional transformation* is defined as:

$$\mathcal{F}_l(T,Q) \stackrel{\Delta}{=} T_{11} + T_{12}Q(I-T_{22}Q)^{-1}T_{21}$$

2.2 The $\mathcal{L}^1$ Optimal Control Problem

Consider the system represented by the block diagram 1, where S represents the system to be controlled; the scalar signals $w \in \mathcal{L}^\infty$ and u represent an exogenous disturbance and the control action respectively; and where ζ and y represent the output subject to performance constraints and the measurements available to the controller respectively. As usual we will assume, without loss of generality, that any weights have been absorbed in the plant S. Then, the $\mathcal{L}^1$ optimal control problem can be stated as: Given the system (S) find an internally stabilizing controller

$$u(s) = K(s)y(s) \qquad (C)$$

such that the worst case (over the set of all $w(t) \in \mathcal{L}^\infty$, $\|w\|_\infty \leq 1$) maximum amplitude of the performance output $\hat{z}(t)$ is minimized.

2.3 Problem Transformation

Assume that the system S has the following state–space realization:

$$\left(\begin{array}{c|cc} A & B_1 & B_2 \\ \hline C_1 & D_{11} & D_{12} \\ C_2 & D_{21} & D_{22} \end{array}\right) \qquad (S)$$

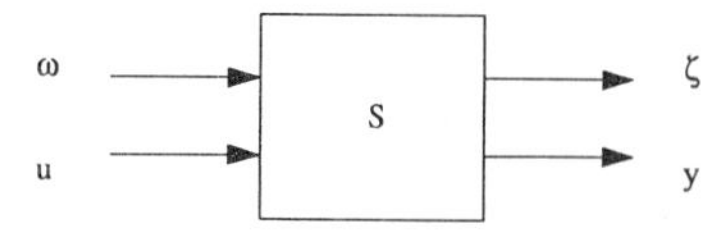

Fig. 1. The Generalized Plant

where the pairs (A, B_2) and (C_2, A) are stabilizable and detectable respectively. It is well known (see for instance [7]) that the set of all internally stabilizing controllers can be parametrized in terms of a free parameter $Q \in \mathcal{H}_\infty$ as:

$$K = \mathcal{F}_l(J, Q) \tag{1}$$

where J has the following state-space realization:

$$\left(\begin{array}{c|cc} A + B_2F + LC_2 + LD_{22}F & -L & B_2 + LD_{22}R_b \\ \hline F & 0 & R_b \\ -R_c(C_2 + D_{22}F) & R_c & -R_cD_{22}R_b \end{array}\right) \tag{J}$$

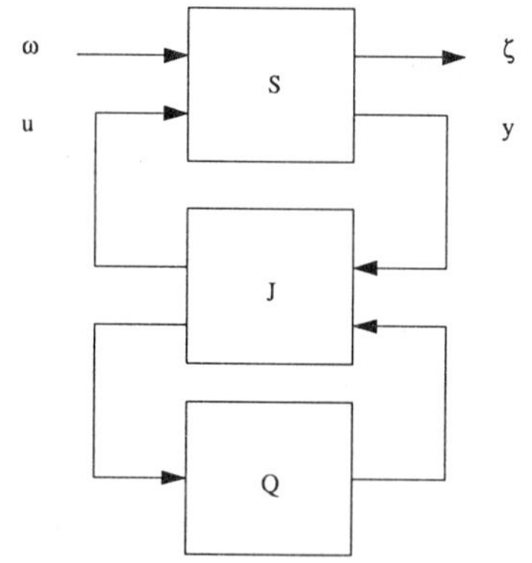

Figure 2. Parametrization of all Stabilizing Controllers

where F and L are selected such that $A + B_2F$ and $A + LC_2$ are stable and R_b and R_c are free non-singular matrices than can be used, for instance, to obtain an inner-outer factorization. By using this parametrization, the closed-loop transfer function $T_{\zeta w}$ can be written as :

$$T_{\zeta w} = \mathcal{F}_l(T, Q) = T_{11} + T_{12}QT_{21} \tag{2}$$

where $T_i \in \mathcal{RH}_\infty$ and where T has the following state-space realization:

$$T_f = \left(\begin{array}{cc|cc} A_F & -B_2F & B_1 & B_2R_b \\ 0 & A_L & B_1 + LD_{21} & 0 \\ \hline C_f + D_{12}F & -D_{12}F & D_{11} & D_{12}R_b \\ 0 & R_cC_2 & R_cD_{21} & 0 \end{array}\right) \tag{3}$$

$A_F = A + B_2F$
$A_L = A + LC_2$

For the SISO case, equation (2) reduces to:

$$T_{\zeta w}(s) = T_1(s) + T_2(s)Q(s) \tag{4}$$

where $T_2(s) = T_{12}(s)T_{21}(s)$. Finally, assume that the following conditions hold:

A1) D_{12} has full column rank and D_{21} has full row rank.

A2) $\begin{pmatrix} A - jwI & B_2 \\ C_1 & D_{12} \end{pmatrix}$ has full column rank for all ω

A3) $\begin{pmatrix} A - j\omega I & B_1 \\ C_2 & D_{21} \end{pmatrix}$ has full row rank for all ω.

These assumptions guarantee that the problem is well-posed: (A1) guarantees that T_{12} and T_{21} have full rank at infinity, while (A2) and (A3) rule-out the existence of zeros on the $j\omega$-axis. By using this parametrization the $\mathcal{L}^1$ control problem can be now precisely stated as solving:

$$\mu^o = \inf_{Q \in \mathcal{H}_\infty} \|T_1 + T_2 * Q\|_1$$

where $*$ denotes convolution and where $T_2(s)$ does not have zeros on the $j\omega$-axis.

- **Theorem 1:** Dahleh and Pearson, [2]Let $T_2(s)$ have n distinct zeros z_k in the open right-half plane and no zeros on the jw-axis. Then:

$$\mu^o = \inf_{K stab} \|T_1 + T_2 * Q\|_1$$
$$= \max_{\alpha_j} \left[\sum_{i=1}^{n} \alpha_i Re\{T_1(z_i)\} + \sum_{i=1}^{n} \alpha_{i+n} Im\{T_1(z_i)\} \right] \tag{5}$$

subject to:

$$\left| \sum_{i=1}^{n} \alpha_i Re\{e^{-z_i t}\} + \sum_{i=1}^{n} \alpha_{i+n} Im\{e^{-z_i t}\} \right| \leq 1 \; \forall t \in \mathcal{R}_+ \tag{6}$$

Furthermore, the optimal error ϕ has the following form:

$$\phi = \sum_{i=0}^{m} \phi_i \delta(t - t_i), \; t_i \in \mathcal{R}_+, \quad \text{m finite}$$
$$\{\phi_i\} \in l^1, \; \|\phi\|_1 = \sum_{i=0}^{m} |\phi_i| \tag{7}$$

and satisfies the interpolation condition:

$$\Phi(z_k) = \sum_{i=0}^{m} \phi_i e^{-z_k t_i} = T_1(z_k), \; k = 1, \ldots, n$$

Remark 1: From (7) it follows that the optimal Q, and hence the optimal compensator K, have non-rational Laplace transforms.

2.4 Existence of Suboptimal Rational Controllers

In this section we consider the problem of approximating the optimal cost μ^o with controllers in $\mathcal{RL}^1$. First note that, without loss of generality, we can assume $t_k = (k-1)T$, $T > 0, k = 1, \ldots, n$. Indeed, from Theorem 9 in [2] it follows that, given $\delta > 0$, we can take T small enough and ϕ_i such that the corresponding cost μ satisfies $\mu^o \leq \mu \leq \mu^o(1 + \delta)$. Define:

$$f_i^\epsilon(t) = \begin{cases} \frac{1}{\epsilon}, & t \in [t_i - \frac{\epsilon}{2}, t_i + \frac{\epsilon}{2}]; \\ 0, & \text{otherwise.} \end{cases}$$

$$f^\epsilon(t) = \sum_{i=0}^{m} f_i^\epsilon \phi_i$$

It is immediate that $f_i^\epsilon \in \mathcal{L}^1$ and, for $\epsilon \leq T$,

$$\|f^\epsilon\|_1 = \sup_{v \in \mathcal{L}^\infty, \|v\|=1} \|f^\epsilon * v\|_\infty = \|\phi\|_1$$

Moreover, it is easily shown that for ϵ small enough there exist ϕ_i^ϵ such that $\hat{f}(t) = \sum_{i=0}^{m} \phi_i^\epsilon f_i^\epsilon(t)$ satisfies the interpolation constraints:

$$\hat{F}(z_k) = T_1(z_k) \; k = 1, \ldots n$$

and such that $\phi_i^\epsilon \to \phi_i$ as $\epsilon \to 0$. Finally, since the set of functions with rational Laplace transfer functions is dense in $\mathcal{L}^1$ [8] it can be shown (see Appendix A) that given $\eta > 0$ small enough, there exist a function $f^r(t) \in \mathcal{RL}^1$ such that $\|f^r(t) - f^\epsilon(t)\|_1 \leq \eta$ and such that $f^r(t)$ satisfies the interpolation constraints. It follows that the suboptimal error $f^r(t)$ can then be achieved by the stabilizing rational compensator $Q(s) = \frac{F^r(s) - T_1(s)}{T_2(s)}$. These results are summarized in the following lemma:

- **Lemma 1:** Suppose that the $\mathcal{L}^1$ optimal control problem has a (non rational) solution with optimal cost μ^o. Then, for any $\mu^r > \mu^o$ there exist a suboptimal internally stabilizing compensator $K^r \in \mathcal{RL}^1$ such that the resulting closed loop transfer function satisfies $\|T_{\zeta w}\|_1 \leq \mu^r$.

3. Problem Solution

Although Lemma 1 guarantees the existence of a suboptimal rational compensator, the proof is not constructive. In this section we address the issue of finding a suboptimal rational controller. To that effect we introduce the concepts of the Euler Approximating System (EAS) and of positively invariant sets [9].

3.1 Definitions

• **Def. 1:** Consider the continuous time system (S). Then, the Euler Approximating System is defined as the following discrete time system:

$$\left(\begin{array}{c|cc} I+\tau A & \tau B_1 & \tau B_2 \\ \hline C_1 & D_{11} & D_{12} \\ C_2 & D_{21} & D_{22} \end{array}\right) \qquad (EAS)$$

where $\tau > 0$.

• **Def. 2:** Consider the following system:

$$\dot{x}(t) = Ax(t) + Bv(t) \qquad (8)$$

where $x \in R^n$ and $v(t) \in \Omega \subset R^m$. A set $\Sigma \subset R^n$ is a *positively invariant set* of (8) if for any initial condition $x_o \in \Sigma$ and for any $v(t)$ the corresponding trajectory $x(t, x_o, v(t)) \in \Sigma$ for all t. A similar definition holds for the case of discrete-time systems.

3.2 Proposed Design Method

In this section we introduce a method for finding suboptimal rational controllers yielding cost arbitrarily close to the optimal. An additional advantage of this method is that it can be used to remove the ill-posedness arising from the existence of zeros on the jw-axis.

• **Theorem 2:** Consider the system:

$$\begin{aligned} \dot{x} &= Ax + B_1 v \\ \hat{z} &= C_1 x + D_{11} v \end{aligned} \qquad (9)$$

Assume that the corresponding (EAS):

$$\begin{aligned} x_{k+1} &= (I+\tau A)x_k + \tau B_1 v_k \\ \hat{z}_k &= C_1 x_k + D_{11} v_k \end{aligned} \qquad (10)$$

is asymptotically stable and such that:

$$\|T^{(EAS)}_{\hat{z}v}\|_1 = \sup_{\substack{v\in l^\infty,\ \|v\|\le 1 \\ x_o=0}} \|\hat{z}_k\|_\infty = \mu_E(\tau)$$

Then the system (9) is asymptotically stable and such that:

$$\|T_{\hat{z}v}\|_1 = \sup_{\substack{v\in \mathcal{L}^\infty,\ \|v\|\le 1 \\ x_o=0}} \|\hat{z}(t)\|_\infty \triangleq \mu_c \le \mu_E(\tau)$$

Conversely, if (9) is asymptotically stable and $\|T_{\hat{z}v}\|_1 \triangleq \mu_c$ then for all $\mu > \mu_c$ there exists $\tau^* > 0$ such that for all $0 < \tau \le \tau^*$ the EAS (9) is asymptotically stable and such that $\|T^{(EAS)}_{\hat{z}w}\|_1 \le \mu$.

Proof: The proof of the Theorem is given in Appendix B.

• **Theorem 3:** Consider a strictly decreasing sequence $\tau_i \to 0$, and the corresponding EAS. Let $\mu_i = \inf_{K\,stabilizing} \|T^{(EAS)}_{\hat{z}w}\|_1$ denote the optimal l^1 cost for the closed-loop system. Then the sequence μ_i is non-increasing and such that $\mu_i \to \mu^o$, the optimal $\mathcal{L}^1$ cost.

Proof: The proof will be split into two parts. First we show that the sequence μ_i is non-increasing. To this aim, let $\Sigma_E(\tau)$ denote the closure of the origin-reachable domain of (10) with the bounded input $|v| \le 1$ and define:

$$\begin{aligned} Z(\epsilon) &\triangleq \left\{x : \|C_1 x + D_{11} v\|_\infty \le \epsilon \text{ for all } \|v\| \le 1\right\} \\ \mu_i &\triangleq \min\{\epsilon > 0 : \Sigma_E(\tau_i) \subseteq Z(\epsilon)\} \end{aligned} \qquad (11)$$

The set $\Sigma_E(\tau_i)$ is positively invariant for the EAS. Therefore, denoting by $\partial\Sigma_E(\tau_i)$ the boundary of $\Sigma_E(\tau_i)$, we have that for all $x \in \partial\Sigma_E(\tau_i)$ and all $\|v\| \le 1$:

$$(I + \tau_i A)x + \tau_i B_1 v \in \Sigma_E(\tau_i)$$

and, by convexity, for $0 < \tau_{i+1} < \tau_i$ we have:

$$(I + \tau_{i+1} A)x + \tau_{i+1} B_1 v \in \Sigma_E(\tau_i)$$

Hence $\Sigma_E(\tau_i)$ is positively invariant for (10) [10], with $\tau = \tau_{i+1}$. Since $\Sigma_E(\tau_i)$ contains the origin, then it includes $\Sigma_E(\tau_{i+1})$ so $\Sigma_E(\tau_{i+1}) \subseteq \Sigma_E(\tau_i) \subseteq Z(\mu_i)$. It follows that:

$$\mu_{i+1} = \min\left\{\epsilon : \Sigma(\tau_{i+1}) \subseteq Z(\epsilon)\right\} \le \mu_i$$

Since μ_i is a non-increasing sequence, bounded below by μ^o (from Theorem 2), it follows that it has a limit $\mu^* \ge \mu^o$. Since from Lemma 1 we have that the optimal cost μ^o can be arbitrarily approximated with a rational controller, it follows from the second part of Theorem 2 that $\mu^* = \mu^o$ $\diamond$.

Next, we recall the main result regarding the SISO discrete-time l^1 Optimal Control Problem:

• **Theorem 4:** Dahleh and Pearson, [2]Let $T_2(z)$ have n distinct zeros z_k outside the closed unit disk. Then:

$$\begin{aligned} \mu^o_d &= \inf_{K\,stab} \|T_1(z) + T_2(z) * Q(z)\|_1 \\ &= \max_{\alpha_j} \left[\sum_{i=1}^n \alpha_i Re\{T_1(z_i)\} + \sum_{i=1}^n \alpha_{i+n} Im\{T_1(z_i)\}\right] \end{aligned} \qquad (12)$$

subject to:

$$\left|\sum_{i=1}^n \alpha_i Re\{z_i^{-k}\} + \sum_{i=1}^n \alpha_{i+n} Im\{z_i^{-k}\}\right| \triangleq r_k \le 1 \quad k = 0, 1, \ldots \qquad (13)$$

Furthermore, the optimal error ϕ satisfies:

$$\begin{aligned} &\phi_k = 0, \quad \text{whenever } |r_k| < 1 \\ &\phi_k r_k \ge 0 \\ &\sum_{k=0}^\infty |\phi_k| = \mu^o_d \\ &\sum_{k=0}^\infty \phi_k z_i^{-k} = T_1(z_i), \quad \text{for all } i = 1, \ldots, n \end{aligned} \qquad (14)$$

From (14) it follows that only finitely many ϕ_i are non-zero. Since $T_1(z)$, $T_2(z)$ are rational, it follows that the optimal compensator is also rational.

Finally, we relate the closed-loop transfer functions of (9) and its EAS (10). From the definitions it is easily seen that the closed-loop transfer function obtained by applying the rational compensator $K(s)$ to (9) is the same as the closed loop transfer function obtained by applying the compensator $K(\frac{z-1}{\tau})$ to the EAS (10) up to the complex transformation $z = \tau s + 1$. Therefore, if a rational compensator $K(z)$ yielding an l^1 cost μ_E is found for (10), then $K(\tau s + 1)$ internally stabilizes (9) and yields an $\mathcal{L}^1$ cost $\mu_c \le \mu_E$. It follows that a rational compensator can be synthesized using the EAS with suitably small τ. By combining this observation with the results of Theorems 2, 3 and 4, we can state now the main result of this section.

• **Theorem 5:** Consider the $\mathcal{L}^1$ Optimal Control Problem for SISO continuous time-systems. A suboptimal rational solution, with cost arbitrarily close to the optimal cost, can be obtained by solving a discrete-time l^1 optimal control problem for the corresponding EAS. Moreover, if $K(z)$ denotes the optimal l^1 compensator for the EAS, the suboptimal $\mathcal{L}^1$ compensator is given by $K(\tau s + 1)$.

Remark 2: The transformation $1+\tau s$ maps the imaginary axis, except the origin, outside the unit disk. Hence, our approach maps plant zeros on $(-j\infty, j\infty) - \{0\}$ outside the unit disk, providing a guaranteed cost rational continuos-time compensator in the cases in which the optimal $\mathcal{L}^1$ theory developed in [2] fails. In particular, it provides rational continuous-time compensators for strictly proper continuous-time plants which have no zeros at the origin. In this case, in view of Theorem 1, we can achieve a cost which is arbitrarily close to the infimum of the set of all costs associated with rational compensators.

4. A Simple Example

Consider the SISO plant used in [2]:

$$P(s) = \frac{s-1}{s-2}$$

and assume that the output and measurement equations are given by:

$$\begin{aligned} \hat{z} &= Pu \\ y &= -Pu + v \end{aligned}$$

where $v \in \mathcal{L}^\infty$. Then the system (S) can be represented by the following state–space realization:

$$\left(\begin{array}{c|cc} 2 & 0 & 1 \\ \hline 1 & 0 & 1 \\ -1 & 1 & -1 \end{array}\right) \qquad (S)$$

The optimal $\mathcal{L}^1$ controller is given by [2]:

$$K_{\mathcal{L}^1} = \frac{(s-2)(1.7071 - 4.1213e^{-0.8814s})}{(s-1)(-0.7071 + 4.1213e^{-0.8814s})} \qquad (15)$$

and yields and optimal cost $\mu^o = 5.8284$. For $\tau = 0.1$ the EAS is given by:

$$\left(\begin{array}{c|cc} 1.2 & 0 & 0.1 \\ \hline 1 & 0 & 1 \\ -1 & 1 & -1 \end{array}\right) \qquad (EAS)$$

and the Youla parametrization with $F = -2.9091$ and $L = 0.3667$ yields:

$$T = \left(\begin{array}{cc|cc} 0.9091 & 0.2909 & 0 & 0.0909 \\ 0 & 0.8333 & 0.3667 & 0 \\ \hline -1.9091 & 2.9091 & 0 & 0.9091 \\ 0 & -0.8333 & 0.8333 & 0 \end{array}\right)$$

$$J = \left(\begin{array}{c|cc} 1.6091 & -0.3667 & -0.2424 \\ \hline -2.9091 & 0 & 0.9091 \\ -1.5909 & 0.8333 & 0.7576 \end{array}\right)$$

Hence we have that:

$$\begin{aligned} T_1 &= \frac{176(z-1.1)}{125(1.1z-1)(1.2z-1)} \\ T_2 &= \frac{(z-1.1)(z-1.2)}{(1.1z-1)(1.2z-1)} \\ T_{\zeta w} &= T_1 + T_2 Q \end{aligned} \qquad (16)$$

Solving for the optimal l^1 compensator yields optimal cost $\mu_d = 6.184$ and optimal error:

$$\phi(z) = 1.8414 - 4.3423z^{-9}$$

The corresponding optimal Q and compensator K_{EAS} are given by:

$$\begin{aligned} Q(z) &= 2.4309 - 0.0525z^{-1} + 0.0607z^{-2} + 0.2089z^{-3} + 0.4004z^{-4} \\ &+ 0.6542z^{-5} + 0.9554z^{-6} + 1.3458z^{-7} + 1.8343z^{-8} - 3.2895z^{-9} \\ K_{EAS} &= \mathcal{F}_l(J, Q) \end{aligned} \qquad (17)$$

Finally, the transformation $z = \tau s + 1$ yields the corresponding compensator for the continuous time system. Although in principle the suboptimal compensator has order 10, by using model reduction techniques we were able to obtain a 4th order compensator yielding a virtually identical impulse response. The closed loop system obtained with the reduced order compensator is given by:

$$T_{\zeta v} = \left(\begin{array}{ccccc|c} 0.1581 & 1.0571 & -1.0913 & 1.3769 & 0.5489 & 1.8419 \\ -1.0571 & 0.6387 & 5.7817 & 0.1740 & -0.0412 & 1.0571 \\ -1.0913 & -5.7817 & -2.3301 & 4.6435 & 1.6090 & 1.0913 \\ -1.3769 & 0.1740 & -4.6435 & -5.3510 & -6.1230 & 1.3769 \\ 0.5489 & 0.0412 & 1.6090 & 6.1230 & -9.2009 & -0.5489 \\ \hline -0.8419 & 1.0571 & -1.0913 & 1.3769 & 0.5489 & 1.8419 \end{array}\right)$$

and it is easily shown that $\|T_{\zeta w}\|_1 = |D| + \int_0^\infty |Ce^{At}B|dt = 6.184$.

5. Conclusions

A recent research effort [1–4] has lead to techniques for designing optimal compensators that minimize the worst case output amplitude with respect to all inputs of bounded amplitude. In the discrete-time SISO case, minimizing the l^1 norm of the closed-loop impulse response yields a rational compensator. Unfortunately, the solution to the continuous-time version of the problem is non–rational. Thus, given the difficulty of physically implementing a system with a non–rational transfer function, in most cases this theory is primarily used to furnish a performance limit for any linear feedback compensator.

In this paper, we have proposed a suboptimal design technique which enables to compute near-optimal *continuous-time* compensators by applying the l^1 theory to the Euler forward approximating system, hence resulting in a rational compensator. We have shown that the continuous-time cost is upper bounded by the l^1 cost and that the cost of the resulting suboptimal closed-loop system converges to the optimal one as the sampling time goes to zero.

One appealing feature of our technique is that, through the use of the simple transformation $z = \tau s + 1$, it removes the ill-posedness due to the presence of zeros on the imaginary axis (except for those at the origin). This property allows us to obtain a guaranteed cost compensator even in the cases (such as strictly proper plants) where the $\mathcal{L}^1$ theory developed in [2] is not applicable.

References

[1]. M. Vidyasagar "Optimal Rejection of Persistent Bounded Disturbances," *IEEE Trans. Autom. Contr.*, 31, pp. 527–535, June 1986.

[2]. M. A. Dahleh and J. B. Pearson "$\mathcal{L}^1$-Optimal Compensators for Continuous–Time Systems," *IEEE Trans. Autom. Contr.*, 32, pp. 889–895, October 1987.

[3]. M Vidyasagar "Further Results on the Optimal Rejection of Persistent Bounded Disturbances", *IEEE Trans. Autom. Contr.*, 36, pp. 642–652, June 1991.

[4]. M. A. Dahleh and J. B. Pearson "l^1-Optimal Feedback Controllers for MIMO Discrete–Time Systems," *IEEE Trans. Autom. Contr.*, 32, pp. 314–322, April 1987.

[5]. M. Khammash and J. B. Pearson "Performance Robustness of Discrete–Time Systems with Structured Uncertainty," *IEEE Trans. Autom. Contr.*, 36, pp. 398–412, April 1991.

[6]. J. B. Pearson and B. Bamieh "On Minimizing Maximum Errors," *IEEE Trans. Autom. Contr.*, 35, pp. 598–601, May 1990

[7]. J. Doyle "Lecture Notes in Advances in Multivariable Control," *ON-R/Honeywell Workshop*, Minneapolis, MN., 1984.

[8]. D. W. Kammler "Approximation with Sums of Exponentials in $\mathcal{L}^p$ $[0, \infty)$, *Journal of Approximation Theory*, 16, pp. 385–408, 1976.

[9]. J. P Lasalle "The Stability and Control of Discrete Processes," *Vol 62 in Applied Mathematics Series*, Springer–Verlag, New–York, 1986.

[10]. F. Blanchini "Constrained Control for Uncertain Linear Systems," *Journal of Optimization Theory and Applications*, 71, 3, pp/ 465–483, 1991.

[11]. J. P. Aubin and A. Cellina "Differential Inclusions," Springer–Verlag, Berlin, 1984.

Appendix A: Proof of Lemma 1

Consider a strictly decreasing sequence $\epsilon_j \to 0$ and define:

$$\mathcal{F} \triangleq \begin{pmatrix} e^{-z_1 t_1} & \dots & e^{-z_1 t_n} \\ \vdots & & \vdots \\ e^{-z_m t_1} & \dots & e^{-z_m t_n} \end{pmatrix}$$
$$\mathcal{F}^{\epsilon_j} \triangleq \begin{pmatrix} F_1^{\epsilon_j}(z_1) & \dots & F_n^{\epsilon_j}(z_1) \\ \vdots & & \vdots \\ F_1^{\epsilon_j}(z_m) & \dots & F_n^{\epsilon_j}(z_m) \end{pmatrix} \qquad (A1)$$
$$t_i = (i-1)T, \; n \geq m$$

Since all z_k are distinct, T can be selected such that $e^{-z_i T} \neq e^{-z_j T}$, $i \neq j$. It follows that $\mathcal{F}$ has full row rank since it contains a Vandermonde matrix. We will show that there exists J such that $\mathcal{F}^{\epsilon_j}$ has full row rank for all $j \geq J$. Assume, to the contrary, that there exist a sequence $\mathcal{J} = \{j_1, j_2, \ldots\}$ such that for $j \in \mathcal{J}$, $\mathcal{F}^{\epsilon_j}$ does not have full row rank. Then, there exists $\lambda^j, \|\lambda^j\|_\infty = 1$, such that $\lambda^j \mathcal{F}^{\epsilon_j} = 0$. Thus, since $\epsilon_i \to 0$ and z_k, $k = 1, \ldots, m$ are in the open right half plane, we have that for any $\delta > 0$ there exists J such that:

$$\begin{aligned} |\sum_{i=0}^{m} \lambda_i^j e^{-z_i t_k}| &= |\sum_{i=o}^{m} \lambda_i^j (e^{-z_i t_k} - F_k^{\epsilon_j}(z_i))| \\ &\leq \sum_{i=0}^{m} \|\lambda^j\|_\infty |e^{-z_i t_k} - F_k^{\epsilon_j}(z_i)| \\ &\leq \sum_{i=o}^{m} |e^{-z_i t_k}||1 - \frac{e^{\frac{z_i \epsilon_j}{2}} - e^{\frac{-z_i \epsilon_j}{2}}}{z_i \epsilon_j}| \\ &\leq O^3(z_i \epsilon_j) \leq \delta \; \forall j \in \mathcal{J}, \, j \geq J, \, k = 1, \ldots n \end{aligned} \qquad (A2)$$

Since $\|\lambda^j\|_\infty = 1$, the sequence λ^j has an accumulation point $\hat{\lambda}$ such that $\|\hat{\lambda}\|_\infty = 1$ and $\hat{\lambda}\mathcal{F} = 0$. But this contradicts the fact that $\mathcal{F}$ has full row rank. Hence there exist coefficients ϕ_i^ϵ such that $\hat{f}(t) = \sum_{i=1}^{m} \phi_i^\epsilon f_i^\epsilon(t)$ satisfies the interpolation constraints $\hat{F}(z_k) = T_1(z_k)$. Moreover, since $\lim_{\epsilon \to 0} F_k^\epsilon(z) = e^{-z t_k}$ it follows that ϕ_i^ϵ can be selected such that $\phi_i^\epsilon \to \phi_i$. Hence $\|\hat{f}\|_1 \to \|\phi\|_1$. To complete the proof consider a sequence F_i^j of rational approximations to F_i^ϵ (in the l_1 topology) and define

$$\mathcal{F}^j \triangleq \begin{pmatrix} F_1^j(z_1) & \dots & F_n^j(z_1) \\ \vdots & & \vdots \\ F_1^j(z_m) & \dots & F_n^j(z_m) \end{pmatrix}$$

since:

$$|F_i^j(z_k) - F_i^\epsilon(z_k)| \leq \int_0^\infty |f_i^j(t) - f_i^\epsilon(t)| dt = \|f_i^j - f_i^\epsilon\|_1$$

a similar argument shows that there exist J such that $\mathcal{F}^j$ has full row rank for $j \geq J$. It follows that, for any $\eta > 0$, there exist ϕ_i^r such that $f^r(t) = \sum_{i=1}^{m} \phi_i^r f_i^r(t)$ satisfies $\|f^r\|_1 - \|\phi\|_1 \leq \eta$; $F^r(s)$ is rational; and satisfies the interpolation constraints $F^r(z_k) = T_1(z_k)$. The suboptimal rational compensator is given by $Q(s) = \frac{F^r(s) - T_1(s)}{T_2(s)}$ ◇.

Appendix B: Proof of Theorem 2

Denote by Λ the set of eigenvalues of A and define $\theta(\Lambda) \triangleq \min_{\lambda \in \Lambda} 2[\frac{-re(\lambda)}{|\lambda|^2}]$. Then (10) is asymptotically stable if and only if (9) is stable and $0 < \tau < \theta(\Lambda)$. Therefore, if A is asymptotically stable then (9) must be so. Let Σ_C and $\Sigma_E(\tau)$ denote the closures of the origin–reachable sets of (9) and (10), with $\|v\| \leq 1$. It follows that $\mu_C = \min\{\epsilon : \Sigma_C \subseteq Z(\epsilon)\}$ and $\mu_E = \min\{\epsilon : \Sigma_E(\tau) \subseteq Z(\epsilon)\}$, where $Z(\epsilon)$ is defined in (11). The set $\Sigma_E(\tau)$ is convex and positively invariant for (10) so, denoting by $\partial\Sigma_E(\tau)$ its boundary we must have that for $x \in \partial\Sigma_E(\tau)$ and for all v such that $\|v\| \leq 1$:

$$(I + \tau A)x + \tau B_1 v \in \Sigma_E(\tau) \qquad (B1)$$

Let $C_{\Sigma_E(\tau)}(x)$ denote the tangent cone to $\Sigma_E(\tau)$ at x. From the convexity of $\Sigma_E(\tau)$ and $(B1)$ it follows that:

$$Ax + B_1 v \in C_{\Sigma_E(\tau)}(x) \qquad (B2)$$

This condition implies [11] that the set $\Sigma_E(\tau)$ is a positively invariant set for (9). Since $\Sigma_E(\tau)$ contains the origin, it follows that it must contain Σ_C. Hence $\Sigma_C \subseteq \Sigma_E(\tau) \subseteq Z(\mu_E(\tau))$ and $\mu_C \leq \mu_E(\tau)$.

To prove the second part of the theorem consider the asymptotically stable continuous time systems:

$$\dot{x} = Ax + B_1 v + \delta w \qquad (B3)$$

$$\dot{x} = Ax + \delta w \qquad (B4)$$

where $w(t) \in \mathcal{L}^\infty$, $\|w(t)\| \leq 1$ is a fictitious disturbance and δ is a positive weighting parameter. Denote by $\Sigma_C^*(\delta)$ and $\Sigma_W(\delta)$ the closures of the respective origin–reachable sets. Then $\Sigma_C^*(\delta)$ is given by the Minkowsky sum of Σ_C and $\Sigma_W(\delta)$. Note that the asymptotic stability of A guarantees that these sets are compact.

For $\mu > \mu_c$ the set $Z(\mu)$ contains $Z(\mu_C)$ in its interior so, by an appropriate choice of δ the set $\Sigma_w(\delta)$ can be made small enough to guarantee that $\Sigma_C^*(\delta) \subseteq Z(\mu)$. To complete the proof, we show that there exists τ^* such that for any $0 < \tau \leq \tau^*$, the set $\Sigma_C^*(\delta)$ is a positively invariant set of (10). Indeed, if this is the case then, since $\Sigma_C^*(\delta)$ contains the origin, it also contains the set $\Sigma_E(\tau)$ and therefore $\Sigma_E(\tau) \subseteq Z(\mu)$. It follows that $\mu_E(\tau) \leq \mu$. The set $\Sigma_C^*(\delta)$ contains the origin in its interior since (B3) is controllable from the input w. Since $\Sigma_C^*(\delta)$ is invariant for (B3), for each $x \in \partial\Sigma_C^*(\delta)$, and for all $\|v\| \leq 1$, $\|w\| \leq 1$, the vector $Ax + B_1 v + \delta w$ belongs to the tangent cone to $\Sigma_C^*(\delta)$ at x. It follows that there exists a strictly positive τ such that:

$$x + \tau(Ax + B_1 v) \in int[\Sigma_C^*(\delta)], \; \forall \|v\| \leq 1 \qquad (B5)$$

where $int(.)$ denotes the interior of the set. Define:

$$\tau(x) = \sup\left\{\tau : x + \tau[Ax + B_1 v] \in \Sigma_C^*(\delta) \; \forall \|v\| \leq 1\right\}$$

Since $\Sigma_C^*(\delta)$ is convex and $x \in \partial\Sigma_C^*(\delta)$ if (B5) holds for some $\tau > 0$, then it holds for all $0 < \tau \leq \tau(x)$ and in particular:

$$\chi = x + \frac{\tau(x)}{2}[Ax + B_1 v] \in int[\Sigma_C^*(\delta)] \; \forall \|v\| \leq 1 \qquad (B6)$$

Finally, we show that $\tau(x)$ is bounded below by a positive number as x varies on the boundary of $\Sigma_C^*(\delta)$. By contradiction, assume that there exist sequences $x_k \in \partial\Sigma_C^*(\delta)$, v_k, $\|v_k\| \leq 1$ and $\tau_k > 0, \tau_k \to 0$, such that :

$$x_k + \tau_k(Ax_k + B_1 v_k) \notin \Sigma_C^*(\delta) \qquad (B7)$$

Since $\partial\Sigma_C^*(\delta)$ and $\mathcal{B} \triangleq \{v : \|v_k\| \leq 1\}$ are compact sets, the sequence $\{x_k, v_k\} \in \partial\Sigma_C^*(\delta) \times \mathcal{B}$ contains a subsequence converging to a point $(\underline{x}, \underline{v})$. Hence, without loss of generality we can assume that $x_k \to \underline{x}$ and $v_k \to \underline{v}$. Select κ such that $0 < \tau_k < \frac{1}{2}\tau(\underline{x})$ for $k > \kappa$. Since $\Sigma_C^*(\delta)$ is convex and $x_k \in \partial\Sigma_C^*(\delta)$, (B7) implies that:

$$\chi_k = x_k + \frac{1}{2}\tau(\underline{x})(Ax_k + B_1 v_k) \notin \Sigma_C^*(\delta) \text{ for } k > \kappa$$

which, in view of the convergence of x_k and v_k, contradicts (B6). Therefore, there exists $\tau' > 0$ such that for $0 < \tau < \tau'$, (B5) holds for all $x \in \partial\Sigma_C^*(\delta)$. It follows [10] that $\Sigma_C^*(\delta)$ is a positively invariant set for (10).The proof is completed by selecting $\tau^* = \min\left\{\tau', \theta(\Lambda)\right\}$ to guarantee asymptotic stability of system (10) ◇.

Proceedings of the
American Control Conference
San Francisco, California • June 1993

POLYNOMIAL AND RATIONAL MATRIX INTERPOLATION: SYSTEMS AND CONTROL APPLICATIONS

Panos J. Antsaklis
Dept. of Electrical Engineering
University of Notre Dame
Notre Dame, IN 46556
Email: antsakli@saturn.ece.nd.edu

Zhiqiang Gao
Dept. of Electrical Engineering
Cleveland State University
Euclid Ave. at E. 24th St.
Cleveland, Ohio 44115

Abstract: In this paper, a theory of polynomial and rational matrix interpolation is introduced and applied to problems in systems and control. The polynomial matrix interpolation theory is first outlined and then applied to solving matrix equations; it is also used in pole assignment and other control problems. Rational matrix interpolation is also discussed and it is used to solve rational matrix equations including the model matching problem.

I. INTRODUCTION

A theory of polynomial and rational matrix interpolation is briefly outlined in this paper and its application to certain systems and control problems is discussed; full details can be found in [21].

Many system and control problems can be formulated in terms of matrix equations where polynomial or rational solutions with specific properties are of interest. It is known that equations involving just polynomials can be solved by either equating coefficients of equal power of the indeterminate s or equivalently by using the values obtained when appropriate values for s are substituted in the given polynomials; in the latter case one uses results from the theory of polynomial interpolation. Similarly one may solve polynomial matrix equations using the theory of polynomial matrix interpolation presented here (also in [1-7], [21]); this approach has significant advantages and these are discussed below. Rational, mostly scalar interpolation has been of interest to systems and control researchers recenly. Note that the rational interpolation results presented here are distinct from other literature results as they refer to matrix case and concentrate on fundamental representation questions. Other results in the literature attempt to characterize rational functions that satisfy certain interpolation constraints and are optimal in some sense and so they rather complement our results than compete with them.

In this paper polynomial matrix interpolation of the type $Q(s_j)\, a_j = b_j$, where Q(s) is a matrix and a_j, b_j vectors, is introduced as a generalization of the scalar polynomial interpolation of the form $q(s_j) = b_j$. This generalization appears to be well suited to study and solve a variety of multivariable system and control problems. The original motivation for the development of the matrix interpolation theory was to be able to solve polynomial matrix equations, which appear in the theory of Systems and Control and in particular the Diophantine equation; the results presented here and in [21] however go well beyond solving that equation.

The use of interpolation type constraints in system and control theory is first discussed and a number of examples are presented.

Interpolation type constraints in Systems and Control theory

Many control system constraints and properties that are expressed in terms of conditions on a polynomial or rational matrix R(s), can be written in an easier to handle form in terms of $R(s_j)$, where $R(s_j)$ is R(s) evaluated at certain (complex) values $s = s_j$ $j=1, \ell$. We shall call such conditions in terms of $R(s_j)$, interpolation (type) conditions on R(s). Next, a number of examples from Systems and Control theory where polynomial and polynomial matrix interpolation constraints are used, are outlined. This list is not complete, by far.

Eigenvalue / eigenvector controllability tests: It is known that all the uncontrollable eigenvalues of $\dot{x} = Ax + Bu$ are given by the roots of the determinant of a greatest left divisor of the polynomial matrices sI - A and B. An alternative, and perhaps easier to handle, form of this result is that s_j is an uncontrollable eigenvalue if and only if $\text{rank}[s_jI-A, B] < n$ where A is nxn (PBH controllability test [11]). This is a more restrictive version of the previous result which involves left divisors, since it is not clear how to handle multiple eigenvalues when it is desirable to determine all uncontrollable eigenvalues. The results presented here can readily provide the solution to this problem.

More recently, stability constraints in the *H^∞ formulation of the optimal control problem* have been expressed in terms of interpolation type constraints[18-20]. It is rather interesting that [18, 19] discuss a "directional" approach which is in the same spirit of the approach taken here (and in [1-7]).

The *output and state feedback pole assignment problems* have a rather natural formulation in terms of interpolation type constraints [6,7,14].

The above are just a few of the many examples of the strong presence of interpolation type conditions in the systems and control literature. A closer look reveals that the relationships between conditions on $R(s_j)$ and properties of R(s) need to be better understood. Our research on matrix interpolation and its applications addresses this need.

The main ideas of the polynomial matrix interpolation results can be found in earlier publications [1-5], with state and static output feedback applications appearing in [6, 7]; some of the material on rational matrix interpolation has appeared before in [5]. A rather complete theory of polynomial and rational matrix interpolation with applications is presented in [21]. Note that all the algorithms in this paper have been successfully implemented in Matlab.

II. POLYNOMIAL MATRIX INTERPOLATION

The basic theorem of polynomial interpolation can be stated as follows:

Given ℓ distinct complex scalars s_j $j = 1, \ell$ and ℓ corresponding complex values b_j, there exists a unique polynomial q(s) of degree $n = \ell - 1$ for which

$$q(s_j) = b_j \quad j = 1, \ell \quad (2.1)$$

That is, an nth degree polynomial q(s) can be uniquely represented by the $\ell = n+1$ interpolation (points or doublets or) pairs (s_j, b_j) $j = 1, \ell$. To see this, write the n-th degree polynomial q(s) as $q(s) = q\,[1, s, \ldots, s^n]'$ where q is the (1x(n+1)) row vector of the coefficients and [ ]' denotes the transpose. The $\ell = n+1$ equations in (2.1) can then be written as

$$qV = q\begin{bmatrix} 1 & \cdots & 1 \\ s_1 & & s_\ell \\ \cdot & & \cdot \\ \cdot & & \cdot \\ \cdot & & \cdot \\ s_1^{\ell-1} & \cdots & s_\ell^{\ell-1} \end{bmatrix} = [b_1, \ldots, b_\ell] = B_\ell$$

Note that the matrix V ($\ell x \ell$) is the well known Vandermonde matrix which is nonsingular if and only if the ℓ scalars s_j $j = 1, \ell$ are distinct. Here s_i are distinct and therefore V is nonsingular. This implies that the above equation has a unique solution q, that is there exists a unique polynomial q(s) of degree n which satisfies (2.1). There are several approaches to generalize this result to the polynomial matrix case. They are special cases of the basic polynomial matrix interpolation theorem that follows [21]:

Let $S(s) := \text{blk diag}\{[1, s, \ldots, s^{d_i}]'\}$ where d_i $i = 1, m$ are non-negative integers; let $a_j \neq 0$ and b_j denote (mx1) and (px1) complex vectors respectively and s_j complex scalars.

Theorem 2.1: Given interpolation (points) triplets (s_j, a_j, b_j) $j = 1, \ell$ and nonnegative integers d_i with $\ell = \Sigma\, d_i + m$ such that the $(\Sigma\, d_i + m)x\ell$ matrix

$$S_\ell := [S(s_1)a_1, \ldots, S(s_\ell)a_\ell] \quad (2.2)$$

has full rank, there exists a unique (pxm) polynomial matrix Q(s), with ith column degree equal to d_i, $i = 1, m$ for which

$$Q(s_j)\, a_j = b_j \quad j = 1, \ell \quad (2.3)$$

Proof: Since the column degrees of Q(s) are d_i, Q(s) can be written as

$$Q(s) = QS(s) \quad (2.4)$$

where Q $(px(\Sigma d_i + m))$ contains the coefficients of the polynomial entries. Substituting in (2.3), Q must satisfy

$$QS_\ell = B_\ell \quad (2.5)$$

where $B_\ell := [b_1, \ldots, b_\ell]$. Since S_ℓ is nonsingular, Q and therefore Q(s) are uniquely determined. □

It should be noted that when $p = m = 1$ and $d_1 = \ell - 1 = n$ this theorem reduces to the polynomial interpolation theorem. To see this, note that in this case the nonzero scalars a_j $j = 1, \ell$, can be taken to be equal to 1, in which case $S_\ell = V$ the well known Vandermonde matrix.

Example 2.1: Let Q(s) be a 1x2 (=pxm) polynomial matrix and let $\ell = 3$ interpolation points $\{(s_j, a_j, b_j)\ j = 1, 2, 3\}$ be specified: { (-1,[1, 0]', 0), (0,[-1, 1]', 0), (1, [0, 1]', 1)}.

In view of Theorem 2.1, Q(s) is uniquely specified when d_1 and d_2 are chosen so that $\ell(=3) = \Sigma d_i + m = (d_1 + d_2) + 2$ or $d_1 + d_2 = 1$ assuming that S_3 has full rank. Clearly there are more than one choices for d_1 and d_2; the resulting Q(s) depends on the particular choice for the column degrees d_i:

(i) Let $d_1 = 1$, and $d_2 = 0$. Then $S(s) = \text{blk diag}\{[1,s]',1\}$ and (2.5) becomes:

$$Q\,S_3 = Q\,[S(s_1)a_1, S(s_2)a_2, S(s_3)a_3] = Q\begin{bmatrix} 1 & -1 & 0 \\ -1 & 0 & 0 \\ 0 & 1 & 1 \end{bmatrix}$$

$$= [0, 0, 1] = B_3$$

from which Q = [1, 1, 1] and Q(s) = QS(s) = [s+1, 1].

(ii) Let $d_1 = 0$, $d_2 = 1$. Then $S(s) = \text{blk diag}\{1, [1, s]'\}$ and (2.5) gives Q = [0, 0, 1] from which Q(s) = [0, s], clearly different from (i) above. □

III. RATIONAL MATRIX INTERPOLATION

Similarly to the polynomial matrix case, the problem here is to represent a (pxm) rational matrix H(s) by interpolation triplets or points (s_j, a_j, b_j) $j = 1, \ell$ which satisfy

$$H(s_j)a_j = b_j \quad j = 1, \ell \quad (3.1)$$

where s_j are complex scalars and $a_j \neq 0$, b_j complex (mx1), (px1) vectors respectively.

It is shown that the rational matrix interpolation problem reduces to a special case of polynomial matrix interpolation. To see this:

Write $H(s) = \tilde{D}^{-1}(s)\tilde{N}(s)$ where $\tilde{D}(s)$ and $\tilde{N}(s)$ are (pxp) and (pxm) polynomial matrices respectively. Then (3.1) can be written as $\tilde{N}(s_j)a_j = \tilde{D}(s_j)b_j$ or as

$$[\tilde{N}(s_j), -\tilde{D}(s_j)]\begin{bmatrix} a_j \\ b_j \end{bmatrix} = Q(s_j)c_j = 0 \;\; j = 1, \ell \quad (3.2)$$

That is the rational matrix interpolation problem for a pxm rational matrix H(s) can be seen as a polynomial interpolation problem for a px(p+m) polynomial matrix $Q(s) := [\tilde{N}(s), -\tilde{D}(s)]$ with interpolation points $(s_j, c_j, 0) = (s_j, [a_j', b_j']', 0)$ $j = 1, \ell$. There is also the additional constraint that $\tilde{D}^{-1}(s)$ exists; note that this is similar to the constraints in the pole assignment problem studied below.

IV. SOLUTION OF MATRIX EQUATIONS

In this section polynomial matrix equations of the form M(s)L(s) = Q(s) are studied. The main result is Theorem 4.1 where it is shown that all solutions M(s) of degree r can be derived by solving equation (4.9). In this way, all solutions of degree r of the polynomial equation, if they exist, are parameterized. The Diophantine equation is an important special case and it is examined at length [21]. It is also shown that Theorem 4.1 can be applied to solve rational matrix equations of the form M(s)L(s) = Q(s).

Consider the equation

$$M(s)L(s) = Q(s) \quad (4.1)$$

where L(s) (txm) and Q(s) (kxm) are given polynomial matrices. Dtermine the polynomial matrix solutions M(s) (kxt) when they exist.

First consider the left hand side of equation (4.1). Let

$$M(s) := M_0 + \ldots + M_r s^r \quad (4.2)$$

and $d_i := \deg_{ci}[L(s)]$ i = 1, m. If

$$\hat{Q}(s) := M(s)L(s) \quad (4.3)$$

then $\deg_{ci}[\hat{Q}(s)] = d_i + r$ for $i = 1, m$. According to the basic polynomial matrix interpolation Theorem 2.1, the matrix $\hat{Q}(s)$ can be uniquely specified using $\Sigma(d_i+r))+m = \Sigma d_i+m)(r+1)$

interpolation points. Therefore consider ℓ interpolation points (s_j, a_j, b_j) $j = 1, \ell$ where

$$\ell = \sum d_i + m(r+1) \quad (4.4)$$

Let $S_r(s) :=$ blk diag$\{[1, s, ..., s^{d_i+r}]'\}$ and assume that the $(\sum d_i + m(r+1)) x \ell$ matrix

$$S_{r\ell} := [S_r(s_1)\, a_1, ..., S_r(s_\ell) a_\ell] \quad (4.5)$$

has full rank; that is the assumptions in Theorem 2.1 are satisfied. Note that for distinct s_j, $S_{r\ell}$ will have full column rank for almost any set of nonzero a_j [21]. Now in view of Theorem 2.1 the matrix $\hat{Q}(s)$ which satisfies

$$\hat{Q}(s_j)a_j = b_j \quad j = 1, \ell \quad (4.6)$$

is uniquely specified given these ℓ interpolation points (s_j, a_j, b_j). To solve (4.1), these interpolation points must be appropriately chosen so that the equation $\hat{Q}(s)$ (= M(s)L(s)) = Q(s) is satisfied:
Write (4.1) as

$$ML_r(s) = Q(s) \quad (4.7)$$

where

$$M := [M_0, ..., M_r] \quad (kxt(r+1))$$

$$L_r(s) := [L(s)', ..., s^r L(s)']' \quad (t(r+1)xm).$$

Let $s = s_j$ and postmultiply (4.7) by a_j $j = 1, \ell$; note that s_j and a_j $j = 1, \ell$ must be so that $S_{r\ell}$ above has full rank. Define

$$b_j := Q(s_j)a_j \quad j = 1, \ell \quad (4.8)$$

and combine the equations to obtain

$$ML_{r\ell} = B_\ell \quad (4.9)$$

where

$L_{r\ell} := [L_r(s_1)\, a_1, ..., L_r(s_\ell)a_\ell]$ $(t(r+1)x\ell)$ and

$B_\ell := [b_1, ..., b_\ell]$ $(kx\ell)$.

<u>Theorem 4.1</u>: Given L(s), Q(s) in (4.1), let $d_i := \deg_{ci}[L(s)]$ i = 1, m and select r to satisfy

$$\deg_{ci}[Q(s)] \le d_i + r \quad i = 1, m \quad (4.10)$$

Then a solution M(s) of degree r exists if and only if a solution M of (4.9) does exist; $M(s) = M\,[I, sI, ..., s^r I]'$. □

It is not difficult to show that solving (4.9) is equivalent to solving

$$M(s_j)c_j = b_j \quad j = 1, \ell \quad (4.11)$$

where

$$c_j := L(s_j)a_j,\ b_j := Q(s_j)a_j \quad j = 1, \ell \quad (4.12)$$

M(s) that satisfy (4.11) are obtained by solving

$$MS_{r\ell} = B_\ell \quad (4.13)$$

where $S_{r\ell} := [S_r(s_1)c_1, ..., S_r(s_\ell)c_\ell]$ $(t(r+1)x\ell)$, with $S_r(s) := [I, sI, ..., s^r I]'$ $(t(r+1)xt)$ and $B_\ell := [b_1, ..., b_\ell]$ $(kx\ell)$. Solving (4.13) is an alternative to solving (4.9).

Constraints on Solutions

When there are more unknowns (t(r+1)) than equations ($\ell = \sum d_i + m(r+1)$) in (4.9) or (4.13), this additional freedom can be exploited so that M(s) satisfies additional constraints. In particular, $k := t(r+1) - \ell$ additional linear constraints, expressed in terms of the coefficients of M(s) (in M), can be satisfied in general. The equations describing the constraints can be used to augment the equations in (4.9). In this case the equations to be solved become

$$M[L_{r\ell}, C] = [B_\ell, D] \quad (4.14)$$

where MC = D represents the k linear constraints imposed on the coefficients M; C and D are matrices (real or complex) with k columns each.

The Diophantine Equation

An important case of (4.1) is the Diophantine equation:

$$X(s)D(s) + Y(s)N(s) = Q(s) \quad (4.15)$$

where the polynomial matrices D(s), N(s) and Q(s) are given and X(s), Y(s) are to be found. Note that if

$$M(s) = [X(s), Y(s)],\quad L(s) = \begin{bmatrix} D(s) \\ N(s) \end{bmatrix} \quad (4.16)$$

it is immediately clear that the Diophantine equation is a polynomial equation of the form (4.1) and all the previous results do apply. That is, Theorem 4.1 guarantees that all solutions of (4.15) of degree r are found by solving (4.9) (or (4.13)). In the theory of Systems and Control the Diophantine equation used involves a matrix L(s) = [D'(s), N'(s)]' which has rather specific properties. These are exploited to solve the Diophantine equation and to derive conditions for existence of solutions to (4.15) of degree r.

<u>Theorem 4.2:</u> Let r satisfy

$$\deg_{ci}[Q(s)] \le d_i + r \quad i = 1, m \text{ and } r \ge v - 1.$$

Then the Diophantine equation (4.15) has solutions of degree r, which can be found by solving (4.9) (or (4.13)).

<u>Example 4.1</u>: Let

$$D(s) = \begin{bmatrix} s-2 & 0 \\ 0 & s+1 \end{bmatrix}, N(s) = \begin{bmatrix} s-1 & 0 \\ 1 & 1 \end{bmatrix}, \text{and } Q(s) = \begin{bmatrix} 1 & 0 \\ 0 & 1 \end{bmatrix}$$

From which $d_1 = d_2 = 1$; $\deg_{ci}Q(s) = 0$, i=1, 2; and $\ell = 2 + 2(r+1)$

For r = 1, s_j = -2, -1, 0, 1, 2, 3 and

$$a_j = \begin{bmatrix} 0 \\ 1 \end{bmatrix}, \begin{bmatrix} 1 \\ 3 \end{bmatrix}, \begin{bmatrix} 0 \\ -1 \end{bmatrix}, \begin{bmatrix} -1 \\ 3 \end{bmatrix}, \begin{bmatrix} -1 \\ 1 \end{bmatrix}, \begin{bmatrix} 1 \\ -1 \end{bmatrix}$$

a solution is

$$M(s) = [X(s), Y(s)] = \begin{bmatrix} s & -1 & -s & s+1 \\ 1/3 & 1/3 & 0 & -1/3s+2/3 \end{bmatrix}. \quad \square$$

Solving Rational Matrix Equations

Now let's consider the rational matrix equation:

$$M(s)L(s) = Q(s) \quad (4.17)$$

where L(s) (txm) and Q(s) (kxm) are given rational matrices. The polynomial matrix interpolation theory developed above will can be used to solve this equation and determine the rational matrix solutions M(s) (kxt). Let $M(s) = \tilde{D}^{-1}(s)\tilde{N}(s)$, a polynomial fraction form of M(s) to be determined. Then (4.17) can be written as:

$$[\tilde{N}(s)\ \ -\tilde{D}(s)] \begin{bmatrix} L(s) \\ Q(s) \end{bmatrix} = 0 \quad (4.18)$$

Note that one could equivalently solve

$$[\tilde{N}(s)\ \ -\tilde{D}(s)] \begin{bmatrix} L_p(s) \\ Q_p(s) \end{bmatrix} = 0 \quad (4.19)$$

where $[L_p(s)'\ Q_p(s)']' = [L(s)'\ Q(s)']'\phi(s)$ a polynomial matrix with $\phi(s)$ the least common denominator of all entries of L(s) and Q(s); in general, $\phi(s)$ could be any denominator in a right fractional representation of [L(s)', Q(s)']'. The problem to be solved is now (4.1), a polynomial matrix equation, where $L(s) = [L_p(s)'\ Q_p(s)']'$ and Q(s) = 0. Therefore, all solutions $[\tilde{N}(s)\ -\tilde{D}(s)]$ of degree r can be determined by solving (4.9) or (4.13). Let $s = s_j$ and postmultiply (4.19) by a_j $j = 1, \ell$ with a_j and ℓ chosen properly [21]. Define

$$c_j := \begin{bmatrix} L_p(s) \\ Q_p(s) \end{bmatrix} a_j \quad j = 1, \ell \tag{4.20}$$

The problem now is to find a polynomial matrix $[\tilde{N}(s) \ \ -\tilde{D}(s)]$ which satisfies

$$[\tilde{N}(s_j) \ -\tilde{D}(s_j)]\, c_j = 0 \qquad j = 1, \ell \tag{4.21}$$

Note that restrictions on the solutions can be easily imposed to guarantee that $\tilde{D}^{-1}(s)$ exists and/or that $M(s) = \tilde{D}^{-1}(s)\tilde{N}(s)$ is proper. Additional constraints can be added so the solution satisfies additional specifications; see (4.14).

V. POLE PLACEMENT AND OTHER APPLICATIONS

Output Feedback. All proper output controllers of degree r (of order mr) that assign all the closed loop eigenvalues to arbitrary locations are characterized in a convenient way using interpolation results. This has not been done before.

We are interested in solutions [X(s), Y(s)] (mx(p+m)) of the Diophantine equation where only the roots of |Q(s)| are specified; furthermore $X^{-1}(s)Y(s)$ should exist and be proper. Here the equation to be solved is

$$(X(s_j)\, D(s_j) + Y(s_j)N(s_j))a_j = 0 \ \ j = 1, \ell \tag{5.1}$$

or $ML_{r\ell} = 0$ ($\ell = \Sigma d_i + mr$) ; that is the Σd_i + mr roots of |X(s) D(s) + Y(s)N(s)| are to take on the values s_j $j = 1, \ell$. Note the difference between the problem studied in Section IV, where Q(s) is known, and the problem studied here where only the roots of |Q(s)| (or |Q(s)| within multiplication by some nonzero real scalar) are given. It is clear that there are many (in fact an infinite number) of Q(s) with the desired roots in |Q(s)|. So if one selects in advance a Q(s) with desired roots in |Q(s)| that does not satisfy any other design criteria as it is typically done, then one really solves a more restrictive problem than the eigenvalue assignment problem. In the scalar polynomial case if Q(s) is selected so that the roots of |Q(s)| are the desired ones then one really arbitrarily selects in addition only the leading coefficient of Q(s), which is not really restrictive. This perhaps explains the tendency to do something analogous in the multivariable case; this however clearly changes and restricts the original problem. It is shown here that one does not have to select Q(s) in advance. The vectors a_j can then be seen as design parameters and they can be selected almost arbitrarily to satisfy requirements in addition to pole assignment; see [6,7, 21]. Note that this design approach is rather well known in the state feedback case as it is discussed later in this section.

Theorem 5.1 Let $r \geq \nu-1$. Then (X(s), Y(s)) exists such that all the n+mr zeros of |X(s) D(s) + Y(s)N(s)| are arbitrarily assigned and $X^{-1}(s)Y(s)$ is proper. □

Example 5.1: Let $D(s) = \begin{bmatrix} s-2 & 0 \\ 0 & s+1 \end{bmatrix}$, $N(s) = \begin{bmatrix} s-1 & 0 \\ 1 & 1 \end{bmatrix}$ with n = deg|D(s)| = 2. Here there are deg|X(s)D(s) + Y(s)N(s)| = n + mr = 2 + 2r closed-loop poles to be assigned. Note that $r \geq \nu - 1 = 1 - 1 = 0$.

i) For r = 0 and $\{(s_j, a_j), j = 1,2\} = \{(-1, [1\ 0]'), (-2, [0\ 1]')\}$, a solution of $ML_{r\ell} = 0$ is

$M = \begin{bmatrix} 2 & 0 & -3 & 0 \\ 0 & 2 & 1 & 2 \end{bmatrix}$. For this case, M = M(s) = [X(s) Y(s)].

ii) For r = 1, and $\{(s_j, a_j), j = 1,4\} = \{(-1, [1\ 0]^T), (-2, [0\ 1]^T), (-3, [-1\ 0]^T), (-4, [0\ -1]^T)\}$

a solution of $ML_{r\ell} = 0$ is $[X(s)\ Y(s)] = \begin{bmatrix} s-7 & -1 & 12 & s+1 \\ 5 & s+4 & -6 & s+4 \end{bmatrix}$

Note that $X(s)^{-1}Y(s)$ exists and it is proper. □

State Feedback Let A, B, F be nxn, nxm, mxn real matrices respectively. Note that $|sI - (A+BF)| = |sI - A|\cdot|I_n - (sI-A)^{-1}BF| = |sI - A|\cdot|I_m - F(sI-A)^{-1}B|$. If now the desired closed-loop eigenvalues s_j are different from the eigenvalues of A, then F will assign all n desired closed loop eigenvalues s_j if and only if

$$F[(s_jI-A)^{-1}Ba_j] = a_j \ \ j = 1,n \tag{5.2}$$

The mx1 vectors a_j are selected so that $(s_jI-A)^{-1}Ba_j$ $j = 1,n$ are linearly independent vectors. Alternatively one could approach the problem as follows: let M(s) (nxm) D(s) (mxm) be right coprime polynomial matrices such that $(sI-A)^{-1}B = M(s)D^{-1}(s)$.

An internal representation equivalent to $\dot{x} = Ax + Bu$ in polynomial matrix form is Dz = u with x = Mz. The eigenvalue assignment problem is then to assign all the roots of |D(s) - FM(s)|; or to determine F so that

$$FM(s_j)a_j = D(s_j)a_j \ \ j = 1,n \tag{5.3}$$

Relation (5.3) was originally used in [6] to determine F. Note that this formulation does not require that s_j be different from the eigenvalues of A as in (5.2). The mx1 vectors a_j are selected so that $M(s_j)a_j$ $j = 1,n$ are independent. Note that $M(s_j)$ has the same column rank as $S(s_j)$ = block diag$\{[1,s,...,s^{d_i-1}]'\}$ where d_i are the controllability indices of (A,B) [10,11]. Therefore, it is possible to select a_j so that $M(s_j)a_j$ $j = 1,n$ are independent even when s_j are repeated. In general, there is great flexibility in selecting the nonzero vectors a_j . Note for example that when s_j are distinct, a very common case, a_j can almost be arbitrarily selected[21]. For all the appropriate choices of a_j ($M(s_j)a_j$ $j = 1,n$ linearly independent), the n eigenvalues of the closed-loop system will be at the desired locations s_j $j = 1,n$. Different a_j correspond to different F (via(5.3)) that produce, in general, different closed loop behavior. The exact relation of the eigenvectors to the a_j can be found as follows: $[s_jI - (A+BF)]M(s_j)a_j = (s_j - A)M(s_j)a_j - BFM(s_j)a_j = BD(s_j)a_j - BD(s_j)a_j = 0$. Therefore $M(s_j)a_j = v_j$ are the closed-loop eigenvectors corresponding to s_j .

One may select a_j in (5.3) to impose constraints on the gain f_{ij} in F. For example one may select a_j so that a column of F is zero (take the corresponding row of all a_j to be nonzero), or an elements of F, $f_{ij} = 0$.

Note that a similar approach for eigenvalue assignment via state feedback is [14]; this approach was developed in parallel but independently to the interpolation method described above (and in [6,7], [21]). The main difference between the two approaches in [6] and [14] is that in [6] a polynomial basis for the kernel of [sI-A, B] is found first and then it is evaluated at $s=s_j$, while in [14] a basis for the kernel of $[s_jI-A,\ B]$ is determined without involving polynomial bases and right factorizations.

Assignment of Characteristic Values and Vectors

In view of the discussion above on state feedback, the characteristic vectors a_j of (D(s) - FM(s)) or the eigenvectors $v_j = M(s_j)a_j$ of sI - (A+BF) can be assigned so that additional design goals are attained, beyond the pole assignment at s_j $j = 1, n$. Two examples of such assignment follow:

Optimal Control: It is possible to select (s_j, a_j) so that the closed-loop system satisfies some optimality criteria. In fact it is straightforward to select (s_j, a_j) so that the resulting F calculated using the above interpolation method, is the unique solution of a Linear Quadratic Regulator (LQR) problem; see for example [11].
Unobservalble eigenvalues: It is possible under certain conditions to select (s_j, a_j) so that s_j become an unobservable eigenvalue in the closed loop system [21].

Choosing a Closed Loop Transfer Function Matrix

One of the challenging problems in control design is to choose an appropriate closed loop transfer function matrix that satisfies all the control specifications which can be obtained from the given plant by applying an internally stable feedback loop. To guarantee the internal stability of feedback control systems, both locations and directions of the RHP zeros of the plant must be considered; these zeros must appear as zeros of the closed loop tranfer function matrix. Consider this in the context of [15]:

Given proper rational matrices H(s) (pxm) and T(s) (pxq), find a proper and stable rational matrix M(s) such that the equation

$$H(s)M(s) = T(s) \tag{5.4}$$

holds. It is known that a stable solution for (5.4) exists if and only if T(s) has as it zeros all the RHP zeros of H(s) together with their directions. Let the coprime fraction representations of H(s) and T(s) be $H(s) = N(s)D^{-1}(s)$ and $T(s) = N_T(s)D_T^{-1}(s)$.

The direction associated with a zero of H(s), z_j, is given by the vector a_j which satisfies $a_jN(z_i) = 0$. Furthermore, T(s) will have the same zero, z_i, together with its direction if T(s) satisfies $a_jN_T(z_i) = 0$ and this must be taken into consideration when T(s) is selected.

Example 5.2: Consider a diagonal T(s); that is the control spécificatons demand diagonal decoupling of the system. Let

$$H(s) = \frac{1}{s+1}\begin{bmatrix} s-1 & 0 \\ 1 & 1 \end{bmatrix}$$

with a zero at s=1. Then aH(1)=0 gives a=[1 0] and T(s) must satisfy aT(1)=[1 0]T(1)=0. Since T(s) must be diagonal, $t_{11}(1) = 0$; that is the RHP zero of the plant should appear in the (1,1) entry of T(s) only. Certainly T(s) can be chosen to have 1 as a zero in both diagonal entries. However, the RHP zeros are undesirable in control and the minimum possible number should be included in T. □

VI. CONCLUDING REMARKS

Interpolation is a very general and flexible way to deal with systems and control problems. Note that only a fraction of existing results [21] were presented here due to space limitations. At the same time note that the results presented in [21] have only opened the way, as there are many more results that can and need be developed to handle the wide range of problems possible to study via polynomial and rational matrix interpolation theory.

REFERENCES

[1] P.J. Antsaklis, "Polynomial Matrix Characterization Using Characteristic Values and Vectors", Publ. No. 80/18, Dept. of Electr. Engr., Imperial College, London, July 1980.
[2] P.J. Antsaklis, "Polynomial Matrix Interpolation in Control Equations: The Diophantine Equation", Proc. of the 1983 Conf. on Info. Sciences and Systems, pp. 873-878, The Johns Hopkins University, March 1983.
[3] P.J. Antsaklis and R.L. Lopez, "Control Design Using Polynomial Matrix Interpolation", Proc. of the 23rd IEEE Conf. on Decision and Control, pp 621-622, Las Vegas, Nevada, Dec. 12-14, 1984.
[4] R. Lopez, Multivariable Control Design via Polynomial Interpolation Methods, M.S.E.E. Thesis, Dept. of Electr. Engr., University of Notre Dame, May 1984.
[5] P.J. Antsaklis and Z. Gao, "On the Theory of Polynomial Matrix Interpolation and its Role in Systems and Control", Twenty-Eighth Annual Allerton Conference on Communication, Control and Computing, Univ. of Illinois at Urbana -Champaign, Sept. 28 - Oct. 1, 1990.
[6] P.J. Antsaklis, Some New Matrix Methods Applied to Multivariable System Analysis and Design, Ph.D. Dissertation, Brown University, 1977.
[7] P.J. Antsaklis and W. A. Wolovich, "Arbitrary Pole Placement Using Linear Output Feedback Compensation", Intern. J. Control, Vol. 25, pp. 915-925, 1977.
[8] P.J. Davis, Interpolation and Approximation, Dover, 1975.
[9] H.H. Rosenbrock, State Space and Multivariable Theory, Wiley, New York, 1970.
[10]W.A. Wolovich, Linear Multivariable Systems, Springer-Verlag, 1974.
[11]T. Kailath, Linear Systems, Prentice-Hall, 1980.
[12]C.T. Chen, Linear Systems Theory and Design, Holt, Rinehart and Winston, New York, 1984
[13] F.M. Brasch and J.B. Pearson, "Pole Placement Using Dynamic Compensators," IEEE Trans. Autom. Contr., Vol. AC-15, pp. 34-43, February 1970.
[14]B.C. Moore, "On the Flexibility Offered by State Feedback in Multivariable Systems Beyond Closed Loop Eigenvalue Assignment," IEEE Trans. Autom. Contr., Vol. AC-21, pp. 689-692, Oct. 1976.
[15]Z. Gao and P.J. Antsaklis, "On Stable Solutions of the One and Two Sided Model Matching Problems", IEEE Transactions on Automatic Control, Vol. AC-34, No. 9, pp. 978-982, September 1989.
[16]G.F. Franklin, J.D. Powell and M.L. Workman, Digital Control of Dynamic Systems, 2nd Edition, Addison-Wesley Publishing Company, Reading, MA, 1990.
[17]P.J. Antsaklis and M.K. Sain, "Unity Feedback Compensation for Unstable Plants," Proc. of the 20th IEEE Conf. on Decision and Control, pp. 305-308, San Diego, December 1981.
[18]H. Kimura, "Directional Interpolation Approach to H^∞ - Optimization and Robust Stabilization", IEEE Transactions on Automatic Control, Vol. AC-32, No. 12, pp.1085-1093, December 1987.
[19]U. Shaked, "The Structure of Inner Matrices that Satisfy Multiple Directional Interpolation Requirements", IEEE Transactions on Automatic Control, Vol. AC-34, No. 12, pp. 1293-1296, December 1989.
[20]B.-C. Chang and J. B. Pearson, Jr., "Optimal Disturbance Reduction in Linear Multivariable Systems", IEEE Transactions on Automatic Control, Vol. AC-29, No. 10, pp. 880-887, October 1984.
[21]P.J. Antsaklis and Z. Gao, "Polynomial and Rational Matrix Interpolation: Theory and Control Applications", Control Systems Technical Report No. 71, Dept. of Electrical Engineering, Univ. of Notre Dame, September 1992. To appear in International Journal of Control.

Proceedings of the
American Control Conference
San Francisco, California • June 1993

WP2 - 16:10

Model Reference Robust Control Scheme for Nonlinear Parametric Uncertain Systems

J. Y. Zhu*, S.C. Martindale*, D. M. Dawson*, and Z. Qu**

*School of Electrical and Computer Engineering
Clemson University
Clemson, SC 29634, U.S.A
803–656–1183

**Department of Electrical Engineering
University of Central florida
Orlando, FL 32826, U.S.A

Abstract

In this paper, we consider the design of a model reference robust controller for a class of SISO, minimum phase, nonlinear systems. The design of the controller does not require the existence of the matching conditions or the feedback linearizability property in the strictest sense; rather, the controller requires a set of assumptions which allow the original nonlinear system to be transformed into the so–called observable canonical form. The robust control scheme guarantees that the overall states are globally uniformly bounded (GUB) and that the output tracking error is globally uniformly ultimately bounded (GUUB).

I. Introduction

In the model reference control (MRC) literature, various design methodologies have been proposed, such as model reference adaptive control (MRAC), variable structure control (VSC) [6,7], and model reference robust control (MRRC) [4]. All the design methodologies above are based on the transfer function; therefore, the problem formulations begin with the assumption of a linear plant. In [5], a nonlinear MRAC approach is presented by K. Nam and A. Arapostathis which is based on state–feedback linearization, so that it is restricted to a class of "well structured" nonlinear systems called pure–feedback systems in which the full states need to be measured. In [9], Kanellakopoulos, *et al* have presented a design procedure for adaptive controllers (i.e., state feedback and output feedback) for uncertain nonlinear systems. In [3] and [8], Marino, *et al* have presented results which include adaptive state observer–based controllers and robust output feedback controllers for uncertain nonlinear systems. In [4,10], Qu, *et al* have presented results for the design of robust controllers (i.e., output feedback and state feedback) for uncertain nonlinear and linear systems.

In this paper, we combine the work in [3] and [4] to design robust output feedback controllers for a class of uncertain nonlinear systems that can be transformed into observable canonical form. The plant uncertainties are in the form of unknown constant parameters which are multiplied by known nonlinear functions of the input and output. The main difference from [4] is that the problem is formulated from a state space point of view rather than by the utilization of a transfer function approach. Therefore, in contrast to [4], the uncertain plant is entirely nonlinear, whereas in [4] the plant is an uncertain linear system with an additive bounded disturbance. This broadening of the class of systems in which robust output feedback controllers can be designed is due to some of the recent work pioneered by Marino and Tomei in [3]. In [3], a set of geometric conditions is given such that a parameter independent coordinate transformation can be utilized to transform an uncertain nonlinear system into a system which is linear with respect to unknown states, parameters, and is nonlinear with respect to the input and the output. A filtered transformation is then used to transform the unknown nonlinear system into observable canonical form. Utilizing the observable canonical form for the uncertain plant, we then use a robust control approach [4], which is based on the integrator backstepping technique [4,9,11], to design a robust output feedback controller which guarantees that the overall states are GUB and that the output tracking error is GUUB. The robust controller developed in this paper has evolved from VSC; however, the resulting control is continous and guarantees robust stability and performance under bounded, additive disturbances. In addition, the controller is of a simpler form than the VSC [7,6] in that it is not based on an adaptation mechanism. The paper is organized as follows. In section II, we formulate the problem and state some preliminary definitions which are related to the transformations presented in [3]. In section III, we design the robust output feedback controller for the case of a relative degree one plant. In section IV, a recursive mapping for the robust control design is proposed when only input–output data is available but the relative degree of the plant is greater than one.

II. Problem Statement

We begin with a system in the form

$$\dot{\zeta} = A_c\zeta + b(\theta)\sigma(y)(u + T_d(y,t)) + \sum_{i=0}^{p}\theta_i\psi_i(y) \tag{2.1}$$

$$y = C_c\zeta$$

with (A_c, b, C_c) in observable canonical form

$$A_c = \begin{bmatrix} 0\,1\,0\ldots0 \\ 0\,0\,1\ldots0 \\ \cdot\;\cdot\;\cdot\quad\cdot \\ 0\,0\,0\ldots1 \\ 0\,0\,0\ldots0 \end{bmatrix}_{n\times n}, \quad b(\theta) = \begin{bmatrix} 0 \\ \vdots \\ b_\beta(\theta) \\ \vdots \\ b_n(\theta) \end{bmatrix}_{n\times 1}, \quad C_c = [1,0,\ldots,0]_{1\times n}$$

where $\sigma(y) \neq 0$ is a known scalar function of y, $\theta_i \in \mathbb{R}^1$ are unknown parameters, $\psi_i(y) \in \mathbb{R}^n$ are known vector functions of y, $T_d(y,t)$ denotes any unknown disturbance or nonlinearity bounded by

$$\|T_d(y,t)\| \leq \rho(y,t) \tag{2.2}$$

where $\rho(y,t)$ is a positive scalar function. Here, $b(\theta) \in \mathbb{R}^{n\times 1}$ is a Hurwitz vector with relative degree β, $b_i(\theta) \in \mathbb{R}^1$ are functions of unknown parameters θ_i, $\zeta \in \mathbb{R}^{n\times 1}$ is the state vector, $u \in \mathbb{R}^1$ is the control input, β is used as the relative degree indicator, $y \in \mathbb{R}$ is the system output which is available for measurement, and $\theta = [\theta_1,\ldots,\theta_p]^T$ is the constant parameter vector belonging to Ω, a closed subset of $\mathbb{R}^p$. Assume without loss of generality that the origin is an equilibrium point.

Remark 2.1

It has been shown in [3] that the system given by (2.1) can be obtained from an SISO, time–invariant, unknown, nonlinear system in the form

$$\dot{x} = f(x) + [g_0(x) + \sum_{i=1}^{p}\theta_i g_i(x)](u + T_d(y,t)) + \sum_{i=1}^{p}\theta_i q_i(x)$$

$$y = h(x) \tag{2.3}$$

where $h \in C^\infty(\mathbb{R}^n)$, $h(0) = 0$, is the output function; f, g_0, g_i and q_i $(1 \leq i \leq p)$ are smooth vector fields on $\mathbb{R}^n$, with $f(0) = 0$ and $q_i(0) = 0$ $(1 \leq i \leq p)$ for every state vector $x \in \mathbb{R}^n$. In order to maintain the controllability of the system, we must assume that

$$g_0(x) + \sum_{i=1}^{p}\theta_i g_i(x) = g(x;\theta) \neq 0, \quad \forall\theta \in \Omega.$$

The new system (2.1) is obtained thru a global coordinate diffeomorphism transformation (independent of θ) given as $\zeta = T(x)$ and $T(0) = 0$ under five geometric conditions. Under the sixth condition the zero dynamics can be expressed by a linear asymptotically stable system [1]. Systems which are not feedback linearizable may belong to such a class as well. We omit the restatement of these results here and the reader is referred to [3] for further detail. Note that we use the same plant and assumptions that are given in [3]. In [3], Marino solved the adaptive observer and stabilization problem while in this paper we solve the robust output tracking problem in the presence of unknown, but bounded disturbances. To develop the controller we assume that all the unknown parameters are bounded and that the bounds are known.

The control problem investigated in this paper is the model reference problem, that is, we will design a controller that forces the output of the plant (2.1) to track the output of a reference model under any given reference signal $r_m(t)$. The reference model is described by

$$\dot{x}_m = \begin{bmatrix} -a_{m1} & 1\;0\ldots0 \\ -a_{m2} & 0\;1\ldots0 \\ \cdot & \cdot\;\;\cdot\quad\;\cdot \\ -a_{m(n-1)} & \cdot\;\;0\ldots1 \\ -a_{mn} & \cdot\;\;0\ldots0 \end{bmatrix}_{n\times n} x_m + \begin{bmatrix} 0 \\ \cdot \\ b_{m\beta} \\ \vdots \\ b_{mn} \end{bmatrix}_{n\times 1} r_m \tag{2.4}$$

$$y_m = [1,0,\ldots,0]_{1\times n}\,x_m$$

where $x_m \in \mathbb{R}^n$ and the a_{mi}'s and the b_{mi}'s $1 \leq i \leq n$ are the coefficients of the denominator and numerator polynomials of the transfer function, respectively.

It is assumed that the reference model is a stable system. Our goal is to determine u for the system given by (2.1) with only measurement of r_m, y_m, and y such that the output tracking error is GUUB for arbitrary initial conditions, unknown but bounded nonlinearities and inexact knowledge of the parameter vector θ. Before continuing with the control development, we now state some basic definitions which will be utilized in the sections following.

Definition 2.1 (see [3])

A vector $b = [b_1, \ldots, b_n]^T$ is said to be Hurwitz of relative degree β if the associated polynomial $b_1 s^{n-1} + b_2 s^{n-2} + \ldots + b_n$ is of degree β $(b_1 = \ldots = b_{\beta-1} = 0\; b_\beta \neq 0)$ and Hurwitz, i.e., all its zeros have real parts less than zero.

Definition 2.2 (see [3])

A filtered transformation is defined as a time–varying global state diffeomorphism, which may depend on the unknown vector θ,

$$z = S(x,\xi,\theta), \quad z \in \mathbb{R}^n,\; x \in \mathbb{R}^n,\; \xi \in \mathbb{R}^{n(n+p+1)\times 1},\; \theta \in \mathbb{R}^p$$

such that there exists a C^∞ function $S^{-1}(z,\xi,\theta)$ satisfying

$$z = S(S^{-1}(z,\xi,\theta)), \quad \xi \in \mathbb{R}^{n(n+p+1)\times 1},\; \theta \in \mathbb{R}^p$$

where ξ is a signal generated by the auxiliary linear asymptotically stable filter

$$\dot{\xi} = \Lambda\xi + \delta(y(t),u(t)), \quad \xi(0) = 0.$$

The filter is driven by the inputs y(t) and u(t), $\Lambda \in \mathbb{R}^{n(n+p+1)\times n(n+p+1)}$ is a Hurwitz matrix, $\delta \in \mathbb{R}^{n(n+p+1)\times 1}$ depends on the original plant, and p is the number of unknown parameters.

III. Robust Control Design: Relative Degree–One Case ($\beta = 1$)

In this section, we begin by demonstrating how to transform both the nonlinear system and the reference model into a similiar observable canonical form represented through a filtered transformation. This operation allows the error dynamics to be constructed in the same form. The robust controller is then developed based on the error dynamics which are stabilized using output feedback. The resulting control makes the tracking error exponentially tend to zero.

Lemma 3.1 (see [3] for proof)

For the system given by (2.1), there exists a time varying coordinate transformation given by

$$z = \zeta - \sum_{j=2}^{n} d_j\xi_{j-1}^T\vartheta, \tag{3.1}$$

where $\vartheta \in \mathbb{R}^{n+p+1}$ is an unknown parameter vector, ζ is defined in (2.1), and the ξ_i are generated by the following auxiliary dynamics:

$$\dot{\xi}_i = -\lambda_i\xi_i + \xi_{i+1} + \phi_{i+1}(y,u,t) \qquad \xi_i(0) = 0,\; \xi_i \in \mathbb{R}^{n+p+1},\; 1 \leq i \leq n-1$$

$$\xi_n = 0 \qquad \xi_n \in \mathbb{R}^{n+p+1}, \tag{3.2}$$

$\phi_{i+1}(y,u,t) \in \mathbb{R}^{n+p+1}$, which is defined in [2], depends on the original plant, and the λ_i are arbitrary positive scalars. The vector $d_j \in \mathbb{R}^{n\times 1}$ in (3.1) is generated by the recursive formula

$$d_n = [0,\ldots,1]^T$$

$$d_j = A_c d_{j+1} + \lambda_i d_{j+1} \quad 1 \leq j \leq n-1, \tag{3.3}$$

Using (3.1) and (3.2), we will transform (2.1) into a new "plant" represented by

$$\dot{z} = A_c z + d_1\left(\sum_{i=0}^{p}\theta_i\psi_i^1(y) + b_1(\theta)\sigma(y)(u + T_d(y,t)) + \xi_1^T\vartheta\right) \tag{3.4}$$

$$y = C_c z$$

where $\psi_i^1(y) \in \mathbb{R}^1$ is the first entry of the vector $\psi_i(y)$ defined in (2.1), $d_1 = [1, d_{12}, \ldots, d_{1n}]^T$ from (3.3) is a known Hurwitz vector of degree 1 satisfying the design equation

$$s^{n-1} + d_{12}s^{n-2} + \ldots + d_{1n} = (s + \lambda_1)\ldots(s + \lambda_{n-1})$$

s is the Laplace transform variable, and $\vartheta \in \mathbb{R}^{n+p+1}$ is an unknown parameter vector.

Lemma 3.2 (see [3] for proof)

Considering the reference model given in (2.4), there exists a filtered transformation

$$z_m = x_m - \sum_{j=2}^{n} d_j\xi_{m(j-1)}^T\theta_m \qquad \theta_m \in \mathbb{R}^{2n-\beta+1} \tag{3.5}$$

where ξ_{mi} is generated by

$$\dot{\xi}_{mi} = -\lambda_i \xi_{mi} + \xi_{m(i+1)} + \phi_{m(i+1)}(y_m, r_m) \quad \xi_{mi}(0)=0,\ \xi_{mi} \in \mathbb{R}^{2n-\beta+1},\ 1 \le i \le n-1$$
$$\xi_{mn} = 0 \quad \xi_{mn} \in \mathbb{R}^{2n-\beta+1}. \tag{3.6}$$

Note that the λ_i are defined in (3.3), d_j is given by (3.3), $\theta_m = [a_{m1},..,a_{mn}, b_{m\beta},..,b_{mn}]^T$, $\phi_{m(i+1)} \in \mathbb{R}^{2n-\beta-1}$ are vectors defined in [2] that depend on r and y_m. By combining (3.5) with (3.6), we can transform (2.4) into

$$\dot{z}_m = A_c z_m + d_1 \zeta(r_m, y_m)$$
$$y_m = C_c z_m \tag{3.7}$$

where d_1 is given in (3.3) and $\zeta(r_m, y_m) \in \mathbb{R}^1$ is given by

$$\zeta(r_m, y_m) = \begin{cases} -a_{m1} y_m + b_{m1} r_m + \xi_{m1}^T \theta_m & \text{if } \beta = 1 \\ -a_{m1} y_m + \xi_{m1}^T \theta_m & \text{if } \beta > 1 \end{cases}$$

Utilizing the dynamics of (3.4) and (3.7), we can construct the error dynamics as follows:

$$\dot{z}_e = A_c z_e + d_1(\zeta(r_m, y_m) - \xi_1^T \vartheta - \sum_{i=0}^{p} \theta_i \psi_i^1(y) - b_1(\theta)\sigma(y)(u + T_d(y,t)))$$
$$e = C_c z_e \tag{3.8}$$

where $z_e = z_m - z$ and $e = y_m - y$.

Note that (A_c, d_1, C_c) in (3.8) is unstable. In order to apply the Kalman–Yakubovich Lemma [12] in the stability proof, we must first stablize the error system (3.8). Here we use output feedback to stabilize the error system. Define the disturbance term $T_r \in \mathbb{R}^1$ as

$$T_r = \zeta(r_m, y_m) - \xi_1^T \vartheta - \sum_{i=0}^{p} \theta_i \psi_i^1(y) - b_1(\theta)\sigma(y) T_d(y,t).$$

Then, rewrite (3.8) as

$$\begin{aligned} \dot{z}_e &= A_c z_e + d_1(T_r - b_1(\sigma(y)u - \mathrm{sgn}(b_1)e)) - d_1 \mathrm{sgn}(b_1) b_1 e \\ &= (A_c - d_1 K) z_e + d_1(T_r - b_1(\sigma(y)u - \mathrm{sgn}(b_1)e)) \\ &= A_k z_e + d_1(T_r - b_1(\sigma(y)u - \mathrm{sgn}(b_1)e)) \\ e &= C_c z_e \end{aligned} \tag{3.9}$$

where $K = [b_1 \mathrm{sgn}(b_1), 0, \ldots, 0] \in \mathbb{R}^{1\times n}$ and $A_K = A_c - d_1 K$ $(A_K \in \mathbb{R}^{n\times n})$. Now the system (A_K, d_1, C_c) in (3.9) is a stable system. Given the error system described by (3.9), we now state a stability theorem for the output tracking error.

<u>Theorem 3.1</u> (for proof see [2])

The plant output tracking error e(t) converges to zero exponentially under the control

$$u = (v_r + \mathrm{sgn}(b_1)e)/\sigma(y) \qquad v_r = \frac{e g^2(y_m, y, r_m, u, t)}{2\underline{b}_1(|e| g + \epsilon e^{-\gamma t})} \tag{3.10}$$

where γ, $\epsilon > 0$ are scalar constants, $\underline{b}_1$, $\bar{b}_1$ are the lower and upper bounds of b_1, and g is a positive, scalar function given by

$$g = 2\mathrm{BND}(|T_r|)$$

where BND(•) denotes the bound of the argument. It is worthwhile to make several comments about the robust controller given in (3.10). First, we note that

$$|v_r| \le \frac{1}{2\underline{b}_1} g(y_m, y, r_m, u, t) \tag{3.11}$$

which implies that v_r is bounded if the input and output are bounded. Second, it is apparent that v_r is continuous since $\gamma > 0$. Therefore the control u is bounded and continuous. Third, the robust controller requires the function $g(y_m, y, r_m, u, t)$ in which

$$|T_r| \le \|\zeta(r_m, y_m) - \sum_{i=0}^{p} \theta_i \psi_i^1(y)\| + \mathrm{BND}(|\xi_1^T|)\|\vartheta\| + |\bar{b}_1(\theta)\sigma(y)\rho(y,t)|.$$
$$\triangleq \mathrm{BND}(|T_r|) \tag{3.12}$$

We also note that the auxiliary signals ξ_1 need not to be calculated on line since v_r requires only the Euclidean bound on ξ_1. It follows from (3.2) that

$$\begin{aligned} \xi_1(s) &= \frac{\phi_2(s)}{s+\lambda_1} + \frac{\phi_3(s)}{(s+\lambda_1)(s+\lambda_2)} + \ldots + \frac{\phi_n(s)}{(s+\lambda_1)(s+\lambda_2)\ldots(s+\lambda_{n-1})} \\ \xi_1(t) &= \int_{t_0}^{t} (e^{-\lambda_1(t-\tau)}\phi_2(\tau) + (A_1^2 e^{-\lambda_1(t-\tau)} + A_2^2 e^{-\lambda_2(t-\tau)})\phi_3(\tau) + \ldots + \\ &\quad (A_1^{n-1} e^{-\lambda_1(t-\tau)} + A_2^{n-1} e^{-\lambda_2(t-\tau)} + \ldots + A_{n-1}^{n-1} e^{-\lambda_{n-1}(t-\tau)})\phi_n(\tau))d\tau \\ &= \int_{t_0}^{t} (\phi_2(\tau) + A_1^2\phi_3(\tau) + \ldots + A_1^{n-1}\phi_n(\tau))e^{-\lambda_1(t-\tau)} + (A_2^2\phi_3(\tau) + \ldots + \\ &\quad A_2^{n-1}\phi_n(\tau))e^{-\lambda_2(t-\tau)} + \ldots + A_{n-1}^{n-1}\phi_n(\tau)e^{-\lambda_{n-1}(t-\tau)})d\tau \\ &= \int_{t_0}^{t} A_1(\tau)e^{-\lambda_1(t-\tau)} + A_2(\tau)e^{-\lambda_2(t-\tau)} + \ldots + A_{n-1}(\tau)e^{-\lambda_{n-1}(t-\tau)})d\tau \end{aligned}$$

where A_i^i $1 \le i \le n-1$ are scalar constants and

$$\begin{aligned} A_1(\tau) &= \phi_2(\tau) + A_1^2\phi_3(\tau) + \ldots + A_1^{n-1}\phi_n(\tau),\ \in \mathbb{R}^{n+p+1} \\ A_2(\tau) &= A_2^2\phi_3(\tau) + \ldots + A_2^{n-1}\phi_n(\tau),\ \in \mathbb{R}^{n+p+1} \\ &\vdots \\ A_{n-1}(\tau) &= A_{n-1}^{n-1}\phi_n(\tau) \in \mathbb{R}^{n+p+1} \\ \|\xi_1\| &\le \int_{t_0}^{t} (\|A_1(\tau)\|e^{-\lambda_1(t-\tau)} + \|A_2(\tau)\|e^{-\lambda_2(t-\tau)} + \ldots + \|A_{n-1}(\tau)\|e^{-\lambda_{n-1}(t-\tau)})d\tau \\ &\triangleq \mathrm{BND}(|\xi_1|) \end{aligned} \tag{3.13}$$

IV. Robust Control Design: General Case ($\beta \ge 2$)

In this section we generalize Lemma 3.1 to the case of any relative degree β. Considering (2.1) for $\beta \ge 2$ and $b = [0, \ldots, 0, b_\beta, \ldots, b_n]^T$, we state the filtered transformation consisting of the filters [3]

$$\begin{aligned} \dot{\varphi}_1 &= -\bar{\lambda}_1 \varphi_1 + \varphi_2 \\ &\vdots \\ \dot{\varphi}_{\beta-2} &= -\bar{\lambda}_{\beta-2}\varphi_{\beta-2} + \varphi_{\beta-1} \\ \dot{\varphi}_{\beta-1} &= -\bar{\lambda}_{\beta-1}\varphi_{\beta-1} + \sigma(y)u \end{aligned} \tag{4.1}$$

$$\begin{aligned} \dot{\bar{\varphi}}_1 &= -\bar{\lambda}_1 \bar{\varphi}_1 + \bar{\varphi}_2 \\ &\vdots \\ \dot{\bar{\varphi}}_{\beta-2} &= -\bar{\lambda}_{\beta-2}\bar{\varphi}_{\beta-2} + \bar{\varphi}_{\beta-1} \\ \dot{\bar{\varphi}}_{\beta-1} &= -\bar{\lambda}_{\beta-1}\bar{\varphi}_{\beta-1} + \sigma(y)T_d(y,t) \end{aligned} \tag{4.1a}$$

with φ_i, $\bar{\varphi}_i \in \mathbb{R}^1$, $1 \le i \le \beta-1$, and the transformation

$$\bar{z} = \zeta - \sum_{i=2}^{\beta} \bar{d}_i(\varphi_{i-1} + \bar{\varphi}_{i-1}) \tag{4.2}$$

where the $\bar{\lambda}_i$, $1 \le i \le \beta-1$, are arbitrary positive scalars, and $\bar{d}_i \in \mathbb{R}^n$, $1 \le i \le \beta$, are unknown vectors given by the recursive formula

$$\begin{aligned} \bar{d}_\beta &= b \\ \bar{d}_{j-1} &= A_c \bar{d}_j + \bar{\lambda}_{j-1}\bar{d}_j \qquad 2 \le j \le \beta. \end{aligned} \tag{4.3}$$

where A_c is defined in (2.1). Note, that since the vector b is Hurwitz by assumption in (2.1), $\bar{d}_1$ is also Hurwitz and its first element is given by $\bar{d}_1^1 = b_\beta$. Differentiating (4.2) and then substituting (2.1), (4.1), (4.1a), and (4.3) into (4.2), the dynamics in the $\bar{z}$–coordinates are given by

$$\begin{aligned} \dot{\bar{z}} &= A_c\bar{z} + \bar{d}_1(\varphi_1 + \bar{\varphi}_1) + \sum_{i=0}^{p} \theta_i \psi_i(y) \\ &= A_c\bar{z} + \bar{d}_1^1 \begin{bmatrix} \varphi_1+\bar{\varphi}_1 \\ 0 \\ \vdots \\ 0 \\ 0 \end{bmatrix}_{n\times 1} + \ldots + \bar{d}_1^n \begin{bmatrix} 0 \\ 0 \\ \vdots \\ 0 \\ \varphi_1+\bar{\varphi}_1 \end{bmatrix}_{n\times 1} + \sum_{i=0}^{p} \theta_i \psi_i(y) \\ \dot{\bar{z}} &= A_c\bar{z} + \sum_{i=1}^{n+p+1} \bar{\theta}_i \bar{\psi}_i(y, \varphi_1, \bar{\varphi}_1) \\ y &= C_c \bar{z} \end{aligned} \tag{4.4}$$

where $\bar{d}_1^i \in \mathbb{R}^1$ are elements of $\bar{d}_1 \in \mathbb{R}^{n\times 1}$ which depend on the unknown parameters $b_i(\theta)$, $\bar{\theta}_i$ represents a compilation of the unknown constant parameters given by θ_i and $\bar{d}_1^i$ defined below, $\psi_i(y) \in \mathbb{R}^{n\times 1}$ is defined in (2.1), and $\bar{\psi}_i(y, \varphi_1, \bar{\varphi}_1) \in \mathbb{R}^{n\times 1}$ represents a compilation of the known functions given by φ_1, $\bar{\varphi}_1$ and $\psi_i(y)$. Note that we can define

$$\bar{\theta}_1 = \bar{d}_1^1, \ldots, \bar{\theta}_n = \bar{d}_1^n, \quad \bar{\theta}_{n+1} = \theta_0, \ldots, \bar{\theta}_{n+p+1} = \theta_p,$$

$$\bar{\psi}_1(y, \varphi_1, \bar{\varphi}_1) = \begin{bmatrix} \varphi_1+\bar{\varphi}_1 \\ 0 \\ \vdots \\ 0 \\ 0 \end{bmatrix}_{n\times 1}, \ldots, \bar{\psi}_n(y, \varphi_1, \bar{\varphi}_1) = \begin{bmatrix} 0 \\ 0 \\ \vdots \\ 0 \\ \varphi_1+\bar{\varphi}_1 \end{bmatrix}_{n\times 1}$$

$$\bar{\psi}_{n+1} = \psi_0(y), \ldots, \bar{\psi}_{n+p+1} = \psi_p(y),$$

and

$$\bar{\psi}_i(y, \varphi_1, \bar{\varphi}_1) = \sum_{j=1}^{n} \phi_{ij} d_j$$

where d_j is constructed using the recursive formula given in (3.3). As in Lemma 3.1, (4.4) can be transformed into a new "plant" in the same form as (3.4). Here, we briefly describe how to use the filtered transformation rather than provide a proof. Rewrite (4.4) as

$$\begin{aligned} \dot{\bar{z}} &= A_c\bar{z} + \sum_{j=1}^{n} d_j \sum_{i=1}^{n+p+1} \phi_{ij}\bar{\theta}_i = A_c\bar{z} + \sum_{j=1}^{n} d_j \phi_j^T(y, \varphi_1, \bar{\varphi}_1)\bar{\theta}_i \\ y &= C_c\bar{z} \end{aligned} \tag{4.5}$$

The auxiliary filter is

$$\dot{\xi}_i = -\lambda_i \xi_i + \xi_{i+1} + \phi_{i+1}(y,\varphi_1,\bar{\varphi}_1),\ \xi_i \in \mathbb{R}^{n+p+1} \quad 1 \le i \le n-1$$
$$\xi_n = 0 \qquad \xi_i(0) = 0,\ \xi_n \in \mathbb{R}^{n+p+1} \tag{4.6}$$

and the transformation is of the form

$$z = \bar{z} - \sum_{j=2}^{n} d_j \xi_{j-1}^T \bar{\theta}. \tag{4.7}$$

Differentiating (4.7) and then substituting (4.5), (4.6), and (3.3) into (4.7) yields

$$\begin{aligned} \dot{z} &= A_c z + d_1 \sum_{i=0}^{p} \theta_i \psi_i^1(y) + d_1 b_\beta(\varphi_1 + \bar{\varphi}_1) + d_1 \xi_1^T \bar{\theta} \\ y &= C_c z \end{aligned} \tag{4.8}$$

where $\psi_i^1(y)$ is the first element of the vector $\psi_i(y)$ defined in (2.1). Using (4.8) and (3.7), we determine the error dynamics to be

$$\begin{aligned} \dot{z}_e &= A_c z_e + d_1(\bar{T}_r - b_\beta \varphi_1) \\ e &= C_c z_e \end{aligned} \tag{4.9}$$

where

$$z_e = z_m - z,\ e = y_m - y, \text{ and } \bar{T}_r = \zeta(r_m, y_m) - \sum_{i=0}^{p} \theta_i \psi_i^1(y) - \xi_1^T \bar{\theta} - b_\beta \bar{\varphi}_1.$$

In order to stablize the error system, we can rewrite (4.9) as

$$\begin{aligned} \dot{z}_e &= A_c z_e + d_1(\bar{T}_r - b_\beta(\varphi_1 - \text{sgn}(b_\beta)e)) - d_1 \text{sgn}(b_\beta) b_\beta e \\ &= (A_c - d_1 K) z_e + d_1(\bar{T}_r - b_\beta(\varphi_1 - \text{sgn}(b_\beta)e)) \\ &= A_K z_e + d_1(\bar{T}_r - b_\beta(\varphi_1 - \text{sgn}(b_\beta)e)) \\ e &= C_c z_e \end{aligned} \tag{4.10}$$

where $K = [b_\beta \text{sgn}(b_\beta), 0, \ldots, 0] \in \mathbb{R}^{1\times n}$, and $A_K = A_c - d_1 K$ ($A_K \in \mathbb{R}^{n\times n}$). Also, φ_1 is the intermediate control which can be designed to make the tracking error small. However, the real control u is related to the intermediate control φ_1 through the differential equations given in (4.1). Our objective is to design the real control u to make the tracking error small. To achieve this objective we will utilize a robust control developed using the integrator backstepping method [9,11]. However, prior to stating the control, we will introduce the following recursive mapping:

$$\begin{aligned} v_1 &= v_{1r} + \text{sgn}(b_\beta)e, \qquad v_{1r} = \frac{e g_1^2}{2\underline{b}_\beta(|e| g_1 + \epsilon_1)}, \\ v_2 &= v_1 - \varphi_1 + \bar{\lambda}_1 \varphi_1 + \frac{(v_1 - \varphi_1) g_2^2}{2(|v_1 - \varphi_1| g_2 + \epsilon_2)}, \\ v_i &= v_{i-2} - \varphi_{i-2} + \bar{\lambda}_{i-1}\varphi_{i-1} + v_{i-1} - \varphi_{i-1} + \frac{(v_{i-1} - \varphi_{i-1}) g_i^2}{2(|v_{i-1} - \varphi_{i-1}| g_i + \epsilon_i)}, \\ v_\beta &= v_{\beta-2} - \varphi_{\beta-2} + \bar{\lambda}_{i-1}\varphi_{i-1} + v_{\beta-1} - \varphi_{\beta-1} + \frac{(v_{\beta-1} - \varphi_{\beta-1}) g_\beta^2}{2(|v_{\beta-1} - \varphi_{\beta-1}| g_\beta + \epsilon_\beta)} \end{aligned} \tag{4.11}$$

where $i = 3,\ldots,\beta$, $\epsilon_i > 0$ are constants, and

$$\begin{aligned} g_1 &= 2\text{BND}(|\bar{T}_r|), \\ g_2 &= 2\bar{b}_\beta |e| + 2|\dot{v}_1|, \text{ and} \\ g_i &= 2|\dot{v}_{i-1}| \quad i = 3, \ldots, \beta. \end{aligned} \tag{4.12}$$

The bounding function is defined as

$$\text{BND}(|\bar{T}_r|) = \|\zeta(r_m, y_m) - \sum_{i=0}^{p} \theta_i \psi_i^1(y)\| + \text{BND}(|\xi_1|)\|\bar{\theta}\| + \bar{b}_\beta \text{BND}(|\bar{\varphi}_1|)$$

where $\text{BND}(|\xi_1|)$ is defined in the same manner as (3.12) from (4.6). We can determine $\text{BND}(|\bar{\varphi}_1|)$ from (4.1a) as follows:

$$\begin{aligned} |\bar{\varphi}_1(t)| &= \left| \frac{\sigma(y) T_d(y,t)}{(s+\bar{\lambda}_1)(s+\bar{\lambda}_2)\ldots(s+\bar{\lambda}_{n-1})} \right| \le \int_{t_o}^{t} \|\bar{C}_2 e^{\bar{A}_2(t-\tau)} \bar{B}_2\| \, |\sigma(y)| \beta(y,t) d\tau \\ &\stackrel{\Delta}{=} \text{BND}(|\bar{\varphi}_1|), \end{aligned}$$

where $\{\bar{A}_2, \bar{B}_2, \bar{C}_2\}$ is a minimum realization of $\dfrac{1}{(s+\bar{\lambda}_1)(s+\bar{\lambda}_2)\ldots(s+\bar{\lambda}_{n-1})}$.

It is worth making two observations on the mapping procedure. First, the function $g_1(y, y_m, r_m, u, t)$ is not an explicit function of u(t) but an implicit one since $g_1(y,u,t)$ depends on auxiliary signals, such as ξ_1, which is a function of u(t). The same property holds for all g_i. Second, the recursive mapping basically involves finding a bounding function of $|\dot{v}_i|$ in order to obtain v_{i+1}. The term $|\dot{v}_i|$ can be bounded by first developing bounds for the first–order partial derivatives of v_i with respect to its variables and then by determining the bounds for the first order time derivative of its variables. Now, utilizing (4.1), (4.10) and (4.11) we state the main result.

Theorem 4.1

If the robust control u(t) is chosen to be

$$u(t) = v_\beta / \sigma(y) \tag{4.13}$$

where v_β is defined by the outcome of the mapping procedure (4.11), then the plant output tracking error e(t) is GUUB. That is, as time approaches infinity, the magnitude of the output tracking error becomes no larger than the design parameter ϵ, where $\epsilon = \sum_{i=1}^{\beta} \epsilon_i$. Furthermore, the robust control $u(t) = v_\beta/\sigma(y)$ is GUB.

The resulting control in Theorem 4.1 requires only input–output data and guarantees global stability and robust performance. Although the output tracking error converges globally and exponentially to the ultimate bound ϵ, the tracking error is not guaranteed to converge to zero despite the fact that the design parameter $\epsilon > 0$ can be made to be arbitrarily small if control energy permits.

Remark 4.1

The backstepping construction in [9,11] begins with a reduced–order system from which we determine a compensator and a Lyapunov function. Then new states are added one at a time, at each step constructing a new compensator and a new Lyapunov function from those of the previous step. Eventually, we obtain a compensator for the original system which has the desired properties. The overall controller is constructed through a recursive procedure in which the controller calculation at each stage needs the controller constructed in the previous stage. In other words, we must choose different Lyapunov functions at each stage. In this paper, we construct the controller through a recursive mapping rather than a recursive procedure from stage to stage. This mapping technique was developed by Qu in [4]. Theoretically, the recursive mapping is actually the same as the recursive procedure, but the recursive mapping has the advantage of being constructed in one step rather than a piece at a time. Therefore, only one Lyapunov function is needed for the whole recursive mapping. Another advantage of the recursive mapping approach is that the controller developed using this proceedure is of a more concise form. In addition, the convergence properties are more easily determined.

Remark 4.2

Theorem 4.1 applies to a single–input, single–output linear system characterized either by a transfer function of known relative degree β

$$w(s) = \frac{b_\beta s^{n-\beta} + \ldots + b_n}{s^n + a_1 s^{n-1} + \ldots + a_n} \tag{4.14}$$

or by the state space form

$$\begin{aligned} \dot{x} &= \bar{A}x + \bar{B}u \\ y &= \bar{C}x \end{aligned} \tag{4.15}$$

where the numerator is a Hurwitz polynomial with unknown coefficients but with b_β of known sign. The denominator is a polynomial with unknown coefficients a_i, $1 \le i \le n$, and $\bar{A} \in \mathbb{R}^{n\text{x}n}$, $\bar{B} \in \mathbb{R}^{n\times 1}$, $\bar{C} \in \mathbb{R}^{1\times n}$ are unknown matrices, $(\bar{A}, \bar{C})$ is observable, u is the input, and y is the output. It can be shown that there exists a nonsingular transformation T: $z = T^{-1}x$ such that (4.15) can be transformed into observable canonical form, therefore, a realization in observable form of both (4.14) and (4.15) can be written as

$$\begin{aligned} \dot{x} &= \begin{bmatrix} -a_1 & 1 & 0 \ldots 0 \\ -a_2 & 0 & 1 \ldots 0 \\ \cdot & \cdot & \cdot \quad \cdot \\ -a_{n-1} & \cdot & 0 \ldots 1 \\ -a_n & \cdot & 0 \ldots 0 \end{bmatrix}_{n\times n} x + \begin{bmatrix} 0 \\ \cdot \\ b_\beta \\ \vdots \\ b_n \end{bmatrix}_{n\times 1} u \\ y &= [1\ 0 \ldots 0]_{1\times n}\, x. \end{aligned} \tag{4.16}$$

If we let $[a_1, \ldots, a_n, b_\beta, \ldots, b_n]^T$ be the $(2n-\beta+1)$–dimensional vector of unknown parameters, then the system (4.16) is of type (2.1). As in Theorem 4.1 (or Theorem 3.2 when $\beta = 1$), for the system in (4.14) or (4.15), there exists a robust, output–feedback control for which the output tracking error is GUUB.

Remark 4.3

Filtered transformations can be viewed as a tool to produce a nonminimal realization of the transfer function (4.14) or an alternative state realization (which are structurally different from the original system) for nonlinear (2.3) or linear systems (4.16). Desired motion can be expressed in terms of the new states (which constitute a SPR subsystem). In other words, through the filtered transformation, the original system is transfered into a SPR matched subsystem together with other subsystems. The control law can be constructed to translate the desired motion specification in terms of the physical output into those in terms of these new states of the SPR subsystems which are driven into a desired trajectory, so that the output tracks the desired motion, while other new states of other subsystems remain globally and uniformly bounded.

Remark 4.4

To find the bounding functions $|\dot{v}_i|$ for obtaining v_{i+1} we need the bounding functions $|e^{(i)}|$ and $|y^{(i)}|$. Actually we only need to calculate the bounding function $|e^{(i)}|$ because $y^{(i)} = y_m^{(i)} - e^{(i)}$. The calculation of $|e^{(i)}|$ can be performed thru the use of (4.10). For a rigorous mathematical treatment of the process of finding the bounding functions using the concept of user–defined functions see [2].

Remark 4.5

There are two major differences between this paper and [3]. First, we introduce unknown dynamics in the plant which robust control can compensate for while adaptive control can not. Second, the adaptive method developed in [3] is observer–based, that is, the error dynamics are stabilized through state feedback in which the states are constructed by an observer. However, in the robust control scheme developed in this paper, the error dynamics are stabilized through output feedback so that the proposed robust control is of a simpler form than the adaptive controller (e.g. no observer and no adaptive law). Also, the tracking error converges exponentially.

VI. Conclusion

For the output tracking problem of minimum–phase nonlinear uncertain systems, model reference robust control is proposed. The method combines both a filtered transformation and robust control approach. Under some geometric conditions the control technique can guarantee robust stability and performance for output tracking while requiring only input–output feedback for a class of system which may not be feedback linearizable. The assumption of the relative degree of the reference model being equal to or greater than that of the plant is relaxed. The theory presented in this paper for robust output tracking also leads to linear systems either in transfer function or state space form.

Acknowledgements

This work is supported in part by U.S. National Science Foundation Grants MSS–9110034 and IRI–9111258.

References.

References are available upon request.

Proceedings of the
American Control Conference
San Francisco, California • June 1993

Robust Tracking Control of an Induction Motor

D. Dawson,* Z. Qu,** and J. Hu*

*School of Electrical and Computer Engineering
Clemson University
Clemson, SC 29634–0915
803–656–5924

**Department of Electrical Engineering
University of Central Florida
Orlando, FL 32816–0450
407–823–5976

ABSTRACT

This paper illustrates a robust control approach for an induction motor driving a load. The proposed controller is robust with regard to parametric uncertainties and additive bounded disturbances throughout the entire motor/load model while yielding a global uniform ultimate bounded (GUUB) stability result for the motor position tracking error. Simulation results are used validate the performance of the controller.

I. INTRODUCTION

For brevity, we only give a short synopsis of some of the nonlinear based control approaches for induction motors. In [1], De Luca *et al* develop an exact nonlinear controller for a reduced order model consisting of the four electrical variables with stator voltages and the slip frequency while the rotor speed was considered a "slowly varying" parameter in relation to the electrical variables. Based on the model given in [2], Teel *et al* develop an indirect adaptive controller. In [3] and [4], nonlinear based input–output linearization controllers are developed to decouple rotor speed from flux dynamics. In [3], Marino *et al* also develop an adaptive feedback linearizing control for an induction motor which is capable of identifying the load torque and rotor winding resistance. In [5], Georgiou also develops an adaptive feedback linearization controller. In [6], Kadiyala develops an indirect adaptive controller which eliminates the overparameterization problem of some of the direct adaptive control approaches. In [7], Kanellakapoulos *et al* develop an exact model based speed controller for induction without the need for flux measurements. In [8], Ortega *et al* develop an adaptive "torque" controller (i.e. for the mechanical parameters) for a induction motor without the need for flux measurements; however, exact knowledge of the electrical parameters is required. In [9], Chiasson *et al* explores the dynamic feedback linearization of the induction motor via the addition of an integrator in one of the system inputs.

This paper illustrates a robust control approach for an induction motor driving a load. The proposed controller is robust with regard to parametric uncertainties and additive bounded disturbances throughout the entire motor/load model while yielding a global uniform ultimate bounded (GUUB) stability result for the motor position tracking error and also ensuring all electromechanical states remain bounded. A disadvantage of the robust induction motor controller is the requirement of full state feedback (i.e. measurement of flux and current). The control development is similar to [7] in that the motor torques are treated simply as a coupling between the electrical and mechanical subsystems. The control technique used in this paper is related to the so–called "backstepping" technique (See [10,11,12] for applications of this techniques for generic control problems). The paper is organized as follows. In Sections II and III, we present the induction motor model and form the error systems required for the stability proof. In Sections IV and V, we design the robust tracking controller and present the corresponding stability result. In Section VI, we present simulation results which are utilized to elucidate the performance of the robust controller.

II. MATHEMATICAL AND MODELING PRELIMINARIES

2.1. Stability Lemmas

Before presenting the motor dynamics and the robust controller, we introduce two stability lemmas which will be exploited later in the development.

Lemma 2.1 [13]

If the $nx1$ state vector $x(t)$ in the continuous system

$$\dot{x}(t) = f(x(t),t) \tag{2.1}$$

has an associated Lyapunov function [14] $V(x,t)$ with the following properties

$$\lambda_1\|x(t)\|^2 \le V(x,t) \le \lambda_2\|x(t)\|^2 \tag{2.2}$$

$$\dot{V}(x,t) \le -\lambda_3\|x(t)\|^2 + \epsilon \tag{2.3}$$

where λ_1, λ_2, λ_3, and ϵ are positive scalar constants, then the state $x(t)$ is GUUB in the sense that

$$\|x(t)\| \le \left[\frac{\lambda_2}{\lambda_1}\|x(0)\|^2 e^{-\lambda t} + \frac{\epsilon}{\lambda_1\lambda}\left[1 - e^{-\lambda t}\right]\right]^{\frac{1}{2}} \tag{2.4}$$

where $\lambda = \lambda_3/\lambda_2$ and e is the natural logarithm exponential. The notation $\|\{\cdot\}\|$ is used to represent the Euclidean norm [15] of the vector $\{\cdot\}$ and a "dot" is used to designate differentiation with respect to time throughout the development.

Lemma 2.2 [13]

Let the signal $y(t)$ be defined in terms of the signal $z(t)$ as shown

$$y(t) = \dot{z}(t) + \alpha z(t) \tag{2.5}$$

where α is a positive scalar constant. If $y(t)$ is upper bounded by the expression

$$|y(t)| \le \sqrt{A} + \sqrt{|B|}e^{-\lambda t/2} \tag{2.6}$$

where $|\cdot|$ is used to represent the absolute value, and A, $|B|$, λ are positive scalar constants, then $z(t)$ can be upper bounded as

$$|z(t)| \le e^{-\alpha t}|z(0)| + \frac{\sqrt{A}}{\alpha}\left[1 - e^{-\alpha t}\right] + \frac{2\sqrt{|B|}}{2\alpha - \lambda}\left[e^{-\lambda t/2} - e^{-\alpha t}\right]. \tag{2.7}$$

2.2. Induction Motor Model

For the general theory and related motor control problems, the reader is referred to [16]. In [17], Krause introduced a two phase equivalent machine representation with two stator windings and two rotor windings. Under the assumption of equal mutual inductance and linear magnetic circuit, the dynamics of an induction motor driving a load are given by

$$J\ddot{q} + N(q,\dot{q}) = K_\tau(\psi_a I_b - \psi_b I_a) \tag{2.8}$$

$$L_I\dot{I}_a + R_a(\psi_a,\psi_b,I_a,I_b,\dot{q}) = V_a \tag{2.9}$$

$$L_I\dot{I}_b + R_b(\psi_a,\psi_b,I_a,I_b,\dot{q}) = V_b \tag{2.10}$$

$$L_r\dot{\psi}_a + N_a(\psi_a,\psi_b,\dot{q}) = K_I I_a \tag{2.11}$$

$$L_r\dot{\psi}_b + N_b(\psi_a,\psi_b,\dot{q}) = K_I I_b \tag{2.12}$$

where q, $\dot{q}$, and $\ddot{q}$ represent the rotor position, velocity, and acceleration, respectively; $(\psi_a\ \psi_b)$, $(I_a\ I_b)$, and $(V_a\ V_b)$, represent the rotor fluxes, stator currents, and stator voltages, respectively; J, K_τ, L_I, L_r, and K_I are positive constants related to the motor parameters (see Appendix A), and $N(\cdot)$, $R_a(\cdot)$, $R_b(\cdot)$, $N_a(\cdot)$, and $N_b(\cdot)$ are nonlinear functions related to the motor parameters, rotor fluxes, motor position/speed, and stator currents (see Appendix A).

Remark 2.1

It is important to emphasize that constant bounds are assumed for each of the parametric quantities represented in (2.8) thru (2.12). For example, the inductance coupling term K_τ is assumed to be bounded as

$$\underline{K}_\tau \le K_\tau \le \bar{K}_\tau \tag{2.13}$$

where $\underline{K}_\tau$ and $\bar{K}_\tau$ are known positive scalar bounding constants. Hence, in the subsequent development, we will use overbars and underbars to denote the known upper bounds and lower bounds; respectively, for all parametric quantities described in (2.8) thru (2.12).

III. Formulation of the Tracking Error System

Our objective is to synthesize a robust controller that achieves GUUB position tracking (i.e. in the sense of Lemma 2.1) in the presence of modeling uncertainty. With this objective in mind, we define the motor position tracking error to be

$$e = q_d - q \tag{3.1}$$

where q_d represents the desired motor position. We will assume that q_d and its first, second, and third derivatives are all bounded functions of time. In addition, we define the filtered tracking error [14] to be

$$r = \dot{e} + \alpha e \tag{3.2}$$

where α is a positive scalar constant.

We now write the mechanical dynamics of (2.8) in terms of the filtered tracking error defined in (3.2) as

$$J\dot{r} = w_\tau - K_\tau u_\tau + K_\tau \eta_\tau \tag{3.3}$$

where

$$w_\tau = J(\ddot{q}_d + \alpha\dot{e}) + N(q,\dot{q}), \tag{3.4}$$

$$\eta_\tau = u_\tau - (\psi_a I_b - \psi_b I_a), \tag{3.5}$$

and u_τ is an auxiliary robust controller embedded inside of the robust voltage controllers, which are to be defined later. After differentiating (3.5) with respect to time and substituting (2.9) thru (2.12), the dynamics of the torque perturbation η_τ can be written in the following form

$$L_I\dot{\eta}_\tau = w_{I1} - (\psi_a V_b - \psi_b V_a) - K_\tau r \tag{3.6}$$

where

$$w_{I1} = L_I\dot{u}_\tau + K_\tau r + \psi_a R_b(\cdot) - \psi_b R_a(\cdot) \tag{3.7}$$
$$+ L_I I_a L_r^{-1}(K_I I_b - N_b(\cdot)) + L_I I_b L_r^{-1}(N_a(\cdot) - K_I I_a).$$

The error system dynamics given by (3.3) and (3.6) constitute one control objective. That is, the design of a voltage controller to ensure that the rotor position tracks a desired rotor position. We now form another set of errors systems to ensure that all the electrical states (i.e. ψ_a, ψ_b, I_a, I_b) remain bounded. This control objective is accomplished by defining the flux tracking error η_ψ in the following way

$$\eta_\psi = \psi_d - \tfrac{1}{2}(\psi_a^2 + \psi_b^2) \tag{3.8}$$

where ψ_d is the "pseudo–magnitude" of the desired flux [7] which is assumed to be second order differentiable with respect to time. After differentiating (3.8) with respect to time and substituting (2.11) and (2.12), the dynamics of the flux tracking error can be written in the following form

$$L_r\dot{\eta}_\psi = w_\psi - K_I u_\psi + K_I\eta_I \tag{3.9}$$

where

$$w_\psi = L_r\dot{\psi}_d + \psi_a N_a(\cdot) + \psi_b N_b(\cdot), \tag{3.10}$$

$$\eta_I = u_\psi - (\psi_a I_a + \psi_b I_b), \tag{3.11}$$

and u_ψ is an auxiliary robust controller embedded inside of the robust voltage controllers, which are to be defined later. After differentiating (3.11) with respect to time and substituting (2.9) thru (2.12), the dynamics of the current perturbation η_I can be written in the following form

$$L_I\dot{\eta}_I = w_{I2} - (\psi_a V_a + \psi_b V_b) - K_I\eta_\psi \tag{3.12}$$

where

$$w_{I2} = L_I\dot{u}_\psi + K_I\eta_\psi + \psi_a R_a(\cdot) + \psi_b R_b(\cdot) \tag{3.13}$$
$$+ L_I I_b L_r^{-1}(N_b(\cdot) - K_I I_b) + L_I I_a L_r^{-1}(N_a(\cdot) - K_I I_a)$$

To simplify the stability proof given later in the paper, we now combine (3.6) and (3.12) into the following error system

$$L_I\dot{\eta}_e = w_e - BV_e - [K_\tau r \quad K_I\eta_\psi]^T \tag{3.14}$$

where

$$V_e = [V_a \quad V_b]^T,\quad \eta_e = [\eta_\tau \quad \eta_I]^T,\quad w_e = [w_{I1} \quad w_{I2}]^T,\quad B = \begin{bmatrix} -\psi_b & \psi_a \\ \psi_a & \psi_b \end{bmatrix}. \tag{3.15}$$

Remark 3.1

The dynamics equations given by (2.8) thru (2.12) have now been rewritten in the tracking error form given by (3.3), (3.9), and (3.14). It should be noted that the form of these new equations, which are similar to those given in [18], are motivated by the robust control strategy and the stability analysis that follows in the succeeding two sections.

IV. Robust Control Formulation

In this section, we present the robust tracking controller which compensates for uncertainties in the motor dynamic model. By utilizing this controller, we are able to prove a GUUB stability result for the motor position tracking error in the next section. The proposed controller is robust with regard to parametric uncertainties and additive bounded disturbances in the motor dynamic model.

Given the tracking error dynamics of (3.3), (3.9), and (3.14), we define the robust controllers u_τ, u_ψ, and V_e to be

$$u_\tau = (k_1 r + u_1)/\underline{K}_\tau,\quad u_\psi = (k_2\eta_\psi + u_2)/\underline{K}_I,\quad V_e = B^{-1}(k_3\eta_e + u_3) \tag{4.1}$$

where k_1, k_2, and k_3 are positive scalar controller gains and u_1, u_2, and u_3 are auxiliary robust controllers. The auxiliary robust controllers u_1, u_2, and u_3 are defined as [18]

$$u_1 = \frac{r\rho_1^2}{\|r\|\rho_1 + \epsilon_1},\quad u_2 = \frac{\eta_\psi\rho_2^2}{\|\eta_\psi\|\rho_2 + \epsilon_2},\quad u_3 = \frac{\eta_e\rho_3^2}{\|\eta_e\|\rho_3 + \epsilon_3} \tag{4.2}$$

where ϵ_1, ϵ_2, and ϵ_3 are positive scalar control gains which are adjusted to achieve a desired motor tracking error performance. The terms ρ_1, ρ_2, and ρ_3 defined in (4.2) are positive scalar functions used to "bound" the uncertainty in the motor model. These bounding functions are defined as follows

$$\rho_1 \geq \|w_\tau\|,\quad \rho_2 \geq \|w_\psi\|,\quad \rho_3 \geq \|w_e\| \tag{4.3}$$

where w_τ, w_ψ, and w_e are defined in (3.4), (3.10) and (3.15), respectively.

Remark 4.1

The procedure for calculating the bounding functions defined in (4.3) will be discussed later in the development. For now, we simply assume their existence. It should be emphasized that these bounding functions depend only on measurement of ψ_a, ψ_b, I_a, I_b, q, and $\dot{q}$.

Remark 4.2

We note that our controller is not well defined for $\psi_a = \psi_b = 0$ since during these operating conditions, the inverse of the matrix B defined in (3.15) does not exist. In actual operation of the induction motor, this singularity will not be a problem since electronic circuitry can be used to provide an initial rotor flux for motor starting.

V. Stability Analysis of the Closed Loop System

By substituting the controller given in (4.2) and (4.3) into the tracking error dynamics given by (3.3), (3.9), and (3.14), we can form the closed loop system. In this section, we give a GUUB stability result for the closed loop system. That is, we show that the position tracking error defined by (3.1) is stable in the sense of Lemma 2.2. Before we give our final result, we first state a GUUB stability theorem for the filtered tracking error defined in (3.2).

Theorem 5.1

The filtered tracking error defined in (3.2) is GUUB in the following sense

$$\|r(t)\| \le [A + Be^{-\lambda t}]^{1/2} \tag{5.1}$$

where

$$A = \frac{\epsilon}{\lambda_1 \lambda}, \quad B = \frac{\lambda_2}{\lambda_1}\|x(0)\|^2 - \frac{\epsilon}{\lambda_1 \lambda}, \quad \epsilon = \epsilon_1 + \epsilon_2 + \epsilon_3 \tag{5.2}$$

$$x(t) = [r(t) \;\; \eta_\psi(t) \;\; \eta_e^T(t)]^T, \quad \lambda = \lambda_3/\lambda_2, \tag{5.3}$$

$$\lambda_1 = \tfrac{1}{2}min(\underline{J},\underline{L}_r,\underline{L}_I), \quad \lambda_2 = \tfrac{1}{2}max(\bar{J},\bar{L}_r,\bar{L}_I), \quad \lambda_3 = min(k_1,k_2,k_3) \tag{5.4}$$

Proof:

Define the following Lyapunov function

$$V = \tfrac{1}{2}rJr + \tfrac{1}{2}\eta_\psi L_r \eta_\psi + \tfrac{1}{2}\eta_e^T L_I \eta_e = x^T P x \tag{5.5}$$

where P is a 4x4 diagonal positive definite matrix given by

$$P = \tfrac{1}{2}diag\{J, L_r, L_I, L_I\}. \tag{5.6}$$

By utilizing the Rayleigh–Ritz Theorem [15], we can state that V defined in (5.5) is upper and lower bounded as in (2.2) where $\lambda_1 = \lambda_{min}\{P\}$ and $\lambda_2 = \lambda_{max}\{P\}$ are defined in (5.4).

After differentiating (5.5) with respect to time and substituting (3.3), (3.9), (3.14), and (4.1), we have

$$\dot{V} = -(rk_1r)(K_\tau/\underline{K}_\tau) - \eta_\psi k_2 \eta_\psi (K_I/\underline{K}_I) - \eta_e^T k_3 \eta_e + rw_\tau - (ru_1)(K_\tau/\underline{K}_\tau) + \eta_\psi w_\psi - (\eta_\psi u_2)(K_I/\underline{K}_I) + \eta_e^T w_e - \eta_e^T u_3 \tag{5.7}$$

After substituting (4.2) for u_1, u_2, and u_3 into (5.7) and utilizing (2.13) and (4.3), $\dot{V}$ can be upper bounded as

$$\dot{V} \le -\lambda_3\|x\|^2 + \left[\|r\|\rho_1 - \left[\frac{\|r\|^2\rho_1^2}{\|r\|\rho_1 + \epsilon_1}\right]\right] + \left[\|\eta_\psi\|\rho_2 - \left[\frac{\|\eta_\psi\|^2\rho_2^2}{\|\eta_\psi\|\rho_2 + \epsilon_2}\right]\right] + \left[\|\eta_e\|\rho_3 - \left[\frac{\|\eta_e\|^2\rho_3^2}{\|\eta_e\|\rho_3 + \epsilon_3}\right]\right] \tag{5.8}$$

where λ_3 is defined in (5.4) and x is defined in (5.3). After combining each of the bracketed terms on the right–hand–side of (5.8) under common denominators, a new upper bound on $\dot{V}$ is found to be in the form of (2.3) where ϵ is defined in (5.2). Therefore, we can apply Lemma 2.1 and utilize the fact that $\|r(t)\| \le \|x(t)\|$ to yield (5.1).

Remark 5.1

After noting that $|r(t)| = \|r(t)\|$ and that the right–hand–side of (2.6) is always greater than or equal to the right–hand–side of (5.1), we can apply Lemma 2.2 with (3.2) to yield a motor position tracking error bound as given by (2.7). Note that the control parameters can be arbitrarily adjusted to give a desired transient response and an ultimate bound for the motor position tracking error.

Remark 5.2

From the above stability proof, we know that r(t) and $\eta_\psi(t)$ (defined in (3.2) and (3.8), respectively) are bounded for all time; therefore, from this information, it is easy to show that q, $\dot{q}$, ψ_a, and ψ_b (and hence u_τ and u_ψ defined in (4.1)) are bounded for all time. From the above stability proof, we also know that $\eta_e(t)$ defined in (3.15) (and hence η_τ and η_I defined in (3.5) and (3.11), respectively) are bounded for all time; therefore, from this information, it is easy to show that the quantities $(\psi_a I_b - \psi_b I_a)$ and $(\psi_a I_a + \psi_b I_b)$ are bounded for all time. After multiplying the first quantity by ψ_a and the second quantity by ψ_b and adding the result, we obtain the bounded expression $I_b(\psi_a^2 + \psi_b^2)$ which shows that I_b (and similarly I_a) is bounded for all time. Note, $I_b(\psi_a^2 + \psi_b^2)$ is always bounded since we always assume $\psi_{ai} = \psi_{bi} = 0$ is never satisfied (see Remark 4.2).

Remark 5.3

It should be noted that the calculation of the bounding functions ρ_2 and ρ_3 defined in (4.3) require substitution of the original electromechanical equations given by (2.8) thru (2.12). For example, in the calculation of ρ_3, we can see from (3.7) that we must bound $\dot{u}_\tau$, which given by the time differentiation of u_τ in (4.1), will depend on q, $\dot{q}$, and $\ddot{q}$. However, we note that by the utilization of (2.8) and the parametric bounds defined in (2.13), the dependency of $\ddot{q}$ can be replaced by a known positive scalar function $\xi(q,\dot{q},I_a,I_b,\psi_a,\psi_b)$ which is always greater than $\|\ddot{q}\|$.

Remark 5.4

The calculation of the robust controllers defined in (4.2) is slightly complicated by the fact that we must calculate bounds on the derivative of the embedded robust controllers (i.e. u_τ and u_ψ defined in (4.1)). In general, the embedded controllers will be functions of the Euclidean norm of states; therefore, in general, the derivative of these terms are not well–defined. This problem can be eliminated by redefining auxiliary robust controllers u_1 and u_2 defined in (4.2). For example, by redefining u_1 as

$$u_1 = \frac{r\rho_{1s}^2}{\|r\|_m \rho_{1m} + \epsilon_1} \tag{5.9}$$

where ρ_{1s} and ρ_{1m} are the same positive scalar function defined in (4.3) (i.e. ρ_1) but with the dependence on the standard Euclidean norm being replaced by the functions $\|\cdot\|_s$ and $\|\cdot\|_m$, respectively. The functions $\|\cdot\|_s$ and $\|\cdot\|_m$ are defined to be

$$\|y\|_s = \sqrt{y^Ty + \sigma} \quad \text{and} \quad \|y\|_m = \sqrt{y^Ty + \sigma} - \sqrt{\sigma} \tag{5.10}$$

where σ is a small positive constant, and y is an arbitrary nx1 vector. Note that as result of (5.10) and the standard definition of the Euclidean norm, we have

$$\|y\|_s \ge \|y\| \ge \|y\|_m \quad \text{and} \quad \rho_{1s} \ge \rho_1 \ge \rho_{1m}. \tag{5.11}$$

It should be noted that the re–defining of u_1 in no way destroys the stability result given by Theorem 5.1. This can be established by utilizing the following additional factoid in the proof of Theorem 5.1

$$\frac{\|r\|^2\rho_{1s}^2}{\|r\|_m\rho_{1m} + \epsilon_1} \ge \frac{\|r\|^2\rho_1^2}{\|r\|\rho_1 + \epsilon_1}. \tag{5.12}$$

VI. SIMULATION

In this section, we give simulation results for the theoretical developments presented in the previous sections. We selected the motor parameter values for (2.8) thru (2.12) to be

$$R_s = 0.18\Omega,\ R_r = 0.15\Omega,\ L_s = L_r = 0.0699H,\ M = 0.068H,$$
$$J = 0.0568Kg\text{–}m^2,\ n_p = 4,\ F_d = 0.01N\text{–}sec. \tag{6.1}$$

The desired motor position trajectory is assumed to be

$$q_d = \sin\left[\left[1 - e^{-5t^3}\right]t\right] rad. \tag{6.2}$$

The desired flux is designed to be

$$\psi_d = 1.3\left[1 - e^{-t^2}\right] + 0.01 \text{ Wb}. \quad (6.3)$$

The initial position error, velocity error, and currents are set to zero. The initial fluxes are set to 0.1wb. The controller gains are assumed to be $k_1 = k_2 = k_3 = 1$, $\epsilon_1 = \epsilon_2 = 60$, $\epsilon_3 = 800$, $\alpha = 30$, and $\sigma = 0.01$. For control purposes, the parameters of (2.9) thru (2.12) are upper and lower bounded at ±50% of the nominal values given in (6.1). In addition, additive disturbances are assumed to be

$$T_{d1} = T_{d2} = T_{d3} = T_{d4} = T_{d5} = 0.2\sin(2t) \quad (6.4)$$

which are also upper bounded by +50%. The resulting position tracking error, fluxes, currents, and voltages are shown in Figures 1 thru 4.

Remark 6.1

Since the most computationally intensive portion of the controller is the calculation of the bounds on the $\dot{u}_\psi$ and $\dot{u}_\tau$, we set these terms equal to zero in bounding function ρ_3 for the simulation. Note that the simulation results yield good link position tracking despite these neglected terms.

VII. CONCLUSION

In this paper, we developed a robust tracking controller for an induction motor driving a load. The proposed controller compensates for the uncertainty in the motor/load model while yielding a GUUB stability result for the motor position tracking error. The proposed controller was designed to be robust with regard to parametric uncertainties and additive bounded disturbances. Although the proposed controller requires full state feedback, the controller is robust with regard to parametric uncertainties and additive bounded disturbances throughout the entire electromechanical system. Future work will involve the elimination of flux measurement.

Acknowledgements

This work is supported in part by U.S. National Science Foundation Grants MSS–9110034, IRI–9111258, DOE Grant DE–AC21–92MC29155, and Westinghouse Savannah River Technology Center through SCUREF task orders #70 and #100.

References

[1] A. De Luca, and G. Ulivi, "Design of Exact Nonlinear Controller for Induction Motors", IEEE Transactions on Automatic Control, Vol. 34, No. 12, pp. 1304–1307, 1989.

[2] A. Teel, R. Kadiyala, P. Kokotovic, and S. Sastry, "Indirect Techniques for Adaptive Input–Output Linearization of Nonlinear Systems, International Journal of Control, Vol. 53, No. 1, 1991, pp. 193–222.

[3] R. Marino, S. Peresada, and P. Valigi, "Adaptive Partial Feedback Linearization of Induction Motors", Proc. IEEE Conf. on Decision and Control, Vol. 6, pp. 3313–3318, Dec. 1990.

[4] Z. Krzeminski, "Nonlinear Control of the Induction Motor", 10th IFAC World Congress, Munich, 1987, pp. 349–354.

[5] G. Georgiou, "Adaptive Feedback Linearization and Tracking for Induction Motors", IFAC Evaluation of Adaptive Control Strategies, Tbilisi, USSR, 1989, pp. 255–260

[6] R. Kadiyala, "Indirect Adaptive Nonlinear Control of Induction Motors", Memorandum No. UCB/ERL M92/23, Electronics Research Laboratory, College of Engineering, University of California, Berkeley.

[7] I. Kanellakopoulos, P. Krein, and F. Disilvestro, "Nonlinear Flux–Observer–Based Control of Induction Motors", Proc. of the American Control Conference, 1992, pp. 1700–1704.

[8] R. Ortega, C. Canudas, and S. Seleme, "Nonlinear Control of Induction Motors: Torque Tracking with Unknown Load Disturbance", Proc. of the American Control Conference, 1992, pp. 206–210.

[9] J. Chiasson, A. Chaudhari, and M. Bodson, "Nonlinear Controllers for the Induction Motors", Proc. of IFAC Nonlinear Control Systems Design Symposium, Bordeaux, France, 1992, pp. 150–155.

[10] I. Kanellakopoulos, P. Kokotovic, and R. Marino, "An Extended Direct Scheme for Robust Adaptive Nonlinear Control", Automatica, Vol. 27, No. 2, pp. 247–255, 1991.

[11] Z. Qu, and D. Dawson, "Lyapunov Direct Design of Robust Tracking Control for Classes of Cascaded Nonlinear Uncertain Systems Without Matching Conditions", Proc. IEEE Conf. on Decision and Control, Vol. 3, pp. 2521–2526, Dec. 1991.

[12] R. Marino and P. Tomei, "Robust Output Feedback Stabilization of Single Input Single Output Nonlinear Systems", Proc. of the IEEE Conference on Decision and Control, 1991, pp. 2503–2508.

[13] M.M. Bridges, D.M. Dawson, and Z. Qu., "Robust Control of Rigid–Link Flexible–Joint Robots with Redundant Actuators", Proc. of the American Controls Conference, June 1992, pp. 1222–1226.

[14] J. Slotine and W. Li, Applied Nonlinear Control, Englewoods Cliff, NJ: Prentice Hall Co., 1991.

[15] H.L. Pearson, Handbook of Applied Mathematics, New York: Van Nostrand Reinhold Company, 1974.

[16] P. Krause, Analysis of Electric Machinery, McGraw Hill, 1986

[17] P. Krause and C. Thomas, "Simulation of Symmetric Induction Motor Machinery", IEEE Transactions on Power Apparatus and System, Vol. PAS–84, No. 11, pp. 1038–1053, 1986.

[18] A. Zinober, Ed., Deterministic Control of Uncertain Systems, London:Peter Peregrinus, Ltd., pp.269–287, 1990.

Appendix A

Before we complete the induction motor model given in Section II, we define the following symbols: R_s – stator resistance, R_r – rotor resistance, n_p – number of pole pairs, L_s – stator inductance, L_r – rotor inductance, M – mutual inductance, J – rotor inertia, and F_d – damping coefficient. To complete the model given in Section II, the following definitions are now given

$$K_\tau = 3n_pM/2L_r, \quad L_I = L_s - M^2/L_r, \quad K_I = R_rM$$

$$N(\cdot) = F_d\dot{q} + T_{d1}(q,\dot{q})$$

$$R_a(\cdot) = -\psi_aMR_r/L_r^2 - \psi_b\dot{q}n_pM/L_r + I_a(M^2R_r + L_r^2R_s)/L_r^2 + T_{d2}(\psi_a,\psi_b,I_a,I_b,\dot{q})$$

$$R_b(\cdot) = \psi_a\dot{q}n_pM/L_r - \psi_bMR_r/L_r^2 + I_b(M^2R_r + L_r^2R_s)/L_r^2 + T_{d3}(\psi_a,\psi_b,I_a,I_b,\dot{q})$$

$$N_a(\cdot) = R_r\psi_a + n_pL_r\dot{q}\psi_b + T_{d4}(\psi_a,\psi_b,\dot{q})$$

$$N_b(\cdot) = R_r\psi_b - n_pL_r\dot{q}\psi_a + T_{d5}(\psi_a,\psi_b,\dot{q})$$

where the T_{di}'s all represent additive bounded disturbances. These additive bounded disturbance terms are used to represent additional modeling uncertainty. For control purposes, we have assumed the existence of known positive bounding functions.

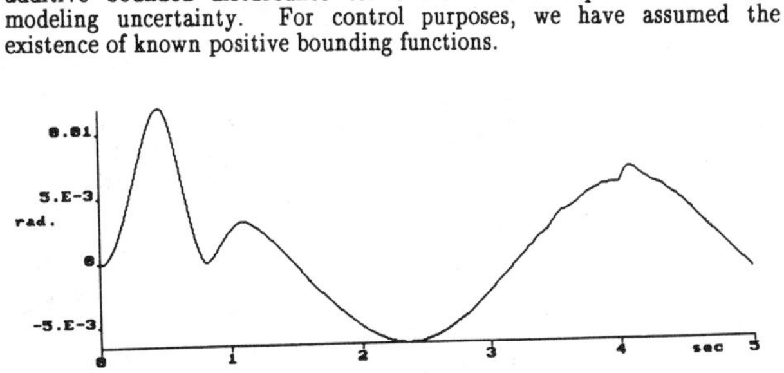

Position Tracking Error – Figure 1

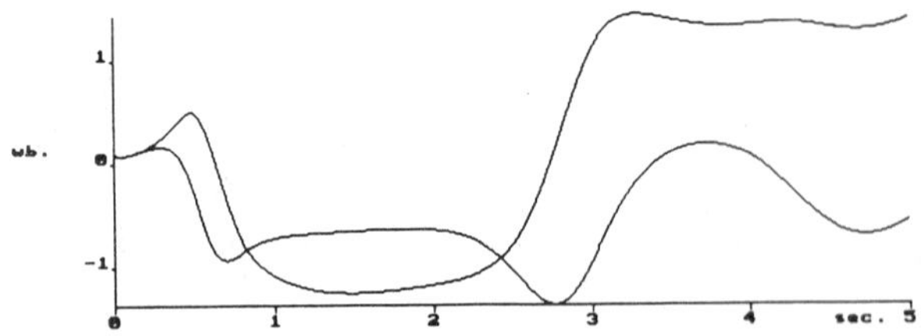

Fluxes – Figure 2

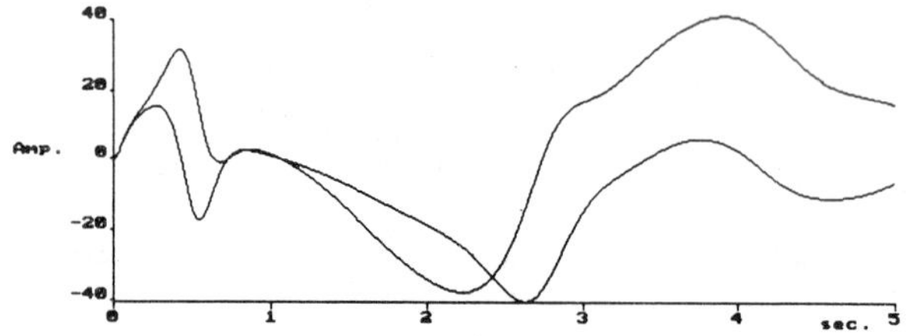

Currents – Figure 3

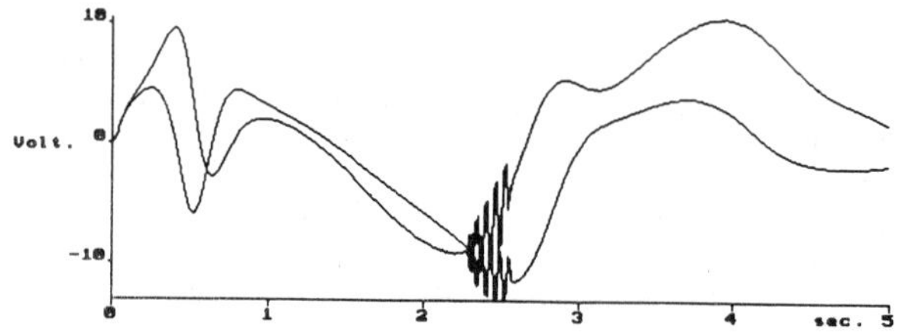

Voltages – Figure 4

Proceedings of the
American Control Conference
San Francisco, California • June 1993

H_∞ LOOP TRANSFER RECOVERY DESIGN WITH AN UNKNOWN INPUT OBSERVER-BASED CONTROLLER

M. Zasadzinski*, K. As'ad*, M. Darouach*, D. Mehdi**
*C.R.A.N. (C.N.R.S. U.A. 821) - E.A.R.A.L., 186 rue de Lorraine, 54400 Cosnes et Romain, France
**L.A.I.I. - E.S.I.P., 40 Avenue du Recteur Pineau, 86022 Poitiers, France

Abstract

In this paper, we derive a stabilizing solution for the H_∞/LTR problem with an unknown input observer-based controller. The solution is parametrized. The recovered transfer function is given by an H_∞ control system with state feedback.

I. Introduction

In [1] and [2], Doyle and Stein have proposed the linear quadratic gaussian loop transfer recovery (LQG/LTR) procedure to improve the robustness of the classical LQG design. LQG/LTR is based on the fact that, for minimum phase plants, the open loop transfer function of an output feedback system composed of an LQ regulator with an observer converges pointwise to that of the state feedback system given, by an LQ regulator as the covariance of a disturbance at plant input becomes larger in LQG theory. The robustness of the LQG/LTR is obtained when the phase and gain margins are closed to those given by the LQ design. Recently, some authors [3]-[5] have introduced a mesure (an H_∞ norm) to estimate the difference of the open loop transfer functions of the state feedback and output feedback respectively, considering the LTR procedure as a kind of model matching problem. The use of an H_∞ criterion for LTR permits to improve the robustness properties of the H_∞ feedback design [6]-[7]. In [3]-[5], the LTR compensators are observer-based controllers. But often, some inputs (disturbances, ...) are unknown. This paper introduces an unknown input observer-based controller in the H_∞/LTR design. The internal stability is guaranteed by defining a recovery error from a suitable target loop transfer function (extracted from an H_∞ state feedback controller) and an unknown input observer-based controller. The paper is organized as follows. Firstly, the LTR problem is stated. In section III, an unknown input observer-based controller is synthesized and parametrized in the frequency domain. The necessary and sufficient conditions for existence of this observer are given. In section IV, after defining the target loop transfer function, the proposed H_∞/LTR design is solved by minimizing the H_∞ norm of the recovery error.

II. Problem statement

Consider the following finite dimensional linear time invariant system (FDLTI)

$$\dot{x} = A\,x + B_1\,w + B_2\,u \qquad (1.1)$$
$$z = C_1\,x + D_{12}\,u \qquad (1.2)$$
$$y = C_2\,x \qquad (1.3)$$

where $x \in \mathbb{R}^n$, $w \in \mathbb{R}^m$, $u \in \mathbb{R}^q$, $z \in \mathbb{R}^k$ and $y \in \mathbb{R}^p$ are the state, the unknown external input, the control input, the controlled output and the measured output respectively with $p > m$, $n > q$ and $k > q$. A, B_1, B_2, C_1, D_{12} and C_2 are constant matrices with appropriate dimensions. Without loss of generality, we assume that $\mathrm{rank}(B_1) = m$ and $\mathrm{rank}(C_2) = p$. The basic block diagram used in this paper has the following form

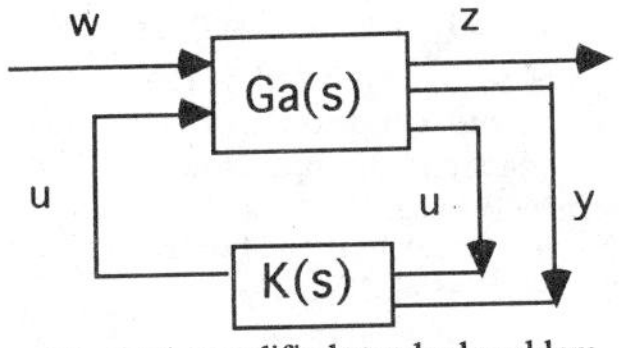

Figure 1 : modified standard problem

where $G_a(s) = \begin{bmatrix} G_{11}(s) & G_{12}(s) \\ G_{21}(s) & G_{22}(s) \\ 0 & I \end{bmatrix}$ is the generalized plant and K(s) is a FDLTI controller. The proposed controller K(s) is designed to stabilize internally the closed loop transfer function $T_{zw}(s)$ between w and z, and to recover the closed loop properties of an H_∞ state feedback controller scheme in the full information case ($C_2 = I$).

In the sequel, we make the following assumptions on the system (1).

A-1 : $G_{21}(s)$ is left-invertible,

A-2 : $G_{21}(s)$ is minimum phase (i.e. $G_{21}(s)$ has no unstable zero),

A-3 : $\mathrm{rank}(C_2 B_1) = \mathrm{rank}(B_1) = m$,

A-4 : $\mathrm{rank}(D_{21}) = q$,

A-5 : (A, B_2) is stabilizable and (C_2, A) is detectable.

Before defining the LTR criterion and the target loop transfer function, we first give the H_∞ control with state feedback and the procedure to design an unknown input observer. Now, we consider that $C_2 = I$, and we find the state feedback control law $u = F\,x$ which stabilizes internally the system (1-1)-(1-2) and satisfies $\|T_{zw}(s)\|_\infty \le \gamma$.

The solution of this problem is given in [7]. Let X_∞ be the symmetric positive definite matrix which satisfies the following algebraic Riccati equation

$$A\,X_\infty + X_\infty A^T + C_1^T C_1 - \theta^T \Sigma^{-1} \theta + X_\infty B_1 B_1^T X_\infty$$
$$+ (F + \Sigma^{-1}\theta)^T \Sigma\, (F + \Sigma^{-1}\theta) = 0 \qquad (2)$$

with $\Sigma = D_{12}^T D_{12}$ and $\theta = D_{12}^T C_1 + B_2^T X_\infty$. The H_∞ state feedback gain matrix is given by $F = -\Sigma^{-1}\theta$.

III. Unknown input observer design in the frequency domain

Hautus [8] has given the necessary and sufficient conditions for the existence of a stable unknown input observer for system (1) in the frequency domain.

Theorem 1 [8]

The system described by

$$x_e(s) = N_y(s)\,y(s) + N_u(s)\,u(s) \qquad (3)$$

is a stable unknown input observer for system (1), where the state estimate x_e converges asymptotically to the state x, if and only if there exist stable matrices M(s) and N(s) such that N(s) is proper and

$$\begin{bmatrix} M(s) & N(s) \end{bmatrix} \begin{bmatrix} sI-A & -B_1 & -B_2 \\ C_2 & 0 & 0 \\ 0 & 0 & I_q \end{bmatrix} = \begin{bmatrix} I_n & 0 & 0 \end{bmatrix} \qquad (4)$$

where $N(s) = \begin{bmatrix} N_y(s) & N_u(s) \end{bmatrix}$. ■

Theorem 2 [8]

The unknown input observer described in theorem 1 exists if and only if assumptions A-2 and A-3 are satisfied.
■

If we introduce vectors $\begin{bmatrix} x^T & w^T & u^T \end{bmatrix}^T$ and $\begin{bmatrix} x_0^T & y^T & u^T \end{bmatrix}^T$ in equation (3), we obtain

$$x = M(s)\,x_0 + N_y(s)\,y + N_u(s)\,u = M(s)\,x_0 + x_e \qquad (5)$$

where M(s) is stable. The FLDTI system $K(s) = F\,N(s)$ is an unknown input observer-based controller for the modified standard problem in figure 1. The following theorem presents the separation principle for such controllers.

Theorem 3

If M(s), N(s) and $(sI - A - B_2F)^{-1}$ are stable, then the closed loop transfer function in figure 1 is internally stable for $K(s) = F\,N(s)$, where M(s) and N(s) are given in theorem 1. ■

Proof

From (5), the state estimation error is given by $e = x - x_e = M(s)\,x_0$. For some unknown input observer N(s), by using (4), we obtain

$$M(s) = (I_n - N_y(s)\,C_2)\,(sI - A)^{-1} \qquad (6)$$

Then M(s) is strictly proper. Let $[\Phi, G, H, 0]$ be a state-space realization of M(s), v the associated state vector and u the command signal given by $u = F\,x_e$. The closed loop state equation given by

$$\begin{bmatrix} \dot{x} \\ \dot{v} \end{bmatrix} = \begin{bmatrix} A+B_2F & -B_2FH \\ 0 & \Phi \end{bmatrix} \begin{bmatrix} x \\ v \end{bmatrix} + \begin{bmatrix} B_1 & 0 \\ 0 & G \end{bmatrix} \begin{bmatrix} w \\ x_0 \end{bmatrix} \qquad (7)$$

is internally stable under the assumptions of theorem 3. ■

Equation (4) can be written as

$$\left[M\_(s)\ N\_y(s)\ N\_u(s)\ D\_(s) \right] \begin{bmatrix} sI-A & -B_1 & -B_2 \\ C_2 & 0 & 0 \\ 0 & 0 & I_q \\ -I_n & 0 & 0 \end{bmatrix} = \left[I_n\ \ 0\ \ 0 \right] \quad (8)$$

where $D\_^{-1}(s) \left[M\_(s)\ N\_y(s)\ N\_u(s) \right]$ is a matrix fraction description (MFD) of the transfer function matrix $\left[M(s)\ N_y(s)\ N_u(s) \right]$. Let $U_1(s)$ and U_2 be two unimodular matrices given by

$$U_1(s) = \begin{bmatrix} 0 & 0 & 0 & -I_n \\ 0 & 0 & I_q & 0 \\ P_1 & 0 & -f_2 & f_1(s) \\ P_2 & 0 & -f_4 & f_3(s) \\ 0 & I_p & 0 & C_2 \end{bmatrix} \text{ and } U_2 = \begin{bmatrix} I_n & 0 & 0 \\ 0 & 0 & I_q \\ 0 & I_m & 0 \end{bmatrix}$$

where $P_1 = -(B_1^T B_1)^{-1} B_1^T$, $f_1(s) = P_1(sI - A)$, $f_2 = -P_1 B_2$, P_2 is a base of the left kernel of B_1, $f_3(s) = P_2(sI - A)$ and $f_4 = -P_2 B_2$. We have the following relation

$$U_1(s) \begin{bmatrix} sI-A & -B_1 & -B_2 \\ C_2 & 0 & 0 \\ 0 & 0 & I_q \\ -I_n & 0 & 0 \end{bmatrix} U_2 = \begin{bmatrix} I_n & 0 & 0 \\ 0 & I_q & 0 \\ 0 & 0 & I_m \\ 0 & 0 & 0 \\ 0 & 0 & 0 \end{bmatrix} \quad (9)$$

From (8) and (9), we obtain

$$D\_(s) = a_1(s)\, f_3(s) + a_2(s)\, C_2 \text{ and } M\_(s) = a_1(s)\, P_2 \quad (10.1)$$

$$N\_y(s) = a_2(s) \text{ and } N\_u(s) = -a_1(s)\, f_4 \quad (10.2)$$

where $a_1(s)$ and $a_2(s)$ are free polynomial matrices, of dimensions (n,n-m) and (n,p) respectively, such that $\det(D\_(s))$ has all its roots strictly in the left half plane. It is easy to see that $G_{21}(s)$ and $\begin{bmatrix} f_3(s) \\ C_2 \end{bmatrix}$ have the same zeros that are roots of $\det(D\_(s))$. Then assumption A-2 is necessary. With $a_1(s)$ and $a_2(s)$, we have a parametrization of all unknown input observers for system (1) in the frequency domain.

$D_t(s)$ and $N_t(s)$ are polynomial matrices of dimensions (p-m,p-m) and (p-m,n+p+q) respectively, such that $\det(D_t(s))$ has all its roots strictly in the left half plane and

$$N_t(s) \begin{bmatrix} sI-A & -B_1 & -B_2 \\ C_2 & 0 & 0 \\ 0 & 0 & I_q \end{bmatrix} = \left[0\ \ 0\ \ 0 \right] \quad (11)$$

Then, for system (1), any unknown input observer L(s) is given by

$$L(s) = N(s) + Q(s)\, T_2(s) \quad (12)$$

where the free parameter $Q(s) \in \mathbb{R}H_\infty$ and $T_2(s) = D_t^{-1}(s)\, N_{t2}(s)$, $N_{t2}(s)$ being the p+q last columns of $N_t(s)$. N(s) is an unknown input observer computed by equation (10).

IV. H_∞/LTR design problem with an unknown input observer-based controller

The closed loop transfer function of the H_∞ control with state feedback, defined in section II, is given by

$$T_{Fzw}(s) = G_{11}(s) + G_{12}(s)\, F\, (I - P_{22}(s)\, F)^{-1}\, P_{21}(s) \quad (13)$$

where

$$P_{21}(s) = (sI - A)^{-1} B_1 \text{ and } P_{22}(s) = (sI - A)^{-1} B_2 \quad (14)$$

We have the following relations

$$G_{21}(s) = C_2\, P_{21}(s) \text{ and } G_{22}(s) = C_2\, P_{22}(s) \quad (15)$$

The realizable closed loop transfer function, defined in figure 1, is given by

$$T_{zw}(s) = G_{11}(s) + G_{12}(s)\, (I - K(s) \begin{bmatrix} C_2 P_{22}(s) \\ I \end{bmatrix})^{-1} K(s) \begin{bmatrix} C_2 \\ 0 \end{bmatrix} P_{21}(s) \quad (16)$$

where K(s) is an unknown input observer-based controller given by

$$K(s) = F\, (N(s) + Q(s)\, T_2(s)) = F\, L(s) \quad (17)$$

and $Q(s) \in \mathbb{R}H_\infty$ is a free parameter defined in (12).

We obtain an exact LTR design if the closed loop transfer functions in (13) and (16) are equal, i.e. $L_t(s)$ and the so-called target loop transfer function $L_{Ft}(s)$ are equal. $L_t(s)$ and $L_{Ft}(s)$ are given by

$$L_t(s) = (I - K(s) \begin{bmatrix} C_2 P_{22}(s) \\ I \end{bmatrix})^{-1} K(s) \begin{bmatrix} C_2 \\ 0 \end{bmatrix} \quad (18)$$

and

$$L_{Ft}(s) = F\, (I - P_{22}(s)\, F)^{-1} \quad (19)$$

Inserting (17) into (18) and equaling the obtained result to (19) give the following recovery error

$$E(s) = F\, (N(s) + Q(s)\, T_2(s)) \begin{bmatrix} C_2 \\ F \end{bmatrix} - F \quad (20)$$

Then, the H_∞/LTR design problem is stated as follows : given assumptions A-1 to A-5, and $T_2(s) \in \mathbb{R}H_\infty$ (12), find $Q(s) \in \mathbb{R}H_\infty$ which minimizes the H_∞ norm of the recovery error E(s) (20). This model matching problem can be solved with the Hankel norm approach [6], [7], [9], or with the H_∞ control with output feedback (2-Riccati equations solution) [7], [10], [11].

Remark

Let $R(s) = \begin{bmatrix} C_2 \\ 0 \end{bmatrix} (sI - A)^{-1} \left[B_1\ B_2 \right] + \begin{bmatrix} 0 & 0 \\ 0 & I \end{bmatrix} = C_R (sI - A)^{-1} B_R + D_R$, assumptions A-2 and A-3 are equivalent to R(s) has no unstable zero and to $\text{rank}(\begin{bmatrix} C_R B_R & D_R \\ D_R & 0 \end{bmatrix}) = \text{rank}(\begin{bmatrix} B_R \\ D_R \end{bmatrix}) + q$ respectively. Let $V(s) = (sI - A)^{-1} B_R$ and $N_R(s) = \left[N_{Ry}(s)\ N_{Ru}(s) \right]$, $N_R(s) \in \mathbb{R}H_\infty$, such that

$$N_R(s)\, R(s) = V(s) \quad (21)$$

and M(s) in (6) is stable if we replace $N_y(s)$ by $N_{Ry}(s)$. We can see that relation (4) is verified, then $N_R(s)$ is an unknown input observer. In addition, the unknown input observer-based controller $K_R(s) = F\, N_R(s)$ gives an exact LTR design.

VI. Conclusion

In this paper, we have derived, in the frequency domain, an unknown input observer for FDLTI systems. The observer is parametrized and the necessary and sufficient conditions of its existence are given. Then, an H_∞ control scheme with state feedback is recovered with an unknown input observer-based controller scheme by minimizing the H_∞ norm of a recovery error. The proposed H_∞/LTR design is reduced to a model matching problem.

References

[1] Doyle J.C. and Stein G., "Robustness with observers", I.E.E.E. Transactions on Automatic Control, Vol AC-24, No 8, pp. 607-611, 1979.

[2] Doyle J.C. and Stein G., "Multivariable feedback design: concepts for a classical/modern synthesis", I.E.E.E. Transactions on Automatic Control, Vol AC-26, No 1, pp. 4-16, 1981.

[3] Moore J.B. and Tay T.T., "Loop recovery via H_∞/H_2 sensitivity recovery", International Journal of Control, Vol 49, pp. 1249-1271, 1989.

[4] Nieman H.H., Søgaard-Andersen P. and Stoustrup J., "Loop transfer recovery for general observer architecture", International Journal of Control, Vol 53, No 5, pp. 1177-1203, 1991.

[5] Saeki M., "H_∞/LTR procedure with specified degree of recovery", Automatica, Vol 28, No 3, pp. 509-517, 1992.

[6] Francis B.A., "A course in H_∞ control theory", Lecture Notes in Control and Information Sciences, Vol 88, Springer-Verlag, 1987.

[7] Dorato P., Fortuna L. and Muscato G., "Robust control for unstructured perturbations - An introduction", Lecture Notes in Control and Information Sciences, Vol 168 Springer-Verlag, 1992.

[8] Hautus M.L.J., "Strong detectability and observers", Linear Algebra and its Applications, Vol 50, pp. 353-368, 1983.

[9] Glover K., "All optimal Hankel-norm approximations of linear multivariable systems and their L_∞-error bounds", International Journal of Control, Vol 39, No 6, pp. 1115-1193, 1984.

[10] Glover K. and Doyle J.C., "State-space formulae for all stabilizing controllers that satisfy an H_∞-norm", Systems and Control Letters, Vol 11, pp. 167-172, 1988.

[11] Doyle J.C., Glover K., Khargonekar P.P. and Francis B.A., "State-solutions to standard H_2 and H_∞ control problems", I.E.E.E. Transactions on Automatic Control, Vol AC-34, No 8, pp. 831-847, 1989.

Proceedings of the
American Control Conference
San Francisco, California • June 1993

AN ADAPTIVE METHOD FOR INDUCTION MOTOR CONTROL

by Jennifer Stephan, Marc Bodson
Department of Electrical and Computer Engineering
Carnegie Mellon University, Pittsburgh, PA 15213
and John Chiasson
Department of Electrical Engineering
University of Pittsburgh, Pittsburgh, PA 15261

ABSTRACT

The paper addresses the problem of adapting model-based control laws for induction motors in the presence of uncertainty or parametric variation. A procedure is presented that can be used for the real-time estimation of the parameters and the rotor fluxes of induction motors. The estimation method is based on a standard model of the induction motor, expressed in rotor coordinates. It is assumed that current and position (or velocity) measurements are available. Experimental results are reported, and the ability of the algorithm to rapidly estimate the motor parameters is demonstrated. The results are validated using different experiments and compared with those obtained using a standard frequency response test at standstill.

1 Introduction

The low price and ruggedness of induction motors make them attractive in a variety of applications. They have been proposed to replace hydraulic actuators in aerospace applications (including the space shuttle) and combustion engines in cars. Control theoreticians have also investigated the application of recent nonlinear control theories to induction motors, including input/output linearization [4], and passivity theory [6]. An interesting problem will be to determine what benefits (if any) can be gained from these new approaches over methods currently used in industry.

Whatever method is used, an important problem is to estimate the uncertain or time-varying parameters that affect control performance. The problem is generally complicated by the fact that some of the state variables (namely the rotor fluxes) are not available for measurement. If the fluxes were measured, then it would be relatively straightforward to design a recursive identifier to estimate the motor parameters. Conversely, if the parameters were known exactly, then it would be possible to design an observer to estimate the fluxes. However, the joint problem is significantly more complicated. It does not fall directly into the framework of adaptive identification because of the nonlinearity of the dynamic model of the induction motor.

In this paper, we describe and evaluate a recently proposed method [7], [8] for the estimation of induction motor parameters. The objectives are similar to those of [1], [2], and [9]. However, the emphasis here is on a method that is fast, efficient, and does not require special test signals or configuration of the machine. The method is suitable for continuous updating of the parameters in the regular operation of the machine, so that tracking of parameter variations is possible. Also, the estimation of the parameters is combined with an estimation of the rotor fluxes, which may be used for feedback.

2 Modelling and Identification

2.1 Induction Motor Model

Standard models of induction machines are available in the literature. See [3] for example, where a model suitable to control applications is discussed. Parasitic effects such as hysteresis, eddy currents, magnetic saturation, and others are generally neglected for control design. The algorithm used here is based on the model in [3], but is expressed in a coordinate frame rotating with the rotor. The current variables are transformed according to

$$\begin{pmatrix} i_{sx} \\ i_{sy} \end{pmatrix} = \begin{pmatrix} \cos(n_p\theta) & \sin(n_p\theta) \\ -\sin(n_p\theta) & \cos(n_p\theta) \end{pmatrix} \begin{pmatrix} i_{sa} \\ i_{sb} \end{pmatrix}$$

where θ is the position of the rotor, n_p is the number of pole pairs, and i_{sa}, i_{sb} are the stator currents of a 2-phase machine (or equivalent). The transformation simply projects the vectors in the (a,b) frame on the axes of the moving coordinate frame. An advantage of this transformation is that the signals in the moving frame (*i.e.*, the (x,y) frame) typically vary slower than those in the (a,b) frame (at the slip frequency instead of stator frequency). At the same time, the transformation does not depend on any unknown parameter. If the stator voltages and the rotor fluxes are transformed similarly, the following model can be obtained ([8])

$$\frac{di_{sx}}{dt} = \frac{1}{\sigma L_s}v_{sx} - \gamma i_{sx} + \frac{\beta}{T_r}\psi_{rx} + n_p\beta\omega\psi_{ry} + n_p\omega i_{sy} \quad (1)$$

$$\frac{di_{sy}}{dt} = \frac{1}{\sigma L_s}v_{sy} - \gamma i_{sy} + \frac{\beta}{T_r}\psi_{ry} - n_p\beta\omega\psi_{rx} - n_p\omega i_{sx} \quad (2)$$

$$\frac{d\psi_{rx}}{dt} = \frac{M}{T_r}i_{sx} - \frac{1}{T_r}\psi_{rx} \quad (3)$$

$$\frac{d\psi_{ry}}{dt} = \frac{M}{T_r}i_{sy} - \frac{1}{T_r}\psi_{ry} \quad (4)$$

$$\frac{d\omega}{dt} = \frac{2Mn_p}{JL_r n_{ph}}(i_{sy}\psi_{rx} - i_{sx}\psi_{ry}) - \frac{\tau_L}{J}. \quad (5)$$

In the above model, the angular speed of the rotor is denoted ω and n_{ph} is the number of phases. The (unknown) parameters of the model are the five electrical parameters, R_s and R_r (the stator and rotor resistances), M (the mutual inductance), L_s and L_r (the stator and rotor inductances), and the two mechanical parameters, J (the inertia of the rotor) and τ_L (the load torque). The symbols $T_r = \frac{L_r}{R_r}$, $\sigma = 1 - \frac{M^2}{L_s L_r}$, $\beta = \frac{M}{\sigma L_s L_r}$ and $\gamma = \frac{R_s L_r^2 + M^2 R_r}{\sigma L_s L_r^2}$ have been used to simplify the expressions (the notation is similar to [4]). T_r represents the rotor time constant and σ is the total leakage factor. The load torque is assumed constant but the techniques presented in this paper can be extended to a torque proportional to speed, for example.

2.2 Linearly Parameterized Model

Measurements of the currents and of the position of the rotor are assumed to be available. Velocity is reconstructed from position measurements by filtered differentiation. The drive is assumed to be controlled through a voltage source inverter, and the commanded voltages are used by the estimation procedure. However, the rotor fluxes are not assumed to be measured.

Standard methods for parameter estimation are based on equalities where known signals depend linearly on unknown parameters. Unfortunately, the induction motor model described above does not fit in this category unless the rotor fluxes are known. To circumvent this problem, an approximate model of the induction machine was introduced in [8], where it was shown that if $\frac{d\omega}{dt} \approx 0$, the model is equivalent to

$$\begin{pmatrix} -\frac{di_{sx}}{dt} & -i_{sx} & n_p\omega i_{sy} & \frac{dv_{sx}}{dt} & v_{sx} \\ -\frac{di_{sy}}{dt} & -i_{sy} & -n_p\omega i_{sx} & \frac{dv_{sy}}{dt} & v_{sy} \end{pmatrix} \begin{pmatrix} K_1 \\ K_2 \\ K_3 \\ K_4 \\ K_5 \end{pmatrix} \tag{6}$$

$$= \begin{pmatrix} \frac{d^2 i_{sx}}{dt^2} - n_p\omega \frac{di_{sy}}{dt} \\ n_p\omega \frac{di_{sx}}{dt} + \frac{d^2 i_{sy}}{dt^2} \end{pmatrix} \tag{7}$$

where a new set of parameters is defined

$$K_1 = \frac{R_s T_r + L_s}{\sigma L_s T_r} \quad K_2 = \frac{R_s}{\sigma L_s T_r} \quad K_3 = \frac{1}{\sigma T_r} \quad K_4 = \frac{1}{\sigma L_s} \quad K_5 = \frac{1}{\sigma L_s T_r} . \tag{8}$$

A nonlinear relationship exists between these five parameters. Specifically,

$$K_1 = \frac{K_2 K_4}{K_5} + K_3 \tag{9}$$

In addition, not all five electrical parameters (R_s, L_s, R_r, L_r and M) can be retrieved from the K's. The five parameters K_1 - K_5 determine only the four independent parameters R_s, L_s, σ and T_r. Specifically,

$$R_s = \frac{K_2}{K_5} \quad L_s = \frac{K_3}{K_5} \quad \sigma = \frac{K_5}{K_3 K_4} \quad T_r = \frac{K_4}{K_5} \tag{10}$$

Since $T_r = \frac{L_r}{R_r}$ and $\sigma = 1 - \frac{M^2}{L_s L_r}$, only $\frac{L_r}{R_r}$ and $\frac{M^2}{L_r}$ can be obtained and not M, L_r and R_r independently. This situation is inherent to the identification problem with unknown rotor fluxes and is not a problem with our method. If rotor fluxes are not measured, machines with different R_r, L_r and M but identical $\frac{L_r}{R_r}$ and $\frac{M^2}{L_r}$ will have the same input/output (voltage/current) characteristics [8].

Equation (7) is linear in the parameters K_1, K_2, K_3, K_4 and K_5 and does not involve the unknown rotor flux signals. This linear form of the motor model enables direct application of a least-squares identification algorithm to estimate the electrical parameters. Note that the need to have flux measurements has been avoided by the assumption that the speed of the motor varies slowly. This is an advantage because flux measurements, which require sensors close to the airgap, are impractical to obtain. A drawback is that derivatives of the currents are required. These may be reconstructed by filtered differentiation. The standard approach of adaptive control using state-variable filters may also be used, but is essentially equivalent.

2.3 Modified Algorithm with Known Stator Resistance

As mentioned earlier, the parameters $K_1 - K_5$ are supposed to satisfy the nonlinear relationship (9). In other words, the system is overparameterized. As is usually the case in such instances, the solution of the least-squares problem was found to be poorly conditioned if the constraint was ignored. Incorporation of the nonlinear relationship (9) is therefore necessary, leading to a more complex, constrained least-squares problem. An indirect way to deal with this difficulty starts by assuming that R_s is known. This assumption is often acceptable because it is possible to measure the resistance of the stator independently by applying a DC voltage to the motor and deriving the voltage to current ratio (applying $R = \frac{V}{I}$). The assumption that R_s is known can be incorporated in the algorithm by letting $R_s = 0$ in the original five parameter K matrix and by replacing v_s by $v_s - R_s i_s$. Then, the new parameters become

$$K_1' = \frac{1}{T_r \sigma} \quad K_2' = 0 \quad K_3' = \frac{1}{T_r \sigma} \quad K_4' = \frac{1}{\sigma L_s} \quad K_5' = \frac{1}{\sigma L_s T_r} \tag{11}$$

An important observation to make is that K_2' is now zero, and thus need not be identified. Additionally, the constraint between the parameters is now simply that K_1' equals K_3'. Therefore, there are only three parameters to be identified and the overall identification problem is

$$\begin{pmatrix} -\frac{di_{sx}}{dt} + n_p\omega i_{sy} & \frac{dv_{sx}}{dt} - R_s\frac{di_{sx}}{dt} & v_{sx} - R_s i_{sx} \\ -\frac{di_{sy}}{dt} - n_p\omega i_{sx} & \frac{dv_{sy}}{dt} - R_s\frac{di_{sy}}{dt} & v_{sy} - R_s i_{sy} \end{pmatrix} \begin{pmatrix} K_3' \\ K_4' \\ K_5' \end{pmatrix} \tag{12}$$

$$= \begin{pmatrix} \frac{d^2 i_{sx}}{dt^2} - n_p\omega \frac{di_{sy}}{dt} \\ n_p\omega \frac{di_{sx}}{dt} + \frac{d^2 i_{sy}}{dt^2} \end{pmatrix} . \tag{13}$$

Once again, the problem is linear in the parameters K_3', K_4' and K_5' and of the form $y = w^T K$. The application of the least-squares algorithm is straightforward. Additionally, the nonlinear relationship is automatically enforced by the fact that $K_1' = K_3'$ is directly accounted for. The electrical parameters can be derived from the K''s according to $L_s = \frac{K_3'}{K_5'}$, $\sigma = \frac{K_5'}{K_3' K_4'}$ and $T_r = \frac{K_4'}{K_5'}$.

2.4 Flux Reconstruction

The second phase of the identification scheme is the reconstruction of the rotor fluxes ψ_{rx} and ψ_{ry}. This procedure is based on the estimates of the electrical parameters R_s, σ, L_s and T_r and on the derivatives calculated in the identification of these parameters. However, no further integration needs to be performed (i.e., no state observer is needed). The fluxes ψ_{rx} and ψ_{ry} can simply be obtained by solving (1) and (2). It turns out that, because the parameters M and L_r cannot be estimated separately, it is impossible to solve for the rotor fluxes themselves. However, it is possible to calculate scaled versions of the fluxes, $\frac{M}{L_r}\psi_{rx}$ and $\frac{M}{L_r}\psi_{ry}$, using the estimated parameters R_s, L_s, σ and T_r. Since the fluxes appear with this scaling factor in the torque equation the scaled versions of the fluxes may be used directly for control, or for estimating the two mechanical parameters.

2.5 Identification of the Mechanical Parameters

The third and final stage of the estimation scheme is the identification of the two mechanical parameters, J and τ_L. Once the fluxes have been reconstructed, a linear form of the mechanical equation can be obtained. As previously, this enables a direct application of a least-squares algorithm to estimate the two last parameters, K_6 and K_7. From K_6

and K_7, the inertia and load torque are calculated. The torque equation (5) can be written as

$$\frac{d\omega}{dt} = \left(\frac{M}{L_r}\psi_{rx}i_{sy} - \frac{M}{L_r}\psi_{ry}i_{sx} \quad -1 \right) \left(\begin{array}{c} K_6 \\ K_7 \end{array} \right) \tag{14}$$

where $K_6 = \frac{2n_p}{Jn_{ph}}$ and $K_7 = \frac{\tau_L}{J}$. Once the parameters K_6 and K_7 are estimated, τ_L and J may be calculated according to $J = \frac{2n_p}{K_6 n_{ph}}$ and $\tau_L = \frac{2K_7 n_p}{K_6 n_{ph}}$. Note that a load torque, τ_L, proportional to speed, (*i.e.*- $\tau_L = B\omega$) can also be estimated by replacing -1 by $-\omega$ in equation (14). Then, $K_7 = \frac{B}{J}$ and $B = \frac{2K_7 n_p}{K_6 n_{ph}}$.

3 Experimental Results

The experimental set-up includes a development system for the Motorola DSP 56001, an input/output board and power electronics developed by Aerotech, Inc. (to carry out the analog/digital conversions and to process the encoder pulses), and an IBM-compatible computer used as a host. The motor is a small, 60W, 3-pole, 2-phase induction motor, with a 2000-line encoder.

3.1 Experiment 1

The first experiment consists in switching the nominal sinusoidal voltages on the motor, resulting in a steady acceleration from zero to a speed close to synchronous in less than a second (see figure 4 shown later). The input voltages are 400 Hz sinusoids with peak amplitude $74.2V$. The currents reached a steady-state peak amplitude of 2A. A total of 1.28 seconds of data, sampled at 3125 Hz (4000 sample points), was used.

By applying a DC voltage to the motor R_s was calculated to be 1.70Ω. A mixed batch/recursive approach was used: the estimates were updated every 200 points (*i.e.* - every 0.0640s). Fig. 1 shows the response of the estimator for the first stage of the identification scheme (parameter K_4') as a function of time. The estimate (solid line) and the envelope (dashed lines) given by uncertainty estimates are shown. Fig. 2 shows the result of the flux estimation. The results of the third stage of the identification scheme (parameter K_7) are provided in Fig. 3.

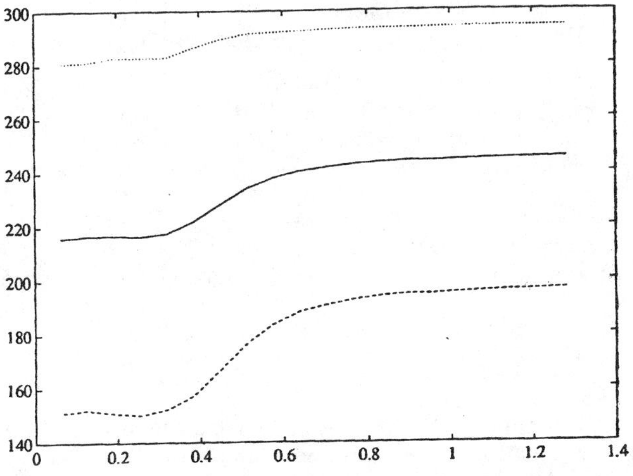

Figure 1: Parameter K_4' Estimate with Uncertainty vs. Time (s)

A summary of the results of the algorithm is provided in table 1 (the uncertainty measures are conservative estimates based on the sensitivity of the residual error to the parameters - see [8]). Based on these results, the actual motor parameters were calculated to be

$$R_s = 1.7\Omega \quad L_s = 0.0137H \quad \sigma = 0.2981 \quad T_r = 0.0036s$$

$$\gamma = 1.0770 \quad J = 0.000110kgm^2 \quad \tau_L = 0.0190Nm.$$

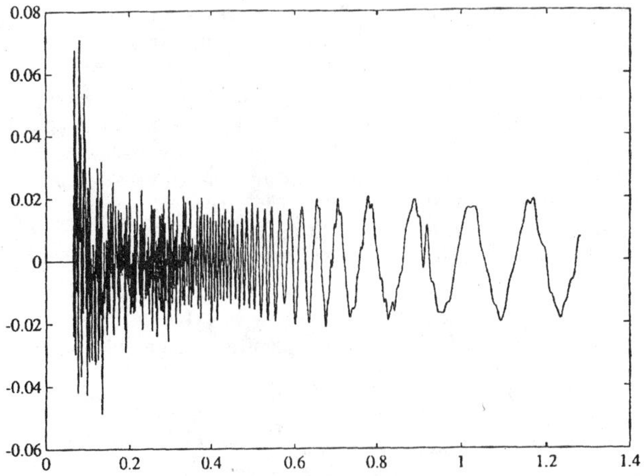

Figure 2: Rotor Flux (ψ_{rx}) Estimate vs. Time (s)

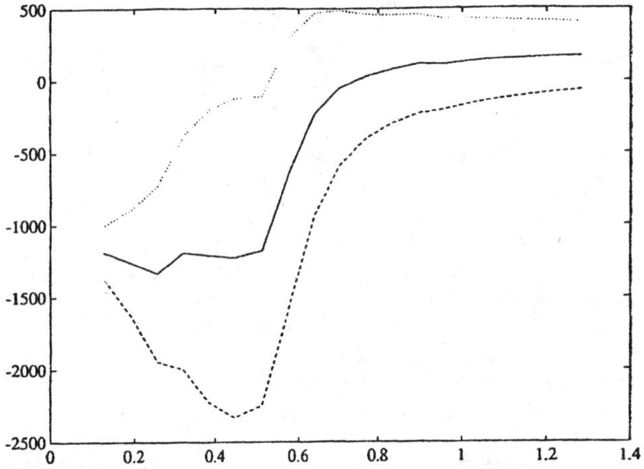

Figure 3: Parameter K_7 Estimate with Uncertainty vs. Time (s)

Table 1: RESULTS - EXPERIMENT 1

Parameter	Estimated Value	Estimated Uncertainty
K_3'	940	565
K_4'	245	49
K_5'	68763	72961
K_6	26596	6218
K_7	168	236

A simulation of the induction motor using the estimated motor parameters was performed. The rotor speed measured in the experiment and calculated in the simulation are shown on Figure 4. They are found to be in very close agreement.

3.2 Experiments 2 and 3

To validate the results presented in section 3.1 and in [8], additional experiments were performed. Specifically, a deceleration experiment and a different acceleration experiment were selected. Both experiments were chosen to collect data with a different trajectory to assess the repeatability of the identification results. The motivation behind the second accelerating experiment was also to eliminate some of the difficulties observed in the first experiment. In the first experiment, the nominal stator frequency of 400 Hz was applied throughout the experiment. The slip frequency therefore varied from 400 Hz to approximately 0 over the course of the experiment. This made filtering of the noise before differentiation somewhat difficult and a filter with a bandwith varying over the course of the experiment was used. In the second experiment, the stator frequency was increased by steps of 20 Hz, so that the frequency content of the x-y variables was much lower throughout the experiment. Note that this is the mode of operation that one would expect from a modern AC drive, since the torque falls for large values of the slip frequency.

Figure 5 shows the rotor speed for the second accelerating trajectory and figure 6 shows the decelerating case. A summary of the results is provided in table 2. Good agreement is observed between the parameters calculated using different experiments.

Table 2: COMPARISON OF THREE EXPERIMENTS

Parameter	Experiment 1 Acceleration	Experiment 2 Acceleration	Experiment 3 Deceleration
K_3'	940.0	779.0	786.0
K_4'	245.0	215.0	234.0
K_5'	68763.0	68786.0	66530.0
σ	0.30	0.41	0.36
T_r	0.0036	0.0031	0.0035
L_s	0.014	0.011	0.012

3.3 Standstill Frequency Response Test

In addition, we compared the results of the estimation procedure with those obtained using a totally different test: the frequency response test at standstill. This procedure was the basis of the method implemented by [1], where the authors measured the impedance using a recursive estimation procedure and a pseudo-random binary signal. Here, we used the more conventional and perhaps more robust method consisting in measuring the frequency response.

When the induction motor model is evaluated for $\omega = 0$ (standstill), the currents become decoupled and the impedance can be calculated for each phase independently. It takes a few manipulations to get the result that the complex admittance is given by

$$\frac{I(s)}{V(s)} = \frac{T_r s + 1}{\sigma R_s T_s T_r s^2 + R_s(T_s + T_r)s + R_s} \tag{15}$$

To obtain the frequency response experimentally, sinusoidal voltages of peak amplitude 2.25 volts were applied to one phase of the induction motor. The sinusoids ranged in frequency from 1 Hz to 420 Hz. A 0 dc voltage was applied to the other phase. A total of thirty three sets of data (input frequencies) were used to generate the frequency response plots shown in figure 7 and 8. The transfer function was also calculated using the identified motor parameters from experiment 1, and the magnitude and phase plots are shown on the figures. Remarkably close matching is observed between the results obtained through the two totally different methods.

4 Conclusions

In this paper, a method for the estimation of induction motor parameters was presented. The estimates of the parameters converge in a short period of time (within a second) using a brief acceleration experiment. The algorithm is fast and simple and may easily be implemented in real-time with existing hardware. The method also simultaneously provides estimates of the rotor fluxes.

The method is applicable for the design of self-tuning AC drives and, in its recursive form, for real-time tracking of variations in motor parameters. The rotor fluxes can be used for state-feedback, in a field-oriented controlled drive, or any of the recently proposed methods based on nonlinear control theory (see [4], [5] and [6]).

The original experiments of [8] were corroborated in this paper by several experiments which strongly validated the results. A frequency response test at standstill gave frequency response data points nearly identical to those calculated using the estimated parameters. Accelerating and decelerating trajectories produced very close estimates for the parameters, and when those parameters were used in a simulation of the induction motor, the computed trajectories matched very closely those measured in the experiment.

5 Acknowledgements

The authors would like to thank S. Botos of Aerotech and J. Frank of Cleveland Machine Controls for their partial support of this research. Special thanks also to Aerotech, Inc., and in particular M. Aiello, for supplying the hardware used to carry out the research. The Motorola Corporation is gratefully acknowledged for donating the DSP 56001 Development System. The authors also thank Andy Blauch, Yong-Chae Kim, and Si Nguyen, for collecting some of the data reported in this paper.

6 References

1. G. Heinemann and W. Leonhard, "Self-Tuning Field Orientated Control of an Induction Motor Drive," *Proc. of the 1990 International Power Electronics Conference*, Tokyo, Japan, 1990, pp. 465-472.

2. A. Khambadkone and J. Holtz, "Vector-Controlled Induction Motor Drive with a Self-Commissioning Scheme," *IEEE Transactions on Industrial Electronics*, Vol. 38, No. 5, Oct. 1991, pp. 322-327.

3. W. Leonhard, *Control of Electrical Drives.* New York: Springer Verlag, 1984.

4. R. Marino, S. Peresada and P. Valigi, "Adaptive Partial Feedback Linearization of Induction Motors," *Proc. of the 29th Conference on Decision and Control*, Honolulu, Hawaii, December 1990, pp. 3313-3318.

5. R. Ortega, C. Canudas and S. Seleme, "Nonlinear Control of Induction Motors: Torque Tracking with Unknown Load Disturbance," *Proc. of the Automatic Control Conference*, Chicago, IL, 1992, pp. 206-210.

6. R. Ortega, and G. Espinosa, "An Exponentially Convergent Controller for Induction Motors," *Proc. of the European Control Conference*, Grenoble, France, 1991.

7. J. Stephan, *Real-Time Estimation of the Parameters and Fluxes of Induction Motors.* Master's Thesis, ECE Department, Carnegie Mellon University, 1992.

8. J. Stephan, M. Bodson and J. Chiasson. "Real-Time Estimation of the Parameters and Fluxes of Induction Motors," *Proc. of the Annual Meeting of the IEEE Industry Applications Society*, Houston, TX, 1992.

9. M. Velez-Reyes, K. Minami and G. Verghese, "Recursive Speed and Parameter Estimation for Induction Machines," *Proc. of IEEE Industry Applications Conference*, San Diego, California, 1989.

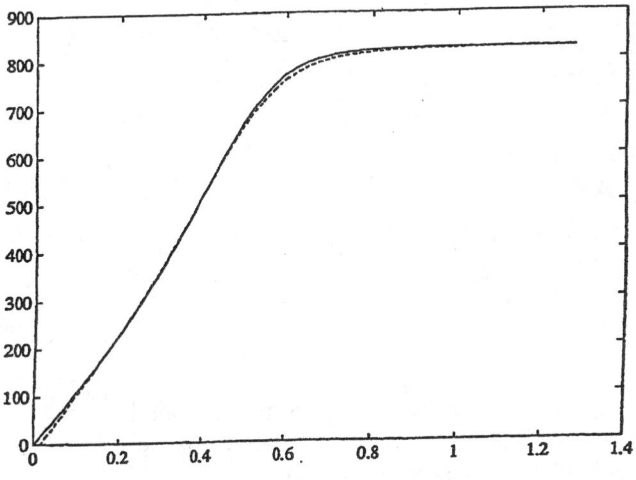

Figure 4: Rotor Speed (rad/sec) - simulation (solid line) vs. experiment

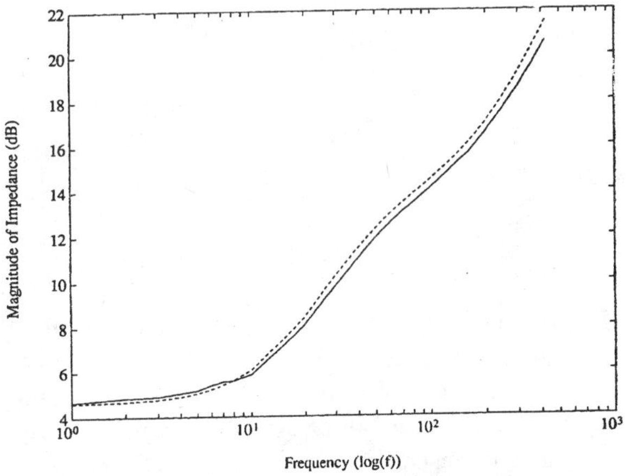

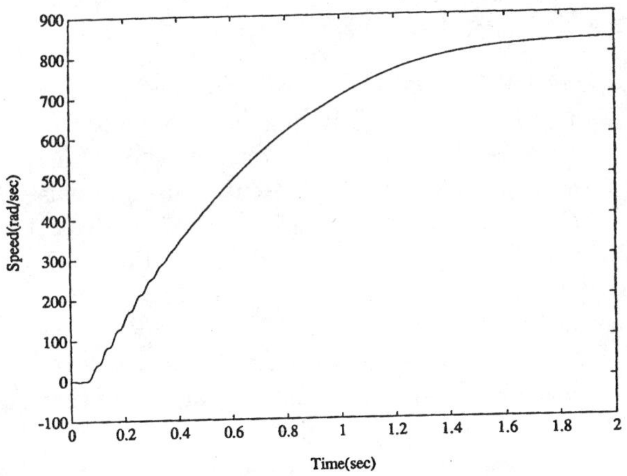

Figure 5: Rotor Speed (rad/sec)

Figure 6: Rotor Speed (rad/sec)

Figure 7: Magnitude of Impedance (dB) as a function of frequency

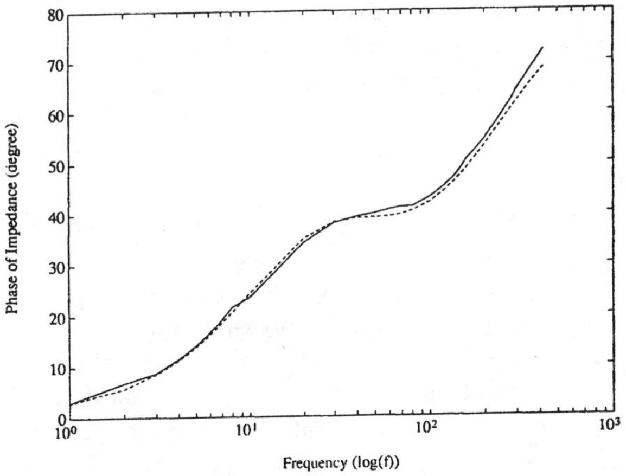

Figure 8: Phase of Impedance (degrees) as a function of frequency

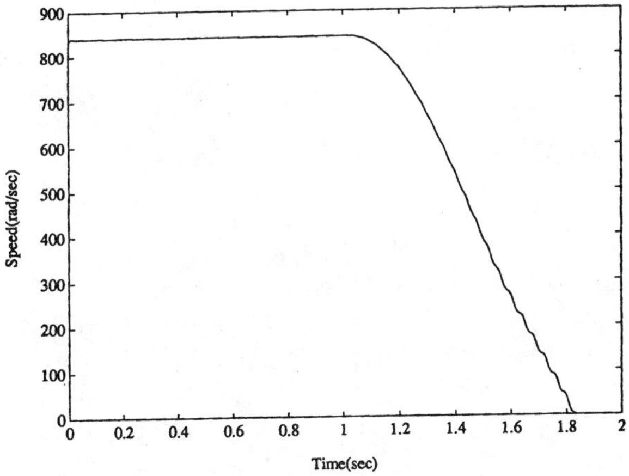

Proceedings of the
American Control Conference
San Francisco, California • June 1993

Sampled-Data Modeling and Control Design for Nonlinear Pulse-Width Modulated Systems*

Alireza Khayatian and David G. Taylor

Georgia Institute of Technology
School of Electrical Engineering
Atlanta, Georgia 30332–0250

Abstract

Techniques for sampled-data modeling and control design of nonlinear pulse-width modulated systems are introduced. The modeling results are based on formal exponential series with Lie derivative operators. The control design is based on a multirate strategy, useful for deadbeat tracking or feedback linearization.

1 Introduction

The most significant areas of applications using pulse-width modulation (PWM) control strategies are power electronics and electric machines. Accurate system descriptions from either area are likely to contain nonlinearities, such as saturating inductors in power electronic circuits and nonlinear torque production mechanisms in electric machines. These PWM systems are cyclically switched systems and, hence, are most naturally modeled as sampled-data systems [3]. However, no methodology has yet been reported for computing sampled-data models of PWM systems containing nonlinearities. The purpose of this paper is to introduce an applicable modeling methodology, and to further design a nonlinear control system based on the sampled-data model that possesses deadbeat tracking or feedback linearization capabilities.

Sampled-data approaches to modeling and control design are considered for three reasons: (i) the power semiconductor switches may not be fast enough to justify the use of averaging approximations [3]; (ii) the microprocessor-based control implementation may not be fast enough to justify the use of emulation design [2]; (iii) the most widely applicable feedback design methods for nonlinear systems require a discrete-time model [1]. The types of nonlinear PWM systems considered in this paper are classified by the topological effects of the switching actions, and by the switching function associated with the operating logic. By incorporating the possibility for nonlinearities, prior research on PWM systems [4,5] is significantly generalized.

*This work was supported in part by the National Science Foundation under Grants ECS-8909329, ECS-9007778, and ECS-9158037.

2 PWM System Modeling

2.1 Switching Logic

The type of PWM operation considered here extends the ideas of low-frequency sampling [2] and multirate control [4] (see also [5]). The key concept behind this approach is to consider three different time intervals $0 < T \leq T_c \leq T_s$: where T is the *switching period*; $T_c := N_1 T$ is the *hold period*, where N_1 is the number of switching periods over which the duty-ratio is held to a constant value; and $T_s := N_2 N_1 T$ is the *sampling period*, where N_2 is the number of distinct duty-ratio values used in between sampling instants. In other words, the $N_2 \geq 1$ duty-ratio values $0 \leq d_i(kT_s) \leq 1$ for $i = 1, \ldots, N_2$ are simultaneously selected at $t = kT_s$, and each duty-ratio value is used over $N_1 \geq 1$ consecutive switching intervals. Consider the switching function

$$\sigma(t) := \begin{cases} 1 & , t \in \mathcal{T} \\ 0 & , \text{otherwise} \end{cases} \tag{2.1}$$

illustrated in Fig. 2.1, where

$$\mathcal{T} := \bigcup_{n_2=0}^{N_2-1} \bigcup_{n_1=0}^{N_1-1} \{t : n_1 T + n_2 T_c + kT_s \leq t < n_1 T + n_2 T_c + kT_s + d_{n_2+1}(kT_s)T, k \geq 0\} \tag{2.2}$$

This definition for $\sigma(t)$ involves a "low sampling frequency" (for $N_1 > 1$) since the switching period is T, whereas the sampling period is $T_s \neq T$ for $N_1 \neq 1$. Also, $\sigma(t)$ defines a "multirate" operating logic (for $N_2 > 1$) since the hold period is T_c, whereas the sampling period is $T_s \neq T_c$ for $N_2 \neq 1$.

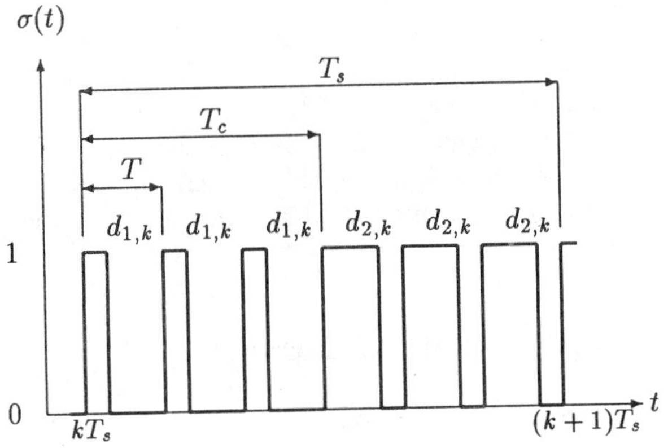

Figure 2.1: Switching function for $(N_1 = 3, N_2 = 2)$.

2.2 Formal Exponential Series

In order to derive a sampled-data model for nonlinear PWM systems, a formal exponential series from [6] will be used. This formal exponential series is defined according to

$$e^{\tau X}(\cdot) := \sum_{i=0}^{\infty} \frac{\tau^i}{i!} X^i(\cdot) \tag{2.3}$$

where X is viewed as an operator. In [6], (2.3) is shown to play a role in the sampled-data modeling of nonlinear systems with piecewise-constant inputs, i.e. pulse-amplitude modulated systems. There it is proved that the exact sampled-data model for the system

$$\begin{aligned} \dot{x} &= f(x) + g(x)u, \quad x \in R^n \quad u \in R & (2.4) \\ u(t) &= u(kT_s), \quad \forall\, kT_s \leq t < (k+1)T_s & (2.5) \end{aligned}$$

is

$$x_{k+1} = e^{T_s(L_f + u_k L_g)} x \Big|_{x_k} \tag{2.6}$$

where $x_k := x(kT_s)$, $u_k := u(kT_s)$, and L_f and L_g are Lie derivative operators. The technical assumptions are: the vector fields $f(x)$ and $g(x)$ are analytic, the input and state sequences u_k and x_k are uniformly bounded, and the sampling interval T_s is sufficiently small. Note that if the $O(T_s^2)$ terms of (2.6) are dropped, then Euler discretization is achieved. The value of the model (2.6) is that greater accuracy can be achieved by including higher order terms (but note that the more accurate model will generally have a nonlinear dependence on u_k).

The model (2.6) is directly useful for the modeling problem of the present paper. Referring to Fig. 2.1, a single switching cycle of a nonlinear PWM system is modeled by applying (2.6) over the interval $[kT_s, kT_s + d_{1,k}T)$ using the constant input associated with $\sigma = 1$, then applying (2.6) again over the interval $[kT_s + d_{1,k}T, kT_s + T)$ using the constant input associated with $\sigma = 0$. This type of procedure needs to be extended through each of the $N_1 N_2$ switching intervals via composition in order to model a nonlinear PWM system over the entire sampling interval $[kT_s, (k+1)T_s)$. A complicated model would be anticipated, due to the repeated compositions. Fortunately, a special property of the formal exponential series results in a computational simplification that is significant for nonlinear PWM systems. Specifically, an $N_1 N_2$-deep nesting of functions can be avoided since the *composition* of exponential series is equivalent to the *concatenation* of the series in reverse order.

2.3 Input-Switched Systems

The first type of PWM system to be considered is the so-called input-switched (IS) system. This is the simpler type of PWM system, in the sense that averaging of just the plant input signal is sufficient to compute an approximate response. An electromechanical system that fits into the IS system format is the permanent-magnet dc motor driven by an H-bridge inverter. Incorporating the switching logic given in (2.1), the IS system is defined by

$$\dot{x} = \begin{cases} f(x) + g(x)U, & \sigma(t) = 1 \\ f(x) - g(x)U, & \sigma(t) = 0 \end{cases} \tag{2.7}$$

where $x \in R^n$ and $U > 0$ is a constant. Note that (2.7) may be interpreted as the system $\dot{x} = f(x) + g(x)u$ where u is switched between $+U$ and $-U$ according to (2.1).

The cycle-to-cycle description of the IS system (2.7) is

$$\begin{aligned} x_{k+1} &= \prod_{i=1}^{N_2} \left(e^{d_{i,k}T(L_f + UL_g)} e^{d'_{i,k}T(L_f - UL_g)} \right)^{N_1} x \Big|_{x_k} \\ &=: F_{IS}(x_k, d_k) & (2.8) \end{aligned}$$

where $x_k := x(kT_s)$, $d_k := [d_{1,k} \cdots d_{N_2,k}]^T$, $d_{i,k} := d_i(kT_s)$, $d'_{i,k} := 1 - d_i(kT_s)$, and $\prod$ denotes a left-to-right increasing-index product. The series in (2.8) is absolutely and uniformly convergent for all T sufficiently small. Closed-form expressions for $F_{IS}(x_k, d_k)$ are not generally possible to obtain, except in very special cases.

Example 2.1 Consider, for instance, the problem studied in [4], where for simplicity $N_1 = N_2 = 1$ is assumed. In this case, there are no nonlinearities since

$$f(x) = Ax \quad g(x) = b$$

It can be shown that when (2.8) is evaluated, the resulting model is

$$x_{k+1} = \Phi(T)x_k + \left(\Gamma(T) - 2\Gamma(d'_k T) \right) U$$

where $\Phi(t) := e^{At}$ and $\Gamma(t) := \int_0^t e^{A\tau} b\, d\tau$. Hence, the model (2.8) recovers the single-rate high-frequency sampling PWM model of [4] as a special case.

More generally, $F_{IS}(x_k, d_k)$ needs to be approximated using a truncation of the power series in (2.8). In Table 2.1, all seven terms needed for the desired $O(T^2)$ truncated model are displayed. Note that the control-dependent polynomials depend only on design parameters N_1 and N_2, whereas all the plant-specific nonlinearities to be evaluated are expressed in terms of simple Lie derivatives.

2.4 State-Switched Systems

The second type of PWM system to be considered is the so-called state-switched (SS) system (which covers the IS system as a special case). This type of PWM system is more complex, due to the fact that averaging of plant dynamics is required to compute an approximate response. An electromechanical system that fits into the SS system format is the permanent-magnet dc motor driven by a buck-boost converter. Incorporating the switching logic given in (2.1), the SS system is defined by

$$\dot{x} = \begin{cases} f_1(x) + g_1(x)U, & \sigma(t) = 1 \\ f_2(x) + g_2(x)U, & \sigma(t) = 0 \end{cases} \tag{2.9}$$

where $x \in R^n$ and $U > 0$ is a constant. Note that (2.9) is expressed in terms of two vector fields (f_i, g_i) in each configuration, in order to most naturally generalize the commonly used linear notation (A_i, b_i).

The cycle-to-cycle description of the SS system (2.9) is

$$\begin{aligned} x_{k+1} &= \prod_{i=1}^{N_2} \left(e^{d_{i,k}T(L_{f_1}+UL_{g_1})} e^{d'_{i,k}T(L_{f_2}+UL_{g_2})} \right)^{N_1} x \Bigg|_{x_k} \\ &=: F_{SS}(x_k, d_k) \end{aligned} \tag{2.10}$$

where $x_k := x(kT_s)$, $d_k := [d_{1,k} \cdots d_{N_2,k}]^T$, $d_{i,k} := d_i(kT_s)$, $d'_{i,k} := 1 - d_i(kT_s)$, and $\prod$ denotes a left-to-right increasing-index product. The series in (2.10) is absolutely and uniformly convergent for all T sufficiently small. Closed-form expressions for $F_{SS}(x_k, d_k)$ are not generally possible to obtain, except in very special cases.

Example 2.2 Consider the problem studied in [5], under the simplifying assumption that $N_1 = N_2 = 1$. In this case, there are no nonlinearities as

$$f_i(x) = A_i x \quad g_i(x) = b_i \quad i = 1, 2$$

When the model (2.10) is evaluated, it reduces to

$$\begin{aligned} x_{k+1} &= \Phi_2(d'_k T)\Phi_1(d_k T)x_k \\ &+ \left(\Phi_2(d'_k T)\Gamma_1(d_k T) + \Gamma_2(d'_k T) \right) U \end{aligned}$$

where $\Phi_i(t) := e^{A_i t}$ and $\Gamma_i(t) := \int_0^t e^{A_i \tau} b_i d\tau$. Hence, the model (2.10) recovers the single-rate high-frequency sampling PWM model of [5] as a special case.

More generally, $F_{SS}(x_k, d_k)$ needs to be approximated using a truncation of the power series in (2.10). In Table 2.1, all seven terms needed for the desired $O(T^2)$ truncated model are displayed. Note that the control-dependent polynomials depend only on design parameters N_1 and N_2, whereas all the plant-specific nonlinearities to be evaluated are expressed in terms of simple Lie derivatives.

3 PWM Control Design

3.1 Sufficient Conditions

Following [1], the objective is to design the control systems for the IS and SS systems (2.7) and (2.9) by inverting their control-to-state maps. This procedure is summarized as follows. Suppose that the design objective is to track some desired state trajectory $\{x_k^d : k \geq 0\}$. This objective will be met if a d_k can be found that satisfies

$$F(x_k, d_k) = x_{k+1}^d \tag{3.1}$$

such that

$$d_k \in \{\delta \in R^{N_2} : 0 \leq \delta_i \leq 1, \ i = 1, \ldots, N_2\} \tag{3.2}$$

where $F = F_{IS}$ or $F = F_{SS}$, depending on which type of system is being considered. Clearly, the design problem is simplified by choosing $N_2 = n$.

The sampled-data models will have equilibrium points defined by $x_k = \bar{X}$ and $d_{i,k} = \bar{d}$ for $i = 1, \ldots, N_2$, where

$$\bar{X} = F(\bar{X}, \bar{D}) \tag{3.3}$$

and $\bar{D} = [\bar{d} \cdots \bar{d}]^T$. Hence, (3.1) will be satisfied at the point $x_k = x_{k+1}^d = \bar{X}$ and $d_k = \bar{D}$. As a consequence, the Implicit Function Theorem implies that for all (x_k, x_{k+1}^d, d_k) in a neighborhood of $(\bar{X}, \bar{X}, \bar{D})$, there exists a function $\Delta(x_k, x_{k+1}^d)$ such that

$$F(x_k, \Delta(x_k, x_{k+1}^d)) = x_{k+1}^d \tag{3.4}$$

provided that

$$\operatorname{rank} \left. \frac{\partial F(\bar{X}, d)}{\partial d} \right|_{d=\bar{D}} = n \tag{3.5}$$

If (3.5) is satisfied, then the implicitly defined feedback controller

$$d_k = \Delta(x_k, x_{k+1}^d) \tag{3.6}$$

meets the control objective locally. Unfortunately, the values of d_k computed from (3.6) may not satisfy the constraints (3.2). However, a tuning procedure for $N_1 \geq 1$ can be established that effectively reduces this saturation problem (see [5]).

Due to the fact that F cannot be computed in closed-form, the rank condition (3.5) might seem impossible to

$\frac{T^i}{i!}$	d Polynomials		x Nonlinearities	
	IS	SS	IS	SS
i=0	1	1	x	x
i=1	$N_1 N_2$	$N_1(\sum_{i=1}^{N_2} d_i)$	$L_f x$	$(L_{f_1}+UL_{g_1})x$
	$N_1(\sum_{i=1}^{N_2} d_i - d_i^{'})$	$N_1(\sum_{i=1}^{N_2} d_i^{'})$	$UL_g x$	$(L_{f_2}+UL_{g_2})x$
i=2	$N_1^2 N_2^2$	$N_1^2(\sum_{i=1}^{N_2} d_i)^2$	$L_f^2 x$	$(L_{f_1}+UL_{g_1})^2 x$
	$\sum_{i=1}^{N_2} N_1^2(1+2(i-1))(d_i-d_i^{'})-2N_1 d_i d_i^{'}$	$\sum_{i=1}^{N_2} N_1(N_1+1)d_i d_i^{'}+2N_1^2 \sum_{j=i+1}^{N_2} d_i d_j^{'}$	$UL_f L_g x$	$(L_{f_1}+UL_{g_1})(L_{f_2}+UL_{g_2})x$
	$\sum_{i=1}^{N_2} N_1^2(1+2(n-i))(d_i-d_i^{'})+2N_1 d_i d_i^{'}$	$\sum_{i=1}^{N_2} N_1(N_1-1)d_i d_i^{'}+2N_1^2 \sum_{j=i+1}^{N_2} d_i^{'} d_j$	$UL_g L_f x$	$(L_{f_2}+UL_{g_2})(L_{f_1}+UL_{g_1})x$
	$N_1^2(\sum_{i=1}^{N_2} d_i - d_i^{'})^2$	$N_1^2(\sum_{i=1}^{N_2} d_i^{'})^2$	$U^2 L_g^2 x$	$(L_{f_2}+UL_{g_2})^2 x$

Table 2.1: Terms of $O(T)$ and $O(T^2)$ IS and SS models.

verify. However, if T is quite small (as it should be in order to have reasonably small switching ripple), then it is possible to relate (3.5) to the controllability properties of various *continuous-time approximate models* corresponding to (2.7) and (2.9). In the IS system case, one considers the input-averaged representation of (2.7)

$$\dot{x} \approx f(x) + g(x)\bar{u} \tag{3.7}$$

where $\bar{u} = U(2d-1)$. The equilibrium points of (3.7) are characterized by

$$0 = f(x_e) + g(x_e)\bar{u}_e \quad \bar{u}_e = U(2\bar{d}-1) \tag{3.8}$$

On the other hand, for the SS system the average dynamics

$$\begin{aligned} \dot{x} \approx\ & (f_2(x) + g_2(x)U) \\ & + ((f_1(x) - f_2(x)) + (g_1(x) - g_2(x))U)\, d \end{aligned} \tag{3.9}$$

are considered, with equilibria characterized by

$$0 = \bar{f}(\bar{x}) + \bar{g}(\bar{x})U \tag{3.10}$$

$$\bar{f}(\bar{x}) = \bar{d}f_1(\bar{x}) + (1-\bar{d})f_2(\bar{x}) \tag{3.11}$$

$$\bar{g}(\bar{x}) = \bar{d}g_1(\bar{x}) + (1-\bar{d})g_2(\bar{x}) \tag{3.12}$$

The following theorem provides the relationship between (3.5) and controllability properties of these continuous-time approximate models.

Theorem 3.1

1. *Given the PWM system (2.7), if the condition*

$$\text{rank}\left[\ g(x_e) \quad ad_f g(x_e) \quad \cdots \quad ad_f^{n-1} g(x_e)\ \right] = n$$

is satisfied, then there exists a T^* such that for all $0 < T < T^*$, the model (2.8) is feedback linearizable.

2. *Given the PWM system (2.9), if the condition*

$$\text{rank}\left[\ \bar{g}(\bar{x}) \quad ad_{\bar{f}}\bar{g}(\bar{x}) \quad \cdots \quad ad_{\bar{f}}^{n-1}\bar{g}(\bar{x})\ \right] = n$$

is satisfied, then there exists a T^* such that for all $0 < T < T^*$, the model (2.10) is feedback linearizable.

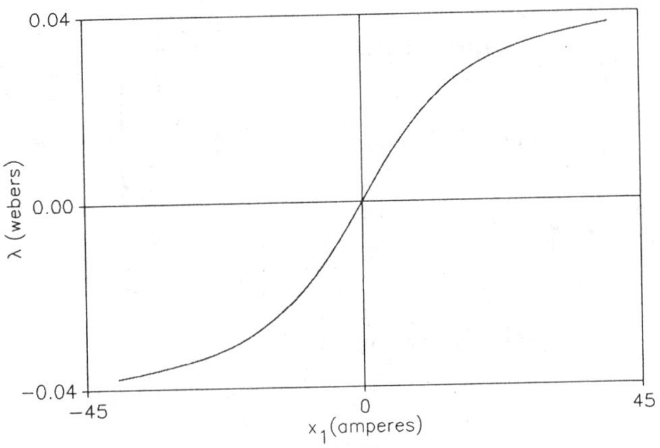

Figure 3.1: The nonlinear inductance model.

3.2 Simulation Example

The purpose of this example is twofold: first, it is shown how the $O(T^2)$ model of Table 2.1 can be more accurate than a traditional Euler discretization scheme; second, the value of the deadbeat tracking algorithm (3.1) is demonstrated. The example system is a buck-boost converter with nonlinear magnetics defined by

$$f_1(x) = \begin{bmatrix} 0 \\ -\frac{x_2}{RC} \end{bmatrix} \quad g_1(x) = \begin{bmatrix} \frac{1}{\lambda'(x_1)} \\ 0 \end{bmatrix}$$

$$f_2(x) = \begin{bmatrix} \frac{x_2}{\lambda'(x_1)} \\ -\frac{Rx_1+x_2}{RC} \end{bmatrix} \quad g_2(x) = \begin{bmatrix} 0 \\ 0 \end{bmatrix}$$

The state variables are inductor current x_1 and capacitor voltage x_2, R and C denote resistance and capacitance, $\lambda(x_1)$ models the inductor flux, and U is the constant input voltage. In SI units, the parameters are $R = 10$, $C = 100 \times 10^{-6}$, $U = 100$, and $\lambda(x_1)$ is displayed in Fig. 3.1. The nonlinearities needed are

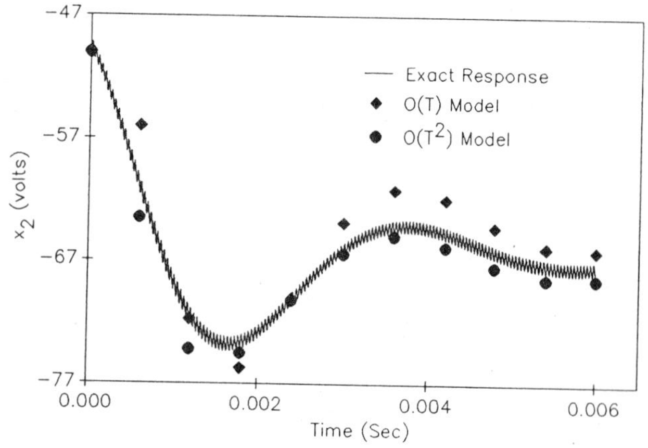

Figure 3.2: Verification of model accuracy.

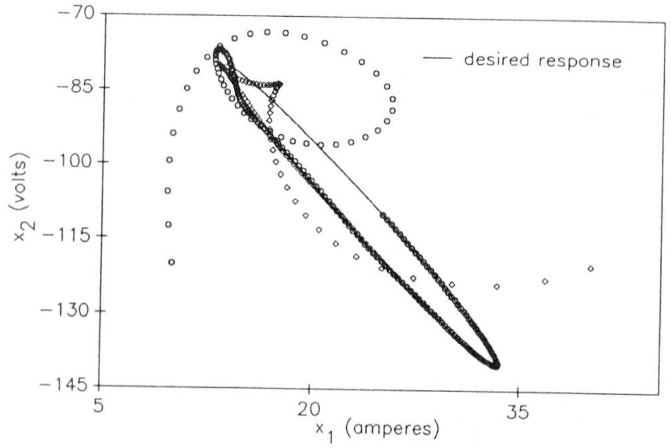

Figure 3.3: Establishing periodic solutions.

$$
\begin{aligned}
(L_{f_1}+UL_{g_1})x &= \begin{bmatrix} \frac{U}{\lambda'(x_1)} \\ -\frac{x_2}{RC} \end{bmatrix} \\
(L_{f_2}+UL_{g_2})x &= \begin{bmatrix} \frac{x_2}{\lambda'(x_1)} \\ -\frac{Rx_1+x_2}{RC} \end{bmatrix} \\
(L_{f_1}+UL_{g_1})^2x &= \\
& \begin{bmatrix} -\frac{U^2\lambda''(x_1)}{\lambda'(x_1)^3} \\ \frac{x_2}{R^2C^2} \end{bmatrix} \\
(L_{f_1}+UL_{g_1})(L_{f_2}+UL_{g_2})x &= \\
& \begin{bmatrix} -\frac{x_2(\lambda'(x_1)^2+URC\lambda''(x_1))}{RC\lambda'(x_1)^3} \\ \frac{x_2\lambda'(x_1)-UR^2C}{R^2C^2\lambda'(x_1)} \end{bmatrix} \\
(L_{f_2}+UL_{g_2})(L_{f_1}+UL_{g_1})x &= \\
& \begin{bmatrix} -\frac{Ux_2\lambda''(x_1)}{\lambda'(x_1)^3} \\ \frac{Rx_1+x_2}{R^2C^2} \end{bmatrix} \\
(L_{f_2}+UL_{g_2})^2x &= \\
& \begin{bmatrix} -\frac{RCx_2^2\lambda''(x_1)+\lambda'(x_1)^2(Rx_1+x_2)}{RC\lambda'(x_1)^3} \\ \frac{-R^2Cx_2+\lambda'(x_1)(Rx_1+x_2)}{R^2C^2\lambda'(x_1)} \end{bmatrix}
\end{aligned}
$$

where λ' and λ'' denote the first and second derivatives of λ with respect to x_1.

In the first simulation, the model accuracy is tested. The test conditions are $T = 40 \times 10^{-6}$, $N_1 = 15$, $N_2 = 1$, $\bar{d} = 0.4$, and $x_0 = [10 \;\; -50]^T$. The sampled-data model trajectories are compared to the exact trajectory of this open-loop system in Fig. 3.2.

In the second simulation, the system of algebraic equations (3.1) is used (in an open-loop fashion with x_k set equal to x_k^d) to pre-compute a control sequence that will impose a sinusoidal output voltage with average value -110, peak-to-peak variation 60, and frequency 100π. Hence, a desired periodic solution x_k is selected that satisfies the elliptical constraint

$$X_1^2 + X_2^2 - 2X_1X_2\cos\theta = \sin^2\theta$$

where $X_1 = (x_1 - x_{1a})/\alpha_1$, $X_2 = (x_2 - x_{2a})/\alpha_2$, $x_{1a} = 23.5$, $x_{2a} = -110$, $\alpha_1 = 10$, $\alpha_2 = 30$, $\theta = 19\pi/20$. The test conditions are $T = 50 \times 10^{-6}$, $N_1 = 1$, $N_2 = 2$, with various values for x_0. The sampled data model trajectories are compared to the desired periodic trajectory in Fig. 3.3.

References

[1] J. W. Grizzle and P. V. Kokotovic, "Feedback linearization of sampled-data systems," *IEEE Trans. Automatic Control*, vol. 33, no. 9, pp. 857–859, 1988.

[2] F. Huliehel and S. Ben-Yaakov, "Low-frequency sampled-data models of switched mode dc-dc converters," *IEEE Trans. Power Electronics*, vol. 6, no. 1, pp. 55–61, 1991.

[3] J. G. Kassakian, M. F. Schlecht and G. C. Verghese, *Principles of Power Electronics*, Addison-Wesley, 1991.

[4] A. Khayatian and D. G. Taylor, "Feedback control of linear continuous systems by pulse-width modulation," *Proc. 1992 American Control Conference*, Chicago, IL, pp. 708–712, June 1992.

[5] A. Khayatian and D. G. Taylor, "Multirate operation of switched-mode power converters," to appear in *IEEE Power Electronics Specialists Conf.: 1993 Record*, Seattle, WA, June 1993.

[6] S. Monaco and D. Normand-Cyrot, "On the sampling of a linear analytic control system," *Proc. 24th IEEE Conf. Decision and Control*, Ft. Lauderdale, FL, pp. 1457–1462, December 1985.

Proceedings of the
American Control Conference
San Francisco, California • June 1993

A BALL AND BEAM TESTBED FOR FUZZY IDENTIFICATION AND CONTROL DESIGN

Eric Laukonen Stephen Yurkovich
The Ohio State University
Department of Electrical Engineering
2015 Neil Avenue
Columbus, Ohio 43210

Abstract

This paper describes a case study from conception through final experimental design of a ball and beam testbed for comparison of conventional and fuzzy control techniques. Control objectives include quick and accurate positioning of the ball to a specified location along the platform. Conventional linear control techniques were employed in simulation and then applied to the experimental apparatus. For comparison purposes, techniques in fuzzy control were utilized in developing alternative control algorithms. Significant non-linearities, such as discrete position sensing capabilities, are designed into the experiemtnal ball and beam apparatus in order to compare control effectiveness when transferring control designs from simulation to a real world testbed.

1. Introduction

Most reported success stories of fuzzy logic are in the control of various processes, too numerous in fact to cite here. Claims are often made with regard to system robustness properties, design simplicity, and overall effectiveness. As control engineers, we naturally question these claims, and many are found to be grossly exaggerated. Moreover, as control engineers we naturally turn to application examples of nonlinear dynamical systems in order to investigate the validity of these claims.

A frequently encountered example of a nonlinear dynamical system for control design purposes is the classical ball-and-beam system. When one turns attention to the actual hardware, several nonlinearities arise which may or may not be modeled, such as surface integrity and uniformity, friction, and dead zone (with regard to the ball and beam), and gear backlash and back emf forces (with regard to the beam actuation system). Moreover, sensing of the ball position (and velocity) raises interesting issues in application, since typical analytical investigations, whether for modeling or control design, assume exact knowledge of these quantities.

This paper describes an apparatus constructed from available materials at a very reasonable cost (less than $300) as an undergraduate design project. A primary objective was to provide a testbed for analysis of control techniques typically encountered in an undergraduate curriculum, including fuzzy logic techniques for system identification and control. Several features of the apparatus make it an ideal platform for such analysis; these include discrete sensing of the ball position achieved via photodiodes which sense the shadow cast by the rolling ball; a gearbox on the motor providing actuation for the beam angle; and, a wooden platform with a groove in which the ball rolls, where no particular attempt has been made at reducing friction nor at creating a homogeneous surface. The uncertainties due to these features make modeling and control design very challenging. For example, static and rolling friction dominate the motion for different ball velocities, and the angle of the shadow detected by the photocells varies with beam angle and ball position, since overhead light is provided by two lamps.

Advanced nonlinear control analysis is difficult due to modeling uncertainties, and probably too much to expect in an undergraduate design project. From the viewpoint of fuzzy control, therefore, a primary objective of this project has been to investigate many of the claims of fuzzy control enthusiasts, such as success with no modeling requirements, short lead time to design and implementation, "robustness" to parameter uncertainty, and so on.

2. System Model

The experimental apparatus, shown in Figure 1, is comprised of a platform which rotates about the center by an actuated angle. The platform contains a machined groove allowing a steel ball to roll freely in one dimension. The object of control includes positioning and subsequently bringing a ball to rest at a specified point along the platform. Assuming

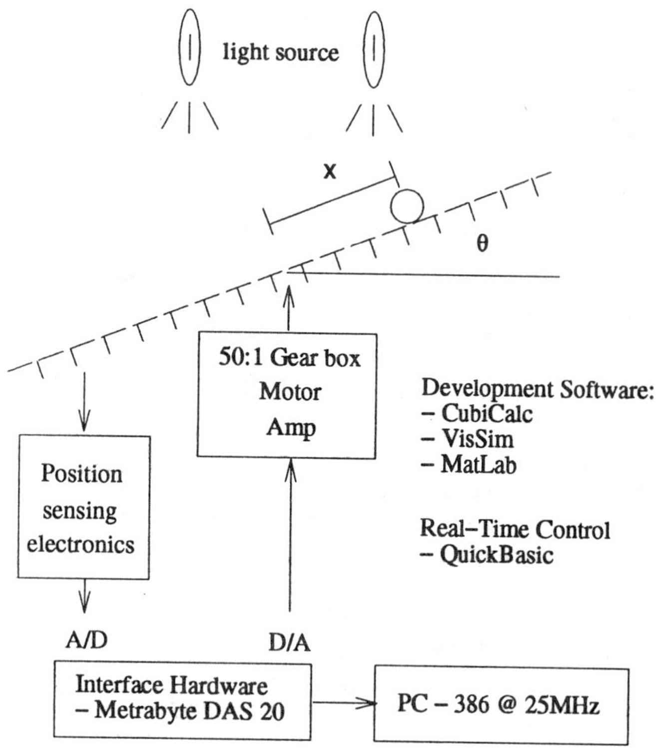

Figure 1: System Setup

ideal conditions, the function relating ball acceleration, $\ddot{x}$, and the control input, θ, is given as

$$\ddot{x} = \frac{5}{2} g \sin\theta \tag{1}$$

where g is the gravitational constant. By assuming a small range in θ we write the system transfer function as

$$\frac{X(s)}{\Theta(s)} = \frac{5g}{2s^2}. \tag{2}$$

The transfer function describes an idealized plant where the platform angle θ is available for direct control.

The experimental apparatus contains several nonlinearities and uncertainties not accounted for in the model. Inconsistencies due to a wooden platform create varied friction as a function of both ball position and velocity. Also, as observed in experiment, the platform contains significant static friction creating a "dead-zone" response, or a large angle needed to produce initial ball movement. The angle actuation is produced by a current controlled DC motor driven through a 50:1 gear ratio leading to additional dynamics and backlash not accounted for in the model.

Although more extensive modeling and system identification of the experimental apparatus would lead to a better approximation of the real plant, we chose not to include these effects in our model. Instead the idealized model was used in simulation to derive both a linear and a fuzzy controller. The design derived through simulation was then applied to the experimental apparatus and tested. Therefore this was an exercise in measuring control effectiveness when transferring control designs from simulation to a real system in the presence of modeling uncertainties.

3. Control Design

A linear controller incorporating position and velocity feedback ($x - x_{\text{ref}}, \dot{x}$), where x_{ref} is the desired position, was designed using simple pole placement. Specifically, the poles of the system (2) were placed to provide a stable response while maintaining a sufficiently small range in the actuator output, θ.

A straightforward approach was taken for the design using fuzzy control. The reader is directed to [1, 2] for a description of fuzzy systems. Both $x_{\text{ref}} - x$ and $\dot{x}$ are inputs to the fuzzy controller. The position, x, is associated with a universe of discourse defined on the interval [-10,10] cm. Five linguistic values describing the linguistic variable x are characterized by membership functions shown in Figure 2. Similarly, $\dot{x}$ is associated with a universe of discourse defined on the interval [-50,50]$\frac{cm}{s}$ with three linguistic values given by membership functions shown in Figure 3.

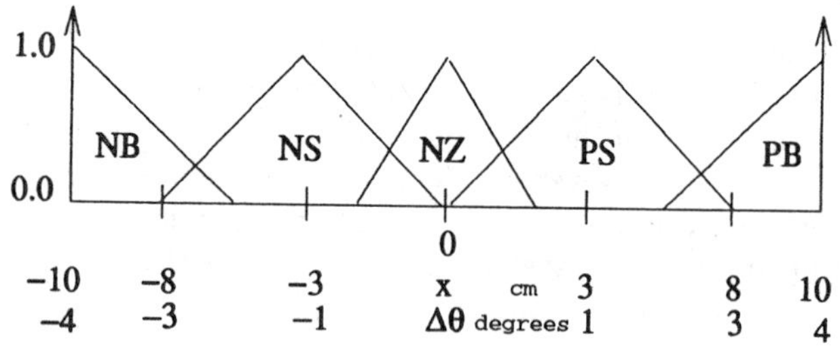

Figure 2: Membership functions for x and $\Delta\theta$

The output computed by the fuzzy controller is $\Delta\theta$, or the change in platform angle. The universe of discourse associated with $\Delta\theta$ is defined on the interval [-4,4] degrees. Five linguistic values are given by membership functions shown in Figure 2. The range of the actuator output θ is limited to $\pm 12^o$. The rule base relating inputs, $\dot{x}$ and

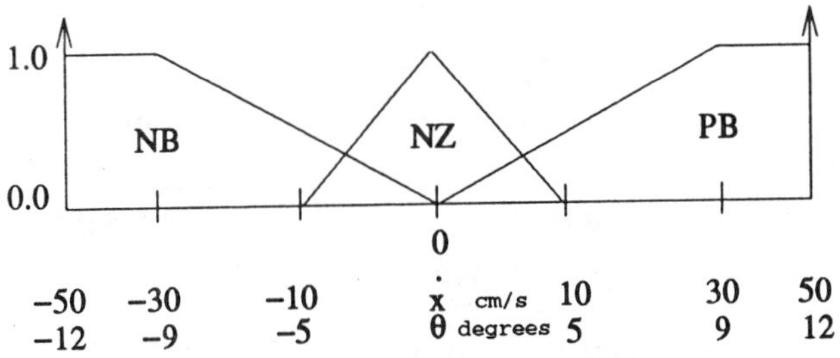

Figure 3: Membership functions for $\dot{x}$ and θ

$$x_e = x_{ref} - x,$$

to output $\Delta\theta$ is governed by the following set of rules:

If x_e is NB and $\hat{\dot{x}}$ is NZ Then $\Delta\theta$ is PB
If x_e is NS and $\hat{\dot{x}}$ is NZ Then $\Delta\theta$ is PS
If x_e is NZ and $\hat{\dot{x}}$ is NZ Then $\Delta\theta$ is NZ
If x_e is PS and $\hat{\dot{x}}$ is NZ Then $\Delta\theta$ is NS
If x_e is PB and $\hat{\dot{x}}$ is NZ Then $\Delta\theta$ is NB
If x_e is NB and $\hat{\dot{x}}$ is PB Then $\Delta\theta$ is PS
If x_e is NS and $\hat{\dot{x}}$ is PB Then $\Delta\theta$ is NZ
If x_e is NZ and $\hat{\dot{x}}$ is PB Then $\Delta\theta$ is NS
If x_e is PS and $\hat{\dot{x}}$ is PB Then $\Delta\theta$ is NS
If x_e is PB and $\hat{\dot{x}}$ is PB Then $\Delta\theta$ is NB
If x_e is NB and $\hat{\dot{x}}$ is NB Then $\Delta\theta$ is PB
If x_e is NS and $\hat{\dot{x}}$ is NB Then $\Delta\theta$ is PS
If x_e is NZ and $\hat{\dot{x}}$ is NB Then $\Delta\theta$ is PS
If x_e is PS and $\hat{\dot{x}}$ is NB Then $\Delta\theta$ is NZ
If x_e is PB and $\hat{\dot{x}}$ is NB Then $\Delta\theta$ is NS

Crisp output is derived via a mean of max defuzzification technique. In the above, the linguistic value symbols have the following meaning: NZ denotes "near zero", NS denotes "negative small", NB denotes "negative big", and so on for positive values.

Figure 4 illustrates the results produced by implementing both the conventional linear and fuzzy controllers in simulation for an ideal plant. Computer simulation tools used in implementation included: CubiCalc, VisSim, and MATLAB. As Figure 4 illustrates, both controllers performed reasonably well in simulation with the linear controller performing somewhat better. The designs in simulation were applied directly to the experimental ball and beam apparatus.

4. Experimental Implementation

Two of the main elements within the control loop for the experimental apparatus include the estimation

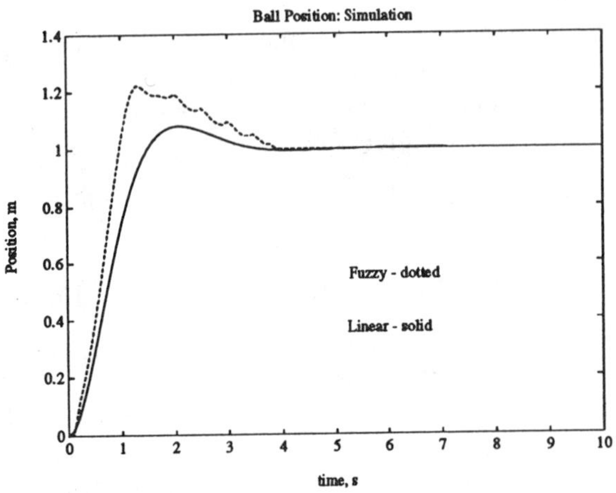

Figure 4: Simulation results

of ball position and velocity based on discrete measurements. Sensing of ball position is implemented with an array of 32 evenly spaced photodiodes (3 cm apart). The action of the ball casting a shadow over a photodiode produces a logic signal polled by a computer which denotes the approximate position of the ball along the platform. Custom electronics and software drive the position sensing mechanism. The size of the ball (1.5 cm) is such that it is possible for no ball detection to take place between successive photodiodes. This feature was purposely designed into the system to allow application of various estimation techniques.

An estimate for the ball position, $\hat{x}$, for the linear controller is simply the location of the photodiode for which a shadow was last sensed. An estimate for ball velocity is based on a time history of sensed ball positions. An estimation of ball velocity $\hat{\dot{x}}$ for the linear controller is given as,

$$\hat{\dot{x}} = 3\frac{(x_n - x_{n-1})}{k_p T}\frac{\text{cm}}{\text{s}} \tag{3}$$

where x_n and x_{n-1} are the photodiodes denoting the current and previous ball positions detected, k_p is the number of polling cycles between successive ball detections, and T is the sampling period between polling cycles. A new estimate $\hat{\dot{x}}$ is computed and held when a position x_n is detected that is different from the previous reading x_{n-1}; or, $\hat{\dot{x}}$ is zero if the ball is detected at the same location for a number of polling cycles (25 cycles). This crude estimation technique produces a very rough, but tractable estimate utilized for conventional linear feedback control.

The fuzzy controller incorporates a fuzzy estimation technique to estimate $\hat{x}$ and $\hat{\dot{x}}$. Specifically, we concede that the shadow of the ball is a function of ball position, location of the light source, the angle of platform, and specific photodiode response. Therefore we include knowledge about the relationship between platform angle and true ball position to create a fuzzy estimate for $\hat{x}$ and $\dot{\hat{x}}$.

Experimentation with the actual apparatus has produced a fuzzy functional mapping given as

$$\hat{x} = f_1(\dot{\hat{x}}, k_p, \theta) \tag{4}$$

where f_1 denotes the fuzzy system between input and output defined by our knowledge base. $\dot{\hat{x}}$ is updated each sampling period based on our fuzzy estimate $\hat{x}$. Specifically, $\hat{x}$ produced by the fuzzy estimator denotes a best guess for ball position in relation to the last position detected with a photodiode.

The platform angle, θ, is associated with a universe of discourse defined on the interval [-12,12] degrees. Three linguistic values describing the linguistic variable θ are characterized by membership functions shown in Figure 3. Similarly, $\dot{\hat{x}}$ is associated with a universe of discourse defined on the interval [-50,50]$\frac{cm}{s}$ with three linguistic values given by the same membership functions shown for $\dot{x}$ in Figure 3. The endpoints, NZ_{k_p} of the membership function NZ extend away from their initial points as a function of k_p, and are given as

$$NZ_{k_p} = \pm\left\{\frac{1}{2}k_p + 10\right\}\frac{\text{cm}}{\text{s}} \tag{5}$$

where k_p is intialized to zero when a photodiode detects a ball position, and is incremented every polling cycle that a ball is not detected.

The output computed by the fuzzy estimator is $\Delta\hat{x}$, or a correction of a ball estimate at each polling cycle that the ball is not detected. The universe of discourse associated with $\Delta\hat{x}$ is defined on the interval $[-\frac{1}{2},\frac{1}{2}]$ cm. Five linguistic values are given by membership functions shown in Figure 5. Output $\hat{x}$ is limited to ± 3 cm (distance between photodiodes) from the most recent detected position. The rule base relating input to output is governed by the following set of *If..Then* rules:

If $\dot{\hat{x}}$ is NB and θ is NB Then $\Delta\hat{x}$ is NB
If $\dot{\hat{x}}$ is NB and θ is NZ Then $\Delta\hat{x}$ is NS
If $\dot{\hat{x}}$ is NB and θ is PB Then $\Delta\hat{x}$ is NZ
If $\dot{\hat{x}}$ is NZ and θ is NB Then $\Delta\hat{x}$ is NS
If $\dot{\hat{x}}$ is NZ and θ is NZ Then $\Delta\hat{x}$ is NZ
If $\dot{\hat{x}}$ is NZ and θ is PB Then $\Delta\hat{x}$ is PS
If $\dot{\hat{x}}$ is PB and θ is NB Then $\Delta\hat{x}$ is NZ
If $\dot{\hat{x}}$ is PB and θ is NZ Then $\Delta\hat{x}$ is PS
If $\dot{\hat{x}}$ is PB and θ is PB Then $\Delta\hat{x}$ is PB

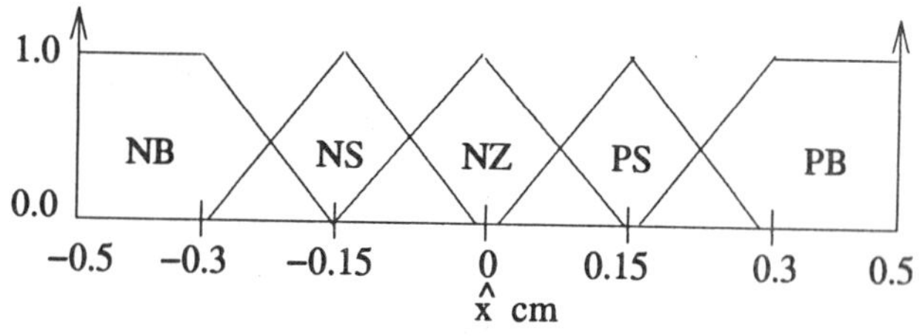

Figure 5: Estimator membership functions

The platform angle θ is driven at the center of the platform via a DC motor coupled through a 50:1 gear ratio. The platform angle is determined through a potentiometer providing angle feedback to a simple digital PID controller wrapped around the mechanical drive. PID parameters are entered interactively. The PID control of angle actuation is the same for both the linear and fuzzy controllers as if angle actuation was an imbedded controller.

The control loop for the linear and fuzzy controllers follows three seperate actions during one cycle. First, each of the photodiodes is polled to detect ball position. The last detected ball position is polled first and the next nearest locations are polled until either the ball is detected or all photodiodes have been polled. Using this information, $\hat{x}$ and $\dot{\hat{x}}$ are computed. Next, either the linear or the fuzzy controller is implemented to determine the desired actuator angle θ. Finally, the desired angle θ is actuated by the PID controller.

5. Experimental Results

Initially, in experimentation the linear controller as designed in simulation produced an unstable response. In order to produce a stable response with desirable transient characteristics, tuning of the feedback gains was necessary. In the case of the fuzzy controller no tuning was necessary from the design derived in simulation.

Experimental results for a command from photodiode #2 to photodiode #5, or a small command input, demonstrated better positioning performance with the fuzzy controller. As Figure 6 illustrates, the linear controller exhibits overshoot and steady state error. Alternatively, the fuzzy controller exhibits no overshoot and zero steady state error for a small command input.

A second experiment measures response to a large position (-5 to 5) as a command input (Figure 7). The linear controller exhibits significant overshoot and steady state error. The response due to the fuzzy controller exhibits no overshoot and

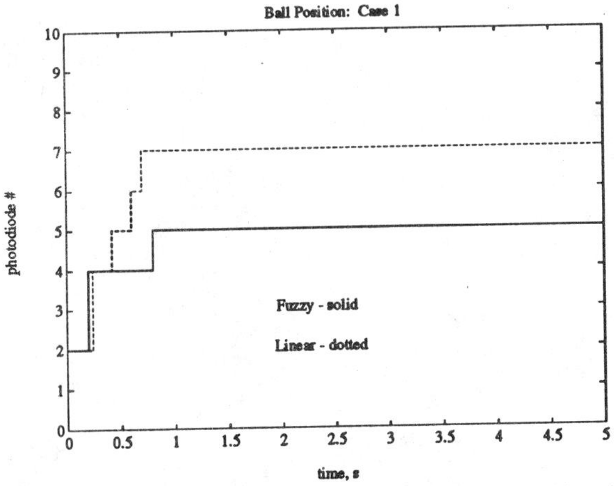

Figure 6: Experimental results: Small command input

zero steady state error. The overshoot present in the linear controller is due to larger gains needed to overcome significant static friction.

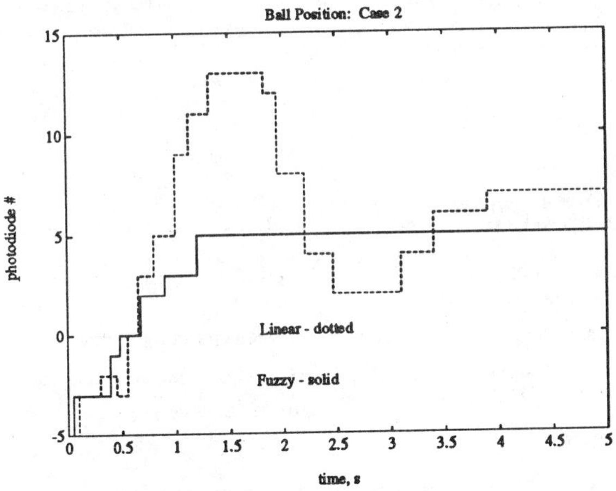

Figure 7: Experimental results: Large command input

6. Conclusion

So what have we learned from this exercise? Certainly the results were not entirely surprising, since simple linear control schemes cannot be expected to outperform the nonlinear fuzzy control scheme. What's more, even though both controllers used the same information for feedback, the fuzzy scheme employed a clever algorithm, utilizing fuzzy logic, for estimation of the ball position and velocity. While no claims can be made with regard to robustness, it was true that after severe degradation in the angle sensor (the potentiometer was badly damaged) the fuzzy controller still gave acceptable performance, whereas the linear controller could not be tuned to provide a stable response. For a more fair comparison, future investigations will involve design of conventional nonlinear controllers, once adequate modeling is achieved (if possible).

Nonetheless, useful conclusions can be drawn from this project. Successful results were achieved with little formal training in the use of fuzzy logic for control, although extensive use was made of "experience factors" aquired during the apparatus development. There was definitely a short lead time to control design and implementation, particularly if one estimates the potential time involved in carrying out extensive nonlinear modeling and design. The fuzzy controller designed in simulation was transfered directly to the apparatus *with no tuning required*. On the other hand, the conventional control scheme needed extensive tuning before acceptable performance was achieved.

One might conclude, therefore, that this project was useful in comparing the *ease* and *convenience* in design approaches, rather than relative effectiveness. Future investigations with nonlinear techniques, as well as with more contraints on the sensing (for example, using only every other photodiode) should delineate some of the more difficult comparison issues.

Acknowledgements

The authors wish to acknowledge the support of Battelle Memorial Institute, Columbus, OH, and the Department of Electrical Engineering at Ohio State, for the hardware employed in this project.

References

[1] M. Sugeno, "An Introductory Survey of Fuzzy Control," *Fuzzy Sets and Systems*, vol. 16, pp. 103-113, 1985.

[2] A. Jones, A. Kaufmann, and H. Zimmermann, eds., *Fuzzy Set Theory and Applications*. Dororecht, Holland: D. Reidel Publishing Company, 1986.

Proceedings of the
American Control Conference
San Francisco, California • June 1993

Adaptive Tracking Control of a Switched Reluctance Motor Turning an Inertial Load

J. J. Carroll and D. M. Dawson

School of Electrical and Computer Engineering
Clemson University
Clemson, SC 29634-0915
803-656-5924

ABSTRACT

Using nonlinear models of the motor and load, an adaptive tracking controller is developed for switched reluctance (SR) motors turning an inertial load. The proposed controller uses full state measurements (i.e., motor position, velocity, and the per phase winding currents) to yield a global uniform asymptotic stability (GUAS) [1] result for the motor position tracking error despite parametric uncertainty throughout the entire electro-mechanical system dynamics.

I. INTRODUCTION

The study of SR motors is motivated by many factors, such as their recent commercial use as direct-drive (DD) robot actuators. The advantages of using SR motors as joint actuators include [4,5]: low cost and high reliability due to simple design and construction, better suited to high temperature environments, and the ability to increase torque production through electromagnetic gearing. Although DD actuators couple additional nonlinear dynamics into the mechanical load dynamics, it is usually possible to develop an accurate structural model of the overall electro-mechanical system. These models facilitate the development of advanced model-based nonlinear controls.

For perspective, a brief review of the advanced control strategies proposed for SR motors is now given. An instantaneous torque control is introduced in [6] under the assumption of constant motor velocity for SR motors turning inertial loads. A detailed nonlinear motor model, an electronic commutation strategy, and a feedback linearizing control was formulated for a single-link robot with a SR actuator in [7]. This work is generalized to an n-link DD manipulator with SR actuation in [8]. A composite control for an *n*-link DD manipulator with SR actuator dynamics is then developed in [4]. Reduced-order feedback linearization techniques are used to develop a similar control in [5], which is shown to reduce the torque ripple in the actuation of an experimental inertial load. A certainty equivalence argument is used in [9] to develop an adaptive feedback linearizing control for a single-link robot with a SR actuator. This control yields asymptotic link tracking despite uncertainty in the mechanical parameters and selected electrical parameters (e.g., winding resistances). A robust controller which compensates for parametric uncertainty and additive bounded disturbances throughout the entire electro-mechanical dynamics of a SR motor turning an inertial load is presented in [12]. This controller yields a global uniform ultimately bounded (GUUB) stability result for the motor position tracking error given full state measurement.

In this paper, an adaptive tracking controller is developed for a SR motor turning an inertial load. The controller is capable of compensating for parametric uncertainty throughout the entire electro-mechanical dynamics. The proposed control is based on the theoretical results of [2,3] but cannot be directly inferred from this work due to the SR motor's unique modeling and electronic commutation. For modeling purposes, we introduce an established set of SR motor dynamics with a linear magnetic circuit [9]. We then apply a control technique commonly referred to as "integrator backstepping" [13] to develop an adaptive tracking controller using full state feedback (i.e., the controller requires measurement of the motor position, velocity, and the per phase winding currents). The resulting closed-loop error system is then shown to yield GUAS motor position tracking error.

II. POSITION TRACKING IN THE PRESENCE OF SR MOTOR DYNAMICS

2.1. ELECTRO-MECHANICAL MODEL DEVELOPMENT

For control purposes, we shall model a SR motor turning an inertial load. Functional dependencies are shown only when the notation adds clarity. The dynamic model of the SR motor's mechanical subsystem is taken to be a single-link robot [14] of the form

$$[J + ML^2]\ddot{q} + MGL\sin(q) + B\dot{q} = \tau. \tag{2.1}$$

where J, M, L, G, and B are scalar parameters representing the motor rotor inertia, load mass, load length, coefficient of gravity, and coefficient of viscous load dampening, respectively; q(t) is a scalar representing the motor displacement; and $\tau(t)$ is a scalar representing the electromechanical coupling torque.

To formulate the SR motor's electrical subsystem, let m designate the total number of phases per single stack (for $m \geq 3$), and N_r represent the total number of rotor saliencies (i.e., poles). Subscript j will be used to refer to the individual motor phases, for $j = 1,\cdots,m$. Using this notation, the number of controls (i.e., motor voltages) and states (i.e., rotor position, velocity, and current variables) are m and $m+2$, respectively. We assume the expression relating the per phase voltage and current for the SR motor with linear magnetic circuit [9] is

$$L_j(q)\dot{\gamma}_j + R_j(q,\dot{q},\gamma_j) = u_j, \tag{2.2}$$

where

$$L_j(q) = L_0 - L_1\cos(x_j) > 0, \tag{2.3}$$

$$R_j(q,\dot{q},\gamma_j) = R_0\gamma_j + N_rL_1\sin(x_j)\gamma_j\dot{q}, \tag{2.4}$$

and

$$x_j = N_rq - \frac{2\pi(j-1)}{m}. \tag{2.5}$$

The scalar positive parameters L_0, L_1, and R_0 represent the motor coefficients of static winding inductance, dynamic winding inductance, and winding resistance, respectively; $\gamma_j(t)$ is a scalar representing the per phase motor winding current; and $u_j(t)$ is a scalar representing the per phase motor winding control voltage. The electromechanical torque coupling between the electrical and mechanical subsystems is given by [9]

$$\tau = \frac{N_rL_1}{2}\sum_{j=1}^{m}\sin(x_j)\gamma_j^2. \tag{2.6}$$

<u>Remark 2.1</u>

For control purposes, all of the parameters associated with the electro-mechanical system dynamics (i.e., M, J, L, B, L_0, L_1, and R_0) are assumed to be unknown positive constants. In addition, the states q, $\dot{q}$, and γ_j are assumed to be measurable, while motor parameters N_r and m are assumed to be known a priori.

2.2. FORMULATION OF THE MOTOR POSITION TRACKING ERROR SYSTEM

Given the dynamics of Section 2.1, our objective is to synthesize a controller which ensure a GUAS result for the motor position tracking error. With this in mind, we define the motor position tracking error to be

$$e = q_d - q, \tag{2.7}$$

where q_d is a scalar representing the desired motor position trajectory. We will assume that q_d and its first, second, and third derivatives are all bounded functions of time. This assumption on the "smoothness" of the desired trajectory ensures that the controller, to be defined later, is bounded (i.e., requires finite control energy). In addition, we define a filtered tracking error [15] to be

$$r = \dot{e} + \alpha e, \tag{2.8}$$

where α is a positive scalar control gain.

To facilitate the control development, we multiply the coupled electro-mechanical subsystem dynamics of (2.1) and (2.6) by $\frac{2}{N_rL_1}$ to obtain

$$\bar{M}\ddot{q} + \bar{N}\sin(q) + \bar{B}\dot{q} = \sum_{j=1}^{m}\sin(x_j)\gamma_j^2, \tag{2.9}$$

where

$$\bar{M} = 2[J + ML^2]/N_rL_1, \quad \bar{N} = 2MGL/N_rL_1, \quad \text{and} \quad \bar{B} = 2B/N_rL_1. \tag{2.10}$$

Given the dynamics of (2.9), we can design an adaptive controller which achieves the stated control objectives if the expression on the right-hand side of (2.9) was assumed to be the control input (even though this expression is a function of the actual system states γ_j). Under this assumption, we assign the "control inputs" using Slotine's [1] adaptive approach

$$\sum_{j=1}^{m}\sin(x_j)\gamma_j^2 = Y\hat{\phi} + k_Lr, \tag{2.11}$$

where Y is a *1×3* regressor vector of known functions defined as

$$Y = [\ddot{q}_d + \alpha\dot{e},\ \sin(q),\ \dot{q}], \tag{2.12}$$

ϕ is a *3×1* vector consisting of the unknown *constant* mechanical subsystem parameters defined as

$$\phi = [\bar{M}, \bar{N}, \bar{B}]^T, \quad (2.13)$$

$\hat{\phi}$ is a 3×1 vector estimate of (2.13), and k_L is a positive scalar control gain. The estimate $\hat{\phi}$ is changed on-line by the following adaptation law

$$\dot{\hat{\phi}} = \Gamma Y^T r, \quad (2.14)$$

where Γ is a 3×3 positive definite constant diagonal gain matrix.

To formulate the closed-loop mechanical subsystem error dynamics, we rewrite (2.9) in terms of the filtered tracking error (2.8) to yield

$$\bar{M}\dot{r} = \bar{M}[\ddot{q}_d + \alpha\dot{e}] + \bar{N}\sin(q) + \bar{B}\dot{q} - \sum_{j=1}^{m}\sin(x_j)\gamma_j^2. \quad (2.15)$$

Given (2.12) and (2.13), we can rewrite (2.15) as

$$\bar{M}\dot{r} = Y\phi - \sum_{j=1}^{m}\sin(x_j)\gamma_j^2. \quad (2.16)$$

Substituting the "control inputs" of (2.11) into (2.16) yields the closed-loop mechanical subsystem error dynamics

$$\bar{M}\dot{r} = Y\tilde{\phi} - k_L r, \quad (2.17)$$

where

$$\tilde{\phi} = \phi - \hat{\phi}, \quad (2.18)$$

is the mechanical subsystem parameter estimate error. Note, $\dot{\tilde{\phi}} = -\dot{\hat{\phi}}$ since ϕ is assumed to be a constant parameter vector. Therefore, we can rewrite (2.14) in terms of (2.18) as

$$\dot{\tilde{\phi}} = -\Gamma Y^T r. \quad (2.19)$$

2.3. STABILITY ANALYSIS OF THE CLOSED-LOOP ERROR SYSTEM

In this section we give a theorem for the stability of the closed-loop mechanical subsystem error dynamics developed in Section 2.2.

Theorem 2.1

Given the mechanical subsystem dynamics of (2.16), the assumed "control inputs" of (2.11) yield a GUAS result for the motor position tracking error of the form

$$\lim_{t\to\infty} \dot{e}(t),\ e(t) = 0. \quad (2.20)$$

Proof:

Define the following "Lyapunov-like" function [1]

$$V = \frac{1}{2}r^T\bar{M}r + \frac{1}{2}\tilde{\phi}^T\Gamma^{-1}\tilde{\phi}. \quad (2.21)$$

Differentiating (2.21) with respect to time yields

$$\dot{V} = r^T\bar{M}\dot{r} + \tilde{\phi}^T\Gamma^{-1}\dot{\tilde{\phi}}. \quad (2.22)$$

Substituting the closed-loop error dynamics of (2.17) and the adaptation up-date law of (2.19) into (2.22) yields

$$\dot{V} = -r^T k_L r. \quad (2.23)$$

Since $\dot{V}$ in (2.23) is negative semi-definite, we can state that V in (2.21) is upper bounded. Given V is upper bounded and the fact that $\bar{M}$ and Γ are positive definite, we can state that r and $\tilde{\phi}$ are bounded. Therefore, using (2.8) and standard linear control arguments [1], we can state that $\dot{e}$ and e (and hence $\dot{q}$ and q) are bounded. Since $\dot{e}$, e, r, and $\tilde{\phi}$ are all bounded, we can use (2.17) to show that $\dot{r}$ and hence $\ddot{V}$, obtained by differentiating (2.23), is bounded. In summary, we can state that V is lower bounded, $\dot{V}$ is negative semi-definite, and $\ddot{V}$ is bounded; therefore, we can apply Barbalat's Lemma [16] to state that

$$\lim_{t\to\infty} \dot{V}(t) = 0, \quad \text{or} \quad \lim_{t\to\infty} r(t) = 0. \quad (2.24)$$

Given (2.24), we can apply standard linear control arguments [1] to (2.8) to yield (2.20). □

2.4. COMMUTATION STRATEGY DEVELOPMENT

An usual feature of the SRM is that it must be electronically commutated to produce a desired motion. Various SRM commutation strategies have been proposed in the literature [4,5,6,7,8,9,17] corresponding to different control objectives and methodologies. These strategies often assume that the motor is fed from a pulse-width-modulated (PWM) voltage or current source. We introduce a new commutation strategy which is motivated by our control approach, which requires the specification of the assumed "control inputs" γ_j such that (2.11) is asymptotically achieved. Inherent in this philosophy is the assumption that these inputs can be practically generated. With these comments in mind, we define the γ_j such that they "share" the control responsibilities dictated by (2.11) in a "smooth" fashion as shown

$$\gamma_j = \sqrt{\frac{\gamma_c\sin(x_j)S(\sin(x_j)\gamma_c)}{S_T} + \gamma_{c0}^2}\ ; \quad (2.25)$$

where γ_c is a auxiliary control term defined as

$$\gamma_c = Y\hat{\phi} + k_L r, \quad (2.26)$$

γ_{c0} is a positive scalar design parameter, S(z) is a continuously differentiable function defined for arbitrary scalars z as

$$S(z) = \begin{cases} 0 & \text{for } z \le 0 \\ 1 - e^{-\epsilon_0 z^2} & \text{for } z > 0, \end{cases} \quad (2.27)$$

ϵ_0 is a positive scalar design parameter, and

$$S_T = \sum_{j=1}^{m}\sin^2(x_j)S(\sin(x_j)\gamma_c). \quad (2.28)$$

Remark 2.2

It is important to note that $\gamma_j(q,\dot{q})$ and $\dot{\gamma}_j(q,\dot{q},\ddot{q})$ as defined above are bounded functions given bounded arguments [see Appendix A].

To verify that the proposed commutation strategy of (2.25) through (2.28) satisfies (2.11), we can substitute (2.25) into the left-hand side of (2.11) to obtain

$$\sum_{j=1}^{m}\sin(x_j)\left[\frac{\gamma_c\sin(x_j)S(\sin(x_j)\gamma_c)}{S_T} + \gamma_{c0}^2\right]. \quad (2.29)$$

Substituting (2.26), (2.28), and applying the fact that the assumed motor geometry implies [see Appendix B]

$$\sum_{j=1}^{m}\sin(x_j) = 0, \quad (2.30)$$

we obtain the right-hand side of (2.11).

2.5. THE ERROR SYSTEM DYNAMICS REVISITED

The proposed "control inputs" given by the right-hand side of (2.11) are actually functions of system states which can not be specified directly. Therefore, we shall design practical current level controllers by adding and subtracting "fictitious" control terms γ_{cj} to the mechanical subsystem error dynamics of (2.16) as shown

$$\bar{M}\dot{r} = Y\phi - \sum_{j=1}^{m}\sin(x_j)\gamma_{cj}^2 + \sum_{j=1}^{m}\sin(x_j)\left[\gamma_{cj} + \gamma_j\right]\eta_j, \quad (2.31)$$

where

$$\eta_j = \gamma_{cj} - \gamma_j, \quad (2.32)$$

are scalar terms representing per phase current perturbations to the mechanical subsystem dynamics. The "fictitious" current controllers γ_{cj} are designed to provide GUAS motor position tracking for the mechanical subsystem dynamics alone (assuming they could be applied directly to the coupled mechanical subsystem). We will show later in the development that these controllers are embedded inside of controllers u_j, the per phase motor voltages.

We define the "fictitious" controllers to be

$$\gamma_{cj} = \sqrt{\frac{\gamma_c\sin(x_j)S(\sin(x_j)\gamma_c)}{S_T} + \gamma_{c0}^2}\ , \quad (2.33)$$

where all terms are as defined in Section 2.4. Substituting (2.33) into (2.31) yields the new mechanical subsystem closed-loop error dynamics

$$\bar{M}\dot{r} = Y\phi - \sum_{j=1}^{m}\sin(x_j)\left[\frac{\gamma_c\sin(x_j)S(\sin(x_j)\gamma_c)}{S_T} + \gamma_{c0}^2\right] + \sum_{j=1}^{m}\sin(x_j)\left[\gamma_{cj} + \gamma_j\right]\eta_j. \quad (2.34)$$

The closed-loop error dynamics can be further simplified by substituting (2.18), (2.26), (2.28), and (2.30) to obtain

$$\bar{M}\dot{r} = Y\tilde{\phi} - k_L r + \sum_{j=1}^{m} \sin(x_j)\left[\gamma_{cj} + \gamma_j\right]\eta_j. \tag{2.35}$$

To obtain GUAS motor position tracking, the motor phase winding currents γ_j must be forced to track the "fictitious" control inputs γ_{cj} of (2.33). This control objective is met using the voltage level control inputs u_j to the electrical subsystem. The electrical subsystem error dynamics are obtained by differentiating η_j in (2.32), multiplying by $L_j(q)$, and substituting (2.2) as shown

$$L_j(q)\dot{\eta}_j = L_j(q)\dot{\gamma}_{cj} + R_j(q,\dot{q},\gamma_j) - u_j. \tag{2.36}$$

To facilitate the stability analysis, we add and subtract the terms $\frac{1}{2}\dot{L}_j(q)\eta_j$ to the electrical subsystem error dynamics of (2.36) as shown

$$L_j(q)\dot{\eta}_j = L_j(q)\dot{\gamma}_{cj} + R_j(q,\dot{q},\gamma_j) + \frac{1}{2}\dot{L}_j(q)\eta_j - u_j - \frac{1}{2}\dot{L}_j(q)\eta_j. \tag{2.37}$$

Note that the proposed commutation strategy has been designed such that $\dot{\gamma}_{cj}$ in (2.37) is well defined. Substituting $\dot{\gamma}_{cj}$ from Appendix A into (2.37) yields the electrical subsystem error dynamics

$$L_j(q)\dot{\eta}_j = W_j\theta_j - u_j - \frac{1}{2}\dot{L}_j(q)\eta_j, \tag{2.38}$$

where W_j is a $1{\times}9$ regressor vector of known functions, and θ_j is a $9{\times}1$ vector of unknown *constant* electro-mechanical parameters [see Appendix C].

We define the voltage level controllers u_j to be

$$u_j = k_J\eta_j + \sin(x_j)\left[\gamma_{cj} + \gamma_j\right]r + W_j\hat{\theta}_j, \tag{2.39}$$

where the parameter estimates $\hat{\theta}_j$ are adjusted on-line according to the update law

$$\dot{\hat{\theta}}_j = \Gamma_j W_j^T \eta_j, \tag{2.40}$$

for positive scalar control gains Γ_j. Substituting (2.39) into the electrical subsystem error dynamics of (2.38) yields the closed-loop electrical subsystem error dynamics

$$L_j(q)\dot{\eta}_j = W_j\tilde{\theta}_j - k_J\eta_j - \sin(x_j)\left[\gamma_{cj} + \gamma_j\right]r - \frac{1}{2}\dot{L}_j(q)\eta_j, \tag{2.41}$$

where

$$\tilde{\theta} = \theta - \hat{\theta}, \tag{2.42}$$

is the electrical subsystem parameter estimate error. Note, $\dot{\tilde{\theta}} = -\dot{\hat{\theta}}$ since θ is assumed to be a constant parameter vector. Therefore, we can rewrite (2.40) in terms of (2.42) as

$$\dot{\tilde{\theta}}_j = -\Gamma_j W_j^T \eta_j. \tag{2.43}$$

<u>Remark 2.3</u>

It should be noted that $W(\gamma_c,\dot{\gamma}_c,q,\dot{q})$ is a bounded function given bounded arguments as a result of Remark 2.2.

2.6. STABILITY ANALYSIS OF THE NEW CLOSED-LOOP ERROR SYSTEM

In this section we give a theorem for the stability of the closed-loop electro-mechanical error dynamics developed in Section 2.5.

<u>Theorem 2.2</u>

Given the electro-mechanical dynamics of (2.31) and (2.38), the control inputs defined in (2.33) and (3.39) yield a GUAS result for the motor position tracking error of the form

$$\lim_{t\to\infty} \dot{e}(t),\ e(t) = 0. \tag{2.44}$$

<u>Proof</u>:

Define the following "Lyapunov-like" function [1]

$$V = \frac{1}{2}r^T\bar{M}r + \frac{1}{2}\sum_{j=1}^{m} \eta_j^T L_j(q)\eta_j + \frac{1}{2}\tilde{\phi}^T\Gamma^{-1}\tilde{\phi} + \frac{1}{2}\sum_{j=1}^{m} \tilde{\theta}_j^T\Gamma_j^{-1}\tilde{\theta}_j. \tag{2.45}$$

Differentiating (2.45) with respect to time yields

$$\dot{V} = r^T\bar{M}\dot{r} + \sum_{j=1}^{m} \eta_j^T L_j(q)\dot{\eta}_j + \tilde{\phi}^T\Gamma^{-1}\dot{\tilde{\phi}} + \sum_{j=1}^{m} \tilde{\theta}_j^T\Gamma_j^{-1}\dot{\tilde{\theta}}_j + \frac{1}{2}\sum_{j=1}^{m} \eta_j^T\dot{L}_j(q)\eta_j. \tag{2.46}$$

Substituting the closed-loop error system dynamics of (2.35) and (2.41), and the adaptation up-date laws of (2.19) and (2.43) into (2.46) yields

$$\dot{V} = -r^Tk_Lr - \sum_{j=1}^{m} \eta_j^T k_J \eta_j. \tag{2.47}$$

Since $\dot{V}$ in (2.47) is negative semi-definite, we can state that V in (2.45) is upper bounded. Given V is upper bounded and the fact that $\bar{M}$, Γ, $L_j(q)$, and the Γ_j are positive definite, we can state that r, $\tilde{\phi}$, η_j, and $\tilde{\theta}_j$ are all bounded. Therefore, using (2.8) and standard linear control arguments [1], we can state that $\dot{e}$ and e (and hence $\dot{q}$ and q) are bounded. Since $\dot{e}$, e, r, $\tilde{\phi}$, η_j, and $\tilde{\theta}_j$ are all bounded, we know from Appendix A that γ_{cj} and hence γ_j are bounded. In addition, we can use (2.35) to show that $\dot{r}$ and hence $\ddot{q}$ are bounded. Since q, $\dot{q}$, and $\ddot{q}$ are all bounded, we know from Appendix A and (2.4) that $\dot{\gamma}_{cj}$ and therefore, u_j and $\dot{\eta}_j$ are bounded. Finally, since r, $\dot{r}$, η_j, and $\dot{\eta}_j$ are bounded, we can differentiate (2.47) to state that $\ddot{V}$ is bounded. In summary, we can state that V is lower bounded, $\dot{V}$ is negative semi-definite, and $\ddot{V}$ is bounded; therefore we can apply Barbalat's Lemma [16] to state that

$$\lim_{t\to\infty} \dot{V}(t) = 0, \quad \text{or} \quad \lim_{t\to\infty} r(t),\ \eta_j(t) = 0, \text{ for all } j. \tag{2.48}$$

Given (2.48), we can apply standard linear control arguments [1] to (2.8) to yield (2.44). □

<u>Remark 2.4</u>

Given (2.48) and (2.32), we can also state that

$$\lim_{t\to\infty} \gamma_j(t) = \gamma_{cj}(t), \text{ for all } j. \tag{2.49}$$

Therefore, the per phase motor winding currents are forced to track the "fictitious" current controls defined in (2.33) of Section 2.5 (i.e., those controls necessary to achieve a GUAS result for the motor position tracking error).

<u>Remark 2.5</u>

Unlike the result presented in [9], the proposed controller is capable of compensating for uncertainty throughout the electro-mechanical system. This includes uncertainty in the so called "interconnection terms" associated with the torque coupling (i.e., uncertainty in the parameter L_1 of (2.6)). In addition, the proposed controller does not exhibit the two singularity problems addressed in [9].

<u>Remark 2.6</u>

While papers in this area often discuss how the proposed controller affects the amount of "torque ripple" produced, we do not. Since our overall control objective is obtain GUAS motor position tracking, we view torque simply as a coupling between the electrical and mechanical subsystems. In this regard, any practical current command γ_{cj} which results in GUAS motor position tracking is acceptable. From this perspective, the concept of "torque ripple" is irrelevant.

III. SIMULATION

In this section, we give simulation results for the theoretical developments presented in Section II. As in [4], a three phase, 4:6 SR motor (i.e., $m = 3$ and $N_r = 4$) is assumed with parameter values of (2.1) and (2.2) taken to be

$$L_0 = 0.2\text{H},\ L_1 = 0.1\text{H},\ R = 5.0\Omega, \tag{3.1}$$

$$J = 0.1\text{Kg-m}^2,\ M = 1.0\text{Kg},\ L = 1.0\text{m},$$

and

$$B = 0.1\text{N-sec, and } G = 9.81\text{Kg-m/sec}^2.$$

The design parameters of Section 2.4 are defined to be

$$\gamma_{c0} = 1.0, \text{ and } \epsilon_0 = 1.0. \tag{3.2}$$

The desired motor position trajectory is assumed to be

$$q_d(t) = \frac{\pi}{2}\sin(t)\left[1 - e^{-0.1t^2}\right]\text{rad}. \tag{3.3}$$

The following initial conditions for the system states are assumed: position error is 0.1m, velocity error is zero, and the motor current perturbations are zero.

<u>Remark 3.1</u>

To simulate the proposed control for uncertainty throughout the entire electro-mechanical system requires a total of 35 integrators (including 3 adaptive integrators for the mechanical subsystem and 9 adaptive integrators per phase for the electrical subsystem). To ease the computational burden on the simulation software we assume exact on the mechanical subsystem parameters $\bar{M}$ and $\bar{N}$. Therefore, only the parameters $\bar{B}$, L_0, L_1, L_0A_2, L_1A_2, and R_0 are adaptively computed on-line. This reduces the total number of integrators required for simulation to 21.

The initial conditions on the adaptive parameters are assumed to differ from their actual values by +50%. In addition, all controller gains are set to 10 (i.e., $k_L = k_J = \alpha = \Gamma_j = 10$, and $\Gamma = 10I_9$ where I_9 is the 9×9 identity matrix).

Given the controls of (2.33) and (2.39), the resulting motor position tracking error, position trajectory, and electro-mechanical coupling torque is shown in Figures 1A through 1C; the per phase winding currents are shown in Figures 2A through 2C; and the per phase winding voltages are shown in Figures 3A through 3C, respectively.

IV. CONCLUSION

In this paper, we presented an approach that is be used to design an adaptive tracking controller for a SR motor turning an inertial load. This hand-crafted approach is intuitively simple since it uses concepts most control engineers can readily identify. The result is a tracking controller which gives a GUAS result for the motor position tracking error despite parametric uncertainty throughout the entire electro-mechanical system. Simulation results show that the proposed tracking controller effectively compensates for the parametric uncertainty in both the mechanical and electrical dynamics.

Acknowledgements

This work is supported in part by the U.S. National Science Foundation Grant IRI-9111258, DOE Grant DE-AC21-92MC29115, the Westinghouse Savannah River Technology Center through SCUREF Tasks Orders #70 and #100, and a DOE/EBSCoR Graduate Fellowship.

References

[1] J. Slotine and W. Li, Applied Nonlinear Control, Englewoods Cliff, NJ: Prentice Hall Co., 1991.

[2] I. Kanellakopoulos, P. Kokotovic, and R. Marino, "An Extended Direct Scheme for Robust Adaptive Nonlinear Control", Automatica, Vol. 27, No. 2, pp. 247-255, 1991.

[3] I. Kanellakopoulos, P. Kokotovic, and A. Morse, "Systematic Design of Adaptive Controllers for Feedback Linearizable Systems", IEEE Transactions on Automatic Control, Vol. 36, No. 11, pp. 1241-1253, 1991.

[4] D. Taylor, "Composite Control of Direct-Drive Robots", Proc. IEEE Conf. on Decision and Control, pp. 1670-1675, Dec. 1989.

[5] D. Taylor, "An Experimental Study on Composite Control of Switched Reluctance Motors", IEEE Control Systems Magazine, pp. 31-36, Feb. 1991.

[6] M. Ilic'-Spong, T. Miller, S. MacMinn, and J. Thorp, "Instantaneous Torque Control of Electric Motor Drives", IEEE Transactions on Power Electronics, Vol. 2, No. 5, pp. 55-61, Jan. 1987.

[7] M. Ilic'-Spong, R. Marino, S. Peresada, D. Taylor, "Feedback Linearizing Control of Switched Reluctance Motors", IEEE Transactions on Automatic Control, Vol. 32, No. 5, pp. 419-426, May 1987.

[8] D. Taylor, M. Ilic'-Spong, R. Marino, S. Peresada, "A Feedback Linearizing Control for Direct-drive Robots With Switched Reluctance Motors", Proc. IEEE Conf. on Decision and Control, pp. 388-396, Dec. 1986.

[9] D. Taylor, "Adaptive Control Design for a Class of Doubly-Salient Motors", Proc. IEEE Conf. on Decision and Control, Vol. 3, pp. 2903-2908, Dec. 1991.

[10] R. Marino, S. Peresada, and P. Valigi, "Adaptive Partial Feedback Linearization of Induction Motors", Proc. IEEE Conf. on Decision and Control, Vol. 6, pp. 3313-3318, Dec. 1990.

[11] N. Hemati, J. Thorp, and M. Leu, "Robust Nonlinear Control of Brushless DC Motors for Direct-Drive Robotic Applications", IEEE Transactions on Industrial Electronics, Vol. 37, No. 6, pp. 498-501, 1990.

[12] J. Carroll, D. Dawson, and Z. Qu, "Robust Tracking Control of a Switched Reluctance Motor Turning an Inertial Load", Proc. American Controls Conf., to appear, June 1992.

[13] I. Kanellakopoulos, P. Kokotovic, and A. Morse, "Adaptive Output-Feedback Control of a Class of Nonlinear Systems", Proc. IEEE Conf. on Decision and Control, Vol. 1, pp. 1082-1087, Dec. 1991.

[14] M. Spong and M. Vidyasagar, Robot Dynamics and Control, New York: John Wiley and Sons, Inc., 1989.

[15] J. Slotine, (1988), "Putting Physics in Control - The Example of Robotics," Controls Systems Magazine, Dec. 1988, Vol. 8, pp 12-17.

[16] S. Sastry and M. Bodson, Adaptive Control: Stability, Convergence, and Robustness, Englewoods Cliff, NJ: Prentice Hall Co., 1989.

[17] G. Buja and M. Valla, "Control Characteristics of the SRM Drives-Part I: Operation in the Linear Region", IEEE Transactions on Industrial Electronics, Vol. 38, No. 5, pp. 313-321, Oct. 1991.

Appendix A is available upon request

Appendix B

Proof of (2.30)

Given (2.5), and the trigonometric identity

$$\sin(a - \beta) = \cos(\beta)\sin(a) - \sin(\beta)\cos(a), \tag{B.1}$$

we can write $\sin(x_j)$ as

$$\sin(x_j) = \cos(\left[\frac{2\pi(j-1)}{m}\right])\sin(N_r q) - \sin(\left[\frac{2\pi(j-1)}{m}\right])\cos(N_r q). \tag{B.2}$$

Substituting (B.2) into the left-hand side of (2.30) yields

$$\sum_{j=1}^{m}\sin(x_j) = \sin(N_r q)\sum_{j=1}^{m}\cos(\left[\frac{2\pi(j-1)}{m}\right]) - \cos(N_r q)\sum_{j=1}^{m}\sin(\left[\frac{2\pi(j-1)}{m}\right]). \tag{B.3}$$

We can interpret each of the summations on the right-hand side of (B.3) as being composed of m unit length phasors (where $m \geq 3$ by assumption), which are equally spaced about the unit circle (starting with the reference phasors $\cos(\frac{2\pi}{m})$ and $\sin(\frac{2\pi}{m})$, respectively). Given this interpretation, the vector sum of each set of phasors is zero; which implies

$$\sum_{j=1}^{m}\cos(\left[\frac{2\pi(j-1)}{m}\right]) = 0, \quad \text{and} \quad \sum_{j=1}^{m}\sin(\left[\frac{2\pi(j-1)}{m}\right]) = 0. \tag{B.4}$$

Given (B.3) and (B.4), (2.30) then follows. □

Appendix C

Definition of W_j and θ_j in (2.38)

Given (A.4), we can partition the term $\dot{\gamma}_c$ as shown

$$\dot{\gamma}_c = \left[\dot{\gamma}_c\right]_k + \left[\dot{\gamma}_c\right]_u = \left[Y\dot{\phi} + \dot{Y}\phi + k_L\dot{r}\right]_k + \left[\dot{Y}\hat{\phi} + k_L\dot{r}\right]_u, \tag{C.1}$$

where the subscript k is used to indicate the known component of the designated quantity and the subscript u is used to indicate the unknown component of the designated quantity. This partition is significant because it allows us to linearly parameterize the electrical subsystem dynamics as shown in (2.38). To determine the individual components, we solve (2.9) for $\ddot{q}$ and substitute into (2.8) to obtain

$$\dot{r} = \left[\ddot{q}_d - \left\{A_0\sum_{j=1}^{m}\sin(x_j)\gamma_j^2 - A_1\sin(q) - A_2\dot{q}\right\}\right] + \alpha\dot{e}, \tag{C.2}$$

where

$$A_0 = \frac{1}{M}, \quad A_1 = \frac{\bar{N}}{M}, \quad \text{and} \quad A_2 = \frac{\bar{B}}{M}. \tag{C.3}$$

Using (2.12), (2.13), (2.14), and (C.2), the known portion of (C.1) is given as

$$\left[Y\dot{\phi} + \dot{Y}\phi + k_L\dot{r}\right]_k = Y\Gamma Y^T r + \left[\left\{\frac{d}{dt}\ddot{q}_d + \alpha\ddot{q}_d\right\}\hat{M} + \cos(q)\dot{q}\hat{N}\right] + k_L[\ddot{q}_d + \alpha\dot{e}], \tag{C.4}$$

while the unknown portion of (C.1) can be partitioned as

$$\left[\dot{Y}\hat{\phi} + k_L\dot{r}\right]_u = \left[\dot{Y}\hat{\phi} + k_L\dot{r}\right]_{u\bar{N}} + \left[\dot{Y}\hat{\phi} + k_L\dot{r}\right]_{u\bar{B}} + \left[\dot{Y}\hat{\phi} + k_L\dot{r}\right]_{u\gamma_j}, \tag{C.5}$$

where $u\bar{N}$, $u\bar{B}$, and $u\gamma_j$ are the components of the unknown quantities in (C.2) associated with the gravity term, the viscous load dampening term, and the per phase motor current terms, respectively. Using (2.12), (2.13), (2.14), and (C.2), these terms are given as

$$\left[\dot{Y}\hat{\phi} + k_L\dot{r}\right]_{u\gamma_j} = A_0\left[-\left\{\alpha\hat{M} - \hat{B} + k_L\right\}\sum_{j=1}^{m}\sin(x_j)\gamma_j^2\right], \tag{C.6}$$

$$\left[\dot{Y}\hat{\phi} + k_L\dot{r}\right]_{u\bar{N}} = A_1\left[\left\{\alpha\hat{M} - \hat{B} + k_L\right\}\sin(q)\right], \tag{C.7}$$

and

$$\left[\dot{Y}\hat{\phi} + k_L\dot{r}\right]_{u\bar{B}} = A_2\left[\left\{\alpha\hat{M} - \hat{B} + k_L\right\}\dot{q}\right]. \tag{C.8}$$

Given (C.1) through (C.8) and the results of Appendix A, we can represent $\dot{\gamma}_{cj}$ as a sum of known and unknown components

$$\dot{\gamma}_{cj} = \left[\dot{\gamma}_{cj}\right]_k + \left[\dot{\gamma}_{cj}\right]_u, \tag{C.9}$$

where

$$\left[\dot{\gamma}_{cj}\right]_k = \Sigma_j\dot{x}_j + \Pi_j\left[\dot{\gamma}_c\right]_k, \tag{C.10}$$

and

$$\left[\dot{\gamma}_{cj}\right]_u = \Pi_j\left[\dot{\gamma}_c\right]_u. \tag{C.11}$$

Given (2.3), (2.4), and (C.9), we can rewrite the electrical subsystem dynamics as

$$L_j(q)\dot{\eta}_j = \left[L_0 - L_1\cos(x_j)\right]\left\{\left[\dot{\gamma}_{cj}\right]_k + \left[\dot{\gamma}_{cj}\right]_u\right\} + R_0\gamma_j + N_rL_1\sin(x_j)\gamma_j\dot{q} + \tfrac{1}{2}L_1\sin(x_j)\eta_j\dot{x}_j - u_j - \tfrac{1}{2}\dot{L}_j(q)\eta_j. \tag{C.12}$$

Substituting (C.11), (C.6), (C.7), and (C.8) for the unknown components of (C.12) yields

$$\begin{aligned} L_j(q)\dot{\eta}_j = {} & L_0\left[\dot{\gamma}_{cj}\right]_k \\ & + L_0A_0\Pi_j\left[-\left\{a\hat{M} - \hat{B} + k_L\right\}\sum_{j=1}^{m}\sin(x_j)\gamma_j^2\right] \\ & + L_0A_1\Pi_j\left[\left\{a\hat{M} - \hat{B} + k_L\right\}\sin(q)\right] \\ & + L_0A_2\Pi_j\left[\left\{a\hat{M} - \hat{B} + k_L\right\}\dot{q}\right] \\ & + L_1\left\{-\cos(x_j)\left[\dot{\gamma}_{cj}\right]_k + N_r\sin(x_j)\gamma_j\dot{q} + \tfrac{1}{2}\sin(x_j)\eta_j\dot{x}_j\right\} \\ & + L_1A_0\cos(x_j)\Pi_j\left[\left\{a\hat{M} - \hat{B} + k_L\right\}\sum_{j=1}^{m}\sin(x_j)\gamma_j^2\right] \\ & + L_1A_1\cos(x_j)\Pi_j\left[-\left\{a\hat{M} - \hat{B} + k_L\right\}\sin(q)\right] \\ & + L_1A_2\cos(x_j)\Pi_j\left[-\left\{a\hat{M} - \hat{B} + k_L\right\}\dot{q}\right] \\ & + R_0\gamma_j - u_j - \tfrac{1}{2}\dot{L}_j(q)\eta_j. \end{aligned} \tag{C.13}$$

The electrical subsystem error dynamics are now linearly parameterized in terms of unknown constant electro-mechanical parameters. Therefore, we can rewrite (C.13) as shown in (2.38) with the 1×9 regressor vector defined as

$$W_j = \left[W_{j1}, \cdots, W_{j9}\right], \tag{C.14}$$

having individual elements

$$W_{j1} = \left[\dot{\gamma}_{cj}\right]_k, \tag{C.15}$$

$$W_{j2} = \Pi_j\left[-\left\{a\hat{M} - \hat{B} + k_L\right\}\sum_{j=1}^{m}\sin(x_j)\gamma_j^2\right], \tag{C.16}$$

$$W_{j3} = \Pi_j\left[\left\{a\hat{M} - \hat{B} + k_L\right\}\sin(q)\right], \tag{C.17}$$

$$W_{j4} = \Pi_j\left[\left\{a\hat{M} - \hat{B} + k_L\right\}\dot{q}\right], \tag{C.18}$$

$$W_{j5} = -\cos(x_j)\left[\dot{\gamma}_{cj}\right]_k + N_r\sin(x_j)\gamma_j\dot{q} + \tfrac{1}{2}\sin(x_j)\eta_j\dot{x}_j, \tag{C.19}$$

$$W_{j6} = \cos(x_j)\Pi_j\left[\left\{a\hat{M} - \hat{B} + k_L\right\}\sum_{j=1}^{m}\sin(x_j)\gamma_j^2\right] = -\cos(x_j)W_{j2}, \tag{C.20}$$

$$W_{j7} = \cos(x_j)\Pi_j\left[-\left\{a\hat{M} - \hat{B} + k_L\right\}\sin(q)\right] = -\cos(x_j)W_{j3}, \tag{C.21}$$

$$W_{j8} = \cos(x_j)\Pi_j\left[-\left\{a\hat{M} - \hat{B} + k_L\right\}\dot{q}\right] = -\cos(x_j)W_{j4}, \tag{C.22}$$

$$W_{j9} = \gamma_j, \tag{C.23}$$

and the 9×1 vector of unknown *constant* electro-mechanical parameters θ_j is defined as

$$\theta_j = \left[L_0, L_0A_0, L_0A_1, L_0A_2, L_1, L_1A_0, L_1A_1, L_1A_2, R_0\right]^T. \tag{C.25}$$

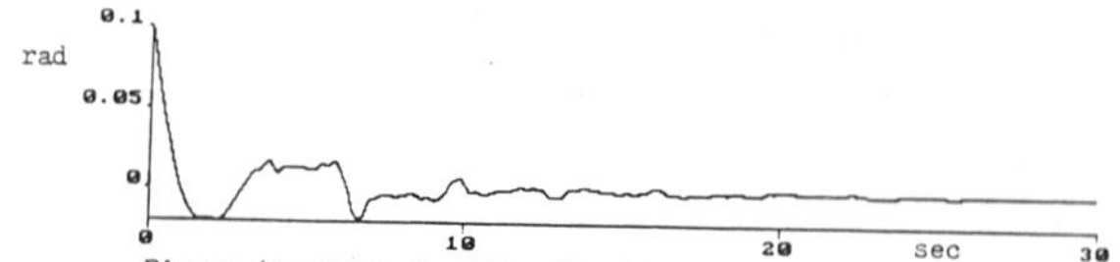

Figure 1A: Motor Position Tracking Error

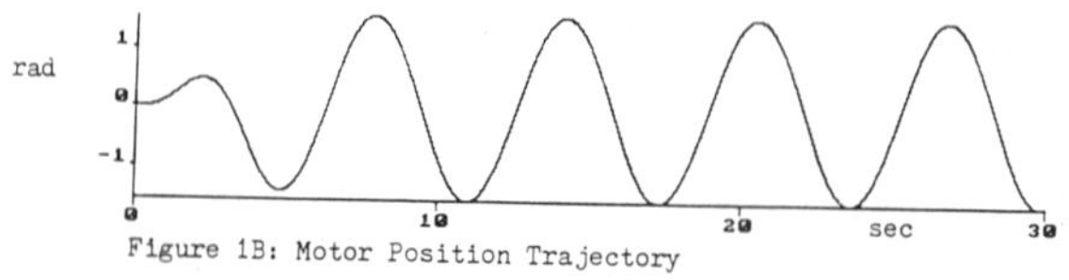

Figure 1B: Motor Position Trajectory

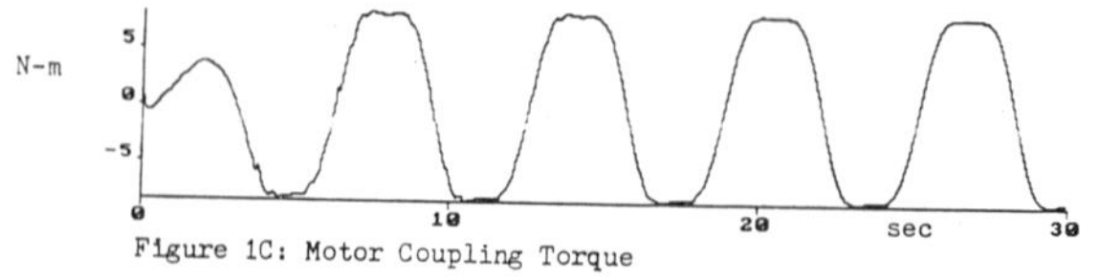

Figure 1C: Motor Coupling Torque

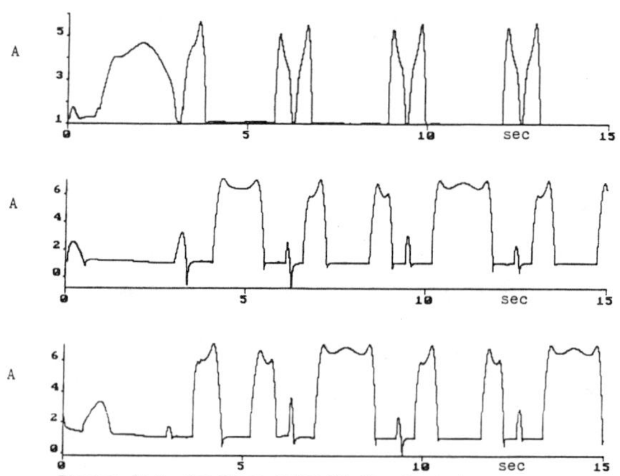

Figures 2A-C: Per Phase Motor Winding Currents

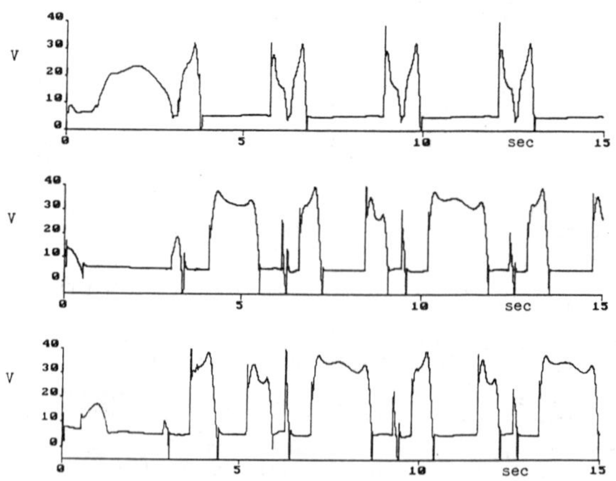

Figures 3A-C: Per Phase Motor Winding Voltages

Proceedings of the
American Control Conference
San Francisco, California • June 1993

Adaptive Sliding Mode Control for PM Synchronous Motor System Driven by PWM Inverter

Shi-Lin Lee[1], *Li-Chen Fu*[1,2], *and Wen-Hai Yu*[1]

Department of Electrical Engineering[1]
Department of Computer Science & Information Engineering[2]
National Taiwan University, Taiwan, R. O. C.

Abstract

The paper proposes an efficient robust control scheme for a permanent magnet (PM) synchronous motor. The motor system considered here consists of a pulsewidth modulated (PWM) inverter which is used to regulate the input current. Initially, a full model of the motor system is derived under the condition that the system parameter are not precisely known or slowly varying, an adaptive controller is proposed to fulfill the task of tracjectory tracking. The controller incorporates the extremely roboust variable-structure sliding mode method and, hence, can be easily implemented in a motor system with PWM inverter, which has been widely adopted. Real experiment with Megatorque Motor from Nippon Seiko K.K. using the proposed scheme is performed, and the results are satisfactory. High potential of the present controller is demonstrated due to its easy implementation in a commercial motor system and its promising performance.

I. Introduction

In recent years, the control problem of motors has been widely discussed. The usual application of motors is in a high-performance servo system, such as an industrial robot, computer numerically controlled (CNC) machine tool, and a military missile. This research is thus motivated by the need of a high-quality control.

Traditional control method for motors is usually the PID control. This kind of control has its advantage of easy implementation and understanding. Unfortunately, its drawback also lies in the so simple controller structure with PID gains. To tune these gains properly is a tedious task. Since a fixed choice of those gains is supposed to deal with only linear or quasi-linear systems, the operation range is not wide enough to cope with uncertainties due to modeling and disturbances from the surrounding environment. Recently, an effort to apply variable-structure sliding mode control (VSSMC) in the motor drive system is made. The disturbance effect can be easily handled because of the inherent robustness property of this control method. Despite the strengh of such a method, it is subjected to a drawback of undergoing switching with excessively high gain unless the system parameter are known to some enough extent.

The control problems of motors can be separated into two part, one is the electrical drive system and another is the controller design. In the past years, many papers were published for discussing how to achieve a good performance of PWM inverter. The PWM inverter is the most important part of electrical drive system. There are fewer papers wholly focused on the controller design.

Although PID controller was the main control technique for motors so far, but some advanced controllers have also been proposed recently. VSSMC controller was presented by Bose, Park & Kim [3][5]. Chan, Liaw, Chen, Marino, & Jean [6]-[9][12] introduced adaptive control methods which are based on a kind of coordinate transformation, such as vector control ⋯ etc. For others, nonlinear control using feedback linearization was introduced by Marino, Hemati, & Zribi *et al.*[9]-[11]. They used complicated nonlinear control theory to transform motor system into linear one and then specified PID control, VSSMC or adaptive control.

In this paper, the proposed scheme is based on PWM (pulse width modulation) current control and the idea coming from Slotine [1][2] named as adaptive sliding control. It composes of adaptive control and VSSMC. The adaptive control part is used for the unkown parameters, and VSSMC for uncertainties and disturbances.

In section II, we proposed the main control theory. In section III, the application to PM synchronous motor is discussed, including mathematical, uncertainly caused by PWM inverter, computer simulation, and experiments. Finally, a conclusion is drawn in section IV.

Before the standard presentation, we summarize the notations used in this paper in the following :

Nomenclature

$v_{ds}, (v_{qs})$	:	d-axis (q-axis) stator voltage
$i_{ds}, (i_{qs})$	:	d-axis (q-axis) stator current
$L_d, (L_q)$	:	$L_{ls} + L_{mq}, (L_{ls} + L_{md})$
$L_{md}, (L_{mq})$	:	$\frac{3}{2}(L_A + L_B), (\frac{3}{2}(L_A - L_B))$
L_{ls}	:	leakage inductances
$L_A, (L_B)$	:	self inductances,(mutual inductances)
r_s	:	stator resistance
λ_m	:	amplitude of flux linkage
P	:	pole number
J	:	inertia of rotor and the payload
T_L	:	torque load
B_m	:	damping constant
$d(t)$	:	bounded disturtance
θ	:	angular position of rotor
w	:	angular velocity of rotor
θ_r	:	electrical angular position of rotor($= \frac{P}{2}\theta$)
w_r	:	electrical angular velocity of rotor($= \frac{P}{2}w$)

$$sgn(S) = \begin{cases} 1 & \text{if } S > 0 \\ 0 & \text{if } S = 0 \\ -1 & \text{if } S < 0 \end{cases}$$

$$sat(\frac{S}{\Phi(t)}) = \begin{cases} 1 & \text{if } S \geq \Phi(t) \\ \frac{S}{\Phi(t)} & \text{if } |S| < \Phi(t) \\ -1 & \text{if } S \leq -\Phi(t) \end{cases}$$

$\Phi(t)$: boundary layer, and chosen > 0

II. Main Control Theory - Adaptive Sliding Control

In this chapter, a new controller is proposed to deal with a class of nonlinear SISO systems. Later it will be shown that dynamics of motor belongs to this class of systems. In the following sections, the modified adaptive sliding controller based on Slotine's [2] is provided and the stability problems will also be discussed.

2.1 Problem Statement

Consider the class of nonlinear SISO systems modeled by the following equation [2] :

$$x^{(n)} + \sum_{i=1}^{r}(a_{si} + a_{vi}(t))f_i(X,t) = (b_s \cdot b_f(t))u + d(t) \tag{2.1}$$

where x is the state and also the output, $x^{(n)}$ is the n-th order derivative , u is the input, a_{si} and b_s are nonzero constant parameters, $a_{vi}(t)$ and $b_f(t)$ are time-varying parameters, $d(t)$ is the output disturbance, and $X = [x, ..., x^{(n-1)}]^T$.

Our problem here is to design an robust adaptive controller so that the output x will asymptotically follow the desired trajectory x_d. The following are some relevant assumptions regarding the system equation (2.1).

Assumptions:

A1: The time-varying functions $a_{vi}(t), b_f(t)$, and $d(t)$ are bounded by some positive constants, i.e. there exist Δa_{vi}, d, and $B > 0$ such that $|a_{vi}(t)| \leq \Delta a_{vi}, |d(t)| \leq d$, and $|b_f(t)| \leq B$.

A2: The function $b_f(t)$ is bounded away from zero for any time $t \geq 0$, and is assumed to be always positive here.

A3: The functions $f_i(X,t)$, $i = 1, 2, \cdots, r$, are bounded for any time t if X is bounded.

Given that the class of nonlinear systems described by (2.1) satisfy the above conditions, in the next section, we will present an adaptive sliding control which is a modified version of the one in [2].

2.2 Discontinuous Control Law

Initially, we rearrange the equation (2.1) as follows,

$$b_f(t)u = (\frac{1}{b_s})x^{(n)} + \sum_{i=1}^{r}(\frac{a_{si}+a_{vi}(t)}{b_s})f_i(X,t) - \frac{d(t)}{b_s} \tag{2.2}$$

Let $h = \frac{1}{b_s}$, $A_{si} = \frac{a_{si}}{b_s}$, $A_{vi}(t) = \frac{a_{vi}(t)}{b_s}$, and $D(t) = \frac{-d(t)}{b_s}$, then the above equation becomes

$$b_f(t)u = hx^{(n)} + \sum_{i=1}^{r}(A_{si}+A_{vi}(t))f_i(t) + D(t) \tag{2.3}$$

If we further denote $\Delta A_{vi} = \frac{\Delta a_{vi}}{b_s}$ and $D = \frac{d}{b_s}$, then the assumption **A1** becomes $|A_{vi}(t)| \leq \Delta A_{vi}$, and $|D(t)| \leq D$.

Let the tracking error between the desired trajectory and the real output be denoted by

$$e = x - x_d \tag{2.4}$$

and the sliding surface as

$$S = (\frac{d}{dt}+\lambda)^{(n-1)}e \tag{2.5}$$

where $\lambda > 0$. We define a new variable $y_r^{(n-1)}$:

$$y_r^{(n-1)} = x_d^{(n-1)} - \sum_{i=1}^{n-1} C_i^{n-1}(\frac{d}{dt})^{n-1-i}\lambda^i e \quad , \tag{2.6}$$

where $C_i^{n-1} = \frac{(n-1)!}{i!(n-1-i)!}$ and choose $\hat{b}_f(t)$ such that $\frac{1}{\beta_f} \leq \frac{b_f(t)}{\hat{b}_f(t)} \leq \beta_f$, where $\beta_f \geq 1$. Note that $S = x^{(n-1)} - y_r^{(n-1)}$, and $\hat{b}_f(t)$ can be chosen as $(b_f(t)_{min} \cdot b_f(t)_{max})^{\frac{1}{2}}$ where $b_f(t)_{min}$ and $b_f(t)_{max}$ denote the minimum and the maximum of $b_f(t)$, respectively. See that in equation(2.5) we can construct another kind of sliding surface, such as

$$S = (\frac{d}{dt}+\lambda)^{(n)}\int_0^t e(\tau)d\tau \quad ,$$

where the integral form of the tracking error is included. This can improve the finite-time steady-state. Another example is to replace the operator $(\frac{d}{dt}+\lambda)^{(n-1)}$ in q.(2.5) by any Hurwitz polynomial of s, $H(s)$, of degree $(n-1)$ where $s = \frac{d}{dt}$. Althogh there are many alternatives to select such a Hurwitz polynomial function, only the form of q.(2.5) is considered here. Now, we state the first theorem in the following.

Theorem 2.1 *Given system (2.1) and assumptions A1-A3 which are valid, if we use the input*

$$u = (\hat{b}_f(t))^{-1}\left[\hat{h}y_r^{(n)} - sgn(h)kS + \sum_{i=1}^{r}\hat{A}_{si}f_i(X,t) + K(X,t)sgn(S)\right] \tag{2.7}$$

where

$$\begin{aligned}
K(X,t) &= -sgn(h)\beta_f\left[|\hat{h}y_r^{(n)} + \sum_{i=1}^{r}\hat{A}_{si}f_i(X,t)|(\beta_f-1)\right.\\
&\quad \left.+\sum_{i=1}^{r}|\Delta A_{vi}f_i(X,t)| + (D+\eta)\right]\\
\frac{d}{dt}\hat{h} &= -sgn(h)my_r^{(n)}S\\
\frac{d}{dt}\hat{A}_{si} &= -sgn(h)mf_i(X,t)S \qquad i=1,\cdots,r \;\;,\;\; \text{and } m,\eta>0,
\end{aligned}$$

then the output x will asymptotically converge to the desired trajectory x_d.

Proof : After equation(2.7) is substituted into equation(2.3), we can get

$$\begin{aligned}
h\dot{S} + \frac{b_f(t)}{\hat{b}_f(t)}sgn(h)kS &= \tilde{h}y_r^{(n)} + (\frac{b_f(t)}{\hat{b}_f(t)}-1)\hat{h}y_r^{(n)} + \sum_{i=1}^{r}\tilde{A}_{si}f_i(X,t)\\
&+ \sum_{i=1}^{r}(\frac{b_f(t)}{\hat{b}_f(t)}-1)\hat{A}_{si}f_i(X,t) - \sum_{i=1}^{r}A_{vi}(t)f_i(X,t)\\
&- D(t) + \frac{b_f(t)}{\hat{b}_f(t)}K(X,t)sgn(S)
\end{aligned} \tag{2.8}$$

Choose the following Lyapunov function candidate

$$V = \frac{1}{2}[m|h|S^2 + \tilde{h}^2 + \sum_{i=1}^{r}\tilde{A}_{si}^2], \tag{2.9}$$

where $\tilde{h} = \hat{h} - h$, $\tilde{A}_{si} = \hat{A}_{si} - A_{si}$, and consider the case $h > 0$, then the time derivative of V can be derived as:

$$\dot{V} = mhS\dot{S} + \tilde{h}\dot{\tilde{h}} + \sum_{i=1}^{r}\tilde{A}_{si}\dot{\tilde{A}}_{si}$$

Using the equation(2.8), we get

$$\begin{aligned}
\dot{V} &= m\left[-\frac{b_f(t)}{\hat{b}_f(t)}kS + \tilde{h}y_r^{(n)} + (\frac{b_f(t)}{\hat{b}_f(t)}-1)\hat{h}y_r^{(n)} + \sum_{i=1}^{r}\tilde{A}_{si}f_i(X,t)\right.\\
&\quad + \sum_{i=1}^{r}(\frac{b_f(t)}{\hat{b}_f(t)}-1)\hat{A}_{si}f_i(X,t) - \sum_{i=1}^{r}A_{vi}(t)f_i(X,t) - D(t)\\
&\quad \left.+\frac{b_f(t)}{\hat{b}_f(t)}K(X,t)sgn(S)\right]S + \tilde{h}\dot{\tilde{h}} + \sum_{i=1}^{r}\tilde{A}_{si}\dot{\tilde{A}}_{si}
\end{aligned} \tag{2.10}$$

Now, because

$$\begin{aligned}
\dot{\tilde{h}} = \dot{\hat{h}} &= -my_r^{(n)}S\\
\dot{\tilde{A}}_{si} = \dot{\hat{A}}_{si} &= -mf_i(X,t)S, \qquad i=1,\cdots,r,
\end{aligned}$$

after some algebraic manipulation, it can be found that

$$\begin{aligned}
\dot{V} &= m\left\{-\frac{b_f(t)}{\hat{b}_f(t)}kS + (\frac{b_f(t)}{\hat{b}_f(t)}-1)\hat{h}y_r^{(n)} + \sum_{i=1}^{r}(\frac{b_f(t)}{\hat{b}_f(t)}-1)\hat{A}_{si}f_i(X,t)\right.\\
&\quad -\sum_{i=1}^{r}A_{vi}(t)f_i(X,t) - D(t) - \frac{b_f(t)}{\hat{b}_f(t)}\beta_f\\
&\quad \cdot\left[|\hat{h}y_r^{(n)} + \sum_{i=1}^{r}\hat{A}_{si}f_i(X,t)|(\beta_f-1)\right.\\
&\quad \left.\left.+\sum_{i=1}^{r}|\Delta A_{vi}f_i(X,t)| + (D+\eta)\right]sgn(S)\right\}S
\end{aligned} \tag{2.11}$$

which can be further simplified into

$$\begin{aligned}
\dot{V} &\leq -\frac{m}{\beta_f}kS^2 - m\eta|S|\\
&\leq -m\eta|S|\\
&\leq 0
\end{aligned} \tag{2.12}$$

It then follows that S, $\tilde{h}$, and $\tilde{A}_{si}$ are bounded, i.e, S, $\tilde{h}$, and $\tilde{A}_{si} \in L_\infty$, and hence V is bounded.

From equation(2.12), we can see that

$$V(\infty) - V(0) \leq -m\eta\int_0^\infty |S|dt \tag{2.13}$$

Because V is bounded, and

$$0 \leq m\eta\int_0^\infty |S|dt \leq V(0) - V(\infty) \tag{2.14}$$

We can get another conclusion that $S \in L_1 \cap L_\infty$. Also, from equation(2.8), we can see that $\dot{S}$ is bounded. Thus, using Barbalat's lemma [15], we can guarantee S will asymptotically converge to zero. Finally, by a stable filter thereom [21], we successfully show that x will converge to x_d asymptotically.

The same conclusion can also be made for the case $h < 0$. The proof is thus completed. *Q.E.D*

2.3 Continuous Control Law

In many cases, the term $-K(X,t)sgn(S)$ will cause the phenomenon known as "chattering" in the variable structure system (VSS). The chattering is generally highly undesirable in practice since it implies extremely high control activity. Futhermore, it may excite high-frequency dynamics neglected in the course of modelling (such as resonant structural mode, neglected actuator time-delays,etc.). In many applications, only the control of motors has achieved satisfactory performance up to now. So, the concept of boundary layer is introduced here to avoid the switching effect.

Here, we introduce saturation function $sat(\frac{S}{\Phi(t)})$ and define new variable S_Δ as the followings:

$$sat(\frac{S}{\Phi(t)}) = \begin{cases} 1 & S > \Phi(t)\\ \frac{S}{\Phi(t)} & |S| \leq \Phi(t)\\ -1 & S < -\Phi(t)\end{cases}$$

$$S_\Delta = S - \Phi(t)sat(\frac{S}{\Phi(t)}),$$

where $\Phi(t)$ denotes the boundary layer width. Note that $\dot{S}_\Delta = \dot{S} - \dot{\Phi}(t)$ outside the boundary layer, while $S_\Delta = 0$ inside the boundary layer.

By following the ideas from Theorem 2.1, we can derive another result in the following.

In fact, instead of using S_Δ[2] to synthesize the adaptation laws,

an alternative which use S can be similarly proposed. This is stated in the following theorem.

Theorem 2.1: *Given system (2.1) and assumptions A1-A3 which are valid, if we use the input*

$$\begin{aligned}
u &= (\hat{b}_f(t))^{-1}\left[\hat{h}y_r^{(n)} - sgn(h)kS + \sum_{i=1}^{r}\hat{A}_{si}f_i(X,t)\right.\\
&\quad \left.+K(X,t)sat(\frac{S}{\Phi(t)})\right]
\end{aligned} \tag{2.15}$$

$$K(X,t) = -sgn(h)\beta_f \left[|\hat{h}y_r^{(n)} + \sum_{i=1}^{r} \hat{A}_{si} f_i(X,t)|(\beta_f - 1) + \sum_{i=1}^{r} |\Delta A_{vi} f_i(X,t)| + (D+\eta) \right]$$

$$\frac{d}{dt}\hat{h} = \begin{cases} -sgn(h) m y_r^{(n)} S & |S| \geq \Phi(t) \\ 0 & |S| < \Phi(t) \end{cases}$$

$$\frac{d}{dt}\hat{A}_{si} = \begin{cases} -sgn(h) m f_i(X,t) S & |S| \geq \Phi(t) \\ 0 & |S| < \Phi(t) \quad i = 1, \cdots, r \end{cases}$$

where η is some positive constant, then the output tracking error will be bounded in a small region which depends on the boundary layer width $\Phi(t)$.

Proof : Now, we choose another Lyapunov function candidate

$$V = \frac{1}{2}[m|h|S^2 + \tilde{h}^2 + \sum_{r=1}^{r} \tilde{A}_{si}] \tag{2.16}$$

, and consider the case $h > 0$. The time derivative of V can be found to be

$$\begin{aligned} \dot{V} &= m\Bigg[-\frac{b_f(t)}{\hat{b}_f(t)} sgn(h) kS + \tilde{h}y_r^{(n)} + (\frac{b_f(t)}{\hat{b}_f(t)} - 1)\hat{h}y_r^{(n)} \\ &+ \sum_{i=1}^{r} \tilde{A}_{si} f_i(X,t) + \sum_{i=1}^{r} (\frac{b_f(t)}{\hat{b}_f(t)} - 1)\hat{A}_{si} f_i(X,t) \\ &- \sum_{i=1}^{r} A_{vi}(t) f_i(X,t) - D(t) + \frac{b_f(t)}{\hat{b}_f(t)} K(X,t) sat(\frac{S}{\Phi(t)}) \Bigg] S \\ &+ \tilde{h}\dot{\tilde{h}} + \sum_{i=1}^{r} \tilde{A}_{si}\dot{\tilde{A}}_{si} \end{aligned} \tag{2.17}$$

where $\dot{S}$ is replaced by substitution of equation(2.15) into equation(2.3), and consider $S > |\Phi(t)|$. Because

$$\begin{aligned} \frac{d}{dt}\hat{h} &= \frac{d}{dt}\tilde{h} = -my_r^{(n)}S \\ \frac{d}{dt}\hat{A}_{si} &= \frac{d}{dt}\tilde{A}_{si} = -mf_i(X,t)S, \end{aligned}$$

$\dot{V}$ can be rewritten as

$$\begin{aligned} \dot{V} &= m\Bigg\{ -\frac{b_f(t)}{\hat{b}_f(t)} kS + (\frac{b_f(t)}{\hat{b}_f(t)} - 1)\hat{h}y_r^{(n)} + \sum_{i=1}^{r} (\frac{b_f(t)}{\hat{b}_f(t)} - 1)\hat{A}_{si} f_i(X,t) \\ &- \sum_{i=1}^{r} A_{vi}(t) f_i(X,t) - D(t) - \frac{b_f(t)}{\hat{b}_f(t)}\beta_f \\ &\cdot \left[|\hat{h}y_r^{(n)} + \sum_{i=1}^{r} \hat{A}_{si} f_i(X,t)|(\beta_f - 1) \right. \\ &\left. + \sum_{i=1}^{r} |\Delta A_{vi} f_i(X,t)| + (D+\eta) \right] sat(\frac{S}{\Phi(t)}) \Bigg\} S \end{aligned} \tag{2.18}$$

It can be similarly verified that $\dot{V}$ will be negative outside the boundary layer.

$$\begin{aligned} \dot{V} &\leq -\frac{b_f(t)}{\hat{b}_f(t)} mkS^2 - m\eta|S| \\ &\leq -\frac{m}{\beta_f} kS^2 \\ &\leq 0 \end{aligned}$$

Until here, we get a conclusion that S, $\tilde{h}$, and $\tilde{A}_{si}$ are bounded. From the modified adaptation law, we can also guarantee that the parameters are bounded in the layer.

Now, consider $hS\dot{S}$

$$\begin{aligned} hS\dot{S} &= -\frac{b_f(t)}{\hat{b}_f(t)} kS^2 + \Bigg[\tilde{h}y_r^{(n)} + (\frac{b_f(t)}{\hat{b}_f(t)} - 1)\hat{h}y_r^{(n)} + \sum_{i=1}^{r} \tilde{A}_{si} f_i(X,t) \\ &+ \sum_{i=1}^{r} (\frac{b_f(t)}{\hat{b}_f(t)} - 1)\hat{A}_{si} f_i(X,t) - \sum_{i=1}^{r} A_{vi}(t) f_i(X,t) - D(t) \\ &+ \frac{b_f(t)}{\hat{b}_f(t)} K(X,t) sat(\frac{S}{\Phi(t)}) \Bigg] S \end{aligned} \tag{2.19}$$

$$\begin{aligned} h\frac{d}{dt}S^2 &\leq -\frac{k}{\beta_f}S^2 + \Bigg\{ \Bigg[\tilde{h}y_r^{(n)} + (\frac{b_f(t)}{\hat{b}_f(t)} - 1)\hat{h}y_r^{(n)} + \sum_{i=1}^{r} \tilde{A}_{si} f_i(X,t) \\ &+ \sum_{r=1}^{r} (\frac{b_f}{\hat{b}_f} - 1)\hat{A}_{si} f_i(X,t) - \sum_{i=1}^{r} A_{vi} f_i(X,t) - D(t) \\ &- \frac{b_f(t)}{\hat{b}_f(t)}\beta_f \left[|\hat{h}y_r^{(n)} + \sum_{i=1}^{r} \hat{A}_{si} f_i(X,t)|(\beta_f - 1) \right. \\ &\left. + \sum_{i=1}^{r} |\Delta A_{vi} f_i(X,t)| + (D+\eta) \right] sat(\frac{S}{\Phi(t)}) \Bigg] S \Bigg\} \end{aligned} \tag{2.20}$$

for S is outside the boundary layer

Because $\tilde{h}$, $\tilde{A}_{si}$, $y_r^{(n)}$, and $f_i(X,t)$ are bounded, there exists a positive constant η, such that these terms in the big bracket, i.e,{}, less than zero. So,

$$\frac{1}{2}h\frac{d}{dt}S^2 < -\frac{k}{\beta_f}S^2 < 0$$

, which can be rewritten into

$$\frac{d}{dt}|S| < \frac{-2}{h}[\frac{k}{\beta_f}|S|] < 0$$

Thus, S will penetrate the boundary layer in finite time, and the tracking error will be bounded in a small region if $\Phi(t)$ is chosen to be small for all $t \geq 0$.
The case $h < 0$ also has the same property and, hence, the proof is completed. *Q.E.D.*

Remark : In this theorem, we cannot guarantee S will fall into the boundary layer if η fails to be chosen sufficiently large. However, from (2.20), η can be chosen as suggested in order to meet the requirement. If it is the case, S will exponentially decay into the boundary layer (also from equation(2.20)). In practice, if the system is not too complicated, a proper η will normally be small.

III. Applications - PM Synchronous Motor

A typical servo drive configuration may consists of command generator, speed and position loop controllers, a current regulated pulsewidth modulated (PWM) inverter, a motor and a load (see Fig.3.1). Vector Control (i.e. field oriented control) [15] is usually employed in formulating control laws for 3-phase motor. This method orients the armature current vector to be perpendicular to the rotor flux in a two-axis coordinate frame and obtains control characteristics that are similar to those of separately excited DC motors.

In the following subsections, the mathematical model of PM synchronous motor is given and then specify the results of Thereom 2.1 in Chapter 2 to design the controllers of motors, and the same definitions of variables are used here if not pointed out. We also assume that the PWM can function well for tracking the desired currents.

3.1 Mathematical Model

Adopting the notations in [15], the math model can be described by the following equation for the PM synchronous motor assumed to be balanced 3-phase, Y-connected, symmetric, and linear magnetic circiuts. resulting system.

$$v_{qs} = (r_s + L_q\frac{d}{dt})i_{qs} + w_r L_d i_{ds} + w_r \lambda_m \tag{3.1a}$$

$$v_{ds} = (r_s + L_d\frac{d}{dt})i_{ds} - w_r L_q i_{qs} \tag{3.1b}$$

$$T_e = J\frac{d}{dt}w + B_m w + T_L + d(t) \tag{3.1c}$$

where

$$T_e = (\frac{3}{2})(\frac{P}{2})[\lambda_m i_{qs} + (L_d - L_q)i_{qs}i_{ds}] \tag{3.1d}$$

3.2 Position Control

Case I : λ_m is unknown

For designing the controller, we first combine equation(3.1c) and equation(3.1d) as follows.

$$i_{qs} + \frac{(L_d - L_q)}{\lambda_m} i_{qs}i_{ds} = \frac{4J}{3P\lambda_m}\frac{d}{dt}w + \frac{4B_m}{3P\lambda_m}w + \frac{4}{3P\lambda_m}T_L + \frac{4}{3P\lambda_m}d(t) \tag{3.2}$$

Let $h = \frac{4J}{3P\lambda_m}$, $D(t) = \frac{4}{3P\lambda_m}d(t)$, $A_1 = \frac{4B_m}{3P\lambda_m}$, $f_1(X,t) = w$, and $\frac{4}{3P\lambda_m}T_L = \sum_{i=2}^{r} A_i f_i(X,t)$ ($X = [w,\theta]$). Equation(3.2) is written as

$$i_{qs} + \frac{(L_d - L_q)}{\lambda_m} i_{qs}i_{ds} = h\ddot{\theta} + \sum_{i=1}^{r} A_i f_i(X,t) + D(t) \tag{3.3}$$

Proposition 3.1 *If we let the current command $i_{ds}^* = 0$, and*

$$i_{qs}^* = \hat{h}\ddot{y}_r - kS + \sum_{i=1}^{r} \hat{A}_i f_i(X,t) - (D+\eta)sgn(S) \tag{3.4}$$

$$\begin{aligned} \frac{d}{dt}\hat{h} &= -mS\ddot{y}_r \\ \frac{d}{dt}\hat{A}_i &= -mSf_i(X,t) \qquad i = 1, \cdots, r \end{aligned}$$

where $e = \theta - \theta_d$, $\dot{y}_r = \dot{\theta}_d - \lambda e$, $S = \dot{\theta} - \dot{y}_r = \dot{e} + \lambda e$, and $\lambda, \eta, k, m, D > 0$, then the angular position of rotor θ will asymptotically converge to the desired trajectory θ_d.

Remark : Note that i_{ds}^* and i_{qs}^* are the current commands which we want the PM synchronous motor to follow (see Fig.3.1). It is why we use these symbols instead of true current states. There is physical meaning for $i_{ds}^* = 0$, i.e., we want to orient the magnet flux of stator to be perpendicular to that of rotor.

Case II: λ_m is known

In most applications, the command input is the torque function. For this case, we can let the current command input be :

$$i_{ds}^* = 0 \quad (3.5a)$$

$$i_{qs}^* = \frac{4}{3P\lambda_m}T_e \quad (3.5b)$$

Now, we only need to decide what kind of torque command should be used. Rewrite equation(3.1c) as

$$T_e = J\ddot{\theta} + \sum_{i=1}^{r} A_i f_i(X,t) + d(t) \quad (3.6)$$

where $A_1 f_1(X,t) = B_m w$ and $T_L = \sum_{i=2}^{r} A_i f_i(X,t)$.

Proposition 3.2 *If we let the torque command*

$$\begin{aligned} T_e^* &= \hat{J}\ddot{y}_r - kS + \sum_{i=1}^{r} \hat{A}_i f_i(X,t) - (d+\eta)sgn(S) \quad (3.7) \\ \frac{d}{dt}\hat{J} &= -mS\ddot{y}_r \\ \frac{d}{dt}\hat{A}_i &= -mSf_i(X,t) \qquad i = 1,\cdots,r \end{aligned}$$

and use equation(3.5), where e, $\dot{y}_r$, and S are the same as those in proposition 3.1, and $k, d, \eta, m > 0$, then the angular position of rotor θ will asymptotically converge to the desired trajectory θ_d.

3.3 Velocity Control

Here, the control object is angular velocity, i.e., we want the angular velocity of the motor to follow some desired trajectory w_d. The same conditions in position control will be considered again.

Case I : λ_m is unknown

Consider the equation(3.3) again, and let $\ddot{\theta}$ be replaced by $\dot{w}$.

Proposition 3.3 : *If we let the current commands $i_{ds}^* = 0$, and*

$$\begin{aligned} i_{qs}^* &= \hat{h}\dot{w}_d - ke + \sum_{i=1}^{r} \hat{A}_i f_i(X,t) - (D+\eta)sgn(e) \quad (3.8) \\ e &= w - w_d \\ \frac{d}{dt}\hat{h} &= -me\dot{w}_d \\ \frac{d}{dt}\hat{A}_i &= -mef_i(X,t) \end{aligned}$$

where k, D, η, and $m > 0$, then, the angular velocity of rotor, w, will asymptotically converge to the desired angular velocity w_d.

Case II : λ_m is known

Considering equation(3.6) again and use $\dot{w}$ instead of $\ddot{\theta}$, then we can derive another similar result.

Proposition 3.4 : *If we let the torque command*

$$\begin{aligned} T_e^* &= \hat{J}\dot{w}_d - ke + \sum_{i=1}^{r} \hat{A}_i f_i(X,t) - (d+\eta)sgn(e) \quad (3.9) \\ \frac{d}{dt}\hat{J}_m &= -me\dot{w}_d \\ \frac{d}{dt}\hat{A}_i &= -mef_i(X,t) \qquad i = 1,\cdots,r \end{aligned}$$

and use equation(3.5), where $e = w - w_d$ and $k, D, \eta, m > 0$,
then, the angular velocity of rotor, w, will asymptotically converge to the de: red angular velocity w_d.

3.4 Uncertainty Caused by PWM Inverter

The performance of PWM is considered to function well in the previous discussion. Although the hysteresis band method [4][16] works almost perfectly, there is still error between true current and current command. We can see in the Fig.4.1. The i_{ds}^* and i_{qs}^* are the inputs. But, in the motor system the actual currents will be $i_{ds}^* + \Delta i_{ds}$ and $i_{qs}^* + \Delta i_{qs}$, i.e, the inputs are disturbed by Δi_{ds} and Δi_{qs} where $|\Delta i_{ds}| < \Delta i_d$ and $|\Delta i_{qs}| < \Delta i_q$.

In the PM synchronous motor system, the torque equation(3.3) can be modified as

$$(i_{qs}+\Delta i_{qs}) + \frac{(L_d - L_q)}{\lambda_m}(i_{qs}+\Delta i_{qs})(i_{ds}+\Delta i_{ds}) = h\ddot{\theta} + \sum_{i=1}^{r} A_i f_i(X,t) + D(t) \quad (3.10)$$

After some calculations, we get

$$\begin{aligned} &(1 + \frac{L_d - L_q}{\lambda_m}\Delta i_{ds})i_{qs} + \frac{L_d - L_q}{\lambda_m}i_{qs}i_{ds} + \Delta i_{qs} \\ &+ \frac{L_d - L_q}{\lambda_m}\Delta i_{qs}i_{ds} + \frac{L_d - L_q}{\lambda_m}\Delta i_{qs}\Delta i_{ds} \\ &= h\ddot{\theta} + \sum_{i=1}^{r} A_i f_i(X,t) + D(t) \quad (3.11) \end{aligned}$$

where obviously $b_s = 1$. We now define $b_f(t) = 1 + (\frac{L_d - L_q}{\lambda_m})\Delta i_{ds}$ and estimate $\hat{b}_f(t)$ such that $\frac{1}{\beta_f} \le \frac{\hat{b}_f(t)}{b_f(t)} \le \beta_f$, $\beta_f > 1$. From the results in Chapter 2, we then can derive the following propositions for designing suitable controller.

Proposition 3.9 (Position Control): *If the current commands $i_{ds}^* = 0$ and*

$$\begin{aligned} i_{qs}^* &= (\hat{b}_f(t))^{-1}\Big[\hat{h}\ddot{y}_r - kS + \sum_{i=1}^{r} \hat{A}_i f_i(X,t) \\ &\quad + K(X,t)sgn(S)\Big] \quad (3.12) \\ K(X,t) &= -\beta_f\Big[|\hat{h}\ddot{y}_r + \sum_{i=1}^{r} \hat{A}_i f_i(X,t)|(\beta_f - 1) \\ &\quad \cdot(D + \eta + \Delta i_q \Delta i_d + \Delta i_q)\Big] \\ \frac{d}{dt}\hat{h} &= -mS\ddot{y}_r \\ \frac{d}{dt}\hat{A}_i &= -mSf_i(X,t) \end{aligned}$$

where e, S, and $\dot{y}_r$ are the same as those in Proposition 3.1, and $k, D, \eta, m > 0$. then the output θ will asymptotically converge to the desired θ_d.

Remark : Generally speaking, the term $\frac{(L_d - L_q)}{\lambda_m}$ is so small that $b_f(t)$ is almost equal to one. In turn, this implies that $\hat{b}_f(t)$ only to be slightly larger than one.

Proposition 3.10 (Velocity Control): *If the current commands $i_{ds}^* = 0$, and*

$$\begin{aligned} i_{qs}^* &= (\hat{b}_f(t))^{-1}\Big[\hat{h}\dot{w}_d - ke + \sum_{i=1}^{r} \hat{A}_i f_i(X,t) \\ &\quad + K(X,t)sgn(e)\Big] \quad (3.13) \\ K(X,t) &= -\beta_f\Big[|\hat{h}\dot{w}_d + \sum_{i=1}^{r} \hat{A}_i f_i(X,t)|(\beta_f - 1) \\ &\quad + (D + \eta + \Delta i_q \Delta i_d + \Delta i_q)\Big] \\ \frac{d}{dt}\hat{h} &= -me\dot{w}_d \\ \frac{d}{dt}\hat{A}_i &= -mef_i(X,t) \end{aligned}$$

where $e = w - w_d$, and k, D, η, $m > 0$. then the output w will asymptotically converge to w_d.

IV. Simulations and Experiments

4.1 Simulation Results

Consider a one-link robot arm drived directly by a PM synchronous motor (see Fig.3.1. The torque equation is

$$J\frac{d}{dt}w = T_e - B_m w - Mgl\sin(\theta) + d(t) \quad (4.1)$$

The system parameters of the servo motor system used here are $L_q = 0.0015$ H, $L_d = 0.00152$ H, $\lambda_m = 0.21\ N\text{-}m/A$, $r_s = 0.6\ \Omega$, $P = 4$, $J = 0.32284\ kg\text{-}m^2$, $B_m = 0.001\ N\text{-}m/rad/sec$, $d(t) = 5\cos(50t)\ N \cdot m$, and $V = 100\ volt$ (input voltage). Those of the robot arm are $M = 1kg$ (mass), $l = 0.5m$ (length), $g = 9.8m/sec^2$. As to the adaptive sliding controller, $\lambda = 10$, $m = 0.01$, $k = 100$ and $D + \eta = 20$. The initial conditions are all zero except that $\theta = 0.25$, $w = 2.5$ and $i_{ds} = 0.5A$ initially. The frequency of PWM is 10 kHz.

For position control, we let the commands θ_d be $\sin(10t)$ *radian*. The result of sinusoidal command is shown in Fig.4.2. In the step response case, a command generator is specified.

$$\dot{\theta}_d = -20\theta_d + 20r$$

where r is the step function.

4.2 Experiments – Velocity Control

There are some experiments of velocity control in this chapter. To execute the adaptive sliding control for velocity control, a PC-based motor control system is implemented in Fig.4.1.

System Description

The setup of the motor system (see Fig.4.1.) consists of a PC486, a 16 bits A/D & D/A converter, an NSK motor, a brake and a signal generator. In the following paragraphs, we will describe these instruments briefly. Note that there are two connectors in the system. The specification for NSK motor is shown below : (see NSK Megatorque Motor System USER'S MANUAL for more detail)

Maximum Torque: 4 $kgf \cdot m$; Maximum Velocity: 3.0 rps ; Maximum Friction Torque: $30kgf \cdot cm$; Moment Load Capacity: $6kgf \cdot m$; Rotor Inertial: 0.031 $kgf \cdot m^2$.

In the following experiments, we let the step velocity command be 25 rpm.

Experiment Results

The sliding surface is

$$S = (\frac{d}{dt} + \lambda) \int_0^t e(\tau) d\tau \qquad (4.2a)$$

$$e = w - w_d \qquad (4.2b)$$

and the relative controller is

$$T_e = \hat{J}\dot{y}_r - KS + \hat{B}_m w - (D+\eta) sgn(S) \qquad (4.3a)$$

$$\dot{y}_r = \dot{w}_d - \lambda e \qquad (4.3b)$$

$$\frac{d}{dt}\hat{J} = -mS\dot{y}_r \qquad (4.3c)$$

$$\frac{d}{dt}\hat{B}_m = -mSw \qquad (4.3d)$$

where $m = 0.01$, $K = 0.3$, $\lambda = 0.1$ and $D + \eta = 0.2$ for no load case. (see Fig.4.3) For load case, we change K, λ to 0.2, 0.09 separately and the others are kept the same. In Fig.4.4, there is also drop phenomenon in the transient phase. In Fig.4.5, we use the extra disturbance. The controller show its robustness too. Note that, the unit of torque command and velocity feedback is the voltage.

What will be happened if we use saturation function $(D+\eta)sat(\frac{S}{\Phi(t)})$. Consider the last case, what difference is that saturation function is used instead of switching one. The boundary layer $\Phi(t) = 0.2$ and the result is shown in Fig.4.6. Comparing Fig.4.5 with Fig.4.6 we can see that the latter is better than the former in the steady state.

V. CONCLUSIONS

A new adaptive sliding control methedology for PM synchronous motor is developed. The control scheme adopts both the adaptive control and the variable-structure sliding mode control. With the integration of these two kinds of control, the dynamic performance and the robustness of the servo motor systems are significantly enhanced. The special features of the new control scheme lies in its excellent dynamic performance and simple adaptation laws, which can be easily implemented by microprocessors. Experimental results are satisfactory. The control scheme is suitable for high-performance robust speed control and position control.

References

[1] J.-J. E. Slotine and Weiping Li, *Applied Nonlinear Control*, Prentice-Hall, International, Inc, 1991.

[2] J.-J. E. Slotine and J. A. Coetsee, " Adaptive Sliding Controller Synthesis for Nonlinear Systems ", *Int. J. Control*, 1986, vol.43, no.6, pp.1631-1651.

[3] Bimal K. Bose, " Sliding Mode Control of Induction Motor ", *IEEE/IAS Annual Metting*, pp.479-486, 1985.

[4] Bimal K. Bose, " An Adaptive Hysteresis-Band Current Control Technique of a Voltage-Fed PWM Inverter for Machine Drive System ", *IEEE Trans. Industry Electronics*, vol.37, no.5, pp.402-408, October 1990.

[5] Min-Ho Park and Kyung-Seo Kim, " Chattering Reduction in the Position Control of Induction Motor Using the Sliding Mode ", *IEEE Trans. Power Electronics*, vol.6, no.3, pp.317-325, July 1991.

[6] C. C. Chan, W. S. Leung, and C. Wing, " Adaptive Decoupling Control of Induction Motor Drives ", *IEEE Trans. Industrial Electronics*, vol.37, no.1, pp.41-47, February 1990.

[7] C. Liaw, C.Pan and Y. Chen, " Design and Implementation of an Adaptive Control for Current-Fed Induction Motor ", *IEEE Trans. Industrial Electronics*, vol.35, no.3, pp.393-401, August, 1988.

[8] Degang Chen and Brad Paden, " Nonlinear Adaptive Torque-Ripple Cancellation for Step Motors ", *Proc. of IEEE CDC*, 1990, pp.3319-3324.

[9] Riccardo Marino, Sergei Peresada, and Paolo Valigi, " Adaptive Partial Feedback Linearization of Induction Motors ", *Proc. of IEEE CDC*, 1990, pp.3313-3318.

[10] Neyram Hemati, James S. Thorp, and Ming C. Leu, " Robust Nonlinear Control of Brushless dc Motors for Direct-Drive Robotic Applications ", *IEEE Trans. Industrial Electronics*, vol.37, no.6, pp.460-468, December 1990.

[11] M. Zribi and J. Chiasson, " Position Control of a PM Stepper Motor by Exact Linearization ", *IEEE Trans. Automatic Control*, vol.36, no.5, pp.620 -625, May 1991.

[12] Jong-Hann Jean and Li-Chen Fu, " A new Adaptive Control Scheme for Induction Motors ", *15th National Symposium on Automatic Control*, pp.593-601, Taiwan, R.O.C., 1991.

[13] Paul C. Krause, *Analysis of Electric Machinery*, McGraw-Hill Book Company, 1986.

[14] *Megatorque Motor System USER'S MANUAL*, Nippon Seiko K.K. , Tokyo, Japan, 1989.

[15] Shankar Sastry and Marc Bodson, *Adaptive Control - Stability, Convergence, and Robustness*, Prentice-Hall, International Edition, 1989.

[16] Tian-Hua Liu, Chung-Ming Young, and Chang-Huan Liu, " Microprocessor -Based Controller Design and Simulation for a Permanent Magnet Synchronous Motor Drive ", *IEEE Trans. Industrial Electronics*, vol.35, no.4, pp.516-523, November, 1988.

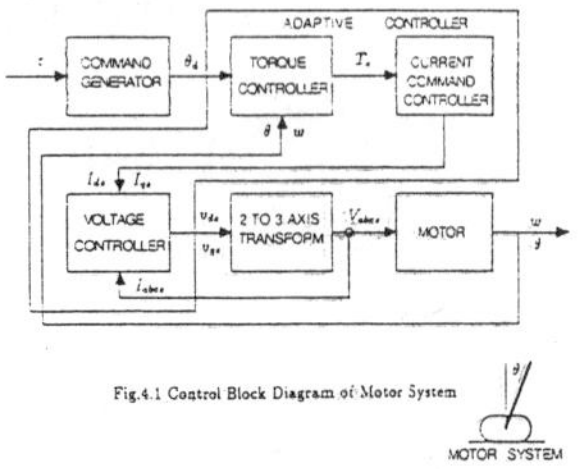

Fig.4.1 Control Block Diagram of Motor System

Fig.4.2 Tracking sin(10t)

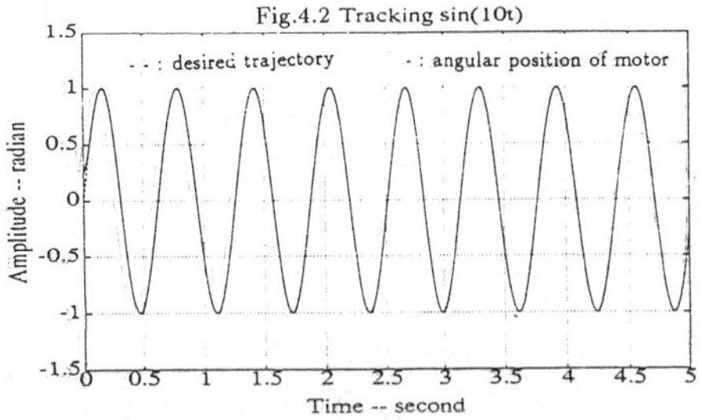

Fig.4.3 No Load

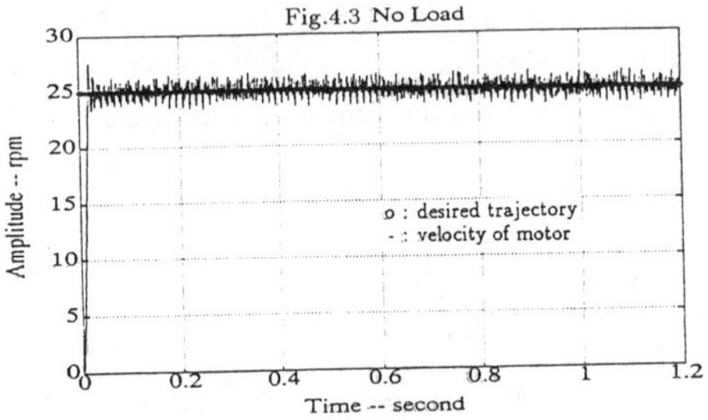

Fig.4.4 Load with Backlash

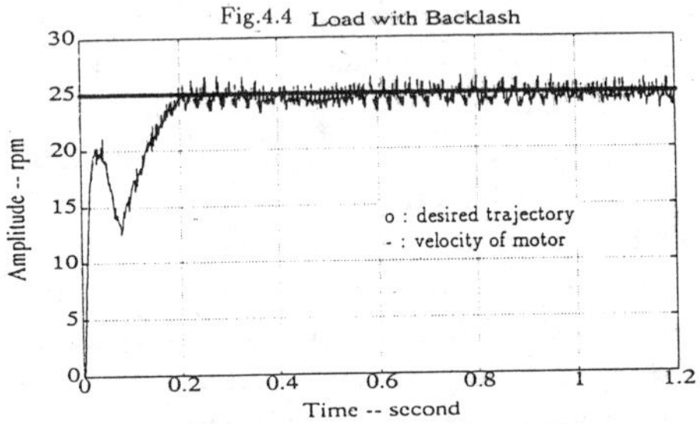

Fig.4.5 Adding Disturbance

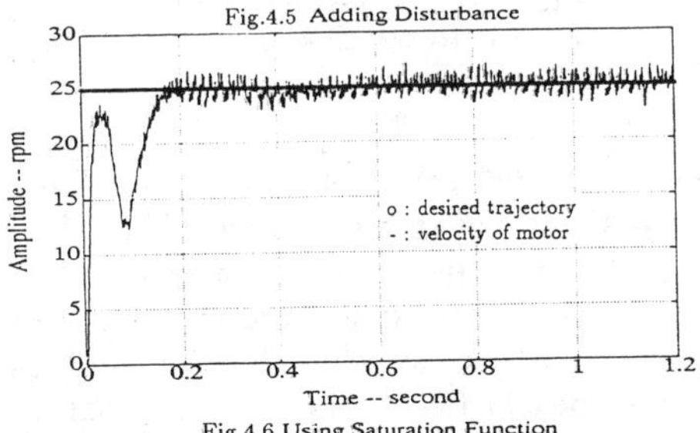

Fig.4.6 Using Saturation Function

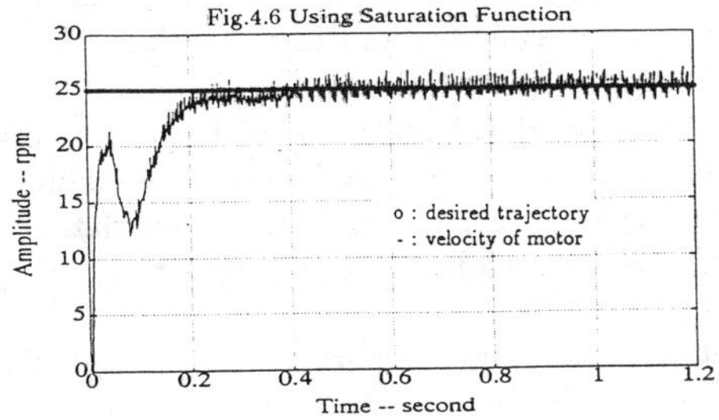

Proceedings of the
American Control Conference
San Francisco, California • June 1993

Controlling Non-Minimum Phase Nonlinear Systems - The Inverted Pendulum on a Cart Example

R. Gurumoorthy* S.R.Sanders†

Abstract

Control design for minimum phase nonlinear systems has been well developed in the literature via the input-output linearization method developed in [Isi89] and elsewhere. Since a minimum phase system has stable internal dynamics, one may only need to design a control for the linear subsystem after performing input-output linearization for such a system. This paper addresses the design of controls for non-minimum phase nonlinear systems that result in stable output regulation or tracking with acceptable closed-loop performance. The approach is based on the decomposition of a system into an input-output subsystem and an internal dynamics. The developed results are applied to the classical inverted pendulum on a cart example. Simulation and experimental results are reported.

1 Introduction

Control design for minimum phase nonlinear systems has been well developed in the literature via the input-output linearization method developed in [Isi89] and elsewhere. Since a minimum phase system has stable internal dynamics, one may only need to design a control for the linear subsystem after performing input-output linearization for such a system. This paper addresses the design of controls for non-minimum phase nonlinear systems that result in stable output regulation or tracking with acceptable closed-loop performance. The approach is based on the decomposition of a system into an input-output subsystem and an internal dynamics. The developed results are applied to the classical inverted pendulum on a cart example. Simulation and experimental results are reported.

The paper is organized as follows. Section 2 introduces an approach based on singular perturbation theory for stable tracking in non-minimum phase nonlinear systems. In particular, this approach makes explicit the tracking error that must be incurred in order to stabilize the internal dynamics. The method developed in this section assumes that a nominal state trajectory is available and known. Since this is not typically the case, Section 3 deals with the issue of generating an approximate nominal trajectory in real time. Section 4 applies the developed theory to the inverted pendulum on a cart example. In particular, the problem of simulataneously stabilizing the inverted pendulum and having the cart follow a desired trajectory in real time is addressed. Simulation and experimental results are given.

*Power Systems Technology, Corporate Research and Development, General Electric Company, Schenectady NY 12301

†EECS Department, University of California, Berkeley, CA 94720

2 Tracking Based on Singular Perturbation Theory

This section develops an approach for stable tracking in non-minimum phase nonlinear systems based on singular perturbation theory. For the purposes here, the reader should keep in mind that a non-minimum phase system has unstable internal dynamics. This notion will be clarified in the sequel. We first deal with tracking of constant trajectories which can be seen, without loss of generality, as regulation of an output to zero. We then consider the extension of the results to the tracking of a time-varying trajectory.

We begin by quoting a theorem on singular perturbation. See Appendix B of [Isi89] for a proof.

Theorem 2.1 (Singular Perturbation)
Given *a system of the form,*

$$\epsilon\dot{\xi} = f(\xi, \eta, \epsilon) \quad (1)$$
$$\dot{\eta} = q(\xi, \eta, \epsilon) \quad (2)$$

where $\xi \in \Re^{\gamma}$, $\eta \in \Re^{n-\gamma}$, $f : \Re^{\gamma} \times \Re^{n-\gamma} \times \Re^{1} \to \Re^{\gamma}$, $q : \Re^{\gamma} \times \Re^{n-\gamma} \times \Re^{1} \to \Re^{n-\gamma}$, *and* $\xi = \xi_0$, $\eta = \eta_0$ *is an equilibrium.*

If

1. *There exists a solution to the equation* $0 = f(\xi, \eta, 0)$ *of the form* $\xi = r(\eta)$.
2. *The system*

   $$w' = f(w + r(\eta_0), \eta_0, 0) \quad (3)$$

   where $w = \xi - r(\eta)$, $\tau = t/\epsilon$ *and* $(\cdot)'$ *represents the derivative of* $(\cdot)$ *with respect to* τ, *is asymptotically stable in the first approximation at* $w = 0$.
3. *The reduced system*

   $$\dot{\eta} = q(r(\eta), \eta, 0) \quad (4)$$

   is asymptotically stable in the first approximation at $\eta = \eta_0$.

Then *for each sufficiently small* $\epsilon > 0$, *the equilibrium* (ξ_0, η_0) *is asymptotically stable in the first approximation.*

Output Tracking Consider a single-input, single-output system of the form

$$\dot{x} = f(x) + g(x)u \quad (5)$$
$$y = h(x) \quad (6)$$

where $x \in \Re^n, f : \Re^n \to \Re^n, g : \Re^n \to \Re^n, h : \Re^n \to \Re$, u is the input, and y is the output. Let the *relative degree* of the system be one, i.e. $L_g h(x) \neq 0$. Systems with relative degree greater than one can be reduced to the relative degree one case. This involves redefining the output to be a combination of the original output and its derivatives. For details on this, see [Gur92] and the example in Section 4. Let $\xi = y$ and η be a set of coordinates such that $L_g \eta = 0$ and the jacobian of $(\xi^T, \eta^T)^T = \Phi(x)$ is nonsingular, i.e. (ξ, η) can serve as a new set of coordinates [Isi89]. After change of coordinates, the system is given by

$$\begin{aligned} \dot{\xi} &= L_f h(\cdot) + L_g h(\cdot) u \\ \dot{\eta} &= q(\xi, \eta) \\ y &= \xi \end{aligned} \quad (7)$$

where $\xi \in \Re^1$ and $\eta \in \Re^{n-1}$. In this coordinate system, the η-subsystem is termed the *internal dynamics*. Note that this subsystem is driven by the output $y = \xi$.

Theorem 2.2
Given *A system of the form (7) ,*
If *the control u is chosen to be*

$$u = \frac{1}{L_g h(x)} (-L_f h(x) - C_1 \xi + C_1 r(\eta)) \quad (8)$$

where $\xi = r(\eta)$ asymptotically stabilizes the η subsystem in the first approximation,
Then *the closed loop system with this feedback is asymptotically stable for sufficiently large C_1.*

Proof: Substituting the control u suggested in equation (8) back into the equation for the ξ dynamics, we obtain

$$\dot{\xi} = -C_1 \xi + C_1 r(\eta) \quad (9)$$
$$(10)$$

Letting $\epsilon = \frac{1}{C_1}$, the system (7) becomes,

$$\epsilon \dot{\xi} = -\xi + r(\eta) = f(\xi, \eta, \epsilon) \quad (11)$$
$$\dot{\eta} = q(\xi, \eta) \quad (12)$$

This gets the system into the form of systems considered in Theorem 2.1. By design, the conditions for Theorem 2.1 are satisfied. Hence, by its hypothesis, for sufficiently small $\epsilon > 0$ (that is, for sufficiently large $C_1 > 0$), $(0, 0)$ is asymptotically stable in the first approximation for the system (7) with control given by (8). •

For tracking time-varying trajectories, the essential difference is that the η-dynamics are time-varying. Then the variation from Theorem 2.2 is to have $\xi = r(\eta, t)$ *uniformly* asymptotically stabilize the η subsystem.

In [Gop92], there is a similar approach for stable tracking. Gopalswamy [Gop92] considers a method for redefinition of the output that results in stable internal dynamics. In contrast our approach modifies the desired trajectory for the output to track, in order to stabilize the internal dynamics. Our method makes explicit the penalty in tracking error due to the non-minimum phase nature of a system, in the form of the required modification of desired trajectory.

The essential requirement for this method to work is that there exist a bounded solution to the η-dynamics, with the output maintained on its desired trajectory. We have assumed the existence and knowledge of a bounded solution η_d to the internal dynamics. We shall discuss in the next section, a method for obtaining an approximation to this bounded solution in real time.

3 Generating η_d

As we have seen in the preceding section, we need to solve for a bounded solution of the system states, consistent with $y = y_d$. In this section, we look at a method for finding an approximate desired trajectory, in real time. We seek a bounded solution η_d to

$$\dot{\eta} = q(\xi_d, \eta) . \quad (13)$$

First, let us assume that we know the model generating ξ_d. That is, ξ_d is the output of a dynamical system:

$$\dot{\nu} = p(\nu) \quad (14)$$
$$\xi_d = m(\nu) \quad (15)$$

Then, we can combine the η and ξ_d subsystems into one system. Letting $z = (\eta^T, \nu^T)^T$, we have

$$\dot{z} = Q(z) \quad (16)$$

Following is a method for extracting an appropriate η_d via center manifold theory [Car81].

Let $F = \left[\frac{\partial Q}{\partial z}\right]_{z=0}$. Suppose the matrix F has n^o eigenvalues with zero real part, n^- eigenvalues with negative real part and n^+ eigenvalues with positive real part. We assume that the ν-dynamics generating ξ_d have no unstable mode since such a mode would lead to an unbounded ξ_d. Typically, the η-dynamics does not have eigenvalues with zero real part. The domain of the linear mapping F can be decomposed into the direct sum of three invariant subspaces, noted E^o,E^- and E^+ of dimension n^o, n^- and n^+ respectively. By using a similarity (linear) transformation the system can be transformed to the form

$$\dot{z}^o = q^o(z^o, z^-, z^+) \quad (17)$$
$$\dot{z}^- = q^-(z^o, z^-, z^+) \quad (18)$$
$$\dot{z}^+ = q^+(z^o, z^-, z^+) \quad (19)$$

where the first approximate linearized model of (17 - 19) is block diagonalized. This is the first step in the procedure.

By center manifold theory, there exist invariant manifolds S^o, S^-, S^+ which are tangent to E^o, E^-, E^+ at the origin [Car81] [Isi89]. The, not necessarily unique, invariant manifolds S^o are called the center manifolds. There exist mappings π^- and π^+ such that a center manifold can be represented by $(z^o, \pi^-(z^o), \pi^+(z^o))$. In the case that there is no S^o, the bounded solution we are looking for is the trivial solution - the equilibrium. But if S^o is non-empty, then we assume that the trajectories on this manifold are bounded, and the bounded solution we are seeking is a solution on this manifold.

This manifold can be found by solving some partial differential equations [Car81]. However, we require just one solution on the center manifold.

In order to find these invariant manifolds, we would have to find a nonlinear coordinate transformation that would decouple the nonlinear system. Since this is computationally difficult (if possible), approximations to these manifolds which are invariant to some order k may be computed [GH90]. These approximate models are called normal forms. For a complete review of an iterative technique (both theory and algorithm with examples) for approximating these invariant manifolds, refer to [CK88, CK89]. It has been shown that when there are no *resonant* eigenvalues [CK88], the manifold can be made invariant to any order. We say there are no resonant eigenvalues if the eigenvalues of the jacobian linearization λ_i $i = 1, 2, \cdots, n$ do not satisfy a relationship of the form

$$\lambda_k = \sum_{i=1}^{n} m_i \lambda_i \tag{20}$$

for nonnegative integers m_i satisfying $\sum_{i=1}^{n} m_i \geq 2$ for any index k satisfying $1 \leq k \leq n$. For example if the eigenvalues were $\lambda_1 = i, \lambda_2 = -i$, where $i = \sqrt{-1}$, they are resonant since

$$\begin{aligned} \lambda_1 &= m\lambda_1 + (m-1)\lambda_2 \\ \lambda_2 &= (m-1)\lambda_1 + m\lambda_2 \end{aligned}$$

for any $m > 1$. When we cannot find the center manifold exactly, we can still approximate it to some order.

Real-Time Generation of η_d In the preceding development, we used information about the model generating ξ_d. Hence, this technique helps in computing η_d, but not in real time. If ξ_d is constant or almost constant ($\dot{\xi}_d \approx 0$), then we could treat ξ_d like a parameter. Then we can get coordinate transformations $(h(\eta, \xi_d), \xi_d)$ which leave $\dot{\xi}_d = 0$ invariant and will transform the η subsystem in a ξ_d dependent way [GH90]. This idea can be used to approximate η_d in real time.

Let us now look at finding an approximate η_d in real time, by first considering a linear example:

$$\dot{x} = x + y_d. \tag{21}$$

Let us reverse the vector field over which x is evolving. That is, let us consider the system

$$\dot{z} = -z - y_d. \tag{22}$$

Comparing the transfer functions $\frac{X}{Y_d} = \frac{1}{s-1}$ and $\frac{Z}{Y_d} = \frac{-1}{s+1}$, we see they agree closely at low frequencies. That is, the trajectory we get by reversing the vector field of the unstable system is a good approximation of the actual trajectory for low frequencies. This reflection of the unstable eigenvalues corresponds to a linear quadratic (LQ) optimal solution for a linear system in the costly control case [KS72]. (Here, y_d is viewed as the control input.)

We can extend this idea to the nonlinear zero dynamics, by essentially reversing the vector field corresponding to the unstable manifold of the internal dynamics (13). With a linear transformation, we would first transform the internal dynamics to

$$\dot{z}^- = q^-(\xi_d, z^-, z^+) \tag{23}$$

$$\dot{z}^+ = q^+(\xi_d, z^-, z^+), \tag{24}$$

for a particular value of the "parameter" ξ_d. Here, we assume there are no neutral modes (modes corresponding to imaginary axis eigenvalues). Then, to generate the nominal state trajectory in a stable manner, we reverse the unstable modes of the internal dynamics. That is, change the z^+ dynamics to

$$\dot{z}^+ = -q^+(\xi_d, z^-, z^+). \tag{25}$$

This idea can be justified for low frequencies, as follows. Let us first assume that we are looking for a constant solution. Then we have $\dot{z}^+ = 0$. Then we obtain the same solution by either solving

$$0 = -q^+(\xi_d, z^-, z^+) \tag{26}$$

or

$$0 = q^+(\xi_d, z^-, z^+)\,. \tag{27}$$

Even when we are not looking for an asymptotically constant trajectory, if it is slowly varying, then $\dot{z}^+$ is approximately zero and the two solutions will be close. Hence, the trajectory obtained by running the system (23, 25) gives an approximation to the bounded solution we seek. Reversing the vector field corresponding to the unstable manifold is also suggested in [Gop92].

4 Inverted Pendulum on a Cart

Let us consider the problem of output tracking for the inverted pendulum on a cart problem [GPEN91]. The system consists of an inverted pendulum freely hinged to a cart, which is free to move on a horizontal plane. The control available is a force applicable to the cart. The equations of motion for this system are given by:

$$(M+m)\ddot{x} + ml(\ddot{\theta}\cos\theta - \dot{\theta}^2\sin\theta) + b\dot{x} = u \tag{28}$$

$$m(\ddot{x}\cos\theta + l\ddot{\theta} - g\sin\theta) = 0 \tag{29}$$

where M is the mass of the cart, m is the mass of the block on the pendulum, l the length of the pendulum, g the acceleration due to gravity, b the coefficient of viscous friction for motion of the cart, θ is the angle the pendulum makes with the vertical, x the position of the cart, and u is the applied force.

With the choice of variables, $x_1 = x, x_2 = \dot{x}, x_3 = \theta, x_4 = \dot{\theta}$, the state space equations of the system are

$$\begin{aligned} \dot{x}_1 &= x_2 \\ \dot{x}_2 &= \frac{1}{M + m\sin^2(x_3)} \left[-mg\sin(x_3)\cos(x_3) + mlx_4{}^2\sin(x_3) - bx_2 + u \right] \\ \dot{x}_3 &= x_4 \\ \dot{x}_4 &= \frac{1}{l(M + m\sin^2(x_3))} \begin{bmatrix} (M+m)g\sin(x_3) \\ -mlx_4{}^2\sin(x_3)\cos(x_3) \\ +bx_2\cos x_3 - u\cos(x_3) \end{bmatrix}. \end{aligned} \tag{30}$$

Let the output of the system be $y = x = x_1$. With this output, the system is non-minimum phase, as well as open loop unstable. We can see that the system has relative degree 2. To convert the system into (ξ, η) coordinates, we take

$$\xi_1 = y\ ,\ \xi_2 = \dot{y} = x_2\ , \eta_1 = x_3\ ,\ \eta_2 = lx_4 + x_2\cos(x_3).$$

Let us redefine an auxiliary variable to be $s = \xi_2$, and group ξ_1 with the internal variables. Then the extended internal dynamics system consists of (ξ_1, η_1, η_2), and takes the form

$$\dot{\xi}_1 = s \quad (31)$$

$$l\dot{\eta}_1 = \eta_2 - s\cos(\eta_1) \quad (32)$$

$$\dot{\eta}_2 = g\sin(\eta_1) + \frac{s}{l}\sin(\eta_1)(\eta_2 - s\cos(\eta_1)) \quad (33)$$

With the auxiliary variable s viewed as the output, the system is relative degree one. Let $(\tilde{\cdot}) = (\cdot) - (\cdot)_d$ for each variable. The partial control

$$\tilde{s} = k_1\tilde{\xi}_1 + k_2\tilde{\eta}_1 + k_3\tilde{\eta}_2 = K\zeta \quad (34)$$

with $k_1 > 0, k_2 > lk_1$ and $k_3 > \frac{k_2}{k_2 - lk_1}$ asymptotically stabilizes the extended zero dynamics (31,32,33) in the first approximation. So by choosing the control u to be

$$u = (M + m\sin^2\theta) \quad \left[-ml\dot{\theta}^2\sin\theta + mg\sin\theta\cos\theta + v\right] \quad (35)$$

$$v = -C\tilde{s} + CK\zeta + \dot{s}_d, \quad (36)$$

the system is stabilized for sufficiently large C, in accord with Theorem 2.2.

The parameters used in the experimental and simulation work are given below.

System Parameters	Value
Cart Mass , M (Kg)	1.378
Pendulum Mass , m (Kg)	0.051
Accel. due to grav. , g (m/sec^2)	9.81
Pendulum Length , l (m)	0.325
Coeff. of Viscous friction, b (Kg/sec)	12.98

Real-Time Generation of η_d In the partial control given by equation (34), we require the desired trajectory η_d. We shall now use the method developed in the previous section to obtain an approximate bounded solution for η_d in real time. For simplicity of computation, we shall approximate the stable and unstable manifold locally by manifolds invariant to the first order. This is done by making the linear coordinate change that diagonalizes the Jacobian linearization of the system. Let us look at the η subsystem.

$$l\dot{\eta}_1 = \eta_2 - \xi_2\cos(\eta_1) \quad (37)$$

$$\dot{\eta}_2 = g\sin(\eta_1) + \frac{s}{l}\sin(\eta_1)(\eta_2 - \xi_2\cos(\eta_1)) \quad (38)$$

The linearization of the η subsystem has eigenvalues $\sqrt{gl}, -\sqrt{gl}$. We can diagonalize the η subsystem in the first approximation, for $\xi_2 = 0$. Then, for small enough ξ_2 the stability properties of the approximately decoupled system will not change. ¿From the linearization, we get the coordinate transformation

$$\begin{pmatrix} \eta^+ \\ \eta^- \end{pmatrix} = E \begin{bmatrix} -\sqrt{gl} & -1 \\ -\sqrt{gl} & 1 \end{bmatrix} \begin{pmatrix} \eta_1 \\ \eta_2 \end{pmatrix} \quad (39)$$

that separates the stable and unstable portion of the linearized system, where $E = -\sqrt{\frac{1+gl}{4gl}}$. We have

$$\dot{\eta}^+ = E[-\sqrt{gl}(\eta_2 - \xi_2\cos(\eta_1)) - g\sin(\eta_1) \quad (40)$$

$$-\frac{s}{l}\sin(\eta_1)(\eta_2 - \xi_2\cos(\eta_1))] \quad (41)$$

$$\dot{\eta}^- = E[-\sqrt{gl}(\eta_2 - \xi_2\cos(\eta_1)) + g\sin(\eta_1) \quad (42)$$

$$+\frac{s}{l}\sin(\eta_1)(\eta_2 - \xi_2\cos(\eta_1))] \quad (43)$$

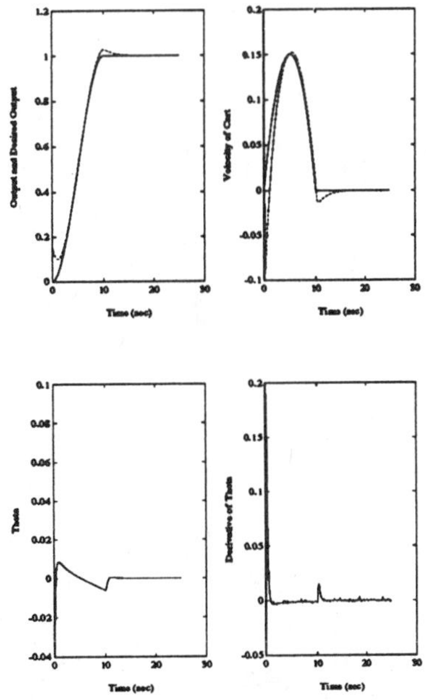

Figure 1: Real time η_d generation: Cubic trajectory. For the position and velocity of the cart, solid curves indicate desired trajectory and dashed indicate actual trajectory.

where η_1, η_2 in the above equations can be replaced in terms of η^+, η^- using the inverse of the transformation (39). Now with ξ_2 replaced by ξ_{2d} and reversing the vector field in the η^+ dynamics, we have

$$\dot{\eta}^+ = -E[-\sqrt{gl}(\eta_2 - \xi_{2d}\cos(\eta_1)) - g\sin(\eta_1) \quad (44)$$

$$-\frac{s}{l}\sin(\eta_1)(\eta_2 - \xi_{2d}\cos(\eta_1))] \quad (45)$$

$$\dot{\eta}^- = E[-\sqrt{gl}(\eta_2 - \xi_{2d}\cos(\eta_1)) + g\sin(\eta_1) \quad (46)$$

$$+\frac{s}{l}\sin(\eta_1)(\eta_2 - \xi_{2d}\cos(\eta_1))]. \quad (47)$$

This is the system that will be used to generate the approximation for η_d in real time. We can now use this η_d in the control (35,36). The results reported below are obtained with the control

$$u = (M + m\sin^2\theta)\left[-ml\dot{\theta}^2\sin\theta + mg\sin\theta\cos\theta + b\dot{x} + v\right] \quad (48)$$

$$v = -900\tilde{s} + 900(3.22\tilde{\xi}_1 + 12\tilde{\eta}_1 + 7.44\tilde{\eta}_2) \quad (49)$$

Cubic Trajectory

Let us first consider tracking a desired trajectory y_d of the form

$$y_d = at^3 + bt^2 + ct + d \quad \text{for } 0 \leq t < t_0$$

$$= at_0^3 + bt_0^2 + ct_0 + d \quad \text{for } t \geq t_0$$

where a, b, c, d are chosen to make $y_d(0) = 0, y_d(t_0) = y_{final}, \dot{y}_d(0) = 0, \dot{y}_d(t_0) = 0$. This is basically moving the cart along a cubic trajectory from an initial point to a final point. Numerical simulation results are given in Figure 1.

This trajectory is an eventually constant trajectory, and hence we expect that the desired trajectory we get for η would

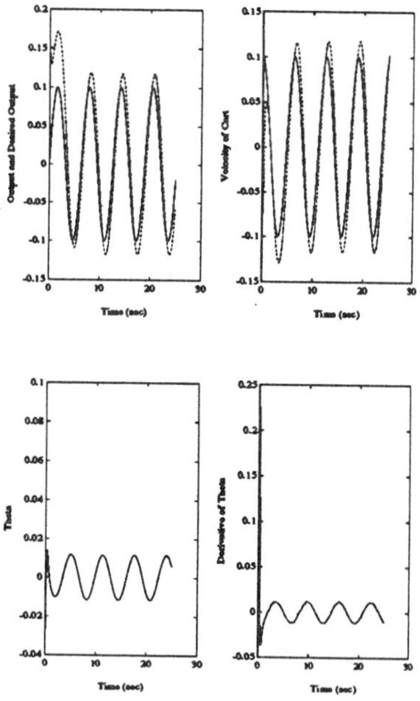

Figure 2: Real time η_d generation: Sinusoidal trajectory.

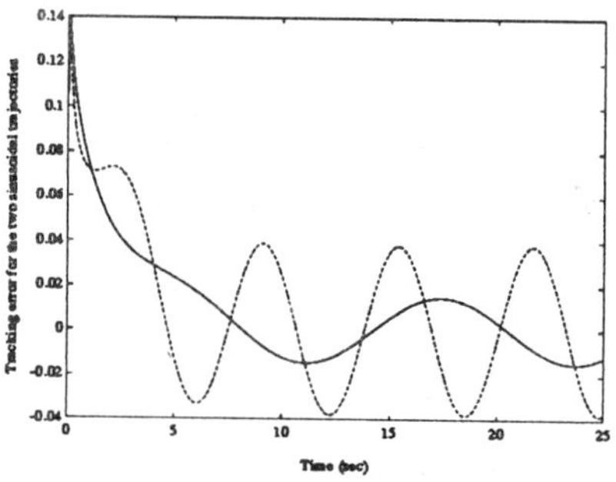

Figure 3: Tracking error for the two sinusoids.

asymptotically converge to the actual asymptotic trajectory and hence will give asymptotic tracking. This is seen from the figures to be true.

Sinusoidal Trajectories

Let us now consider tracking of sinusoidal trajectories $y_d = A\sin(wt)$. These are not asymptotically constant, and hence the desired trajectory we generate for η is only an approximation (even asymptotically) to the actual desired trajectory. A steady state error is expected. Numerical simulation results are given in Figure 2 for $y_d = 0.1sin(t)$ meter. The frequency of the desired trajectory was then decreased to 0.5rad/sec. As expected, the tracking error shown in Figure 3 is reduced for the lower frequency sinusoid.

In order to fully characterize the behavior, a set of simulations was carried out using $y_d = 0.1\sin(wt)$ meter. The results are tabulated below. As seen in the table, the tracking error increases sharply with frequency. Note the unstable zero (of the linearized input-output model) is at 5.49rad/sec.

Simulation with $y_d = 0.1\sin(wt)$ m	
Freq. of desired traj. (rad/sec)	Amp. tracking error percentage
0	0.0
0.25	5.0
0.5	17.0
1.0	40.0
1.5	65.0
2.0	82.5
2.5	100.0

Experimental Results

We implemented the real time desired trajectory generation and control in an experimental set-up. The parameters of the hardware were the same as those considered in the simulations above. We used the control given in equations (48,49), but with an additional term to cancel inherent static friction. The control implementation was personal-computer-based, with sampling frequency of 40Hz.

The result using a sinusoidal desired trajectory $y_d = 0.05\sin(t)$ meters is given in Figure 4. With the frequency of the sinusoidal trajectory increased to 1.5rad/sec, the result is given in Figure 5. Note the close agreement with the simulation.

We tabulate below, the amplitude of the error in tracking (as a percentage of the amplitude of the desired trajectory). The results with the desired trajectory $0.1\sin(wt)$ meter, are tabulated below.

Experiment with $y_d = 0.1\sin(wt)$ m	
Freq. of desired traj. (rad/sec)	Amp. tracking error percentage
0.25	15.0
0.5	30.0
1.0	65.0
1.5	80.0

With the desired trajectory chosen to be $0.05\sin(wt)$ meter, we obtained the following results.

Experiment with $y_d = 0.05\sin(wt)$ m	
Freq. of desired traj. (rad/sec)	Amp. tracking error percentage
0.5	40.0
1.0	60.0
1.5	87.5
2.0	120.0
2.5	180.0

As indicated in the tabulated data, there is a strong trend of increasing tracking error with increasing frequency. This is a consequence of the non-minimum phase character of the plant. The tracking error does not appear to be strongly dependent on amplitude for the nominal excursions of 0.05m and 0.10m.

5 Summary

This paper develops a method for stable tracking in non-minimum phase nonlinear systems. The method modifies the desired trajectory for tracking for the purpose of stabilizing the internal dynamics. Singular perturbation theory was used for demonstrating stability of the combined system dynamics. The method gives a penalty on tracking error due to the non-minimum phase nature of the plant, in the form of a modification of desired trajectory.

The essential requirement for the method to work is the existence of a bounded solution to the internal dynamics, when the output is maintained on its desired trajectory. The paper develops a method for obtaining an approximation to this bounded solution in real time.

We have applied the generation of the approximate η_d in real time, and used it in conjunction with the developed control scheme, for tracking in an experimental non-minimum phase nonlinear system. We report results on numerical simulations, as well as experimental work. Both the simulation and the experimental results show similar trends of increasing errors with increasing frequency of the desired trajectory, as predicted by the theory.

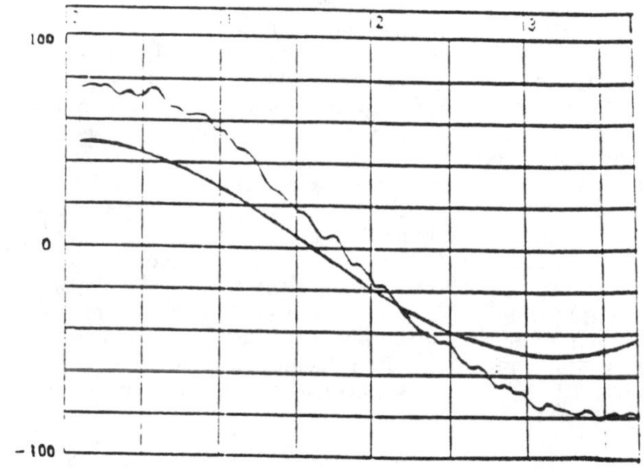

Figure 4 : Actual Output and Desired Trajectory (mm)

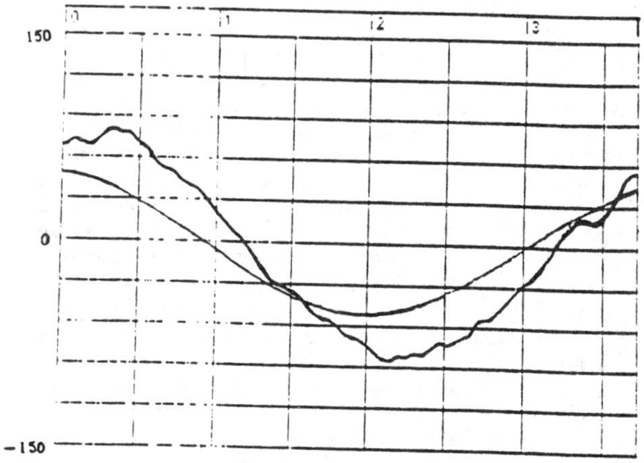

Figure 5 Actual Output and Desired Trajectory (mm)

References

[Car81] Carr.J. *Applications of centre manifold theory.* Springer Verlag, 1981.

[CK88] Chua.L.O. and Kokubu.H. Normal forms for nonlinear vector fields - part i: Theory and algorithm. *IEEE Transactions on Circuits and Systems,* 35(7):863–880, 1988.

[CK89] Chua.L.O. and Kokubu.H. Normal forms for nonlinear vector fields - part ii: Theory and algorithm. *IEEE Transactions on Circuits and Systems,* 36(1):51–70, 1989.

[GH90] Guckenheimer.J. and Holmes.P. *Nonlinear Oscillations, Dynamical Systems and Bifurcations of Vector Fields.* Springer Verlag, 3rd edition, 1990.

[Gop92] Gopalswamy.S. *Adaptive control of Nonlinear Nonminimum Phase Systems.* PhD thesis, UCB, 1992.

[GPEN91] Franklin G.F., Powell.D.J., and Abbas Emami-Naeini. *Feedback Control of dynamic systems.* Addison-Wesley, 2nd edition, 1991.

[Gur92] Gurumoorthy.R. *Output Tracking of Nonminimum Phase Nonlinear Systems.* PhD thesis, UCB, 1992.

[Isi89] Isidori.A. *Nonlinear Control Systems.* Springer Verlag, 2nd edition, 1989.

[KS72] Kwakernaak.H. and Sivan.R. *Linear Optimal Control Systems.* New York, Wiley Interscience, 1972.

Proceedings of the
American Control Conference
San Francisco, California • June 1993

Experimental Results of Adaptive Periodic Disturbance Cancellation in a High Performance Magnetic Disk Drive*

Alexei Sacks†, Marc Bodson and Pradeep Khosla

Data Storage Systems Center
Department of Electrical and Computer Engineering
Carnegie Mellon University, Pittsburgh, PA 15213-3890, U.S.A.

Abstract

This paper considers the implementation of an adaptive algorithm for periodic disturbance cancellation. It is shown that the maximum rate of adaptation can be calculated precisely based on measurements of the system's frequency response. The response of the closed-loop system to additional disturbances can also be computed on that basis. The results are verified experimentally on a high track density magnetic disk drive. Excellent matching between the theoretical and experimental results is observed. An improved method is also proposed that leads to faster convergence of the adaptive algorithm and better disturbance rejection capabilities. The results of this paper significantly enhance the ability of the control engineer to design and analyze adaptive feedforward algorithms for a variety of applications where periodic disturbances are encountered.

1 Introduction

The problem of rejecting periodic disturbances appears in a variety of applications involving rotating mechanical systems. For example, DC motors and stepper motors exhibit torque pulsations at the frequency of rotation due to the tendency of the permanent magnets to align themselves along directions of minimum reluctance [5]. In [13], active vibration control is applied to a cryocooler expander to eliminate several harmonics originating from a rotating pump. The control of rotating magnetic bearing systems is another recent application of great interest [2].

This paper concerns high performance magnetic disk drives. Data is written in concentric tracks on the surface of each disk in a disk stack. The current trend in disk drives is to smaller sizes (form-factors) and larger data capacity. Tracks must be spaced closer together in the radial direction to achieve higher data capacities. This paper focuses on one of the problems in tracking: large periodic components (runout) in the position error signal (PES). A tilting of the disk with respect to the head, or an actual warping of the disk, will cause repeatable runout. These disturbances usually occur at integer multiples of the frequency of rotation of the disk, but non-integer multiples are often present due to the ball bearing geometries in the spindle.

There are several methods to design linear control systems for eliminating periodic disturbances. Probably the most common approach is based on the *internal model principle* (IMP) [6], which states that a model of the disturbance generation system should be included in the feedback system for perfect disturbance rejection. The underlying property is that a linear feedback system has perfect disturbance rejection at some frequency if the controller gain is infinite at that frequency. For sinusoidal disturbances, the controller must have a pair of poles on the $j\omega$-axis in the s-plane at a location corresponding to the frequency of the disturbance.

Another method is *repetitive control*, which is a subset of *learning control* [1]. The idea is to use information from the previous performance of a task to improve the current performance, i.e., a "betterment" process [7]. Current algorithms based on this idea can be shown to be closely related to those based on the internal model principle.

The method that is discussed in this paper is *adaptive feedforward cancellation* (AFC). The disturbance is cancelled at the input of the plant by adding the negative of its value. AFC continually estimates the parameters describing the sinusoidal disturbance and adapts to variations in time. A comparison of the above methods is presented in [9].

In [5], it was shown that a simple AFC algorithm was capable of reducing harmonics that it was not designed to cancel. The analytical results of [4] allowed for the calculation of an upper bound on the adaptation gain, based on the fact that the AFC algorithm was *equivalent* to a linear time-invariant controller. In this paper, the analytical results are extended with the inclusion of a parameter to improve the transient response of the adaptive closed-loop system. The main contribution of this paper is an extensive set of experimental results of AFC applied to a high performance, commercial magnetic disk drive.

2 An Adaptive Feedforward Cancellation Algorithm

We consider a relatively simple continuous-time adaptive feedforward cancellation (AFC) scheme. In this method, the Fourier coefficients of a periodic disturbance of known frequency are estimated by an adaptive algorithm. It is assumed that the unknown disturbance consists of a sum of sinusoids of known frequencies of the form

$$d(t) = \sum_{i=1}^{n} \{a_i \cos(\omega_i t) + b_i \sin(\omega_i t)\} \tag{1}$$

while the output of the system is

$$y(t) = P(s)\,[u(t) - d(t)] \tag{2}$$

with $P(s)$ the plant transfer function acting on the time domain signals in the brackets. It is desired to remove the disturbance observed at the output of the system by forming a control input that exactly cancels the disturbance. This control input is selected to be

$$u(t) = \hat{d}(t) = \sum_{i=1}^{n} \left\{\hat{a}_i(t)\cos(\omega_i t) + \hat{b}_i(t)\sin(\omega_i t)\right\} \tag{3}$$

The disturbance is exactly cancelled when the estimates of the coefficients have the nominal values

$$\hat{a}_i = a_i \qquad \hat{b}_i = b_i \tag{4}$$

An adaptive algorithm to adjust estimates of a_i and b_i consists of the update laws (cf. [5], [4])

$$\dot{\hat{a}}_i(t) = -g_i\; y(t)\; \cos(\omega_i t) \tag{5}$$

$$\dot{\hat{b}}_i(t) = -g_i\; y(t)\; \sin(\omega_i t) \tag{6}$$

where the parameters g_i are positive constants. The subscript i refers to the ith frequency of the disturbance (typically the ith harmonic of the fundamental frequency).

2.1 Stability Properties of the Algorithm

It can be shown that the adaptive algorithm is exponentially stable if the transfer function $P(s)$ is strictly positive real (SPR) (cf. [5]). Roughly speaking, the SPR condition requires that $P(s)$ be stable, minimum phase, and $Re[P(j\omega)] > 0$ for all ω [8]. From a practical perspective, an important question is what happens when $P(s)$ is not SPR, or $d(t)$ contains more harmonics than the algorithm is designed to cancel. Indeed, physical systems

*This project has been supported by the National Science Foundation under grant ECD-890768. The government has some rights in this material.

†Partially supported by a National Science Foundation Fellowship.

are rarely minimum phase, or SPR. The second question is important in light of the rich spectrum of disturbance frequencies (see Fig. 4, shown later). Both questions can be addressed analytically. For example, averaging analysis shows that one only needs to have $Re[P(j\omega_1)] > 0$ when one sinusoid is being cancelled and the gain is sufficiently small. In fact, $Re[P(j\omega_1)]$ can be less than zero if the sign of the adaptation gain is switched to be negative. Therefore, the plant can be non-minimum phase, but the magnitude of the adaptation gain is limited. In addition, it is possible to show that the generation of harmonics within the adaptive feedforward algorithm can yield attenuation or amplification of other harmonics than those being directly cancelled.

In [4], it was shown that the AFC algorithm was *equivalent* to a linear time-invariant controller. Given the same disturbance $d(t)$, the response $y(t)$ is identical (for zero initial conditions) to that resulting from

$$U(s) = -\sum_{i=1}^{n} g_i \left\{ \frac{s}{s^2+\omega_i^2} \right\} Y(s) \tag{7}$$

Such a control law is equivalent to a control law based on the internal model principle. This equivalence is discussed in detail in [4]. We would like, however, to make two important points. The first is that the overall adaptive system is linear time-varying. In particular, the transformation from $y(t)$ to the adaptive parameters *cannot* be described by a linear time-invariant system. The transformation from y to u, however, is equivalent to a linear time-invariant system. The second point is that while the equivalence is extremely useful to analyze and design the adaptive system, there are significant practical advantages to the adaptive system over one based on the internal model principle. The advantages are discussed in the concluding section of this paper.

2.2 Gain Margin

The result (7) allows one to predict precisely the stability/instability boundary of the adaptive system. If a rational transfer function describing the plant is known, it is possible to use (7) to obtain an equivalent closed-loop transfer function. A simple root-locus test for a single frequency with g_1 as the proportional feedback gain would yield an upper bound on the adaptation gain. The accuracy of the result would depend on the precision of the fit of a rational transfer function to the experimental data.

A simple and more accurate method can be derived which uses only experimentally obtained frequency response data. The result is based on the Nyquist criterion, and it is shown in [11] that

$$g_{max} = \frac{|\omega_1^2 - \omega_0^2|}{\omega_0\,|\mathrm{Im}\,[P(j\omega_o)]|} \tag{8}$$

The quantities ω_0 (the frequency where the phase of $P(s)$ is $\pm 90°$) and $\mathrm{Im}[P(j\omega_0)]$ (the magnitude of the frequency response at $\pm 90°$ phase) can be determined from the experimental frequency response data.

For the case when several frequency components are present, the stability of the closed-loop system can still be determined numerically from the denominator polynomial of the closed-loop system or from the Nyquist diagram, but (8) *cannot* be applied to the individual g_i's separately.

2.3 Disturbance Rejection

In addition, the attenuation/amplification of other harmonics (in fact, any other frequency) can be predicted. The effect on other frequencies can be quantified by comparing the magnitude of the closed-loop system

$$P_{cl}(s) = \frac{P(s)}{1+P(s)C(s)} \tag{9}$$

with the magnitude of $P(s)$ at the desired frequency. Specifically, the coefficient of rejection of an arbitrary frequency ω while directly cancelling ω_1 is (by dividing the magnitude of (9) by $|P(s)|$)

$$R(\omega) = \left| \frac{1}{1+g\frac{j\omega}{\omega_1^2-\omega^2}P(j\omega)} \right| \tag{10}$$

If $R(\omega) = 1$, then the frequency ω, if different from ω_1, is not altered by the adaptation scheme. If $R(\omega) < 1$, the frequency component is reduced, and if $R(\omega) > 1$, there will be amplification. The formula (10) is based on the rejection of a single frequency, but can easily be extended to multiple frequencies.

2.4 Averaging Analysis

It is also possible to carry out an averaging analysis of the AFC algorithm (see [3] and [12] for details). This analysis leads to an *averaged* system representation of the form

$$\dot{\varphi}_{av} = A_{av}\varphi_{av} \tag{11}$$

It is shown in [11] that for a single frequency

$$\begin{aligned} A_{av} &= -g_1 AVG\left[\nu P[\nu^T]\right] \\ &= -\tfrac{1}{2}g_1 \begin{pmatrix} Re[P(j\omega_1)] & Im[P(j\omega_1)] \\ -Im[P(j\omega_1)] & Re[P(j\omega_1)] \end{pmatrix} \end{aligned} \tag{12}$$

The eigenvalues of the averaged system A_{av} are

$$\lambda_{1,2} = -\frac{1}{2}g_1 \left\{ Re[P(j\omega_1)] \pm jIm[P(j\omega_1)] \right\} \tag{13}$$

The averaging analysis requires that the transfer function $P(s)$ be stable and that g_1 be sufficiently small. Equation (13) then allows one to conclude that stability will be guaranteed if $g_1 Re[P(j\omega_1)] > 0$. In other words, the SPR condition can be avoided and the minimum phase property is not required; $Re[P(j\omega)]$ does not need to be positive for all frequencies, but only at the frequency of cancellation ω_1 (this is the result of [10]). $Re[P(j\omega_1)]$ could even be negative if the sign of g_1 is changed correspondingly. The price to pay is that the range of gain is limited, but the previous results allow one to calculate the margin of gain precisely, using (8).

Equation (13) also gives valuable information about the parameter convergence properties of the algorithm. Specifically, $\frac{2}{g_1 Re[P(j\omega_1)]}$ is a measure of the time constant associated with the parameter convergence. We also would expect undesirable oscillatory behavior when $Re[P(j\omega_1)] \ll Im[P(j\omega_1)]$. This problem can be resolved with the alternate algorithm described later in this paper.

The result can easily be extended to an arbitrary disturbance input. In this case $y = P[u-d]$. The result for the averaged system is the same as before except that φ is replaced by $\begin{pmatrix} \hat{a}_1 - a_1 \\ \hat{b}_1 - b_1 \end{pmatrix}$, where a_1 and b_1 are the frequency components of $d(t)$ at the frequency ω_1, i.e., $a_1 = AVG[d(t)\cos(\omega_1 t)]$, $b_1 = AVG[d(t)\sin(\omega_1 t)]$.

If several harmonics are cancelled, A_{av} can be calculated similarly. For more than one harmonic, A_{av} becomes block diagonal where each block is of the form (12). A_{av} is stable if $g_i Re[P(j\omega_i)] > 0$ for all i. The eigenvalues of A_{av} again give valuable information about the convergence properties of the closed-loop system.

3 Modifications to AFC

3.1 Phase Advance Modification

A simple modification to the original AFC structure can add an additional parameter to stabilize and reduce the sensitivity of the adaptive controller. The averaging analysis predicts that when $Re[P(j\omega_1)] \simeq 0$ the eigenvalues will be close to the $j\omega$ axis in the s-plane. Consequently, the transient response will be oscillatory. Consider Fig. 6(a). In this experiment, a step input was applied to the system while AFC was used on the fourth harmonic[1]. This resulted in lightly damped oscillations. Also, as seen in Table 1, the maximum adaptation gain is

[1] The step input was a single track move while leaving the adaptation on. For actual implementation, the adaptation would be turned off when moving from track to track.

small for this frequency. This is a consequence of this frequency being near the $-270°$ crossing of the open-loop frequency response. From the averaging analysis, the eigenvalues for the averaged system for the parameters are $\lambda_{1,2} = -1.7 \pm j21$. This result gives an indication of the type of response to be expected: oscillatory transient behavior.

The modification of the original AFC structure consists of adding a phase shift to the parameter update equations (5) and (6). These modified equations are

$$\dot{a}_i(t) = -g_i\ y(t)\ \cos(\omega_i t + \phi_i) \quad (14)$$

$$\dot{b}_i(t) = -g_i\ y(t)\ \sin(\omega_i t + \phi_i) \quad (15)$$

The estimate of the disturbance is kept the same (3). The Laplace transform analysis of the resulting AFC scheme yields the following expression for the AFC controller

$$C(s) = -\sum_{i=1}^{n} g_i \left\{ \frac{\cos(\phi_i)s + \sin(\phi_i)\omega_i}{s^2 + \omega_i^2} \right\} \quad (16)$$

The value of g_{max} also can be determined and the averaging analysis extended. The eigenvalues of the averaged modified system A_{av} for one frequency are

$$\lambda_{1,2} = -\tfrac{1}{2}g_1\{Re[P(j\omega_1)]\cos(\phi_1) + Im[P(j\omega_1)]\sin(\phi_1) \\ \pm j\,(Re[P(j\omega_1)]\sin(\phi_1) - Im[P(j\omega_1)]\cos(\phi_1))\} \quad (17)$$

As was noted earlier, when $\phi_1 = 0°$ and $Re[P(j\omega_1)] \ll Im[P(j\omega_1)]$, the system will perform poorly by exhibiting oscillatory responses to disturbances. Therefore, it would be desirable to have two poles on the negative real axis of the s-plane. This can be accomplished by setting ϕ_1 equal to the phase of $P(j\omega_1)$. The eigenvalues of the system are then

$$\lambda_{1,2} = -\frac{1}{2}g_1|P(j\omega_1)| \quad (18)$$

Note that $Re[P(j\omega_1)] = |P(j\omega_1)|\cos(\phi_1)$ and $Im[P(j\omega_1)] = |P(j\omega_1)|\sin(\phi_1)$, where ϕ_1 is the phase of the transfer function $P(s)$ at the frequency ω_1.

4 Experimental Setup and Results

The development system used for experiments consists of a 3.5" form-factor magnetic disk drive, a Digital Signal Processor board using a TMS320C30 floating-point microprocessor, and an IBM-compatible host computer. The original servo processor was removed and replaced by the 'C30 with the appropriate interface circuitry. The DSP development system has access to the PES[2] as well as to the Digital-to-Analog Converter (DAC) that controls the current in the rotary voice coil actuator.

A block diagram of the disk drive base controller and adaptive compensation is shown in Fig. 1. In the base controller, the DSP receives a raw position error signal and converts it into a PES, which is then used in a state-feedback controller. The velocity is estimated, and along with the PES and integral of the PES, is fed back through the state-feedback gain vector K to form the control input. Figure 2 shows the open-loop frequency response of the disk drive system, i.e., without AFC added to the loop. The frequency responses generated for this paper were taken from $\hat{d}$ to the PES signal, which is what the adaptive algorithm "sees" (the double dashed lines in the figure). Note that, in the implementation, the control input u, i.e., the estimate of the disturbance $\hat{d}(t)$, was *subtracted* from the input to the plant.

Figure 3 shows a typical PES over two revolutions of the disk (27.8 ms or a frequency of rotation of 71.9 Hz). A significant repeatable runout is visible. The track width for the experimental drive used is approximately 11.35 microns, and the head deviates about ±4% off-track (± 0.454 microns). Figure 4(a) shows that the disk drive used for experiments has a rich spectrum.

[2]In all of the data obtained from the experiments, the PES is the signal coming directly from the dedicated servo platter. There is no compensation for the relative difference between the servo head position and the data head positions.

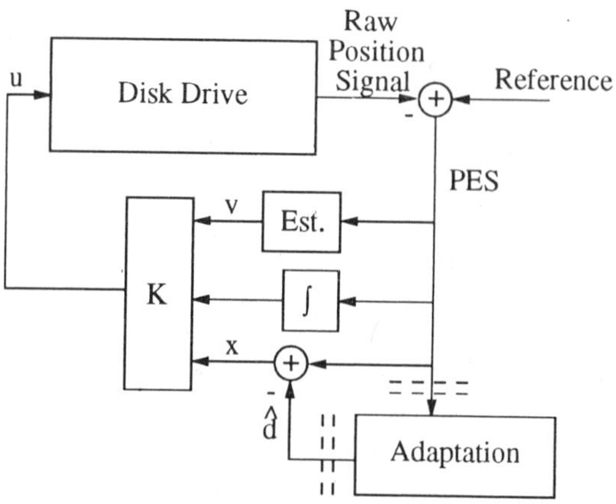

Figure 1: Block diagram of overall control structure.

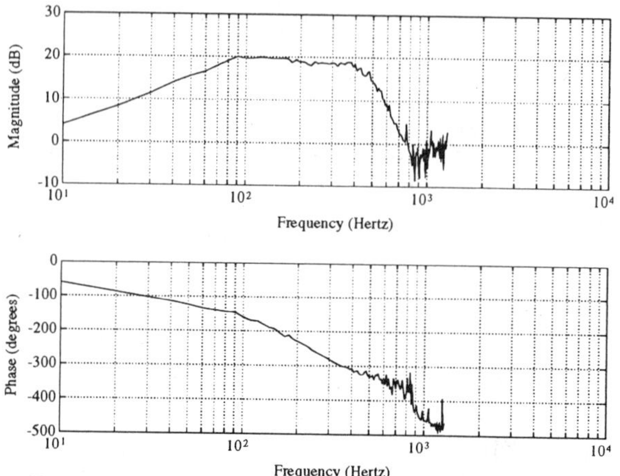

Figure 2: Open-loop frequency response (no AFC)

It was observed in [5] that not only was the intended frequency component attenuated, but also other frequency components could be attenuated when using AFC. This effect, which originates in the time variation of the parameters, can be seen in Fig. 4(b), where AFC has been applied to the eighth harmonic. The eighth and seventh harmonics are attenuated. The sixth and seventh harmonics are, however, amplified.

4.1 Experimental Verification of Upper Gain Bound

Table 1 shows a comparison of calculated and experimental results for g_{max} at the first 10 harmonics. The calcu-

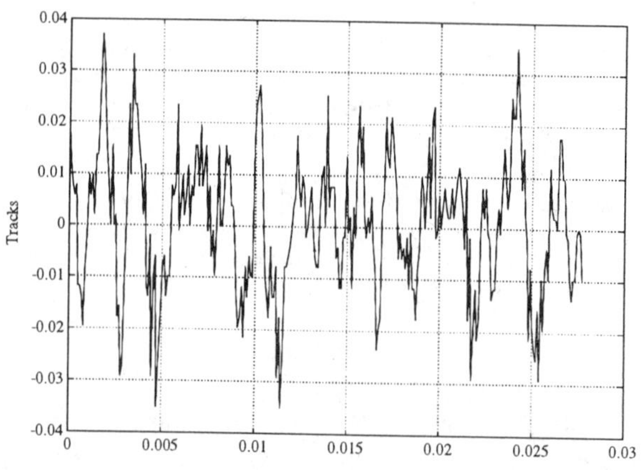

Figure 3: Time domain PES signal over two revolutions

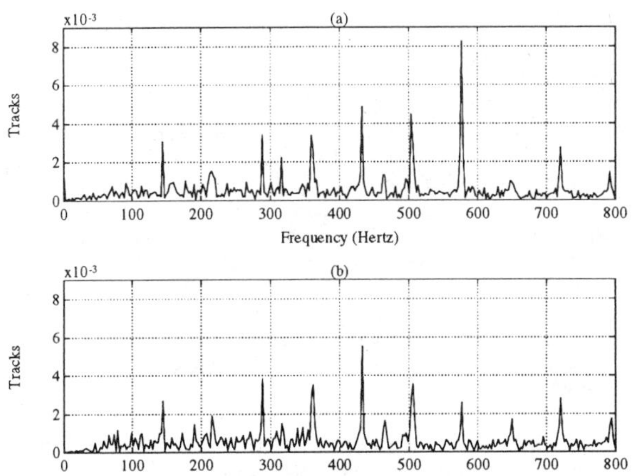

Figure 4: PES spectra for (a) Fig. 3 (b) after application of AFC to the eighth harmonic

Harmonic	Frequency (Hz)	g_{max} Exp.	g_{max} Calc.
1	71.9	-0.019	-0.018
2	143.8	-0.015	-0.014
3	215.7	-0.0083	-0.0072
4	287.6	0.0028	0.0022
5	359.5	0.015	0.014
6	431.4	0.030	0.029
7	503.3	0.049	0.047
8	575.2	0.070	0.067
9	647.1	0.093	0.090
10	719.0	0.11	0.12

Table 1: Calculated and Experimental g_{max} values

lated values were obtained from (8) and then by multiplication by the sampling period T. The calculated and experimental g_{max} values match very well. The fourth harmonic exhibits the largest relative error because the frequency is close to the $-270°$ point in the frequency response ($\sim$ 270 Hz), which is where the real part of the transfer function changes sign. The sensitivity of the transfer function is very large near such frequencies.

4.2 Prediction of Attenuation/Amplification

It is possible to predict the attenuation or amplification of harmonics other than those being directly cancelled by AFC. Calculated (7) and measured frequency responses (with AFC for the 6th harmonic) are shown in Fig. 5, and they match well. The magnitude of the adaptation gain,

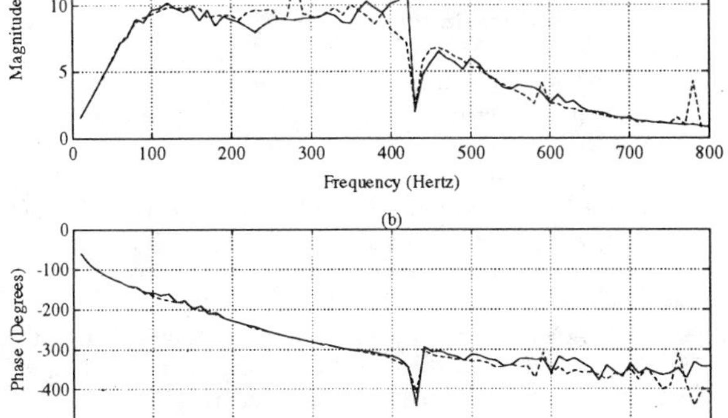

Figure 5: Measured frequency response (solid) versus calculated frequency response (dashed) for AFC for the sixth harmonic with $g_6 = 0.001$

however, will have an effect on how well the calculated matches the measured closed-loop response. It was found that, for larger adaptation gains, the fit between calculated and measured responses becomes worse. This effect may be due to approximations made in the discretization.

4.3 Phase Advance Modification

The modified AFC method was implemented to reject the fourth harmonic. The calculated value of g_{max} was -0.012, and the experimental value was -0.013. The response of the parameters to a step input is oscillatory and lightly damped. Figure 6(a) shows a typical time domain plot of this cosine coefficient. This type of response is expected after calculating the system matrix $A_{av} = \begin{pmatrix} -1.7 & -21 \\ 21 & -1.7 \end{pmatrix}$ where the angle of the poles with the negative real axis is 85°. After compensation,

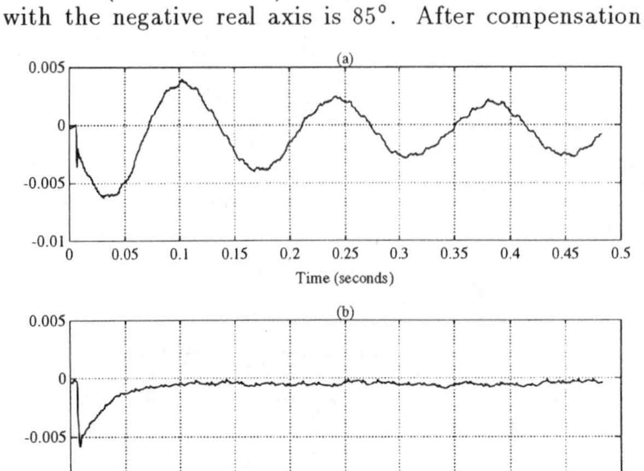

Figure 6: Time domain plot of fourth harmonic cosine coefficient for (a) AFC (b) modified AFC

$A_{av} = \begin{pmatrix} -22 & 0 \\ 0 & -22 \end{pmatrix}$. That is, the phase modification created a system with two repeated real poles on the negative real axis. The magnitude of the real part (22) is much larger than previously (1.7). The associated time domain response, is shown in Fig. 6(b).

The effect of the phase advance on the AFC structure is also apparent in the frequency domain. Figure 7 shows two frequency responses for fourth harmonic cancellation. The solid line is the original AFC method (no phase advance), and the dashed line is the AFC method with phase advance. The phase advance has greatly reduced the sensitivity of the overall system around the fourth harmonic frequency.

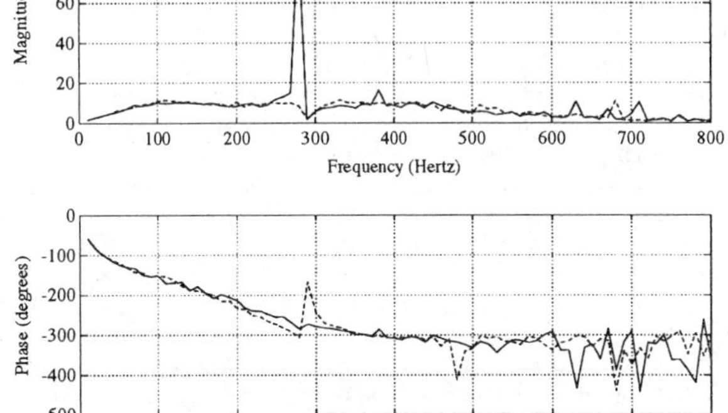

Figure 7: Frequency responses for original AFC method (solid), and with phase advance (dashed)

4.4 Multiple Frequency Compensation

An AFC design for multiple frequencies was implemented. On the first attempt, the design was attempted using AFC with no phase advance. It was found that it was not possible to cancel more than three harmonics without causing the adaptive system to go unstable except at very low adaptation gains. This result was caused by the increase in sensitivity observed when using AFC. The phase advance method, however, allowed us to cancel six of the harmonics present in the PES. Figure 8 shows the before and after frequency spectra, where the overall reduction in PES at the cancelled harmonics can be observed.

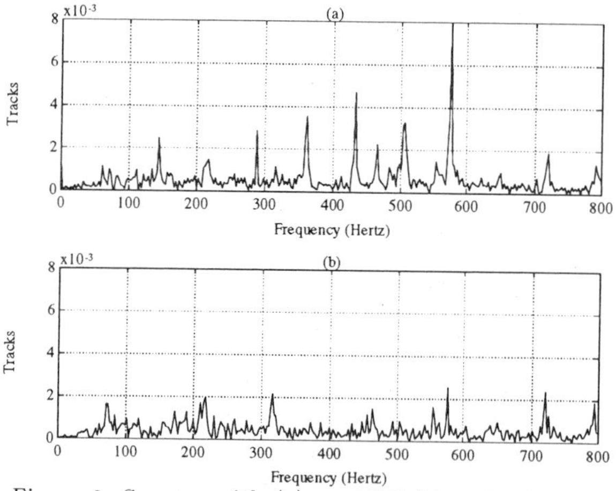

Figure 8: Spectra with (a) no AFC (b) multiple AFC

5 Conclusions

This paper has explored the issues of implementing adaptive feedforward cancellation in a magnetic disk drive. The disturbance rejection of the adaptive closed-loop system is shown by calculating the closed-loop frequency response using the open-loop frequency response data and the equivalent linear time-invariant transfer function of the adaptive controller. An averaging analysis of the original AFC algorithm allows one to predict the convergence of the adaptive closed-loop system from the locations of the poles of the averaged system. These results are extended in this paper by considering a modification of the original AFC method. The addition of a phase advance term to the parameter update equations can greatly improve the transient response. An averaging analysis for the modified system shows that it is advantageous to let the phase advance be equal to the phase of the open-loop frequency response at the frequency that it is desired to cancel. Then, the closed-loop system will have two repeated real poles on the negative real axis. The system behaves as expected in experiments.

The analytical results provide useful guidelines for design. There are two design parameters for the adaptive system, the adaptation gain g and the phase modification ϕ. Stability and disturbance rejection characteristics can be verified numerically, as quantified by the analytical results presented in this paper. The use of the phase advance ϕ can greatly reduce the sensitivity of the adaptive system and thus allow for cancellation of more harmonics. In fact, it may not be possible to actively cancel enough harmonics to achieve a reduction in the periodic disturbance unless this modification is used. In addition, reducing the sensitivity allows for a higher adaptation gain to be used, which means a faster convergence time, up to some point. The unique results for the AFC algorithm allow for a design of the system based on available frequency response data, which is commonly available during the overall design process.

There are important advantages to the AFC scheme over a scheme based on high-gain (internal model principle). An actual design would incorporate switching the algorithm off during seeks to another track, and it would store previous parameter values to minimize convergence delay. The ability to switch the algorithm on and off is in contrast to a controller based on the internal model approach, which cannot be turned off. Also, the AFC algorithm can be easily adapted to slowly varying frequencies. In many applications, an encoder provides position information which can be used to address the look-up tables for the sine and cosine functions. In such cases, the frequency of the compensation is directly tied to the frequency of the disturbance. A varying speed of rotation, and thus of the harmonic frequencies, occurs in optical applications, e.g., CD players. The speed of rotation is changed to maintain the same data rate depending on where the optical head is placed radially. AFC would easily allow for a varying harmonic frequency for cancellation. Again, this is in contrast to the internal model approach.

The method of adaptive periodic disturbance cancellation presented in this paper has application beyond magnetic hard drives. Removable optical and magnetic disks have larger periodic components in their PES because of imperfect alignment in the disk drive. In addition, there are a number of applications with rotating machinery in which adaptive periodic cancellation and the results of this paper are of immediate interest.

References

[1] S. Arimoto, et. al., "Learning Control Theory for Dynamical Systems," *Proc. of the 24th Conference on Decision and Control*, Ft. Lauderdale, FL, 1985, pp. 1375-1380.

[2] S. Beale, B. Shafai, P. LaRocca & E. Cusson, "Adaptive Forced Balancing for Magnetic Bearing Control Systems." *Proc. of the 31st IEEE Conference on Decision and Control*, Tucson, Arizona, 1992, pp. 3535-3539.

[3] M. Bodson, "Effect of the Choice of Error Equation on the Robustness Properties of Adaptive Control Systems," *International Journal of Adaptive Control and Signal Processing*, Vol. 2, 1988, pp. 249-257.

[4] M. Bodson, A. Sacks & P. Khosla, "Harmonic Generation in Adaptive Feedforward Cancellation Schemes," *Proc. of the 31st IEEE Conference on Decision and Control*, Tucson, Arizona, 1992, pp. 1261-1266.

[5] D. Chen & B. Paden, "Nonlinear Adaptive Torque-Ripple Cancellation for Step Motors," *Proc. of the IEEE Conference on Decision and Control*, Honolulu, Hawaii, 1990, pp. 3319-3324.

[6] B. Francis & B. Wonham, "The Internal Model Principle of Control Theory," *Automatica*, Vol. 12, No. 5, 1976, pp. 457-465.

[7] S. Hara, T. Omata & M. Nakano, "Synthesis of Repetitive Control Systems and Its Applications," *Proc. of the 24th Conference on Decision and Control*, Ft. Lauderdale, FL, 1985, pp. 1387-1392.

[8] P.A. Ioannou & G. Tao, "Frequency Domain Conditions for Strictly Positive Real Functions," *IEEE Trans. on Automatic Control*, Vol. AC-32, No. 1, pp. 53-54, 1987.

[9] C. Kempf, W. Messner, M. Tomizuka & R. Horowitz, "A Comparison of Four Discrete-Time Repetitive Control Algorithms," *Proc. of the Automatic Control Conference*, Chicago, Illinois, 1992, pp. 2700-2704.

[10] B. Riedle & P. Kokotovic, "A Stability-Instability Boundary for Disturbance-Free Slow Adaptation with Unmodeled Dynamics," *IEEE Trans. on Automatic Control*, Vol. 30, No. 10, 1985, pp. 1027-1030.

[11] A. Sacks, M. Bodson & P. Khosla, "Experimental Results of Adaptive Periodic Disturbance Cancellation in a High Performance Magnetic Disk Drive," submitted for publication.

[12] S. Sastry & M. Bodson, *Adaptive Control: Stability, Convergence, and Robustness*, Prentice Hall, Englewood Cliffs, NJ, 1989.

[13] Y. Wei & A. Wu, "Demonstration of Active Vibration Control of the Hughes Cryocooler Testbed," *Proc. of the 31st Conference on Decision and Control*, Tucson, Arizona, 1992, pp. 2580-2585.

Proceedings of the
American Control Conference
San Francisco, California • June 1993

Nonlinear Differential-Geometric Techniques for Control of a Series DC Motor

John Chiasson
Department of Electrical Engineering
348 BEH, University of Pittsburgh
Pittsburgh, PA 15261

Abstract

The problem of controlling a Series DC motor using only current measurements is considered. It is shown that both speed and load-torque may be estimated from the current measurements for use in two proposed nonlinear controllers. The two proposed feedback laws are based on feedback linearization and input-output linearization. Further, both the speed/torque estimation scheme and the control schemes are valid in the prescence of magnetic saturation in the field circuit and when high-speed field-weakening is employed. The estimation is accomplished by using nonlinear state-space and output-space transformations to construct an observer with linear error-dynamics whose rate of convergence may be arbitrarily specified. (Such an observer could provide reliability to existing systems in the event of a speed sensor failure.) The feedback-linearization controller involves a non-trivial state-space transformation allowing control of the full state trajectory. It is then shown that a simpler input-output linearization controller with stable internal dynamics exists and is explicitly constructed.

1. Introduction

A DC motor in which the field circuit is connected in series with the armature circuit is referred to as a *series* DC motor. Due to this electrical connection, the electromagnetic torque put out by this motor is proportional to the *square* of the current (below field saturation). As a result, the series-connected DC motor puts out more torque per ampere of current than any other DC motor. It is used in applications that require high torque at low speed, e.g., electric cable cars and subway trains [2]. In fact, the series motor is the most widely used DC motor for electric traction applications [16]. However, as the series motor can only produce torque in one direction, it is typically used only in speed control applications.

The list of nonlinear control systems for which the differential- geometric approach is an important tool for the design of a controller continues to expand. Many of these applications have been for electro- mechanical systems. Marino has applied the techniques to synchronous generators [13] and applications to stepper motors are given in [14] and [15]. Isidori [6, page 226] has applied the techniques to a separately- excited field-controlled DC motor while in [19] a feedback linearization control algorithm was developed for the DC shunt motor. The standard electrical configuration for a DC motor used in servo applications is the separately-excited armature-controlled DC motor which is well known to have a *linear* mathematical model [1],[2]. In this paper, the singly-excited series-connected DC motor is considered.

The mathematical model of the series DC motor is nonlinear. The traditional method of nonlinear control, i.e., linearization about an operating point, is unable to provide high-performance. However, the advances made in the differential-geometric approach to nonlinear control theory (see e.g., [4],[5],[6],[7]) have opened up new avenues to controlling such systems. In particular, using the results of Keller [8], Krener and Isidori [9], Krener and Respondek [10] and, Xia and Gao [11], a nonlinear observer with linear error dynamics may be constructed which estimates the speed and load torque based on measurements of the current. Finally, it is shown that feedback-linearizing and input-output linearization controllers for speed may be constructed for the Series DC motor.

2. Mathematical Models of a Series DC Motor [1][2]

As previously mentioned, a series DC motor is one in which the field circuit is connected in series with the armature circuit. This is illustrated in the simplified picture of a DC motor below by connecting terminal T_2' to terminal T_1 and applying the voltage between terminals T_1' and T_2.

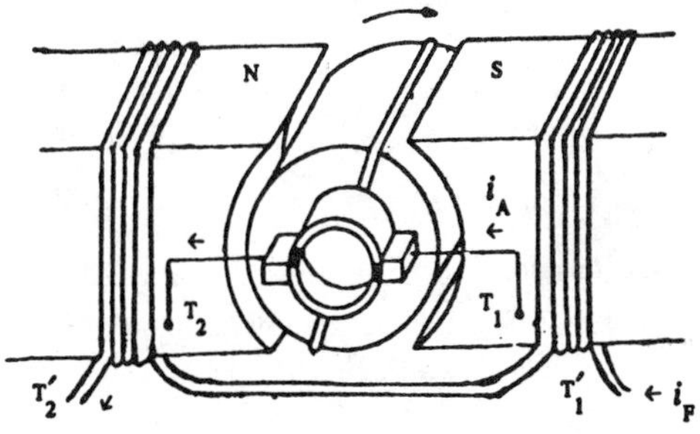

Figure 1 *Series Connected DC Motor*

The armature inductance is denoted by L_a and the field flux is given by $\phi_f(i_f) = f(i_f)$ where $f(\cdot)$ is the *magnetization curve* as shown in figure 2. The magnetization curve is symmetric with respect to origin and satisfies $if(i) > 0$ for $i \neq 0$. Below saturation, ϕ_f is linear and may be written as $\phi_f = L_f i_f$. In a typical series wound DC motor for traction applications the condition $L_f \gg L_a$ holds. In figure 2 below, R_a and R_f denote the resistance of the armature and field windings, respectively. The resistance

R_p placed in parallel with the field winding is for field-weakening. (R_p is not indicated in figure 1.) The constant K_m denotes the torque/back-emf constant.

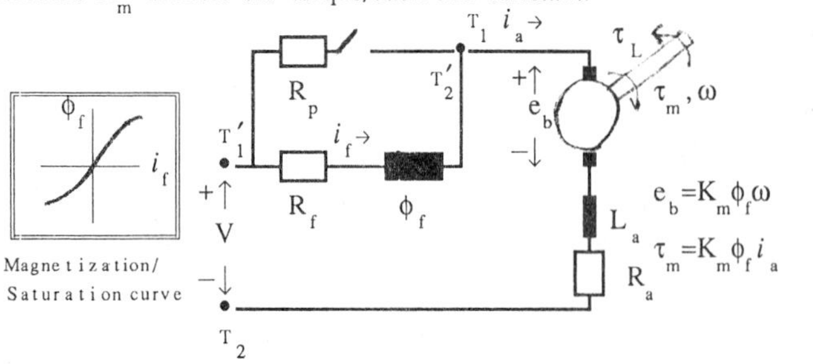

Figure 2 *Schematic Circuit for a Series Connected DC Motor*

The dynamic equations describing a series-wound DC motor are [2, page 58]:

$$L_a di_a/dt = V - R_a i_a - R_p(i_a - i_f) - K_m\phi_f(i_f)\omega$$

$$d\phi_f/dt = -R_f i_f + R_p(i_a - i_f) \tag{1}$$

$$J d\omega/dt = K_m\phi_f(i_f)i_a - B\omega - \tau_L$$

These equations are valid in the *field-weakening* region. That is, at high speeds (above the so-called *base speed*) the switch is closed so that the field current i_f is less than the armature current i_a. The field flux is then less than it would be with full armature current, i.e., $\phi_f(i_f) < \phi_f(i_a)$. As can be seen from the first equation of (1), the applied voltage V must be greater than the back-emf voltage $K_m\phi_f(i_f)\omega$ in order to produce armature current i_a. The back-emf being less allows the speed ω to be larger with the same voltage than it would be if the field windings had full armature current. The trade-off is that the torque put out by the motor is now less for the same armature current as can be seen from the third equation of (1).

If the first two equations of (1) are added, we have

$$d\left(\phi_f(i_f) + L_a i_a\right)/dt = -R_f i_f - R_a i_a - K_m\phi_f(i_f)\omega + V$$

$$J d\omega/dt = K_m\phi_f(i_f)i_a - B\omega - \tau_L \tag{2}$$

We shall find this form to be very useful for speed-observer design. Below the base-speed, field-weakening is not present, i.e., the switch is open so that $R_p = \infty$ and equations (2) reduce to

$$d\left(\phi_f(i) + L_a i\right)/dt = -(R_f + R_a)i - K_m\phi_f(i)\omega + V$$

$$J d\omega/dt = K_m\phi_f(i)i - B\omega - \tau_L \tag{3}$$

where $i = i_a = i_f$.

Note that the torque put out by the motor $K_m\phi_f(i)i$ is always positive which is a direct result of the series connection. In more detail, when the armature current is reversed, so is the field current (as they are the same current!) thus reversing the magnetic field in the air-gap and keeping the torque positive. If a negative torque is required, the terminal T_2' of the field circuit must be connected to terminal T_2 of the armature circuit instead of T_1 (see Figure 1). Even at high speeds where field-weakening is employed, it is easy to that i_a and i_f have the same sign and thus the torque is again always positive (or, negative depending on the connection of the terminals). As a consequence of this unidirectional torque production, the series DC motor is typically used for speed control applications and not in positioning control systems. Note that the motor is slowed down only by the load torque (neglecting the viscous-friction torque $B\omega$). That is, the physical mechanism by which the controller reduces the motor speed is by lowering the current in the motor so that the load torque may slow it down. Consequently, one *never* unloads a series motor nor connects it to the load by a belt (or other mechanism that could break) as the result could be disastrous [3, page 306].

In summary, below the base-speed (i.e., no field-weakening), the system is described by (3) while above the base-speed the system is described by (1) (or (2)).

3. Nonlinear Observers with Linear Error Dynamics

The idea of a nonlinear observer with linear error dynamics is briefly explained as follows [9]: Consider a nonlinear system in the following *special* form:

$$\dot{x} = \begin{bmatrix} 0 & 1 & 0 \\ 0 & 0 & 1 \\ 0 & 0 & 0 \end{bmatrix} x + \begin{bmatrix} \varphi_1(y) \\ \varphi_2(y) \\ \varphi_3(y) \end{bmatrix} + \begin{bmatrix} g_1(y) \\ g_2(y) \\ g_3(y) \end{bmatrix} u \tag{4}$$

$$y = [1\ 0\ 0]x$$

where the $\varphi_i(y)$ are arbitrary (nonlinear) functions of the output y. The key point here is that in this special form, the system is nonlinear only in the measured output $y = x_1$ and *linear* in the unknown state variables x_2, x_3. As y is a known (measured) output, one defines an observer by

$$\dot{\hat{x}} = \begin{bmatrix} 0 & 1 & 0 \\ 0 & 0 & 1 \\ 0 & 0 & 0 \end{bmatrix} \hat{x} + \begin{bmatrix} \varphi_1(y) \\ \varphi_2(y) \\ \varphi_3(y) \end{bmatrix} + \begin{bmatrix} g_1(y) \\ g_2(y) \\ g_3(y) \end{bmatrix} u + \begin{bmatrix} \ell_0 \\ \ell_1 \\ \ell_2 \end{bmatrix} (y - \hat{y}) \tag{5}$$

$$\hat{y} = [1\ 0\ 0]\hat{x}$$

Subtracting (5) from (4) and the obvious definitions for A_o and c_o, the dynamic equations for the error $\varepsilon \triangleq x - \hat{x}$ are

$$\dot{\varepsilon} = (A_o - \ell c_o)\varepsilon \tag{6}$$

which is a *linear* system. As the pair (c_o, A_o) is observable, a straight-forward choice of the gain vector ℓ leads to a stable error equation so that $\varepsilon(t) \to 0$ and $\hat{x}(t) \to x(t)$ as $t \to \infty$.

With the currents i_a, i_f as the available measurements, we now consider constructing an observer with linear error dynamics to estimate the speed ω and load torque τ_L. With the models given by (1), (2) or (3) above, it is not possible to design such an observer. However, by using engineering judgment, one can simplify the problem and still obtain an accurate observer. The key approximation is to note that $L_a i_a$ is very small compared to $\phi_f(i_f)$. For example, below the saturation current level where $\phi_f(i_f) = L_f i_f$ the ratio L_a/L_f can be 10^{-4} [1, page 90]. Even in the field-weakening region, $\phi_f(i_f) \gg L_a i_a$ [2, page 59]. Making this approximation in (2), defining $x_1 = \phi_f(i_f)$, $x_2 = \omega$ and modeling the (constant) load torque as an additional state variable $x_3 = \tau_L/J$ results in

$$\begin{aligned} dx_1/dt &= -k_1 x_1 x_2 - R_f i_f - R_a i_a + V \\ dx_2/dt &= -k_2 x_2 - x_3 + (K_m/J)\phi_f(i_f) i_a \\ dx_3/dt &= 0 \end{aligned} \tag{7}$$

$$y = [1\ 0\ 0]x = x_1.$$

where $k_1 = K_m$, $k_2 = B/J$. Note that the measurement is now the field flux $x_1 = \phi_f(i_f)$ which is available by physically measuring the field current and using the magnetization curve to determine ϕ_f. However, (7) is *not* linear in the unmeasured state variables due to the term $x_1 x_2$ in the first equation as $x_2 = \omega$ is not available. As shown in the literature [6]-[12], the idea is to find out if a coordinate transformation $x^* = T(x)$ exists (with inverse $x = S(x^*)$) which will transform (7) to the form (4). For $x_1 = \phi_f(i_f) > 0$, consider the change of coordinates

$$\begin{aligned} x_1^* &= \ln(x_1) = \ln(\phi_f) \\ x_2^* &= x_2 = \omega \\ x_3^* &= x_3 = \tau_L/J \end{aligned} \tag{8}$$

and change of output transformation

$$y^* = \ln(y) = \ln(\phi_f)$$

The reason for the transformation becomes clear upon computing $\dot{x}_1^*$ as

$$\begin{aligned} \dot{x}_1^* = (1/x_1)dx_1/dt &= (1/x_1)(-k_1 x_1 x_2 - R_f i_f - R_a i_a + V) \\ &= -k_1 x_2 + (-R_f i_f - R_a i_a + V)/x_1 \\ &= -k_1 x_2^* + (-R_f i_f - R_a i_a + V)/\phi_f(i_f) \end{aligned}$$

which is now *linear* in the unmeasured state variable $x_2^* = \omega$. Defining the known (measurable) vector φ and system matrices A,c as

$$\varphi(i_f, i_a, V) \triangleq \begin{bmatrix} \left(-R_f i_f - R_a i_a + V\right)/\phi_f(i_f) \\ (K_m/J)\phi_f(i_f) i_a \\ 0 \end{bmatrix}, \quad A \triangleq \begin{bmatrix} 0 & -k_1 & 0 \\ 0 & -k_2 & -1 \\ 0 & 0 & 0 \end{bmatrix},$$

$c \triangleq [\ 1\ 0\ 0\ ]$, the transformed system becomes

$$\begin{aligned} \dot{x}^* &= Ax^* + \varphi(i_f, i_a, V) \\ y^* &= cx^* = \ln(\phi_f) \end{aligned} \tag{9}$$

A simple calculation shows that the pair (c,A) is observable so that an observer may be defined by

$$\begin{aligned} \dot{\hat{x}}^* &= A\hat{x}^* + \varphi(i_f, i_a, V) + \ell(y^* - \hat{y}^*) \quad \ell = [\ell_1\ \ell_2\ \ell_3]^T \\ \hat{y}^* &= c\hat{x}^* \end{aligned} \tag{10}$$

Remark 1 In the development of the observer, the assumption that $\phi_f(i_f) > 0$ was made. (Conversely, the condition $\phi_f(i_f) < 0$ may be used with $x_1^* = \ln|\phi_f|$ to construct an observer.) That is, the field current must be kept positive and bounded away from zero to use this observer. However, as the torque put out by the motor $\phi_f(i_f)i_a$ is always positive, irrespective of the direction of the current, there is no reason to have the current change sign. At start-up of the motor, the observer would not be initiated until the measured field current is above a certain level, say .1 amp. In fact, a controller must be designed to keep the current bounded away from zero for controlled operation of the motor. This can be easily understood by noting that if the system (3) is linearized about $i_f = 0$, the resulting linear system is not controllable. Again, at start-up of the motor, a control strategy would be to just command an open-loop voltage to the motor to build up enough current in order to control the motor.

Remark 2 It is quite interesting that the structure of the observer does not change as the motor goes into (or out of) field-weakening, although the dynamics of the motor do change! The structural change in dynamics, that is, from (1) to (3) is accounted for in (2) by the redundancy of the current measurements at speeds below field-weakening since then $i_f = i_a$.

Remark 3 Note that to achieve the observer form, it was necessary to do a coordinate transformation *and* an output transformation. It seems surprising that the natural logarithm of the flux $y^* = \ln(\phi_f)$ is taken as output rather than just the flux itself. The Krener-Isidori [9] necessary and sufficient conditions for the existence of a nonlinear observer with linear error dynamics is given in terms of a *particular* output equation. It turns out that if $y = \phi_f$ were chosen as the output, the conditions given in [9] would *not* hold. In [10], conditions are given (theorem 4.1 of [10]) in more general terms where a new output may be required which is an *invertible* function of the original output. The above output function comes out quite naturally from theorem 4.1 of [10] or by solving equation (25) in [8]. Using the output equation $y^* = h(x) = \ln(\phi_f)$, the simpler conditions in [9] may be checked to show an observer exists.

4. Nonlinear Speed Controllers for the Series DC Motor

A speed controller for the series DC motor may be designed using the concepts of feedback linearization and input-output linearization [6], [7]. That is, by a combination of a change of coordinates and state feedback, the original nonlinear system (1) can be made linear. To do so, let $i_f = \psi(\varphi_f)$ where $\psi(\cdot)$ is the inverse of $\varphi_f = \varphi_f(i_f) = f(i_f)$. Then (1) may be rewritten as

$$di_a/dt = V/L_a - ((R_a+R_p)/L_a)i_a + (R_p/L_a)\psi(\phi_f) - (K_m/L_a)\phi_f\omega$$

$$d\phi_f/dt = -(R_f + R_p)\psi(\phi_f) + R_p i_a \quad (11)$$

$$d\omega/dt = (K_m/J)\phi_f i_a - \tau_L/J$$

where the viscous-friction coefficient has been set to zero ($B = 0$) for ease of exposition.

4.1 Feedback Linearization with Field-Weakening

Consider the nonlinear transformation

$$x_1^* = T_1(x) = \omega - (K_m/2R_pJ)\phi_f^2$$

$$x_2^* = T_2(x) = (K_m/J)(R_f/R_p + 1)\phi_f\psi(\phi_f) - \tau_L/J = dx_1^*/dt \quad (12)$$

$$x_3^* = T_3(x) = (K_m/J)(R_f/R_p + 1)d\left(\phi_f\psi(\phi_f)\right)/dt$$

$$= \alpha\left(\psi(\phi_f) + \phi_f\psi'(\phi_f)\right)\left(-(R_f + R_p)\psi(\phi_f) + R_p i_a\right) = dx_2^*/dt$$

where $\alpha \triangleq (K_m/J)(R_f/R_p + 1)$, $\psi' = d\psi/d\phi_f$.

In this new coordinate system, the system equations are then

$$dx_1^*/dt = x_2^*$$

$$dx_2^*/dt = x_3^* \quad (13)$$

$$dx_3^*/dt = a(i_a,\phi_f,\omega) + b(\phi_f)V$$

where $b(\phi_f) = \alpha\left(\psi(\phi_f) + \phi_f\psi'(\phi_f)\right)(R_p/L_a)$. The quantity $a(i_a,\phi_f,\omega)$ is a messy expression but straightforward to compute. Setting $V = (-a(i_a,\phi_f,\omega) + u)/b(\phi_f)$ results in a third-order *linear* system from the new input u to the new state space coordinates x^*. Clearly, the condition $b(\phi_f) \neq 0$ must hold for this controller to be valid. It is easy to see that $\psi(\phi_f) + \phi_f\psi'(\phi_f) > 0$ as long as $i_f > 0$. That is, the saturation (magnetization) curve $\phi_f = f(i_f)$ and its inverse $i_f = \psi(\phi_f)$ are both strictly increasing so that $\phi_f > 0$ for $i_f > 0$ and $\psi > 0$ for $\phi_f > 0$. Further, $\psi'(\phi_f) > 0$ for all ϕ_f. As this controller is designed for the field-weakening region, the current i_f is bounded above zero and the controller is thus valid. The value of τ_L/J would be obtained from the observer described in the previous section. Note that the load torque has been canceled out using feedforward of its estimate.

This feedback controller is sensitive to the value of L_a which, as noted previously, is quite small. We now consider a controller designed with L_a taken to be zero which is consistent with the approximation made in the observer design. To this end, set $L_a = 0$ in (1) (again with $B = 0$ for simplicity) and solve for i_a to get

$$i_a = \left(V + R_p i_f - K_m\phi_f(i_f)\omega\right)/(R_a + R_p) \quad (14)$$

This is then substituted into the second and third equations of (1) to get

$$d\phi_f/dt = -(R_f + R_p)\psi(\phi_f) + \left(R_p/(R_a + R_p)\right)\left(V + R_p\psi(\phi_f) - K_m\phi_f\omega\right) \quad (15)$$

$$d\omega/dt = (K_m/J)\phi_f\left(V + R_p\psi(\phi_f) - K_m\phi_f\omega\right)/(R_a + R_p) - (\tau_L/J)$$

However, as i_a does not appear in the first two equations of (12) it is easy to see that the transformation for this second-order system is just the first two equations in (12)

$$x_1^* = T_1(x) = \omega - (K_m/2R_pJ)\phi_f^2$$

$$x_2^* = T_2(x) = (K_m/J)(R_f/R_p + 1)\phi_f\psi(\phi_f) - \tau_L/J = dx_1^*/dt \quad (16)$$

and further that

$$dx_2^*/dt = (K_m/J)(R_f/R_p + 1)d\left(\phi_f\psi(\phi_f)\right)/dt$$

$$= \alpha\left(\psi(\phi_f) + \phi_f\psi'(\phi_f)\right)\left(-(R_f + R_p)\psi(\phi_f) + R_p i_a\right)$$

where $\alpha \triangleq (K_m/J)(R_f/R_p + 1)$ and i_a is given by (14). That is, we may write

$$dx_2^*/dt = a(\phi_f,\omega) + b(\phi_f)V$$

where $b(\phi_f) = \alpha\left(\psi(\phi_f) + \phi_f\psi'(\phi_f)\right)R_p/(R_a + R_p)$ and $a(\phi_f,\omega)$ is a known function. Thus, setting $V = (-a(\phi_f,\omega) + u)/b(\phi_f)$ results in a *linear* system from the new input u to the new state variables x^*.

4.2 Input-Output Linearization with Field-Weakening

The feedback linearization controllers are complicated and inconvenient due to the fact that neither of the transformed state variables x_1^*, x_2^* is the speed. As a consequence, any reference trajectory for the speed ω would have to be transformed to the x^* coordinates and then the feedback controller could be designed to track this reference. It would be simpler and more like standard engineering practice not to require this. This can be accomplished using *input-output* linearization rather than feedback linearization. To do so, one just sets V in the second equation of (15) equal to

$$V = - R_p\psi(\phi_f) + K_m\phi_f\omega + u(R_a + R_p)/((K_m/J)\phi_f) \quad (17)$$

to get

$$d\omega/dt = u - \tau_L/J \quad (18)$$

so that the output (speed) is linearly related to the new input u and hence input-output linearization has been achieved. Further, with the controller (17), the first equation of (15) becomes

$$d\phi_f/dt = -(R_f + R_p)\psi(\phi_f) + uJR_p/(K_m\phi_f) \quad (19)$$

To check the stability of (19), multiply both sides by $2\phi_f$ to obtain

$$d\phi_f^2/dt = -2(R_f + R_p)\phi_f\psi(\phi_f) + u(2JR_p/K_m)$$

The saturation curve is such that $|\phi_f(i_f)| \leq |L_f i_f|$ where $L_f = \phi_f'(0)$. Thus we may write (recall that $i_f = \psi(\phi_f)$)

$$d\phi_f^2/dt = -\gamma_1\phi_f^2 - \gamma_1\phi_f(L_f i_f - \phi_f) + \gamma_2 u$$

$$\leq -\gamma_1\phi_f^2 + \gamma_2 u, \text{ where } \gamma_1 \triangleq 2(R_f + R_p)/L_f,\ \gamma_2 \triangleq 2JR_p/K_m$$

Thus

$$\phi_f^2 \le \phi_f^2(i_{f0})e^{-\gamma_1(t-t_0)} + \int_{t_0}^{t} e^{-\gamma_1(t-\tau)}\gamma_2 u(\tau)d\tau$$

were t_0 is the time that field-weakening was initiated and i_{f0} is the field current at t_0. From this last expression, it is clear that ϕ_f^2 is bounded if the input u is bounded (i.e., bounded acceleration, see (18)). Thus, the second-order system (15) with the feedback control strategy (17) is BIBO stable. Again, the load torque can be compensated by using its estimate given in the previous section. Note this controller gives a simple straightforward way to control the speed.

4.3 Controller below Field-Weakening

The above controller designs were done assuming field-weakening was in effect. We now consider the case where $R_p = \infty$ so that the system equations are given by (3). In this case, consider the coordinate transformation

$$x_1^* = T_1(x) = \omega$$
$$x_2^* = T_2(x) = (K_m/J)\phi_f(i)i - \tau_L/J = dx_1^*/dt \tag{20}$$

which results in

$$dx_1^*/dt = x_2^*$$
$$dx_2^*/dt = (K_m/J)\left[\phi_f'(i)i + \phi_f(i)\right]di/dt \tag{21}$$
$$= (K_m/J)\left[(\phi_f'(i)i + \phi_f(i))/\phi_f'(i)\right]\left[-(R_f + R_a)i - K_m\phi_f(i)\omega + V\right]$$

where L_a has been set to zero. With $V = (R_f + R_a)i/\phi_f'(i) + K_m\phi_f(i)/\phi_f'(i)\omega + (J/K_m)\left[\phi_f'(i)/(\phi_f'(i)i+\phi_f(i))\right]u$, the system is then *linear* from the new input u to the new state coordinates x*. As $\phi_f(i)$ is strictly increasing, $\phi_f'(i) > 0$ for all i and $\phi_f'(i)i + \phi_f(i) > 0$ for $i > 0$ so that the controller is valid for $i > 0$. In this case (i.e., without field weakening), the feedback and input-output linearization controllers are identical. If the field flux is not in saturation so that $\phi_f(i) = L_f i$, (20) and (21) reduce to the results given in [20], [21]. Finally, note that by taking $R_p = \infty$, the first two equations of (12) reduce to the transformation (20) as expected.

5. Conclusions It has been shown that the nonlinear differential-geometric techniques can be successfully applied to the series DC motor. In order to estimate the load torque and speed from measurements of the current, a nonlinear observer with linear error dynamics was shown to exist and explicitly constructed. This observer is valid even with magnetic saturation present and when field-weakening is employed. The observer structure remains unchanged when moving into and out of field-weakening regimes assuming the field and armature currents are measurable. Further, feedback and input-output linearizing controllers were constructed which make use of the estimated speed and load torque. The observer and controller are valid as long as the field current is nonzero which is the standard operating condition of a series connected DC motor. Note that such an observer scheme would provide *reliability* to existing series motors in that if the speed sensor were to fail, the control scheme proposed here would provide the capability for continued controlled operation of the motor. In particular, large series DC motors are often used as the propulsion system for *autonomous* (unmanned) transportation systems where such reliability would be particularly important.

This application of the differential-geometric theory to the control of the series DC motor vividly illustrates the power of these new techniques. This is especially true in regards to the observer, as it does not appear that it would have otherwise naturally arose.

References

[1]P. Krause, *Analysis of Electric Machines*, McGraw Hill, 1986.
[2]W. Leonhard, *Control of Electrical Drives*, Springer-Verlag, 1985.
[3]Chapman, S.J., *Electric Machinery Fundamentals*, McGraw-Hill, 1985.
[4]B. Jakubczyk, and W. Respondek, *On Linearization of Control Systems*, **Bull. Acad. Polon. Sci., Ser. Sci. Math Astronom. Phys.** 28, 517-522, 1980.
[5]R. Su, G. Meyer, and L.R. Hunt, *Design for multi-input nonlinear systems*, in **Differential Geometric Control Theory**, edited by R.W. Brockett, R.S. Millman and H.J. Sussman, Birkhauser, Boston, pp. 268-298, 1983.
[6]A. Isidori, *Nonlinear Control Systems*, Second Edition, 1989.
[7]H. Nijmeijer and A.J. van der Schaft, *Nonlinear Dynamic Control System* Springer-Verlag, 1990.
[8]Keller, H., *Nonlinear Observer Design by Transformation into a Generalized Observer Canonical Form*, **International Journal of Control**, vol. 46, n. 6, pgs. 1915-1930, 1987.
[9]Krener, A.J. and Isidori, A., *Linearization by Output Injection and Nonlinear Observers*, **Systems and Control Letters**, 3, pgs. 47-52, 1983.
[10]A.J. Krener and W. Respondek, *Nonlinear Observers with Linearizable Error Dynamics*, **Siam Journal of Control and Optimization**, Vol 23, pp 197-216, 1985.
[11]X. Xia and W. Gao, *Nonlinear Observer Design by Observer Linearization,* **Siam Journal of Control and Optimization,** Vol. 27, No. 1, pp. 199-216, January, 1989.
[12]Bestle, D. and M. Zeitz, *Canonical Form Observer Designs for Nonlinear Time-variable Systems*, **International Journal of Control**, 38 (1983), pp. 419-431.
[13]R. Marino, *An example of a Nonlinear Regulator*, **IEEE Transactions on Automatic Control**, Vol. AC-29, No.3, March 1989.
[14]M. Zribi, and J. Chiasson, *Position Control of a PM Stepper Motor by Exact Linearization*, **IEEE Transactions on Automatic Control**, Vol. 36, No. 5, May 1991.
[15]M. Bodson, and J. Chiasson, *Application of Nonlinear Control Methods to the Positioning of a Permanent Magnet Stepping Motor*, **Proceedings of the 1989 CDC**, Tampa Fl.
[16]R.D. Begamudre, *Electro-Mechanical Energy Conversion with Dynamics of Machine*, Wiley 1988.
[17]Kailath, T., *Linear Systems*, Prentice-Hall, 1980.
[18]Sastry, S., and M. Bodson, *Adaptive Control - Stability, Convergence and Robustness*, Prentice-Hall, 1989.
[19]Bodson, M. and J. Chiasson, *Nonlinear and Adaptive Control of a Shunt DC Motor*, **Proceedings of the IEEE International Conference on Systems Engineering**, Dayton, Ohio, August 1-3, 1991.
[20]Oliver, Philip D., *Feedback Linearization of DC Motors*, **IEEE Transactions on Industrial Electronics**, Vol. 38, No. 6, December 1991.
[21]Chiasson, J., *Nonlinear Control Systems - EE 3648 Class Notes*, May 1989.

WP4 - 14:30

Proceedings of the
American Control Conference
San Francisco, California • June 1993

DESIGN OF ACTIVE SUSPENSION SYSTEM IN THE PRESENCE OF PHYSICAL PARAMETRIC UNCERTAINTIES

László Palkovics
Dept. of Road Vehicles, TU Budapest, H-1521 Budapest, Hungary
Péter Gáspár
József Bokor
System and Control Laboratory
Computer and Automation Institute of Hungarian Academy of Sciences
H-1518 Budapest, P.O.Box 63, Hungary

ABSTRACT

The purpose of the paper is to study the design of the active wheel suspension system. The goal of the control design is the disturbance attenuation with respect to the road disturbances when some of the physical parameters of the system are uncertain. On the basis of a linear quarter-car model the tire stiffness and suspension stiffness are assummed to be uncertain. In this paper the authors deal with some new robust design methods. They examine the applicability of H_∞ control in case of the active suspension system using a quarter-car model. The problem is solved as a direct state-feedback H_∞ control problem and in case of structured uncertainties as an *RLQR* (Robust LQR) design task. On the basis of combination of these two methods new procedure is proposed.

1. INTRODUCTION

The first design procedures of the active wheel suspension system can be dated back to the beginning of eighties. The investigators mainly used the well-known "sky-hook" principle or the standard LQR/LQG methodology for the design of active suspension system. The results achieved by using controlled elements in the suspension were very significant comparing them to those reached by optimisation of parameters of the conventional (passive suspension system). The backdraws of the above mentioned control strategies became soon clear: the quarter-car model used in the design is much more complicated one as it was thought. First it cannot be considered as a linear one, there are several non-linearities: wheel-hoop, bump stop etc. On the other hand in the standard LQR strategy it is assumed that the parameters of the system are perfectly known however uncertainties in the quarter-car model can appear both in unmodelled dynamics and in physical parameters. The quarter-car model extended with the mentioned uncertainties is shown in Figure 1. The effect of the wheel-hop phenomenon, non-linear spring and time delay of the actuator on the behaviour of the active suspension system design by means of LQG/LQR strategy is examined in [9]. This study demonstrates the disadvantages of the LQR control problem very well.

In the early studies of the control of wheel-suspension system the LQR problem was solved assuming that the states of the system are available or they can be estimated. The basic study of the problem can be found in [13]. In this case the author assumes perfect (broad-bandwidth) actuator, which does not have any dynamics and all of the modes of the system can be controlled with it. The same approach to the problem can be found in [6] using LQG design method with Kalman-filter. The limited bandwidth actuator problem is examined in [11]. In the design of active suspension system the critical point is always the estimation of the states of the vehicle. For the use of state-observers we can find several examples in the literature. The design and tuning of the Kalman-filter for vehicle application is investigated in [14]. Reduced order Luenberger observer is examined and applied for the state-estimation of the quarter-car model in [3]. Detailed review of the field is given in [7].

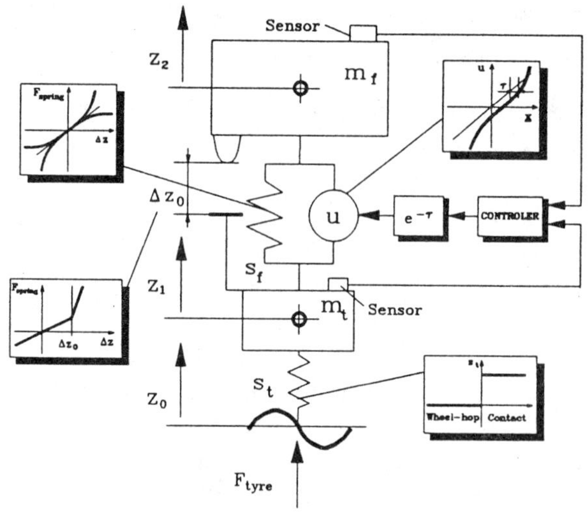

Figure 1 Quarter-car model

In the second half of eighties and in the beginning of the nineties several publications have been appeared which approach to the design problem different way. We can consider these as a "second generation" control design methods. An eigenstructure assignment approach is presented in [8]. The control system is designed on the basis of reference model following control in [12]. The adaptive system design can be found in [4], which compares the adaptive LQG and the nonlinear design procedures. The robustness of the LQG method is examined in [15]. A Benchmark problem is carried out for several "second generation" design strategies in [5].

In this paper the authors study the applicability of H_∞ control in the case of linear quarter-car model. The solution of the direct state-feedback problem is presented. The problem is solved when structured uncertainty is present in the system (the tyre stiffness is not perfectly known). The link between the *RLQR* and H_∞ is explained and modified design procedure is proposed.

2. PROBLEM FORMULATION

In the paper the spring stiffness is assumed to be not perfectly known, which is quite realistic since it is a function of the internal tyre pressure, vehicle speed, temperature, etc. Assume that the tyre stiffness is varying arbitrary in the following range:

$$s_t \in [s_{t0}-\delta s_t, s_{t0}+\delta s_t]$$

where the s_{t0} is the nominal value of s_t and the δs_t the range of variation. Figure 2 shows if the stiffness is decreased, the gain in the acceleration of the vehicle body is higher in the lower frequency range, which is undesired from the viewpoint of the ride comfort. Increasing the value of the stiffness we can expect harshness problem: in the higher frequency range the gain of the system is larger. Of course, the uncertainty of this parameter does not give the most demonstrative results, but the need for robust system design straightforward.

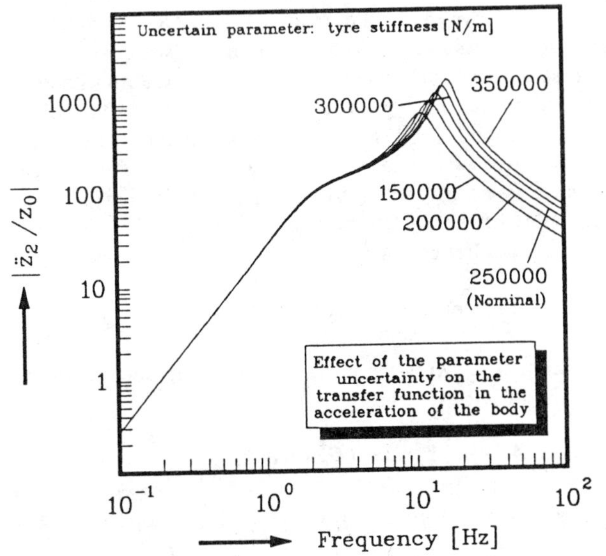

Figure 2 Effect of the uncertain tyre stiffness on the transfer function in acceleration of the vehicle body

In the paper only the parametric uncertainty is considered, altough several non-linearities are present in the system as it can be seen in Figure 1. The aim of this study is to demonstrate the applicability of the robust design methodology in case of the active suspension system based on simple quarter-car model. Let us consider the state-matrix of the linear uncertain system by separating the nominal part from the uncertain one:

$$A = A_0 + \sum_{i=1}^{p} q_i E_i \tag{1}$$

where p is the number of the uncertain parameters in the system. Let us assume that

$$|q_i| \leq 1, \quad rank(E_i) = 1 \quad (i=1,2,\dots,p)$$

The matrices E_i contain all the information about the structure and size of the uncertainties, q_i are the uncertain variables. The rank condition ensures that the matrices E_i can be written as a diad of two vectors:

$$E_i = l_i n_i^T \tag{2}$$

and we can define the following hyper-vectors:

$$L = [\, l_1 \;\; l_2 \dots l_p \,], \qquad N = [\, n_1 \;\; n_2 \dots n_p \,] \tag{3}$$

When the uncertainty in the tyre stiffness written above is considered the state-matrix of the uncertain system can be written as follows:

$$A = \begin{bmatrix} 0 & 0 & 1 & 0 \\ 0 & 0 & 0 & 1 \\ -\dfrac{s_f+s_{t0}}{m_t} & \dfrac{s_f}{m_t} & 0 & 0 \\ \dfrac{s_f}{m_f} & -\dfrac{s_f}{m_f} & 0 & 0 \end{bmatrix} + q_1 \begin{bmatrix} 0 & 0 & 0 & 0 \\ 0 & 0 & 0 & 0 \\ -\dfrac{\delta s_t}{m_t} & 0 & 0 & 0 \\ 0 & 0 & 0 & 0 \end{bmatrix} \tag{4}$$

and the matrixes of Eq.3. can be considered as:

$$L^T = \begin{bmatrix} 0 & 0 & \sqrt{\dfrac{\delta s_t}{m_t}} & 0 \end{bmatrix}, \quad N^T = \begin{bmatrix} -\sqrt{\dfrac{\delta s_t}{m_t}} & 0 & 0 & 0 \end{bmatrix}. \tag{5}$$

The matrix representing the uncertainties of the system can be written in diagonal form:

$$\Delta = diag\{ q_1, q_2, \dots, q_p \} \tag{6}$$

The state equation of the uncertain system can be written

$$\dot{x} = A_0 x + L \Delta N^T x + B_1 u_1 + B_2 u_2 \tag{7}$$

with state-vector:

$$x^T = [\, z_1 \;\; z_2 \;\; \dot{z}_1 \;\; \dot{z}_2 \,]$$

The remaining two vectors in Eq.7. can be considered as input vector of the disturbances acting on the system and the control input vector, respectively:

$$B_1^T = \begin{bmatrix} 0 & 0 & \frac{s_t}{m_t} & 0 \end{bmatrix}, \quad B_2^T = \begin{bmatrix} 0 & 0 & \frac{1}{m_t} & -\frac{1}{m_f} \end{bmatrix}$$

In this paper we will consider the vertical acceleration of the vehicle body as a measurable output of the system.

$$y_1 = C_1 x + D_{12} u_2 \tag{8}$$

where

$$C_1 = \begin{bmatrix} \frac{s_{f0}}{m_f} & -\frac{s_{f0}}{m_f} & 0 & 0 \end{bmatrix} \quad D_{12} = -\frac{1}{m_f}$$

The block diagram of the uncertain control system described by Eq.7. and Eq.8. can be seen in Figure 3.

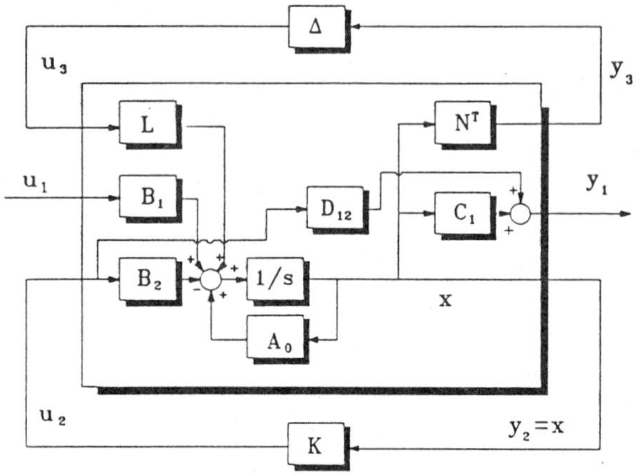

Figure 3 Block diagram of the uncertain problem

3. H_∞ SOLUTION OF THE CONTROL PROBLEM

Related to the minimax control value on u_1 is supposed to maximize while u_2 is supposed to minimize the following cost function:

$$J_\infty(u_1, u_2, \gamma) = \lim_{T\to\infty} \frac{1}{T} \int_0^T [\, x^T Q_0 x + u_2^T R_0 u_2 - \gamma^2 u_1^T u_1 \,] \, dt \tag{9}$$

The solution is obtained by using direct state-feedback

$$K_\infty^T(\gamma) = R_0^{-1} B_2^T X_\infty(\gamma) \tag{10}$$

where the X_∞ is the positive semi-definit solution of the following ARE (c.f. in [2]):

$$X_\infty A_0 + A_0^T X_\infty + Q_0 + X_\infty \left(\frac{1}{\gamma^2} B_1 B_1^T - B_2 R_0^{-1} B_2^T\right) X_\infty = 0 \tag{11}$$

where $Q_0 = C_1^T C_1$ and $R_0 = D_{12}^T D_{12}$ for the sake of simlicity. The controller described by Eq.10. is admissible if the Hamiltonian matrix relating to ARE in Eq.11. does not have roots on the imaginary axis, that is the closed-loop system is stable. As it can be seen from Eq.11. in this case there is no unique solution to the control design problem: finding the minimal value of γ needs an iteration. For the nominal parameter values given in Table 1 the minimal value of $\gamma_{min} = 1250$, which means that in the transfer function in acceleration of vehicle body the highest peak is 1250 ($1/s^2$) as it can be seen in Figure 4.

Parameter	Symbol	Unit	Value
Tyre mass	m_t	kg	33
Body mass	m_f	kg	200
Suspension stiffness	s_f	N/m	9000
Nominal tyre stiffness	s_{t0}	N/m	250000
Variation	δs_t	N/m	100000

Table 1 Parameters of the quarter-car model

As it can be seen in Figure 4, the standard LQR solution gives very poor stability for the same set of the parameters and the maximum gain of the transfer function is higher than 1250. On the other hand it can be seen that in some ranges (4...8 Hz and above 11 Hz) the gain of the robust solution is much higher than it would be required, it is the price of the robustness: the bandwidth of the system becomes larger.

4. ROBUST LQR (RLQR) PROBLEM

As it was shown earlier the standard LQR/LQG controller has poor robustness in face of the uncertainties (see in Figure 2). In case of direct state-feedback H_∞ problem the robustness is ensured by the Small Gain Theorem. In this part the robust solution to the LQR design method is adopted to the problem of the active suspension system. The problem of the RLQR solution is investigated [10]. Further examination of some properties of the RLQR solution can be found in [1]. The RLQR controller can be written as

$$K_{RLQR}^T(\lambda) = R_0^{-1} B_2^T X_{RLQR}(\lambda) \tag{12}$$

where the $X_{RLQR}(\lambda)$ is the positive semi-definit solution of the following RARE (if exists):

$$X_{RLQR} A_0 + A_0^T X_{RLQR} + (Q_0 + \lambda N N^T) - X_{RLQR}\left(B_2 R_0^{-1} B_2^T - \frac{1}{\lambda} L L^T\right) X_{RLQR} = 0 \tag{13}$$

The performance index of the RLQR problem can be written

$$J_{RLQR}(u_2, d, \lambda) = \lim_{T\to\infty} \frac{1}{T} \int_0^T [\, x^T (Q_0 + \lambda N N^T) x + u_2^T R_0 u_2 + \frac{1}{\lambda} x^T X_{RLQR} L L^T X_{RQLR} x \,] \, dt \tag{14}$$

where $d(t)$ is defined in Eq.17. Examining the performance index Eq.14. the following can be concluded:

(*i*) the second term in Eq.14. means that the potential energy in the uncertain spring which is minimized. Expanding this term in case of quarter-car model (assuming that there is no road input) the following expression can be obtained:

$$x^T N N^T x = \frac{1}{m_t} s_t z_1^2 \tag{15}$$

that is proportional to the potential energy stored in the uncertain spring. The controller minimizes the potential energy in the uncertain tyre and tries to return back to the equilibrium position the perturbed system as fast as possible.

(*ii*) The last term in performance index Eq.14. is similar to the H_∞ term in performance index Eq.9. and it has the same function: tries to minimize the effect of the disturbances arising from the uncertainties. It is a kind of "worst case disturbance" term considering the parameter uncertainties:

$$\frac{1}{\lambda} x^T X_{RLQR} L L^T X_{RLQR} x = -\lambda d_{RLQR}^T d_{RLQR} \tag{16}$$

The free parameter λ means the trade-off between the above mentioned two effect of the RLQR controller, i.e. increasing the value of λ the system becomes more robust, decreasing it the performance of the system will be better but the robustness is lost as it can be seen in Figure 4.

5. COMBINED H_∞/RLQR PROBLEM

According to the form of the performance index Eq.14. of RLQR problem the optimal controler minimizes the potential energy in the location of the uncertainty and it tries to attenuate the effect of the "internal disturbances" coming from the parameter uncertainty. The external disturbance rejection of the RLQR controler was investigated by [1] for some special cases, the worst case design for joint external and internal disturbance attenuation was not considered. Hereby the authors combine the H_∞ and RLQR procedures where both the parametric uncertainties and the external disturbances are considered in the design procedure. Define the "actual disturbance" in Eq.7. arising from the structured uncertainties as follows:

$$d(t) = \Delta N^T x(t) \tag{17}$$

The resulted control problem is summarized in the following Theorem. Similar form of the scaled H_∞ problem is investigated in [16].

Theorem. Consider the uncertain system described by

$$\dot{x}(t) = A_0 x(t) + L d(t) + B_1 u_1(t) + B_2 u_2(t) \tag{18}$$

where the $u_1(t)$ is the external disturbance, $d(t)$ stands for the internal disturbance defined by Eq.17. and the $u_2(t)$ is the control input. Controler minimizing the following performance index at the supremum of both external and internal disturbances

$$J(u_1^*, d^*, u_2^*, \lambda, \gamma) = \lim_{T\to\infty} \frac{1}{T} \int_0^T [x^T(Q_0 + \lambda N N^T) x + u_2^T R_0 u_2 - \gamma^2 u_1^T u_1 - \lambda d^T d]\, dt \tag{19}$$

can be written as

$$u_2^*(t) = -K_{H_\infty/RLQR}^T x(t) \tag{20}$$

where

$$K_{H_\infty/RLQR}^T(\gamma, \lambda) = R_0^{-1} B_2^T X_{H_\infty/RLQR}(\gamma, \lambda) \tag{21}$$

and the $X_{H_\infty/RLQR}$ is the positive semi-definit solution of the following ARE:

$$A_0^T X_{H_\infty/RLQR} + X_{H_\infty/RLQR} A_0 + (Q_0 + \lambda N N^T) + X_{H_\infty/RLQR} \left[\frac{1}{\gamma^2} B_1 B_1^T + \frac{1}{\lambda} L L^T - B_2 R_0^{-1} B_2^T \right] X_{H_\infty/RLQR} = 0 \tag{22}$$

Proof. Assume that (A,B_1), (A,L) and (A,B_2) are controllable. This conditions ensure that the optimal controler u_2^* exists. Denote the "external" worst case disturbance by u_1^* and the "internal" worst case disturbance by d^*. The usual saddle point condition can be written as

$$J(u_1^*, d^*, u_2) \geq J(u_1^*, d^*, u_2^*) \geq J(u_1, d, u_2^*)$$

Defining an appropriate input matrices the problem yields formally the same results as a standard H_∞ control problem.□

The worst case disturbance can be written as

$$\hat{u}_1^* = \frac{1}{\gamma^2} \hat{B}_1^T X_{H_\infty/RLQR} x = \frac{1}{\gamma^2} B_1^T X_{H_\infty/RLQR} x + \frac{1}{\lambda} L^T X_{H_\infty/RLQR} x \tag{23}$$

As it can be seen in Eq.23. the first term is the worst case disturbance due to the external road excitation and the second term is the worst case disturbance due to the parametric uncertainties. If we neglect either the external disturbance attenuation or the consideration of the structured uncertainties in the design the controller will be identical either to the H_∞ control problem or to the RLQR problem, respectively.

The performance index means that the controller tries to minimize the effect of the disturbances acting on the system due to the parameter uncertainty and external disturbance due to the road excitation and makes the system robust via the intelligent choice of weighting matrices containing information about the structure of the uncertainties. It can be seen the finding the stabilizing solution always needs two parameter iteration and the most suitable controller is a trade-off between the robustness and performance.

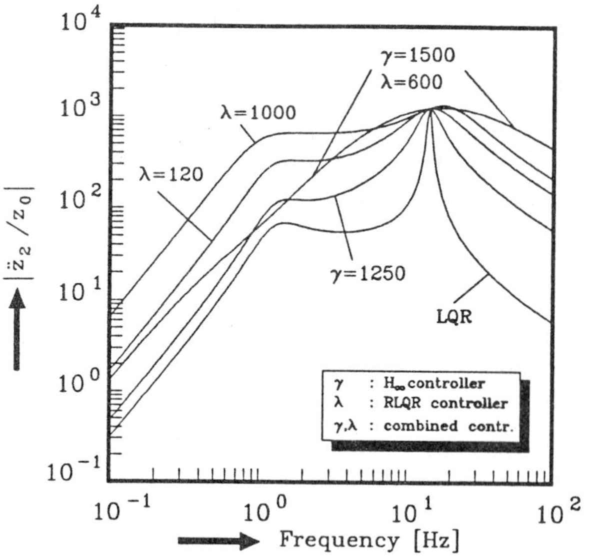

Figure 4 Comparison of several control strategies

One can deduct from the above contribution that the controller design is a trade-off between the robustness and performance requirements and there is no unique optimal controller exists and its computation always needs one or two parameter iteration.

3. CONCLUSIONS

In the paper the authors directed attention to the problems of the standard LQR/LQG strategies used in the design of an active wheel suspension system. It was shown that the controller designed by means of LQR/LQG does not give the optimal behaviour of the system when structured parametric uncertainty presents in the system which results in the need for the robust control design. In the first case the pure H_∞ control problem is formulated and solved. The aim of the control system design is the external disturbance attenuation. The stability robustness of this controller is ensured by the Small-Gain Theorem. In the second part of the paper the structured parametric uncertainty is considered in the design procedure solving the Robust LQR problem. In this case the controller minimizes the potential energy in the location of the uncertainty and tries to reject the internal disturbances arising from the uncertainties. There is a free parameter indicating a trade-off between these two above mentioned facts. On the basis of two methods a modification of the robust control design procedure is proposed. The joint internal and external worst case design procedure is derived and proven. In this case both the external disturbance attenuation and the structured uncertainties are considered in the design. The resulted controller is not unique, its computation always need two parameter iteration.

ACKNOWLEDGEMENTS

This research project was supported by **Hungarian Scientific Research Fund** (OTKA 102-061 and F-4084) and by **For the Hungarian Science Foundation** of the Hungarian Creditbank.

REFERENCES

[1] Douglas, J.; Athans, M. "Robust linear quadratic design with respect to parametric uncertainty", Proc. ACC, Chicago, 1992.

[2] Doyle, J.C.; Glover, K.; Khargonekar, P.; Francis, B. "State-space solution to standard H_2 and H_∞ control problems", Proc. American Contr. Conf., Atlanta, GA., 1988.

[3] Fulton, T.O.L. "Design of active suspension system for road vehicles using linear quadratic control law and reduced order observer", C Sc Theses, MTA TMB., 1988.

[4] Gordon, T.J.; Marsch, C.; Milsted, M.G. "A comparision of adaptive LQG and nonlinear controllers for vehicle suspension system", Vehicle System Dynamics, vol. 20, pp.321-340., 1991.

[5] Gordon, T., Venhovens, P., Palkovics, L., Truscott, T., Sharp, R. "Second generation approaches to active and semi-active suspension control system design", Submitted to IAVSD Conference, China, 1993.

[6] Hac, A. "Stochastic optimal control of vehicles with elastic body and active suspension", Trans. ASME J.of Dynamic Systems, Measurement and Control, Vol. 108, pp. 106-110., 1986.

[7] Hedrick, J.K.; Wormley, D.N. "Active suspensions for ground transport vehicles - a state of the art review", ASME AMO, Vol. 15, pp. 21-40., 1975.

[8] Michelberger, P.; Bokor, J.; Keresztes, A.; Várlaki, P. "Design of active suspension system for road vehicles: an eigenstructure assignment approach", SAE Paper No. 905146., 1990.

[9] Palkovics, L., Venhovens, P.Th.J. "Investigation on stability and possible chaotic motions in the controlled wheel suspension system", Vehicle System Dynamics, vol. 21, 1992.

[10] Petersen, I.R.; Hollot, C.V. "A Ricatti equation approach to the stabilization of uncertain linear systems", Automatica, vol. 22(4), pp.397-411., 1986.

[11] Sharp, R.S.; Hassan, S.A. "Performance and design considerations for dissipative semi-active suspension systems for automobiles", Proc. Instn. Mech. Engrs. Vol. 201(D2), pp. 1-5., 1987.

[12] Sunwoo, M.; Cheok, C.; Huang, J. "Application of model reference control to active suspension system", 1990 ACC, San Diego, pp.1340-1346., 1990.

[13] Thompson, A.G.; Pearce, C.E.M. "Optimal suspension for an automobile on a random road", SAE Prepr., No. 790478., 1979.

[14] Venhovens, P.J.Th. "Active and semi-active automotive suspension systems. Quarter car model analysis.", University report, TU Delft, Rp.nr. 92.3.VT.2935., 1992.

[15] Ulsoy, A.G.; Hrovat, D. "Stability robustness of LQG active suspensions", ACC, San Diego, pp.1347-1356., 1990.

[16] Xie, L.; De Souza, C.E. "Robust H_∞ control for linear systems with norm-bounded time varying uncertainty", IEEE Trans. on Automatic Contr., vol. 37, no.8., 1992.

Proceedings of the
American Control Conference
San Francisco, California • June 1993

Including the Force Generation Process in Active Suspension Control Formulation

G.H. Engelman
Ford Motor Company
Alpha Simultaneous Engineering

G. Rizzoni
The Ohio State University
Department of Mechanical Engineering

Abstract

In this paper, the dynamic behavior of hydraulic, quarter car suspensions are investigated by using linear models. These linear models include the sprung and unsprung masses with a linear visco-elastic model of the tire as well as a hydraulic cylinder and two stage electro-hydraulic servovalve model.

Using a reduced order linear model, the active suspension control problem is addressed using linear optimal control. Specifically, the linear quadratic regulator formulation is used to formulate a closed loop control strategy for the suspension with the force generation process considered. Results show that the force generation process is dynamically coupled with the suspension system and should be considered when formulating the control strategy.

Introduction

Even though the active suspension concept has great potential for advancing suspension technology, it has not yet achieved ideal characteristics. The difficulties arise in realizing the forces on the suspension and body required to achieve isolation and good handling. Most current control efforts consider what force is required to meet performance objectives, but do not address the realization of these forces [1-5]. A comprehensive non-linear simulation of a hydraulic quarter car suspension along with some experimental validation was presented in [6], however the control problem was not formally addressed. Due to the complexity of this problem and the lack of rigorous control development, a large portion of the control advances in active suspension technology have been made by trial and error methods.

The Ideal, Active Suspension Model

Understanding the compromise that must be made in conventional suspension design, a motivation for an alternative design becomes evident. The alternative to be investigated in this work is that of the "fully active" suspension. In particular, this system will be configured in what is typically known as the broad bandwidth design. This is characterized by having the suspension spring and the hydraulic actuator in parallel rather than in series. To investigate the possibilities of this "fully active" suspension concept , consider eliminating the shock absorber and replacing it with an ideal source of force that can be determined by a suitable algorithm. The resulting model can be seen in Figure 1. Applying Newton's law to the masses results in (1) and (2). These equations now represent an ideal active suspension since no mention of how this force is to be produced is mentioned.

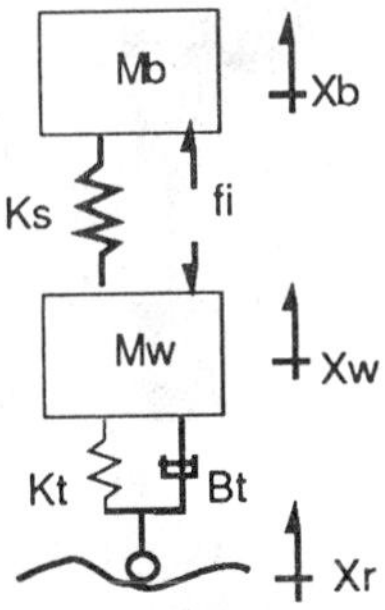

Figure 1: Ideal Fully Active Suspension Model

$$M_w\ddot{x}_w = K_t(x_r - x_w) + B_t(\dot{x}_r - \dot{x}_w) - K_s(x_w - x_b) - f_i \quad (1)$$

$$M_b\ddot{x}_b = K_s(x_w - x_b) + f_i \quad (2)$$

$$f_i = K_{ol}(x_w - x_b) + B_{ol}(\dot{x}_w - \dot{x}_b) - B_{sh}\dot{x}_b \quad (3)$$

Let the control force be defined as in (3) to be comprised of spring and shock absorber terms as well as a skyhook damper term. Note that any force could be specified here but this particular choice allows "conventional" modifications to the suspension through the spring and shock terms as well as "active" modifications in the form of the inertially referenced skyhook damper term. For the remainder of this work, this specification of the force command shall be distinguished as the "outer-loop" control scheme. This will eliminate confusion between the process of determining what control force should be applied by the actuator ("outer-loop control") and the process of actually generating this desired force ("inner-loop" control). Figure 2 shows the advantage of the skyhook damper on body accelerations or ride characteristics in the frequency domain. Notice that the primary "body bounce" resonant mode has been greatly attenuated without affecting the high frequency isolation of the sprung mass.

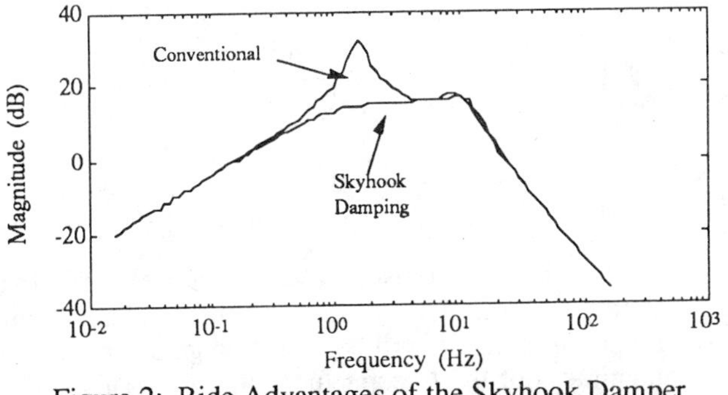

Figure 2: Ride Advantages of the Skyhook Damper

The Hydraulic Servo Model

To continue the model development, the previous linear suspension model will be modified to incorporate a hydraulic actuator and servovalve. The model to be studied in this section can be seen in Figure 3.

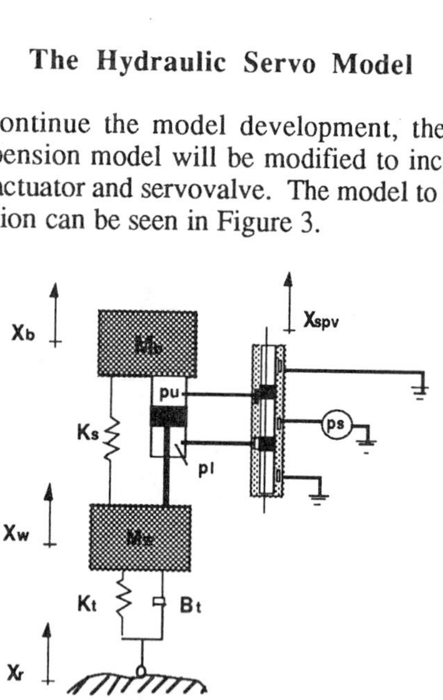

Figure 3: Hydraulic Suspension Schematic

Applying conservation of mass to the upper and lower cylinder volumes yields

$$C_d W x_{spv}\sqrt{\frac{2(ps-pu)}{\rho}} - A_p\frac{dxb}{dt} = \frac{V_u}{\beta}\frac{dpu}{dt} \quad (4)$$

$$-C_d W x_{spv}\sqrt{\frac{2(pl-pr)}{\rho}} + A_p\frac{dxb}{dt} = \frac{V_l}{\beta}\frac{dpl}{dt} \quad (5)$$

Linearizing using perturbations about operating points,

$$C_x x_{spv} + C_p(0 - p_u) - A_p\frac{d}{dt}(x_b) = \frac{V}{\beta}\frac{d}{dt}(p_u) \quad (6)$$

$$-C_x x_{spv} - C_p(p_l - 0) + A_p\frac{d}{dt}(x_b) = \frac{V}{\beta}\frac{d}{dt}(p_l) \quad (7)$$

and subtracting (7) from (6) yields

$$2C_x x_{spv} - 2\,Ap\frac{d}{dt}(x_b) = \frac{V}{\beta}\frac{d}{dt}(p_u - p_l) + Cp\,(p_u - p_l) \quad (8)$$

substituting $F = A_p(p_u - p_l)$,

$$2C_x x_{spv} + 2Ap\frac{d}{dt}(x_w - x_b) = \frac{V}{\beta Ap}\frac{d}{dt}(F) + \frac{Cp}{Ap}(F) \quad (9)$$

Applying Newton's law to the body and wheel masses yields

$$Mw\frac{d^2}{dt^2}(xw) = K_t(x_r - x_w) + B_t\frac{d}{dt}(x_r - x_w) - K_s(x_w - x_b) - F \quad (10)$$

$$Mb\frac{d^2}{dt^2}(xb) = F + K_s(xw - xb) \quad (11)$$

In order to gain insight from this model, typical values for the variables will be used and the resultant frequency domain information will be presented graphically using the magnitudes of the transfer function only. This will allow qualitative interpretation of the system characteristics . If the body acceleration as a function of road displaceme velocity is considered with spool valve position fixed, t graph of Figure 4 results. As can be seen, two prima resonances can still be seen in the suspension. Howev due to the stiffness of the oil column in the actuator, the resonances now appear as a 3 Hz vehicle bouncing on t tire mode and an 80 Hz body bouncing on the hydrau cylinder mode instead of the more familiar 1 Hz bo bounce and 10 Hz wheel hop modes.

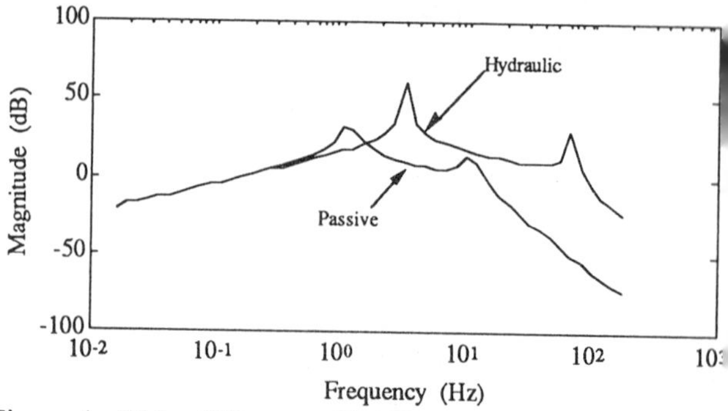

Figure 4: Ride of Uncontrolled Hydraulic Suspension

In addition to looking at road disturbance inputs an their effects on body accelerations, the ability of the spo valve to generate desired forces in the actuator should b investigated. If the open-loop transfer function betwee spool valve displacement and actuator force is considere the frequency response of Figure 5 results. It is interestin to note that the spool valve readily excites the resona modes of the mechanical suspension elements. I particular, the high frequency vibrations associated with th stiffness of the oil column are sensitive to spool valv motions. In addition to being highly sensitive at som frequencies, the actuator forces show lower sensitivity t spool valve motions near 1 and 10 Hz.

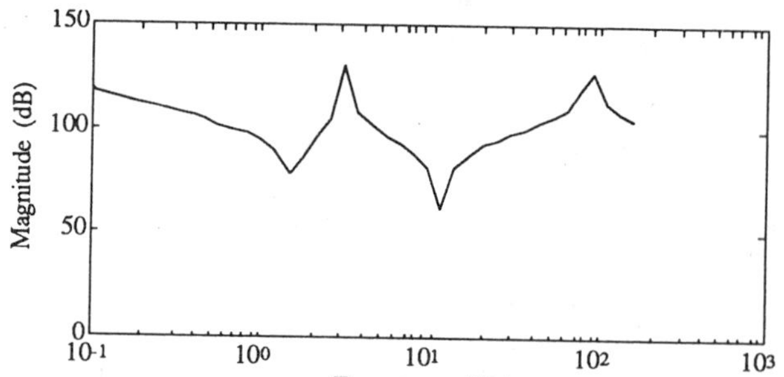

Figure 5: Force Response to Spool Displacement

Completion of the Force Generation Process

Up to this point, the modeling has been focused only on the interaction from the main spool valve to the force generated in the actuator as well as the disturbance added by the road. Another important aspect of the force generation process is the actuation of the spool valve. In the case of the hydraulic suspension, this takes the form of a torque motor interacting with a hydraulic amplifier. Solving (12) and (13) indicates that the valve dynamics are third order and will therefore contribute three poles to the force generation process.

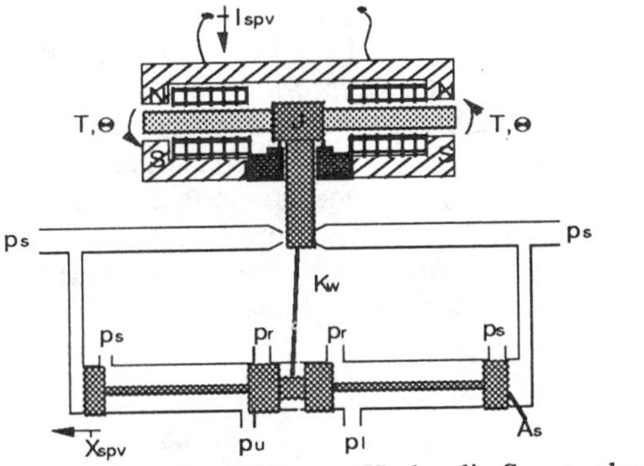

Figure 6: Two Stage Electro-Hydraulic Servovalve

$$J_f \frac{d^2\theta}{dt^2} + B_f \frac{d\theta}{dt} + K_f\,\theta + K_w x_{spv} = K_t i_{spv} \qquad (12)$$

$$K_h\theta = A_s \frac{dx_{spv}}{dt} \qquad (13)$$

A Classical Perspective on Model Reduction

Previously, a model of the active suspension was developed to represent the process of spool valve displacements generating forces in the hydraulic cylinder. If proportional feedback of force were applied to this system, a root locus plot would have the basic shape as seen in Figure 7 (note that this plot is not in proportion but shows the basic directions that the closed loop poles would move). Clearly this system is inherently stable since no poles can migrate to the right half plane.

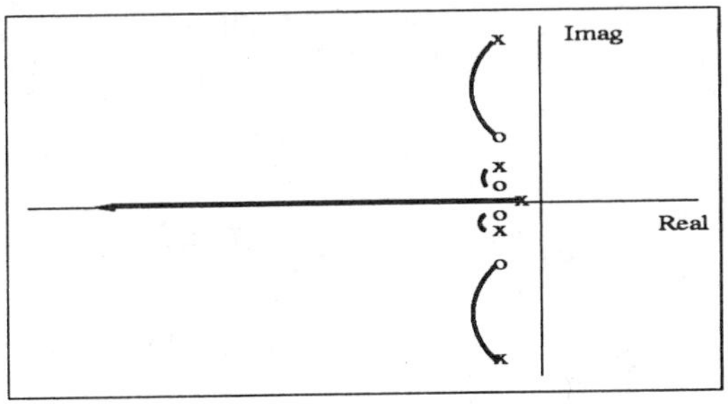

Figure 7: Root Locus for Proportional Force Control

It was acknowledged that some sort of electro-mechanical actuator would be needed in order to implement computer control of the spool valve. The model of the electro-hydraulic two stage servovalve resulted in a model from torque motor command current to spoolvalve displacement. Thus the actuator for the spool will add three poles to the force generation system. If these poles are added to the system, the loci of the characteristic equation migrate as in Figure 8. The importance of the valve dynamics can be easily seen . The inherently stable system of Figure 7 now tends very quickly toward instability with the addition of proportional force feedback control.

The highest resonant frequency in the mechanical system corresponds to 80 Hz and is represented in Figure 8 by the complex poles which tend toward the right half plane. The corresponding highest resonant frequency in the valve dynamics is 815 Hz and is represented in Figure 8 by the complex poles tending toward infinity on the left side of

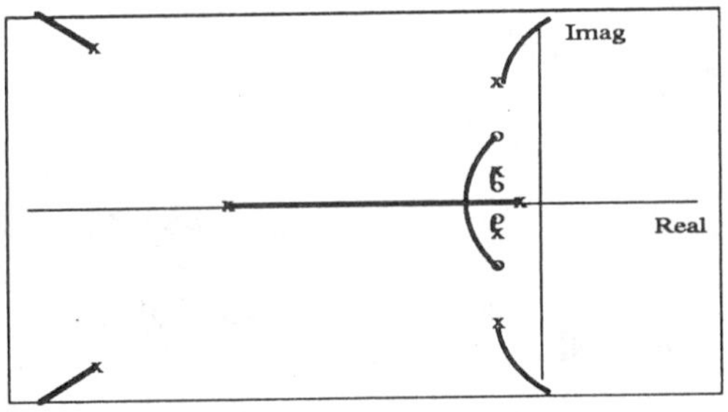

Figure 8: Root Locus with Valve Dynamics

the plot. Due to the large difference in relative speed of these dynamics, the present model could neglect the high frequency poles of the valve dynamics without a significant decrease in modeling accuracy and thereby reduce the computational size of the problem. If the valve dynamics are modeled as first order, the root locus of the system would appear as in Figure 9 Note that the general shape of the root locus has been preserved indicating that the model reduction was reasonable. With this model of the force production system, the formulation of the LQR problem can proceed.

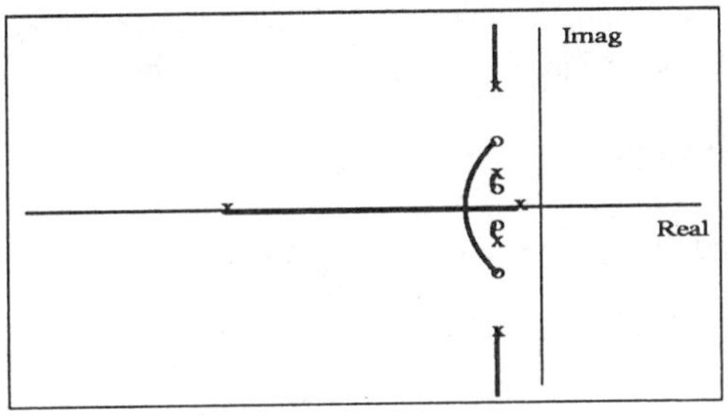

Figure 9: Root Locus with First Order Valve Dynamics

Derivation of the State Equations

Using the results from the model reduction in the previous section, the dynamic equations for the system can now be expressed as:

$$2C_x x_{spv} + 2Ap \frac{d}{dt}(x_w - x_b) = \frac{V}{\beta A_p}\frac{d}{dt}(F) + \frac{Cp}{A_p}(F) \qquad (14)$$

$$M_w \frac{d^2}{dt^2}(xw) = K_t(x_r - x_w) + B_t\frac{d}{dt}(x_r - x_w) - K_s(x_w - x_b) - F \qquad (15)$$

$$M_b \frac{d^2}{dt^2}(x_b) = F + K_s(x_w - x_b) \qquad (16)$$

$$\tau\frac{d}{dt}(x_{spv}) + x_{spv} = K_v i_{spv} \qquad (17)$$

Defining the vectors

$$\underline{x} = [\ F\ \ (xr-xw)\ \ \dot{x}w\ \ (xw-xb)\ \ (\dot{x}w-\dot{x}b)\ \ xspv\ ]^T \qquad (18)$$

$$\underline{u} = [\ ispv\ ] \qquad (19)$$

$$\underline{d} = [\ \dot{x}r\ ] \qquad (20)$$

equations (14-17) can now be expressed as

$$\dot{\underline{x}} = A\underline{x} + B\underline{u} + W\underline{d} \quad (21)$$
$$\underline{y} = C\underline{x} + D\underline{u} \quad (22)$$

Linear Quadratic Regulator Theory

Given a linear system with full feedback of a normalized state vector described by

$$\dot{\underline{z}} = T^{-1}AT\underline{z} + T^{-1}B\underline{u} \quad (23)$$
$$\underline{y} = CT\underline{z} + D\underline{u} \quad (24)$$

then the linear, optimal regulator problem consists of finding a control law

$$\underline{u} = -K\underline{z} \quad (25)$$

which minimizes the performance index

$$J = \lim_{t \to \infty} E\,[\, z^T(t)\, Q\, z(t) + u^T(t)\, R\, u(t)\,] \quad (26)$$

where E is the expectation operator and Q and R are positive definite symmetric matrices. It can be shown that the steady state solution to this problem involves solving the algebraic Riccati equation

$$(T^{-1}AT)^T P + P(T^{-1}AT) + Q - P(T^{-1}B)R^{-1}(T^{-1}B)^T P = 0 \quad (27)$$

and that the feedback law is satisfied by

$$K = -R^{-1}(T^{-1}B)^T P\underline{z} \quad (28)$$

or in terms of the original state variable $\underline{x}$

$$K = -R^{-1}(T^{-1}B)^T P T^{-1}\underline{x} \quad (29)$$

This formulation of the control problem presents a convenient method for dealing with the multiple feedback of the so called "inner" and "outer" loop control problems and eliminates the coupling problem when treating these separately. A graphical interpretation of this regulator problem can be seen in Figure 10.

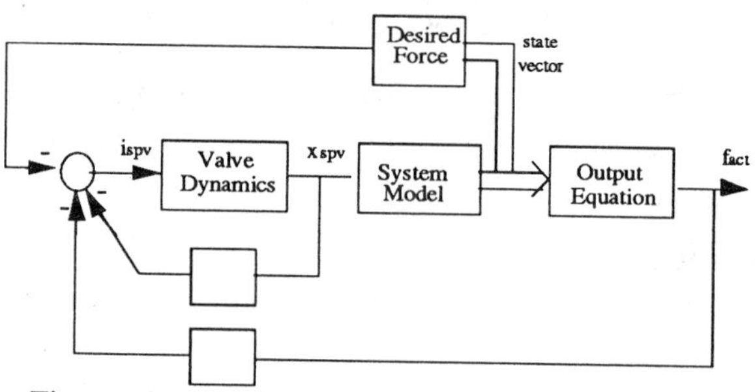

Figure 10: Graphical Interpretation of the Regulator

Results of the Controller Design

Figure 11 shows the body acceleration response of the closed loop (solid) to an integrated white noise road profile and compares this with a passive system (dashed). The vibration levels no longer show the dominance of the hydraulic resonances as was the case with the open lo system. The plots of Figure 12 show the system respon to a 3 inch step road profile. These responses represen very severe input to the suspension and therefore can used to appropriately size components of the hydrau supply. It is important to note that these results represe only one solution of the optimal control problem. Mo solutions as well as validation of the linear models using non-linear model can be found in [9].

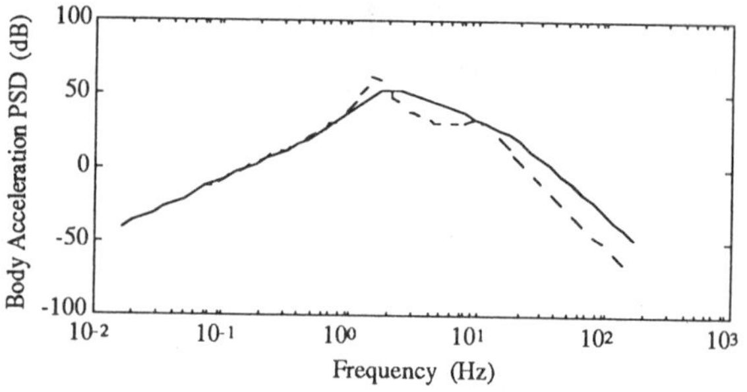

Figure 11: Ride Quality

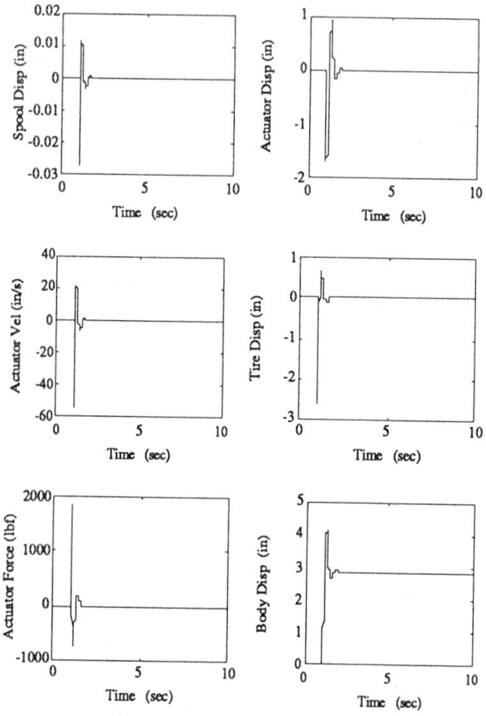

Figure 12: System Step Response

Conclusions

In this work, linearized models of a hydraulic active suspension were developed. The open loop characteristics of the system revealed a far from ideal force generation capability dominated by resonances around 3 and 80 Hz. These represent the familiar body bounce and wheel hop modes normally associated with suspension systems. These frequencies vary from the traditional 1 and 10 Hz frequencies due to the stiffness of the oil column in the actuator. In addition to the resonances, two anti-resonances or notches were found in the open loop force generation plant due to the mechanical resonances of the suspension system. This interaction of the mechanical resonances with the characteristics of the hydraulic system is an important issue for control. Namely, the "inner" loop and "outer" loop controllers considered in most previous works are in fact dynamically coupled and cannot be treated separately.

Using ideas from classical control, the importance of the servovalve dynamics on system behavior was made evident. Namely, the high frequency dynamics of the torque motor cause the system to tend toward instability. This conclusion again solidifies the need to consider actuator dynamics in control system design.

Using linear optimal control theory, a controller was designed that incorporated the effects of the coupling between the "inner" and "outer" control loops. Closed loop system performance failed to achieve the desired characteristics of an active suspension. This was caused by the hydraulic resonances dominating the controller design. In order to control these resonant modes of the system, the force produced in the actuator had to be kept at a minimum. Since the actuator force is the means by which the system is controlled, this constraint of small forces reduced the amount of active control that could be achieved. In fact, as the force in the actuator was kept low by the controller, the system behaved with the characteristics of a passive suspension with the actuator functioning as a shock absorber.

Future Work

Future work on the active suspension could endeavor to dampen the hydraulic resonances which dominate the current control design. By dealing with these resonances in the hardware, the controller would be more free to generate active control forces without degrading the passenger ride characteristics. One method of controlling the high frequency vibrations would be to introduce a bushing into the system model. This would add another degree of freedom to the suspension design and allow a greater roll off of vibrations at the high frequencies. This bushing would also introduce a new resonance and anti-resonance into the force generation process thus complicating the control design. However, the exact effects this would have on performance remain unclear. Another possible means of dealing with the resonances could come from within the control strategy. Gupta [10] introduced weighting of the LQR problem in the frequency domain. This allows selected frequencies to be penalized more than others. Preliminary studies on simplified models showed that this method can work although by penalizing certain frequencies, other frequencies receive less control action. Further work could try to implement this strategy by penalizing the resonances while letting frequencies of little or no interest to suspension performance receive less control effort.

Nomenclature

Xw	= wheel displacement
Xb	= body displacement
Xr	= road profile displacement
Xspv	= spool valve displacement
Ps	= hydraulic supply pressure
Pr	= hydraulic return pressure
Pu	= hydraulic pressure in upper chamber of cylinder
Pl	= hydraulic pressure in lower chamber of cylinder
Mw	= 1/4 of unsprung mass of vehicle
Mb	= 1/4 of sprung mass of vehicle
Kt	= tire stiffness
Bt	= viscous damping associated with tire
Ks	= suspension spring stiffness
Cd	= orifice discharge coefficient
Cx	= flow gain for spool displacements
Cp	= flow gain for orifice pressure drop
W	= width of rectangular flow port
Ap	= area of actuator piston
Vu	= volume of upper cylinder chamber
Vl	= volume of lower cylinder chamber
β	= effective fluid bulk modulus
J_f	= torque motor rotor inertia
B_f	= net damping on armature/flapper
K_f	= net stiffness on armature/flapper
K_w	= torque motor feedback wire stiffness
K_t	= torque motor gain
K_h	= nozzle/flapper flow gain
A_s	= flow area of spool
τ	= time constant for first order valve model

References

[1] D. Karnopp, "Active Damping in Road Vehicle Suspension Systems," Vehicle System Dynamics,12,1983,pp.291-311.
[2] A.G. Thompson., "An Active Suspension System with Optimal Linear State Feedback," Vehicle System Dynamics, Vol. 5, pp. 187-203, 1976.
[3] L.R. Ray, "Robust Linear Optimal Control Laws for Active Suspension Systems," DE-Vol. 40, Advanced Automotive Technologies, ASME 1991.
[4] S. Kiriczi and R. Kashani, "Robust Control of Active Car Suspension with Model Uncertainty using H_∞ Methods," DE-Vol. 40, Advanced Automotive Technologies, ASME 1991.
[5] D.A. Crolla and M.B.A. Abdel-Hady, "Active Suspension Control; Performance Comparisons Using Control Laws Applied to a Full Vehicle Model," Vehicle System Dynamics, 20, pp. 107-120,1991.
[6] R. Ben Mrad, J.A. Levitt, and S.D. Fassois, "Modeling and Simulation of an Automobile Hydraulic Active Suspension System," DE-Vol. 40, Advanced Automotive Technologies, ASME 1991.
[7] D. McCloy and H.R. Martin,"Control of Fluid Power: Analysis and Design 2nd Ed.," Wiley and Sons, New York, 1980
[8] Brian D.O. Anderson and John B. Moore, "Optimal Control: Linear Quadratic Methods," Prentice Hall, Englewood Cliffs, 1990
[9] G.H. Engelman, " Modeling and Control of a Hydraulic, Broad Bandwidth Active Suspension," Master's Thesis, The Ohio State University, 1992.
[10] Gupta, "Frequency Shaped Cost Functionals," Vol.3, Journal of Guidance and Control, pp.529-35, 1980

Proceedings of the
American Control Conference
San Francisco, California • June 1993

Adaptive Observer for Active Automotive Suspensions[1]

R. Rajamani and J.K. Hedrick

Department of Mechanical Engineering
University of California at Berkeley
Berkeley, CA 94720.

Abstract

An adaptive observer for a class of nonlinear systems is developed. Conditions for convergence of state estimates and parameters are presented. The developed theory is used for observer-based parameter identification in the active suspension system of an automobile. The observer uses measurements from two accelerometers and an LVDT. It adapts on dry friction which is usually present in significant magnitudes in hydraulic actuators of active suspensions. Experimental results on a half-car suspension test rig are presented.

Nomenclature

k_s	spring stiffness
b_s	damping coefficient
m_s	sprung mass
m_u	unsprung mass
μ	friction coefficient
x	state
y	measured outputs
z_r	road disturbance input
u	control input
L_∞	set of finite ∞-norm functions
L_2	set of finite 2-norm functions

I. Active Automotive Suspension

1.1 Introduction

An automotive suspension supports the vehicle body on the axles. The vehicle body is represented by the "sprung" mass m_s and the tire and axles by the "unsprung" mass m_u in the quarter-car model shown in Fig. 1. The spring, shock absorber and the variable force element placed between the sprung and unsprung masses constitute the suspension. The tire is modeled as a spring with stiffness k_t and its damping is assumed to be negligible. For automobiles with independent suspensions four such quarter-cars can be used to represent the entire car.

The presence of the variable-force element F_A is what differentiates an active or semi-active suspension from a passive one [4].

[1] This work supported by a grant from the Ford Motor Company

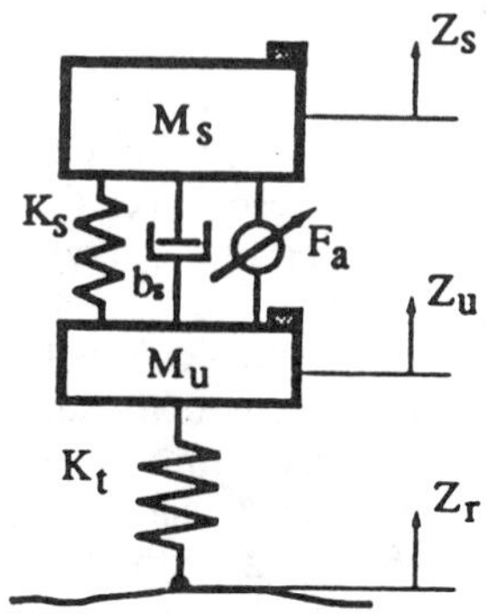

Fig. 1 Quarter-car Suspension

This element is used to generate a time-varying force that in some measure compensates for the uneven road that keeps disturbing the system.

In the case of an active suspension the variable force element is usually a spool-valve controlled hydraulic actuator (Fig. 2). Movement of the spool valve u causes high pressure hydraulic fluid to flow into one side of the piston. The pressure difference across the piston is what provides the force F_A to the suspension.

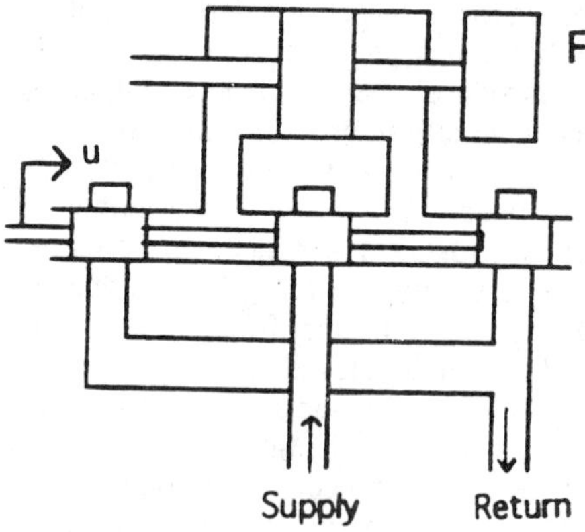

Fig. 2 Hydraulic Actuator

The relation between the spool valve movement u and the output force of this actuator F_A is dynamic and nonlinear [10] :

$$\dot{F}_A = c_1\, u\, \sqrt{c_2 - c_3\, sgn(u)\, F_A} - c_4\,(\dot{z}_s - \dot{z}_u) - c_5\, F_A \quad (1.1)$$

where c_i depend on various parameters of the actuator.

Movement of the piston inside the actuator is also opposed by friction between the piston seals and the cylinder wall. This friction is usually of a significant magnitude (> 200 N) and cannot be neglected.

To describe this system in state space we need five states in all :

$$x = \begin{Bmatrix} z_s - z_s \\ \dot{z}_s \\ z_u - z_r \\ \dot{z}_u \\ F_A \end{Bmatrix}$$

Considering the friction force and the actuator dynamics, the system in state space is :

$$\dot{x} = A\,x + \Phi\,(x,\,u) + b\;sgn(x_2 - x_4)\;\mu + \Gamma\;\dot{z}_r \qquad (1.2)$$

where

$$A = \begin{bmatrix} 0 & 1 & 0 & -1 & 0 \\ \dfrac{-k_s}{m_s} & \dfrac{-b_s}{m_s} & 0 & \dfrac{b_s}{m_s} & \dfrac{1}{m_s} \\ 0 & 0 & 0 & 1 & 0 \\ \dfrac{k_s}{m_u} & \dfrac{b_s}{m_u} & \dfrac{-k_t}{m_u} & \dfrac{-b_s}{m_u} & \dfrac{-1}{m_u} \\ 0 & -c_4 & 0 & c_4 & c_5 \end{bmatrix}$$

$$\Phi\,(x,\,u) = \begin{Bmatrix} 0 \\ 0 \\ 0 \\ 0 \\ c_1\,u\,\sqrt{c_2 - c_3\;sgn(u)\;x_5} \end{Bmatrix}$$

$$b = \begin{Bmatrix} 0 \\ \dfrac{-1}{m_s} \\ 0 \\ \dfrac{1}{m_u} \\ 0 \end{Bmatrix} \quad \text{and} \quad \Gamma = \begin{Bmatrix} 0 \\ 0 \\ -1 \\ 0 \\ 0 \end{Bmatrix}$$

A more complete model would include the ability of the friction to lock-up the system i.e. a calculation of the friction value when the relative velocity $(x_2 - x_4)$ is zero.

A simple and very effective vibration isolation strategy is to choose the desired time-varying force to be ([3], [5], [6]).

$$F_{sky} = g_{opt}\;\dot{z}_s \qquad (1.3)$$

This strategy is referred to as "sky-hook" damping. It attempts to attach a damper between the sprung mass and inertial space. As far as improvement of ride quality is concerned, sky-hook damping provide nearly as good a performance as full-state feedback does ([5], [6]).

To provide a net suspension force equal to F_{sky}, F_A must track the desired force of

$$F_{A_{des}} = F_{sky} + \mu\;sgn(x_2 - x_4)$$

Thus, the friction force must be canceled by the actuator at every instant of time so that the net force is equivalent to sky-hook damping. μ is therefore an important variable necessary for control. Even an error of 20% in the value of μ can lead to poor tracking with spikes present in the tracking error whenever the relative velocity changes sign.

Given μ and access to state variables, nonlinear control methods like sliding surface and feedback linearization can be used to obtain a control law with good tracking performance capabilities.

II. Adaptive Observer

Consider the class of nonlinear dynamical systems described by

$$\dot{x} = A\,x + \Phi\,(x,\,u) + b\,f(y)\;\theta \qquad (2.1a)$$

$$y = C\,x \qquad (2.1b)$$

where
$x \in R^n$, $y \in R^m$, $\theta \in R^p$, $f : R^m \to R^{sxp}$ $\Phi : R^n \to R^n$,
$b \in R^{nxs}$, $C \in R^{mxn}$

If

i) There exists a positive definite symmetric matrix P such that $b^T P = C$

ii) Φ is Lipschitz in x with Lipschitz constant γ.

iii) A gain matrix L can be chosen such that

$$\gamma < \frac{\lambda_{min}(Q)}{2\lambda_{max}(P)}$$

where Q is a positive definite symmetric matrix satisfying the Lyapunov equation

$$(A - L\,C)\,P + P\,(\,A - L\,C) \;=\; -Q$$

then the adaptive observer

$$\dot{\hat{x}} = A\,\hat{x} + \Phi\,(\hat{x},\,u) + b\,f(y)\;\hat{\theta} + L\,[\,y - C\,\hat{x}\,] \qquad (2.2a)$$

$$\dot{\hat{\theta}} = \gamma\,[\,y - C\,\hat{x}\,] \qquad (\gamma > 0) \qquad (2.2b)$$

is stable, $\tilde{x} \to 0$ as $t \to \infty$ and $b\,f(y)\;\tilde{\theta} \to 0$ as $t \to \infty$.

Proof :

Part A : Lyapunov Stability

Let $\tilde{x} = x - \hat{x}$ be the estimation error. The error dynamics are then given by

$$\dot{\tilde{x}} = (A - L\,C)\;\tilde{x} + \Phi(x,\,u) - \Phi(\hat{x},\,u) + b\,f(y)\;\tilde{\theta} \qquad (2.3)$$

Consider the Lyapunov function candidate

$$V = \tilde{x}^T\,P\,\tilde{x} + k\,\tilde{\theta}^T\,\tilde{\theta}$$

with P chosen so as to satisfy (i), $k \in R^+$.

$$\dot{V} = \tilde{x}^T\,[(A - L\,C)^T\,P + P\,(A - L\,C)]\;\tilde{x}$$
$$+\,2\,\tilde{x}^T\,P\,[\Phi(x,u) - \Phi(\hat{x},u)] + 2\,\tilde{\theta}^T\,f(y)^T\,b^T\,P\,\tilde{x} + 2\,k\,\tilde{\theta}^T\,\dot{\tilde{\theta}}$$

$$\dot{V} \le -\tilde{x}^T Q \tilde{x} + 2\gamma \lambda_{max}(P) \tilde{x}^T \tilde{x} + 2\tilde{\theta}^T f(y)^T b^T P \tilde{x} + 2k \tilde{\theta}^T \dot{\tilde{\theta}}$$

Choose L such that

$$\gamma < \frac{\lambda_{min}(Q)}{2\lambda_{max}(P)}$$

i.e.

$$\gamma - \frac{\lambda_{min}(Q)}{2\lambda_{max}(P)} = \beta > 0$$

Then

$$\dot{V} \le -\beta \tilde{x}^T \tilde{x} + 2\tilde{\theta}^T [f(y)^T b^T P \tilde{x} + k \dot{\tilde{\theta}}]$$

Choose

$$\dot{\tilde{\theta}} = -\frac{f(y)^T}{k} b^T P \tilde{x} = -\frac{f(y)^T}{k} C \tilde{x}$$

Hence

$$\dot{V} \le -\beta \tilde{x}^T \tilde{x}$$

and so the system is Lyapunov stable.

This implies $\tilde{x} \in L_\infty$ and $\tilde{\theta} \in L_\infty$.

Part B : Convergence of $\tilde{x}$

$$\dot{V} \le -\beta \tilde{x}^T \tilde{x}$$

Integrating

$$V(t) \le V(0) - \beta \int_0^t \tilde{x}^T \tilde{x}\, dt$$

Since $V(t) \in L_\infty$ and $V(0)$ is finite, this implies that $\tilde{x} \in L_2$.

Also, from eqn. (2.3) for $\dot{\tilde{x}}$, we see that $\dot{\tilde{x}} \in L_\infty$.

Thus,

$\tilde{x} \in L_\infty$, $\tilde{x} \in L_2$ and $\dot{\tilde{x}} \in L_\infty$.

Therefore, by Barbalat's Lemma [7], $\tilde{x} \to 0$.

Part C : Convergence of $\tilde{\theta}$

$$\int_0^\infty \ddot{\tilde{x}}\, dt = \lim_{t \to \infty} \dot{\tilde{x}}(t) - \dot{\tilde{x}}(0) = -\dot{\tilde{x}}(0)$$

which is finite.

Also, from eqn. (2.3), using the Lipschitz continuity of Φ, $\ddot{\tilde{x}}$ is uniformly continuous.

Hence, again by Barbalat's lemma [7], $\dot{\tilde{x}} \to 0$. From eqn. (2.3), this implies that $b\, f(y)\, \tilde{\theta} \to 0$.

III. Observer Design for the Suspension System

The active suspension system is a disturbance-affected nonlinear system. Due to the presence of the disturbance, $\dot{z}_r$, it is not of the form given by eqn. (2.1a). Further, the nonlinearity $\sqrt{c_2 - c_3\, sgn(u)\, F_A}$ is not globally Lipschitz. The results of sec. II are, therefore, not directly applicable to this system.

A globally stable observer with exponentially convergent error dynamics, even in the presence of the disturbance and the nonlinearity, can be designed by "decoupling". Such an observer for this system is presented in [1] and [2]. This observer, however, needs accurate values of the friction force F_f.

The results of sec. II will be used to construct an off-line observer-based method for identification of the friction magnitude. The value of friction obtained can then be used for control as well as by the decoupled observer of [1] for on-line state estimation. We shall choose the road input $\dot{z}_r$ to be zero. The system is excited by suitably changing u, the spool valve movement. On an actual automobile this amounts to keeping the car stationary and then exciting it by means of the hydraulic actuator.

The input u has to be properly chosen so that the term $\sqrt{c_2 - c_3\, sgn(u)\, F_A}$ is Lipschitz within the operating range. Note that this term is Lipschitz if F_A can be bounded to be strictly less than $\frac{c_2}{c_3}$. Physically, c_2 is a function of the supply pressure and F_A is guaranteed not to exceed $\frac{c_2}{c_3}$. It can however, easily equal this value. This is seen, for instance, when u is kept at a constant value. F_A rapidly approaches $\frac{c_2}{c_3}$.

Since the system is not being controlled, however, we have a complete freedom in choosing u and so we can ensure that the nonlinearity does remain Lipschitz.

Under these constraints, the active suspension system is exactly of the form (2.1a). We have

$$\theta = \mu$$

and

$$f(y) = sgn(\dot{z}_s - \dot{z}_u)$$

Since $b\, f(y)\, \tilde{\theta} \to 0$ for the adaptive observer, this automatically implies **parameter convergence** in the case of the active suspension system.

We shall use the same sensor measurements as in [1]. These are the sprung and unsprung mass accelerations $\ddot{z}_s$ and $\ddot{z}_u$ and the suspension deflection $z_s - z_u$. These are easily accessible and inexpensively measured.

Since $\ddot{z}_s$ and $\ddot{z}_u$ depend on μ(*i.e.*θ), they cannot be written in the form $y = C\,x$. We shall hence use $m_s \ddot{z}_s + m_u \ddot{z}_u$ and $z_s - z_u$ as our outputs

$$m_s \ddot{z}_s + m_u \ddot{z}_u = [0\ 0\ -k_t\ 0\ 0]\, x$$

$$z_s - z_u = [1\ 0\ 0\ 0\ 0]\, x$$

$sgn(\dot{z}_s - \dot{z}_u)$ is also needed by the observer. We will integrate $\ddot{z}_s - \ddot{z}_u$ in real-time and high pass filter it to obtain $\dot{z}_s - \dot{z}_u$.

A choice of

$$P = \begin{bmatrix} 1 & 0 & 0 & 0 & 0 \\ 0 & m_s & 0 & 0 & 0 \\ 0 & 0 & 1 & 0 & 0 \\ 0 & 0 & 0 & m_u & 0 \\ 0 & 0 & 0 & 0 & 1 \end{bmatrix}$$

ensures that $b^T P = C_1$ where

$$C_1 = [0\ -1\ 0\ 1\ 0]$$

A sinusoidal excitation at 2 hz with an amplitude of 3.75×10^{-5} was used. F_A with this input takes a maximum value of 600 N. The Lipschitz constant under these conditions is $\gamma = 0.0086$.

The observer gain matrix

$$L = \begin{bmatrix} 5 & 0 \\ 0 & 0 \\ 0 & -0.01 \\ 0 & -1 \\ 0 & 0 \end{bmatrix}$$

yields

$$\frac{\lambda_{min}(Q)}{2\ \lambda_{max}(P)} = 0.0172$$

ensuring that inequality (ii) is satisfied and making $(A - L\ C)$ stable.

IV. Experimental Results

Experimental performance of the above design on a half-car suspension test rig is shown in Figs. 3-6. A comparison of actual and estimated actuator forces is shown in Fig. 3. A plot of actual vs estimated tire force is shown in Fig. 4 and a comparison of actual and estimated sprung mass velocities is shown in Fig. 5. The state estimates , after the quick transient, are seen to be excellent. Variation of the estimated friction magnitude ($\hat{\mu}$) is shown in Fig. 6. An initial value of $\hat{\mu}$=400 was used. $\hat{\mu}$ is seen to converge rapidly to a steady value of around 240 N. The parameter convergence algorithm was modified so as to make the estimate value constant when the error in the estimated output $\tilde{y}$ becomes very small. This is to eliminate the influence of noise from exciting the parameter estimate.

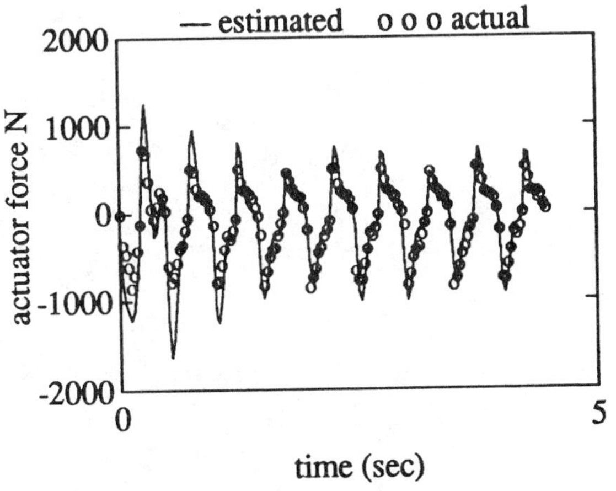

Fig. 3 Estimated Vs. Actual Actuator Force

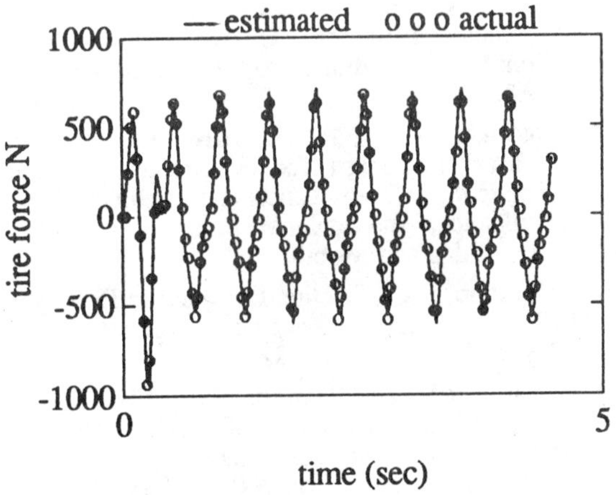

Fig. 4 Estimated Vs. Actual Tire Force

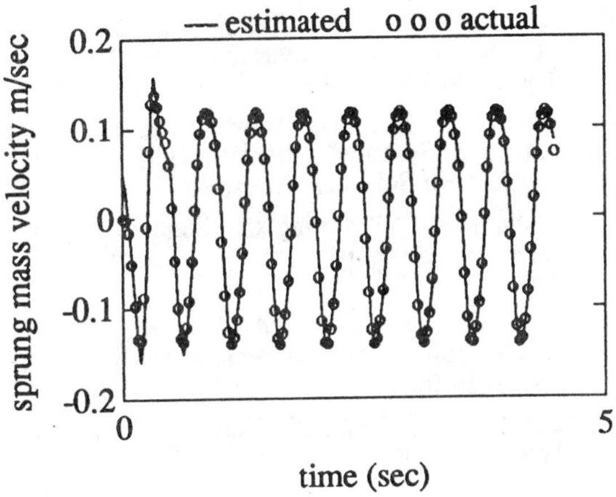

Fig. 5 Estimated Vs. Actual Sprung Mass Velocity

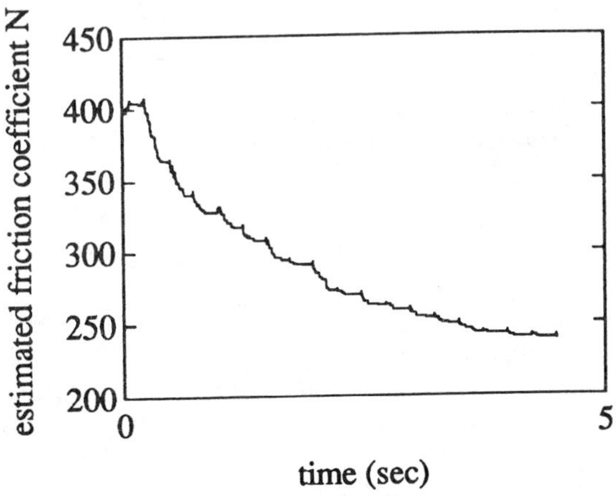

Fig. 6 Variation of Estimated μ

References :

[1] Rajamani, R. and Hedrick, J.K.,"Observer-Based Control of an Active Suspension", Proceedings of the 1st IEEE Conference on Control Applications, Dayton, Ohio, Sep 13-16, 1992.

[2] Hedrick, J.K., Yi, K. and Rajamani, R., "Observer Design for Electronic Suspension Applications", to appear in Vehicle System Dynamics, International Journal for Vehicle Mechanics and Mobility.

[3] Karnopp, D.C., "Active Damping in Road Vehicle Suspension Systems", Vehicle System Dynamics, Vol. 11, 1982.

[4] Sharp, R.S. and Hassan, S.A., "The Relative Performance Capabilities of Passive, Active and Semi-Active Car Suspension Systems", Proc. Inst. Mech. Eng., Vol. 200, No. D3, 1986.

[5] Yue, C, Butsuen, T. and Hedrick, J.K., "Alternative Control Laws for Automotive Active Suspensions", Proceedings, 1988 American Control Conference, Atlanta, GA, 1988.

[6] Butsuen, T., "The Design of Semi-Active Suspensions for Automotive Vehicles", Ph.D. Thesis, M.I.T., 1989.

[7] Narendra, K.S. and Annaswamy, A., "Stable Adaptive Systems", Prentice Hall Information and System Sciences Series, 1989.

[8] Thau, F.E., "Observing the State of Nonlinear Dynamic Systems", Int. J. Control., 17, 3, 1973.

[9] Raghavan, S. and Hedrick, J.K., "Observer Design for a Class of Nonlinear Systems", to appear in Int. J. Control.

[10] Meritt, H.E., "Hydraulic Control Systems", John Wiley & Sons, Inc., 1967.

Proceedings of the
American Control Conference
San Francisco, California • June 1993

Observer Based Identification of Nonlinear Vehicle Suspension Parameters

Kyongsu Yi and Karl Hedrick
Department of Mechanical Engineering
University of California, Berkeley, CA 94720

Abstract

This paper deals with an observer-based nonlinear system parametr identification method utilizing repetitive excitation. Although methods for physical parameter identification of both linear and nonlinear systems are already available, they are not attractive from a practical point of view since the methods assume that all the system states, $\underline{x}$, and the system input are available. The proposed method is based on a "sliding observer" and a least-square method. A sufficient condition for the convergence of the parameter estimates is provided in the case of "Lipschitz" nonlinear systems. The observer is used to estimate signals which are difficult or expensive to measure. Using the estimated states of the system with repetitive excitation, the parameter estimates are obtained.

The observer based identification method has been tested on a half car simulation and used to identify the parameters of a half car suspension test rig. The estimates of nonlinear damping coefficients of a vehicle suspension, suspension stiffness, pitch moment inertia, equivalent sprung mass and unsprung mass are obtained by the proposed method. Simulation and experimental results show that the identifier estimates the vehicle parameters accurately.

The proposed identifier will be useful for parameter identification of actual vehicles since vehicle parameters can be identified only using vehicle excitation tests rather than component testing.

1 Introduction

Parameter identification methods for linear systems are well established [6] and the parameters of linear systems can be identified only using input and output data [6]. It is possible to design an adaptive observer-identifier in the case of linear systems such that both the estimated states and parameter estimation converge to system state and true parameter values [5]. An observer based identifier for linear systems is described in [6]. If the system response, i.e., all the system states, $\underline{x}$, and input are available and the parameters of the nonlinear system are "linear-in-the-parameters", i.e.,the nonlinear system can be parametrized linearly in the unknown terms, then the parameters can be estimated by using a least square method [1] or by an "observer-based" nonlinear system identification method [11] [3]. If some of the system states are not available or are difficult to measure, adaptive observer-based identification methods can be used for parameter identification of the nonlinear systems. For a very special case such that the nonlinear system can be parameterized linearly in the unknown parameters and the parametrized nonlinear term can be represented as a function of the system output rather than the full state, the parameters of the nonlinear system can be exactly identified [2]. It was shown that both state and parameter estimations with bounded errors can be obtained by using an adaptive observer-identifier if the parametrized term satisfies not only Lipschitz, but also boundedness conditions [3].

Identification of vehicle parameter values such as vehicle sprung mass, pitch moment inertia, unsprung mass, suspension stiffness and damping coefficient is the first step to the study of vehicle dynamics and suspension control. Active and semi-active suspension control laws are derived based on the assumption that we have the correct vehicle parameter values [8]. In the case of a semi-active suspension, the damping rate of each damper setting should be known to determine the damper setting for the generation of the desired force at a given suspension velocity.

In this paper we present an "observer-based" identification method which can be applied to the identification of a class of nonlinear systems. The proposed method has been used to identify nonlinear vehicle suspension parameters with measurements which can be made with ease via vehicle excitation tests. The proposed method is based on a "sliding observer" and a least square method. The sliding observer is used to estimate the unavailable states with parametric uncertainty since the major potential advantage of the sliding observer, over a linear observer such as a Luenberger observer, is that the sliding observer can be made considerably more robust to parametric uncertainty [4]. The least square method is effective in general because the principle of minimizing sums of quadratic error functions is robust.

To check the performance of the proposed identification method, half car simulation studies and experimental studies using a half car test rig were made. The simulation results showed that the vehicle parameters including nonlinear suspension damping rates can be identified accurately using vehicle excitation test data by the proposed method. Experimental results are presented and identified damping rates are verified using suspension force measurement which is made via a load cell and is not used for the parameter identification.

2 Observer-Based Parameter Identification

Consider the system

$$\ddot{x}_1 = f_0(t, x, \theta) + E(t)$$

where $f_0(t, x, \theta)$ is a nonlinear function of the state $x = [\ x_1 \ \ x_2(= \dot{x}_1)\ ]^T$, time t and unknown parameter θ, and $E(t)$ is a known repetitive or periodic excitation with period T, i.e.,

$$E(iT + t_1) = E(jT + t_1), \quad i, j = 0, 1, 2, \cdots.$$

We assume that $f_0 : R \times R^2 \times R^m \rightarrow R$ is a nonlinearity Lipschitz in x, and dependent on the unknown parameter vector θ. Assuming that $f_0(t, x, \theta)$ can be parametrized linearly in the unknown parameters, as follows:

$$f_0(t, x, \theta) = \theta^T f(t, x),$$

we can represent the system as following state equations:

$$\dot{x}_1 = x_2 \tag{1}$$

$$\dot{x}_2 = \theta^T f(t, x) + E(t) \tag{2}$$

where f is a nonlinear function of the state $x = [x_1, x_2]^T$ and time t.

2.1 Identification with Exact Measurements

In order to identify the parameter, θ, based on the measurements, x_1, $y = \dot{x}_2$ and known excitation, $E(t)$, firstly, the state x_2 is estimated using an observer and then the parameter θ is estimated based on the measured and estimated states.

For the estimation of the state x_2, we use an sliding observer [4] of the form

$$\dot{\hat{x}}_1(t) = \hat{x}_2 + \alpha_1 e_1 + k_1 sgn(e_1) \quad (3)$$

$$\dot{\hat{x}}_2(t) = \hat{\theta}^T(k) f(t, \hat{x}) + \alpha_2 e_1 + k_2 sgn(e_1) + E(t) \quad (4)$$

where

$$kT < t \le (k+1)T,$$

$e = x - \hat{x}$, $\hat{\theta}(k)$ is the estimate of the parameter θ based on the estimated states $\hat{x}(t)$ for $(k-1)T < t \le kT$, $f(t, \hat{x})$ is the estimated vector of $f(t, x)$ based on the estimated state $\hat{x}$, and the constants α_i are linear observer gains chosen as in a Luenberger observer. The resulting error dynamics can be written as follows:

$$\dot{e}_1(t) = e_2 - \alpha_1 e_1 - k_1 sgn(e_1) \quad (5)$$

$$\dot{e}_2(t) = \tilde{\theta}^T(k) f(t, x) + \hat{\theta}^T(k) \tilde{f}(t, \hat{x}) - \alpha_2 e_1 - k_2 sgn(e_1) \quad (6)$$

where

$$\tilde{\theta}(k) = \theta - \hat{\theta(k)}$$

$$\tilde{f}(t, \hat{x}) = f(t, x) - f(t, \hat{x}).$$

Theorem 1 *Consider the error dynamics in equation (5) and (6). In the sliding patch [4], the error is bounded as follows:*

$$e_{max}(k) \le \beta \frac{1}{(\frac{k_2}{k_1} - \mid \hat{\theta}(k) \mid L)} \mid \tilde{\theta}(k) \mid f_1, \qquad kT < t \le (k+1)T$$

where

$$e_{max}(k) = max \mid e(t) \mid, \quad kT < t \le (k+1)T,$$

$$f_1 = max \mid f(t_i, x) \mid, \quad kT < t_i \le (k+1)T,$$

L is Lipschitz constant of the function $f(t, x)$, i.e., for any x_i, x_j,

$$\mid f(t, x_i) - f(t, x_j) \mid \le L \mid x_i - x_j \mid,$$

and β is a constant.

Proof: see [12].

Theorem 2 *Consider the observer described by the equation (3) and (4), and the estimated parameter $\hat{\theta}(k)$ which is obtained based on the estimated state $\hat{x}$. If the sliding observer gains, k_1 and k_2, is chosen as follows:*

$$\frac{k_2}{k_1} \ge (1+\varepsilon) \cdot \beta \cdot n \cdot F_1 f_1^2 L \mid \theta^* \mid + L \mid \hat{\theta}(k) \mid \quad (7)$$

where

$$F_1 = \mid F(n, x) \mid$$

$$f_1 = max \mid f(t_i, x) \mid, \quad (k-1)T < t_i \le kT,$$

and θ^* is the estimate of the parameter θ with the true state x and is given by

$$\theta^* = F(n, x) \sum_{i=1}^{n} y(t_i) f(t_i, x)$$

then both e and $\tilde{\theta}(k)$ converge asymptotically to zero as k increases.

Proof: see [12].

We remark that Theorem 2 provides a sufficient condition for the convergence of the parameter estimates in case of Lipschitz nonlinear system. Theorem 2 implies that there exists observer gain (k_1, k_2) which guarantees the convergence of the parameter estimates to true parameter values.

2.2 Identification with Noisy Measurements

In case of noisy measurement, i.e., the measurement of x_1 is corrupted by noise $v_1 = v_1(t)$, the observer error dynamics can be written as follows:

$$\dot{e}_1(t) = e_2 - \alpha_1(e_1 + v_1) - k_1 sgn(e_1 + v_1)$$

$$\dot{e}_2(t) = \underbrace{\tilde{\theta}^T(k) f(t, x) + \hat{\theta}^T(k) \tilde{f}(t, \hat{x})}_{\Delta_{f\theta}} - \alpha_2(e_1 + v_1) - k_2 sgn(e_1 + v_1).$$

If v_1 is white noise and uniformly distributed on the interval $[-\bar{v}_1, \bar{v}_1]$, then it can be shown that the observer error bound can be expressed as [12]

$$e_{max}(k) \le \beta \frac{1}{\sigma_{min}(A_a{}^T + A_a) - \mid \hat{\theta}(k) \mid L} \mid \tilde{\theta}(k) \mid \cdot f_1 + \lambda \bar{v}_1$$

where β and λ are constants, $\sigma_{min}(A_a{}^T + A_a)$ is minimal singular value of matrix $A_a{}^T + A_a$ and

$$A_a = \begin{pmatrix} -(\alpha_1 + \frac{k_1}{\bar{v}_1}) & 1 \\ -(\alpha_2 + \frac{k_2}{\bar{v}_1}) & 0 \end{pmatrix}.$$

In case of the identification with measurement $y(t_i) = \dot{x}_2(t_i) - E(t_i)$, now corrupted by noise $v_2(t)$, it can be shown that [12], if

$$\sigma_{min}(A_a{}^T + A_a) > \Phi \beta f_1 \mid \theta^* \mid + \mid \hat{\theta}(k) \mid L,$$

then

$$\hat{\theta}(k+1) = \hat{\theta}(k) \quad as \ k \to \infty$$

and

$$\mid \tilde{\theta}(k) \mid \le \frac{\Phi \lambda \bar{v}_1 \mid \theta^* \mid}{1 - \rho \mid \theta^* \mid} \quad as \ k \to \infty$$

where

$$\Phi = (1+\varepsilon) \cdot F_1 \cdot n \cdot f_1 \cdot L$$

$$\rho = \frac{\Phi \beta f_1}{\sigma_{min}(A_a{}^T + A_a) - \mid \hat{\theta}(k) \mid L}.$$

In addition, it can be shown that [12]

$$lim_{k \to \infty} \hat{\theta}(k) \to \theta^* \quad as \ \bar{v}_1 \to 0,$$

and

$$\theta^* \to \theta \quad as \ \bar{v}_2 \to 0.$$

3 Observer-based Identification of Vehicle Suspension Parameters

This section describes the vehicle parameter identification method via vehicle excitation tests using measurable states such as accelerations, suspension deflections and tire forces. Although the tire force is very difficult to measure in road tests, it can be measured using a load cell in excitation tests.

3.1 Vehicle Model

Figure 1 shows the four-degree of freedom model of a half car with nonlinear suspension components. The equations of motion can be written as follows:

$$m_b \ddot{z}_b = f_1 + f_2,$$

$$I_c \ddot{\theta}_b = -l_1 f_1 + l_2 f_2,$$

$$m_{u1} \ddot{z}_{u1} = -k_{t1}(z_{u1} - z_{r1}) - f_1,$$

$$m_{u2} \ddot{z}_{u2} = -k_{t2}(z_{u2} - z_{r2}) - f_2,$$

where f_1 and f_2 are the suspension forces.

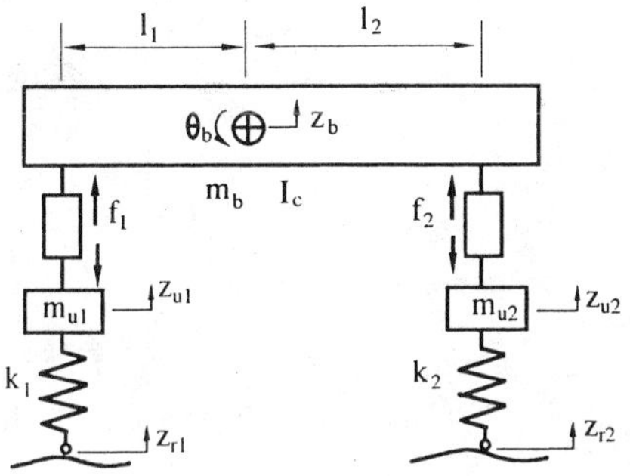

Figure 1: Model of a Half Car Suspension Test Rig

The suspension forces depend on the suspension components such as spring and damper. In case of a suspension with a linear spring and a nonlinear damper which has different damping rates for compression and extension, the suspension force is represented as follows:

$$f_1 = -k_s z_{sus1} - (\frac{1 + sgn(\dot{z}_{sus1})}{2}) b_1 \dot{z}_{sus1} - (\frac{1 - sgn(\dot{z}_{sus1})}{2}) b_2 \dot{z}_{sus1},$$

$$f_2 = -k_s z_{sus2} - (\frac{1 + sgn(\dot{z}_{sus2})}{2}) b_1 \dot{z}_{sus2} - (\frac{1 - sgn(\dot{z}_{sus2})}{2}) b_2 \dot{z}_{sus2},$$

where k_s is the suspension stiffness, k_t is the tire stiffness, b_1 and b_2 are damping rates for extension and compression, respectively, sgn is the sign function and

$$z_{sus1} = z_b - l_1 \theta_b - z_{u1},$$

$$z_{sus2} = z_b + l_2 \theta_b - z_{u2}.$$

3.2 Observer-based Identification

The vehicle parameters to be identified are:
(1) the suspension stiffness, k_s,
(2) damping coefficients, b_1 and b_2,
(3) vehicle pitch moment inertia, I_c,
(4) unsprung masses, m_{u1}.

The equations of motion for the front quarter car model is written as follows:

$$\begin{aligned} m_{s1} \ddot{z}_{s1} &= -k_s z_{sus1} \\ &\quad -(\frac{1 + sgn(\dot{z}_{sus1})}{2}) b_1 \dot{z}_{sus1} - (\frac{1 - sgn(\dot{z}_{sus1})}{2}) b_2 \dot{z}_{sus1}, \end{aligned} \quad (8)$$

$$\begin{aligned} m_{u1} \ddot{z}_{u1} &= k_s z_{sus1} + (\frac{1 + sgn(\dot{z}_{sus1})}{2}) b_1 \dot{z}_{sus1} + (\frac{1 - sgn(\dot{z}_{sus1})}{2}) b_2 \dot{z}_{sus1} \\ &\quad -k_t(z_{u1} - z_{r1}), \end{aligned} \quad (9)$$

where

$$z_{s1} = z_b - l_1 \theta_b,$$

$$z_{s2} = z_b + l_2 \theta_b.$$

From the above two equations, error Δ_i is defined as follows:

$$\Delta_1 = \hat{\theta}^T(k) \phi_1 \quad (10)$$

$$\Delta_2 = \hat{\theta}^T(k) \phi_2 + k_t(z_{u1} - z_{r1}) \quad (11)$$

where

$$\hat{\theta}^T(k) = [\hat{k}_s(t_i) \ \hat{b}_1(t_i) \ \hat{b}_2(t_i) \ \hat{m}_{s1}(t_i) \ \hat{m}_{u1}(t_i) \ ],$$

$$(k-1)T \ < \ t_i \ \leq \ kT \ .$$

$$\phi_1 = \begin{bmatrix} z_{sus1} \\ \frac{1+sgn(\dot{z}_{sus1})}{2} \dot{z}_{sus1} \\ \frac{1-sgn(\dot{z}_{sus1})}{2} \dot{z}_{sus1} \\ \ddot{z}_{s1} \\ 0 \end{bmatrix}, \quad \phi_2 = \begin{bmatrix} -z_{sus1} \\ -\frac{1+sgn(\dot{z}_{sus1})}{2} \dot{z}_{sus1} \\ -\frac{1-sgn(\dot{z}_{sus1})}{2} \dot{z}_{sus1} \\ 0 \\ \ddot{z}_{u1} \end{bmatrix}.$$

Defining an error cost Φ as follows:

$$\Phi(k) = \sum_{i=1}^{n} [\Delta_1(t_i)^2 + \Delta_2(t_i)^2],$$

we can obtain a least square estimation of the suspension parameters $\hat{\theta}(k)$ based on the estimated states as follows:

$$\hat{\theta}(k) = -[\sum_{i=1}^{n} (\hat{\phi}_1(t_i) \hat{\phi}_1(t_i)^T + \hat{\phi}_2(t_i) \hat{\phi}_2(t_i)^T)]^{-1} \quad (12)$$

$$\sum_{i=1}^{n} k_t(z_{u1}(t_i) - z_{r1}(t_i)) \hat{\phi}_2(t_i), \ (k-1)T \ < \ t_i \ \leq \ kT.$$

Equation (12) indicates that estimates of the suspension parameters, $\hat{\theta}(k)$, can be obtained using suspension deflection, z_{sus1}, suspension velocity, $\dot{z}_{sus1}$, acceleration of the equivalent sprung mass, $\ddot{z}_{s1}$, sprung mass acceleration, $\ddot{z}_{u1}$ and dynamic tire force, $k_t(z_{u1} - z_{r1})$. Although the suspension velocity can be obtained by numerical differentiation of the suspension deflection measurement, it is very sensitive to measurement noise. Since the measurement of the suspension velocity cannot be made directly, it will be estimated using a sliding observer which is robust to parametric uncertainty. By defining state variables for the quarter car model as follows:

$$x_1 = z_{s1} - z_{u1}, \quad (13)$$

$$x_2 = \dot{z}_{s1} - \dot{z}_{u1}, \quad (14)$$

we can write the state equation as follows:

$$\dot{x}_1 = x_2 \quad (15)$$

$$\dot{x}_2 = f(x_1, x_2) + \frac{1}{m_{u1}} k_t(z_{u1} - z_{r1}) \quad (16)$$

where

$$\begin{aligned} f(x_1, x_2) &= -(\frac{1}{m_{s1}} + \frac{1}{m_{u1}}) k_s x_1 - (\frac{1}{m_{s1}} + \frac{1}{m_{u1}}) \\ &\quad \times [(\frac{1 + sgn(\dot{x}_2)}{2}) b_1 x_2 + (\frac{1 - sgn(\dot{x}_2)}{2}) b_2 x_2] \end{aligned}$$

From the state equation, a sliding observer can be designed based on the measurement of x_1 and the dynamic tire force, $y_1 =: k_t(z_{u1} - z_{r1})$ as follows:

$$\dot{\hat{x}}_1 = \hat{x}_2 + \alpha_1 \tilde{x}_1 + k_1 sgn(e_1) \quad (17)$$

$$\dot{\hat{x}}_2 = \hat{f}(\hat{x}_1, \hat{x}_2) + \frac{1}{\hat{m}_{u1}} y_1 + \alpha_2 e_1 + k_2 sgn(e_1) \quad (18)$$

where $e_1 = x_1 - \hat{x}_1$. $\hat{f}$ is the estimated value of f, the constants α_i are observer gains chosen as in a Linear observer such as a Luenberger observer, and the constants k_i are sliding observer gains. The resulting error dynamics can be written as follows:

$$\dot{e} = \begin{bmatrix} -\alpha_1 & 1 \\ -(k_s + \alpha_2) & -b_s \end{bmatrix} e - \begin{bmatrix} 0 & 0 \\ \tilde{k}_s & \tilde{b}_s \end{bmatrix} \begin{bmatrix} \hat{x}_1 \\ \hat{x}_2 \end{bmatrix} - \begin{bmatrix} k_1 sgn(e_1) \\ k_2 sgn(e_1) \end{bmatrix} \quad (19)$$

where $e_i = x_i - \hat{x}_i$, $\tilde{k}_s = k_s - \hat{k}_s$, $b_s = b_1$ *or* b_2 and $\tilde{b}_s = b_i - b_j$ (i,j depend on x_2 and $\hat{x}_2$). It can be shown that [12] [4]

$$|e_2{}^2| \leq \beta \frac{|\tilde{k}_s(|\hat{x}_1|)_{max} + \tilde{b}_s(|\hat{x}_2|)_{max}|}{(\frac{k_2}{k_1} + b_s)}.$$

where β is a constant. Furthermore, if $\tilde{k}_s \to 0$ and $\tilde{b}_s \to 0$ then $|e_2| \to 0$.

4 Experimental Parameter Identifications

The parameters of the laboratory half car test rig were identified by the observer-based identification method. The laboratory half car test rig used in the experimental study is shown in Figure 2. The half car test rig is equipped with various sensors for the measurement of important states of the system such as sprung and unsprung mass accelerations (accelerometers), suspension deflection (LVDT), tire and damper force (load cells), sprung mass displacement and road input displacement (linear encoders). Since the proposed observer-based identification method may be useful in real vehicle parameter identification only if it requires easily measurable states from the vehicle excitation tests, the damper force measurement, sprung mass and road input displacement measurements were not used. The measured damper force was used for a verification of the identification results.

Figure 2: Laboratory Half Car Test Rig

The road displacement used in excitation tests and the measured sprung mass accelerations (axle accelerations) are shown in Figure 3.

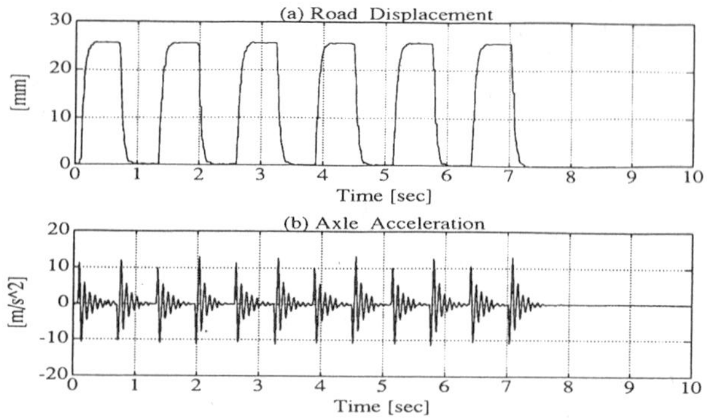

Figure 3: Road Displacement and Axle Acceleration (Rear side of the half car suspension test rig)

The linear observer gains, α_i, and the sliding observer gains, k_i, used in this simulations are as follows:

$$\begin{bmatrix} \alpha_1 \\ \alpha_2 \end{bmatrix} = \begin{bmatrix} 25.0 \\ 150.5 \end{bmatrix}, \begin{bmatrix} k_1 \\ k_2 \end{bmatrix} = \begin{bmatrix} 0.01 \\ 2.3 \end{bmatrix}.$$

The identified damping coefficients are shown in Figure 4. The suspension stiffness, unsprung mass, sprung mass and pitch moment inertia are shown in Figure 5 and Figure 6. The identified values which are the optimal parameter estimates at $k = 6$ are given in Table 1. These experimental results show that the estimated parameter values converge to a constant value at $k = 4$.

For the verification of the identification results, the measured damper force - velocity relation and identified nonlinear damping coefficients are compared in Figure 7. The scattering of data in the measured force - velocity relation is due to measurement noise, and possibly friction in the damper. As can be seen in Figure 7, the identified damping coefficients represent the nonlinear damper characteristics with good accuracy.

Table 1: Identified Parameter Values (Test Rig) (Damper Setting = 9)

Parameter	Value	unit
Suspension Stiffness k_s	15896.0	N/m
Equivalent Sprung Mass m_{s1}	207.9	kG
Unsprung Mass m_{u1}	60.6	kG
Pitch Moment Inertia I_c	466.4	kGm^2
Damping Coefficient b_1	670.7	$N/(m/sec)$
Damping Coefficient b_2	1135.1	$N/(m/sec)$

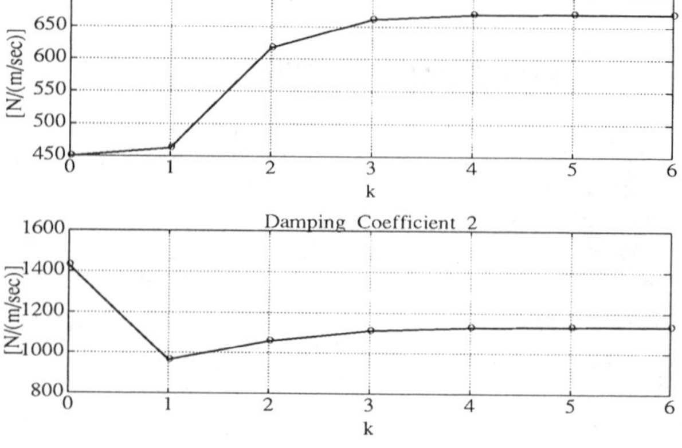

Figure 4: Parameter Identification (Damping Coefficient)

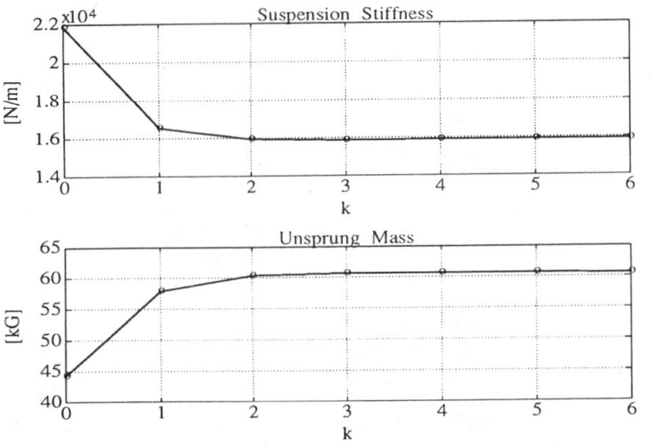

Figure 5: Parameter Identification (Suspension Stiffness and Unsprung Mass)

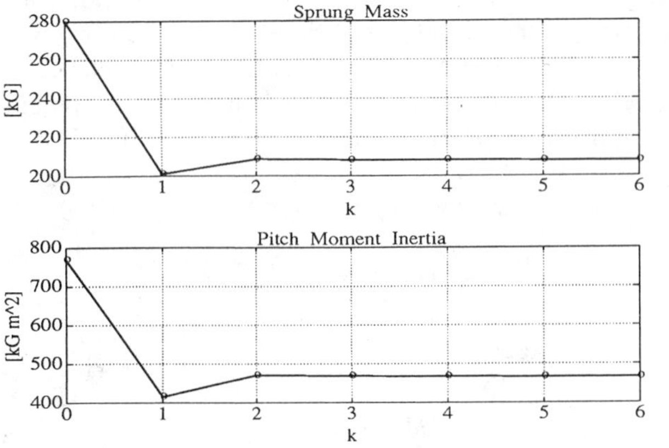

Figure 6: Parameter Identification (Sprung Mass and Pitch Moment Inertia)

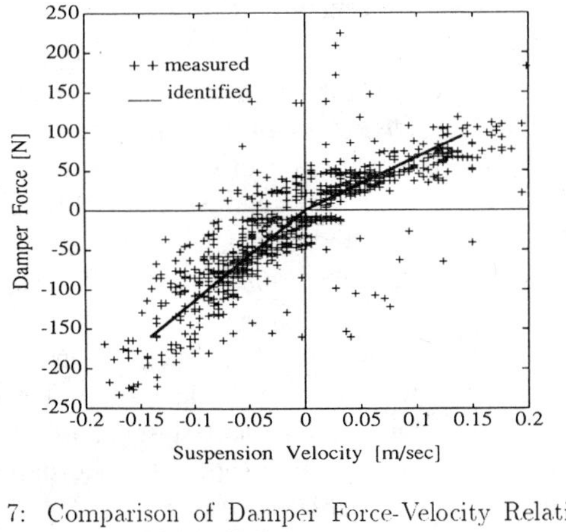

Figure 7: Comparison of Damper Force-Velocity Relations between Measured and Identified

5 Conclusions

A observer-based parameter identification method has been proposed. The identification methodology includes a sliding observer for robustness and the least square method for computational efficiency. The method is verified via simulations and used in the nonlinear vehicle parameter identifications of the laboratory half car test rig. Experimental identification results have been verified by the measured damper force-velocity relation which is available on the laboratory test rig.

This parameter identification method will be useful for parameter identification of real vehicles since the vehicle parameters can be identified using easily measurable data from vehicle excitation tests rather than by individual component testings.

References

[1] Lin, Y., and Kortum, W., "Identification of System Physical Parameters for Vehicle Systems with Nonlinear Components", Vehicle System Dynamics, Vol. 20, pp.354-365, 1991.

[2] Bastin, G., and Gevers, M., "Stable adaptive observers for nonlinear time varying systems", IEEE Trans on Automatic Control, Vol. 33, pp. 650-658. July 1988.

[3] Raghavan, S., "Observers and Compensators for Nonlinear Systems, with Application to Flexible-Joint Robots", Ph.D. Thesis, submitted to the Dept. of Mechanical Engineering, University of California at Berkeley, January 1992.

[4] Slotine, J.J.E., Hedrick, J.K., and Misawa, E.A., "On Sliding Observers for Nonlinear Systems", ASME Trans. of Dynamic Systems, Measurement, and Control, Vol. 109, pp. 245-252, September 1987.

[5] Kreisselmeier, G., "Adaptive Observers with Exponential Rate of Convergence", IEEE Trans on Automatic Control, Vol. 22, No. 1, pp. 2-8, February 1977.

[6] Sastry, S. and Bodson, M., "Adaptive Control, Stability, Convergence, and Robustness", Prentice Hall, 1989.

[7] Masmoudi, R.A. and Hedrick, J.K., "Estimation of Vehicle Shaft Torque using Nonlinear Observers", ASME Trans. of Dynamic Systems, Measurement and Control, Vol. 114, No. 3, 1992.

[8] Yi, K., Wargelin, M.M., and Hedrick, J.K., "Dynamic Tire Force Control by Semi-active Suspensions", To appear, ASME Trans. of Dynamic Systems, Measurement and Control, 1992.

[9] Bailey, J.R., Hedrick, J.K., and Wormley, D.N., "Suspension Model Identification from Rail Vehicle Characterization Tests", Proc. of 11th IAVSD-Symp., Ont., Aug. 1989, pp 57-71.

[10] Bailey, J.R., Hedrick, J.K., and Wormley, D.N., "Rail Vehicle Suspension Parameter Identification", ASME Winter Annual Meeting, Chicago, Dec. 1988.

[11] Teel, A., Kadiyala, R., Kokotovic, P., and Sastry, S. S., "Indirect Techniques for Adaptive Input Output Linearization of Nonlinear Systems," UCB/ERL memo M89/93, March 1990.

[12] Yi, K. and Hedrick, J.K., "Observer Based Identification of Nonlinear System Parameters", To be submitted, ASME Trans. of Dynamic Systems, Measurement and Control, 1993.

Proceedings of the
American Control Conference
San Francisco, California • June 1993

Parameter Estimation of Shock Absorbers with Artificial Neural Networks

S. Leonhardt*, J. Bußhardt*,
R. Rajamani**, K. Hedrick**,
and R. Isermann*

* Technical University of Darmstadt
Institute of Control Engineering
Landgraf-Georg-Str. 4
6100 Darmstadt, FRG
e-mail : LEO@IRT1.RT.E-TECHNIK.TH-DARMSTADT.DE

** University of California at Berkeley
Department of Mechanical Engineering
6185 Etcheverry Hall
Berkeley, CA 94720, USA

Abstract

A method for identification of adjustable shock absorbers is presented which combines a modern QR-RLS parameter estimation algorithm (DSFI) with an artificial neural network (ANN) for classification purposes. The parameter estimation algorithm is based on a discrete-time linear model. Thus, no state variable filter (SVF) as for continuous time identification problems is required. For the ANN, a multilayer feedforward perceptron trained by backpropagation is used.

The method was tested by simulation and with data drawn from shock absorber test stands at UC Berkeley and TU Darmstadt.

1. Introduction

Shock absorbers are one of the most important parts of a vehicle suspension system. Besides the spring, the tire and other components, the shock absorber influences the performance of a vehicle in a large range and is mainly responsible for driving safety and comfort.

Today, some of the modern shock absorbers are capable of somehow adjusting their damping coefficients. There are three basic concepts : passive, semi-active and active dampers. The first two concepts deal with those dampers which do not put energy into the system and adjust their dynamics passively, often by changing the valve diameter of a hydraulic bypass. Semi-active dampers are faster, though, their adjusting frequency is in the range of the vertical eigendynamics resulting in modified overall dynamics. For reference see [1] or [2]. Active dampers are different in the way that they use external energy supply, see e.g. [3]. Within the scope of this paper, only passive and semi-active dampers are concerned.

To design proper control rules for adjustable dampers, a good knowledge of the actual physical parameters is desirable. On-line identification schemes to estimate unknown or non-measurable vehicle coefficients (damping coefficient, masses, stiffnesses) by measuring vertical movements (e.g. suspension deflection, wheel or body acceleration) have recently been developed, see e.g. [1]. The method presented in this work combines such an estimation scheme with an artificial neural network (ANN) which allows to further interpret the estimation results, see Fig. 1.

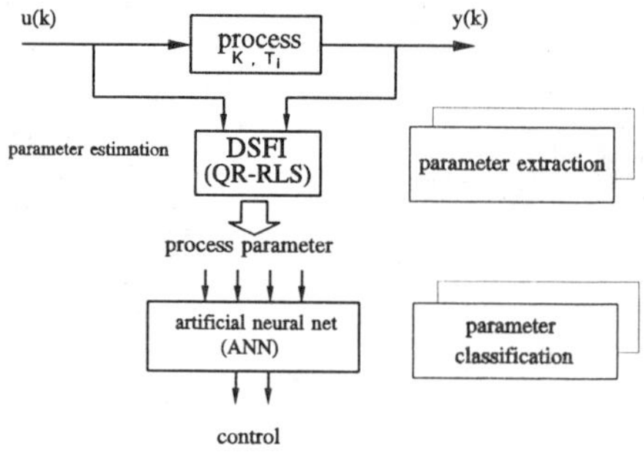

Fig. 1 : general estimation scheme

The presented scheme requires a linear mathematical model of the vertical vehicles dynamics in z- and s-domain. For the extraction of characteristics (z-domain model parameters), a recursive QR-RLS algorithm (DSFI) is used. Afterwards, the estimated parameters are classifed by a perceptron featuring backpropagation training.

The concept has been tested by simulation and by measurements taken on the half car test rig of UC Berkeley and the quarter car test stand of TU Darmstadt and may be applied on-board for real-time control of suspension and vehicle components.

2. Physical Models

For rigorous testing of new control and estimation schemes, a test stand allowing to simulate realistic vehicle conditions is required. In the following, the test rigs of UC at Berkeley and of TU Darmstadt will shortly be presented.

At the Institute of Control Engineering of the Technical University of Darmstadt, a quarter car test rig has been designed. Fig. 2 gives a block diagram.

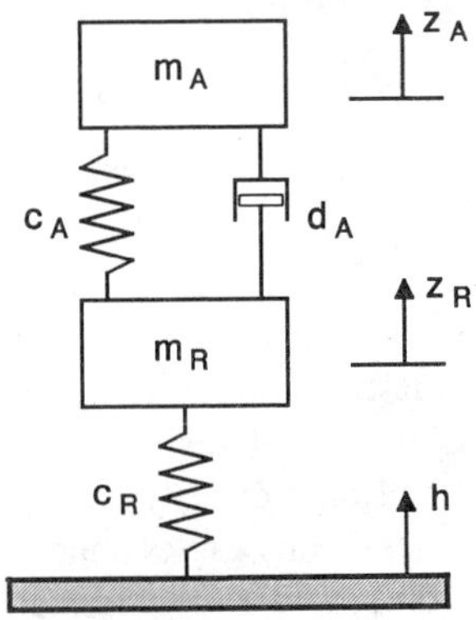

Fig. 2 : scheme of quarter car

From first principles, the following equations are obtained

$$m_A \ddot{z}_A = c_A (z_R - z_A) + d_A (\dot{z}_R - \dot{z}_A) \quad (1)$$

$$m_R \ddot{z}_R = - c_A (z_R - z_A) - d_A (\dot{z}_R - \dot{z}_A) + c_R (h - z_R) \quad (2)$$

Note that c_R stands for tire stiffness and that c_A counts for the shock absorber spring. d_A denotes the damping coefficient, m_R and m_A stand for wheel and body mass, respectively. Eq. (3) and (4) give the transfer functions for the vehicle body

$$G_A(s) = \frac{(z_R - z_A)}{\ddot{z}_A} = \frac{\frac{m_A}{c_A}}{1 + \frac{d_A}{c_A} s} \quad (3)$$

and for wheel and body

$$G_R(s) = \frac{z_R - z_A}{h - z_R} = \frac{\frac{m_A c_R}{c_A (m_R + m_A)}}{1 + \frac{d_A}{c_A} s + \frac{m_A m_R}{c_A (m_A + m_R)} s^2} \quad (4)$$

In Fig. 3, the physical construction of the test stand is shown. The input (road displacement h) is generated by a hydraulic actuator.

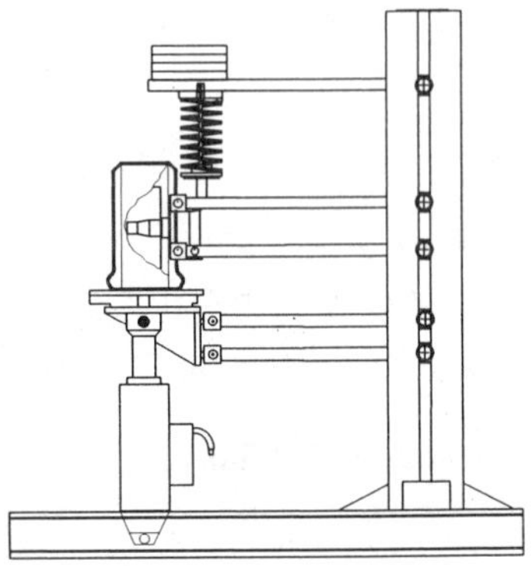

Fig. 3 : quarter car test stand

The half-car test rig at UC Berkeley is a full-scale model incorporating both pitch and heave dynamics for the sprung mass. Fig. 4 gives the block diagram.

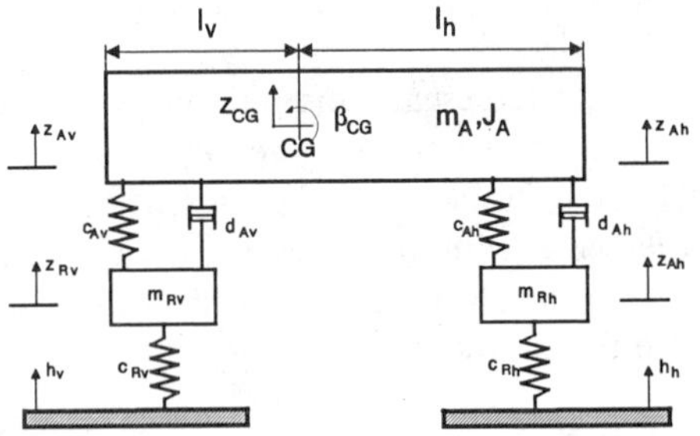

Fig. 4 : scheme of half car

For the dynamic behaviour, model equations can again be derived from first principles, see [4]. Let m_A, m_{Rv} and m_{Rh} be physical parameters (body mass and wheel masses, respectively). Let further be J_A the moment of inertia relative to the body center of gravity. Three masses and an additional rotational degree of freedom would lead to four equations. However, only two shall be given here

$$m_A \ddot{z}_{CG} = c_{Av} (z_{Rv} - z_{Av}) + d_{Av} (\dot{z}_{Rv} - \dot{z}_{Av}) + c_{Ah} (z_{Rh} - z_{Ah}) + d_{Ah} (\dot{z}_{Rh} - \dot{z}_{Ah}) \quad (5)$$

$$J_A \ddot{\beta}_{Rh} = l_h c_{Ah} (z_{Rh} - z_{Ah}) + l_h d_{Ah} (\dot{z}_{Rh} - \dot{z}_{Ah}) - l_v c_{Av} (z_{Rv} - z_{Av}) - l_v d_{Av} (\dot{z}_{Rv} - \dot{z}_{Av}) \quad (6)$$

For small angles β_{CG}, the following geometric relationships are valid

$$z_{Av} = z_{CG} - l_v \beta_{CG}, \quad z_{Ah} = z_{CG} + l_h \beta_{CG} \quad (7)$$

Taking derivates of eq. (7) and plugging in eq. (5) and

(6), the following two equations are obtained

$$\ddot{z}_{Av} = a_{0vv}\,(z_{Rv} - z_{Av}) + a_{1vv}\,(\dot{z}_{Rv} - \dot{z}_{Av}) + a_{0hv}\,(z_{Rh} - z_{Ah}) + a_{1hv}\,(\dot{z}_{Rh} - \dot{z}_{Ah}) \qquad \textbf{(8)}$$

$$\ddot{z}_{Ah} = a_{0vh}\,(z_{Rv} - z_{Av}) + a_{1vh}\,(\dot{z}_{Rv} - \dot{z}_{Av}) + a_{0hh}\,(z_{Rh} - z_{Ah}) + a_{1hh}\,(\dot{z}_{Rh} - \dot{z}_{Ah}) \qquad \textbf{(9)}$$

where the a_{ijk} are functions of the physical parameters.

3. QR-RLS Parameter Estimation

For extracting characteristics from a dynamical system, recursive parameter estimation algorithms have often been applied during the last decades. For example, within adaptive controllers RLS estimators are often used, see e.g. [5].

Let b_i , a_i represent a discrete time model where input and output signals are given by u(k) and y(k), respectively. A dc offset shall be named y_∞. Let the process order be n with m the order of the numerator ($m \leq n$). Let d denote a possible discrete time delay. This leads to the following model

$$y(k) = \psi^T(k)\ \theta \qquad \textbf{(10)}$$

with the data vector

$$\psi^T(k) = [-y(k-1), \ldots, -y(k-m), u(k-d-1), \ldots, u(k-d-m), 1] \qquad \textbf{(11)}$$

and the parameter vector

$$\theta = [a_1, \ldots, a_m, b_1, \ldots, b_m, y_\infty]^T \qquad \textbf{(12)}$$

After N+1 samples one can construct a $(N+1)$-dimensional output vector $Y(k)$ and a rectangular data matrix Ψ with dimension $(N+1, m+n+1)$. The error vector $\varepsilon(k)$ and the loss function $V(k)$ are given by

$$\varepsilon(k) = Y(k) - \Psi(k)\ \theta_{est}(k-1) \qquad \textbf{(13)}$$

$$V(k) = \varepsilon^T(k)\ \varepsilon(k) = \| I\ \varepsilon \|^2 \qquad \textbf{(14)}$$

Minimizing eq. (14) solves the Least Squares (LS) estimation problem and leads to the "normal equation"

$$\theta_{est} = [\ \Psi^T\ \ \Psi\ ]^{-1}\ \Psi^T\ Y \qquad \textbf{(15)}$$

When using the LS algorithm recursively, the inversion of the squared data matrix may be avoided by applying the matrix inversion lemma. The resulting algorithm is the well established Recursive Least Square algorithm (RLS), see e.g. [5]. However, squaring the data matrix may cause numerical instability. In such cases, so called QR-RLS algorithms are a good alternative. In this study, a specific algorithm referred to as DSFI (Discrete Square Root Filter in the Information Form) was used which directly factorizes Y into Ω R (with R an upper triangular and Ω an orthogonal matrix).

$$Y = \Psi\ \theta \quad \overset{\Omega}{\Rightarrow} \quad \begin{bmatrix} R \\ 0 \end{bmatrix} \theta = \Omega\ Y = \begin{bmatrix} c \\ d \end{bmatrix} \qquad \textbf{(16)}$$

$$\Leftrightarrow\ \theta = R^{-1}\ c \qquad \textbf{(17)}$$

This algorithm actually avoids squaring the data matrix by applying the orthogonal transformation as shown in eq. (16) and (17) and then directly solves the resulting system of linear equations. QR transformations are usually either a Householder transformation or, as in this study, a set of Givens rotations, see [6]. Details on the recursive implementation can be found in [7].

4. Artifical Neural Networks (ANNs)

ANNs are motivated by biological central nervous systems (CNS). Here, the central processing element is a cell called neuron which actually integrates input signals in space and time and sends out a frequency coded output signal if a certain threshold is reached. When building artificial neural networks, however, some major simplifications are made. Most artifical neurons do not integrate over space and are synchronized with system time. Also, frequency coding is substituted by a nonlinear activation function **f**.

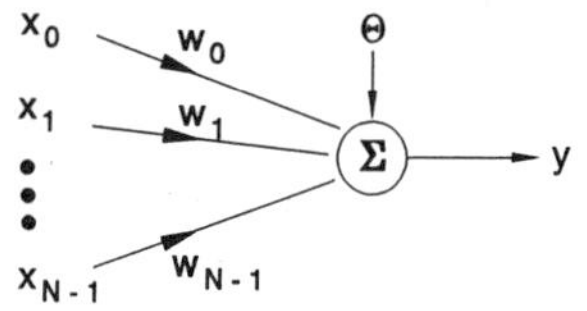

Fig. 5 : artificial neuron

The resulting neuron is known as the McCulloch-Pitts neuron (1943), see Fig. 5 and eq. (18).

$$y(k) = f\left(\sum_{i=0}^{N-1} w_i\ x_i(k) - \theta \right) = f(a) \qquad \textbf{(18)}$$

When "backpropagation", see [8], is used for training, the network "learns" data by adjusting its weights w_{ji} to minimize the quadratic loss function

$$E = \frac{1}{2}\sum_j (g_j - y_j)^2 \tag{19}$$

g_j stand for the desired output while y_j is the current output of the network. Usually, a gradient descent method is used for weight adjusting

$$w_{ji}(n+1) = w_{ji}(n) - \eta \frac{\partial E}{\partial w_{ji}(n)} \tag{20}$$

with the learning rate η. Each iteration, the weight adjustment propagates backwards from output to the input layers. Fig. 6 shows a feedforward multilayer network.

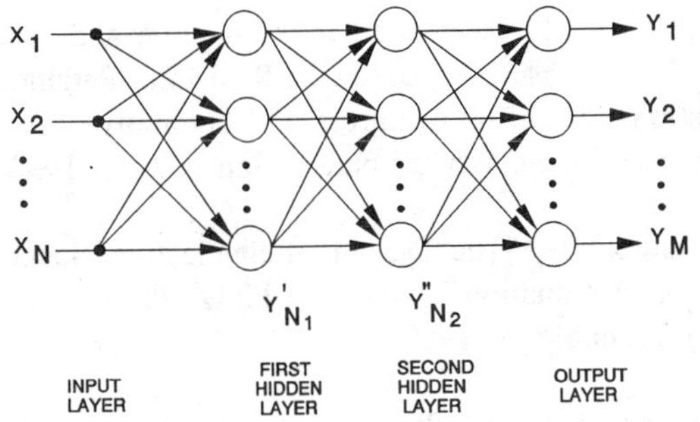

Fig. 6 : multilayer perceptron

Thus, the network actually performs a nonlinear mapping. For reference on classification with ANNs see e.g. [9].

5. Experimental Results

Static Damping Curves

Fig. 7 shows the characteristic curves of the damper used for the experiments in Darmstadt.

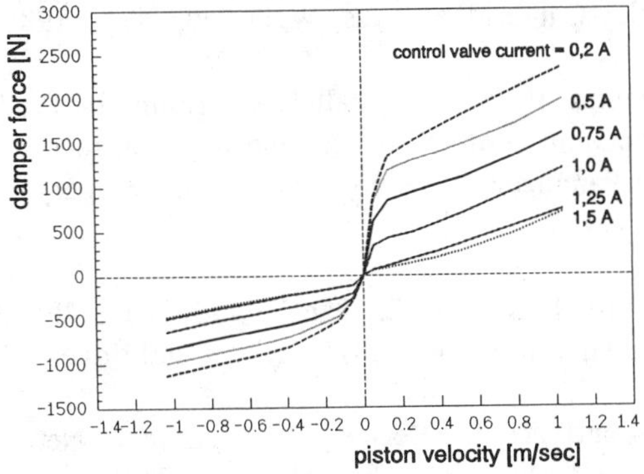

Fig. 7 : damping curve of Darmstadt shock absorber

Note that the linear model asumption in section 2 actually linearizes these curves by an average slope.

The following setup was used

body mass m_A	: 200 - 300 kg
wheel m_R	: 32 kg
tire	: radial-ply tire 195/65 VR 15
tire stiffness c_R	: 203 kN/m at 2.0 bar, adjustable by changing air pressure
damper	: continuously adjustable double-tube gas pressure shock absorber
input	: hydraulic, 200 mm at 10 kN

Fig. 8 shows different damping curves for the damper used for the experiments in Berkeley. Numbers 1 .. 20 indicate different settings of the stepper motor.

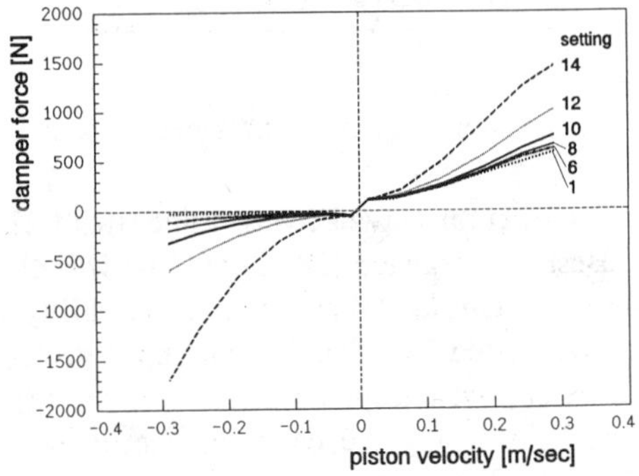

Fig. 8 : damping curves of shock absorber

The following setup was used for the first shock absorber (the second was an active one):

body mass m_A	: 580 kg
moment of inertia J	: 770 kg m^2
unsprung mass m_R	: 59.5 kg
tire stiffness c_R	: 190000 N/m
spring stiffness c_A	: 16812 N/m
damper	: 22-state double tube shock absorber using a stepper motor to switch between states
input	: hydraulic actuators using a supply pressure of 1500 psi

Classification of Parameter Changes

For the quarter car test rig of TU Darmstadt, the following changes were implemented

- class 1/2 : damping coefficient d_A too high/low
- class 3/4 : tire stiffness c_R too high/low

Classes 3 and 4 indicate a wrong tire air pressure resulting in a different tire stiffness. Together with class 0 (no changes), one finds a total of 5 classes which were mapped on a binary coded 4-dimensional output vector. The parameters of the discrete-time model, a_1, a_2, b_1 and b_2 form the 4-dimensional input vector. Fig. 9 shows the decision regions of the (reduced) parameter space a_1 and b_1 when damping coefficient or tire stiffness were changed (the complete 4-dimensional parameter space can not be plotted for obvious reasons).

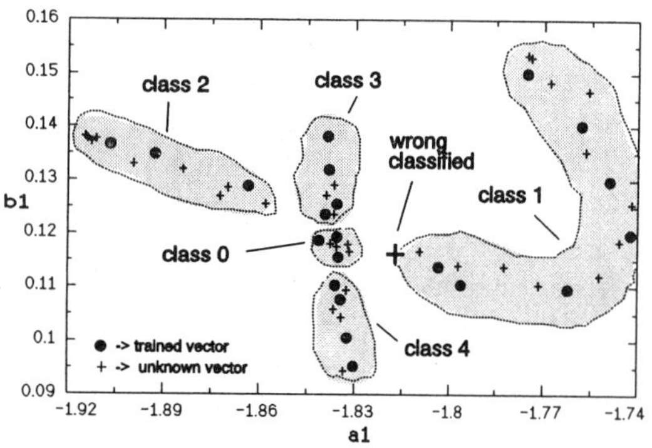

Fig. 9 : decision regions in parameter space

The artificial neural network was trained with 21 input vectors. Best convergence (288 iterations) was obtained for a 4-16-4 network. After training, the ability to generalize was tested by 32 unknown input vectors and found to be correct except for one input, see fig. 9.

At Berkeley, only the damping coefficient of the passive shock absorber was modified (the second absorber was an active one). Fig. 10 gives the variation of discrete-time parameters a'_{0v} and a'_{0h} as a function of the damping coefficient. Three classes were formed

- class 1 : weak damping (1, 6, 8)
- class 2 : medium damping (10, 12)
- class 3 : stiff damping (14, 16, 18, 20)

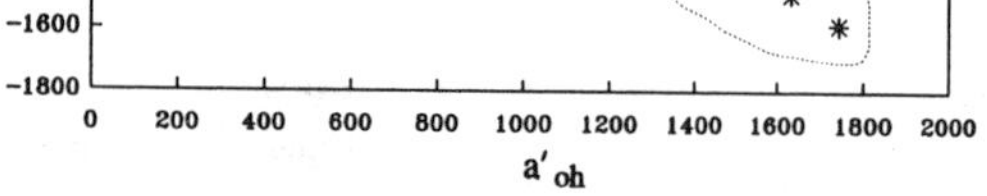

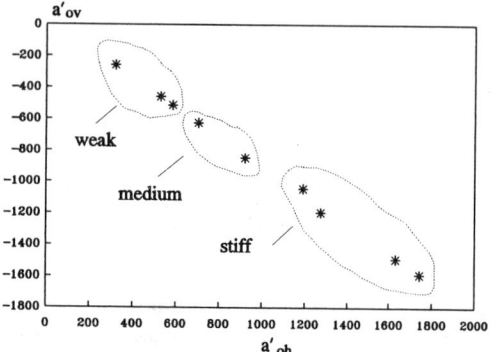

Fig. 10 : half car shock absorber variations

6. Conclusions

The combined algorithm presented in this work has been shown to work successfully on two specific shock absorbers. Despite the fact that the two processes are actually nonlinear, a parameter estimation based on a discrete linear model works satisfactory. Furthermore, feedforward multilayer ANNs proved to be useable for classification of process properties. Both techniques may well be used for adaptive control and supervision of shock absorbers.

Acknowledgements

The cooperation between our two research groups was partly funded by grants from German Research Foundation (DFG) and by the UC Berkeley - TU Darmstadt academic exchange program.

References

[1] **Bußhardt, J., Isermann, R.**, "Adaptive and Semi-active Shock Absorbers Based on Real-time Parameter Estimation", 24. Fisita Congress 92 "Automotive Technology Serving Society", London, June 07-11, 1992.

[2] **Butsuen, T.**, "The Design of Semiactive Suspensions for Automation Vehicles", Ph.D. thesis, Mass. Inst. of Technology, 1989.

[3] **Alleyne, A., Hedrick, J.K.**, "Nonlinear Control of a Quarter Car Active Suspension", American Control Conference, Chicago, July 24-26, 1992, pp. 21-25.

[4] **Rajamani, R., Hedrick, K.**, "Semi-active Suspension - a comparison between theory and experiment", 12th IAVSD Symposium on the dynamics of vehicels on roads and on tracks, Lyon, Aug. 26-30, 1991

[5] **Isermann, R.**, "Identifikation dynamischer Systeme", Springer Verlag, Berlin, 1988.

[6] **Strang, G.**, "Introduction to Applied Mathematics", Wellesley-Cambridge Press, Wellesley, USA, 1986.

[7] **Leonhardt, S.**, "A Parallel Algorithm for Process Identification", 9th IFAC Symposium on Ident. and System Parameter Estimation, Budapest, Hungary, July 8-12, 1991.

[8] **Rummelhart, D. E., McCleland, J.L.**, "Parallel Distributed Processing", MIT Press, Cambridge, 1989.

[9] **Barschdorff, D., Becker, D.**, "Neuronale Netze als Signal- und Musterklassifikatoren", Technisches Messen (tm) 57, No. 11, 1990, pp. 437-444.

Proceedings of the
American Control Conference
San Francisco, California • June 1993

Driver Simulation used in Dynamical Engine Test Stands for Exhaust Emission Test Cycles

K. Pfeiffer and R. Isermann

Technical University of Darmstadt, Institut für Regelungstechnik
Landgraf-Georg-Str. 4, D-6100 Darmstadt, F.R.G.

Tel. : (49) 6151-163704, FAX : (49) 6151-293445

Abstract

A *driver simulation used in dynamical engine test stands* is discribed which may be used to control the velocity and acceleration during exhaust emission test cycles. A model of the car body including drive line, differential and wheels has been developed and implemented on the test stand to simulate the dynamics of load changes occurring in a driving vehicle. A comparison between a human driver and the control results of the driver simulation (realized as a digital controller) is presented and discussed.

1. Introduction

Today exhaust emission analysis are performed on a chassis dynamometer with a real car and a human test driver. This procedure is capable of finding family characteristics for an existing combination of vehicle body and combustion engine. The test results are not reproducible because of the different and time variant behaviour of human drivers.

With a *dynamical engine test stand* exhaust emission test cycles may be performed automatically under defined conditions. The dynamics of a real car are simulated by a *dynamical* model. Therefore exhaust emission analysis can be performed for an existing combustion engine and a non existing vehicle body.

Conceptionally, the structure of the test stand may be divided into three parts :

- the **plant** including the different hardware components
- the three **software modules**
- the **user interface** (cockpit and terminals)

As shown in Fig. 1, the plant consists of the actual Diesel engine and the dynamometer. A flat belt drive is used to reduce the moment of inertia of the dynamometer and its speed.

The different software modules, i.e. the torque controller, the driver simulation and the drive line simulation, run on a real-time computer. To compensate the undesired dynamics of the dynamometer itself a torque-controller is employed. The drive line simulation uses a simplified mechanical model of a vehicle drive line. The driver simulation for exhaust emission test cycles based on a digital velocity controller is presented in this paper, for exhaust emission test cycles. Finally, the user interface

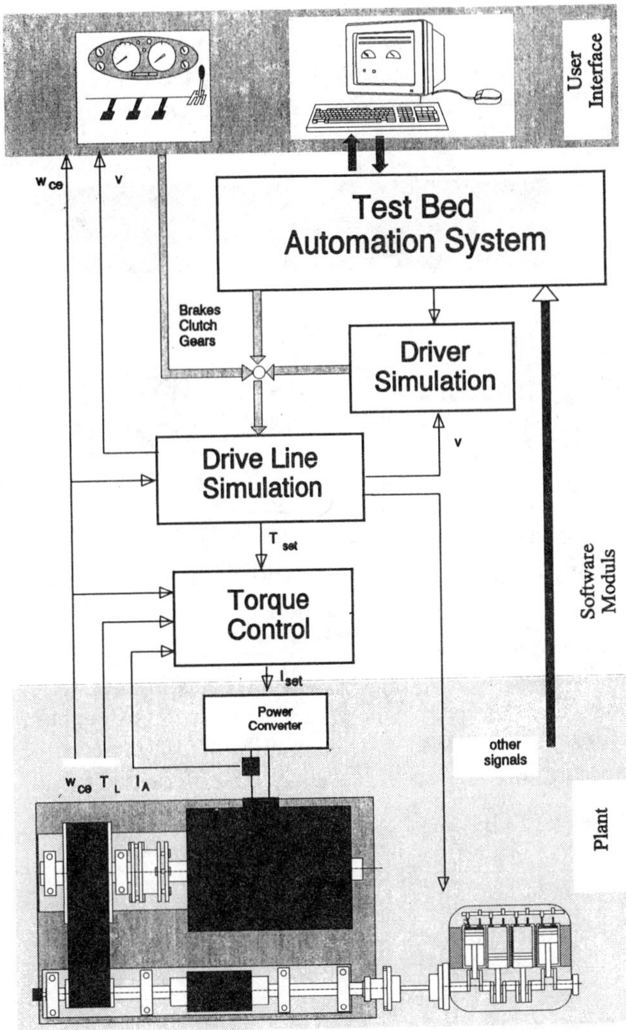

Fig. 1 Components of the dynamical test stand

allows interaction with an operator.

2. Driver Simulation

To consider the actions of a human operator, a car cockpit simulation and a driver simulation has been included which interacts with the drive chain simulation. This feature allows two modes of operation :

- driving with a human operator and a car cockpit
- automatically driving under control of the driver simulation

The car cockpit features acceleration, brake and clutch pedals and gear stick. These components are directly connected to one VME-bus computer, which controls the dynamometer by steadily calculating the states of the vehicle model. Thus, operators may drive the engine in a way similar to the conditions in a real car.

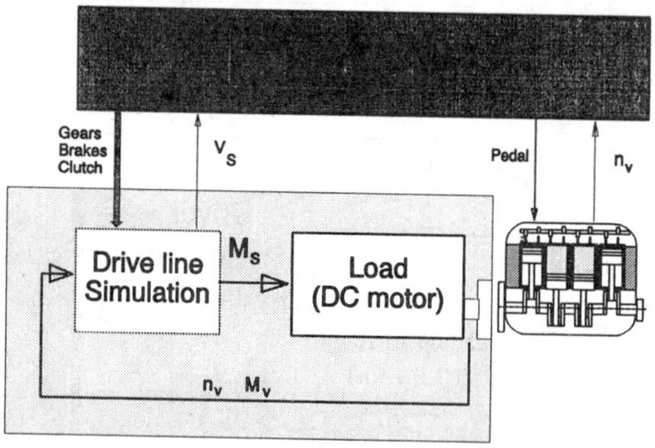

Fig. 2 Concept for test stand with human driver and driver simulation

The standardized test cycles, e.g. FTP75, ECE-cycle, are implemented to allow automatic testing of engines. Velocity and acceleration profiles will be simulated according to the requirements of the different countries.

3. Control concept

The control process can be divided into two parts

- combustion engine
- drive line

The model of the vehicle body includes the drive chain consisting of shaft, differential and wheels. Fig. 3 gives an overview of the vehicle parts involved.

The behaviour of a vehicle is also influenced by the road condition, wind velocity and other environmental factors, resistance to air flow and road ascent are considered in the simulation as well.

On the dynamical engine test stand the drive line is simulated based on a reduced mechanical model. Fig. 4 shows the mechanical model of the drive line with interfaces to road, driver and tested engine. Inputs to the

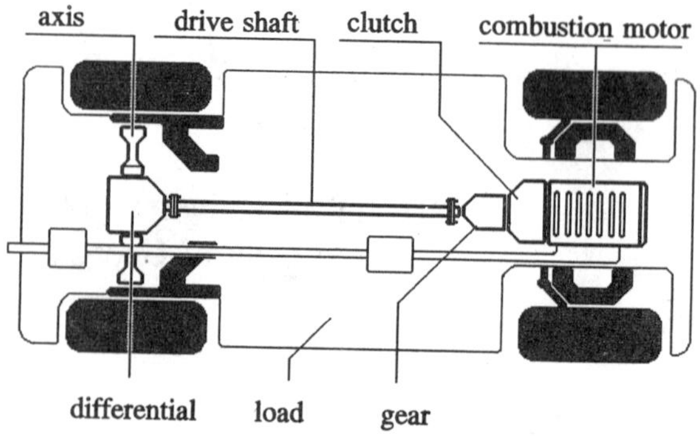

Fig. 3 Scheme of a vehicle

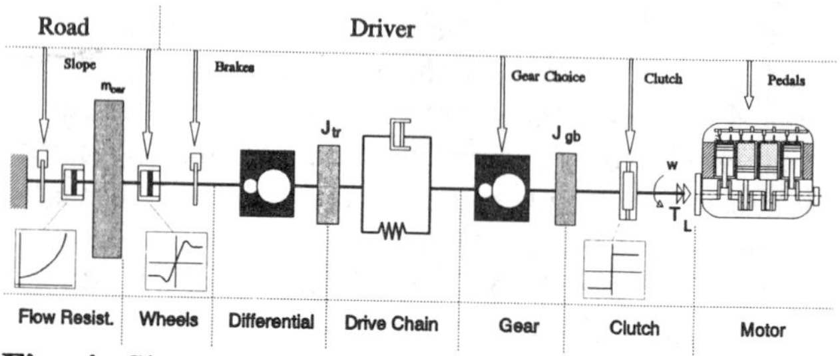

Fig. 4 Simplified mechanical model of a vehicle driveline

simulation are measured signals as engine torque T_{ce} and driver commands like brake pedal, gear shift and clutch pedal as well as road condition parameters. The acceleration pedal is directly connected to the tested engine and not used for the drive line simulation. The drive line simulation does not need any information about the engine. Output of the simulation is the engine speed and the vehicle velocity. Main parts of the model are clutch, gear box, transmission shaft, wheel and vehicle body.

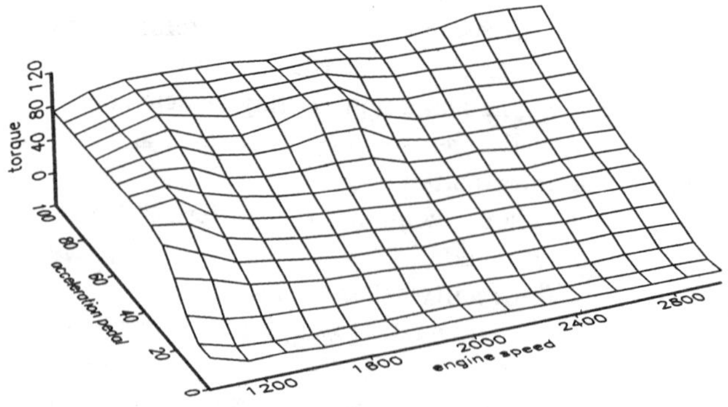

Fig. 5 Engine look up table

For the driver simulation a minimal information about the engine is necessary. The engine can be described by its

look-up-table, which includes the torque and the speed characteristics of a Diesel-engine. This look-up-table was recorded through variations of the acceleration pedal, Fig. 5.
For exhaust emission tests the controller input is the difference between the nominal value and the simulated value of the velocity, the controller output is the position of the acceleration pedal, no matter if the velocity-closed-loop is working with a human driver or the driver simulation. The control concept for the closed loop is shown in Fig. 6.

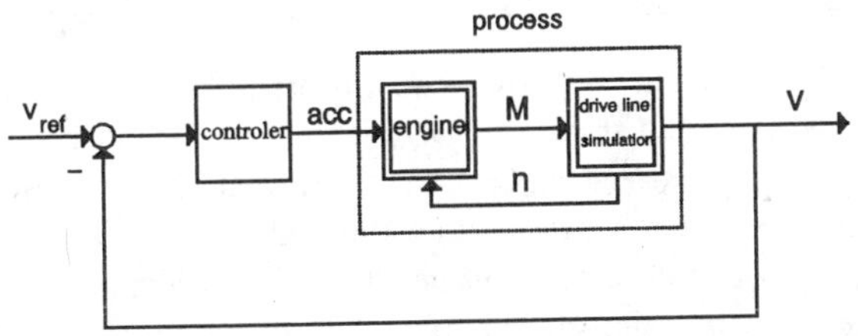

Fig. 6 Velocity control loop

3.1 Controller design

To design a feedback controller for the acceleration pedal it is necessary to get a parametric model of the process, consisting the real engine and the drive line simulation. The transfer-function of this process, with the acceleration pedal as input value and the vehicle velocity as output value, has general an integral behaviour, see Fig. 7.

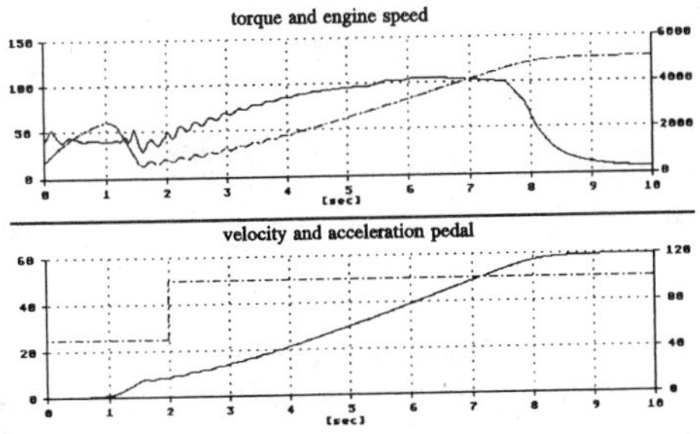

Fig. 7 Step response 1. gear

The reason for the differences between a linear integral behaviour and this behaviour is the nonlinearity of the diesel engine. This is also the reason for the P-behaviour for higher engine speeds.
In Laplace-domain, the process is given approximately by

$$G_s(s) = \frac{K_I}{s} \qquad (1)$$

The process parameter K_I can be determined from the linear part of the step response. This parameter K_I depends on the transmission ratio, see Table 1.

Tab 1 Process parameters

gear	K_I	T_I
1.	9,28	0,1077
2.	5,58	0,1792
3.	3,68	0,2717
4.	2,54	0,3932

For controller design it is necessary to define a performance criterion, The desired behaviour of the control-loop is:

- no control difference
- fast operation of the controller by variation of the reference velocity.
- smooth changes of the manipulated variable

To avoid a permanent control difference, the open loop must have an integral behaviour. The integral behaviour is sufficient to avoid a permanent control difference. A fast operation of the controller can be achieved with an differential part in the control-algorithm. A PD control algorithm is not efficient as driver simulation because of a limited controller output. Therefore a PD control algorithm with a lime lag T_1 (PDT_1-Controller) was designed. In Laplace-domain, the PDT_1 control algorithm is given by

$$G_C(s) = K_C\,(1 + \frac{T_D s}{1 + T_1 s}) \qquad (2)$$

3.2 Stability conditions

The stability conditions can be determined by the root locus. For the characteristic polynomial of the closed loop

$$D(z) = z^2 + d_1 z + d_0 = 0 \qquad (3)$$

The poles result in

$$z_{1/2} = -\frac{d_1}{2} \pm \sqrt{(\frac{d_1}{2})^2 - d_0} \qquad (4)$$

The discrete-time closed loop is stable, if

$$|z| \le 1 \qquad (5)$$

The stability conditions for the controller parameters are given by

$$K_C \geq 0 \tag{6}$$

$$K_C \leq \frac{2}{T_0/T_I} \tag{7}$$

$$\frac{T_D}{T_1} \leq \frac{2}{K_C * T_0/T_1} - 1 \tag{8}$$

As result of these stability conditions the stability area of the velocity-closed-loop is obtained, Fig. 8.

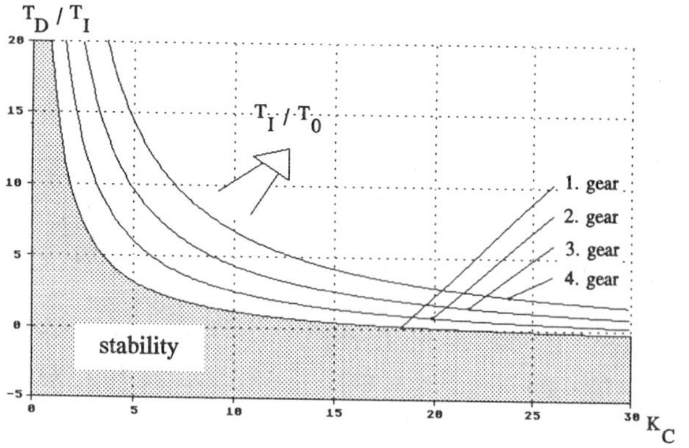

Fig. 8 Stability area of the velocity control loop with PDT_1 controller

The critical controller gain is determined by the ratio T_0/T_I. A variation of the sampling time T_0 causes a reduction or expansion of the stability area.

4. Closed loop with driver simulation

After designing the controller for the acceleration pedal the driver simulation has to replace the human driver. First the driver simulation has to learn and to copy the vehicle startup and the transmission shifting, because the clutch pedal and therefore the transmission shifting will be feedforward controlled.

Tab 2 Vehicle startup time

	street				roller test stand
	slow	normal	drafty	fast	
vehicle startup time [sec]	1.65	1.47	1.32	1.31	2.35

Tab 3 Time of transmission shifting from 1 to 4

	street				roller test stand
	slow	normal	drafty	fast	
gear 1-2	1.38	0.99	0.94	0.66	0.92
gear 2-3	1.42	1.02	0.96	0.67	0.98
gear 3-4	1.28	0.92	0.82	0.56	0.88

Table 2 and Table 3 shows the different behaviour for vehicle startup and transmission shifting of human drivers driving on the street and on a roller test stand. After learning the gear shifting and the vehicle startup the controller for the acceleration pedal can be implemented.

Theoretically, the closed loop will reach the limit of stability for a ratio $T_D/T_I=1$ ($T_D/T_0=10.7$) at $K_C=0.955$, see Fig. 8, but practically the limit of stability is reached at $K_C=2.0$, see Fig. 9.

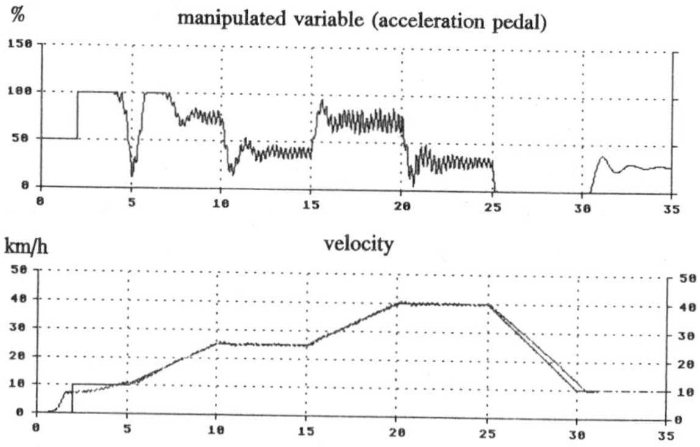

Fig. 9 PDT_1-Controller with $K_C=2$ at stability limit

The difference between theoretical and practical stability of the closed loop is the inexact identification of the process parameter T_I. This is a problem of theoretical stability examination.

To reach stability the distance between the controller gain K_C and the limit of stability must be magnificent. A fit value for the controller gain is reached at $K_C=1.0$, see Fig. 10. The reference behaviour is quite good, nevertheless the variation of the reference signal provokes an oscillating operation of the manipulated variable. This oscillation is asymptotic stable. However this controller can not be used as a driver simulation for exhaust emission tests, because it provokes higher exhaust emission. The PDT_1 control must be modified, so that the manipulated variable trend will be damped.

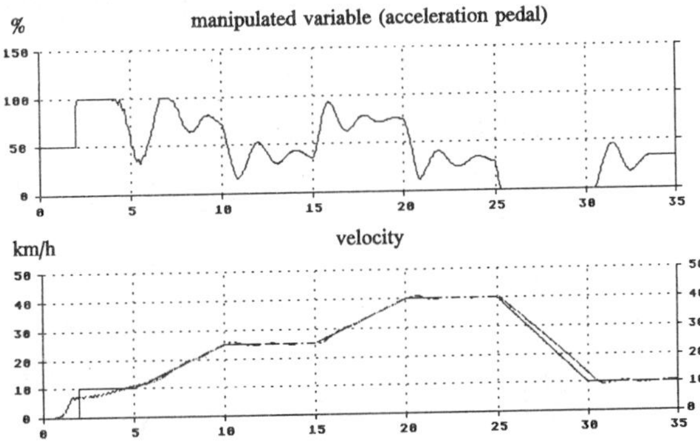

Fig. 10 PDT$_1$-Controller with $K_C=1$ (optimized controller parameters)

5. Closed loop with human driver

A normal human driver, who is not trained in driving exhaust emission test cycles, has to practise a lot to drive these test cycles with the required control performance. It is more difficult for human drivers to follow pretended velocity trends as to follow the daily traffic.

The advantage of a human driver is, that he has more a priori knowledge about the reference values than the presented PDT$_1$ controller, because he knows the reference values from the future. Therefore a trained driver provokes a smoother trend of the manipulated variable and therefore less exhaust emissions than the presented controller. The operation of a trained human driver is presented in Fig. 11.

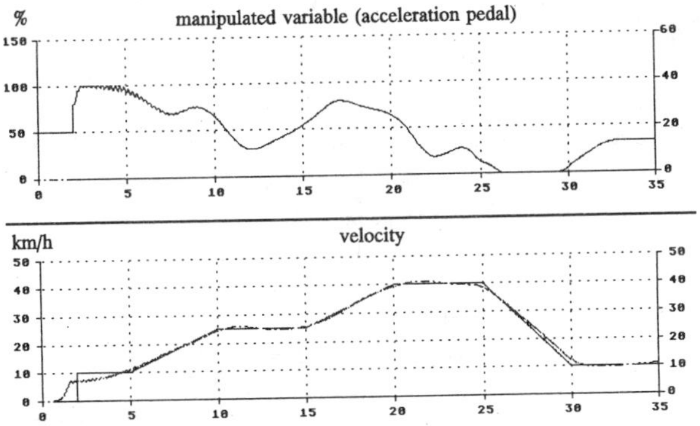

Fig. 11 Human Driver

6. Conclusions

As presented in this paper a driver simulation used in dynamical engine test stands could be a proper tool for exhaust emission tests. The main disadvantage of the presented driver simulation is oscillating manipulated variable. The definition of the performance criterion needs to be revised to achieve a smoother trend of the manipulated variable. A smoother behavior of the acceleration pedal can be obtained by:

- predictive filtering of the reference value for an optimized PDT$_1$ controller
- predictive control concepts
- other control concepts with neural networks or Fuzzy logic

To make the driver simulation as intelligent as the human driver, a proper feedback controller for the brake pedal as second manipulated variable needs to be designed.

7. References

(1) von Thun, H.J., "A New Dynamic Combustion Engine Test Stand with Real-time Simulation of the Vehicle Driveline", SAE-Paper No. 870085, 1987

(2) Gebauer, W., "An Engine Test Stand with High Dynamic Response with Simulation of Driver, Vehicle and Road Resistance", VDI-Berichte 681, VDI-Verlag, Düsseldorf, 1988

(3) Müller, F.M., " Modellbildung und Digitale Simulation des Antriebsstarnges von Kraftfahrzeugen (Modelling and Digital Simulation of Vehicle Drivelines)", Studienarbeit, Technical University of Darmstadt, 1988

(4) Danz, W,"Entwurf und Implementierung verschiedener Regelungskonzepte für den Einsatz als Fahrregler an einem dynamischen Motorenprüfstand (Design and Implementation of different Control Concepts for Use as Driver Simulation on a Dynamical Engine Test Stand)", Diplomarbeit, Technical University of Darmstadt, 1990

(5) Voigt, K.U., A Control Scheme for a Dynamical Engine Test Stand", IEE Control '91, Edinburgh, U.K., March 25-28, 1991

(6) Bosch GmbH, "Automotive Handbook", 2nd edition, VDI-Verlag, Düsseldorf, 1986

(7) Leonhardt, Schmidt, Voigt, Isermann: "Real-Time Simulation of Drive Chaines for Use in Dynamical Engine Test Stands", ACC '92, Chicago, USA, June 24-26, 1992

(8) Isermann, R.: "Digital Control Systems, Vol. 1 and 2)", Springer-Verlag, Berlin, 1989, 1990

(9) Isermann, R.: "Identifikation dynamischer Prozesse, Band 1 u. 2, (Identification of dynamical processes, Vol 1 and 2)",Springer-Verlag, Berlin, 1992

Proceedings of the
American Control Conference
San Francisco, California • June 1993

IDENTIFICATION OF VEHICLE-DRIVER STABILITY DOMAIN USING HUMAN PILOT STRUCTURAL MODEL

Mostafa S. Habib

Department of Mechanical Engineering
University of Bahrain, P. O. Box:32038, Bahrain

ABSTRACT

This paper presents the simulation of the vehicle-driver closed-loop directional stability domain using human pilot structural model. A two degrees of freedom model is used to describe the yaw and lateral velocity of the vehicle motion. The human driver is represented by a low and a high frequency cascade compensations. The low frequency part is a simple lead compensation, while the high frequency compensation takes into account the structural behavior of the driver. The directional stability of the closed-loop system is investigated from which a stability domain is detected without assuming specific values for the driver's adaptive parameters. Simulation results show that the stability region is significantly improved when the front tires cornering stiffness and the distance from the CG to the front axle are reduced and when the rear tires cornering stiffness is increased. Simulation results of the vehicle-driver system also demonstrates the effectiveness of the identified stability domain to track lateral displacement step input for various gains representing various locations in the domain.

1. INTRODUCTION

The identification of a vehicle-driver directional stability domain is of prime importance as far as safety is concerned. The accuracy of the stability domain is basically determined by the mathematical functions that describe the behaviors of both of the human pilot and the vehicle during lane-keeping driving task on curving roadways. The two degrees of freedom vehicle model has been used in the simulation to describe the yaw and lateral velocity of the vehicle motions with adequate degree of accuracy [1]. On the other hand, a pilot model which (1) allows the bandwidth and stability requirements of aggressive steering tasks to be met, (2) includes a neuromuscular system mode, (3) exhibits the desirable open-loop return ratio characteristics of the "crossover" model of the human operator, and (4) requires a minimum of "art" in its application, is a good candidate for a driver model. A review of past work on pilot models can be found in [4]. According to [2], non of these models meet the four criteria stated above. However, the so called "structural model" of the human operator presented in [2] appears to satisfy the above requirements.

The usual approach to the driver-vehicle stability problem consists of simulating the motion of the closed-loop system by setting the deriver's adaptive parameters (to be defined later) to specific values [3,4]. The criterion of stability during lane-keeping driving task on a curving road is strongly influenced by this choice. References [4-6] have considered the drivers adaptive characteristics in determining the pilot-vehicle stability domain. However, the pilot models used in [4-6] were lead-lag compensator or a lead compensator with a time delay which do not satisfy all the requirements mentioned previously since the effects of higher frequency neuromuscular system modes have been ignored [2]. It is evident, however, that the accuracy of the directional stability domain is expected to be significantly improved if the "structural model" is used to describe the driver behavior during the steering process. It is, therefore, the objective of the present work to identify a directional stability domain in which the driver is described by the "structural model" of the human operator while the vehicle heading and lateral motions are represented by a two degrees of freedom vehicle model. The stability domain is determined as a function of the pilot-vehicle parameters. To demonstrate the effectiveness of the identified stability domain, numerical simulation of the closed-loop system is used to 1) study the effect of vehicle parameters on the detected domain, 2) track a unit step lateral position for various locations in the domain and 3)assume parameters for a hypothetical vehicle and compare its stability domain with the typical one.

2. DRIVER-VEHICLE MODEL

Figures 1 and 2 show the steering task geometry and the feedback system of the driver-vehicle used in this article. The block diagram in Fig. 2 suggests that the driver generates steering corrections to the front wheels based upon the perceived heading and/ or the lane lateral position errors as determined by behavioral transfer function $G_p(s)$ which closes the loop.

2.1 Driver Model: The pilot block, G_p shown in Fig. 2 consists of a low and a high frequency cascade compensations. The low frequency part G_L (Fig. 3 [2]) includes the equalization lead term ($T_L s + 1$) and the gain k_{yt}. Therefore the low frequency compensation G_L is given by:

$$G_L(s) = K_{yt}(T_L s + 1) = \bar{K}_y(s + \frac{1}{T_L}) \qquad (1)$$

where $\bar{K}_y = K_{yt}\, T_L$. The high frequency compensation (the so called "structural model"), G_H consists of four main blocks. The block G_{HNM} is a simple second order representation of the neuromoscular system of the driver's arms:

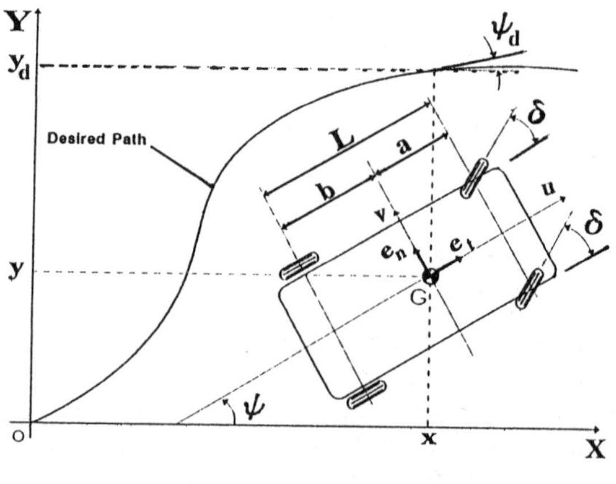

Fig. 1 Vehicle configuration for transient handling model during steering control task.

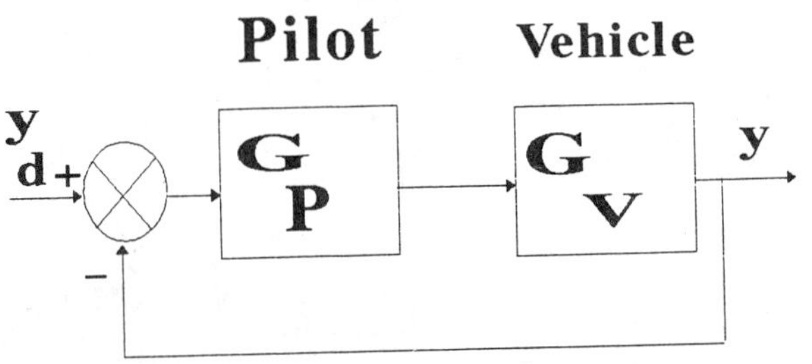

Fig. 2 Feedback control of the driver-vehicle system.

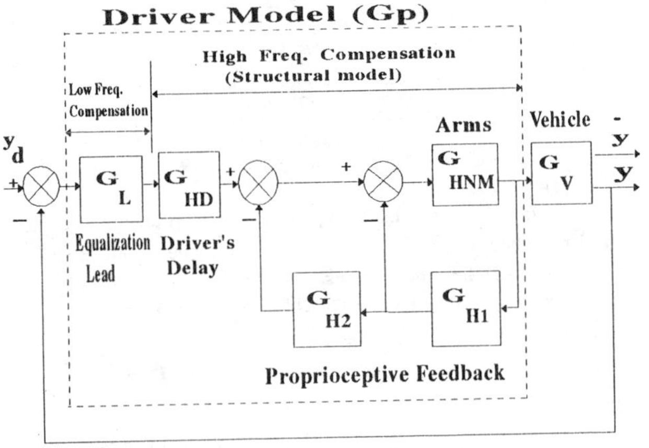

Fig. 3 Driver-vehicle control structure.

$$G_{HNM}(s) = \frac{\omega_\nu^2}{s^2 + 2\zeta\omega_\nu s + \omega_\nu^2} \tag{2}$$

where the nominal values of the natural frequency ω_ν and the damping ratio ζ of the neuromuscular system of his arms are 10 rad/s and .707 respectively[2]. The feedback structural blocks G_{H1} and G_{H2} receive the steering wheel angular position signal δ_{sw} and process it as shown in Fig 3. Both of these functions represent feedback of variables derived from the motion of the human limbs and muscle tissue and are referred to as "proprioceptive" feedback elements. These blocks are described by [2,10]:

$$G_{H1}(s) = \frac{K_1 s}{s + \frac{1}{T_1}} \tag{3}$$

$$G_{H2}(s) = \frac{K_2}{(s + \frac{1}{T_2})^{k-1}} \tag{4}$$

The block G_{H2} accounts for the type of driver control action (i.e. proportional; k = 1 derivative; k = 2 or integral; k = 0). The value of the proprioceptive feedback gain k_1 is 1 while that of k_2 is 2, 10 or 2 for P-, D- or I- driver control action respectively. The pole of G_{H1} is located at $s = -1/T_1$ = -.2, -4 or -.2 for P-, D- or I- compensation respectively. The magnitude of T_2 in $G_{H2}(s)$ is selected to achieve the desirable crossover characteristics. The fourth structural block, G_{HD} represents the human signal processing delays which is expressed as:

$$G_{HD} = e^{-T_o s} \tag{5}$$

An average value of the driver time delay T_o is .15 sec. Combining (1-5), the driver transfer function $G_p(s)$ is:

$$G_p(s) = \frac{G_L G_{HD} G_{HNM}}{1 + G_{H1}G_{HNM} + G_{H2}G_{HNM}} \tag{6}$$

2.2 Vehicle Handling Model: Lateral maneuvers in response to steer angle inputs can be obtained with a useful degree of accuracy by the widely used two degree-of-freedom vehicle model. In this model the vehicle is assumed to be travelling at a constant speed u. The two degrees of freedom are represented by lateral velocity v and the yaw rate Ω (see Fig.2, where e_n and e_t are unit vectors fixed to the vehicle body at its CG.). These two velocities together with the lateral displacement y and the heading angle ψ form four state-space variables which represent the vehicle model. The derivation of the equations of motion and the transfer functions relating the directional outputs to the steering input can be found in [4,12 and 13]. For the purpose of this study, the vehicle dynamics are summerized by the following transfer function:

$$G_v(s) = y(s)/\delta_{sw}(s) = k_s \frac{c_{1v}s^2 + c_{2v}s^2 + c_{3v}}{s^2(s^2 + c_{4v}s + c_{5v})} \tag{7}$$

where K_s is the steering ratio. The values of the coefficients c_{iv} are provided in the appendix.

2.3 Driver-Vehicle Closed-Loop Transfer Function: The closed-loop transfer function of the lateral displacement is expressed by:

$$\frac{y(s)}{y_d(s)} = \frac{G_p(s)G_v(s)}{1 + G_p(s)G_v(s)} \tag{8}$$

From which the characteristic equation is given by:

$$\Delta(s) = 1 + G_p(s)G_v(s) \tag{9}$$

In the analysis, the steering ratio k_s and the driver gain $\bar{K}_y$ are replaced by K_y, where $Ky = Ks\ \bar{K}y$

3. Driver-Vehicle Stability Analysis:

In this article the stability domain is determined without assuming specific values of the deriver's adaptive parameters. The high-frequency driver compensation involves an eight parameter model. Four of these parameters (i.e., ω_ν, ζ, T_o and K_1) can, however, be considered invariant, while the remaining four depend on the compensation action (Proportional, Derivative or Integral). The low frequency compensation incorporates two parameters (e.g., the lead time T_L and the gain K_y). These parameters are system dependent and may take a variety of values according to particular maneuvers, climatic conditions [4]. Therefore for a particular structural compensation, the stability domain is determined by considering the gain K_y and the equalization lead-time T_L as variables, while other coefficients of the system are taken as constants. The following is a typical procedure for determining the stability domain for all types of the driver compensations. Due to the space limitation, only one control action is presented here, namely for k=0; i. e., I-compensation..

3.1. Stability Domain: A necessary condition for the driver-vehicle system to be at the limit of stability is to have at least one pole of the closed_loop transfer function (8) on the imaginary axis of the s-plane. Therefore, by letting $s \Rightarrow j\omega$ in (9), yields:

$$\Delta(j\omega) = 1 + G_p(j\omega)G_v(j\omega) = 0 \tag{10}$$

Substituting (6 and 9) into (10), separating the imaginary and real parts and solving for T_L and k_y ($=\bar{K}_y K_S$), one obtains:

$$T_L(\omega) = \frac{n_2(\omega)D_1(\omega) - n_1(\omega)D_3(\omega)}{n_1(\omega)D_4(\omega) - n_2(\omega)D_2(\omega)} \tag{11}$$

$$K_y(\omega) = \frac{n_1(\omega)^2 D_4(\omega) - n_1(\omega)n_2(\omega)D_2(\omega)}{n_1(\omega)D_1(\omega)D_4(\omega) - n_1(\omega)D_2(\omega)D_3(\omega)} T_L(\omega) \tag{12}$$

where the values of n_i ($i = 1,2$) and D_j ($j = 1..4$) are provided in the appendix. For each frequency $\omega > 0$, equations (11 and 12) result in a point in the (T_L-k_y) plane. Over some range of ω, the stability curves can be obtained. Figure 4 shows a typical stability domain of the driver-vehicle system for a Dodge "Monaco" at a forward velocity of 90 Km/hr. The values of the parameters of the vehicles together with the code for "MCAD" used in the simulation are displayed in the appendix. The system stability in the domain is evaluated by studying the root locus of $G_p(S)\ G_v(s)$ at a given T_L. Figure 5 shows the root loci at T_L =2 and 1.2 Sec (i.e.; at point C Fig. 4). At T_L = 2 sec, one branch of the locus crosses the imaginary axis at ω = 0, .57, and 1.65 at gains K_y = 0, .045 and .34 respectively. Therefore only the area enclosed by the limiting curve is stable. Figures 6 and 7 show the simulation results of the lateral displacement time response and its corresponding control effort $\delta(t)$ due to a unit step command input (y_d=1 m i.e., $y_d(s)$ = 1/s in (8)) for gains k_y =.25, .34 and .4 at T_L= 2 Sec. This is done here in order to demonstrate the accuracy of the identified stability domain. In obtaining the response, Pade' approximation is used to simplify the time delay term in (5). For an integral control action (k = 0), the driver adjusts the

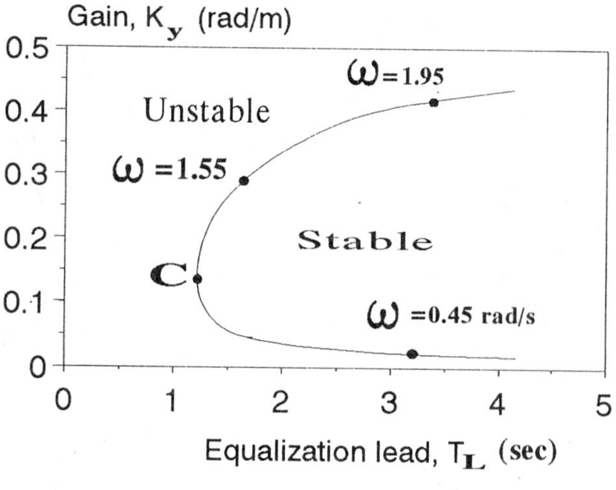

Fig.4 Stability domain for the driver-vehicle system.

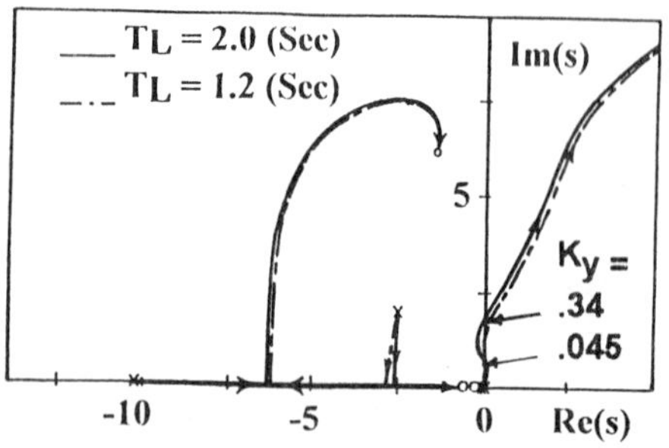

Fig.5 The root locus of $G_p(s)G_v(s)$ at T_L=2 and 1.2S.

value of T_2 to achieve the highest possible stable area. A value of T_2 = .1 Sec is considered in this article. In the K_y-T_L- plane, there exists a point, C (Fig 4) where: $\frac{\partial K_y}{\partial T_L} = \left(\frac{\partial k_y}{\partial \omega} \cdot \frac{\partial \omega}{\partial T_L}\right) = \infty$. This point does represent the minimum stable equalization lead time T_{LC} required to achieve stability when a gain K_{yc} is applied on the front tires. It is driver-vehicle parameters dependent and it gives an indication about the maneuverability of the system.

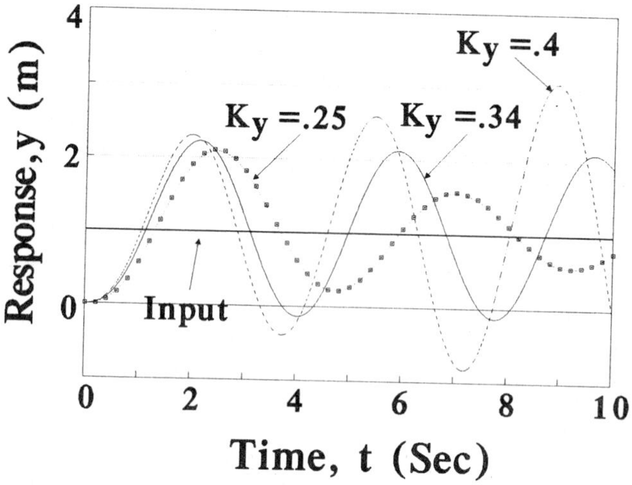

Fig. 6 Controlled lateral position-time response to track a unit step input for various control gains.

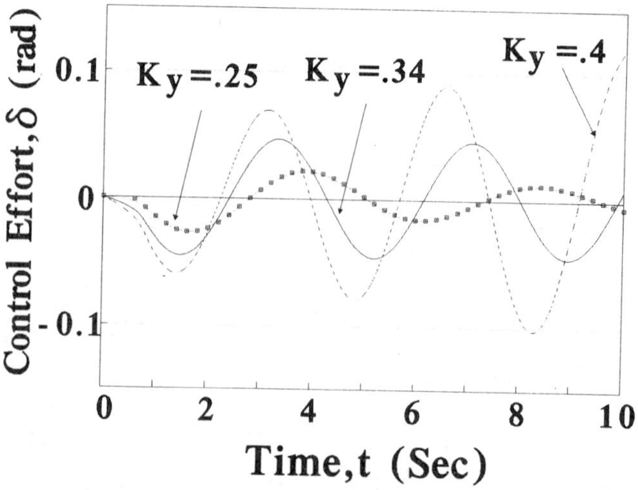

Fig. 7 Control effort, $\delta(t)$ generated at various gains.

3.2. Effect of vehicle parameters on the stability domain: To achieve a robust vehicle-pilot control system, the vehicle should be less sensitive to disturbances and imbalances due to crosswinds, road surfaces, tire differences and other causes which are themselves independent of a particular base vehicle or design. It is evident that an optimization process to the pilot-vehicle system should take into consideration both of the pilot as well as vehicle behaviors. The contribution of the pilot towards a robust system can be achieved by his professionality in driving. Unfortunately, a debate may not be acceptable as long as a person can drive a vehicle once he is capable of attaining a driver's license. As such, though the alertness of the driver would help make the problem much easier, a solution that fundamentally depends, on the vehicle robustness should be the basic concern.

In this article, the effects of the cornering stiffnesses c_f, c_r and the longitudinal CG position from the front axle on the stability domain for a Dodge "Monaco" are investigated (see the appendix). The parameters under investigation are allowed to vary from their nominal values and the stability domain is detected for each increment or of the parameter.

While keeping the wheel base of the typical vehicle as constant, the effect of varying the CG location was studied. Figure 8 shows the effect of the parameter a on the stability domain **at** u = 90 Km/hr. In general, one can easily conclude that when a is reduced from its nominal value, the stability domain is significantly improved. Figures 9 and 10 display the effect of C_f and C_r on the stability domain. one can conclude that when the front tires cornering stiffness C_f gets smaller from its nominal value, the stability domain becomes better and the opposite is true for the rear tires. The obtained results indicate a very good agreement with the basic principles concerning the theory of vehicle directional stability [11,14]. As an example, consider a hypothetical model having the same mass, moment of inertia and wheel base as those of Dodge "Monaco" while the values of a =.7 m, C_f=14325 N/rad and C_r=57300 N/rad. These values are then used to build a corresponding hypothetical vehicle model which is compared with the typical one. Figure 11 show the stability domains of the typical and proposed vehicle. It can be seen from Fig. 11 that the accuracy of the proposed vehicle model is significantly improved.

4. CONCLUSION

The simulation study of the vehicle-driver closed-loop system using human pilot structural model has shown the effectiveness of the identified directional stability domain. The human driver was represented by a low and a high frequency cascade compensations. The low frequency part was a simple lead compensation, while the high frequency compensation took into account the structural behavior of the driver. The vehicle is represented by a two degrees of freedom model describing the yaw and lateral velocity motion. The directional stability of the closed-loop system is investigated from which a stability domain is detected without assuming specific values for the driver's adaptive parameters. Simulation results of the vehicle-driver system demonstrated the effectiveness of the identified stability domain to track lateral displacement step input for various gains representing various locations in the domain. Simulation results also showed that the stability region was significantly improved when the front tires cornering stiffness and the distance from the CG to the front axle were reduced and when the rear tires cornering stiffness was increased. Based on the parametric study, parameters of a hypothetical vehicle were assumed as an example. The stability domain comparison for both vehicles demonstrated the effectiveness of the hypothetical over the typical vehicle.

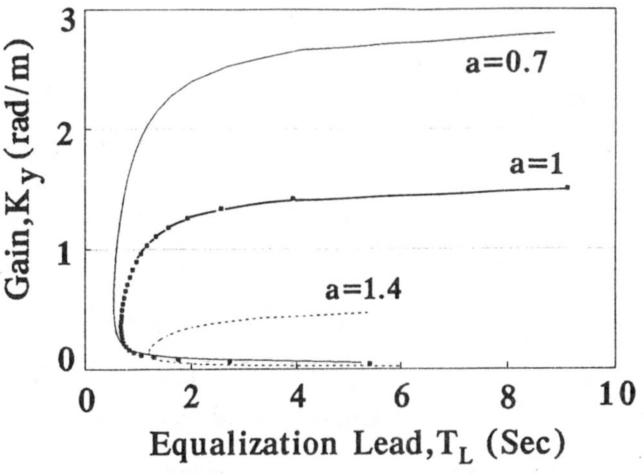

Fig. 8 Effect of CG location from the front axle on the stability domain.

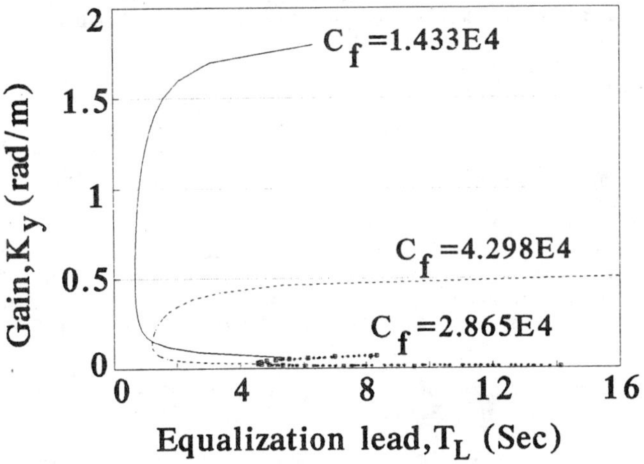

Fig. 9 Effect of the front tire cornering stiffness on the stability domain.

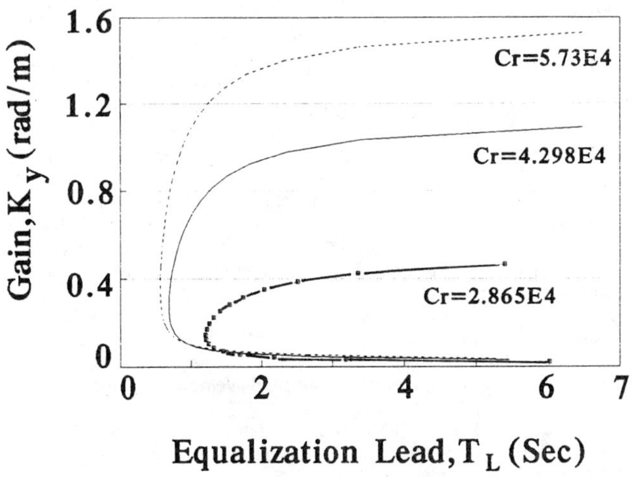

Fig. 10 Effect of the rear tire cornering stiffness on the stability domain.

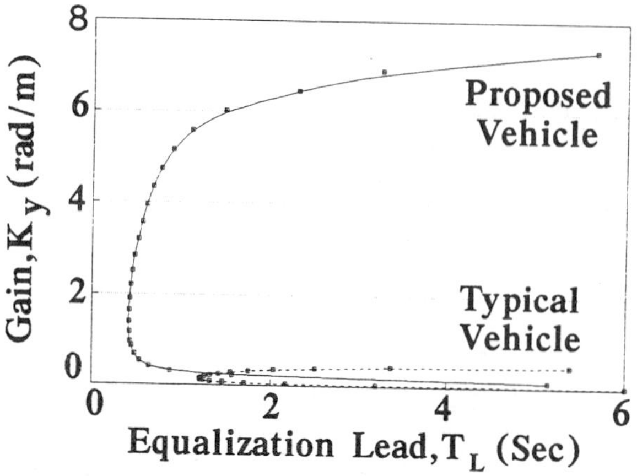

Fig. 11 Stability domain comparison for the typical and proposed vehicles.

Based on the identified stability region a controller could be augmented with the steering gear to force the car to be driven inside the stable area. It can also be used as a basis for determining optimal vehicle directional design parameters.

REFERENCES

[1] MacAdam, C.j Fancher, P.S.,"Study of the Closed-Loop Directional Stability of Various Commercial Vehicle Configurations", Vech Syst Dyn, V14 n1-3, Jun 1985

[2] Hess, R.A., and Modjtahed Zadeh, A., A Control Theoretic Model of Driver Steering Behavior, IEEE Control Systems Magazine, August 1990, pp 3 - 8.

[3] McRuer, D. and Klein, R.:"Effects of Automobile Steering Characteristics on driver-Vehicle Performance for Regulation Task", SAE paper 760778.

[4] Legouis, T.; Laneville, A.; Bourassa, P., and payre, G., "characterization of Dynamic Vehicle Stability Using Two Models of the Human Pilot Behavior", Vehicle System Dynamics, 15 (1986), PP. 1-18

[5] Habib, M.S., "On the evaluation of An Accurate Driver-Vehicle Directional Stability Region", Submitted to the J. of Vehicle System Dynamics.

[6] Habib, M.S. and Bakr, E. M.," The Selection of Optimum Vehicle Parameters Based on The Pilot-Vehicle Directional Stability", To appear in the Proceedings of the 13Th IAVSD Symposium, China, Aug. 23-27, 1993.

[7] Hirao, O.,"Improvement of Safety of Automobile as a Man-Machine System at High Speed", XIIe FISITA-memo 2-15

[8] MacAdam, C.C., Sayers, M.W., Pointer, J.D., and Gleason, M., "Crosswind Sensitivity of Passenger Cars and Influence of Chassis and Aerodynamic Properties on Driver Performance", Vehicle System Dynamics, Vol. 19 1990.

[9] Good, M.C., "Sensitivity of Driver-Vehicle Performance to Vehicle Characteristics Revealed in Open-Loop Tests", Vehicle System Dynamics, Vol. 6, No. 4, 1977, P 245-277.

[10] Hess, R.A.,"A Model-Based Theory for Analyzing human Control Behavior",in Advances in Man-Machine Systems Research, W. B. Rouse, Ed., Vol.2. London:JAI Press, 1985, pp. 129-175.

[11] Iguchi, M.,"Application of Active Control technology to motor Vehicle Control", Int. J.Vehicle Des., Vol. 9, No.3,PP.287-294, 1988.

[12] Wong, J. Y.," Theory of Ground Vehicles", John Wiley & Sons, New York, New York, 1978.

[13] Cole, D.E., "Elementary Vehicle Dynamics", Department of Mechanical Engineering, University of Michigan, Ann Arbor, MI, 1972.

[14] Bergman, W., "Measurement and Subjective Evaluation of Handling", SAE Paper 730492, Automotive Engineering Meeting, Detroit, May 14-18, 1973.

APPENDIX

Vehicle parameters:

$m := 1900 \quad I_z := 4500 \quad a := 1.4$

$C_f := 28650 \quad C_r := 28650 \quad b := 1.7 \quad u := 25$ m/s

Pilot parameters:

$K := 0 \quad K_1 := 1 \quad K_2 := 2 \quad T_1 := 5$

$\zeta := 0.707 \quad \omega_v := 10 \quad T_2 := 0.1 \quad T_0 := 0.15$

Coefficients for stability domain:

$$A_{11} := -2\cdot\frac{C_f + C_r}{m\cdot u} \qquad A_{12} := -u - 2\cdot\frac{C_f\cdot a - C_r\cdot b}{m\cdot u}$$

$$A_{21} := -2\cdot\frac{C_f\cdot a - C_r\cdot b}{I_z\cdot u} \qquad A_{22} := -2\cdot\frac{C_f\cdot a^2 + C_r\cdot b^2}{I_z\cdot u}$$

$$B_1 := 2\cdot\frac{C_f}{m} \qquad B_2 := 2\cdot C_f\cdot\frac{a}{I_z} \qquad C_{1v} := 2\cdot\frac{C_f}{m}$$

$$C_{2v} := 2\cdot C_f\cdot\left[a\cdot\frac{A_{12}+u}{I_z} - \frac{A_{22}}{m}\right] \qquad C_{3v} := 2\cdot u\cdot C_f\cdot\left[-a\cdot\frac{A_{11}}{I_z} + \frac{A_{21}}{m}\right]$$

$$C_{4v} := -\left[A_{11} + A_{22}\right] \qquad C_{5v} := A_{11}\cdot A_{22} - A_{21}\cdot A_{12}$$

$$A_1 := \omega_v^2 \qquad A_2 := 2\cdot\zeta\cdot\omega_v \qquad L_1 := T_1\cdot T_2$$

$$L_2 := A_2\cdot T_1\cdot T_2 + T_1\cdot T_2\cdot C_{4v} + T_2 + K_1\cdot T_1\cdot T_2\cdot A_1\cdot K_2$$

$$L_3 := T_1\cdot T_2\cdot A_1 + T_1\cdot T_2\cdot A_2\cdot C_{4v} + T_1\cdot T_2\cdot C_{5v} + T_2\cdot A_2 + T_2\cdot C_{4v} \ldots + K_1\cdot T_1\cdot T_2\cdot A_1 + K_1\cdot T_1\cdot T_2\cdot A_1\cdot K_2\cdot C_{4v} + K_1\cdot T_1\cdot A_1\cdot K_2$$

$$L_4 := C_{4v}\cdot A_1\cdot T_1\cdot T_2 + C_{5v}\cdot A_2\cdot T_1\cdot T_2 + A_1\cdot T_2 + C_{4v}\cdot A_2\cdot T_2 + C_{5v}\cdot T_2 \ldots + K_1\cdot T_1\cdot T_2\cdot A_1\cdot C_{4v} \ldots + K_1\cdot T_1\cdot T_2\cdot A_1\cdot K_2\cdot C_{5v} + K_1\cdot T_1\cdot A_1\cdot K_2\cdot C_{4v}$$

$$L_6 := C_{5v}\cdot T_1\cdot A_1\cdot T_2 + C_{4v}\cdot A_1\cdot T_2 + C_{5v}\cdot A_2\cdot T_2 + K_1\cdot T_1\cdot A_1\cdot T_2\cdot C_{5v} \ldots + K_1\cdot T_1\cdot K_2\cdot A_1\cdot C_{5v}$$

$$L_7 := A_1\cdot T_1\cdot T_2\cdot C_{2v} + A_1\cdot T_2\cdot C_{1v} \qquad L_8 := T_1\cdot T_2\cdot A_1\cdot C_{1v}$$

$$L_9 := T_2\cdot C_{5v}\cdot A_1 \qquad L_{10} := T_1\cdot T_2\cdot A_1\cdot C_{3v} + T_2\cdot A_1\cdot C_{2v}$$

$$L_{11} := T_1\cdot T_2\cdot A_1\cdot C_{2v} + T_2\cdot A_1\cdot C_{1v} \qquad L_{12} := T_2\cdot A_1\cdot C_{3v}$$

$$L_{13} := T_1\cdot T_2\cdot A_1\cdot C_{3v} + T_2\cdot A_1\cdot C_{2v} \qquad L_{14} := T_2\cdot A_1\cdot C_{3v}$$

$$L_5 := T_1\cdot T_2\cdot A_1\cdot C_{1v}$$

Incrementation of ω

$$\omega := 0, .05 .. 2$$

$$D_1[\omega] := -L_8\cdot\sin[T_0\cdot\omega]\cdot\omega^3 - L_{11}\cdot\cos[T_0\cdot\omega]\cdot\omega^2 + L_{13}\cdot\sin[T_0\cdot\omega]\cdot\omega \ldots + L_{14}\cdot\cos[T_0\cdot\omega]$$

$$D_2[\omega] := L_5\cdot\cos[T_0\cdot\omega]\cdot\omega^4 - L_7\cdot\sin[T_0\cdot\omega]\cdot\omega^3 - L_{10}\cdot\cos[T_0\cdot\omega]\cdot\omega^2 \ldots + L_{12}\cdot\sin[T_0\cdot\omega]\cdot\omega$$

$$D_3[\omega] := -L_8\cdot\cos[T_0\cdot\omega]\cdot\omega^3 - L_{14}\cdot\sin[T_0\cdot\omega] + L_{11}\cdot\sin[T_0\cdot\omega]\cdot\omega^2 \ldots + L_{13}\cdot\cos[T_0\cdot\omega]\cdot\omega$$

$$D_4[\omega] := -L_5\cdot\sin[T_0\cdot\omega]\cdot\omega^4 - L_7\cdot\cos[T_0\cdot\omega]\cdot\omega^3 + L_{10}\cdot\sin[T_0\cdot\omega]\cdot\omega^2 \ldots + L_{12}\cdot\cos[T_0\cdot\omega]\cdot\omega$$

$$n_1[\omega] := L_2\cdot\omega^6 - L_4\cdot\omega^4 + L_9\cdot\omega^2 \qquad n_2[\omega] := L_1\cdot\omega^7 - L_3\cdot\omega^5 + L_6\cdot\omega^3$$

$$T_L[\omega] := \frac{n_2[\omega]\cdot D_1[\omega] - n_1[\omega]\cdot D_3[\omega]}{n_1[\omega]\cdot D_4[\omega] - n_2[\omega]\cdot D_2[\omega]}$$

$$K_y[\omega] := \frac{n_1[\omega]^2\cdot D_4[\omega] - n_1[\omega]\cdot n_2[\omega]\cdot D_2[\omega]}{n_1[\omega]\cdot D_1[\omega]\cdot D_4[\omega] - n_1[\omega]\cdot D_2[\omega]\cdot D_3[\omega]}\cdot T_L[\omega]$$

Proceedings of the
American Control Conference
San Francisco, California • June 1993

Robustness Analysis of Piecewise Dynamical Cycles

Hatem M. Hmam Dale A. Lawrence

Dept of Aerospace Engineering Sciences
University of Colorado
Boulder, Colorado 80309, USA

Abstract

A general perturbation analysis for piecewise dynamical cycles is presented. Singular and regular perturbations are discussed, showing that if a simplified design system dynamics possess a stable attractor and if the fast (unmodeled) dynamics are asymptotically stable, then the asymptotic motion of the entire physical system is qualitatively similar to that of the design system. It is shown that simple, robust controllers can be designed to effectively control complex dynamical systems, where the desired behavior of the simple control design model is "passed along" to the realistic physical system for small enough perturbation parameters.

Introduction

This paper is motivated by the example of legged locomotion [5-10]. A theoretical analysis of the topological properties of systems containing a chain of piecewise smooth dynamics is carried out. Explicit recognition of the need to develop simplified models for control design is made by phrasing the problem as one of providing desired motion in the presence of perturbations. Both singular and regular perturbations are treated [11-14]. In this paper, we focus on two systems. The first is the physical system which will be considered to be too complex for direct control design, and too complex to model the *significant* modes of system behavior. Therefore, the physical system contains unmodeled dynamics. The second system is called the design system. It is a simplified version of the physical system, and is constructed to be tractable for control design, yet representative of the essential system dynamics. It is shown in this paper that if the unmodeled dynamics are of "small significance" and are "well behaved" in a specific sense, then robust control of the design system can be constructed which also provides stable, qualitatively similar asymptotic motion of the physical system.

Perhaps the best example of the study of piecewise dynamical systems can be found in the variable structure control literature [1-3]. However, these works construct a piecewise *controller* to modify the behavior of a nominally smooth system, and the effects of unmodeled dynamics are not of central importance. The objective in this paper is to investigate the behavior of systems which are inherently piecewise in their dynamics, under the influence of nonlinear control design. The focus of this work is the effect of perturbations. Our work is also similar to [4] where feedback control stability in the presence of unmodeled (or parasitic) dynamics is discussed. The contribution of the present paper is an extension of perturbation analysis to systems which contain non-smooth transitions between different dynamical phases.

1 Problem Description

Consider a problem of controlling a physical system consisting of n different dynamical phases where fast unmodeled dynamics and model uncertainties exist. The physical system is represented as

$$\begin{aligned}\dot{X}_i &= \mathbf{f}_i(X_i, Z_i, U_i),\\ \epsilon\dot{Z}_i &= \mathbf{g}_i(X_i, Z_i, U_i),\end{aligned} \tag{1}$$

where the subscript i $(1 \leq i \leq n)$ refers to the ith phase of dynamics taking place in the dynamical cycle. The vectors U_i stand for the vector control. Each dynamical phase ends as soon as a corresponding phase termination index $\mathbf{F}_i$ vanishes

$$\mathbf{F}_i(X_i, Z_i, U_i) = 0. \tag{2}$$

In robotic applications, a phase termination index can be for example the normal component of the end effector contact force with an object surface. This quantity therefore delineates two distinct dynamics namely, robot and environment dynamics when $\mathbf{F}_i > 0$ and robot dynamics alone when $\mathbf{F}_i = 0$. The ith dynamical phase remains active as long as $\mathbf{F}_i(X_i, Z_i, U_i) > 0$. We should add here that the quantity $\mathbf{F}_i$ may also depend on $\epsilon\dot{Z}_i$ which then may be replaced by $\mathbf{g}_i(X_i, Z_i, U_i)$. For example, $\epsilon\dot{Z}_i$ could represent ignored inertias, link flexibilities, etc. Another example is legged locomotion, where the system state evolves through different dynamics depending on the number of legs in contact with the ground. The phase termination indexes in this case are simply a description of the ground "attachment constraints". Examples of such constraints are found in [5,6] where biped sitting, standing, walking, squatting, jumping and laying down are investigated.

The purpose of this paper is to analyze the dynamics of the actual system (1) when the simpler **design system**

$$\dot{\tilde{X}}_i = \mathbf{f}_{i_d}(\tilde{X}_i, U_i) \qquad 1 \leq i \leq n \tag{3}$$

$$\mathbf{F}_{i_d}(\tilde{X}_i) = 0, \qquad 1 \leq i \leq n, \tag{4}$$

is subject to state feedback control of the type $U_i = \mathbf{G}_i(X_i)$. The physical system (1) under feedback control is therefore

$$\begin{aligned}\dot{X}_i &= f_i(X_i, Z_i), & X_i \in \Omega_{X_i} \subset I\!R^p,\\ \epsilon\dot{Z}_i &= g_i(X_i, Z_i), & Z_i \in \Omega_{Z_i} \subset I\!R^q,\end{aligned} \tag{5}$$

and

$$F_i(X_i, Z_i) = 0. \quad (6)$$

where i runs from 1 to n. The functions f_i, g_i, and F_i are smooth functions (C^∞) defined as $f_i : \mathbb{R}^p \times \mathbb{R}^q \longrightarrow \mathbb{R}^p$, $g_i : \mathbb{R}^p \times \mathbb{R}^q \longrightarrow \mathbb{R}^q$, and $F_i : \mathbb{R}^p \times \mathbb{R}^q \longrightarrow \mathbb{R}$. The sets Ω_{X_i} and Ω_{Z_i} are compact sets. The assumption of smoothness on these functions may be relaxed to C^r continuity for some $r \geq 1$, but this will not be pursued here. The associated **reduced system** of (5) are obtained by setting $\epsilon = 0$ [11-14]. That is

$$\begin{array}{l} \dot{\bar{X}}_i = f_i(\bar{X}_i, \bar{Z}_i), \\ 0 = g_i(\bar{X}_i, \bar{Z}_i). \end{array} \quad (7)$$

We assume that in the sets Ω_{X_i} and Ω_{Z_i}, the algebraic (or transcendental) equations $g_i(\bar{X}_i, \bar{Z}_i) = 0$ ($i = 1 \ldots n$) each possess a unique solution $\bar{Z}_i = \varphi_i(\bar{X}_i)$. We assume further that the obtained functions φ_i are smooth. Hence, the reduced dynamical systems become

$$\begin{array}{ll} \dot{\bar{X}}_i = f_{i_r}(\bar{X}_i, \varphi_i(\bar{X}_i)) & 1 \leq i \leq n, \\ \bar{Z}_i = \varphi_i(\bar{X}_i). \end{array} \quad (8)$$

Similarly, the phase termination indexes (2) reduce to

$$F_{i_r}(\bar{X}_i, \varphi_i(\bar{X}_i)) = 0, \quad 1 \leq i \leq n. \quad (9)$$

At this point, we assume that the design system under state feedback control

$$\dot{\tilde{X}}_i = f_{i_d}(\tilde{X}_i) \quad 1 \leq i \leq n \quad (10)$$

$$F_{i_d}(\tilde{X}_i) = 0, \quad 1 \leq i \leq n, \quad (11)$$

is within a μ-neighborhood of the reduced system (8). In other words

$$\begin{array}{l} \|f_{i_r}(X_i) - f_{i_d}(X_i)\| < \mu, \\ |F_{i_r}(X_i) - F_{i_d}(X_i)| < \eta \end{array} \quad (12)$$

in the compact set Ω_{X_i}. The equations ($F_{i_d} = 0$) define each a hypersurface

$$S_i = \{X \in \mathbb{R}^p | F_{i_d}(X) = 0\} \quad 1 \leq i \leq n$$

of dimension $n-1$. The ith phase dynamics terminate as soon as the associated flow "pierces" the surface defined by S_i.

The results of structural stability [15-17] can not be used for our work because the design system dynamics are only piecewise continuous and because of the kind of perturbation dealt with. Specifically,

1. The system dynamical flow during the transition between phase i to $i+1$ is only C^0 continuous and not C^1.

2. The perturbed system (5) is not an ϵ-perturbation of the reduced system. This is because $\|f_i(X_i, Z_i) - f_{i_r}(X_i, \varphi_i(X_i))\|$ can be large at the initial layer[1].

[1] The initial layer is the initial time interval during which the fast vector Z_i joins the slow manifold $\bar{Z}_i = \varphi_i(\bar{X}_i)$

Moreover, the theorems of structural stability [15-17] require the C^0 *equivalence* condition which is too restrictive and distinguishes between *periodic* and *quasi−periodic* orbits. As an example, in an application like locomotion [5-10], the system state does not necessarily evolve on a *periodic* orbit, and hence we wish to associate *quasi − periodic* and *periodic* orbits to the same class. The controlled design system (10) is robust if the physical system orbits generated by (5) are close to their design system counterparts regardless of how the orbits are "winding up"[2] in the phase space.

In the sequel, several assumptions about the design system dynamics are made. We first assume that all the dynamical phases occur consecutively in a cyclic fashion. In other words, i and k index the same phase if $i \equiv k \pmod{n}$. The expression *complete system dynamics* refers to the system dynamics when evolving through the n dynamical phases. The design flow associated to the complete system dynamics is denoted by $\mathcal{F}_d$. Finally and most importantly, we will assume the following:

1. During the dynamical phase i, the phase termination index F_{i_d} is positive.

2. The flow of the ith phase dynamics is *transversal* to the surface S_i.

3. A single stable attractor $\Omega(\mathcal{F}_d)$ [15-17] of the design system flow exists and is located inside some closed "ring" R_d (a torus-like shape in $\mathbb{R}^p$)[3]. The attracting set $\Omega(\mathcal{F}_d)$ consists of either periodic or quasi-periodic orbits. We further assume that in some phase (say phase 1), the vector field on the surface of the ring R_d points inside the ring. We denote by $A_X \subset \Omega_X = \cup_{i=1}^n \Omega_{X_i}$ a closed subset of the interior of the basin of attraction and assume further that the flow in A_X is invariant under $\mathcal{F}_d$ and $R_d \subset A_X$.

The second assumption makes sure that F_{i_d} for a given phase i turns negative once the ith design system flow impacts the surface S_i. How these dynamical features are implemented for a given system is not discussed in this paper. However, an example of control design that meets assumption 3 is provided in [9,10]. Roughly speaking, assumption 3 requires that the propagating state of the flow $\mathcal{F}_d$ never leaves the closed region A_X and enters eventually the invariant region R_d.

For the physical system (5), not all fast dynamics (generated by the vector field g_i) lead to a stable motion, but the physical system is stable if both the fast and slow dynamics are stable. Hence, in addition we note the following two assumptions for the fast dynamics [12].

1. If t_i is the initial instant of the ith dynamical phase, then the equilibrium $\bar{Z}_i(t_i)$ is asymptotically stable for initial states $Z_i(t_i)$ in its basin of attraction.

[2] That is the non-wandering set of the design system flow is either a limit-cycle or a "complex" set where the dynamics are quasi-periodic (the state never visits a previously visited state with the same tangent vector field.)

[3] In other words, we assume that the ring R_d is invariant

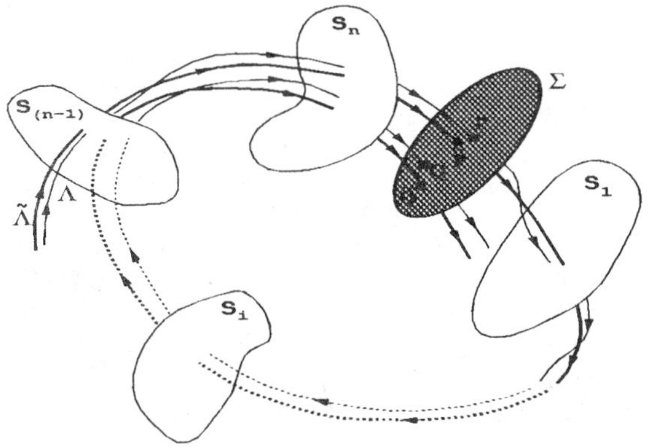

Figure 1: Poincaré maps of the perturbed and unperturbed flows. Λ and $\tilde{\Lambda}$ are respectively two perturbed and unperturbed orbits.

2. The Jacobian J_z (with respect to the fast vector Z_i) associated with the second equation of (5) has negative real part eigenvalues.

These two assumptions constrain the fast dynamics to converge to their slow manifolds. The other assumption needed to ensure the alternation of phases for the complete physical system is

$$F_i(X_i(t_i), Z_i(t_i)) \geq \beta_i > 0,$$

where t_i is the initial instant of the ith dynamical phase. This assumption ensures that the ith dynamical phase is not skipped.

The object of this paper is to demonstrate rigorously that the stability and robustness features of the design system flow of the complete system are "transmitted" to the perturbed system for small but nonzero perturbation parameters.

2 Perturbation Analysis

In the mathematical literature, the physical system as given in (5) is often known as the perturbed system whereas the design system is the unperturbed system. The natural workspace for the physical system dynamics is the space $\mathbb{R}^{(p+q)}$, however, we are most concerned with the dynamics of the "slow" states X_i which occur in $\mathbb{R}^p$. Let $\mathbf{S} \subset \mathbb{R}^p$ be the hyperplane crossing the flow midway between S_n and S_1 and define $\mathbf{\Sigma} = \mathbf{S} \cap A_X$ (see Figure 1) as the *poincaré* section. This section is chosen transversal to the incoming flow associated to the dynamics of phase 1. Let $\tilde{P} = \tilde{X}(t=0)$ be an arbitrary point on $\mathbf{\Sigma}$ and define $\tilde{\phi} : \mathbf{\Sigma} \longrightarrow \mathbf{\Sigma}$ as the first return map defined by the unperturbed flow $\mathcal{F}_d$. Let $\tilde{Q} = \tilde{\phi}(\tilde{P})$ be the first mapped return of the point $\tilde{P}$ on[4] $\mathbf{\Sigma}$. Clearly, given the assumed stability of the unperturbed flow (assumption 3 section 1), the map $\tilde{\phi}$ is stable. Similarly, let $\phi_{\epsilon,\mu,\eta} : \mathbf{\Sigma} \longrightarrow \mathbf{\Sigma}$ be the first return map associated to the perturbed flow of the slow dynamics given by (5) on the section $\mathbf{\Sigma}$.

[4] Starting at the state $\tilde{P}$, $\tilde{Q}$ is obtained by propagating consecutively the unperturbed dynamics through one cycle of n phases until impact with the surface $\mathbf{\Sigma}$.

We wish to show that the perturbed flow remains in a "neighborhood" of the stable unperturbed trajectory. A notion of a neighborhood of a trajectory $\tilde{\Lambda}$ is therefore needed.

Definition 2.1 *A trajectory Λ is in a δ-neighborhood of $\tilde{\Lambda}$ in $\mathbb{R}^p$ if it is contained in the set $C^\delta_{\tilde{\Lambda}}$ of radius δ and of central axis $\tilde{\Lambda}$. More precisely,*

$$C^\delta_{\tilde{\Lambda}} = \bigcup_{X \in \tilde{\Lambda}} B^\delta_X,$$

where B^δ_X is the open ball centered at X and of radius δ.

The first proposition introduced below starts by extracting properties of the dynamics of individual phases. In particular, the proposition shows that by controlling the size of the perturbation parameter ϵ, μ and η of phase i and the distance between the initial perturbed and unperturbed impact states $X_{(i-1)i}$ and[5] $\tilde{X}_{(i-1)i}$, we can bring the ith perturbed orbit branch together with its next impact state $X_{i(i+1)}$ to a close neighborhood of their unperturbed counterparts. More precisely, we have

Proposition 2.1 *For any positive number δ_i, there exist $\epsilon_i > 0$, $\mu_i > 0$, $\eta_i > 0$, and $\delta_{i-1} > 0$ such that*

$$\begin{aligned} &\|X_{(i-1)i} - \tilde{X}_{(i-1)i}\| < \delta_{i-1} \text{ and } \epsilon < \epsilon_i,\ \mu < \mu_i,\ \eta < \eta_i \\ &\text{imply} \\ &\|X_i(t) - \tilde{X}_i(t)\| < \delta_i \quad \text{for } t_i \leq t \leq t_{i+1}, \quad \text{and} \\ &\|X_{i(i+1)} - \tilde{X}_{i(i+1)}\| < \delta_i. \end{aligned} \tag{13}$$

where time interval $[t_i\ t_{i+1}]$ is large enough to allow for the termination of the ith unperturbed dynamical phase and t_i is the starting time of the dynamical phase[6] *i.*

Proof: (Outline) Informally, the proof proceeds as follows: the objective is to have an upper bound estimate of the "closeness" of the perturbed trajectory emanating at $X_{(i-1)i}$ to that of the unperturbed trajectory emanating at $\tilde{X}_{(i-1)i}$. To achieve this goal, intermediate trajectories are introduced so to allow the application of known theorems such as Tikhonov's theorem [11,14] for singularly perturbed systems.

The first intermediate trajectory is obtained by integrating (8) starting from the state $\tilde{X}_{(i-1)i}$. The associated state is $\hat{X}_i(t)$ (refer to Figure 2). Using the continuity of the ODE (8) with respect to initial conditions [18], an upper bound on the distance of the propagating states $\|\tilde{X}_i(t) - \hat{X}_i(t)\|$ may be found.

[5] The double index refers to the dynamical transition from phase $(i-1)$ to phase i.

[6] It may be argued that the perturbed and unperturbed dynamics do not necessarily enter phase i at the same instant. However given the autonomous nature of the dynamics at hand, we only wish to show that their respective orbits remain close. Thus, the perturbed and unperturbed states may become separated (unsynchronized) in time.

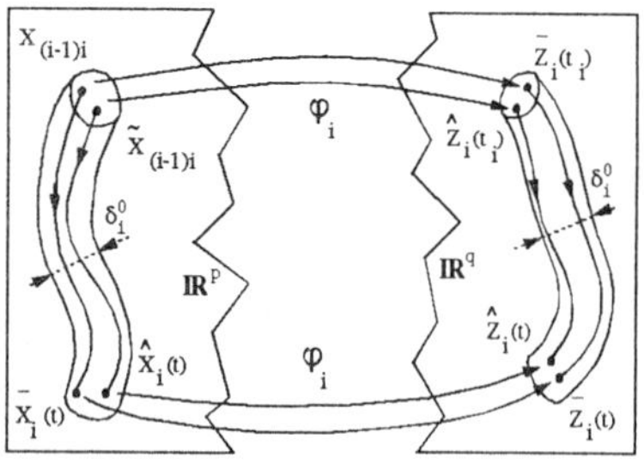

Figure 2: Dynamics of the reduced system (8) starting from the two initial states $\tilde{X}_{(i-1)i}$ and $X_{(i-1)i}$. Both fast and slow states are close (within δ_i^0) to each other provided that $\tilde{X}_{(i-1)i}$ and $X_{(i-1)i}$ are close within δ_{i-1}.

Next, we use Tikhonov's theorem to relate the perturbed dynamics to those of the reduced system (8) and find an upper bound on $||\hat{X}_i(t)-X_i(t)||$. Using the inequality (12), we compute an upper bound estimate of $||\tilde{X}_i(t)-\hat{X}_i(t)||$. Using the triangle inequality, an arbitrary upper bound estimate δ_i of $||\tilde{X}_i(t)-X_i(t)||$ is found provided that $||\tilde{X}_{(i-1)i}-X_{(i-1)i}|| < \delta_{i-1}$ and the perturbation parameters ϵ, μ, and η are small enough.

The next step is to show that the state $X_{i(i+1)}$ associated to the vanishing of the termination index F_i can be controlled within a δ_i-neighborhood of $\tilde{X}_{i(i+1)}$. The proof uses basically the smoothness of F_i and F_{i_r} and consequently applies Lipshitz conditions leading to an upper bound estimate for $|F_i(X_i(t), Z_i(t)) - F_{i,d}(\tilde{X}_i(t))|$. □

Thus, the slow dynamics in each phase closely approach their design system counterparts for small enough ϵ, μ, η and for close enough starting initial conditions. The following proposition extends these results to show similar properties on a complete cycle of n dynamical phases. Specifically, the proposition shows that the first return $Q = \phi_{\epsilon,\mu,\eta}(P)$ of a point P close to $\tilde{P}$ lies in the neighborhood of $\tilde{Q} = \tilde{\phi}(\tilde{P})$ with $\tilde{P}$ a fixed arbitrary point on $\overset{o}{\Sigma}$.[7]

Proposition 2.2 *For any open neighborhood $O_\delta(\tilde{Q}) = B_\delta(\tilde{Q}) \cap \Sigma$, there[8] exist an open ball $I_{\delta_0}(\tilde{P}) = B_{\delta_0}(\tilde{P}) \cap \Sigma$ and $\epsilon_0, \mu_0, \eta_0 > 0$ small enough such that for any $P \in I_{\delta_0}(\tilde{P})$ $\epsilon < \epsilon_0$, $\mu < \mu_0$ and $\eta < \eta_0$, $\phi_{\epsilon,\mu,\eta}(P) \in O_\delta(\tilde{Q})$.*

Proof Define the set $C^\delta_{\tilde{\Lambda}} \subset A_X$ where δ is positive and $\tilde{\Lambda}$ is the complete unperturbed trajectory emanating at $\tilde{P} = \tilde{X}_1(0)$ and ending at $\tilde{Q} = \tilde{\phi}(\tilde{P})$ on Σ. The initial state of the perturbed dynamics is $(X_1(0), Z_1(0))$ where $Z_1(0)$ is in the basin of attraction associated to the fast dynamics. The proof uses the previous general result, patch the individual dynamics and show global properties of the complete perturbed dynamics. Hence in order to "fit" the complete perturbed trajectory inside $C^\delta_{\tilde{\Lambda}}$, we start by choosing[9] $\delta_{n+1} \leq \delta$ and then find $\delta_n \leq \delta$, ϵ_{n+1}, μ_{n+1} and η_{n+1} as described earlier in proposition 2.1. We recursively repeat the same procedure over the n phases so that if $\epsilon_0 = \min\{\epsilon_1, \epsilon_2 \ldots \epsilon_n, \epsilon_{n+1}\}$, $\mu_0 = \min\{\mu_1, \mu_2 \ldots \mu_n, \mu_{n+1}\}$ and $\eta_0 = \min\{\eta_1, \eta_2 \ldots \eta_n, \eta_{n+1}\}$, the slow perturbed trajectory is in a δ- neighborhood of its reduced counterpart. The perturbed initial state P on Σ is in $I_{\delta_0}(\tilde{P})$ and its first mapped return Q is in $O_\delta(\tilde{Q})$. □

[7] $\overset{o}{\Sigma}$ is the interior of Σ

[8] $B_\delta(\tilde{Q})$ is an open ball in $I\!R^p$ of radius δ and centered at $\tilde{Q}$.

Thus far, we have shown that for an initial point $\tilde{P}$ on $\overset{o}{\Sigma}$, there exist perturbation parameters ϵ_0, μ_0, η_0 for which all initial perturbed states in a δ_0-neighborhood of $\tilde{P}$ on Σ map to a δ-neighborhood of $\tilde{Q}$. In particular, Proposition 2.2 holds for $P = \tilde{P} = X(0)$. Thus after one complete cycle, we have the approximation

$$X(t) = \tilde{X}(t) + \mathcal{O}(\delta).$$

The next step of the perturbation analysis is to show how the local results extend to a "global" characterization of perturbed dynamics (note the choice of ϵ_0, μ_0, η_0 depends on $\tilde{P}$). The following proposition shows that one set of the perturbation parameters $(\tilde{\epsilon}, \tilde{\mu}, \tilde{\eta})$ is sufficient to approximate the perturbed dynamics by those of the unperturbed dynamics on a whole closed set of initial states.

Proposition 2.3 *For any closed bounded subset I in Σ, there exists $\tilde{\epsilon}$, $\tilde{\mu}$, $\tilde{\eta}$ small enough such that $\phi_{\epsilon,\mu,\eta}(M) \in O_\delta(\tilde{\phi}(M))$ for any point $M \in I$ and $\epsilon < \tilde{\epsilon}$, $\mu < \tilde{\mu}$, $\eta < \tilde{\eta}$.*

Proof: The set I is closed and bounded, hence it is compact. It follows that among the infinite family $\{I_{\delta_0}(M)\}$ of open sets of Σ that cover I, a finite number of these sets $\{I_{\delta_{0_k}}(M_k)\}$ $k = 1 \ldots m$ can cover I. Let $\tilde{\epsilon} = min\{\epsilon_{0_k}\}$, $\tilde{\mu} = min\{\mu_{0_k}\}$, $\tilde{\eta} = min\{\eta_{0_k}\}$, $k = 1 \ldots m$. Thus for all $\epsilon < \tilde{\epsilon}$, $\mu < \tilde{\mu}$, $\eta < \tilde{\eta}$, we have necessarily $\phi_{\epsilon,\mu,\eta}(M) \in O_\delta(\tilde{\phi}(M))$ for any point $M \in I$. □

The topological (qualitative) properties of the complete perturbed dynamics can now be analyzed. In particular, knowing the attraction property of the flow of the design system to a torus-like set, we expect the perturbed dynamics to exhibit the same behavioral features. A preliminary result concerning the behavior of the perturbed dynamics in the vicinity of $\Omega(\tilde{\phi})$ is provided in the following proposition which shows that the map $\phi_{\epsilon,\mu,\eta}$ is invariant[10] for some closed set containing $\Omega(\tilde{\phi}) \cap \Sigma$.

Proposition 2.4 *There exists a closed set W in Σ containing $\Omega(\tilde{\phi}) \cap \Sigma$ and $\tilde{\epsilon} > 0$, $\tilde{\mu} > 0$, $\tilde{\eta} > 0$ small enough such that $\phi_{\epsilon,\mu,\eta}(W) \subset W$ for any $\epsilon < \tilde{\epsilon}$, $\mu < \tilde{\mu}$, $\eta < \tilde{\eta}$.*

Proof: Let $W = R_d \cap \Sigma$ be the closed set consisting of the intersection of Σ with the ring R_d. This set contains $\Omega(\tilde{\phi}) \cap \Sigma$. If we map W once under $\tilde{\phi}$ then $\tilde{\phi}(W)$ is

[9] $(n+1) \equiv 1 \ (mod\ n)$.

[10] A set S is invariant under $\phi_{\epsilon,\mu,\eta}$ if $\phi_{\epsilon,\mu,\eta}(S) \subset S$.

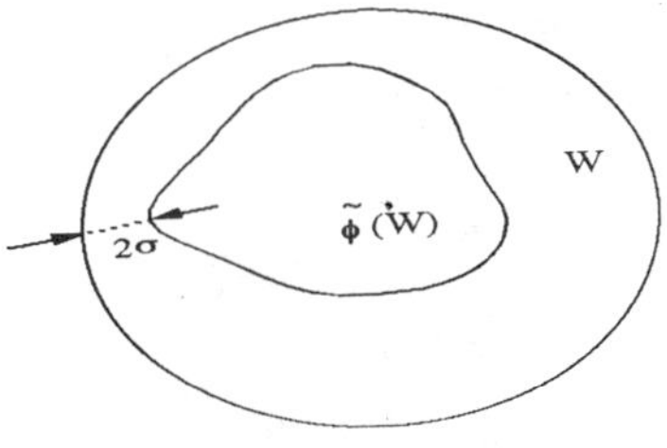

Figure 3: The flow $\mathcal{F}_d$ is invariant in R_d and contracts volumes during phase 1. Hence $\tilde{\phi}(W)$ is strictly inside W.

strictly contained in W ($\tilde{\phi}(W) \cap \partial W$ is empty). In particular $\tilde{\phi}(W) \subset W$ and $\inf_{X \in \partial W, Y \in \partial \tilde{\phi}(W)} \|X - Y\| > 2\sigma > 0$ (refer to Figure 3). This is so because of the assumption that the flow points inwards on the surface of the ring R_d during phase 1.

Now, if M is a point in W, then according to proposition 2.3, there corresponds for σ perturbation parameters $\tilde{\epsilon}$, $\tilde{\mu}$ and $\tilde{\eta}$ for which

$$(\epsilon < \tilde{\epsilon}, \quad \mu < \tilde{\mu}, \quad \eta < \tilde{\eta}) \Longrightarrow \phi_{\epsilon,\mu,\eta}(M) \in O_\sigma(\tilde{\phi}(M)).$$

But then by construction, $O_\sigma(\tilde{\phi}(M)) \subset W$. Hence, it follows that W is invariant under the perturbed mapping $\phi_{\epsilon,\mu,\eta}$. □

This proposition shows the flow invariance to hold locally in the vicinity of the torus-like structure $\Omega(\tilde{\phi})$. But how about the perturbed dynamical flow behavior for initial states far away from this set? The next theorem provides an answer to this question and uses all the previous results to make a general assessment regarding the global stability of the complete perturbed system dynamics.

Theorem 2.1 *There exist $\tilde{\epsilon} > 0$, $\tilde{\mu} > 0$, $\tilde{\eta} > 0$ small enough such that for any $\epsilon < \tilde{\epsilon}$, $\mu < \tilde{\mu}$, $\eta < \tilde{\eta}$, the trajectory of the propagating state X in A_X of the perturbed dynamics is eventually located inside R_d.*

Proof: Under the dynamics of the unperturbed model, the evolving state $\tilde{X}$ asymptotically approaches $\Omega(\mathcal{F}_d)$. Thus, the propagating state $\tilde{X}(t)$, starting from the initial state at M, eventually impacts the set $\overset{o}{W}$ after a finite time t_m corresponding to m dynamical cycles. It was shown earlier in proposition 2.3 that $\phi_{\epsilon,\mu,\eta}(M)$ is uniformly continuous at $\epsilon = \mu = \eta = 0$ in $\mathbf{\Sigma}$. The same is true for the iterated map $\phi^j_{\epsilon,\mu,\eta}(M)$. In particular for that number of dynamical cycles $j = m$, and given that $\mathbf{\Sigma}$ is closed and bounded, there exist (proposition 2.3) $\check{\epsilon}$, $\check{\mu}$, $\check{\eta}$ positive such that $\phi^m_{\epsilon,\mu,\eta}(\Sigma) \subset W$ for all $\epsilon < \check{\epsilon}$, $\mu < \check{\mu}$, $\eta < \check{\eta}$. On the other hand, W is shown to be invariant (proposition 2.4) under $\phi_{\epsilon,\mu,\eta}$ for $\epsilon < \check{\epsilon}$, $\mu < \check{\mu}$, $\eta < \check{\eta}$. Now, a choice of $\tilde{\epsilon} = \min\{\check{\epsilon}, \check{\epsilon}\}$, $\tilde{\mu} = \min\{\check{\mu}, \check{\mu}\}$, and $\tilde{\eta} = \min\{\check{\eta}, \check{\eta}\}$ guarantee $\phi^r_{\epsilon,\mu,\eta}(M) \in W$ for $r \geq m$ and $\epsilon < \tilde{\epsilon}$, $\mu < \tilde{\mu}$, $\eta < \tilde{\eta}$. Moreover, all perturbed orbits after r cycles are contained in R_d. □

Conclusion

This paper addresses the control design problem of a "complex" system exhibiting cyclic motions using model reduction techniques. The basic idea is to reduce the complexity of the system dynamics to a simpler design model for which a robust controller can be designed. A theoretical foundation is provided which motivates this control design method. The main contribution of this work is a rigorous analysis of cyclic perturbed motions obtained by patching several distinct dynamics. Both singular and regular perturbation theory are used for the analysis. This paper extends beyond the work of the legged locomotion dynamics [9,10] to encompass more general systems.

The analysis results are similar to those for ordinary systems possessing only one type of dynamics: If the controlled design dynamics possess a single stable attractor and if the fast (or unmodeled) dynamics are asymptotically stable, then the physical system asymptotic motion is qualitatively similar to that of the design system. In particular, theorem 2.1 shows that for small enough perturbation parameters, both physical and design biped motions share the same qualitative properties.

References

[1] V. I. Utkin, *J. of Automatic Control*, Vol. 2, pp. 212-220, 1977.

[2] J. J. Slotine and S. S. Sastry, *Int. J. of Control*, Vol. 38, pp. 465-492, 1983.

[3] B. Fernandez and J. K. Hedrick, *Int. J. of Control*, Vol. 46, pp. 1019-1040, 1987.

[4] H. K. Khalil, *IEEE Transactions on Automatic Control* , Vol. 26, No. 2, April 1981, pp. 524-526.

[5] H. Hemami, R. Tomovic, and A. Z. Ceranowicz, *J. of Bioengineering*, Vol. 2, pp. 477-494, 1978.

[6] H. Hemami, and V. Jaswa, *IEEE Transactions on systems, man and cybernetics*, Vol. 8, 1978, pp. 477-494.

[7] M. H. Raibert, *Legged robots that balance*, MIT Press, Cambridge, 1986.

[8] R. Katoh and M. Mori, *Automatica* Vol. 20, 1984, pp. 405-414.

[9] H. M. Hmam and D. A. Lawrence, the 31st *IEEE Conference on Decision and Control*, December 1992.

[10] H.M. Hmam, *Biped Control Via Nonlinear Dynamics*, Ph. D dissertation, University of Cincinnati, June 1992.

[11] P. V. Kokotovic, H. K. Khalil, and J. O'Reilly, *Singular Perturbation Methods in Control: Analysis and Design*, Academic Press, London, 1986.

[12] P. V. Kokotovic, *SIAM Review* , Vol. 26, No. 4, Oct 1981, pp. 501-550.

[13] A. B. Vasil'eva, *Russian Mathematical surveys*, Vol. 18, 1963, pp. 13-81.

[14] P. V. Kokotovic and H. K. Khalil, *Singular Perturbations in Systems and Control*, IEEE Press, 1986.

[15] D. R. J. Chillingworth, *Differential Topology with a View to Applications*, Pitman, 1976.

[16] J. Guckenheimer, and P. Holmes, *Nonlinear Oscillations, Dynamical Systems and Bifurcations of Vector fields*, Springer-Verlag, New York, 1983.

[17] D. K. Arrowsmith and C. M. Place, *An Introduction to Dynamical Systems*, Cambridge University Press, Cambridge, 1990.

[18] M. W. Hirsh and S. Smale, *Differential equations, Dynamical Systems and Linear Algebra*, Academic Press, New York, 1974.

Proceedings of the
American Control Conference
San Francisco, California • June 1993

Destabilizing effects of muscular co-contraction in human-machine interaction

Karin Hollerbach
Graduate Group in Bioengineering

C. F. Ramos
Neurosciences Division

H. Kazerooni
Department of
Mechanical Engineering

University of California, Berkeley, CA 94720

Abstract

We are studying the control of human arm movements that are constrained by physical interaction with a machine such as a hand controller or a telerobotic system. One of the difficulties in controlling this type of constrained interaction is instability in the human arm-machine system. In this article, we present simulation results showing that increasing muscular co-contraction destabilizes human-machine interaction. Results of this work may have an impact on the design of machines that are to interact with humans.

Nomenclature

L	=	agonist muscle
R	=	antagonist muscle
a	=	joint acceleration
Bh	=	muscle damping constant
Bp	=	passive tissue damping
$B_{vL,R}$	=	muscle damping element
$f_{L,R}$	=	actual muscle tension
Jp	=	passive tissue inertia
K_1	=	muscle spring stiffness
K_2	=	muscle spring stiffness
Kp	=	passive tissue stiffness
$n_{L,R}$	=	neural input to muscle
$t_{L,R}$	=	hypothetical muscle tension
T	=	time constant
v	=	joint velocity
$v_{L,R}$	=	muscle velocity
$x_{L,R}$	=	muscle position
θ	=	joint position

1. Instability in human-machine interaction

When the human arm is interacting directly with a machine, its movement is constrained through physical contact with the machine; i.e., the human arm moves in such a way that the machine continuously exerts a dynamic constraint on the arm. Examples of constrained movements can be seen when the arm is operating a hand controller [1] or a telerobotic system [3] or is moving an exercise machine or an orthotic device. In systems of this nature, the human arm dynamics are integrated with the machine dynamics, resulting in behavior specific to the total system. The performance and stability of the system taken as a whole are both functions of not only the machine dynamics, but also the human arm dynamics. Evidence for instability in a human-machine system involving an interaction force between the human and the machine, as well as force feedback compensation within the machine, has been shown [1,3]. The goal of this article is to determine whether increasing muscular co-contraction levels may be a cause of such instability.

Kazerooni [1] has demonstrated a relationship between stability in active hand controllers and compliance in the hand controller and in the human arm. (Active hand controllers are defined as powered, multi-degree-of-freedom joystick-like mechanisms that are maneuvered by a human to generate command signals.) In order to guarantee stability, some compliance in either the hand controller or in the human arm is required. We extend these results by presenting simulation results that demonstrate the destabilizing effects of increasing arm impedance by increasing muscular co-contraction levels explicitly.

Empirical evidence has shown that "rigidity" of a limb is increased by simultaneous co-contraction of antagonist muscles, resulting in more effective postural maintenance [5,9]. Furthermore, model simulation studies have shown that high co-contraction levels cause a strong resistance to low-frequency disturbing forces [5,10]. We note, however, that the focus of our studies is not posture maintenance in the presence of disturbing forces and torques; instead, we are interested in the behavior of the arm-machine system as the arm is constrained by continuous contact with the machine. The instability in this type of interaction may be described as an increasing tremor in the arm, rather than an inability to reject disturbing forces. The hypothesis of the present study is that increased co-contraction levels in the human arm contribute significantly to instability in the human-machine system.

2. Simulation study

In the simulation study described here, we used a non-linear, lumped-parameter, antagonist muscle model of single-joint movements of the human arm [4,7,8,10]. A brief description of the model and of external torques ("load disturbances") and position constraints applied to the model in the present study is shown in Figure 1. The undisturbed agonist-antagonist muscle model is described by the following set of equations:

L = agonist muscle
R = antagonist muscle

$$\frac{d}{dt}\theta = v$$

$$\frac{d}{dt}x_L = \frac{t_L - f_L}{Bv_L} = v_L$$

$$\frac{d}{dt}x_R = \frac{-t_R + f_R}{Bv_R} = v_R$$

$$\frac{d}{dt}v = \frac{-K_p\theta - B_p v + f_L - f_R}{J_p} = a$$

$$\frac{d}{dt}t_L = \frac{n_L - t_L}{T}$$

$$\frac{d}{dt}t_R = \frac{n_R - t_R}{T}$$

$$f_L = K_1 (e^{K_2(x_L - \theta)} - 1)$$

$$f_R = K_1 (e^{K_2(x_R - \theta)} - 1)$$

$$Bv_L = \frac{1.25\, t_L}{B_h + |v_L|}$$

$$Bv_R = \frac{1.25\, t_R}{B_h + |v_R|}$$

The disturbances and constraints applied to the antagonist muscle model were used to model the possible modes of interaction of the human arm with the machine: it is possible for the machine to either apply a specific joint torque to the human arm, while allowing the human to determine the position; on the other hand, the machine may impose a position constraint, while the human imposes forces on the machine.

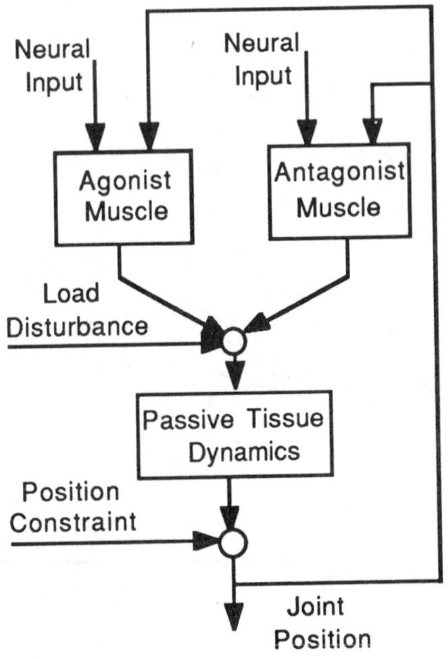

Figure 1. Model used in simulation studies. The model consists of an antagonist pair of muscles, a passive load, and neurological control signals to each muscle. Disturbances modeling machine input to the human arm may be imposed as load disturbances or as position constraints.

In the first three sets of simulations, we applied an external, time-varying load disturbance and examined the response of the system to the applied torque. These simulations involve predictable (constant or periodic) applied torques on the simulated arm. The model was simulated with varying co-contraction levels. Load disturbance amplitudes and co-contraction levels were normalized in the model, with minimum muscle forces at 80 grams and maximum muscles forces at 10,000 grams. The simulations were run for several seconds to observe long-term trends. However, plotted in each figure are the first 1000 milliseconds only, as this time proved to be sufficient to show the observed behavior.

In the first set of simulations, we applied a constant joint torque with an amplitude of 1000, comparable to a muscle force of 1000 grams (Figure 2). Co-contraction levels were varied from 6000 grams to 10,000 grams. In the results, increased levels of co-contraction correspond to an overall decrease in the position response (a smaller deviation from the initial position), and an increase in joint oscillation. The decrease in the amplitude of the position response represents an increase in the arm's ability to maintain its posture. The increase in joint oscillation (tremor) with increasing co-contraction levels, however, suggests a decrease in stability when the arm is disturbed by external forces. The frequency of the oscillations that result from a constant, externally applied joint torque in the presence of high co-contraction levels, is approximately 10 Hz.

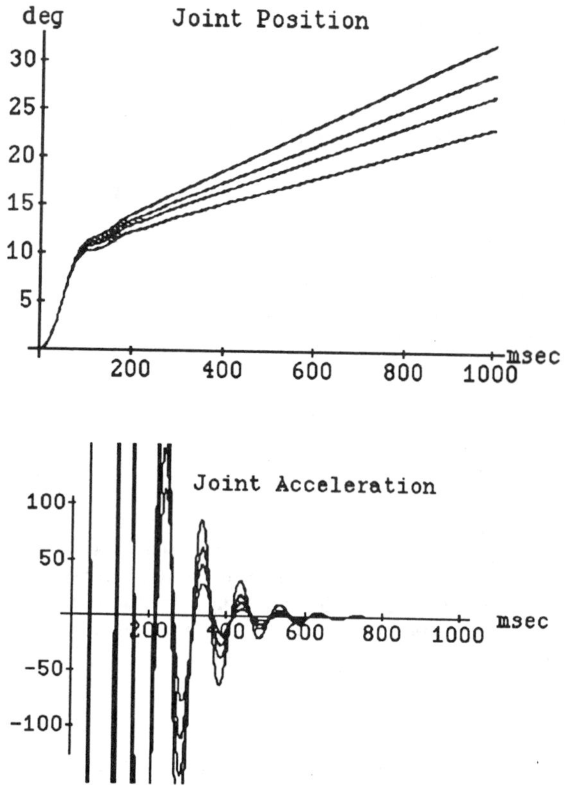

Figure 2. Joint position and acceleration as functions of time in response to a load disturbance with amplitude = 1000 grams. Co-contraction levels varied from 6000 grams to 7000, 8000, and 10,000 grams.

In the second set of simulations, we applied a sinusoidal torque disturbance with an amplitude of 1000 and a frequency of 10 Hz (Figure 3). In the steady state, the increase in co-contraction levels, from 5000 grams to 10,000 grams, caused an increase in the amplitude and a small decrease in the phase shift of the oscillations. As before, the increasing amplitude of the oscillations with increasing levels of co-contraction suggests a decrease in the stability of the arm.

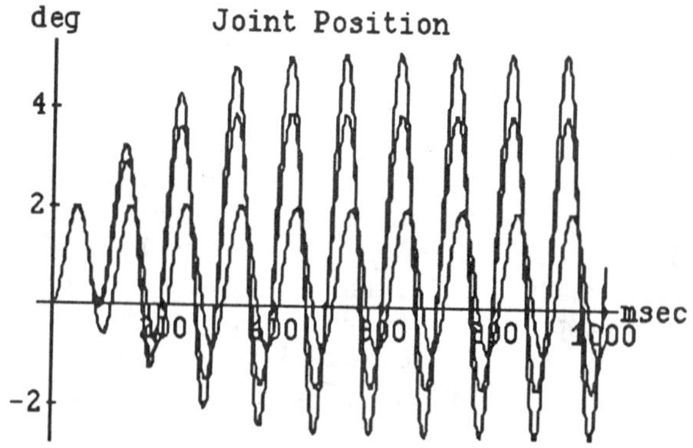

Figure 3. Joint position as a function of time in response to a sinusoidal applied torque with amplitude = 1000 grams and frequency = 10 Hz. Co-contraction levels varied from 5000 grams to 8000 grams and 10,000 grams.

In the third set of simulations (Figure 4) we examined the system's response to varying frequencies in the applied torque. The torque frequency was varied in order to determine whether the behavior pattern in response to the 10 Hz load is specific to 10 Hz loads. In Figure 4, the disturbance amplitude is 1000 grams, and co-contraction levels are high, at 9000 grams. An increase in disturbance frequency from 1 Hz to 5 Hz may be observed to cause a decrease in the amplitude of the position response. A further increase in frequency to 10 Hz decreased the mean position response but increased the amplitude.

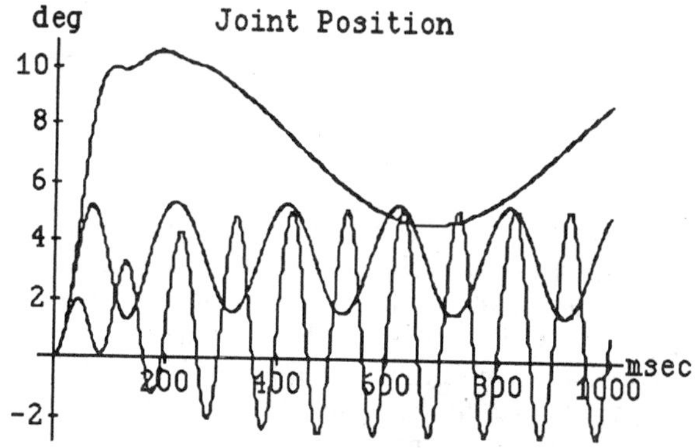

Figure 4. Joint position as a function of time in response to sinusoidal applied torque with amplitude = 1000 grams and frequencies = 1 Hz, 5 Hz, and 10 Hz. Co-contraction was kept high, at 9000 grams.

In the final set of simulations, we added a disturbance to the system, in the form of a position constraint imposed upon the arm. As before, we simulated the resulting model under varying mean co-contraction levels. The position constraint was taken from data measured in experiments with a real arm and machine; the resulting simulated contact force (between the human arm and the hypothetical machine imposing the position constraint in the simulation) was calculated and compared with the actual, experimental force data. The simulation, in this case, was run for several seconds. The applied position constraint is shown in Figure 5. Simulations were carried out at three different levels of co-contraction, 2000 grams, 5000 grams, and 9000 grams. The contact force, between the arm's endpoint (hand) and a hypothetical machine imposing the position constraint, was calculated and is shown in Figure 6. The force behavior at all three co-contraction levels is qualitatively similar to that observed in the laboratory. Increasing co-contraction levels, however, increases the amplitude of the contact force response.

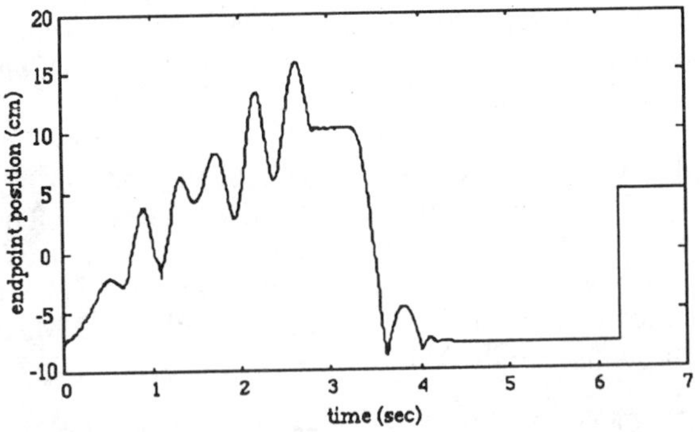

Figure 5. The joint position as a function of time. The position constraint shown here was imposed upon the arm, and the resulting contact forces between the human arm (hand) and a hypothetical machine imposing the constraint were calculated in the simulation and are shown in Figure 6.

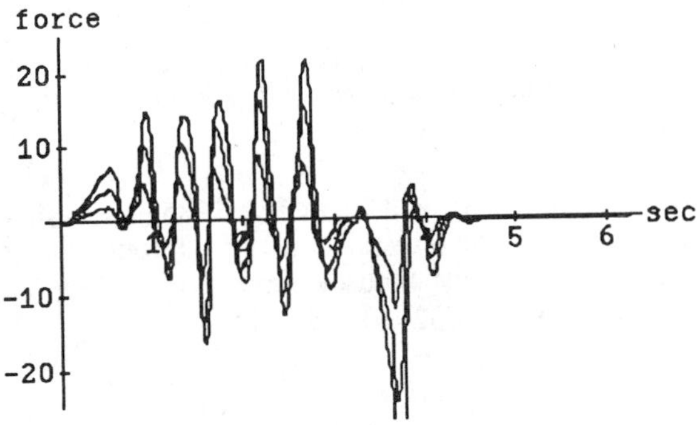

Figure 6. The contact force between the human arm (hand) and a hypothetical machine imposing the position constraint shown in Figure 5. The contact force is shown for three different co-contraction levels, 2000 grams, 5000 grams, and 9000 grams.

3. Discussion

It has been observed [1,2] that increasing human arm impedance leads to instability in human-machine interaction. The significance of the work presented here is to examine the specific link between increasing muscular co-contraction levels in the arm and instability. In order to test the hypothesis that increased co-contraction leads to instability, we simulated single joint arm behavior with load disturbances and position constraints that might be imposed on the arm by an actual machine.

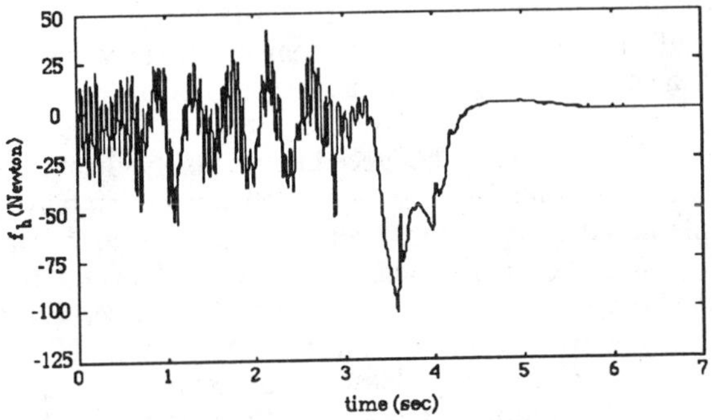

Figure 7. The contact force between the arm (hand) and the machine, as measured by sensors in the machine. The contact force was generated in response to the imposed position constraint shown in Figure 5. For more information on how these data were gathered, the reader is referred to (2).

Our simulations indicate that high co-contraction levels lead to smaller steady-state displacements of the arm, in response to applied load disturbances; i.e., high co-contraction levels improve the disturbance rejection properties of the arm. This result supports previous data [5,10] regarding the role of co-contraction levels in posture maintenance. However, our simulation results indicate that, in the presence of such externally imposed constraints, high co-contraction levels do lead to increasing transient oscillation of the arm. This oscillation, unless it is sufficiently filtered out by the machine, could be enough to cause growing oscillations, leading to total (unbounded) instability of the human-machine system.

The model used in the simulations permitted us to specify the co-contraction levels explicitly. We tested the effects of co-contraction levels in several sets of circumstances. The first included constant and periodic applied joint torques. In all cases, increasing co-contraction in the muscles led to increased tremor. Increased co-contraction in the presence of applied joint torques, thus, tended to destabilize the system. In the last set of simulations, a position constraint was applied to the arm, and the resulting contact force was calculated at three different co-contraction levels. The position constraint data were taken directly from an experiment using a real machine and human. In that experiment, the machine was commanded to move along a trajectory, imposing the position constraint shown in Figure 5. The contact forces in the resulting, unstable system were measured and are shown in Figure 7, for comparison with the calculated contact forces shown in Figure 6. We note the similarity of the low frequency components of the measured force in Figure 7[1] to the calculated force in Figure 6. In addition, we observe that, while qualitatively the force response is similar at all co-contraction levels, the amplitude of the force increases with increasing co-contraction. Thus, the simulations that were used to verify the arm model's predictions appear to be in agreement with experimental data gathered using a real machine and human.

The results of the preceding sections indicate that co-contraction of the muscles in the human arm plays a role in determining the relative stability of the human arm-machine-load system. Increasing co-contraction increases the magnitude of the arm's impedance. When it becomes great enough, the magnitude of the impedance causes at least a conservative Nyquist stability condition describing the human-machine system to fail [2] As a result, the stability of the system can no longer be guaranteed. Thus, the model predicts one cause of instability in the arm-machine-load system: increasing muscular co-contraction.

4. Summary

In this article, we use a model of the human arm to predict one cause of instability in a human arm-machine-load system: increased co-contraction of the arm muscles. This prediction is based on experimental observations indicating that varying arm impedance causes instability. The prediction of the model is verified using data from a simulation and compared with experimental observations. Other factors that may play a significant role in causing instability include machine and compensator design. It is the interaction of each of these factors that ultimately determines the stability of the system, and it is the understanding of this interaction that is the goal of this research. In future research, we plan to test these simulation results with an actual machine simulating the modeled arm behavior.

[1]The high frequency components of the force shown in Figure 7 represent unmodeled dynamics of the sensors in the real robot and should not be expected to be duplicated in the simulation results.

5. References

[1] Kazerooni, H., 1990, Human-robot interaction via the transfer of power and information signals. *IEEE Trans. on Systems and Cybern.*, Vol. 20, No. 2, 450-463.

[2] Kazerooni, H., 1992, Human-induced instability in powered hand controllers. *Proc. of the 1992 IEEE Intl. Conf. on Robotics and Automation.*

[3] Kazerooni, H., Tsay, T.I., and Hollerbach, Karin, 1993, A controller design framework for telerobotic systems (to appear).

[4] Kim, W. S., Lee, S. H., Hannaford, B. and Stark, L., 1984, Inverse Modeling to obtain head movement controller signal. *Proc. of the IEEE 20th Annual Conf. on Manual Control.* 601-620.

[5] Murray, W. R. and Hogan, N., 1989, Experimental observations on the maintenance of elbow posture in the presence of disturbances. *Issues in The Modeling and Control of Biomechanical Systems* (Edited by J. L. Stein, J. A. Ashton-Miller, and M. G. Pandy), pp. 19-28. ASME.

[6] Ogata, K., 1970, *Modern control engineering.* Prentice-Hall, Inc., pp. 407-417.

[7] Ramos, C. F. and Stark, L., 1987, Simulation studies of descending and reflex control of fast movements. *J. Motor Behav.* **19**:38-62.

[8] Ramos, C. F., Hacisalihzade, S. S., and Stark, L., 1990, Behavior Space of a stretch reflex model and its implications for the neural control of voluntary movements. *Med. & Biol. Eng. & Comput.*, **28**:15-23.

[9] Wilkie, D. R., 1950, The relation between force and velocity in human muscle. *J. Physiol.* K110, pp. 248-280.

[10] Winters, J. M. and Stark, L., 1985, Analysis of fundamental human movement patterns through the use of in-depth antagonistic muscle models. *IEEE Trans. on Biomed. Engr.* BME32, 10, 826-839.

Proceedings of the
American Control Conference
San Francisco, California • June 1993

Kinematics and Workspace of a Rolling Disk between Planar Manipulators

Sunil Kumar Agrawal, Assistant Professor
R. Pandravada, Graduate Student

Department of Mechanical Engineering
Ohio University, Athens, OH 45701.

Abstract

The following properties are well known for systems with rolling constraints: (a) constraints of rolling are expressed in terms of rate variables that describe the system, (b) these constraints are nonintegrable for systems having spatial motion and integrable for systems restricted to a plane. The integrability of the rolling constraint equations for planar systems has the following consequences: (a) the position kinematics equations explicitly contain the initial conditions unlike the position kinematics equations for robots without rolling constraints, (b) the presence of initial conditions in the position kinematics equations makes the joint solutions, workspace, and motion plans dependent on the initial conditions. In other words, the start conditions determine whether the robot will reach a desired goal position. This behavior is quite different from the behavior of industrial robots which have fixed workspace and kinematic solutions independent of start configuration.

This paper presents studies on a rolling disk between two planar manipulators. The objectives of this paper are to: (a) present position kinematics, list upper bounds on the number of solutions, and investigate the effects of initial conditions, and (b) compute workspace analytically and study the effects of initial conditions. These studies are worthy of presentation because the work described in this paper on the effects of initial conditions on kinematics and workspace of planar rolling systems is novel. The planar rolling systems also act as an important subset of spatial rolling systems for which a variety of algorithms for motion planning have been proposed.

1 Introduction

Over the last few decades, extensive efforts have been devoted by researchers in developing intelligent mechanical systems that can perform fine manipulation. Multifingered systems such as Stanford-JPL hand [8], Utah Dextrous hand [2], In-parallel actuated mechanisms [10] were designed to study algorithms for coordination and control. A variety of studies were conducted on mechanics of grasping and multifingered hands ([3], [5]). During assembly, it is not uncommon to encounter situations where the contact between bodies is pure rolling. The motion planning of spatial rolling systems becomes difficult due to non-integrability of the constraints ([9], [7], [4]). The rolling constraints can not be integrated to give constraint equations on the position variables that describe the system. Non-holonomic constraints are also encountered in the study of wheeled mobile robots and free-floating space robots[1].

In planar manipulation, such as rolling disks between planar manipulators, the rolling constraints are integrable. The rolling constraints can be expressed as displacement equations in the appropriate joint variables and their initial conditions. The study of planar rolling systems is challenging, unique, and worthy of study due to the presence of initial conditions in the governing kinematic equations. It is demonstrated in this paper that the inclusion of rolling contsraints results in a higher upper bound on the joint solutions compared to structurally similar mechanisms without rolling constraints. The reachable workspace changes with initial assembly configuration of the mechanism. As a result, the question of selection of initial conditions during path planning becomes important. The organization of this paper is as follows: Section 2 describes the rolling system under study and its governing equations. Section 3 describes the kinematic solutions and the effects of initial conditions. Section 4 outlines an analytical procedure to find the workspace of the disk center along with the effects of the initial conditions.

2 A Planar Rolling System

A computer solid model of the system under study is shown in Fig. 1. The system has two planar chains A and B with two revolute joints. A rolling gear D meshes in racks at the end of the two chains. As a result, pure rolling is achieved between the gear and the two manipulators. For kinematic modeling, a stick figure of the rolling system is shown in Figure 2. This figure reduces to that of the designed exper-

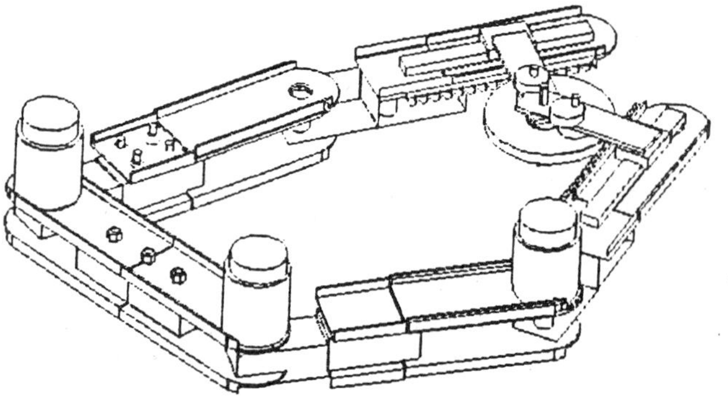

Figure 1: A computer solid model of a planar rolling system constructed at Ohio University.

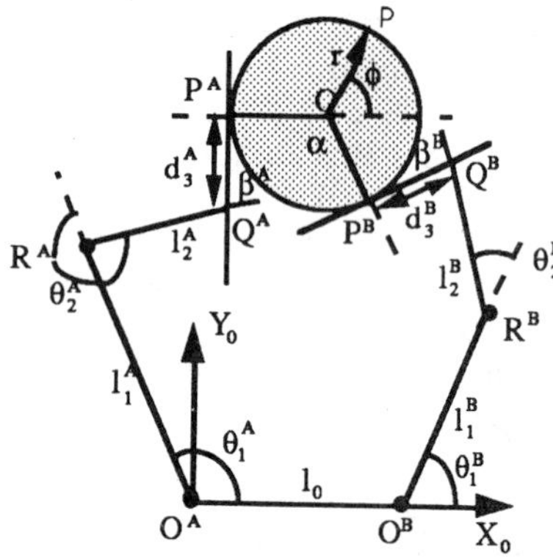

Figure 2: A stick figure of a rolling disk between two planar manipulators.

iment when $\beta^A = 0$ and $\beta^B = \pi$.

The link dimensions and the joint angles of the chains A and B are identified respectively with superscripts A and B. The dimension of the links i, $i \in 1,2$ of chain j, $j \in (A, B)$, are l^j_i. A chain j is described by three variables: θ^j_1, θ^j_2, and d^j_3 which are shown in the figure. The lines R^jQ^j and Q^jP^j make an angle β^j with each other. An inertially fixed coordinate frame $\mathcal{F}_0$ is attached to the base at O^A. The distance O^AO^B is l_0. The radius of the disk is r and the coordinates of the disk center O is (x_e, y_e). The normals P^AO and P^BO at the point of contact between the disk and the end-effector link subtend an angle α as shown in the figure.

The loop closure of the X position of the disk center via chains A and B results in the following equations:

$$\begin{aligned} x_e &= l^A_1c^A_1 + l^A_2c^A_{12} + d^A_3c^A_{12'} + rc^A_{12''} \\ &= l_0 + l^B_1c^B_1 + l^B_2c^B_{12} + d^B_3c^B_{12'} + rc^B_{12''} \end{aligned} \quad (1)$$

and the Y position of the center of the disk results in:

$$\begin{aligned} y_e &= l^A_1s^A_1 + l^A_2s^A_{12} + d^A_3s^A_{12'} + rs^A_{12''} \\ &= l^B_1s^B_1 + l^B_2s^B_{12} + d^B_3s^B_{12'} + rs^B_{12''} \end{aligned} \quad (2)$$

where $c^j_i = cos(\theta^j_i)$ and $s^j_i = sin(\theta^j_i)$. The angles in the last two equations are: $12^j = \theta^j_1 + \theta^j_2$, $12'^j = \theta^j_1 + \theta^j_2 + \beta^j$, $12''^j = \theta^j_1 + \theta^j_2 + \beta^j + \frac{3\pi}{2}$, $j \in A, B$. The loop closure on the angle loop gives:

$$\theta^A_{12''} + \alpha = \theta^B_{12''} \quad (3)$$

Commonly, the rolling constraints are non-holonomic, i.e., they are described as a non-integrable function of the joint rates in the system. However, in the planar case, these constraints are integrable, i.e., they can be described in terms of displacement of the disk along the surface of the manipulator chain. These rolling constraints can be obtained in the following way: Let us assume that in the initial assembly configuration of the manipulator, a line OP fixed on the disk is coincident with the normal at P^A. At a later instant, let the angle between this line OP and P^AO be ϕ. From the equations of rolling in a plane, the following must be satisfied:

$$d^A_3 - d^A_{30} = r\phi \quad (4)$$

where d^A_{30} is the value of d^A_3 in the initial assembly configuration. At this same instant, the rolling of the disk relative to the other chain B gives:

$$d^B_3 - d^B_{30} = r(-\alpha + \phi) + r\alpha_0 \quad (5)$$

where d^B_{30} is the value of d^B_3 and α_0 is the value of α in the initial assembly configuration. Eliminating ϕ between equations (4) and (5), we obtain the following equation for rolling:

$$d^B_3 - d^A_3 = d^B_{30} - d^A_{30} + r(\alpha_0 - \alpha) \quad (6)$$

These equations can be summarized as follows: The system is described by nine variables x_e, y_e, α, θ^A_1, θ^A_2, d^A_3, θ^B_1, θ^B_2, d^B_3 and three initial conditions d^A_{30}, d^B_{30}, and α_0. The angles β^A and β^B are parameters. These nine variables are subjected to six constraint equations (1)-(3), and (6). Hence, all nine variables can be determined when a set of three independent variables are specified.

3 Kinematic Solutions

The constraint equation (6) relates d^A_3 and d^B_3 linearly to the joint angle α. d^A_3 and d^B_3, on the other hand, are 'trig' functions of α in (1)-(2). With this form of the governing equations, for an arbitrary set of three variables, closed-form solution of the other six variables is not possible. In order to plan motion of the disk center, one needs to relate x_e, y_e and a third variable to the joint angles of the system. It is shown in this section that a closed-form analytical solution of θ^A_1, θ^A_2, d^A_3, and θ^B_1, θ^B_2, d^B_3 is possible only if α is chosen as the third independent variable. Even though, this is not the classical inverse kinematics described in the literature, it is justified to take α as an independent variable due to the following reasons: (a) α measures the relative approach angle between the end-effectors of the two manipulators and is an important manipulation variable. A very low or a very high α makes the system unstable from the perspective of force closure. (b) closed form solutions of the joint angles is computationally more attractive than solving sets of transcendental equations.

The X and Y position loop closure equations of chain A from eqs. (1) and (2) can be written as follows:

$$x_e - (l_2^A + d_3^A c_\beta^A + r s_\beta^A) c_{12}^A - (-d_3^A s_\beta^A + r c_\beta^A) s_{12}^A = l_1^A c_1^A$$
$$y_e - (l_2^A + d_3^A c_\beta^A + r s_\beta^A) s_{12}^A - (d_3^A s_\beta^A - r c_\beta^A) c_{12}^A = l_1^A s_1^A \quad (7)$$

On squaring and adding, we eliminate θ_1^A and the resulting equation can be written as:

$$d_3^{A^2} + K_2 d_3^A + K_1 = 0 \quad (8)$$

where K_1 and K_2 are functions of the angles θ_{12}^A. From the above equation, d_3^A can be solved as:

$$d_3^A = \frac{-K_2 \pm \sqrt{K_2{}^2 - 4K_1}}{2} \quad (9)$$

Similarly, the X and Y position loop closure equations of chain B can be written as:

$$(x_e - l_0) - (l_2^B + d_3^B c_\beta^B + r s_\beta^B) c_{12}^B - (-d_3^B s_\beta^B + r c_\beta^B) s_{12}^B$$
$$= l_1^B c_1^B$$
$$y_e - (l_2^B + d_3^B c_\beta^B + r s_\beta^B) s_{12}^B - (d_3^B s_\beta^B - r c_\beta^B) c_{12}^B$$
$$= l_1^B s_1^B \quad (10)$$

On squaring and adding the above two equations, we eliminate θ_1^B. Substituting from the angle loop closure $\theta_{12}^A + \beta^A + \alpha = \theta_{12}^B + \beta^B$, we can rewrite the equation as:

$$d_3^{B^2} + K_3 d_3^B + K_4 = 0 \quad (11)$$

where K_3 and K_4 are functions of the joint angle θ_{12}^A. From the above equation, d_3^B can be solved as:

$$d_3^B = \frac{-K_3 \pm \sqrt{K_3{}^2 - 4K_4}}{2} \quad (12)$$

Substituting the values for d_3^A from (9) and d_3^B from (12) in equation (6), we obtain:

$$-K_3 \pm \sqrt{K_3{}^2 - 4K_4} + K_2 \pm \sqrt{K_2{}^2 - 4K_1} = 2K \quad (13)$$

The equation (13) is a function of only one variable θ_{12}^A. On simplification and collecting the coefficients, it can be shown that the above equation can be rewritten as:

$$K_6 s_{12}^{A^3} + K_7 c_{12}^{A^3} + K_8 c_{12}^A s_{12}^{A^2} + K_9 s_{12}^A c_{12}^{A^2}$$
$$+ K_{10} s_{12}^A c_{12}^A + K_{11} c_{12}^{A^2} + K_{12} s_{12}^{A^2}$$
$$+ K_{13} s_{12}^A + K_{14} c_{12}^A + K_{15} = 0 \quad (14)$$

On substituting $s_{12}^A = \frac{2x}{1+x^2}$ and $c_{12}^A = \frac{1-x^2}{1+x^2}$ in (14), the equation reduces to a sixth degree polynomial in x:

$$a_6 x^6 + a_5 x^5 + a_4 x^4 + a_3 x^3 + a_2 x^2 + a_1 x + a_0 = 0 \quad (15)$$

This equation has a maximum of 6 real roots of x, hence upto 6 solutions of θ_{12}^A are possible. For every θ_{12}^A, there are two solutions of d_3^A from (9) and two solutions of d_3^B from (12). For a set of θ_{12}^A, d_3^A, and d_3^B there is a single θ_1^A and θ_1^B which can be calculated using eqns. (7) and (10) respectively. Hence, a maximum of 24 real joint solution sets are possible for every specified x_e, y_e, α and d_{30}^A, d_{30}^B, α_0. The expressions for K_i and a_i appearing in this section are not listed to keep the paper short but are available in the forthcoming M.S. thesis[6]. It is important to point out that if the rolling contacts between the disk and the manipulator were replaced by prismatic or revolute joints, the maximum number of kinematic solutions are limited to 4, as opposed to 24 solutions obtained in this paper.

3.1 Representative Solutions

Figure 3 shows sixteen inverse solutions of the mechanism for a given position and orientation of the disk. The numerical values chosen for this display are: (a) $l_1^A = l_2^A = l_1^B = l_2^B = 1.0$, $r = 0.75$, $l_0 = 2.0$, (b) $\alpha_0 = -285.6°$, $d_{30}^A = 0.3848$, $d_{30}^B = 0.476$, (c) $x_e = 0.999$, $y_e = 2.402$, $\alpha = -287.6°$, and $\beta^A = \beta^B = 90°$. At this point, 4 real solutions of the polynomial (15) were obtained and the resulting 16 mechanism configurations are shown in Fig 3. From our simulations, we observed that even though the predicted upper bound on the number of solutions is 24, only 16 real solutions were obtained.

3.2 Dependence on Initial Condition

The initial conditions appear in the inverse solutions through the rolling constraint eq. (6) which can be rewritten as:

$$d_3^B - d_3^A + r\alpha = d_{30}^B - d_{30}^A + r\alpha_0 = K \quad (16)$$

where the effects of the initial conditions d_{30}^B, d_{30}^A, and α_0 are aggregated on the right hand side of this equation by a constant K. The constant K determines a unique plane in the d_3^A, d_3^B, and α space. The ranges of d_3^A and d_3^B will be limited by the physical design of the robot system and $\alpha \in (0, 2\pi)$. A K plane is shown in Figure 4. An interpretation of this picture is that during the motion, d_3^A, d_3^B, and α are limited to this K plane. A second interpretation is that the joint solutions for a x_e, y_e, and α with any initial conditions d_{30}^B, d_{30}^A, and α_0 on a K plane are the same. This follows because in computing the joint solutions the effects of d_{30}^A, d_{30}^B, and α_0 are aggregated into the constant K. Hence all initial conditions with the same K will give the same joint solutions at a x_e, y_e, and α.

4 Workspace of the Disk Center

The workspace of the system plays an important role in path-planning algorithms. Typically, for manipulator systems without rolling, the workspace is fixed and depends only on the geometry of the mechanism. However, the workspace of rolling systems depends not only on the geometry of the mechanism but also on the start configuration. This property of planar rolling systems is unique and differs from conventional manipulator systems without rolling constraints.

Analytically, the workspace can be determined as follows: Given the range on d_3^A and d_3^B, the closure constraints, and the rolling constraint, find the workspace of the disk center. The algorithm to determine the workspace is as

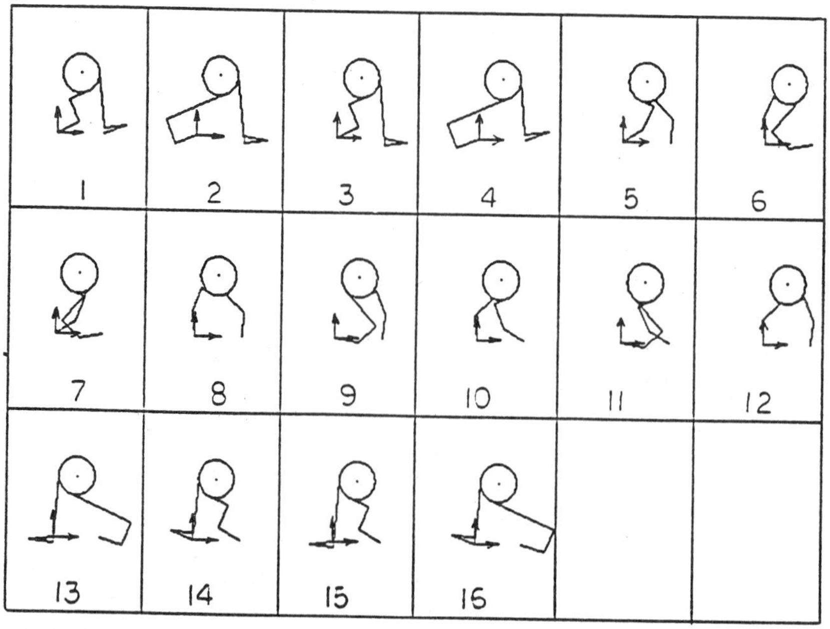

Figure 3: The kinematic solutions for a position of the disk center and an orientation α.

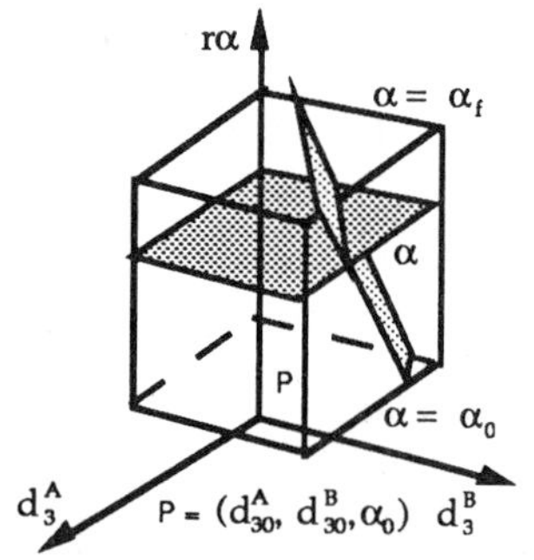

Figure 4: A K plane: Initial conditions d_{30}^A, d_{30}^B, and α_0 which lies on a K plane result in same joint solutions at a given x_e, y_e, and α.

Figure 5: Two typical forms of loci of the disk center in the Cartesian space for grid points (d_3^A, d_3^B).

follows: (a) Divide the feasible region of (d_3^A, d_3^B) into grid points and choose a (d_3^A, d_3^B), (b) compute α using eq. (6) and the initial conditions d_{30}^A, d_{30}^B, α_0, (c) Eliminate θ_{12}^A using eq.(8) and (11) and obtain a locus of x_e and y_e for a given d_3^A and d_3^B. This locus is a sixth degree polynomial in x_e and y_e. The coefficients of this polynomial are functions of d_3^A, d_3^B, d_{30}^A, d_{30}^B, α_0 and the link geometry. The points on this locus are determined by computing the roots of the y_e polynomial using a numerical procedure over the values of x_e. Some typical forms of the locus of the disk center obtained at grid points (d_3^A, d_3^B) using this procedure are shown in Fig. 5. (c) This procedure is repeated over all grid points in d_3^A-d_3^B space and the resulting union of these loci is the workspace of the disk center. We must note that a point in this workspace may not be reached for any value of α because α is unique for a d_3^A, d_3^B and the initial conditions. If d_3^A, d_3^B are chosen respectively as d_{30}^A and d_{30}^B, the x_e-y_e locus is the set of points where the mechanism is assemblable in the initial configuration for a unique value of α_0. The workspace of the disk center for two different start configurations are shown in Figure 6, where all other parameters are held the same.

4.1 Dependence on initial condition

The initial conditions appear in the analysis due to the rolling constraint. With similar reasoning as in the section on kinematics, we can conclude that all start configurations which lie on a K plane such as shown in Fig. 4 result in same workspace of the disk center. If the initial conditions

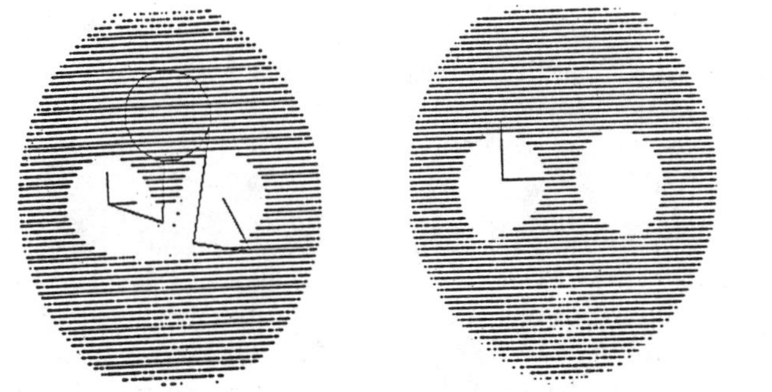

Figure 6: The x_e-y_e workspace for two different start configurations where all other parameters are held the same.

are changed, a new K plane is chosen, and the workspace changes.

5 Conclusions

For planar systems, the rolling constraints are integrable and can be included as additional constraints in solving the inverse kinematics and workspace. We showed in this paper that the number of kinematic solutions for a rolling disk between planar manipulators is much higher than kinematic solutions for structurally similar closed-chain manipulators without rolling. We presented an analytical method to determine the workspace boundaries of the center of the rolling disk. We observed that with rolling constraints, the inverse kinematic solutions and the workspace are dependent on the initial configuration of the system. Planes were determined with the property that every initial condition results in the same kinematic solutions at a generic point and the same overall workspace of the disk center. The mechanism is restricted to this plane during motion.

6 Acknowledgments

We thank Prof. V. Kumar for giving us initial statements of the problem, G. Desmier for designing the experiment setup, J. Rambhaskar and M. Annapragada for interfacing the electronics and software for experimentation. The support of the National Science Foundation under the Research Initiation Program and Stocker Fellowship from Ohio University are gratefully acknowledged.

References

[1] S.K. Agrawal and J. Garimella, "Workspace Boundaries of a Free-floating Open and Closed-Chain Planar Manipulators", to appear in *Journal of Mechanical Design, Transactions of the ASME*, 1993.

[2] S. Jacobsen , "Development of the Utah Artificial Arm", *IEEE Transactions on Biomedical Engineering*, vol. BME-29, No. 4, April 1982.

[3] Z. Ji, *Dextrous Hands: Optimizating Grasp by Design and Optimization*, Ph.D. Dissertation, Dept. of Mechanical Engineering, Stanford University, 1987.

[4] X. Yun, V. Kumar, N. Sarkar, and E. Paljug, "Control of Multiple Arm Systems with Rolling Constraints", In proceedings, *IEEE International Conference on Robotics and Automation*, 1992.

[5] P.R. McAree, A.E. Samuel, K.H. Hunt, and C.G. Gibson, "A Dexterity Measure for the Kinematic Control of a Multifinger, Multifreedom Robot Hand", *The International Journal of Robotics Research*, Vol. 10, No. 5, October 1991.

[6] R. Pandravada, "A Study of a Planar Mechanisms With Rolling Constraints", M.S. Thesis (under preparation), Dept. of Mechanical Engineering, Ohio University, 1993.

[7] R.M. Murray, "Robotics Control and Nonholonomic Motion Planning", Ph.D. Thesis, UCB/ERL M90/117, Berkeley, Dec. 1990.

[8] J.K. Salisbury and B. Roth,"Kinematics and Force Analysis of Articulated Mechanical Hands", *Journal of Mechanisms, Transmission and Automation in Design, Transactions of the ASME*, vol. 105, March 1983, pp. 35-41.

[9] S. Sastry and Z. Li, "Robot Motion Planning with Nonholonomic Constraints", In Proceedings, *28th IEEE CDC*, pp. 211-216, Florida, 1989.

[10] K.J. Waldron, M. Raghavan and B. Roth, "Kinematics of a Hybrid Series-Parallel Manipulation System", *Journal of Dynamic Systems, Measurements, and Control, Transactions of the ASME*, vol. 11, 1989, pp. 211-221.

Proceedings of the
American Control Conference
San Francisco, California • June 1993

Estimation of Angular Velocity of a Moving Object Using Line Correspondences

Ming Lei & Bijoy K. Ghosh
Department of Systems Science and Mathematics
Washington University, St. Louis, MO 63130

ABSTRACT

The change in orientation of a moving object is modeled in this paper. The associated angular velocity is determined through an orthonormal interpolation technique in two steps. This involves solving a linear equation and a polynomial equation of order 5. Simulation shows that the method works effectively even when large errors occur in data measurement and processing.

1. INTRODUCTION

The problem of tracking and grasping of a moving object by a robot manipulator has been discussed in the literature[6, 7, 8]. However in these papers, the orientation of the moving object is assumed to change in a known fashion and hence no estimation is needed. We are interested in a general case where the change of orientation is assumed to be unknown. Our solution to the tracking and grasping problem is to subdivide the problem into two subproblems, namely, centroid tracking and orientation tracking. In order for the manipulator to track the motion of the centroid of an object, the feedback control law has to depend on the motion parameters of the object which can be recursively estimated on-line based on the information extracted from the cameras [2]. Similarly the angular velocity of the object needs to be estimated for the gripper to align its orientation with that of the object such that the grasping may occur at any point.

Suppose the object has features such as line segments. By using Plücker coordinates[1], the direction of each line can be found from its images. The estimation of the angular velocity turns out to be an orthonormal interpolation which is presented in detail in section 3. Section 4 gives an illustrative example of the orthonormal interpolation. Section 5 is the conclusion.

2. MODELING THE CHANGE OF ORIENTATION

2.1 The setup of visually-guided tracking system

Figure 1 illustrates the configuration of the tracking system where two fixed cameras are facing the workspace of a robot manipulator. The base coordinate frame of the manipulator is chosen as the world coordinate frame(WCF) of the system, which is denoted by $o_w x_w y_w z_w$. For i=1,2, each camera coordinate frame CCFi, denoted by $o_{ci}x_{ci}y_{ci}z_{ci}$, is related to the WCF respectively by

$$\begin{bmatrix} x_w \\ y_w \\ z_w \end{bmatrix} = \begin{bmatrix} -1 & 0 & 0 \\ 0 & 0 & 1 \\ 0 & 1 & 0 \end{bmatrix} \begin{bmatrix} x_{ci} \\ y_{ci} \\ z_{ci} \end{bmatrix} + \begin{bmatrix} d_1 + d^{(1)} \\ d_2 \\ d_3 \end{bmatrix} \tag{1}$$

where $d^{(1)} = d$, $d^{(2)} = 0$. d, d_1, d_2 and d_3 are known calibration data.

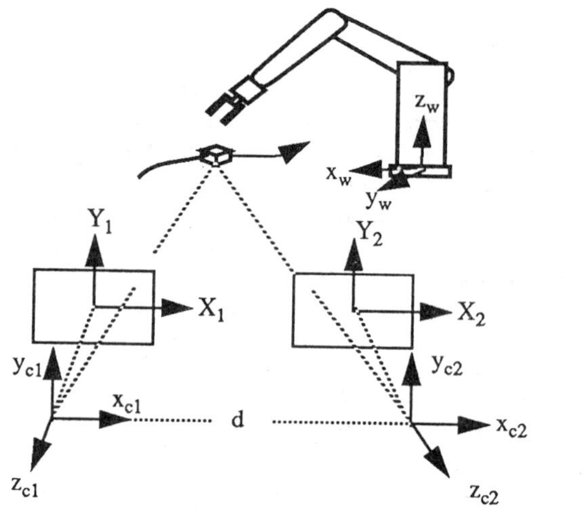

Figure 1 The configuration of the tracking grasping system

Perspective projection is used as the projection model of our cameras. For a point having coordinates (x_{ci}, y_{ci}, z_{ci}) in the CCFi, its image in the image plane X_iY_i is described by

$$X_i = \frac{x_{ci}}{z_{ci}} f, \quad Y_i = \frac{y_{ci}}{z_{ci}} f \quad (i = 1, 2) \tag{2}$$

where f is the focal length of each camera.(assumed to be the same)

Two feedback control schemes have been proposed in [2] for the end-effector of the manipulator to track the motion of the moving centroid of an object. However, in order to direct the gripper to grasp the object, the change in orientation of the object must be estimated. In this paper we concentrate only on estimating the angular velocity.

2.2 A model of orientation change

A coordinate frame with three unit vectors **n**, **s**, **a** is commonly used to represent the orientation of the end-effector(gripper) in the robotics literature. For convenience, we use the same notation **n**, **s**, **a** to represent a coordinate frame attached to the moving object. By grasping, we mean to align these two coordinate frames. When object moves, the orientation of the object coordinate frame changes according to

$$[\dot{\mathbf{n}}\ \dot{\mathbf{s}}\ \dot{\mathbf{a}}] = \Omega\, [\mathbf{n}\ \mathbf{s}\ \mathbf{a}] \tag{3}$$

with

$$\Omega = \begin{bmatrix} 0 & -\omega_3 & \omega_2 \\ \omega_3 & 0 & -\omega_1 \\ -\omega_2 & \omega_1 & 0 \end{bmatrix}$$

where $[\omega_1\ \omega_2\ \omega_3]^T$ is the angular velocity.

Suppose that the object has features such as line segments. From [1], a 3D line can be represented in the WCF by

$$\begin{bmatrix} m_1 & m_2 & m_3 & m_4 \\ m_5 & m_6 & m_7 & m_8 \end{bmatrix} \begin{bmatrix} x_w \\ y_w \\ z_w \\ 1 \end{bmatrix} = 0. \tag{4}$$

Using (4), the Plücker coordinates $[\xi_1\ \xi_2\ \xi_3\ \xi_4\ \xi_5\ \xi_6]^T$ of the line can be defined. Since $[\xi_4\ \xi_5\ \xi_6]^T$ is the unit vector in the direction of the line, there exist k_1, k_2, $k_3 \in \mathbf{R}^1$ such that

$$\begin{bmatrix} \xi_4 \\ \xi_5 \\ \xi_6 \end{bmatrix} = k_1\mathbf{n} + k_2\mathbf{s} + k_3\mathbf{a}. \tag{5}$$

Differentiating (5) and using (3) yields

$$\begin{bmatrix} \dot\xi_4 \\ \dot\xi_5 \\ \dot\xi_6 \end{bmatrix} = \Omega \begin{bmatrix} \xi_4 \\ \xi_5 \\ \xi_6 \end{bmatrix}. \tag{6}$$

Equation (6) describes how the angular velocity of a moving object is related to a 3D line on the object.

2.3 Determination of ξ_4, ξ_5 and ξ_6

By (1), equation (4) can be written as

$$\begin{bmatrix} -m_1 & m_3 & m_2 & u_1 \\ -m_5 & m_7 & m_6 & u_2 \end{bmatrix} \begin{bmatrix} x_{c1} \\ y_{c1} \\ z_{c1} \\ 1 \end{bmatrix} = 0 \tag{7}$$

where u_1, u_2 represent some fixed quantities which need not be computed. Using (7), the Plücker coordinates of the line in the the CCF1 has the form of

$$[\xi_1'\ \xi_2'\ \xi_3'\ \ -\xi_4\ \xi_6\ \xi_5]^T$$

where ξ_1', ξ_2' and ξ_3' are some quantities related to $u1$ and $u2$. By [1], the perspective projection (2) of the line in image plane X_1Y_1 is the 2D line

$$\xi_1'X_1 + \xi_2'Y_1 + \xi_3'f = 0.$$

Let (a_1, b_1) denote the measurement

$$a_1 = \xi_1'/(\xi_3'f), \quad b_1 = \xi_2'/(\xi_3'f),$$

then applying the quadratic relation

$$\xi_1'(-\xi_4) + \xi_2'\xi_6 + \xi_3'\xi_5 = 0$$

yields

$$-a_1f\xi_4 + \xi_5 + b_1f\xi_6 = 0. \tag{8}$$

In the same way, let (a_2, b_2) denote the measurement of the line in image plane X_2Y_2, then

$$-a_2f\xi_4 + \xi_5 + b_2f\xi_6 = 0. \tag{9}$$

Therefore, if the stereo measurement pair (a_1, b_1) and (a_2, b_2) satisfies $a_1b_2 \neq a_2b_1$, the unit vector $(\xi_4\ \xi_5\ \xi_6)^T$, namely, the direction of the line, can be determined from solving (8) and (9).

3. Determination of Angular Velocity: Orthonormal Interpolation

In this section, we first introduce an approach to orthonormal interpolation. Then apply it to the problem of estimating angular velocity.

3.1 Orthonormal interpolation

Definition: For given data pairs (X_k, Y_k), $X_k, Y_k \in \mathbf{S}^{n-1} \subset \mathbf{R}^n$, $k = 1, \cdots, N$, where $\mathbf{S}^{n-1}$ denotes the $n-1$ dimensional unit sphere. To fit an orthonormal matrix R to the data such that $Y_k = RX_k$ is called orthonormal interpolation.

For convenience, we only consider the orthonormal interpolation problem for $n = 3$ in this paper. The results we obtain hereafter can be extended to those in $\mathbf{S}^{n-1} \in \mathbf{R}^n$ without any difficulty.

Since R has distinct eigenvalues $e^{i\theta_m}$, $(m = 1, 2, 3)$, $\theta_1 = 0$ or π, $\theta_2 = \theta$, $\theta_3 = -\theta$, there always exists a nonsingular matrix V such that

$$VRV^{-1} = diag(e^{i\theta_1}, e^{i\theta_2}, e^{-i\theta_3}).$$

Hence, fitting the R to $Y_k = RX_k$, $(k = 1, \cdots, N)$ is equivalent to fitting the V and θ's to

$$[VY_1\ VY_2\ \cdots\ VY_N] = diag(e^{i\theta_1}, e^{i\theta_2}, e^{-i\theta_3})\, [VX_1\ VX_2\ \cdots\ VX_N]. \tag{10}$$

Let

$$V = [v_{ij}]_{3\times 3}, \quad X_k = \begin{bmatrix} x_{1k} \\ x_{2k} \\ x_{3k} \end{bmatrix}, \quad Y_k = \begin{bmatrix} y_{1k} \\ y_{2k} \\ y_{3k} \end{bmatrix}.$$

One approach to solving the orthonormal interpolation is to minimize

$$J = \sum_{m=1}^{3}\sum_{k=1}^{N}[v_{m1}y_{1k} + v_{m2}y_{2k} + v_{m3}y_{3k} - e^{i\theta_m}(v_{m1}x_{1k} + v_{m2}x_{2k} + v_{m3}x_{3k})]^2$$
$$= \sum_{m=1}^{3}\sum_{k=1}^{N}[v_{m1}(y_{1k} - e^{i\theta_m}x_{1k}) + v_{m2}(y_{2k} - e^{i\theta_m}x_{2k}) + v_{m3}(y_{3k} - e^{i\theta_m}x_{3k})]^2.$$

Setting

$$\frac{\partial J}{\partial v_{mn}} = 0, \quad (m,n = 1,2,3)$$

yields

$$\Phi(\theta_m)\begin{bmatrix} v_{m1} \\ v_{m2} \\ v_{m3} \end{bmatrix} = 0 \qquad (11)$$

where

$$\Phi(\theta_m) = A - e^{i\theta_m}B + e^{2i\theta_m}C,$$
$$A = (a_{mn})_{3\times3}, \quad B = (b_{mn})_{3\times3}, \quad C = (c_{mn})_{3\times3},$$
$$a_{mn} = \textstyle\sum_{k=1}^{N} y_{mk}y_{nk},$$
$$b_{mn} = \textstyle\sum_{k=1}^{N}(x_{mk}y_{nk} + x_{nk}y_{mk}),$$
$$c_{mn} = \textstyle\sum_{k=1}^{N} x_{mk}x_{nk}. \quad (m,n = 1,2,3)$$

If for some $m \in \{1,2,3\}$, $\Phi(\theta_m)$ is nonsingular, then $v_{m1} = v_{m2} = v_{m3} = 0$, which contradicts the nonsingularity of T. Therefore, the determinant of $\Phi(\theta_m)$ *must* be zero for $m = 1,2,3$. Let $A_1, A_2, A_3, B_1, B_2, B_3, C_1, C_2, C_3$ denote the column vectors of matrices A, B and C, respectively. It is straightforward to check that the determinant of $\Phi(\theta_m)$ is

$$\det(\Phi(\theta_m)) = \sum_{n=0}^{6} h_n \cos n\theta_m + i\sum_{n=1}^{6} h_n \sin n\theta_m$$

where

$$\begin{aligned}
h_0 =& \det(A),\\
h_1 =& \det([A_1\ A_2\ B_3]) + \det([A_1\ B_2\ A_3]) + \det([B_1\ A_2\ A_3]),\\
h_2 =& \det([A_1\ A_2\ C_3]) + \det([A_1\ C_2\ A_3]) + \det([C_1\ A_2\ A_3]) + \det([A_1\ B_2\ B_3]) + \det([B_1\ A_2\ B_3]) + \det([B_1\ B_2\ A_3]),\\
h_3 =& \det(B) + \det([A_1\ C_2\ B_3]) + \det([A_1\ B_2\ C_3]) + \det([C_1\ A_2\ B_3]) + \det([B_1\ A_2\ C_3]) + \det([C_1\ B_2\ A_3]) + \det([B_1\ C_2\ A_3]),\\
h_4 =& \det([A_1\ C_2\ C_3]) + \det([C_1\ C_2\ A_3]) + \det([C_1\ A_2\ C_3]) + \det([C_1\ B_2\ B_3]) + \det([B_1\ C_2\ B_3]) + \det([B_1\ B_2\ C_3]),\\
h_5 =& \det([C_1\ C_2\ B_3]) + \det([C_1 B_2\ C_3]) + \det([B_1\ C_2\ C_3]),\\
h_6 =& \det(C).
\end{aligned}$$

Since $\det(\Phi(\theta_m))$ is in general a complex quantity, the best one can hope is to make it as close to the origin of the complex plane as possible.

The squared magnitude of $\det(\Phi(\theta_m))$ is

$$d(\theta_m) = \textstyle\sum_{k=0}^{6} h_k^2 - 2\cos\theta_m \sum_{k=0}^{5} h_k h_{k+1} + 2\cos2\theta_m \sum_{k=0}^{4} h_k h_{k+2} - 2\cos3\theta_m \sum_{k=0}^{3} h_k h_{k+3} + 2\cos4\theta_m \sum_{k=0}^{2} h_k h_{k+4} - 2\cos5\theta_m \sum_{k=0}^{1} h_k h_{k+5} + 2h_0h_6\cos6\theta_m.$$

Setting $d'(\theta_m) = 0$ and using trigonometric identities yields

$$\sin\theta_m\ (r_0 - r_1\cos\theta_m + r_2\cos^2\theta_m - r_3\cos^3\theta_m + r_4\cos^4\theta_m - r_5\cos^5\theta_m) = 0 \qquad (12)$$

where

$$r_0 = 0.25\textstyle\sum_{k=0}^{5} h_k h_{k+1} - 0.75\sum_{k=0}^{3} h_k h_{k+3} + 1.25\sum_{k=0}^{1} h_k h_{k+5},$$
$$r_1 = \textstyle\sum_{k=0}^{4} h_k h_{k+2} - 4\sum_{k=0}^{2} h_k h_{k+4} + 9h_0h_6,$$
$$r_2 = 3\textstyle\sum_{k=0}^{3} h_k h_{k+3} - 15\sum_{k=0}^{1} h_k h_{k+5},$$
$$r_3 = 8\textstyle\sum_{k=0}^{2} h_k h_{k+4} - 48h_0h_6,$$
$$r_4 = 20\textstyle\sum_{k=0}^{1} h_k h_{k+5},$$
$$r_5 = 48h_0h_6.$$

Clearly, $\theta_1 = 0$ or π is a solution to the equation (12) .

Polynomial

$$P(s) = r_0 - r_1 s + r_2 s^2 - r_3 s^3 + r_4 s^4 - r_5 s^5 \qquad (13)$$

has at least one real root. If $r_i's$ $(i = 0,1,\ldots,5)$ come from the observations of a rotation or its reflection, equation (12) has to be satisfied with some $\pm\theta$, i.e., $s = cos(\pm\theta)$ is a real root of (13) . Thus by finding the real root $s^* \in [-1,1]$ of (13) which minimizes $d(\theta_m)$, we have $\theta_2 = \cos^{-1}(s^*)$, $\theta_3 = -\cos^{-1}(s^*)$.

Suppose that we have solved $\theta_1, \theta_2, \theta_3$, by the singularity of $\Phi(\theta_1), \Phi(\theta_2)$ and $\Phi(\theta_3)$, the corresponding

$$v_m = \begin{bmatrix} v_{m1} \\ v_{m2} \\ v_{m3} \end{bmatrix} \qquad (m = 1,2,3)$$

can be solved from (11) .

From the algorithmic point of view, the measured data pairs (X_k, Y_k) are generic so that the following assumptions are reasonable.

Let $\lambda_1 = e^{i\theta_1}, \lambda_2 = e^{i\theta_2}, \lambda_3 = e^{-i\theta_3}$

(A1) $[B - (\lambda_1 + \lambda_3)C]\zeta_1$ and $[B - (\lambda_2 + \lambda_3)C]\zeta_2$ are linearly independent.

(A2) $[B - (\lambda_1 + \lambda_2)C]\zeta_1$ and $[B - (\lambda_2 + \lambda_3)C]\zeta_3$ are linearly independent.

(A3) $[B - (\lambda_1 + \lambda_2)C]\zeta_2$ and $[B - (\lambda_1 + \lambda_3)C]\zeta_3$ are linearly independent.

Lemma 1: Assume (A1) or (A2) or (A3) is true, then it follows that ζ_1, ζ_2, ζ_3 are linearly independent.

Lemma 2: Assume (A1), (A2) and (A3) are true, then $rank(\Phi(\theta_m)) = 2$ for $m = 1,2,3$.

Lemma 1 tells us that $V = [v_1\ v_2\ v_3]^T$ is nonsingular, hence

$$R = V^{-1}\ diag(\pm1, e^{i\theta}, e^{-i\theta})\ V. \qquad (14)$$

Theorem 1: R is a (real) orthonormal matrix.

The proofs of lemma 1, 2 and theorem 1 can be found in Appendix 1, 2, 3.

3.2 Estimation of ω_1, ω_2 and ω_3

Suppose the motion of the object with p feature lines is observed over q frames which are taken at a sequence of equally spaced time points $t_1, t_2, \cdots, t_q$, with space T. Using (6), we have

$$\begin{bmatrix} \xi_4^{(m)}(t_1+(k+1)T) \\ \xi_5^{(m)}(t_1+(k+1)T) \\ \xi_6^{(m)}(t_1+(k+1)T) \end{bmatrix} = R \begin{bmatrix} \xi_4^{(m)}(t_1+kT) \\ \xi_5^{(m)}(t_1+kT) \\ \xi_6^{(m)}(t_1+kT) \end{bmatrix},$$

with $R = e^{\Omega T}, k = 0, 1, \cdots, q-1; m = 1, 2, \cdots, p$. From the discussion in section 2.3, $\xi_4^{(m)}$, $\xi_5^{(m)}$ and $\xi_6^{(m)}$ can be obtained at each vision sampling instant. Therefore the corresponding $\Phi(\theta_m)$ can be generated. We have

Theorem 2: ω_1, ω_2 and ω_3 can be solved from

$$A \begin{bmatrix} \omega_1 \\ \omega_2 \\ \omega_3 \end{bmatrix} = 0, \quad (15)$$

$$P(cos\omega) = 0 \quad (16)$$

where $\omega = \sqrt{\omega_1^2+\omega_2^2+\omega_3^2}$.

Proof: Since $R = e^{\Omega T}$, there exists a $\bar{V}$ such that

$$\bar{V}R\bar{V}^{-1} = diag(1, e^{i\omega T}, e^{-i\omega T}).$$

By (14), it is readily seen that $\omega = \theta$ and $\bar{V} = V$, where $cos\theta$ and V satisfy equations (13) and (11) respectively. So

$$R^T \left[v_{11}\ v_{12}\ v_{13}\right]^T = \left[v_{11}\ v_{12}\ v_{13}\right]^T.$$

But

$$R^T = (e^{\Omega T})^T = e^{\Omega^T T} = e^{-\Omega T}$$
$$= I - \Omega T + \tfrac{1}{2!}\Omega^2 T^2 - \cdots + \tfrac{(-1)^k}{k!}\Omega^k T^k + \cdots,$$

So

$$R^T \left[\omega_1\ \omega_2\ \omega_3\right]^T = \left[\omega_1\ \omega_2\ \omega_3\right]^T,$$

so

$$\left[\omega_1\ \omega_2\ \omega_3\right]^T = \alpha \left[v_{11}\ v_{12}\ v_{13}\right]^T$$

for some $\alpha \neq 0$. On the other hand, v_{11}, v_{12} and v_{13} are solved from (11) with $\theta_1 = 0$. So

$$\Phi(0) \begin{bmatrix} \omega_1 \\ \omega_2 \\ \omega_3 \end{bmatrix} = A \begin{bmatrix} \omega_1 \\ \omega_2 \\ \omega_3 \end{bmatrix} = 0.$$

□

Remark: Define $n1 = \omega_1/\omega$, $n2 = \omega_2/\omega$, $n3 = \omega_3/\omega$. $n1$, $n2$ and $n3$ are indeed that directional cosines of the axis of rotation of the object. Clearly, $(n1\ n2\ n3)^T$ satifies equation (15). Since the computation of the $n1$, $n2$ and $n3$ does not depend on the solution of (13), it is expected to be robust to noisy measurement.

Algorithm 1:
(1)Solve (15) for $n1, n2$ and $n3$.
(2)Solve (13) for $cos\omega T$ and hence ω_1, ω_2 and ω_3.

4. Simulation and Error Analysis

Given angular velocity $[\omega_1\ \omega_2\ \omega_3]^T$ (hence $n1, n2, n3$ and $cos\omega$), we have a reference rotation matrix $R_{re} = exp(\Omega)$. We can generate a sequence of observations of p feature lines over q frames according the following equation:

$$\eta_{k+1}^{(m)} = R_{re}\eta_k^{(m)}, \quad m = 1, \cdots, p; \ k = 1, 2, \cdots, q-1$$

where $\eta_1^{(m)} \in \mathbf{S}^2$ $(m = 1, \cdots, p)$ are arbitrarily chosen. In order to simulate the measurement noise, a Gaussian process with zero mean and variance σ^2 is added to $\{\eta_k^{(m)}, m = 1, \cdots, p; k = 1, 2, \cdots, q-1\}$. Since $\|\eta_k^{(m)}\| = 1$, the components of $\eta_k^{(m)}$ have an average magnitude of 1/3. Hence it is reasonable to say that $\sigma^2 = 0.0033r$ represents a noise perturbation of about $r\%$ in the measurement.

For $p = 2$, simulations have been done for $q = 3, 5, 8$ and $r = 0, 1, 5$ respectively. It is found that if $|cos\omega T|$ is far less than 1, then algorithm 1 works well even for perturbation as large as 5 percent no matter what $(n1\ n2\ n3)$ initially is. However, the performance deteriorates when $|cos\omega T|$ is nearly equal to 1, which is the case when the sampling period is short and ωT is small. Nevertheless, algorithm 1 still manages to recover the correct axis of rotation and reasonably good rotation angle ωT, which is illustrated in the following example.

Suppose that the angular displacement in time T is: $(\omega_1 T\ \omega_2 T\ \omega_3 T) = (0.0157\ 0.0209\ 0.0453)$. It is equivalent to $(n1\ n2\ n3) = (0.3\ 0.4\ 0.866)$, $\omega T = 0.0524 (= 3^o)$, $cos\omega T = 0.9986$. The reference rotation matrix can be calculated as

$$R_{re} = e^{\Omega T} = \begin{bmatrix} 0.9988 & -0.0452 & 0.0213 \\ 0.0455 & 0.9988 & -0.0152 \\ -0.0206 & 0.0162 & 0.9997 \end{bmatrix}.$$

We have the following simulation results with $p = 2$, $\eta_1^1 = (0.4082\ 0.8165\ -0.4082)^T$, $\eta_1^2 = (-0.3162\ 0\ 0.9487)^T$.

Estimated angular velocity from algorithm 1

q	Perturbation	n1	n2	n3;	ωT
3	0%	.30	.40	.87;	2.5^o
	1%	.35	.39	.86;	3.3^o
	5%	-.31	-.82	.49;	13.0^o
5	0%	.30	.40	.87;	2.5^o
	1%	.33	.48	.81;	3.8^o
	5%	.11	-.21	.97;	11.3^o
8	0%	.30	.40	.87;	2.5^o
	1%	.29	.36	.89;	2.9^o
	5%	.07	-.13	.99;	7.0^o

We see that even if the noise perturbation is 0, there is still some error in the estimation of ωT. This is due to the sensitivity of function $cos^{-1}s^*$ to the change of s^* when s^* is near ± 1, which can be easily seen from

$$\frac{d}{ds^*}(cos^{-1}s^*) = -\frac{1}{\sqrt{1-s^{*2}}}.$$

Therefore, accurately solving s^* from (13) is crucial to the recovery of ωT. Indeed, when Laguerre's method (or finding the eigenvalues of an associated companion matrix) is used to find the roots of $P(s)$ in (13), the resulting five roots seem to be repeated and their average usually gives the best estimation of $\cos\omega T$. For example, in the case when $p = 2$, $q = 5$ and perturbation is zero, the five roots of (13) are respectively 1.0004, 0.9994±0.0009i, 0.9981±0.0006i whose average 0.9991 best approximates the reference value 0.9986.

5. Concluding Remarks

Using stereo cameras to observe a moving object having features such as line segments, the change in orientation of the object is easily modeled and measured. The associated angular velocity is estimated through the orthonormal interpolation in which only a polynomial equation of order 5 and a system of linear equtions are required to be solved. The design of feedback control law for the grasping incorporating the estimated angular velocity will be discussed in the future paper.

We finally comment that the orthonormal interpolation on $\mathbf{S}^{n-1} \subset \mathbf{R}^n$ is similarly solved from finding the roots of a polynomial of order $2n-1$ and solving several eigenvector-type of linear equations.

Appendix 1

Proof of Lemma 1: Let $k_1\zeta_1 + k_2\zeta_2 + k_3\zeta_3 = 0$, by (11), $0 = A(k_1\zeta_1 + k_2\zeta_2 + k_3\zeta_3) = k_1\lambda_1 B\zeta_1 + k_2\lambda_2 B\zeta_2 + k_3\lambda_3 B\zeta_3 - k_1\lambda_1^2 C\zeta_1 - k_2\lambda_2^2 C\zeta_2 - k_3\lambda_3^2 C\zeta_3$. But $k_1\lambda_3 B\zeta_1 + k_2\lambda_3 B\zeta_2 + k_3\lambda_3 B\zeta_3 = k_1\lambda_3^2 C\zeta_1 + k_2\lambda_3^2 C\zeta_2 + k_3\lambda_3^2 C\zeta_3 = 0$, so $k_1(\lambda_1 - \lambda_3)[B-(\lambda_1+\lambda_3)C]\zeta_1 + k_2(\lambda_2-\lambda_3)[B-(\lambda_2+\lambda_3)C]\zeta_2 = 0$. By (A1), $k_1(\lambda_1-\lambda_3) = k_2(\lambda_2-\lambda_3) = 0$. Hence $k_1 = k_2 = 0$ and $k_3 = 0$. Similar argument holds for (A2) or (A3).

Appendix 2

Proof of Lemma 2: WLOG, assume $rank(\Phi(\theta_1)) = 1$, then $\Phi(\theta_1)\zeta = 0$ has two linearly independent solutions ζ_{11}, ζ_{12}. Let $k_{11}\zeta_{11} + k_{12}\zeta_{12} + k_2\zeta_2 + k_3\zeta_3 = 0$, by the same argument as in lemma 1, $k_2 = k_3 = 0$ by (A3). So $k_{11}\zeta_{11} + k_{12}\zeta_{12} = 0$ implies $k_{11} = k_{12} = 0$. Hence we find four linearly independent vectors in $\mathbf{R}^3$, a contradiction.

Appendix 3

Proof of Theorem 1: $R^TR = I$ is easy to check by (14). We must show $R^* = R$ where ' * ' stands for complex conjugation. Suppose $\Phi(\theta_1)\zeta_1 = \Phi(\theta_2)\zeta_2 = \Phi(\theta_3)\zeta_3 = 0$, since $\Phi(\theta_1)$ is a real matrix, there exist $k_1, a_1, a_2, a_3 \in \mathbf{R}^1$, $k_1 \neq 0$ such that $\zeta_1 = k_1[a_1\ a_2\ a_3]^T$. Since $\Phi^*(\theta_3) = \Phi(\theta_2)$, $\Phi(\theta_2)\zeta_3{}^* = \Phi^*(\theta_3)\zeta_3{}^* = \Phi(\theta_3)\zeta_3{}^* = 0$. But $rank(\Phi(\theta_2)) = 2$, there exist $c_1, c_2, c_3, k_2, k_3 \in \mathbf{C}^1, k_2, k_3 \neq 0$ such that $\zeta_2 = k_2[c_1\ c_2\ c_3]^T$, $\zeta_3{}^* = k_3[c_1\ c_2\ c_3]^T$. So

$$T = \begin{bmatrix} k_1a_1 & k_1a_2 & k_1a_3 \\ k_2c_1 & k_2c_2 & k_2c_3 \\ k_3{}^*c_1{}^* & k_3{}^*c_2{}^* & k_3{}^*c_3{}^* \end{bmatrix}.$$

Denote $T^{-1} = [s_{ij}]$, by $T^{-1}T = I$,

$$T^{-1}\begin{bmatrix} k_1a_1 & k_1a_2 & k_1a_3 \\ k_2c_1 & k_2c_2 & k_2c_3 \\ k_3{}^*c_1{}^* & k_3{}^*c_2{}^* & k_3{}^*c_3{}^* \end{bmatrix} = I. \quad (17)$$

Taking conjugate of (17) and comparing the resulted equation with (17) yields

$$T^{-1} = \begin{bmatrix} s_{11}{}^* & s_{13}{}^* & s_{12}{}^* \\ s_{21}{}^* & s_{23}{}^* & s_{22}{}^* \\ s_{31}{}^* & s_{33}{}^* & s_{32}{}^* \end{bmatrix}\begin{bmatrix} 1 & 0 & 0 \\ 0 & k_3/k_2 & 0 \\ 0 & 0 & k_2{}^*/k_3{}^* \end{bmatrix}$$

So s_{m1} $(m = 1,2,3)$ are real, $k_3{}^*[s_{13}\ s_{23}\ s_{33}]^T = k_2{}^*[s_{12}{}^*\ s_{22}{}^*\ s_{32}{}^*]^T$. Using this relationship, it is easy to verify $R^* = R$ from $R = T^{-1}\ diag(\pm 1,\ e^{i\theta},\ e^{-i\theta})\ T$.

References

[1] M. Lei and B. K. Ghosh,"New Geometric Methods in Computing the Motion Parameters of A Rigid Body Using Straight Line Correspondences", *Proc. 1992 American Control Conference,* Chicago, pp1500-1504, Jun. 1992.

[2] M. Lei and B. K. Ghosh, "Visually-guided Robotic Motion Tracking", *Proc. of the 30th Allerton Conference on Communication, Control, and Computing,* Allerton House, Monticello, Illinios, Sep. 1992.

[3] B. L. Yen and T. S. Huang, "Determining 3-D Motion/Structure of a Rigid Body Using Straight Line Correspondences", *Image Sequence Processing and Dynamics Scene Analysis,* ed. by T. S. Huang, Springer-Verlag, 1983.

[4] R. Y. Tsai and T. S. Huang, "Uniqueness and Estimation of Three-Dimensional Motion Parameters of Rigid Objects with Curved Surfaces", *IEEE Trans. PAMI,* Vol.6, No. 1, Jan. 1984.

[5] A. Ruhe, "Fitting Empirical Data by Positive Sums of Exponentials", *SIAM J. Sci. Stat. Computation,* Vol.1, NO. 4, Dec. 1980.

[6] P. K. Allen, A. Timcenko, B. Yoshimi, P. Michelman, "Trajectory Filtering and Prediction for Automated Tracking and Grasping of a Moving Object", *Proc. 1992 Int. Conf. Rob. Auto.,* Nice, France, 1992

[7] A. J. Koivo, N. Houshangi, "Real-Time Vision Feedback For Servoing Robotic Manipulator With Self-Tuning Controller", *IEEE Trac. systems, man, and cybernetics,* Vol. 21, No. 1, pp134-142, Jan. 1991.

[8] J. Feddema, C. S. G. Lee, "Adaptive Image Feature Prediction and Control for Visual Tracking with a Hand-Eye Coordinated Camera",*IEEE Trac. systems, man, and cybernetics,* Vol. 20, No. 5, pp1172-1183, Sept. 1990.

Proceedings of the
American Control Conference
San Francisco, California • June 1993

COMPARISON OF INVERSE MANIPULATOR KINEMATICS APPROXIMATIONS FROM SCATTERED INPUT-OUTPUT DATA USING ANN-LIKE METHODS

Dimitry M. Gorinevsky* and Thomas H. Connolly

Lehrstuhl B für Mechanik, Technische Universität München
8000 München 2, Germany

Abstract

We compare the application of five different methods for the approximation of the inverse kinematics of a robot arm from a number of joint angle/Cartesian coordinate training pairs. The first method is a standard feed-forward neural network with error back-propagation learning. The next two methods employ an extended Kohonen Map that we combine with Shepard interpolation for the forward computation. We consider learning of the Kohonen Map with the method of Ritter et al. and compare it to our own method based on steepest descent optimization. We also study two scattered data approximation algorithms, namely Gaussian Radial Basis Function interpolation and a Local Polynomial Fit method that could be considered as a modification of McLain's method. We propose extensions of the considered scattered data approximation algorithms to make them suitable for vector-valued multivariable functions, such as the mapping of Cartesian coordinates into joint angle coordinates.

1 Introduction

A modern trend in control system research and application is the transition from analytical models, that are never completely precise, to approximate models, that never pretend to be precise but could lead to a more realistic and convenient description of system input/output properties. The recent expansion of research in Artificial Neural Networks (ANN) is the most visible indication of this tendency.

Although various ANN approaches are being increasingly used in control systems, their comparative benefits and drawbacks are not quite well understood. In most important applications, an ANN performs an approximation of some multivariable input-output mapping. In this paper we compare the performance of several such methods in their application to a rather basic problem related to robot control, that of inverse kinematics computation.

Recently, several papers on applications of ANNs to the approximation of inverse manipulator kinematics were published. Two commonly used methods are multilayer feed-forward networks with error back-propagation learning [12, 19, 15, 28] and Kohonen self-organizing maps [14, 25, 27].

Generally, in robotics applications the data to be approximated are multivariable and not available on a regular grid, resulting in the so called Scattered Data Approximation problem. In the past 20 years much of the work in this area has been made in applied mathematics., e.g. see [1]-[9],[23, 24] .

Most Scattered Data Approximation methods compute the approximation from the available data directly in a single step. On the other hand, most ANN methods are based on relatively simple computational algorithms that can be used only after a lengthy and computationally intensive optimization of the network internal weights (learning). One should, however, mention that the distinction between these two groups of methods is simply a terminology question [22].

A Scattered Data Approximation problem is typically stated as follows. Let us consider a scalar-valued multivariable function $y = \phi(x)$. Let the function value y be known at points $x^{(i)}, (i = 1, ..., N)$ in the given argument domain: $y^{(i)} = \phi(x^{(i)})$. The problem is to build an approximation $\hat{y}$ of the function value $\phi(x)$ for an arbitrary x in the given domain.

In many control-related problems a vector-valued mapping $\phi(x)$ is to be approximated. Some of the Scattered Data Approximation methods can be used for a vector-valued function without the need for multiple solutions of a scalar-valued function approximation problem. These methods compute the estimate of the form

$$\hat{y} = \sum_{i=1}^{N} w_i y^{(i)}, \qquad (1)$$

where $w_i = w_i\left(x, \{x^{(j)}\}\right), (i = 1, ..., N)$ are scalar weights that depend on the relative position of the points x and $x^{(j)}$ and do not depend on the known function values $y^{(j)}$. Since estimate (1) could be applied to each component of the vector-valued function, one can just consider $y^{(i)}$ in (1) as vectors.

Although relatively extensive literature on ANN and Scattered Data Approximation methods exists, little attempt has been made to compare their performance in applications (exceptions are the papers [2] and [26]). The goal of this paper is to present such a comparison for an inverse manipulator kinematics problem. The parameters compared are: precision, sensitivity to noise in the data, and computation speed.

In this study we are not concerned whether the approximation obtained is smooth or continuous, but we rather put emphasis on its accuracy.

2 Inverse Kinematics Approximation Problem

Let us consider an inverse kinematics problem for a three link anthropomorphic manipulator. This basic problem in robotics is a convenient testbed for the comparison of the approximation methods since the precise analytic expressions are readily available and we can use them to check the accuracy of the approximation.

Given the manipulator link lengths, the forward kinematics with respect to the base, shoulder and elbow joint angles, θ_1, θ_2 and θ_3 respectively, can be written in vector

*Presently with *Robotics and Automation Laboratory, University of Toronto, 5 King's College Road, Toronto, Ontario, CANADA, M5S 1A4*

form as

$$X = f(\Theta); \qquad \Theta = \mathrm{col}(\theta_1, \theta_2, \theta_3) \tag{2}$$
$$\Theta = g(X); \qquad X = \mathrm{col}(X_1, X_2, X_3) \tag{3}$$

Generally, for a given vector X two solutions exist. We assume that the function $g(\Theta)$ represents the solution with $\theta_3 \geq 0$. In our numerical study the links have unit length and the joint angles Θ are in the domain

$$\mathcal{D} = \{0.0 \leq \theta_1, \theta_2 \leq 0.5; 0.5 \leq \theta_3 \leq 1.0\} \tag{4}$$

We consider the following approximation problem. Let N joint angle space points $\Theta^{(j)}, (j = 1, ..., N)$ be randomly placed in the domain (4) and let the N corresponding Cartesian coordinate points be related to them as

$$X^{(j)} = f(\Theta^{(j)}), \ \Theta^{(j)} \in \mathcal{D}; \ (j = 1, ..., N) \tag{5}$$

The problem is: given an arbitrary vector $X \in f(\mathcal{D})$ and the data (5), compute an approximation $\hat{\Theta}$ for the inverse kinematics solution (3). We will further refer to the data set (5) as the training set.

We check the accuracy of the solution in the following way. Let us consider a test set of N_t points $\Theta_t^{(k)}$ randomly placed in the domain (4) and let $X_t^{(k)} = f(\Theta_t^{(k)})$. Using a chosen approximation method, we compute an approximation $\hat{\Theta}_t^{(k)} = \hat{g}(X_t^{(k)})$ and the approximation error for each of the test set points

$$e_\Theta^{(k)} = \| \hat{\Theta}_t^{(k)} - \Theta_t^{(k)} \|, \tag{6}$$

By averaging the errors in (6) over the test data set and finding the maximal value over the set, one can get an impression of the approximation method's accuracy.

In addition to the training data set (5), we use a training data set with added noise

$$X^{(j)} = f(\Theta^{(j)}) + \eta^{(j)}, \ \Theta^{(j)} \in \mathcal{D}; \ (j = 1, ..., N), \tag{7}$$

where $\eta^{(j)}$ are random independent variables uniformly distributed over the interval $[-\eta_0, \eta_0]$. In the numerical experiments we choose a noise intensity of $\eta_0 = 5 \times 10^{-3}$, which is less than the approximation error of the considered methods. Thus, the noise influence represents just the robustness of the methods and not a degree of data degradation.

3 Approximation Methods

In this section we formulate each of the approximation methods for a general Scattered Data Approximation problem for a smooth function $\phi(x)$

$$y = \phi(x) : \ R^K \mapsto R^M, \text{ where} \tag{8}$$
$$x^{(j)}, \ y^{(j)} = \phi\left(x^{(j)}\right), \ (j = 1, \ldots, N) \text{ are known.}$$

Then, if necessary, we describe peculiarities in the application of each of the methods to the inverse kinematics approximation problem stated in Section 2. Section 4 presents the application results.

Feed-forward Multilayered Network

In this method, which is one of the most popular ANN methods, the network nodes are organized in several layers so that the input signal is processed consecutively from the input to the output layer. In the ANN literature the nodes are called neurons. The input layer of K neurons supplies the components x_i of the input vector x; the output layer of M neurons gives the components $\hat{y}_j$ of the output vector $\hat{y}$. Nodes of the intermediate (hidden) layers compute shifted linear transformations of their input signals and a sigmoidal activation function of the form $\sigma(x) = \tanh(\beta x)$ were applied to them [18]. As usual no sigmoidal function was applied to the output layer neurons. In order for the network node state equations, which map the input vector x into the output vector y, to approximate the mapping $y = \phi(x)$, the correct values of the neuron weights and activation thresholds must be determined. This is typically done by minimizing the mean square approximation error of the training set. A complete explanation of the minimization procedure known as error back-propagation learning, can be found elsewere, e.g. in [18].

The two hidden layer network implemented in our study has three input and three output neurons corresponding to the components of vectors X and Θ in the mapping (3). For two considered network architectures the hidden layers contained six and 15 neurons each (as in [15] and [28]) since for more neurons the iterative minimization (network training) process does not converge in a reasonable time. We employ the standard notations 3-6-6-3 and 3-15-15-3 for the implemented networks.

Kohonen Map

Along with multilayered feedforward networks, Kohonen's self-organizing mapping algorithm is one of the most popular ANN methods in robotics applications, e.g. see [25]. In this subsection we first formulate our own version of the method and then the version developed by Ritter et al. [25], which is specific for an inverse manipulator kinematics approximation. Numerical study shows that our version is superior in several respects.

We begin by describing the forward computations of the method, which are the same for the two versions. What differs is the procedure for acquiring (tuning) the network parameters such as the weights, etc.

The Kohonen Map network consists of L nodes with a vector $z_\mathbf{r} \in R^K$, a vector $\psi_\mathbf{r} \in R^M$ and a gradient matrix $W_\mathbf{r} \in R^{M,K}$ associated with each node $\mathbf{r}$.

Suppose that a vector x is input to the network. Following [25], one finds a node $\mathbf{s}$ so that $\| x - z_\mathbf{s} \|$ is minimal over all the nodes and approximates the value $y = g(x)$ of the function (8) as

$$y_\mathbf{s} = \psi_\mathbf{s} + W_\mathbf{s}(x - z_\mathbf{s}) \tag{9}$$

Let us note, that the linear approximation (9) of the mapping (3) is continuous only piecewise. That is, if the input vector x experiences an infinitely small variation so that the closest node $\mathbf{s}$ changes, the output value of (9) will generally experience a finite change. Therefore, we propose to use the Kohonen Map algorithm (9) together with Shepard interpolation, which is commonly applied if one knows the function and its gradient at some scattered points [8, 9, 24].

With Shepard interpolation we compute an approximation $\hat{y}$ to $y = \phi(x)$ as a weighted sum of the form

$$\hat{y} = \sum_{\mathbf{r}=1}^{L} \left[h(z_\mathbf{r}, x) y_\mathbf{r} / \sum_{\mathbf{r}=1}^{L} h(z_\mathbf{r}, x) \right], \tag{10}$$

where the summation is performed over the network nodes, $y_\mathbf{r}$ is an approximation of the form (9) and $h(z_\mathbf{r}, x)$ are scalar weighing functions. We used functions h of the form

$$h(x, z) = \exp(- \| x - z \|^2 / d^2), \tag{11}$$

where d is the interpolation radius.

The approximation (9)-(11) can be computed once the network parameters z_r, ψ_r, w_r are found. The following subsections present two methods for determining them.

The forward computations, according to (9) and (10), include a search of the neighboring nodes making it necessary to compute the distances $\| z_r - x \|$ for all nodes. For a large network this is the most computationally intensive part of the forward algorithm. Since the Gaussian function (11) vanishes quickly, computations according to (9)-(11) are done only for a relatively small number of the nodes closest to x and do not require much computation time.

Gradient Descent Optimization. One can determine the network parameters z_r, ψ_r, W_r in a quite natural way by demanding them to minimize the mean square approximation error of the training set (8)

$$D = \frac{1}{2} \sum_{\mu=1}^{N} \| y^{(\mu)} - \hat{y}^{(\mu)} \|^2 \rightarrow \min, \qquad (12)$$

where $\hat{y}^{(\mu)}$ denotes the network output (10) when the input vector $x^{(\mu)}$ of the training set pair $\{x^{(\mu)}, y^{(\mu)}\}$ in (8) is fed as the input.

To find the optimum network parameters we use an iterative minimization of the cost function (12) with the steepest descent method (back-propagation). More detail on the procedure can be found in [11].

By using the gradient descent optimization (referred as GDO in Table 1 and Figure 1), we learn the network parameters that provide a minimum of the cost function (12). Therefore, the accuracy of the proposed method in the numerical study of Section 4 is better than that for the algorithm of Ritter et al. [25] considered in the next section.

Method of Ritter et al. The extended Kohonen self-organizing mapping algorithm in [25] is specific for an inverse manipulator kinematics approximation. In other considered methods the approximations are built from the training set data (5). Unlike them, the learning procedure proposed in [25] requires additional training data in the learning process. It assumes that we are able to move the manipulator to a rough approximation $\hat{\Theta}$ and then measure the Cartesian tip coordinates X to further refine the approximation, therefore, producing additional input/output pairs for the mapping (3).

After learning, the accuracy is tested by presenting each of the test input vectors to the network and calculating the output using (9)-(11). See [11] for a further explanation.

Radial Basis Functions

The Radial Basis Function (RBF) approximation is one of the most commonly used Scattered Data Approximation method groups. Although initially some of the methods belonging to this group were applied just empirically, presently they are acknowledged to give an approximation that minimizes a certain regularization performance index [4, 22, 23], describing the roughness of the surface being approximated. We consider here only so-called exact RBF interpolation, which requires no iterative minimization. However, some recent papers consider RBF approximation as an ANN algorithm [3, 13, 17],[20]-[22] and compute the approximation as a result of an iterative minimization process.

For a scalar-valued function (8) ($M = 1$) the RBF interpolation has the form

$$\hat{y} = \sum_{j=1}^{N} c_j h\left(\|x - x^{(j)}\|\right), \qquad (13)$$

where $h(\cdot)$ is a function of the distance, or the radius (thus the name of the method). The weights c_j are chosen to ensure zero approximation error at the points $x^{(j)}$. The latter condition could be written in vector form as $Hc = Y$, where $c = \mathrm{col}(c_1, \ldots, c_N)$, $Y = \mathrm{col}(y^{(1)}, \ldots, y^{(N)})$ and H is a symmetric $N \times N$ matrix with entries $H_{ij} = h\left(\| x^{(i)} - x^{(j)} \|\right)$.

If the radial function $r(\| \cdot \|)$ is chosen properly, the matrix H is invertible. Thus, we find that approximation (13) could be written in form (1), where the weights w_j are computed as

$$w = H^{-1} R(x), \; w = \mathrm{col}\left(\{w_j\}_{j=1}^{N}\right), \qquad (14)$$

$$R(x) = \mathrm{col}\left(\{h(\|x - x^{(j)}\|)\}_{j=1}^{N}\right)$$

For the approximation of a vector-valued function $y = \phi(x)$, one can still use expression (14) to find the weights w_j and compute the linear combination (1) of the known vectors $y^{(j)}$. If all the available data are taken into account (the approximation is global), matrix H in (14) is the same for any point x. Therefore, H^{-1} could be computed beforehand, reducing the volume of the computations for each new approximation (1), (14). For a local version of the method, the set of the neighboring points depends on the considered vector x, making this precomputation impossible.

We present numerical results for a Gaussian radial function (13), $h(r) = \exp\left(-r^2/d^2\right)$. For the Gaussian radial function, matrix H in (14) could be proved to be nondegenerate [16]. Since the Gaussian function vanishes quickly as its argument increases, the terms with $\|x - x^{(i)}\| \gg d$ in (13) have little influence on the result. Therefore, we used a local version of the method. That is we take into account only the points $x^{(i)}$ closest to x. In our numerical study $L = 25$ closest data points provided the best precision.

Another popular choice of the radial function is Hardy multiquadrics (e.g. see [8]). The numerical results we obtained for multiquadrics differ insignificantly from those obtained for Gaussian RBF [11].

For the considered local version of the RBF interpolation, the 'bottleneck' of the forward computations is the search of the closest points in the data set (this includes computing the distances to each of the points) and the solution of the linear equation system $H^T w = R(x)$ in (14).

Local Multivariable Polynomial Fit

The method in its below form was suggested in [10]. For presentation simplicity we consider a second-order polynomial approximation here. We compute an estimate of the form (1) for the function $\phi(x)$ in (8) at the point $x = x^{(0)}$ by solving a classical regression problem. We assume that the points $x^{(i)}, (i = 1, \ldots, L)$ lie 'in the vicinity' of the point $x^{(0)}$ so that we can write the Taylor expansion as

$$\mathrm{y}^{(\mathrm{i})} = \phi + \sum_{\mathrm{q}=1}^{\mathrm{L}} \phi_{,\mathrm{q}} \mathrm{h}_{\mathrm{q}}^{(\mathrm{i})} + \frac{1}{2} \sum_{\mathrm{q,r}=1}^{\mathrm{L}} \phi_{,\mathrm{qr}} \mathrm{h}_{\mathrm{q}}^{(\mathrm{i})} \mathrm{h}_{\mathrm{r}}^{(\mathrm{i})} + \mathrm{e}^{(\mathrm{i})} + \eta^{(\mathrm{i})}, \quad (15)$$

where $\phi_{,q}$ and $\phi_{,qr}$ denote partial derivatives, of $\phi(x)$ at $x^{(0)}$, $h^{(i)} = x^{(i)} - x^{(0)}$, $\eta^{(i)}$ are random measurement errors, and $e^{(i)}$ is the mismatch of the Taylor expansion. To compute an estimate for $y^{(0)} = f(x^{(0)})$, we consider $\phi(x^{(0)})$, $\phi_{,q}(x^{(0)})$, $\phi_{,rs}(x^{(0)})$, $\eta^{(i)}$ and $e^{(i)}$ as independent zero-mean random variables. We further assume that for $(q, r = 1, \ldots, L)$

$$\mathbf{D}(\phi(x)) = c^2,\ \mathbf{D}(\phi_{,q}) = \alpha^2 c^2,\ \mathbf{D}(\phi_{,qr}) = \alpha^4 c^2/4,$$

$$\mathbf{D}\left(e^{(i)}\right) = \frac{\alpha^6 c^2}{36} \| h^{(i)} \|^6,\ \mathbf{D}\left(\eta^{(i)}\right) = \psi^2, \qquad (16)$$

where $\mathbf{D}(\cdot)$ denotes covariance and parameter α has the meaning of "wave length" of the function $\phi(x)$. That is, if the input vector (8) varies so that $\| \Delta x \| = \alpha$, the output value significantly changes. Parameter α could be assigned a value by considering a physical meaning of the input and output variables. The expression for $\mathbf{D}\left(e^{(i)}\right)$ in (16) follows from the estimate of the Taylor expansion residual in (15).

We represent the regression problem in the form

$$Y^T = F^T H + \mathcal{E}^T, \qquad (17)$$

$$F = \text{col}\,(\phi;\ \phi_{,1};\ldots,\ \phi_{,q};\ldots,\ \phi_{,rs};\ldots)\big|_{x\,=\,x^{(0)}},$$

$$H^{(i)} = \text{col}(1,\ h_1^{(i)},\ldots,\ h_q^{(i)},\ldots,\ h_r^{(i)} h_s^{(i)},\ldots),$$

$$H = \left[H^{(1)},\ldots,H^{(L)}\right],\ Y = \text{col}(\{y^{(i)}\}),$$

$$\mathcal{E} = \text{col}(\{e^{(i)} + \eta^{(i)}\}),$$

where H and Y are known matrices and $\mathcal{E}$ and F are zero-mean vectors with known covariances. The problem is to estimate $y^{(0)} = \phi(x^{(0)}) = F^T l$, where $l = \text{col}(1,0,\ldots,0)$. We search for the least covariance estimate of the form (1) $\hat{y}^{(0)} = Y^T w,\ w = \text{col}(\{w_i\}_{i=1}^{L})$. Taking into account (17) we can write (1) in the form

$$\hat{y}^{(0)} = Y^T w = F^T l + \zeta \qquad (18)$$

Solving (18) and (16) for a least-covariance zero-mean estimation error ζ results in

$$w = (\Xi + H^T \Psi H)^{-1} H^T \Psi l\,, \qquad (19)$$

where the diagonal covariance matrices $\Xi = \mathbf{E}\left(\mathcal{E}\mathcal{E}^T\right)$, and $\Psi = \mathbf{E}\left(FF^T\right)$ are defined by (16) and (17).

The method could be obviously generalized for a polynomial regression of any order and in the numerical study we used a third-order polynomial fit.

For a vector-valued function (8) we suppose that the stochastic model (16) is the same for each vector component or matrix entry. Therefore, the weight vector w (19) is the same for all components and the approximation still has the form (1). In the numerical study we set $\alpha = 1$ and $\psi/c = 10^{-3}$.

A similar solution to the polynomial fitting problem could be found in [2]. However, in [2] an expression of the form (19) is obtained just as a regularized solution to the ill-posed polynomial fitting problem.

4 Numerical Study

We compare the precision of the approximation methods of Section 3 as described in Section 2. First, a large initial training data set was generated by a random number generator so that each component of the vector Θ is independent and distributed in the domain (4). The training set was the same for all methods. Next, a random test data set of 100 more independent vectors $\Theta_t^{(j)}$ was generated in the same domain $\mathcal{D}$. For the training and test sets the corresponding Cartesian vectors were determined using the manipulator's forward kinematics.

We checked the approximation error as defined by (6) for training sets of different sizes. Each time we took N consecutive points from the initial data set. To get representative results, the procedure was repeated with different training data sets of the same size. For $N = 25$ training points we used $M = 8$ training sets; for $N = 50$, $M = 8$; for $N = 100$ and $N = 200$, $M = 4$; for $N = 400$, $M = 2$; for $N = 800$, $M = 1$.

Figure 1 displays the mean value of the joint angle error (6), depending on the training set size N. Figure 1 also illustrates respective results obtained for the training data contaminated with noise according to (7). The analysis of the results is summarized in Table 1. In the description of the computation volume L denotes the number of neighboring data points.

The two ANN schemes have the advantage of relatively fast forward computation. Our modification of the Kohonen Map method has approximately the same accuracy as the 3-15-15-3 feed-forward network and almost an order of magnitude better accuracy than the Kohonen Map method of Ritter et al. All ANN methods are rather robust to noise in the data. The considered Scattered Data Approximation methods have approximately the same accuracy, much better than that of the ANN methods. Of them the Local Polynomial Fit is much more robust to the presence of noise in the data. This method can be recommended for off-line computations or if the approximation should be computed for a small number of training pairs.

Acknowledgements

Work of the first author was supported by Alexander von Humboldt International Research Fellowship from Alexander von Humboldt Foundation, Bonn, Germany and of the second author by BMFT Grant 413-5839-01 IN 104 D/7.

References

[1] Alfeld, P. "Scattered Data Interpolation in Three or More Variables". In T. Lyche and L.L. Schumaker, editors, *Math. Methods in Computer Aided Geometric Design.* Academic Press, Boston, 1989.

[2] Atkenson, C.G. "Using Locally Weighted Regression for Robot Learning". *Proc. of IEEE Int. Conf. on Robotics and Automation*, vol. 3:958–963, April 1991.

[3] Bishop C. "Improving the Generalization Properties of Radial Basis Function Neural Networks". *Neural Computation*, vol. 3:579–88, 1991.

[4] Dyn, N. "Interpolation of Scattered Data by Radial Functions". In C.K.Chui, L.L. Schumaker and F.I. Utreras, editor, *Topics in Multivariable Approximation.* Academic Press, Boston. pp. 47-61, 1987.

[5] Farwig, R. "Multivariable Interpolation of Arbitrary Spaced Data by Moving Least Squares Methods". *J. of Computational and Applied Math*, vol. 16:79–93, 1987.

[6] Foley, T.A. "Scattered Data Interpolation and Approximation with Error Bounds". *Comp. Aided Geometry and Design*, vol. 3:163–177, 1986.

[7] Franke, R. "Recent Advances in the Approximation of Surfaces from Scattered Data". In C.K.Chui, L.L. Schumaker and F.I. Utreras, editor, *Topics in Multivariable Approximation.* Academic Press, Boston. pp. 79-98, 1987.

[8] Franke, R. "Scattered Data Interpolation: Test of Some Methods". *Math. of Computation*, 38(157):181–200, 1982.

[9] Franke, R. and Nielson, G. "Smooth Interpolation of Large Sets of Scattered Data". *Int. J. for Numerical Methods in Engineering*, vol. 15:1691–1704, 1980.

[10] Gorinevsky, D.M. "Experiments in Direct Learning of Feedforward Control for Manipulator Path Tracking". *Robotersysteme*, vol. 8:139–147, 1992.

[11] Gorinevsky, D.M. and Connolly, T.H. "Comparison of Neural Network and Scattered Data Approximations for Inverse Manipulator Kinematics". Technical Report 92-07, Lehrstuhl B fü Mechanik, Technische Universität München, 1992.

[12] Guez A. and Ahmad, Z. "Solution to the Inverse Kinematics Problem in Robotics by Neural Networks". *Proc. of IEEE Int. Joint Conf. on Neural Networks*, vol. 2:617–624, July 1988.

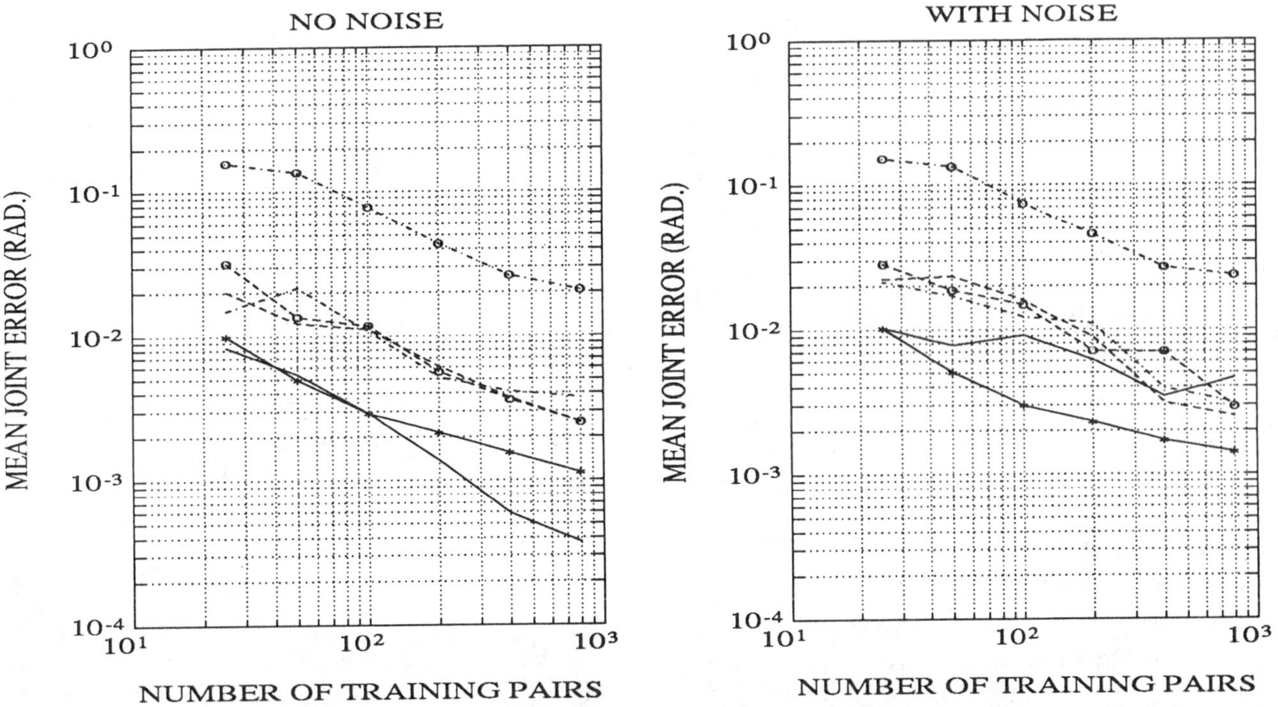

Figure 1: Mean Error of Joint Angle Approx. for the Test Set: **dashed line with circles** – Feed-For. Multilayered Net. (3-6-6-3), **dashed line** – Feed-For. Multilayered Net. (3-15-15-3), **dash – dot line** – Koh. Map (GDO), **dash-dot line with circles** – Koh. Map (Rit.), **solid line** – Gauss. RBF, **solid line with stars** – Local Multivariable Polynomial Fit

Method		Accuracy	Noise sensitivity	Forward computation time (bottleneck)	optimization (learning)
Feed-forward Networks		good	low	very small	long
Kohonen Map with Shepard Interpolation	GDO	good	low	small (search of the neighboring neurons)	long
	Rit.	good	low		moderate (extra input/output pairs are needed)
Local Gaussian Radial Basis Functions		very good	high	large (search of the neighboring data points, inversion of $L \times L$ matrix)	No
Third Order Local Polynomial Fit		very good	low	large (search of the neighboring data points, multiplications of a $L \times 20$ matrices, and an inversion of a $L \times L$ matrix)	No

Table 1: Performance Comparison of the Approximation Methods

[13] Hartman, E. and Keeler, D. . "Predicting the Future: Advantages of Semilocal Units". *Neural Computation*, vol. 3:566–578, 1991.

[14] Kieffer S., Morellas V. and Donath M. "Neural Network Learning of the Inverse Kinematic Relationships for a Robot Arm". *Proc. of IEEE Int. Conf. on Robotics and Automation*, vol. 3:2418–2425, April 1991.

[15] Kozakiewicz, C., Ogiso, T. and Miyake, N. "Partitioned Neural Network Architecture for Inverse Kinematic Calculation of a 6 DOF Robot Manipulator". *Proc. of IEEE Int. Joint Conf. on Neural Networks*, vol. 3:2001–2006, 1991.

[16] Micchelli, C.A. "Interpolation of Scattered Data: Distance Matrices and Conditionally Positive Definite Functions". *Const. Approx.*, vol. 2:11–22, 1986.

[17] Moody, J. and Darken, C.J. . "Fast Learning in Networks of Locally-Tuned Processing Units". *Neural Computation*, vol. 1:281–284, 1989.

[18] Müller, B. and Reinhardt, J. *Neural Networks*. Springer-Verlag, Berlin, 1990.

[19] Nguyen, L., Patel, R.V. and Khorasani, K. "Neural Network Architectures for the Forward Kinematics Problem in Robotics". *Proc. of IEEE Int. Joint Conf. on Neural Networks*, vol. 3:393–399, 1990.

[20] Park, J. and Sandberg, I.W. . "Universal Approximation Using Radial-Basis-Function Networks". *Neural Computation*, vol. 3:246–57, 1991.

[21] Platt, J. . "A Resource-Allocating Network for Function Interpolation". *Neural Computation*, vol. 3:213–225, 1991.

[22] Poggio, T. and Girosi, F. "Networks for Approximation and Learning". *Proceeding of the IEEE*, 78(9):1481–1497, September 1990.

[23] Powell, M.J.D. "Radial Basis Functions for Multivariable Interpolation: A Review". In J.C. Mason and M.G. Cox, editors, *Algorithms for Approximation*. Clarendon Press, Oxford, 1987. pp. 143-168.

[24] Renka, R.J. "Multivariable Interpolation of Large Sets of Scattered Data". *ACM Trans. on Math. Software*, 14(2):139–148, 1988.

[25] Ritter H., Martinez T. and Schulten K. *Neuronale Netze*. Addison-Wesley, Bonn, 1991.

[26] Tolle, H., Militzer, J. and Erzue, E. "Zur Leistungsfähigkeit Lokal Verallgemeinender assoziativer Speicher und Ihren Einsatzmöglichkeiten in Lernenden Regelungen". *Messen Steuern Regeln*, 32(3):98–105, 1991.

[27] Walter, J.A. and Schulten, K.J. "Implementation of Self-organizing Neural Networks for Visuo-motor Control of an Industrial Robot". *IEEE Trans. on Neural Networks*, 4(1):86–95, 1993.

[28] Watanabe, T. et al. . "The Calibration of Position and Orientation of Robot Manipulators Using a Neural Network". *Japan/USA Symp. on Flexible Automation*, pages 219–225, 1992.

Proceedings of the
American Control Conference
San Francisco, California • June 1993

Development of A New Kind of Robot Slipping Sensor

H. Liu, P. Meusel

Institute of Robot and System Dynamics
DLR, German Aerospace Research Establishment
D-8031 Oberpfaffenhofen, Germany

Abstract

A novel force/position sensor based on FPSR™ (Force Position Sensing Resistor) has been developed which can measure the normal force to the sensor surface and the position where the force is applied. The compact SMD circuitry was located in the back of the sensor to process the initial signals and send it to the other interface circuits. The sensing area is 0.5 in × 4.0 in. The minimum detecting force and position resolution are 50g and ± 0.15mm respectively. Because of its fast response to the physical contact (2.2 ms) and high displacement resolution, the FPSR™ is a good candidate for dexterous robot hand to detect the contact force and the slipping between robot hand and a grasping object. With this kind of sensor, some object grasping and holding experiments have been implemented successfully.

1. Construction and Principle of the FPSR™

Interlink FPSR™ shown in Fig.1 is based on two polymer films. A conducting pattern is deposited on one polymer in the form of a set of interdigital electrodes called wiper. The electrode pattern is on the order of 0.375mm finger width and spacing. There is a fixed resistor strip between the 'Hot' and 'Ground' which is used to measure the displacement where the force is applied. Next, a proprietary semiconducting polymer called force sensing layer is deposited on the other sheet. The sheets are faced together so that the conducting fingers are shunted by the conducting polymer. When no force is applied to the sandwich, the resistance between the interdigitial electrodes is quite high, usually 20MΩ or more.

A voltage is applied between the 'Hot' and 'Ground' ends of the fixed resistor strip. When force is applied to the force sensing layer, the wiper contacts are shunted through that layer to one of the conducting fingers of the resistor strip. The voltage read from the wiper is thus proportional to the distance along the strip that force is applied. An equivalent circuit for this arrangement is shown in Fig.2(a).

To sense force, a resistance measurement is made between the wiper terminal and either the 'Hot' or 'Ground' end(or both, connected together) of the fixed resistor strip as shown in Fig.2(b). It is obvious that the two measurements are not totally independent. However, the position measurement can be made unambiguously if the measuring device draws negligible current so that there is no voltage drop across the wiper resistance. Section 2 will discuss the coupling error between the force and position measurements in detail.

2. Force / Position Measure Accuracy Analysis

2.1. Force Measurement

Force measurements are not quite so unambiguous, but good approximate measurements can be obtained by shorting the two fixed resistor ends(Hot and Ground) together, and measuring the resistance between the combined leads and the wiper. Some error results from the fixed resistor being in series with the FSR™. For example, if the force is applied at the middle of the FPSR, the FSR™ part will have an additional series resistance of 1/2 of the total fixed resistance, because the resulting middle contact effectively parallels the two halves of the fixed resistor. If, on the other hand, force is applied to either end of the device active area, the fixed resistance is essentially shorted out.

Fig.3. shows the simplified circuit for exact force measure. The actual output V_{act} and the desired output V_{dsi} are:

$$R_{par} = R_1 // R_2 \quad (1)$$

$$V_{act} = V_{ref} \cdot (R_{par} + R)/(R_{par} + R + R_k) \quad (2)$$

$$V_{dsi} = V_{ref} \cdot R/(R + R_k) \quad (3)$$

where,

- R_{par} is the parallel resistance of R_1 and R_2, from 0 to 4.25KΩ,
- R is the measured resistance , from 1MΩ to 2KΩ,
- R_k is the sampling resistance , 47KΩ.

Using MATLAB, the force error distribution vs. position and force is shown in Fig.4. The maximum error(approximate 3%) happens on the middle position when great load is applied.

2.2. Position Measurement

From the Fig.3, the position measurement can be made unambiguously if the measuring device draws negligible current so that there is nearly no voltage drop across the wiper resistance. However, because of the force "footprint", the position accuracy can only reach +/-7%, with which FPSR can not be used as a accurate position potentiometer.

Resolution of a measurement device must be distinguished from accuracy. Resolution refers to the smallest change in position that can be detected. The position resolution of a FPSR depends on the width of the applied force distribution and the fineness of the conductive fingers on the FPSR. For a force "footprint" large compared to the conductive finger width, the barycentric position average can be expressed as

$$\bar{x} = \frac{\int_{x1}^{x2} x \cdot F(x)dx}{\int_{x1}^{x2} F(x)dx} \quad (4)$$

where, F(x) is the force distribution, x1, x2 are the inferior limit and superior limit of the applied force area respectively. Resolution can be approximated by

$$\Delta X = 2 \cdot W_s^2 / W_f \quad (5)$$

where, w_s is the width of the conductive fingers and w_f is the width of the applied force. This approximation assumes a relatively constant force across the force "footprint". In practice, the resolution can achieve ± 0.15mm.

Because of its quick dynamic response, approximately 2.2ms, and high position resolution , ±0.15mm, the FPSR can be used to detect "touch" and "slipping" easily.

3. Data Acquisition Electronics

3.1. Data Processing

The basic requirement is that current through the device can not exceed a limit value, e.g. 0.5mA/cm^2. Secondly, because the position and force measurements can not be made at the same time, there is a problem of the selection of switching frequency. Normally the more high the sampling frequency is, the better the measure accuracy is. However, there exists a small capacity between the 'Wiper' and the 'Ground' of the FPSR , which changes from 2000pf to 68pf with the increase of the applied force. This small capacity combined with the very great initial touching resistance (MΩ) will limit the sampling frequency of the whole sensor system to be 1KHz or less.

3.2. Interface

The circuit uses only 5 ICs, several resistors and capacities. There are 5 I/O lines connecting the circuit to the outside. Two of these are the analogue force and position output signals, one is for power supply +12V, and other two digital outputs are the initial touch signal and the position detecting signal which indicates the valid position signal.

4. Object Grasping with the FPSR™

4.1. Experimental Setup

With this kind of FPSR force/position sensor, we build a test bed for slipping feedback control shown in Fig.5. The FPSR can provide a initial touch signal '1' or '0', a force signal, a position signal and a position detecting pulse. The current coil is used as a actuator which increases output force when the input current is raised.

The digitisation is performed using a DS1002 data acquisition module installed in an IBM-386 personal computer. This module is equipped with a high-performance CMOS TMS320C30 floating-point microprocessor with an instruction time of 60 nsec. The DS2002 A/D converter offers 32 channels, and 8bit, 10bit, 12bit, and 16bit selective resolution with 5μs conversion time. The DS4001 PIO provides 32- bidirection TTL digital I/O lines with some handshake and interrupt lines, which were used to receive the 'touch' signal and slip detecting signal. The analogue current to the PWM was sent by the programmable DS2101 D/A converter which has five fully parallel analogue ranges with 3 μs settling time. Also, the DS1002 is equipped with 2K Word of true dual-port memory. This memory has separate data and address busses to the host and DSP thus allowing data transfers without the typical arbitration losses of shared memory systems.

4.2. Initial Experimental Results

The initial tests were proceeded on several kinds of objects, metal, plastic and paper box with different geometric shapes. The slipping test has been implemented as follows:

- an approach phase in which the current coil moves straight upon a object until the initial contact signal is detected;
- a holding or grasping phase where the output force of the current coil keeps in minimum value not to let the object slipping;
- a sudden impact is used to investigate the response of the FPSR.

Using the real time trace TRACE30 provided by DSPACE, one cycle of the touching and grasping signals were captured and shown in Fig. 6.

5. Conclusions and Future Efforts

In this paper, the force/position FPSR slipping sensor has been discussed, which has flexible structure, easier interface, high dynamic response and small displacement resolution. Initial experiment has proved its effectiveness for grasping task. In the near future, the integration of several sensors to a robot finger will be proceeded to provide more intelligence to the robot hand for fine manipulation.

6. Acknowledgements

The authors would like to express their severe thanks to Prof. G. Hirzinger, the director of the Institute of Robot and System Dynamics, DLR, for many helpful suggestions and his constant encouragement.

References [omitted]

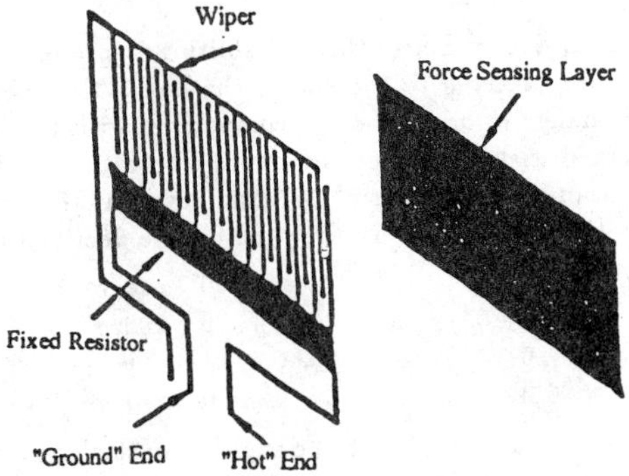

Fig.1. Construction of FPSR™

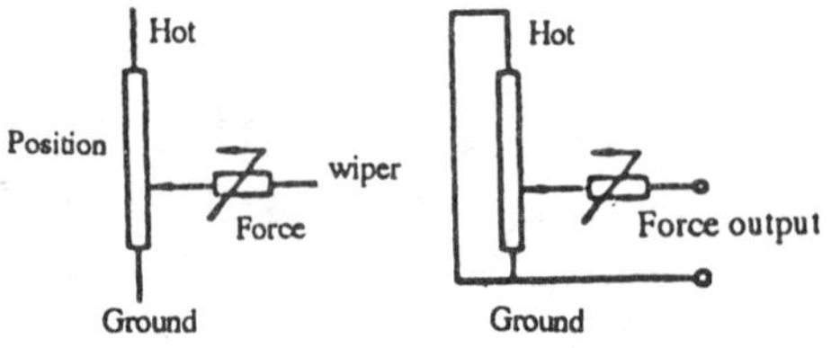

(a). position measure (b). force measure

Fig.2. Principle of the force/position measurement

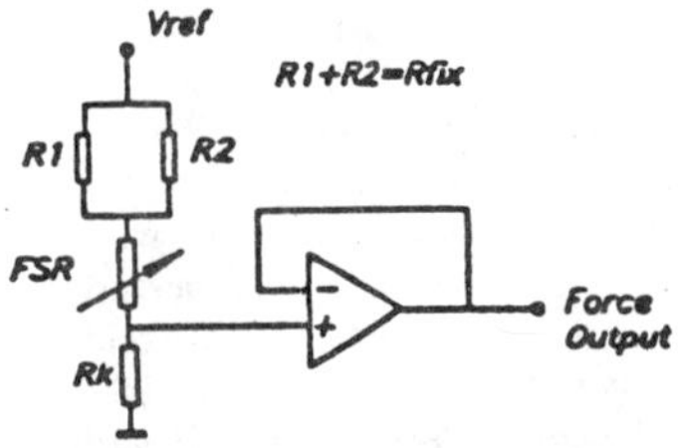

Fig.3. The equivalent circuit of the force measure

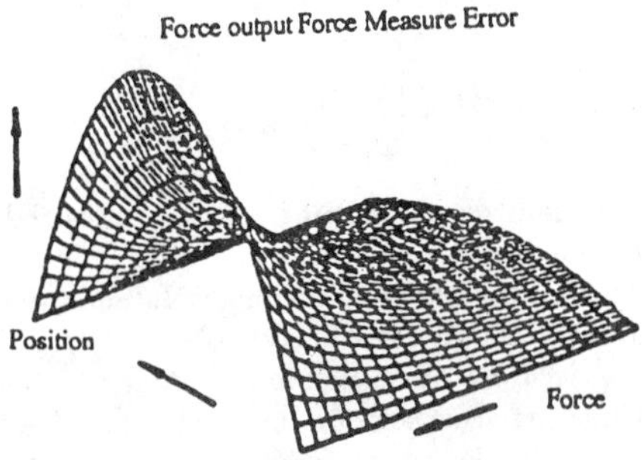

Fig.4. The error distribution of the FPSR.

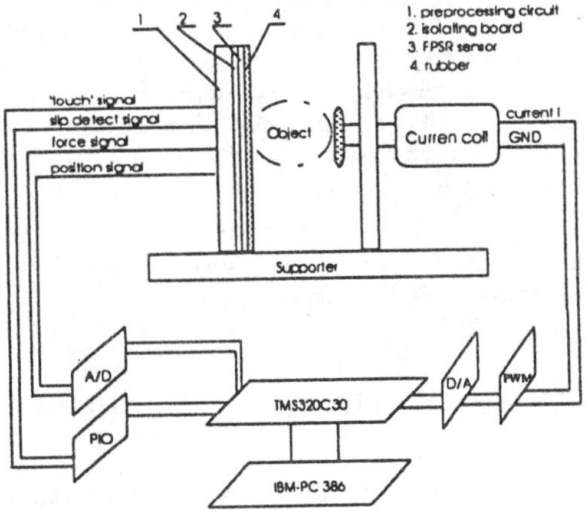

Fig.5. Test bed for the FPSR

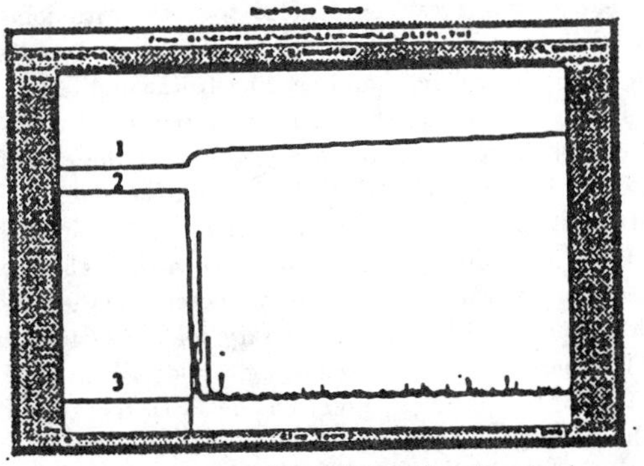

1. current signal 2. initial touch signal 3. position signal

Fig. 6. Test results of the FPSR for object grasping

Proceedings of the
American Control Conference
San Francisco, California • June 1993

An Optical Measurement System for High Accuracy Positioning of Robots

G. Quick and P. C. Müller

Safety Control Engineering, University of Wuppertal
Gaußstr. 20, D-5600 Wuppertal 1, FRG

Abstract

This paper describes a system for high accuracy measurement of robot axis position using CCD image sensors and a set of laser-beams driven by an additional motor. The system works during normal operation such that the measurements can be used for axis control. The principle is explained on a single flexible link. With the given system of sensors and control, it is possible to realize a robot with high absolute positional accuracy.

1 Introduction

The dominant reason for programming industrial robots in-teach in mode or correcting off-line programms produced by CAM (also with teach in), is the inadequate absolute position accuracy. The intention to design (less bulky) robots especially decreased the position accuracy again due to flexible joints. Some methods for improving the accuracy of a standard joint drive for a robot with revolute joints, based on encoder, motor, gearing, and joint, are presented in [1,2,3]. All cited examples are available to reduce the effects of special faults in robot positioning and control but not the total errors. For exact measurement of the tool center point (TCP) or an end effector, the use of an independent measurement system is more suitable. Realized systems with a laser interferometer [4], laser beam triangulation [5], or automatic theodolites [6] are used only for robot calibration. A measurement system for on line correction, i. e. on line control with high accuracy, and the practicability of an implementation on a robot with revolute joints is presented in the following chapter.

2 Design of the Laser-Beam-System

The measuring equipment is to be assigned for each link of the manipulator. Fig. 1 gives an overview of the elements involved in link i. Link i is driven by joint i, which is fixed to link $i-1$. The end of link i can be coupled togehter with joint $i+1$ for driving link $i+1$. The operation is based on two laser beams which emitted in joint i and heading to the end of link i parallel the link length a_i. Both beams are received by a position sensitive light detector (PSD), one mounted at the end of the link, the other with a known distance b_i from the end. The identical light emitters are pivoted on the same axis as joint i, but however there is no direct connection between the light emitters and link i. Rather the emitters are connected together and equiped with a separate drive. It is necessary for the system that a special last part b_i is constructed as rigid body. With measuring the position of the produced point on the PSD, the known direction of the laser beam, the position of joint i, and the lenght a_i, the position of the end point of link i can be calculated. The second measured position together with the measurement at the end of the link are rendering possible calculation of the changing orientation of the end of the link. This value is used for correcting the orientation error with the angle of the following joint of a multi-axis robot. Usually the drive of the laser beams must be a system with high positional accuracy because the measuring accuracy really depends directly on the beam direction. In this application a stepping motor is used for driving the laser beam. Working without commutator and collector ring and positioning without feedback are the advantages of the stepping motor. On the other hand this motor is characterized by an insufficient angular resolution and variations between the steps, so a microstep generator is used with the stepping motor. Normally a rotary encoder can be used for feedback of the stepping motor drive control to compensate positioning errors based on overload. In the actual application the primary aim is the measurement of the actual beam direction so that the systematic positioning error, i. e. 1 mrad, and effects based on friction don't reduce the accuracy of the system. Loosing steps are not possible because of a low and constant load. The PSDs for position measuring in a plane are usually built up with CCD image sensors which are implemented in CCD cameras also. It is easy to find out the coordination values of lighted pixles in such an image plane but comparatively the bandwidth of the system is low and insufficient for control of link vibration. The application of CCD linear image sensors are characterized by a higher resolution and a possible bandwidth above 10kHz. Width and position of the lighted interval can be interpreted as a position in the PSD plane.

3 Calculation for Correcting Values

The represented side view of the system, see fig. 2, describes the different angles in the example of an elastic link. The description by DH-parameters would be significant only with additional information on a given robot, so the introduced coordinate systems xyz, $x^*y^*z^*$, and the desired value for the joint angle q yield the transformation matrix

$$\underline{T} = \begin{pmatrix} \cos q & -\sin q & 0 & a\cos q \\ \sin q & \cos q & 0 & a\sin q \\ 0 & 0 & 1 & 0 \\ 0 & 0 & 0 & 1 \end{pmatrix} \tag{1}$$

for the ideal link. Nevertheless the real shifting is presented by the actual angle q^* refered to the end of the link. Also there is an additional change in orientation in comparison with the ideal link. It is marked with β^* and correspondes to a rotation of the z^*-axis of the coordinate system $x^*y^*z^*$ brought in at the end of the link. Now the complete transformation can be decribed by

$$\underline{T}^* = \begin{pmatrix} \cos(q^*+\beta^*) & -\sin(q^*+\beta^*) & 0 & a\cos q^* \\ \sin(q^*+\beta^*) & \cos(q^*+\beta^*) & 0 & a\sin q^* \\ 0 & 0 & 1 & 0 \\ 0 & 0 & 0 & 1 \end{pmatrix}. \tag{2}$$

The used angle q^* is calculated with the angle q_m of the laser beam drive and the difference angle q_{PSD} presented by the measurement with PSD:

$$q^* = q_m - q_{PSD}. \tag{3}$$

With the assumption of constant length a and small angles q_{PSD} and β^* the angle q_{PSD} is calculated by

$$q_{PSD} \approx \arcsin \frac{c_{I_y}}{a}. \qquad (4)$$

The values c_i are demonstrated in fig. 3 and make it possible to compute the change in orientation β^* using the equation

$$\beta^* = \arctan \frac{c_{II_y} - c_{I_y}}{b}. \qquad (5)$$

For the deflection c_{II_y}, it is necessary to measure w_{II_y} and to use informations about the laserpoint diameter d of PSD II for calculating

$$c_{II_y} = \frac{\sqrt{d^2 - w_{II_y}^2}}{2}. \qquad (6)$$

The measurement of c_{II_z} is usefull in vibration control for a revolute joint of vertical axis.

4 Control Improvement

Control of flexible links are presented in a lot of papers. For example the controller in [7,8,9] are based on a two layer control. Static errors in positioning are not considered or there is an offline calculation of static errors. In this case it is not possible to compensate changes in load or other faults. An axis controller with the presented measuring system shows a possibility to improve the control using on line values of the new measuring system. There is a feedback of the calculated values q^* with seperate filters for the position controller and the vibration controller. In relationship with the implemented drive there must be a change of the controller structure or the controller parameters, because the feedback of a position sensor mounted on a joint or a drive is replaced by the new system. The new position controller is able to control q^* with the desired value q_d.

5 Conclusions

The proposed measuring system is independent on the selected joint drive, such that an economical and efficient drive system can be used. The absolute position accuracy and the accuracy in repeatability depends only on the precision of the CCD sensors, the incremental encoder of the additional beam drive, and the adjustment of these elements. Using the new system only for compensation of errors like gear elasticity, it is sufficient to have one system of laser beam and a CCD sensor. Another possibility is to extend the present system by an extra laser beam. Now there are three light emitters based at the joint. The direction of the additional laser beam is with a known angle to the both of the other beams. Differences in the length of the link are affected by changes of light position of a third PSD sensor at the end of the link.

References

[1] Bühler, C.: Regelung direkt angetriebener Roboterachsen am Beispiel eines sechsachsigen Industrieroboters, Dissertation, University of Dortmund 1989

[2] Henrichfreise, H.: Aktive Schwingungsdämpfung an einem elastischen Knickarmroboter, Dissertation, University of Paderborn 1987

[3] Wurst, K.-H.: Leichtbaustrukturen im Roboterbau - Probleme und Einsatz, VDI/VDE-GMA 5.5-Tagung, Jan. 1992, Aachen

[4] Weule, H. and Reichling, B.: Optisches Meßsystem zur Genauigkeitsprüfung von Industrierobotern, Robotersysteme 3(1987), pp. 189-198

[5] ASL CTD Lasertrack system, technical documetation, Bradville, England

[6] Driels, M. R.; Pathre, U. S.: Vision-based automatic theodolite for robot calibration. IEEE Trans. on Robotics and Automation 3(1991), pp.351-360

[7] Pfeiffer, F., Richter, K. and Kovacsne-Bende, M.: Augmented flexible link manipulator trajectory control for moving a filled glass, Robotersysteme 8(1992), 74-78

[8] Kleemann, U.: Dynamics and control of a robot system with elastic arms. Proc. Int. Symp. Rob. Manip., Modelling, Control and Edu., Albuquerque, pp. 487-492, 1986

[9] Pfeiffer, F.; Gebler, B.: A multistage approach to the dynamics and control of elastic robots. Proc. IEEE Int. Conf. Rob. and Autom., pp. 2-8, Philadelphia, USA, 1988

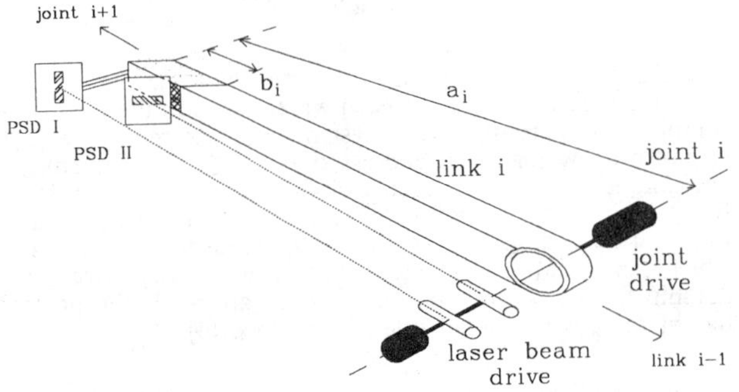

Fig.1. Measurement system for link i

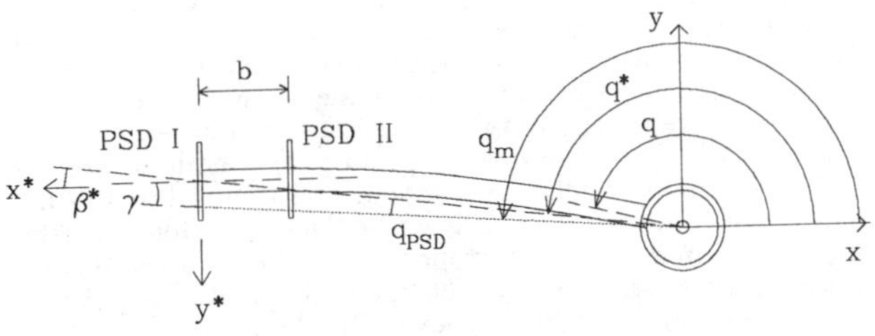

Fig.2. Sectional view of the link

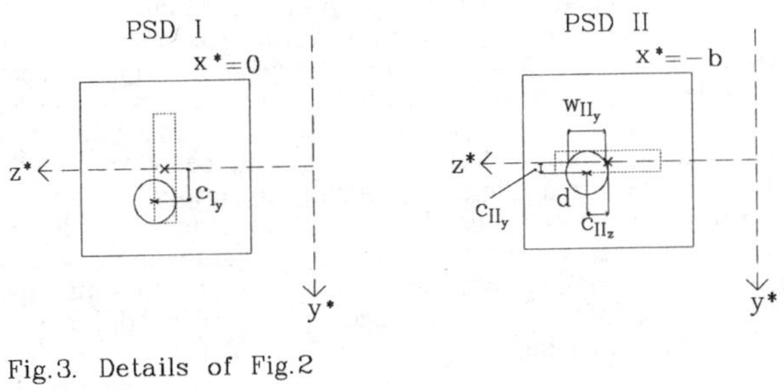

Fig.3. Details of Fig.2

Proceedings of the
American Control Conference
San Francisco, California • June 1993

KNOWLEDGE BASE DECOUPLING IN FUZZY-LOGIC CONTROL SYSTEMS

Clarence W. de Silva

NSERC Professor of Industrial Automation
Department of Mechanical Engineering
The University of British Columbia
Vancouver, Canada

Abstract

In a coupled rule base, more than one condition variable may link with more than one action variable within the same rule. This paper develops an analytical framework for decoupling such a rule base, with specific reference to fuzzy-logic control. Since control decisions are made through the use of the compositional rule of inference, the computational problem of fuzzy-logic is greatly simplified through the use of an uncoupled rule base. Conditions are derived, under which inferencing through an uncoupled rule base becomes equivalent to that through a coupled rule base. A laboratory prototype of a single-axis servo motor system which incorporates a knowledge-based tuner is employed to demonstrate the effective use of an uncoupled rule base. Experiments are carried out by operating the system, with only a segment of the rule base active. By comparing the tuning response of the servo motor when such subgroups of rules are sequentially activated, with that when all rules are activated simultaneously, it can be established whether rule base decoupling has resulted in a performance degradation.

1. Introduction

The theory of fuzzy sets, first developed by Zadeh [1], and associated fuzzy logic, have been widely used in the control of complex and partially known systems (For example, see [2]). Use of a knowledge base expressed as a set of if-then rules is not unique to fuzzy-logic control (For example, see [3]). In fuzzy-logic control (FLC), however, the rules may contain fuzzy terms such as "fast", "poor" and "reasonably accurate", which can be expressed as fuzzy sets with representative membership functions, and control decisions are made through the use of the compositional rule of inference [4].

In many applications, at least some of the control knowledge is generated through experience of control engineers, control system designers, and system operators. It is generally not possible to express such knowledge as hard algorithms or analytical formulas, but may be conveniently expressed as a set of linguistic statements. FLC is appropriate in such situations in particular. Even though FLC has been used in low-level direct control, as in [5], it is more appealing at least intuitively, in high-level control, self-organization, and tuning [6]. In manual tuning of a controller, it is convenient to perform the tuning actions in a sequential manner according to some form of priority. There, the person who tunes the controller may observe some set of attributes, determine the conditions that occur, prioritize them, and perform the tuning actions sequentially. In many problems, the governing relations (rules) of conditions and actions may be interpreted as being uncoupled, in the sense that only one condition variable is related to only one action variable in a given rule. In a general and more complex rule base, each rule may relate more than one condition variable and more than one action variable. This latter situation gives a coupled rule base. It should be clear that the action variables in a rule can be uncoupled simply by repeating the rule with the same condition part but providing only one action at a time, without sacrificing any accuracy in the knowledge base, assuming that the rules are processed simultaneously during inferencing. But, uncoupling the condition variables is not as trivial.

Clearly, the computational and developmental advantages of using an uncoupled rule base in FLC are tremendous. Generally, however, some accuracy is lost by assuming that the rules in a knowledge base are uncoupled. In view of this, it is important to examine the conditions under which this assumption can be made without sacrificing the control accuracy. First, this problem is analytically investigated in the present paper. Next, experiments are carried out employing a prototype servo-motor system which incorporates a fuzzy-logic based tuner, to illustrate the effective use of an uncoupled rule base, and to examine whether the performance could be improved through coupling of the rule base.

2. Theory Of Rule Base Decoupling

In this section, the theoretical basis of rule base decoupling is presented. First, the general fuzzy-logic control problem with a coupled rule base is formulated. This represents a multi-degree-of-freedom decision making problem. Next, the method of single-degree-of-freedom decision making using a coupled rule base is given. Finally, the assumption of decoupled rule base is incorporated into the single-degree-of-freedom decision making problem. On that basis, conditions are established for rule-base decoupling in the problem of single degree-of-freedom decision making.

Fuzzy Logic Control Problem

Consider a knowledge base of fuzzy-logic control, given as a set of linguistic rule in the general form

$$\underset{i,j,\cdots,k}{\textbf{Else}}\ [\textbf{If } e_1 \text{ is } E_1^i \text{ and } \ldots \text{ and } e_n \text{ is } E_n^a \textbf{ then } c_1 \text{ is } C_1^j \text{ and } \ldots \text{and } c_p \text{ is } C_p^b] \tag{1}$$

with $\underline{e} \,\underset{=}{\Delta}\, [e_1, \ldots, e_n]^T \in \mathbf{R}^n$ and $\underline{c} \,\underset{=}{\Delta}\, [c_1, \ldots, c_p]^T \in \mathbf{R}^p$.

Here $\underline{e}$ is the vector of condition variables (antecedents), which is monitored for subsequent control. Each antecedent e_s may assume one of m discrete fuzzy states $E_s^1, E_s^2, \ldots, E_s^m$. It follows that the integer m is a measure of the *fuzzy resolution* in e_s. Similarly, $\underline{c}$ is the vector of control actions (consequents). Each consequent c_q may assume one of r discrete fuzzy states $C_q^1, C_q^2, \ldots, C_q^r$. Again, the integer r is a measure of the fuzzy resolution of c_q. Also, note that the fuzzy states assumed by the action variables depend on (i.e., are functions of) those of the condition variables. The fuzzy states E_s and C_q are fuzzy sets [1] which are completely represented by their membership functions

$\mu_{E_s}(e_s) : \mathbf{R} \rightarrow [0, 1]$ and $\mu_{C_q}(c_q) : \mathbf{R} \rightarrow [0, 1]$.

The rule base given by (1) may be expressed in the compact notation

$$R : \underset{\underline{i},\, \underline{j}(\underline{i})}{\textbf{Else}}\ [\textbf{If } \underline{e} \text{ is } \underline{E}^{\underline{i}} \textbf{ then } \underline{c} \text{ is } \underline{C}^{\underline{j}}] \tag{2}$$

Note that $\underline{i}$ is a set of m integers which denotes a general fuzzy state taken up by the condition vector $\underline{e}$. Then $\underline{j}$ is a set of r integers which depends on $\underline{i}$, and denotes the corresponding fuzzy state of the action vector $\underline{c}$.

The membership function of the rule base R is a mapping in the cartesian product space of the universes of the fuzzy sets : $\underline{E} \times \underline{C} \,\underset{=}{\Delta}\, E_1 \times E_2 \times \ldots \times E_n \times C_1 \times C_2 \times \ldots \times C_p$, and is expressed as

$\mu_R(\underline{e}, \underline{c}) : \mathbf{R}^n \times \mathbf{R}^p \rightarrow [0, 1]$.

Using the *sup–min* connectives of fuzzy logic [4], this membership function is determined by

$$\mu_R(\underline{e}, \underline{c}) = \sup_{i, j(i)} \min[\mu_{\underline{E}^i}(\underline{e}), \mu_{\underline{C}^j}(\underline{c})] \quad (3)$$

in which, the set of membership functions of the fuzzy state vector $\underline{E}^i$ of condition variables is defined as

$$\mu_{\underline{E}^i}(\underline{e}) \underset{=}{\Delta} \{\mu_{E_1^i}(e_1), \ldots, \mu_{E_n^a}(e_n)\} \quad (4)$$

and the set of membership functions of the corresponding fuzzy state vector $\underline{C}^j$ of action variables is defined as

$$\mu_{\underline{C}^j}(\underline{c}) \underset{=}{\Delta} \{\mu_{C_1^j}(c_1), \ldots, \mu_{c_p^b}(C_p)\} \quad (5)$$

Once the knowledge base of control is available as a membership function, the control problem becomes a matter of estimating a control action $\hat{\underline{c}}$ corresponding to a context $\hat{\underline{e}}$ which is available through monitoring of the system behavior.

The computation of $\hat{\underline{c}}$ is performed by using the compositional rule of inference, and specifically applying the *sup–min* composition [4,2,].

Inferencing through a Coupled Rule Base

Suppose that by monitoring the condition vector $\underline{e}$ of the system, a fuzzy context $\hat{\underline{E}} \underset{=}{\Delta} [\hat{E}_1, \hat{E}_2, \ldots, \hat{E}_n]^T$ has been established at a given instant. Note that with crisp data, a process of fuzzification [7] will be needed to obtain the context $\hat{\underline{E}}$. For example, the crisp data $\hat{\underline{e}}$ may be taken as fuzzy singletons. Alternatively, the crisp data may be classified into fuzzy states through the use of the membership functions of those states. These procedures will provide the membership function $\mu_{\hat{\underline{E}}}(e)$ of the context.

The control decision $\hat{\underline{C}} \underset{=}{\Delta} [\hat{C}_1, \hat{C}_2, \ldots, \hat{C}_p]^T$ corresponding to the context $\hat{\underline{E}}$ is computed through the use of the compositional rule of inference [4]. Specifically, by the *sup–min* composition of the context $\hat{\underline{E}}$ with the rule base R, we get

$$\mu_{\hat{\underline{C}}}(\underline{c}) = \sup_{\underline{e}} \min[\mu_{\hat{\underline{E}}}(\underline{e}), \mu_R(\underline{e}, \underline{c})] \quad (6)$$

Then, crisp control actions $\hat{\underline{c}}$ have to be computed from fuzzy $\hat{\underline{C}}$. In this process, first the action membership function, given by equation (6), is projected along each axis c_q and then the centroid method is applied to compute the corresponding control action.

__Definition:__ Consider a membership function $\mu(\underline{x}, \underline{y}) : \mathbf{R}^n \times \mathbf{R}^p \rightarrow [0, 1]$. Its *projection* in the $X_i \times Y_j$ subspace is denoted by $Proj\ [\mu(\underline{x}, \underline{y})]\ (x_i, y_j) : \mathbf{R} \times \mathbf{R} \rightarrow [0, 1]$ and is given by

$$Proj\ [\mu(\underline{x}, \underline{y})]\ (x_i, y_j) \underset{=}{\Delta} \sup_{\substack{\forall x_k \neq x_i \\ \forall y_l \neq y_j}} \mu(\underline{x}, \underline{y}) \quad (7)$$

Using this version of the familiar definition of projection [7] the crisp control actions corresponding to equation (6) are computed by

$$\hat{c}_q = \frac{\int c_q\ Proj\ [\mu_{\hat{\underline{C}}}(\underline{c})]\ (c_q)\ dc_q}{\int Proj\ [\mu_{\hat{\underline{C}}}(\underline{c})]\ (c_q)\ dc_q} \quad (8)$$

$$q = 1, 2, \ldots, p$$

in which, each integration is performed over the support set of the particular membership function.

Arguably, the greatest potential of fuzzy logic control is in applications where there is a useful knowledge base of manual control, which can be expressed as a set of linguistic rules. Then, tuning and self-organization of a control system, rather than direct low-level control, are better suited for the particular approach [6]. Knowledge-base acquisition by human operators can be quite effective if only one condition variable and one action variable are considered at a time. Also, control actions determined by human thought process are often provided one at a time. In complex situations, the control actions will be carried out in a quick succession and some prioritization of the actions will occur naturally, again depending on factors such as the complexity or urgency of the situation, operator experience, and available expertise. It follows that, use of pairs of a single condition variable and a single action variable is quite realistic in fuzzy logic control. For this purpose, however, the specific variables of the knowledge base have to be carefully chosen, particularly making use of expert experience [9]. Now let us address the inferencing problem in this particular point of view.

Consider a coupled rule base R as given by equation (1), (2) or (3), with membership function $\mu_R(\underline{e}, \underline{c})$. Suppose that a crisp observation $\hat{e}_s$ of the condition variable e_s is available, and it is required to determine a crisp control value $\hat{c}_q$ for the corresponding action variable c_q . First the projection of μ_R in the $E_s \times C_a$ subspace is determined as $Proj\ [\mu_R(\underline{e}, \underline{c})]\ (e_s, c_q)$ using equation (7). The crisp condition $\hat{e}_s$ may be expressed as a fuzzy singleton whose membership function is

$$\mu_{\hat{E}_s}(e) \underset{=}{\Delta} s(e - \hat{e}_s) \begin{array}{l} = 1 \text{ for } e = \hat{e}_s \\ = 0 \text{ elsewhere} \end{array} \quad (9)$$

Then, by applying the compositional rule of inference (6) and the centroid equation (8), it can be shown that

$$\hat{c}_q = \frac{\int c_q\ Proj\ [\mu_R(\underline{e}, \underline{c})]\ (\hat{e}_s, c_q)\ dc_q}{\int Proj\ [\mu_R(\underline{e}, \underline{c})]\ (\hat{e}_s, c_q)\ dc_q} \quad (10)$$

$$q = 1, 2, \ldots, p \qquad s = 1, 2, \ldots, n$$

This result is used in making control decisions in the case of a coupled rule base.

Inferencing through an Uncoupled Rule Base

Here the rule base is assumed to be uncoupled, and subgroups of rules are considered separately, where each subgroup relates just one condition variable e_s and one action variable c_q ; thus

$$R_{s,q} : \underset{i, j(i)}{Else}\ [\text{If } e_s \text{ is } E_s^i \text{ then } c_q \text{ is } C_q^j] \quad (11)$$

The complete, uncoupled rule base is given by

$$R = \underset{s, q(s)}{U} R_{s,q} \quad (12)$$

Note that the membership function of the rule base subgroup $R_{s,q}$ is

$$\mu_{R_{s,q}}(e, c) : \mathbf{R} \times \mathbf{R} \rightarrow [0, 1] \quad (13)$$

and is given by

$$\mu_{R_{s,q}}(e, c) = \sup_{i, j(i)} \min\left[\mu_{E_s^i}(e), \mu_{C_q^j}(c)\right] \quad (14)$$

For a fuzzy context $\hat{E}_s$ that is given at a particular instant, the corresponding fuzzy action $\hat{C}_q$ is obtained by applying the compositional rule of inference in the usual manner, as

$$\mu_{\hat{C}_q}(c) = \sup_{e} \min\left[\mu_{\hat{E}_s}(e), \mu_{R_{s,q}}(e, c)\right] \quad (15)$$

If the context is assumed to be a fuzzy singleton of value $\hat{e}_s$, the corresponding crisp action is determined by the centroid method

$$\hat{c}_q = \frac{\int c\,\mu_{R_{s,q}}(\hat{e}_s, c)\,dc}{\int \mu_{R_{s,q}}(\hat{e}_s, c)\,dc} \tag{16}$$

It follows that the computational requirements of inferencing can be significantly reduced by the assumption of an uncoupled rule base. But, of course, some accuracy is lost here. This will be addressed in the next section. But, note that the concepts of a coupled rule base can be directly applied to an uncoupled rule base, through the use of the familiar concept of *cylindrical extension* [8], which is defined next

Definition : Consider $\underline{x} \triangleq [x_1, x_2, ..., x_n]^T \in \mathbf{R}^n$,

$\underline{y} \triangleq [y_1, y_2, ..., y_p]^T \in \mathbf{R}^p$, and $\mu(x_i, \underline{y}) : \mathbf{R} \times \mathbf{R}^p \rightarrow [0,1]$

with $1 \le i \le n$. The *cylindrical extension* of $\mu(x_i, \underline{y})$ over the entire space $\mathbf{R}^n \times \mathbf{R}^p$ is given by

$$cyl\,[\mu(x_i, \underline{y})]\,(\underline{x}, \underline{y}) \;:\; \mathbf{R}^n \times \mathbf{R}^p \rightarrow [\,0,1\,] \tag{17}$$

$$= \mu(x_i, \underline{y}), \quad \forall\, \underline{x},\, \underline{y};\; 1 \le i \le n$$

With this definition, it is clear that the membership function of the entire rule base is the *intersection* of the cylindrical extensions of the membership functions of the subgroups; thus

$$\mu_R(\underline{e}, \underline{c}) = \bigwedge_{s,\,q(s)} cyl\left[\mu_{R_{s,q}}(e_s, c_q)\right](\underline{e}, \underline{c}) \tag{18}$$

The uncoupled rule base will not suffer any further loss of accuracy through this extension in view of the fact that, in the uncoupled case we have

$$Proj\left[cyl[\mu_{R_{s,q}}(e_s, c_q)]\,(\underline{e}, \underline{c})\right](e_s, c_q) = \mu_{R_{s,q}}(e_s, c_q) \tag{19}$$

Equivalence Condition

From the developments presented thus far, it is clear that the control inferences made using a coupled rule base is generally not the same as those made by assuming an uncoupled rule base, for the system parameters and data. But, it can be shown that if a certain condition is satisfied by the membership functions of the rule-base variables, the control inferences in the two cases become identical, with an obvious computational advantage in the case of the uncoupled rule base. A condition for this equivalence is established in the present section.

Zadeh [10] developed the concept of separability of fuzzy restrictions, and showed that a fuzzy restriction is separable if and only if the *join* of the projections of the restriction results in the original restriction. Note that the join is the intersection of the cylindrical extensions. This concept can be extended to establish the equivalence condition mentioned above. Again consider the coupled rule base given by (1). Its membership function is expressed using the *sup-min* connectives, as

$$\mu_R(\underline{e}, \underline{c}) = \sup_{i,\,j(i)} \min\Big[\mu_{E_1^{i(1)}}(e_1),\, \mu_{E_2^{i(2)}}(e_2), ..., \mu_{E_n^{i(n)}}(e_n),$$

$$\mu_{C_1^{j(1)}}(c_1),\, \mu_{C_2^{j(2)}}(c_2), ..., \mu_{C_p^{j(p)}}(c_p)\Big] \tag{20}$$

where i denotes a coupled rule in the rule base, and hence representing the associated set of fuzzy states of the condition variables, and j denotes the associated set of fuzzy states of the action variables. The *min* operation of the membership functions in equation (20) may be interpreted as the intersection of their cylindrical extensions in $\mathbf{R}^n \times \mathbf{R}^p$. Then, when using equation (20) in (10) for inferencing through a coupled rule base, it is required to determine the projection $\mathbf{R}^n \times \mathbf{R}^p \rightarrow \mathbf{R} \times \mathbf{R}$ given by

$$Proj\,[\mu_R(\underline{e}, \underline{c})]\,(e_s, c_q) = \sup_{\substack{\forall e_k \ne e_s \\ \forall c_t \ne c_q}} \{\mu_R(\underline{e}, \underline{c})\} \tag{21}$$

Now, by substituting equation (20) into (21) it can be shown that

$$Proj[\mu_R(\underline{e}, \underline{c})](e_s, c_q) = \sup_{i,\,j(i)} \min\left[\mu_{E_s^{i(s)}}(e_s), \mu_{C_q^{j(q)}}(c_q), \mu_i\right] \tag{22}$$

in which

$$\mu_i = \min_{\substack{k \ne s \\ t \ne q}} \; \sup_{e_k,\, c_t} \left[\mu_{E_k^{i(k)}}(e_k)\,,\, \mu_{C_t^{j(t)}}(c_t)\right] \tag{23}$$

Then by comparing equation (22) with (14) it follows that the equivalence condition is

$$\mu_i \ge \min\left[\sup_{e_s} \mu_{E_s^{i(s)}}(e_s)\,,\; \sup_{c_q} \mu_{C_q^{j(q)}}(c_q)\right] \quad \forall i \tag{24}$$

A special case in which the condition (24) is satisfied is when all the fuzzy variables in the rule base are *normal* (i.e., when they have peak membership grades of unity).

3. Experimental Illustration

To demonstrate the use of an uncoupled rule base in a realistic application, and to study the effect of uncoupled rules, an experimental system of knowledge-based tuning is used. This application is consistent with the assertion that tuning is more appropriate than low-level direct control, as an application of fuzzy-logic based, on-line decision making.

System Description

The prototype system that is used in our experiments is shown in Figure 1. It consists of a DC motor with a servo loop complete with a servo amplifier, optical encoder, and a commercial digital controller. This is a single-axis servo system that can drive a single-degree-of-freedom load as shown. The servo loop has proportional and integral actions along with a lead compensator. The servo system is interfaced with a desktop computer which serves as the system host. Software modules have been developed in the host computer for tuning the servo system [9]. Several key features of the tuning system should be pointed out. The system uses a reference model for comparison purposes in evaluating the performance of the servo motor. A common test input (typically a sequence of steps or a pulse train) is applied to both the servo motor and the reference model, and their responses are transmitted to the Performance Evaluator Module (*P*). Note that the required performance is implicitly specified by the reference model, with respect to which the numerical values of "performance indicators" are computed by *P*. These indicators are given in a nondimensional index form, with values ranging from 0 denoting an overspecification, and infinity denoting a completely unacceptable performance. Performance grades such as Overspecified, In-specification, Marginal, Poor, and Very Poor are expressed by a set of membership functions, through which the values of the performance indicators are fuzzified to generate the "context" (or the condition-variable values) for the tuning knowledge base. Note here that the reference model serves several functions, more notably as a means of performance specification and to serve as a buffer against unrealistic specifications. Also, in the present context, the performance evaluator *P* is intended to behave somewhat like a human, and the evaluation can be rather qualitative. Then, the availability of a reference model can greatly facilitate graphic and experience-based evaluations.

An uncoupled rule base is employed to represent the tuning knowledge. This is not an arbitrary decision, and the condition-action variable pairs have to be chosen in a realistic manner. Accordingly, another important feature of the present system is to use an intermediate set of controller parameters, termed "controller attributes", rather than the direct tuning parameters. Then a transformation unit, denoted as the "Tuner Mapping Module" (*T*) in Figure 1, is used to compute the actual tuning-parameter values from the inference values (controller attributes). The *T* module typically contains a set of algebraic relations, but it may use other types such as fuzzy relations as well. Decision making is carried out using the compositional rule of inference, as given by equation (15) for an uncoupled rule base. Defuzzification of the tuning inferences is done according to the centroid method (see equation (16)).

The rule base used in servo tuning is presented in Figure 2. Note that the rules are uncoupled, and furthermore grouped

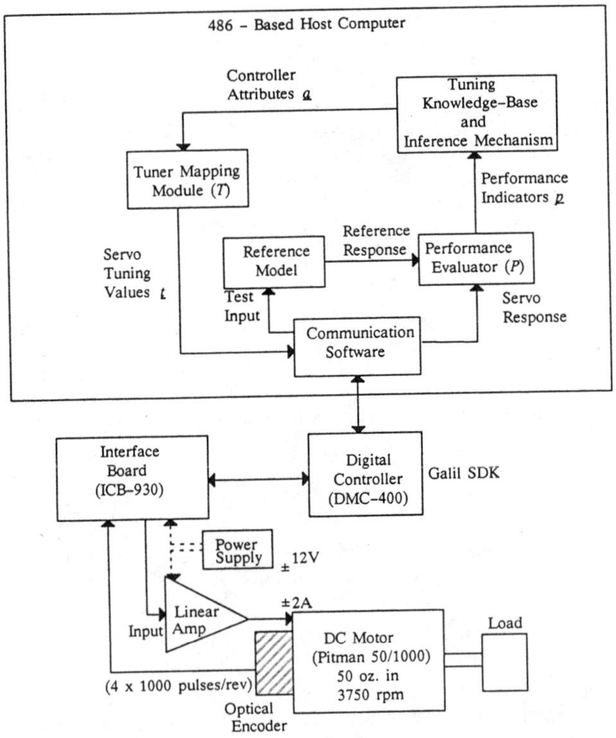

Figure 1. A Schematic Diagram of the Prototype Servo System with Knowledge-Based Tuning

Context

RT = 95% Rise Time
FD = Damped Natural Frequency
DR = Damping Ratio
OS = Response Overshoot
OF = Response Offset

Actions

PX = Phase Lead at Crossover
GX = Gain at Crossover
XF = Crossover Frequency
LF = Low Frequency of Integrator for Crossover Gain

Rule Base

1. For Rise Time:

   Else [**If** *RT* **is** *X* **then** *PX* **is** *A*]
   X, A(X)

   Else [**If** *RT* **is** *X* **then** *GX* **is** *A*]
   X, A(X)

   Else [**If** *RT* **is** *X* **then** *XF* **is** *A*]
   X, A(X)

2. For Damped Natural Frequency:

   Else [**If** *FD* **is** *X* **then** *GX* **is** *A*]
   X, A(X)

3. For Damping Ratio:

   Else [**If** *DR* **is** *X* **then** *PX* **is** *A*]
   X, A(X)

   Else [**If** *DR* **is** *X* **then** *GX* **is** *A*]
   X, A(X)

4. For Response Overshoot:

   Else [**If** *OS* **is** *X* **then** *PX* **is** *A*]
   X, A(X)

   Else [**If** *OS* **is** *X* **then** *XF* **is** *A*]
   X, A(X)

5. For Response Offset:

   Else [**If** *OF* **is** *X* **then** *GX* **is** *A*]
   X, A(X)

   Else [**If** *OF* **is** *X* **then** *LF* **is** *A*]
   X, A(X)

Figure 2. The Rule Base of Servo Tuning

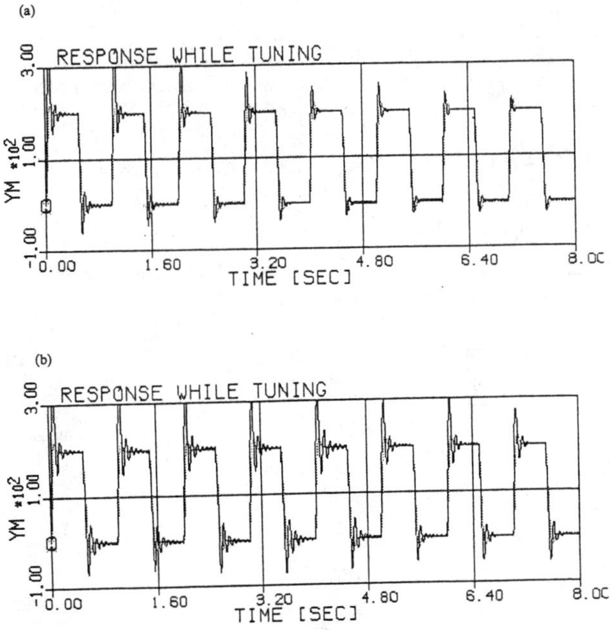

Figure 3. The Response of the Prototype Servo Motor During Tuning
(a) With All Rules Active
(b) With the Rule Subgroup Sequence 1–2–3–4

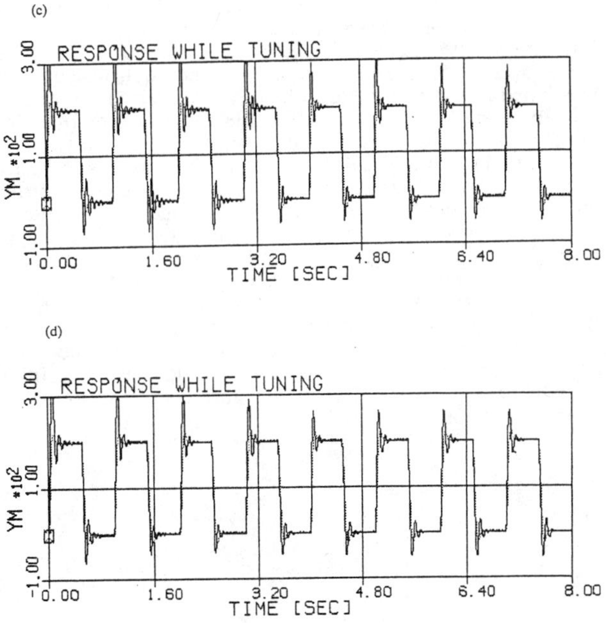

Figure 3 (cont'd)
(c) With the Rule Subgroup Sequence 2–3–4–1
(d) With the Rule Subgroup Sequence 3–4–1–2

according to the condition variable. Each rule, given in the abbreviated form, is actually a set of rules which takes into account various fuzzy states that have been defined for the condition and action variables. In particular, five fuzzy states are used for each of the action variables and condition variables.

The action variables used in the rule base are known to be very familiar to the control engineers and designers of conventional servo systems. The direct tuning parameters of the servo controller are the pole and zero locations of the lead compensator, proportional gain of the servo loop, and the gain of the integral controller. They are related to the action variables (controller attributes) through well-known algebraic relations (see for example, [11]). These relations form the Module T in Figure 1.

Experimental Results

The rule base that has been implemented in the servo motor system is uncoupled, as clear from Figure 2. First, the entire rule base is executed at high speed to carry out the tuning of an initially oscillatory system. The response of the servo motor with an inertial load, in this case, is shown in Figure 3(a). It could be argued that if reasoning is carried out sufficiently fast, characteristics of a coupled rule base would be retained here, at least to a limited extent. For example, the two uncoupled rules

If RT **is** X **then** PX **is** A
and

If FD **is** Y **then** GX **is** B

may exhibit the behavior of the coupled rule

If RT **is** X **and** FD **is** Y **then** PX **is** A **and** GX **is** B

if the uncoupled rules are executed very fast (i.e., almost in parallel), which is the case for the result shown in Figure 3(a).

Next, the four subgroups of rules, as denoted by 1 through 4 in Figure 2, were sequentially activated, for uniform intervals of time, one at a time. It was found that in each case proper tuning could be achieved if the sequence was cycled for a sufficient length of time. It follows that tuning accuracy is not compromised due to sequencing a set of uncoupled rules, instead of executing a coupled rule base. Since the membership functions in the rule base were chosen to be normal, this behavior was to be expected, in view of the equivalence result developed in this paper. But, when the duration of a sequence was fixed and the order in which the subgroups of rules are sequenced was changed, the end results were found to differ depending on the particular sequence. This too was to be expected because different subgroups of rules emphasize different characteristics of the servo response. Since these characteristics of the response vary with time, the end result of tuning depends on the time segment of the response in which a particular subgroup of rules is activated. Three such results are presented in Figures 3 (b) through (d). In these experiments, the switching sequence of the rule-base subgroups was maintained the same, in a cyclic sense, but the starting subgroups of rules were not identical. Hence, the efficiency of tuning is seen to depend on the time period during which a particular subgroup of rules is active.

Conclusion

This paper presented an analytical framework for studying the equivalence of an uncoupled rule base and a coupled one, in the context of fuzzy logic control systems. A prototype servo-motor system with a fuzzy-logic-based parameter tuning system is employed to illustrate the realistic application of an uncoupled rule base. The rule base was subdivided, and the subgroups of rules were activated sequentially to study the effect of each subgroup of rules on the tuner performance. Rule base coupling might be neglected in this example, in view of the fact that the fuzzy quantities in the rule base were normal. The experimental results supported this analytical finding.

Acknowledgment

This work was supported by grants from the *Advanced Systems Institute of B.C.*, and from the *Natural Sciences and Engineering Research Council of Canada* for an NSERC Research Chair in industrial automation. The assistance of Mr. S. Barlev in obtaining the experimental results is greatly appreciated.

References

[1]. L.A. Zadeh, "Fuzzy Sets", *Inf. Control*, Vol. 8, 1965, pp. 338–353.

[2]. E.H. Mamdani, "Application of Fuzzy Logic to Approximate Reasoning Using Linguistic Synthesis", *IEEE Trans. Comp.*, Vol. C-26(12), 1977, pp. 1182–1192.

[3]. K.J. Astrom, J.J. Anton, and R.E. Arzen, "Expert Control", *Automatica*, Vol. 22, No. 3, 1986, pp. 277–286.

[4]. L.A. Zadeh, "Outline of a New Approach to the Analysis of Complex Systems and Decision Processes", *IEEE Trans. Systems, Man and Cybernetics*, Vol. SMC-3, No. 1, 1973, pp. 28–44.

[5]. W. Pedrycz, *Fuzzy Control and Fuzzy Systems*, Research Studies Press, Ltd., Somerset, England, 1989.

[6]. C.W. de Silva and A.G.J. MacFarlane, *Knowledge-Based Control with Application to Robots*, Springer-Verlag, Berlin, 1989.

[7]. D. Dubois and H. Prade, *Fuzzy Sets and Systems*, Academic Press, Orlando, FL, 1980.

[8]. L.A. Zadeh, "Calculus of Fuzzy Restrictions", *Fuzzy Sets and Their Applications to Cognitive and Decision Processes*, (L.A. Zadeh, K.S. Fu, K. Tanaka and M. Shimura, eds.), Academic Press, NY, 1975, pp. 1-39.

[9]. C.W. de Silva and S. Barlev, "Hardware Implementation and Evaluation of a Knowledge-Based Tuner for a Servo System", *Proc. IFAC Symposium on ACASP*, Grenoble, France, 1992, (in press).

[10] L.A. Zadeh, "The Concept of a Linguistic Variable and Its Application to Approximate Reasoning", Parts 1-3, *Inf. Sci.*, 1975, pp. 43–80, 199–249, 301–357.

[11] G.F. Franklin, J.D. Powell, and A.E. Naeini, *Feedback Control of Dynamic Systems*, Addision-Wesley, Reading, MA, 1986.

Proceedings of the
American Control Conference
San Francisco, California • June 1993

A DESCRIBING FUNCTION APPROACH FOR THE EVALUATION OF FUZZY LOGIC CONTROL

Derek P. Atherton
School of Engineering, The University of Sussex
Falmer, Brighton BN1 9QT, U.K.

Abstract

The paper presents a describing function for modelling a two dimensional fuzzy logic controller. An example is given to show how the approach can be used for controller design.

1. Introduction

One of the major problems facing control engineering design at the current time is the need for theoretically based methods for the design of controllers for nonlinear plants. Complex algorithms involving dynamics, nonlinear functions and rules can now be implemented in microprocessor based controllers at costs far less than those for a PID controller two decades ago. The technology is here but the theory to complete designs which make efficient use of these technological capabilities is not. In a subject which is rightly proud of the theoretical developments it has made to linear systems theory, the occurrence of nonlinearity can lead to the acceptance of approaches, such as fuzzy logic, which have a negligible theoretical basis. To quote from a recent opinion [1] 'what is true is that fuzzy control lets one solve control problems with no mathematical education whatsoever'. How well does it solve them? Rarely does this question seem to be answered. Clear performance specifications for system designs which have been described using this approach are rarely given and imprecise statements such as 'it worked satisfactorily' accepted as justification. Even when presentations admit the resulting design is nonlinear, system responses are never given covering a large range of input amplitudes. Comparisons with other design techniques are only made infrequently and when this is done it is usually with a linear, often PID, controller. This hardly seems a fair comparison since one cannot expect a linear controller to adequately control a highly nonlinear plant. Certainly it is easy to find examples where difficulties can occur[2].

It is often claimed that fuzzy logic control is appropriate for use when no plant model is available. This raises two questions, including the obvious one as to why no model is available. Are no simple identification experiments possible and are no approximate physical laws describing the behaviour known? The second, more difficult question is, what is an adequate plant model for a satisfactory control system design? Certainly a complete mathematical model in terms of, say, linear or nonlinear state equations is not essential. Good results have been obtained based on frequency response descriptions, both for linear and nonlinear systems [2,3], and autotuning, which uses two numbers to describe the plant, namely the critical gain and critical frequency, has proved successful in process control.

The purpose of this investigation is to develop an approximate theoretical approach for the study of fuzzy logic control based on the describing function method. The initial studies presented here consider a fuzzy controller using error and derivative of error information so that its output, u, is a nonlinear function of these two variables.

2. Evaluation of the Describing Function

Denoting the controller output u by $n(x,\dot{x})$ and assuming the input x to be $a\cos\theta$, $\theta = \omega t$, the describing function, DF, is given by

$$N(a,\omega) = N_p(a,\omega) + jN_q(a,\omega) \qquad (1)$$

where the in phase $N_p(a,\omega)$ and quadrature $N_q(a,\omega)$ components are given by

$$N_p(a,\omega) = \frac{1}{a\pi}\int_{-\pi}^{\pi} n(x,\dot{x})cos\theta d\theta, \quad \text{and} \qquad (2)$$

$$N_q(a,\omega) = -\frac{1}{a\pi}\int_{-\pi}^{\pi} n(x,\dot{x})sin\theta d\theta \qquad (3)$$

The average value, or bias, of the output signal is zero if the two dimensional nonlinearity is odd symmetric, that is if

$$n(x,\dot{x}) = -n(-x,-\dot{x}) \qquad (4)$$

Assuming this to be the case taking the values of $n(x,\dot{x})$ as $h3_{j,k}$ and $h4_{j,k}$ for the constant values in the (j,k) regions of the third and fourth quadrants it can be shown that

$$N_p(a,\omega) = \frac{2}{a\pi}\sum_{j,k}\left(h4_{j,k} - h3_{j,k}\right)\left(sin\phi_{j,k} - sin\theta_{j,k}\right) \qquad (5)$$

and

$$N_q(a,\omega) = \frac{2}{a\pi}\sum_{j,k}\left(h4_{j,k} + h3_{j,k}\right)\left(cos\phi_{j,k} - cos\theta_{j,k}\right) \qquad (6)$$

Fig. 1 illustrates the computation where the angle α increases clockwise from the x axis and the angles $\theta_{j,k}$ and $\phi_{j,k}$ are the values of α at which the rectangular regions (j,k) are entered and left by a circle of radius a in the $x - \dot{x}/\omega$ plane. A MATLAB program has been written to compute $N(a,\omega)$ for given values of $h3_{j,k}$ and $h4_{j,k}$ as a function of script a for different values of ω.

3. A Design Application

The design of a controller for a nonlinear plant which has the frequency responses shown in Fig. 2 for input sinusoidal amplitudes of 2 and 4, respectively, and which bound the responses for intermediate amplitudes. The values of $h3$ and $h4$ for the first fuzzy controller investigated are given in Table 1. The divisions of j and k on the axes of Fig. 1 are taken equal to 0, 0.5, 1.5, 2.5, 3.5, 4.5, so that the first figure in the table for $h4_{j,k}$ is the height in the square with the corners $(0,0)$ and $(0.5,0.5)$, and the last in the square with corners $(4.5,4.5)$ and $(20,20)$. Similarly for $h3_{j,k}$, the first number in the table is in the square nearest the origin. Also shown on Fig. 2 are the $-1/N(a,\omega)$ curves for

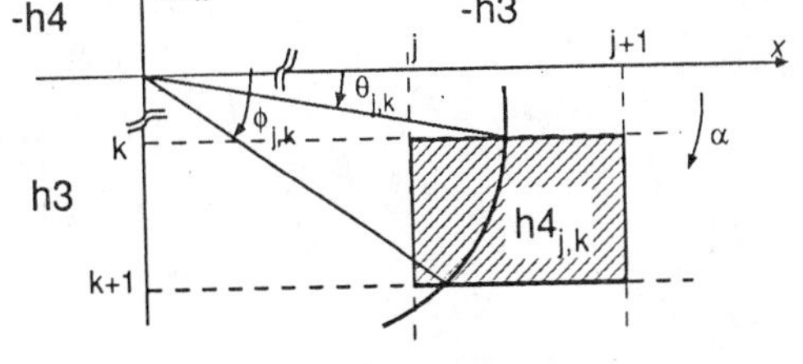

Fig. 1: Illustration of describing function calculation

frequency values of 1.8, 2.0, 2.2 and 2.4 for amplitudes from 0 to 4.6. The results displayed on this figure indicate the system should

Table 1: Values of $h3$ and $h4$ for controller 1

parameters of $h4_{j,k}$						parameters of $h4_{j,k}$					
0	1	2	3	4	5	0	-1	-2	-3	-4	-5
-1	0	1	2	3	4	-1	-2	-3	-4	-5	-6
-2	-1	0	1	2	4	-2	-3	-4	-5	-6	-7
-3	-2	-1	0	1	2	-3	-4	-5	-6	-7	-8
-4	-3	-2	-1	0	1	-4	-5	-6	-7	-8	-9
-5	-4	-3	-2	-1	0	-5	-6	-7	-8	-9	-10

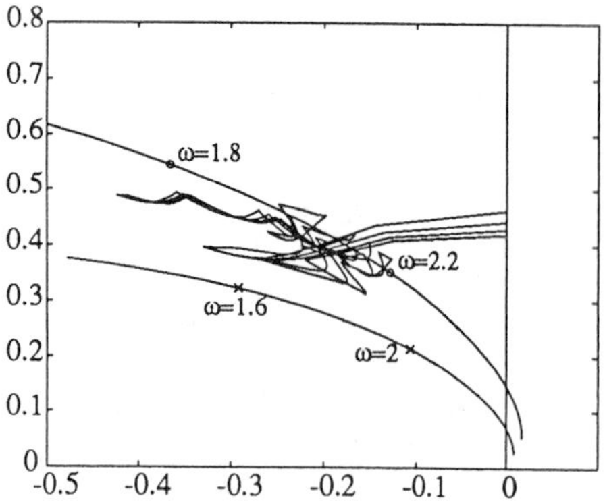

Fig. 2: DF for controller 1 and plant frequency responses

be stable for small input amplitudes but not for larger ones. This indeed was found to be the case and Fig. 3 shows the unstable response resulting from a step input of 5.

To stabilise the system the controller values were increased less rapidly in the proportional direction of the table being changed to the values indicated in Table 2. Fig. 4 shows the new $-1/N(a,\omega)$ loci for the same values of ω as previously and a from 0 to 5.2 together with the plant frequency response for an input of 4. Since the $-1/N(a,\omega)$ loci lie outside the frequency response locus for amplitudes greater than 4 the system should now be stable for all input amplitudes. This was indeed confirmed by simulation for several step input amplitudes and Fig. 5 shows the simulation result for an input step of 5.

4. Conclusions

The paper has presented a describing function for modelling a fuzzy controller which is described by a two dimensional quantization. An example has been given to show how a controller can be designed to stabilise a nonlinear plant. The numbers in the controller table provide a large number of parameters which can be varied, however, it is not clear what is the best way to do this to achieve a specific system performance.

Table 2: Values of $h3$ and $h4$ for controller 2

parameters of $h4_{j,k}$					
0	1	1.3	1.6	1.9	2.2
-1	0	0.3	0.6	0.9	1.2
-2	-1	-0.7	-0.4	-0.1	0.2
-3	-2	-1.7	-1.4	-1.1	-0.8
-4	-3	-2.7	-2.4	-2.1	-1.8
-5	-4	-3.7	-3.4	-3.1	-2.8

parameters of $h3_{j,k}$					
0	-1	-1.3	-1.6	-1.9	-2.2
-1	-2	-2.3	-2.6	-2.9	-3.2
-2	-3	-3.3	-3.6	-3.9	-4.2
-3	-4	-4.3	-4.6	-4.9	-5.2
-4	-5	-5.3	-5.6	-5.9	-6.2
-5	-6	-6.3	-6.6	-6.9	-7.2

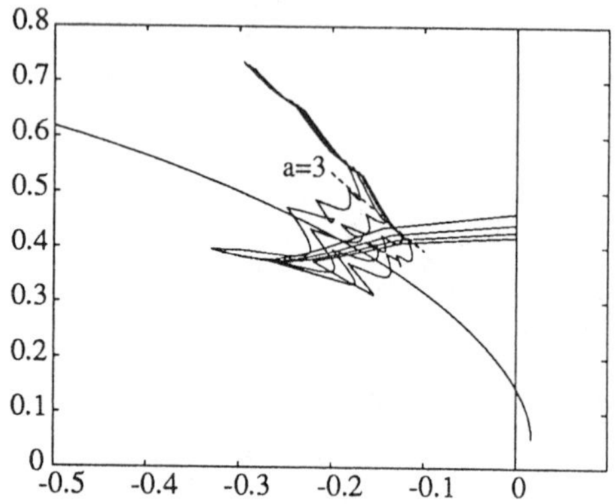

Fig. 4: DF for controller 2 and plant frequency response

5. References

[1] Bernhard P, Fuzzy Control, Facts, Japan and Europe, The European Control Newsletter, (TEC News), No 1, pp 4-5, June 1992.

[2] Nanka-Bruce O and Atherton D P, Design of Nonlinear Controllers for Nonlinear Plants, IFAC Congress, Tallinn, Volume 6, pp 75-80, 1990.

[3] Taylor J H and Stobel K L, Nonlinear Control System Design Based on Quasilinear System Models, Control '85, Cambridge, UK, pp 469-473, 1983.

[4] Procyk T J and Mandani E H, A Linguistic Self-Organising Process Controller, Automatica, Vol 15, pp 15-30, 1979

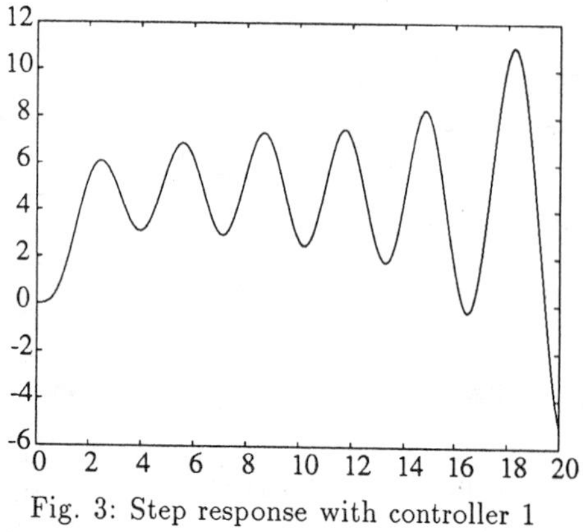

Fig. 3: Step response with controller 1

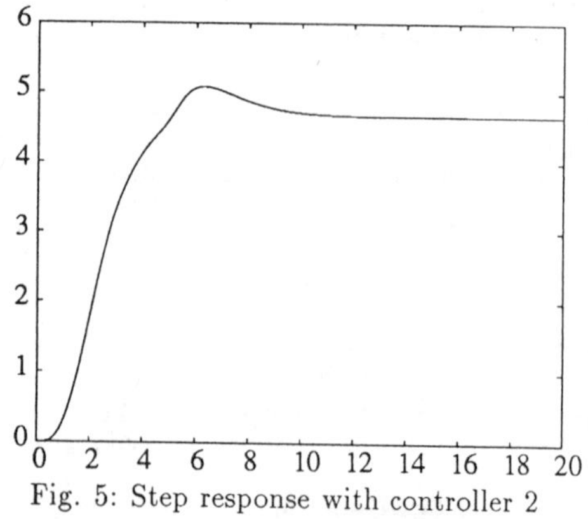

Fig. 5: Step response with controller 2

Proceedings of the
American Control Conference
San Francisco, California • June 1993

Automatic Knowledege Acquisition for Multivariable Fuzzy Control Using Neural Network Approach

Junhong Nie and D. A. Linkens***

*Department of Electrical Engineering
National University of Singapore, Singapore 0511

**Department of Automatic Control & Systems Engineering
University of Sheffield, Sheffield S1 3JD, U.K.

Abstract: This paper introduces a simple and systematic scheme capable of self-organizing and self-learning the required control knowledge for use with multivariable fuzzy controllers. The starting point of the approach is to structurally map a simplified fuzzy control algorithm (SFCA) into a counterpropagation network (CPN) in such a way that the control knowledge is explicitly represented in the form of connection weights of the nets, the control rule-base is gradually self-constructed with the fulfillment of the prespecified performance requirements, and finally the approximate reasoning is carried out by replacing a winner-take-all competitive scheme with a soft matching cooperative strategy. Two problems of multivariable control of blood pressure and anaesthesia have been studied as demonstration examples.

1. Introduction

There is an increasing interest in combining neural networks with ordinary expert systems in general and with fuzzy rule-based systems in particular. Basically, two approaches to performing this combination can be distinguished. The first approach aims at seeking a functional mapping between fuzzy reasoning algorithms and neural network paradigms [5,8-10]. The second approach, by its very nature, is intended to find a structural mapping from a fuzzy reasoning system (algorithm) to a kind of neural network, thereby usually leading to a localized network implementation. This paper is mainly concerned with the second approach. Although the fundamental issues we address here remain the same as those in the first approach, that is, rule-base acquisition, computational representation, and approximate reasoning, our objective here is to deal with these different but correlated problems under a unified framework of neural networks with a particular attention on the rule-base acquisition. In particular, we describe a simple and efficient scheme capable of self-organizing and self-learning the required control knowledge in a real-time manner under multivariable controlled environments. The starting point of the approach is to structurally map a simplified fuzzy control algorithm (SFCA) developed by the authors [7] into a counterpropagation network (CPN) developed by Hecht-Nielsen [1-2], which is very simple in structure but is often overlooked, in such a way that the control knowledge is explicitly represented in the form of connection weights of the nets. Then by introducing a valid radius into the Kohonen layer and providing a on-line learning teacher to the Grossberg layer, the control rule-base, starting from empty, is gradually self-organized and self-constructed with the fulfillment of the prespecified performance requirements. Finally the approximate reasoning is carried out by replacing a winner-take-all competitive scheme with a soft matching cooperative strategy. As demonstration examples, two problem of multivariable control of blood pressure and anaesthesia have been studied using the proposed approach.

2. Simplified fuzzy control algorithms (SFCA)

The operation of a fuzzy controller typically involves many stages within one sampling instant. However by taking the nonfuzzy property regarding the input/output of the fuzzy controller into account, we have derived a kind of very simple but efficient fuzzy control algorithm SFCA which consists of only two main steps, pattern matching and weighted averaging, and this is described below.

Assume that the controlled process is multivariable with m inputs and m outputs. The inputs to the fuzzy controller are various combination of control error, change-in-error, and sum of error with respect to each process output. In what follows, it is assumed that a $n \times m$ controller is used to control a $m \times m$ process with $n > m$ in general. Furthermore, assume that there are P rules in the rule-base, each of which has the form:

$$IF\ U_1\ is\ A_1^j\ AND\ \cdots\ AND\ U_n\ is\ A_n^j$$

$$THEN\ V_1\ is\ B_1^j\ AND\ \cdots\ AND\ V_m\ is\ B_m^j$$

where U_i and V_k are linguistic variables corresponding to the numerical variables u_i and v_k, A_i^j and B_k^j are fuzzy subsets representing some linguistic terms which are defined on the corresponding universes of discourse. Assume that A_i^j and B_k^j are normalized fuzzy subsets whose membership functions are defined uniquely in triangular form, each of which is characterized only by two parameters, $M_{u,i}^j$ and $\delta_{u,i}^j$, or $M_{v,k}^j$ and $\delta_{v,k}^j$ with the understanding that $M_{u,i}^j$ ($M_{v,k}^j$) is the center element of the support set of A_i^j (B_k^j), and $\delta_{u,i}^j$ ($\delta_{v,k}^j$) is the half width of the support set. Hence, the jth rule can be written as

$$IF\ \ (M_{u,1}^j, \delta_{u,1}^j)\ AND\ \ \ldots\ldots\ (M_{u,n}^j, \delta_{u,n}^j)$$

$$THEN\ \ (M_{v,1}^j, \delta_{v,1}^j)\ AND\ \ \ldots\ldots\ (M_{v,m}^j, \delta_{v,m}^j)$$

Let $M_u^j = (M_{u,1}^j, M_{u,2}^j, \ldots\ldots, M_{u,n}^j)$ and $\Delta_u^j = (\delta_{u,1}^j, \delta_{u,2}^j, \ldots\ldots, \delta_{u,n}^j)$ be two n-dimensional vectors. Then the *condition* part of the jth rule may be viewed as creating a subspace or a *rule pattern* whose center and radius are M_u^j and Δ_u^j respectively. Thus the *condition* part of the jth rule can be simplified further to " IF $M\Delta_u(j)$ ", where $M\Delta_u(j) = (M_u^j, \Delta_u^j)$. Similarly n current inputs $u_{0i} \in \overline{U}_i$ (i=1, 2, ..., n), with u_{0i} being a singleton, can also be represented as a n-dimensional vector u_0 or a *input pattern* .

The fuzzy control algorithm can be considered to be a process in which an appropriate control action is deduced from a current input and P rules according to some prespecified reasoning algorithms. We split the whole reasoning procedure into two phases: pattern matching and weighted averaging. The first operation deals with the IF part for all rules, whereas the second one involves an operation on the THEN part of the rules. From the patter concept introduced above, we need first to compute the matching degrees between the current input pattern and each rule pattern. Denote the current input by $u_0 = (u_{01}, u_{02}, \ldots\ldots, u_{0n})$. Then the matching degree denoted by $S^j \in [0, 1]$ between u_0 and the jth rule pattern $M\Delta_u(j)$ can be measured by the complement of the corresponding relative distance given by

$$S_j = 1 - D^j(u_0, M\Delta_u(j)) \quad (1)$$

where $D^j(u_0, M\Delta_u(j)) \in [0, 1]$ denotes relative distance from u_o to $M\Delta_u(j)$. D^j can be specified in many ways. With the assumption of an identical width δ for all fuzzy sets A_i^j, the computational definition of D^j is given by

$$D^j = \begin{cases} \dfrac{\|M_u^j - u_0\|}{\delta} & \text{if } \|M_u^j - u_0\| \le \delta \\ 1 & \textit{otherwise} \end{cases} \tag{2}$$

For a specific input u_0 and P rules, after the matching process is completed, the kth component of the deduced control action v_k is given by

$$v_k = \frac{\sum_{q=1}^{Q} S^q \cdot M_{v,k}^q}{\sum_{q=1}^{Q} S^q} \tag{3}$$

where it is assumed that all the membership functions $b_k^j(v)$ are symmetrical about their respective centers and have an identical width. We notice that because only the centres of the THEN parts of the fired rules are utilized and they are the only element having the maximum membership grade 1 on the corresponding support sets, the algorithm can be understood as a modified maximum membership decision scheme in which the global centre is calculated by the *Center of Gravity* algorithm. Thus the rule form can be further simplified as

$$IF\ \ M\Delta_u(j)\ \ THEN\ \ M_v^j \tag{4}$$

where $M_v^j = [M_{v,1}^j, M_{v,2}^j, \ldots\ldots, M_{v,m}^j]$ is a center value vector of the THEN part.

3. Representation and reasoning by CPN

CPN network

By combining a portion of the self-organizing map of Kohonen and the outstar structure of Grossberg, Hecht-Nielsen has developed a new type of neural networks named counterpropagation network (CPN) [2]. Functionally CPN is designed to approximate a continuous function $f: A \in R^n \rightarrow R^m$, defined on a compact set A by means of a set of samples (μ^s, v^s). A CPN network with forward-only version consists of an input layer, a hidden Kohonen layer, and a Grossberg output layer with n, N, and m units respectively. In what follows, the forward algorithm used during normal operation of the CPN is presented, whereas the backward algorithm used during training will be described in the next section. Denote input vector, and output vectors at Kohonen and Grossberg layers by $\mu = [\mu_1, \mu_2, \ldots\ldots, \mu_n]^T$, $\zeta = [\zeta_1, \zeta_2, \ldots\ldots, \zeta_N]^T$, and $v = [v_1, v_2, \ldots\ldots, v_m]^T$ respectively, the *single winner* forward algorithm of the CPN with regard to a particular input μ_0 is outlined as follows:

a) Determine the winner unit J at the Kohonen layer competitively according to the distances of weight vector $\omega^j(t)$ with respect to μ_0

$$D(\omega^J, \mu_0) = \min_{j=1,N} D(\omega^j, \mu_0) \tag{5}$$

where $\omega^j = [\omega_1^j, \omega_2^j, \ldots\ldots, \omega^j]$ is the weight vector connecting n input units to the jth unit at the Kohonen layer.

b) Calculate the outputs $\zeta^j \in \{0,1\}$ of the Kohonen layer by a winner-take-all rule

$$\zeta^j = \begin{cases} 1 & \text{if } j=J \\ 0 & \textit{otherwise} \end{cases} \tag{6}$$

c) Compute the outputs of the Grossberg layer by

$$v_k = \sum_{j=1}^{N} \zeta^j \cdot \pi_k^j \tag{7}$$

where $\pi^j = [\pi_1^j, \pi_2^j, \ldots\ldots, \pi_m^j]$ is the weight vector connecting the jth Kohonen unit to m Grossberg output units and $k = 1, 2, \ldots, m$.

Equivalence between SFCA and CPN

We are seeking structural mapping from the SFCA algorithm onto the CPN network such that control knowledge represented formerly in rule form can be represented by the CPN network, and the reasoning algorithm can be carried out by operating directly the network. By carefully examining these two paradigms, we have found that there exist some striking similarities between the SFCA and CPN.

The first aspect of similarity involves the issue of knowledge representation. More specifically, after training is terminated, the CPN network has been trained and arranged in such a way that N associations (ω^j, π^j) can function as a look-up table. Each ω^j is a representative of a set of vectors surrounding it. It becomes very clear that, by being analogous to the simplified rule form (4), each CPN association (ω^j, π^j) can be expressed as a rule:

$$IF\ \ \omega^j\ \ THEN\ \ \pi^j \tag{8}$$

Equivalently, each Kohonen unit defines a rule by regarding the weight vectors connecting to and emanating from that unit as IF and THEN parts respectively. In this view, each rule in the form of (4) can be directly mapped into a Kohonen unit with M_u^j and M_v^j being corresponding weight vectors.

The similarity between these two system can be made more clear by exploring the algorithmic aspect in CPN and reasoning process in SFCA. Both of them are intended to provide an approximate output v or v by operating the existing knowledge (ω^j, π^j) or (M_u^j, M_v^j) with respect to the current input μ or u. Comparing (1), (2), and (3) in SFCA with (5), (6), and (7) in CPN, it can be concluded that the matching degree stage in SFCA is functionally similar to the competition process in CPN, whereas the weighted averaging in SFCA corresponds to the computation of the output at the Grossberg layer. However, we notice that the SFCA adopts a graded matching scheme and works in an *interpolation* mode.

4. Automatic knowledge acquisition

So far the knowledge representation and reasoning problems have been solved by structural mapping and an associated forward algorithm provided that the rule-base is available. As mentioned previously, our main interest however lies in automatic acquisition of control knowledge directly from a controlled process. In terms of CPN, this means that the number of units in the Kohonen layer must be self-organized and the associated weights with each unit must be self-learned.

CPN training algorithm

Basically, the CPN training algorithm is a supervised training process by which the weights of the network are determined by being exposing to a set of paired training samples (μ^s, v^s). The algorithm consists of two parts: a Kohonen scheme which is unsupervised in nature and is used to learn ω^j, and a Grossberg scheme which is truly supervised and is used to learn π^j.

More specifically, assuming that the number of Kohonen units is specified in advance and remains fixed during the training, the update law is given by

$$\omega^j(t) = \omega^j(t-1) + \alpha_t \cdot [\mu^s(t) - \omega^j(t-1)] \cdot \zeta^j \tag{9}$$

where $\zeta \in \{0, 1\}$ is determined by (5) and (6). $0 < \alpha_t < 1$ is a gain sequence decreasing monotonically with time. Once the Kohonen layer has stabilized, ω^j can be frozen and the Grossberg layer begins to learn the desired output v for each frozen weight vector ω^j by adjusting the weights connecting the Kohonen units to the Grossberg units. More specifically, the update law at this layer is given by

$$\pi_k^j(t) = \pi_k^j(t-1) + \beta\cdot[-\pi_k^j(t-1) + v_k^s]\cdot\zeta^j \qquad (10)$$

where π_k^j is a weight from the jth Kohonen unit to the kth Grossberg (output) unit. β is a constant update rate within the range [0,1]. v_k^s is the kth component of the training sample v^s.

Self-construction of rule-base
There are several difficulties in applying the CPN training algorithm described above to our case. The major problems lie in the fact that: (a) the number M of the Kohonen units must be specified in advance; and (b) the correct or desired output at the Grossberg layer must be supplied. By assumption, the above required knowledge is unavailable and instead must be learned on-line apart from the learning of associated weight vectors.

Self-organizing: IF part: Comparing the IF part of (4) in SFCA with (8) in CPN, there is a width vector Δ_u^j associated with the former. As discussed before, Δ_u^j can be roughly visualized as defining a neighbourhood for the jth rule centered at M_u^j. This viewpoint, together with the concept of relative distance (2), provides some insight into finding a solution for the problem. A vital idea is to associate with each existing Kohonen unit a valid radius and a local update gain such that each subregion, represented by the weight vector ω and restricted by the associated radius, is treated as a completely localized region although overlap along the boundaries between the adjacent regions is allowed. By assigning each Kohonen unit with a predefined width δ, the winner J not only has a minimum distance among all the existing units in regard to the current input μ as determined by (5), but also must satisfy the condition of μ falling into the winner's neighbourhood as designated by δ. Thus if these two conditions are met, then unit J is considered to be the winner and the associated weight vector is adjusted using (9) but with a local update gain. On the other hand, if these conditions are not satisfied with respect to all the units, it indicates that no existing unit is adequate to assign μ as its member and therefore a new unit should be created. It is clear that, starting from an empty state, the Kohonen layer can be dynamically self-organized in terms of the number of units and weight vectors ω associated with each unit, thereby establishing the IF part of the rule-base.

Self-learning: THEN part: As mentioned previously, the major difficulty in deriving the weight vectors π^j connecting the Kohonen layer to the Grossberg layer, or equivalently the THEN parts of the rules, stems from the unavailability of the teacher signals v^j guiding the supervised training. Here, we propose a simple but efficient scheme capable of carrying out the task of training π^j. At the beginning of each iteration, the teacher signals are constructed explicitly by means of an iterative learning approach [6]. Then the derived signals are supplied to the Grossberg layer of the CPN so as to adjust π vectors using the standard algorithm (10). Fig 1 shows a block diagram of the learning system. The reference mode is designed to specify what the process responses y_p should be when both the model and the process are subject to the same command signal r. For the sake of simplicity, we adopt a non-interacting model with second-order linear transfer functions. The overall goal of the learning system is to force the learning error $y_d - y_p$ asymptotically to zero or to a predefined tolerance region ε within a time interval of interest [0, T] by repeatedly operating the system. By taking the process time delay into account, the learning law is given by

$$\gamma^{l+1}(t) = \gamma^l(t) + P_L\cdot e_{L,l}(t+\lambda) + Q_L\cdot c_{L,l}(t+\lambda) \qquad (11)$$

where $\gamma^l, \gamma^{l+1} \in R^m$ are on-line learning teacher vector-valued functions at the lth and the $(l+1)$th iterations respectively, $e_{L,l}$, $c_{L,l} \in R^m$ are learning error and change of learning error defined by $c_{L,l}(t) = e_{L,l}(t+1) - e_{L,l}(t)$, λ is an estimated time advance corresponding to time delay of the process, and $P_L, Q_L \in R^{m\times m}$ are constant learning gain matrices. Since at the beginning of each iteration, γ is available at each time instant t, it can be used to guide the weight vector adjustment at the Grossberg layer by

$$\pi_k^j(t) = \pi_k^j(t-1) + \beta\cdot[-\pi_k^j(t-1) + \gamma_k^l(t)]\cdot\zeta^j \qquad (12)$$

Assume that, by appropriately choosing P_L and Q_L, the desired output y_d can be approached asymptotically with a learned control sequence γ^d which is in turn embedded into π^j vectors by (16) with a suitably chosen β. Thus with the increase of the iteration, THEN parts of the rules are gradually learned along with the learning process of γ.

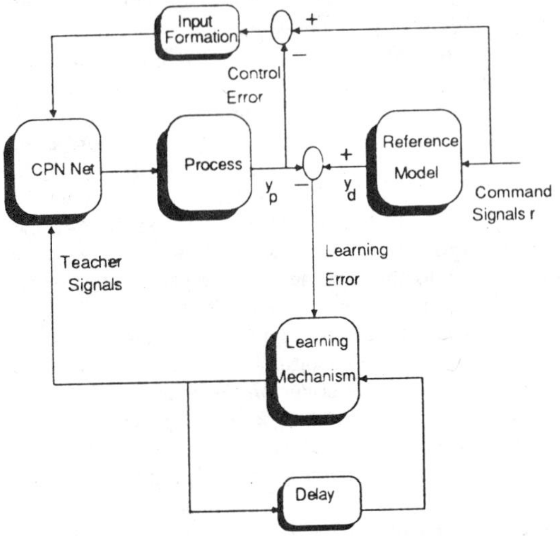

Fig 1 A diagram of on-line learning system

5. Simulation results

Multivariable blood pressure control
It is required to regulate simultaneously the cardiac output (CO) and the mean arterial pressure (MAP) of a patient in hospital intensive care using two drugs dopamine (DOP) an inotropic drug, and sodium nitroprusside (SNP) a vasoactive drug. For the purpose of this simulation study, we adopt the same model as used before [4,8] which is given by

$$\begin{bmatrix}\Delta CO\\ \Delta MAP\end{bmatrix} = \begin{bmatrix}1.0 & -24.76\\ 0.6636 & 76.38\end{bmatrix}\begin{bmatrix}\dfrac{K_{11}e^{-\tau_1 s}}{sT_1+1} & \dfrac{K_{12}e^{-\tau_2 s}}{sT_1+1}\\ \dfrac{K_{21}e^{-\tau_2 s}}{sT_2+1} & \dfrac{K_{22}e^{-\tau_2 s}}{sT_2+1}\end{bmatrix}\begin{bmatrix}I_1\\ I_2\end{bmatrix}$$

where ΔCO (ml/s) and ΔMAP (mmHg) are the changes in cardiac output and in mean arterial pressure due to I_1 and I_2 ; I_1 (μg /Kg/min) and I_2 (ml/h) are the infusion rates of dopamine and nitroprusside; K_{11}, K_{12}, K_{21} and K_{22} are steady-state gains with typical values of 8.44, 5.275, − 0.09 and −0.15 respectively; τ_1 and τ_2 represent two time delays with typical values of τ_1 = 60s and τ_2 = 30s; and T_1 and T_2 are time constants typified by the values of 84.1s and 58.75s respectively.

The proposed CPN-based controller can work in two modes: real-time control with or without learning. In the latter case, it is assumed that an appropriate CPN structure with corresponding weights has been obtained during the learning stage. With this learned CPN or rule-base, it is expected that the controller can perform similar tasks in an acceptable manner by replacing a winner-take-all competitive scheme with a soft matching cooperative strategy. By using a controller with 4 inputs (errors & change-in-errors) and 2 outputs, Fig 2 shows the actual and the desired (dotted line) outputs of the process after 10 iterations with 14 rules being created, where the following controller parameters were used: learning gain matrices P_L=diag{0.05, -0.05} and Q_L=0, Grossberg update date β=0.5, and Euclidean distance with the valid radius δ=0.1. Fig 3 shows the outputs of the process using the learned 14 rules but with the approximate reasoning scheme with δ=0.6. It can be seen that the responses given by the latter are as good as those given by the former.

We have carried out a set of simulations aiming at examining adaptive ability and convergence property of the system with respect to a variety of situations including variations of process parameters, various desired responses, noise measurements , and various controller parameters. As an example, Fig 4 shows the outputs of the process at the 10th iteration with a measured noise amplitude of 10% at the setpoints. It can be seen that the responses are satisfactory. While space prevents us from presenting all the results, it is interesting to mention two of the controller parameters which have direct effect on the number of the rules produced during the learning. The first one is valid radius δ which is mainly used to control the self-organizing process in the CPN. Intuitively, the bigger δ is, the more units the CPN creates, and therefore the more rules in the rule-base. By choosing δ=0.01, 0.1, and 1.0 respectively, we obtained the respective rule bases with the rule numbers being 22, 14, and 8. However, as expected, we have observed that convergence is not very sensitive to this parameter. The second one is the form of the distance metric used in the self-organizing process at the Kohonen layer. Because different distance metrics define different shapes of the neighbourhood of each rule, it is expected that they have some effect on the number of created rules and less effect on the control or learning performances. We carried out a comparative studies by using three frequently used metrics: Euclidean, Hamming, and Maximum distances D_E, D_H, and D_M. Three almost identical convergence processes verified our expectation. However, it is interesting to note that the rule numbers produced by these metrics were 14, 16, and 13 respectively. These results can be explained by the fact that, with the same valid radius δ, the neighbourhood defined by D_M has the biggest "volume", therefore the fewest rule number 13, the one defined by D_H has the smallest "volume", therefore the highest rule number 16, leaving the defined "volume" and the produced rule number by D_E in the middle.

Nonlinear multivariable anaesthesia control

The second simulation study involved a simultaneous control of relaxation and unconsciousness during anaesthesia by using two drugs: atracurium for producing muscle relaxation and isoflurane for producing unconsciousness. The overall simulation model has been experimentally justified and has been studied in [3] and is given by

$$y_1 = E_{eff}(L^{-1}[H_{11}(s)U_1(s)]) + L^{-1}[H_{12}(s)U_2(s)]$$

$$y_2 = L^{-1}[H_{21}(s)U_1(s)] + L^{-1}[H_{22}(s)U_2(s)]$$

where y_1 and y_2 denote the degree of paralysis (%) and the increase of arterial pressure (mmHg). u_1 and u_2 denote atracurium and isoflurane drugs. L^{-1} is inverse Laplace transformation, and

$$H_{11}(s) = \frac{1.0e^{-s}(1+10.64s)}{(1+3.08s)(1+4.81s)(1+34.42s)}$$

$$H_{12}(s) = \frac{0.27e^{-s}}{(1+2.83s)(1+1.25s)}$$

$$H_{21}(s) = 0$$

$$H_{22}(s) = \frac{-15.0e^{-0.42s}}{(1+2s)}$$

$$E_{eff}(E) = \frac{E_{max}}{1+\frac{E^{\alpha}(50)}{E^{\alpha}}}$$

where E is the drug concentration, $E(50)$=0.404 $ml^{-1}\mu g$ is the drug concentration at 50% effect, E_{max}=1.0, and α=2.98. It is evident that the system is characterized by interactions between variables and strong nonlinearity existing in the first channel.

By employing a controller with 6 inputs (errors, change-in-errors, and sum-of-errors) and two outputs, Fig 5 shows one of the results obtained at the 20th iteration with 20 rules being produced, where the controller parameter settings were P_L=diag{0.09, -0.02} and Q_L=0, Grossberg update date β=0.5, and valid radius δ=5.0. It can be seen that while a nearly ideal response of the *MAP* was obtained, the response of the relaxation was by no means perfect, this being attributed to nonlinearity and disturbance produced by the change of isoflurane drug. However the result was acceptable, indicating the high ability of the learning system to accommodate unknown and complex processes.

6. Conclusion

We have introduced a unified framework for constructing automatically a control rule-base constrained by prespecified control performance requirements. The approach reported here outperforms the existing fuzzy control algorithms in many aspects. In particular, we claim that the approach is very generic in the sense that, in principle, arbitrary dimensional control rule-bases can be constructed automatically while satisfying arbitrary desired but physically achievable performance requirements. The learning process involved is extremely fast due to the simple network topology and the efficient learning algorithms. Another point is that very little prior knowledge about the controlled process is required in the implementation of the algorithm. The simulation studies have demonstrated the capability of the proposed approach in controlling complex processes characterized by interaction, delay, and nonlinearity.

7. Reference

[1] R. Hecht-Nielsen, 1987, Counterpropagation network, *Applied Optics* , **26** , pp 4979-4984.

[2] R. Hecht-Nielsen, 1988, Applications of counterpropagation network, *Neural Networks* , **1** , pp 131-139.

[3] D.A.Linkens, M.Mahfouf and M.Abbod, 1992, Self-adaptive and self-organizing control applied to nonlinear multivariable anaesthesia,*IEE Proc.-D*, **139**, pp 381-394.

[4] D. A. Linkens and Junhong Nie, 1992, A unified real time approximate reasoning approach for use in intelligent control. Part 2: application to multivariable blood pressure control, *Int. J. Control*, **56**, pp 365-398.

[5] D. A. Linkens and Junhong Nie, 1992, Rule extraction for BNN neural network-based fuzzy control systems by self-learning, in *Artificial Neural Networks 2* ,I. Aleksander and J. Taylor Eds., Noth-Holland, pp 459-462.

[6] D. A. Linkens and Junhong Nie, 1993, Constructing rule-bases for multivariable fuzzy control by self-learning. Part 1 : system structure and learning algorithms, *Int. J. System Science* , **24**, pp 111-127.

[7] Junhong Nie, 1989, A class of new fuzzy control algorithms, *Proc. IEEE Int. Conf. on Control and Applications*, Israel.

[8] Junhong Nie, 1992, *Fuzzy-neural control: principles, algorithms and applications*, Ph.D thesis, Department of Automatic Control and Systems Engineering, The University of Sheffield.

[9] Junhong Nie and D. A. Linkens, 1992, Neural network-based approximate reasoning: principles and implementation, *Int. J. Control*, **56**, pp 399-414.

[10] Junhong Nie and D.A. Linkens, A hybrid neural network-based self-organizing fuzzy controller, *Int. J. Control*, under review.

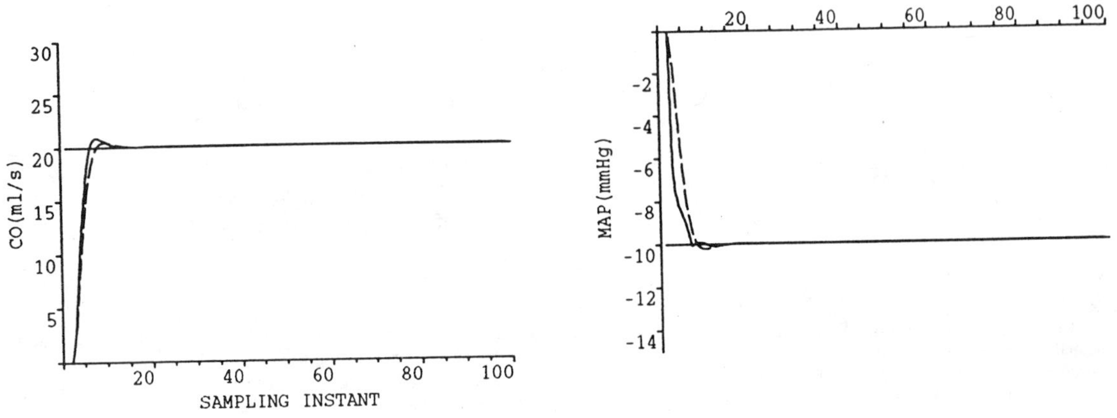

Fig 2 Learning output responses of blood pressure control

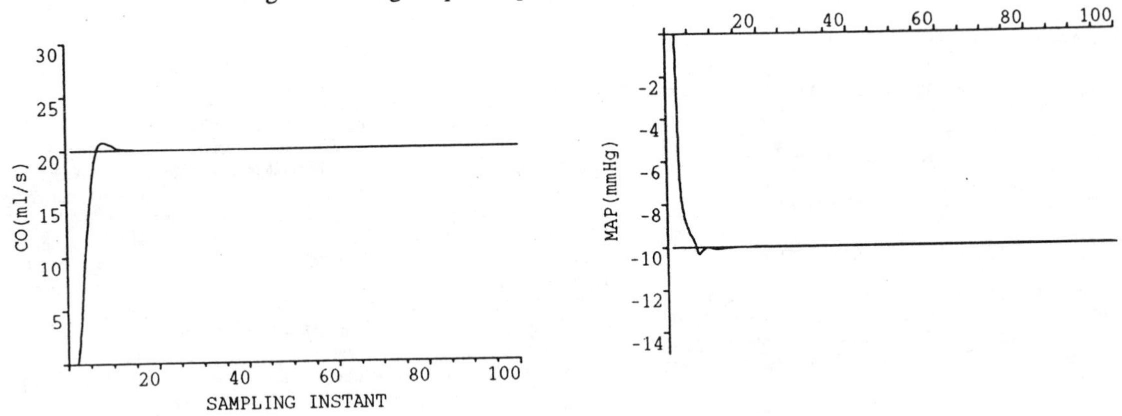

Fig 3 Output responses of the process using learned rules

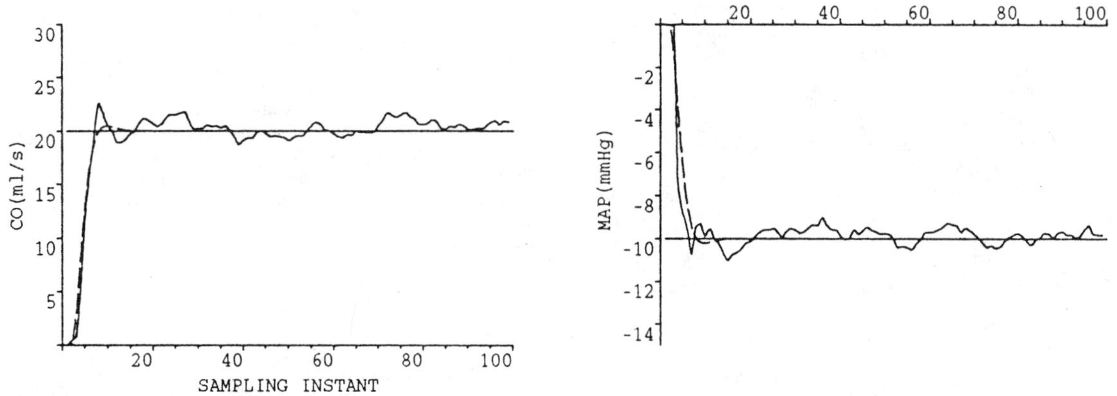

Fig 4 Learning outputs under noise measurements

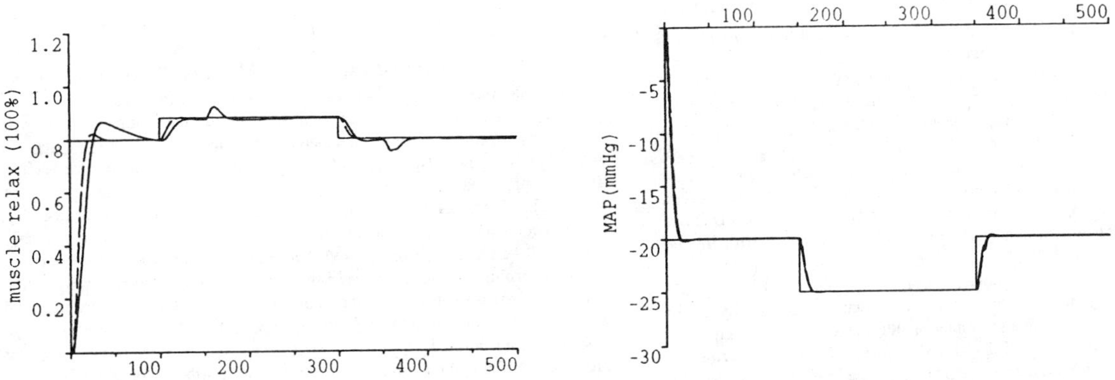

Fig 5 Learning output responses of anaesthesia control

Proceedings of the
American Control Conference
San Francisco, California • June 1993

INVERSE FUZZY MODEL CONTROLLERS

Celal Batur* Arvind Srinivasan
Department of Mechanical Engineering

Chien-Chung Chan
Department of Mathematical Sciences

The University of Akron, Akron, OH 44325.

1. INTRODUCTION

Certain aspects of fuzzy controllers are still not well understood and the lack of this understanding makes the industry shy away from serious applications of such controllers. The first problem is the lack of explicit use of process models in the fuzzy controller design. Currently there is no systematic way to incorporate the knowledge about the process dynamics into the fuzzy controller design. The second problem is the analysis of stability of the feedback control system operating under a fuzzy inference engine. It is difficult to check the stability of these controllers. Our motivation is to offer a solution to the first problem, namely, the development of fuzzy model based fuzzy controllers.

We propose to model the forward and the inverse process dynamics in terms of a set of fuzzy rules that are obtained from input output data. We accomplish this by the following procedure:

(1) quantify input output data in terms of a priori selected fuzzy membership functions,

(2) generate fuzzy models using an automated knowledge acquisition algorithm.

Once fuzzy models are determined, we use the models to construct fuzzy controllers by the following steps.

(A) Consider the fuzzy model as a knowledge base of an expert system.

(B) In the case of forward model, consider the set-points as the conclusion states and run an inference engine in a backward reasoning scheme to determine the control action, that if applied, can generate process outputs close to the set-points.

(C) In the case of inverse fuzzy model, use it directly as controller.

To analyze the stability of the control system, we consider the fuzzy controller as a nonlinear, time variant map between the current information set and the controller output. The current information set is determined by the past values of process inputs, outputs and the set-point. If the process is linear, we use the circle criterion to check the stability. If the process is strongly nonlinear, we linearize the process dynamics around the current operating point and apply the circle stability criterion.

A typical fuzzy controller design starts with the assumption that process operators' knowledge can be represented by a set of production rules. This assumption leads to a fuzzy version of the proportional plus derivative control law design [Daley and Gill, 1987 1989], [Kosko, 1992]. The process dynamics has not been considered explicitly as part of the knowledge base. Only the process output $y(t)$ and the change in the process output $y'(t)$ are used as knowledge about the process dynamics, despite the fact that fuzzy process modeling techniques have been proposed by almost fifteen years ago, for example, [Tong, 1978], [Pedrycz, 1984], [Xu, 1989], [Xu and Lu, 1987] and [Sugeno, 1985]. The main reason for the lack of fuzzy model usage is probably due to the fact that these models tend to create a large number of production rules, therefore, they are not practical.

Recently, [Wang and Mendel, 1991] developed a fuzzy modeling algorithm that uses a set of fuzzy reference membership functions to quantify the process input output data. To prune the resulting rule set and therefore, to reduce the model complexity, they attached a measure of confidence for each generated rule. This process reduces the number of rules, and therefore, makes the fuzzy model practical. [Batur et al, 1992] have extended this approach and used Quinlan's decision tree algorithm, ID3 [Quinlan, 1986 1987] to generate a set of production rules to represent the process dynamics. The quantization of process data is accomplished through reference fuzzy membership functions. We use an automated knowledge acquisition methodology, LERS3 [Chan, 1991] to identify both the forward and the inverse dynamics of the process. This approach has an advantage that the resulting models can be directly used as process controllers which attempts to cancel the dynamics of the process. This methodology promises a much tighter control than a generic PD based fuzzy controller. However, it also shares the problems associated with inverse model based controllers.

The stability of fuzzy controllers is first analyzed by Lyapunov functions, [Chen, 1987]. His approach assumes that an 'expert' Lyapunov function can be found and imposes limits on the fuzzy controller output for stability. [Ray and Majumder, 1984, 1985] applied the circle criterion for stability analysis of fuzzy control systems. This analysis assumes that the process is linear and the fuzzy controller output is sector bounded [Cook, 1986]. The concept of energetistic stability is used by [Kiszka et al, 1985]. They conjectured rules for the stability analysis. We assume that the stability of our fuzzy controller can be analyzed similarly if a suitable Lyapunov function can be determined.

The paper is organized as follows. The fuzzy process modeling is described in Section 2. Section 3 presents the predictive fuzzy controller. Simulated applications of the technique are presented in Section 4. Conclusions are given in Section 5.

2. FUZZY PROCESS MODELING

The process of building fuzzy models for dynamic systems has four steps, namely, determination of model structure, choice of reference membership functions, construction of models and validation of models. Two popular representations of fuzzy models are relational equations and fuzzy rules. The former approach has been used in [Pedrycz, 1984] and [Xu, 1989]. The latter methodology has been proposed in [Tong, 1978], [Wang and Mendel, 1991] and [Batur et al, 1992]. In this work, a fuzzy model is represented by a set of fuzzy rules generated by an inductive learning algorithm LERS3 [Chan, 1991]. Each rule has the form: "If condition then decision with a confidence factor (CF)." The condition is a conjunctive statement of process inputs and the decision is a statement for process output. Each rule is interpreted as: if conditions are true then the decision is granted with certainty factor (CF). Figure 1 presents the main components of the fuzzy model building methodology. In the following subsections, we describe the requirements and steps for building a rule based model.

2.1 Determination of Model Structure

A fixed number of past process inputs and outputs are used to characterize the process output. The problem of determining how many past inputs and outputs to use corresponds to the model order determination in process identification. Following the same technique used there, one has to determine the number of past inputs and outputs so that a given performance index is minimized. In process identification, this performance index, such as the sum of squares of the prediction errors, is the same index that is used to determine the process model. Although our model building technique does not use the same index, nevertheless we can still employ the variance of one step ahead prediction as the criterion to determine the required number of past inputs and outputs. This criterion is defined below

$$V = \sum_{t=1}^{N} e^2(t) = \sum_{t=1}^{N} \left(y(t+1) - \hat{y}(t)\right)^2 \tag{2.1.1}$$

where $e(t)$ is the one step prediction error, $y(t)$ and $\hat{y}(t)$ are the outputs of process and fuzzy model respectively and N is the number of data in the training set. A second rationale behind this criterion is that, our control algorithm determines $u(t)$ so that the difference between the set point $r(t)$ and the one step ahead predicted process output $\hat{y}(t)$ is minimum.

2.2. Determination of Reference Membership Functions

Our methodology uses fuzzy membership functions as levels of quantization. For example, the numerical value of $y(t)$ may belong to both small positive and medium positive membership functions, therefore, $y(t)$ may be quantified with these two levels of quantization. If exponential membership functions are used, there are as many membership values as the number of membership functions used for a given data point. Although every membership function contributes to the quantization of data, nevertheless, most membership values will be close to zero. To limit the number of data points that goes into the rule-learning algorithm, we use a threshold level for the membership value. If the membership value of the data point does not exceed this threshold, the attribute corresponding to this membership function is not used for this particular data point. In the extreme case, one may even consider accepting only one attribute for a given data point. This attribute corresponds to the membership function that generates the maximum membership value for that data point. In conclusion, the type of membership function is not critical as long as a certain threshold on the membership function values is implemented.

The number of membership functions determines how fine the data are quantized. Too fine a quantization generates unnecessarily large number of modeling rules. Furthermore, it becomes increasingly difficult to interpret these rules in terms of linguistic variables such as small positive, large positive, etc. This creates extra difficulty in fusing the operator based rules into the knowledge base. On the other hand, too coarse a quantization decreases the accuracy of the fuzzy model based prediction. The optimum number of reference membership functions is chosen manually. The criterion used is such that further increase in the number of membership functions does not significantly reduce the prediction error variance.

Finally, the quantization of data points by reference membership functions may introduce conflicts i.e., two data points with the same values in condition attributes may have different decision values. This can be resolved by using learning programs that are capable of dealing with conflicts such as LERS3 , which is based on the rough set theory introduced in [Pawlak, 1982].

2.3. Model Construction

Construction of fuzzy model is automated by feeding the quantized training data set into LERS3 inductive learning algorithm. For a given experimental data set of N entries. Each entry is the interpretation of the current and past data in terms of the reference membership functions. For example, if the vector $x(t)=[u(t-1) \quad u(t-2) \quad y(t) \quad y(t-1) \quad y(t-2)]$ represents the number of input and output elements used in modeling, in terms of reference membership functions, the quantized vector may read like $x_q(t)$=[*small positive, medium positive, small positive, large positive, small negative*]. The collection of *N* quantized vectors is then sent to the LERS3 learning program. The outputs of LERS3 are two sets of rules called certain rules and possible rules [Grzymala-Busse, 1988], which can be interpreted as the lower and upper approximation of the original data points. The set of certain rules is a subset of possible rules. We use the set of possible rules to represent the fuzzy model learned from the quantized vectors.

2.4. Model Validation

The compositional rule of inference operator is applied to the test data and the independent data to validate the fuzzy model. During the application of the compositional rule of inference, each fuzzy rule contributes with an appropriate membership function. The contributing membership function is determined by minimum (min) or product operator [Kosko, 1992]. Except for the experimental work by [Thole et al, 1979], there is no theoretical result guiding on which operator performs better. In fact, the min and product operators are special cases of the t-norms [Pedrycz, 1989]. It is our opinion that the product operator should be used in determining the contribution of the rule because the min operator simply chooses the minimum value and completely ignores the magnitude of other arguments.

Finally, if there are rules imposed by the process operators, these rules can also be combined with the fuzzy rules generated by the algorithm. The combined rule set, i.e.,

$$R_i; \quad i=1,2,\cdots,n_R \tag{2.4.1}$$

defines the fuzzy model of the system in terms of n_R number of rules.

3. FUZZY PREDICTIVE CONTROLLER

Following the fuzzy modeling phase, the dynamics of the system is characterized by a set of n_R fuzzy rules as,

$$R_i; \quad i=1,2,\cdots,n_R \tag{3.1}$$

Where a typical rule may take the following form:

"If u(t-1) is small positive and y(t-1) is large positive then y(t) is medium positive." This set of rules can be contrasted with a non-fuzzy model:

$$y(t)=f(y(t-1),y(t-2)\ldots,u(t-1),u(t-2),\ldots,\eta(t),\eta(t-1),\ldots,\theta) \tag{3.2}$$

where u, y and η are the process input, output, and noise respectively and θ denotes the parameters representing the dynamics. The structure of the function *f(.)* is assumed a priori. Since we intend to use the fuzzy model (3.1) as a predictor, it is instructive to compare the fuzzy and the non-fuzzy models as far as their use as predictors.

(a) The prediction of one step ahead process output , *y(t+1)*, given old process inputs and outputs such as *(y(t), y(t-1),... u(t), u(t-1),....)* is straightforward in (3.2). This task only requires the prediction of the noise term $\eta(t+1)$. If the model is linear, the prediction can be obtained by the minimum variance predictors. In the case of unstructured *f(.)*, however, there is no straightforward technique to determine the prediction for $\eta(t+1)$.

(b) The fuzzy model represented by (3.1) does not explicitly contain the noise term. The one step ahead prediction of the process output can be determined by the compositional rule of inference. For the example rule given above, the rule can be interpreted as *"If u(t) is small positive and y(t) is large positive then y(t+1) is medium positive."* Under this interpretation, we effectively increment the time index (*t*) of the original rule by one and restate the rule again. After applying the same interpretation to each rule of (3.1), a set of predictive rules for the fuzzy model can be obtained. To predict the one step ahead process output, the compositional rule inference operator is applied to the set of predictive rules.

(c) Although no benchmark problem is designed and solved to demonstrate the predictive power of the fuzzy models, it has been demonstrated that fuzzy predictive models are as powerful as the conventional time series models [Tong ,1978], [Pedrycz, 1984], [Sugeno ,1985] and [Xu and Lu, 1987].

There are two ways to design a fuzzy model based controller. The first and the obvious one is to invert the fuzzy model and use it as controller. The second and perhaps a more direct way is to identify an inverse fuzzy model from data and use it as controller. In the following, we denote these controllers as the forward and the inverse model based controller respectively.

3.1 Forward Model Based Controller

The task of inverting a fuzzy model and using as fuzzy controller can be performed within the following steps.

(1) The fuzzy model (3.1) is considered as a knowledge base of an expert system. This model consists of a set of fuzzy rules expressing the predicted process output in terms of current and past values of input output data.

(2) The process set-points *r(t)* are considered as conclusion states and we run an inference engine on the knowledge base in a backward reasoning scheme to determine the control action that , if applied, would generate the process output close to the set-point. This can be considered as reverse fuzzy reasoning process in which we already know the conclusion, however, one of the condition elements that generates this conclusion is missing. This missing element in our case is the required controller output at time *t*. To demonstrate the determination of the controller output, consider the rule that explains the process behavior in the form: *"If u(t) is small positive and y(t) is large positive then y(t+1) is medium positive."* We interpret this rule for the controller design as : *"medium positive y(t+1) and large positive y(t) implies small positive u(t)"* . The contribution of each rule to the controller output can be determined by the compositional rule of inference. Assume that the fuzzy model (3.1) can be written as

$$y(t)=u(t-1)\circ u(t-2)\circ\ldots\circ u(t-m)\circ y(t-1)\circ y(t-2)\circ\ldots\circ y(t-n) \tag{3.1.1}$$

where ($\circ$) denotes the compositional rule of inference operator. The one step ahead predictor form of (3.1.1) becomes

$$y(t+1)=u(t)\circ u(t-1)\circ\ldots\circ u(t-m+1)\circ y(t)\circ y(t-1)\circ\ldots\circ y(t-n+1) \tag{3.1.2}$$

Interpreted as controller outputs, (3.1.2) takes the form

$$u(t)=y(t+1)\circ y(t)\circ y(t-1)\circ\ldots\circ y(t-n+1)\circ u(t-1)\circ\ldots\circ u(t-m+1) \tag{3.1.3}$$

Finally, upon substitution of the control task *y(t+1)=r(t)*, the control rules become

$$u(t)=r(t)\circ y(t)\circ y(t-1)\circ\ldots\circ y(t-n+1)\circ u(t-1)\circ\ldots\circ u(t-m+1) \tag{3.1.4}$$

The variables on the right hand side of (3.1.4) are known at time t, therefore, the contribution of each rule can be determined with the compositional rule of inference operator. Figure 2 illustrates how the controller output is determined.

3.2 Inverse model Based Controllers

Under this methodology, we identify the inverse process model directly from input output data using the LERS3 algorithm. The training data has the condition and conclusion variables $[y(t) \quad y(t-1) \quad \cdots \quad y(t-n) \quad u(t-1) \quad \cdots \quad u(t-n)]$,and *u(t-1)* respectively. Figure 3 shows how the forward and inverse model based controllers are obtained.

Note that both controllers outlined above act as inverse process models. In the first case, the rules of the forward fuzzy model are interpreted such that the resulting controller acts as an inverse process. Whereas in the second case an inverse process model is explicitly identified from data and used as controller.

4. EXAMPLES

In this section, we present two simulated application where we use the inverse model based controller as presented in Section 3.2. The forward model based controller described in Section 3.1 can be found in [Batur 1992].

In the first example, we attempt to construct an inverse fuzzy controller for the following linear system

$$y(t) = y(t-1) - 0.4y(t-2) + 0.5u(t-1) - 0.1u(t-2) + e(t) \quad (4.1)$$

where $u(t)$, $y(t)$ are the process inputs and outputs, $e(t)$ is the associated noise. Note that the fuzzy models makes no assumption on the distribution of e. Initially, this system is simulated by applying a random input with mean 10 and variance 5.75. A part of the resulting input-output data is shown in Figure 5. The order of the system is two and hence two past inputs and outputs are used as attributes for predicting the future output. In case this is not known, we can determine the number of past inputs and outputs by the techniques mentioned in Section 2.1.

At this point we have raw input-output data. Each data point can be interpreted as in the following example

if $y(t+1) = 10.4$ & $y(t) = 10$ & $y(t-1) = 6$ & $u(t-1) = 2$ then $u(t-1) = 6$

These input-output data are fuzzified to give a set of fuzzified input-output data. The shape of the fuzzy reference membership function is assumed to be triangular. For all u's and y's, 10 fuzzy membership functions are assumed in the range 5 to 15 in a similar fashion as in Figure 4. Notice that there are input and outputs actually that lie outside the (5-15) range. However, the objective is to learn the response of the system in (5-15) range. The resulting membership functions are used to fuzzify the raw input-output data. As mentioned earlier, each attribute may belong to more than one fuzzy set. For example

$y(t) = 10.0$ implies $y(t)$ belongs 5th and 6th fuzzy set.

In a similar fashion, other attributes can belong to more than one fuzzy set. Thus, a single data point may result in multiple fuzzy data points. In this paper, we restrict the number of resulting fuzzy data point by associating each attribute to only one fuzzy set corresponding to the maximum membership value. Thus the fuzzified data for the above example becomes

if $y(t+1) = 6$ & $y(t) = 6$ & $y(t-1) = 2$ & $u(t-1) = 1$ then $u(t) = 1$.

The inverse fuzzy model is learnt from 750 fuzzified data points using LERS3 learning algorithm. The LERS3 algorithm gives two set of rules, namely, certain rules and possible rules. The certain rules are a subset of possible rules. In this paper, we use the possible rules for prediction and control. In order to illustrate the prediction capability of the fuzzy model, we try to predict $u(t)$ on the same data set used for training. A small section of the prediction is shown in Figure 6. Notice that the prediction is very good in the region between 5 and 15 and outside this range the model cannot predict. This is due to the choice of our fuzzy reference membership function. Finally, the inverse fuzzy model is used to follow certain references. The system response and controller outputs are shown in Figure 7. Notice, the system is able to reach the set-point. However, the process output is oscillating almost all the times. The controller output is also oscillating. This is a problem shared by almost all inverse controller. This can be alleviated by using all the fuzzified rules of a particular raw input-output data instead of just using the maximum. Also, there is steady state errors with the reference following. Hence, further research is necessary for the practicality of these controllers.

In the second example, we try to control a highly non-linear system as given below

$$y(t) = \left(0.5 - 0.5e^{-y^2(t-1)}\right)y(t-1) - \left(0.3 + 0.9e^{-y^2(t-1)}\right)y(t-2)$$
$$+ u(t-1) + 0.2u(t-1)u(t-2) + e(t) \quad (4.2)$$

where $u(t)$, $y(t)$ are the process inputs and outputs. $e(t)$ is the noise associated. The same non-linear system is used by [Chen et al 1990] to test their neural network based modeling techniques. This system is simulated by applying a random input with mean 2.0 and variance 0.3. Some of the resulting input-output data are shown in Figure 8. As in the previous example, the shape of the fuzzy reference membership function is assumed to be triangular. For all u's , 10 fuzzy membership functions are assumed in the range (1.5 , 2.5) and similarly 10 membership functions are used in the range (4.0, 7.0) to fuzzify all y's.

The inverse fuzzy model of this system is learnt from 750 fuzzified data points using LERS3 learning algorithm. Again, only possible rules are used for prediction and control of this system. The prediction capability of the fuzzy model is illustrated in Figure 9. The inverse fuzzy model is used to make the system to follow certain references. The system response and controller outputs are given in Figure 10. The system is able to follow trajectories. However, there is still oscillations in the system response and steady state error.

5. CONCLUSION

This paper presents a methodology to identify predictive fuzzy models for process dynamics. In addition, a fuzzy model based controller is also proposed. Dynamics of the inverse process is identified in terms of a set of fuzzy rules. The resulting fuzzy model is used as controller. In this capacity, the controller attempts to cancel the dynamics of the process. The cancellation is never exact because it requires an infinite number of membership functions to quantize the process input output variables. Furthermore, since the controller is based on the inverse process model, it can not be directly applied to non-minimum phase systems. The performance of the control system depends strongly on the accuracy of the fuzzy process model. Simulated examples on the predictive fuzzy model building and on the inverse model based fuzzy controller design are presented.

6. REFERENCES

Batur C., Srinivasan A., Chan Chien-Chung, " Automated rule base model generation for uncertain complex dynamic systems " Eng. Applications. of Artificial Intelligence. Vol.4 No. 4, 1991.

Batur C., Srinivasan A., Chan Chien-Chung, "Fuzzy model based fuzzy predictive control", Proceedings of First Int. Conf. on Fuzzy Teory and Technology, pp 176-180, 1992.

Chan Chien-Chung "Incremental learning production rules from examples under uncertainty: a rough set approach" Int. Journal. of Software and Knowledge Eng. Vol.1 No.4 1991.

Chen, S., Billings, S.A., Grant, P.M., "Non-linear system identification using neural networks" , Int. J. Control, 1990 Vol. 51 No. 6 , pp 1191-1214.

Chen, Y.Y., "Stability analysis of fuzzy control: a Lyapunov approach" CH 2503-187, 1027-1031, IEEE, 1987.

Cook P.A. Nonlinear Dynamical Systems Prentice Hall 1986.

Daley, S ., Gill, K.F. " A design study of self organizing fuzzy logic controller" Proceed. of the Inst. of Mech. Eng. Pt C, 200, (C1) 56-59, and "Attitude control of a space craft using an extended self organizing fuzzy logic controller. Ibid, 201 C 1987.

Daley, S ., Gill, K.F. " Comparison of fuzzy logic controller with a P+D control law" Trans. of the ASME pp. 128-137 Vol 111, June 1989.

Grzymala-Busse, J.W., "Knowledge acquisition under uncertainty: a rough set approach," J. Intell. Robotic Syst., Vol. 1, 3-16, 1988.

Kiszka, J.B., Gupta M. M., Nikiforuk P.N "Energetistic stabilty of fuzzy dynamic systems" IEEE Trans. SMC, Vol. SMC-15, No.6, Nov.-Dec., pp.783-792.

Kosko B. Neural networks and fuzzy systems. Prentice Hall 1992.

Pawlak, Z., "Rough sets," Int. J. Computer Inf. Sci., Vol. 11, 341-356, 1982.

Pedrycz W "An identification algorithm in fuzzy relational systems" Fuzzy Set and Systems, 13, 153-167 1984.

Pedrycz W. Fuzzy Control and Fuzzy Systems, R.S.P and John Wiley 1989

Quinlan, J. R. "Induction of decision trees" Machine learning 1, pp. 81-106 1986

Quinlan, J. R. "Simplifying decision trees" Int. J. Man-Machine Studies 27, pp 221-234., 1987.

Ray K.S., Majumder D. " Application of circle criteria for stability analysis of linear SISO and MIMO systems associated with fuzzy logic controller." IEEE Trans. on Systems, Man and Cybernetics, SMC-14 , No.2 1984.

Ray K.S., Majumder D. " Fuzzy logic control of nonlinear multivariable steam generating unit using decoupling theory IEEE Trans. on Systems, Man and Cybernetics, SMC-15 , No. 4 July/August 1985.

Sugeno, M. Takagi, T. "Fuzzy identification of systems and its applications to modeling and control, IEEE Trans. on Syst. Man and Cybernetics, SMC-15, 1985.

Thole U. Zimmermann H.J., Zysno " The suitability of minimum and product operators for the intersection of fuzzy sets" Fuzzy Sets and Systems 2, 167-180 1979

Tong, R.M., "Synthesis of fuzzy models for industrial processes " Int. Journ. of Generating Systems, 4, 143-162.1978.

Wang Li-Xin., Mendel Jerry M. " Generating fuzzy rules by learning from examples" Proc. of the 1991 Int. Symp. on Intelligent Control. CH3019-7/91/0000, 1991

Xu Chen-Wei " Fuzzy system identification" IEE Proceed. Vol. 136 Pt.D No. 4 July. pp. 146-149, 1989.

Xu Hen-Wei ., Lu Yong-Zai " Fuzzy model identification and self learning for dynamic systems" IEEE Trans. on Systems, Man and Cybernetics Vol. SMC-17 No.4 1987.

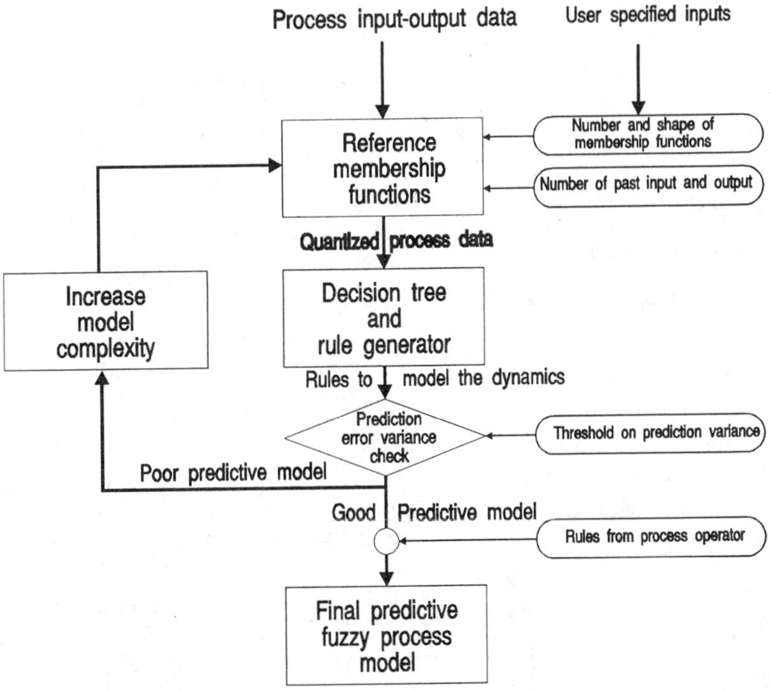

Figure 1. Components of fuzzy model building methodology.

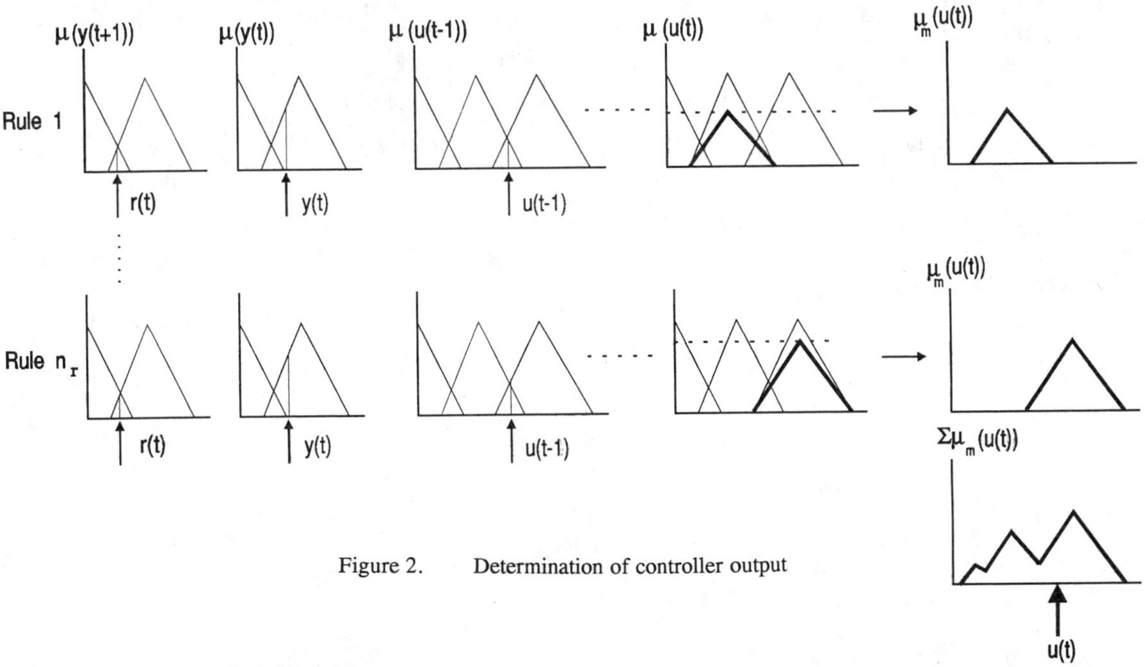

Figure 2. Determination of controller output

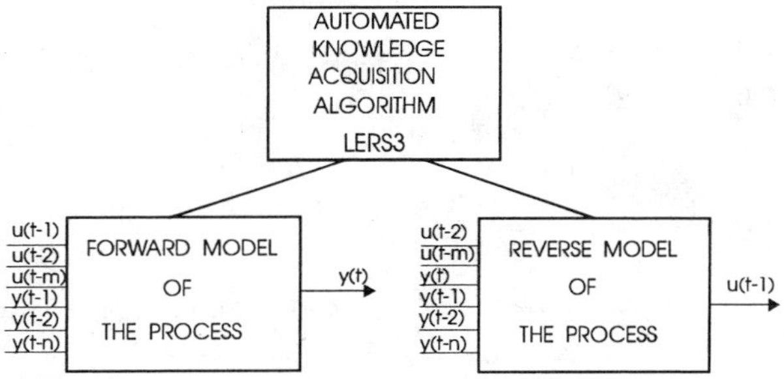

Figure 3. Forward and inverse fuzzy models obtained.

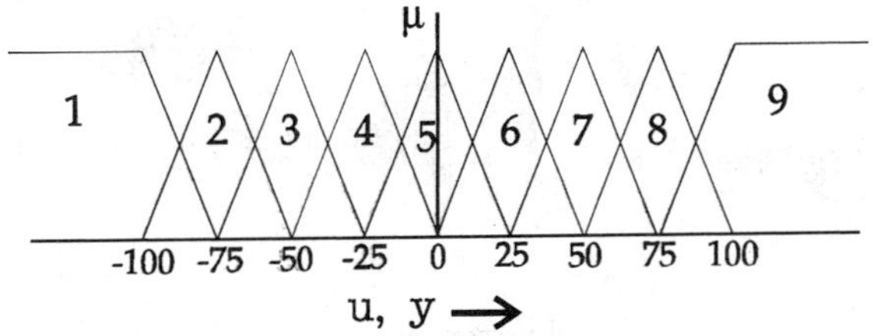

Figure 4. Fuzzy membership functions

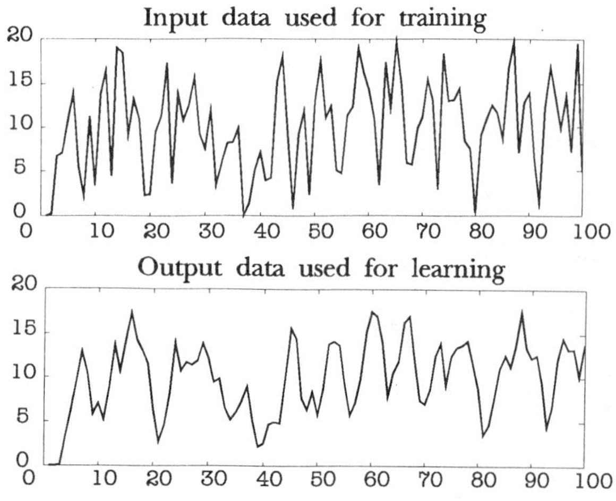

Figure 5. Input-output training data for linear system

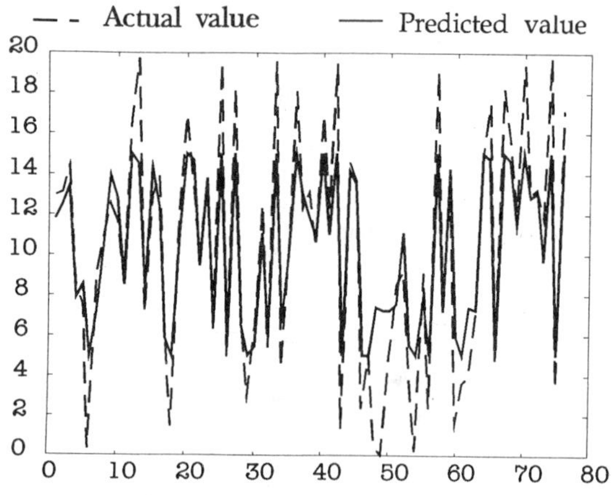

Figure 6. Prediction of output for linear system

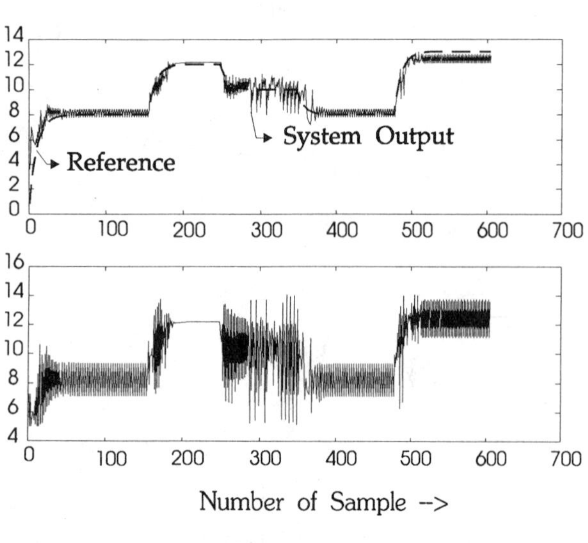

Figure 7 · Performance of the control system

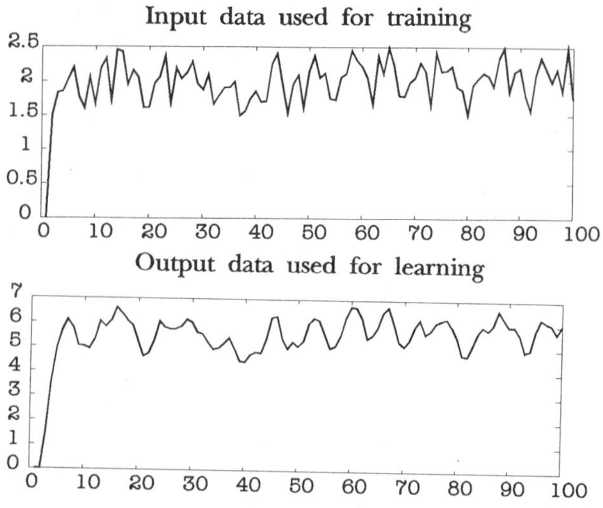

Figure 8. Input-output training data for nonlinear system

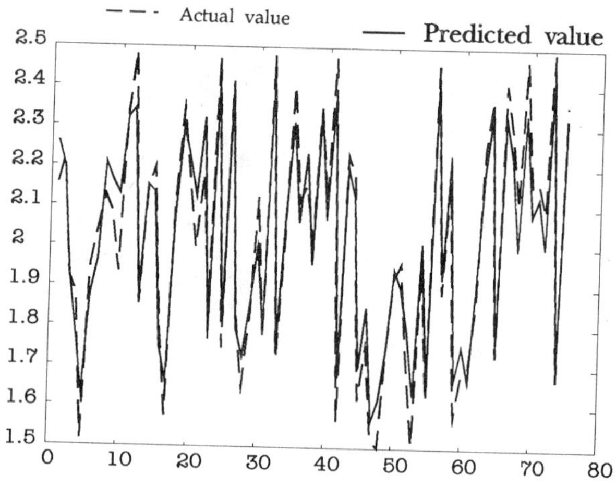

Figure 9. Prediction of output for nonlinear system

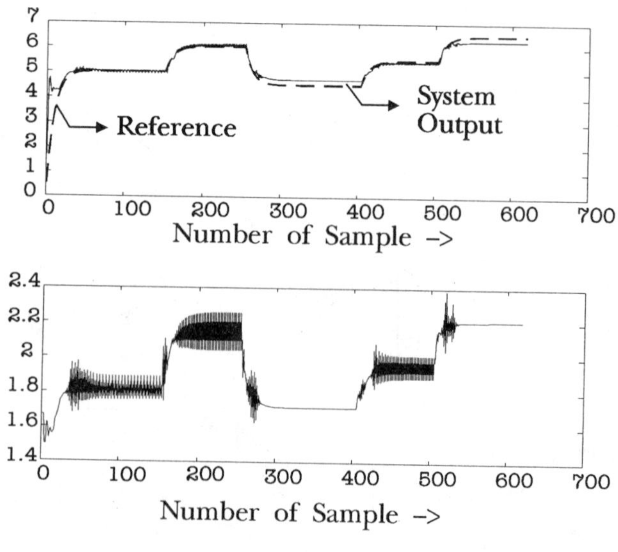

Figure 10. Performance of the control system

Proceedings of the
American Control Conference
San Francisco, California • June 1993

STABILITY ANALYSIS OF LINGUISTIC FUZZY MODEL SYSTEMS

Won C. Kim
Samsung Data Systems Co.
Automation Business Team
C.P.O. BOX 4284 Seoul

Wook H. Kwon, H.D. Kim
Information Systems Laboratory
Dept. of Contr. & Instr. Engr.
Seoul National University
Seoul 151-742,KOREA

ABSTRACT

In this paper we propose a new stability theorem for linguistic fuzzy model systems. The model used here is a continuous version of Tanaka and Sugeno's model by which nonlinear system can be identified precisely. This theorem enables us to check the stability of fuzzy model by solving certain simple matrix equations. A simple example is also included to illustrate an application of the method.

I. INTRODUCTION

Fuzzy set theory, which was suggested by Zadeh[1] in 1965, was developed as a fuzzy logic controller(FLC)[2]. The controller has been applied to the control of cement kiln, robot and power electric plants to result in good performances. Since the controller can be implemented directly from the knowledge and explanation of experts, it has been used widely for controlling systems or systems which are not exactly known.

The fuzzy reasoning method in FLC is also used to model nonlinear systems[3]. The system modeled by FLC was identified better than other methods like GMDH[4]. The fuzzy model may be regarded as one of the piecewise linear functions, but the former can approximate a function with less partitions and is a continuous function unlike the latter. Therefore, when we model and analyze a nonlinear system from its input-output informations, the fuzzy model is very useful. But it is very difficult to find its characteristics such as stability and controllability because it can not be represented with traditional operators.

The methods of fuzzy modeling - linguistic modeling and relational matrix modeling - are basically the same. Strictly speaking, the relation matrix modeling is a numerical representation of a part of the linguistic modeling. But in the case of state space fuzzy modeling, with which the plant is described by $x_n = x_{n-1} \circ R$, many researches relating to stability and controllability have been conducted[5][6]. But unlike the case of the traditional one which is a combined form of fuzzification, reasoning and defuzzification and which maps real values to real values, the state space fuzzy model maps fuzzy set to fuzzy set. Thus, it is hard to find a real plant which can be modeled with this model.

On the other hand, the linguistic model and its numerically represented relation matrix model can be used for modeling almost all real plants, but only a few[7][8] have studied about its characteristics. Among them, Tanaka and Sugeno suggested effective method to test the stability of systems[9]. And since the model he used can be identified from the input-output data[4], the method can be used effectively for determining the stability of nonlinear plants. However, the common solution matrix P of Lyapunov equations which is difficult to find is required in the method. And even if the system is stable there may not be such a solution, because the solution of Lyapunov equation depends on system matrix A. Besides, the method does not use the constraint that the summation of all coefficients of the system matrix is always 1.

The model which is used here is a continuous version of Tanaka and Sugeno's. We suggest a method to determine the stability from the uncertainty bounds of a system. The method allows us to determine its stability not from the defuzzified equation but from each rule which is independent from the other rules. Thus, we can check the stability easily. And since the stability of a fuzzy model system can be determined from the equation of each rule, the method makes the finding of stabilizing control easy. This method is more useful when nonlinearity is not prominent. And the discrete version of this method can be found straightforwardly.

The example determining the stability of a fuzzy model system using this method is also presented.

II. SYSTEM

Generally, nonlinear systems have the following state equation.

$$\dot{x} = f(x, u) \qquad (1)$$

where $x \in R^n$, $u \in R^p$, $f \in R^n X R^n$. Since the function f(x,u) can be well approximated by the fuzzy function F(x,u), the system can be modeled by

$$\dot{x} = F(x, u) \qquad (2)$$

where F is derived from the following rules.

Rule 1: x_1 is R^1_1, x_2 is R^1_2, ... , x_n is R^1_n, then

$$x_1 = a^1_{11}x_1 + a^1_{12}x_2 \cdots + a^1_{1n}x_n$$
$$x_2 = a^1_{21}x_1 + a^1_{22}x_2 \cdots + a^1_{2n}x_n$$
$$\cdots\cdots$$
$$x_n = a^1_{n1}x_1 + a^1_{n2}x_2 \cdots + a^1_{nn}x_n$$

Rule 2: x_1 is R^2_1, x_2 is R^2_2, ... , x_n is R^2_n, then

$$x_1 = a^2_{11}x_1 + a^2_{12}x_2 \cdots + a^2_{1n}x_n$$
$$\cdots\cdots$$

....

Rule m: x_1 is R^m_1, x_2 is R^m_2, ... , x_n is R^m_n, then

$$x_1 = a^m_{11}x_1 + a^m_{12}x_2 \cdots + a^m_{1n}x_n$$
$$x_2 = a^m_{21}x_1 + a^m_{22}x_2 \cdots + a^m_{2n}x_n$$
$$\cdots\cdots$$
$$x_n = a^m_{n1}x_1 + a^m_{n2}x_2 \cdots + a^m_{nn}x_n$$

where R^i_j's are fuzzy sets.

This function can be represented briefly by

$$\dot{x}=\sum_{i=1}^{m} \alpha_i A_i x_i \tag{3}$$

where A_i is a system matrix of i-th rule, $\alpha_i = \omega_i/\Sigma_j\,\omega_j$, and ω_i is a membership value of rule i which is the minimum among membership values in the rule,i.e. among $A_{ik}(x_k)$'s, which mean the membership x_k to fuzzy set R^i_k. Thus the range of α_i is from 0 to 1 and the summation of all α_i is 1.

III. STABILITY

At any state, the fuzzy mapping F can be defined by system matrices of Eq.(3) with appropriate α_i's.Thus if Eq.(3) is stable for all possible α_i's, then nonlinear state Eq.(2) is stable.

We first explain the useful theorem suggested by Zhou and Khargonekar[10].

Let us consider a linear system with multiple uncertain parameters

$$\dot{x}=Ax+\sum_{i=1}^{m} k_i\,\delta A_i x \tag{4}$$

where $x\epsilon R^n$,A is constant stable matrix,δA_i's are constant perturbation matrices, and k_i's are uncertain parameters.

Let P be the solution of the following Lyapunov equation.

$$A^T P+PA=I \tag{5}$$

And F_k's are matrix from the following equation.

$$\frac{\delta A_k^T P + P\,\delta A_k}{2} = F_k \tag{6}$$

Then, system (4) is stable if

$$\sum_{i=1}^{m} k_i \sigma_M(F_i)<1 \tag{7}$$

or

$$|k_i| < \frac{1}{\sigma_M\left(\sum_{j=1}^{m} |F_j|\right)} \qquad i=1,2,...m \tag{8}$$

where $\sigma_M(A)$ is the maximum singular value of matrix A.

To use this method we need to find a divided form of the constant matrix and perturbed matrices which corresponds to A and δA_k respectively. The divided form can be found from Eq.(3) or from each rules. The constant matrices, A, can be assumed as the value when all states are zero or when the α_i's have certain values.

In many nonlinear systems, since they have many linear terms and a few nonlinear terms, it is not strange that a nonlinear system is divided into constant and perturbed terms.

A system devided by the method is described by

$$\dot{x}=\sum_{i=1}^{m} \alpha_i\,(A+\delta A_i)\,x \tag{9}$$

where $A\epsilon R^{nxn}$ is a constant system matrix which corresponds to linear term, $\delta A_i \epsilon R^{nxn}$ are perturbation matrices which correspond to nonlinear terms and $\alpha_i \epsilon[0,1]$, $\Sigma\alpha_i = 1$. This may be assumed as the case that the nonlinear part of a system is modeled by fuzzy logic.

If the rule is divided, α_i's always have values between 0 and 1. But If Eq.(3) is divided, then δA_i has to be adjusted to make α_i's have their values between 0 and 1 but $\Sigma\alpha_i = 1$ is not reserved. In this case, the system is described by

$$\dot{x}=(A+\sum_{i=1}^{m} \alpha_i\,\delta A_i)\,x \tag{10}$$

where $A\epsilon R^{nxn}$, $\delta A_i \epsilon R^{nxn}$ and $\alpha_i \epsilon[0,1]$. This is almost the same form with Eq.(9) except $\Sigma\alpha_i$ is not always 1.

Theorem: Assume that the constant system matrix A of Eq.(9) and (10) is stable,

i) the system is stable if the F_i defined in Eq.(6) satisfies the following inequalities.

$$\sum_{i=1}^{m} \sigma_M(F_i)<1 \tag{11}$$

ii) if system (9) satisfies the following inequalities, or system (10) satisfies $\Sigma\alpha_i = 1$ and the following, then the system is stable.

$$\sigma_M(F_i)<1 \quad i=1,2,...m \tag{12}$$

proof: Eq.(9), since $\Sigma\alpha_i = 1$, can be represented by Eq.(10) which is the same form with Eq.(4). If Eq.(11) holds, then

$$\sum_{i=1}^{m} |\alpha_i|\sigma_M(F_i)<1 \tag{13}$$

From Eq.(7), the system is stable. The first part has proved. And if $\Sigma\alpha_i = 1$ and if Eq.(12) holds, the Eq.(11) is satisfied all $\alpha_i \epsilon [0,1]$. Thus, the system is stable. **Q.E.D.**

Now we will show how to divide A_i's into a constant and perturbation matrices. The system matrices of each rule may be given from the initial stage. That is, by identifying the nonlinear parts only, fuzzy rule can be represented by

Rule 1: x_1 is $R^1{}_1$, x_2 is $R^1{}_2$, ······ , x_n is $R^1{}_n$,
then $x = Ax+\delta A_i x$
Rule 2: x_1 is $R^2{}_1$, x_2 is $R^2{}_2$, ······ , x_n is $R^2{}_n$,
then $x = Ax+\delta A_i x$
....
Rule m: x_1 is $R^m{}_1$, x_2 is $R^m{}_2$, ······ , x_n is $R^m{}_n$,
then $x = Ax+\delta A_i x$

Thus for any state, the system is described by Eq.(9). And since Eq.(14) holds,

$$\dot{x}=(A+\sum_{i=1}^{m} \alpha_i\,\delta A_i)\,x \tag{14}$$

When devision is completed, we have to choose a constant matrice A. The recommended one is to choose when all states are zero and the other one is an average value of all system matrices. The differences between the chosen constant matrix and one of the system matrices are considered as a perturbation matrices. When we devide defuzzified equation (9) not the rules, if one perturbation matrix can cover a part of another perturbation matrices, then they can be treated as common perturbation, since $\Sigma\alpha_i = 1$.

An example of the division is given. When a nonlinear system is modeled by a fuzzy model with 3 rules whose system matrices, A_i's, are

$$A_1=\begin{pmatrix}1 & 1.2\\ 0 & 1\end{pmatrix} \quad A_2=\begin{pmatrix}0.7 & 0\\ 0 & 0.7\end{pmatrix} \quad A_3=\begin{pmatrix}1 & 0\\ 0.6 & 1\end{pmatrix} \tag{15}$$

For all states, the system can be described by

$$\dot{x}=(\alpha_1 A_1+\alpha_2 A_2+\alpha_3 A_3)\,x \tag{16}$$

By choosing the average value as constant matrix, it can be described by

$$\dot{x}=(A+\beta_1\delta A_1+\beta_2\delta A_2+\beta_3\delta A_3)\,x \tag{17}$$

where

$$A=\frac{1}{3}(A_1+A_2+A_3)=\begin{pmatrix}0.9 & 0.4\\ 0.2 & 0.9\end{pmatrix}$$

$$\delta A_1=\begin{pmatrix}0.1 & 0.8\\ -0.2 & 0.1\end{pmatrix} \quad \delta A_2=\begin{pmatrix}-0.2 & -0.4\\ 0.2 & -0.2\end{pmatrix} \quad \delta A_3=\begin{pmatrix}0.1 & -0.4\\ 0.4 & 0.1\end{pmatrix}$$

IV. EXAMPLE

In this section we present an example which shows how to determine the stability of fuzzy model system.

consider a system whose fuzzy model is

Rule 1: x_1 is $R^1{}_1$, x_2 is $R^1{}_2$, then $x_1 = A_1x$
Rule 2: x_1 is $R^2{}_1$, x_2 is $R^2{}_2$, then $x_2 = A_2x$
Rule 3: x_1 is $R^3{}_1$, x_2 is $R^3{}_2$, then $x_3 = A_3x$
where

$$A_1=\begin{pmatrix}-1 & 0.7\\ 1.1 & -1.5\end{pmatrix} \quad A_2=\begin{pmatrix}-0.8 & 0.4\\ 0.9 & -0.7\end{pmatrix} \quad A_3=\begin{pmatrix}-1.2 & 0.4\\ 0.3 & -0.8\end{pmatrix}$$

By dividing, we can rewrite the rules by
Rule 1: x_1 is $R^1{}_1$, x_2 is $R^1{}_2$, then $x_1 = (A + \delta A_1)x$
Rule 2: x_1 is $R^2{}_1$, x_2 is $R^2{}_2$, then $x_2 = (A + \delta A_2)x$
Rule 3: x_1 is $R^3{}_1$, x_2 is $R^3{}_2$, then $x_3 = (A + \delta A_3)x$
where

$$A=\frac{1}{3}(A_1+A_2+A_3)=\begin{pmatrix}-1 & 0.5\\ 0.5 & -1\end{pmatrix}$$

$$\delta A_1=\begin{pmatrix}0 & 0.2\\ 0.6 & -0.5\end{pmatrix} \quad \delta A_2=\begin{pmatrix}0.2 & -0.1\\ 0.4 & 0.3\end{pmatrix} \quad \delta A_3=\begin{pmatrix}-0.2 & -0.1\\ -0.2 & 0.2\end{pmatrix}$$

From the Lyapunov equation (5) with constant matrix A,

$$P=\begin{pmatrix}\frac{2}{3} & \frac{1}{3}\\ \frac{1}{3} & \frac{2}{3}\end{pmatrix}$$

Then, for each F_k which is computed from A_k, k=1,2,3,

$\sigma_M(F_1) = 0.6583$, $\sigma_M(F_2) = 0.4534$, $\sigma_M(F_3) = 0.4060$

Thus the system is stable.

V. CONCLUSION

In this paper, we suggested a new stability theorem using robust stability. This is a sufficient condition and the stability can be tested with less computation than the Tanaka and Sugeno's method. Unlike the method which is obiligatory to find a common solution of Lyapunov equations, this method proposed here can determine the stability from a simple matrix equation. Thus it needs less computation and can determine the stability of a system whose rules do not have a common Lyapunov solution.

This theorem works better if the perturbation is not large. Thus if we find the system matrices after dividing the model into appropriate intervals according to fuzzification, we sometimes find a model with less perturbation.

The most important characteristics of this theorem is that it can determine its stability from each rule and not from a defuzzified value. Thus this theorem can be used to find a stabilizing control law.

REFERENCES

[1] L.A.Zadeh,"Fuzzy sets," Information and control,vol.8, pp.338-353,1965.

[2] E.H.Mamdani,"Application of fuzzy logic to approximate reasoning using linguistic synthesis," IEEE Tr. on computer, pp.1182-1191,Dec.,1977.

[3] T.Takagi and M.Sugeno,"Fuzzy identification of systems and its applications to modeling and control,"IEEE Tr.on SMC,vol.15,pp.116-132,Feb.,1985.

[4] M.Sugeno and G.T.Kang,"Structure identification of fuzzy model," Fuzzy set and systems 28,pp.15-33,1988.

[5] J.B.Kiszka, M.M.Gupta and P.N.Nikiforuk,"Energetic stability of fuzzy dynamic systems,"IEEE Tr. on SMC, vol.15,Nov.,1985.

[6] R.M.Tong,"Analysis and control of suzzy systems using finite discrete relations," int. J. control,vol.27,no.3,pp.431-440,1978.

[7] K.S.Ray and D.D.Majumder,"Application of circle criteria for stability analysis of linear SISO and MIMO systems associated with fuzzy logic controller," IEEE Tr. on SMC.,MAR./APR.,1984.

[8] P.Z.Wang and H.M.Zhang,"Pad-analysis of fuzzy control stability," Fuzzy set and systems 38,pp.27-42,1990.

[9] K.Tanaka and M.Sugeno,"Stability analysis of fuzzy control systems using Lyapunov's direct method," Proc. of NAFIPS '90, pp.133-136,1990.

[10] K.Zhou and P.P.Khargonekar,"Stability robustness bounds for linear state-space models with structured uncertainty," IEEE Tr. on Automat. Contr.,vol.32, pp.621-623,Jul.,1987.

Proceedings of the
American Control Conference
San Francisco, California • June 1993

ANALYSIS OF FUZZY NONLINEARITY - ONE DIMENSIONAL CASE

J. H. Tarn and L. T. Kuo

Institute of Aeronautics and Astronautics
National Cheng Kung University
Tainan, Taiwan, ROC

Abstract

Analysis of nonlinear dynamics of one-dimensional fuzzy control system is achieved indirectly. The fuzzy control law is decomposed into a linear control law and a superimposed nonlinearity. The linear part is treated as variable-level bang-bang control and analyzed by applying Lyapunov stability theorem. Superimposed nonlinearity can then be categorized according to its effects on the stability and transient performance of the closed loop system. With fuzzy nonlinear control law formulated explicitly, the design parameters can then be synthesized to satisfy control system requirements.

1. Introduction

The purposes of this study are

(1) to establish relations between design parameters of the fuzzy control system and nonlinear dynamics introduced by it;

(2) to categorize the fuzzy nonlinearities according to their analytic properties such as stability, robustness, and transient performance.

It is known that fuzzy logic control is a nonlinear control strategy. The nonlinearity has been studied by [4][5]. It is also recognized that fuzzy control system usually inherits good robustness for system uncertainties.[3] To further study their relations, groups of fuzzy nonlinearities are formulated explicitly with dependents of fuzzy parameters such as input, output fuzzy partition, compositional operator, and defuzzification strategy. Analytical studies of these nonlinear dynamics are pursued by forming a fuzzy bang-bang control law. First, output of the proposed fuzzy control system is decomposed into a linear and a super-imposed nonlinear control law. The linear part is treated as a variable-level bang-bang system and analyzed by applying Lyapunov Theorem. Based on this, the nonlinear control laws form various groups are categorized according to their effects to system stability, robustness and transient performances.

In the next section the control rules are expressed linguistically and form a fuzzy bang-bang control system. Nonlinearity of the proposed fuzzy control system is formulated explicitly with various dependent variables in section 3. Effects of the superimposed nonlinear control law, introduced by fuzziness, on system dynamics are studied in section 5 with simulation results.

2. Fuzzy Bang-Bnag Control

It is well known that the fuzzy control is a nonlinear control strategy. In order to

(i) establish relations between parameters of fuzzy control systems and various characteristics of nonlinear dynamics;

(ii) analyze the dynamics of the nonlinearity of FLC,

a simple three rules fuzzy controller imitating the bang-bang behaviors is utilized for brevity.
Linguistically, the bang-bang control can be expressed with three fuzzy rules:

R_1 : If X_2 is "Positive", Then U is "Negative."
R_2 : If X_2 is "Zero", Then U is "Zero".
R_3 : If X_3 is "Negative", Then U is "Positive".

Fuzzy Partition of Input Fuzzy Spaces

The input fuzzy space is divided into three fuzzy terms "Negative", "Zero ","Positive" and their membership functions are shown is Fig.1

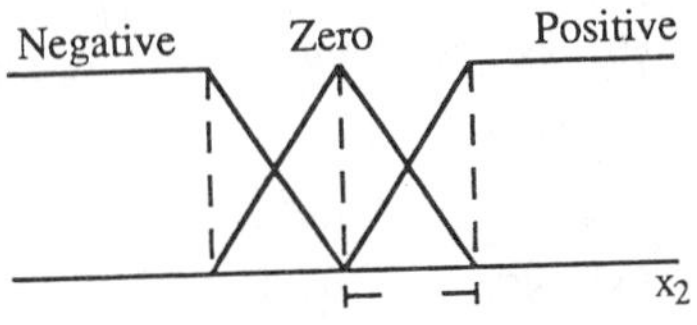

Fig.1 Fuzzy Terms of State x_2

From Fig.1 it can be seen that, for $x_2 \leq -\epsilon$ or $x_2 \geq \epsilon$, only fuzzy rule R_2 or R_3 is triggered. In order to make the state feedback gain critical *i.e.* "$\frac{k}{c}$", for comparison, the base semi-length ϵ for membership function "Zero" is set to be equal to "$\frac{K}{(\frac{k}{c})}$".

As shown in Fig.2, the state feedback gain is "critical" and the gain schedule between positive and negative saturation bounds is linear. The output fuzzy variable "u" is also divided into three term negative, zero, and positive. And their membership functions are shown in Fig.3

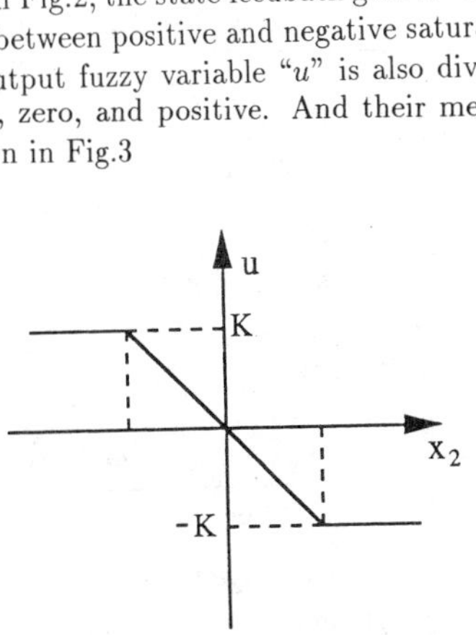

Fig.2 Linear Feedback Law with Saturation Bound

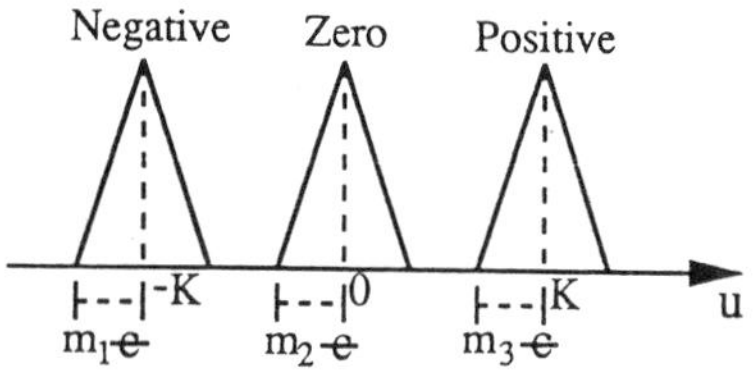

Fig.3 Output Fuzzy Terms.

Defuzzification Strategy

Three kinds of defuzzification strategies are used.[1]

MOM(Mean of Maximum)

$$u = \frac{\sum^{n} \mu_i U_i}{\sum^{n} \mu_i}$$

COA (Center of Area)

$$u = \frac{\int_{\forall \mu(x)\neq 0} \mu(x) x dx}{\int_{\forall \mu(x)\neq 0} \mu(x) dx}$$

GCOA (Generalized Center of Area)

$$U = \frac{\sum^{n} A_i U_i}{\sum^{n} A_i}$$

Where

$\cdot \mu_i$ is the firing strength (matching level) of the fuzzy rule R_i.

$\cdot U_i$ is u_i of fuzzy variable $\tilde{U}_i$ with max membership value.

$\cdot A_i$ is the inferred area of fuzzy variable $\tilde{U}_i$.

$\cdot n$ is the number of rules been excited.

3. Nonlinearity of Fuzzy Bang-Bnag Control

To formulate the control laws for $-\epsilon \leq x_2 \leq \epsilon$, assume that $x_2 = d\epsilon, 0 \leq d \leq 1$. Under this assumption, there are two fuzzy rules R_2 and R_3 been excited. With "sup-min" compositional operator, the matching level of each rule is listed in Table.

Antecedent	Strength	Control Action	Inference Area
"Zero"	$1-d$	0 "Zero"	$(1+d_1)(1-d_1)m_k\epsilon$
"Positive"	d	$-K$"Negative"	$(2-d)dm_{k+1}\epsilon$

By utilizing the GCOA defuzzification strategy, the output control action becomes.

$$\begin{aligned} u &= \frac{-(2-d)d \cdot m_{k+1}\epsilon \cdot K}{(1+d)(1-d)m_k\epsilon + (2-d)dm_{k+1}\epsilon} \\ &= -\frac{(2-d)d \cdot m_{k+1} \cdot S_k\epsilon}{(1-d^2)m_k + (2d-d^2)m_{k+1}} \qquad (\text{let} K = S_k\epsilon) \\ &= \underbrace{-S_k \cdot d\epsilon}_{\text{linear}} - \underbrace{\frac{(d^3-d)m_k + (d^3-3d^2+2d)m_{K+1}}{(1-d^2)m_k + (2d-d^2)m_{k+1}} S_k\epsilon}_{\text{superimposed nonlinear}} \end{aligned}$$

From this, it is clear that fuzzy logic control defines a nonlinear control strategy. The nonlinear control action can be further decomposed into (i) a linear control law and (ii) a superimposed nonlinearity. Studies will focus on the nonlinear part of the output control action.

Let $m = \frac{m_k}{m_{k+1}}$ be the area ratio between two adjacent membership functions of the output fuzzy variable. In this case, the superimposed nonlinear control law becomes

$$u_{NL} = \frac{[(2-m)d - 3d^2 + (m+1)d^3}{m + 2d - (m+1)d^2}$$

Fig.4 shows the nonlinearity for $0.2 \leq m \leq 2$ with increment 0.2.

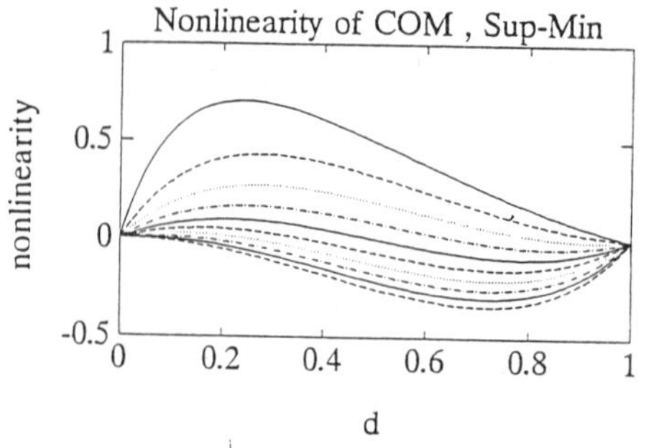

Fig.4 Nonlinearity of GAOA Sup-Min, $m = 0.2 \sim 2$; Increment 0.2.

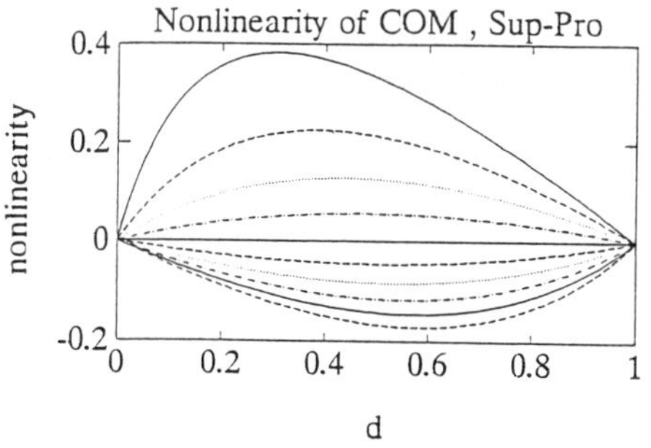

Fig.5 Nonlinearity of GCOA, Sup-Product, $m = 0.2 \sim 2$; Increment 0.2

It's clear that variation of the area ratio m changes the nonlinear curve greatly, thus the nonlinear dynamics. Other fuzzy parameters that affect the nonlinearity are compositional operator, defuzzification strategy. By "sup-product" compositional operator, the control law becomes

$$u = -S_k * d\epsilon - \frac{(1-m)(1-d) \cdot d\epsilon}{m + (1-m)d} * S_k \qquad 0 \leq d \leq 1$$

Fig.5 shows the corresponding nonlinear curves for m from 0.2 to 2 with increment 0.2. For $m = 1$, in this case, the FLC becomes a piecewise linear control strategy without nonlinearity.

4. Analysis of Fuzzy Logic Control Law

To illustrate the effects on stability, imposed by various nonlinearities, time responses of a fuzzy control law with and without superimposed nonlinear strategies are compared. First, time response of "critical" linear state feedback law depicts simple harmonic motion . By arranging the fuzzy operators properly, the fuzzy control laws applied all have the same linear control law. However, the nonlinear part of control law induced by fuzzy inference is different for each by varying the "area ratio" m defined in the former section. For "Sup-Min1" , m equals to 1 and the corresponding nonlinear control law is shown in Fig.4. Obviously the system become unstable from initial condition (5,0) as in Fig.6. For m equals to 0.875, 0.5 and 0.125, the nonlinear curves for fuzzy controller are shown in Fig.7, and time responses are shown in Fig.8 respectively. It is interesting that the system becomes stable again when m is set to be 0.875. Continuous decrease of m to 0.5 improves the transient responses. Finally for m=0.125, the control law is more like bang-bang strategy. And the corresponding response, in this case, decays slowly.

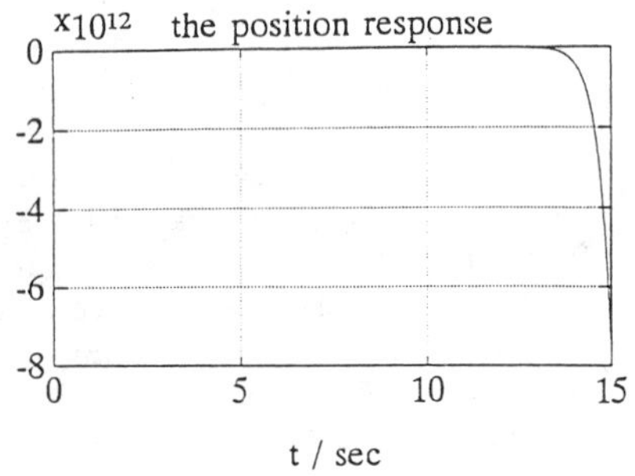

Fig.6 Time Response of COA, Sup-Min and $m = 1$

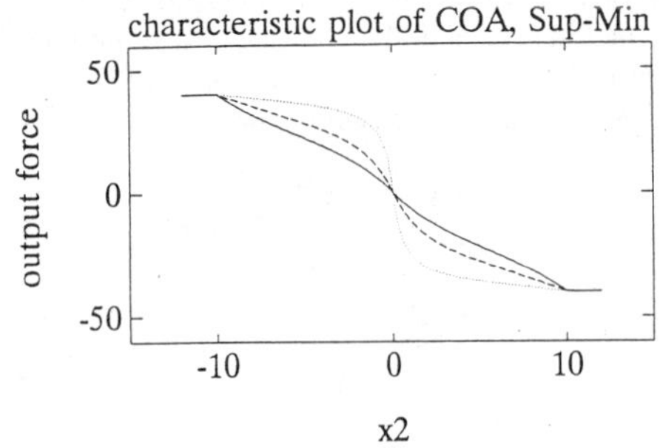

Fig.7 Nonlinearity Curve of Sup-Min COA $m = 0.875, 0.5, 0.125$

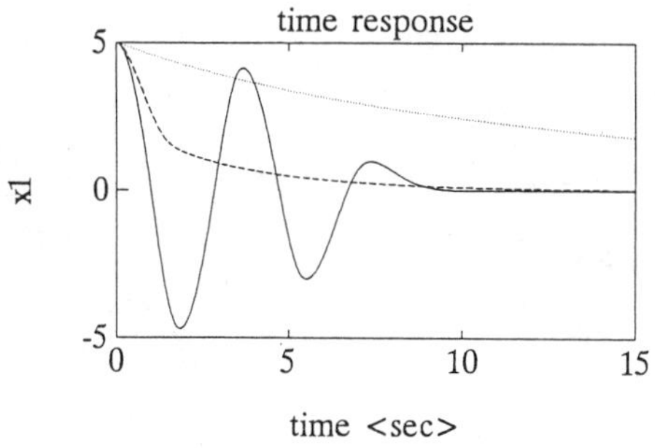

Fig.8 Time Response of Fuzzy Control Law in Fig.9

Stability Analysis

With system and control law formulated, it is assumed that the system is stable if the feedback gain is greater than $-\frac{c}{k}$.Therefore the system will be stable if and only if *" the control law falls side the shaded area except for some finite points of x_2"* in Fig.11 . With input and output membership functions defined in Fig.12; "Sup-Min" compositional rule; and COA defuzzification strategy, the linear part of fuzzy control matches the "critical "linear control law. Together with the nonlinear portion, the resulted fuzzy control law are as the dotted line in Fig.11. x this case, it is clear that. The fuzzy controlled system is locally stable for $-5 < x_2 < 5$; is locally unstable for $-5 < x_2 < 10$ and$-10 < x_2 < -5$.

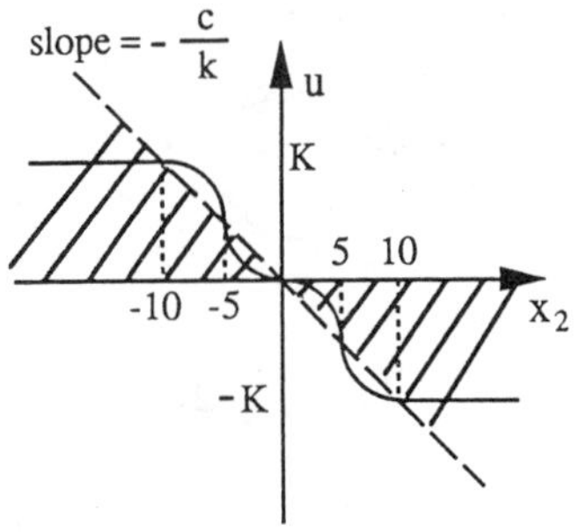

Fig.9 Fuzzy Control Force Induced by Sup-Min, COA.

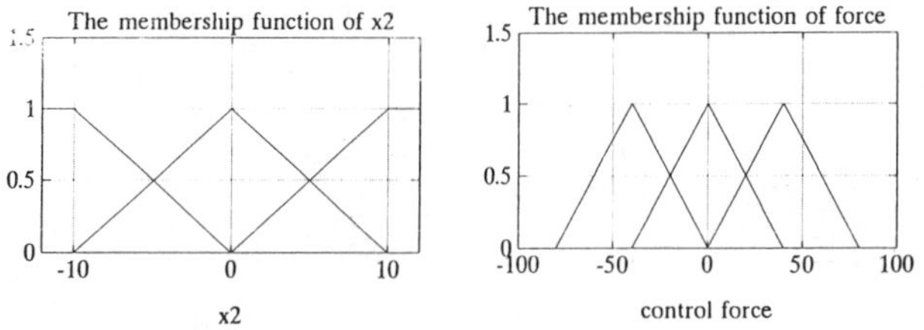

Fig.10 Input, Output Membership Functions.

A contrast can be formulated by using the "Sup-product" compositional rule. With the same fuzzy parameters except inference rule, the results nonlinear control law is depicted in Fig.11.

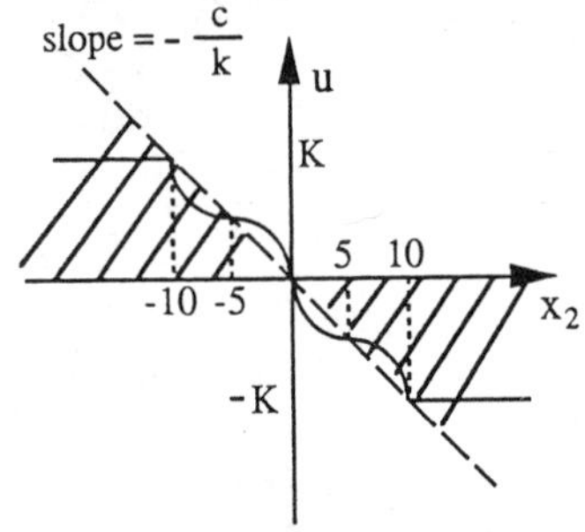

Fig.11 Fuzzy Control Force induced by Sup-Pro COA.

Contrary to the "Sup-Min" case, the small error region $-5 \leq x_2 \leq 5$ becomes unstable and the large error regions, $5 < x_2 \leq 10$, and ,$-10 \leq x_2 < -5$, become stable. The resulted time response is shown in Fig.12. On the other hand, the phase-plane trajectory clearly reveals the existence of a limits cycle. (Fig.13). To decrease the " area ratio" m

continuously from 1 to 0.2 shrinks the small error unstable zone; thus results in smaller limit cycles till the whole region become stable. Fig.14 shows some typical nonlinear control curves. The corresponding time responses are shown in Fig.15.

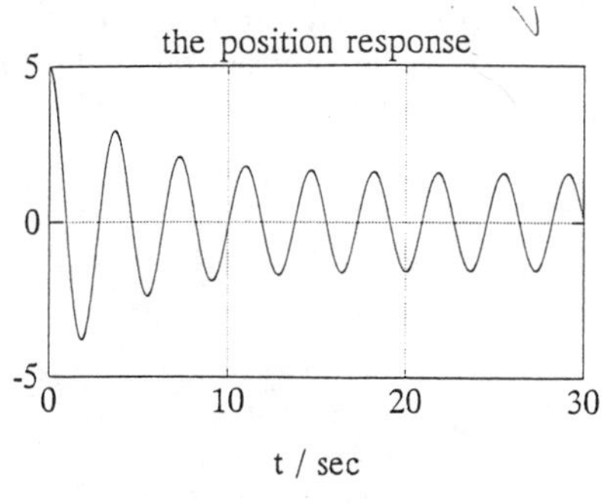

Fig.12 Simulation Results of Sup-Min COA

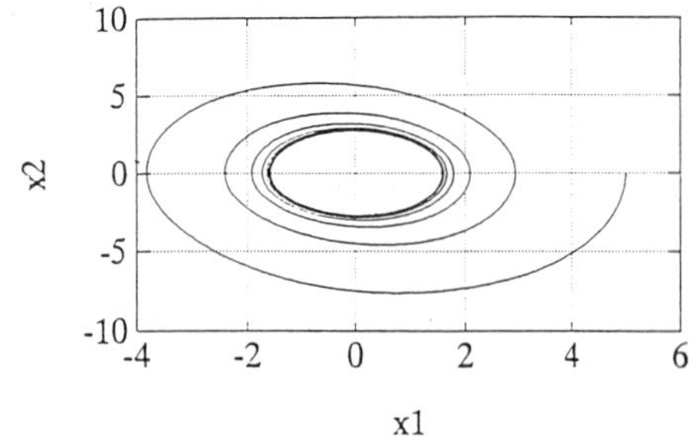

Fig.13 Phase Plane Trajectory of Sup-Pro, COA.

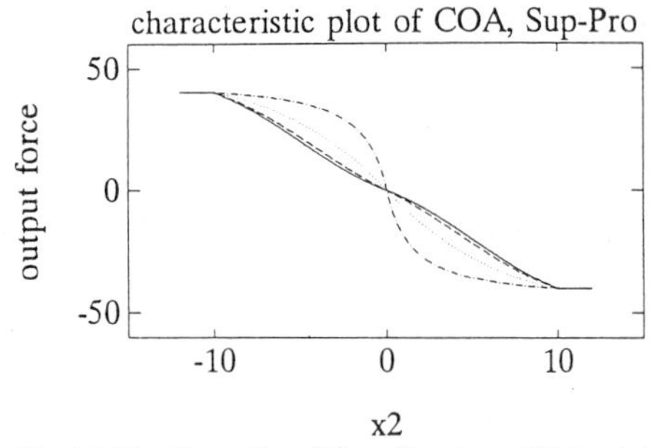

Fig.14 Nonlinearity of Sup-Product COA with different m.

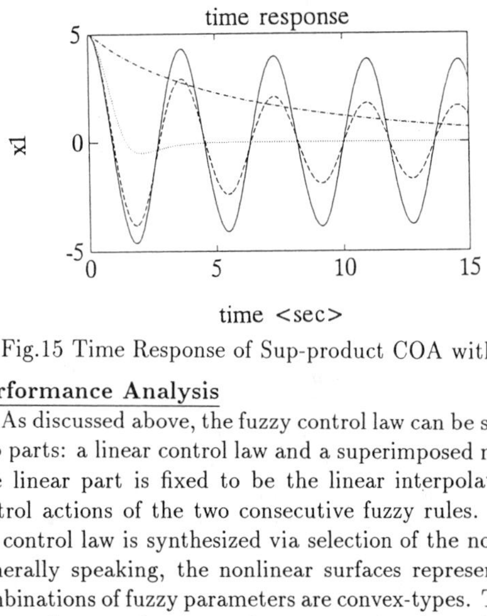

Fig.15 Time Response of Sup-product COA with different m.

Performance Analysis

As discussed above, the fuzzy control law can be separated into two parts: a linear control law and a superimposed nonlinear law. The linear part is fixed to be the linear interpolation between control actions of the two consecutive fuzzy rules. Thus finally the control law is synthesized via selection of the nonlinear part. Generally speaking, the nonlinear surfaces representing various combinations of fuzzy parameters are convex-types. This property reflects the more fuzziness when moves away from the center of a fuzzy rule.

Fig.16. shows the interpolating strategies from thorough confidence on fuzzy rule R_i to fully relying on rule R_{i+1}. The former corresponds to a "zero" slope interpolation and the latter a "∞" slope interpolation scheme. These covers the control strategies

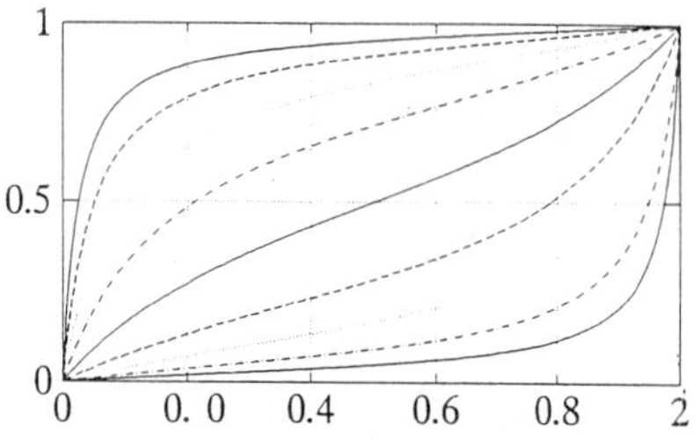

Fig.16 Fuzzy Interpolations.

under the minimum assumptions of "minimum phase" and " finite actuator saturation limit." It is also clear that tuning of the inter-strategy is absurd unless the boundary rules in this case R_i and R_{i+1} are effective control rules; this is undoubtedly reasonable by all means.

Fig.17 shows the fuzzy nonlinear control law of the system described above with m equal to $1, 0.8, 0.6, 0.4, 0.2$, and the corresponding time responses. It is clear that with the superimposed nonlinear part becoming bigger and bigger, the resulted control law become more robust in the Lyapunov sense. The transient responses improves also in the beginning. However, the high-gain feedback of the state variable in this case, " velocity" makes the system heavy damped and become irresponsive when nonlinear part becomes larger.

It is clear that "sup-min" introduces higher gain in small error region; while "sup-product" exceeds in large error region. Defuzzification strategies also reshaped the gain curses. All these characteristics together with design laws in linear design paradigm guides the utilization of different fuzzy control laws under different design requirements and circumstances.

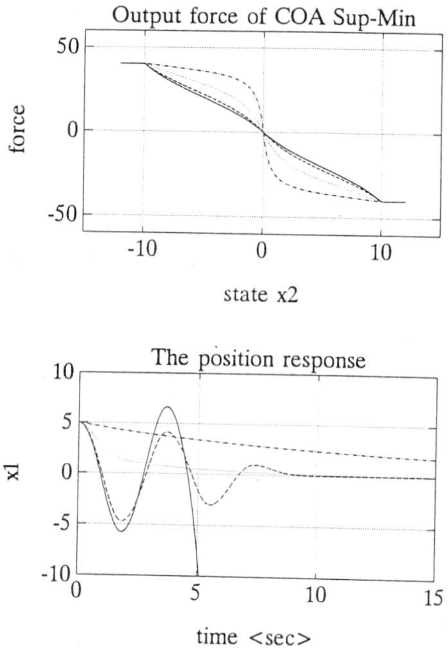

Fig.17 shows the fuzzy nonlinear control law of the system

5. Conclusion

Analytical properties of one-dimensional fuzzy control system is studied in this paper. Therefore synthesis of fuzzy parameters in building a fuzzy logic control system is guided by control system requirements explicitly. Extensions of the results to general fuzzy logic control system are pursued in the future studies.

Reference

[1] **C. C. Lee**,"Fuzzy Logic in Control Systems: Fuzzy Logic Controller, Part I and II," *IEEE Transactions on Systems, Man,And Cybernetics*, Vol.20, No.2. March/April 1990.

[2] **G. Langari** and **M. Tomizuka**, " Analysis and Synthesis of Linguistic Control System," *1990 ASME Winter Annual Meeting.*

[3] **L. I. Larkin**, "A Fuzzy Logic Controller for Aircraft Flight Control," *Industrial Applications of Fuzzy Control, M. Sugeno, Ed. Amsterdam: North-Holland*, 1985, pp. 87-104.

[4] **P. Z. Wang** and **H. M. Zhang**,"Pad-Analysis of Fuzzy Control Stability," *Fuzzy Sets and Systems*, vol. 38, pp. 27-42, 1990.

[5] **H. Ying, W. Siler** and **J. J. Buckley**,"Fuzzy Control Theory: A Nonlinear Case," *Automatica*, 1990.

Proceedings of the
American Control Conference
San Francisco, California • June 1993

On the Tuning of Nonlinear Model Predictive Control Algorithms

Emad Ali and Evanghelos Zafiriou*

Department of Chemical Engineering and Institute for Systems Research
University of Maryland, College Park, MD 20742

Abstract

Nonlinear Model Predictive Controllers determine appropriate control actions by solving an on-line optimization problem. A nonlinear process model is utilized for on-line prediction, making such algorithms particularly appropriate for the control of chemical reactors. The algorithm presented in this paper incorporates an Extended Kalman Filter, which allows operations around unstable steady-state points. The paper proposes a formalization of the procedure for tuning the several parameters of the control algorithm. This is accomplished by specifying time-domain performance criteria and using an interactive multi-objective optimization package off-line to determine parameter values that satisfy these criteria. A reactor example is used to demonstrate the effectiveness of the proposed on-line algorithm and off-line tuning procedure.

1. Introduction

In order to meet the increasing needs of designing control systems that take into account the nonlinear process characteristics, a number of Model Predictive Control (MPC) algorithms have emerged in the last decade, which directly utilize nonlinear models for on-line prediction. A description of various MPC algorithms is given in a review paper by Bequette [2].

The performance may deteriorate in the presence of model-plant mismatch. One attempt to address this issue is to couple the NLMPC algorithm with an optimization-based parameter estimation method as reported by Wright *et al.* [19], Li and Biegler [12], and Eaton and Rawlings [5]. Another approach is the combined parameter and state estimation via nonlinear programming. This algorithm is studied by Jang *et al.* [10] and Sistu and Bequette [3]. An alternative way to compensate for the impact of model uncertainty is by augmenting the controller with a state estimator by Kalman Filtering as proposed by Ricker [16] for linear MPC. This approach was successfully extended by Gattu and Zafiriou [7] to Nonlinear Quadratic Dynamic Matrix Control [6] for disturbance rejection of open-loop unstable processes. In this study, we show that it is advantageous to couple our NLMPC algorithm with on-line Extended Kalman Filter (EKF).

*Author to whom correspondence should be addressed. E-mail: zafiriou@src.umd.edu

Li *et al.* [13], and Gattu and Zafiriou [8] used the concept of contraction mapping to establish sufficient closed-loop stability conditions for their algorithms for the case of open-loop stable plants. These conditions, however, are not useful from a practical point of view, since they are usually conservative [8]. The situation is much more complicated when constraints are included in the on-line optimization. For linear process dynamics, Zafiriou and Marchal [20] proved the presence of hard constraints in the MPC algorithm can lead to instability, even though the unconstrained algorithm may be stable.

The difficulties in developing theoretical conditions that guarantee stability and good performance of NLMPC, especially in the presence of disturbances, model uncertainty, and output constraints, lead designers to trial-and-error tuning of the NLMPC parameters. The trade-off problem, however, for several competing objectives can be quite complex.

This paper attempts a formalization of what is currently a trial-and-error procedure for NLMPC parameter tuning. The real-valued parameters of the algorithm are determined by an off-line optimization. While the integer parameters such as the prediction horizon and the control horizon are found by grid search. The objective of the off-line optimization is to ensure that certain performance specifications, e.g., required speed of response and limited overshoot, are satisfied in the presence of modeling error and disturbances that lie within certain maximum bounds. The off-line problem is solved by an interactive multi-objective optimization tool called CONSOLE, developed by Tits *et al.* [18].

2. NLMPC Algorithm

On-line Optimization

The algorithm finds a sequence of M future manipulated variables by minimizing on-line an objective function based on the desired output trajectories over a prediction horizon P. After the optimization, the first element of this future sequence is implemented. Then at the next sampling time, after a new measurement has been obtained, a new optimization is carried out. The objective function is as follows:

$$\min_{u(t_k),\ldots,u(t_{k+M-1})} \sum_{l=1}^{P} \| \Gamma e(t_{k+l}) \|^2 + \sum_{l=1}^{M} \| D\Delta u(t_{k+l-1}) \|^2 \quad (1)$$

where k denotes the current sampling point, $t_i = iT$, with T the sampling time, and $\| \cdot \|$ the Euclidean vector norm. The predicted error is defined as $e(t_{k+l}) = y(t_{k+l}) - r(t_{k+l}) + d(t_{k+l})$, where r is the setpoint, y is the model output, and d is the deviation of the process measurement from the model output. Since future measurements are not known, the disturbance $d(t_{k+l})$, for $l = 1, \ldots, P$, is considered constant in the future and equal to $d(t_k)$. The inputs u are constant between sampling points. Δu indicates the change in manipulated inputs ($\Delta u(t_{k+l}) = u(t_{k+l}) - u(t_{k+l-1})$). The inputs are assumed constant after $k + M - 1$, i.e., $\Delta u(t_{k+i}) = 0, i > M$. Γ and D are the diagonal matrices of weights on the outputs and the change of manipulated variables respectively. Constraints on both u and Δu are also included in the optimization problem. The optimization is carried out with the NPSOL software, written by Gill *et al.* [9], which uses a Successive Quadratic Programming algorithm.

The output prediction is obtained via numerical integration of the nonlinear model differential equations for specified inputs, using the software package DASSL [15]. Incorporation of state estimation in the output prediction to compensate for model-plant mismatch and disturbances is discussed in the following section.

State Estimation

State reseting is achieved with an Extended Kalman Filter (EKF) which allows an *additive* state correction formulation. The correction term is then used to reset not only the current state variables, but also the state variables at each future sampling point during the prediction. The construction of the EKF for nonlinear models is discussed in Lewis [11]. Here we extend the calculational procedure of the filter gain [11] to evaluate its steady state value. The correction term is then equal to the product of the calculated steady state filter gain and the deviation of the current predicted output from its actual measured value.

Let the model equations be represented by:

$$\dot{x} = f(x, u, t) + w \quad (2)$$

$$y = h(x) + v \quad (3)$$

where w~(0,Q) and v~(0,R) are white Gaussian noise processes assumed to be independent of each other, and to characterize the unmeasured disturbances and the measurement noise respectively. Q and R are the respective covariances of w and v and they are assumed to be diagonal matrices of the form $Q = q^2 I$ and $R = r^2 I$. In the absence of accurate knowledge of the disturbance and noise characteristics, we further simplify the filter tuning method. Defining $\sigma^2 = q^2/r^2$ and letting $r^2 = 1.0$ will uniquely determine the Kalman Filter gain and simplify its tuning to determining only one parameter [17].

The model output prediction is described by the following steps:

step 1: Initialization. *Known at the current sampling time, k, are the plant measurement* $\tilde{y}(t_k)$*, the model state vector* $x(t_k)$*, and the manipulated variable vector* $u(t_{k-1})$*. Set* $P_k = I$.

step 2: Linearization. *Obtain the following jacobians:*

$$A_k = \nabla_x f(x, u, t) \mid_{x=x(t_k), u=u(t_{k-1}), t=t_k} \quad (4)$$

$$H_k = \nabla_x h(x) \mid_{x=(t_k)} \quad (5)$$

step 3: Time update. *Integrate numerically the error covariance equation:*

$$\dot{P}(t) = A_k P(t) + P(t) A_k^T + Q \quad (6)$$

for one sampling interval using DASSL, with initial condition P_k*. Define the solution as* $\bar{P}_k$*.*

step 4: Measurement update. *Compute the Kalman Gain:*

$$K_k = \bar{P}_k H_k^T [H_k \bar{P}_k H_k^T + R]^{-1} \quad (7)$$

and update the error covariance:

$$P_k = [I - K_k H_k] \bar{P}_k \quad (8)$$

Repeat steps 3 and 4 till steady state value of P_k *is reached.*

step 5: Correction factor. *Compute the Kalman Filter correction factor :*

$$F_k = K_k[\tilde{y}_k - h(x(t_k))] \quad (9)$$

step 6: Output prediction. *Set* $\hat{x}(t_k) = x(t_k) + F_k$ *and integrate the state equation over one sampling time to get* $x(t_{k+1})$*, then reset the value of the new state to* $\hat{x}(t_k)$ *by adding* F_k*, and evaluate the output* $y(t_{k+1}) = h(\hat{x}(t_{k+1}))$*. Repeat the last step over the prediction horizon P.*

3. Tuning Procedure

This section formulates the tuning parameter selection problem as an off-line optimization carried out with the interactive CONSOLE software. This is a flexible formulation that allows one to use several types of performance criteria. The off-line optimization can, e.g., determine the tuning parameter values that make the closed-loop response stay within a preset constraint envelope over defined time domain as shown in Fig. 1. The envelope is used to represent various performance objectives. For example, constraints can be used to limit overshoot or undershoot, and/or maintain desired response speed. The values of constraints can be specified as functions of the setpoint change values, e.g., proportional to them. Alternatively one could choose to directly minimize the maximum possible overshoot [21].

The procedure can be described by the loop shown in Fig. 2. The desired performance specifications, e.g., the

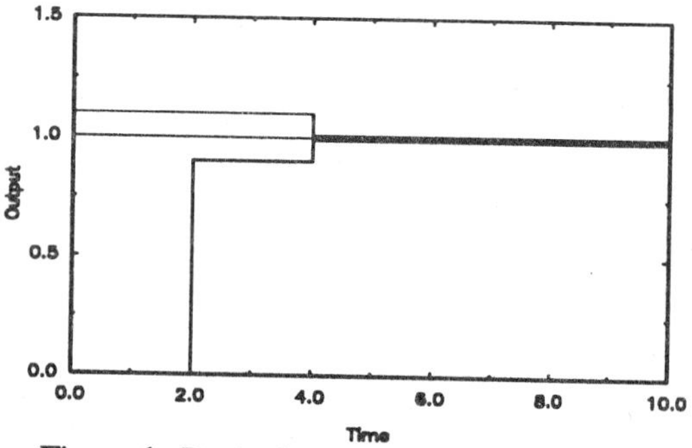

Figure 1: Desired response profile for setpoint tracking

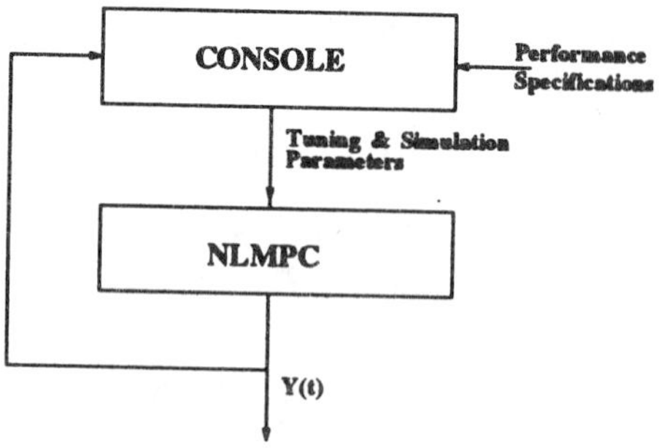

Figure 2: Tuning procedure

envelope of Fig. 1 are given to CONSOLE. Also possible setpoint changes, disturbances, model parameter errors etc, can be specified. By discretizing the range of possible values of these quantities one can define multiple objectives or constraints for CONSOLE, each of which corresponds to a particular set of values, and require that the specified performance criteria be satisfied or optimized. CONSOLE will then find suitable tuning parameter values that force every NLMPC response obtained for different discretized value of modeling error, setpoints, or disturbances to lie within the maximum bounds.

During the optimization carried out by CONSOLE, simulations of the closed-loop control system under NLMPC have to be run repeatedly for different tuning parameters, setpoints, disturbances, as well as model and plant. CONSOLE determines the next set of values to be tried, based on optimization theory, instead of trial-and-error. An added feature of CONSOLE is its interactive nature, which allows the designer to specify "good" and "bad" values for each performance constraint specification and interactively change them if CONSOLE can not find tuning parameter values to satisfy them. More detailed discussion is given in Nye and Tits [14].

It should be emphasized that CONSOLE treats all design variables as continuous real variables. Since the NLMPC algorithm uses only integer values for M and P, the optimal M and P are determined, in this paper, by performing a grid search. For each grid point (i.e., each fixed values of M and P) CONSOLE is used to determine the real-valued parameters. Note, also, that beyond the usual MPC tuning parameter, the sampling time (T), and the covariance ratio (σ) can also be used as such parameters.

4. Illustration

A catalytic CSTR example is studied. In all simulations, the effect of the upper and lower performance constraints are balanced by equating the difference between their "good" and "bad" values. In this case CONSOLE will try to satisfy both bounds equally.

For each off-line optimization solved with CONSOLE we report the total number of NLMPC simulations. Several NLMPC simulations (corresponding to different values of disturbances) are required every time that a new point in the variable space (NLMPC tuning parameter space) has to be tried. This includes simulations made for numerical derivative computations. CONSOLE uses a forward difference formula for each parameter. The number of total NLMPC simulations is provided as an alternative to CPU time. The type of software that one uses for solving the on-line NLP has a significant effect on CPU time for each simulation.

The example is taken from the paper by Brengel and Seider [4]. An exothermic catalytic reaction in the form of $A + B \rightarrow P$ is taking place. The reactor model is:

$$\dot{x}_1 = u_1 + u_2 - 0.2x_1^{0.5} \tag{10}$$

$$\dot{x}_2 = \frac{(C_{b1} - x_2)u_1}{x_1} + \frac{(C_{b2} - x_2)u_2}{x_1} - \frac{k_1 x_2}{(1 + k_2 x_2)^2} \tag{11}$$

The process outputs are $y_1 = x_1$ (tank level), and $y_2 = x_2$ (concentration of B in the reactor). C_{b1}, C_{b2} are the concentrations in the inlet feeds of condensed and dilute B. The corresponding flow rates u_1 and u_2 are the manipulated variables. The model parameter values are $k_1 = k_2 = 1$, $C_{b1} = 24.9$, and $C_{b2} = 0.1$.

The control goal is to move the process from initial stable steady state conditions of $u_1 = u_2 = 1$, $y_1 = 40$, and $y_2 = 0.4$, to a new unstable steady state at $y_1 = 100$ and $y_2 = 2.787$ by manipulating u_1, and u_2. This step change test is carried out in the presence of disturbance on the inlet concentration C_{b1}, and physical constraints on the manipulated variables between 0 and 10. For this situation the concentration response suffers from excessive overshoot and slow disturbance rejection as reported by Brengel and Seider.

Tuning of the NLMPC parameters is necessary to reduce the overshoot, reject the disturbance, and maintain proper speed of the response. In order to impose these desired properties with CONSOLE, they are translated into transient upper and lower bounds on the response of the process outputs y_1 and y_2. For y_2 tight upper bounds of 2.86 and 2.8 for the intervals 0-10 and 10-30 respectively are employed to prevent overshoot. Lower bounds of 2.6 and 2.73 for the intervals 5-10 and 10-30 respectively are also imposed to avoid sluggishness and ensure convergence of the response to its final steady state. For y_1 a constant upper bound of 101 and a lower bound of 99 from time

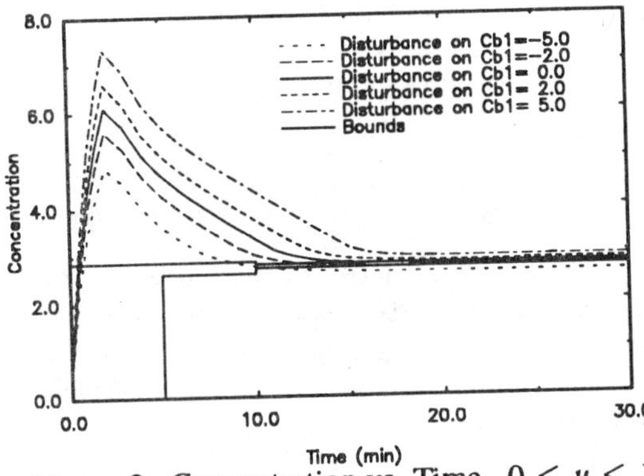

Figure 3: Concentration vs. Time. $0 \leq u \leq 10$, $M = 1$, $P = 3$, $\sigma = 0$, D =diag[0,0], Γ =diag[1,1].

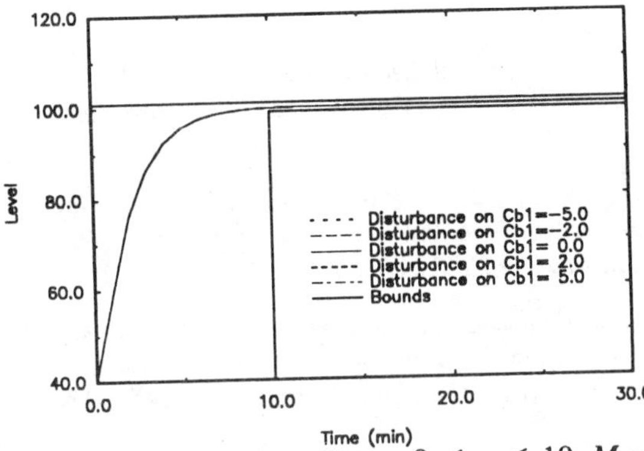

Figure 4: Level vs. Time. $0 \leq u \leq 10$, $M = 1$, $P = 3$, $\sigma = 0$, D =diag[0,0], Γ =diag[1,1].

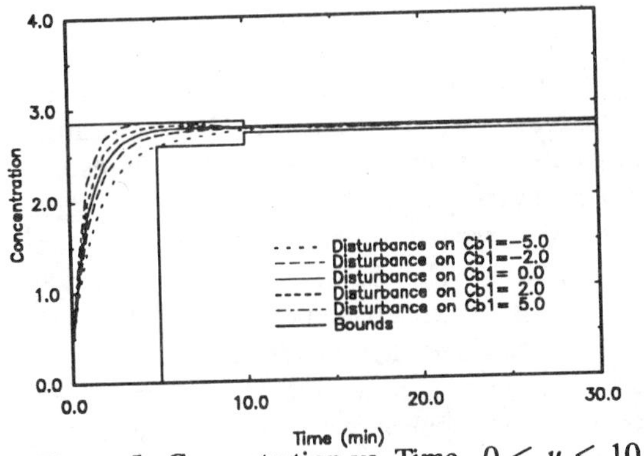

Figure 5: Concentration vs. Time. $0 \leq u \leq 10$, $M = 1$, $P = 3$, $\sigma = 0.087$, D =diag[15.4,0], Γ =diag[1,108.6].

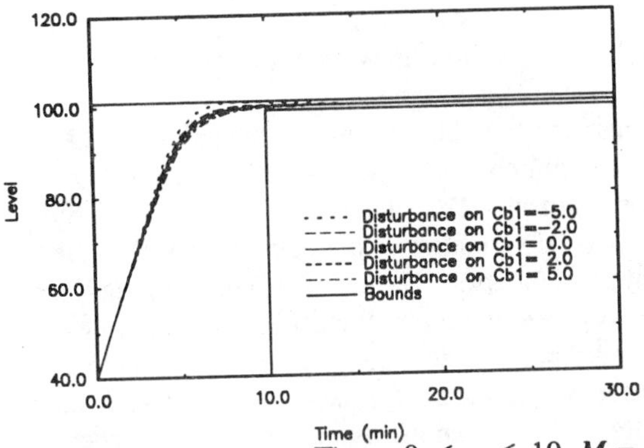

Figure 6: Level vs. Time. $0 \leq u \leq 10$, $M = 1$, $P = 3$, $\sigma = 0.087$, D =diag[15.4,0], Γ =diag[1,108.6].

10 to 30 were used to avoid performance degradation due to penalty weight variation. The performance bounds are represented by the solid lines in Figures 3 to 6.

Grid search along with CONSOLE is used to determine the optimal values of M, P, σ, D, and the weight on the second output (Γ_2) that simultaneously force the responses of the setpoint change under three different values of disturbances to fulfill the performance constraints. In particular step disturbances of magnitude 5.0, 0, and -5.0 on C_{b1} were used. The results of this search, which uses a sampling time of $1min$, are summarized in Table 1. At each fixed value of M and P, The parameters σ, D, and Γ_2 in Table 1 are the final values found by runing CONSOLE starting with initial values of 0.0, diag[0,0], and 1.0 respectively. The table indicates whether the three responses at the obtained parameter values satisfy the bounds or not. In case they are not, the corresponding performance is then the best achievable one for that case. The table also shows the total required NLMPC simulations which have been used for each grid point.

For small values of P the response is so aggressive that CONSOLE was not able to move from the initial values of the tuning parameters. For large values of M and P the response of y_1 is slower and further decrease of the overshoot was not possible because it forces the response to violate the lower bounds. Only at $M = 1$ and $P = 3$ optimal tuning parameters that successfully satisfy the desired objectives were found. Figures 3 and 4 show the setpoint responses of y_1 and y_2 at $M = 1$, $P = 3$, and initial values of the tuning parameters. While Figures 5 and 6 show the responses for the same values of M and P but at the final values of the tuning parameters. The figures also show the responses at additional disturbances values of +2.0 and -2.0. Since this system has slow dynamics it takes longer time to settle down to its final steady state value which would be clear if longer simulation time was used in the figures. Finally one should note that the NLMPC simulations required by CONSOLE would have been reduced by about one third, if the case of zero disturbance on C_{b1} was not used in CONSOLE.

Table 1.

M=1

P	Γ_2	σ	D [diag]	B	N
1	1.0	0.0	[0,0]	No	12
2	1.9	4.0e-9	[0,0]	No	12
3	108.6	0.087	[15.46,0]	Yes	147
4	18.44	0.097	[0,0]	No	129
5	168.6	0.109	[1.8,5.3]	No	363
6	18.83	0.134	[1.85,13.2]	No	255
7	9.88	0.157	[21.6,13.3]	No	328

B=Bounds satisfied, N=NLMPC simulations

5. Discussion

This paper considered the question of tuning a nonlinear Model Predictive Control algorithm. A differential equation model is assumed for the process and an Extended Kalman Filter is incorporated to allow stable operation around open-loop unstable steady state points and better disturbance rejection. The use of the software package CONSOLE proved very effective in obtaining solutions to an off-line optimization problem used to tune the NLMPC parameters. One can expect the technique to work even more efficiently when applied to problems in which simulations of MPC algorithms are less computationally demanding, as, for example, the case of discrete nonlinear models, link neural networks, or linear models. Although in the case of linear models theoretical design techniques are available, the time-domain orientation of this approach may be preferable to a designer.

The integer nature of the control (M) and prediction (P) horizons create difficulties for the off-line optimization and require a grid search. The situation can be improved by treating P as a real variable by a simple modification of the on-line objective function. The use of differential equation model allows prediction at non-integer P. For cases where the model prediction is not computationally demanding, an alternative is to select a large fixed P. The formulation for non-integer P is given in Ali and Zafiriou [1], where also certain stability questions are discussed in the context of satisfying the off-line time domain specification.

Acknowledgements

Support for this project is provided by the National Science Foundation (PYI grant CTS-9057292), the Institute for Systems Research, and grants from Shell and Texaco. The authors are grateful to Dr. Jian Zhou and Prof. André Tits for making the CONSOLE software available, and for their help in using it.

References

[1] Ali, E., and Zafiriou, E., "Optimization-Based Tuning of Nonlinear Model Predictive Control with State Estimation", submitted to the J. of Process Control, 1993.

[2] Bequette, B. W. "Nonlinear Control of Chemical Processes- A Review", *Ind. & Eng. Chem. Res.*, **30**, 1391-1413, 1991.

[3] Sistu, P. B., and Bequette, B. W. "Nonlinear Predictive Control of Uncertain Processes: Application to a CSTR", *AICHE J.*, **37**, 1711-1723, 1991.

[4] Brengel, D. D., and Seider, W. D. "Multistep Nonlinear Predictive Controller", *Ind. & Eng. Chem. Res.*, **28**, 1812-1822, 1989.

[5] Eaton, J. W., and Rawlings, J. B. "Feedback Control of Chemical Processes Using On-line Optimization Techniques", *Comp. and Chem. Eng.*, **14**, 469-479, 1990.

[6] Garcia, C. E. "Quadratic Dynamic Matrix Control of Nonlinear Processes: An Application to a Batch Reaction Process", *AICHE ann. mtg.*, San Francisco, CA, 1984.

[7] Gattu, G., and Zafiriou, E. "Nonlinear Quadratic Dynamic Matrix Control with State Estimation", *Ind. & Eng. Chem. Res.*, **31**, 1096-1104, 1992.

[8] Gattu, G., and Zafiriou, E. "On the Stability of Nonlinear Quadratic Dynamic Matrix Control", In *IFAC/DYCORD+ '92 Preprints*, College Park, MD, USA, 303-308, 1992.

[9] Gill, P. E., Murray, W., Sauders, M. A., and Wright, M. H., "User's Guide for NPSOL (version 4.0): A Fortran Program for Nonlinear Programming", Technical Report SOL 86-2, Department of Operations Research, Stanford University, 1986.

[10] Jang, S. S., Joseph, B., and Mukai, H. "Control of Constrained Multivariable Nonlinear Process Using Two-Phase Approach", *Ind. & Eng. Chem. Res.*, **26**, 2106-2114, 1987.

[11] Lewis, F. L., "Optimal Estimation with Introduction to Stochastic Control Theory", Wiley and Sons, New York, 1986, 260.

[12] Li, W. C., and Biegler, L. T. "Newton-Type Controllers for Constrained Nonlinear Processes with Uncertainity", *Ind. & Eng. Chem. Res.*, **29**,1647-1657, 1990.

[13] Li, W. C., Biegler, L. T., Economou, C. G., and Morari, M., "A Constrained Pseudo-Newton Control Strategy for Nonlinear Systems", *Comp. and Chem. Eng.*, **14**, 451-468, 1990.

[14] Nye, W. T., and Tits, A. L., "An Application-Oriented, Optimization-based Methodology for Interactive Design of Engineering Systems", *Int. J. Cont.*, **43**, 1693-1721, 1986.

[15] Petzold, L. R., "A Description of DASSL: A Differential-Algebraic System Solver", in *Scientific Computing*, R. S. Stepleman, Ed., North-Holand 1983.

[16] Ricker, N. L. "Model Predictive Control with State Estimation", *Ind. & Eng. Chem. Res.*, **29**, 374-382, 1990.

[17] Hamilton, J. C., Seborg, D. E., and Fisher, D. G. "An Experimental Evaluation of Kalman Filtering", *AICHE J.*, **19**, 901-908, 1973.

[18] Tits, A. L., Fan, M. K., Zhou, J., Wang, L., and Koninckx, J., "Console User's Manual (version 1.1)", System Research Center, University of Maryland, Technical Report SRC-TR 87-212r2, College Park, MD, 1990.

[19] Wright, G. T., Breedijk, T. B., and Edgar, T. F., "On-line Parameter Estimation and Adaptation in Nonlinear Model-Based Control", American Control Conference, Boston, MA, 2782-2787, 1991.

[20] Zafiriou, E., and Marchal, A. L. "Stability of SISO Quadratic Dynamic Matrix Control with Hard Output Constraints", *AICHE J.*, **37**, 1550-1560, 1991.

[21] Zhou, J., "Fast, Globally Convergent Optimization Algorithms, with Application to Engineering System Design", *Ph.D. Dissertation*, Electrical Engineering Department, University of Maryland, College Park, MD, USA, 1992.

Proceedings of the
American Control Conference
San Francisco, California • June 1993

MODEL PREDICTIVE CONTROL FOR OPEN LOOP UNSTABLE PROCESS

Kent Z. Qi, D. Grant Fisher [1]
Department of Chemical Engineering
University of Alberta
Edmonton, Alberta, Canada T6G 2G6

Abstract

The discrete models used in Predictive Controllers are usually in non-parametric step response or parametric ARMA form. This paper shows how both models can be combined into a state space formulation that will handle both stable and unstable processes. A feedback system based on the use of an observer with user specified poles is also developed which shows that control can be maintained even in the presence of model process mismatch.

1 Introduction

Over the past decade, the concept of Long Range Predictive Control (LRPC) has been widely accepted and refined by people in both industry and academia. The generic term "Model Predictive Control" covers the large MPC family which includes MPHC (Richalet et al., 1978), DMC (Cutler and Ramaker, 1980), IMC (Garcia and Morari, 1982), MAC (Rouhani and Mehra, 1982), QDMC (Garcia and Morshedi, 1984), MOCCA (Sripada and Fisher, 1985), etc. These control algorithms differ in detail but are usually formulated using a non-parametric, step response model to describe the process. The step response model representation requires very little a prior information (*e.g.* the dynamic order of the process) and the variables usually have intuitive interpretations. One disadvantage of using step response models is that they require a large number of model coefficients.

Another class of LRPC systems includes adaptive control schemes such as Generalized Predictive Control (GPC) (Clarke *et al.*, 1987). Even though the philosophy behind MPC and GPC is similar, there are significant differences between the models used for predicting the future output trajectory. GPC uses a parametric ARMA representation which has a more compact mathematical form than step response models.

MPC typically uses an explicit step response model and hence only past control inputs are required in the output prediction equations. The infinite dimension of past control action requires that truncation be used in MPC algorithms. The prediction error resulting from truncation may result in 'internal instability' problems (Morari and Lee, 1991). In GPC, an ARMA model is used to calculate the prediction based on both past output measurements and past control actions. Semi-implicit in nature, the ARMA model has a finite order and can handle stable or unstable open-loop poles and zeros.

The state space, or recursive, formulation of MPC put forwarded by Li *et al.*(1989) is in an observable and controllable canonical form. Although it is non-minimal in order, it provides a direct link between step response and state space models and allows the use of modern control theory. Depending on how the open-loop step response behaves after the initial transient dynamics have decayed, it can be truncated and represented by a state space formula for open-loop stable processes(Li *et al.*, 1989) and integrating systems(Morari and Lee, 1991). But conventional MPC schemes can not handle general open-loop unstable processes.

This paper extends the state space formulation of MPC to handle open loop unstable processes. A new structure is proposed which combines a step response model and an ARMA model into a state space formulation. It keeps the advantages of using the non-parametric model to describe the initial process dynamics but uses an auto regressive formula to represent the final or unstable portion of the output response. The state space model can be used for system analysis or the design of components such as observers, controllers etc.

2 Non-Parametric Model Prediction

The output of a general process can be described by a set of step response data as

$$\{a_j,\ j = 1, 2, \ldots\}$$

which is the discrete response of the open-loop process to a unit step input.

Obviously, the step response data includes the effects of both stable and unstable poles. If there is no RHP pole, the step response can be truncated and defined as a finite impulse response(FIR) model. Otherwise, it is an infinite impulse response(IIR) model.

The effect of the stable poles will eventually decay to zero provided the number of step response points (*i.e.* N) is large enough. The rest of the step response points, *i.e.* $\{a_{N+k}, k = 1, 2, \ldots,\}$, therefore reflect the process steady state or the effects of the unstable poles. The final part of the step response ($k > 0$) may behave as a:

- stable process, a_{N+k} =constant.
- 1st order integrating process, Δa_{N+k} =constant.
- integrating process of order i, $\Delta^i a_{N+k}$ =constant.
- continuously oscillating process, *i.e.* pure imaginary poles.
- exponentially unstable process, *i.e.* real RHP poles.
- oscillatory unstable process, *i.e.* complex RHP poles.

Based on the superposition principle of linear systems, the model prediction using discrete step response data is formulated in convolution form and can be expressed as an infinite impulse response (IIR) model of the form:

$$\begin{aligned} Y(k+i \mid k+i) &= \sum_{j=1}^{\infty} a_j \Delta u(k+i-j) \\ &= \sum_{j=1}^{i} a_j \Delta u(k+i-j) + \sum_{j=i+1}^{\infty} a_j \Delta u(k+i-j) \\ &= \sum_{j=1}^{i} a_j \Delta u(k+i-j) + Y_m^*(k+i \mid k) \qquad (1) \\ i &= 0, 1, 2, \ldots \end{aligned}$$

where $\{Y_m^*(k+i \mid k), i = 0, 1, 2, \ldots\}$ is the contribution to the future output trajectory due to all past control actions where k represents the current time interval.

[1] Author to whom correspondence should be directed

Assume N is the number of points selected for the truncated IIR model. For the first (*N-1*) terms of the prediction $Y_m^*(k+i \mid k)$, the following recursive relations (Li *et al.*) add the effect of the latest control action, $\Delta u(k-1)$, to the known prediction from time $(k-1)$.
For $i = 0, 1, 2, \ldots, N-1$

$$Y_m^*(k+i \mid k) = Y_m^*(k+i \mid k-1) + a_{i+1}\Delta u(k-1) \quad (2)$$

For $i = N$,

$$Y_m^*(k+N \mid k) = Y_m^*[(k-1)+(N+1) \mid k-1] + a_{N+1}\Delta u(k-1) \quad (3)$$

where

$$\begin{aligned} Y_m^*[(k-1) &+ (N+1) \mid k-1] \\ &= a_{N+2}\Delta u(k-1) + a_{N+3}\Delta u(k-2) + \ldots \quad (4) \\ Y_m^*[(k-1) &+ (N) \mid k-1] \\ &= a_{N+1}\Delta u(k-1) + a_{N+2}\Delta u(k-2) + \ldots \quad (5) \\ Y_m^*[(k-1) &+ (N-1) \mid k-1] \\ &= a_N\Delta u(k-1) + a_{N+1}\Delta u(k-2) + \ldots \quad (6) \\ &\vdots \end{aligned}$$

In Equations (4), (5) and (6), if a recursive or auto regressive relation can be found among the step response data $\{a_{N+i}, i = 1, 2, \ldots\}$, *i.e.* after the initial stable dynamics have decayed, then this recursive relationship can be used in the prediction of the corresponding output trajectory at time $k-1$, *i.e.* $\{Y_m^*(k-i+N \mid k-1), i = 0, 1, 2, \ldots\}$. The output prediction at the current time interval (*e.g.* *k*) in Equation (3) can be obtained by calculating recursively based on the prediction from last time interval (*e.g.* *k-1*). The derivation of such a recursive relationship is presented in the next section.

3 ARMA Formulation of The Step Response Data

A general process in the Laplace domain can be represented as

$$Y(s) = G_s(s)G_u(s)U(s)$$

where $G_s(s)$ includes all the zeros and stable poles, $G_u(s)$ includes only the unstable poles. The process output Y, and the input U, are perturbation variables with initial conditions equal to zero.

Define an intermediate variable $P(s)$ with

$$P(s) = s\,G_s(s)U(s)$$

For a unit step input, $U(s) = \frac{1}{s}$ and

$$P(s) = G_s(s)s\frac{1}{s} = G_s(s)$$

so that

$$Y(s) = \frac{G_u(s)}{s}P(s)$$

Since $P(s) = G_s(s)$ has all its poles located in the LHP, the final value theorem can be applied and

$$\lim_{t\to\infty} p(t) = \lim_{s\to 0} s\,P(s) = 0$$

i.e. for large N, $k \geq 0$

$$p(N+k) = 0 \quad (7)$$

Then the sampled step response coefficient is

$$a_{N+k} = \mathcal{Z}(\frac{G_u(s)}{s})p(N+k) \quad (8)$$

Define

$$\mathcal{Z}(\frac{G_u(s)}{s}) = \frac{N(z^{-1})}{1 - S(z^{-1})z^{-1}} \quad (9)$$

where $S(z^{-1})$ is a n_s order polynomial and can be described as

$$S(z^{-1}) = s_0 + s_1 z^{-1} + \ldots + s_{n_s}z^{n_s} \quad (10)$$

Then from (8) and (9)

$$a_{N+k} = \frac{N(z^{-1})}{1 - S(z^{-1})z^{-1}}p(N+k) \quad (11)$$

and

$$(1 - S(z^{-1})z^{-1})a_{N+k} = N(z^{-1})p(N+k) \quad (12)$$

Combining Equation (7) and Equation (12) gives a recursive relationship for the step response coefficients after time $N+k$ as:

$$a_{N+k} = S(z^{-1})a_{N+k-1} \quad (13)$$

Then an AR model can be obtained by substituting Equation (4) into (3) and noting the obvious relationship between the step response coefficients

$$\begin{aligned} Y_m^*(k+N \mid k) &= S(z^{-1})\,Y_m^*[(k-1)+N \mid k-1] \\ &\quad + a_{N+1}\Delta u(k-1) \quad (14) \\ k &= 1, 2, \ldots \end{aligned}$$

The polynomial $S(z^{-1})$ is defined in Equation (9) and will be illustrated later.

4 State Space Formulation of MPC

Define the state space variables as

$$\begin{aligned} X(k) &= [Y_m^*(k \mid k)\; Y_m^*(k+1 \mid k)\; \cdots\; Y_m^*(k+N \mid k)]^T \\ X(k-1) &= [Y_m^*(k-1 \mid k-1)\; Y_m^*(k \mid k-1)\; \cdots \\ &\quad Y_m^*(k+N-1 \mid k-1)]^T \quad (15) \end{aligned}$$

The state space form of MPC can then be written as:

$$\begin{aligned} X(k) &= \Phi\,X(k-1) + \theta\,\Delta u(k-1) \\ Y(k) &= H\,X(k) \end{aligned} \quad (16)$$

which has the same structure form as suggested by Li *et al.* except for the last row of Φ and

$$\Phi = \begin{bmatrix} 0 & 1 & 0 & \cdots & 0 & 0 & \cdots & 0 & 0 \\ 0 & 0 & 1 & \cdots & 0 & 0 & \cdots & 0 & 0 \\ \vdots & \vdots & \vdots & \ddots & \vdots & \vdots & \ddots & \vdots & \vdots \\ 0 & 0 & 0 & \cdots & 0 & 0 & \cdots & 0 & 1 \\ 0 & 0 & 0 & \cdots & 0 & s_{n_s} & \cdots & s_1 & s_0 \end{bmatrix}$$

$$\theta = [\; a_1 \;\; a_2 \;\; a_3 \;\; \cdots \;\; a_{N+1} \;]^T$$

$$H = [\; 1 \;\; 0 \;\; 0 \;\; \cdots \;\; 0 \;]$$

It is clear from Equation (16) that a state space model can be formed by using the first $N+1$ step response coefficients in θ and the parametric AR model coefficients from Equation (9) and (10) in the last row of Φ. Therefore all MPC strategies based on step response models can be modified to use a step response model for prediction of the first N points of the output response and an autoregressive model to predict the balance of the response. This modelling approach will handle unstable as well as stable processes as shown below.

Note that for this MPC state space formulation:

- The step response data used for the controller design includes the effects of both stable and unstable poles.

- The unstable poles must be identified separately. The unstable parts of some physical processes (*cf.* level control processes) are obvious from physical analysis. Identification algorithms must be used for the more general cases. Since the latter part of the step response $\{a_{N+i}, i = 1, 2, \ldots\}$, by definition, reflects only the effects of unstable poles, it is relatively easy to estimate the locations of these poles.

- The length of the step response series (N) must be long enough so that all effects of the zeros and stable poles decay to zero within $(N - n_s)$ steps.

The following examples show the form of the $S(z^{-1})$ polynomial for several common applications.

1. **Open Loop Stable Process**

$$\begin{aligned} G_u(s) &= 1 \\ \mathcal{Z}(\frac{1}{s}) &= \frac{1}{1-z^{-1}} \\ S(z^{-1}) &= 1 \end{aligned}$$

i.e. $s_0 = 1$ and $n_s = 0$

This result is identical to that suggested by Li *et al.* (1989).

2. **Integrating Process**

Let T_s be the sample interval

$$\begin{aligned} G_u(s) &= \frac{1}{s} \\ \mathcal{Z}(\frac{1}{s^2}) &= \frac{T_s z^{-1}}{1-2z^{-1}+z^{-2}} \\ S(z^{-1}) &= 2 - z^{-1} \end{aligned}$$

i.e. $s_0 = 2,\ s_1 = -1$ and $n_s = 1$

This result is identical to that suggested by Morari and Lee (1991).

3. **2nd Order Integrating Process**

$$\begin{aligned} G_u(s) &= \frac{1}{s^2} \\ \mathcal{Z}(\frac{1}{s^3}) &= \frac{\frac{1}{2}T_s^2 z^{-1}(1+z^{-1})}{(1-z^{-1})^3} \\ S(z^{-1}) &= 3 - 3z^{-1} + z^{-2} \end{aligned}$$

i.e. $s_0 = 3,\ s_1 = -3,\ s_2 = 1$ and $n_s = 2$

4. **Exponentially Unstable Process**

$$\begin{aligned} G_u(s) &= \frac{1}{s-p},\ p > 0 \\ \mathcal{Z}(\frac{1}{s(s-p)}) &= \frac{\frac{1}{p}z^{-1}(e^{pT_s}-1)}{1-(1+e^{pT_s})z^{-1}+e^{pT_s}z^{-2}} \\ S(z^{-1}) &= (1+e^{pT_s}) - e^{pT_s}z^{-1} \end{aligned}$$

i.e. $s_0 = 1 + e^{pT_s},\ s_1 = -e^{pT_s}$, and $n_s = 1$

5. **Continuously Oscillating Process**

$$\begin{aligned} G_u(s) &= \frac{s}{s^2+\omega^2} \\ \mathcal{Z}(\frac{s}{s(s^2+\omega^2)}) &= \frac{\frac{1}{\omega}z^{-1}\sin(\omega T_s)}{1-2z^{-1}\cos(\omega T_s)+z^{-2}} \\ S(z^{-1}) &= 2\cos(\omega T_s) - z^{-1} \end{aligned}$$

i.e. $s_0 = 2\cos(\omega T_s),\ s_1 = -1$, and $n_s = 1$

It is easy to verify that the combined models based on Equation (16) accurately represent the unstable responses of the corresponding open-loop processes. If $S(z^{-1})$ is unknown, it can be obtained by fitting the experimental process step response for time > (N).

5 Feedback Observer Design

The state space formulation in Equation (16) describes the open-loop dynamic behaviour of stable and unstable processes. With this formulation, the so called 'internal instability' problem due to incorrect open loop prediction can be avoided. However, noise and unexpected disturbances may still cause severe problems in control performance. Also, the controller must be robust enough to handle changes in the location of the unstable pole(s) of the actual process. A feedback system can be designed to reject noise, estimate the effects of disturbances and provide the necessary robustness.

Obviously, since the state space formulation (16) is in a controllable canonical form, the observability matrix is:

$$[H\ H\Phi\ \cdots\ H\Phi^{N+1}] = I$$

The model is therefore observable and hence all state variables $X(k)$ can be estimated based on measurements of the output. An MPC observer can be designed using classical observer theory. For example, with a Kalman type, two stage observer form (Navratil *et al.*, 1988), the MPC observer can be written as:

$$\begin{aligned} \widehat{X}(k) &= \Phi X^*(k-1) + \theta\Delta u(k-1) \\ \widehat{Y}(k) &= H\widehat{X}(k) \\ X^*(k) &= \widehat{X}(k) + K[Y(k) - \widehat{Y}(k)] \end{aligned} \tag{17}$$

where $X^*(k)$ is the estimated state variable vector. $Y(k)$ is the actual output measurement in (16) and K is the generalised feedback gain.

Then, introducing the state error vector

$$\overline{X}(k) = X(k) - X^*(k) \tag{18}$$

and combining Equation (16), (17) and (18), the following homogenous equation is obtained

$$\overline{X}(k) = (I - KH)\Phi\overline{X}(k-1) \tag{19}$$

For an asymptotically stable predictor, it is required that

$$\lim_{k\to\infty}\overline{X}(k) = 0$$

The characteristic equation of the observer is

$$det[\lambda I\ -\ (I - KH)\Phi] = 0 \tag{20}$$

For an asymptotically stable observer, all eigenvalues of the observer should be within the unit circle. The feedback gain K can be designed to shift the original eigenvalues to desired locations.

Assume

$$K = [k_1\ k_2\ \cdots\ k_{N+1}]^T$$

Equation (20) can be expanded as:

$$\begin{aligned} det[\lambda I &- (I-KH)\Phi] \\ &= \lambda^{N+1} \\ &+ (k_2 - s_0)\lambda^N \\ &+ (k_3 - s_0k_2 - s_1)\lambda^{N-1} \\ &+ \cdots \\ &+ (k_{i+1} - \sum_{j=0}^{i} s_j k_{i-j})\lambda^{N+1-i} \\ &+ \cdots \\ &+ (k_{N+1} - \sum_{j=0}^{N} s_j k_{i-j})\lambda \\ &= 0 \end{aligned} \tag{21}$$

where $s_j = 0$, if $j > n_s$.

From this equation, the properties of the MPC observer can be summarized as:

- The coefficients of the characteristic equation (CE) are independent of k_1. For convenience, let $k_1 = 1$.
- Equation (21) is a (N+1) order polynomial but without a constant term so that at least one root is at the origin. *i.e.* one eigenvalue is $\lambda = 0$.

The feedback gain K can therefore be calculated using standard pole placement techniques to obtain the desired observer performance. For example, three cases are presented below

1. **Open loop predictor(no feedback)**

   With $\{k_i = 0, i = 1, 2, \ldots, N+1\}$, Equation (21) becomes

   $$\lambda^{N+1} - s_0\lambda^N - s_1\lambda^{N-1} - \cdots - s_{n_s}\lambda^{N+1-n_s} = 0$$

   or

   $$\lambda^{N-n_s}(\lambda^{n_s+1} - s_0\lambda^{n_s} - \cdots - s_{n_s}) = 0$$

   so that there are $(N - n_s)$ eigenvalues located at the origin and $(n_s + 1)$ eigenvalues are determined by the equation

   $$\lambda^{n_s+1} - s_0\lambda^{n_s} - \cdots - s_{n_s} = 0$$

   - For open loop stable processes, $n_s = 0$, $s_0 = 1$. Therefore, the eigenvalue $\lambda = 1$ is on the boundary of the unit circle and the output will be biased if there are any disturbances.
   - For integrating processes, $n_s = 1$, $s_0 = 2$ and $s_1 = -1$, the CE becomes

     $$\lambda^2 - 2\lambda + 1 = 0$$

     There are two eigenvalues on the stability boundary.
   - For open loop unstable processes, all of the n_s eigenvalues decided by CE are outside the unit circle.

   The general conclusion is that without a proper feedback system, any noise or small disturbance will result in severe problems.

2. **DMC feedback design**

   The simplest feedback design used in DMC is simply to let the gain vector

   $$K = [1\ 1\ \cdots\ 1]^T$$

   Equation (21) becomes

   $$\begin{aligned}\lambda^{N+1} + (1 - s_0)\lambda^N &+ (1 - s_0 - s_1)\lambda^{N-1} + \cdots \\ &+ (1 - \sum_{j=0}^{n_s+1} s_j)\lambda^{N+1-n_s} = 0\end{aligned}$$

   - For open loop stable processes, $n_s = 0$ and $s_0 = 1$, so that all eigenvalues are at the origin. Therefore, this kind of feedback can give perfect control performance.
   - For integrating processes, $n_s = 1$, $s_0 = 2$ and $s_1 = -1$. The CE becomes $\lambda(\lambda - 1) = 0$, so there is an eigenvalue on the stability boundary which is unsatisfactory.
   - For open loop unstable processes, the eigenvalues are decided by the coefficients of the $S(z^{-1})$ polynomial. They can be inside, on, or outside the unit circle so that there is no guarantee that this kind of feedback design will result in a stable observer.

3. **Deadbeat feedback design**

   If all coefficients in Equation (21) are assigned to zero, then deadbeat performance can be obtained. Since all the eigenvalues of the observer are equal to zero, the feedback gain K must satisfy following recursive equations:

   $$\begin{aligned} k_{i+1} &= \sum_{j=0}^{i} s_j k_{i-j}, \quad i = 1, 2, \ldots, N \qquad (22) \\ k_1 &= 1 \end{aligned}$$

   - For example, open loop stable processes have $s_0 = 1$ and $s_2 = s_3 = s_{N+1} = 0$, so the solution of Equation (22) is

     $$K = [1\ 1\ \cdots\ 1]^T$$

     i.e. the basic DMC feedback option is a deadbeat observer for open loop stable processes.
   - For integrating processes, $n_s = 1$, $s_0 = 2$, $s_1 = -1$, the solution of Equation (22) is

     $$K = [1\ 2\ \cdots\ N+1]^T$$

     This feedback design is also mentioned by Morari *et al.*(1992).
   - For open loop unstable processes, a deadbeat observer can be designed by solving the simple algebraic Equation (22). In the next section some examples are given to show how deadbeat performance is achieved.

6 Simulation Results

Three examples will be given in this section to demonstrate the performance of the MPC observer and controller. The discussion focuses on the stability of MPC when controlling open loop unstable processes rather than on the regulatory performance. For simplicity, it is assumed that there are no constraints and that only one control move is calculated. However, the proposed approach can be applied to more general MPC problems. (The main problem to watch out for is that if sufficient control is not available, *e.g.* due to constraints, then the process response could be unstable).

For open-loop unstable process, the sample interval should be chosen using the same guidelines as for stable processes.

6.1 Case 1: Integrating Process with Gain Mismatch

The first example is an integrating process

$$\begin{aligned} G(s) &= \frac{K_p}{s(s^2+s+1)} \\ G_s(s) &= \frac{K_p}{s^2+s+1} \\ G_u(s) &= \frac{1}{s} \end{aligned}$$

The MPC was designed with following parameters

$$T_s = 0.3, \quad N = 25, \quad P = 10,$$

and the state space formulation results in

$$\begin{aligned} S(z^{-1}) &= 2 - z^{-1} \\ K &= [1\ 2 \cdots\ (N+1)]^T \end{aligned}$$

At step 80, the actual process gain K_p was increased by 100% (The gain of the model used in the controller was unchanged). Fig. 1 shows that this MPC structure can stabilize the close loop system even with strong gain mismatch.

6.2 Case 2: Exponentially Unstable Process with Uncertainty

The actual process in this example is an underdamped exponentially unstable process.

$$G_p(s) = \frac{1}{(s-0.5)(s^2+s+1)}$$

However, the model used for controller design is the same as that used in Example 1 (*i.e.* an underdamped integrating model). All parameters and the MPC state space formulation are identical to those in Example 1. There is a large error in the location of the unstable pole of the actual process and the pole used for MPC control (*i.e.* $p = 0.5$ versus $p = 0$). Fig. 2 shows that the MPC formulation developed in this paper still gives good tracking performance. (The oscillations are inherent in the process and would require stronger faster control to eliminate).

6.3 Case 3: Unstable Process with Deadbeat Feedback Observer

The state space model can be used for prediction and for the design of a state feedback observer. The poles of the observer can be specified using a pole-placement type design procedure.

The process simulated here is

$$G_p(s) = \frac{1}{s-1}$$

and there is no Model-Plant Mismatch for the controller design.

The performance of the deadbeat observer is illustrated by introducing a step type disturbances in the output at step 60 in Fig. 3. A deadbeat feedback observer was designed such that the disturbance was rejected almost immediately. A similar disturbance at step 140 shows that a basic DMC type observer results in a much large output disturbance. (Note that since the unit step disturbance is added directly to the output the full effect of the disturbance is visible in the output after one sampling interval and can not be reduced by feedback control.)

7 Conclusion

The state space formulation of MPC is extended by using an explicit step response model combined with an implicit AR model to model open loop unstable systems. The only extra requirement is that the open loop unstable pole(s) be estimated separately. Theoretically, if the number of step response points (*i.e.* N) is large enough and the AR model of the unstable mode(s) are correct, there is no truncation error in the output prediction. Pole-placement techniques are employed so that the observer in the feedback path exhibits deadbeat performance. Simulation results also show that MPC based on this approach gives good performance even in the presence of mismatch in the stable and/or unstable models.

References

[1] Cutler, C. R. and B. L. Ramaker (1980). Dynamic Matrix Control — A Computer Control Algorithm. *Proc. Automatic Control Conf.*, San Francisco, Paper WP5-B.

[2] Clarke, D.W., C. Mohtadi and P. S. Tuffs (1987). Generalized Predictive Control. *Automatica*, 23, 137-160.

[3] Li, S., K. Y. Lim and D. G. Fisher (1989). A State Space Formulation for Model Predictive Control. *AICHE Journal*, Vol.35, No.2, 241-249.

[4] Isermann, R., K. H. Lachmann and D. Matko (1992). Adaptive Control System. *Prentice Hall International (UK) Ltd.*

[5] Morari, M. and J. H. Lee (1991). Model Predictive Control: The Good, the Bad, and the Ugly. *Chemical Process Control (CPC) IV*, 419-444.

[6] Morari, M., N. L. Ricker and E. Zafiriou (1992), Model Predictive Control. *ACC'92 Workshop (No. 4)*, Chicago, IL.

[7] Navratil, J. P., K. Y. Lim and D. G. Fisher (1988). Feedback Prediction Options in Model Predictive Control Systems. *Proceeding of IFAC International Workshop on Model Based Process Control*, Page 6, Atlanta.

[8] Richalet J., A. Rault, J. L. Testud, and J. Papon, (1978). Heuristic Control: Application to Industrial Processes, *Automatica*, 14, 413.

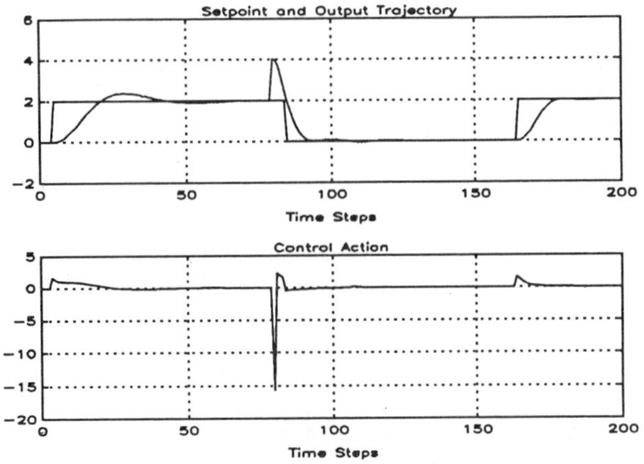

Fig 1a-1b Output and Control Action with Gain Mismatch

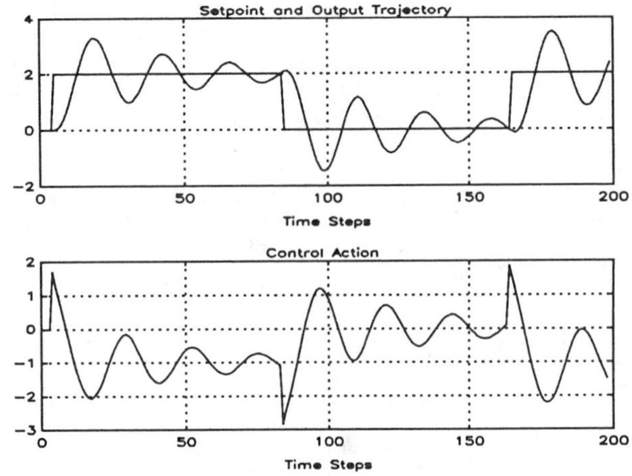

Fig 2a-2b Output and Control Action with Uncertain Unstable Pole

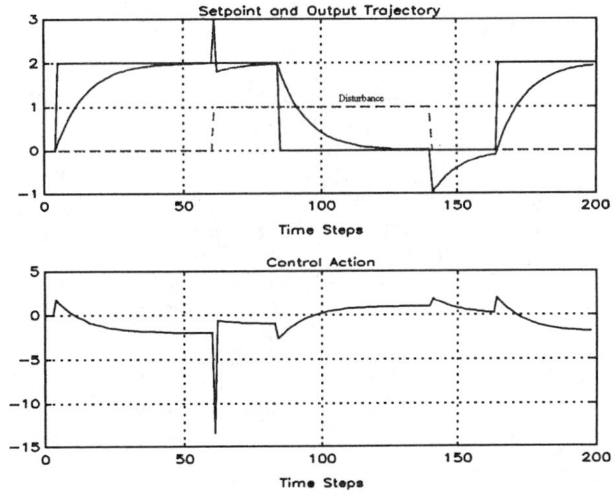

Fig 3a-3b Output and Control Action with Different Feedback Options

Proceedings of the
American Control Conference
San Francisco, California • June 1993

Information Forgetting Using the Augmented UD Identification Algorithm

Shaohua Niu and D. Grant Fisher[1]
Department of Chemical Engineering
University of Alberta
Edmonton, Canada, T6G 2G6

ABSTRACT

Fundamental analysis of information forgetting in recursive identification shows that there are only two basic approaches: relative and absolute forgetting. Using the augmented UD identification (AUDI) algorithm developed by the authors, it is found that all the information pertinent to identification and information forgetting is contained in a single matrix called the information accumulation matrix (IAM). Analysis of the UD factored form of this IAM shows that the effect of the new information contained in the regressor, relative to the information (*e.g.*, parameter values) already contained in the current IAM can be controlled by relative and/or absolute modification of the diagonal D matrix produced by the UDU^T factorization. This simplifies the interpretation of new and existing information forgetting approaches and provides a basis for developing effective design guidelines. Also, since AUDI is a least-squares (LS) type algorithm, the basic principles and interpretation carry over to other LS algorithms.

1 Introduction

Tracking the time varying dynamics of a process is a fundamental problem in control and signal processing. Since most real processes are nonlinear in nature, linear process models provide an accurate description of the process dynamics only in the vicinity of the current operating point. The parameters of the linear model change as the process moves from one operating condition to another and hence a recursive forgetting mechanism is needed to appropriately discard old data and put more emphasis on the recently obtained information which represents the latest process dynamics. Recursive forgetting is a very important but also very difficult area of recursive identification.

Many different information forgetting schemes exist in the literature, including exponential forgetting (EF) (Åström, Borisson, Ljung & Wittenmark 1977, Ljung & Söderström 1983), variable forgetting factor (Fortescue, Kershenbaum & Ydstie 1981, Cordero & Mayne 1981), directional forgetting (Saelid & Foss 1983, Hägglund 1983, Kulhávy & Kàrny 1984), covariance resetting (Goodwin & Teoh 1983, Vogel & Edgar 1982) and the constant trace method (Sripada & Fisher 1987, Irving 1979), *etc.* However, with the AUDI notation, all these methods can be conveniently grouped into two categories: *relative forgetting* and *absolute forgetting*. The Augmented UD Identification (AUDI) algorithm, proposed by Niu, Fisher & Xiao (1992), is an efficient implementation of the least-squares algorithm. An information accumulation matrix (IAM) is defined which contains all the information on parameter estimates and loss functions. The AUDI algorithm has a compact and stable structure very similar to the UD factorization method (Bierman 1977), and simultaneously produces multiple models from order 1 to a user-specified order n, with approximately the same computational effort as nth order least-squares. This is referred to as *the multiple model structure* or *the AUDI structure*. The AUDI formulation facilitates the interpretation and implementation of the information forgetting principles.

[1]To whom all correspondence should be directed

Relative forgetting methods use a forgetting factor to scale the information accumulation matrix (IAM) to proportionally forget old information. Absolute forgetting schemes forcibly modify the information accumulation matrix with user-specified values, which may not necessarily be related to the previous information accumulation matrix. For example, the exponential forgetting method, which falls into the relative forgetting category, uses a constant forgetting factor to scale the IAM at every time step, *i.e.*, the new IAM is a scalar multiple of the previous IAM. On the other hand, the covariance resetting algorithm, which is an absolute forgetting method, simply resets all or part of the IAM to a user-specified value, which is not necessarily a function of the previous IAM.

In this paper, information forgetting is discussed from a very general point of view, based on the AUDI algorithm, since it provides deeper insight into the information forgetting principles. By using the concept of *relative forgetting* and *absolute forgetting*, information forgetting in recursive identification is simplified into the problem of controlling the weight that the new information from the process is given when it is used to update the information accumulation matrix. Simple and convenient guidelines are derived for analyzing and designing new information forgetting schemes.

2 Information Accumulation

Consider a process described by the following linear difference equation model

$$z(t)+a_1z(t-1)+\cdots+a_nz(t-n) = b_1u(t-1)+\cdots+b_nu(t-n)+v(t) \quad (1)$$

Define *the augmented data vector* as

$$\varphi(t) = [-z(t-n), u(t-n), \cdots, -z(t-1), u(t-1), -z(t)]^\tau \quad (2)$$

As shown by the AUDI structure in Niu et al. (1992), all the information on the process parameters and loss functions for all models from order 1 to a user-specified maximum number n are contained, implicitly, in the information accumulation matrix (IAM)

$$C(t) = \left[\sum_{j=1}^{t} \varphi(j)\varphi^\tau(j)\right]^{-1} \quad (3)$$

or equivalently, in the data product moment matrix (DPMM)

$$S(t) = \sum_{j=1}^{t} \varphi(j)\varphi^\tau(j) = C^{-1}(t) \quad (4)$$

Batch identification methods collect all the input/output data first, then use them simultaneously to construct the Information Accumulation Matrix (IAM) or the Data Product Moment Matrix (DPMM). In recursive algorithms, the new information from the input/output data is accumulated in the IAM/DPMM as it is obtained, that is

$$S(t) = S(t-1) + \varphi(t)\varphi^{\tau}(t), \text{ or } C^{-1}(t) = C^{-1}(t-1) + \varphi(t)\varphi^{\tau}(t) \tag{5}$$

In the AUDI algorithm, the concept of recursive identification becomes the recursive accumulation of process information into the information accumulation matrix (IAM) using (5). As will be shown later, this simplifies the interpretation and implementation of the existing information forgetting schemes, and also makes it easier to design new information forgetting methods.

Notice that the diagonal elements of the rank-one matrix $\varphi(t)\varphi^{\tau}(t)$ are always non-negative, therefore, the matrix $S(t)$ (or $C^{-1}(t)$)is always non-decreasing. The new information $\varphi(t)\varphi^{\tau}(t)$ from the process at each different time interval t is accumulated into the IAM with exactly the same weight. As time goes on, the DPMM will eventually go to infinity, and the new information will be "buried" in the DPMM, *i.e.*,

$$\lim_{t\to\infty} S(t) \approx \lim_{t\to\infty} S(t-1) \to \infty$$

and the identification algorithm is no longer aware of the new information in $\varphi(t)\varphi^{\tau}(t)$ and effectively shuts itself off. This is the main reason that an information forgetting mechanism is needed for tracking time varying process. To keep the DPMM from going to infinity (or, in other words, to keep the IAM from going to zero), the updating formula (5) must be modified. A general formula is

$$S(t) = \mathcal{F}(S(t-1), \varphi(t)) \tag{6}$$

where $\mathcal{F}$ represents a particular relationship or function. *All existing information forgetting methods are based on this principle and they differ only in the choice of the function $\mathcal{F}$.* In essence, information forgetting is simply a problem of controlling the weight that the new information $\varphi(t)\varphi^{\tau}(t)$ takes in the update of the IAM/DPMM matrix. In other words, the mechanism for information forgetting is to appropriately control the relative importance of the new information $\varphi(t)\varphi^{\tau}(t)$ as compared with that already contained in the information accumulation matrix. A less general formula deduced from (6) is

$$\left\{ \begin{array}{rcl} \bar{S}(t) & = & S(t-1) + \varphi(t)\varphi^{\tau}(t) \\ S(t) & = & \mathcal{F}(\bar{S}(t)) \end{array} \right. \tag{7}$$

which still covers most of the existing methods as special cases. The information forgetting problem actually reduces to the problem of appropriately updating the information accumulation matrix with (6) or (7). A general information forgetting method requires some means of determining the information content of the new matrix $\varphi(t)\varphi^{\tau}(t)$ relative to that contained in the current IAM. This is the key step in developing a good information forgetting mechanism.

3 Information Forgetting Using the AUDI Algorithm

In the last section, it was seen that information forgetting is basically a problem of appropriately updating the information accumulation matrix. In this section, the concept of information forgetting is simplified further by using the Augmented UD Identification (AUDI) algorithm (Niu et al. 1992). The AUDI algorithm is a simultaneously order and parameter identification method with excellent numerical performance. A detailed derivation and discussion of the AUDI algorithm can be found in Niu et al. (1992) but a brief review is given below.

First, decompose the information accumulation matrix (IAM) in (3) into its UDU^{T} form, *i.e.*,

$$C(t) = U(t)D(t)U^{\tau}(t) \tag{8}$$

Then, through careful analysis of (8), it can be shown that the following structure exists (Niu et al. 1992)

1. The $U(t)$ matrix, with the unit-upper-triangular form

$$U(t) = \begin{bmatrix} 1 & \hat{\alpha}_1^{(0)} & \hat{\theta}_1^{(1)} & \hat{\alpha}_1^{(1)} & \hat{\theta}_1^{(2)} & \cdots & \hat{\alpha}_1^{(n-1)} & \hat{\theta}_1^{(n)} \\ & 1 & \hat{\theta}_2^{(1)} & \hat{\alpha}_2^{(1)} & \hat{\theta}_2^{(2)} & \cdots & \hat{\alpha}_2^{(n-1)} & \hat{\theta}_2^{(n)} \\ & & 1 & \hat{\alpha}_3^{(1)} & \hat{\theta}_3^{(2)} & \cdots & \hat{\alpha}_3^{(n-)} & \hat{\theta}_3^{(n)} \\ & & & 1 & \hat{\theta}_4^{(2)} & \cdots & \hat{\alpha}_4^{(n-1)} & \hat{\theta}_4^{(n)} \\ & & & & 1 & \cdots & \hat{\alpha}_5^{(n-1)} & \hat{\theta}_5^{(n)} \\ & & & & & \ddots & \vdots & \vdots \\ & & & & & & 1 & \hat{\theta}_{2n}^{(n)} \\ & & & 0 & & & & 1 \end{bmatrix} \tag{9}$$

is *the parameter matrix* of the process model (1). It contains all the parameter estimates for all models from order 1 to a user specified value n. More specifically, the ith order model parameter estimates $\hat{\theta}^{(i)}(t)$ are contained in the $(2i+1)$th column of the $U(t)$ matrix, where $i \in [1, n]$.

2. The diagonal matrix $D(t)$

$$D(t) = \text{diag}\left[J^{(0)}(t), L^{(0)}(t), \cdots, J^{(n-1)}(t), L^{(n-1)}(t), J^{(n)}(t)\right] \tag{10}$$

is *the loss function matrix* and contains all the loss functions corresponding to the n models defined in $U(t)$ matrix. That is, the $(2i+1)$th diagonal element $J^{(i)}(t)$ in the loss function matrix is the loss function of the ith order model, with $i \in [1, n]$.

3. The AUDI algorithm has a clear, compact structure and provides much more information than ordinary least-squares, with the same computational requirement. The AUDI algorithm also has better numerical properties and is therefore recommended for use in place of the ordinary least-squares method for all applications. See Niu et al. (1992) for more details.

Using AUDI notation and noting that $C(t) = U(t)D(t)U^{\tau}(t)$, the recursive information accumulation formula (5) can be rewritten as

$$[U(t)D(t)U^{\tau}(t)]^{-1} = [U(t-1)D(t-1)U^{\tau}(t-1)]^{-1} + \varphi(t)\varphi^{\tau}(t) \tag{11}$$

Successful identification implies that the parameter matrix $U(t)$ converges to a constant matrix, and the loss function matrix $D(t)$ converges to a zero matrix, *i.e.*,

$$\lim_{t\to\infty} D(t) = 0, \quad \Rightarrow \quad \lim_{t\to\infty}\{U(t)D(t)U^{\tau}(t)\} = 0$$

It follows that the tracking ability of the AUDI identification algorithm is controlled by the diagonal loss function matrix $D^{-1}(t)$. Consequently, a general information forgetting formula for AUDI algorithms can be written very simply as

$$\left\{ \begin{array}{l} \left[U(t)\bar{D}(t)U^{\tau}(t)\right]^{-1} = [U(t-1)D(t-1)U^{\tau}(t-1)]^{-1} + \varphi(t)\varphi^{\tau}(t) \\ D(t) = \mathcal{G}(\bar{D}(t)) \end{array} \right. \tag{12}$$

that is, $D(t-1) \to \bar{D}(t) \to D(t)$. $\mathcal{G}$ is a function analogous to $\mathcal{F}$ in (7). Since D is diagonal, it is much easier to interpret and work with than the full IAM/DPMM matrices in (6) and (7). Therefore, from now on, the emphasis in the discussion of information forgetting will be shifted from the IAM/DPMM to the loss function matrix D in (10).

3.1 Relative Forgetting

The *relative forgetting* approach using the AUDI algorithm is very simple. The main idea is to scale the loss function matrix with a diagonal matrix $\Lambda(t)$, *e.g.*,

$$D(t) = \bar{D}(t)\Lambda(t) \tag{13}$$

where the key design decision is the selection of the $\Lambda(t)$ matrix. A special case of (13) is

$$\Lambda(t) = \frac{1}{\lambda(t)} I \quad (14)$$

which is equivalent to

$$C(t) = U(t)D(t)U^\tau(t) = U(t)\left[\frac{\bar{D}(t)}{\lambda(t)}\right]U^\tau(t)$$
$$= [U(t)\bar{D}(t)U^\tau(t)]/\lambda(t) = C(t-1)/\lambda(t)$$

or in terms of DPMM

$$S(t) = \lambda(t)S(t-1)$$

this shows that scaling the loss function matrix $D(t)$, which is a simple diagonal matrix with clear physical meaning, has the same effect as scaling the information accumulation matrix $C(t)$. The new loss function matrix is simply a multiple of the previous loss function matrix and this approach is therefore referred to as *relative forgetting*. Relative forgetting includes exponential forgetting, variable forgetting and directional forgetting as special cases, since they all use a forgetting factor $\lambda(t)$ as in (14) . The AUDI-LS algorithm with a variable forgetting factor $\lambda(t)$ is shown in Table 1. Note that the loss function is updated in

Table 1: The Recursive AUDI Algorithm

$\varphi(t) = [-z(t-n), u(t-n), \cdots, -z(t-1), u(t-1), -z(t)]^\tau$
$f = U^\tau(t-1)\varphi(t),\ g = D(t-1)f,\ \beta_0 = \lambda(t)$
For $j = 1$ **to** d, **do**
  $\beta_j = \beta_{j-1} + f_j g_j$
  $D_{jj}(t) = D_{jj}(t-1)\beta_{j-1}/\beta_j/\lambda(t)$
  $\mu_j = -f_j/\beta_{j-1},\ \nu_j = g_j$
  For $i = 1$ **to** $j-1$, **do (skip for** $j = 1$)
    $U_{ij}(t) = U_{ij}(t-1) + \nu_i \mu_j$
    $\nu_i = \nu_i + U_{ij}(t-1)\nu_j$

Table 1 by

$$D_{jj}(t) = D_{jj}(t-1)\beta_j/\beta_{j-1}/\lambda(t) \quad (15)$$

or after rearrangement

$$D_{jj}(t) = \bar{D}_{jj}(t)/\lambda(t), \quad \text{and} \quad \bar{D}_{jj}(t) = D_{jj}(t)\beta_{j-1}/\beta_j$$

which is exactly the same as formula (13) or (14). Thus the *relative forgetting method* can be interpreted as a generalization of the variable forgetting methods. Since the forgetting factor $\lambda(t)$ is used directly in the updating of the diagonal $D(t)$ matrix rather than the full matrix $C(t)$, it is much more convenient and easier to interpret. However, the problem of how to evaluate the information content of the IAM matrix still exists.

Consider the following properties of the IAM that are affected by the introduction of a forgetting factor defined by (14)

1. DETERMINANT. Without information forgetting, the determinant of the information accumulation matrix $C(t)$ would converge to zero. Note that the determinant of the parameter matrix $U(t)$ is always unity, thus the determinant of the IAM equals the determinant of the $D(t)$ matrix, which is a diagonal matrix, *i.e.*,

$$\det\{C(t)\} = \det\{U(t)D(t)U^\tau(t)\} = \det\{D(t)\}$$

Introducing a forgetting factor is equivalent to

$$C(t) = \frac{\bar{C}(t)}{\lambda(t)} \quad \Rightarrow \quad \det\{D(t)\} = \frac{\det \bar{D}(t)}{\lambda^m(t)}$$

The constant determinant method maintains the determinant of the IAM at a constant value by using a forgetting factor $\lambda(t)$, which is equivalent to maintaining the determinant of the $D(t)$ matrix at a constant value. From the AUDI structure, it is known that the $D(t)$ matrix contains all the loss functions for all models, and thus the determinant of the loss function matrix is the product of all the loss functions of *all* models. Clearly, there is no solid theoretical ground to take this product as the information criterion.

2. TRACE. The forgetting factor scales the trace of the IAM/DPMM by a factor of $\lambda(t)$, that is

$$\text{tr}\{C(t)\} = \frac{\text{tr}\{\bar{C}(t)\}}{\lambda(t)} \quad \text{or} \quad \text{tr}\{S(t)\} = \lambda(t)\text{tr}\{S(t-1)\}$$

The constant trace method tries to maintain the trace of the IAM at a constant value through the use of a forgetting factor. However, for least-squares estimators, if the process noise is white noise with zero mean and variance σ_v^2, then $\sigma_v^2 C(t)$ is the covariance matrix of the parameter estimates, which implies that *the trace of the $C(t)$ matrix equals to the sum of the variances of the parameter estimates of all n models.* Clearly, the trace can be affected by many factors such as the noise level and model order. Using the trace of $C(t)$ as the information criterion would therefore be a very *ad hoc* method of choosing the value of this criterion and would require a great deal of experience.

3. CONDITION NUMBER. The condition number of the IAM is approximately a linear function of the condition number of the loss function matrix since the parameter matrix converges to a constant matrix, that is

$$\text{cond}\{C(t)\} = \text{cond}\{U(t)D(t)U^\tau(t)\} \approx \kappa \cdot \text{cond}\{D(t)\}$$

where κ is a constant positive number determined by the condition number of $U(t)$. In another words, the condition number of the IAM is mainly determined by the condition of the loss function matrix. Since the loss function matrix is a diagonal matrix, its condition number can be conveniently calculated as

$$\text{cond}\{D(t)\} = \frac{\max\limits_{1\le i\le m}\{D_{ii}(t)\}}{\min\limits_{1\le i\le m}\{D_{ii}(t)\}}$$

Introducing a forgetting factor as $C(t) = \bar{C}/\lambda(t)$ is equivalent to scaling $D(t)$ as $D(t) = \bar{D}(t)/\lambda(t)$, and since

$$\text{cond}\{D(t)\} = \text{cond}\{\frac{\bar{D}(t)}{\lambda}\} = \text{cond}\{\bar{D}(t)\}$$

introducing a forgetting factor can not, in theory, improve the condition of the IAM. However, the forgetting factor does prevent the IAM from going to zero. This means that the round-off errors are less serious, and hence gives the impression that introducing a forgetting factor makes the identification numerically more stable.

3.2 Absolute Forgetting

As mentioned earlier, the information forgetting problem is simply a problem of determining the relative weight given to the new information $\varphi(t)\varphi^\tau(t)$ when it is accumulated into the IAM. Relative forgetting schemes scale the IAM in order to give the new information an appropriate weight. The absolute forgetting schemes, however, simply reassign the information accumulation matrix to a value, which can be completely unrelated to its previous values. The covariance resetting method (Goodwin & Sin 1984, Xie & Evans 1984, Vogel & Edgar 1982) is an example of absolute forgetting.

The main idea behind absolute resetting method is to regularly reset the information accumulation matrix to appropriate values, in accordance with a user-specified criterion. This keeps the IAM from going to zero *and* also assigns an appropriate weight for the new information from the process. With the IAM updating formula

$$[\bar{C}(t)]^{-1} = [C(t-1)]^{-1} + \varphi(t)\varphi^\tau(t)$$

the absolute forgetting schemes usually take one of the following two forms, *i.e.*,

$$C(t) = \bar{C}(t) + Q, \quad e.g., \quad Q = \sigma I \tag{16}$$

or

$$C(t) = Q, \quad e.g., \quad Q = \sigma I \tag{17}$$

The above IAM resetting schemes can be very effective but are quite *ad hoc* as to when and how much the IAM should be reset, and this is the major problem with the covariance resetting methods in the literature. Many approaches exist but they are more or less based on trial and error or application-specific results.

Another problem with IAM resetting is that the parameters exhibit a drift towards the origin (Ljung & Gunnarsson 1990), *i.e.*, IAM resetting can also produce unexpected parameter resetting. This is made clear by the following simple example.

Consider the IAM updating formula (16), and rewrite it in UDU^T form as

$$U(t)D(t)U^{\tau}(t) = \bar{U}(t)\bar{D}(t)\bar{U}^{\tau}(t) + \sigma I$$

where σI is the resetting term. Assuming the IAM (before being reset) is

$$\begin{aligned}\bar{C}(t) &= \bar{U}(t)\bar{D}(t)\bar{U}^{\tau}(t) \\ &= \begin{bmatrix} 1 & \theta \\ 0 & 1 \end{bmatrix} \begin{bmatrix} d_1 & \\ & d_2 \end{bmatrix} \begin{bmatrix} 1 & \theta \\ 0 & 1 \end{bmatrix}^{\tau} \\ &= \begin{bmatrix} d_1 + d_2\theta^2 & \theta d_2 \\ \theta d_2 & d_2 \end{bmatrix}\end{aligned}$$

Then resetting $\bar{C}(t)$ with σI by using (16) leads to

$$\begin{aligned}C(t) &= \bar{C} + \sigma I = \begin{bmatrix} d_1 + d_2\theta^2 + \sigma & \theta d_2 \\ \theta d_2 & d_2 + \sigma \end{bmatrix} \\ &= \begin{bmatrix} 1 & \frac{\theta d_2}{d_2 + \sigma} \\ 0 & 1 \end{bmatrix} \\ &\quad \begin{bmatrix} d_1 + d_2\theta^2(1 - \frac{d_2}{d_2 + \sigma}) + \sigma & \\ & d_2 + \sigma \end{bmatrix} \begin{bmatrix} 1 & \frac{\theta d_2}{d_2 + \sigma} \\ 0 & 1 \end{bmatrix}^{\tau}\end{aligned}$$

which indicates that resetting the IAM by σI causes the parameter θ to drift from θ to $\frac{\theta d_2}{d_2+\sigma}$. After the parameters converge, d_2, the inverse of a loss function term, becomes a very small positive number. Thus $\frac{\theta d_2}{d_2+\sigma}$ becomes a very small number, which indicates that the parameter θ drifts towards zero.

If the resetting of the second kind (17) is used, then

$$\begin{aligned}C(t) &= \sigma I \qquad (\text{not related to } \bar{C}(t)) \\ &= \begin{bmatrix} 1 & 0 \\ 0 & 1 \end{bmatrix} \begin{bmatrix} \sigma & \\ & \sigma \end{bmatrix} \begin{bmatrix} 1 & 0 \\ 0 & 1 \end{bmatrix}^{\tau}\end{aligned}$$

This resets the parameters to 0, which is not desirable for the general case.

In the AUDI algorithm, information accumulation into the IAM is controlled by the loss function matrix and thus IAM resetting can be replaced by loss function matrix resetting. This has obvious advantages over IAM resetting. The resetting, from $\bar{C}(t)$ to $C(t)$, is accomplished by setting

$$U(t) = \bar{U}(t) \quad \text{and} \quad D(t) = \bar{D}(t) + Q \tag{18}$$

this means that

$$\begin{aligned}\bar{C}(t) &= \begin{bmatrix} 1 & \theta \\ 0 & 1 \end{bmatrix} \begin{bmatrix} d_1 & \\ & d_2 \end{bmatrix} \begin{bmatrix} 1 & \theta \\ 0 & 1 \end{bmatrix}^{\tau} \\ C(t) &= \begin{bmatrix} 1 & \theta \\ 0 & 1 \end{bmatrix} \begin{bmatrix} d_1 + \sigma & \\ & d_2 + \sigma \end{bmatrix} \begin{bmatrix} 1 & \theta \\ 0 & 1 \end{bmatrix}^{\tau}\end{aligned}$$

In this way, $C(t)$ is prevented from approaching zero, and at the same time, the tracking ability is effectively restored and parameter drift is avoided.

The following properties of the $D(t)$ matrix provide a theoretical guideline for resetting the loss function matrix

1. With no information forgetting, the elements of the loss function matrix increase linearly with time step t, that is

$$\lim_{t\to\infty} D^{-1}(t) = \lim_{t\to\infty}(t \cdot R_0) = \infty$$

where R_0 is a constant diagonal matrix. The first element of the $D^{-1}(t)$ matrix equals the squared sum of the process outputs (Niu & Fisher 1993*b*), *i.e.*

$$\lim_{t\to\infty} J^{(0)}(t) = \lim_{t\to\infty} \sum_{j=1-n}^{t-n} z^2(j) = t\,\mathbf{E}z^2(t) \tag{19}$$

where $\mathbf{E}$ stands for expectation. The last element, which is the loss function of the nth order model, is the squared sum of the residuals

$$\lim_{t\to\infty} J^{(n)}(t) = \lim_{t\to\infty} \sum_{j=1}^{t} \varepsilon^2(j) = \lim_{t\to\infty} \sum_{j=1}^{t} \{z(j) - \varphi^{\tau}(j)\hat{\theta}(t)\}^2 = t\,\sigma_v^2$$

where $\varepsilon(t)$ represents the residual at time t and σ_v^2 is the variance of the process noise.

2. With a constant forgetting factor $0 < \lambda < 1$, the loss function matrix $D^{-1}(t)$ converges to a constant matrix which is dependent on the forgetting factor, that is

$$\lim_{t\to\infty} D^{-1}(t) = \frac{1}{1-\lambda} R_0$$

Here $N = \frac{1}{1-\lambda}$ is called the "asymptotic memory length", or the "asymptotic data window". It indicates that the information dies away with a time constant of approximately N sampling intervals. This principle can be extended to variable forgetting factors, where $\lambda(t)$ means that at time interval t, the identification algorithm is implementing a data window with an asymptotic length $N = 1/(1 - \lambda(t))$. The first element, $J^{(0)}(t)$, of the loss function matrix becomes

$$\lim_{t\to\infty} J^{(0)}(t) = \frac{1}{1-\lambda}\mathbf{E}z^2(t) = N\,\mathbf{E}z^2(t) \tag{20}$$

and the last element, $J^{(n)}(t)$, becomes

$$\lim_{t\to\infty} J^{(n)}(t) = \frac{1}{1-\lambda}\mathbf{E}\varepsilon^2(t) = N\,\mathbf{E}\varepsilon^2(t)$$

3. From (19) and (20), it is seen that the value of the loss function matrix is directly related to the forgetting factor and equation (19) provides an estimate of the mathematical expectation of the outputs, which is $\mathbf{E}z^2(t)$. Setting the first element of the $D^{-1}(t)$ matrix to $N\,\mathbf{E}z^2(t)$ is equivalent to setting the asymptotic memory length to N which in turn is equivalent to setting the current forgetting factor value to $\lambda(t) = 1 - 1/N$, regardless of its previous value. This leads to remark 4.

4. For AUDI algorithms, the following actions have the same effect in terms of information forgetting

1. Introducing a forgetting factor $\lambda(t)$.
2. Setting the "asymptotic memory length" to $N = 1/(1 - \lambda(t))$.
3. Setting the loss function matrix to $D^{-1}(t) = N\,R_0$.

3.3 Matrix Regularization

Matrix regularization is a way of keeping the information accumulation matrix $C(t)$ well conditioned (Ljung & Söderström 1983). This is done by specifying an upper and a lower bound on the IAM

$$\alpha_{\min} I \leq C(t) \leq \alpha_{\max} I \tag{21}$$

where I is the identity matrix and α_{min} and α_{max} are positive constants, with $0 < \alpha_{min} < \alpha_{max} < \infty$. The lower bound maintains the algorithm's ability to track time-varying parameters, and the upper bound prevents blow up. Normally the objective of matrix regularization is to improve numerical performance. For RLS algorithms, matrix regularization results in boundedness of the estimation errors. If the input signal $\varphi(t)$ is persistently exciting and bounded as well, then the convergence of the parameter estimates is guaranteed and the convergence rate is at least exponentially fast (Parkum, Poulsen & Holst 1992). The AUDI algorithm is inherently a LS algorithm, and hence the above results also apply.

In the AUDI algorithm, with the decomposition of $C(t) = U(t)D(t)U^{\tau}(t)$, only the diagonal loss function matrix needs to be regularized. The parameter matrix $U(t)$ is an upper triangular matrix with all the diagonal elements being unity. Its determinant is always unity and thus does not need to be regularized. Matrix regularization of $D(t)$ is very trivial

$$\alpha_{\min} \leq D_{ii}(t) \leq \alpha_{\max} \quad \text{for} \quad i = 1, \cdots, m \tag{22}$$

Actually, matrix regularization of the $D(t)$ matrix can be expressed in an even simpler way, *i.e.*, apply an upper bound to the largest element of the loss function matrix and a lower bound to the smallest element. For ARMA models, the largest element of the loss function matrix is $J^{(0)}$ or $L^{(0)}$, depending on whether $\sum_{j=1}^{t} z^2(j)$ is larger than $\sum_{j=1}^{t} u^2(j)$. The smallest element is usually the last element in the loss function matrix, *i.e.*, $J^{(n)}(t)$ (Niu & Fisher 1993*b*). Matrix regularization thus puts an upper bound on the largest element of the loss function matrix and a lower bound on the smallest element and thus sets the maximum condition number of the loss function matrix which in turn determines the maximum condition number of the information accumulation matrix. It thereby guarantees that the condition number of the information accumulation matrix is always smaller than that specified by matrix regularization. In this sense, matrix regularization improves the condition of the matrices.

The AUDI formulation/analysis shows that the upper and lower bounds on the loss function matrix, set by matrix regularization, also determine the maximum and minimum "asymptotic memory length" of the algorithm. Once these maxima/minima are exceeded, the algorithm resets the memory length to the upper/lower bounds which has the same effect as the loss function resetting discussed in Section 3.2 and thus *matrix regularization has the dual function of improving matrix condition and limiting maximum memory length of the identification algorithm.*

The above analysis and guidelines were used to improve the *variable forgetting method* (Fortescue et al. 1981). Simulations produce excellent results. However, due to space limitations, the examples are not presented here. (They will be included in the ACC presentation and are available from the authors.)

4 Conclusions

With the AUDI notation, it is found that information forgetting in recursive identification reduces to the simple problem of controlling the weight of the new process information contained in the regressor, $\varphi(t)$, relative to the information already contained in the information accumulation matrix. This can be done conveniently by modifying the diagonal loss function matrix, which actually controls the information accumulation. Based on the above analysis it is shown that all information forgetting methods can be classified into two categories: relative forgetting and absolute forgetting. This simplifies the interpretation and provides convenient guidelines for designing new information forgetting schemes.

References

Åström, K., Borisson, U., Ljung, L. & Wittenmark, B. (1977), 'Theory and application of self-tuning regulators', *Automatica* **13**, 457.

Bierman, G. J. (1977), *Factorization Methods for Discrete Sequential Estimation*, Academic Press, New York.

Cordero, A. & Mayne, D. Q. (1981), 'Deterministic convergence of a self-tuning regulator with variable forgetting factor', **128**(1), 19 – 23.

Fortescue, T. R., Kershenbaum, L. S. & Ydstie, B. E. (1981), 'Implementation of self-tuning regulator with variable forgetting factor', *Automatica* **17**, 831–835.

Goodwin, G. C. & Sin, K. S. (1984), *Adaptive Filtering Prediction and Control*, Prentice Hall.

Goodwin, G. C. & Teoh, E. K. (1983), Adaptive control of a class of linear time-varying systems, *in* 'Prepr. IFAC Workshop Adaptive System Control, Signal Processing', San Francisco.

Hägglund, T. (1983), The problem of forgetting old data in recursive estimation, *in* 'Prepr. IFAC Workshop Adaptive System Control, Signal Processing', San Francisco. Paper SAC-6.

Irving, E. (1979), New developments in improving power network stability with adaptive control, *in* 'Yale Workshop Application Adaptive Control', Yale.

Kulhávy, R. & Kàrny, M. (1984), Tracking of slowly varying parameters by directional forgetting, *in* 'Proceedings of the 9Th IFAC Triennial World Congress', Vol. 2, Budapest, Hungary, pp. 687 – 692.

Ljung, L. & Gunnarsson, S. (1990), 'Adaption and tracking in system identification — a survey', *Automatica* **26**(1), 7–21.

Ljung, L. & Söderström, T. (1983), *Theory and Practice of Recursive Identification*, MIT Press.

Niu, S. & Fisher, D. G. (1993*a*), 'Multiple model least squares method'. Submitted to *Automatica*.

Niu, S. & Fisher, D. G. (1993*b*), 'On-line identification of noise variance and signal-to-noise ratio'. Submitted to *IEEE Transactions on Acoustics, Speech and Signal Processing*.

Niu, S., Fisher, D. G. & Xiao, D. (1992), 'An augmented UD identification algorithm', *International Journal of Control* **56**(1), 193 – 211.

Parkum, J. E., Poulsen, N. K. & Holst, J. (1992), 'Recursive forgetting algorithms', *International Journal of Control* **55**(1), 109 – 128.

Saelid, S. & Foss, B. (1983), Adaptive controllers with a vector variable forgetting factor, *in* 'Proceedings of the 22Nd IEEE Conference on Decision and Control', San Antonio, Texas, pp. 1488 – 1494.

Sripada, N. R. & Fisher, D. G. (1987), 'Improved least-squares identification', *International Journal of Control* **46**(6), 1889 – 1913.

Vogel, E. F. & Edgar, T. F. (1982), Application of an adaptive pole-zero placement controller to chemical process with variable deadtime, *in* 'Proc. 1982 American Control Conference', Washington, D.C., U.S.A.

Xie, X. & Evans, R. J. (1984), 'Discrete time adaptive control for deterministic time-varying systems', *Automatica* **20**(3), 309 – 319.

Proceedings of the
American Control Conference
San Francisco, California • June 1993

PREDICTIVE CONTROLLER DESIGN WITH IMPLICIT ECONOMIC CRITERIA

Athanassios Kassidas and Thomas Marlin

Chemical Engineering Department, McMaster University
Hamilton, Ontario, Canada L8S 4L7

The importance of real-time operations optimization has gained increasing recognition (Culter and Perry, 1982). This interest has spawned research in model formulation (Forbes et al, 1992A), model updating using real-time data (Roberts and Williams, 1981), and model-based optimization (Beigler, 1992), along with industrial case studies (Bailey et al, 1992). Another important facet of successful operations optimization is the design of a process control system that is compatible with operations optimization, which is the topic of this paper.

1. Control Design with Implicit Economic Criteria

Typically, the operations optimization problem is solved for a single set of conditions, although the plant never operates at exactly these conditions, because the externally determined inputs vary over time and introduce disturbances to the process. Therefore, the actual operating conditions of the process and the resulting profit depend strongly on how the process under feedback control responds to input changes.

In this paper, a general method is presented for designing a control system which maintains the profit at a high value. One obvious approach would be to solve the economic optimization explicitly at every controller execution; however, this would normally require excessive execution time and unreliable convergence at the process control level. Also, simplified explicit economic models in the controller have been shown to be sensitive to modelling errors (Forbes et al, 1992B).

Therefore, the approach proposed in this paper utilizes the best available model in the operations optimization level to determine adjustable parameters in the controller. In this approach, the controller algorithm is unchanged, i.e., it optimizes the trajectory of controlled and manipulated variables, usually in the error squared sense. However, the controller parameters are selected to result in high profit; thus the term implicit economic criteria.

The process conditions considered in this paper are

1) the execution period of the operations optimization is infrequent compared with process dynamics and disturbance frequencies.
2) the period of major disturbances, i.e., those which significantly influence profit, is long with respect to the process dynamics and short with respect to the optimization frequency
3) the ranges of the expected major disturbances can be predicted.

The result of these conditions is that the process (under control) operates at a number of quasi-steady states between each optimization, with each quasi-steady state the response to a major disturbance. For these conditions, the best controller design from an economic point of view can be determined by evaluating the performance at these steady-states.

The predictive controller selected for this study is the standard, unconstrained Dynamic Matrix Controller (DMC) (Culter and Ramaker, 1979). The optimizer can influence the behavior of the control system by determining the adjustable parameters in the DMC objective function.

$$P = \sum_{j=1}^{m}\sum_{k=1}^{r} \gamma_j\,(y_{jk} - y_{j,T})^2 + \sum_{j=1}^{m}\sum_{k=1}^{r} w_j\,(x_{jk} - x_{j,T})^2 + \sum_{j=1}^{m}\sum_{k=1}^{r} \lambda_j\,(\Delta x_{jk})^2 \qquad (1)$$

The parameters λ_j, the weights on the changes in the manipulated variables, influence the transient behavior of the system but assuming stability, do not affect the steady-state values of the controlled and manipulated variables. Thus, these parameters are not determined by the optimizer and can be given values that yield good transient behavior.

The remaining parameters are the targets for the controlled, $y_{j,T}$, and manipulated, $x_{j,T}$, variables and the weights on the deviations of these variables from their targets, γ_j and w_j respectively. All of these parameters influence the steady-state response of the system to disturbances and are determined to achieve high profit. There are two possible approaches to posing this problem.

Method I - All weights on the manipulated variable deviations from their targets are zero, and the targets for the controlled variables are allowed to take values which will increase profit. Assuming a square control problem and non-zero weights on the controlled variable deviations, the controlled variables will have zero steady-state offset. Thus the controlled variables do not change in response to disturbances, while the manipulated variables change as required by the process relationships.

Method II- All parameters are free to take values which increase profit. In this case, the system will not have zero steady-state offset, since both controlled and manipulated variables will deviate from their target values in response to disturbances.

Clearly, Method I, with only a subset of the adjustable parameters in Method II, can never give a profit greater than Method II. Also, recall that both methods will in general yield profit below the results with a complete operations optimization considering economics explicitly at each disturbance.

2. Mathematical Formulation

The challenge is to determine the values of the adjustable controller parameters,

$$\xi^T = (\ y_{1,T} \cdot\cdot\ x_{1,T} \cdot\cdot\ \gamma_1 \cdot\cdot\ w_1 \cdot\cdot) \qquad (2)$$

which results in a high profit for the expected disturbance. The problem involves

1) defining a steady-state process model and profit measure
2) defining the disturbances, d_i, i=1,n
3) defining the model equations which calculate the quasi-steady-state profit for all disturbances for the process under closed-loop control.
4) determining the parameters ξ which maximize the total profit

This can be formally stated as

$$\max_{\xi} \sum_{i=1}^{n} P(X_i, Y_i, d_i) \quad \{\text{Profit}\} \qquad (3)$$

$$\text{s.t.} \quad \text{for } i=1,n$$

$$F(X_i, Y_i, d_i) = 0 \qquad \{\text{Plant model}\}$$

$$G(X_i, Y_i, d_i) \leq 0$$

$$\min_{X_i} \ p(X_i, Y_i, \xi) \qquad \{\text{Controller}\}$$

$$\text{s.t.}$$

$$f(X_i, Y_i) = 0 \qquad \{\text{Controller}$$

$$g(X_i, Y_i) \leq 0 \qquad \text{model}\}$$

The statement in equation (3) involves a bilevel optimization problem, with the outer profit optimization requiring the inner controller optimization to be satisfied. A solution approach requiring two optimizations is generally considered unlikely to be successful due to accumulated numerical errors; thus, an alternative bilevel solution approach similar to that developed by Clark and Westerberg (1990) is employed. The inner optimization is replaced by its first order optimality conditions, which involves an equation for each manipulated variable defined by $\partial p/\partial x_j = 0$, i.e., $\nabla_x p = 0$. (Second order conditions were not included in the solution, but they were verified in post-solution analysis.) This approach replaces the inner optimization with an equivalent set of algebraic equations, which greatly improves the numerical performance of the formulation.

The reformulated problem can be stated as.

$$\max_{\xi} \sum_{i=1}^{n} P(X_i, Y_i, d_i) \quad \{\text{Profit}\} \qquad (4)$$

$$\text{s.t.} \quad \text{for } i=1,n$$

$$F(X_i, Y_i, d_i) = 0 \qquad \{\text{Plant model}\}$$

$$G(X_i, Y_i, d_i) \leq 0$$

$$\nabla_x p(X_i, Y_i, \xi) = 0 \qquad \{\text{Controller stationarity}\}$$

3. Case Study

The controller design approach was applied to the two-product distillation tower shown in Figure 1 with a feed rate of 532 kgmoles/hr of a mixture of propane and propylene. The tower was modelled as a tray-to-tray, binary component system, with the vapor liquid equilibrium defined by the relative volatility, α. No equipment constraints were active.

The profit measure was based on the cost of impurities in the product streams (0.242 $/kg in bottoms and 0.176 $/kg in distillate) and the cost of reboiler energy (3 $/MBTU).

The disturbances in the relative volatility and the feed composition are defined in Table 1. A complete operations optimization at every disturbance showed that the optimum values of both the controlled and manipulated variables changed in response to disturbances; the variability in the controlled variable indicated that Method II could provide improved economic performance.

For this case, the energy balance control was employed, so that the DMC controller adjusts the reflux flow and reboiler duty to control the distillate and bottoms compositions. The solution to the controller design in equation (4) determines for

Method I	the targets for the product compositions.
Method II	i) the targets for the product compositions and weights for the deviations of the product compositions from their targets and ii) the targets for the reflux and reboiler and weights for the deviations of these manipulated variables from their targets.

The mathematical problem involving 406 equations was formulated in the equation management system in GAMS and solved using the MINOS non-linear programming solver (Brooke et al, 1988).

The results of the optimization calculations are summarized in Table 2. The non-zero weights for the manipulated variables in Method II indicate that the controlled and manipulated variables should be allowed to vary in response to disturbances. The profit achieved by Method II is substantially higher than Method I, and it is not too different from the highest profit possible (-3730 $/hr), which could only be achieved by reoptimizing at each disturbance. The results demonstrate that Method II, which allows controlled and manipulated variables to deviate from their targets, results in a higher profit (a smaller loss) than Method I, which maintains the controlled variables at their constant target values.

The transient performances are presented in Figures 2, 3 and 4 for re-optimization at each disturbance, and for DMC control with the parameters ξ determined by Method I and Method II. In the Figures, the disturbances are entered in the numerical order indicated in Table 1. Note that the values of the controlled variables for Method II follow closely the values for the (perfect) reoptimization at each disturbance case, although the controller in Method II does not explicitly consider economics. Additional results with disturbances in α and x_F different from those used to determine the parameters ξ demonstrated the Method II still achieved higher profit than Method I. Also, the results demonstrate that the controller in Method II, with targets for the manipulated variables, provides dynamic performance as good as the conventional DMC controllers in the other approaches.

4. Conclusions

Two methods (I and II) have been presented for determining controller parameter values that increase the overall profit for a process, under feedback control, which is subject to disturbances. For either method, the optimization problem in equation (4) would be solved by the operations optimizer and the parameters ξ would be transmitted to the controller. Method II has been shown to have the potential to yield higher profit for situations in which the optimal controlled variables have different values for different disturbance levels. In essence, Method II determines a control strategy which approximately follows the optimum operating conditions, rather than maintaining a fixed values for the controlled variables. While there is no guarantee that the approach in Method II will always provide substantial improvement in all cases, it appears worthy of a careful evaluation.

NOMENCLATURE

d= disturbance
P= economic objective function
p= steady-state component of controller objective function, i.e., equation (1)
w= weights on the manipulated variable deviations from target
x= manipulated variables
X^T_i= $[x_{1i}\ x_{2i}\ ....]$, steady-state values at each disturbance, i
y= controlled process variables
Y^T_i= $[y_{1i}\ y_{2i}\ ....]$, steady-state values at each disturbance, i

α= relative volatility
ξ= adjustable controller parameters , the same for all cases, i=1,n
γ= weights on the controlled variable deviations from target
λ= weights on the changes in manipulated variables at each step

subscripts
i= cases for each disturbance, i=1,n
j= manipulated and controlled variables, j=1,m
k= steps in the control trajectory, k=1,r
T= target value

REFERENCES

Bailey, J., A. Hrymak, S. Treiber, and R. Hawkins, Non-linear Optimization of a Hydrocracker Fractionation Plant, submitted to Comp Chem Eng, 1992

Beigler, L., Successive Quadratic Programming for Real-Time Optimization, Algorithmic Concepts and Issues, CSChE Conf, Oct. 1992

Brooke, A., D. Kendrick, and A. Meeraus, GAMS Users Manual, The Scientific Press, San Francisco, 1988

Clark, P. and A. Westerberg, Bilevel Programming for Steady-state Chemical Process Design - I. Fundamentals and Algorithms, Comp Chem Eng, 14, 1, pp 87-97 (1990)

Cutler, C. and R. Perry, Real-time Optimization with Multivariable Control is Required to Maximize Profit, AIChE Meet, Oct. 1982

Cutler, C. and B. Ramaker, Dynamic Matrix Control - A Computer Control Algorithm, AIChE Meet, April 1979

Forbes, J., T. Marlin and J. MacGregor, Model Adequacy Requirements for Optimizing Plant Operations, submitted to Comp Chem Eng, 1992A

Forbes, J., T. Marlin and J. MacGregor, Model Accuracy Requirements for Economic Optimizing Model Predictive Controllers - the Linear Programming Case, ACC, pp. 1587-1593 (1992B)

Roberts, P. and T. Williams, On an Algorithm for Combined System Optimization and Parameter Estimation, Automatica, 17, 1, pp 199-209 (1981)

Table 1. Definition of expected disturbances

	relative volatility, α		
feed composition, x_F, % light key	1.454	1.494	1.534
60	case 1	case 4	case 7
70	case 2	case 5	case 8
80	case 3	case 6	case 9

Table 2. Results of controller design and implementation with disturbances in Table 1

	Method I		Method II	
variable	target	weight on deviation	target	weight on deviation
X_D (% L.K.)	94.88	*	95.19	10.0
X_B (% L.K.)	9.19	*	8.55	6.5
LR (kgmole/hr)	N/A	0	3243	0.020
V (kgmole/hr)	N/A	0	3660	0.0775
Total profit for nine steady states ($/hr)	-3868		-3771	

* = any non-zero values will yield zero-steady-state offset

Note: The optimum product qualities for case 5 is x_D= 95.18% and x_B= 8.68% which differ from the results of Method I

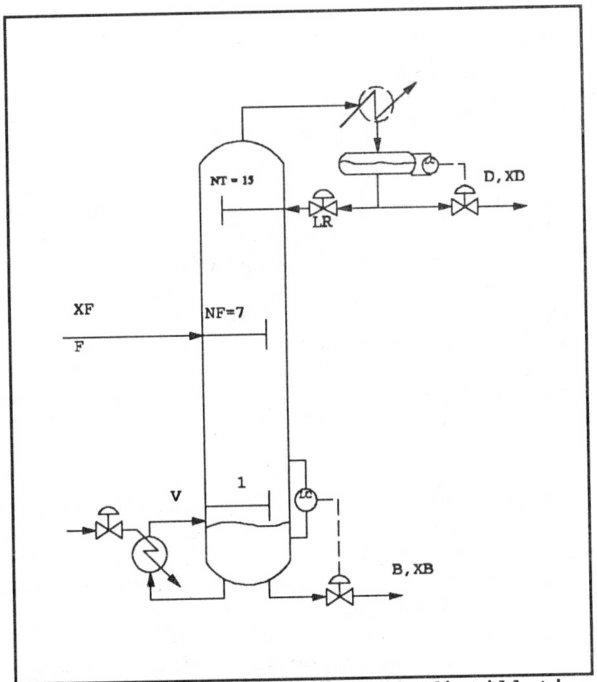

Figure 1. Schematic of distillation column used in case study

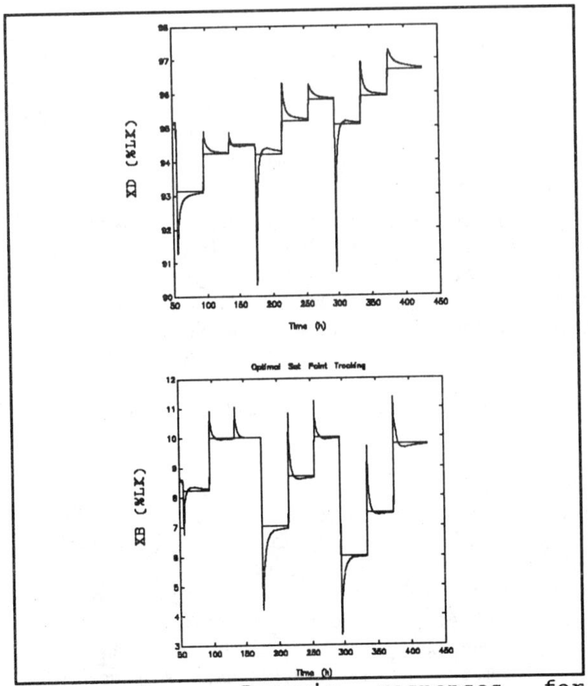

Figure 2. Dynamic responses for operations optimization at each disturbance

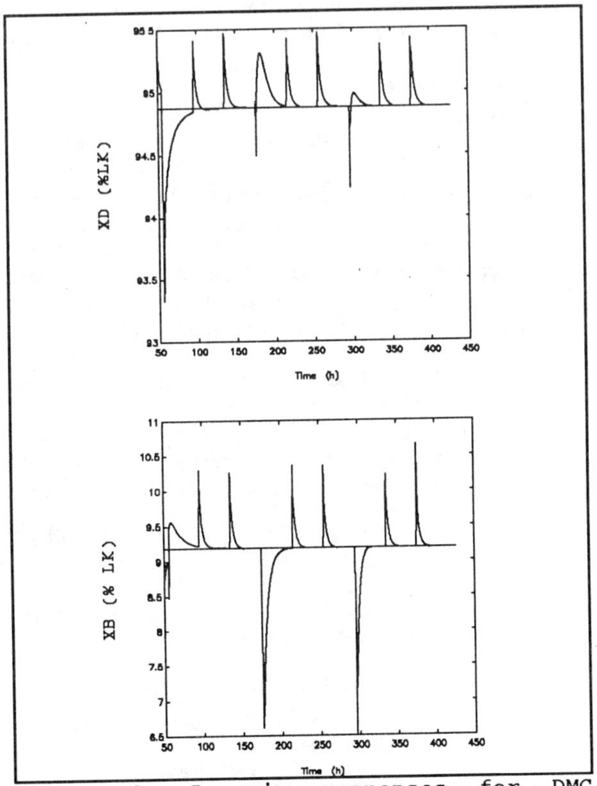

Figure 3. Dynamic responses for DMC controller designed according to Method I

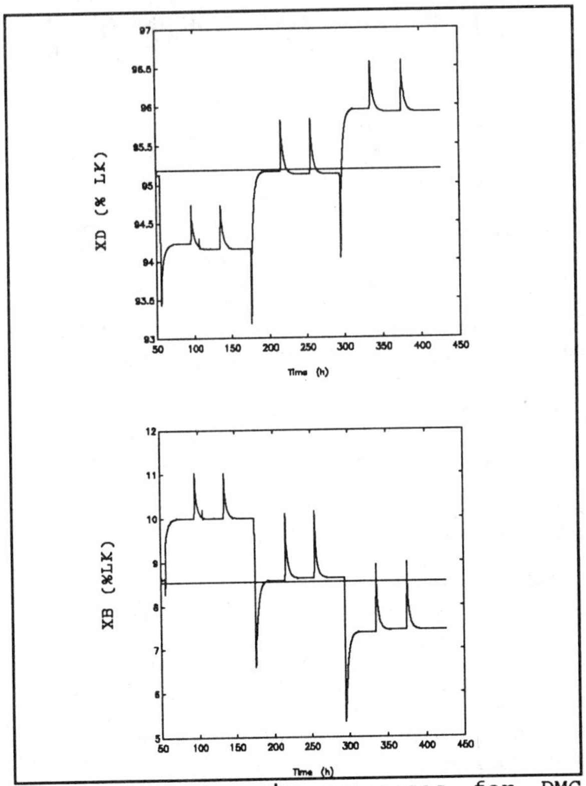

Figure 4. Dynamic responses for DMC controller designed according to Method II

Proceedings of the
American Control Conference
San Francisco, California • June 1993

HIERARCHICAL WAVELET CONTROLLER

Alexander Meystel, Predrag Filipovic
Electrical and Computer Engineering Department
Drexel University, Philadelphia, PA 19104

Abstract
This paper introduces a new control architecture and its design for feedback control systems. Our goal is to develop an architecture that will exploit the opportunities given by modern computational advances and create a structure that will eventually embrace intelligence features. Nested feedback loops are derived from the multiresolutional representation of control variables and hierarchical prediction of the next sample error vector. Method leads to a simple design process and demonstrates the advantages over other approaches.

Introduction
In existing controllers, hierarchies are built heuristicaly. Albus and Meystel [1-3], elaborated on the Nested Hierarchical Controllers principles. Multirate properties emerging from Sampled Data Control Systems were recognized by T. Hagiwara and M. Araki [4] and other works related to these basic ideas.We were also motivated by the advances in the area of signal processing, in particular by techniques of wavelet signal representation that matches the concept of hierarchical control [5,6].

Our goal is to design a hierarchical compensator based on multiresolutional signal decomposition and the tracking error prediction. Thus designed feedback system, will be shown to lead to significant improvement of tracking, increase of control robustness, higher utilization of existing computational power and, above all, creating a structure evolutionary proven to be a good ground for adaptivity, learning, and implementation of other features of the intelligent control.

Error Prediction
Equations of the plant are accepted as follows :

$$\mathbf{x}(n+1) = (\mathbf{A}+\Delta\mathbf{A})\mathbf{x}(n) + (\mathbf{B}+\Delta\mathbf{B})\mathbf{u}(n) + \mathbf{H}\mathbf{w}(n) \quad (1)$$

Δ's are unknown parameter variations from the values presumed in the model, $\mathbf{w}(n)$ is input disturbance propagated through unknown matrix **H**. Given the desired output trajectory $\mathbf{y}^*$ (state trajectories $\mathbf{x}^*$ too), our controller will have to make up for all parametric imperfections of the feedforward controller, output and the state disturbances.

Off-line feedforward input $u^{ff}(n)$ is computed to satisfy requirements for the presumed ideal model :

$$\mathbf{B}u^{ff}(n) + \mathbf{A}\mathbf{X}^*(n) = \mathbf{X}^*(n+1) \quad (2)$$

so that application of (2) to the plant (1) will yield error (3):

$$\mathbf{e}(n+1) = \Delta\mathbf{A}\mathbf{x}(n) + \Delta\mathbf{B}\,u^{ff}(n) + \mathbf{H}\mathbf{w}(n) + \mathbf{A}\mathbf{e}(n) \quad (3)$$

Introduction of their state error difference as an additional compensator $u^{fb}(n) = \mathbf{K}(x^*(n) - \mathbf{x}(n))$, can reduce the influence of the last member of (3):

$$\mathbf{A}\mathbf{e}(n) \;\text{-->}\; [\mathbf{A}-(\mathbf{B}+\Delta\mathbf{B})\mathbf{K}]\mathbf{e}(n) \quad (4)$$

It is obvious, that the error propagation can be reduced by proper choice of a feedback matrix **K** (optimal control e.g.). Let's assume for a moment that we have ability to perfectly predict $\mathbf{e}(n+1)$ if no extra action applied. Single input can then be calculated as $u^{pr}(n) = u^{pr}(n-1) - \mathbf{P}\mathbf{e}(n+1)$, where matrix **P** is a prediction gain. Entry matrix **B** prevents our intention to annul alleged error vector since **BP** matrix has rank = m. Matrix **P** choice is a topic of further investigation, one particular method will be proposed in a simulation example. Impossibility of a perfect predictor existence demands introduction of the predicted error vector as a sum of correct prediction and random error $\mathbf{z}(n)$. Quality of prediction determines the error distribution, so that search for control improvement should be directed in this manner.

Hierarchical Controller Architecture
The initial level control signal is state error feedback difference. First level feedback controller signal is a representation of original signal at a lower resolution (less frequent samples). Each level predicts within his representation of the error signal and computes the control action of its sampling time duration . Next level (n+1-st) computes the action upon its prediction (within his signal representation derived from signal representation at n-th level) and thus applied action has duration of its representation sample time. Procedure continues recursively until the point where new level introduction does not improve performance (illustrated by Figure 1). In order to determine such a limit frequency domain analysis of wavelet transform would be used as a tool .

Averaging Wavelet
Heuristical treatment of hierarchical and nested multiresolutional controller is known [1-3] however, no formalism has been introduced for dealing with analytical control design. In this paper, we propose an analytical technique based upon wavelet theory which allows for: a) selection of the number of resolution levels per controller, b)selection of resolution ratios between two consecutive levels. The derived analysis is suboptimal since computational complexity was not introduced as a part of cost evaluation.

Having set of signal samples, we would like to find a systematic way of building one sample representation with lower resolution required for the next adjacent level (const. to represent m samples). Tcherbysheff inequality holds regardless of density function which allows one to use time sequence as a random variable, minimization of $E\{(x(k) - \text{const})^2\}$ gives that the best constant is the average if $\mathbf{x}(k)$ sequence .

Multiresolutional signal representation is therefore done by usage of averaging wavelet transformation. Let us now define the averaging wavelet function $\Psi(k) \in I^2(Z)$:

$$k \in Z, \quad \Psi(k) = \begin{cases} 1 \;;\; -1 < k \le 0 \\ 0 \;;\; \text{elsewhere} \end{cases} \quad (5)$$

Multiresolutional signal representation using averaging wavelet will be defined as ($s_j \in Z$ is a resolution factor):

$$D^j(f(k)) = \sum_{n=-\infty}^{\infty} \left\langle f(k),\ \Psi^j(k - s_j n) \right\rangle \Psi^j(k - s_j n)$$

Hierarchical Controller Design

Presuming that starting level of signal representation corresponds to measured error samples. How many samples should we use to build next resolution level (the value of $s_1 \in Z,\ s_1 > 1$)? Optimal solution should take into account computational cost as well as performance goals. If we decide to pursue suboptimality, problem will require minimizing function **J**, the distance between the signal and its representation:

$$J = \max \mid f(k) - D^1 f_w \mid_{k \in (-s_1+1,\ 0\ )} \qquad (6)$$

which is minimal for $s_1 = 2$. Since similar argument can be applied for all consecutive levels, suboptimal level generation can be achieved by wavelet transform with $s_j = 2^j$.

Practical feedback compensator design procedure (to be used in our example) runs as follows:

- Record tracking error of a system with FF and FB.
- Find its next level AWT.
- Evaluate the usefulness of its application to control .
- The same for next levels regarding previous as compact sys.

Overall System Evaluation

Our unconventional approach to feedback compensator design can be analyzed using 'classical' tools. Let's for example start with the simplest case: two levels of hierarchy, non zero initial conditions problem. With system as in (Figure 1), recursion yields general formula:

$$\mathbf{x}(i+1) = T_i \mathbf{x}(i) \qquad (7)$$

$$T_{i_{even}} = (\mathbf{A} - \mathbf{B}K_1 - 0.5\mathbf{B}K_2 - 0.5\mathbf{B}K_2 T_{i-1}^{-1}) \qquad (8)$$

$$T_{i_{odd}} = (\mathbf{A} - \mathbf{B}K_1 - 0.5\mathbf{B}K_2 T_{i-1}^{-1} - 0.5\mathbf{B}K_2 T_{i-2}^{-1} T_{i-1}^{-1}) \qquad (9)$$

where $T_0 = I$, $T_1 = \mathbf{A} - \mathbf{B}K_1$ as compared to $T = \mathbf{A} - \mathbf{B}K_1$ for the state feedback controller.

Simulation Results

A single link manipulator is considered the plant in our simulation example. DC motor second order linearized system with no dry friction will be used for driving the link. The nonlinearity due to gravitation will be introduced as a source of the error to be compensated by the control system.

$$x'(t) = \begin{bmatrix} -1.5 & 501.1 \\ -15.7 & -361.5 \end{bmatrix} x(t) + \begin{bmatrix} 0 \\ 118.9 \end{bmatrix} v(t) \qquad (10)$$

Trajectory reach in frequencies is chosen to be our control goal. Parametric disturbances will be checked by change of plant parameters during control simulation.Comparison is done with PID controller since it has shown the best experimental results. PID gains are determined by exhaustive search for values that minimize tracking error. Prediction gain vector **p** for each level of hierarchy was found by minimization of **J**:

$$\mathbf{J} = \mathbf{w}_0^t(\mathbf{I}-\mathbf{bp})^t(\mathbf{I}-\mathbf{bp})\mathbf{w}_0 + S_{i=1}^{i=k}\mathbf{w}_i^t(\mathbf{A}^i\mathbf{bp})^t\mathbf{A}^i\mathbf{bpw} \qquad (11)$$

where vector $\mathbf{w}_i$ represents weighting factor. Matrices **A**, **b**, **c** are computed from continuous space state system with different "sampling" time for different levels. Function **J** reflects our desire to have perfect match, resulting in zero error in next step as well as minimizing the influence of this action in the future steps. Since new control will be applied while i>0 events occur, less significance should be given to these membersThe table for comparison and graphic illustration shows the superiority of the hierarchical AWT-prediction controller over PID in all aspects of performance. Compared are sum of errors and maximum absolute value. Third controller is PID with two levels addition which shows that hierarchical structure is not bound to prediction: it introduces new way of dealing with phenomenon which was hidden by information overflow at one level.

Conclusion

This research paper presents Nested Hierarchical Control Architecture implemented using AWT. Its suboptimal form is derived and performance evaluation experiment confirmed our theoretical results.

References

[1] J. Albus, A. Meystel, Foundations of Cognitive Architecture for Intelligent Machines, NIST/Drexel University Technical Report, 1991

[2] J. Albus, "Outline for a Theory of Intelligence", IEEE Transactions on Systems Man and Cybernetics, Vol. SMC-21, No. 3, May/June, 1991

[3] A. Meystel, "Theoretical Foundations of Planning and Navigation for Autonomous Robots", *Int. J. Intelligent Systems*, No.2, 1987

[4] T. Hagiwara, T. Fujimura, M. Araki "Genarilized multirate output controllers", *Int. J. control, 1990, vol 52, no. 3*

[5] Y. Maximov, A. Meystel, "Optimum design of multiresolutional hierarchical control systems", Proceedings of the 1992 International Conference of Intelligent Control, Glasgow, UK, 1992

[6] S. G. Mallat, "A Theory for Multiresolution Signal Decomposition: The Wavelet Representation", *IEEE transactions on Pattern Analysis and Machine Intelligence*, July 1989

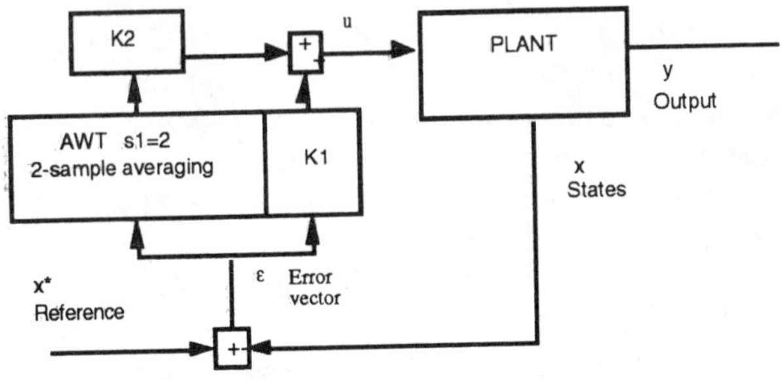

Figure 1 - Two-level Hierarchical Regulator

Controller		input noise gravitation	parametric disturbance	all suorces of disturbances
PID	Error sum	12.7	18.4	22.6
	Max abs	0.2	0.2	0.3
Hierarchy 2 levels	Error sum	2.4	7.0	9.6
	Max abs	0.2	0.1	0.1
PID with 2 additional levels	Error sum	12.	16.	21.
	Max abs	0.2	0.2	0.3

Table 1 - Performance evaluation

Proceedings of the
American Control Conference
San Francisco, California • June 1993

ESTIMATION OF PROCESS STEP RESPONSE WEIGHTS BASED ON CLOSED-LOOP STEP RESPONSE DATA

L. Wang and W.R. Cluett

Department of Chemical Engineering
University of Toronto, Toronto, Canada M5S 1A4

Abstract

Dynamic matrix controllers (DMC) and model predictive controllers (MPC) have found wide application in the process industries. In order to design such a controller, a step response model of the process is often used. This paper will provide an algorithm for obtaining the step response model of a process based on closed-loop operating data generated by a step change in the setpoint. This algorithm is intended for application to closed-loop systems where a DMC or MPC is being designed to replace an arbitrary existing controller.

1 Introduction

In the procedure of process identification, a step response test is often performed as a simple means to obtain approximate values for the process gain, time constant and time delay. This experiment is generally used only as a precursor to the design of further identification experiments (e.g. to choose the sampling interval and the frequency content of the input signal) for use in the fitting of a more accurate model. However, there is tremendous incentive to explore the possibility of obtaining a quality model from the step response data itself (i.e. reduced experimental time and ease of implementation). Recently, we have been studying the development of Laguerre models from open-loop step response data[2,1,7]. This paper extends these results to the closed-loop situation where a Laguerre model relating the setpoint to the closed-loop process response is used to derive a frequency response model of the process itself. This model is then converted directly to a step response model (i.e. the step response weights) for use in the design of a DMC or MPC.

2 Laguerre Modelling from Step Response Data

This section will present the identification algorithm for estimating a continuous-time transfer function model in the form of a Laguerre model on the basis of step response data.

2.1 The Laguerre model structure

The continuous-time Laguerre model has the following structure, for $p > 0$

$$G(s) = \sum_{i=1}^{\infty} c_i L_i(s) \tag{1}$$

where $L_i(s)$ is defined as

$$L_i(s) = \sqrt{2p}\frac{(s-p)^{i-1}}{(s+p)^i} \tag{2}$$

The inverse Laplace transform of equation (1) gives the corresponding impulse response model in the time domain

$$h(t) = \sum_{i=1}^{\infty} c_i l_i(t) \tag{3}$$

where $l_i(t)$ are the Laguerre functions defined by

$$\begin{aligned} l_1(t) &= \sqrt{2p} \times e^{-pt} \\ l_2(t) &= \sqrt{2p}(-2pt+1)\, e^{-pt} \\ \vdots &= \vdots \\ l_i(t) &= \sqrt{2p}\tfrac{e^{pt}}{(i-1)!}\tfrac{d^{i-1}}{dt^{i-1}}[t^{i-1}e^{-2pt}] \end{aligned} \tag{4}$$

which satisfy the orthonormal properties

$$\int_0^{\infty} l_i(t) l_j(t) dt = 0 \quad i \neq j \tag{5}$$

and

$$\int_0^{\infty} l_i(t)^2 dt = 1 \tag{6}$$

It is well known that for any piece-wise continuous impulse response function $h(t)$ with

$$\int_0^{\infty} h^2(t) dt < \infty \tag{7}$$

and any $\varepsilon > 0$, there exists an integer N such that

$$\int_0^{\infty} (h(t) - \sum_{i=1}^{N} c_i l_i(t))^2 dt < \varepsilon \tag{8}$$

In practical situations, the infinite dimensional model in equation (1) is approximated by a finite dimensional model of order N

$$G_A(s) = \sum_{i=1}^{N} c_i L_i(s) \qquad (9)$$

The parameters to be determined in the Laguerre model are the pole location p, the coefficients c_i, and the model order N. A step response model can be directly constructed from the Laguerre functions and the model parameters as follows

$$\begin{aligned} g_A(t) &= C^T \int_0^t L_N(\tau)d\tau \\ &= \frac{1}{p}C^T A_N^{-1}[L_N(0) - L_N(t)] \qquad (10) \end{aligned}$$

where
$C^T = [c_1 c_2 \ldots c_N]$, $L_N(t) = [l_1(t) l_2(t) \ldots l_N(t)]^T$ and A_N is the $N \times N$ matrix given by

$$A_N = \begin{bmatrix} 1 & 0 & \ldots & 0 \\ 2 & 1 & \ldots & 0 \\ \vdots & & & \\ 2 & \ldots & 2 & 1 \end{bmatrix} \qquad (11)$$

2.2 Estimation of the Laguerre coefficients from noisy step response data

Assume that for a unit step input change, the output response of a stable, linear, time-invariant system is given by

$$\hat{g}(t) = g(t) + \xi(t) \qquad (12)$$

where $g(t)$ denotes the true step response, and $\xi(t)$ denotes the output additive disturbance effect with the assumption that $|\xi(t)| < \infty$. Assuming that the disturbance $\xi(t)$ is differentiable, the following loss function is chosen as the modelling criterion

$$E_c = \int_0^\infty \left(\frac{d\hat{g}(t)}{dt} - \sum_{i=1}^{N} c_i l_i(t)\right)^2 dt \qquad (13)$$

where $\frac{d\hat{g}(t)}{dt}$ is an estimate of the unit impulse response. Note, however, that we will not actually require that the step response be differentiated in the estimation algorithm. Using the orthonormal property of the Laguerre functions (equations (5) and (6)), this loss function can be readily minimized, which yields the following analytical solution of the Laguerre coefficients

$$\hat{c}_i = \int_0^\infty \frac{d\hat{g}(t)}{dt} l_i(t)dt \qquad (14)$$

$$i = 1, 2, 3, ..., N$$

To avoid differentiation of the measured step response data $\hat{g}(t)$, which can amplify noise effects and cause numerical problems, integration by parts is introduced in equation (14) so that the derivative is transferred from the step response to the Laguerre functions. Here, the Laguerre function is being used as a type of modulating function in that the approximation of a derivative from a noisy signal is avoided [5,3]. Equation (14) then becomes

$$\hat{c}_i = [\hat{g}(t) l_i(t)]_0^\infty - \int_0^\infty \hat{g}(t)\dot{l}_i(t)dt \qquad (15)$$

Since for any $p > 0$, $\lim_{t\to\infty} l_i(t) = 0$, and taking $\hat{g}(0) = 0$, the first term on the right-hand side of equation (15) is equal to zero. Let T_m denote an overestimate of the settling time of the process (i.e. time to reach steady-state), and g_m be an estimate of the new steady-state value of the process. Then, equation (15) can be written as

$$\hat{c}_i = -\int_0^{T_m} \hat{g}(t)\dot{l}_i(t)dt - g_m \int_{T_m}^\infty \dot{l}_i(t)dt \qquad (16)$$

which leads to the following set of equations for estimating the Laguerre coefficients

$$\begin{aligned} \hat{c}_1 &= p\int_0^{T_m} \hat{g}(t)l_1(t)dt + g_m l_1(T_m) \\ \hat{c}_2 &= 2p\int_0^{T_m} \hat{g}(t)l_1(t)dt \\ &+ p\int_0^{T_m} \hat{g}(t)l_2(t)dt + g_m l_2(T_m) \\ &\vdots \\ \hat{c}_N &= 2p\sum_{i=1}^{N-1}\int_0^{T_m} \hat{g}(t)l_i(t)dt \\ &+ p\int_0^{T_m} \hat{g}(t)l_N(t)dt + g_m l_N(T_m) \qquad (17) \end{aligned}$$

Remarks:
(1) It is important to point out that the algorithm presented here does not involve the inversion of a data matrix that typically arises with the application of least-squares based estimation algorithms. Therefore, any numerical problems associated with inversion of this matrix when using a step input signal are avoided.
(2) Each coefficient $\hat{c}_i$ is estimated independently and therefore, an increase or decrease in the model order N does not affect the previously estimated coefficients.
(3) Although the assumption of differentiability of the disturbance is made to define the loss function, the algorithm itself does not require differentiation of the step response data.

2.3 Choice of pole location p

In theory, choice of the pole location p does not affect the existence and convergence of the Laguerre model. In practice, a poor choice of p will require a high order Laguerre model in order to achieve a desired model accuracy. Thus, the pole location p should be chosen such that some measure of the modelling error is minimized for a given model order N. The modelling error considered here is referred to as the step response error. Upon obtaining the coefficients $\hat{c}_i$, $i = 1, 2, ..., N$, the step response of the Laguerre model $g_A(t)$ can be evaluated by using equation (10). Hence, the integral square error between the plant step response and the Laguerre model step response can be calculated as

$$E_{step} = \int_0^{T_m} (\hat{g}(t) - g_A(t))^2 dt \tag{18}$$

Based on this step response error function, the pole location p can be chosen such that E_{step} is minimized. Note that to find the best value for p, (18) can be readily minimized using an algorithm for the solution of a one-dimensional unconstrained optimization problem.

3 Closed-loop Identification Algorithm Based on Step Response Data

The closed-loop identification algorithm consists of two stages: the first stage is to identify the frequency response of the plant, and the second stage is to transform the frequency response into a step response model.

3.1 Estimation of the plant frequency response

Consider a standard feedback control system, where $G(s)$ denotes the unknown plant transfer function, $K(s)$ denotes the feedback controller, ξ is the additive disturbance, and r is the setpoint signal. It is assumed that the feedback system is closed-loop stable. The control signal u is given by

$$u = \frac{K}{1+KG} r - \frac{K}{1+KG} \xi \tag{19}$$

and the plant output y is given by

$$y = \frac{KG}{1+KG} r + \frac{1}{1+KG} \xi \tag{20}$$

The objective in the first stage is to estimate the frequency response of the plant G, subject to a step change in r. Here, we will assume that the structure and the parameters of the feedback controller K are known. Then, define the following transfer function

$$M_1(s) = \frac{KG}{1+KG} \tag{21}$$

which is the closed-loop transfer function which relates r to y. If we assume that M_1 is stable and strictly proper, then M_1 can be represented by a finite dimensional Laguerre model, i.e.

$$M_1(s) = \sum_{i=1}^{N} c_i L_i(s) \tag{22}$$

Hence, the coefficients c_i and the parameter p are obtained from the closed-loop step response y using the algorithm presented in section 2. Using the frequency responses of M_1 and K, the frequency response of the plant can be estimated by solving the following equation

$$\hat{G}(jw) = \frac{M_1(jw)}{[1 - M_1(jw)]K(jw)} \tag{23}$$

at the values of w where $[1 - M_1(jw)]K(jw) \neq 0$. The approach is simple and straightforward, particularly if K is a proportional controller.

3.2 Transforming the frequency response data into step response weights

We will now derive step response weights in the continuous-time domain, which gives the user complete flexibility with respect to the selection of the final sampling interval. Note that the continuous-time unit step response $g(t)$ of the process is given by

$$g(t) = \int_0^t h(\tau) d\tau \tag{24}$$

where $h(.)$ is unit impulse response. Substituting the inverse Fourier transform of $h(t)$ into equation (24) gives a direct relationship between the process step response and its frequency response $G(jw)$ [4]

$$\begin{aligned} g(t) &= \frac{1}{2\pi} \int_{-\infty}^{\infty} G(jw) \int_0^t e^{jw\tau} d\tau dw \\ &= \frac{1}{2\pi} \int_{-\infty}^{\infty} \frac{G(jw)}{jw} (e^{jwt} - 1) dw \end{aligned} \tag{25}$$

A numerical solution of equation (25) may be used to evaluate the step response weights. A plot of the weighting function $\frac{(e^{jwt}-1)}{jw}$ is given in Figure 1 for two values of t. This shows that the weighting function emphasizes low frequencies more as t increases and is finite for all finite values of t. Note that this function does not depend on the plant transfer function $G(jw)$.

4 Simulation Results

Consider the following 12th order process with transfer function

$$G(s) = \frac{(15s+1)^2(4s+1)(2s+1)}{(20s+1)^3(10s+1)^3(5s+1)^3(0.5s+1)^3} \quad (26)$$

The output disturbance ξ is taken to be of the form

$$\xi(t) = 0.01 \times (cos3t + cos5t + d(t)) \quad (27)$$

with $d(t)$ chosen as a zero-mean, white noise sequence with variance equal to one.

Two experiments were performed on this simulated process using a proportional controller with two different values of the controller gain. The magnitude of the step setpoint change in both cases was 5.0. The measured plant output y for a gain of 0.1 is shown in Figure 2. The Laguerre model fit ($N = 5$, $p = 0.031$) to the closed-loop response is also shown in Figure 2. The first 32 values of the measured output, which equals 12.8 seconds at the sampling rate of 2.5 Hz, were set equal to zero to improve the model fit. The estimated process frequency response obtained from applying Equation (23) is shown in Figure 3 and the estimated process step response obtained from applying Equation (25) is shown in Figure 4. In both figures, the true responses are also given for comparison.

The same set of results for a gain of 1.0 are given in Figures 5-7. The Laguerre model fit shown in Figure 5 was obtained with $N = 12$ and $p = 0.034$. Again, the first 32 values were set equal to zero to improve the model fit.

In both cases, the frequency response and step response estimates are very close to those of the true system. The algorithm is very robust in the presence of the disturbance, although the procedure of zeroing some of the initial measured data is important, particularly in the case with $K = 0.1$. This procedure and other detailed analysis of the step response algorithm are discussed in [6].

5 Conclusions

This paper presents an algorithm for estimating step response weights directly from closed-loop operating data generated by a step setpoint change. Simulation examples have been used to demonstrate the effectiveness and the accuracy of the algorithm. The potential application of this algorithm lies in the area of design of model predictive and dynamic matrix controllers for the process industries.

References

[1] W. R. Cluett and L. Wang. Modelling and robust controller design using step response data. *Chemical Engineering Science*, Vol.46:2065–2077, 1991.

[2] W. R. Cluett and L. Wang. Process modelling using step response data. *Presented at the 1990 Annual AIChE Meeting, Recent Advances in Process Control, Chicago*, 1990.

[3] T. B. Co and B. E. Ydstie. System identification using modulating functions and fast fourier transforms. *Computers and Chemical Engineering*, Vol.14:1051–1066, 1990.

[4] D. R. Coughanowr and L. B. Koppel. *Process Systems Analysis and Control.* McGraw-Hill Book Company, New York, 1965.

[5] P. Eykhoff. *System Identification.* Wiley, New York, 1974.

[6] L. Wang and W. R. Cluett. Building transfer function models from step response data using the Laguerre network. *Submitted for publication.*

[7] L. Wang and W. R. Cluett. The Laguerre network- a bridge from plant data to process models. *Proceedings of 4th International Symposium on Process Systems Engineering, Montebello, Quebec*, III.6.1–III.6.15, 1991.

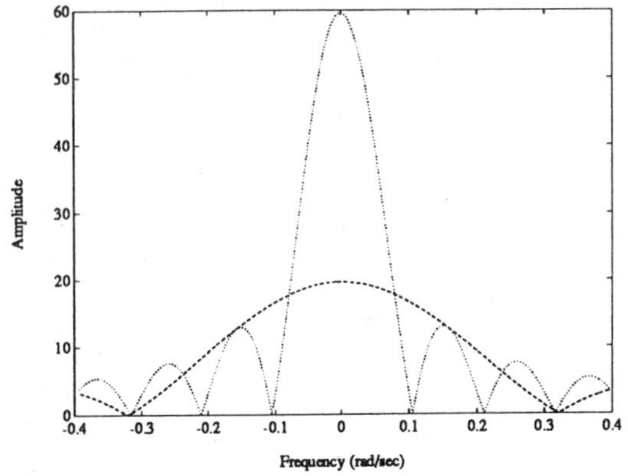

Figure 1: Frequency weighting function (dashed: $t = 20$; dotted: $t = 60$)

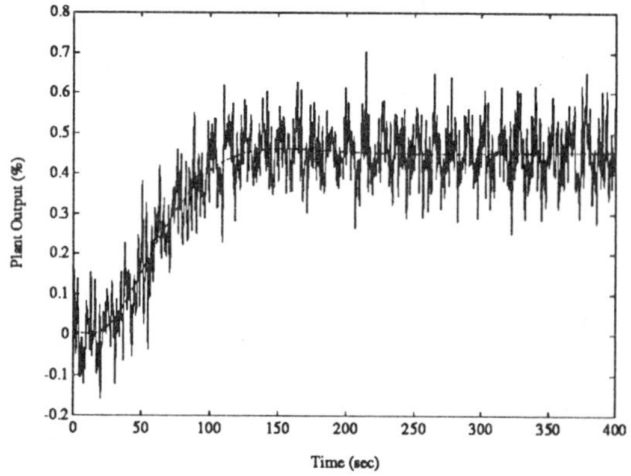

Figure 2: Closed loop process output response for $K = 0.1$ (solid: measured response; dashed: Laguerre model fit)

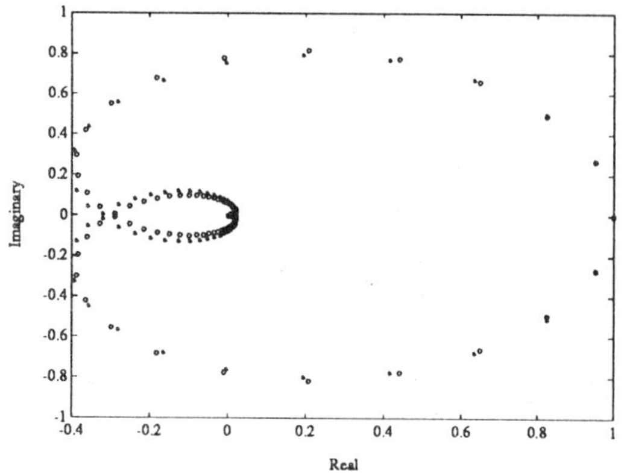

Figure 3: Process frequency response (*-true process; o-estimated process)

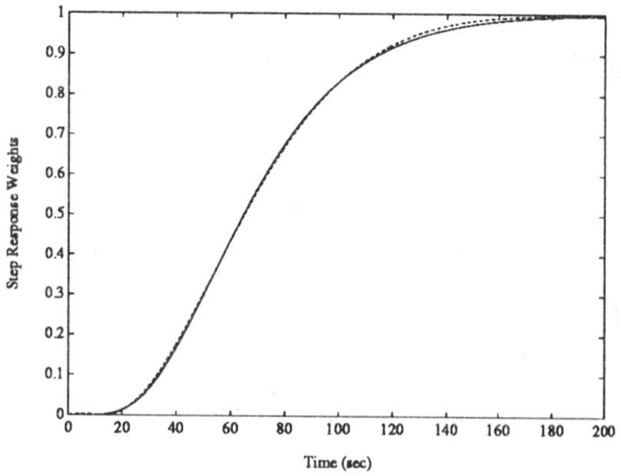

Figure 4: Process step response (solid: true; dashed: estimated)

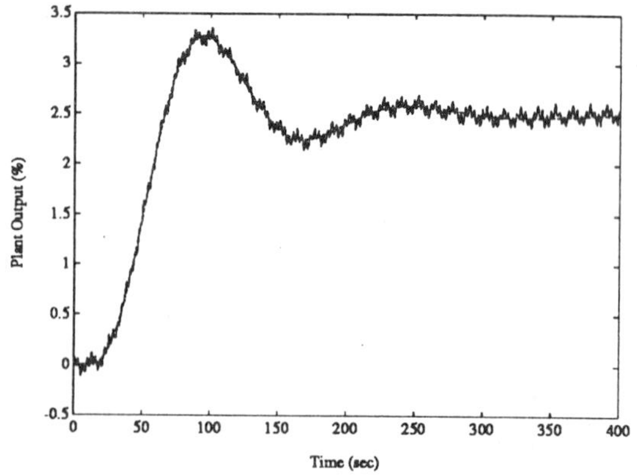

Figure 5: Closed loop process output response for $K = 1.0$ (solid: measured response; dashed: Laguerre model fit)

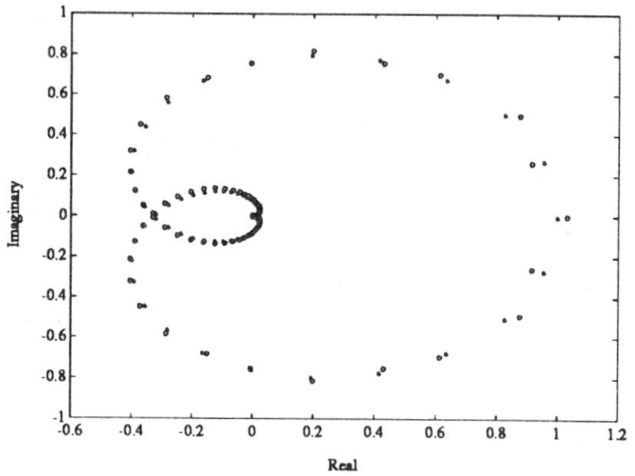

Figure 6: Process frequency response (*-true process; o-estimated process)

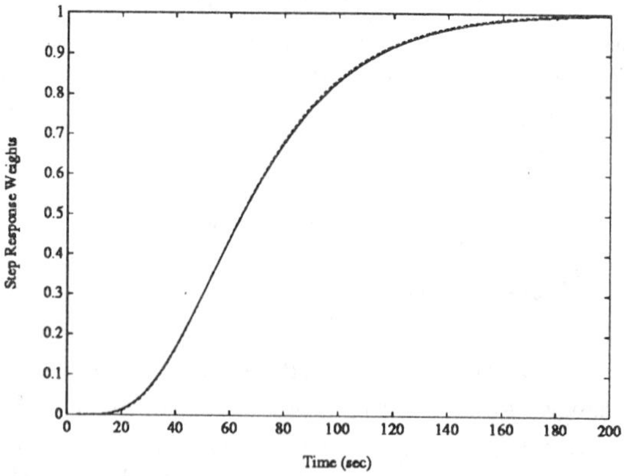

Figure 7: Process step response (solid: true; dashed: estimated)

Proceedings of the
American Control Conference
San Francisco, California • June 1993

Long Range Non-Linear Predictive Control

Yousef Al-Assaf
Department of Industrial Engineering
University of Jordan

Abstract:

Self-tuners based on linear models have shown their ability to achieve adequate control for special class of processes, such those which are slowly time-varying and weakly non-linear. However, many practical applications are highly non-linear and embarking on designing a linear self-tuner could be a fruitless exercise.

In this research the dynamic process to be controlled is described by a non-linear model (namely the Hammerstein model) and a long-range, incremental and non-linear predictive self-tuner is obtained accordingly.

Various simulation examples indicated that the long range and non-linear predictive controller gives a superior performance in comparison with linear self-tuners as long as the controlled process is adequately represented by Hammerstein model.

1. Introduction:

A major assumption made on most of the work performed in the area of self-tunning control [3,10,11] is that the process to be controlled is linear or can be linearised around the current operating point. Those controllers produced adequate results to a certain extant when applied to processes which are slowly time varying and weakly non-linear. Certain design knobs where carefully chosen in order to assist the controller to overcome the shortcomings produced by assuming that the process is linear. For example the forgetting factor was chosen to be small so that the estimator would give more weight to new coming data and consenquently a more suitable linear model for the present operating condition is produced. Furthermore, digital filters are adapted in order to detune any model mismatch between the estimator model and the actual one. Other methods [4] use cascade control in extreme non-linear cases to partially linearise the forward loop. The principle justification is that the methods based on that assumption have been seen to work in practice. However other research [8] noted that basic and linear self-tuners are not amenable to actuator non-linearites and non-linear model has to be adapted to improve performance.

In this paper the Hammerstein model which was shown [8] to be practically suitable for a certain class of non-linearites is used to describe the non-linear dynamic process to be controlled. Consequently, a non-linear incremental predictive self-tuner is obtained accordingly. Section 2 presents the continuous and discrete forms of the Hammerstein models with a special structure for the noise signal. Based on this model a prediction of the process output is obtained. The objective of this controller is to set this predicted output to the desired set-point by manipulating the present and future control signals. Although there are many strategies which give unique control, section 3 describes the one which is used in this paper. Simulation examples to demonstrate the ability of this controller are presented in section 4. Conclusions are included in section 5.

2. Non-linear plant model and predictor:

In the theory of self-tuning control [5] the process to be controlled is assumed to be linear and can be represented in CARIMA (Controlled Auto-Regressive Integrated Moving Average) form as follows:

$$A(z^{-1})y(t) = B(z^{-1})u(t-k) + C(z^{-1})\zeta(t)/\Delta \qquad 1$$

Where

y(t) & u(t) : are the process output and input respectively.
A, B & C : are polynomials in backward shift operator z^{-1}.
k : is the process time delay.
ζ : is an uncorrelated noise signal.
Δ : is the difference operator $1-z^{-1}$

The use of the CARIMA model introduces an integral action which gives an offset free closed loop behaviour. To produce a non-linear sampled-data model, the process can be described as a Volterra series [2,8,9] while the noise structure is taken as in CARIMA model, then:

$$Ay(t) = g_o + \sum_{\tau_1=0}^{t} g_1(\tau_1)u(t-k-\tau_1) +$$
$$\sum_{\tau_1=0}^{t}\sum_{\tau_2=0}^{t} g_2(\tau_1,\tau_2)u(t-k-\tau_1).u(t-k-\tau_2) + ..$$
$$.. + \sum_{\tau_1=0}^{t} \cdots \sum_{\tau_n=0}^{t} g(\tau_1,\ldots,\tau_n)\prod_{\tau=\tau_1}^{\tau_n} u(t-k-\tau) + \ldots + C\zeta(t)/\Delta \qquad 2$$

Where $g_n(\tau_1,\ldots\ldots,\tau_n)$ are the n-th order Volterra Kernels. Since the recursive parameter estimator requires the system to be linear in the parameters and of finite number of elements [7] a discrete description of eq.(2) can be written as follows [8]:

$$A(z^{-1})y(t) = g_o + B_1(z^{-1})u(t-k)$$
$$+ \sum_{\beta 1=0}^{h} B_{2\beta 1}(z^{-1})u(t-k)u(t-k-\beta_1)$$
$$+ \ldots + \sum_{\beta_1=0}^{h} \cdots \sum_{\beta_{p-1}=\beta_{p-2}}^{h_1} B_{p\beta_1\ldots\beta_{p-1}} u(t-k)\prod_{\beta=\beta}^{\beta_{p-1}} u(t-k-\beta) + C\zeta(t)/\Delta \qquad 3$$

Where
P : is the degree of non-linearity
$A(z^{-1})$: $1 + a_1 z^{-1} + \ldots\ldots\ldots + a_{\delta_a} z^{-\delta_a}$
$B_{p\beta_1\ldots\beta_{p-1}}(z^{-1})$: $b_{p\beta_1\ldots\beta_{p-1}} z^{-1} + \ldots + b_{p\beta_1\ldots\beta_{p-1}} z^{-\delta_b}$
g_o : time-invariant constant
For most physical systems it is sufficient to set h_1=h=0 [8]. So, eq.(3) becomes:

$$A(z^{-1})y(t)=g_o+B_1(z^{-1})u(t-k)+\ldots+B_p(z^{-1})u^p(t-k)+C(z^{-1})\xi(t)/\Delta \tag{4}$$

To derive the non-linear predictor it will be assumed that $B_1, B_2, \ldots\ldots, B_p$ are all having the same degree. Let C be chosen as 1 or alternatively C^{-1} is absorbed and computed within the other polynomials to give the model:

$$Ay(t)=g_o+Bu(t-k)+\ldots+B_pu^p(t-k)+\xi(t)/\Delta \tag{5}$$

To derive an N step ahead predictor of y(t+N) consider the identity

$$1=E_N(z^{-1})A\Delta+z^{-N}F_N(z^{-1}) \tag{6}$$

Where E and F are polynomials of degree N-1 and δ_a-1 respectively. From eq.(5) and eq.(6) it can be shown that:

$$y(t+N)=F_Ny(t)+G_1\Delta u(t+N-k)+\ldots+G_p\Delta u^p(t+N-k)+E_N\xi(t+N) \tag{7}$$

Where $G_j=E_nB_j$ j=1,2,.........,p

G_j are polynomials of degree $N+\delta b-1$. As E_N is of degree N-1 all the noise components are in the future so the optimal N-step ahead predictor given the measured output data up to time t is:

$$\hat{y}(t+N/t)=F_Ny(t)+G_1\Delta u(t+N-k)+\ldots+G_p\Delta u^p(t+N-k) \tag{8}$$

It can be seen from eq.(8) that if p = 1 then the predictor corresponds to a linear one.Eq.(8) is unsuitable for parameter estimation using RLS techniques because it contains a mixture of differenced and positional data [6]. However F can be modified to give a zero-mean equation which is suitable for RLS estimation, such as:

$$F_N=1+\Delta F \tag{9}$$

From eq.(9) and eq.(8) it can be shown that:

$$\hat{y}(t+N)=y(t)+F\Delta y(t)+G_1\Delta u(t+N-k)+\ldots+G_p\Delta u^p(t+N-k) \tag{10}$$

A RLS estimator similar to the one discussed in [11] is used to estimate the parameters of F, G_1, G_2, ..., G_p in eq.(10). It is to be emphasised here that the non-linear model is assumed linear in parameters.

3. Control strategy:

The objective of the predictive control law is to derive the future $\hat{y}(t+N)$ to the desired set-point. It can be seen from eq.(10) that in order to do that some decisions and assumptions must be made concerning the future control signals which are not available at time t. It is easy to note that G can be written as:

$$G_j=G_{j1}+z^{-(N-k+1)}G_{j2} \tag{11}$$

Where G_{j1} are polynomials of degree N-k and G_{j2} are polynomials of degree $\delta b+k-1$, such that:

$$G_j=g_{j0}+g_{j1}z^{-1}+\ldots+g_{jN-k}z^{-(N-k)}+g_{jN-k+1}z^{-(N-k+1)}+\ldots g_{jN+\delta b-1}z^{-(N+\delta b-1)} \tag{12}$$

Substituting eq.(11) into eq.(10) gives:

$$\hat{y}(t+N)=y(t)+F\Delta y(t)+G_{11}\Delta u(t+N-k)+\ldots+G_{12}\Delta u(t-1)+G_{p1}\Delta u^p(t+N-k)+G_{p2}\Delta u^p(t-1) \tag{13}$$

Assume it is desired to satisfy

$$\hat{y}(t+N)=W \tag{14}$$

Where W is the desired set-point. Then eq.(13) becomes:

$$\mu=G_{11}\Delta u(t+N-k)+G_{21}\Delta u^2(t+N-k)+\ldots+G_{p1}\Delta u^p(t+N-k) \tag{15}$$

where μ consists of all known signals values at time t, such that:

$$\mu=W-y(t)-F\Delta y(t)-G_{12}\Delta u(t-1)-G_{22}\Delta u^2(t-1)-\ldots-G_{p2}\Delta u^p(t-1) \tag{16}$$

Although there are many strategies which give unique control, in this implementation all the future control increments are assumed to be zero while the present control signal is calculated from eq.(15). Then it can be shown that eq.(15) becomes:

$$\mu-\lambda_1u(t-1)-\lambda_2u^2(t-1)-\ldots-\lambda_pu^p(t-1)=\lambda_1u(t)+\lambda_2u^2(t)+\ldots+\lambda_pu^p(t) \tag{17}$$

Where $\lambda_j=g_{jN-k}$

At each sampling instant any polynomial solving iterative technique can be used to calculate the control signal from eq.(17). However, according to the degree of eq.(17), p real or complex roots could result and decisions must be made about which root must be chosen and implemented. To avoid the possibility of all roots of eq.(17) turning out complex, p is restricted to an odd value. If p is chosen as 1 then there is only one solution and the controller is linear. However if p is equal to 3, then in this case there are two possible situations:

1- Eq.(17) gives one real and two complex roots, the real one is implemented.

2- The solution to eq.(17) are three real roots, although in theory any of the three roots should satisfy the objectives, one must be taken. Anbumani [1] chooses the real root with the least magnitude. Although no justification is given it is believed that the reason is to keep the control signal as small as possible. The controller used in that research was a positional minimum variance. The control signal which it has been chosen in this study is the closed action to the previous applied control signal ie. the one which gives minimum $\Delta u(t)$. This will give the minimum possible valve activity which is a desired feature from a practical point of view.

If p is chosen as an odd value greater than 3, same analysis discussed above is applied.

4. Simulation examples:

In the following simulation examples p=1 is taken to represent the linear controller.

<u>Example 1:</u>

Assume it is desired to control the process shown in Fig.1 with an input actuator given by:

$$U_o=u^3(t)$$

In this simulation, N is chosen as 1 for both the linear and non-linear self-tuner with $\delta a=2$ and $\delta b=3$. For the non-linear controller p was taken as 3. The rest of the parameters are the same for both controllers. Fig.2 shows how the linear predictive controller behaves while Fig.3 shows the performance of the non-linear controller. As it can be seen from Fig.2 the linear controller has to obtain a new linear model for the process at each operating condition. Hence during the set-point changes massive control signals and poor set-point tracking is experienced. However essential improvements has been achieved by the non-linear model since it is more adequate in representing the non-linearity.

In Fig.2 and Fig.3 at the first shown arrow a DU (load disturbance at input) of 5 units is applied and the released, and at the second arrow a DAY (load disturbance at the output) of 5 units is applied and then released. It can be seen that the rejection properties of both controllers are similar since the changes produced by disturbances were not strong enough to damage the creditability of the local model at that set-point.

<u>Example 2:</u>

Consider that it is desired to control the process shown in Fig.4 with the following input non-linearity:

$$U_o=u+0.1u^2+0.03u^3$$

In this simulation N is chosen as 1 with $\delta a=2$, $\delta b=3$ and p=3 for the non-linear controller. Similar other parameters were used.

Fig.5 shows that the linear controller is unable to control this process adequately. Large overshoots, oscillatory behaviour and limit cycles are present at most operating conditions. This is due to the fact that a strong non-linearity has been introduced in the input. However the non-linear controller finds no difficulty to produce good results as shown in Fig.6. The linear-model estimator produced reasonable linearised model for the initial operating condition but did not have the momentum to give adequate models in other operating levels.

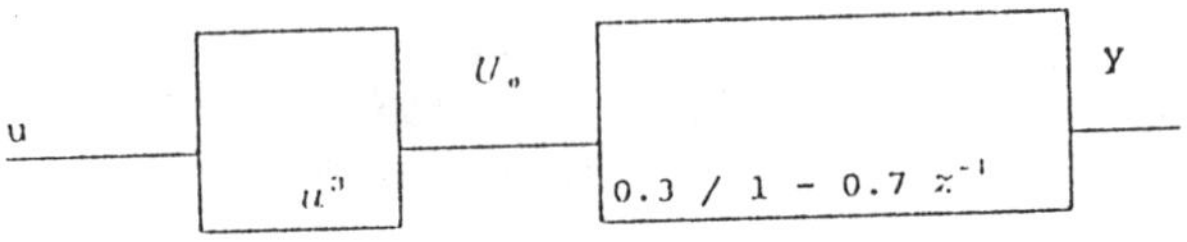

Fig.1: Input non-linearity 1.

5. Conclusions:

Through simulations, although the linear predictive controller manages to control and adapt implicitly to a certain non-linearities in some cases, the control performance is not entirely satisfactory. The non-linear predictive controller which is based on a non-linear model for the process not only had a good adaptation mechanism but also gave excellent performance. One of the major problems facing this controller is the huge number of parameters to be estimated, particularly if the value of the prediction horizon is large. Estimating such large value of parameters affect the convergence speed and accuracy of the parameter estimator which make the use of such controller in practice hard to accept.

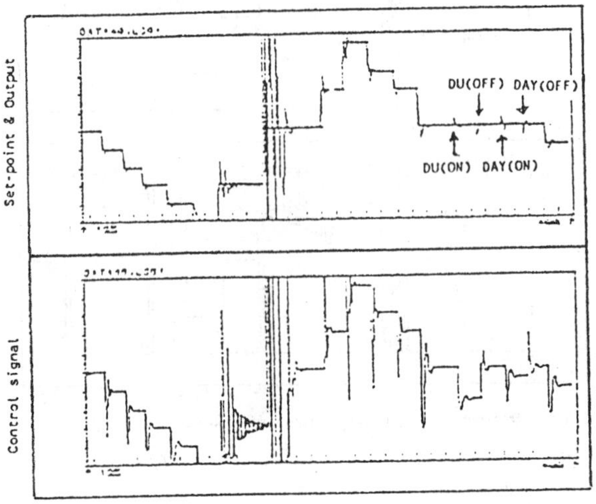

Fig.2: Performance of linear self-tuner with above non-linearity.

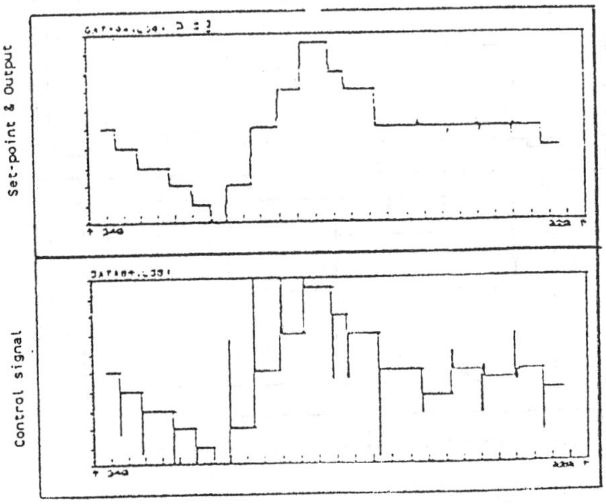

Fig.3: Performance of non-linear self-tuner with above non-linearity.

6. Acknowledgements:

The author would like to thank Dr. D.Clarke from Oxford University/U.K for his help and support in this research.

7. References:

1-Anbumani,K., Sarma,I.G and Patnaik,L.M, (1981), "Self-tuning control of non-linear systems characterized by Hammerstien models": Proc. of 9th IFAC World Congress, Kyoto, Japan.

2-Billings, S.A., (1985), "An overview of non-linear systems identification": IFAC aymp. on identification and system parameter estimation, York.

3-Clarke,D.W (1981), "Self-tuning and adaptive control: Introduction to self-tuning controllers": (ed. Harris and billings) peter Peregrinus.

4-Clarke, D.W. and Gawthrop, P.J., (1981), "Implementation and application of microprocessor-based self-tuners": Automatica, Vol.17, No.1, pp.233-244.

5-Clarke,D.W., Mohtadi,C and Tuffs,P.S, (1987), "Generalized predictive control", (2 parts): Automatica, Vol.23, No.2, pp.137-160.

6-Hodgson,A.J., (1983), "Problems of integrity in applications of adaptive controllers": D.Phil Thesis, Oxford University-U.K.

7-John,J., (1980), "Non-linear models, linear in parameters": IFAC/IFIP conference on digital computer applications to process control, Dusseldorf, FRG.

8-Lachmann,K.H., (1982), "Parameter adaptive control of a class of non-linear processes": Proc. of the 6th IFAC symp., Washinghton.

9-Leontaritis,J.J and Billings,S.A., (1984), "Input-output Parameteric models for non-linear systems": Report 252, Dep. of control eng., Sheffield University.

10-Mohtadi,C.,(1986), "Studies in adavanced self-tuning algorithms": D.phil. Thesis,Oxford University-U.K.

11-Tuffs,P.S., (1984), "Self-tuning control:Algorithms and applications": D.Phil. Thesis, Oxford University-U.K.

12-Zanker,P.M. and Wellstead,P.E., (1979),"Practical features of self-tuning": IEE conference on trends in on-line computer control systems, pp.160-164.

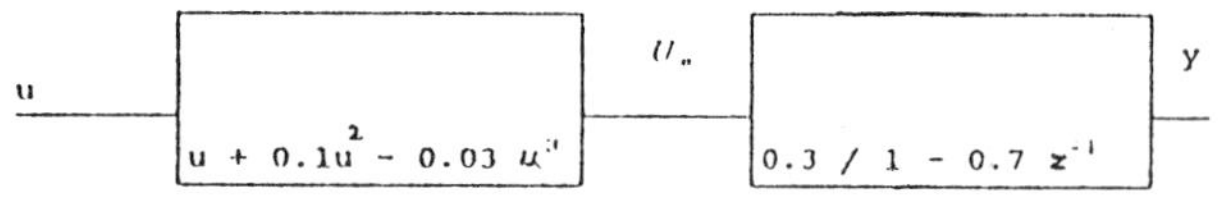

Fig.4: Input non-linearity 2.

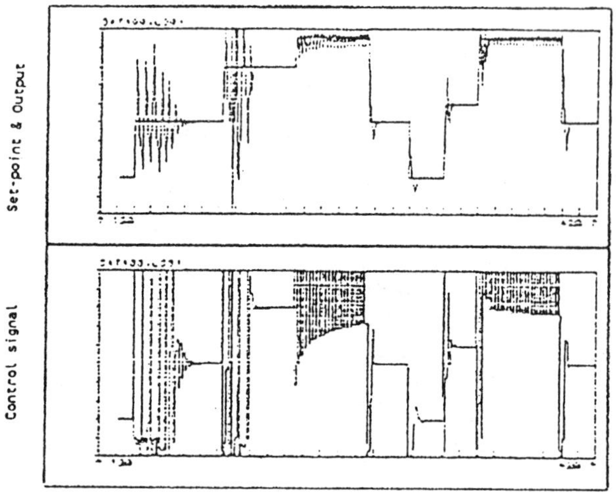

Fig.5: Performance of linear self-tuner with above nonlinearity.

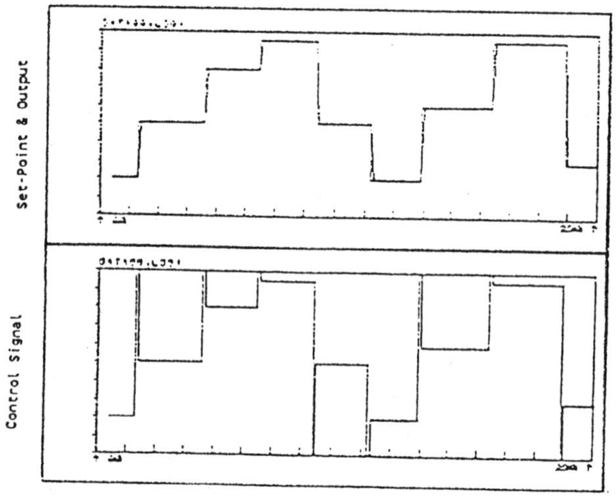

Fig.6: Performance of non-linear self-tuner with above non-linearity.

Proceedings of the
American Control Conference
San Francisco, California • June 1993

NONLINEAR TRACKING CONTROLLERS DESIGN

Ping Lu

Dept. of Aerospace Engineering and Engineering Mechanics
Iowa State University, Ames, IA 50011

Abstract

In this paper we present a new technique for design of nonlinear feedback controllers that yield satisfactory tracking performance for a class of dynamic systems. The controller is based on minimization of predicted tracking errors. Some tracking convergence properties of the controller are established. In the face of model uncertainties, we show that the unique structure of the controller allows robust stable tracking via high-gain feedback. Possible modifications for adaptive control in the presence of parameter uncertainties are discussed. Practical usefulness and effectiveness of the approach are exemplified by an autopilot design problem for a missile.

1. Introduction

In many control problems of nonlinear dynamics systems, a reference trajectory $\mathbf{q}(t)$ that represents the desired state of the system at each time is first obtained off-line. This allows a thorough trade-off study of various conflicting objectives and constraints, satisfaction of output requirements, and careful mission planning. Frequently $\mathbf{q}(t)$ is a product of some type of optimization process; then the actual state of the dynamic system is controlled to follow the reference trajectory on-line. Many complex aerospace systems, such as aircrafts, launch vehicles, spacecraft and space shuttles, often operate in this way. The control problem amounts to finding a controller to drive the system to follow $\mathbf{q}(t)$.

The state-tracking problem for robotic systems has seen impressive progress in recent years. Luo and Saridis [1] obtained an linear optimal feedback control by minimizing an integral of tracking errors. Slotine and Sastry [2] proposed a variable-structure sliding-control approach. More recently, Johansson [3] obtained a nonlinear feedback tracking control by minimizing an energy-like performance index. However, all these techniques are invariably based on some distinct features of the rigid body dynamics of the robot. They include an independent control for each degree of freedom, a positive definite mass-inertia matrix, and some skew symmetric property. Many other nonlinear dynamic systems, notably aerospace vehicles, do not share this luxury. Little in the literature reports more general nonlinear state tracking. Thus, in the case of aircraft control, linear control techniques such as model-following and linear quadratic controller design have been the main tools applied to the linearized model. Although the success has been tremendous, ever-increasing high performance requirements now demand that a modern aircraft operate in regimes of large angles and angular rates where nonlinearities are dominant. The traditional linearization technique is far from adequate in those situations. The following simple example illustrates the inadequacy of linearization technique and lack of nonlinear state-tracking technique.

<u>Example 1.1</u>.
Consider a subsonic aircraft flying in a horizontal plane. The speed of the aircraft is maintained at a constant $V = 150$ m/sec by proper throttling. Assume a quadratic drag polar for the aircraft. The point-mass equations of motion are

$$\frac{dx}{dt} = V\cos\psi \tag{1}$$

$$\frac{dy}{dt} = V\sin\psi \tag{2}$$

$$\frac{d\psi}{dt} = \frac{g}{V}\tan\sigma \tag{3}$$

where x and y are position coordinates, ψ the heading angle, σ the bank angle (treated as the control variable). g is the gravitational acceleration at the flight altitude. Suppose that the reference state trajectory is specified by

$$x^*(t) = R\cos\omega t,\ y^*(t) = R\sin\omega t,\ \psi^*(t) = \frac{\pi}{2} + \omega t \tag{4}$$

where $R = 1000$ meters and $\omega = V/R = 0.15$ rad/sec. Clearly the reference trajectory is a great circle of radius $R = 1000$ m centered at the origin. Given the initial state of the aircraft

$$x(0) = y(0) = \psi(0) = 0 \tag{5}$$

we want to find the required control $\sigma(t)$ to bank the aircraft so that $x(t)$, $y(t)$, and $\psi(t)$ follow the desired history of Eq. (4). σ is subject to the constraint

$$|\sigma| \le 80^\circ \tag{6}$$

Linearizing the trajectory around the reference trajectory is not valid because of the large initial errors ($\Delta x_0 = 1000$ m and $\Delta\psi_0 = 90^\circ$). Even when linearization is feasible, the linearized system will be time-varying, which leaves little advantage for control law design. There is no readily available nonlinear state-tracking technique to apply.

An equally important problem closely related to state-tracking is the output-tracking problem. In this case an output vector $\mathbf{y}$ which is a function of the state variables is defined for the system and $\mathbf{q}(t)$ represents the desired output. The output-tracking problem has been under intensive study. The most popular approach is the input/output linearization approach using differential geometric technique [4]. This technique involves nonlinear static feedback for cancelling system nonlinearities and replaces the input/output dynamic behavior with desired linear dynamics. One lingering problem of this approach is that exact knowledge of the system nonlinearities is needed for cancellation. The input/output linearization applications in aerospace control are examplified by the studies of Refs. [5-7]. We will treat both state- and output-tracking problems within the same framework. It turns out, however, that for the output-tracking problem, our approach will naturally lead to results that are consistent with those obtained by using input/output linearization.

We present a general tracking controller design methodology in this paper. Section 2 describes the approach to obtain the controller based on minimization of predicted tracking errors. Section 3 discusses tracking properties, robustness and possible modification of the controller. The output-tracking problem is treated in Section 4. In Section 5 a missile autopilot is designed using the preceeding results. Section 6 summarizes the work.

2. Control Law Development

2.1 Problem Formulation

We consider the system of the form

$$\dot{\mathbf{x}}_1 = \mathbf{f}_1(\mathbf{x}) \tag{7}$$

$$\dot{\mathbf{x}}_2 = \mathbf{f}_2(\mathbf{x}) + \mathbf{B}_2(\mathbf{x})\mathbf{u} \tag{8}$$

where $\mathbf{x}_1 \in R^{n_1}$ and $\mathbf{x}_2 \in R^{n_2}$, $n_1 + n_2 = n$, and $\mathbf{x} = (\mathbf{x}_1^T\ \mathbf{x}_2^T)^T \in \mathbf{X} \subset R^n$ is the state vector. $\mathbf{u} \in \mathbf{U} \subset R^m$ represents the control. We assume that $m \le n$ since this is the case for most physical systems. $\mathbf{X}$ and $\mathbf{U}$ are some connected sets containing the origin. $\mathbf{f}_1 : R^n \to R^{n_1}$ is sufficiently differentiable; $\mathbf{f}_2 : R^n \to R^{n_2}$ and $\mathbf{B}_2 : R^n \to R^{n_2 \times m}$ only need to be C^1. Without loss of generality, we assume that none of the rows of $\mathbf{B}_2(\mathbf{x})$ are constantly zero. For mechanical systems, Eq. (7) typically represents the kinematics in the sysytem, as did Eqs. (1) and (2) in Example 1.1. Equation (8) is the dynamic part of the system; the kinematic part is usually well defined by physical relations. It is the dynamic part, Eq. (8), that is more complicated and more easily subject to uncertainties. The system can be rewritten in a conventional format

$$\dot{\mathbf{x}} = \mathbf{f}(\mathbf{x}) + \mathbf{G}(\mathbf{x})\mathbf{u} \tag{9}$$

with

$$\mathbf{f} = \begin{pmatrix} \mathbf{f}_1 \\ \mathbf{f}_2 \end{pmatrix}$$

$$\mathbf{G} = \begin{pmatrix} 0 \\ \mathbf{B}_2 \end{pmatrix} \triangleq [\mathbf{g}_1\ \mathbf{g}_2 \ldots \mathbf{g}_m]$$

We will assume that the reference trajectory, $\mathbf{q}(t) = (\mathbf{q}_1^T(t)\ \mathbf{q}_2^T(t))^T \in R^n$, $0 \le t \le t_f$, is generated from the same system model [Eqs. (7)-(8)] with a reference control $\mathbf{u}^*(t)$

$$\dot{\mathbf{q}}_1 = \mathbf{f}_1(\mathbf{q}) \quad (10)$$

$$\dot{\mathbf{q}}_2 = \mathbf{f}_2(\mathbf{q}) + \mathbf{B}_2(\mathbf{q})\mathbf{u}^* \quad (11)$$

We wish to find a feedback control law $\mathbf{u} = \mathbf{s}(\mathbf{x}, t)$ so that $\mathbf{x}(t)$ tracks $\mathbf{q}(t)$ for an arbitrary initial condition $\mathbf{x}(0) \in \mathbf{X}_0 \subset \mathbf{X}$.

2.2 Predictive Controllers

Let r_i, $i = 1, ..., n$, be the lowest order of derivative of x_i in which any component of $\mathbf{u}$ first appears at $\mathbf{x}(t)$, $t \in [0, t_f]$. Define $\mathbf{v}(\mathbf{x}(t)) = (v_1(\mathbf{x}(t)), \ldots, v_n(\mathbf{x}(t)))^T$, where

$$v_i = hL_f^0(f_i) + \frac{h^2}{2!}L_f^1(f_i) + ... + \frac{h^{r_i}}{r_i!}L_f^{r_i-1}(f_i),\ i = 1, ..., n \quad (12)$$

where $h > 0$ is a real number. $L_f^k(f_i)$ denotes the k−th order Lie derivative of f_i with respect to $\mathbf{f}$

$$L_f^0(f_i) = f_i$$

$$L_f^1(f_i) = \frac{\partial f_i}{\partial \mathbf{x}}\mathbf{f}$$

$$L_f^2(f_i) = \frac{\partial L_f^1(f_i)}{\partial \mathbf{x}}\mathbf{f}$$

and so on. By state equation (9), at any instant $t \in [0, t_f]$, the current state $\mathbf{x}(t)$ and control $\mathbf{u}(t)$ determine the future state. If we expand each $x_i(t+h)$ for a small $h > 0$ in an r_i-th order Taylor series at t, we can write $\mathbf{x}(t+h)$ in a compact form

$$\mathbf{x}(t+h) = \mathbf{x}(t) + \mathbf{v}(\mathbf{x}(t)) + \Lambda(h)\mathbf{W}(\mathbf{x}(t))\mathbf{u}(t) \quad (13)$$

where $\Lambda(h) \in R^{n\times n}$ is a diagonal matrix with the elements on the main diagonal being

$$\lambda_{ii}(h) = \frac{h^{r_i}}{r_i!},\ i = 1, ..., n \quad (14)$$

and $\mathbf{W}(\mathbf{x}) \in R^{n\times m}$ has each of its rows in the form

$$\mathbf{w}_i = [L_{\mathbf{g}_1}(L_f^{r_i-1}(x_i)), ..., L_{\mathbf{g}_m}(L_f^{r_i-1}(x_i))],\ i = 1, ..., n \quad (15)$$

where the Lie derivative with respect to $\mathbf{g}_j$ is similarly defined

$$L_{\mathbf{g}_j}(L_f^{r_i-1}(x_i)) = \frac{\partial L_f^{r_i-1}(x_i)}{\partial \mathbf{x}}\mathbf{g}_j,\ j = 1, ..., m$$

Obviously, by assumption for $i = n_1 + 1, ..., n$

$$r_i = 1,\quad v_i = hf_i,\quad \text{and } \mathbf{w}_i = \text{the } i\text{-th row of } \mathbf{G}$$

Consider a performance index that penalizes the tracking error at next instant and current control expenditure

$$J(\mathbf{u}(t)) = \frac{1}{2}(\mathbf{x}(t+h)-\mathbf{q}(t+h))^T\mathbf{Q}(\mathbf{x}(t+h)-\mathbf{q}(t+h)) + \frac{1}{2}\mathbf{u}^T(t)\mathbf{R}\mathbf{u}(t) \quad (16)$$

where $\mathbf{Q} \in R^{n\times n}$ is positive definite and $\mathbf{R} \in R^{m\times m}$ is at least positive semidefinite. Likewise, we may expand the i-th component of $\mathbf{q}(t+h)$ in an r_i-th order Taylor series,

$$\mathbf{q}(t+h) = \mathbf{q}(t) + \mathbf{d}(t) \quad (17)$$

where the i-th component of $\mathbf{d}(t) \in R^n$ is

$$d_i(t) = h\dot{q}_i(t) + \frac{h^2}{2!}\ddot{q}_i(t) + ... + \frac{h^{r_i}}{r_i!}q_i^{(r_i)}(t),\ i = 1, ..., n$$

Replace $\mathbf{x}(t+h)$ and $\mathbf{q}(t+h)$ in Eq. (16) by Eqs. (13) and (17), respectively. For given $\mathbf{x}(t)$ and $\mathbf{q}(t)$, the minimization of J with respect to $\mathbf{u}(t)$ yields a best predictive controller

$$\mathbf{u}(t) = -[(\Lambda(h)\mathbf{W}(\mathbf{x}))^T\mathbf{Q}\Lambda(h)\mathbf{W}(\mathbf{x}) + \mathbf{R}]^{-1} \\ [(\Lambda(h)\mathbf{W}(\mathbf{x}))^T\mathbf{Q}(\mathbf{e}(t) + \mathbf{v}(\mathbf{x}) - \mathbf{d}(t)] \quad (18)$$

where $\mathbf{e}(t) = \mathbf{x}(t) - \mathbf{q}(t)$ is the current tracking error.

When the dynamic system is linear and discrete in time, and h equals the sample period, performance index (16) reduces to the so called one-step-ahead control formulation which was discussed in [8]. In this respect, Eq. (18) may be viewed as a generalized nonlinear version of the one-step-ahead control for continuous systems. But the indefiniteness of the "step" h here can actually serve to provide some desired properties that are not shared by discrete systems, as we shall see shortly. Explicit formulas of (18) for two common cases are as follows.

Case 1. $n_1 = 0$. In this case,

$$\mathbf{u}(t) = -\frac{1}{h}(\mathbf{G}^T(\mathbf{x})\mathbf{Q}\mathbf{G}(\mathbf{x}) + h^{-2}\mathbf{R})^{-1}\mathbf{G}^T(\mathbf{x})\mathbf{Q}[\mathbf{e}(t) + h(\mathbf{f}(\mathbf{x}) - \dot{\mathbf{q}}(t))] \quad (19)$$

Case 2. $n_1 \neq 0$, and $r_i = 2$ for $i = 1, ..., n_1$. Let

$$\mathbf{Q} = \begin{pmatrix} \mathbf{Q}_1 & 0 \\ 0 & h^2\mathbf{Q}_2 \end{pmatrix}$$

$\mathbf{Q}_1$ and $\mathbf{Q}_2$ are positive definite matices of $n_1 \times n_1$ and $n_2 \times n_2$, respectively. Define

$$\mathbf{F}_{11} = \frac{\partial \mathbf{f}_1}{\partial \mathbf{x}_1},\quad \mathbf{F}_{12} = \frac{\partial \mathbf{f}_1}{\partial \mathbf{x}_2}$$

Equation (18) becomes

$$\mathbf{u}(t) = -\mathbf{P}\{\frac{1}{2h^2}(\mathbf{F}_{12}\mathbf{B}_2)^T\mathbf{Q}_1[\mathbf{e}_1 + h\dot{\mathbf{e}}_1 + \frac{h^2}{2}(\mathbf{F}_{11}\mathbf{f}_1 + \mathbf{F}_{12}\mathbf{f}_2 - \ddot{\mathbf{q}}_1(t))] \\ + \frac{1}{h}\mathbf{B}_2^T\mathbf{Q}_2[\mathbf{e}_2 + h(\mathbf{f}_2 - \dot{\mathbf{q}}_2(t))]\} \quad (20)$$

where

$$\mathbf{P} = (\frac{1}{4}(\mathbf{F}_{12}\mathbf{B}_2)^T\mathbf{Q}_1\mathbf{F}_{12}\mathbf{B}_2 + \mathbf{B}_2^T\mathbf{Q}_2\mathbf{B}_2 + h^{-4}\mathbf{R})^{-1} \quad (21)$$

$$\mathbf{e}_i(t) = \mathbf{x}_i(t) - \mathbf{q}_i(t),\quad i = 1, 2$$

Case 1 is seen in some simplified missile and aircraft dynamics. A great majority of mechanical systems fall into Case 2 if the outputs of actuators are taken as the controls.

3. Controller Performance

We shall discuss in this section some important properties of the controller derived above and some possible modifications. All the results will be stated without proof for lack of space. The detailed proofs will be included in a forthcoming paper.

3.1 Tracking Accuracy

The foremost concerned property will be the tracking capability. First, we state a property of the controller by the following Proposition.

Lamma 3.1

If the tracking error $\mathbf{e}(t) = 0$ *at any* $t \in [0, t_f]$, *controller (18) will reproduce exactly* $\mathbf{u}^*(t)$, *the reference control at t, provided that* $\mathbf{R} = 0$ *and* $\mathbf{W}(\mathbf{q}(t))$ *is of full rank.*

Remark 3.1

A direct result of Lemma 3.1 is that if $\mathbf{e}(0) = 0$ and $\mathbf{W}(\mathbf{q}(t))$ has full rank for all $t \in [0, t_f]$, then $\mathbf{e}(t) = 0$ for all $t \in [0, t_f]$ under controller (18).

When $\mathbf{e}(0) \neq 0$, let us first make the following simple observation. Consider Eq. (19). Assume that $m = n$ and G has full rank at $\mathbf{x}(t) \in \mathbf{X}$. Let $\mathbf{R} = 0$. Then for any $\mathbf{Q} > 0$ we have

$$\dot{\mathbf{e}} = -\frac{1}{h}\mathbf{e}(t)$$

that is, globally asymptotic tracking for any $\mathbf{q}(t)$.

Next, let us consider a class of systems the dynamic equations of which are

$$\dot{\mathbf{x}}_1 = \mathbf{C}\mathbf{x}_2 \quad (23)$$

$$\dot{\mathbf{x}}_2 = \mathbf{f}_2(\mathbf{x}) + \mathbf{B}_2(\mathbf{x})\mathbf{u} \quad (24)$$

In this case we assume that $n_1 = n_2 = m$, $\mathbf{C}$ is a nonsingular constant matrix, and $\mathbf{B}_2(\mathbf{x})$ is of full rank for all $\mathbf{x}$. We have the following result:

Lemma 3.2

For system (23)-(24), the controller (18) with $\mathbf{R} = 0$ *achieves global asymptotic tracking of any reference trajectory* $\mathbf{q}(t)$.

The proof uses the Lyapunove stability theory and La Salle's invariant Theorem (Refs. [9–10]).

Remark 3.2

System (23)–(24) reduces to the dynamics of a rigid body robot when $\mathbf{C} = \mathbf{I}$ in (23). For the case where $\dot{\mathbf{x}}_1 = \mathbf{f}_1(\mathbf{x}_2)$, where $\mathbf{f}_1(\mathbf{x}_2)$ is a nonlinear function and $\mathbf{f}_1(0) = 0$, by Lyapunov indirect method [10], the above lemma also establishes that the nonlinear feedback control law (20) stabilizes the system at (0, 0) if $\partial \mathbf{f}_1(0)/\partial \mathbf{x}_2$ is nonsingular.

To see what may be expected for more general systems, we return to the Example in the Introduction. Let the control $u = \tan\sigma$. The system of Eqs. (1)-(3) fits to use controller (20) but does not have enough controls as robotic systems. Use Eq. (4) as the reference trajectory and apply control law (20) which becomes

$$u = \tan\sigma = \frac{-1}{P}\{\frac{1}{2h^2}[-Q_1(\Delta x + h\Delta\dot{x})\sin\psi + Q_2(\Delta y + h\Delta\dot{y})\cos\psi] - 0.25R\omega^2(Q_1\sin\psi\cos\omega t - Q_2\cos\psi\sin\omega t) + \frac{Q_3}{hV}(\Delta\psi - \omega)\} \quad (31)$$

where $Q_i > 0$, $i = 1, 2, 3$ are weighting coefficients, $R = 1000$ meters, $\omega = 0.15$ rad/sec, and

$$P = 0.25g(Q_1\sin^2\psi + Q_2\cos^2\psi) + \frac{gQ_3}{V^2}$$

Figure 1 shows the tracking trajectory in x-y plane in dashed line for $Q_i = 1$ and $h = 0.5$. Despite its large initial errors, the trajectory quickly merges onto the circle, which is the trace of the reference trajectory. But the aircraft always lags behind the reference point $[x^*(t), y^*(t)]$ about 417 meters. It can be shown that this lagging distance can be reduced to zero if the aircraft has throttle control.

3.2 Robustness

When system uncertainties are present, it is desired that the controller maintains satisfactory performance. The feedback nature of our controller is expected to provide a certain degree of robustness. For instance, in the above example, if the aircraft speed V is not exactly 150 m/sec, the effect is equivalent to variation of the controller weighting $\mathbf{Q}$. Since the tracking performance is found to be extremely insensitive to changes in $\mathbf{Q}$, the uncertainty in V practically has no effect on tracking. In more general situations, we can achieve robustness through high-gain feedback. To illustrate this prospective, we consider unmodeled dynamics $\Delta\mathbf{f}(\mathbf{x})$ and $\Delta\mathbf{G}(\mathbf{x})$ in the system (9)

$$\dot{\mathbf{x}} = \mathbf{f}(\mathbf{x}) + \Delta\mathbf{f}(\mathbf{x}) + [\mathbf{G}(\mathbf{x}) + \Delta\mathbf{G}(\mathbf{x})]\mathbf{u} \quad (32)$$

Let us again assume that $m = n$ and $\mathbf{G}(\mathbf{x}(t))$ is of full rank at $\mathbf{x}(t)$. Under these conditions,we have tracking robustness as stated by the following Lemma.

Lemma 3.3

Suppose that the unmodeled dynamics in Eq. (32) satisfy the following conditions

$$||\Delta\mathbf{f}(\mathbf{x})|| < N_1, \text{ for all } \mathbf{x} \in \mathbf{X} \quad (33)$$

$$\Delta\mathbf{G}(\mathbf{x}) = \delta(\mathbf{x})\mathbf{G}(\mathbf{x}), \text{ and } -1 < \delta(\mathbf{x}) < N_2 \text{ for all } \mathbf{x} \in \mathbf{X} \quad (34)$$

where N_1 and N_2 are positive constants. Moreover, we assume that $||\mathbf{f}(\mathbf{x})||$ and $||\dot{\mathbf{q}}(t)||$ are bounded for all $\mathbf{x} \in \mathbf{X}$ and $t \in [0, t_f]$. Then for any given $\varepsilon > 0$ there are an $\eta > 0$ and h_{max} such that for $||\mathbf{e}(0)|| < \eta$ and $0 < h < h_{max}$ in controller (18), we have $||\mathbf{e}(t)||$ for all $t \in [0, t_f]$.

The proof employs Malkin's Theorem [9, 11]. Note that small h means high controller gain from Eq. (18).

Remark 3.3

For system (23)-(24), if there are unmodeled dynamics $\Delta\mathbf{f}_2(\mathbf{x})$ and $\Delta\mathbf{B}_2(\mathbf{x})$ in Eq. (24) that satisfy Eqs.(33) and (34), it can be similarly shown that controller (20) can also maintain tracking accuracy $||\mathbf{e}(t)|| < \varepsilon$ for any $\varepsilon > 0$.

3.3 Adaptive Control

Suppose that the system (9) has some parameters denoted by a vector $\theta^* \in R^p$ for which exact values are unknown. Assume that θ^* appears linearly in the system equations. Regroup the system equations to obtain

$$\dot{\mathbf{x}} = \mathbf{f}_0(\mathbf{x}) + \mathbf{M}(\mathbf{x})\theta^* + \mathbf{G}(\mathbf{x})\mathbf{u} \quad (35)$$

where $\mathbf{f}_0$ and $\mathbf{M}$: $R^n \to R^{n\times p}$ are known. Let θ be an estimate of θ^*. Let $\mathbf{f}(\mathbf{x})$ in control law (19) be replaced by $\mathbf{f}_0(\mathbf{x}) + \mathbf{M}(\mathbf{x})\theta$

$$\mathbf{u}(t) = -\frac{1}{h}(\mathbf{G}^T(\mathbf{x})\mathbf{Q}\mathbf{G}(\mathbf{x}) + h^{-2}\mathbf{R})^{-1}\mathbf{G}^T(\mathbf{x})\mathbf{Q}[\mathbf{e}(t) + h(\mathbf{f}_0(\mathbf{x}) + \mathbf{M}(\mathbf{x})\theta - \dot{\mathbf{q}}(t)) \quad (36)$$

Again assume that $n = m$ and $\mathbf{G}(\mathbf{x})$ is nonsingular. Then we have

Lemma 3.4

Under controller (36) with $\mathbf{R} = 0$ and a parameter updating law

$$\dot{\theta} = \mathbf{M}^T(\mathbf{x})\mathbf{e} \quad (37)$$

the tracking error $\mathbf{e}(t)$ tends to zero for any $\mathbf{e}(0)$. Furthermore, if $p \leq n$ and $\mathbf{M}(\mathbf{q}(t))$ has full rank for all $t \in [0, t_f]$, it follows that $\theta \to \theta^*$ for any $\theta(0)$.

The proof again is based on Lyapunov stability theory and Invariant Theorem.

Remark 3.4

Result similar to Proposition 3.4 holds for system Eqs. (23)-(24) if the parameter uncertainties appear in the dynamic part of the system [Eq. (24)].

4. Output-Tracking

The approach developed in the preceding sections can be readily extended to the output-tracking problem. Suppose that in addition to the system state-equations (7)-(8) or (9), we have output equations

$$\mathbf{y} = \mathbf{c}(\mathbf{x}) \quad (40)$$

where $\mathbf{y} \in R^l$ and $\mathbf{c}$: $R^n \to R^l$ is sufficiently differentiable. Let $\mathbf{q}(t)$, $0 \leq t \leq t_f$, denote the reference output in this section.

4.1 Output-Tracking Controller

Let r_i, $i = 1, ..., l$, be the lowest order of derivative of y_i in which any component of $\mathbf{u}$ first appears at $\mathbf{x}(t)$, $t \in [0, t_f]$. In exactly the same way as in Section 2.2, we expand each $y_i(t+h)$ and $q_i(t+h)$ in a Taylor expansion of r_i-th order. Then by minimizing a performance index

$$J(\mathbf{u}(t)) = \frac{1}{2}(\mathbf{y}(t+h)-\mathbf{q}(t+h))^T\mathbf{Q}(\mathbf{y}(t+h)-\mathbf{q}(t+h)) + \frac{1}{2}\mathbf{u}^T(t)\mathbf{R}\mathbf{u}(t) \quad (41)$$

we obtain an output-tracking control law

$$\mathbf{u}(t) = -((\Lambda(h)\mathbf{W}(\mathbf{x}))^T\mathbf{Q}\Lambda(h)\mathbf{W}(\mathbf{x}) + \mathbf{R})^{-1}[(\Lambda(h)\mathbf{W}(\mathbf{x}))^T\mathbf{Q}(\mathbf{e}(t) + \mathbf{z}(\mathbf{x}) - \mathbf{d}(t)] \quad (42)$$

where $\mathbf{Q} \in R^{l\times l}$ is positive definite and $\mathbf{R} \in R^{m\times m}$ at least positive semidefinite; $\mathbf{e}(t) = \mathbf{y}(t) - \mathbf{q}(t)$; $\Lambda(h) \in R^{l\times l}$ is a diagonal matrix with the elements on the main diagonal being

$$\lambda_{ii}(h) = \frac{h^{r_i}}{r_i!}, \ i = 1, ..., l \quad (43)$$

the i-th component of $\mathbf{z} \in R^l$ is

$$z_i = hL_f(c_i) + \frac{h^2}{2!}L_f^2(c_i) + ... + \frac{h^{r_i}}{r_i!}L_f^{r_i}(c_i), \quad i = 1, ..., l \quad (44)$$

and the i-th component of $\mathbf{d}$ is defined as before

$$v_i(t) = h\dot{q}_i(t) + \frac{h^2}{2!}\ddot{q}_i(t) + ... + \frac{h^{r_i}}{r_i!}q_i^{(r_i)}(t), \ i = 1, ..., l \quad (45)$$

The i-th row the $l \times m$ matrix $\mathbf{W}$ takes the form

$$\mathbf{w}_i = [L_{\mathbf{g}_1}(L_f^{r_i-1}(c_i)), ..., L_{\mathbf{g}_m}(L_f^{r_i-1}(c_i))], \quad i = 1, ..., l \quad (46)$$

4.2 Tracking Performance

In this section we shall make the standard assumption that the numder of outputs is equal to that of the controls, i.e., $l = m$. Moreover, we assume that $\mathbf{W}(\mathbf{x})$ is nonsingular for all $\mathbf{x} \in \mathbf{X}$. Let $\mathbf{R} = 0$ in the controller (42).

Lemma 4.1

Assume that $\mathbf{W}(\mathbf{x})$ is nonsingular for all $\mathbf{x} \in \mathbf{X}$. Let $\mathbf{R}$=0 in the Eq. (42). Control law (42) achieves asymptotic tracking of an arbitrary output history $\mathbf{q}(t)$ for any $h > 0$ and $\mathbf{Q} > 0$, if $r_i \leq 4$ for $i = 1, ..., l$.

Proof: The error dynamics can be shown to be

$$\frac{h^{r_i}}{r_i!}e_i^{(r_i)} + \frac{h^{r_i-1}}{(r_i-1)!}e_i^{(r_i-1)} + \ldots + h\dot{e}_i + e_i = 0 \quad (47)$$

The lemma follows application of Nyquist Criterion to system (47).

Remark 4.1

The error dynamics (47) is linear, time-invariant. We see that the proposed tracking controller that minimizes the tracking error naturally leads to input/output linearization. For most of the mechanical systems with actuator dynamics neglected, $r_i = 1$ or $r_i = 2$. In these cases, the eigenvalues of the error dynamics are

$$s_1 = -\frac{1}{h}, \quad \text{if } r_i = 1 \quad (48)$$

$$s_{1,2} = \frac{1}{h}(-1 \pm j), \quad \text{if } r_i = 2 \tag{49}$$

Interestingly, we notice that the damping ratio of the complex roots in Eq. (49) is 0.707, a well accepted best choice in classic control theory. In all cases, the value of h only influences the magnitude of the time constant.

Note that the damping ratio of the complex roots in Eq. (49) is 0.707, a well accepted best choice.

When actuator dynamics are included in the system equations, the index r_i can be higher than two. It is easily verified by the Routh criterion that for up to $r_i = 4$, the error dynamics (47) is stable. The value of $h > 0$ only influences the magnitude of the time constant. When $r_i \geq 5$, the error dynamics becomes unstable. In those situations, the controls only affect the fifth and higher order derivatives of y_i. The minimization of performance index (41) with higher order Taylor expansions for $y_i(t+h)$ cannot generate sufficient influence on the behavior of $y_i(t)$. An immediate remedy is to incorporate additional term that penalizes the derivative of $e_i = y_i - q_i$ in (41)

$$J(\mathbf{u}(t)) = \frac{1}{2}(\mathbf{y}(t+h) - \mathbf{q}(t+h))^T \mathbf{Q}_1(\mathbf{y}(t+h) - \mathbf{q}(t+h)) + \frac{1}{2}(\dot{\mathbf{y}}(t+h) - \dot{\mathbf{q}}(t+h))^T \mathbf{Q}_2(\dot{\mathbf{y}}(t+h) - \dot{\mathbf{q}}(t+h)) + \frac{1}{2}\mathbf{u}^T(t)\mathbf{R}\mathbf{u}(t) \tag{50}$$

where $\mathbf{Q}_2$ is a positive semidefinite diagonal matrix with a nonzero i-th element on the main diagonal only if $r_i \geq 5$. Then the same procedure can be carried out to obtain a control law. For instance, if one sets $(\mathbf{Q}_2)_{ii} = h^2(\mathbf{Q}_1)_{ii}$ for $r_i = 5$, it can be shown that the resulting ith error dynamics is stable again. For even higher order cases, incorporating derivatives of second or higher order in the performance index (50) will stabilize the error dynamics.

Let us assume that the error dynamics have been stabilized. We can write m output dynamic equations for $y_i^{(r_i)}$, $i = 1, \ldots, m$ as

$$\begin{pmatrix} y_1^{(r_1)} \\ \vdots \\ y_m^{(r_m)} \end{pmatrix} = \begin{pmatrix} L_f^{r_1}(c_1) \\ \vdots \\ L_f^{r_m}(c_m) \end{pmatrix} + \mathbf{W}(\mathbf{x})\mathbf{u} \triangleq \mathbf{p}(\mathbf{x}) + \mathbf{W}(\mathbf{x})\mathbf{u} \tag{51}$$

If there are unmodeled dynamics $\Delta\mathbf{p}(\mathbf{x})$ and $\Delta\mathbf{W}(\mathbf{x})$ in the form of Eqs. (33) and (34), or parameter uncertainties in the form of $\mathbf{p}(\mathbf{x}) = \mathbf{p}_0(\mathbf{x}) + \mathbf{M}(\mathbf{x})\theta^*$, by similar analysis we can conclude that the robustness discussion and modification for adaptive control in Sections 3.2 and 3.3 are applicable to the output-tracking problem.

To demonstrate the robustness of the tracking controller with high-gain feedback, we again use Example 1.1. Suppose that there is an unmodeled wind with constant velocity. The two equations of motion affected are

$$\frac{dx}{dt} = V\cos\psi + w_x \tag{52}$$

$$\frac{dy}{dt} = V\sin\psi + w_y \tag{53}$$

where w_x and w_y are the constant wind velocity components in x and y direction, respectively. Suppose that the objective is to fly the aircraft in a great circle with radius $R = 1000$ meters centered at the origin. Choose the output as

$$r = x^2 + y^2 \tag{54}$$

The reference output then is $q = R^2 = 10^6$ meters. For this output the index $r_i = 2$. It is straightforward to show that the resulting umodeled dynamics in the $\ddot{r}$ equation is

$$\Delta p = 2[\cos\psi(1+V)w_x + \sin\psi(1+V)w_y + w_x^2 + w_y^2] \tag{55}$$

Clearly $|\Delta p|$ is bounded by a constant for all x, y, and ψ. The tracking controller based on Eq. (42) for the nominal dynamics (no wind) is

$$u = \tan\sigma = -\frac{(e + h\dot{e} + h^2V^2)}{gh^2(y\cos\psi - x\sin\psi)} \tag{56}$$

For $w_x = w_y = 15$ m/sec, Fig. 2 shows two histories of the flight radius $\sqrt{x^2+y^2}$ with two different values of h as used in (56). The dashed line shows that when $h = 4.0$ the maximum steady-state tracking error $|e|_{max} = \max|\sqrt{x^2+y^2} - 1000|$ is about 100 meters. When the controller gain is increased by reducing h to 0.5, the solid line tells that the steady-state $|e|_{max}$ is less than 10 meters.

5. Missile Autopilot Design

Extensive applications of the above design techniques to the flight control of a high-performance fighter aircraft will be reported in another paper. In this section we shall be content to demonstrate the practical usefulness of the approach with the following missile control problem

Consider the longitudinal rigid-body dynamics of a missle. The model is taken from [12] for a missile traveling at Mach 3 at an altitude of 6,096 m (20,000 ft).

$$\dot{\alpha} = \frac{180gQS}{\pi WV}\cos(\pi\alpha/180)\phi_n(\alpha) + q + \frac{180gQS}{\pi WV}\cos(\pi\alpha/180)b_n\delta \tag{57}$$

$$\dot{q} = \frac{180QSd}{I_{yy}}\phi_m(\alpha) + \frac{180QSd}{I_{yy}}b_m\delta \tag{58}$$

where α is the angle of attack (deg); q pitch rate (deg/sec); δ fin deflection (deg); g gravitational acceleration (9.8 m/sec); W weight (4,410 kg); V speed (947.6 m/sec); I_{yy} pitch moment of inertia (247.44 kg-m^2); Q dynamic pressure (293,638 N/m^2); S reference area (0.04087 m^2); d reference diameter (0.2286 m). The normal force and pitch moment aerodynamic coefficients for $|\alpha| \leq 20^\circ$ are given by

$$C_n = \phi_n(\alpha) + b_n\delta = 0.000103\alpha^3 - 0.00945\alpha|\alpha| - 0.17\alpha - 0.034\delta \tag{59}$$

$$C_m = \phi_m(\alpha) + b_m\delta = 0.000215\alpha^3 - 0.0195\alpha|\alpha| + 0.051\alpha - 0.206\delta \tag{60}$$

For convenience, we rewrite Eqs. (57)–(58) as

$$\dot{\alpha} = f_1(\alpha) + q + c_1\cos(\pi\alpha/180)\delta \tag{61}$$

$$\dot{q} = f_2(\alpha) + c_2\delta \tag{62}$$

with $f_1(\alpha)$, $f_2(\alpha)$ and two constants c_1 and c_2 obviously defined. We approximate the tail fin actuator dymamics by a first-order lag

$$\dot{\delta} = -10\delta + 10u \tag{63}$$

where u represents the commanded fin deflection (deg). The system equations are now Eqs. (61)–(63). The objective is to design an autopilot that maintains an equilibrium flight condition at $\alpha = q = \delta = 0$ for possibly large perturbations. Appreciable modeling errors of the aerodynamic coefficients are expected to be present. Following the controller design approach in Section 2.2, we denote $\mathbf{x}_1 = (\alpha\ q)^T$ and $\mathbf{x}_2 = \delta$. The reference trajectory is $\mathbf{q}(t) = 0$. By Eq. (20), we arrive at a control law

$$\begin{aligned} u = -\frac{1}{P}\{&\frac{5Q_1c_1\cos(\pi\alpha/180)}{h^2}[\alpha + h\dot{\alpha} \\ &+ 0.5h^2(F_{1\alpha} - c_1\pi\sin(\pi\alpha/180)\delta/180)f_1 + f_2 - 10c_1\cos(\pi\alpha/180)\delta] \\ &+ \frac{5Q_2c_2}{h^2}[q + h\dot{q} + 0.5h^2(F_{2\alpha}f_1 - 10c_2\delta)] + \frac{10Q_3}{h}(\delta - 10h\delta)\} \end{aligned} \tag{64}$$

where

$$P = 25Q_1c_1^2\cos^2(\pi\alpha/180) + 25Q_2c_2^2 + 100Q_3$$

and

$$F_{1\alpha} = \frac{\partial f_1(\alpha)}{\partial\alpha}, \quad F_{2\alpha} = \frac{\partial f_2(\alpha)}{\partial\alpha}$$

$Q_i > 0$, $i = 1, 2, 3$, are weighting coefficients. It can be shown by using Lyapunov indirect method [10] that under control law (64) the missile closed-loop dynamics is asymptotically stable at $(0, 0, 0)$. To test the effectiveness of the design, we choose the initial conditions

$$\alpha(0) = 20^\circ, \quad q(0) = 20 \text{ (deg/sec)} \tag{65}$$

To count for possible modeling uncertainties of the aerodynamic coefficients C_n and C_m, we tested three cases: C_n and C_m have nominal values as given by Eqs. (59) and (60); C_n and C_m simultaneously have +25%, and then −25% perturbations. Figures 3 and 4 illustrate the variations of $\alpha(t)$ and $q(t)$ in these three cases for $Q_i = 1$ and $h = 0.1$. It is seen that the controller performs remarkably well in all cases. The fin deflections (not shown here) are not excessive.

6. Concluding Remarks

A new design methodology for nonlinear feedback controllers that yield satisfactory tracking performance is proposed. The design technique is applicable to systems more general than robotic systems, particularly including aerospace systems. With the proposed formulation, the state- and output-tracking problems can be treated in the same framework. In the output-tracking problem, the approach naturally leads to input/output linearization. Some asymptotic tracking convergence properties have been established. It is shown that the controller can maintain robust performance in the presence of unmodeled dynamics via high-gain feedback. Minor modifications of the controller allow stable adaptive control of the system in the face of parameter uncertainties. A missile autopilot is designed by using the technique to demonstrate its practical usefulness and effectiveness.

Acknowledgements

Helpful discussions with Tang Cheng in the early stage of the work and a suggestion by M. Asif Khan regarding Eq. (50) are gratefully acknowledged.

References

[1] Luo, G. L., and Saridis, G. N., "L-Q Design of PID Controller of Robot Arms", *IEEE Journal of Robotics and Automation*, vol. RA-1, no. 3, Sept. 1985, pp. 152–159.

[2] Slotine, J. J. E., and Sastry, S. S., "Tracking Control of Nonlinear Systems Using Sliding Surfaces with Applications to Robot Manipulators", *International Journal of Control*, Vol. 38, 1983, pp. 465–492.

[3] Johansson, R., "Quadratic Optimization of Motion Coordination and Control", *IEEE Transactions on Automatic Control*, Vol. 35, No. 11, 1990, pp. 1197–1210.

[4] Isidori, A., *Nonlinear Control Systems: An Introduction*, 2nd Edition, Springer-Verlag, 1989.

[5] Lane, S. H., and Stengel, R. F., "Flight Control Design Using Nonlinear Inverse Dynamics", *Automatica*, Vol. 24, No. 4, July 1988, pp. 471–483.

[6] Van Buren, M. A., and Mease, K. D., " Aerospace Plane Guidance Using Time-Scale Decomposition: A Geometric Approach", *Proceedings of AIAA Guidance, Navigation and Control Conference*, Vol. 1, 1991.

[7] Wise, K. A., "Nonlinear Aircraft Control Using Dynamic Inversion", *Proceedings of American Control Conference*, Vol. 2, 1992.

[8] Goodwin, G. C., and Sin, K. S., *Adaptive Filtering, Prediction and Control*, Prentice-Hall, 1984.

[9] La Salle, J., and Solomon, L., *Stability by Lyapunov's Direct Method with Application*, Academic Press, 1961.

[10] Vidyasagar, M., *Nonlinear Systems Analysis*, Prentice-Hall, 1978.

[11] Malkin, I. G., "Questions Concerning Transformation of Lyapunov Theorem On Asymptotic Stability", *PMM*, Vol. 18, 1954, pp. 129–138.

[12] Reichert, R., "Modern Robust Control for Missile Autopilot Design", *Proceedings of American Control Conference*, San Diego, CA, June 1990.

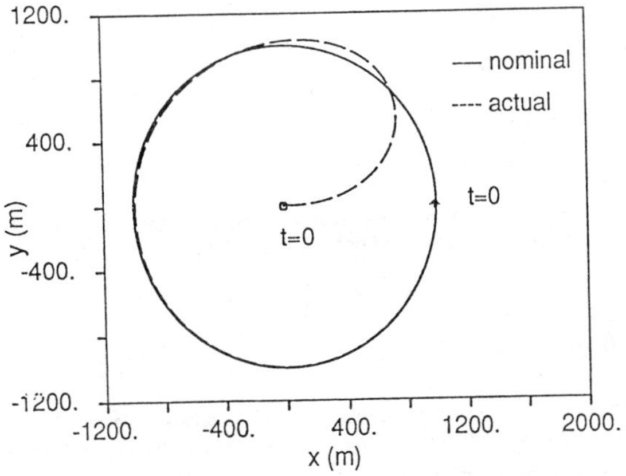

Fig. 1 State-tracking trajectory of the aircraft

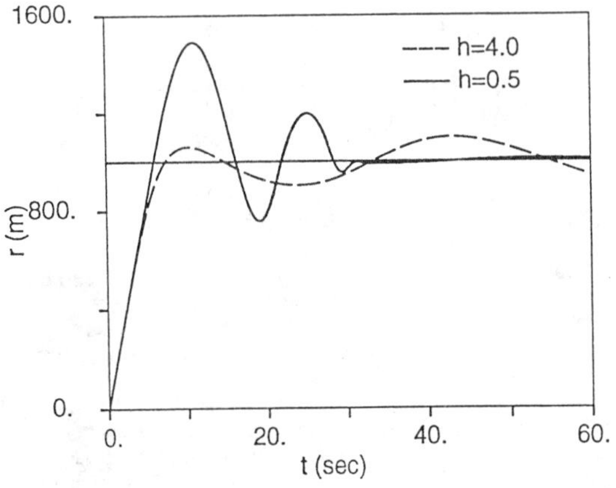

Fig. 2 Variations of flight radius of the aircraft (output-tracking)

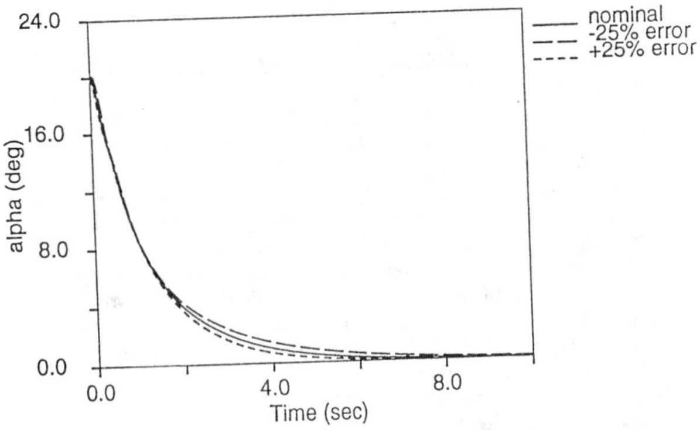

Fig. 3 Variations of angle of attack of the missile

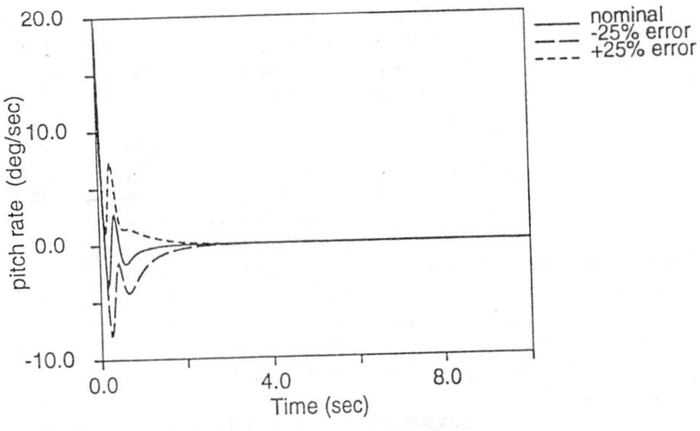

Fig. 4 Variations of pitch rate of the missile

Proceedings of the
American Control Conference
San Francisco, California • June 1993

Resonance Averaging in Dynamics and Control of Flexible Structures

Mark A. Pinsky and Bill Essary
Dept. of Mathematics, University of Nevada, Reno
Reno, Nevada 89557

Abstract

In this paper we address a novel averaging method for analysis and control of high dimensional, stiff nonlinear differential equations governing the dynamics of a variety of flexible structures. The method yields significant reduction of the initial equations by the averaging of high oscillatory elastic distortions over slow rigid-body motions which can be given in either analytical or numerical form. The averaging allows the stiff property to be overcome. In the averaging equations only exceptional resonance nonlinear terms persist which actually control the plant's stability. A stabilization problem is addressed for an averaging nonlinear plant and the error involved in such an approximation is estimated. A nonlinear stabilizing control is then evaluated in terms of the averaging normal form and the resonance feedback is shown to be an efficient design procedure.

Introduction

Nonlinear dynamics of flexible structures has attracted increasing attention within the past decade. In a variety of recent publications in this area (Anthony and Wie, 1990, Meirovitch and Kwak, 1989a, 1989b, Meirovitch et al., 1989, van Shoor and von Flotow 1990), concern is given to deriving the equations of motion in a conventional form (Meirovitch and Kwak, 1989b) and to developing a strategy to control a nonlinear plant in the presence of system uncertainties. While the mathematical formulation of flexible structure dynamics consists of a set of coupled PDEs and ODEs, the PDEs are often approximated by spatial discretization throughout the corresponding set of ODEs. The set of equations obtained in this manner are usually high dimensional and possess an intrinsic stiff property due to the persistence in their solutions of both slow and fast oscillatory components. Analysis of these complex nonlinear systems rests on highly elaborate direct numerical simulations. Due to the complexity of analysis of flexible structure dynamics, there have been proposed decentralized control schemes which simplify feedback design (Meirovitch et al., 1989). A decentralized control strategy rests on feedback gains which are designed independently for each substructure. A few techniques using feedback linearization have also been applied to controlling the dynamics of flexible structures (Di Benedetto and Lucibello, 1990). Note that the proposed techniques do not adapt to the peculiarities of the specific nonlinear plant and therefore are not very efficient.

Indeed, inherent complexity of flexible structure dynamics can be used in a way that simplifies its analysis. The key idea is to average high oscillatory elastic distortions over slow rigid-structure motions. Observe that equations governing flexible structure dynamics usually possess a multiple resonance property that complicates or makes fail known averaging techniques. Although no averaging techniques are completely general, we report here an effective method which overcomes the essential limitation imposed by multiresonance flexible-body dynamics. The averaging technique is applied to high dimensional equations governing elastic oscillations which are coupled to known rigid-body motions. It is assumed in addition, that the magnitude of elastic oscillations is sufficiently small with respect to a characteristic displacement of rigid-structure. The ratio of the norms of elastic oscillations and motions of the rigid-structure determines the value of the small parameter involved in this averaging technique. The main part of the proposed technique consists of the derivation of the resonance normal form; after that, separation of fast and slow motions is given in a closed form. Averaging overcomes the stiff property and yields significant decoupling of the initial equations. The number of coupled nonlinear equations in the averaging form are determined by the structure of resonances and are independent of the order of the initial system. In major applications only very few averaging equations are coupled by nonlinear resonance terms. Indeed, the terms persisting in an averaging normal form actually control stability and are responsible for transition of the plant's stability. The averaging equations are convenient for both analysis of a plants behavior and design of a stabilizing feedback control.

1. Generalized Normal Forms Method and Averaging Normal Forms

Unfortunately, lack of computability prevents direct use of both standard averaging and the normal forms method in solving many applied problems. We describe here a more general approach to finding normal forms that is computationally more efficient and is applicable to a broader class of systems than established algorithms.

Our approach is based on a simple recursive formula which has been implemented in computer software that allows one to find the normal form for a high dimensional nonlinear plant possessing complex resonances. It is remarkable that in the context of the following algorithm the nonlinear resonance condition is shaped in a form congruent with an analogous relation from the theory of linear forced oscillations. Although it is easy to verify that Poincare resonance monomials (Arnold, 1983, Wiggins, 1990) are caught by the new condition, it is important to note that this approach may also be used when the known relation is invalid. Note also that for equations written in the normal form, separation of slow and fast variables becomes rather routine and is presented in a closed form in this section.

Write an equation in the form:

$$\dot{x} = Ax + \varepsilon f(x,t,\varepsilon) \tag{1}$$

where f is a power series in x periodic with respect to t and A=diag(λ_1, ..., λ_n). Note that we do not have to assume here that $f(0,t,\varepsilon) = 0$. We attempt to simplify (1) with the aid of a close to identity change of variables:

$$x = y + \varepsilon r(y,t,\varepsilon) \tag{2}$$

Suppose that in the new variables (1) takes the form:

$$\dot{y} = Ay + \varepsilon B(y,t,\varepsilon) \tag{3}$$

From (1)-(3) we get:

$$Ar - r_y Ay - r_t = -f(y+\varepsilon r) + B + \varepsilon r_y B, \tag{4}$$

where r_y is the Jacobian with respect to y and r_t is a partial derivative of r with respect to t. We consider (4) as a system of partial differential equations with respect to r. We seek a particular solution of (4) satisfying an additional condition:

$$\|f\| \to 0 \Rightarrow \|r\| \to 0$$

where $\|\cdot\|$ is a certain norm of a vector valued function. In other words, we are looking for a particular solution such that the norm of r tends to zero if the norm of f tends to zero also. For small ε one can try to approximate the solution of (4) by iterations:

$$Ar_1 - r_{1,y}Ay - r_{1,t} = -f(y)$$
$$Ar_k - r_{k,y}Ay - r_{k,t} = -f(y+\varepsilon r_{k-1}) + B_k + \varepsilon r_{k-1,y}B_{k-1},\ k>1 \tag{5}$$

Note that (5) represents a set of linear partial differential equations with respect to r_k. Let us write a characteristic equation for (5) :

$$\dot{r}_1 = Ar_1 + f(y,t) - B_1 \tag{6}$$
$$\dot{r}_k = Ar_k + f(y+\varepsilon r_{k-1}) - \varepsilon r_{k-1,y}B_{k-1} - B_k,\ k>1 \tag{7}$$
$$\dot{y} = Ay \tag{8}$$

It is clear that $y = e^{At}c$.

The time-dependent terms in (6)-(8) should be split up into two distinct groups, namely, resonance and nonresonance terms.

Definition: F(t) is called a resonance perturbation if

$$F(t) = e^{At}N(c), \tag{9}$$

where $N(c) \in R^n$ is a vector dependent upon c, otherwise F is called a nonresonance perturbation. In order to annihilate nonresonance terms we set: $B_k = e^{At}N_k(c)$ (recall that $c=e^{-At}y$). So, one is able to write:

$$B_k(y,t) = e^{At}N_k(e^{-At}y). \tag{10}$$

The preceding derivations naturally express a nonlinear resonance condition in a form adapted from the theory of linear forced oscillations.

Although (10) looks distinct from the Poincare resonance condition it turns out to be equivalent in the case when $f_s(x) = \alpha_{ms}x^m e_s$, $\alpha_{ms} = \text{const}$, e_s a unit vector of the s-axis. Recalling that A is a diagonal matrix, and $f_s(e^{At}c) = \alpha_{ms}e^{(m;\lambda)t}c^m e_s$, we see that f_s admits form (9) if $(m;\lambda) = \lambda_s$. Note also in this case $B_s = \alpha_{ms}y^m e_s$.

Observe that (6)-(8) coincide with the set of linear ODEs given by naive iterations if one sets $B_k=0$, $k \geq 1$. As is known, the resonance terms usually present in these recursive sequences force these iterations to diverge on large time intervals. The problem with naive iterations is that they do not distinguish between resonance and nonresonance terms. In spite of this, one can use the available B_k to annihilate resonance terms in (6)-(8) and place them into the normal form.

Because the resonance terms are exceptional, the normalization yields significant reduction of the initial system. Moreover, the normal forms admit complementary reduction in both the so-called slow and especially in the amplitude-phase variables.

Let us write the normal form equation in such a way:

$$\dot{y} = Ay + \varepsilon e^{At}N(e^{-At}y, \varepsilon) + O(\varepsilon^K)$$

Address a slow variable c(t) by the formula:

$$y(t) = e^{At}c(t)$$

Then one obtains:

$$\dot{c} = \varepsilon N(c, \varepsilon) + O(\varepsilon^K)$$

Assuming now that all eigen-values are complex conjugate:

$$\lambda_k = \alpha_k + I\omega_k; \quad \bar{\lambda}_k = \alpha_k - I\omega_k, \quad k = 1, \ldots, n/2, \quad I = \sqrt{-1}$$

We choose related c_k as complex conjugate couples:

$$c_k(t) = a_k(t)e^{I(\omega_k t + \rho_k(t))}, \quad \bar{c}_k(t) = a_k(t)e^{-I(\omega_k t + \bar{\rho}_k(t))}, \quad k = 1, \ldots, n/2$$

Assume also that the vector $\lambda = \{\lambda_1, \ldots, \lambda_{n/2}\}$ is not resonant. Namely, there is no vector m satisfying the Poincare resonance condition $\lambda_s = (m;\lambda)$, s=1,...,n/2. In this case we have:

$$\dot{a} = \alpha a + \tfrac{1}{2}\varepsilon(N(a,\varepsilon) + \bar{N}(a,\varepsilon)) + O(\varepsilon^K)$$
$$\dot{\rho} = \tfrac{-I}{2a}\varepsilon(N(a,\varepsilon) - \bar{N}(a,\varepsilon)) + O(\varepsilon^K) \tag{11}$$

where $a = \{a_1, \ldots a_{n/2}\}$, $r = \{r_1, \ldots, r_{n/2}\}$. The the most notable feature of the above equations is that the amplitude variables are separated from the phase ones.

For zero eigen-values, related eigen-vectors can be treated as slow variables directly. Assume that critical eigen-values consist of both a number of zero eigenvalues and a certain number of noncomensurable complex conjugate couples. In this case an averaging normal form also assumes the form (11). In fact, the vector of slow variables consists of additional components corresponding to zero eigen-vectors.

In the face of additional resonances: $\lambda_s = (m; \lambda)$, s = 1, ..., p conforming combinations of phase variables, namely

$$\psi_s = (m;\rho) - \rho_s, \quad s = 1, \ldots, p \tag{12}$$

persist in (11). Defining by (12) new variables $\psi = \{\psi_1, \ldots, \psi_p\}$ and leaving the same notation for the remaining variables, we write (11) in the modified form

$$\dot{a} = \alpha a + \tfrac{1}{2}\varepsilon(N(a,\psi,\varepsilon) + \bar{N}(a,\psi,\varepsilon)) + O(\varepsilon^K)$$
$$\dot{\psi} = \tfrac{-I}{2a}\varepsilon(N(a,\psi,\varepsilon) - \bar{N}(a,\psi,\varepsilon)) + O(\varepsilon^K)$$
$$\dot{\rho} = \tfrac{-I}{2a}\varepsilon(N(a,\psi,\varepsilon) - \bar{N}(a,\psi,\varepsilon)) + O(\varepsilon^K) \tag{13}$$

where 1<k. The last equation represents the effect of (k-1) iterations which yield averaging.

Thus additional p resonances yield additional p active variables: ψ in the averaging normal form.

2. Estimation of Residual Terms

We present here a simple upper bound on residual terms that guides the formulation of sufficient conditions for local stability of a steady state solution. This bound also provides us with an estimate for the acceptable value of the small parameter.

Terminating iterations (6)-(8) on the k-th step by setting $r_{k+1} = r_k$ gives the residual term in the form: $R = B_{k+1} = Ar_k - \dot{r}_k + \gamma(y + \varepsilon r_k) - \varepsilon r_{k,y}B$. It is clear that R=R(a,ρ,ε) depends on both amplitude and phase variables. Therefore, (6)-(8) can be written in the following form:

$$\dot{a} = \alpha a + \tfrac{1}{2}\varepsilon(N(a,\varepsilon) + \bar{N}(a,\varepsilon)) + \varepsilon^K E(a,\rho,\varepsilon)$$
$$\dot{\rho} = \tfrac{-I}{2a}\varepsilon(N(a,\varepsilon) - \bar{N}(a,\varepsilon)) + \varepsilon^K e(a,\rho,\varepsilon) \tag{14}$$

where E and e are periodic functions with respect to each ρ_k, k = 1, ..., p, with periods T_k.

It is important to notice that the above equations are given by the closed form change of variables and are therefore accurate. The residuals E and e can be effectively bounded.

Indeed, the bounds are:

$$E \leq \max_{\rho_1 \in [0:T_1]} \ldots \max_{\rho_n \in [0:T_n]} E(a,\rho,\varepsilon) = E^0(a)$$
$$e \leq \max_{\rho_1 \in [0:T_1]} \ldots \max_{\rho_n \in [0:T_n]} e(a,\rho,\varepsilon) = e^0(a) \tag{15}$$

Using these bounds we will formulate in the following section conditions of the Lyapunov stability of the trivial solution a=0 of (14) with the aid of the method of Lyapunov functions which are addressed in amplitude variables. Observe that the solution a=0 may represent either an equilibrium or a periodic or almost periodic solution in the initial equations.

Note that in analysis of applied problems ε usually assigns the ratio of the norms of nominal and perturbed solutions. Though the last norm is not available, we propose to estimate the value of ε indirectly by using (15). An assumed value of ε can be chosen such that

$$E^0(a,\varepsilon) < \eta, \quad a_0 \leq a \leq a^0,$$

where η is an admitting error and a_0, a^0 assign a region about the trivial solution a = 0.

3. Stabilization of an Averaging System

Design of stabilization feedback control for critical dynamical systems (faced with bifurcations) was studied by several authors. Existence of smooth feedback which asymptotically stabilized an equilibrium point was studied by Brocket, 1983. His consideration rests on Lyapunov functions. Aeyels, 1985, 1986 studied the same problem for a critical nonlinear system which exhibits Hopf bifurcation. His approach was based on the center manifold reduction to the standard Hopf bifurcation problem in two dimensions. Abed and Fu, 1986, 1987 obtain sufficient conditions for local smooth feedback stabilization in the critical cases when the linearized system has either a pair of pure imaginary eigen-values or a single zero eigen-value. The latter results were extended to certain cases of codimension two in Betash and Sastry, 1988, by employing center manifold/normal forms reduction. Note that derivation of stabilizing conditions in this paper ignores the effect of residuals of the normal forms reduction. Although the normalized part of the system overcomes residuals in a certain small neighborhood of a steady-state solution, these discarded terms may contribute essentially in an estimation of the basin of stability.

Our approach to designing a stabilizing feedback control rests on the above described normal forms and averaging methodology. We address feedback as a function of amplitude variables with coefficients adjustable due to imposed stability conditions. Such a procedure intrinsically voids a portion of feedback invalid in stabilization. In the last step a feedback is mapped to the original measurable variables.

Though (14) is equivalent to the initial system, it allows us to formulate stability conditions in a more clear and direct way in the cases when we are able to estimate the influence of residuals $E(a,\rho,\varepsilon)$ and $e(a,\rho,\varepsilon)$ on a systems behavior. Note that amplitude variables a are normalized with respect to characteristic measure ε of a chosen neighborhood of steady state solution such that $a=O(1)$. Residuals decay if $\varepsilon \to 0$ and its magnitudes are bounded by (15). We will see in the following examples that the actual magnitude of residuals turns out to be essentially less than the theoretically predicted upper bounds of (15).

Let us describe briefly a design of resonance stabilizing feedback control. The phase variables can be disregarded in stability analysis, thus we are able to concentrate on controlling the amplitude variables. Address the amplitude equations (14) with feedback in the form:

$$\dot{a} = \alpha a + \tfrac{1}{2}\varepsilon(N(a,\varepsilon) + \overline{N}(a,\varepsilon)) + \varepsilon^K E(a,\rho,\varepsilon) + U + V(a), \qquad (16)$$

where V is feedback, U initializes the bounded uncertainties $U^- \le U \le U^+$.

Let us consider a certain Lyapunov function $L=L(a)$. Let

$$G(a,\rho,\varepsilon) = \alpha a + \tfrac{1}{2}\varepsilon(N(a,\varepsilon) + \overline{N}(a,\varepsilon)) + \varepsilon^K E(a,\rho,\varepsilon) + U + V(a) \text{ and}$$
$$G^0(a,\varepsilon) = \alpha a + \tfrac{1}{2}\varepsilon(N(a,\varepsilon) + \overline{N}(a,\varepsilon)) + \varepsilon^K E^0(a,\varepsilon) + U + V(a).$$

The trivial solution $a=0$ of (16) is asymptotically stable if

$$\sum_{i=1}^{\frac{n}{2}} \frac{\partial L}{\partial a_i} G_i < 0 \quad \text{for } 0 \le a < a^0$$

where equality is admitted only for $a=0$ and a^0 assigns a margin of the basin of stability. We will use in the control design a slightly modified condition which ensures decay of distortions at the required rate

$$\sum_{i=1}^{\frac{n}{2}} \frac{\partial L}{\partial a_i} G_i \le -D \quad \text{for } a_0 \le a \le a^0$$

where D assigns the degree of relative stability, $a_0>0$ is a certain small value.

Due to the inequality $G(a,\rho,\varepsilon) \le G^0(a,\varepsilon)$, we are able to simplify the above relation

$$\sum_{i=1}^{\frac{n}{2}} \frac{\partial L}{\partial a_i} G_i^0 \le -D, \quad a_0 \le a \le a^0 \qquad (17)$$

Thus the design procedure may be specified as follows:

1. Choose a Lyapunov function $L=L(a)$.
2. Find a feedback $V(a)$ which allows the inequality (17) to be satisfied in a prescribed neighborhood of the solution $a = 0$.
3. Map feedback back to the original measurable variable. The last step is rather routine because all involved changes of variables are smooth one-to-one maps.

The resonance control procedure is especially efficient in a certain neighborhood of the trivial solution $a=0$, where the bound of residual $E^0(a,\varepsilon)$ is sufficiently small and resonance terms are dominant. Observe that a particular equation in system (14) consists of nonlinear resonance terms only if relevant modes of (1) are critical/close to critical, regardless of order and structure of the initial system. In other words, nonlinear resonance terms persist in (14) in exceptional cases when the linear resonance terms are either zero or are small. In addition, nonlinear coupling of distinct critical modes (amplitude variables) is possible only if complimentary resonance relations of type: $\lambda_s=(m;\lambda)$ occur. We will see that in flexible-body-dynamics such coupling occurs between rigid-body-modes associated with zero critical eigen-values and oscillatory modes which relate to close-to-pure imaginary eigen-values. At the same time generic oscillatory modes are uncoupled from each other if the system does not possess additional symmetry. Thus feedback V(a) is applied only to the critical modes in order to suppress or annihilate both residual and destabilizing resonance terms in (16). Indeed the linear and nonlinear resonance components enhancing stability remain unchanged. While a variety of Lyapunov functions can be considered, the most simple one $L=\sum a_i^2$ usually yields stability criteria desirable from an engineering point of view.

4. Analysis and Control of a Simplified Model of an Elastic Rotating Bar

The averaging normal forms method is used in this section to detail analysis of an elastic rotating bar modeled by the single mass-spring system shown in figure 1. The energy dissipation in both bar and joint is modeled by viscous friction dampers. Note that this simplified model consists of such essential characteristics of more complex flexible structures as multiple resonances and the stiff property of governing differential equations. We demonstrate a significant simplification of the initial system which is enriched by the averaging of elastic distortion over rigid-body dynamics. The effect of resonances on the averaging of high oscillatory elastic vibrations is revealed in this section, and resonance control is designed in order to suppress elastic distortion to an acceptable level in a chosen time interval.

Let us write the governing differential equation in the form:

$$J\dot{w} + m(L+x)^2\dot{w} + 2mw(L+x)\dot{x} + \beta L w = C$$
$$m\ddot{x} - mw^2(L+x) + kx + \alpha\dot{x} = 0 \qquad (18)$$

where w is the angular velocity of the bar, x is elastic displacement of the mass, α and β are viscous friction coefficients, $C = C(t)$ is applied torque, and J and L are moment of inertia and length of the rotating bar. One obtains equations of a rigid-body motion by discarding x in (18):

$$\dot{w}_0[J + mL^2] + \beta L w_0 = C \qquad (19)$$

where w_0 is the angular velocity for the rigid-body. Assuming torque in the form $C = C_0 \cos \omega t$, we deduce from (19):

$$w_0 = A\cos\omega t + B\sin\omega t,$$

where

$$A = \frac{\beta L C_0}{\beta^2 L^2 + (J+mL^2)^2\omega^2}, \qquad B = \frac{(J+mL^2)\omega C_0}{\beta^2 L^2 + (J+mL^2)^2\omega^2}$$

Setting $w = w_0 + w_1$, yields

$$\dot{w}_1 = \frac{-2m(w_0+w_1)(L+x_1)x_2(J+ml^2) - Cm(2Lx_1+x_1^2) + \beta L(w_0 m(2Lx_1+x_1^2) - w_1(J+mL^2))}{(J+mL^2)^2\left(1+\frac{m(2Lx_1+x_1^2)}{J+mL^2}\right)}$$
$$\dot{x}_1 = x_2$$
$$\dot{x}_2 = (w_0+w_1)^2(L+x_1) - \tfrac{k}{m}x_1 - \alpha x_2 \qquad (20)$$

By expanding

$$\left(1+\frac{m(2Lx_1+x_1^2)}{J+mL^2}\right)^{-1}$$

in a power series and by using a linear change of variables, one represents the above equations in the eigen-basis of the linearized system. The computations have been made for the following parameter values: $J=0.2\,kg/m^2$, $m=0.1\,kg$, $k=10^3\,N/m$, $L=1\,m$, $\alpha=0.02\,Ns/m$, $\beta=0.06\,N/m$, $C_0=7$ and $I=(-1)^{1/2}$.

Rewrite (20) in the form

$$\dot{y} = Ay + \varepsilon f(y,t)$$

where

$$A = \begin{bmatrix} 100\,I & & 0 \\ & -100\,I & \\ 0 & & 0 \end{bmatrix}, \quad T = \begin{bmatrix} 0.01 & 0.01 & 0 \\ I & -I & 0 \\ 0 & 0 & 1 \end{bmatrix}.$$

Matrix T assigns a linear mapping to the eigen-basis of the linearized system: $Ty = (w_1, x_1, x_2)^T$.

Notice that the small linear friction terms have been moved to f(y,t). Two resonances occur in this case. The first corresponds to a single zero eigen-value and the other one relates to a pair of complex conjugate eigen-values. Additional resonance arises if $\omega = 100p/q$, where p and q are integers. This last resonance condition will have the greatest effect when p and q take on relatively small values.

Assume that $\omega_o = 10\pi \neq 100p/q$. In this case, the normal form of the second order is

$$\dot{z}_1 = (-0.00999 + 100\mathrm{I})z_1 + (-0.00001 + 0.001666\mathrm{I})z_1 z_3^2 - 0.000001\mathrm{I}z_1^2 z_2 z_3^2$$
$$\dot{z}_2 = (-0.00999 z_1 - 100\mathrm{I}) + (-0.00001 - 0.001666\mathrm{I})z_2 z_3^2 - 0.000001\mathrm{I}z_1 z_2^2 z_3^2$$
$$\dot{z}_3 = -0.20002 z_3 - 0.000004 z_1 z_2 z_3 - 0.666667 z_3^2 + 0.0001 z_1 z_2 z_3^2$$

These equations in the amplitude-phase variables take the following form:

$$\dot{A} = -0.00999A - 0.00001Az_3^2$$
$$\dot{\rho} = -0.000001A^3 z_3^2 + 0.00166Az_3^2$$
$$\dot{z}_3 = -0.20002z_3 - 0.00004A^2 z_3 - 0.666667z_3^3 + 0.00001A^2 z_3^2 \qquad (21)$$

In (21) only the first and last equations are coupled by nonlinear terms. While this set of equations is not integrable, it does admit clear numerical observation. The solutions of (21) are plotted in figure 2. In figure 3 is plotted the highly oscillatory time history of the system's coordinates given by straight numerical integration. Both sets of solutions have been obtained with the Runge-Kutta method using both adjustable step size and fixed tolerable error. The integration has shown that maximum admissible step size in the case of averaging equations (21) is $1.1 \cdot 10^5$ times larger than the step of integration for (20). At the same time (21) yields an accurate approximation to the exact solution. Comparison of solutions shows that errors do not accumulate with time and on the chosen time interval do not exceed 10^{-7}.

The most significant advantage of averaging normal forms is that it assigns a new set of governing parameters which determine the system behavior. For example, discarding the small terms in (21), one obtains

$$\dot{A} = -0.00999A$$
$$\dot{\rho} = 0.00166z_3^2$$
$$\dot{z}_3 = -0.20002z_3 - 0.6666667z_3^3 \qquad (22)$$

The last equations are integrable. The time history of the errors due to such simplification are on the order of 10^{-9}. Notice that such additional reduction is invisible in original coordinates and is exposed only in terms of the averaging normal form.

It is known that for a flexible robot, natural friction is small and, as a rule, incapable of suppressing elastic oscillations. We will design a feedback control which ensures an acceptable rate of decay of elastic distortions.

While the reduction (22) permits us to design control for a very simple plant, we are going to apply a more general approach to design a robust control. We choose a control u(a) which ensures that

$$G(a) = g(a) + u(a) \leq -d, \text{ for } a > a_0 \qquad (23)$$

In other words, control should ensure asymptotic stability for all $a \geq 0$, and outside of a small regime about zero (initialized by the vector a_0) the least rate of decay of the amplitude variable should be equal to d. Let $a_0=0.1$ and d=0.1. Combining the equation for the amplitude of elastic oscillations (21) and the estimated error $E(a,\rho,\varepsilon)=10^{-7}$ we have

$$g(a) = -0.00999A - 0.00001Az_3^2 + 10^{-7}$$

Choose control

$$u(a) = kA$$

Then determining k that satisfies (23), we get

$$u(a) = -0.990004A$$

Figure 4a displays the time history of controlled and uncontrolled amplitude of elastic distortions and figure 4b displays the required control force.

Summary

In many engineering applications numerical simulation of nonlinear and high-dimensional systems of ODEs arising in flexible structure dynamics is belabored by its stiff property. Approximate solutions are also rare in this field. Direct numerical simulation is not adequate in revealing a mechanism of nonlinear resonance interaction of distinct dynamical modes and not acceptable in control design. Indeed, inherent complexity of flexible structures is used in this paper in a way that essentially reduces its analysis and control. The key physical idea is to average high oscillatory elastic distortions over slow rigid-structure dynamics. The main part of the averaging procedure described in this paper consists of a novel, computationally efficient technique of selecting a resonance normal form. Utilized in symbolic computer software, this technique yields successive approximations for a normal form, a normalized change of variable and residuals of such an approximation. The separation of fast and slow modes turns out to be trivial for equations written in the normal form and is given in closed form. The averaging overcomes stiffness, and substantially reduces the governing equations. In addition, the structure of resonance terms clearly reveals the mechanism and intensity of resonance coupling of distinct dynamical modes (such as slow modes of rigid-bodies and fast elastic oscillations). Although residuals of the normal form approximation are coupled by both fast and slow variables, we deduce a sharp bound which depends only upon slow variables. Using these bounds, we reveal in terms of the slow variable the Lyapunov stability of a chosen steady-state solution.

A robust stabilization with the required rate of asymptotic conversion is ensured by a novel and efficient control design procedure linked with the method of stability analysis. We choose feedback as a function of the averaging kernel of a system and fit required behavior by adjusting free feedback parameters. Note that such a design procedure intrinsically voids the nonresonance portion of the system which does not effect stability. The proposed method has been applied to analysis and control of a simplified model of an elastic rotating bar. Even though elasticity was modeled by a single elastic degree of freedom, the system possesses coupled resonances linked with a single zero and a single pure imaginary couple of eigen-values. The deduced averaging equations present clearly the mechanism and intensity of resonance interaction of the rotation mode of rigid-bar and the mode of elastic oscillations. Note that the averaging equations introduce a reduced set of system parameters allowing additional simplifications which are invisible in the original coordinates. Though the original model is stable, we design a resonance feedback control which ensures an acceptable rate of decay of elastic distortions.

References

Abed, E.H. and J.-H. Fu, 1986, "Local feedback stabilization and bifurcation control, I. Hopf bifurcation," System and Control Letters, Vol. 7, pp. 11-17.

Abed, E.H. and J.-H. Fu, 1987, "Local feedback stabilization and bifurcation control, II. Stationary bifurcation," Systems and Control Letters, Vol. 8, pp. 467-473.

Aeyels, D., 1985, "Stabilization of a class of nonlinear systems by a smooth feedback control," Systems and Control Letters, Vol. 5, pp. 289-294.

Aeyels, D., 1986, "Local and global stabilizability for nonlinear systems," in Theory and Applications of Nonlinear Control Systems, C.I. Byrnes and A. Lindquist (editors), pp. 93-105, North-Holland, Amsterdam.

Anthony, T.C and B. Wie, 1990, "Pulse-Modulated Control Synthesis for a Flexible Spacecraft," Journal of Aircraft, Vol. 13 (6), pp. 1014 - 1112.

Arnold, V.I., 1983, *Geometrical methods in the theory of ordinary differential equations*, Springer-Verlag, New York.

Betash, S. and S. Sastry, 1988, "Stabilization of Nonlinear Systems with Uncontrollable Linearization," in *Dynamical systems Approaches to Nonlinear Problems in Systems and Circuits*, editors: F. M. A. Salam and M. L. Levi, SIAM, Philadelphia.

Bogolubov, N.N. and V.A. Mitropolsky, 1974, *Asymptotic Methods in the Theory of Nonlinear Oscillations*, Nauka. (In Russian)

Brockett, R.W., 1983, *Asymptotic stability and feedback stabilization, Differential geometric control theory*, in: R.W. Brockett, R.S. Milmann, and H.J. Sussman, eds., Progress in Mathematics, Birkhauser, Boston.

Di Benedetto, M.D. and P. Lucibello, 1990, "A Nonlinear Observer for Flexible Mechanisms using Canonical Forms," Proceedings of the American Control Conference, pp. 144-147.

Meirovitch, L. and M.K. Kwak, 1989, "Control of Flexible Spacecraft with Time-Varying Configuration," Proceedings of the AAS/AIAA Astrodynamics Specialist Conference, Stowe,Vermont.

Meriovitch, L. and M.K. Kwak, 1989, "State Equations for a Spacecraft with Maneuvering Flexible Appendages in Terms of Quasi-Coordinates," Presented at the Pan-American Congress of Applied Mechanics, Rio de Janeiro, Brazil.

Meriovitch,L. and M.K. Kwak and T. Stemple, 1989, "A Substructure Synthesis Approach to the Control of Flexible Multi-Body Systems," Multi-Body Dynamics and Control at the ASME Winter Annual Meeting, San Francisco, CA.

Silverberg, L.M. and P. Sungtae, 1990, "Interactions between Rigid-Body and Flexible-Body Motions in Maneuvering Spacecraft," Journal of Guidance and Control, Vol. 13(1), pp. 73-81.

van Shoor, M.C. and A.H. von Flotow, 1990, "Aeroelastic Characteristics of a Highly Flexible Aircraft," Journal of Aircraft, Vol. 27(10), pp. 901-908.

Wiggins, S., 1990, *Introduction to Applied Nonlinear Dynamical Systems and Chaos*, Springer-Verlag, New York.

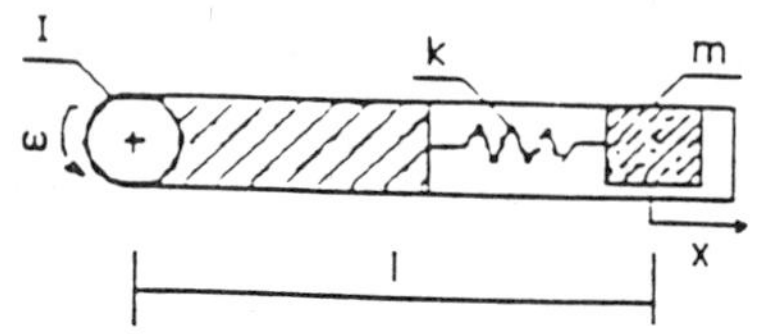

Figure 1

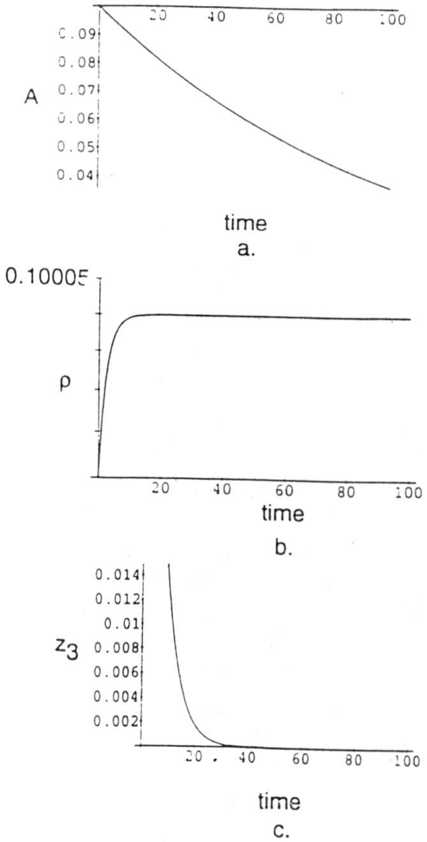

Figure 2

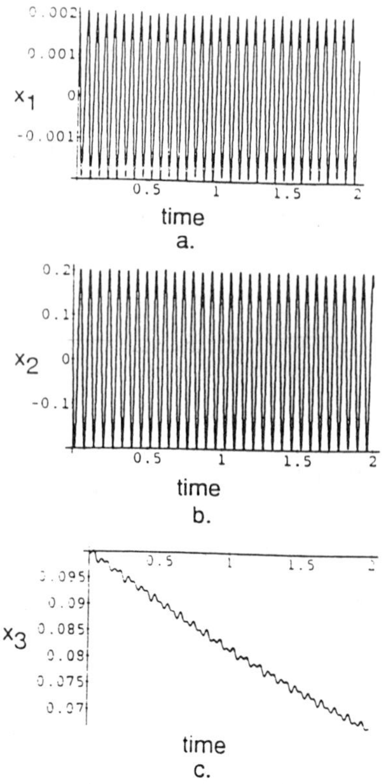

Figure 3

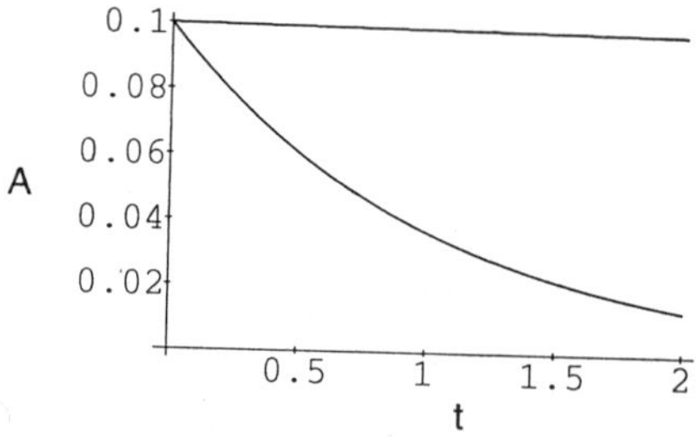

Figure 4a: Uncontrolled amplitude of unstable mode (thin), and controlled amplitude (thick)

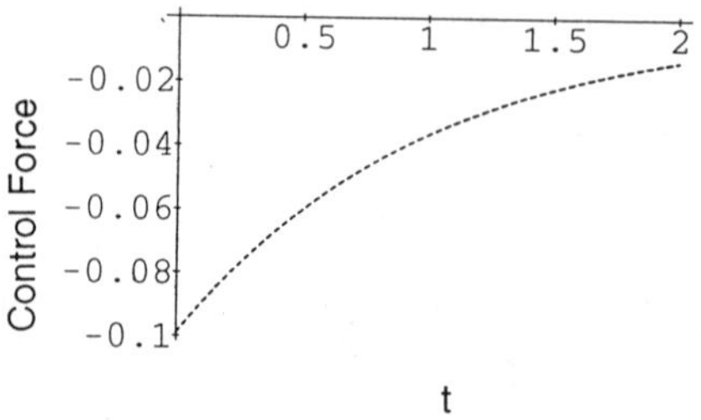

Figure 4b: Control force

Proceedings of the
American Control Conference
San Francisco, California • June 1993

ON EQUATIONS OF MOTION AND CONTROL FOR SYSTEMS WITH NONHOLONOMIC EQUALITY CONSTRAINTS

J.S. Chen **Y.H. Chen**

The George W. Woodruff School of Mechanical Engineering
Georgia Institute of Technology
Atlanta, GA 30332-0405, USA

ABSTRACT

A procedure to derive the equation of motion for a class of systems under nonholonomic equality constraints is discussed in detail. Two approaches, namely, adjoining and embedding, to derive equations of motion without Lagrange multiplier are introduced. The equations of motion for systems with nonholonomic constraints are then transformed into a format used in non-constrained problems. The final formulation is suitable for control design. We also address a new robust control design.

1. Introduction

Nonholonomic constraints appear in many physical systems, such as wheeled carts (Kanayama *et al.* 1990), space robots (Masutani *et al.* 1989), and dexterous manipulation of robot fingers (Sastry and Li 1989). Due to the nature of the constraints, the equations of motion are difficult to formulate, not to mention the controller design.

So far, only a few work discussed the control problems for nonholonomic systems (see, for example, Bloch and McClamroch 1989, Bloch *et al.* 1990). Various specific physical systems are addressed. A general approach for the formulation of the equation of motion is still in need. This paper serves to complement the previous work in this regard. We propose a general but detailed procedure on how to formulate the equations of motion for systems with nonholonomic (equality) constraints. We show how to simplify these equations for control purpose. Two algorithms to derive the equations of motion are discussed. These are the *Adjoining (Lagrange multiplier) approach* and the *embedding approach.* Since our setting is based upon the Pfaffian form, the approaches are applicable to holonomically constrained systems as well. We also introduce a new control design suitable for the type of nonlinear systems under consideration when uncertainties exist.

2. Fundamental setting

By Hamilton's Principle, the fundamental motion equation can be written as (Pars, 1965)

$$\left[\frac{d}{dt}\frac{\partial T(q,\dot{q})}{\partial \dot{q}} - \frac{\partial T(q,\dot{q})}{\partial q} - Q^{\mathrm{T}}(q,u)\right]\delta q = 0. \quad (2.1)$$

Here $t \in \mathbf{R}$ is the independent variable, $q \in \mathbf{R}^n$ is the generalized displacement, $\dot{q} \in \mathbf{R}^n$ is the generalized velocity, $u \in \mathbf{R}^r$ is the external input, $T(q,\dot{q}) \in \mathbf{R}$ is the kinetic energy, $Q(q,u) \in \mathbf{R}^n$ is the generalized force, δq is the generalized virtual displacement. In (2.1), the partial derivatives of a scalar function $U(p)$ with respect to $p \in \mathbf{R}^n$ is defined as

$$\frac{\partial U}{\partial p} := \left[\frac{\partial U}{\partial p_1}\ \frac{\partial U}{\partial p_2}\ \cdots\ \frac{\partial U}{\partial p_n}\right],$$

where p_i is the i-th component of the vector p.

We shall focus our attention to a class of systems in which equation (2.1) will lead to

$$[M(q)\ddot{q} + C(q,\dot{q})\dot{q} - B(q)u]^{\mathrm{T}}\,\delta q = 0, \quad (2.2)$$

$$\dot{M}(q) - 2C(q,\dot{q}) \quad \text{is skew symmetric.} \quad (2.3)$$

Here $M(q) \in \mathbf{R}^{n\times n}$, $C(q,\dot{q}) \in \mathbf{R}^{n\times n}$, $B(q) \in \mathbf{R}^{n\times r}$.

A sufficient condition for this is that the generalized force is linear with respect to u. Furthermore, the kinetic energy $T(q,\dot{q})$ is in a quadratic form of the generalized velocity, i.e,

$$T(q,\dot{q}) = \frac{1}{2}\dot{q}^{\mathrm{T}}A(q)\dot{q}, \quad (2.4)$$

where $A(q) \in \mathbf{R}^{n\times n}$. Very often, a system is modelled first via a set of *natural coordinates.* If the natural coordinates, which are dependent on the *generalized coordinates*, do not depend explicitly on t, then (2.2) is *sufficiently* assured, provided that the linearity of Q on u holds. Furthermore, for every element $a_{ij}(q)$ of $A(q)$, one has $a_{ij}(q) = a_{ji}(q)$ for all i, j.

We assume that the system has m nonholonomic equality constraints. These are put in the following compact form:

$$J(q)\dot{q} = 0, \qquad (2.5)$$

where $J \in \mathbf{R}^{m\times n}$ $(m \leq n)$ has full row rank. Note that these constraints are not integrable according to the definition of nonholonomic constraint. Using the notion of virtual displacement, the nonholonomic constraints are expressed by

$$J(q)\ \delta q = 0. \qquad (2.6)$$

The virtual displacement δq in (2.2) is *arbitrary* if no constraints are imposed on the system motion. Because constraints arise, δq in (2.2) is now the *possible* one and can *not* vary arbitrarily. It is constrained by (2.6). Therefore, the bracket term in (2.2) is not necessary zero. We shall discuss two approaches to simplify the setting (2.2) and (2.6).

The *equality* constraints considered are of the Pfaffian form in classical mechanics

$$A_1(q,t)\ dq + A_2(q,t)\ dt = 0, \qquad (2.7)$$

where $A_1(q,t)$ and $A_2(q,t)$ are sufficiently smooth functions. In this article, we restrict the discussions to *equality* constraints only. We emphasize that nonholonomic constraints may be described by *inequalities* (Pars 1965).

2.1 Algorithm I – Adjoining (Lagrange multiplier) approach

To satisfy both (2.2) and (2.6), the transpose of the bracket term is equation (2.2) must lie in the range space spanned by the rows of $J(q)$. That is

$$[M(q)\ddot{q} + C(q,\dot{q})\dot{q} - B(q)u]^{\mathrm{T}} = \lambda^{\mathrm{T}} J(q), \qquad (2.8)$$

where $\lambda \in \mathbf{R}^m$ is the Lagrange multiplier. After rearrangng the equation, we have

$$M(q)\ddot{q} + C(q,\dot{q})\dot{q} = J(q)^T\lambda + B(q)u. \qquad (2.9)$$

This is the form which many researchers are familiar with. The matrix equations (2.9) and (2.5) represent n and m scalar equations, respectively. There are $n+m$ variables (i.e., the components of q and λ) involved.

The setting can be further simplified. Find a matrix $R(q) \in \mathbf{R}^{n\times(n-m)}$ such that (Campion *et al.* 1991)

$$J(q)R(q) = 0. \qquad (2.10)$$

Note that it is always possible to find an $R(q)$. One most obvious choice for $R(q)$ is

$$R(q) = \begin{bmatrix} -J_1^{-1}(q)J_2(q) \\ I \end{bmatrix}, \qquad (2.11)$$

where I is an $(n-m)\times(n-m)$ identity matrix and $J_1(q) \in \mathbf{R}^{m\times m}$ and $J_2(q) \in \mathbf{R}^{m\times(n-m)}$ are the submatrices of $J(q)$:

$$J(q) = [\,J_1(q) \quad J_2(q)\,]. \qquad (2.12)$$

Note that $J_1^{-1}(q)$ always exists since the matrix $J(q)$ is assumed to have full rank. The scalar equations may need to be reordered to obtain $J_1^{-1}(q)$.

Lagrange multiplier λ in equation (2.9) can be eliminated by multiplying $R^{\mathrm{T}}(q)$ to the equation:

$$R^{\mathrm{T}}(q)M(q)\ddot{q} + R^{\mathrm{T}}(q)C(q,\dot{q})\dot{q} = R^{\mathrm{T}}(q)B(q)u. \qquad (2.13)$$

These are $n-m$ (scalar) equations with n variables. This together with (2.5) form the equation of motion with n equations and n variables.

A common confusion that may arise in *eliminating the Lagrange multiplier*, especially as $a_{ij}(q) \equiv c_{ij} = $ constant and $Q(q,u) = Q(u)$, is the following: One first decomposes (2.5) into the block form

$$[J_1 \quad J_2]\begin{bmatrix} \dot{q}_1 \\ \dot{q}_2 \end{bmatrix} = 0 \qquad (2.14)$$

and therefore has

$$\dot{q}_1 = -J_1^{-1}J_2\dot{q}_2. \qquad (2.15)$$

Substituting (2.4) into the kinetic energy $T(q,\dot{q})$ results in

$$\begin{aligned} T =& \dot{q}_1^{\mathrm{T}}A_{11}\dot{q}_1 + \dot{q}_1^{\mathrm{T}}A_{12}\dot{q}_2 + \dot{q}_2^{\mathrm{T}}A_{21}\dot{q}_1 + \dot{q}_2^{\mathrm{T}}A_{22}\dot{q}_2 \\ =& \dot{q}_2^{\mathrm{T}}(J_2^{\mathrm{T}}J_1^{-\mathrm{T}}A_{11}J_1^{-1}J_2 \\ & - J_2^{\mathrm{T}}J_1^{-\mathrm{T}}A_{12} - A_{21}J_1^{-1}J_2 + A_{22})\dot{q}_2 \\ =:& \ \dot{q}_2^{\mathrm{T}}\tilde{J}\dot{q}_2, \end{aligned} \qquad (2.16)$$

where

$$A(q) = \begin{bmatrix} A_{11}(q) & A_{12}(q) \\ A_{21}(q) & A_{22}(q) \end{bmatrix} \qquad (2.17)$$

with the submatrices $A_{ij}(q)$, $i,j = 1,2$, of appropriate dimensions. Substituting the T in (2.16) into the Lagrange equation

$$\frac{d}{dt}\frac{\partial T}{\partial \dot{q}} - \frac{\partial T}{\partial q} - Q^{\mathrm{T}} = 0 \qquad (2.18)$$

yields a set of *incorrect* equations of motion. This is since an incorrect constraint was embedded in the

Lagrange equation which requires *possible virtual displacement* rather than *possible velocity*.

2.2 Algorithm II – Embedding approach

We now introduce the second algorithm. The advantage in using it is to avoid the use of Lagrange multiplier in the entire setting. This is desirable from the control point of view if positioning is the main task and force is not considered (The physical correspondence of the lagrange multiplier is the constraint force). The approach was first introduced by Rosenberg (1977).

In order to satisfy equation (2.6), δq must stay in the vector space which is orthogonal to the space spanned by the rows of matrix $J(q)$. From equation (2.10), we know that columns of matrix $R(q)$ span the subspace orthogonal to row vectors of $J(q)$. Therefore, δq is equal to

$$\delta q = R(q)\delta z, \tag{2.19}$$

where $\delta z \in \mathbf{R}^{n-m}$ is a time dependent vector. Note that δz, unlike δq, can vary arbitrarily. Substituting above equation into equation (2.2), we have

$$[M(q)\ddot{q} + C(q,\dot{q})\dot{q} - B(q)u]^{\mathrm{T}} R(q)\delta z = 0. \tag{2.20}$$

It also lead to equation (2.13) since δz can vary arbitrarily.

2.3 Further simplification

The equations of motion, equation (2.13) and (2.5), can be further simplified. From (2.19), we have

$$\dot{q} = R(q)\dot{z}. \tag{2.21}$$

According to the definition of $R(q)$, equation (2.5) is automatically satisfied when $\dot{q}$ is restricted to be $R(q)\dot{z}$. Differentiate above equation with time, we get

$$\begin{aligned}\ddot{q} =& \dot{R}(q)\dot{z} + R(q)\ddot{z} \\ & R'(q)\dot{q}\dot{z} + R(q)\ddot{z},\end{aligned} \tag{2.22}$$

where $R'(q)$ is the derivative of $R(q)$ with respect to q. Plugging q and $\dot{q}$ into (2.13), we have

$$R^{\mathrm{T}}(q)M(q)R(q)\ddot{z} + \left[R^{\mathrm{T}}(q)C(q,\dot{q})R(q) + R^{\mathrm{T}}(q)M(q)R'(q)\dot{q}\right]\dot{z} = R^{\mathrm{T}}(q)B(q)u. \tag{2.23}$$

This equation has the following form:

$$\bar{M}(q)\ddot{z} + \bar{C}(q,\dot{q})\dot{z} = \bar{B}(q)u. \tag{2.24}$$

According to the definition of $\bar{M}(q)$, $\bar{C}(q,\dot{q})$ and the property in equation (2.3), we also have the following property:

$$\dot{\bar{M}}(q) - 2\bar{C}(q,\dot{q}) \quad \text{is skew symmetric.} \tag{2.25}$$

Therefore, the equations of motion for systems with nonholonomic constraints is transformed into equations similar to systems without constraints.

3. Robust control design

We wish the system to follow a desired trajectory $z^d(t)$, $t \in [t_0, t_1]$, with the desired velocity $\dot{z}^d(t)$. Assume $z^d(\cdot) : [t_0, \infty) \to \mathbf{R}^n$ is of class $\mathbf{C}^2$ and $z^d(t)$, $\dot{z}^d(t)$, and $\ddot{z}^d(t)$ are uniformly bounded. Let

$$e(t) := z(t) - z^d(t), \tag{3.1}$$

and hence $\dot{e}(t) = \dot{z}(t) - \dot{z}^d(t)$, $\ddot{e}(t) = \ddot{z}(t) - \ddot{z}^d(t)$.

The system (2.24) can be rewritten as

$$\bar{M}(q)(\ddot{e} + \ddot{z}^d(t)) + \bar{C}(q,\dot{q})(\dot{e}(t) + \dot{z}^d(t)) = \bar{B}(q)u. \tag{3.2}$$

In many practical situations, there may be modeling uncertainty and/or computational difficulty which prevents one from using the precise knowledge of $\bar{M}$, $\bar{C}$. Uncertainty includes, for example, payload mass and friction force parameters. Here we assume it is possible to estimate the bound of the model uncertainty.

We first choose *nominal* matrices $\hat{M}$, $\hat{C}$. Next, for a given $S = \mathrm{diag}[s_i]_{n\times n}$, $s_i > 0$, we *choose* (and hence we know) a scalar function $\rho : \mathbf{R}^n \times \mathbf{R}^n \times \mathbf{R} \to \mathbf{R}_+$ such that

$$\rho(e,\dot{e},q,\dot{q},t) \geq \|\phi(e,\dot{e},q,\dot{q},t)\|, \tag{3.3}$$

where

$$\begin{aligned}\phi(e,\dot{e},q,\dot{q},t) :=& (\hat{M}(q) - \bar{M}(q))(\ddot{z}^d(t) - S\dot{e}) \\ &+ (\hat{C}(q,\dot{q}) - \bar{C}(q,\dot{q}))(\dot{z}^d(t) - Se)\end{aligned} \tag{3.4}$$

Here $\rho(e,\dot{e},q,\dot{q},t)$ is based on the assumed bound of uncertainty. For a given $\epsilon > 0$ (often chosen to be "small") and k_{p_i}, $k_{v_i} > 0$, $i = 1,2,\cdots,n$, the control torque is given by

$$\bar{B}u = \hat{M}(\ddot{z}^d - S\dot{e}) + \hat{C}(\dot{q}^d - Se) - K_p e - K_v\dot{e} + p \tag{3.5}$$

where

$$p = \begin{cases} -\dfrac{\mu}{\|\mu\|}\rho & \text{if } \|\mu\| > \epsilon, \\ -\dfrac{\mu}{\epsilon}\rho & \text{if } \|\mu\| \leq \epsilon, \end{cases} \tag{3.6}$$

$$\mu = (\dot{e} + Se)\rho, \tag{3.7}$$

$$K_p := \text{diag}[k_{p_i}]_{n\times n}, \tag{3.8}$$

$$K_v := \text{diag}[k_{v_i}]_{n\times n}. \tag{3.9}$$

Assumption 1. The inertia matrix $\bar{M}(q)$ is uniformly positive definite; that is, there exists a constant $\underline{\sigma} > 0$ such that

$$\bar{M}(q) \geq \underline{\sigma} I \qquad \forall q \in \mathbf{R}^n. \tag{3.10}$$

We state this as an assumption rather than a fact. Let

$$\underline{e}(t) := [\, e^T(t) \quad \dot{e}^T(t)\,]^T. \tag{3.11}$$

Theorem 1. Subject to Assumption 1, the control (3.5) renders $\underline{e}(t)$ of the system (3.2) uniformly bounded and uniformly ultimately bounded. The size of the ultimate boundedness ball can be made arbitrary small by a suitable choice of ϵ.

The theorem can be proven by chossing

$$\begin{aligned} v(\underline{e}, t) :=& \frac{1}{2}(\dot{e} + Se)^{\mathrm{T}} \bar{M}(e + q^d(t))(\dot{e} + Se) \\ &+ \frac{1}{2} e^{\mathrm{T}}(K_p + SK_v)e. \end{aligned} \tag{3.12}$$

as the Lyapunov function (Corless and Leitmann 1981). The proof is omitted here.

The (positive) gain parameters s_i, k_{p_i}, and k_{v_i} are arbitrary. No restrictions are imposed. The designer has the discretion of choosing these parameters based on a number of practical factors such as the actuator saturation limits. In a sense the matrices $\hat{M}$ and $\hat{C}$ define the input for the nominal portion of the system. However, no restrictions on their choices are imposed. In the special case that there is no modeling uncertainty and one can afford sufficiently fast on-line computation, one naturally chooses $\hat{M} = \bar{M}$, $\hat{C} = \bar{C}$, and therefore $\rho = 0$. The errors $e(t)$ and $\dot{e}(t)$ converge to zero as $t \to \infty$.

Example: Consider the control problem of a knife edge which is under contact with a plane at one point. Let x, y denote the coordinates of the contact point and ϕ denotes the heading angle of the knife edge with respect to the x-axis. Let also u_f be the applied force per unit mass in the heading direction and u_t be the applied torque per unit moment of inertia. The fundamental equations of motion are

$$(\ddot{x} - \cos\phi\; u_f)\delta x + (\ddot{y} - \sin\phi\; u_f)\delta y + (\ddot{\phi} - u_t)\delta\phi = 0. \tag{3.13}$$

Let $z := [\, x \quad y \quad \phi\,]^{\mathrm{T}}$ and $u := [\, u_f \quad u_t\,]^{\mathrm{T}}$. According to (2.2), we have

$$M(q) = \begin{bmatrix} 1 & 0 & 0 \\ 0 & 1 & 0 \\ 0 & 0 & 1 \end{bmatrix}, \qquad C(q, \dot{q}) = 0,$$

$$B(q) = \begin{bmatrix} \cos\phi & 0 \\ \sin\phi & 0 \\ 0 & 1 \end{bmatrix}.$$

The velocity of the knife edge must always coincide with heading direction. Therefore, there is one nonholonomic constraint:

$$\sin\phi\; \dot{x} - \cos\phi\; \dot{y} = 0. \tag{3.14}$$

According to equation (2.5), we have

$$J(q) = [\, \sin\phi \quad -\cos\phi \quad 0\,]. \tag{3.15}$$

When $\phi \neq 0$, $R(q)$ can be chosen as

$$R(q) = \begin{bmatrix} -\cot\phi & 0 \\ 1 & 0 \\ 0 & 1 \end{bmatrix}. \tag{3.16}$$

From equation (2.21), we know that for this choice

$$z = \begin{bmatrix} y \\ \phi \end{bmatrix}. \tag{3.17}$$

The equation of motion becomes

$$\begin{bmatrix} \csc^2\phi & 0 \\ 0 & 1 \end{bmatrix} \begin{bmatrix} \ddot{y} \\ \ddot{\phi} \end{bmatrix} + \begin{bmatrix} -\cot\phi\csc^2\phi & 0 \\ 0 & 0 \end{bmatrix} \begin{bmatrix} \dot{y} \\ \dot{\phi} \end{bmatrix} = \begin{bmatrix} -\csc\phi\sin 2\phi & 0 \\ 0 & 1 \end{bmatrix} \begin{bmatrix} u_f \\ u_t \end{bmatrix}. \tag{3.18}$$

After divide the first row by $\csc^2\phi$, it becomes

$$\begin{bmatrix} 1 & 0 \\ 0 & 1 \end{bmatrix} \begin{bmatrix} \ddot{y} \\ \ddot{\phi} \end{bmatrix} + \begin{bmatrix} -\cot\phi & 0 \\ 0 & 0 \end{bmatrix} \begin{bmatrix} \dot{y} \\ \dot{\phi} \end{bmatrix} = \begin{bmatrix} -\sin\phi\sin 2\phi & 0 \\ 0 & 1 \end{bmatrix} \begin{bmatrix} u_f \\ u_t \end{bmatrix}. \tag{3.19}$$

In this system, we can directly control y and ϕ by the input u_f and u_t when ϕ is not zero. However, we can only indirectly control x and $\dot{x}$ through (3.14). The system is uncontrollable when ϕ is equal to zero. The control problem of the knife edge and other similar nonholonomic systems, such as wheeled carts and a rolling disk on a plane, may be divided into two categories. The first is the *trajectory planning* problem. That is, subject to the nonholonomic constraints, determine all desirable yet achievable trajectories. The second is the *tracking* problem. That is, design feasible controller(s) (preferably in a continuous manner) such that the deviation between the desired and actual trajectories is within a prespecified threshold. More research is underway for such control problems.

Acknowledgment

This research was supported by the National Science Foundation under Grant MSS-9014714.

References

Bloch, A.M. and McClamroch, N.H., 1989, "Control of mechanical systems with classical nonholonomic constraints", *Proceedings of the 28th IEEE Conference on Decision and Control*, Tampa, FL, pp. 201-205.

Bloch, A.M., McClamroch, N.H., and Reyhanoglu, M., 1990, "Controllability and stabilizability properties of a nonholonomic control system", *Proceedings of the 29th IEEE Conference on Decision and Control*, Honolulu, HA, pp. 1312-1314.

Campion, G., d'Andrea-Novel, B. and Bastin, G., 1991, "Controllability and state feedback stabilization of nonholonomic mechanical systems", in C. Canudas de Wit (Ed), *Advanced Robot Control*, Spring-Verlag, New York, N.Y., pp. 106-124.

Corless, M.J. and Leitmann, G., 1981, "Continuous state feedback guaranteeing uniform ultimate boundedness for uncertain dynamics systems," *IEEE Transactions on Automatic Control*, Vol. 26, No. 5, pp. 1139-1144.

Kanayama, Y., Kimura, Y., Miyazaki, F., and Noguchi, T., 1990, "A stable tracking control method for a autonomous mobile robot", *Proceedings of the IEEE International Conference on Robotics and Automation* , Cincinnati, OH, pp. 384-389.

Masutani, Y., Miyazaki, F. and Arimoto, S, 1989, "Sensory feedback control for space manipulator", *Proceedings of the IEEE International Conference on Robotics and Automation*, Washington, D.C., pp. 1346-1351.

Pars, L.A., 1965, *A Treatise on Analytical Dynamics*, John Wiley and Sons, New York, N.Y.

Rosenberg, R.M., 1977, *Analytical Dynamics of Discrete Systems*, Plenum Press, New York, N.Y.

Sastry, S. and Li, Z., 1989, "Robot motion planning with nonholonomic constraints", *Proceedings of the 28th IEEE Conference on Decision and Control*, Tampa, FL, pp. 211-216.

Proceedings of the
American Control Conference
San Francisco, California • June 1993

Nonlinear Controllers for Positive Real Systems with Arbitrary Input Nonlinearities

Dennis S. Bernstein
Department of Aerospace Engineering
The University of Michigan
Ann Arbor, MI 48109-2140

Wassim M. Haddad
Department of Mechanical and
Aerospace Engineering
Florida Institute of Technology
Melbourne, FL 32901

1. Introduction

In certain applications, such as the control of flexible structures, the plant transfer function is known to be positive real. This property arises if the sensor and actuator are colocated and also dual, for example, force actuator and velocity sensor, or torque actuator and angular rate sensor. In practice the prospects for controlling such systems is quite good since, if sensor and actuator dynamics are negligible, then stability is unconditionally guaranteed so long as the controller is strictly positive real [1,2]. Although there is no general theory yet available for designing positive real controllers, a variety of techniques have been proposed based upon H_2 theory [3-5] and H_∞ theory [6-8].

The purpose of this note is to address the following question: Given a positive real plant and strictly positive real compensator, how should the compensator be modified if the plant is found to possess an input nonlinearity? For example, proof mass and piezoelectric actuators have force constraints that lead to saturation nonlinearities [9]. There exists an extensive literature devoted to the control saturation problem; see, for example, [10-14] and the numerous references cited therein.

Our main result (Theorem 1) implies that closed-loop stability is guaranteed so long as the compensator is modified to include a suitable input nonlinearity. Although this result is limited to positive real plants, it turns out that it is not limited to saturation nonlinearity, but rather applies to a large class of input nonlinearities. We require only that the nonlinearity be memoryless and that either its characteristics be known or its output be measurable. The proof of this result is based upon Lyapunov function theory applied to positive real systems. An alternative, more succinct proof based upon dissipative system theory [15, 16] is also given. This result shows that the nonlinear controller modification counteracts the effects of the input nonlinearity by recovering the passivity of the plant.

Since our results focus on positive real plants, it is natural to suspect that our results are related to classical absolute stability criteria such as the circle or Popov criterion. Such results are often used to verify stability of closed-loop systems involving saturation nonlinearities [10,11]. However, such criteria require a gain or phase constraint on the linear portion of the loop transfer function. Such constraints are not satisfied in our formulation since *both* the plant and compensator are positive real so that the loop gain need not possess either a gain or phase constraint. In addition, the approach of [10,11] assumes beforehand that only a finite portion of the nonlinearity is used in closed-loop operation, or, equivalently, that the state is confined to a finite region of the state space. Our approach, however, guarantees unconditional global asymptotic stability.

In certain special cases, however, absolute stability criteria can be used to guarantee closed-loop stability in the presence of an input nonlinearity and without modifying the compensator [17]. Specifically, if the input nonlinearity is sector-bounded and either monotonic or odd monotonic, then closed-loop stability is guaranteed if the product $G(s)G_c(s)Z(s)$ is positive real, where $G(s)$ and $G_c(s)$ denote the linear portion of the plant and the linear compensator, respectively, and $Z(s)$ denotes a frequency domain multiplier of a specified class [18]. If $G_c^{-1}(s)$ belongs to this class of multipliers, then by choosing $Z(s) = G_c^{-1}(s)$ it follows that the closed-loop is stable. Our results, however, are valid for nonlinearities that are not necessarily either sector-bounded or odd or monotonic and positive real compensators that are otherwise arbitrary. Closed-loop stability for this class of systems is guaranteed by employing the modified nonlinear compensator introduced herein.

2. Input Nonlinearities

Consider the positive real plant

$$\dot{x}(t) = Ax(t) + Bu(t), \tag{1}$$
$$y(t) = Cx(t) + Du(t) \tag{2}$$

with the positive real feedback compensator

$$\dot{x}_c(t) = A_c x_c(t) + B_c y(t), \tag{3}$$
$$u(t) = -\left[C_c x_c(t) + D_c y(t)\right], \tag{4}$$

where $x(t) \in \mathbb{R}^n, u(t), y(t) \in \mathbb{R}^m, x_c(t) \in \mathbb{R}^{n_c}$, and all matrices are real with appropriate dimensions. In (4) the minus sign denotes the fact that the positive real plant (A, B, C, D) and positive real compensator (A_c, B_c, C_c, D_c) are in a negative feedback configuration. As discussed in the Introduction, such compensators may be designed by means of a variety of techniques [3-8]. Also, by standard theory [1] the closed-loop system is guaranteed to be stable in the sense of Lyapunov and, furthermore, is asymptotically stable if either the plant or the compensator is strictly positive real.

Now suppose that the plant is found to possess an input nonlinearity so that, in reality, (1) is not valid. Rather, in place of (1) a more accurate plant model is

$$\dot{x}(t) = Ax(t) + B\sigma(u(t)), \tag{5}$$

$$y(t) = Cx(t) + D\sigma(u(t)), \tag{6}$$

where σ: $\mathbb{R}^m \to \mathbb{R}^m$ denotes the input nonlinearity. We shall require the following assumption concerning $\sigma(\cdot)$. Let $u = [u_1 \cdots u_m]^{\mathrm{T}}$ and $\sigma(u) = [\sigma_1(u) \cdots \sigma_m(u)]^{\mathrm{T}}$ denote the components of u and σ.

Assumption 1. For all $i = 1, \ldots, m$, if $u_i = 0$, then $\sigma_i(u) = 0$. That is, the ith component of $\sigma(u)$ vanishes whenever the ith component of u vanishes.

To illustrate the allowable input nonlinearities, consider first the special case $\sigma(u) = [\hat{\sigma}_1(u_1) \cdots \hat{\sigma}_m(u_m)]^{\mathrm{T}}$ of decoupled nonlinearities. In this case, the ith component $\hat{\sigma}_i(u_i)$ of $\sigma(\cdot)$ depends only upon the ith component u_i of u. Now $\hat{\sigma}_i(\cdot)$ can represent an arbitrary scalar nonlinearity that vanishes at the origin. For example, the saturation nonlinearity $\hat{\sigma}_1(u_1) = \operatorname{sat}(u_1)$ is allowable as well as deadzone, quantization

*This research was supported in part by the Air Force Office of Scientific Research under Grant F49620-92-J-0127 and the National Science Foundation under Research Initiation Grant ECS-9109558.

and relay nonlinearities. Note that different types of nonlinearities are permissible. For example, $\sigma(u) = [\text{sat}(u_1) \quad \text{sgn}(u_2)]^{\text{T}}$ is allowed, where $\text{sgn}(0) = 0$.

More generally, $\sigma(u)$ may also denote a nonlinearity whose coordinates are not necessarily decoupled. For example, the nonlinearity

$$\begin{aligned} \sigma(u) &= u, \quad \|u\|_2 \leq 1, \\ &= 1, \quad \|u\|_2 > 1, \end{aligned}$$

where $\|u\|_2 = \sqrt{u^{\text{T}}u}$, satisfies Assumption 1 and has the form of a radial saturation function on $\mathbb{R}^m$.

In the presence of such nonlinearities, closed-loop stability and performance may be affected. In the next section we modify the controller (3), (4) to account for the input nonlinearity in order to guarantee closed-loop stability.

3. Nonlinear Controller Modification

To counteract the effect of the input nonlinearity $\sigma(u)$ in (5), (6) we modify the controller by replacing the compensator dynamics (3) and control inputs (4) by

$$\dot{x}_c(t) = A_c x_c(t) + B_c\beta(u(t))y(t), \tag{7}$$
$$u(t) = -[C_c x_c(t) + D_c\beta(u(t))y(t)], \tag{8}$$

where the controller nonlinearity $\beta(u)$ is the diagonal matrix

$$\beta(u) = \begin{bmatrix} \beta_1(u) & & 0 \\ & \ddots & \\ 0 & & \beta_m(u) \end{bmatrix}, \tag{9}$$

where, for $i = 1, \ldots, m$,

$$\begin{aligned} \beta_i(u) &= \sigma_i(u)/u_i, \quad u_i \neq 0, \\ &= \text{arbitrary}, \quad u_i = 0. \end{aligned} \tag{10}$$

Because of Assumption 1, it can be seen that $\beta_i(u)u_i = \sigma_i(u)$, for all $i = 1, \ldots, m$ and $u \in \mathbb{R}^m$. Since $\sigma_i(u) = 0$ whenever $u_i = 0$, it can also be seen that $\beta_i(u)u_i = \sigma_i(u)$ is satisfied for arbitrary $\beta_i(u)$ whenever $u_i = 0$. Consequently, it follows that

$$\beta(u)u = \sigma(u), \quad u \in \mathbb{R}^m. \tag{11}$$

It thus turns out that the value of $\beta_i(u)$ when $u_i = 0$ plays no role in the subsequent stability analysis.

The form of the controller nonlinearity $\beta(u)$ to be implemented in (7) and (8) is quite simple, requiring only knowledge of $\sigma(u)$ and division by u_i. For the case $m = 1$ and several common nonlinearities, the required controller nonlinearity $\beta(u)$ is illustrated in Table 1. It can be seen that a relay nonlinearity $\sigma(u) = \text{sgn}(u)$ leads to unbounded $\beta(u)$ for u near zero. Hence in this case it may be desirable to artificially implement a deadzone so that $\beta(u)$ is bounded. Finally, although all of the input nonlinearities shown in Table 1 are sector-bounded and odd monotonic, our results are valid for nonlinearities that are not necessarily either sector-bounded or odd or monotonic.

The modified nonlinear controller (7), (8) can be implemented in two different ways. If a model of the input nonlinearity $\sigma(u)$ is known, then $\beta(u)$ can be constructed from (10) by evaluating $\sigma(u)$. If, however, the model $\sigma(u)$ is not available but $\sigma(u(t))$ can be measured during closed-loop operation, then $\beta(u(t))$ can be formed from $u(t)$ and $\sigma(u(t))$ as shown in Figure 1. If, however, neither a model of $\sigma(u)$ nor a measurement of $\sigma(u(t))$ is available, then $\beta(u(t))$ cannot be formed and our approach does not apply. We assume, however, that an accurate model of $\sigma(u)$ is available or that the signal $\sigma(u(t))$ is available for feedback. This latter scheme is illustrated in Figure 1.

In the case in which the controller is proper but not strictly proper, that is, $D_c \neq 0$, then the controller output equation contains an algebraic constrant on u. For each choice of D_c and $\beta(u)$ this equation must be examined for solvability in terms of u. For the PI controller with saturation nonlinearity considered in Section 6, it can be shown that (8) has a unique solution u for each x.

4. Closed-Loop Stability

Our goal now is to show that in spite of the input nonlinearity, closed-loop stability is preserved if the modified controller (7), (8) is implemented in place of (3), (4). To do this we invoke the positive real lemma [19,20] which states that there exist a positive integer p and matrices $P \in \mathbb{R}^{n \times n}, L \in \mathbb{R}^{n \times p}$, and $W \in \mathbb{R}^{m \times p}$, where P is positive definite, such that

$$0 = A^{\text{T}}P + PA + L^{\text{T}}L, \tag{12}$$
$$0 = B^{\text{T}}P - C + W^{\text{T}}L, \tag{13}$$
$$0 = D + D^{\text{T}} - W^{\text{T}}W. \tag{14}$$

Furthermore, since the compensator is positive real there exist a positive integer p_c and matrices $P_c \in \mathbb{R}^{n_c \times n_c}, L_c \in \mathbb{R}^{n_c \times p_c}$, and $W_c \in \mathbb{R}^{m \times p_c}$, where P_c is positive definite, such that

$$0 = A_c^{\text{T}}P_c + P_cA_c + L_c^{\text{T}}L_c, \tag{15}$$
$$0 = B_c^{\text{T}}P_c - C_c + W_c^{\text{T}}L_c, \tag{16}$$
$$0 = D_c + D_c^{\text{T}} - W_c^{\text{T}}W_c. \tag{17}$$

If the plant or compensator is strictly positive real [21, 22], then (L, A) or (L_c, A_c) is observable, respectively.

Theorem 1. Consider the closed-loop system consisting of the nonlinear plant (5), (6) and the nonlinear controller (7), (8), where the input nonlinearity $\sigma(\cdot)$ satisfies Assumption 1. If the linear plant (1), (2) and the linear compensator (3), (4) are both positive real, then the closed-loop system (5)-(8) is stable in the sense of Lyapunov. Furthermore, if the linear plant (1), (2) and the linear compensator (3), (4) are both strictly positive real and at least one of them is strictly proper, then the closed-loop system (5)-(8) is globally asymptotically stable.

Proof. Using (5) and (7) we can form the closed-loop system

$$\begin{bmatrix} \dot{x} \\ \dot{x}_c \end{bmatrix} = \begin{bmatrix} Ax + B\sigma(u) \\ A_cx_c + B_c\beta(u)y \end{bmatrix}, \tag{18}$$

where $u = -C_cx_c - D_c\beta(u)y, y = Cx + D\sigma(u)$, and the Lyapunov function candidate

$$V(x, x_c) = x^{\text{T}}Px + x_c^{\text{T}}P_cx_c, \tag{19}$$

where P and P_c are given by (12)-(17). Since $V(x, x_c)$ is a positive-definite function, it remains to examine $\dot{V}(x, x_c)$ to determine closed-loop stability. Using the identities (11)-(17) it thus follows that

$$\begin{aligned}
\dot{V}(x, x_c) &= 2x^{\text{T}}P[Ax + B\sigma(u)] + 2x_c^{\text{T}}P_c[A_cx_c + B_c\beta(u)y] \\
&= -x^{\text{T}}L^{\text{T}}Lx - x_c^{\text{T}}L_c^{\text{T}}L_cx_c + 2x^{\text{T}}PB\sigma(u) + 2x_c^{\text{T}}P_cB_c\beta(u)y \\
&= -x^{\text{T}}L^{\text{T}}Lx - x_c^{\text{T}}L_c^{\text{T}}L_cx_c + 2x^{\text{T}}[C^{\text{T}} - L^{\text{T}}W]\sigma(u) + 2x_c^{\text{T}}[C_c^{\text{T}} - L_c^{\text{T}}W_c]\beta(u)y \\
&= -x^{\text{T}}L^{\text{T}}Lx - x_c^{\text{T}}L_c^{\text{T}}L_cx_c + 2x^{\text{T}}C^{\text{T}}\sigma(u) - 2x^{\text{T}}L^{\text{T}}W\sigma(u) + 2x_c^{\text{T}}C_c^{\text{T}}\beta(u)y \\
&\quad - 2x_c^{\text{T}}L_c^{\text{T}}W_c\beta(u)y \\
&= -x^{\text{T}}L^{\text{T}}Lx - x_c^{\text{T}}L_c^{\text{T}}L_cx_c + 2[y^{\text{T}} - \sigma^{\text{T}}(u)D^{\text{T}}]\sigma(u) \\
&\quad - 2x^{\text{T}}L^{\text{T}}W\sigma(u) - 2u^{\text{T}}\beta(u)y - 2y^{\text{T}}\beta^{\text{T}}(u)D_c^{\text{T}}\beta(u)y - 2x_c^{\text{T}}L_c^{\text{T}}W_c\beta(u)y \\
&= -x^{\text{T}}L^{\text{T}}Lx - 2x^{\text{T}}L^{\text{T}}W\sigma(u) - \sigma^{\text{T}}(u)[D + D^{\text{T}}]\sigma(u) - x_c^{\text{T}}L_c^{\text{T}}L_cx_c \\
&\quad - 2x_c^{\text{T}}L_c^{\text{T}}W_c\beta(u)y - y^{\text{T}}\beta^{\text{T}}(u)[D_c + D_c^{\text{T}}]\beta(u)y + 2y^{\text{T}}[\sigma(u) - \beta(u)u] \\
&= -[Lx + W\sigma(u)]^{\text{T}}[Lx + W\sigma(u)] - [L_cx_c + W_c\beta(u)y]^{\text{T}}[L_cx_c + W_c\beta(u)y] \\
&\leq 0,
\end{aligned}$$

which proves stability in the sense of Lyapunov.

To prove asymptotic stability we assume that the plant and compensator are both strictly positive real so that (L, A) and (L_c, A_c) are observable pairs and, without loss of generality, we assume that the plant is strictly proper. Then, using $W = 0$ (since $D = 0$) and applying the invariant set theorem, $\dot{V}(x, x_c) = 0$ implies that $Lx = 0$. Now, by the PBH test for observability it follows that $Ax = \lambda x$ for some complex number λ. However, (12) implies that $\lambda x^{\mathrm{T}} P x = 0$. Since $\lambda \neq 0$, and P is positive definite, it follows that $x = 0$. Now $\dot{V}(x, x_c) = 0$ implies that $L_c x_c = 0$. A similar argument yields $x_c = 0$. This proves global asymptotic stability of the closed-loop system (5)-(8). □

An alternative proof of Theorem 1 can be obtained by using dissipative system theory [15, 16]. Let $V_s(x) = \frac{1}{2}x^{\mathrm{T}}Px$ be a storage function and consider the supply rate $r(u, \hat{y}) = u^{\mathrm{T}}\hat{y}$, where $\hat{y}$ is obtained by rewriting the closed-loop system (5)-(8) as

$$\dot{x}(t) = Ax(t) + Bu(t), \tag{20}$$
$$\hat{y}(t) = \beta(u(t)Cx(t) + \beta(u(t))Du(t), \tag{21}$$
$$\dot{x}_c(t) = A_c x_c(t) + B_c\hat{y}(t), \tag{22}$$
$$u(t) = -\left[C_c x_c(t) + D_c\hat{y}(t)\right]. \tag{23}$$

It thus follows that

$$\begin{aligned}\dot{V}(x) &= \frac{1}{2}x^{\mathrm{T}}(A^{\mathrm{T}}P + PA)x + \sigma^{\mathrm{T}}(u)B^{\mathrm{T}}Px \\ &= -\frac{1}{2}x^{\mathrm{T}}L^{\mathrm{T}}Lx + \sigma^{\mathrm{T}}(u)Cx \\ &\leq u^{\mathrm{T}}\beta(u)Cx \\ &= \hat{y}^{\mathrm{T}}u,\end{aligned}$$

which shows that the modified plant (20), (21) is passive. Consequently, by dissipative system theory [15, 16] the closed-loop system is asymptotically stable. This alternative proof thus shows that the nonlinear controller modification counteracts the effects of the input nonlinearity by recovering the passivity of the plant.

5. An Illustrative Example Involving a Quadratic Nonlinearity

As a first example we consider the quadratic nonlinearity $\sigma(u) = u^2$, and, for simplicity, we set $G(s) = G_c(s) = \frac{1}{s+1}$. As shown in Figure 2, this nonlinearity leads to a finite escape time instability for certain initial conditions. The modified nonlinear controller, however, is guaranteed by Theorem 1 to yield global closed-loop stability. This property is confirmed by Figure 2.

6. Application to Integrator Windup

In this section we apply our approach to the problem of integrator windup with a saturation nonlinearity. This problem has been extensively studied by prior researchers; see, for example, [11-13] and the numerous references cited therein. Since our results are limited to positive real plants, we cannot make general comparisons with the results of [11-13] and others. We can, however, investigate the performance of the modified nonlinear controller in a situation that typically entails integrator windup. We thus consider the illustrative example considered in [12] in which $G(s) = \frac{1}{s}, G_c(s) = \frac{s}{s+1}$, the signal $r(t)$ shown in Figure 1 is a unit step command, and the saturation limits are set at $\pm.1$. Note that because the compensator $G_c(s)$ is not strictly proper, it follows that D_c in (8) is nonzero. Thus the algebraic constraint on u in (8) must be taken into account. However, it is easy to show that (8) has a unique solution u for each value of x. For the simulation results shown below, we took advantage of the MATLAB/Simulink feature of automatically solving algebraic loops by means of a Newton-Raphson iteration. Figure 3 shows the ideal system behavior in the absence of the saturation nonlinearity and compares the performance of the linear controller with the performance of the modified nonlinear controller. The performance improvement attained by the nonlinear controller is directly attributable to the decreased integrator windup as shown in Figure 4. Finally, the signals $u, \sigma(u) = \mathrm{sat}(u)$, and $\beta(u) = \mathrm{sat}(u)/u$ are shown in Figure 5. Note that, in accordance with the form of $\beta(u)$ shown in Table 1, the multiplicative coefficient $\beta(u)$ is small when β is large, thus effectively "shutting down" the integrator to reduce windup.

7. Conclusions

A new approach based upon Lyapunov stability theory has been developed for addressing the problem of input nonlinearities. The approach assumes that the linear plant and compensator are positive real, while the class of input nonlinearities that can be addressed is quite general. To guarantee global asymptotic stability, the linear compensator is modified to form a nonlinear compensator that counteracts the effects of the input nonlinearity by recovering the passivity of the plant. We demonstrated special cases of this result by simulating control systems having quadratic and saturation nonlinearities. Future extensions will focus on extending the result to larger classes of linear plants and compensators.

Acknowledgment. We wish to thank Elmer Gilbert for helpful suggestions and an anonymous reviewer for providing the dissipative system theory proof of Theorem 1.

References

1. R.J. Benhabib, R.P. Iwens, and R.L. Jackson, "Stability of Large Space Structure Control Systems Using Positivity Concepts," *J. Guid. Contr.*, Vol. 4, pp. 487-494, 1981.

2. S.M. Joshi, *Control of Flexible Space Structures*, Springer-Verlag, New York, 1989.

3. M.D. McLaren and G.L. Slater, "Robust Multivariable Control of Large Space Structures Using Positivity," *J. Guid. Contr. Dyn.*, Vol. 10, pp. 393-400, 1987.

4. R. Lozano-Leal and S.M. Joshi, "On the Design of Dissipative LQG-Type Controllers," *Proc. Conf. Dec. Contr.*, pp. 1645-1646, Austin, TX, December 1988 .

5. M. Jacobus, M. Jamshidi, C. Abdallah, P. Dorato, and D.S. Bernstein, "Design of Strictly Positive Real, Fixed-Order Dynamic Compensators," *Proc. Conf. Dec. Contr.*, pp. 3492-3495, Honolulu, HI, December 1990.

6. M.G. Safonov, E.A. Jonckheere and D.J.M. Limebeer, "Synthesis of Positive Real Multivariable Feedback Systems," *Int. J. Contr.*, Vol. 45, pp. 817-842, 1987.

7. D.G. MacMartin and S.R. Hall, "Control of Uncertain Structures Using an H_∞ Power Flow Approach," *J. Guid. Contr. Dyn.*, Vol. 14, pp. 521-530, 1991.

8. W.M. Haddad, D.S. Bernstein, and Y.W. Wang, "Dissipative H_2/H_∞ Controller Synthesis," submitted for publication.

9. D.K. Lindner, T. P. Celano, and E. N. Ide, "Vibration Suppression Using a Proofmass Actuator Operating in Stroke/Force Saturation," *ASME J. Vibr. Acoustics*, Vol. 113, pp. 423-433, 1991.

10. R. L. Kosut, "Design of Linear Systems with Saturating Linear Control and Bounded States," *IEEE Trans. Autom. Contr.*, Vol. AC-28, pp. 121-124, 1983.

11. A. H. Glattfelder and W. Schaufelberger, "Stability Analysis of Single Loop Control Systems with Saturation and Antireset Windup Circuits," *IEEE Trans. Autom. Contr.*, Vol. AC-28, pp. 1074-1081, 1983.

12. K.J. Astrom and L. Rundqwist, "Integrator Windup and How to Avoid It," *Proc. Amer. Contr. Conf.*, pp. 1693-1698, Pittsburgh, PA, 1989.

13. P.J. Campo, M. Morari, and C.N. Nett, "Multivariable Anti-Windup and Bumpless Transfer: A General Theory," *Proc. Amer. Contr. Conf.*, pp. 1706-1711, Pittsburgh, PA, 1989.

14. E.D. Sontag and H.J. Sussmann, "Nonlinear Output Feedback Design for Linear Systems with Saturating Controls," *Proc. Conf. Dec. Contr.*, pp. 3414-3416, Honolulu, HI, 1990.

15. J. C. Willems, "Dissipative Dynamical Systems Part I: General Theory", *Arch. Rational Mech.*, Vol. 45, pp. 321-351, 1972.

16. D. J. Hill and P. J. Moylan, "Dissipative Dynamical Systems: Basic Input-Output and State Properties", *J. Franklin Institute*, Vol. 309, pp. 708-711, 1980.

17. S. R. Hall, Private Communication, 1992

18. K. S. Narendra and J. H. Taylor, *Frequency Domain Criteria for Absolute Stability*, Academic Press, 1973.

19. B.D.O. Anderson, "A System Theory Criterion for Positive Real Matrices," *SIAM J. Contr. Optim.*, Vol. 5, pp. 171-182, 1967.

20. B.D.O. Anderson and S. Vongpanitlerd, *Network Analysis and Synthesis: A Modern Systems Theory Approach*, Prentice-Hall, Englewood Cliffs, NJ, 1973.

21. J.T. Wen, "Time Domain and Frequency Domain Conditions for Strict Positive Realness," *IEEE Trans. Autom. Contr.*, Vol. 33, pp. 988-992, 1988.

22. R. Lozano-Leal and S. Joshi, "Strictly Positive Real Transfer Functions Revisited," *IEEE Trans. Autom. Contr.*, Vol. 35, pp. 1243-1245, 1990.

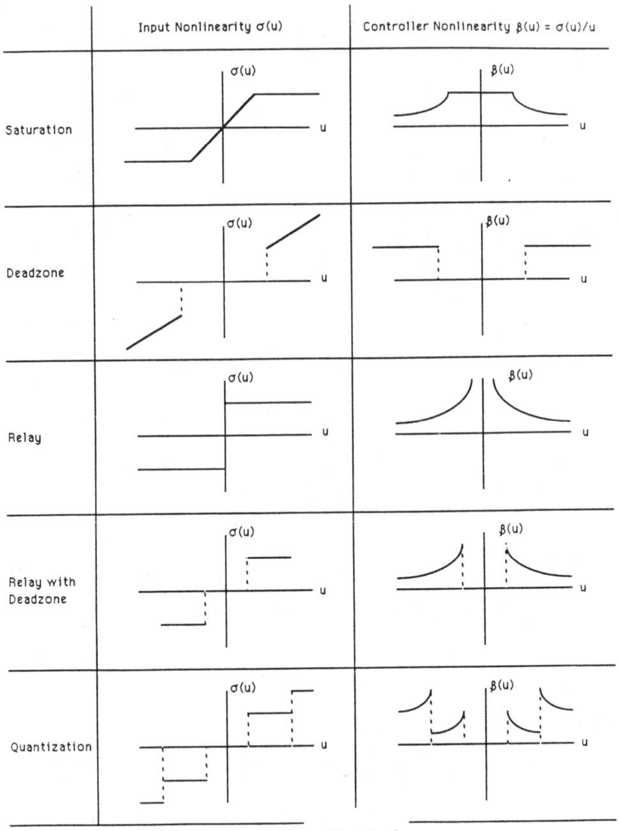

Table 1

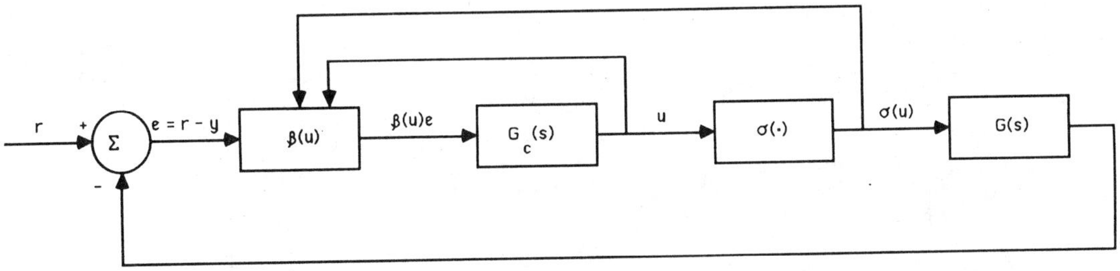

Figure 1

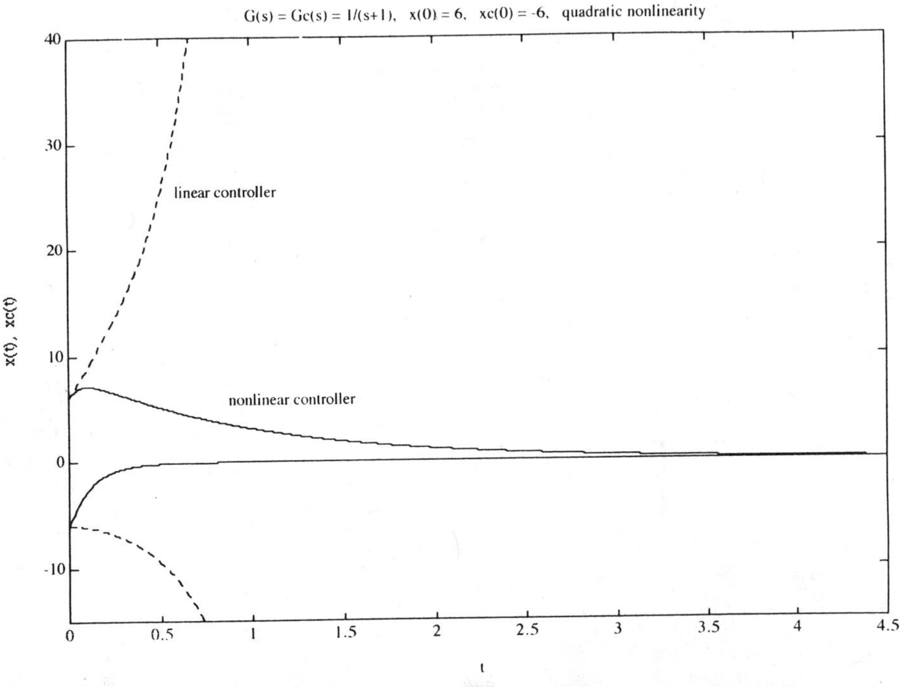

Figure 2

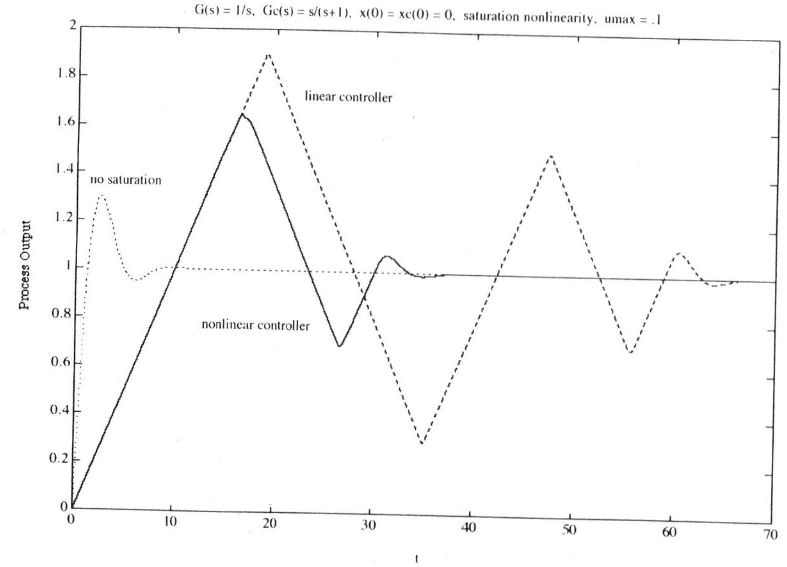
G(s) = 1/s, Gc(s) = s/(s+1), x(0) = xc(0) = 0, saturation nonlinearity, umax = .1
Process Output
t
linear controller
no saturation
nonlinear controller

Figure 3

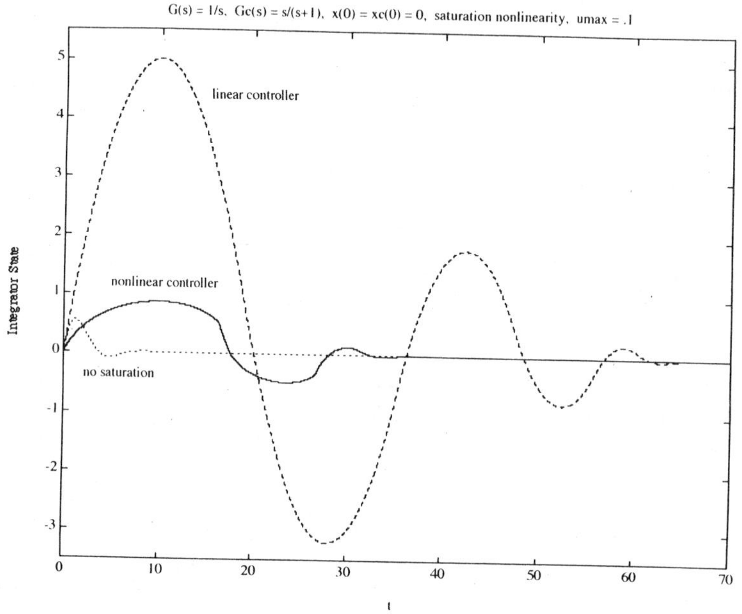
G(s) = 1/s, Gc(s) = s/(s+1), x(0) = xc(0) = 0, saturation nonlinearity, umax = .1
Integrator State
t
linear controller
nonlinear controller
no saturation

Figure 4

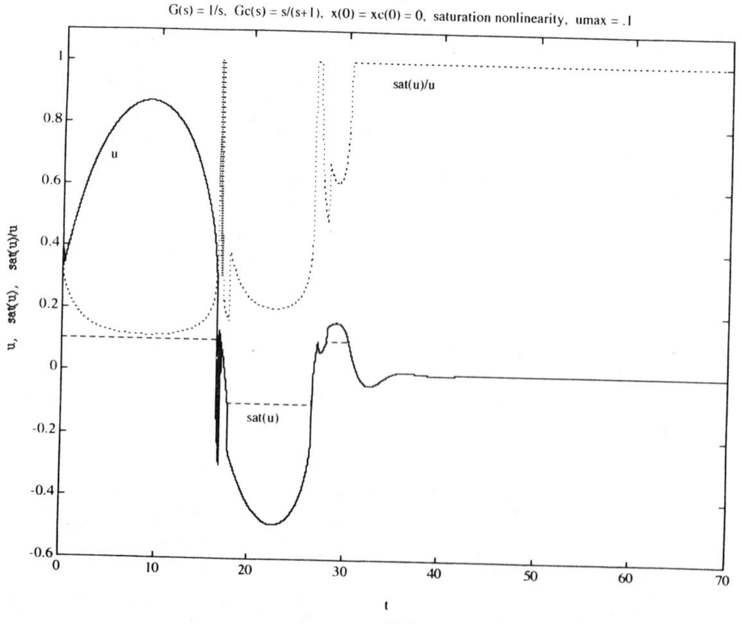
G(s) = 1/s, Gc(s) = s/(s+1), x(0) = xc(0) = 0, saturation nonlinearity, umax = .1
u, sat(u), sat(u)/u
t
sat(u)/u
u
sat(u)

Figure 5

Proceedings of the
American Control Conference
San Francisco, California • June 1993

TRACKING IN CONTROL SYSTEMS DESCRIBED BY NONLINEAR DIFFERENTIAL-ALGEBRAIC EQUATIONS WITH APPLICATIONS TO CONSTRAINED ROBOT SYSTEMS*

Hariharan Krishnan and Harris McClamroch
Department of Aerospace Engineering
University of Michigan
Ann Arbor, Michigan 48109-2140

Abstract

In this paper, we consider the problem of designing a feedback control law so that the outputs track desired reference inputs in control systems described by a class of nonlinear differential-algebraic equations. Assumptions are introduced and a procedure is developed such that an equivalent state realization of the control system described by nonlinear differential-algebraic equations is expressed in a familiar normal form. A nonlinear feedback control law is then proposed which ensures, under appropriate assumptions, that the tracking error in the closed loop differential-algebraic system approaches zero exponentially. Applications to simultaneous contact force and position tracking in constrained robot systems with rigid joints, constrained robot systems with joint flexibility, and constrained robot systems with significant actuator dynamics are discussed.

1. Introduction

We begin by introducing a control system described by a class of nonlinear differential-algebraic equations defined by

$$\dot{x} = f(x) + g(x)v + h(x)u \ , \tag{1}$$

$$y = 0 = k(x) \ , \tag{2}$$

$$z = l(x) + m(x)v \ , \tag{3}$$

where $x \in R^n$, $v \in R^m$, $u \in R^p$, $y \in R^m$, $z \in R^p$. Let $g(x) = [g_1(x), \cdot, \cdot, \cdot, g_m(x)]$, $h(x) = [h_1(x), \cdot, \cdot, \cdot, h_p(x)]$, and $k(x) = [k_1(x), \cdot, \cdot, \cdot, k_m(x)\ ]^T$. Here $f(x)$, $g_i(x)$, $i = 1, \cdot, \cdot, m$, $h_i(x)$, $i = 1, \cdot, \cdot, p$ are smooth vector fields on R^n and $k(x)$, $l(x)$ and $m(x)$ are smooth mappings on R^n. We subsequently refer to v as the constraint input variables, to u as the control input variables, to y as the constraint output variables, and to z as the control output variables. The constraint input variables v cannot be directly changed and must be viewed as extra variables which appear in the dynamic equations due to the presence of constraints defined by (2). However the control inputs u can be directly controlled. The control system described by nonlinear differential-algebraic equations (1)-(3) is also referred to as a constrained system. Control systems of the form (1)-(3) represent an important special class among systems referred to as singular systems or implicit differential equations [2,17,18].

The class of nonlinear differential-algebraic equations considered in this paper represents a number of physical systems which include mechanical systems with classical holonomic and nonholonomic constraints [7]. Robotic systems with kinematic constraints, which arise in force and position control tasks, are also represented by the class of nonlinear differential-algebraic equations studied here [7,11]. Differential-algebraic equations are also known to arise as dynamic models in electrical circuits, interconnected large scale systems, power systems and in quantum mechanics. In general, differential-algebraic equations are the basic model of a number of systems while state-space models are a simplification.

Control systems described by nonlinear differential-algebraic equations of the form (1)-(3) were introduced in [12]. Existence and uniqueness of solutions, and the feedback stabilization problem for systems described by (1)-(3) were introduced. The concept of an equivalent state realization for the class of nonlinear differential-algebraic equations (1)-(3) was developed. Analysis and control design for a class of linear differential-algebraic equations, having the same structure as (1)-(3), have been developed in detail in [7,10]. A tracking problem associated with the class of nonlinear differential-algebraic equations (1)-(3), under the assumption that the reference inputs are sufficiently slowly varying, is considered in [9].

We emphasize that equations (1)-(3) do not provide a state realization for the constrained system. Consequently, the existence of well-defined solutions of equations (1)-(3) requires justification. In order to guarantee the well-posedness of a control system described by nonlinear differential-algebraic equations (1)-(3), additional assumptions are necessary. Our fundamental assumptions for the class of nonlinear constrained systems defined by equations (1)-(3) are now introduced. Assume there are finite positive integers $r_1, \cdot, \cdot, r_m \geq 2$ such that

(A1) $L_{g_j} L_f^k k_i(x) = 0, \ \forall k = 0, \cdot, \cdot, r_i{-}2, \ i, j = 1, \cdot, \cdot, m, \ \forall x \in R^n$;

(A2) rank $A(x) = m, \ \forall x \in R^n$ where $A(x) \in R^{m \times m}$ whose element on the i-th row and j-th column is $a_{ij} = L_{g_j} L_f^{r_i - 1} k_i(x)$;

(A3) $L_{h_j} L_f^k k_i(x) = 0, \ \forall k = 0, \cdot, \cdot, r_i{-}2, \ i = 1, \cdot, \cdot, m,$

$$j = 1, \cdot, \cdot, p, \ \forall x \in R^n \ .$$

The notation $L_f k_i(x)$ denotes $\partial k_i(x)/\partial x f(x)$, and $L_f^k k_i(x) = L_f(L_f^{k-1} k_i(x))$. Assumptions (A1)-(A3) are essentially that the constraint (strong) relative degree vector of (f, g, k) is $(r_1, \cdot, \cdot, r_m)$ and is not greater than the control (strong) relative degree vector of (f, h, k), componentwise [4]. If $r_i = r$, $i = 1, \cdot, \cdot, \cdot, m$, these assumptions are equivalent to the assumption that the index, as defined for nonlinear singular (or implicit) equations as in [2], is $r + 1$. The following theorem from [12] states that the nonlinear differential-algebraic equations (1)-(3) are well-posed.

Theorem 1: Define

$$N^* = \{ \ x \in M \mid L_f^k k_i(x) = 0, \ k = 0, \cdot, \cdot, \cdot, r_i{-}1, \ i = 1, \cdot, \cdot, \cdot, m \} \ . \tag{4}$$

Then N^* is an $n - (r_1 + \cdot \cdot + r_m)$ dimensional smooth submanifold of M. Assume that the initial condition $x(0) \in N^*$ and the input function $u : [0, \infty) \to R^p$ is a given integrable function. Then there exists a unique solution $(x(t), v(t))$ (at least locally defined) of the initial value problem corresponding to equations (1)-(3) and the solution satisfies $x(t) \in N^*$ for each t for which the solution is defined.

Thus under the stated assumptions, it is possible to explicitly specify the state-space for the differential-algebraic equations considered. In fact the state-space is the manifold N^*. In this paper, we consider the problem of designing a feedback control law so that the control outputs $z(t)$ track desired reference inputs in control systems described by a class of nonlinear differential-algebraic equations (1)-(3) for which assumptions (A1)-(A3) hold. Additional assumptions are introduced so that an equivalent state realization of the control system described by nonlinear differential-algebraic equations (1)-(3) is expressed in a familiar normal form [4]. A nonlinear feedback control law is then proposed which ensures, under appropriate assumptions which are made precise later, that the tracking error in the closed loop system approaches zero exponentially. Applications to simultaneous contact force and position tracking in constrained robot systems are discussed in particular.

2. Feedback Control Design

Suppose $r(t) \in R^p$ is a vector of reference inputs to the differential-algebraic system. In this section, we describe a procedure for designing a nonlinear feedback control law so that the control outputs $z(t)$ track the given reference inputs $r(t)$ and the tracking error in the closed loop system approaches zero exponentially. Let $f^*(x)$, $h^*(x)$, $l^*(x)$ and $n^*(x)$ be defined as

$$f^*(x) = f(x) + g(x)\alpha(x) \ , \tag{5}$$

$$h^*(x) = h(x) + g(x)\beta(x) \ , \tag{6}$$

$$l^*(x) = l(x) + m(x)\alpha(x) \ , \tag{7}$$

$$n^*(x) = m(x)\beta(x) \ , \tag{8}$$

where $\alpha(x)$ and $\beta(x)$ are defined as

$$\alpha(x) = -A^{-1}(x) \begin{bmatrix} L_f^{r_1} k_1(x) \\ \cdot \\ \cdot \\ \cdot \\ L_f^{r_m} k_m(x) \end{bmatrix} , \tag{9}$$

$$\beta(x) = -A^{-1}(x) \begin{bmatrix} L_{h_1} L_f^{r_1 - 1} k_1(x) & \cdot \ \cdot & L_{h_p} L_f^{r_1 - 1} k_1(x) \\ \cdot & \cdot \ \cdot & \cdot \\ \cdot & \cdot \ \cdot & \cdot \\ \cdot & \cdot \ \cdot & \cdot \\ L_{h_1} L_f^{r_m - 1} k_m(x) & \cdot \ \cdot & L_{h_p} L_f^{r_m - 1} k_m(x) \end{bmatrix} . \tag{10}$$

* This research was supported by NSF grant No. MSS - 9114630 and NASA grant No. NAG-1-1419.

Without loss of generality, the control outputs $z(t)$ can be ordered so that $n^*(x)$ is of the form

$$n^*(x) = \begin{bmatrix} 0_{s\times p} \\ B_2(x) \end{bmatrix}, \tag{11}$$

where $B_2(x) \in R^{(p-s)\times p}$ and $0 \le s \le p$. Let $h^*(x) = [h_1^*(x), \cdot, \cdot, \cdot, h_p^*(x)]$ and $l^*(x) = [l_1^*(x), \cdot, \cdot, \cdot, l_p^*(x)]^T$. We further assume there exists positive integers $\mu_1, \mu_2, \cdot, \cdot, \mu_s \ge 2$ such that the following assumptions hold:

(A4) $L_{h_j^*} L_{f^*}^k l_i^*(x) = 0, \ \forall k = 0, \cdot, \cdot, \mu_i - 2, \ j = 1, \cdot, \cdot, p,$

$i = 1, \cdot, \cdot, s, \ \forall x \in R^n$.

(A5) rank $B(x) = p, \ \forall x \in R^n$ where $B(x) \in R^{p\times p}$ is defined by

$$B(x) = \begin{bmatrix} B_1(x) \\ B_2(x) \end{bmatrix} \tag{12}$$

where the element in the i-th row and j-th column of $B_1(x) \in R^{s\times p}$ is defined by

$$[B_1(x)]_{i,j} = L_{h_j^*} L_{f^*}^{\mu_i - 1} l_i^*(x), \ i = 1, \cdot, \cdot, s, \quad j = 1, \cdot, \cdot, p .$$

We now consider new variables defined by

$$\begin{pmatrix} \tilde{x} \\ \overline{x} \\ \xi \end{pmatrix} = \begin{pmatrix} \Psi_0(x) \\ \Psi_1(x) \\ \Psi_2(x) \end{pmatrix} = \Phi(x), \tag{13}$$

where

$$\tilde{x}_1 = k_1(x), \ \tilde{x}_2 = L_f k_1(x), \ \cdot, \ \cdot, \ \tilde{x}_{r_1} = L_f^{r_1-1} k_1(x),$$

$$\tilde{x}_{r_1+1} = k_2(x), \ \tilde{x}_{r_1+2} = L_f k_2(x), \ \cdot, \ \cdot, \ \tilde{x}_{r_1+\cdots+r_m} = L_f^{r_m-1} k_m(x),$$

$$\overline{x}_1 = l_1^*(x), \ \overline{x}_2 = L_{f^*} l_1^*(x), \ \cdot, \ \cdot, \ \overline{x}_{\mu_1} = L_{f^*}^{\mu_1-1} l_1^*(x), \tag{14}$$

$$\overline{x}_{\mu_1+1} = l_2^*(x), \ \overline{x}_{\mu_1+2} = L_{f^*} l_2^*(x), \ \cdot, \ \cdot, \ \overline{x}_{\mu_1+\cdots+\mu_s} = L_{f^*}^{\mu_s-1} l_s^*(x),$$

and

$$\xi = \Psi_2(x). \tag{15}$$

Here the vector $\xi \in R^{n-(r_1+\cdots+r_m)-(\mu_1+\cdots+\mu_s)}$ and $\Psi_2(\cdot)$ is a smooth mapping. The assumptions guarantee that there exists a nonlinear coordinate change defined above which is a local diffeomorphism in a neighborhood of every $x \in R^n$ [7]. Here we assume that the nonlinear coordinate transformation defined above is a global diffeomorphism. Sufficient conditions which guarantee the global validity of such a diffemorphism are given in [3]. However the conditions are very restrictive. The differential-algebraic equations (1)-(3) in the transformed coordinates are given by

$$\begin{aligned}
\dot{\tilde{x}}_1 &= \tilde{x}_2 \\
&\ \ \vdots \\
\dot{\tilde{x}}_{r_1-1} &= \tilde{x}_{r_1} \\
\dot{\tilde{x}}_{r_1} &= L_f^{r_1} k_1(x) + \sum_{j=1}^{m} (L_{g_j} L_f^{r_1-1} k_1(x)) v_j + \sum_{j=1}^{p} (L_{h_j} L_f^{r_1-1} k_1(x)) u_j \\
&\ \ \vdots \\
\dot{\tilde{x}}_{r_1+\cdots+r_{m-1}+1} &= \tilde{x}_{r_1+\cdots+r_{m-1}+2} \\
&\ \ \vdots \\
\dot{\tilde{x}}_{r_1+\cdots+r_m-1} &= \tilde{x}_{r_1+\cdots+r_m} \\
\dot{\tilde{x}}_{r_1+\cdots+r_m} &= L_f^{r_m} k_m(x) + \sum_{j=1}^{m} (L_{g_j} L_f^{r_m-1} k_m(x)) v_j + \sum_{j=1}^{p} (L_{h_j} L_f^{r_m-1} k_m(x)) u_j \\
\dot{\overline{x}} &= \frac{\partial \Psi_1(x)}{\partial x} (f(x) + g(x) v + h(x) u) \\
\dot{\xi} &= \frac{\partial \Psi_2(x)}{\partial x} (f(x) + g(x) v + h(x) u) \\
y_i &= 0 = \tilde{x}_{r_{i-1}+1}, \quad i = 1, \cdots, m, \quad r_0 = 0 \\
z &= l(x) + m(x) v
\end{aligned} \tag{16}$$

where

$$x = \Phi^{-1} \begin{pmatrix} \tilde{x} \\ \overline{x} \\ \xi \end{pmatrix}. \tag{17}$$

Imposing the constriants in the transformed variables amounts to setting the variables $\tilde{x}$ identically equal to zero. Eliminating the constraints we obtain

$$v = \alpha(x) + \beta(x) u \tag{18}$$

where $\alpha(x)$ and $\beta(x)$ are defined by (9), (10). Moreover the nonlinear differential-algebraic equations are equivalent to the $n - (r_1 + r_2 + \cdots r_m)$ dimensional nonlinear state realization given by

$$\begin{aligned}
\dot{\overline{x}}_1 &= \overline{x}_2 \\
&\ \ \vdots \\
\dot{\overline{x}}_{\mu_1-1} &= \overline{x}_{\mu_1} \\
\dot{\overline{x}}_{\mu_1} &= L_{f^*}^{\mu_1} l_1^*(x) + \sum_{j=1}^{p} (L_{h_j^*} L_{f^*}^{\mu_1-1} l_1^*(x)) u_j \\
&\ \ \vdots \\
\dot{\overline{x}}_{\mu_1+\cdots+\mu_{s-1}+1} &= \overline{x}_{\mu_1+\cdots+\mu_{s-1}+2} \\
&\ \ \vdots \\
\dot{\overline{x}}_{\mu_1+\cdots+\mu_s-1} &= \overline{x}_{\mu_1+\cdots+\mu_s} \\
\dot{\overline{x}}_{\mu_1+\cdots+\mu_s} &= L_{f^*}^{\mu_s} l_s^*(x) + \sum_{j=1}^{p} (L_{h_j^*} L_{f^*}^{\mu_s-1} l_s^*(x)) u_j \\
\dot{\xi} &= \frac{\partial \Psi_2(x)}{\partial x} f^*(x) + \frac{\partial \Psi_2(x)}{\partial x} h^*(x) u \\
z &= l^*(x) + \begin{bmatrix} 0_{s\times p} \\ B_2(x) \end{bmatrix} u
\end{aligned} \tag{19}$$

where

$$x = \Phi^{-1} \begin{pmatrix} 0 \\ \overline{x} \\ \xi \end{pmatrix}. \tag{20}$$

The equivalent state realization for the nonlinear differential-algebraic equations are in a familiar normal form [4]. Suppose the control outputs $z(t)$ are required to track the reference inputs $r(t)$; i.e., we want

$$z(t) \to r(t) \ \text{as} \ t \to \infty .$$

Then a nonlinear feedback control law can be chosen as

$$u(x, R) = \begin{bmatrix} B_1(x) \\ B_2(x) \end{bmatrix}^{-1} \left\{ - \begin{bmatrix} a_1(x) \\ a_2(x) \end{bmatrix} + \overline{u} \right\} \tag{21}$$

where

$$R(t) = (r_1(t), \cdot, \cdot, r_1^{\mu_1-1}(t), \cdot, \cdot, r_s(t), \cdot, \cdot, r_s^{\mu_s-1}(t), r_{(s+1)}(t), \cdot, \cdot, r_p(t))^T,$$

$$\overline{u}_i = r_i^{\mu_i}(t) - \sum_{j=1}^{\mu_i} K_{i,j} (L_{f^*}^{j-1} l_i^*(x) - r_i^{j-1}(t)), \ i = 1, \cdot, \cdot, s,$$

$$\overline{u}_i = r_i(t), \ i = s+1, \cdot, \cdot, p,$$

$$a_1(x) = \begin{bmatrix} L_{f^*}^{\mu_1} l_1^*(x) \\ \cdot \\ \cdot \\ L_{f^*}^{\mu_s} l_s^*(x) \end{bmatrix}, \ a_2(x) = \begin{bmatrix} l_{s+1}^*(x) \\ \cdot \\ \cdot \\ l_p^*(x) \end{bmatrix},$$

and $\gamma^j(t)$ denotes the j-th time derivative of $\gamma(t)$. Using such a control law the tracking errors in the closed loop differential-algebraic system defined by

$$e_i(t) = z_i(t) - r_i(t), \ i = 1, \cdot, \cdot, p \tag{22}$$

satisfy the following equations:

$$e_i^{\mu_i}(t) + K_{i,\mu_i} e_i^{\mu_i - 1}(t) + \cdots + K_{i,1} e_i(t) = 0, \quad i = 1, \cdot, \cdot, s \ , \tag{23}$$

$$e_i(t) = 0, \quad i = s+1, \cdot, \cdot, p \ . \tag{24}$$

If the gains $K_{i,j}$ are chosen such that the polynomials

$$s^{\mu_i} + K_{i,\mu_i} s^{\mu_i - 1} + \cdots + K_{i,1} = 0, \quad i = 1, \cdot, \cdot, s \tag{25}$$

are Hurwitz then the tracking error for the closed loop differential-algebraic system for the control outputs $z_i(t)$, $i = 1, \cdot, \cdot, s$ approaches zero exponentially; i.e.,

$$e_i(t) = z_i(t) - r_i(t) \to 0 \text{ as } t \to \infty, \quad i = 1, \cdot, \cdot, s \ . \tag{26}$$

The tracking error for the control outputs $z_i(t)$, $i = s + 1, \cdot, \cdot, p$ is identically equal to zero at all time; i.e.,

$$e_i(t) = 0 \ , \ \forall t \geq 0 \ , \ i = s+1, \cdot, \cdot, p \ . \tag{27}$$

Additionally, in order to guarantee the boundedness of all the internal states and the control inputs in the closed loop system the following assumption is necessary.

Assumption 2: The subsystem

$$\dot{\xi} = \frac{\partial \Psi_2(x)}{\partial x} f^*(x) + \frac{\partial \Psi_2(x)}{\partial x} h^*(x) u(x, R) \ , \tag{28}$$

where

$$x = \Phi^{-1} \begin{bmatrix} 0 \\ \bar{x} \\ \xi \end{bmatrix} \ , \tag{29}$$

is bounded input bounded state stable with $\bar{x}$, R as inputs.

If Assumption 2 is satisfied then the control inputs and all the internal states of the closed loop differential-algebraic system are bounded. Sufficient conditions which guarantee Assumption 2 are given in [19]. They are as follows:

(i) the subsystem defined by (28) with $\bar{x}(t)$, $R(t)$ set identically equal to zero is globally exponentially stable.

(ii) the vector field defined by the right hand side of equation (28) is globally Lipschitz.

3. Simultaneous Force and Position Tracking in Constrained Robot Systems

Robotic systems often operate in a constrained environment and interact with these environmental constraints to perform certain tasks. Examples of such challenging tasks include parts insertion and assembly, crank turning, polishing, grinding, deburring, contour following, writing etc; these tasks may involve a single robot or multiple robots working together. Thus constrained robot systems and more generally constrained mechanical systems represent a class of dynamical systems of both practical and theoretical importance. Constraint forces, which maintain satisfaction of the constraints, are important aspects of these systems. Successful accomplishment of constrained tasks requires simultaneous force and position control. In this section, we consider the problem of designing feedback control laws that achieve simultaneous force and position tracking in constrained robot systems. The control laws are designed based on the theory presented in Section 2.

3.1. Constrained Robot Systems with Rigid Joints

In this section, we consider mathematical representations which model a class of constrained robot systems. The joints of the robotic manipulator are assumed to be actuated by direct drive actuators and it is also assumed that the robot joints are rigid; i.e., there is no joint flexibility. The constraints are modeled as holonomic constraints. The model of the constrained robot system, under such an assumption, is represented as [7,11,13]

$$M(q)\ddot{q} + H(q, \dot{q}) = J^T(q)\lambda + u \ , \tag{30}$$

$$y = 0 = \phi(q) \ , \tag{31}$$

$$z_1 = h_1(q) \ , \tag{32}$$

$$z_2 = \lambda \ , \tag{33}$$

where $q \in R^n$ denotes the vector of generalized displacements, $M(q)$ is the inertia matrix which is symmetric and positive definite, $H(q, \dot{q})$ denotes the vector of nonlinearities which include the coriolis, centripetal and gravity forces, $u \in R^n$ represents the vector of generalized forces applied at each joint, $\lambda \in R^m$ is a vector of multipliers corresponding to the constraint vector function $\phi(\cdot) : R^n \to R^m$, and

$$J(q) = \frac{\partial \phi(q)}{\partial q} \ , \tag{34}$$

is the Jacobian matrix of $\phi(q)$ which is assumed to have full row rank. The control outputs represented by the vector $z_1 \in R^{n-m}$ are chosen such that together with the constraints $\phi(q) = 0$, they specify completely the position vector q. The control outputs represented by the vector $z_2 \in R^m$ are chosen to be the constraint forces λ. For this model, the constraint manifold N^* defined by (4) is given by

$$N^* = \left\{ (q, \dot{q}) : \phi(q) = 0, J(q)\dot{q} = 0 \right\} . \tag{35}$$

Simultaneous force and position control for constrained robot systems modeled by equations (30)-(33) has been an active area of recent research (see [7,8,11,13,14,15,16,21] and the references therein). A number of approaches have been proposed for designing control laws which acheives local regulation of contact force and position vectors, and tracking of contact force and position trajectories. In this section, we design a feedback control law for tracking desired force and position trajectories based on the development in Section 2.

Suppose $r_1(t)$ and $r_2(t)$ are vectors of desired position and force trajectories. Our goal is to design a feedback control law so that the position outputs $z_1(t)$ and the force outputs $z_2(t)$ for the constrained robot system track the desired position and force trajectories $r_1(t)$ and $r_2(t)$ respectively. We use the development in Section 2 to design a feedback control law so that the closed-loop system has the desired force and position tracking properties. Equations (30)-(33) can be rewritten in a first order form as

$$\begin{bmatrix} \dot{q} \\ \ddot{q} \end{bmatrix} = f(q, \dot{q}) + g(q, \dot{q})\lambda + h(q, \dot{q})u \ , \tag{36}$$

$$y = 0 = k(q, \dot{q}) \ , \tag{37}$$

$$z = l(q, \dot{q}) + m(q, \dot{q})\lambda \ , \tag{38}$$

where $f(q, \dot{q})$, $g(q, \dot{q})$, $h(q, \dot{q})$, $k(q, \dot{q})$, $l(q, \dot{q})$ and $m(q, \dot{q})$ are defined appropriately. The differential-algebraic equations satisfy assumptions (A1)-(A3) of Section 1 with a constraint relative degree vector $(r_1, r_2, \cdot, \cdot, r_m) = (2, 2, \cdot, \cdot, 2)$ and control relative degree vector $(2, 2, \cdot, \cdot, 2)$. From equations (5)-(10), $f^*(q, \dot{q})$, $h^*(q, \dot{q})$, $l^*(q, \dot{q})$, and $n^*(q, \dot{q})$ for the constrained robot model (30)-(33) are calculated. Assumptions (A4)-(A5) of Section 2 are satisfied in this case with $(\mu_1, \mu_2, \cdot, \cdot, \mu_{n-m}) = (2, 2, \cdot, \cdot, 2)$. Now the coordinate change defined by (13)-(15) in this case is given by

$$\tilde{x}_1 = \phi(q) \ , \tag{39}$$

$$\tilde{x}_2 = J(q)\dot{q} \ , \tag{40}$$

$$\bar{x}_1 = h_1(q) \ , \tag{41}$$

$$\bar{x}_2 = \frac{\partial h_1(q)}{\partial q}\dot{q} = P(q)\dot{q} \ . \tag{42}$$

Following equations (16) through (20), an equivalent state realization is obtained for the differential-algebraic equations (30)-(33) which is given by

$$\dot{\bar{x}}_1 = \bar{x}_2 \ , \tag{43}$$

$$\begin{aligned} \dot{\bar{x}}_2 = {} & \dot{P}(q)\dot{q} - P(q)M^{-1}(q)\{H(q, \dot{q}) \\ & - J^T(q)(J(q)M^{-1}(q)J^T(q))^{-1}[J(q)M^{-1}(q)H(q, \dot{q}) - \dot{J}(q)\dot{q}]\} \\ & + P(q)M^{-1}(q)\{I - J^T(q)(J(q)M^{-1}(q)J^T(q))^{-1}J(q)M^{-1}(q)\}u \end{aligned} \tag{44}$$

$$z_1 = \bar{x}_1 \ , \tag{45}$$

$$\begin{aligned} z_2 = {} & (J(q)M^{-1}(q)J^T(q))^{-1}[J(q)M^{-1}(q)H(q, \dot{q}) \\ & - \dot{J}(q)\dot{q} - J(q)M^{-1}(q)u] \ , \end{aligned} \tag{46}$$

where from (39)-(42) we have

$$q = \psi(\bar{x}_1) \ , \ \dot{q} = Q(q)\bar{x}_2 \ . \tag{47}$$

The nonlinear feedback control law defined by (21) is now given by

$$\begin{aligned} u(t) = {} & M(q)Q(q)(\ddot{r}_1 - \Lambda_1(h_1(q) - r_1) - \Lambda_2(P(q)\dot{q} - \dot{r}_1)) + H(q, \dot{q}) \\ & + M(q)\dot{Q}(q)P(q)\dot{q} - J^T(q)r_2 + J^T(q)\bar{G}(\lambda - r_2) \ , \end{aligned} \tag{48}$$

where $\bar{G} \in R^{m \times m}$ is a positive semidefinite matrix and Λ_1 and Λ_2 are positive definite matrices. The tracking errors in the closed-loop constrained system satisfy the equations

$$\ddot{e}_1(t) + \Lambda_2 \dot{e}_1(t) + \Lambda_1 e_1(t) = 0 \ , \tag{49}$$

$$(J(q)M^{-1}(q)J^T(q))(I_m + \bar{G})e_2(t) = 0 \ , \tag{50}$$

where the position tracking error is defined as

$$e_1(t) = h_1(q) - r_1(t) \ , \tag{51}$$

and the force tracking error is defined as

$$e_2(t) = \lambda(t) - r_2(t) . \quad (52)$$

Since Λ_1 and Λ_2 are chosen as positive definite matrices, the tracking error $e_1(t)$ for the position outputs approach zero exponentially and the force tracking error $e_2(t)$ is identically zero at all time. In addition, all the internal states of the constrained robot system and the control inputs remain bounded since Assumption 2 of Section 2 is satisfied trivially. The control law requires feedback of position and velocity variables. Although force feedback is included, it is not essential since $\overline{G}$ may be taken as a zero matrix.

3.2. Constrained Robot Systems with Flexible Joints

In this section, we consider mathematical representations which model a class of constrained robot systems which include the effects of joint flexibility. The model, obtained by modifying equations (30)-(33) to include effects of joint flexibility [20], is represented as

$$M(q_1)\ddot{q}_1 + H(q_1, \dot{q}_1) = J^T(q_1)\lambda + K_2(q_2 - q_1) , \quad (53)$$

$$M_2\ddot{q}_2 + K_2(q_2 - q_1) = u , \quad (54)$$

$$y = 0 = \phi(q_1) , \quad (55)$$

$$z_1 = h_1(q_1) , \quad (56)$$

$$z_2 = \lambda , \quad (57)$$

where $q_1 \in R^n$ denotes the vector of generalized displacements of the links of the robot, $q_2 \in R^n$ denotes the vector of generalized displacements of the actuator shafts, M_2 is a constant positive definite matrix which represents the actuator inertia and K_2 is a constant positive definite matrix representing the stiffness coefficients of the joints of the robot. All the other variables have the same description as in equations (30)-(35) with q replaced by q_1. Approaches to simultaneous contact force and position control in constrained robot systems with joint flexibility have been proposed in [1,5,8,15]. In this section, we use the development in Section 2 for designing a feedback control law in order to achieve tracking of contact force and position in constrained robot systems with joint flexibility.

Suppose $r_1(t)$ and $r_2(t)$ are vectors of desired position and force trajectories. Equations (53)-(57) can be rewritten in a first order form as

$$\begin{bmatrix} \dot{q}_1 \\ \ddot{q}_1 \\ \dot{q}_2 \\ \ddot{q}_2 \end{bmatrix} = f(q_1, \dot{q}_1, q_2, \dot{q}_2) + g(q_1, \dot{q}_1, q_2, \dot{q}_2)\lambda + h(q_1, \dot{q}_1, q_2, \dot{q}_2)u$$

$$y = 0 = k(q_1, \dot{q}_1, q_2, \dot{q}_2) ,$$

$$z = l(q_1, \dot{q}_1, q_2, \dot{q}_2) + m(q_1, \dot{q}_1, q_2, \dot{q}_2)\lambda ,$$

where f, g, h, k, l, m are defined appropriately. These differential-algebraic equations satisfy assumptions (A1)-(A3) of Section 1 with a constraint relative degree vector $(r_1, r_2, \cdot, \cdot, r_m) = (2, 2, \cdot, \cdot, 2)$ and control relative degree vector $(4, 4, \cdot, \cdot, 4)$. Define

$$\alpha(q_1, \dot{q}_1, q_2) = (J(q_1)M^{-1}(q_1)J^T(q_1))^{-1}[J(q_1)M^{-1}(q_1)H(q_1, \dot{q}_1) - \dot{J}(q_1)\dot{q}_1 - J(q_1)M^{-1}(q_1)K_2(q_2 - q_1)] .$$

From equations (5)-(10), f^*, h^*, l^*, and n^* are calculated. Assumptions (A4)-(A5) of Section 2 are satisfied in this case with $(\mu_1, \cdot, \cdot, \mu_{n-m}, \mu_{n-m+1}, \cdot, \cdot, \mu_n) = (4, \cdot, \cdot, 4, 2, \cdot, \cdot, 2)$. Now the coordinate change defined by (13)-(15) in this case is given by

$$\tilde{x}_1 = \phi(q_1) ,$$

$$\tilde{x}_2 = J(q_1)\dot{q}_1 ,$$

$$\overline{x}_1 = h_1(q_1) ,$$

$$\overline{x}_2 = \frac{\partial h_1(q_1)}{\partial q_1}\dot{q}_1 = P(q_1)\dot{q}_1 ,$$

$$\overline{x}_3 = L_{f^*}^2 h_1(q_1) = f_1(q_1, \dot{q}_1) + B_1(q_1)q_2 ,$$

$$\overline{x}_4 = L_{f^*}^3 h_1(q_1) = f_2(q_1, \dot{q}_1, q_2) + B_1(q_1)\dot{q}_2 ,$$

$$\overline{x}_5 = \alpha(q_1, \dot{q}_1, q_2) = f_3(q_1, \dot{q}_1) + B_2(q_1)q_2 ,$$

$$\overline{x}_6 = L_{f^*}\alpha(q_1, \dot{q}_1, q_2) = f_4(q_1, \dot{q}_1, q_2) + B_2(q_1)\dot{q}_2 ,$$

where f_1, B_1, f_2, B_2, f_3, f_4 can be calculated. Following equations (16) through (20), an equivalent state realization is obtained for the differential-algebraic equations which is given by

$$\dot{\overline{x}}_1 = \overline{x}_2 ,$$

$$\dot{\overline{x}}_2 = \overline{x}_3 ,$$

$$\dot{\overline{x}}_3 = \overline{x}_4 ,$$

$$\dot{\overline{x}}_4 = A_1(q_1, \dot{q}_1, q_2, \dot{q}_2) + B_1(q_1)M_2^{-1}u ,$$

$$\dot{\overline{x}}_5 = \overline{x}_6 ,$$

$$\dot{\overline{x}}_6 = A_2(q_1, \dot{q}_1, q_2, \dot{q}_2) + B_2(q_1)M_2^{-1}u ,$$

$$z_1 = \overline{x}_1 ,$$

$$z_2 = \overline{x}_5 ,$$

where

$$q_1 = \psi(\overline{x}_1) , \quad \dot{q}_1 = Q(q_1)\overline{x}_2 ,$$

$$q_2 = \begin{bmatrix} B_1(q_1) \\ B_2(q_2) \end{bmatrix}^{-1} \left\{ - \begin{bmatrix} f_1(q_1, \dot{q}_1) \\ f_3(q_1, \dot{q}_1) \end{bmatrix} + \begin{bmatrix} \overline{x}_3 \\ \overline{x}_5 \end{bmatrix} \right\} ,$$

$$\dot{q}_2 = \begin{bmatrix} B_1(q_1) \\ B_2(q_2) \end{bmatrix}^{-1} \left\{ - \begin{bmatrix} f_2(q_1, \dot{q}_1, q_2) \\ f_4(q_1, \dot{q}_1, q_2) \end{bmatrix} + \begin{bmatrix} \overline{x}_4 \\ \overline{x}_6 \end{bmatrix} \right\} ,$$

and A_1 and A_2 can be calculated. The nonlinear feedback control law defined by (21) is now given by

$$u(t) = M_2 \begin{bmatrix} B_1(q_1) \\ B_2(q_1) \end{bmatrix}^{-1} \left\{ - \begin{bmatrix} A_1(q_1, \dot{q}_1, q_2, \dot{q}_2) \\ A_2(q_1, \dot{q}_1, q_2, \dot{q}_2) \end{bmatrix} + \begin{bmatrix} v_1(t) \\ v_2(t) \end{bmatrix} \right\} , \quad (58)$$

where

$$v_1(t) = r_1^{(4)}(t) - \Lambda_1(h_1(q_1) - r_1(t)) - \Lambda_2(P(q_1)\dot{q}_1 - r_1^{(1)}(t)) - \Lambda_3(f_1(q_1, \dot{q}_1) + B_1(q_1)q_2 - r_1^{(2)}(t)) - \Lambda_4(f_2(q_1, \dot{q}_1, q_2) + B_1(q_1)\dot{q}_2 - r_1^{(3)}(t)) , \quad (59)$$

$$v_2(t) = r_2^{(2)}(t) - \Lambda_5(f_3(q_1, \dot{q}_1) + B_2(q_1)q_2 - r_2(t)) - \Lambda_6(f_4(q_1, \dot{q}_1, q_2) + B_2(q_1)\dot{q}_2 - r_2^{(1)}(t)) , \quad (60)$$

and $r_1^{(i)}(t)$ and $r_2^{(i)}(t)$ denote the i-th derivative of $r_1(t)$ and $r_2(t)$ with respect to time. The tracking errors in the closed-loop constrained system satisfy the equations

$$e_1^{(4)}(t) + \Lambda_4 e_1^{(3)}(t) + \Lambda_3 e_1^{(2)}(t) + \Lambda_2 e_1^{(1)}(t) + \Lambda_1 e_1(t) = 0 , \quad (61)$$

$$e_2^{(2)}(t) + \Lambda_6 e_2^{(1)}(t) + \Lambda_5 e_2(t) = 0 , \quad (62)$$

where the position tracking error is defined as

$$e_1(t) = h_1(q_1) - r_1(t) ,$$

and the force tracking error is defined as

$$e_2(t) = \lambda(t) - r_2(t) .$$

If Λ_1 through Λ_6 are chosen such that the equations (61)-(62) are Hurwitz, then the tracking error $e_1(t)$ for the position outputs and the force tracking error $e_2(t)$ approach zero exponentially. In addition, all the internal states of the constrained robot system and the control inputs remain bounded since Assumption 2 of Section 2 is satisfied trivially. The control law requires feedback of position and velocity variables of the links of the robot, and the position and velocity variables of the actuator shafts. Force feedback is not necessary. However, if measurement of the contact force $\lambda(t)$ is available it may be included in the feedback loop by replacing the term $f_3(q_1, \dot{q}_1) + B_2(q_1)q_2$ in (60) by $\lambda(t)$.

3.3. Constrained Robot Systems with Significant Actuator Dynamics

In this section, we consider mathematical representations which model a class of constrained robot systems which include the effects of significant actuator dynamics. We consider the case where the joints of the robot are driven by armature controlled direct-current motors. The joints of the robot are assumed to have no flexibility. The model, obtained by modifying equations (30)-(33) to include the significant actuator dynamics, is represented as

$$M(q)\ddot{q} + H(q, \dot{q}) = J^T(q)\lambda + NK_m I_a , \quad (63)$$

$$L\dot{I}_a + RI_a + K_m N\dot{q} = u , \quad (64)$$

$$y = 0 = \phi(q) , \quad (65)$$

$$z_1 = h_1(q) , \quad (66)$$

$$z_2 = \lambda , \quad (67)$$

where $q \in R^n$ denotes the vector of generalized displacements of the links of the robot, $I_a \in R^n$ denotes the vector of currents in the armature circuit of the motors, L, R and N are constant diagonal nonsingular matrices which represent the armature inductances, armature resistances and the gear ratios respectively. The matrix K_m is a nonsingular diagonal matrix which represents the back e.m.f constants of the motors (which are the same as the torque constants when SI units are used), and $u \in R^n$ denotes the vector of control inputs which are the armature voltages of the motors. All the other variables have the same description as in equations (30)-(35).

Suppose $r_1(t)$ and $r_2(t)$ are vectors of desired position and force trajectories. Equations (63)-(67) can be rewritten in a first order form as

$$\begin{bmatrix} \dot{q} \\ \ddot{q} \\ \dot{I}_a \end{bmatrix} = f(q, \dot{q}, I_a) + g(q, \dot{q}, I_a)\lambda + h(q, \dot{q}, I_a)u ,$$

$$y = 0 = k(q, \dot{q}, I_a) ,$$

$$z = l(q, \dot{q}, I_a) + m(q, \dot{q}, I_a)\lambda ,$$

where f, g, h, k, l, m are defined appropriately. These differential-algebraic equations satisfy assumptions (A1)-(A3) of Section 1 with a constraint relative degree vector $(r_1, r_2, \cdot, \cdot, r_m) = (2, 2, \cdot, \cdot, 2)$ and control relative degree vector $(3, 3, \cdot, \cdot, 3)$. Define

$$\alpha(q, \dot{q}, I_a) = (J(q)M^{-1}(q)J^T(q))^{-1}[J(q)M^{-1}(q)H(q, \dot{q}) - \dot{J}(q)\dot{q} - J(q)M^{-1}(q)NK_m I_a .$$

From equations (5)-(10), f^*, h^*, l^*, and n^* are calculated. Assumptions (A4)-(A5) of Section 2 are satisfied in this case with $(\mu_1, \cdot, \cdot, \mu_{n-m}, \mu_{n-m+1}, \cdot, \cdot, \mu_n) = (3, \cdot, \cdot, 3, 1, \cdot, \cdot, 1)$. Now the coordinate change defined by (13)-(15) in this case is given by

$$\tilde{x}_1 = \phi(q) ,$$

$$\tilde{x}_2 = J(q)\dot{q} ,$$

$$\bar{x}_1 = h_1(q) ,$$

$$\bar{x}_2 = \frac{\partial h_1(q)}{\partial q}\dot{q} = P(q)\dot{q} ,$$

$$\bar{x}_3 = L_{f^*}^2 h_1(q) = f_5(q, \dot{q}) + B_3(q)I_a ,$$

$$\bar{x}_4 = \alpha(q, \dot{q}, I_a) = f_6(q, \dot{q}) + B_4(q)I_a ,$$

where f_5, B_3, f_6, B_4 can be calculated. Following equations (16) through (20), an equivalent state realization is obtained for the differential-algebraic equations which is given by

$$\dot{\bar{x}}_1 = \bar{x}_2 ,$$

$$\dot{\bar{x}}_2 = \bar{x}_3 ,$$

$$\dot{\bar{x}}_3 = A_3(q, \dot{q}, I_a) + B_3(q)L^{-1}u ,$$

$$\dot{\bar{x}}_4 = A_4(q, \dot{q}, I_a) + B_4(q)L^{-1}u ,$$

$$z_1 = \bar{x}_1 ,$$

$$z_2 = \bar{x}_4 ,$$

where

$$q = \psi(\bar{x}_1) , \quad \dot{q} = Q(q)\bar{x}_2 ,$$

$$I_a = \begin{bmatrix} B_3(q) \\ B_4(q) \end{bmatrix}^{-1} \left\{ - \begin{bmatrix} f_5(q, \dot{q}) \\ f_6(q, \dot{q}) \end{bmatrix} + \begin{bmatrix} \bar{x}_3 \\ \bar{x}_4 \end{bmatrix} \right\} ,$$

and A_3 and A_4 can be calculated. The nonlinear feedback control law defined by (21) is now given by

$$u(t) = L \begin{bmatrix} B_3(q) \\ B_4(q) \end{bmatrix}^{-1} \left\{ - \begin{bmatrix} A_3(q, \dot{q}, I_a) \\ A_4(q, \dot{q}, I_a) \end{bmatrix} + \begin{bmatrix} v_1(t) \\ v_2(t) \end{bmatrix} \right\} , \quad (68)$$

where

$$v_1(t) = r_1^{(3)}(t) - \Lambda_1(h_1(q) - r_1(t)) - \Lambda_2(P(q)\dot{q} - r_1^{(1)}(t)) - \Lambda_3(f_5(q, \dot{q}) + B_3(q)I_a - r_1^{(2)}(t)) \quad (69)$$

$$v_2(t) = r_2^{(1)}(t) - \Lambda_4(f_6(q, \dot{q}) + B_4(q)I_a - r_2(t)) \quad (70)$$

and $r_1^{(i)}(t)$ and $r_2^{(i)}(t)$ denote the i-th derivative of $r_1(t)$ and $r_2(t)$ with respect to time. The tracking errors in the closed-loop constrained system satisfy the equations

$$e_1^{(3)}(t) + \Lambda_3 e_1^{(2)}(t) + \Lambda_2 e_1^{(1)}(t) + \Lambda_1 e_1(t) = 0 , \quad (71)$$

$$e_2^{(1)}(t) + \Lambda_4 e_2(t) = 0 , \quad (72)$$

where the position tracking error is defined as

$$e_1(t) = h_1(q) - r_1(t) ,$$

and the force tracking error is defined as

$$e_2(t) = \lambda(t) - r_2(t) .$$

If Λ_1 through Λ_4 are chosen such that the equations (71)-(72) are Hurwitz, then the tracking error $e_1(t)$ for the position outputs and the force tracking error $e_2(t)$ approach zero exponentially. In addition, all the internal states of the constrained robot system and the control inputs remain bounded since Assumption 2 of Section 2 is satisfied trivially. The control law requires feedback of position and velocity variables of the links of the robot, and the armature currents of the motors.

References

[1] Ahmad, S., "Constrained Motion (Force/Position) Control of Flexible Joint Robots", *Proceedings of the IEEE Conference on Decision and Control*, Brighton, England, 1991, pp. 1397-1402.

[2] Brenan, K. E., Campbell, S. L. and Petzold, L. R., "Numerical Solution of Initial-Value Problems in Differential-Algebraic Equations", Elsevier Science, 1989.

[3] Byrnes, C. I. and Isidori, A., "Asymptotic Stabilization of Minimum Phase Nonlinear Systems", *IEEE Transactions on Automatic Control*, Vol. 36, No. 10, 1991, pp. 1122-1137.

[4] Isidori, A., "Nonlinear Control Systems", Springer-Verlag, Second Edition, Berlin, 1989.

[5] Jankowski, K. P. and Elmaraghy, H. A., "Nonlinear Decoupling for Position and Force Control of Constrained Robots with Flexible Joints", *Proceedings of the IEEE International Conference on Robotics and Automation*, Sacramento, California, 1991, pp. 1226-1231.

[6] Kaprielian, S., Turi, J. and Hunt, L. R., "Vector Input-Output Linearization for a Class of Descriptor Systems", *Proceedings of the IEEE Conference on Decision and Control*, Brighton, England, 1991, pp. 1951-1954.

[7] Krishnan, H., "Control of Nonlinear Systems with Applications to Constrained Robots and Spacecraft Attitude Stabilization", *Ph.D Thesis, Department of Aerospace Engineering, University of Michigan*, September, 1992.

[8] Krishnan, H. and McClamroch, N. H., "A New Approach To Position and Contact Force Regulation in Constrained Robot Systems", *Proceedings of the IEEE International Conference on Robotics and Automation*, Cincinnati, Ohio, 1990, pp. 1344-1349.

[9] Krishnan, H. and McClamroch, N. H., "Tracking Reference Inputs in Control Systems Described by a Class of Nonlinear Differential-Algebraic Equations", *Proceedings of the IEEE Conference on Decision and Control*, Brighton, England, 1991, pp. 1796-1801.

[10] Krishnan, H. and McClamroch, N. H., "Computation of State Realizations for Control Systems Described by a Class of Linear Differential-Algebraic Equations", *International Journal of Control*, Vol. 55, No. 6, 1992, pp. 1425-1441.

[11] McClamroch, N. H., "Singular Systems of Differential Equations as Dynamical Models for Constrained Robot Systems", *Proceedings of the IEEE International Conference on Robotics and Automation*, San Francisco, California, 1986, pp. 21-28.

[12] McClamroch, N. H., "Feedback Stabilization of Control Systems Described by a Class of Nonlinear Differential-Algebraic Equations", *Systems and Control Letters*, 15, 1990, pp. 53-60.

[13] McClamroch, N. H., and Wang, D., "Feedback Stabilization and Tracking of Constrained Robots," *IEEE Transactions on Automatic Control*, Vol. 33, No. 5, 1988, pp. 419-426.

[14] McClamroch, N. H., and Wang, D., "Linear Feedback Control of Position and Contact Force for a Nonlinear Constrained Mechanism," *ASME Journal of Dynamic Systems, Measurement and Control*, 112, 1990, pp. 640-645.

[15] Mills, J. K., "Stability and Control of Elastic-Joint Robotic Manipulators During Constrained Motion Tasks", *IEEE Transaction on Robotics and Automation*, Vol. 8, No. 1, 1992. pp. 119-125.

[16] Mills, J. K., and Goldenberg, A. A., "Force and Position Control of Manipulators During Constrained Motion Tasks," *IEEE Journal of Robotics and Automation*, Vol. 5, No.1, 1989, pp. 30-46.

[17] Reich, S., "On a Geometrical Interpretation of Differential-Algebraic Equations", *Circuits, Systems and Signal Processing*, Vol. 9, No. 4, 1990, pp. 369-382.

[18] Rheinboldt, W. C., "Differential-Algebraic Systems as Differential Equations on Manifolds", *Mathematics of Computation*, Vol. 43, No. 168, 1984, pp. 473-482.

[19] Sastry, S. S. and Isidori, A., "Adaptive Control of Linearizable Systems", *IEEE Transactions on Automatic Control*, Vol. 34, No. 11, 1989, pp. 1123-1131.

[20] Spong, M. W., "Modeling and Control of Elastic Joint Robots", *ASME Journal of Dynamic Systems, Measurment and Control*, Vol. 109, 1987, pp. 310-319.

[21] Yun, X., "Dynamic State Feedback Control of Constrained Robot Manipulators", *Proceedings of the IEEE Conference on Decision and Control*, Austin, Texas, 1988, pp. 622-626.

Proceedings of the
American Control Conference
San Francisco, California • June 1993

LOW-DIMENSIONAL INTERMITTENT CHAOS ON A CATALYTIC WAFER

Chien-Chong Cheng, Eduardo E. Wolf and Hsueh-Chia Chang

Department of Chemical Engineering
University of Notre Dame, Notre Dame, IN 46556

Abstract

The chaotic distributed dynamics of an exothermic reaction on a catalytic wafer is shown to evolve on a low-dimensional invariant manifold. The dominant spatial patterns during CO oxidation on a Rh black/SiO_2 wafer is obtained by carrying out a statistical Karhunen-Loeve (KL) analysis on the recorded IR thermograph in video images. The entire video sequence is then projected onto the phase space spanned by the 5 leading "empirical eigenfunctions" from the analysis. Statistical properties of the projected trajectories, such as the Lyapunov exponent, is of low dimensions ($n<5$) and is fully captured by the KL technique. The more conventional delayed-embedding phase-space reconstruction technique from a point measurement is shown to be far less robust.

1. Introduction

Distributed systems often exits spatio-temporal chaos with spatially varying fluctuations as well as temporal ones, (A good example is wave dynamics under the Golden Gate on a typical windy day.) Analysis of such distributed dynamics is extremely difficult because of the large degrees of freedom involved. Consequently, while lumped systems have been shown to exhibit low-dimensional temporal chaos, it seems unlikely that the dynamics of distributed systems can be low-dimensional. This would mean that the recent advances in chaos theory can only be applied to the extremely restrictive limit of lumped dynamics. However there is an important class of distributed dynamics that exhibits low-dimensional chaos. The spatial structures of such systems are quite robust and coherent even though the temporal dynamics is irregular. An academic example of such dynamics is inviscid fluid dynamics. The dynamics of a planar inviscid flow is, for example, dominated by interaction among a small number of indestructible and identical vortices. Each vortex is rather irregular in shape and requires a large number of spatial Fourier modes to resolve. Consequently, if one attempts to resolve the distributed dynamics using the conventional Galerkin or spectral projection, a large dimensional dynamical system results which renders it difficult to decipher its low-dimensional dynamics. However, if one expands the flow filed using an isolated vortex as the "basis" the dynamics involving n vortices yields only 2n equations for the speed and location of each vortex. This is essentially the underlying principle behind the "vortex blob" numerical scheme for turbulent flow dynamics. The planar vortex "coherent structure" of inviscid flow can be constructed analytically from the Euler equation and the dynamical system governing vortex interaction can be readily derived. It is far more difficult to identify such coherent structures for a distributed system whose governing equations are unknown. Recently, a Karhunen-Loeve (KL) "Empirical Eigenfunction" technique [1] has been proposed for the construction of the coherent structure and deciphering the low-dimensional distributed chaos.

We demonstrate there that the above KL scheme can indeed reconstruct the spatio-temporal dynamics of an exothermic CO oxidation reaction on a Rh/SiO_2 catalytic wafer. We also demonstrate that the embedding reconstruction technique [2] from a point measurement fails to extract the correct Lyapunov exponent from the system. After the projection of the distributed dynamics, we are able to associate the observed chaotic dynamics with the Melnikov mechanism from chaos theory, thus linking spatio-temporal dynamics with the well-studied low-dimensional dynamics. (This result will be presented at 14:50, Friday of this ACC meeting.)

2. Reaction System

A schematic representation of experimental setup is the same as described in Kellow and Wolf [3]. The reactor, shown, in Figure 1,

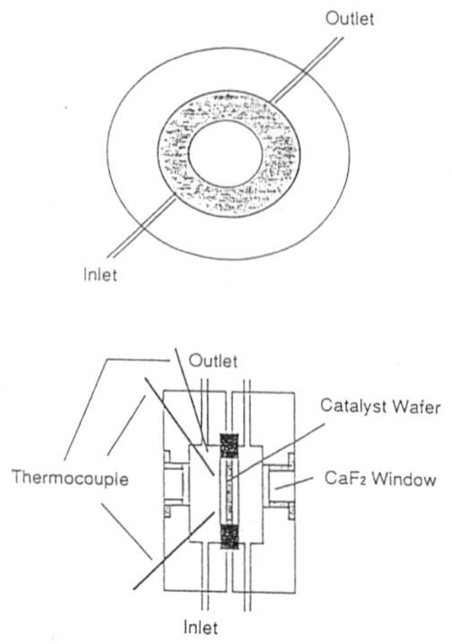

Figure 1. Schematic of the reactor housing the wafer.

consists of a small-volume (6 cm^3) chamber made of two vacuum flanges with infrared transparent CaF_2 windows attached to their centers. Two electric heaters are used to maintain the reactor wall and gas temperatures at a nearly identical given value. Gas flow rates are regulated by a flow controller. The catalyst is a mixture of Rh black powder and SiO_2, with a weight content of Rh of 5%. The catalyst powder is pressed into a wafer by using a pressure of 7000 psi. The circular catalyst wafer about 2.5 cm in diameter is supported by an aluminum gasket pressed between the two flanges that seal the reactor. The feed gas enters from either the bottom left corner or the top right corner and exits diagonally. Mixing in the gas phase is not significant and there is a negative gradient in the gas-phase concentration in the direction of the gas pretreatment. It also means that the most fuel-rich region during reaction is located near the inlet. An AGA 782 infrared camera, measuring the IR radiation emitted through a transparent window, is used to obtain spatial temperature patterns. (It should be noted that, due to the relatively uniform heating, the gas-phase temperature is almost gradientless.) Signals collected by this camera are digitized by a scan converter with a resolution of 105 x 68 pixels per frame with 8 bits/pixel at a maximum rate of 1 frame/s. The digitized signals are sent to a monitor for real-time display, recorded by a VCR, and stored in a computer for future analysis.

Many classes of spatio-temporal dynamics have been observed from the above experimental set up [3]. We shall, however, focus on the most complex one involving a migrating hot spot. A single coherent thermal structure appears on the waver and seems to wander back and forth across it. During its traverse, the hot spot rotates and blinks but its shape remains essentially the same. (A video display will be presented in the Video Session on Thursday 11:00 am of this ACC meeting.) The hot spot remains near the gas feed for a long duration and migrates away intermittently. It returns to the same position after a maximum of 3 loops around the wafer.

The reaction product CO_2 is monitored by analyzing outlet gas via an IR analyzer. All the temperature and concentration signals are sent to a chart recorder as well as an ADDA board, which digitized analog signals with finer resolution and sent the digitized signals to a computer. The CO_2 concentration fluctuations for a 3000-s run with approximately 40 traverses of the hot spot for the second type of thermal pattern dynamics are shown at the top of Figure 2. It is clear that oscillations of CO_2 concentration from a high to lower value occur intermittently in time. At each pulse, a rapid decline is

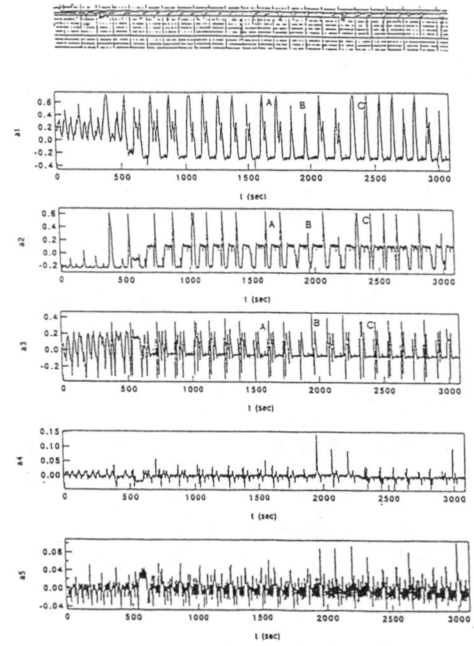

Figure 2. Fluctuations of the CO_2 exit concentration and the first five empirical eigen functions during a chaotic time series.

followed by a gradual relaxation to the original value. The distribution of the time interval between pulses is a narrow one centered at about 125 s, which also corresponds to the relaxation time of each pulse. The pulses occur when the hot spot wanders off the active region and hence provides a lower reaction rate. The pattern will return eventually to the original spot as a pulse is completed. The pulses are quite irregular. Some are doublets with two closely spaced peaks and some have two relaxation stages. Since the CO_2 signal is essentially an integrated quantity averaged over the entire reactor, it misses much of the fine spatial patterns. The Karhunen-Loeve procedure in the next section shows even some of seemingly identical CO_2 peaks correspond to different spatial structures. Nevertheless, the intermittent temporal character of the instability is already in evidence with a laminar phase of the high CO_2 regions and a turbulent phase corresponding to the irregular dips in the CO_2 concentration. The former occurs when the hot spot resides at the active site while the latter corresponds to its intermittent migration.

Denoting the (i,j) pixel recording of frame m in our video as

$$g_m = f_m - \langle f \rangle \tag{1}$$

where $\langle f \rangle = (1/M)\sum_{m=1}^{M} f$ is the ensemble average of all frames. (Typically, M = 1000 frames is used.) A correlation tensor is then reconstructed from the snap-shot method of Sirovich [1]

$$K(i,j,k,l) = \langle g_m(i,j) g_m(k,l) \rangle \tag{2}$$

This fourth-order tensor is symmetric with respect to the index change $i \rightarrow k$ and $j \rightarrow l$, Consequently, the following eigenvalue problem is self-adjoint

$$\sum_{k,l} K(i,j,k,l)\Psi_n(k,l) = \mu_n \Psi_n(i,j) \tag{3}$$

and the real eignevectors are orthonormal

$$\sum_{k,l} \Psi_n(k,l)\Psi_n(k,l) = \delta_{mn} \tag{4}$$

The ensemble averaging in (2) ensures that the dominant structure in all of our video images are represented by leading eigenfunctions $\{\Psi_n\}_{n=1}^{N}$.

The dominant eigenfucntion $n = 1$ resembles the observed thermal hot spot, indicating the coherent structure is faithfully captured. From the magnitude of the eigenvalues μ_m we conclude that the first empirical eigenfuction contains 85% of the total fluctuation energy, μ_m = (432.8, 40.1, 17.4, 6.1, 2.9). With two empirical eigenfunctions 92% of the energy is captured and the higher modes only contribute marginally to the dynamics. This reflects the spatially localized nature of the coherent structure-dominated dynamics (If one represents each reduced frame $g_m(i,j)$ by the orthonormal basis $\{\Psi_n\}$

$$g(i,j) = \sum_{n=1}^{N} a_n \Psi_n(i,j) \tag{5}$$

it is then clear that the mean energy of each mode is

$$\langle a_n^{\,2} \rangle = \langle (g,\Psi_n)(g,\Psi_n) \rangle = \mu_m \tag{6}$$

and the rapid decay in μ_m signifies the higher modes do not contribute significantly. We shall further confirm the fast convergence of the empirical eigenfunction expansion by examining the convergence of the Lyapunov exponent later in this section.

The decomposition

$$g(x,y,t) = \sum_{n=1}^{N} a_n(t)\Psi_n(x,y) \tag{7}$$

which is a continuous version of (5), then allows one to reduce the infinite-dimensional phase space of $\{a_n\}_{n=1}^{N}$. The projected time series is shown in Figure 2.

To confirm that we have obtained an accurate reconstruction, we estimate the Lyapunov exponents from our projected trajectory $\{a_n\}_{n=1}^{N}$ in Figure 2. As shown in Table 1, the estimated Lyapunov exponents show satisfactory convergence with respect to N in contrast to the divergence of the delayed embedding technique from a point measurement in Table II. Exponential divergence of nearby trajectories seems to occur over a time scale of 2 s, which is much smaller than the characteristic period. The existence of 2 positive Lyapunov exponents clearly demonstrate that the observed pattern dynamics comes from a low-dimensional deterministic strange attractor.

Table 1 Lyapunov exponents from the KL method

N	λ_1	λ_2	λ_3	λ_4
2	2.05	0.798		
3	1.417	0.519	-0.716	
4	1.076	0.378	-0.593	-0.950

Table 2 Leading Lyapunov exponent from the delayed-embedding method from a point measurement

N	2	3	4	5	6	7
λ_1	0.436	0.559	0.287	0.101	0.002	0.147

References

[1] Sirovich, L., Physics, D37, pp 126-135, 1989.
[2] Packard, N. H., Cruthfield, J. P. Farmer, J. D. and Shaw, R. S., Phys. Rev. Lett., 45, 712-716, 1985.
[3] Kellow, J. C. and Wolf, E. E., Chem. Eng. Sci., 45, 2597-2602, 1990.

Acknowledgement - This work is supported by NSF grants CTS-9112977 and 9200210.

Proceedings of the
American Control Conference
San Francisco, California • June 1993

On the Discrete-Time Nonlinear Servomechanism Problem

J. Huang, C.F. Lin
American GNC Corporation
9131 Mason Ave.
Chatsworth, CA 91311

Abstract The servomechanism problem for discrete-time nonlinear systems is investigated.

1. Introduction

The objective of this paper is to establish the nonlinear discrete-time servomechanism theory parallel to the continuous-time servomechanism theory developed in [BI], [HR1], [HR2], [HR3], and [IB]. The key result of this paper is, in Section 2, the discovery of a set of nonlinear algebraic functional equations that play exactly the same role as the partial differential equation given by Isidori and Byrnes [IB] for the solvability of continuous-time servomechanism problem. Using the center manifold theory for map [C], it is shown that the solvability of this set of equations leads to the solution of the discrete-time servomechanism problem. Due to the result of Section 2, the discrete-time servomechanism problem boils down to the solution of the aboved mentioned algebraic equation. The solvability of this set of algebraic equations is investigated in Section 3. In Section 4, we present a result on the approximate solution of the discrete-time servomechanism problem which parallels that in [HR2] on continuous-time systems.

Note that the same problem was studied recently by Castillo and Gennaro in [CG] for SISO nonlinear discrete-time systems. However, their results rely on the assumption of the exsitence of relative degree and are proved by means of the normal form. Since the main strength of the continuous time servomechanism theory resides in that it depends on neither the existence of relative degree nor the coordinates transform, the results of this paper significantly generalizes those in [CG].

2. Discrete-Time Nonlinear Servomechanism Problem

We consider a plant described by

$$\begin{aligned} x(t+1) &= f(x(t), u(t), w(t)), \quad x(0) = x_0 \\ y(t) &= h(x(t), u(t), w(t)), \quad t \geq 0 \end{aligned} \tag{2.1}$$

where $x(t)$ is the n-dimensional plant state, $u(t)$ is the m-dimensional plant input, $y(t)$ is the p-dimensional plant output, and $w(t)$ is the q_1-dimensional disturbance signal generated by the exogenous system

$$w(t+1) = a_1(w(t)), \quad w(0) = w_0 \tag{2.2}$$

In addition, there is a reference input generated by a q_2-dimensional exogenous system

$$r(t+1) = a_2(r(t)), \quad r(0) = r_0 \tag{2.3}$$

and the tracking error is defined by

$$e(t) = y(t) - d(r(t)) \tag{2.4}$$

For simplicity, all the functions involved in this setup are assumed to be defined globally on the appropriate Euclidean spaces, with the value zero at the respective origins, all our results are stated locally in terms of open neighborhoods of origins of appropriate Euclidean spaces, and for technical reasons they are assumed to be sufficiently smooth. We will focus on the state feedback control law of the form

$$u(t) = k(x(t), r(t), w(t)) \tag{2.5}$$

where the function $k(\cdot,\cdot,\cdot)$ is required to be sufficiently smooth and zero for zero arguments. Extensions to the output feedback is straitforward. Let the closed-loop system be described as follows

$$\begin{aligned} x(t+1) &= f_c(x(t), r(t), w(t)), \quad x(0) = x_0 \\ y(t) &= h_c(x(t), r(t), w(t)), \quad t \geq 0 \end{aligned} \tag{2.6}$$

where $f_c(\cdot,\cdot,\cdot)$ and $h_c(\cdot,\cdot,\cdot)$ are defined as

$$\begin{aligned} f_c(x, r, w) &= f(x, k(x, r, w), w) \\ h_c(x, r, w) &= h(x, k(x, r, w), w) \end{aligned} \tag{2.7}$$

Then the requirements for the closed-loop system are that (i) all the eigenvalues of the matrix

$$\frac{\partial f_c}{\partial x}(0, 0, 0) \tag{2.8}$$

have modulus less than one, and (ii) for all sufficiently small initial conditions x_0, r_0 and w_0, the tracking error (2.4) satisfies

$$\lim_{t \to \infty} e(t) = 0 \tag{2.9}$$

To characterize the solvability conditions on the above problem, we introduce the following definition.

Definition 2.1: For an open neighborhood Γ of the origin in $R^{q_1+q_2}$, suppose there exist C^2 functions $\mathbf{x}:\Gamma \rightarrow R^n$, $\mathbf{u}:\Gamma \rightarrow R^m$ such that $\mathbf{x}(0,0) = 0$, $\mathbf{u}(0,0) = 0$, and for $(r,w) \in \Gamma$

$$\begin{aligned} \mathbf{x}(a_1(w), a_2(r)) &= f(\mathbf{x}(r,w), \mathbf{u}(r,w), w) \\ h(\mathbf{x}(r,w), \mathbf{u}(r,w), w) &= d(r) \end{aligned} \quad (2.10)$$

Then the functions $\mathbf{u}(r,w)$ and $\mathbf{x}(r,w)$ are called (steady state) *zero-error constrained input* and (steady state) *zero-error constrained manifold* for the plant and the exosystems, respectively.

Equation (2.10) can be viewed as the discrete-time counterpart of the following partial differential equations

$$\begin{aligned} \frac{\partial \mathbf{x}(r,w)}{\partial w} a_1(w) + \frac{\partial \mathbf{x}(r,w)}{\partial r} a_2(r) &= f(\mathbf{x}(r,w), \mathbf{u}(r,w), w) \\ h(\mathbf{x}(r,w), \mathbf{u}(r,w), w) &= d(r) \end{aligned} \quad (2.11)$$

established by Isidori and Byrnes in [IB] that characterize the solvability conditions on the continuous-time nonlinear servomechanism problem.

It is interesting to note that, for the special case where the plant and exosystems are linear, that is

$$\begin{aligned} f(x,u,w) &= Ax + Bu + Ew \\ h(x,u,w) &= Cx + Du + Fw, \quad t \geq 0 \\ a_1(w) &= A_1 w \\ a_2(r) &= A_2 r \\ d(r) &= dr \end{aligned} \quad (2.12)$$

where A, B, C, D, E, F, A_1, A_2, d are constant matrices of appropriate dimensions. Both the functional equation (2.10) and the partial differential equation (2.11) become the same matrix equations established by Francis [F] as follows

$$\begin{aligned} \mathbf{x}S &= A\mathbf{x} + B\mathbf{u} + [0, E] \\ 0 &= C\mathbf{x} + D\mathbf{u} + [0, F] - [d, 0] \end{aligned} \quad (2.13)$$

where $S \stackrel{def}{=} diag\ [A_2\ A_1]$.

Once the two functions $\mathbf{x}(r,w)$ and $\mathbf{u}(r,w)$ are available, a control law achieving asymptotic tracking and disturbance rejection is easily constructed under some standard assumptions.

2.2 Theorem: Under the assumptions that the pair

$$\frac{\partial f}{\partial x}(0,0,0), \quad \frac{\partial f}{\partial u}(0,0,0) \quad (2.14)$$

is stabilizable, the eigenvalues of

$$\frac{\partial a_1}{\partial w}(0), \quad \frac{\partial a_2}{\partial r}(0) \quad (2.15)$$

have modulus 1, and the equilibria of (2.2) and (2.3) at the origins are stable, then there exist state feedback control laws of the form (2.5) such that the closed-loop system satisfies the two requirements (2.8) and (2.9) provided that (2.10) admits a solution of C^2 functions $\mathbf{x}(r,w)$, $\mathbf{u}(r,w)$.

Proof: Let K be such that all the eigenvalues of the matrix

$$\frac{\partial f}{\partial x}(0,0,0) + \frac{\partial f}{\partial u}(0,0,0)\ K \quad (2.16)$$

have modulus less than one. Then under the state feedback control law

$$u(t) = \mathbf{u}(r(t), w(t)) + K(x(t) - \mathbf{x}(r(t), w(t))) \quad (2.17)$$

The closed-loop system is such that all the eigenvalues of the matrix

$$\frac{\partial f_c}{\partial x}(0,0,0) \quad (2.18)$$

have modulus less than one, and, for $(r,w) \in \Gamma$,

$$\begin{aligned} \mathbf{x}(a_1(w), a_2(r)) &= f_c(\mathbf{x}(r,w), r, w) \\ h_c(\mathbf{x}(r,w), r, w) - d(r) &= 0 \end{aligned} \quad (2.19)$$

By the assumptions on the exosystems (2.2) and (2.3), it follows from the center manifold theory for map [C] that there exist positive constants k and $\beta < 1$ such that for sufficiently small x_0, w_0 and r_0, the solution $x(t)$ of the closed-loop system satisfies

$$||x(t) - \mathbf{x}(r(t), w(t))|| \leq k\beta^t \quad (2.20)$$

Further, there exists a compact set M in $R^{n+q_1+q_2}$ such that for $t \geq 0$,
$(x(t),\ r(t),\ w(t)) \in M$, $(\mathbf{x}(r(t), w(t)),\ r(t),\ w(t)) \in M$, therefore, there exists a finite constant L such that

$$||\frac{\partial h_c}{\partial x}(x, r, w)|| < L \quad (2.21)$$

for $(x,\ r,\ w) \in M$. As a result of (2.19)-(2.21), we have

$$\begin{aligned} \lim_{t\rightarrow\infty} ||e(t)|| &= \lim_{t\rightarrow\infty} ||(h_c(x(t), r(t), w(t)) - d(r(t)))|| \\ &= \lim_{t\rightarrow\infty} ||(h_c(x(t), r(t), w(t)) \\ &- h_c(\mathbf{x}(r(t), w(t)), r(t), w(t)))|| \\ &\leq \lim_{t\rightarrow\infty} L||x(t) - \mathbf{x}(r(t), w(t))|| = 0 \end{aligned} \quad (2.22)$$

3. Solvability of (2.10)

In this section, we will establish conditions for the solvability of the key equation (2.10). For convenience, a more compact notation will be used. That is, let $v(t) = (w(t),\ r(t))$ with the dimension of v defined as $q = q_1 + q_2$, we will write (2.1) in the form

$$\begin{aligned} x(t+1) &= f(x(t), u(t), v(t)), \quad x(0) = x_0 \\ y(t) &= h(x(t), u(t), v(t)), \quad t \geq 0 \end{aligned} \quad (3.1)$$

where the composite exogenous system and the error signal are written as

$$v(t+1) = a(v(t)), \quad v(0) = v_0 \quad (3.2)$$
$$e(t) = y(t) - d(v(t)) \quad (3.3)$$

Finally, let $\bar{h}(x,u,v) = h(x,u,v) - d(v)$, then (2.10) can be compactly written as

$$\begin{aligned} \mathbf{x}(a(v)) &= f(\mathbf{x}(v), \mathbf{u}(v), v) \\ 0 &= \bar{h}(\mathbf{x}(v), \mathbf{u}(v), v) \end{aligned} \quad (3.4)$$

Now consider the following constrained system:

$$\begin{aligned} x(t+1) &= f(x(t), u(t), v(t)) \\ v(t+1) &= a(v(t)) \\ 0 &= \bar{h}(x(t), u(t), v(t)) \end{aligned} \quad (3.5)$$

For convenience, in the sequel, we call (3.4) the AFE (Algebraic Functional Equation) associated with (3.5).

Let us first consider three special cases of (3.4)

Case 1: $n = 0$, in this case, (3.4) becomes

$$0 = \bar{h}(\mathbf{u}(v), v) \quad (3.6)$$

Clearly (3.6) is solvable iff

$$rank\ \frac{\partial \bar{h}}{\partial u}(0,0) = p \quad (3.7)$$

Case 2: $p = 0$, in this case, (3.4) becomes

$$\mathbf{x}(a(v)) = f(\mathbf{x}(v), \mathbf{u}(v), v) \quad (3.8)$$

Solvability of this equation can be established using the center manifold theorem for map [C] as shown by the following theorem.

3.1 Theorem: Suppose all the eigenvalues of the matrix $\frac{\partial a}{\partial v}(0)$ have modulus one, then (3.8) is solvable if there exists a smooth feedback control $u = \theta(x)$ satisfying $\theta(0) = 0$ such that none of the eigenvalues of the matrix

$$\frac{\partial\ f(x, \theta(x), 0)}{\partial x} \quad (3.9)$$

evaluated at $x = 0$ have modulus one.

Proof: By the assumptions and center manifold therory for map, locally there exists a C^2 function $\mathbf{x} : R^q \to R^n$ with $\mathbf{x}(0) = 0$, such that

$$\mathbf{x}(a(v)) = f(\mathbf{x}(v), \theta(\mathbf{x}(v)), v) \quad (3.10)$$

Let $\mathbf{u}(v) = \theta(\mathbf{x}(v))$. Then it is clear that $\mathbf{x}(v)$ and $\mathbf{u}(v)$ are the solution of (3.8).

Case 3: $m = 0$ and $p > 0$, in this case, (3.4) becomes

$$\begin{aligned} \mathbf{x}(a(v)) &= f(\mathbf{x}(v), v) \\ 0 &= \bar{h}(\mathbf{x}(v), v) \end{aligned} \quad (3.11)$$

This is kind of ill-posed problem, and is *generically* unsolvable.

In general, we have neither $p = 0$ nor $n = 0$ nor $m = 0$. Nevertheless, using the reduction algorithm to be introduced below, we can show that, under certain regular assumptions, the solvability of (3.4) can always be reduced to one of the above three cases.

Reduction Algorithm:

Let $D_x(x,u,v) = \frac{\partial \bar{h}}{\partial x}(x,u,v)$, and $D_u(x,u,v) = \frac{\partial \bar{h}}{\partial u}(x,u,v)$. Assume that
(i) $D_u(x,0,v)$ has constant rank r_0 in a neighborhood of $0 \in R^{n+q}$ and
(ii) $rank\ [D_x(0,0,0)\ D_u(0,0,0)] = p$.
Then by the Implicit Function Theorem, there exist partitions $u = (u^0, \bar{u}^0)$ with $u^0 \in R^{r_0}$, $\bar{u}^0 \in R^{m-r_0}$, $x = (x^0, \bar{x}^0)$ with $x^0 \in R^{p-r_0}$, $\bar{x}^0 \in R^{n-p-r_0}$ and two locally defined smooth functions $u^0 = k^0(\bar{x}^0, \bar{u}^0, v)$ and $x^0 = d^0(\bar{x}^0, v)$ that satisfy

$$\bar{h}(d^0(\bar{x}^0, v), \bar{x}^0, k^0(\bar{x}^0, \bar{u}^0, v), \bar{u}^0, v) = 0 \quad (3.12)$$

Corresponding to the partition $x = (x^0, \bar{x}^0)$, we can write

$$\begin{aligned} x^0(t+1) &= f^0(x^0(t), \bar{x}^0(t), u^0(t), \bar{u}^0(t), v(t)) \\ \bar{x}^0(t+1) &= \bar{f}^0(x^0(t), \bar{x}^0(t), u^0(t), \bar{u}^0(t), v(t)) \end{aligned} \quad (3.13)$$

with an abuse of notation, let

$$\begin{aligned} f^0(\bar{x}^0, \bar{u}^0, v) &= f^0(d^0(\bar{x}^0, v), \bar{x}^0, k^0(\bar{x}^0, \bar{u}^0, v), \bar{u}^0, v) \\ \bar{f}^0(\bar{x}^0, \bar{u}^0, v) &= \bar{f}^0(d^0(\bar{x}^0, v), \bar{x}^0, k^0(\bar{x}^0, \bar{u}^0, v), \bar{u}^0, v) \end{aligned}$$

then we can define a reduced-order system as follows

$$\begin{aligned} \bar{x}^0(t+1) &= \bar{f}^0(\bar{x}^0(t), \bar{u}^0(t), v(t)) \\ v(t+1) &= a(v(t)) \\ 0 &= h^0(\bar{x}^0(t), \bar{u}^0(t), v(t)) \end{aligned} \quad (3.14)$$

where

$$h^0(\bar{x}^0, \bar{u}^0, v) = f^0(\bar{x}^0, \bar{u}^0, v) - d^0(\bar{f}^0(\bar{x}^0, \bar{u}^0, v), a(v))$$

Finally let $p_0 = p - r_0$, $n_0 = n - p + r_0$ and $m_0 = m - r_0$. □

Since (3.14) has the same form as (3.5), we can associate an AFE of the form

$$\begin{aligned} \bar{\mathbf{x}}^0(a(v)) &= \bar{f}^0(\bar{\mathbf{x}}^0(v), \bar{\mathbf{u}}^0(v), v) \\ 0 &= h^0(\bar{\mathbf{x}}^0(v), \bar{\mathbf{u}}^0(v), v) \end{aligned} \quad (3.15)$$

with (3.14). The solution of (3.15) $\bar{\mathbf{x}}^0(v)$ and $\bar{\mathbf{u}}^0(v)$ are required to be C^2 functions locally defined in a neighborhood of $0 \in R^q$, and satisfy $\bar{\mathbf{x}}^0(0) = 0$ and $\bar{\mathbf{u}}^0(0) = 0$.

The following result shows that the solvability of (3.4) is equivalent to that of (3.15).

3.3 Theorem: Under the two rank conditions in the reduction algorithm, (3.4) is solvable if and only if (3.15) is solvable.

Proof: Assume $\bar{\mathbf{x}}^0(v)$ and $\bar{\mathbf{u}}^0(v)$ are solution of (3.15). Then we have, by the definition of h^0,

$$d^0(\bar{f}^0(\bar{\mathbf{x}}^0(v), \bar{\mathbf{u}}^0(v), v), a(v)) = f^0(\bar{\mathbf{x}}^0(v), \bar{\mathbf{u}}^0(v), v) \quad (3.16)$$

Let $\mathbf{x}^0(v) = d^0(\bar{\mathbf{x}}^0(v), v)$ and $\mathbf{u}^0(v) = k^0(\bar{\mathbf{x}}^0(v), \bar{\mathbf{u}}^0(v), v)$, then we have from (3.15)

$$\begin{aligned} & d^0(\bar{f}^0(\bar{\mathbf{x}}^0(v), \bar{\mathbf{u}}^0(v), v), a(v)) \\ = \ & d^0(\bar{x}^0(a(v)), a(v)) = \mathbf{x}^0(a(v)) \end{aligned} \quad (3.17)$$

Therefore (3.16) can be writen as

$$\mathbf{x}^0(a(v)) = f^0(\bar{\mathbf{x}}^0(v), \bar{\mathbf{u}}^0(v), v) \quad (3.18)$$

Also from (3.12), we have

$$\bar{h}(\mathbf{x}^0(v), \bar{\mathbf{x}}^0(v), \mathbf{u}^0(v), \bar{\mathbf{u}}^0(v), v) = 0 \quad (3.19)$$

Now let $\mathbf{x}(v) = (\mathbf{x}^0(v), \bar{\mathbf{x}}^0(v))$ and $\mathbf{u}(v) = (\mathbf{u}^0(v), \bar{\mathbf{u}}^0(v))$, then it is clear from (3.15) and (3.18) and (3.19) that $\mathbf{x}(v)$ and $\mathbf{u}(v)$ satisfy (3.4).

On the contrary, assume $\mathbf{x}(v)$ and $\mathbf{u}(v)$ satisfy (3.4), then corresponding to the partition $x = (x^0, \bar{x}^0)$ and $u = (u^0, \bar{u}^0)$, we can make partitions $\mathbf{x}(v) = (\mathbf{x}^0(v), \bar{\mathbf{x}}^0(v))$ and $\mathbf{u}(v) = (\mathbf{u}^0(v), \bar{\mathbf{u}}^0(v))$. Clearly, $\bar{\mathbf{x}}^0(v)$ and $\bar{\mathbf{u}}^0(v)$ are the solution of (3.15). □

Note that in case $p - r_0 = n$ or $r_0 = p$ or $r_0 = m$, (3.15) takes the form of either (3.6) or (3.8) or (3.11), then the solvability of (3.15) is given by the previous discussions. In general, we have neither $p - r_0 = n$ nor $r_0 = p$ nor $r_0 = m$. However, if (3.14) also satisfies the two rank conditions of the reduction algorithm, then the reduction algorithm can be applied to (3.14) again. Thus, iteratively, beginning from a system Σ^{l-1} of the form

$$\begin{aligned} \bar{x}^{l-1}(t+1) &= \bar{f}^{l-1}(\bar{x}^{l-1}(t), \bar{u}^{l-1}(t), v(t)) \\ v(t+1) &= a(v(t)) \\ 0 &= h^{l-1}(\bar{x}^{l-1}(t), \bar{u}^{l-1}(t), v(t)) \quad (3.20) \end{aligned}$$

where $\bar{x}^{l-1} \in R^{n_{l-1}}$, $\bar{u}^{l-1} \in R^{m_{l-1}}$, and $h^{l-1} \in R^{p_{l-1}}$ with $n_{l-1} > 0$, $m_{l-1} > 0$, and $p_{l-1} > 0$, under the assumption that the system (3.20) satisfies the two rank conditions of the reduction algorithm, we can obtain a reduced-order constrained system Σ^l.

$$\begin{aligned} \bar{x}^{l}(t+1) &= \bar{f}^{l}(\bar{x}^{l}(t), \bar{u}^{l}(t), v(t)) \\ v(t+1) &= a(v(t)) \\ 0 &= h^{l}(\bar{x}^{l}(t), \bar{u}^{l}(t), v(t)) \quad (3.21) \end{aligned}$$

where $\bar{x}^l \in R^{n_l}$, $\bar{u}^l \in R^{m_l}$, and $h^l \in R^{p_l}$. Note that with $r_l \overset{def}{=} rank\ \frac{\partial h^{l-1}}{\partial u}(0,0,0)$, we have $p_l = p_{l-1} - r_l$, $m_l = m_{l-1} - r_l$, and $n_l = n_{l-1} - p_{l-1} + r_l$. These dimensional relations imply either $n_l < n_{l-1}$ or $m_l < m_{l-1}$ and $p_l < p_{l-1}$. Therefore, for some finite l (In fact, l is bounded by n), either the system Σ^l violates the two rank conditions or one of the following three cases will occur.

Case 1: $p_l - r_{l+1} = n_l$ where $r_{l+1} = rank\ \frac{\partial h^l}{\partial u}(0,0,0)$.

Case 2: $r_{l+1} = p_l$

Case 3: $r_{l+1} = m_l$

Now we can show that applying the reduction algorithm once more will lead to one of the three special cases as discussed in the beginning of this section.

For **Case 1**, by the Implicit Function Theorem, there exist partitions $\bar{u}^l = (u^{l+1}, \bar{u}^{l+1})$ with $u^{l+1} \in R^{r_{l+1}}$, $\bar{u}^{l+1} \in R^{m_l - r_{l+1}}$, and locally defined smooth functions $\bar{x}^l = \bar{d}^{l+1}(v)$ and $u^{l+1} = k^{l+1}(\bar{u}^{l+1}, v)$ that satisfy

$$h^l(\bar{d}^{l+1}(v), k^{l+1}(\bar{u}^{l+1}, v), \bar{u}^{l+1}, v) = 0$$

Then we can define an algebraically constrained equation in $\bar{u}^{l+1}$ and v as follows

$$h^{l+1}(\bar{u}^{l+1}, v) = 0 \quad (3.22)$$

where

$$h^{l+1}(\bar{u}^{l+1}, v) = \bar{f}^l(d^{l+1}(v), k^{l+1}(\bar{u}^{l+1}, v), \bar{u}^{l+1}, v) - \bar{d}^{l+1}(a(v))$$

Now by Theorem 3.3, the solvability of (3.4) is equivalent to the existence of some smooth function $\bar{\mathbf{u}}^{l+1}(v)$ satisfying

$$h^{l+1}(\bar{\mathbf{u}}^{l+1}(v), v) = 0$$

This clearly belongs to the first special case as discussed in the beginning of this section.

Now consider **Case 2**. This happens only when $p_l \le m_l$ or equivalently $p \le m$. It is clear, we have $m_l - p_l = m - p$. By the Implicit Function Theorem, there exist partitions $\bar{u}^l = (u^{l+1}, \bar{u}^{l+1})$ with $u^{l+1} \in R^{r_{l+1}}$, $\bar{u}^{l+1} \in R^{m-p}$, (With an abuse of notation, we allow zero dimension of $\bar{u}^{l+1}$ when $p = m$) and a locally defined smooth function $u^{l+1} = k^{l+1}(\bar{x}^l, \bar{u}^{l+1}, v)$ that satisfies

$$h^{l+1}(\bar{x}^l, k^{l+1}(\bar{x}^l, \bar{u}^{l+1}, v), \bar{u}^{l+1}, v) = 0$$

Let

$$\bar{f}^{l+1}(\bar{x}^l, \bar{u}^{l+1}, v) = \bar{f}^l(\bar{x}^l, k^{l+1}(\bar{x}^l, \bar{u}^{l+1}), \bar{u}^{l+1}, v)$$

then we obtain an unconstrained system as follows

$$\begin{aligned} \bar{x}^{l}(t+1) &= \bar{f}^{l+1}(\bar{x}^{l}(t), \bar{u}^{l+1}(t), v(t)) \\ v(t+1) &= a(v(t)) \quad (3.23) \end{aligned}$$

Thus we have reduced the solvability of (3.4) to the second special case as discussed in the beginning of this section. Solvability of the AFE associated with (3.23) is given by Theorem 3.1.

Now we turn to **Case 3**. This case happens only when $p_l \ge m_l$ or equivalently $p \ge l$. It is clear that $p_l - m_l = p - m$. If $p = m$, then this case has been covered in **Case 2**. Assume $p > m$. Then it is not difficult to see that applying the reduction algorithm to (3.21) will result in a reduced-order system of the form

$$\begin{aligned} \bar{x}^{l+1}(t+1) &= \bar{f}^{l+1}(\bar{x}^{l+1}(t), v(t)) \\ v(t+1) &= a(v(t)) \\ 0 &= h^{l+1}(\bar{x}^{l+1}(t), v(t)) \quad (3.24) \end{aligned}$$

where $\mathbf{x}^{l+1} \in R^{n_l - p_l + r_{l+1}}$ and $h^{l+1} \in R^{p-m}$. Clearly, this case is the third special case as discussed in the beginning of this section.

3.4 Remark: Conceptually, the reduction algorithm is related to the zero dynamics algorithm [I] and the constrained dynamics algorithm [VDS]. However, here the operations are performed on both the states and the inputs rather than outputs or/and inputs. The two rank conditions in the algorithm clearly specify the conditions for the existence of certain maximal constrained invariant manifold. In the special case of the SISO discrete-time system with the relative degree ρ as discussed in [CG], it is not difficult to see that applying the reduction algorithm ρ times will reduce (3.4) to **Case 2** as discussed in the beginning of this Section. Similarly , for the MIMO square discrete-time system with the relative degree $(\rho_1, \cdots, \rho_m)$, applying the reduction algorithm max $(\rho_1, \cdots, \rho_m)$ times will also reduce (3.4) to **Case 2**. Moreover, this algorithm does not rely on the existence of the relative degree. In fact, what is implied by the two rank conditions is kind of *right invertibility*. Therefore, our approach applies to a very broad class of systems.

4. Approximate solution for (3.4)

The establishment of the algebraic equation (3.4) also offers a framework for approximately solving the servomechanism problem. An approximate solution for (3.4) will be given in this section. This is of interest since an exact solution is rarely possible due to the nonlinear nature of the equation.

Our consideration of (3.4) will involve polynomial representation for the unknown functions $\mathbf{x}(v)$ and $\mathbf{u}(v)$, and this entails the following notation. For the $q \times 1$ vector v, let $v^{[l]}$ denote the vector

$$v^{[l]} = [v_1^l \; v_1^{l-1}v_2 \; \cdots \; v_1^{l-1}v_q \; v_1^{l-2}v_2^2 \; v_1^{l-2}v_2v_3 \; \cdots \; v_1^{l-2}v_2v_q \; \cdots \; v_q^l]^T$$

Then we seek polynomial of the form

$$\mathbf{x}_{(k)}(v) = \sum_{l=1}^{k} \phi v^{[l]}, \quad \mathbf{u}_{(k)}(v) = \sum_{l=1}^{k} \psi v^{[l]} \qquad (4.1)$$

such that (3.4) is satisfied up to the order of $v^{[k+1]}$. We have the following result.

Theorem 4.1 : (3.4) has an approximate solution of the form (4.1) up to the order of $v^{[k+1]}$ if

$$rank \begin{bmatrix} \frac{\partial f}{\partial x}(0,0,0) - \lambda & \frac{\partial f}{\partial u}(0,0,0) \\ \frac{\partial h}{\partial x}(0,0,0) & \frac{\partial h}{\partial u}(0,0,0) \end{bmatrix} = n + p \qquad (4.2)$$

for all λ given by

$$\lambda = \lambda_{i_1} \times \cdots \times \lambda_{i_l} \qquad (4.3)$$

where $l = 1, \cdots, k$, $i_1, \cdots, i_l \in \{1, 2, \cdots, q\}$, and $\lambda_1, \cdots, \lambda_q$ are eigenvalues of $\frac{\partial a}{\partial v}(0)$.

Proof: The proof is similar to that in [HR2] and is omitted.

4.2 Remark: It can be shown that the controller

$$u(t) = \mathbf{u}_{(k)}(r(t), w(t)) + K(x(t) - \mathbf{x}_{(k)}(r(t), w(t)))$$

will result in a closed-loop system with the property that the steady state tracking error is in the order of $v^{[k+1]}$. The proof can be established using the same technique as used in [HR3].

5. Conclusions

A fairly complete investigation on the nonlinear discrete-time servomechanism problem has been carried out in this paper. In contrast to the continuous-time case, the problem is centered on the solvability of a set of nonlinear algebraic equations. This set of equations can also be viewed as a natural extension of the matrix equations characterizing the solvability of the linear servomechanism problem to the nonlinear case. Once this solution is available, many results on the continous-time nonlinear servomechanism problem can be carried over to the discrete-time case.

Acknowledgement:

Part of the work of J. Huang is done in the Department of Electrical and Computer Engineering at the Johns Hopkins University. He wish to thank Professor W.J. Rugh for his financial support and encouragement.

REFERENCES

[BI] Byrnes, C.I., Isidori, A., 1989, "Output Regulation of General Nonlinear Systems," *C.R. Acad. Sci. Paris*, June.

[C] Carr,J., 1981, "Applications of the Center Manifold Theory," *Springer Verlag*.

[CG] B. Castillo, S. Di Gennaro, 1991, "Aymptotic Output Tracking for SISO Nonlinear Discrete Systems," *Proceedings of the 30th Conference on Decision and Control*, pp 1802-1806, Brighton, England, December 1991.

[VDS] Van Der Schaft, A.J., 1988, "On Clamped Dynamics of Nonlinear Systems", (eds. C.I. Byrnes, C.F. Martin, R.E. Saeks), North Holland, Amsterdam, pp. 499-506.

[F] Francis, B.A., 1977, "The Linear Multivariable Regulator Problem," *SIAM Journal on Control and Optimization*, Vol. 15, pp. 486 - 505.

[HR1] Huang, J., Rugh, W.J., 1990, "On a Nonlinear Multivariable Servomechanism Problem," *Automatica*, Vol. 26, No. 6. pp. 963-972.

[HR2] Huang, J., Rugh, W.J., 1992, "Stablization on Zero-Error Manifolds and the Nonlinear Servomechanism Problem," *IEEE Transactions on Automatic Control*, July 1992, pp. 1009-1013. to appear.

[HR3] Huang, J., Rugh, W.J., 1992, "An Approximation Method for the Nonlinear Servomechanism Problem," *IEEE Transactions on Automatic Control*, September 1992, pp. 1395-1398.

[IB] Isidori. A, Byrnes, C.I., 1990, "Output Regulation of Nonlinear Systems," *IEEE Transactions on Automatic Control*, Vol. 35, No.2, pp. 131 - 140.

Proceedings of the
American Control Conference
San Francisco, California • June 1993

PRECISE POINT-TO-POINT CONTROL FOR NONLINEAR SYSTEMS

Slim Choura

Department of Mechanical Engineering
King Saud University
PO Box 800, Riyadh 11421, Saudi Arabia

Abstract

A novel control strategy for designing point-to-point controllers for non- linear systems is proposed. The control law combines feedback and feedforward for the purpose of finite time settling of a non-linear system to its desired state. The feedback is designed separately to satisfy certain performance specifications in the time domain. The feedforward control law is determined from the feedback part and it is approximated via numerical methods. The point-to-point control problem is shown to be reduced to a boundary value problem in time, where its solution can be estimated via classical numerical methods, such as using the Galerkin, the least square, and the finite element techniques. Two methods for approximating the feedforward control part with the aid of the least-square technique are proposed. In the first method, the point-to-point control problem reduces to minimizing the norm of an error vector as integrated from zero to the final time. The size of the error vector is equal to the system's dimension. In the second method a truncation in the size of the error vector is suggested. It has been shown that the second method leads to better approximations and less computation times. The robustness of the proposed control strategy is addressed, and computer simulations are presented to justify the viability of the proposed control strategy.

1. Introduction

A major area in control system design is the synthesis of continuous and bounded control laws that drive a system from its initial state to a prespecified final state in finite time. This area has evolved primarily for precise point-to-point maneuvering of flexible structures, such as robot manipulators and large flexible structures. Unlike systems subject to control laws that are based on state feedback do not theoretically converge to a desired final state in finite time.

Two major directions for solving the point-to-point control problem have appeared in the literature. One emphasizes the minimization or the reduction of residual vibrations in robot manipulators after their maneuver time by input shaping. Such direction has been undertaken by several researchers including Aspinwall [2] and Swigert [9] with applications to large space structures, and Meckl and Seering [7,8] with applications to robotics. The other approach is rather concerned with zero residual vibrations with a proper selection of the control input. Such approach has been adopted by other researchers including Bhat and Miu [3,4] and Jayasuriya and Choura [6].

Recently, Choura [5] has studied the finite time settling control problem for linear systems, including linear time-varying systems. He has developed a control strategy that combines feedback and feedforward for the precise point-to-point state transfer in a prespecified finite time. The feedback is separately designed primarily for the purpose of closed loop stability. The feedforward which is determined from the feedback part can be either obtained in closed form or via numerical schemes. The combination of feedback and feedforward has resulted in a robust finite time settling control strategy.

In the light of the recent study by Choura [5], this paper investigates control laws that transfer the initial state of a non-linear system to its desired final state in finite time. Since it is cumbersome to solve non-linear systems in closed form, the computation of the feedforward term would be examined in different ways vis-a-vis that in the linear case. Here, the feedforward control law is determined from the solution of a time boundary value problem. The robustness of the point-to-point control strategy proposed in this paper is examined through computer simulations.

The remainder of this paper is organized as follows. In the next section, the precise point-to-point control problem is formulated for systems described by a set of first order differential equations, and methods for designing the feedback and the feedforward parts are proposed. In section 3, a similar formulation is followed for the design of precise point-to-point control laws for systems described by a set of second order differential equations. Conclusions appear in section 4.

2. Precise Point-to-Point Control Design for Systems Described by First Order Differential Equations

In this section, numerical schemes for approximating precise point-to-point controllers for non-linear systems are developed. The precise point-to-point control law proposed in this study is constructed based on combining feedback and feedforward. The concept of properly combining feedback and feedforward has yielded a robust finite time settling control strategy for linear systems [5]. This paper examines the properties of the precise point-to-point control strategy developed for non-linear systems via-a-vis those of the finite time settling control developed for linear systems.

Consider the class of n-dimensional non-linear systems described by

$$\dot{x} = h(x,t) + B(x,t)u(t) \tag{1}$$

where the elements of vector h and those of matrix B are non-linear functions of the state variables and time t, and u is the input vector of dimension p. The non-linear vector h and the non-linear matrix B are assumed to be bounded and continuous functions in both x and t.

The emphasis of this study is on the design of bounded control laws u that transfer the initial state vector $x(0)$ to a desired state vector $x(t_f)$ in finite time t_f. We require that such design be accompanied with adequate system robustness against uncertainties that result from the measurement of the initial state variables, from parameter identification and from sensor and/or actuator noise. The robustness is expected to ensure that the state transfer in a finite time be achieved while closed loop asymptotic stability is maintained.

The set of control laws u proposed in this study combines feedback and feedforward in the form:

$$u(t) = g(x,t) + v(t) \tag{2}$$

The feedback part g is primarily designed for the purpose of closed loop stability, and it can be determined independently from the feedforward control law v. Methods for designing stabilizing feedback for non-linear systems is very well known in the literature, such as using feedback stabilization [10]. It is therefore assumed that the feedback part is designed apriori to satisfy certain performance specifications in the time domain. For instance, in the control of multi-link robot manipulators, control laws commonly consist of two feedback parts. One is employed to cancel certain non-linear terms (if not all) from the original dynamics, and the other to stabilize the resulting dynamics using linear state feedback [1].

The feedforward is responsible of the point-to-point state transfer in finite time. It is proposed to satisfy the following time history:

$$\begin{cases} v(t) = G(t)\Gamma & \text{for} 0 \le t \le t_f \\ B\left[x(t),t\right]v(t) = -h\left[x(t_f),t\right] - B\left[x(t_f),t\right]g\left[x(t_f),t\right] & \text{for } t > t_f \end{cases} \tag{3}$$

where the design parameters G $(p \times n)$ and Γ $(n \times 1)$ must be properly selected to meet the finite time settling constraint of system (1-3). The need for correcting the tracking of the desired state at the final time t_f in the presence of uncertainties is behind the purpose for selecting the special form of the control law (3) for $t > t_f$. The feedforward part given by Eq. (3) resembles that developed for linear systems by Choura [5]. In particular, the finite time settling control law associated with the linear system described by

$$\dot{x} = A(t)x(t) + B(t)u_l(t)$$

is given by

$$u_l(t) = K(t)x(t) + v_l(t)$$

where

$$\begin{cases} v_l(t) = G(t)\Gamma & 0 \le t \le t_f \\ B(t)v_l(t) = -\left[A(t) + B(t)K(t)\right]x(t_f) & t > t_f \end{cases}$$

The non-constant matrix G and the vector Γ in Eq. (3) are determined from the following claim.

Claim

Let $Q\left[x(t), t\right]$ be an $n \times n$ matrix. The control law $(2-3)$ transfers $x(0)$ to $x(t_f)$ in finite time t_f if the constant vector Γ is determined from:

$$\begin{aligned} \Gamma &= M^{-1}\Big\{Q\left[x(t_f), t_f\right]x(t_f) - Q\left[x(0), 0\right]x(0) \\ &- \int_0^{t_f} \dot{Q}\left[x(\zeta), \zeta\right]x(\zeta) + Q\left[x(\zeta), \zeta\right]h\left[x(\zeta), \zeta\right]d\zeta \\ &- \int_0^{t_f} Q\left[x(\zeta), \zeta\right]B\left[x(\zeta), \zeta\right]\, g\left[x(\zeta), \zeta\right]d\zeta\Big\} \end{aligned} \quad (4)$$

where the matrices G and Q must be properly selected such that the $n \times n$ matrix

$$M = \int_0^{t_f} Q\left[x(\zeta), \zeta\right]B\left[x(\zeta), \zeta)\right]G(\zeta)\,d\zeta$$

is invertible

Proof

The multiplication of both sides of Eq. (1) by a matrix $Q\left[x(t), t)\right]$ with the use of Eqs. (2-3), and the integration of the resulting equation from 0 to t_f lead to

$$\begin{aligned} &\int_0^{t_f} Q\left[x(\zeta), \zeta\right]\dot{x}(\zeta)\,d\zeta \\ &= \int_0^{t_f} Q\left[x(\zeta), \zeta\right]\left\{h\left[x(\zeta), \zeta\right] + B\left[x(\zeta), \zeta\right]\, g\left[x(\zeta), \zeta\right]\right\}d\zeta \\ &+ \left\{\int_0^{t_f} Q\left[x(\zeta), \zeta\right]B\left[x(\zeta), \zeta\right]G(\zeta)\,d\zeta\right\}\Gamma \end{aligned} \quad (5)$$

Integration by parts with some arrangement of Eq. (5) yields Eq. (4).

Note that requiring the matrix M to be non-singular is the only condition stated in the aforementioned claim. Additional design conditions, if desired, such as the control effort, can be further imposed resulting in less freedom in the selection of G and Q. It can be observed that the singularity of matrix M depends on how the matrices G and Q are selected. The multiplication by a matrix Q is necessary, because for some cases the presence of G by itself in M is not sufficient to make the latter nonsingular, as it will be demonstrated in the examples considered in this paper. From Eq. (4), it should be noted that the feedforward part is determined from the feedback control law; i.e., one-way coupling exists between the feedback and the feedforward parts. The dependence of the feedforward control law on feedback is a key to robustness of the point-to-point control strategy. Such robustness has been analytically shown to exist in the case of linear systems [5].

If a non-linear system is operating in the neighborhood of a fixed or dynamic equilibrium, denoted by $\bar{x}(t)$, a possible choice for Q is

$$Q = \Phi(t, \tau)$$

where $\Phi(t, \tau)$ is the state transition matrix that satisfies

$$\begin{aligned} &\frac{\partial}{\partial t}\Phi(t, \tau) = A(t)\Phi(t, \tau) \\ &\Phi(\tau, \tau) = I \quad \text{(the } n \times n \text{ identity matrix)} \end{aligned} \quad (6)$$

and

$$A(t) = \frac{\partial}{\partial x}\left[f(x, t) + B(x, t)g(x, t)\right]\Big|_{x=\bar{x}(t)}$$

is the Jacobian with respect to the equilibrium. For instance, the above choice can be adopted for path planning of multi-link robots that are commanded to follow certain reference trajectories. In this case, since the transition matrix satisfies $\Phi^{-1}(t, \tau) = \Phi(\tau, t)$, it can be easily shown that the constant vector Γ reduces to

$$\begin{aligned} \Gamma &= M^{-1}\Big\{x(t_f) - \Phi(t_f, 0)x(0) \\ &- \int_0^{t_f} \Phi(t_f, \zeta)\left\{h\left[x(\zeta), \zeta\right] + B\left[x(\zeta), \zeta\right]\, g\left[x(\zeta), \zeta\right]\right\}d\zeta \\ &- \int_0^{t_f} \Phi(t_f, \zeta)A(\zeta)x(\zeta)\,d\zeta\Big\} \end{aligned} \quad (7)$$

with

$$M = \int_0^{t_f} \Phi(t_f, \zeta)B\left[x(\zeta), \zeta)\right]G(\zeta)\,d\zeta$$

where τ is set to t_f. For the finite time settling control of linear systems, the results obtained by Choura [5] can be easily drawn from Eq. (7).

Note that calculating the constant vector Γ would require the full knowledge of the state vector x. It is, therefore, necessary to investigate numerical methods for finding Γ_a, an approximate value for Γ, such that the Euclidian norm $\|\Gamma - \Gamma_a\| \le R$, where R is a small scalar number characterizing the error resulting from the approximation. It will be later shown that in the presence of feedback, the error R can be made small. An approximate Γ_a can be determined by noting that the precise point-to-point control dynamics given by

$$\dot{x} = h(x, t) + B(x, t)g(x, t) + B(x, t)G(t)\Gamma \quad 0 \le t \le t_f \quad (8)$$

where Γ is replaced with its expression in Eq. (4), is a boundary value problem in time that satisfies

$$\begin{aligned} x &= x(0) \quad \text{at } t = 0 \\ x &= x(t_f) \quad \text{at } t = t_f \end{aligned} \quad (9)$$

Therefore, classical methods, such as the Galerkin, collocation, least-square and finite element techniques, can be employed for the integration of Eqs. (8-9) from $t = 0$ to $t = t_f$ resulting in an approximate solution denoted by x_a. Γ_a is obtained by replacing x with x_a in Eq. (4). Next we present two methods for approximating the vector Γ, where the least square technique is illustrated.

Method 1

Let the n-dimensional error vector E be defined by

$$E(t) = \dot{x}_a - h(x_a, t) - B(x_a, t)g(x_a, t) - B(x_a, t)G(t)\Gamma_a \quad (10)$$

where $x_a(t)$ is an approximate vector of $x(t)$. Each element $x_{a_i}(t)$, $i = 1, 2, ..., n$, of $x_a(t)$ must satisfy the following time boundary conditions

$$x_{a_i}(0) = x_i(0) \quad \text{and} \quad x_{a_i}(t_f) = x_i(t_f) \quad i = 1, 2, ..., n \quad (11)$$

where $x_i(0)$ and $x_i(t_f)$ are the initial and final time conditions, respectively. Let the elements of the approximate state $x_a(t)$ be selected as

$$x_{a_i}(t) = F_{i0}(t) + \sum_{j=1}^{p} c_{ij}F_{ij}(t) \quad i = 1, 2, ..., n, \quad (12)$$

where F_{i0} and F_{ij} satisfy $F_{i0}(0) = x(0)$, $F_{i0}(t_f) = x(t_f)$, and $F_{ij}(0) = F_{ij}(t_f) = 0$. Note that the number of terms in the above summation can be selected distinct for every $i = 1, 2, ..., n$. If less approximation errors and less computation times are required, the selection of the approximate states should be compatible with the system dynamics. For instance, in vibration problems, the approximate states should include sinusoids and/or polynomials of high orders. For the purpose of error reduction, we require that the quantity

$$\int_0^{t_f} \|E(\zeta)\|^2 d\zeta = \int_0^{t_f} \left\{ \sum_{i=1}^{n} E_i^2(\zeta) \right\} d\zeta$$

be minimized with respect to the constants c_{ij}, $i = 1, 2, ..., n$ and $j = 1, 2, ..., p$. The minimization requirement leads to

$$\int_0^{t_f} \left\{ \sum_{i=1}^{n} E_i(\zeta) \frac{\partial E_i}{\partial c_{jk}}(\zeta) \right\} d\zeta = 0$$
$$j = 1, 2, ..., n \qquad k = 1, 2, ..., p \tag{13}$$

Eq. (13) consists of $n \times p$ non-linear algebraic equations with the same number of unknowns. Next, an example is given to illustrate the above method.

Example 1

Consider a harmonic oscillator with a non-linear stiffness described by the following time boundary value problem:

$$\ddot{x} + \pi^2(x - x^3) = u(t) \tag{14}$$
$$x(0) = x_0 \quad \dot{x}(0) = 0 \quad x(t_f) = 0 \quad \dot{x}(t_f) = 0$$

In this example, the control law is selected to be of the feedforward control type in order to show the validity of the proposed approximation in the absence of feedback. A combined control law will be considered in a later example. Let the feedforward control law be given by

$$u(t) = \Gamma_1 + \Gamma_2 t \tag{15}$$

In state space form, Eqs. (14-15) reduce to

$$\begin{bmatrix} \dot{x}_1 \\ \dot{x}_2 \end{bmatrix} = \begin{bmatrix} x_2 \\ -\pi^2(x_1 - x_1^3) \end{bmatrix} + \begin{bmatrix} 0 & 0 \\ 1 & t \end{bmatrix} \begin{bmatrix} \Gamma_1 \\ \Gamma_2 \end{bmatrix} \tag{16}$$

It is clear from Eq. (16) that solving for Γ_1 and Γ_2 after the integration of both sides of the equation from $t = 0$ to $t = t_f$ is not possible. Therefore, Eq. (16) is pre-multiplied by a matrix Q given by

$$Q = \begin{bmatrix} 1 & t \\ 0 & 1 \end{bmatrix}$$

It can be shown that the vector Γ in Eq. (4) is precisely determined from

$$\begin{bmatrix} \Gamma_1 \\ \Gamma_2 \end{bmatrix} = \begin{bmatrix} -\frac{6}{t_f^2} & \frac{4}{t_f} \\ \frac{12}{t_f^3} & -\frac{6}{t_f^2} \end{bmatrix}$$
$$\cdot \begin{bmatrix} -x_0 - \int_0^{t_f} \{2x_2(\zeta) - \pi^2\zeta(x_1(\zeta) - x_1^3(\zeta))\} d\zeta \\ \int_0^{t_f} \{\pi^2 (x_1(\zeta) - x_1^3(\zeta))\} d\zeta \end{bmatrix} \tag{17}$$

Let the approximate states be selected as

$$x_{a_1}(t) = \frac{t_f - t}{t_f} x_0 + \sum_{j=1}^{p} c_{1j} t^j (t_f - t)$$
$$x_{a_2}(t) = \sum_{j=1}^{p} c_{2j} t^j (t_f - t) \tag{18}$$

It should be verified that the time boundary conditions are satisfied with the above choice (18). The error vector E is therefore given by

$$E(t) = \begin{bmatrix} \dot{x}_{a_1} - x_{a_2} \\ \dot{x}_{a_2} + \pi^2(x_{a_1} - x_{a_1}^3) - \Gamma_1 - \Gamma_2 t \end{bmatrix} \tag{19}$$

A set of computer simulations are summarized in the following table

x_0	p	Γ_{a_1}	Γ_{a_2}	$x_1(t_f)$	$x_2(t_f)$
0.1	1	0.3967	0.1855	-0.0004	0.0354
0.1	2	0.4462	0.0921	0.0002	0.0164
0.5	1	1.0549	1.9124	-0.0334	0.1009
0.5	2	1.3828	1.7331	0.0231	0.0567

Table 1: Approximate design parameters using method 1

with the final time $t_f = 1$. In the above table, $x_1(t_f)$ and $x_2(t_f)$ are the actual values of the state variables at the final time. They are obtained via numerical integration of system (16) where Γ_1 and Γ_2 are replaced with Γ_{a_1} and Γ_{a_2}, respectively. The non-linear algebraic equations are solved using Newton's method, where in this example and the ones given later, our computer simulations give one solution set of real constants. If less errors are required, one should accommodate more terms in the series given in Eq. (18). Note that higher initial deflections x_0 would require a larger p for better approximations. This is expected because for small deflections the non-linear system possesses a linear behavior in which the approximation of the design parameters Γ_1 and Γ_2 yields a small error R.

Method 2

For large dimensions n, the solution of the n non-linear algebraic equations may become cumbersome. Instead, we propose an alternative method where the size of the error vector is truncated to a lower one. Assume that the dimension of E can be truncated to $q \leq n$. This implies that $n - q$ equations in $x_a(t)$ must hold for all times $t \geq 0$. We anticipate that this method yields more precise approximations as compared to the previous one. For more details of this method, the oscillator example is re-visited with the same time boundary conditions.

Example 2

Note that x_2 is the time derivative of x_1. Therefore, the first equation holds if $x_{a_2}(t) = \dot{x}_{a_1}(t)$. We choose the following approximate states as

$$x_{a_1}(t) = \left(2\frac{t^3}{t_f^3} - 3\frac{t^2}{t_f^2} + 1\right) x_0 + \sum_{j=1}^{p} c_{1j} t^{j+1} (t_f - t)^2$$
$$x_{a_2}(t) = \dot{x}_{a_1}(t) \tag{20}$$

It can be checked that all time boundary conditions are satisfied in the above equations. A scalar error must be minimized, and it is given by

$$E(t) = \dot{x}_{a_2} + \pi^2(x_{a_1} - x_{a_1}^3) - \Gamma_1 - \Gamma_2 t \tag{21}$$

Computer simulations showing the effectiveness of the second meth od are summarized in table 2.

x_0	p	Γ_{a_1}	Γ_{a_2}	$x_1(t_f)$	$x_2(t_f)$
0.5	1	1.3925	1.5045	0.0011	0.0102
0.5	2	1.4068	1.4580	-0.0005	0.0005

Table 2: Approximate design parameters using method 2

It is obvious that in this method, the use of one term of the series leads to less errors as compared to taking two terms in the first method.

Next the oscillator example is examined in the case where feedback and feedforward are combined to gain insight into the robustness behavior of the point-to-point control strategy proposed in this study. Here, linear state feedback can be employed for the purpose of closed loop stability. Therefore, the equation of motion of the oscillator becomes

$$\begin{bmatrix} \dot{x}_1 \\ \dot{x}_2 \end{bmatrix} = \begin{bmatrix} x_2 \\ -\pi^2(x_1 - x_1^3) - Kx_2 \end{bmatrix} + \begin{bmatrix} 0 & 0 \\ 1 & t \end{bmatrix} \begin{bmatrix} \Gamma_1 \\ \Gamma_2 \end{bmatrix} \qquad (22)$$

where K is a constant feedback gain. Using the same Q (see example 1), the precise point-to-point problem is stated as finding the vector Γ from

$$\begin{bmatrix} \Gamma_1 \\ \Gamma_2 \end{bmatrix} = \begin{bmatrix} -\frac{6}{t_f^2} & \frac{4}{t_f} \\ \frac{12}{t_f^3} & -\frac{6}{t_f^2} \end{bmatrix}$$
$$\begin{bmatrix} -x_0 - \int_0^{t_f} \{2x_2(\zeta) - K\zeta x_2(\zeta) \\ \quad -\pi^2\zeta(x_1(\zeta) - x_1^3(\zeta))\} \, d\zeta \\ \int_0^{t_f} \{\pi^2 (x_1(\zeta) - x_1^3(\zeta)) + Kx_2(\zeta)\} \, d\zeta \end{bmatrix} \qquad (23)$$

Simulations are shown in table 3 for $x_0 = 0.5$ and $K = 2$, where methods 1 and 2 are employed for the computation of Γ_{a_1} and Γ_{a_2}.

	p	Γ_{a_1}	Γ_{a_2}	$x_1(t_f)$	$x_2(t_f)$
Method 1	1	0.5199	1.9318	0.0762	0.0303
	2	0.1028	1.8794	0.0101	0.0210
Method 2	1	0.1002	1.7565	0.0007	0.0045
	2	0.1121	1.7231	0.000015	0.000054

Table 3: Approximate design parameters with feedback ($K = 2$)

With feedback ($K = 2$), the results from both methods are improved if table 3 is compared with tables 1 and 2. It should be reminded that the feedforward part is determined from the feedback part. Figures 1a-b show the approximate and actual responses using method 1. The responses using method 2 are shown in Figs. 2a-b. If more feedback is added ($K = 5$), the resulting approximations are listed in table 4.

	p	Γ_{a_1}	Γ_{a_2}	$x_1(t_f)$	$x_2(t_f)$
Method 1	1	0.5010	0.4512	0.1428	-0.1994
	2	-2.0924	2.9699	0.0098	-0.0569
	3	-2.6461	3.8113	-0.0018	-0.0019
Method 2	1	-2.5656	3.6830	-0.0004	-0.0072
	2	-2.6086	3.7751	0.000027	0.000141
	3	-2.6095	3.7764	0.000009	-0.000053

Table 4: Approximate design parameters with feedback ($K = 5$)

If tables 3 and 4 are compared, then it can be observed that an increase in feedback, while keeping the same number of terms p, may not yield a further reduction of the computation error with the aid of the first method. However, if an increase in feedback is accompanied with an increase in p, then it is possible to reduce the error as shown in table 4. Note that the use of the second method results in relatively unaffected approximations. It has been verified that solving the time boundary problem described by Eqs. (22-23) via numerical techniques other than the least square one had lead to the same observations.

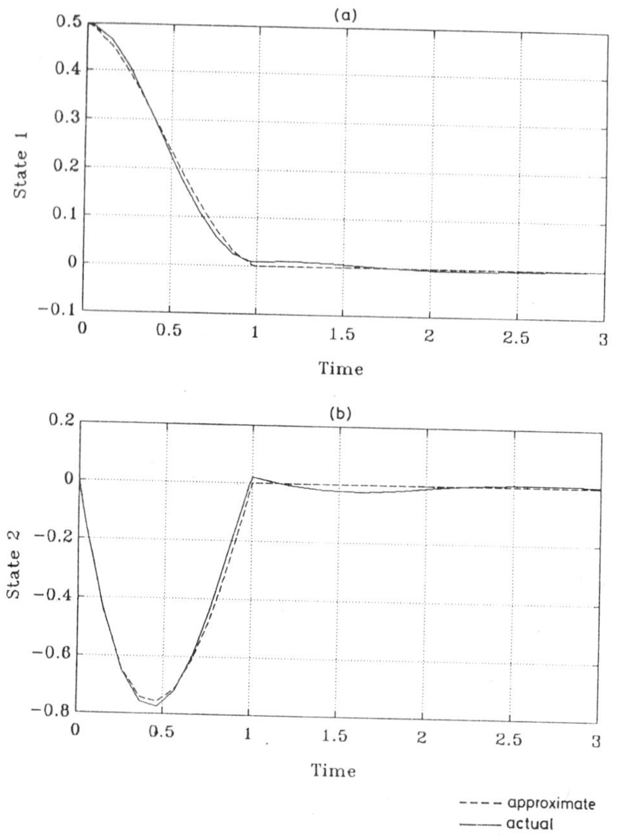

fig. 1: State response using method 1

3. Precise Point-to-Point Control Design for Systems Described by Second Order Differential Equations

Several systems, such as flexible structures, are described by a set of second order differential equations. Instead of rewriting these equations in state space form and then using Eq. (4) to compute the feedforward control law, an alternative formulation is sought. Flexible structures are usually described by a set of n second order differential equations in the form

$$M(q,\dot{q})\ddot{q} + k(q,\dot{q}) = F(q,\dot{q})u(t) \qquad (24)$$

where M is the mass matrix, k is the vector of non-linear terms representing centrifugal, coriolis and stiffness terms, q is the vector of generalized coordinates, u is the vector of generalized actuator forces, and F is a rectangular matrix whose rank is equal to the dimension of u. The goal is to find a control law u that transfers the initial conditions given by the pair $\{q(0),\ \dot{q}(0)\}$ to the final conditions $\{q(t_f),\ \dot{q}(t_f)\}$ in finite time t_f. Since, flexible structures described by Eq. (24) have nonsingular mass matrices [11], it can be written as:

$$\begin{aligned} \ddot{q} + h(q,\dot{q}) &= B(q,\dot{q})u(t) \qquad (25) \\ h(q,\dot{q}) &= M^{-1}(q,\dot{q})k(q,\dot{q}) \\ B(q,\dot{q}) &= M^{-1}(q,\dot{q})F(q,\dot{q}) \end{aligned}$$

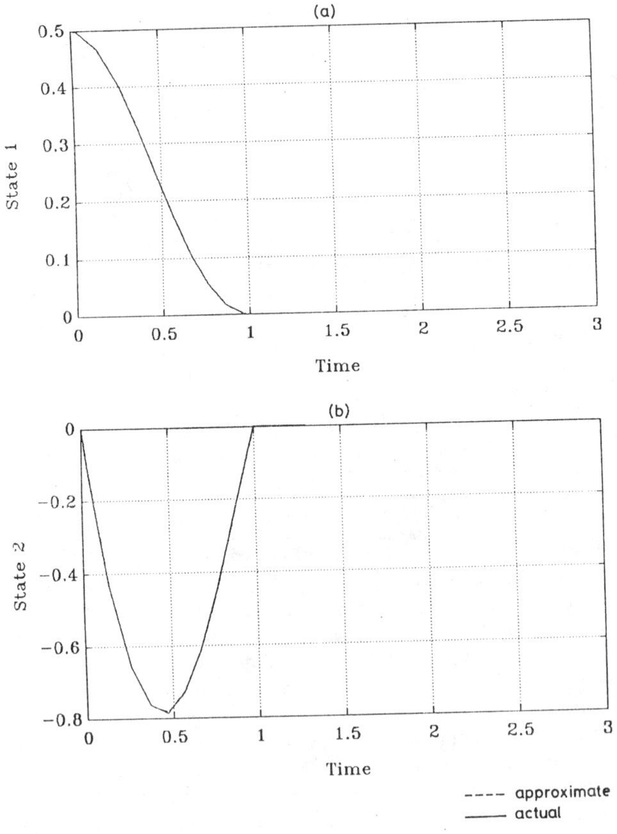

fig. 2: State response using method 2

A control law similar to that given in (2-3) is suggested as:

$$u(t) = g(q, \dot{q}) + v(t) \tag{26}$$

with

$$\begin{cases} v(t) = G(t)\Gamma \ \text{ for } \ 0 \leq t \leq t_f \\ B(q,\dot{q})v(t) = -h(q(t_f), \dot{q}(t_f)) \\ \qquad -B(q(t_f),\dot{q}(t_f))g(q(t_f),\dot{q}(t_f)) \ \text{ for } \ t > t_f \end{cases} \tag{27}$$

where the design parameters G and Γ are now $p \times 2n$ and $2n \times 1$, respectively. Here, instead of transforming (25-27) in state space form and using Eq. (4) for the construction of the feedforward control law, the vector Γ in Eq. (27) can be found from

$$\begin{aligned} \Gamma &= M^{-1}\{Q\left[q(t_f),\dot{q}(t_f)\right]\dot{q}(t_f) - Q\left[q(0),\dot{q}(0)\right]\dot{q}(0) \\ &- \dot{Q}\left[q(t_f),\dot{q}(t_f)\right]q(t_f) + \dot{Q}\left[q(0),\dot{q}(0)\right]q(0) \\ &+ \int_0^{t_f} \ddot{Q}\left[q(\zeta),\dot{q}(\zeta)\right]q(\zeta) + Q\left[q(\zeta),\dot{q}(\zeta)\right]h\left[q(\zeta),\dot{q}(\zeta)\right]d\zeta \\ &+ \int_0^{t_f} Q\left[q(\zeta),\dot{q}(\zeta)\right]B\left[q(\zeta),\dot{q}(\zeta)\right]g\left[q(\zeta),\dot{q}(\zeta)\right]d\zeta\Big\} \end{aligned} \tag{28}$$

$$M = \{Q\left[q(\zeta),\dot{q}(\zeta)\right]B\left[q(\zeta),\dot{q}(\zeta)\right]G(\zeta)\}\, d\zeta \tag{29}$$

where Q is a $2n \times n$ matrix. Similarly, the matrices G and Q in Eqs. (28-29) must be properly selected such that M is nonsingular. It can be verified that if the oscillator of example 1 is examined as a system described by a second order differential equation, and if Q is selected as

$$Q = \begin{bmatrix} t \\ 1 \end{bmatrix}$$

then the results in table 2 will be reproduced.

4. Conclusions

The precise point-to-point control problem for a class of nonlinear systems was investigated. This problem resulted in a time boundary value one in which the feedforward, the part responsible of the point-to-point transfer, is determined. Two methods were proposed for approximating the feedforward control part. In the first method, an error vector, whose size is equal to the dimension of the system, is minimized as its norm is integrated from zero to the final time. In the other method, the error vector is truncated to a lower-size one by a proper selection of the approximate state functions. The second method was shown to yield better approximations and less computation times. It was suggested that properly combining feedback with feedforward could result in a robust point-to-point control strategy. Simulations were presented to justify the viability of the proposed control strategy.

References

[1] H. Asada and J.J. E. Slotine, *Robot Analysis and Control,* John Wiley and Sons, Inc., 1986.
[2] D. M. Aspinwall, "Acceleration Profiles for Minimizing Residual Response," ASME Journal of Dynamic Systems, Measurement and Control, Vol. 102, No. 2, pp. 3-6, 1980.
[3] S. P. Bhat and D. K. Miu, "Precise Point-to-Point Positioning Control of Flexible Structures," ASME Journal of Dynamic Systems, Measurement and Control, Vol. 112, No. 4, pp. 667-674, 1990.
[4] S. P. Bhat and D. K. Miu, "Solutions to Point-to-Point Control Problems Using Laplace Transform Technique," ASME Journal of Dynamic Systems, Measurement and Control, Vol. 112, No. 4, pp. 667-674, 1991.
[5] S. Choura, "On the Design of Finite Time Settling Control for Linear Systems," ASME Journal of Dynamic Systems, Measurement and Control, Vol. 114, pp. 359-368, and presented at the American Control Conference, Chicago, June 24-26, 1992.
[6] S. Jayasuriya and S. Choura, "Active Quenching of a Set of Pre-Determined Vibratory Modes of a Beam by a Single Actuator," International Journal of Control, Vol. 51, No. 2, pp. 445-467, 1990.
[7] P. Meckl and W. Seering, "Active Damping in Three-Axis Robotic Manipulator," ASME Journal of Vibrations, Acoustics, Stress and Reliability in Design, Vol. 107, No. 1, pp. 38-46, 1985.
[8] P. Meckl and W. Seering, "Reducing Residual Vibration in Systems with Time-varying Resonances," Proc. International Conf. on Robotics and Automation, pp. 1690-1695, 1987.
[9] C. J. Swigert, "Shaped Torque Techniques," ASME Journal of Dynamic Systems, Measurement and Control, Vol. 3, No. 5, pp. 460-467, 1980.
[10] M. Vidyasagar, *Nonlinear Systems Analysis,* Prentice Hall, Inc., 1978.
[11] A. S. Yigit and A. G. Ulsoy, "Controller Design for Rigid-Flexible Multibody Systems," *Proc. 28th Conference on Decision and Control,* pp.665-673, 1989.

Proceedings of the
American Control Conference
San Francisco, California • June 199

Overview of Data Fusion Activities

David D. Freedman
Peter A. Smyton

The MITRE Corporation
202 Burlington Road
Bedford, MA 01730

Abstract

This paper will review the data fusion problem and some of the techniques used to solve various components of the problem, including registration, association/correlation, filtering, identification, threat assessment, and situational awareness/ resource allocation. The paper will describe how these techniques have been applied from the perspective of the military services. Specific applications will be discussed.

1.0 Introduction

Combat and combat support systems take advantage of a variety of data from an assortment of different sources (e.g., radar, infrared, television, acoustics, electronic intelligence data and communications) to locate and identify targets of interest. The data from these sources may be complimentary or at times contradictory. It is necessary to provide the system operators with a way to integrate this data together in a timely manner to provide an accurate estimate of a target's location, its identity, its intent and an appropriate course of action.

Interest in sensor data integration has grown tremendously in the last five years. The Department of Defense has placed it on its list of critical technologies. The Joint Directors of Laboratories (JDL) has created a Sensor Fusion Subpanel which has, among other achievements, established an annual symposium and published surveys concerning the current activity in data fusion technology and a data fusion lexicon aimed at establishing a common language and concepts in the data fusion community. Due to increased emphasis on data fusion by the Department of Defense, companies, both small businesses and large defense contractors, are investing millions of dollars in research money to develop fusion algorithms. Universities have expressed interest in developing laboratory environments for data fusion research.

There are a number of reasons for this interest. First and foremost, the political and economic world climate, and the manner in which military operations are conducted, are changing dramatically. In particular, the threat and how it is countered in evolving. Low observable "stealthy" targets (e.g., highly maneuverable aircraft, "quiet" submarines, etc.) are detectable by traditional primary sensors only occasionally. Further, with sales of military and weapon systems to foreign customers and their subsequent shifting affiliations, identifying target classification (e.g., friend or hostile) has become increasingly difficult. In response to this evolving threat, new sensor types, with diverse update rates, dimensionality of measurement state, quality, and timeliness, have been developed to augment the primary sensors in order to improve detectability of targets using a multispectral sensor suite.

In addition to the threat, the downsizing of the military requires existing systems to become more effective and more interoperable, and to minimize upgrades; this implies the need to find new ways to share and merge data.

2.0 Data Fusion Techniques

Data fusion has been defined by the JDL to be "a process dealing with the association, correlation, and combination of data and information from single and multiple sources to achieve refined position and identity estimates and complete and timely assessments of situation and threats as well as their significance."[4] A functional model of the data fusion process has been developed by the Data Fusion Subpanel of the JDL. The data fusion process has been broken down into three levels. Level 1 processing includes registration, association and correlation, filtering or tracking, and identification. Level 2 processing is situation assessment and level 3 processing is threat assessment. It is also possible to consider a fourth level of processing which would deal with collection management. This would include issues such as sensor tasking/cueing, task prioritization, sensor reliability/performance monitoring, scheduling and resource allocation. This fourth level of processing is beyond the scope of the paper and is not discussed further. In addition to the four levels of processing there are additional support functions that are required by a data fusion system. These include database management, a human-computer interface between the human operator and the processor, and a set of measures to evaluate the performance of data fusion algorithms. The functional model of the data fusion process is illustrated in figure 1.

2.1 Registration

The registration problem in data fusion occurs when there are multiple sensors that are not colocated. For example, multiple radars may track or report on the same target, and provide the track data to a central processing site for data fusion. This can be illustrated with two radars at different locations detecting the same target. Both radars detect the target in range and azimuth. Each radar will track the target and generate state estimates in a Cartesian coordinate system. Registration is the process of estimating the bias errors between the two radar sites based on the sensor measurements or track estimates. The central processor needs to first determine if the two observations come from the same target (correlation) and, second, estimate the bias. The first problem of correlation will be discussed later. The second problem is typically be solved using least squares estimation [3].

2.2 Association/Correlation

Association and correlation, considered to be the most challenging problem in data fusion, is the process of deciding which objects (sensor measurements or tracks) from separate sources represent the same entity. Data association is performed at three levels. The first level, measurement to measurement association, typically is used to perform single sensor or single system track initiation. The second level, measurement to track association, is used as part of the track maintenance process (e.g., track update). The third level, track to track association, is used as part of a multisensor fusion process in which each sensor or system performs independent tracking. This section will focus on the measurement to track and track to track association problem. There are four common categories of techniques to solve the association problem: sequential nearest neighbor, global nearest neighbor, joint probabilistic data association (JPDA) and multiple hypothesis; there are a myriad of subtle and significant differences within each category that result in a countless variety of techniques. In addition to the traditional techniques, research is being performed to investigate the design of data fusion algorithms in a distributed sensor network where the decision rules of the individual sensors are known [7].

Association techniques rely on metrics to establish report and track pairings. The metrics that are typically used include Euclidean, weighted Euclidean, Mahalanobis (or chi-square), Bhattacharya, likelihood and log likelihood. For example, the Euclidean distance metric is given by

$$\left[\left(x_r - \hat{x}_s\right)^2 + \left(y_r - \hat{y}_s\right)^2\right]^{1/2} \leq G_r$$

where x_r, y_r represent the sensor measurement in a Cartesian coordinate system, $\hat{x}_s$, $\hat{y}_s$ represent an estimate of the position of a track, and G_r represents a threshold for acceptable pairings.

In a dense environment the association and correlation process can be computationally intensive and it is necessary to reduce the number of report to track pairings that exist. Ad hoc approaches such as gating and clustering are typically used. For gating either a gross rectangular or elliptical gate around a report is created and only those tracks that are within the gate will be considered for correlation. Typically the association algorithm will take into account heuristics such as the possible motion of the maneuver and maneuver windows may be built around each track and the "best" report that is within the smallest window will be used to update the track. If no such pairing exists the report will be compared against the successively larger windows. If this is satisfied the report will be used to update the track. The model used in the Kalman filter described below will be changed to reflect a maneuver. Clustering techniques group reports and tracks together that do not interact with any other group of reports and tracks.

Nearest neighbor association techniques select at most one report from each sensor and one track for correlation. Sequential nearest neighbor is a sub-optimal technique that processes each track (or report) one at a time and the closest report to the track is picked (closest is the one that is closest in the metric used). Global nearest neighbor association results in an optimal solution to the association problem. The problem reduces to a one-to-one integer programming problem. Techniques based upon the Hungarian method such as Munkres algorithm have been used to generate an optimal one-to-one pairing of reports to tracks. The report is then used to update the track.

JPDA uses all the reports to update the track. The process uses weights or association probabilities based upon the false alarm rate, the probability of detection of the reporting sensor, the gate size and filter residuals to weight the reports associating with the track to update the track.

Multiple hypothesis tracking (MHT) techniques will maintain several candidate hypotheses to represent possible report to track correlations. The algorithm will select at most one hypothesis (with the highest confidence) to be used or displayed to an operator. As additional measurements are received each hypothesis will be modified to reflect the new information. If the confidence level of the hypothesis falls below a threshold level and an alternative hypothesis has a confidence level above a set threshold the new hypothesis will be used. MHT is computationally intensive and extensive work has been done to reduce the number of candidate hypotheses that are maintained. Limits can be placed on the number of hypotheses. Track pruning techniques use heuristics concerning the kinematic state of the target or the staleness of the data to limit the number of hypotheses. Other techniques include retaining only the M highest confidence track branches or retaining only those exceeding a certain threshold. N scan memory filters can also be used to merge two hypotheses with the same track history over N scans.

2.3 Filtering

Filtering or tracking is the process that transforms sensor measurements into updated states and covariances for entity tracks. The dominent technique to perform filtering is the Kalman filter although α–β look-up tables using a fixed set of gains to approximate the Kalman filter gains are frequently used when processing capabilities limited. A target is typically modeled as a linear Gauss Markov process with equations

$$x^{k+1} = \Phi x^k + q^k + f^{k+1}$$

where x^k is the state of the target at time k, Φ is the state transition matrix, q^k is a zero mean, white Gaussian process noise with covariance Q, and f^{k+1} is a known deterministic input. The basic Kalman filter equations are

$$\hat{x}_s^k = \hat{x}_p^k + K\left(y^k - H\hat{x}_p^k\right)$$

$$K = P_p^k H^T \left(H P_p^k H^T + R\right)^{-1}$$

$$P^k = (I - KH) P_p^k$$

$$\hat{x}_p^{k+1} = \Phi \hat{x}_s^k + f^{k+1}$$

$$P_p^k = \Phi P^k \Phi^T + Q$$

where $\hat{x}_s^k$ is the estimated target state at time interval k, $\hat{x}_p^k$ is the predicted target state at the time interval k, K is the kalman gain matrix, y^k is the measurement at time interval k, H is the measurement matrix, P^k is the estimate of the covariance matrix at time k, P_p^k is the predicted covariance matrix at time k, and R is the covariance matrix of the measurement noise.

Significant research has been conducted to improve the Kalman filter's performance which has resulted in many different adaptive and state augmentation techniques. A variety of alternative state coordinates have been used including two and three dimensional cartesian, polar, spherical and modified spherical. In some environments the Kalman filter is required to react to target maneuvers (e.g., maneuvering aircraft). Research has been conducted into using parallel Kalman filters with multiple motion models and acceleration input estimation for maneuver response.

2.4 Identification

Identification fusion or classification is the process by which some level of identity of an entity is established, either as a member of a class (e.g., friendly, hostile, neutral), a type within a class (e.g., platform type), or a specific unit within a type (e.g., tail number). The first step is the identification problem is to identify features that can be used to identify the target (e.g., shape and size from a high resolution radar or infrared sensor, emitters from an ESM sensors, sonar detections, etc.). The second step of the identification problem is typically a decision theoretic problem. Techniques to perform identification fall into two categories, Bayesian and non Bayesian. The data that may be used in the identification process may include attribute data generated by a hard decision, with no confidence level or a soft decision with an associated confidence level.

Bayesian estimation uses Bayes rule, give by

$$P(H_i|Z) = \frac{P(Z|H_i)\,P(H_i)}{\sum_i P(Z|H_i)\,P(H_i)}$$

where $P(H_i|Z)$ is the a posteriori probability of hypothesis H_i being true given the observation Z, $P(H_i)$ is the a priori probability of hypothesis H_i being true and $P(Z|H_i)$ is the probability of observing Z giving H_i. The hypothesis with the highest a posteriori probability may be chosen provided a set threshold is exceeded.

An example of a non Bayesian identification technique is the Dempster-Shafer method based on Dempster's rule of combination. This method uses probability intervals and uncertainty to determine the likelihood of a proposition. The basic issue is how belief, derived from evidence, is distributed over propositions. A sensor assigns a probability mass or measure of belief $m(A_i)$ to each proposition A_i based upon evidence. Dempster's rule of combination is then used to combine the probability masses from independent sources

$$m(U_l) = \frac{\sum_{A_i B_j = U_l} m_1(A_i)\, m_2(B_j)}{\left(1 - \sum_{A_j B_n = \phi} m_1(A_k)\, m_2(B_n)\right)}$$

where U_l is the proposition defined by the combination of hypothesis A_i and B_j.

Simple rule based techniques have also been used to establish identity. For example if a particular sensor attribute is consistently associated with a track on N successive scans then the track is given that attribute; if M out of N attributes from correlated sensor reports agree then assign the track an ID based on the attributes. Other systems may perform a simple table look-up to establish ID.

2.5 Situational Awareness/Resource Allocation/Threat Assessment

Situation assessment is the process by which the distribution of fixed and tracked entities are associated with environmental, doctrine and performance data to produce estimates of the situation elements and the behavioral activities of these targets. Threat assessment is a multiperspective assessment of the distribution of fixed and track entities which results in estimating items such as enemy lethality and the appropriate course of action. The above problems are more complex than the level 1 data fusion problem. Techniques typically employ extensive databases with information such as behavioral data about different targets, information about flight corridors and flight plans, and intelligence information on enemy forces. Traditional estimation techniques (Bayesian and Dempster-Shafer) or correlation techniques that use pre-defined templates may be used. Artificial intelligence techniques that require a blackboard architecture have been studied [8]. New areas of research such as abductive technology which allows a system to learn from a set of general principles under uncertainty are being applied to electronic combat to attain estimates of lethality and intent [6].

3.0 Applications

The applications of data fusion are as diverse as the military inventory. They include areas such as tactical air defense, antisubmarine warfare, strategic defense, counter narcotics, intelligence, and air traffic control. For example, in tactical air defense, operators need information (position and identification) for broad area surveillance such as provided by sensors on board a C^3I platform whereas an operator on board a tactical fighter needs such information for quick reaction decisions. In the area of missile defense, data fusion is used to track, identify and help intercept reentry vehicles (RVs), decoys, post-boost vehicles (PBVs) and debris during boost, post-boost, midcourse and terminal phases of a ballistic missile's trajectory. Data fusion is also being applied in the commercial arena in such fields as robotics, automobile, and remote sensing.

4.0 Summary

In general, data fusion continues to be an emerging field rich in technological possibilities. Techniques exist in abundance, but the main thrust remains in the R&D area trying to match technique to specific applications. Typical "real world" challenges today include (1) tuning the algorithms for particular sensor/target environments to satisfy system-specific requirements, with emphasis on achieving adequate performance in stressing environments, (2) allocating tasks between the user and the computer, and (3) integrating data fusion concepts into existing architectures.

The future of data fusion is uncertain--it is imperative that technique emerge soon in fielded systems in increasing number to begin to realize the promise that fusion holds. Without this emergence, the credibility that fusion can address future problems will disappear and trhere will be no acceptance, let alone reliance, of fusion by the user community. As a result, a continued coalescing of the field, and continued use of academia as an area where research and training can occur, is needed. Data fusion is also necessary for commercial applications and a new architecture is required to support industrial requirements.

References

1. S. Blackman, Multiple Target Tracking with Radar Applications, Artech House, 1986.

2. Y. Bar-Shalom, Multitarget-Multisensor Tracking: Advanced Applications, Artech House, 1990.

3. E. Dela Cruz, A. Alovani, T. Rice and W. Blair, "Sensor Registration in Multisensor Systems", SPIE Vol. 1698 Signal and Data Processing of Small Targets, 1992.

4. F. White, Data Fusion Lexicon, Data Fusion Subpanel of Joint Directors of Laboratories, 1991.

5. D. Hall, Mathematical Techniques in Multisensor Data Fusion, Artech House, 1992.

6. G. Montgomery, P. Hess, J. Hwang, "Abductive Networks Applied to Electronic Combat", SPIE Application of Artificial Neural Networks, 1990

7. Z. Chair, and P. K. Varshney, "On Hypothesis Testing in Distributed Sensor Networks", RADC-TR-87-180, Rome Air Development Center, Griffiss AFB, NY, November 1987

8. D. Buede, J. Martin, and J. Sipos "Comparison of Bayesian and Dempster-Shafer Fusion", 1989 Tri-Service Data Fusion Symposium, John Hopkins Applied Physics Laboratory, Laurel, MD, June 1987

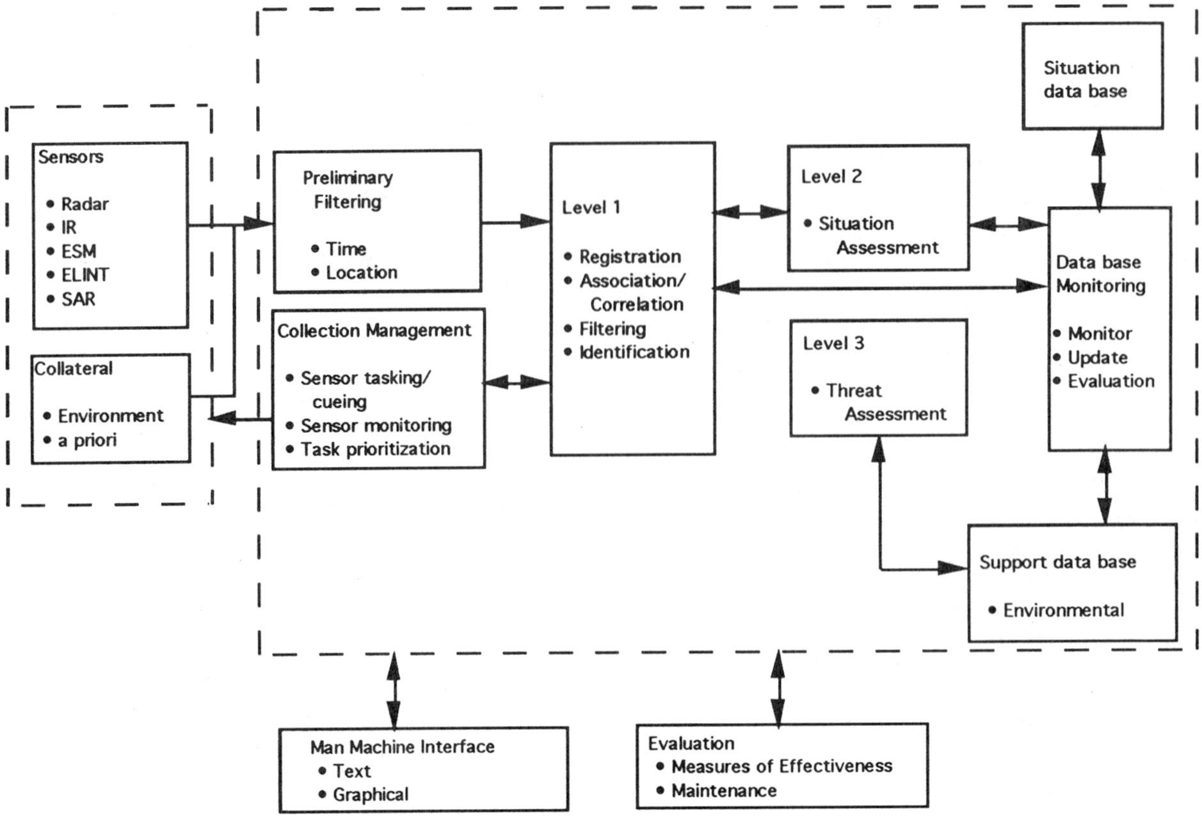

Figure 1: Data Fusion Processing Model [5]

Proceedings of the
American Control Conference
San Francisco, California • June 1993

Multisensor Fusion Algorithms for Tracking

Sean D. O'Neil and Lucy Y. Pao *

Signal Processing Department
The MITRE Corporation
Bedford, Massachusetts 01730

Abstract

In this paper we extend a multitarget tracking algorithm for use in multisensor tracking situations. The algorithm we consider is Joint Probabilistic Data Association (JPDA). JPDA is extended to handle an arbitrary number of sensors under the assumption that the sensor measurement errors are independent across sensors. We also show how filtering can be handled in multisensor JPDA (MSJPDA) without leading to an exponential increase in filtering complexity. Simulation results are presented comparing the performance of the MSJPDA with another multisensor fusion algorithm and with the single-sensor JPDA algorithm.

1 Introduction

Because of the limitations of using a single sensor for tracking (such as accuracy, resolution, measurement space, sensitivity, robustness), many tracking systems are being designed with multiple sensors. These multiple sensors provide large amounts of data with which to detect, track, and identify targets of interest. However, current tracking algorithms usually (a) use information from only one sensor for detection and tracking and use information from the other sensors only for coarse identification, or (b) combine information from the multiple sensors in an *ad hoc* manner. In an effort to upgrade the processing capabilities of trackers to bring them closer to their sensing capabilities, more sophisticated *multisensor* fusion algorithms are now being developed [2, 6, 7, 8, 10, 11].

Issues that need to be addressed in multisensor fusion include registration and estimation and data association. Registration problems may arise when the reference frames for the different sensors are inconsistent, and this can lead to a severe degradation in performance [2]. These issues are not addressed here. In this paper, we address the estimation and data association process, where the different measurement types must be integrated into one common estimation process, and consistent probability metrics must be established for all sensor types.

The paper is organized as follows. In section 2, we review the single-sensor JPDA algorithm and then extend the algorithm to the multisensor MSJPDA in section 3. Filtering in MSJPDA is discussed in section 4. Simulation results comparing the MSJPDA with a multiple-sensor nearest neighbor (NN) algorithm and with the single-sensor JPDA algorithm are presented in section 5. Finally, concluding remarks are given in section 6.

*This work was performed under MITRE's Mission Oriented Investigation and Experimentation Program, Air Force contract F19628-89-C-0001.

2 Single-Sensor JPDA

Consider the problem of tracking T targets in clutter. At discrete time intervals, observations are made, each observation consisting of several measurements (also called reports or returns). Some of the measurements arise from targets, and some arise from clutter; some targets may not yield any measurement at all in a particular observation.

Let $\mathbf{x}^t(k)$ $(1 \leq t \leq T)$ denote the state vectors of each target t at the time of the kth measurement. Suppose the target dynamics are determined by known matrices $\mathbf{F}^t$ and $\mathbf{G}^t$ and random noise vectors $\mathbf{w}^t(k)$ as follows:

$$\mathbf{x}^t(k+1) = \mathbf{F}^t(k)\mathbf{x}^t(k) + \mathbf{G}^t(k)\mathbf{w}^t(k), \tag{1}$$

where $t = 1, \ldots, T$. The noise vectors $\mathbf{w}^t(k)$ are stochastically independent Gaussian random variables with zero mean and known covariance matrices.

Let m_k denote the number of validated (or gated) returns [1] at time k. The measurements are determined by

$$\mathbf{z}_l(k) = \mathbf{H}(k)\mathbf{x}^t(k) + \mathbf{v}^t(k), \tag{2}$$

where $t = 1, \ldots, T$, and $l = 1, \ldots, m_k$. The $\mathbf{H}(k)$ matrix is known, each $\mathbf{v}^t(k)$ is a zero-mean Gaussian noise vector uncorrelated with all other noise vectors, and the covariance matrices of the noise vectors $\mathbf{v}^t(k)$ are known. Let $\mathcal{Z}(k) = (\mathbf{z}_1(k), \ldots, \mathbf{z}_{m_k}(k))$ denote the observation at time k, and let $\mathcal{Z}^k = (\mathcal{Z}(1), \ldots, \mathcal{Z}(k))$ denote the sequence of the first k observations.

In any time interval, a target can give rise to at most one measurement from the sensor. Further, each measurement can originate from at most one target. Finally, we assume that false measurements (*i.e.*, clutter) are uniformly distributed throughout the surveillance region.

Based on these assumptions, the goal of JPDA is to associate the targets with the measurements on the basis of current estimates of target states (position, velocity, *etc.*), and to update those estimates. The actual association of targets to returns being unknown, the conditional estimate is determined by taking a weighted average over all possible associations. An association for the kth observation is a mapping

$$a : \{1, \ldots, T\} \rightarrow \{0, 1, \ldots, m_k\}$$

that associates with each t the number $a(t)$ of the return associated with it, or $a(t) = 0$ if no return is associated with the tth target. For $t_1 \neq t_2$, the associated returns $a(t_1)$ and $a(t_2)$ are equal if and only if both are zero.

Let $\Theta_a(k)$ denote the event that a is the correct association for the kth observation. For $1 \leq t \leq T$ and $0 \leq l \leq m_k$, let $\theta_l^t(k)$ denote the event that $a(t) = l$ for the correct association $a(t)$ for the kth observation. The event $\theta_l^t(k)$ is a disjoint union of events $\Theta_a(k)$:

$$\theta_l^t(k) = \biguplus_{a:a(t)=l} \Theta_a(k), \tag{3}$$

where the union is over all mappings a associating measurement l to target t. Let $\hat{\mathbf{x}}_l^t(k|k)$ denote the estimate of $\mathbf{x}^t(k)$ given by the Kalman filter on the basis of the previous estimate and the association of the tth target with the lth return. The conditional estimate $\hat{\mathbf{x}}^t(k|k)$ for $\mathbf{x}^t(k)$ given $\mathcal{Z}^k$ is [1, 5]

$$\hat{\mathbf{x}}^t(k|k) = \sum_{l=0}^{m_k} \beta_l^t(k) \hat{\mathbf{x}}_l^t(k|k), \tag{4}$$

where

$$\beta_l^t(k) = \sum_{a:a(t)=l} P(\Theta_a(k)|\mathcal{Z}^k) \tag{5}$$

is the conditional probability of the event $\theta_l^t(k)$ given $\mathcal{Z}^k$. The set of probabilities $\beta_l^t(k)$ can be computed efficiently as the permanents of a set of submatrices [9].

3 Extension to Multiple Sensors

In this section, we extend the single-sensor JPDA algorithm described in the previous section to a Multisensor JPDA (MSJPDA) algorithm. Suppose there are N_s sensors. Let $m_{k_i}, i = 1, 2, \ldots, N_s$, be the number of validated reports from each sensor i at time k. The measurements are now determined by

$$\mathbf{z}_l^i(k) = \mathbf{H}_i(k)\mathbf{x}^t(k) + \mathbf{v}_i^t(k), \tag{6}$$

where $t = 1, \ldots, T$, $i = 1, \ldots, N_s$, and $l = 1, \ldots, m_{k_i}$. The measurement $\mathbf{z}_l^i(k)$ is interpreted as the lth measurement from the ith sensor at time k. Generalizing from the single-sensor case, the $\mathbf{H}_i(k)$ matrices are known, and $\mathbf{v}_i^t(k)$ are stochastically independent zero-mean Gaussian noise vectors with known covariance matrices. The observation at time k is now

$$\mathcal{Z}(k) = \Big(\mathbf{z}_1^1(k), \ldots, \mathbf{z}_{m_{k_1}}^1(k), \mathbf{z}_1^2(k), \ldots, \mathbf{z}_{m_{k_2}}^2(k), \ldots, \mathbf{z}_1^{N_s}, \ldots, \mathbf{z}_{m_{k_{N_s}}}^{N_s}(k)\Big).$$

We assume that measurement errors due to measurements from one sensor are independent of those from other sensors.

Let

$$a_{ms} : \{1, \ldots, T\} \rightarrow \{\{0, 1, \ldots, m_{k_1}\}, \{0, 1, \ldots, m_{k_2}\}, \ldots \{0, 1, \ldots, m_{k_{N_s}}\}\}$$

be the mapping that associates each target t with a set of N_s numbers (one for each sensor) $a_{ms}(t)$ of returns. The return number 0 for a sensor indicates the possibility of no return from that sensor being associated with the tth target. For each mapping a_{ms}, there is a set of N_s mappings $a_i : \{1, \ldots, T\} \rightarrow \{0, 1, \ldots, m_{k_i}\}$ that associate return $a_i(t)$ from sensor i with each target t.

For each association a_{ms}, let $\Theta_{a_{ms}}(k)$ and each $\Theta_{a_i}(k)$ denote the events that a_{ms} and each a_i, respectively, are the correct associations for the kth observation. For $1 \leq t \leq T$ and $\mathcal{L} = (l_1, l_2, \ldots, l_{N_s})$ where $0 \leq l_1 \leq m_{k_1}, \ldots, 0 \leq l_{N_s} \leq m_{k_{N_s}}$, let $\theta_{\mathcal{L}}^t(k)$ denote the event that $a_{ms}(t) = \mathcal{L}$ for the correct association a_{ms} for the kth observation. For $1 \leq t \leq T$, $1 \leq i \leq N_s$, and $0 \leq l \leq m_{k_i}$, let $\theta_{l,i}^t(k)$ indicate the event that $a_i(t) = l$ for the correct association a_i of sensor i for the kth observation. The event $\theta_{\mathcal{L}}^t(k)$ is a disjoint union of events $\Theta_{a_{ms}}(k)$:

$$\theta_{\mathcal{L}}^t(k) = \biguplus_{a_{ms}:a_{ms}(t)=\mathcal{L}} \Theta_{a_{ms}}(k), \tag{7}$$

and $\theta_{l,i}^t(k)$ is a disjoint union of events $\Theta_{a_i}(k)$:

$$\theta_{l,i}^t(k) = \biguplus_{a_i:a_i(t)=l} \Theta_{a_i}(k). \tag{8}$$

Let $\beta_{\mathcal{L}}^t(k)$ denote the conditional probability of $\theta_{\mathcal{L}}^t(k)$ given $\mathcal{Z}^k$, and let $\beta_{l,i}^t(k)$ denote the conditional probability of the event $\theta_{l,i}^t(k)$ given $\mathcal{Z}^k$. The probability $\beta_{l,i}^t(k) = P(\theta_{l,i}^t(k)|\mathcal{Z}^k)$ is just the single-sensor JPDA event probability that return l of sensor i is associated with target t.

The MSJPDA event probability that we seek, $\beta^t_{\mathcal{L}}(k)$, is given by

$$\begin{aligned}\beta^t_{\mathcal{L}}(k) &= P(\theta^t_{\mathcal{L}}(k)|\mathcal{Z}^k) \\ &= \sum_{a_{ms}:a_{ms}(t)=\mathcal{L}} P(\Theta_{a_{ms}}(k)|\mathcal{Z}^k). \end{aligned} \quad (9)$$

Assuming that measurement errors are independent across sensors,

$$P(\Theta_{a_{ms}}(k)|\mathcal{Z}^k) = \prod_{i=1}^{N_s} P(\Theta_{a_i}(k)|\mathcal{Z}^k). \quad (10)$$

Substituting (10) into (9) and performing some manipulations yield

$$\begin{aligned}\beta^t_{\mathcal{L}}(k) &= \sum_{a_{ms}:a_{ms}(t)=\mathcal{L}} \prod_{i=1}^{N_s} P(\Theta_{a_i}(k)|\mathcal{Z}^k) \\ &= \sum_{a_1:a_1(t)=l_1,\ldots,a_{N_s}:a_{N_s}(t)=l_{N_s}} \prod_{i=1}^{N_s} P(\Theta_{a_i}(k)|\mathcal{Z}^k) \\ &= \prod_{i=1}^{N_s} \sum_{a_i:a_i(t)=l_i} P(\Theta_{a_i}(k)|\mathcal{Z}^k) \\ &= \prod_{i=1}^{N_s} P(\theta^t_{l_i,i}(k)|\mathcal{Z}^k) \\ &= \prod_{i=1}^{N_s} \beta^t_{l_i,i}(k). \end{aligned} \quad (11)$$

Hence, we see that the multisensor event probability $\beta^t_{\mathcal{L}}(k)$ is just the product of the single-sensor JPDA event probabilities $\beta^t_{l_i,i}(k)$.

4 Multisensor Filtering

The conditional estimate for the MSJPDA algorithm is given by

$$\begin{aligned}\hat{\mathbf{x}}^t(k|k) &= \sum_{\mathcal{L}} \beta^t_{\mathcal{L}}(k)\hat{\mathbf{x}}^t_{\mathcal{L}}(k|k) \\ &= \sum_{\mathcal{L}} \prod_{i=1}^{N_s} \beta^t_{l_i,i}(k)\hat{\mathbf{x}}^t_{\mathcal{L}}(k|k), \end{aligned} \quad (12)$$

where equation (11) has been used, and the sums are over all possible sets of associations $\mathcal{L}$ with target t. The estimate $\hat{\mathbf{x}}^t_{\mathcal{L}}(k|k)$ of $\mathbf{x}^t(k)$ is based on the prediction $\hat{\mathbf{x}}^t(k|k-1)$ and the association of the tth target with the set of $\mathcal{L}$ returns from the N_s sensors:

$$\begin{aligned}\hat{\mathbf{x}}^t_{\mathcal{L}}(k|k) &= \hat{\mathbf{x}}^t(k|k-1) \\ &\quad + \sum_{i=1}^{N_s} \mathbf{K}_i(k)\left[z^i_{l_i}(k) - \mathbf{H}_i(k)\hat{\mathbf{x}}^t(k|k-1)\right], \end{aligned} \quad (13)$$

where $\hat{\mathbf{x}}^t(k|k-1) = \mathbf{F}^t(k)\hat{\mathbf{x}}^t(k-1|k-1)$ is the prediction of $\mathbf{x}^t(k)$ and $\mathbf{K}_i$ is the Kalman gain for measurements from the ith sensor.

At first glance it seems that equation (12) with (13) substituted in for $\hat{\mathbf{x}}^t_{\mathcal{L}}(k|k)$ implies that filtering must be performed for each of the $\prod_{i=1}^{N_s} m_{k_i}$ possible multisensor mappings for a given target, which implies an exponential increase in computational burden as a function of the number of sensors. However, it can be shown that the equations (12)-(13) can be implemented as a series of N_s nested single-sensor filterings, reducing the filtering complexity to a linear function of the number of sensors, N_s.

If we stack the Kalman gains $\mathbf{K}_i(k)$, measurements $\mathbf{z}^i_{l_i}(k)$, and measurement transformation matrices $\mathbf{H}_i(k)$ as follows:

$$\begin{aligned}\mathbf{K}(k) &= [\mathbf{K}_1(k)\ldots\mathbf{K}_{N_s}(k)], \\ \mathbf{H}(k) &= \left[\mathbf{H}_1^T(k)\ldots\mathbf{H}_{N_s}^T(k)\right]^T, \\ \mathbf{Z}_{\mathcal{L}}(k) &= \left[\left(\mathbf{z}^1_{l_1}\right)^T(k)\ldots\left(\mathbf{z}^{N_s}_{l_{N_s}}\right)^T(k)\right]^T, \end{aligned}$$

then (13) can be written as

$$\hat{\mathbf{x}}^t_{\mathcal{L}}(k|k) = \hat{\mathbf{x}}^t(k|k-1) + \mathbf{K}(k)\left[\mathbf{Z}_{\mathcal{L}}(k) - \mathbf{H}(k)\hat{\mathbf{x}}^t(k|k-1)\right]. \quad (14)$$

Substituting (14) into (12) gives

$$\begin{aligned}\hat{\mathbf{x}}^t(k|k) &= \sum_{\mathcal{L}} \beta^t_{\mathcal{L}}(k)\Big\{\hat{\mathbf{x}}^t(k|k-1) \\ &\quad + \mathbf{K}(k)\left[\mathbf{Z}_{\mathcal{L}}(k) - \mathbf{H}(k)\hat{\mathbf{x}}^t(k|k-1)\right]\Big\} \\ &= \hat{\mathbf{x}}^t(k|k-1) + \sum_{\mathcal{L}} \beta^t_{\mathcal{L}}(k)\mathbf{K}(k)\mathbf{Z}_{\mathcal{L}}(k) \\ &\quad - \mathbf{K}(k)\mathbf{H}(k)\hat{\mathbf{x}}^t(k|k-1), \end{aligned} \quad (15)$$

where the fact that $\sum_{\mathcal{L}} \beta^t_{\mathcal{L}}(k) = 1$ has been used in the first and third terms. The second term of (15) can be rewritten as

$$\begin{aligned}&\sum_{\mathcal{L}} \beta^t_{\mathcal{L}}(k)\mathbf{K}(k)\mathbf{Z}_{\mathcal{L}}(k) \\ &= \mathbf{K}(k)\sum_{\mathcal{L}} \beta^t_{\mathcal{L}}(k)\mathbf{Z}_{\mathcal{L}}(k) \\ &= \sum_{i=1}^{N_s} \mathbf{K}_i(k)\sum_{\mathcal{L}} \beta^t_{\mathcal{L}}(k)\mathbf{z}^i_{l_i}(k) \\ &= \sum_{i=1}^{N_s} \mathbf{K}_i(k)\sum_{\mathcal{L}} \prod_{j=1}^{N_s} \beta^t_{l_j,j}(k)\mathbf{z}^i_{l_i}(k) \\ &= \sum_{i=1}^{N_s} \mathbf{K}_i(k)\sum_{l_1=0}^{m_{k_1}} \cdots \sum_{l_{N_s}=0}^{m_{k_{N_s}}} \prod_{j=1}^{N_s} \beta^t_{l_j,j}(k)\mathbf{z}^i_{l_i}(k) \\ &= \sum_{i=1}^{N_s} \mathbf{K}_i(k)\Bigg\{\underbrace{\sum_{l_1=0}^{m_{k_1}} \cdots \sum_{l_{N_s}=0}^{m_{k_{N_s}}}}_{\neq l_i} \prod_{\substack{j=1 \\ j\neq i}}^{N_s} \beta^t_{l_j,j}(k)\Bigg\} \\ &\qquad \times \sum_{l_i=0}^{m_{k_i}} \beta^t_{l_i,i}(k)\mathbf{z}^i_{l_i}(k), \end{aligned} \quad (16)$$

where the nested series of summations within the brackets in the last expression does not include a sum over returns for sensor i. The bracketed expression is the sum of the multisensor probabilities for the set of sensors excluding the ith sensor, and the sum of these probabilities is 1. Hence, equation (16) can be simplified to

$$\sum_{\mathcal{L}} \beta^t_{\mathcal{L}}(k)\mathbf{K}(k)\mathbf{Z}_{\mathcal{L}}(k) = \sum_{i=1}^{N_s} \mathbf{K}_i(k) \sum_{l_i=0}^{m_{k_i}} \beta^t_{l_i,i}(k)\mathbf{z}^i_{l_i}(k). \quad (17)$$

Substituting (17) back into (15) gives the final equation for computing $\hat{\mathbf{x}}^t(k|k)$.

Thus, since Kalman filtering is a linear operation, MSJPDA filtering can be implemented by forming N_s pseudomeasurements that are weighted sums of measurements from each sensor. The Kalman filter is then applied once to each weighted pseudomeasurement. This results in a linear growth in filtering complexity as a function of the number of sensors N_s compared with the exponential growth that would occur if (12)-(13) were implemented directly.

5 Simulation Results

In this section, we present some simulation results comparing the MSJPDA with a multisensor nearest neighbor (NN) algorithm [3, 4] and with the single-sensor JPDA algorithm. The results in this section are all for scenarios that run for 250 intervals or seconds.

Figures 1 and 2 compare the multisensor NN (MSNN) and MSJPDA approaches for tracking of a single target that is moving north in a straight line. There are false measurements at the rate of two expected clutter points per gate per scan. The truth, track, and report information are shown projected onto a plane parallel to the Earth's surface. The solid line represents the truth (*i.e.*, actual target trajectory). Single dots represent reports from either targets or clutter, and dots with circles around them represent gated reports. The track position at each *interval* is plotted as a single dot, thus causing the track history to appear as a dotted line or path. The sensor platform is located at (0, 0) and is also moving north at half the speed of the target. Two sensors are used: (1) a radar giving range, azimuth, elevation, and range rate, and (2) an electronic support measures (ESM) sensor giving azimuth data. The radar gives measurements for the target once per scan or every 10 seconds, and the ESM gives measurements every 3 seconds.

From Figures 1 and 2, the MSJPDA approach clearly outperforms the MSNN. The MSNN algorithm loses track of the target before the end of the simulation. At lower clutter densities (fewer than one expected clutter point per gate per scan), both the MSNN and MSJPDA algorithms maintain track of the target, but the RMS position error with the MSNN algorithm was still found to be much larger (about 40%) than with the MSJPDA algorithm. Simulations with maneuvering targets were also run, and the MSJPDA was again found to perform better than the MSNN algorithm.

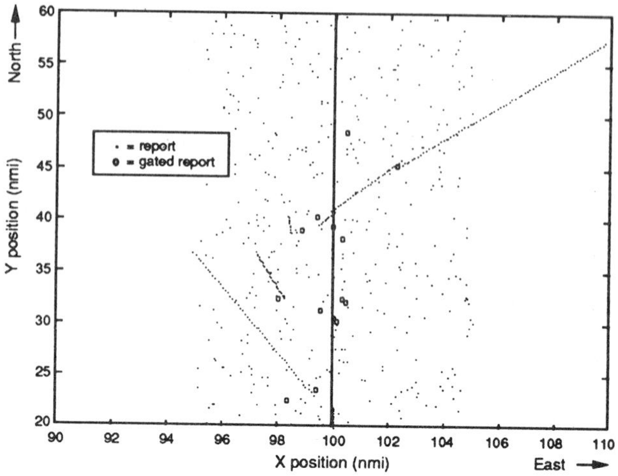

Figure 1: MSNN Tracking of a Target Moving in a Straight Line with a Clutter Density of Two Expected False Reports Per Gate Per Scan.

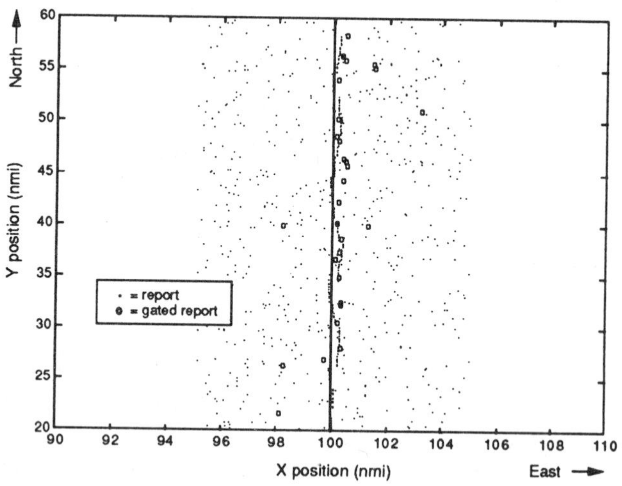

Figure 2: MSJPDA Tracking of a Target Moving in a Straight Line with a Clutter Density of Two Expected False Reports Per Gate Per Scan.

Figure 3 shows the performance of the single-sensor JPDA algorithm, which uses only radar measurements, in tracking a target. The tracking errors in Figure 3 for the single-sensor JPDA are much larger than those in Figure 2 for the MSJPDA algorithm, which uses both radar and ESM sensor measurements.

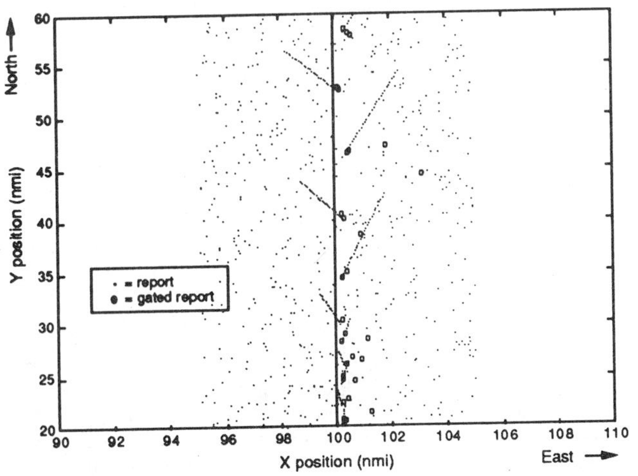

Figure 3: JPDA Tracking of a Target Moving in a Straight Line with a Clutter Density of Two Expected False Reports Per Gate Per Scan.

From the "swinging" estimates from East to West in Figures 1 and 3, we see that the heading estimates are moderately unstable. Our filtering was designed to recover quickly from target maneuvers (turns and accelerations); but, there is a trade-off between fast response to maneuvers and heading stability.

The small biases of about 0.3 nmi (to the East) that appear in the figures are due to sensor and navigational biases (position and rotation) that have been incorporated into the sensor models in our fusion evaluation program. These biases can be estimated and removed from the target state estimates, but this was not a focus of this investigation. The performance of the multisensor fusion algorithms without navigation and sensor biases can be roughly approximated by subtracting the biases observed in the first scan in the remaining scans.

In summary, the examples shown indicate that the MSJPDA approach provides superior resistance to track loss over the MSNN approach. Furthermore, the use of two sensors has also been shown to give better tracking performance than using data from one sensor alone.

6 Conclusions

We have extended the single-sensor JPDA algorithm for use when measurements are available from multiple sensors. Assuming that measurement errors are independent across sensors, extending the JPDA algorithm to the MSJPDA algorithm results in the multisensor data association probabilities to be the product of the single-sensor data association probabilities. Moreover, we showed how filtering for MSJPDA can be performed such that the computational complexity for filtering grows only linearly with the number of sensors. Finally, simulation results were presented showing the superior performance of the MSJPDA algorithm over a multisensor NN algorithm as well as over the single-sensor JPDA algorithm.

References

[1] Bar-Shalom, Y., and T. E. Fortmann. *Tracking and Data Association*, Academic Press, San Diego, 1988.

[2] Bar-Shalom, Y., editor. *Multitarget-Multisensor Tracking: Advanced Applications*, Artech House, Norwood, MA, 1990.

[3] Blackman, S. S. *Multiple-Target Tracking with Radar Applications*, Artech House, Norwood, MA, 1986.

[4] Bogler, P. L. *Radar Principles with Applications to Tracking Systems*, Wiley, New York, 1990.

[5] Fortmann, T. E., Y. Bar-Shalom, and M. Scheffe. "Sonar Tracking of Multiple Targets Using Joint Probabilistic Data Association," *IEEE Journal of Oceanic Engineering*, 8(3): 173–183, 1983.

[6] Hall, D. L. *Mathematical Techniques in Multi-Sensor Data Fusion*, Artech House, Norwood, MA, 1992.

[7] Houles, A., and Y. Bar-Shalom. "Multisensor Tracking of a Maneuvering Target in Clutter," *IEEE Trans. Aerospace and Electronics Systems*, AES-25:176–189, March 1989.

[8] Kurien, T., and M. E. Liggins. "Report-to-Target Assignment in Multisensor Multitarget Tracking," *Proc. 27th IEEE Conf. Decision and Control*, Austin, TX, pp. 2484–2488, December 1988.

[9] O'Neil, S. D., and M. F. Bridgland. "Fast Algorithms for Joint Probabilistic Data Association," *Proceedings of the National Symposium on Sensor Fusion*, Orlando, FL, 1991.

[10] Waltz, E., and J. Llinas. *Multisensor Data Fusion*, Artech House, Norwood, MA, 1990.

[11] Willner, D., C. B. Chang, and K. P. Dunn. "Kalman Filter Algorithms for a Multi-Sensor System," *Proc. IEEE Conf. Decision and Control*, pp. 570–574, November 1976.

Proceedings of the
American Control Conference
San Francisco, California • June 1993

Practical Considerations in Censored Distributed Detection Systems

Constantino Rago Peter Willett Yaakov Bar-Shalom
University of Connecticut
Storrs, CT 06269-3157 *

Abstract

Censored distributed detection schemes represent an interesting alternative to quantization when communication between the sensors and the *Data Fusion Center* (DFC) is to be minimized. The idea of censoring is that each sensor sends only "informative" observations, and leaves those deemed "uninformative" un-transmitted. The problem, naturally, is to decide what is "informative" and what is not. In [1] this was (at least in principle) solved under both Bayes and Neyman-Pearson criteria; this paper is a more practically-oriented treatment. We shall search for simplification in design, specifically in the most interesting case that the DFC threshold is high and the communication constraint is severe. We shall also examine the problem from a distance-measure viewpoint. We shall compare censoring to the more classical binary-transmission framework and observe its considerable decrease in communication needs. Finally, we shall explore the use of feedback to achieve optimal probability of error at a fraction of the bandwidth.

1 Introduction

The *censored* decentralized (or distributed) detection paradigm was introduced in [1]. The assumption is of a parallel topology network in which a group of sensors receive statistically-independent data. From this data information relevant to testing of a common hypothesis is extracted and transmitted to a *fusion center* for an ultimate decision. The rate of information flow is limited, either by bandwidth or to avoid "data-choking" at the fusion center, and in most studies it is assumed that a quantized likelihood ratio is sent. We make a key observation: most of the resolution cells being tested will be empty, and for a binary-quantization scheme as described above this amounts to transmission of a large number of *zeros*.

The idea of censoring uninformative data prior to fusion is perhaps not entirely new: current suites of sensors, particularly of the imaging variety, are already using the technique in an *ad hoc manner*, in that only reports of possible targets as observed from various "look-angles" are fused. However, the idea appears to have been largely ignored by the general decentralized detection community, and it is our intention both to correct this and to formalize the technique.

The new approach pre-supposes that with each sensor i (let us say there are N sensors) we have an associated observation space partition, R_i and $\bar{R}_i$. Transmissions to the fusion center take the form of

$$\left\{ \begin{array}{ll} l_i(\mathcal{X}_i) \in R_i & l_i(\mathcal{X}_i) \text{ is sent} \\ l_i(\mathcal{X}_i) \in \bar{R}_i & \text{nothing is sent} \end{array} \right\} \quad (1)$$

*This research was supported by the Naval Undersea Warfare Center under ONT Grant N66604-92-C-1386

where $\mathcal{X}_i$ is the observation at the ith sensor and $l_i(\cdot)$ denotes the local likelihood ratio (llr). Note that if $l_i(\mathcal{X}_i)$ lies in R_i (the *send* region) then its likelihood ratio is sent unquantized: the motivation here is that with so many "gaps" in the data it will be necessary to time/space/doppler tag all sensor-to-fusion-center transmissions, and as such there is little point in following all this by adulterated information.

In [1] it was shown that in a Bayesian situation and subject to an average communication constraint of the form

$$\Pi_H \sum_{i=1}^{N} Pr(\mathcal{X}_i \in R_i|H) + \Pi_K \sum_{i=1}^{N} Pr(\mathcal{X}_i \in R_i|K) \leq \kappa_B \leq N \quad (2)$$

and assuming that at the fusion center a likelihood ratio test is performed, then optimally we have

$$\bar{R}_i = \{l_i : \tau_{i1} \leq l_i(\mathcal{X}) \leq \tau_{i2}\} \quad (3)$$

(*i.e.*, the no-send region for each sensor is a single interval).

In the Neyman-Pearson case there are no reasonable prior probabilities for the hypotheses; however, by an appropriate re-definition of the constraint to

$$\sum_{i=1}^{N} Pr(l_i(\mathcal{X}_i) \in R_i|H) \leq \kappa_{NP} \leq N \quad (4)$$

a similar result is true. That is, in both cases only *extremal*, or very informative, likelihood ratios are transmitted; optimization is thus simplified in that instead of a search for some arbitrary sets $\{R_i\}_{i=1}^N$, only $\{\tau_{i1}, \tau_{i2}\}_{i=1}^N$ must be chosen. Note that the lack of transmission from sensor i does not indicate that no information is sent, but rather that the fusion center is aware only of the *imprecise* knowledge that $l_i \in \bar{R}_i$. The idea is schematically presented in Figure 1.

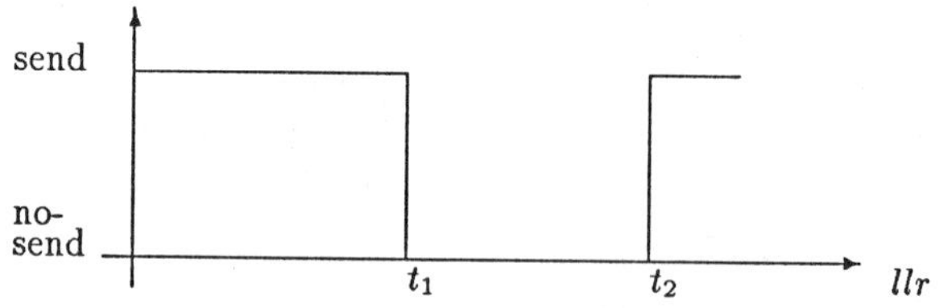

Figure 1: A Censoring Sensor.

The "censoring" scheme is characterized then by the send regions R_i and no-send regions $\bar{R}_i$, and a *Data Fusion Center* that implements the optimal fusion rule (a likelihood ratio test) over the received and non-received llr's given by

$$L_{FC}(l) = \prod_{i:l_i \in R_i} l_i \times \prod_{i:l_i \in \bar{R}_i} \frac{Pr(l_i \in \bar{R}_i|K)}{Pr(l_i \in \bar{R}_i|H)} \quad (5)$$

where $l = \{l_1, l_2, \ldots\}$ and l_i is the llr of sensor i.

Let us begin by examining the benefits of censoring. We shall pose the "cell-averaging constant false-alarm rate" (CA-CFAR) problem, in which the sensors' observations are governed by

$$\begin{aligned} Pr(X_i > x|H) &= (1+x)^{-m} \\ Pr(X_i > x|K) &= \left(1+\frac{x}{1+S}\right)^{-m} \end{aligned} \quad (6)$$

under the target-absent and target-present hypotheses, respectively. The model above describes the situation that a Swerling I squared-envelope return is normalized by the sum of m such others within a "noise-alone" reference window. If a target is present, then it is assumed to have signal-to-noise ratio (SNR) S, and we shall assume that this value is the same for all sensors. We have chosen $m = 8$ as a typical window size.

We shall compare a *censored* distributed detection system to one in which the communication from sensor to fusion center is binary. In the latter case, it may be shown that the optimal performance is given by

$$\beta_g = \max_{1 \leq k \leq N} \left\{ g_k \left[\beta_{local} \left(g_k^{-1}[\alpha_g] \right) \right] \right\} \quad (7)$$

where

$$g_k(x) = \sum_{l=k}^{N} \binom{N}{l} x^l (1-x)^{N-l} \quad (8)$$

Here β_g and α_g are respectively the overall probabilities of detection and false-alarm, and $\beta_{local}(\cdot)$ refers to the receiver operating characteristic (ROC) for each sensor. as described by (6).

The results are given in Figure 2. What is shown here is the average communication needed for censoring system, for various number of sensors, to achieve the *same probability of detection* as a binary scheme, for a global false-alarm rate of 10^{-4}. Note that the result for a binary scheme is shown as a straight line whose value is 1/24: to be fair, we have assumed that 24 bits must accompany each censored transmission to account for the tag information and a reasonably faithful quantization of the local likelihood ratio. The SNR is here given as a parameter; note that as it increases there is a "saturation" effect. The reason for this is that when the average communication is less than $1-(1-\alpha_{global})^N$ a randomized rule at the DFC becomes necessary, and performance deteriorates rapidly.

It should be noted that we have used a result derived subsequently in this paper in order to simplify calculation. That is, we assume that the communication constraint is sufficiently severe, and the threshold sufficiently high, that the "no-send" regions extend from zero to a threshold. Whether this is optimal or not in each situation is not at issue: the results can only be more impressive than those shown.

2 Censoring and Ali-Silvey Distance Measures

In this section we prove a result similar to (3), but under a Ali-Silvey distance measure criterion [2]. An Ali-Silvey distance measure is defined as:

$$d = f\left(E_H\left[C(L)\right]\right) \quad (9)$$

where $f(\cdot)$ is increasing, $C(\cdot)$ is a strictly convex function, and E_H denotes the expectation under the null hypothesis. Examples of Ali-Silvey distance measures are the Bhattacharyya distance, J-divergence, and Matsushita distance.

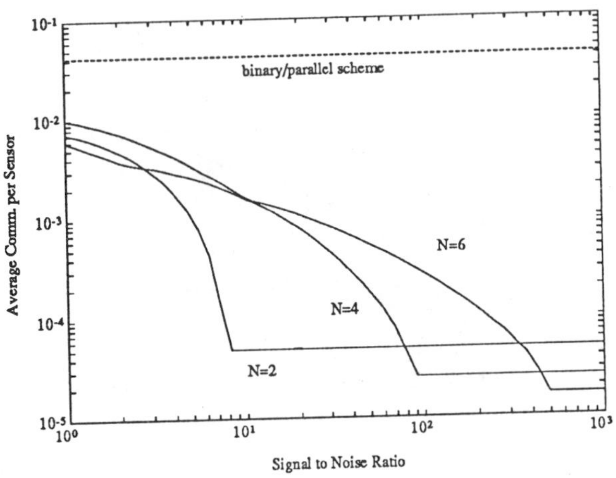

Figure 2: Average communication per sensor needed in a censoring scheme to reach the same global probability of detection as that of an optimal binary scheme (CA-CFAR, $\alpha = 10^{-4}$ in all cases).

To begin with, let us discard the increasing function $f(\cdot)$, which serves merely as a form of normalization and does not contribute to optimization. Second, note that under independence the overall maximization is equivalent to the maximization over one sensor alone. Hence, we shall examine

$$E_o\left[C(L_n)\right] \quad (10)$$

for a single sensor n. We have that

$$d = f\left(\int C(l)\, dP_H(l) + C\left(\frac{P_K(\bar{R}_n)}{P_H(\bar{R}_n)}\right) P_H(\bar{R}_n) - \sum_{i=1}^{M} \int_{A_i} C(l) dP_H(l) \right) \quad (11)$$

and hence it is the difference between the third and second terms which we seek to minimize. Before we proceed, we need a trivial, but tricky, lemma.

Lemma: with $C(.)$ a strictly convex function and a set of six ordered points such that

$$a_1 \leq a_2 \leq a_3 \leq a_4 \leq a_5 \leq a_6 \quad (12)$$

and

$$\begin{aligned} \int_{a_1}^{a_2} dP_H(l) + \int_{a_5}^{a_6} dP_H(l) &= \int_{a_3}^{a_4} dP_H(l) \\ \int_{a_1}^{a_2} l\, dP_H(l) + \int_{a_5}^{a_6} l\, dP_H(l) &= \int_{a_3}^{a_4} l\, dP_H(l) \end{aligned} \quad (13)$$

then

$$\int_{a_1}^{a_2} C(l)\, dP_H(l) + \int_{a_5}^{a_6} C(l)\, dP_H(l) > \int_{a_3}^{a_4} C(l)\, dP_H(l) \quad (14)$$

Proof: The situation is shown in Figure 3. Let

$$\begin{aligned} m &= \frac{C(a_4) - C(a_3)}{a_4 - a_3} \\ b &= C(a_3) - m a_3 \end{aligned} \quad (15)$$

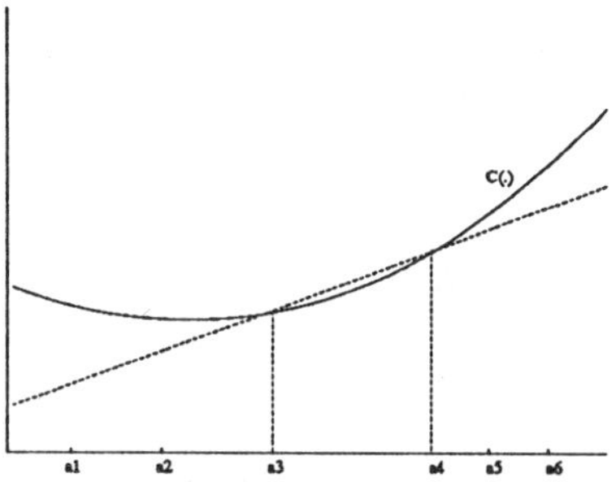

Figure 3: The convex function of Lemma 1.

We have

$$
\begin{aligned}
& \int_{a_1}^{a_2} C(l)\,dP_H(l) + \int_{a_5}^{a_6} C(l)\,dP_H(l) \\
& \qquad\qquad - \int_{a_3}^{a_4} C(l)\,dP_H(l) \\
> & \int_{a_1}^{a_2} [ml+b]\,dP_H(l) + \int_{a_5}^{a_6} [ml+b]\,dP_H(l) \\
& \qquad\qquad - \int_{a_3}^{a_4} [ml+b]\,dP_H(l) \\
= & \; m\left[\int_{a_1}^{a_2} l\,dP_H(l) + \int_{a_5}^{a_6} l\,dP_H(l) - \int_{a_3}^{a_4} l\,dP_H(l)\right] \\
+ & \; b\left[\int_{a_1}^{a_2} dP_H(l) + \int_{a_5}^{a_6} dP_H(l) - \int_{a_3}^{a_4} dP_H(l)\right] \\
= & \; 0 \qquad\qquad (16)
\end{aligned}
$$

If $a_3 = a_4$ the same result holds with $m = C'(a_3)$.□

Theorem: The Ali-Silvey distance is maximized by choosing $\bar{R}_n$ to be a single interval.

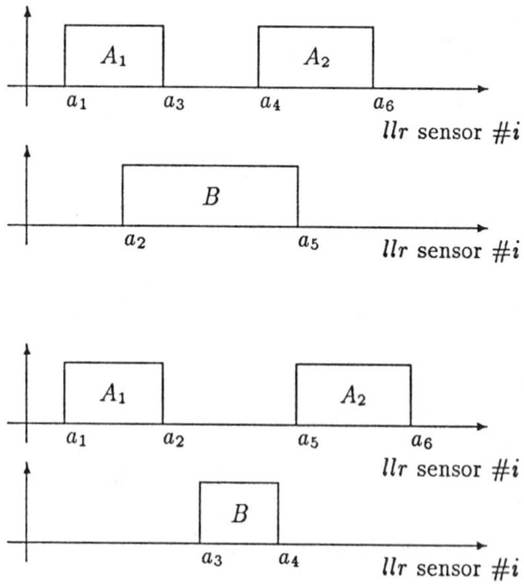

Figure 4: Two possible merging situations

Proof: Assume that $\bar{R}_n$ is not a single interval, and instead is comprised of non-overlapping intervals $\bigcup_{i=1}^{M} A_i$. Let us attempt to merge intervals A_1 and A_2 into interval B such that

$$
\begin{aligned}
\int_{A_1} dP_H(l) + \int_{A_2} dP_H(l) &= \int_B dP_H(l) \\
\int_{A_1} l\,dP_H(l) + \int_{A_2}^{a_6} l\,dP_H(l) &= \int_B l\,dP_H(l) \qquad (17)
\end{aligned}
$$

The situation is as one of those depicted in Figure 4. Regardless of which is the case, we have

$$
\begin{aligned}
& \int_{A_1} C(l)\,dP_H(l) + \int_{A_2} C(l)\,dP_H(l) - \int_B C(l)\,dP_H(l) \\
= & \int_{a_1}^{a_2} C(l)\,dP_H(l) + \int_{a_5}^{a_6} C(l)\,dP_H(l) - \int_{a_3}^{a_4} C(l)\,dP_H(l) \\
> & \; 0 \qquad \text{by the previous Lemma} \qquad (18)
\end{aligned}
$$

Note that the second term in (11) is unaffected by merging A_1 and A_2 into B subject to (13) ; however, the absolute magnitude of the third term is decreased, and hence the Ali-Silvey distance is increased. By continuing to merge intervals, the theorem is proven. □

To explore the result, we have computed the optimal thresholds for two different distance measures, J-divergence and Bhattacharyya, for which we have

$$
\begin{aligned}
f_J(x) &= x & C_J(x) &= (x-1)\log(x) \\
f_B(x) &= -\log(1-x/2) & C_B(x) &= \left(\sqrt{x}-1\right)^2
\end{aligned}
$$

respectively. The problem here is the standard Gaussian change in mean: under the null hypothesis the observation at each sensor has mean zero and variance unity, while under the alternative the mean is positive. All observations are assumed to be independent conditioned on the hypothesis. In Figure 5 we show the thresholds as a function of the Signal to Noise Ratio (SNR) for a constant average communication per sensor of 10%. We see that the no-send region moves downward as the SNR increases; this behavior reflects the fact that with increasing SNR a value of the llr that was "uninformative" but near the upper threshold becomes "informative".

In Figure 6 we show the thresholds as a function of the average communication per sensor, for a fixed SNR.

3 A Further Simplification

The results above (or in (3)) yield considerable simplification; nevertheless, optimization of the *send/no-send* regions is by no means trivial. Further simplification is possible, however, through noting that in most Bayesian situations of interest the prior probability of a target being present is small; this, after all, is our motivation for censoring. We have the following result:

Proposition 1 *For Π_K and the average communication both sufficiently small, we have that $\tau_{i1} = 0$.*

The "polarity" of the result may be reversed to show that $\tau_{i2} = \infty$ for sufficiently large Π_K.

Proof

For a general Bayesian testing situation we write the minimum probability of error as

$$
P_e = \Pi_K \left[1 - \int_{\Omega_K} dF_H(t-\tau)\right] \qquad (19)
$$

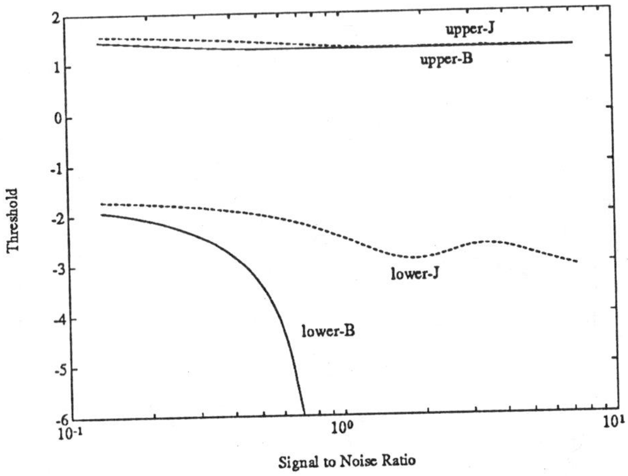

Figure 5: Upper and lower thresholds for the Gaussian case (average communication rate = 10%, $\sigma^2 = 1$ in all cases) for J-divergence and Bhattacharyya distance measures.

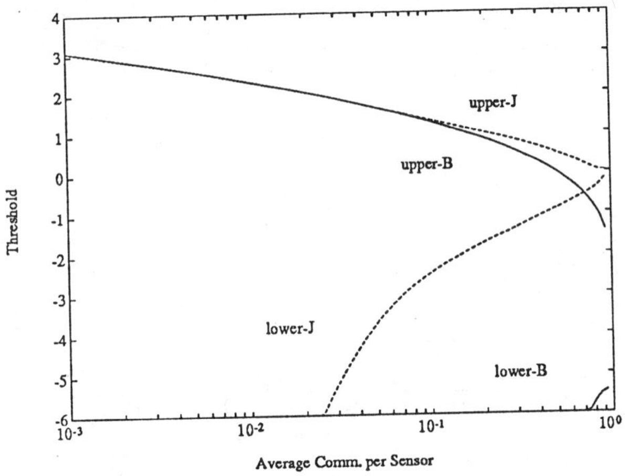

Figure 6: Upper and lower thresholds for the Gaussian case (SNR = 1, $\sigma^2 = 1$ in all cases) for J-divergence and Bhattacharyya distance measures.

where $F_H(\cdot)$ denotes the distribution function of the likelihood ratio under the null hypothesis. In our case we can rewrite (19) as:

$$\begin{aligned} P_e/\Pi_K &= 1 - \int_0^{t_1} p_H(l) \int_{\frac{\tau}{\Upsilon}}^{\infty} dP_H(l\,u - \tau) \\ &\quad - \int_{t_1}^{t_2} p_H(l) \int_{\frac{\tau}{\Upsilon}}^{\infty} dP_H(l\,u - \tau) \\ &\quad - \int_{t_2}^{\infty} p_H(l) \int_{\frac{\tau}{\Upsilon}}^{\infty} dP_H(l\,u - \tau) \qquad (20) \end{aligned}$$

where Υ is the likelihood ratio of $\bar{R}_i$. We now take the derivative of P_e. For this, we will need the derivative of t_2 with respect to t_1 and the derivative of Υ with respect to t_1; this latter can be shown to have a second order effect, and hence we ignore it. As to the former, let us start from the average communication constraint for one sensor:

$$\frac{\kappa_B}{N} = \Pi_H \left(1 - \int_{t_1}^{t_2} p_H(l)\right) + \Pi_K \left(1 - \int_{t_1}^{t_2} p_K(l)\right) \qquad (21)$$

Taking the differential, we find

$$\frac{dt_2}{dt_1} = \frac{p_H(t_1)(\tau + t_1)}{p_H(t_2)(\tau + t_2)} \qquad (22)$$

The derivative of the probability of error is given by

$$\begin{aligned} \frac{1}{\Pi_K}\frac{\partial P_e}{\partial t_1} &= - \; p_H(t_1) \int_{\frac{\tau}{t_1}}^{\infty} dP_H(t_1\,u - \tau) \\ &\quad - \; p_H(t_1)\frac{\tau + t_1}{\tau + t_2} \int_{\frac{\tau}{\Upsilon}}^{\infty} dP_H(t_2\,u - \tau) \\ &\quad + \; p_H(t_1) \int_{\frac{\tau}{\Upsilon}}^{\infty} dP_H(t_1\,u - \tau) \\ &\quad + \; p_H(t_1)\frac{\tau + t_1}{\tau + t_2} \int_{\frac{\tau}{t_2}}^{\infty} dP_H(t_2\,u - \tau) \end{aligned} \qquad (23)$$

or

$$\begin{aligned} \frac{1}{\Pi_K}\frac{\partial P_e}{\partial t_1} &= p_H(t_1)(\tau + t_1) \\ &\times \left[-\frac{\int_{\frac{\tau}{\Upsilon}}^{\frac{\tau}{t_1}} dP_H(\frac{\tau}{t_1} - u)}{\tau + t_1} + \frac{\int_{\frac{\tau}{t_2}}^{\frac{\tau}{\Upsilon}} dP_H(u - \frac{\tau}{t_2})}{\tau + t_2} \right] \end{aligned} \qquad (24)$$

Now, as $\tau \to \infty$ and $\kappa_B \to 0$ (which implies $\Upsilon \to 1$), we have that

$$\frac{\int_{\frac{\tau}{t_2}}^{\frac{\tau}{\Upsilon}} dP_H(u - \frac{\tau}{t_2})}{\frac{\tau}{t_2} + 1} > 1 - \varepsilon \qquad (25)$$

and

$$\frac{\int_{\frac{\tau}{\Upsilon}}^{\frac{\tau}{t_1}} dP_H(\frac{\tau}{t_1} - u)}{\frac{\tau}{t_1} + 1} < \delta \qquad (26)$$

for arbitrarily small ϵ and δ. The derivative of the probability of error is thus positive, and hence $t_1 = 0$ is a global minimum.

If the prior probability of a target being present and the average communication constraint are sufficiently small, then the ith sensor transmits to the fusion center only when its local likelihood ratio *exceeds* some value τ_{i2}. Intuition suggests that as the prior probability of K decreases information supportive of H should become less important. However, it is shown in [1] that in some cases (most notably the Gaussian) τ_{i1} and τ_{i2} do *not* decrease monotonically with Π_K, and hence the result is by no means trivial.

4 A Censoring Scheme with Feedback

In some situations an immediate decision is necessary; in others a certain amount of delay is tolerable if it brings greater accuracy. This idea was explored in [3]: there sensor-to-fusion-center communication was binary and consisted of two "rounds", between which the fusion center's tentative decision was made available to all sensors. For the second round the sensors' local thresholds were raised or lowered accordingly and further information was extracted from the data. The idea was extended in [4] to the case that the "bantering" continued until a consensus was reached.

In the censoring scheme the "further information" does not take the form of a refined likelihood ratio quantization, but rather of all the information which was not previously sent. The problem, including all the ramifications of apportionment of communication between the first and second round of decisionmaking, is highly complex. Here we shall explore a simple and sub-optimal, but effective, scheme:

$$\begin{cases} \text{decide for } H & L_{FC} \leq \tau_{FC} \\ \text{request further information} & L_{FC} > \tau_{FC} \end{cases} \quad (27)$$

where L_{FC} is the first-round likelihood-ratio at the fusion center. Note that unlike [3], a second round of communication is not always necessary.

There are two possible advantages to the use of feedback: to reduce communication, and to improve probability-of-error performance. These may, naturally, be traded off one for the other as is seen fit, but in this paper we shall opt solely for the latter. Specifically, we shall impose the condition that the censored/feedback scheme have the *same* probability of error as the unquantized or *centralized* network. To do this we shall specify, with τ_i representing a threshold below which sensor i transmits nothing, that

$$\prod_{i=1}^{N} \tau_i = \tau_{FC} \quad (28)$$

Notice that if nothing is transmitted to the fusion center, then the product of the local likelihood ratios must have been less than the DFC threshold, and hence a DFC decision for H is appropriate. Likewise, note that any other combination results in full communication, and hence, again, the decision matches that of the unquantized network. This approach is strongly reminiscent of the Nth-root approach described in [4], and indeed, since the sensors are assumed *iid* in the examples which follow, we shall take $\tau_i^N = \tau_{FC}$. In this section we shall be working with a Neyman-Pearson criterion, and τ_{FC} is set accordingly.

The results are given in Figures 7 and 8 for the Gaussian and CA-CFAR (see equation (6)) situations respectively. Note that in both cases, in order to achieve uniformity, the SNRs are adjusted for each probability of false-alarm such that the overall probability of detection is constant (β = 75% in the CA-CFAR case, β = 99% in the Gaussian). Two items are of note in these plots: first, that the savings in communication (with respect to centralized) can be highly impressive; and second, that the advantages are less apparent as the number of sensors (N) increases. This latter is due to the suboptimality of the scheme used: as the number of sensors increases it becomes difficult to control the probability that at least one of the sensors transmits.

5 Summary

In [1] we introduced censoring formally and derived an essential property of the "no-send" regions: that assuming sensor-to-sensor conditional independence these are compact likelihood ratio intervals under both Neyman-Pearson and Bayes criteria. Optimization in these cases is difficult, and hence in this paper we have presented results of a more practical nature. Specifically we have shown that the same result is true under the easy-to-compute Ali-Silvey distance measures. We have also proven that under certain conditions the "no-send" regions correspond to the local likelihood ratio values being lower than a threshold.

We have further shown by example that censoring can involve impressive savings in communication. A feedback scheme to retrieve lost data (when necessary) was also presented, and it was demonstrated that optimal (unquantized) performance is possible at a fraction of the communication cost.

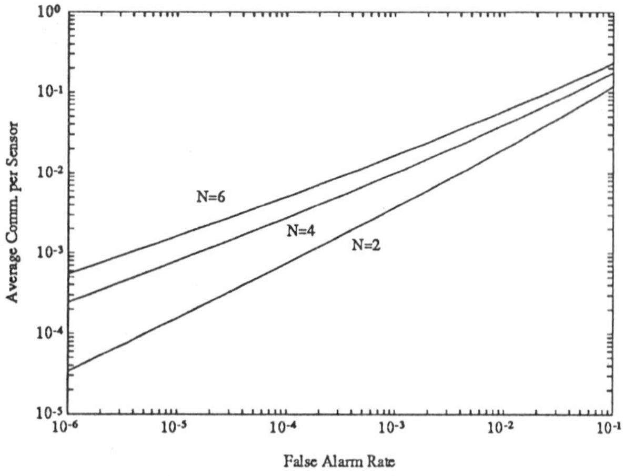

Figure 7: Average communication per sensor needed to reach a specific global probability of detection (β_g = 99%) in a censoring scheme with feedback (Gaussian case σ^2 = 1 in all cases).

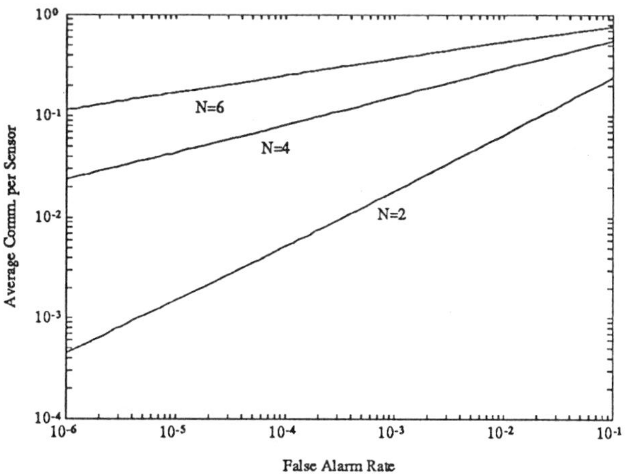

Figure 8: Average communication per sensor needed to reach a specific global probability of detection (β_g = 75%) in a censoring scheme with feedback (CA-FAR case).

References

[1] C. Rago, P. Willett, and Y. Bar-Shalom, "A Low Communication Rate Scheme for Distributed Detection", *Proceedings of the 1993 American Control Conference.*

[2] H.V. Poor, *An Introduction to Signal Detection and Estimation*, Springer-Verlag, 1987.

[3] S. Alhakeem and P. Varshney, "A Bayesian Formulation of Decentralized Detection Systems with Feedback", *Proceedings of the 1990 Conference on Information Sciences and Systems*, March 1990.

[4] B. Tober, P. Willett, and P. Swaszek, "Fully-Connected Non-Hierarchical Decentralized Detection Networks", *Proceedings of the 1992 Conference on Control Applications*, September 1992.

Proceedings of the
American Control Conference
San Francisco, California • June 1993

Application of a Recursive Method for Registration Error Correction in Tracking with Multiple Sensors

S. Dhar

The MITRE Corporation
Burlington Road
Bedford, MA 01730

Abstract

This paper addresses the issue of the correction of registration errors due to the presence of biases in the measurements when multiple sensors are used for tracking targets. The problem is formulated as one of recursively estimating biases, and is addressed by an application of the technique, using an augmented Kalman filter, of simultaneously estimating the sensor biases and the state vector (of track parameters), the latter assuming that no biases are present. Simulation results are presented comparing the performance of the recursive algorithm with that of a generalized least squares method, which is applicable when targets with known positions are available for measurement by the sensors. Results are also presented for a two-sensor case when the extended Kalman filter is used as the tracking filter.

1. Introduction

In target tracking applications, measurements from multiple sensors, e.g., from radars at various sites, are often simultaneously used by the tracking algorithm in estimating the track parameters. Measurements from each of these sensors are corrupted by two kinds of errors, a random error and a systematic or bias error. Random errors are modeled in the estimation algorithm used by the tracking filter, and the filter performance is usually adequate if the random error models are fairly accurate. The effect of unmodeled bias errors can be quite severe, e.g., (1) poor tracking performance, (2) multiple tracks for the same target, or (3) loss of a track when the target moves from the field of view of one set of sensors to that of another. Figure 1 shows a scenario where two targets are in the surveillance volume of two sensors, both measuring the range and the azimuth angle. The presence of the bias errors and the fact that measurements from both the sensors may not be always available can affect tracking performance in the following way. If measurements from one sensor are used in tracking for a time and then the other sensor becomes the only source of measurements, the target is likely to be lost when a window is used for correlating a measurement with a filter-predicted target position, as the measured position of the target will be outside the correlation window. Errors due to unknown sensor measurement biases are called registration errors. To correct for registration errors one can use a generalized least squares approach where a large number of targets with known positions are measured by the individual sensors to estimate the biases, or a recursive approach where the biases are estimated as part of the tracking process and the track parameter estimates are corrected for the presence of biases with the bias estimates. The focus of this paper is the second method as it is more general because it does not require targets with known positions and can adapt to changing biases.

The generalized least squares method, a stand-alone process, was originally proposed by Fischer et al. [1] and its application to the registration error correction problem has been discussed in detail by Dana [2]. It has also found application in a related problem of position location with multiple sensors [3]. The technique for estimating the biases and making necessary corrections to the track parameter estimates is adapted from the recursive bias estimation algorithm of Friedland [4]. Friedland formulates the problem of linear state estimation in the presence of biases as a Kalman filtering problem with state augmentation, and the algorithm decouples the estimation procedure into two parts: one of bias estimation and the other of state estimation assuming that no biases are present. The unbiased estimates are obtained as a linear combination of the two above mentioned estimates. Ignagni [5] has shown that the decoupled algorithm of [4] is equivalent to the full augmented Kalman filter algorithm if a particular relationship between the initial values of the filter parameters in the two algorithms holds. Limitations on the convergence of the above algorithm when the biases are driven by noise, have been discussed in [6], [7] and [8]. Our application described in the following sections is restricted to the case when there is no driving noise in the dynamics of the biases. Finally, Blom et al. [9] have recently proposed applying the joint bias and state estimation algorithm similar to [4], with an extended Kalman filter, to the Air Traffic Control problem.

2. Problem Formulation

Consider the case of tracking a target by two radars located at two different sites as shown in figure 2. We assume that the tagret motion is in the x-y plane. The track parameters that are estimated are the x and y coordinates of the target, denoted by the state vector $\mathbf{X}$. Each radar measures the range r and the angle θ of the target, denoted by r_{ik} and θ_{ik}, where i (= 1 or 2) identifies the radar and k is the time index. Associated with each measurement pair by radar 1, (r_{1k}, θ_{1k}) are bias or registration errors $(\Delta r_1, \Delta\theta_1)$ and random errors $(\delta r_{ik}, \delta\theta_{ik})$, and similarly for radar 2. The problem is to obtain the estimate, $\hat{\mathbf{X}}_k$ of $\mathbf{X}_k$ using all the measurements Ψ_k up to time k, where

$$\Psi_k = (r_{1k}, \theta_{1k}, r_{2k}, \theta_{2k}). \tag{1}$$

The presence of unknown bias errors, $(\Delta r_1, \Delta\theta_1, \Delta r_2, \Delta\theta_2)$ requires that they also have to be estimated for obtaining good track parameter estimates, $\hat{\mathbf{X}}_k$ of $\mathbf{X}_k$. The correction of registration errors is then formulated as the estimation of bias errors in the sensor measurements, followed by the correction of the track parameter estimates using the bias estimates. We describe below two approaches to solving this problem. Our purpose is to analyze the performance of these two methods, with special focus on the second, when they are applied to the multisensor registration problem.

3. Bias Estimation Techniques

The basic features of the two methods are described here. Detailed description of the first method can be found in [2], and that of the second in [4] and [5]. The first method considers the bias estimation as a separate stand-alone process, and utilizes the generalized least squares technique. The second method models the bias estimation and the estimation of the tracking parameters as parts of the same algorithm, and consequently both estimates are obtained simultaneously.

Generalized Least Squares Method:

This method is a generalization of the estimation of unknown parameters by the method of least squares. It is assumed that there are N targets available for simultaneous measurement by both radars (Figure 2). The x-y coordinates of these targets are known from independent sources. In the x-y plane, the difference between the two kth measurements, $(\Delta x_k, \Delta y_k)$ may be expressed as

$$\Delta x_k = g_x(r_{1k}, \theta_{1k}) - g_x(r_{2k}, \theta_{2k}) - u, \tag{2}$$

$$\Delta y_k = g_y(r_{1k}, \theta_{1k}) - g_y(r_{2k}, \theta_{2k}) - v, \tag{3}$$

where $g_x(r_{1k}, \theta_{1k}) = r_{1k}\cos(\theta_{1k})$, $g_y(r_{1k}, \theta_{1k}) = r_{1k}\sin(\theta_{1k})$, and (u, v) are the x-y coordinates of radar 2 relative to radar 1. Because of the bias and random errors, $r_{ik} = r_i^t(k) - \Delta r_i - \delta r_{ik}$, and $\theta_{ik} = \theta_{ik}^t - \Delta\theta_i - \delta\theta_{ik}$, where r_{ik}^t and θ_{ik}^t are the error-free measurements by radar i.

We define the set of biases as the vector,

$$\beta = (\Delta r_1, \Delta\theta_1, \Delta r_2, \Delta\theta_2)^T, \tag{4}$$

where T is the transpose, and the set of measurement differences as $f(\Psi_k, \beta) = (\Delta x_k, \Delta y_k)^T$. The least squares criterion is now employed to determine the value β^* that satisfies the following:

$$f(\Psi_k, \beta^*) = 0. \tag{5}$$

To obtain β^*, assuming that all its components are small, a Taylor series expansion of $f(\Psi_k^t, \beta)$ is made about $\beta = 0$ and $\Psi_k = \Psi_k^t$, where Ψ_k^t are the error-free measurements.

Using a simplified notation, the Taylor expansion can be written in the familiar least squares problem form as

$$\mathbf{X}\beta + \xi = \mathbf{Y}, \tag{6}$$

where

$$\mathbf{X} = (G_1, G_2, \ldots, G_N)^{\mathrm{T}}, \tag{7}$$

$$\xi = (F_1(\Psi_1 - \Psi_1^t), F_2(\Psi_2 - \Psi_2^t), \ldots, F_N(\Psi_N - \Psi_N^t))^{\mathrm{T}}, \tag{8}$$

$$\mathbf{Y} = (-f(\Psi_1, 0), -f(\Psi_2, 0), \ldots, -f(\Psi_N, 0))^{\mathrm{T}}, \tag{9}$$

where G_k and F_k are the Jacobian matrices of partial derivatives with respect to β and Ψ_k, respectively, evaluated at $\beta = 0$ and $\Psi_k = \Psi_k^t$.

Assuming that random errors , e.g., δr_{ik}, are uncorrelated from one measurement to another, the least squares solution, β^* for β is given by

$$\beta^* = (\mathbf{X}^{\mathrm{T}}\Sigma_\xi^{-1}\mathbf{X})^{-1}\mathbf{X}^{\mathrm{T}}\Sigma_\xi^{-1}\mathbf{Y}, \tag{10}$$

where $\Sigma_\xi = E(\xi\xi^{\mathrm{T}})$ is the block diagonal matrix, $diag[\Sigma_1, \Sigma_2 \ldots, \Sigma_N]$, $E(x)$ is the expected value of x, $\Sigma_k = F_k\Sigma_{(\Psi_k - \Psi_k^t)}F_k^{\mathrm{T}}$, $\Sigma_{(\Psi_k - \Psi_k^t)}$ is the diagonal matrix, $diag[\sigma_{r_1}^2, \sigma_{\theta_1}^2, \sigma_{r_2}^2, \sigma_{\theta_2}^2]$. The variances, $\sigma_{r_i}^2$ and $\sigma_{\theta_i}^2$ are the noise variances for range and angle measurements, respectively, for radar i.

Because of the block-diagonal form of Σ_ξ, the of computation β^* may be simplified by using the the following:

$$\mathbf{X}^{\mathrm{T}}\Sigma_\xi^{-1}\mathbf{X}^{\mathrm{T}} = \sum_{k=1}^{N} G_k^{\mathrm{T}}\Sigma_k^{-1}G_k, \tag{11}$$

$$\mathbf{X}^{\mathrm{T}}\Sigma_\xi^{-1}\mathbf{Y} = -\sum_{k=1}^{N} G_k^{\mathrm{T}}\Sigma_k^{-1}f(\Psi_k, 0). \tag{12}$$

Equation (10) is the important result of the generalized least squares method, and equations (11) and (12) show how N independent target measurements by the two radars are used for computing the bias vector β^*. The bias estimation is done separately from and prior to target tracking.

For track parameter estimation, the measured ranges and angles are corrected with the corresponding estimated biases, Δr_i^* or $\Delta\theta_i^*$.

Recursive Bias Estimation Method:

The generalized least squares method described above requires a number of targets of known positions, and also is not suitable for scenarios where the bias errors change because different sets of sensors are employed for measurements in different parts of the surveillance volume. The method to be described here attempts to address these problems by the recursive estimation of the biases and the correction of the track parameter estimation errors simultaneously.

The basic algorithm incorporates the biases, or bias vector as an augmentation of the state vector, and estimates the track parameters with the biased measurements and the augmented state vector. Friedland [4] developed an algorithm within the linear Kalman filter formalism where the estimation of the augmented state vector is decoupled, one part estimating the original state vector of track parameters as if the measurements contain no bias errors (assumed bias-free), and another that estimates the bias vector. The bias-corrected estimates are obtained by adding a projection of the estimated bias vector to the assumed bias-free estimates. The computational advantage derived from this algorithm is that both the unaugmented state vector and the bias vector estimation processes involve matrices of smaller dimensions. Also, the estimation of biases may be performed at a rate different from that of the track parameters. We present the basic features of the algorithm from [4] and [5].

Consider the following coupled transition and measurement equations for the original state, $\mathbf{x}_n$ and the bias, $\mathbf{b}_n$ vectors:

$$\mathbf{x}_n = \mathbf{A}_n\mathbf{x}_{n-1} + \mathbf{B}_n\mathbf{b} + \xi_n, \tag{13}$$

$$\mathbf{y}_n = \mathbf{H}_n\mathbf{x}_n + \mathbf{C}_n\mathbf{b} + \eta_n, \tag{14}$$

where at time n, $\mathbf{x}_n$ is the original (unaugmented) state vector, $\mathbf{y}_n$ the measurement vector, $\mathbf{b}$ the constant bias vector, ξ_n Gaussian state noise, η_n Gaussian measurement noise, $\mathbf{A}_n$ the state transition matrix, $\mathbf{B}_n$ the bias transition matrix, $\mathbf{H}_n$ the measurement matrix for the original state vector, and $\mathbf{C}_n$ is the measurement matrix for the bias vector.

The state and measurement noise processes are assumed to be uncorrelated with covariances, $\mathbf{Q}_n^x$ and $\mathbf{R}_n^y$, respectively.

We do not discuss the estimation of the augmented state vector, and its relationship to the decoupled approach to be given below. Reference [5] discusses the relationship between the two methods. We also assume $\mathbf{B}_n = 0$, and the bias vector $\mathbf{b}_n$ is constant in time and there is no driving noise in its state transition equation.

Assumed Bias-Free Estimator: The assumed bias-free estimator is obtained by incorrectly modeling the measurements as having no bias. The errors and the transition matrix are, however, correctly modeled. Because of the presence of unmodeled biases in the measurements, the estimates produced by the Kalman filter are also biased.

The unaugmented state transition and the measurement models for the assumed bias-free estimation problem are given as follows:

$$\mathbf{x}_n = \mathbf{A}_n\mathbf{x}_{n-1} + \xi_n, \tag{15}$$

$$\mathbf{y}_n = \mathbf{H}_n\mathbf{x}_n + \eta_n. \tag{16}$$

For this case let $\tilde{\mathbf{x}}_{n|m}$ denote the estimate of $\mathbf{x}_n$ with measurements up to time m, and use a similar notation for other quantities that follow. The Kalman gain and the estimation error covariance are denoted by $\tilde{\mathbf{K}}_n$ and $\tilde{\mathbf{P}}_{n|m}$, respectively. Standard Kalman filter gain and covariance update equations [10] can then be used to produce the state vector estimates,

$$\tilde{\mathbf{x}}_{n|n-1} = \mathbf{A}_n\tilde{\mathbf{x}}_{n-1|n-1}, \tag{17}$$

$$\tilde{\mathbf{x}}_{n|n} = \tilde{\mathbf{x}}_{n|n-1} + \tilde{\mathbf{K}}_n(\mathbf{y}_n - \mathbf{H}_n\tilde{\mathbf{x}}_{n|n-1}). \tag{18}$$

These estimates are not optimal because the measurement model does not take into account the presence of the biases. In order to obtain optimal estimates, one has to remove the effects of the biases from the estimates. For this, one has to recursively estimate the biases and the coefficient matrix for adding the estimated bias vector to the assumed bias-free estimate of the original state vector. Before we present the procedure for estimating biases and the coefficient matrices, we consider the special case where the biases are known exactly.

Exactly Known Bias: We discuss this case because it demonstrates how the assumed bias-free estimates can be corrected when biases are known exactly. The extension to the case of unknown biases is straightforward. Because the bias vector $\mathbf{b}$ is known exactly, it can be modeled in the state transition and measurement equations (13) and (14). The measurement vector $\mathbf{y}_n$ can be replaced by $\mathbf{y}'_n$, which is equal to $\mathbf{y}_n - \mathbf{C}_n\mathbf{b}$.

Denoting the estimate of the state vector as $\bar{\mathbf{x}}_{n|n}$, and similarly denoting the others, one can easily show that the following recursive relations are satisfied:

$$\bar{\mathbf{x}}_{n|n-1} = \mathbf{A}_n\bar{\mathbf{x}}_{n-1|n-1}, \tag{19}$$

$$\bar{\mathbf{x}}_{n|n} = \bar{\mathbf{x}}_{n|n-1} + \tilde{\mathbf{K}}_n(\mathbf{y}_n - \mathbf{H}_n\bar{\mathbf{x}}_{n|n-1} - \mathbf{C}_n\mathbf{b}). \tag{20}$$

Notice that the exactly known bias vector is correctly modeled in this case, hence the estimates, $\bar{\mathbf{x}}_{n|n}$, are optimal.

Comparing the expressions for $\tilde{\mathbf{x}}_{n|n}$ and $\bar{\mathbf{x}}_{n|n}$, and using their linear dependence on the bias vector $\mathbf{b}$, one can express the general relationship between the two as follows:

$$\bar{\mathbf{x}}_{n|n} = \tilde{\mathbf{x}}_{n|n} + \mathbf{V}_n \mathbf{b}, \qquad (21)$$

$$\bar{\mathbf{x}}_{n|n-1} = \tilde{\mathbf{x}}_{n|n-1} + \mathbf{U}_n \mathbf{b}, \qquad (22)$$

where $\mathbf{V}_n$ and $\mathbf{U}_n$ are the coefficient matrices that are to be determined. The relationships among $\mathbf{V}_n$, $\mathbf{U}_n$, and $\mathbf{A}_n$ can be obtained as follows:

$$\mathbf{U}_n = \mathbf{A}_n \mathbf{V}_{n-1}, \qquad (23)$$

$$\mathbf{V}_n = \mathbf{U}_n - \tilde{\mathbf{K}}_n \mathbf{S}_n, \qquad (24)$$

where $\mathbf{S}_n$ is defined by

$$\mathbf{S}_n = \mathbf{H}_n \mathbf{U}_n + \mathbf{C}_n. \qquad (25)$$

The matrices $\mathbf{V}_n$ and $\mathbf{U}_n$ play the role of projection matrices, and $\mathbf{S}_n$ is the new measurement matrix for the bias vector estimator.

The residuals of the assumed bias-free estimator can be expressed in terms of $\mathbf{b}$, $\mathbf{S}_n$, and η_n. Let $\mathbf{r}_n$ denote the residual as defined below:

$$\mathbf{r}_n = \mathbf{y}_n - \mathbf{H}_n \tilde{\mathbf{x}}_{n|n-1}$$

$$= \mathbf{S}_n \mathbf{b} + \mathbf{v}_n, \qquad (26)$$

where $\mathbf{v}_n$ is the measurement residual in the exactly known bias case, with covariance, $\mathbf{R}^v_n$ given by

$$\mathbf{v}_n = \mathbf{y}_n - \mathbf{H}_n \bar{\mathbf{x}}_{n|n-1} - \mathbf{C}_n \mathbf{b}. \qquad (27)$$

$$\mathbf{R}^v_n = \mathbf{H}_n \tilde{\mathbf{P}}_{n|n-1} \mathbf{H}^T_n + \mathbf{R}^y_n. \qquad (28)$$

From the recursion relations given above, once $\mathbf{V}_0$ is specified, using $\tilde{\mathbf{K}}_n$, the new measurement matrix sequence $\mathbf{S}_n$ can be readily computed. In the case where $\mathbf{b}$ is not exactly known, a linear model for the state equation for $\mathbf{b}$ is used to obtain estimates $\hat{\mathbf{b}}_{n|n}$, as discussed next.

Bias Estimator: When the bias vector $\mathbf{b}$ is not exactly known, it can be estimated using the following state transition and measurement models:

$$\mathbf{b}_n = \mathbf{b}_{n-1}, \qquad (29)$$

$$\mathbf{r}_n = \mathbf{S}_n \mathbf{b} + \mathbf{v}_n. \qquad (30)$$

The Kalman filter estimates, $\hat{\mathbf{b}}_{n|n-1}$, $\hat{\mathbf{K}}^{(b)}_n$, $\hat{\mathbf{P}}^{(b)}_{n|n}$, etc. are then obtained as they are for the assumed bias-free case, with $\mathbf{H}_n$ and $\mathbf{R}^y_n$ replaced by $\mathbf{S}_n$ and $\mathbf{R}^v_n$, respectively.

Bias Corrected Original State Vector Estimator: The difference between the case where the bias vector $\mathbf{b}$ is known exactly and where $\mathbf{b}$ is estimated is that the bias vector is now a random vector. An estimate $\hat{\mathbf{x}}_{n|n}$ of $\mathbf{x}_n$ is obtained by replacing $\mathbf{b}$ by $\hat{\mathbf{b}}_{n|n}$ in equation (21),

$$\hat{\mathbf{x}}_{n|n} = \tilde{\mathbf{x}}_{n|n} + \mathbf{V}_n \hat{\mathbf{b}}_{n|n}, \qquad (31)$$

and the estimation error covariance matrix, $\hat{\mathbf{P}}_{n|n}$ is now given by

$$\hat{\mathbf{P}}_{n|n} = \tilde{\mathbf{P}}_{n|n} + \mathbf{V}_n \hat{\mathbf{P}}^{(b)}_{n|n} \mathbf{V}^T_n. \qquad (32)$$

Application to Nonlinear Measurements: The procedure described above uses linear models for both the state transition and measurement equations. In order to apply the method to the problem of tracking with two radars, one has to linearize the estimation problem by using a linear approximation, e.g., the extended Kalman filter [10]. In the next section we present some simulation results with the extended Kalman filter implementation of the track parameter estimator using biased measurements from two radars.

Remarks: The structure of the decoupled bias estimation and bias correction algorithm is very similar to the input estimation algorithm [11] for estimating maneuver parameters and correcting the track parameter estimates for a maneuvering target when the target maneuver is not modeled in the estimator. In the input estimation case, the maneuver or acceleration is estimated from the residuals (similar to $\mathbf{r}_n$) of the assumed maneuver-free estimates, using a new measurement matrix (similar to $\mathbf{S}_n$) at each update time. These estimates are then used to correct the track parameters.

4. Simulation Results

The performance of the two techniques described in section 3 was determined by simulating the tracking of a target with two radars. Figure 2 shows the geometry of the target and the radars. Two simulation experiments were conducted; one for comparing the performance of the two methods using linear state and measurement models, and the other using an extended Kalman filter implementation of the recursive method.

Case 1 (Linear models):

We consider a target moving along the perpendicular bisector of the line joining the two sensor positions (x axis). The sensors measure the range and the angle of the target. Biases and measurement noises are present only in the angle measurements. We restrict measurements to a short segment of the trajectory at near 45 degrees and near 135 degrees, respectively, from the two sensors. Then any biases in the angle measurements translate into nearly constant biases in x-position measurements. For the recursive bias estimation method this translates into the problem of estimating a one dimensional state, x and two bias variables, $\mathbf{b}_x^{(1)}$ and $\mathbf{b}_x^{(2)}$, for the two radars. After a fixed number of sampling intervals for the recursive bias estimation method and the same number of target measurements for the least squares method, we can compare the two bias estimates.

We consider the case when both biases have the same sign, for which the assumed bias-free estimator has the worst performance. The constant bias values for $\mathbf{b}_x^{(1)}$ and $\mathbf{b}_x^{(2)}$ are $(0.5, 0.7)$, while the true value of x is held fixed at 10. The variance of the x-measurement noise for both sensors is 0.4. The range and angle biases and noise variances are chosen so that the corresponding bias and noise in the x coordinate are the same as in the case of one-dimensional recursive method. The initial value of the state is set close to 10, and accordingly, the estimation error covariance is assumed small. This will simulate the situation where the steady state condition has been reached and a new set of sensors are brought into operation. Results are shown for 50 Monte Carlo simulations.

Figure 3 shows the performance of the recursive method for obtaining the bias-corrected state estimate. It is clear that without bias correction, the steady-state estimate is biased with respect to the true value; and the bias correction process removes most of the bias and is much closer to the true value.

Figures 4 and 5 show the estimated bias values and the normalized error variance as a function of the number of sampling intervals for the recursive bias estimation method and the number of target measurements for the generalized least squares method. With about 20 sampling intervals or target measurements, the estimated values become comparable. The variances also become comparable after about 20 sampling intervals.

Case 2 (Nonlinear measurements):

For this we choose a two-dimensional state vector, $\mathbf{X}$ in the x-y plane, and the range and angle measurements are nonlinear functions of $\mathbf{X}$. An extended Kalman filter is used to estimate the four bias variables, $\mathbf{b}_x^{(1)}$, etc., as well as to obtain bias-corrected estimates. The same scenario as in case 1 is simulated. The angle biases are chosen so that both radar neasurement biases, $\mathbf{b}_x^{(1)}$ and $\mathbf{b}_x^{(2)}$ are of the same sign (.05).

Figure 6 shows the improvement in the estimate of x, when bias estimates are made using an extended Kalman filter. Without any bias correction, the assumed bias-free estimate converges to the biased value, while with unbiased measurements, the correct value is obtained. The inclusion of the recursive bias estimation and correction algorithm in the estimator significantly improves the performance.

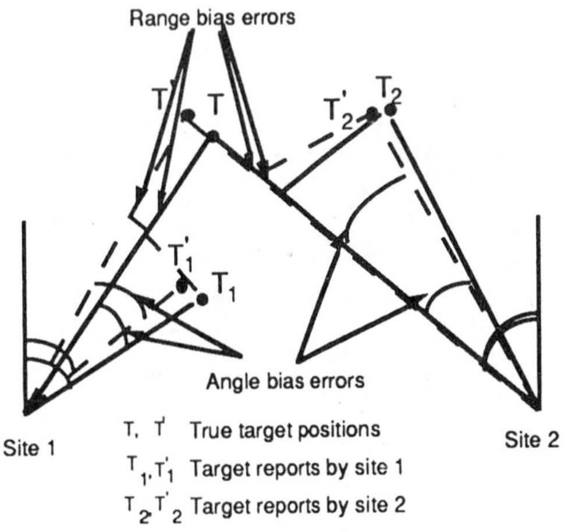

Figure 1. Source of Registration Errors in a Two-Sensor System

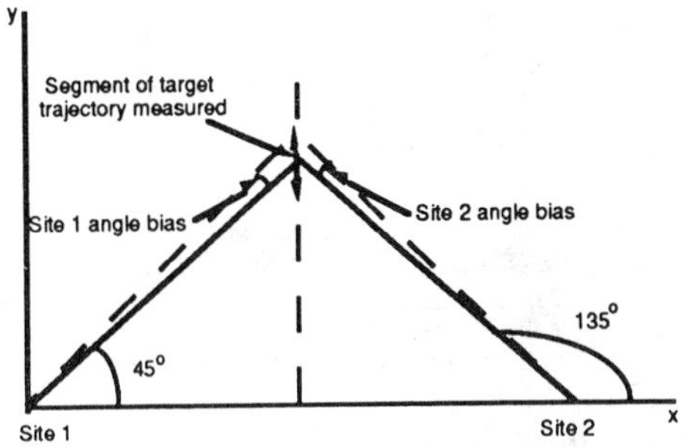

Figure 2. Target and Sensor Geometry for a Two Radar System

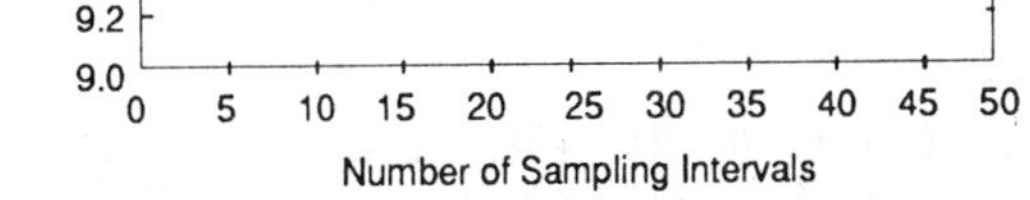

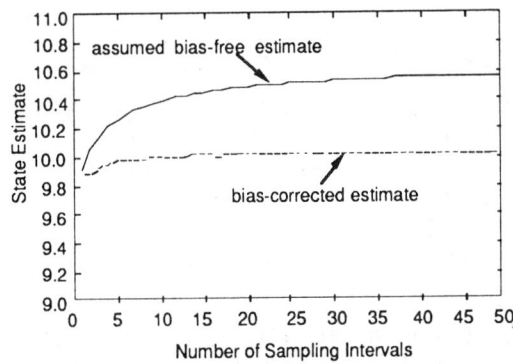

Figure 3. Assumed Bias-Free and Bias-Corrected Estimates: Recursive method

5. Summary and Conclusions

In this paper we have considered two methods for registration error correction for application in tracking with multiple sensors. The registration errors are modeled as bi-

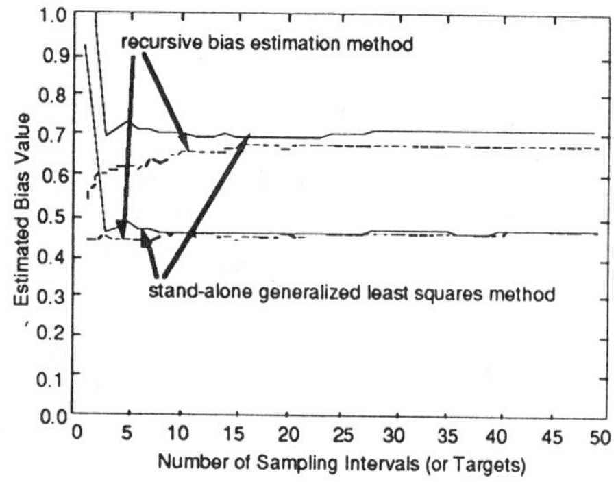

Figure 4. Comparison of Bias Estimates by Two Methods

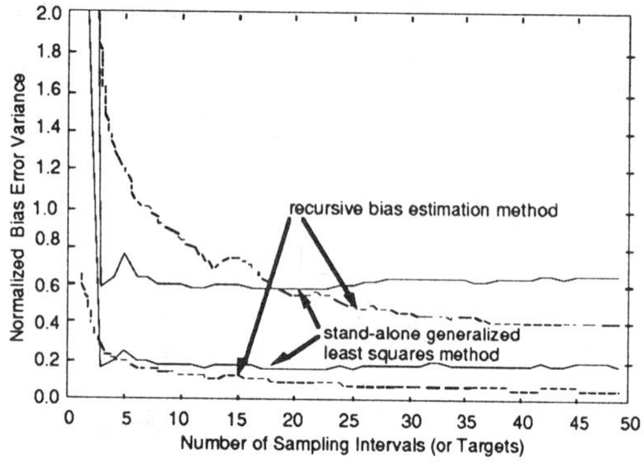

Figure 5. Comparison of Error Variance for Two Methods

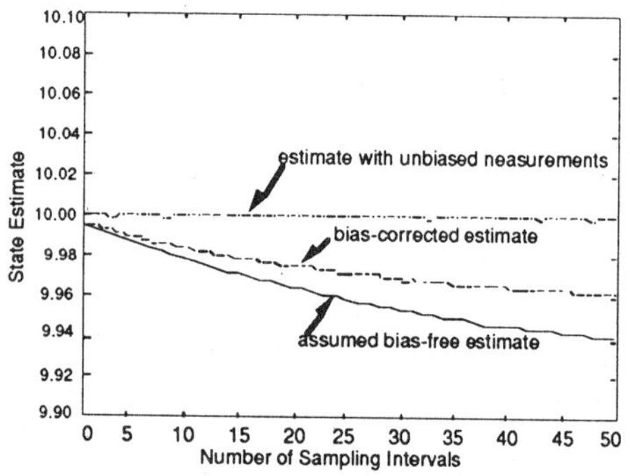

Figure 6. State Estimate from the Extended Kalman Filter

ases in the measurements. The two methods are the generalized least squares and the recursive bias estimation techniques. Using linear models for state transition and measurement, we obtained simulation results for a two radar measurement system, and showed that they provide comparable performance for the special scenario considered. We also showed that for the nonlinear measurement case, using an extended Kalman filter, the recursive bias estimation algorithm provides performance improvement over the case when biases are ignored. As discussed in [4] and [5], the actual performance depends strongly on the validity of the assumptions about the initial conditions of the filter parameters.

References

1. Fischer, W. L., C. E. Muehe, and A. G. Cameron, 1980, "Registration Errors in a Netted Air Surveillance System," Technical Note 1980-40, MIT Lincoln Laboratory, Lexington, MA.
2. Dana, M. P., 1989, "Registration: A Prerequisite for Multiple Sensor Tracking," Chapter 5 of *Multitarget-Multisensor Tracking: Advanced Applications*, edited by Y. Bar-Shalom, Artech House, Needham, MA.
3. Wax, M., 1983, "Position Location from Sensors with Position Uncertainty," *IEEE Transactions on Aerospace and Electronic Systems* AES-19, 658–662.
4. Friedland, B., 1969, "Treatment of Bias in Recursive Filtering," *IEEE Transactions on Automatic Control* AC-14, 359–367.
5. Ignagni, M. B., 1981, "An Alternate Derivation and Extension of Friedland's Two-Stage Kalman Estimator," *IEEE Transactions on Automatic Control* AC-26, 746-750.
6. Ignagni, M. B., 1990, "Separate-Bias Kalman Estimator with Bias State Noise," *IEEE Transactions on Automatic Control* AC-35, 338–341.
7. Alouani, A. T., T. R. Rice, and W. D. Blair, 1992, "A Two-Stage Filter for State Estimation in the Presence of Dynamical Stochastic Bias," *Proceedings of the American Control Conference (1992)*, 1784–1788.
8. Agee, W. S., and R. A. Turner, 1972, "Optimal Estimation of Measurement Bias," Technical Report No. 41, Defense Logistics Agency, Defense Technical Information Agency, Alexandria, VA.
9. Blom, H. A. P., R. A. Hogendoorn, and B. A. van Doorn, 1992, "Design of Multisensor Tracking System for Advanced Air Traffic Control," Chapter 2 of *Multitarget-Multisensor Tracking: Applications and Advances, Vol. II*, edited by Y. Bar-Shalom, Needham, MA: Artech House.
10. Brown, R. G., and P. Y. C. Hwang, 1992, *Introduction to Random Signals and Applied Kalman Filtering*, New York, NY: John Wiley and Sons.
11. Chan, Y. T., A. G. C. Hu, and J. B. Plant, 1979, "A Kalman Filter Based Tracking Scheme with Input Estimation," *IEEE Transactions on Aerospace and Electronic Systems* AES-15, 237–244.

Proceedings of the
American Control Conference
San Francisco, California • June 1993

WP9 - 15:50

REGISTRATION IN MULTI-SENSOR DATA FUSION AND TRACKING

Derek C. Cowley and Bahram Shafai
Communications and Digital Signal Processing (CDSP)
Center for Research and Graduate Studies
Department of Electrical and Computer Engineering
Northeastern University, Boston MA 02115

Abstract

This report presents a simple and direct method of solving the registration problem associated with multiple radar tracking. The registration proceedure is split into two distinct parts that are independent from one another. The first part is a deterministic transformation from the measurement domain to the measurement error or bias variable domain, and the second part is a filtering to track the actual value of the bias variables. Only the transformation part will be covered.

1. Introduction

Radar are devices used for measuring information about objects that are normally unobservable to the human eye. By emitting electro-magnetic energy and listening for an echo off an object, a radar can determine much about that object. Inherent in such information are distortions produced by several sources: (a) the media in which the electro-magnetic energy travels, (b) the radar receiver, (c) the object itself, and (d) other transmitting devices and objects in the measurement environment. The distortions that add to the information being gathered are in the form of (1) background noise , (2) multiple reflection paths between objects and receiver, (3) diffraction of electro-magnetic energy across impedance boundries or around large objects in the environment, (4) mechanical and electronic uncertainty about the receiver equipment itself. The result is that the radar makes errors in judgement about objects that it is trying to measure.

In particular, there are certain errors that the receiver introduces that are in the form of additive constants called bias errors or systematic errors. These bias errors are essentially deterministic in nature and are often constant over time. Determining the values of the bias errors is very useful, so that the signal processing device associated with the radar sensors can subtract them out of the raw and possibly biased measurements. The process of determining the bias errors of a particular radar station is called *registration*. Several articles have appeared in the reference literature relating to the solution of the registration process. References [4, 1, 3, 2] all provide overviews of the registration with various solutions. This report attempts to provide a consolidation of solutions based on the references cited above but with a slightly different topological view of the registration process as a whole.

1.1. Multi-Radar Tracking

Multi-radar tracking is a process of using more than one radar to make simultaneous measurements of an object or cluster of objects. It is a way of getting a view of an object from two or more angles simultaneously. There are several advantages and disadvantages when using more than one radar.

Advantages

- Better resolution in the face of noise and detection uncertainties.
- More reliable target data.
- Can solve bias errors of all radar involved simultaneously.
- Can extrapolate position of other radar platforms through object track data.

Disadvantages

- Requires constant communication between radar platforms.
- Requires more processing of object data.
- Radar coverage has to overlap extensively.

Radar are prone to detection errors, in that they either miss an object report on a particular sweep (antenna rotation), or receive a false report from just noise. Using two or more radar helps eliminate these errors because the errors from each radar are independent from one another. It is much less likely for both radar to miss an object on a given sweep than it is for just one radar to miss it. The same holds true for false reports. Hence if both radar report an object at a certain place and time, then the probability of being a real object is increased.

Noise corrupts the estimated position of an object from radar data, but many such noisy estimates can be used to reduce the effect of the noise. The nett effect is better resolution and accuracy when combining data from multiple radar.

Bias errors that get added into the measurements can be mutually cancelled by registering the radar.

If a radar is receiving track data from another radar but doesn't know where that remote radar is, then this can be calculated by combining the track data from both radar. If for example, the remote radar is moving and doesn't know exactly where it is, then it can calculate its position by receiving track data on mutually measured objects from a radar (maybe a fixed site) that knows where itself is. This is an indirect way for a radar to measure its position, and is by no means the only way, or even the fastest way, most of the time.

The advantages of multi-radar tracking are very desirable. However there are disadvantages as well, but these are bearable in the face of the advantages. Firstly, it is necessary for two radar sites to communicate continuously and therefore have a dedicated channel for this purpose. Such exclusive use of communications channels is very costly in terms of resources available in a theatre of operation. If such channels are interrupted or broken, then combining of track data ceases and multi-radar measurement ceases. Also, if any of the radar are airborne or ground-mobile, then the channel has to be omnidirectional.

Another disadvantage is that combining of data from multiple radar requires each radar to do more signal processing. This again is an expense that must be accounted for in terms of processing power, which directly impacts the cost, electrical and heat dissipation requirements of a radar.

A third disadvantage is that coverage of all radar involved has to overlap to a great extent. This constraint can serve to reduce the overall coverage for a given number of radar.

Therefore, for situations where the advantages outweigh the disadvantages (for example a radar wall like that used to monitor political borders), then it is of interest to consider the details of multi-radar tracking.

2. Registration Proceedure

The registration process can be considered in two stages. The first stage transforms the radar data from the report domain to the sensor bias domain. If noisy reports are used, then this transformation will result in noisy bias estimates. Therefore the translated data has to be filtered to remove the noise as much as possible, to get an accurate estimate of the sensor biases.

The catch is that the transformation process requires apriori paired reports, but then how can we have paired reports before registration? The answer is that not all data need be used for registration. If the sensor biases are known to be constant over a large period of time, then registration need only be done very infrequently, daily for example. If the sensor biases are not known to be constant, then registration needs to be done more frequently. Only the widely separated targets, and hence easily pairable reports, need be used. Registration can be performed when this kind of data are available, and then the resulting bias estimates can be used to untangle the reports of clustered targets, that were initially unpairable. To help in finding initially paired data, the old estimate of the sensor biases (possible incorrect) can be used to partially register the reports. If no old values exist, then initial guesses can be used. The result is a feedback of estimated data into the registration process.

2.1. Data Transformation

This is a deterministic proceedure whereby the raw (unregistered) radar data (reports) are converted to the bias variable domain. The reports in general have noise added to then with associated noise variances. The transformation step does not consider the noise, it simply converts data from one form to another for further processing. The noise variances, treated separately, are also converted to the bias variable domain.

To start the development of the transformation step, the geometry and parameterization must be estabilshed. Figure 1 shows the geometry of the "two radar problem" in two dimensions. To simplify things for the initial development, The remote radar B will have known position (this will be relaxed later) and there will only be 4 bias variables. Let ψ denote the vector of bias variables

$$\psi = [\ r_A \quad \theta_A \quad r_B \quad \theta_B\ ]^T \tag{1}$$

where $\{r_A, r_B\}$ are the measured range to target from radar's A and B respectively, and similarly $\{\theta_A, \theta_B\}$ are the measured bearings to to target. Let β be the vectorized bias variable

$$\beta = [\ \Delta r_A \quad \Delta\theta_A \quad \Delta r_B \quad \Delta\theta_B\ ]^T \tag{2}$$

where the Δ in front of each variable designates it as a bias variable instead of a measurement.

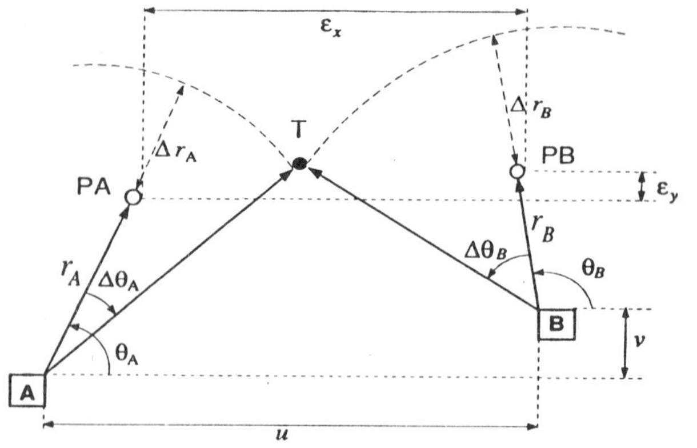

Figure 1: Geometry of registration with 4 bias variables

A is the local radar and B is the remote radar of known position relative to A. T is the target position, which is not known to either radar, and (PA,PB) are the measured positions of the target from radar A and B respectfully. Let us eliminate noise from this problem for this stage of the development, and concern ourselves only with bias variable distortions. The two empty circles in figure 1 are the two unregistered but pre-paired reports. Let the apparent report separation be denoted by ε, where $\{\varepsilon_X, \varepsilon_Y\}$ are the rectangular components of ε in the X (horizontal) and Y (vertical) directions. Radar B is spatially separated from radar A by $\{u, v\}$ in the X and Y directions. The geometry of the problem is fully defined, now all we have to do is solve for β, the vectorized bias variable.

Lets start by defining ε in terms of ψ and β.

$$\begin{aligned} \varepsilon_X &= (r_A + \Delta r_A)\cos(\theta_A + \Delta\theta_A) \\ &\quad -(r_B + \Delta r_B)\cos(\theta_B + \Delta\theta_B) - u \end{aligned} \tag{3}$$

$$\begin{aligned} \varepsilon_Y &= (r_A + \Delta r_A)\sin(\theta_A + \Delta\theta_A) \\ &\quad -(r_B + \Delta r_B)\sin(\theta_B + \Delta\theta_B) - v \end{aligned} \tag{4}$$

Vectorizing ε we get,

$$\varepsilon = \begin{bmatrix} \varepsilon_X \\ \varepsilon_Y \end{bmatrix} \triangleq \mathcal{F}(\psi, \beta) \tag{5}$$

and defining the non-linear function $\mathcal{F}$ as in (3) and (4), where ψ and β are its parameters. Now lets define β^* as the true value of β

$$\mathcal{F}(\psi, \beta^*) = 0 \tag{6}$$

since a perfectly registered radar pair will yield reports (PA,PB) to be collocated at T, making ε_X and ε_Y both equal to zero. All we have to do is solve (6) for unknown β, which is equivalent to finding the root of a non-linear equation. This is, in general, hard to solve nonlinear equations analytically. A standard method for solving roots of a nonlinear equation is the *Newton-Raphson method* in its multi-dimensional form. This is an iterative method based on solving linear approximations the a nonlinear function. We start the first iteration of the Newton-Raphson method by choosing an initial guess for β (commonly zero), and designating this guess as β'. Then, linearizing $\mathcal{F}$ around β', involves a first order approximation of the *Taylor series expansion* of $\mathcal{F}$ around β'. Designate this approximation of $\mathcal{F}$ by $\mathcal{F}'$

$$\mathcal{F}'(\psi, \beta) = \mathcal{F}(\psi, \beta') + \nabla_\beta [\mathcal{F}(\psi, \beta)]_{\beta=\beta'} (\beta - \beta') \tag{7}$$

where $\mathcal{F}(\psi, \beta')$ is a constant since both ψ and β' are known. ∇_β is the gradient of $\mathcal{F}$ with respect to β at a particular value of ψ.

$$\nabla_\beta [\mathcal{F}(\psi, \beta')] = \left.\frac{\partial \mathcal{F}(\psi, \beta)}{\partial \beta}\right|_{\beta=\beta'} = \left.\frac{\partial \varepsilon}{\partial \beta}\right|_{\beta=\beta'}$$

$$= \begin{bmatrix} \frac{\partial \varepsilon_X}{\partial \Delta r_A} & \frac{\partial \varepsilon_X}{\partial \Delta \theta_A} & \frac{\partial \varepsilon_X}{\partial \Delta r_B} & \frac{\partial \varepsilon_X}{\partial \Delta \theta_B} \\ \frac{\partial \varepsilon_Y}{\partial \Delta r_A} & \frac{\partial \varepsilon_Y}{\partial \Delta \theta_A} & \frac{\partial \varepsilon_Y}{\partial \Delta r_B} & \frac{\partial \varepsilon_Y}{\partial \Delta \theta_B} \end{bmatrix}_{\beta=\beta'} \quad (8)$$

Note that $\mathcal{F}'$ is linear in β, and

$$\mathcal{F}'(\psi, \beta') \approx \mathcal{F}(\psi, \beta') \quad \text{for small } (\beta^* - \beta')$$

To solve for β, we set $\mathcal{F}'(\psi, \beta') = 0$. However, this set of linear equations has 4 scalar unknowns and only 2 scalar equations. Therefore there is no unique solution based on this information alone. What is needed are two more independent equations to make a complete set of solvable equations. This can be achieved by simultaneously solving for another target T2 that is spatially separated from the first target redesignated as T1. T2 will yield another measurement vector ψ_2. Redesignate the measurement vector of T1 as ψ_1. Solve β with both measurement vectors simultaneously.

$$\beta = \beta' - J_\beta(\psi_1, \psi_2, \beta') \begin{bmatrix} \mathcal{F}(\psi_1, \beta') \\ \mathcal{F}(\psi_2, \beta') \end{bmatrix} \quad (9)$$

where J_β is the Jacobian of $\mathcal{F}$.

$$J_\beta(\psi_1, \psi_2, \beta') = \begin{bmatrix} \nabla_\beta \left[\mathcal{F}(\psi_1, \beta)\right]_{\beta=\beta'} \\ \nabla_\beta \left[\mathcal{F}(\psi_2, \beta)\right]_{\beta=\beta'} \end{bmatrix} \quad (10)$$

J_β is guaranteed to be invertible if both radar and both targets are spatially separated by any amount (for the noiseless case). For the noisy case, there is always a probability that J_β may become singular $\{\psi_1, \psi_2\}$, and in that case, just ignore this data and move to the next time instant of $\{\psi_1, \psi_2\}$.

Since $\mathcal{F}'$ is only an approximation of $\mathcal{F}$, the calculated value of β is only an approximation of β^*. But for small $(\beta' - \beta^*)$ then $\beta \approx \beta^*$. However, we do not know β^*, so we cannot make this determination. Therefore the algorithm must proceed to the second step of the Newton-Raphson method.

The Newton-Raphson method moves to its second iteration by setting $\beta' \leftarrow \beta$ and resolve for β. Keep repeating this recursion until β converges to β^*.

The Newton-Raphson method is robust, in that it will always find a root of $\mathcal{F}$ given enough iterations. However, $\mathcal{F}$ has an infinite number of roots since

$$\sin(\alpha) = \sin(\alpha + 2n\pi)$$

where $n \in \mathcal{Z}$. We want the principle root where $\alpha + 2n\pi \in (-\pi, \pi]$. This is easy to find by taking any angle calculated for β at an iteration step, and finding its principle value.

It has been determined experimentally that, given $\mathcal{F}$ as it is defined, not many iterations are needed to find an exact solution for β even for very large $(\beta' - \beta^*)$. For the case of 4 bias variables, 4 iterations has always yielded an answer within the limits of double precision floating point accuracy, mostly less than 4 iterations are required.

For noisy $\{\psi_1, \psi_2\}$, the calculated (converged) value of β is not β^*, but somewhere in the neighborhood of β^*. The noise in the measurements is translated directly into noise in β. Using successive paired reports $\{\psi_1(k), \psi_2(k)\}$, we calculate successive for β, designated as $\beta(k)$, where k is the time step (not the iteration step within the Newton-Raphson method). With a sequence of noisy $\beta(k)$, we can filter out the noise component using an appropriet filter. Note that $\psi_1(k)$ do not have to come from successive measurements of the same target for all k, it can be from any target for any k. Similarly for $\psi_2(k)$. Also, to reiterate, all pairs of $\{\psi_1(k), \psi_2(k)\}$, regardless of the time step, must both be paired data at the same time instant. That is, $\psi_1(k)$ is a pre-paired measurement vector and similarly for $\psi_2(k)$, and both measurement vectors must be measured simultaneously.

2.2. Transformation of the Noise Covariance Matrix

If the radar measurements have noise, then there is a corresponding transformation of the measurement covariance matrix into the bias variable space, yielding a bias covariance matrix. To start with, assume that the noise in each bias variable in the bias vector is independent, then the measurement covariance matrix Σ_ψ is simply:

$$\underset{4\times4}{\Sigma_\psi} = \text{diag}\left(\sigma^2_{r_A} \quad \sigma^2_{\theta_A} \quad \sigma^2_{r_B} \quad \sigma^2_{\theta_B} \right) \quad (11)$$

where σ^2 stands for the variance of the noise in a particular bias variable. Σ_ψ is a diagonal 4×4 matrix since all 4 bias variables are independent of one another. The covariance matrix of the association error ε is Σ_ε

$$\underset{2\times2}{\Sigma_\varepsilon} = J_\psi \Sigma_\psi J_\psi^T \quad (12)$$

where J_ψ is the Jacobian of $\mathcal{F}$ with respect to ψ

$$\underset{2\times4}{J_\psi} = \nabla_\psi \left[\mathcal{F}(\psi, \beta)\right] \quad (13)$$

where ∇_ψ is the gradient of $\mathcal{F}$ with respect to ψ.

Since we treat two independent targets $\{\psi_1, \psi_2\}$ simultaneously, the overall measurement covariance is

$$\underset{8\times8}{\Sigma_{\psi 12}} = \begin{bmatrix} \Sigma_{\psi 1} & 0 \\ 0 & \Sigma_{\psi 2} \end{bmatrix} \quad (14)$$

where $\Sigma_{\psi 1} = \Sigma_{\psi 2} = \Sigma_\psi$ since all measurements have the same noise convariances. The corresponding association error covariance matrix is

$$\underset{4\times4}{\Sigma_{\varepsilon 12}} = J_{\psi 12} \Sigma_{\psi 12} J_{\psi 12}^T = \begin{bmatrix} \Sigma_{\varepsilon 1} & 0 \\ 0 & \Sigma_{\varepsilon 2} \end{bmatrix} \quad (15)$$

where

$$\underset{4\times8}{J_{\psi 12}} = \begin{bmatrix} J_{\psi 1} & 0 \\ 0 & J_{\psi 2} \end{bmatrix} \quad (16)$$

and

$$\underset{2\times4}{J_{\psi 1}} = \nabla_\psi \left[\mathcal{F}(\psi, \beta)\right]_{\psi=\psi_1} \quad (17)$$

$$\underset{2\times4}{J_{\psi 2}} = \nabla_\psi \left[\mathcal{F}(\psi, \beta)\right]_{\psi=\psi_2} \quad (18)$$

Therefore

$$\underset{2\times2}{\Sigma_{\varepsilon 1}} = J_{\psi 1} \Sigma_\psi J_{\psi 1}^T \quad (19)$$

$$\underset{2\times2}{\Sigma_{\varepsilon 2}} = J_{\psi 2} \Sigma_\psi J_{\psi 2}^T \quad (20)$$

Finally, the covariance matrix of the bias vector β is

$$\underset{4\times4}{\Sigma_\beta} = \left(J_{\beta 12}^T \Sigma_{\varepsilon 12}^{-1} J_{\beta 12}\right)^{-1} \quad (21)$$

where

$$\underset{4\times4}{\Sigma_{\varepsilon 12}^{-1}} = \begin{bmatrix} \Sigma_{\varepsilon 1}^{-1} & 0 \\ 0 & \Sigma_{\varepsilon 2}^{-1} \end{bmatrix} \quad (22)$$

and

$$\underset{4\times4}{J_{\beta 12}} = \begin{bmatrix} J_{\beta 1} \\ J_{\beta 2} \end{bmatrix} \quad (23)$$

where

$$\underset{2\times4}{J_{\beta 1}} = \nabla_\beta \left[\mathcal{F}(\psi_1, \beta)\right] \quad (24)$$

$$\underset{2\times4}{J_{\beta 2}} = \nabla_\beta \left[\mathcal{F}(\psi_2, \beta)\right] \quad (25)$$

hence

$$\underset{4\times4}{\Sigma_\beta} = \left[J_{\beta 1}^T \Sigma_{\varepsilon 1}^{-1} J_{\beta 1} + J_{\beta 2}^T \Sigma_{\varepsilon 2}^{-1} J_{\beta 2}\right]^{-1} \quad (26)$$

Note that Σ_β is not diagonal, hence the noise in the bias variables is not independent, and it also depends on β.

3. Extending the Bias Vector

All analysis up to this point has been performed with only four bias variables Δr_A, $\Delta\theta_A$, Δr_B, $\Delta\theta_B$. The problem can be expanded by defining more systematic errors induced by radar receivers.

3.1. Remote Radar Position Uncertainty

The first extension is to include variables relating to the uncertainty of the remote radar position Δr_{AB}, $\Delta\theta_{AB}$, which are polar variables added to the relative position r_{AB}, θ_{AB}, of the remote radar to the local radar. The bias vector is now of size six

$$\beta = [\ \Delta r_A \quad \Delta\theta_A \quad \Delta r_B \quad \Delta\theta_B \quad \Delta r_{AB} \quad \Delta\theta_{AB}\ ]^T \quad (27)$$

The equations that describe the geometry with remote position uncertainty are as follows.

$$\begin{aligned} \varepsilon_X &= (r_A + \Delta r_A)\cos(\theta_A + \Delta\theta_A) - \\ &\quad (r_B + \Delta r_B)\cos(\theta_B + \Delta\theta_B) - \\ &\quad (r_{AB} + \Delta r_{AB})\cos(\theta_{AB} + \Delta\theta_{AB}) \quad (28) \\ \varepsilon_Y &= (r_A + \Delta r_A)\sin(\theta_A + \Delta\theta_A) - \\ &\quad (r_B + \Delta r_B)\sin(\theta_B + \Delta\theta_B) - \\ &\quad (r_{AB} + \Delta r_{AB})\sin(\theta_{AB} + \Delta\theta_{AB}) \quad (29) \end{aligned}$$

The solution of β from these equations is similar to the solution from equations (3,4) except that there are six unknowns now, and therefore 3 targets must be measured simultaneously to generate six independent equations. The Jacobian for these equations is then

$$J_\beta(\psi_1, \psi_2, \psi_3, \beta') = \begin{bmatrix} \nabla_\beta\,[\mathcal{F}(\psi_1, \beta)]_{\beta=\beta'} \\ \nabla_\beta\,[\mathcal{F}(\psi_2, \beta)]_{\beta=\beta'} \\ \nabla_\beta\,[\mathcal{F}(\psi_3, \beta)]_{\beta=\beta'} \end{bmatrix} \quad (30)$$

where ∇_β is a 2×6 matrix. However, this Jacobian is rank deficient, and therefore cannot be inverted to solve for β. There is too much freedom in the geometry of the problem, in the form of an undefined rotation with the combination of the three bias variables $\Delta\theta_A$, $\Delta\theta_B$, and $\Delta\theta_{AB}$. Only five of the six variables can be solved for at any instant, therefore one angle related variable must be chosen to be eliminated from the problem. If $\Delta\theta_{AB}$ is chosen, then the solution of the other five bias variables is called a *base-line relative* solution, since there is no correction for base-line errors (θ_{AB} defines the direction of the base-line between two radar). This form of solution is appropriate if both radar are fixed ground stations where the actual base-line angle is known. For mobile and airborne radar, base-line relative solutions are not appropriate because the base-line is unknown. However, there are two other angle related bias variables $\Delta\theta_A$ or $\Delta\theta_B$ that can be chosen to be eliminated from the problem in order to solve for β. In general, the angle related variable with the lowest variance (most well known) can be eliminated to find the solution of the other five bias variables relative to the assumed value of the variable chosen to be eliminated. Relative solutions are the best that can be achieved with unknown or uncertain remote radar position.

3.2. Range Gain Errors

Another possible extension to the bias variable set is to add range gain errors, Δg_A, and Δg_B, by replacing r_A and r_B range measurements in (3,4) or (28,29) with $e^{\Delta g_A} r_A$ and $e^{\Delta g_B} r_B$ respectively. The gradient and Jacobian have to be redefined accordingly. However, this extension to the bias variable set introduces another degree of excess freedom to the problem. The combination of the five range related bias variables Δr_A, Δg_a, Δr_B, Δg_B, and Δr_{AB} create a scale uncertainty that cannot be corrected unless one of the range related variables is assumed fixed, then the other range related variables can be solved relative to the value assumed for the fixed (or eliminated) variable. This situation is the same as that of the rotational uncertainty associated with the angle related bias variables.

If all eight parameters described above (3 angle related bias variables and 5 range related bias variables) are defined in the problem, then one range related variable must be eliminated to fix the scaling freedom, and one angle related variable must be eliminated to fix the rotational freedom. Therefore only six out of the eight bias variables can be solved for at any instant in time. For example, if both radar stations are fixed and of known relative position, then the two variables relating the remote radar position (one angle and one range related variable) can be eliminated satisfying both rotational and scaling uncertainties.

3.3. Elevation Measurement Errors

Another extension the β is to add elevation measurement errors, $\Delta\phi_A$, $\Delta\phi_B$ and possibly $\Delta\phi_{AB}$. These elevation measurement offsets are the errors incorporated by each radar in measuring targets, and in measuring their relative elevation from eachother. The geometry of this case can be described by the following equations.

$$\begin{aligned} \varepsilon_X = \ & (e^{\Delta g_A} r_A + \Delta r_A) \ \cos(\theta_A + \Delta\theta_A) \\ & \qquad \cos(\phi_A + \Delta\phi_A) - \\ & (e^{\Delta g_B} r_B + \Delta r_B) \ \cos(\theta_B + \Delta\theta_B) \\ & \qquad \cos(\phi_B + \Delta\phi_B) - \\ & (r_{AB} + \Delta r_{AB}) \ \cos(\theta_{AB} + \Delta\theta_{AB}) \\ & \qquad \cos(\phi_{AB} + \Delta\phi_{AB}) \end{aligned} \quad (31)$$

$$\begin{aligned} \varepsilon_Y = \ & (e^{\Delta g_A} r_A + \Delta r_A) \ \sin(\theta_A + \Delta\theta_A) \\ & \qquad \cos(\phi_A + \Delta\phi_A) - \\ & (e^{\Delta g_B} r_B + \Delta r_B) \ \sin(\theta_B + \Delta\theta_B) \\ & \qquad \cos(\phi_B + \Delta\phi_B) - \\ & (r_{AB} + \Delta r_{AB}) \ \sin(\theta_{AB} + \Delta\theta_{AB}) \\ & \qquad \cos(\phi_{AB} + \Delta\phi_{AB}) \end{aligned} \quad (32)$$

$$\begin{aligned} \varepsilon_Z = \ & (e^{\Delta g_A} r_A + \Delta r_A) \ \sin(\phi_A + \Delta\phi_A) - \\ & (e^{\Delta g_B} r_B + \Delta r_B) \ \sin(\phi_B + \Delta\phi_B) - \\ & (r_{AB} + \Delta r_{AB}) \ \sin(\phi_{AB} + \Delta\phi_{AB}) \end{aligned} \quad (33)$$

The separation vector ε has components in three dimensions using rectangular coordinates. Elevation bias variables do not add any uncertainty (do not contribute to any rank deficiency of the Jacobian) to the problem so all three of the elevation bias variables can be solved for. Out of the 11 bias variables presented in the equations above, one bearing and one range related variable have to go so that the other 9 can be solved. Three simultaneously measured paired targets have to be aquired in order to provide 9 independent equations to solve for the 9 remaining bias variables. The Jacobian is a 9×9 matrix that is guaranteed full rank (in the noiseless case).

3.4. Registration of Three Radar Simultaneously

Another 7 bias variables associated with a third radar can be solved simultaneously while only using three targets simultaneously measured with pre-associated (in threes) reports. The bias variables relating to the third radar are Δg_C, Δr_C, $\Delta\theta_C$, $\Delta\phi_C$, Δr_{AC}, $\Delta\theta_{AC}$, $\Delta\phi_{AC}$. With 18 possible bias variables, two must be eliminated and the remaining 16 can be solved. The geometry equations are

$$
\begin{aligned}
\varepsilon_{X_{AB}} = \; & (e^{\Delta g_A} r_A + \Delta r_A) \; \cos(\theta_A + \Delta\theta_A) \cos(\phi_A + \Delta\phi_A) - \\
& (e^{\Delta g_B} r_B + \Delta r_B) \; \cos(\theta_B + \Delta\theta_B) \cos(\phi_B + \Delta\phi_B) - \\
& (r_{AB} + \Delta r_{AB}) \; \cos(\theta_{AB} + \Delta\theta_{AB}) \cos(\phi_{AB} + \Delta\phi_{AB})
\end{aligned} \qquad (34)
$$

$$
\begin{aligned}
\varepsilon_{Y_{AB}} = \; & (e^{\Delta g_A} r_A + \Delta r_A) \; \sin(\theta_A + \Delta\theta_A) \cos(\phi_A + \Delta\phi_A) - \\
& (e^{\Delta g_B} r_B + \Delta r_B) \; \sin(\theta_B + \Delta\theta_B) \cos(\phi_B + \Delta\phi_B) - \\
& (r_{AB} + \Delta r_{AB}) \; \sin(\theta_{AB} + \Delta\theta_{AB}) \cos(\phi_{AB} + \Delta\phi_{AB})
\end{aligned} \qquad (35)
$$

$$
\begin{aligned}
\varepsilon_{Z_{AB}} = \; & (e^{\Delta g_A} r_A + \Delta r_A) \; \sin(\phi_A + \Delta\phi_A) - \\
& (e^{\Delta g_B} r_B + \Delta r_B) \; \sin(\phi_B + \Delta\phi_B) - \\
& (r_{AB} + \Delta r_{AB}) \; \sin(\phi_{AB} + \Delta\phi_{AB})
\end{aligned} \qquad (36)
$$

$$
\begin{aligned}
\varepsilon_{X_{AC}} = \; & (e^{\Delta g_A} r_A + \Delta r_A) \; \cos(\theta_A + \Delta\theta_A) \cos(\phi_A + \Delta\phi_A) - \\
& (e^{\Delta g_C} r_C + \Delta r_C) \; \cos(\theta_C + \Delta\theta_C) \cos(\phi_C + \Delta\phi_C) - \\
& (r_{AC} + \Delta r_{AC}) \; \cos(\theta_{AC} + \Delta\theta_{AC}) \cos(\phi_{AC} + \Delta\phi_{AC})
\end{aligned} \qquad (37)
$$

$$
\begin{aligned}
\varepsilon_{Y_{AC}} = \; & (e^{\Delta g_A} r_A + \Delta r_A) \; \sin(\theta_A + \Delta\theta_A) \cos(\phi_A + \Delta\phi_A) - \\
& (e^{\Delta g_C} r_C + \Delta r_C) \; \sin(\theta_C + \Delta\theta_C) \cos(\phi_C + \Delta\phi_C) - \\
& (r_{AC} + \Delta r_{AC}) \; \sin(\theta_{AC} + \Delta\theta_{AC}) \cos(\phi_{AC} + \Delta\phi_{AC})
\end{aligned} \qquad (38)
$$

$$
\begin{aligned}
\varepsilon_{Z_{AC}} = \; & (e^{\Delta g_A} r_A + \Delta r_A) \; \sin(\phi_A + \Delta\phi_A) - \\
& (e^{\Delta g_C} r_C + \Delta r_C) \; \sin(\phi_C + \Delta\phi_C) - \\
& (r_{AC} + \Delta r_{AC}) \; \sin(\phi_{AC} + \Delta\phi_{AC})
\end{aligned} \qquad (39)
$$

Each target triple provides 6 equations, therefore 3 targets are necessary to provide enough independent equations to solve for 16 out of the 18 possible bias variables. The Jacobian will have the form of (30), and will be guaranteed full rank (in the noiseless case).

3.5. Summary of Extended Bias Variables

The following table is a summary of all bias variables discussed so far.

	Range Gain Unknowns	Sensor Offset Unknowns	Unknown Remote Radar Position	Elevation Measurement Unknowns
Radar A	Δg_A	Δr_A $\Delta\theta_A$		$\Delta\phi_A$
Radar B	Δg_B	Δr_B $\Delta\theta_B$	Δr_{AB} $\Delta\theta_{AB}$	$\Delta\phi_B$ $\Delta\phi_{AB}$
Radar C	Δg_C	Δr_C $\Delta\theta_C$	Δr_{AC} $\Delta\theta_{AC}$	$\Delta\phi_C$ $\Delta\phi_{AC}$

The following table is a summary of the exclusion principles that guarantee solvability of the Newton-Raphson equation in the noiseless case. One variable must be eliminated from the scaling and rotation columns only.

Scaling	Rotation	Elevation
Δg_A	$\Delta\theta_A$	$\Delta\phi_A$
Δr_A		
Δg_B	$\Delta\theta_B$	$\Delta\phi_B$
Δr_B		
Δr_{AB}	$\Delta\theta_{AB}$	$\Delta\phi_{AB}$
Δg_C	$\Delta\theta_C$	$\Delta\phi_C$
Δr_C		
Δr_{AC}	$\Delta\theta_{AC}$	$\Delta\phi_{AC}$

Noisy measurements will require targets that are used for registration to be spaced apart with certain minimum margins that depend on the noise level. The greater the noise level, the larger the minimum spacing will be, for rank of the equations and stability of the solution.

The number of simultaneously measured and associated targets required to solve the registration equations is either two or three. An equation is presented to determine which.

$$
\#targets = \frac{\#bias\ variables}{(\#spatial\ dimensions) \times (\#radar - 1)} \qquad (40)
$$

4. Conclusion

Presented in this report is a simple and robust method of registering multiple radar together in order to perform multi-radar tracking. The algorithm can easily be extended to handle other bias variables, more than two radar, and more that 2 spatial dimensions. Not covered in this report are the important issues of filtration of noisy bias estimates, apriori data association of target reports, time synchronization of paired data, timing errors associated with moving radar, registration of track based data and overdetermined data.

Acknowledgement

This work is supported in part by a grant from Mitre Corporation through CDSP Research Center.

REFERENCES

[1] M. P. Dana, "Multiple Sensor Registration: A Prerequisite for Multisensor Tracking," Y. Bar-Shalom (ed.), *Multitarget-Multisensor Tracking: Advanced Applications*, Artech House, Norwood, MA, 1990, pp. 155-185 (Chapter 5).

[2] A. Farina and F. A. Studer, *Radar Data Processing*, Vol. 1, *Introduction to Tracking*, Research Studies Press, 1985.

[3] S. S. Blackman, *Multiple Target Tracking with Radar Applications*, Artech Book Company, London, 1986.

[4] K. A. Cabana and M. K. Cimini, *Necessary and Sufficient Conditions for Radar Registration*, The MITRE Corporation internal publication, MTR10658, August 1989.

Proceedings of the
American Control Conference
San Francisco, California • June 1993

Utilization of Qualitative Information For Multisensor Target Tracking

Kwang H. Kim
20 Lakin St.
Pepperell, MA 01463

Abstract -- Qualitative reasoning is especially appealing for multisensor target tracking because of its ability to accomodate uncertainty and conflict. This paper presents a rule-based modeling approach for manuever target tracking, and a qualitative track/data association technique by combining numerical data with often informational but seldom used surveillance operator's intuition. Computer simulations validate the contribution of such information particularly in a stressful target tracking environment.

1. Introduction

Classical estimation theory uses prior modeling knowledge which is deterministic, statistical or both. In such a framework, it is very difficult to utilize non-numerical qualitative information. This paper explores the use of such information in estimation, especially in target tracking, where previously ignored surveillance operators' expertise may impact system performance. First, we examine some problems that arise in multiple target tracking.

Most tracking filters are model-based and thus, if a target trajectory deviates from the assumed model, then the tracker performance starts to degrade. This is a well-known problem and numerous techniques to deal with it have been published in literature. The most popular techniques are: (i) adjustable noise variances [1-5], (ii) augmenting states [6-11], (iii) input estimation [12-15], and (iv) multiple model [16-18] and interactive multiple model [19-21]. Tracking in clutter causes another uncertainty due to the uncertain origin of measurements. There are many techniques ranging from the simple nearest neighbor association to the more complex multiple hypotheses [22,23]. However, even with these sophisticated algorithms, tracking of maneuvering targets remains elusively challenging.

In section 2, we revisit the α-β tracking algorithm and analyze its characteristics to explore the possible utilization of a rule-based logic for maneuvering target tracking. Section 3 reviews the most widely used track and data association algorithms in current tracking systems, and presents a formulation of qualitative knowledge-augmented track/data association algorithms. Computer simulation results are presented in section 4.

2. Maneuver Target Tracking

Qualitative reasoning has been known to be useful when rigorous mathematical modeling is too difficult or computationally too expensive: balancing double pendulum, truck backup, etc. Another example is the tracking of maneuvering targets, since such target dynamics cannot be exactly described. Fuzzy logic, as introduced by Zadeh [24] has been suggested as being appropriate for describing systems that are too complex or too ill-defined to apply precise mathematical analysis. Thus, it is quite logical to consider a fuzzy logic based tracker to process maneuvering targets. Since Mamdani's seminal work [25] on a control application of fuzzy set theory, fuzzy control has drawn tremendous interest throughout industry and academia, and has reached fruition in numerous practical applications [26-31]. In this section, we reexamine the α-β tracking algorithm and attempt to deduce fuzzy control rules.

2.1. α-β Tracker

The α-β algorithms are the most extensively applied fixed-coefficient filters. These filters are defined by the following equations and are used when only position measurement is available:

$$\hat{x}(k|k) = \hat{x}(k|k-1)+\alpha[x_m(k)-\hat{x}(k|k-1)] \quad (2\text{-}1)$$
$$\hat{\dot{x}}(k|k) = \hat{\dot{x}}(k|k-1)+(\beta/T)[x_m(k)-\hat{x}(k|k-1)] \quad (2\text{-}2)$$
$$\hat{y}(k|k) = \hat{y}(k|k-1)+\alpha[y_m(k)-\hat{y}(k|k-1)] \quad (2\text{-}3)$$
$$\hat{\dot{y}}(k|k) = \hat{\dot{y}}(k|k-1)+(\beta/T)[y_m(k)-\hat{y}(k|k-1)] \quad (2\text{-}4)$$

Note that the smoothing is performed in each coordinate separately. The predicted target position is simply a linear extrapolation from the previous smoothed position with a constant velocity.

The range of smoothing gains α and β, can be obtained from the characteristic equation of the filter, $z^2 + (\alpha+\beta-2) + (1-\alpha) = 0$. Applying the Jury's test yields the stability region which provides admissible α, β values:

$$\beta > 0$$
$$2\alpha + \beta < 4$$
$$0 < \alpha < 2.$$

Most of the α-β tracking algorithms use two sets of smoothing equations: region coordinate smoothing (RCS) and track coordinate smoothing (TCS). The RCS is employed for non-maneuvering targets, with the equations given by (2-1) through (2-4), while the TCS is used for maneuvering targets. In TCS, the filter residuals are decomposed into the radial and the crossing direction with separate smoothing gains, so that the residual in the crossing direction may produce significantly greater response in the perpendicular direction, which is characteristic of turning aircraft. Separate sets of smoothing parameters are usually provided for different validation gates in both RCS and TCS. In addition, the velocity smoothing parameter β is a function of target speed. Smoothing is also controlled by the correlation gates and the track mode (normal, transition or maneuver). The normal mode is assigned to tracks which have correlated with data in the small validation gate. This mode implies good quality straight line tracking. Transition between the modes depends on the correlation, current target mode, and maneuver detection test.

2.2 Rule Based Manuever Logic

Recognizing that maneuver dynamics cannot be rigorously described, we attempt to design a fuzzy tracker which may provide a faster and more precise maneuver response. Observable parameters are the filter residual and change of the residual, and the control parameters are the gain constants, α and β. For feasibility evaluation, a simple benign target environment is used, i.e. no false alarms, probability of detection $P_D<1.0$ and a single target.

A fuzzy algorithm consists of defining membership functions, formation of control rules, and making decisions. It is imperative to formulate an extensive rule set based on experts' experience and to derive input-output relationships from the rules. The control rules are generally expressed in if-then statements. In addition, it is necessary to quantize the qualitative statements expressed in terms of linguistic variables. These variables are:

LP = large positive,
MP = medium positive,
SP = small positive,
ZE = zero.
SM = small negative,
MN = medium negative,
LN = large negative,

After formulating control rules, the next step is to define the membership functions of linguistic sets. The shape of membership functions is quite arbitrary and heavily depends on system requirements.

Membership Functions:

The membership functions chosen for the fuzzy tracker are taken to be the polygonal curves converting the values below:

Dc	0	2	4	6	8	10	12	14	16
ZE	1.0	0.8	0.2	0	0	0	0	0	0
SP	0.2	0.8	1.0	0.8	0.2	0	0	0	0
MP	0	0	0.2	0.8	1.0	0.8	0.2	0	0
LP	0	0	0	0	0.2	0.8	1.0	1.0	1.0

ΔD	0	20	40	60	80	100	120	140	160
ZE	1.0	0.8	0.2	0	0	0	0	0	0
SP	0.2	0.8	1.0	0.8	0.2	0	0	0	0
MP	0	0	0.2	0.8	1.0	0.8	0.2	0	0
LP	0	0	0	0	0.2	0.8	1.0	1.0	1.0

α	0	.1	.2	.3	.4	.5	.6	.7	.8
ZE	1.0	0.8	0.4	0.1	0	0	0	0	0
SP	0.4	0.8	1.0	0.8	0.4	0.1	0	0	0
MP	0	0.1	0.4	0.8	1.0	0.8	0.4	0.1	0
LP	0	0	0	0.1	0.4	0.8	1.0	0.8	0.4

β	0	.1	.2	.3	.4	.5	.6	.7	.8
ZE	1.0	0.8	0.2	0	0	0	0	0	0
SP	0.8	0.1	0.8	0.2	0	0	0	0	0
MP	0.2	0.8	1.0	0.8	0.2	0	0	0	0
LP	0	0.2	0.8	1.0	0.8	0.2	0	0	0

where Dc is a current deviation between the current measurement and the current predicted position,

$$Dc = \sqrt{[x_m(k) - x_p(k)]^2 + [y_m(k) - y_p(k)]^2}$$

$$x_p(k) \equiv \hat{x}(k|k-1), \ x_p(k) \equiv \hat{x}(k|k-1)$$

and $\Delta D = ABS\{Dc(k) - Dc(k-1)\}$, change of deviations.

Control Rules:

Control rules for the feasibility evaluation of a fuzzy tracker are a simplified correlation algorithm that have been implemented in a currently deployed system:

(1) If Dc = SP and ΔD = SP or ZE then α,β = ZE.
(2) If one no correlation, then α,β =SP
(3) If Dc = MP and ΔD = SP, then α=MP, β=SP
(4) If two consecutive no correlations, then α,β = MP
(5) If Dc = MP and ΔD = MP, then α,β = MP
(6) If Dc = MP and ΔD = LP, then α = MP, β = LP
(7) If Dc = LP and ΔD = LP, then α,β = LP
(8) If no 3 correlations in a row, then α,β = LP.

Fuzzy Decision:

Suppose the tracker produces a filter deviation of 5 (nmi) and change of deviation of 30 (knots). It can be shown that rules 1, 3 and 5 are applicable. The points of intersection of value 5 (nmi) and the deviation curves have membership grades,

$$\mu_D = (0.9,\ 0,\ 0.5,\ 0,\ 0.5,\ 0.6,\ 0,\ 0).$$

Similarly, the second curves show that deviation change of 30 knots has the membership function,

$$\mu_{\Delta D} = (0.9,\ 0,\ 0.9,\ 0,\ 0.1,\ 0,\ 0,\ 0).$$

Membership function of the control is obtained from the intersection of two input sets,

$$\mu_{D\cdot\Delta D} = (0.9,\ 0,\ 0.5,\ 0,\ 0.1,\ 0,\ 0,\ 0)$$

whose elements represent the proportions of the contribution by each rule.

Thus, the weighted average of smoothing gains are computed as:

$$\alpha = \frac{0\cdot 0.9 + 0.4\cdot 0.5 + 0.4\cdot 0.1}{0.9 + 0.5 + 0.1} = 0.16$$

$$\beta = \frac{0\cdot 0.9 + 0.1\cdot 0.5 + 0.2\cdot 0.1}{0.9 + 0.5 + 0.1} = 0.047$$

3. Combining Qualitative Information

In this section, we examine the utility of subjective information provided by operators or intelligence sources for another applications: track/data association and track/track fusion.

3.1 Track and Data Association

Correlation of radar data and tracks (called data association) is prerequisite to any filtering process. Data association (DA) is accomplished according to a priority scheme based on the type of sensor data: IFF or search, and the validation gates about the predicted target position where the data may fall. There are typically two or more validation gates which are of circular or elliptic shape.

The simplest DA technique is the Nearest Neighbor method that selects the measurement nearest to a predicted target position. However, this method can lead to very poor performance in an environment where spurious measurements occur frequently. Another widely used approach is to compute a simple arithmetic average of measurements that fall in the validation region. Although the averaging DA is very simple, it provides reasonably good performance and thus has been implemented in many air defense systems. The most complex and optimal method is the multiple hypothesis tracking (MHT) [15,23]. It considers all the possibilities of not only track maintenance but also track initiation and deletion. Major drawback of the MHT is the exponentially growing computational complexity based on the increasing number of returns.

A compromise between the two extremes is the probabilistic data association (PDA) [15,23]. This is a multiple hypothesis data association but the association decision is made after each scan. PDA is designed for association of a single target in clutter. The number of false alarms is usually modelled by a Poisson density and false alarms are assumed to be distributed uniformly in space.

When there are multiple targets in a surveillance area, the PDA does not perform well because the false alarm model is no longer valid. It is mainly due to the persistent returns generated by interfering targets. Thus, joint association probabilities should be considered to resolve this mis-association problem. Like the PDA, the joint probabilistic data association (JPDA) [15,21,23] assumes that tracks have been established and the number of targets are known. In this technique, a hypothesis table is formed by enumerating all the possible track/return pairings and computing the corresponding hypothesis probabilities. Suppose there are n targets and m false alarms in the surveillance area. The probability of H_0 (no returns originated from targets) is

$$P(H_0) \simeq (1-P_D)^n \lambda^m \qquad (3\text{-}1)$$

since no target detection is made and m false alarms are detected. The probability of any other hypotheses H_+ is of the form

$$P(H_+) \simeq P_D{}^k (1-P_D)^{n-k} \lambda^{m-k} \prod_{i,j} g_{ij} \qquad (3\text{-}2)$$

where the likelihood of measurement j being originated from track i is assumed to be a Gaussian, denoted by g_{ij} of distance $\nu_{ij} = y_j - H\hat{X}_i$, P_D denotes the probability of correct target detection, λ is the false alarms density, and k is number of detected targets. The association probabilities are computed by summing up hypothesis probabilities for given target and measurement assignments from the hypothesis table. Several JPDA implementations have been proposed to reduce computational complexity by approximating the association probabilities. However, all of these JPDA-like algorithms suffer severely as number of sensor measurements increases.

Recognizing the shortcomings of JPDA, we have developed an intuitive approach using surveillance operator's subjective knowledge. When only position information is measured by sensors, it is not surprising to note that the $\chi^2 = \nu^T S^{-1} \nu$ variable includes effects of distance residual and sensor accuracy, not target direction explicitly. This can be easily verified from an error ellipse drawn along the target trajectory. Observe that the major axis of the error ellipse does not generally coincide with the target direction. But, this is quite counter-intuitive since it seems reasonable to give more weight to the measurements that fall around the longitudinal target direction, reflecting one of the notable observations often made by surveillance operators, "Target is flying nearly in a straight line." How then, can such a feature be incorporated? Should the subjective knowledge override the numerical information? Wang and Mendel [32,33] attempted to combine numerical information and linguistic IF-THEN rules. They converted input-output numerical data pairs into fuzzy rules and combined with the rest of other linguistic rules. But, such a transformation of multisource information to a common frame of discernment tends to adversely obscure objective knowledge due to the influence by subjective information. Considering this, we decided to adopt the Zadeh's definition of a probability of a fuzzy event [34], as shown below:

$$P(A) = \int_A dP = \int_{R^n} \mu_A(x)\, dP = E(\mu_A) \qquad (3\text{-}3)$$

where P is a probability measure over R^n, probability space = (R^n, Ξ, P), $A \in \Xi$, $x \in R^n$, and μ_A denotes a membership function of A. Here, we interpret the probability density function of a fuzzy set, A as a probability density modulated by a membership function; $\mu_A(x)f(x)$, where $dP=f(x)dx$.

Thus, the modification to JPDA includes: defining a membership function to encode the statement "nearly straight line," and modulating the association probabilities by a membership function

$$P_{ij}' = P_D{}^n \cdot (1-P_D)^{N-n} \cdot \lambda^m \cdot \prod g_{ij}(\nu_{ij}) \cdot f_{ij}(\Delta_{ij})$$

where $f_{ij}(\Delta_{ij})$ is a function of the difference in directions. Here, we chose the functional form of a Gaussian given by

$$f_{ij} = \exp\{\Delta_{ij}{}^T \sigma_\phi{}^{-1} \Delta_{ij}\} \qquad (3\text{-}4)$$

where σ_ϕ is the variance of target heading. The angle difference, Δ_{ij} between the measurement direction and predicted direction at the kth scan determines the membership grade.

Unfortunately, in many cases, the direction of measurement is not directly obtained, and thus a pseudo direction needs to be generated. One possible approach is to compute the direction by connecting the measurement point with the previous predicted target position, $\hat{X}(k-1|k-2)$ or another possibility is to compute an average heading from the past predicted headings (3 or 5). In section 4, we discuss performance comparison of these various data association algorithms.

3.2. Multisensor Track to Track Fusion

In a multiple sensor environment, two different types of processing architectures are often employed: sensor level and central level tracking [21,23]. In central level tracking, all of the sensor measurements are transmitted to a central site and processed. In some applications, however, it may be desirable for the measurements are processed at the sensor site instead of transmitting them to the central processor. The local processed results (local tracks) are then sent over a communication network to be used by the central processor to update system tracks. Most of algorithms developed for single sensor tracking can be applied to the central tracking scheme while the distributed tracking requires additional processing: to determine whether two tracks are originated by the same target, and if so, to combine two tracks (this is called track-to-track fusion). Track fusion problems have been well studied and published in the literature [21]. Basically, two tracks $X_i(k)$ and $X_j(k)$ are combined by a convex combination as below

$$X_{ij}(k) = \alpha X_i(k) + (1-\alpha) X_j(k) \qquad (3\text{-}5)$$

where $\alpha = (P_j - P_{ji})/(P_i + P_j - P_{ij} - P_{ji})$, P_{ij} = cross variance, and $P_{ji} = P_{ij}{}^T$.

However, this technique also suffers from a problem similar to what we encountered in maneuver target tracking, namely modeling inaccuracy. As shown in equation (3-5), the track fusion is based on the state error covariance matrices and thus if target dynamic does not match the assumed model, the covariance does not provide a good measure of confidence. Even though some algorithms such as JPDA and IMM partly moderate the ill-conditioning of the covariance matrices (that is, premature collapse of a covariance matrix resulting in incorrect weights), model mismatch is a recurring problem. Thus, it is desirable to have a rule based track fusion logic. Following control rules have been formed from a few salient features observed on situation display consoles.

Control Rules for Hypothesis Test:

1. If ΔP and ΔV are ZE or SP then T is VL.
2. If ΔP and ΔD are ZE or SP then T is LK.
3. If ΔP is MP and ΔV is ZE or SP then T is LK.
4. If ΔP is ZE or SP and ΔV is LP then T is UL.
5. If ΔP is LP or ΔV is LP then T is VU.

where ΔP is position difference in two tracks, ΔV is velocity difference, ΔD is direction difference, VL = very likely, LK = likely, UL = unlikely, VU = very unlikely, and T = hypothesis that two tracks are originated from the same target.

Control Rules for Track Combination:

1. If ΔT_{ij} is ZE or SP, and D_1 and D_2 are NL then α is MP.
2. If T_j is ZE or SP, and D_1 is NL then α is HP.
3. If T_j is ZE or SP, and D_1 is NL, and T_i is MP, then α is HP.
4. If T_j is ZE or SP, and D_1 is NL, and T_i is LP, then α is LP
5. If T_i is ZE or SP, and D_2 is NL then α is LoP.
6. If T_i is ZE or SP, and D_2 is NL, and T_j is MP, then α is LoP.
7. If T_i is ZE or SP, and D_2 is NL, and T_j is LP, then α is SP.

where T_i = sum of squares of diagonal terms in P_i, T_j = that of P_j, $\Delta T_{ij} = |T_i - T_j|$, D_i = direction of track i, NL = nearly linear, HP=high positive, LoP=low positive. Note that numerical information, P_i and P_j are included as the conditioning of fusion rules.

4. Discussion

Computer simulation was conducted to demonstrate performance improvement by the new data association technique described in section 3.1. Figure 4.1 depicts target trajectories generated by five crossing targets, moving from the right to the left. The unit of each axis is nautical miles (nmi). The targets travel in straight lines at constant speed: target 1 and 5 at 940 knots, and target 2, 3 and 5 at 780 knots. The flight times are 9 minutes. Radar scan time is 10 seconds, probability of detection, Pd=0.7 and the false alarms density is $50X10^{-5}$, Poisson distributed (false alarms are not plotted in the figure).

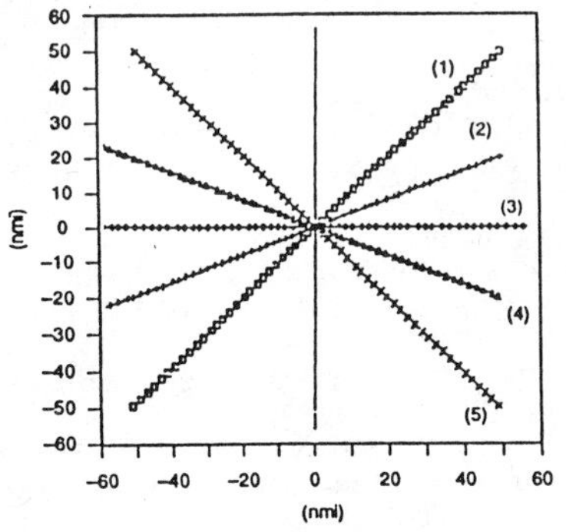

Figure 4.1. Target Trajectories

Tracker responses using the current DA techniques are illustrated in figure 4.2. Figure 4.2(a) is from the nearest neighbor DA algorithm where none of targets are correctly associated after crossing the origin. Target 1 is miss-correlated and merged with target 3. Target 4 is completely lost and coasted to the opposite direction. Target 5 is correlated with returns from target 4. Only, target 2 is successfully associated with its own data.

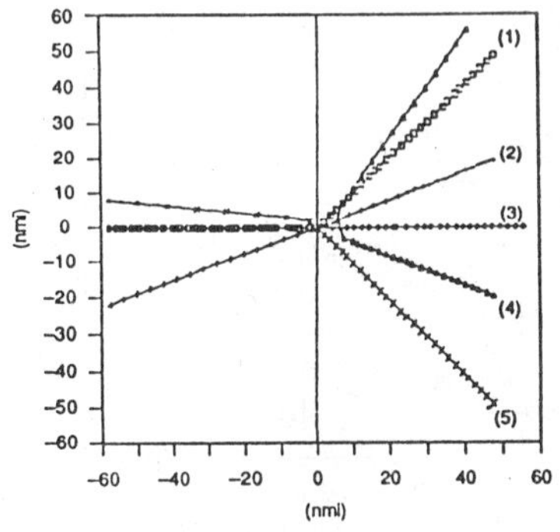

(a) Nearest Neighbor DA

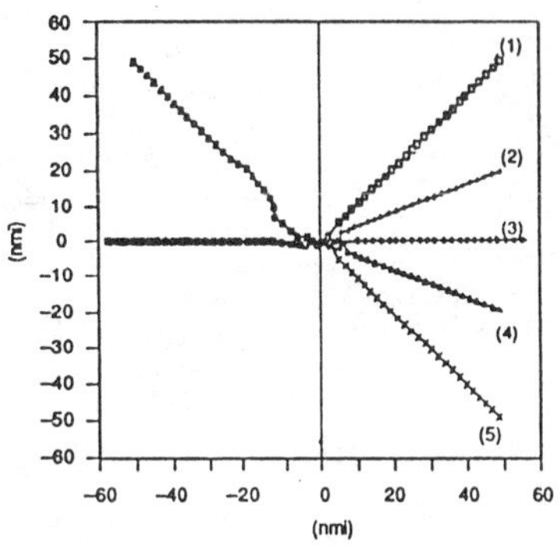

(b) PDA

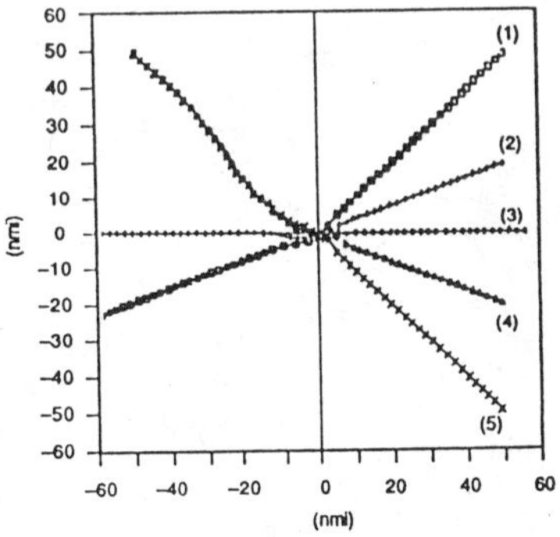

(c) JPDA

Figure 4.2. Tracker Responses from Classical DA Algorithms

Figure 4.2(b) is the response from the PDA tracker, where target 1 is miss-correlated with target 3, and the rest four targets are merged to target 5. The response from the JPDA tracker is shown in figure 4.2(c). Here, target 1 is confused with target 2 and target 2 is miss-correlated with target 3. Target 3 and 4 are merged to target 5.

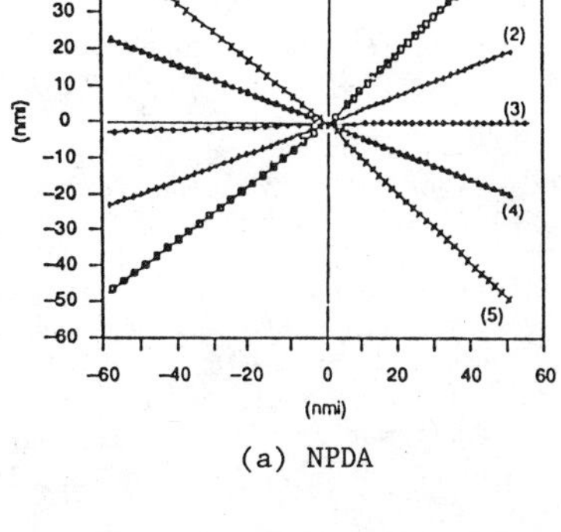

(a) NPDA

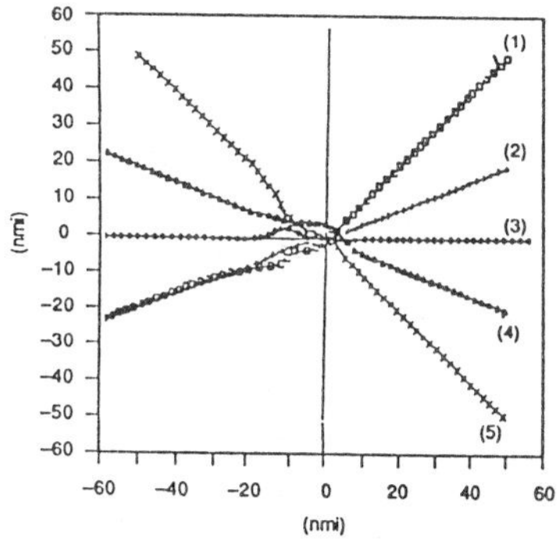

(b) NJPDA

Figure 4.3. Tracker Responses From Modified DA Algorithms

Figure 4.3(a) and (b) show the responses from the modified PDA and JPDA, denoted by NPDA and NJPDA respectively. NPDA exhibits superior association capability but seems to develop heading bias as indicated by target 3. Although NJPDA does not show any bias problem, target 1 and 2 are not able to be resolved as illustrated in figure 4.3(b)

From the above simulation results, we observe the following. Fuzzy logic and rule based systems are a means of dealing with imprecision, a method of modeling human behavior, and a means of achieving control of industrial systems that cannot be modeled rigorously. The principal difference from the conventional techniques is that the fuzzy approach uses qualitative information. We have implemented a fuzzy tracker based on the existing α-β smoothing algorithm and developed a subjective knowledge augmented data association algorithms. An intuitive reason why the fuzzy logic provides better performance is the fuzzified decision boundaries resulting in a weighted average of possible decision rules, and utilization of information features that cannot be easily quantified or are overlooked in conventional techniques. However, it should be noted that the fuzzy method requires comprehensive knowledge acquisition to formulate a successful rule base. Other factors including a proper calibration technique and judicious choice of membership functions are crucial in designing a good fuzzy system.

References

[1] A.H. Jazwinski, "Stochastic Processes and Filtering Theory,"New York, Academic, 1970.

[2] K.A. Myers and B.D. Tapley, "Adaptive Sequential Estimation with Unknown Noise Statistics," IEEE Tr. AC, 520-523, Aug. 1976.

[3] Raman K. Mehra, "Approaches to Adaptive Filtering," IEEE Tr. AC, 693-698, Oct. 1972.

[4] Raman K. Mehra, "On the Identification of Variances and Adaptive Kalman Filtering," IEEE Tr. AC-15, 175-181, Apr. 1970.

[5] M. Athans and D. Willner, "Properties of Matched and Mismatched Kalman Filters," MIT TN 1976-22, Apr. 1976.

[6] C.B. Chang, R.H. Whiting and M. Athans, "On the State and Parameter Estimation for Maneuvering Re-entry vehicles," IEEE Tr. AC-22, 99-105, Feb. 1977.

[7] C.B. Chang and M. Athans, "State Estimation for Discrete Systems with Switching Parameters," IEEE Tr. AES-14, 418-425, May 1978.

[8] R.L. Moose, H.F. Van Landingham and D.H. McCabe, "Modeling and Estimation for Tracking Maneuvering Targets," IEEE Tr. AES-15, 448-456, May 1979.

[9] N.H. Gholson R.L. Moose, "Maneuvering Target Tracking Using Adaptive State Estimation," IEEE Tr. AES-13, 310-317, May 1977.

[10] R.R. Tenney, R.S. Hebert and N.R. Sandell, "A Tracking Filter for Maneuvering Sources," IEEE Tr. AC-22, 246-251, Apr. 1977.

[11] Y. Bar-Shalom and K. Birmiwal, "Variable Dimension Filter for Maneuvering Target Tracking," IEEE Tr. AES-18, Sep. 1982.

[12] Y.T. Chan, A.G.C. Hu and B. Plant, "A Kalman Filter Based Tracking Scheme with Input Estimation,", IEEE Tr. AES-15, No.2, 237-244, Mar. 1979.

[13] P.L. Bogler, "Tracking a Maneuvering Target Using Input Estimation," IEEE Tr. AES-23, No.3, 298-310, May 1987.

[14] Y. Bar-Shalom, K.C. Chang and H.A.P. Blom, "Tracking a Maneuvering Target Using Input Estimation vs. Interacting Multiple Model Algorithms," IEEE Tr. AES-25, 296-300, March 1989.

[15] Y. Bar-Shalom and T. Fortmann, Tracking and Data Association, New York, Academic Press, 1988.

[16] D.T. Magill, "Optimal Adaptive Estimation of Sampled stochastic Processes," IEEE Tr. AC-10, Oct. 1965.

[17] D.G. Lainiotis, "Optimal Adaptive Estimation: Structure and Parameter Adaptation," IEEE Tr. AC-16, Apr. 1971.

[18] M. Athans and C.B. Chang, "Adaptive Estimation and Parameter Identification Using Multiple Model Estimation Algorithms," MIT TN 1976-28, Jun 1976.

[19] H.A.P. Blom, "An Efficient Filter For Abruptly Changing Systems," 23rd CDC, 656-658, Dec. 1984.

[20] A. Houles and Y. Bar-Shalom, "Multisensor Tracking of a Maneuvering Target in Clutter," IEEE Tr. AES-25, 176-189, March 1989.

[21] Y. Bar-shalom, Editor, Multitarget-Multisensor Trackingt: Advanced Applications, Vol.1 and Vol.2, Artech House.

[22] D.B. Reid, "An Algorithm for Tracking Multiple Target," IEEE Tr. AC-24, 43-854, Dec. 1979.

[23] S.S. Blackman, Multiple Target Tracking with Radar Applications, Artech House, 1986.

[24] L.A. Zadeh, "Fuzzy Sets," Information Control, vol.8, 338-353, 1965.

[25] E.H. Mamdani, "Application of Fuzzy Algorithms for Control of a Simple Dynamic Plant," Proc. IEEE, vol. 121, 1585-1588, 1974.

[26] M. Sugeno, "An Introductory Survey of Fuzzy Control," Inf. Sc., vol.36, 59-83, 1985.

[27] J.A. Bernard, "Use of a Rule-Based System for Process Control," IEEE Con. Sys. 3-13, Oct. 1988.

[28] Y.F. Li and C.C. Lau, "Development of Fuzzy Algorithms for Servo Systems," IEEE Con. Sys, 65-72, Apr. 1989.

[29] S. Chiu, S. Chand, D. Moore and A. Chaudhary, "Fuzzy Logic for Control of Roll and Moment for a Flexible Wing Aircraft." IEEE Con. Sys. 42-48, June 1991.

[30] K. Self, "Designing with Fuzzy Logic," IEEE Spectrum, 42-105, Nov. 1990.

[31] S. Yoshida and N. Wakayabashi, "A Fuzzy Logic Controller for a Rigid Disk Drive," IEEE Con. Sys. 65-70, June 1992.

[32] L. Wang and J Mendel, "Generating Fuzzy Rules by Learning from Examples," Proc. of 1991 International Sym on Intelligent Control, 263-268.

[33] L. Wang and J. Mendel, "Fuzzy Basis Functions and Orthogonal Least Squares Learning," FUZZ-IEEE 92, March, 1992.

[34] L.A. Zadeh, "Probability Measures of Fuzzy Events," Jou. of Math Anal and Appl, Vol.23, 421-427, 1968.

Proceedings of the
American Control Conference
San Francisco, California • June 1993

Multiple Sensor Tracking with Retrospective Probabilistic Data Association

Oliver E. Drummond, Ph.D., P.E.

Hughes Missile System Company
10900 E. 4th Street, Rancho Cucamonga, CA 91730

Abstract

A probabilistic data association approach is described for tracking multiple targets with multiple sensor. This approach employs multiple frames of data in the data association processing. The approach offers improved performance over Joint Probabilistic Data Association tracking. This improved performance is obtained, however, at the expense of increased processing load. In the algorithm is a design parameter that can be selected to adjust performance to suit a specific application. The algorithm is retrospective in that as each new frame of sensor data becomes available earlier tracks are modified and the changes have an impact on subsequent tracks.

1. Introduction

Typically, tracking a few bright targets in a sparse population of observations (sometimes called threshold exceedances, returns or reports) does not pose a particularly challenging data association problem. Tracking requirements are, however, growing more demanding as the need arises to track dim targets or to track in a dense population of observations due to background clutter, false signals or targets that are close or crossing.

In tracking, there are two major processes: data association and filtering. Data association deals with the uncertainty of which observation goes with a track or observation from a prior frame of data. Filtering provides an updated estimate of the target state and possibly additional information. Typically the inputs to a filter are current observations and either a time sequence of prior observations or prior track data. For the purpose of this paper, it is assumed that a Kalman filter (or an algorithm that provides its mathematical equivalent) is used. The data association function is the principle interest of this paper. Some pertinent data association approaches are summarized in Section 2.

Processing with multiple sensors can significantly improve tracking performance for the more challenging conditions. For tracking with multiple sensors, there are many applicable algorithm architectures (also called processing chains) and a variety of track or data association approaches for each architecture. Tracking with data from multiple sensors introduces additional conceptual complexities compared to single sensor processing. Four generic algorithm architectures are summarized in Section 3.

Note that Sections 2 and 3 provide a very simple description of data association approaches and types of algorithm architectures. These sections present overview material pertinent to the subject of this paper. Liberties are taken to simplify the discussion and to concentrate on the concepts involved. Multiple target tracking is a complex subject with some very subtle issues, however, the overview in these two sections omits many important details because of page limitations.

This paper concentrates on algorithms for track maintenance to process multiple sensor data with a centralized algorithm architecture. The approach described in Section 4 uses multiple frames of data in data association to tracking multiple targets with multiple sensor. The approach employs a few multiple frames of data in the data association processing as compared to optimal tracking that uses all available frames of data in data association. In the approach, the number of frames used in data association is a design parameter. The algorithm uses a retrospective approach to probabilistic data association in that, as each new frame of sensor data becomes available, earlier tracks are modified and these changes have an impact on subsequent tracks.

2. Data Association

There has been a proliferation of data and track association approaches. With a dense population of observations, the optimal approaches for tracking a single target [1] and for tracking multiple targets [2] require enumerating an ever increasing number of hypotheses. Thus optimal tracking is impractical because it requires too much processing. Consequently, there is the continual search for good sub-optimal approaches that can be readily adapted to the requirements of an application.

Data association algorithms can be classified as single frame and multiple frame approaches [3,4]. A single frame association approach typically enumerates most or all the possible tracks for a frame of data, based on prior tracks. Then the number of candidate tracks is reduced to at most one track per apparent target for use with the next frame of data. A single frame association approach does not reprocess sensor data from prior frames, does not update the prior hypothesis probabilities, and carries forward in time at most one track per apparent target. Typically the number of current candidate tracks is reduced by either eliminating some, combining some, or both.

Note that in this paper, the term hypothesis refers to a global hypothesis. A global hypothesis for a given time takes into account all tracks available from the prior frame of data and all observations for the current frame of data. For a hypothesis, each prior track is assigned to an observation or there is no detection for that track. Similarly, each observation is assigned to a prior track or is from a new source, i.e., due to a false signal or a new target.

Due to the uncertainty of the source for an observation, there are frequently more than one possible assignment of observations for a prior track. Thus multiple candidate tracks can be generated from a single prior track. A local composite track is the best single track given a sub-set of candidate tracks for an apparent target. In this paper, best track refers to best in the minimum mean square error sense. A (global) composite track is the best track based on all candidate tracks for an apparent target.

A track consists of a state vector, its covariance matrix and possibly additional information. A target state vector can include sensor signal signature information, estimated target attributes, target classification or recognition information, target features, and estimated target size and shape, along with kinematic information. For this discussion, however, it is assumed that the target is small so that there is not enough information available from a single frame of data to do target classification or recognition [5]. Consequently, the performance of the data association function can be critical.

Single frame data association approaches include the nearest neighbor algorithm [6]; Joint Probabilistic Data Association (JPDA) [6,7]; and the unique assignment approach [6], which is a Sequentially Most Probable Hypothesis (SMPH) approach. In the JPDA approach, the intention is to combine all current hypotheses to obtain a single track for each apparent target, a global current composite track. These composite tracks are used to provide to the user the estimated state and its covariance matrix for each target. Also, for processing the next frame of data, the composite tracks are used instead of the candidate tracks. Accordingly, the number of hypotheses that must be enumerated for the next frame of data is greatly reduced.

Multiple frame data association approaches include Multiple Hypothesis Tracking (MHT) [6], the algorithm by Singer, Sea and Housewright (SSH) [8], and optimal tracking [1,2]. MHT typically maintains more than one candidate track per apparent target. In MHT, for practical reasons the number of candidate tracks is limited by both eliminating and combining some hypotheses and tracks. In MHT, the typical combining process is local rather than global. Given three candidate tracks for a target, for example, two similar candidate tracks might be combined to form one candidate track, a local composite. Many different versions of MHT have been developed since its original conception by Reid [9].

In optimal tracking, all hypotheses and all the candidate tracks must be retained for use in processing the subsequent frames of data [1,2]. The optimal single estimate (in the minimum mean square sense) for a target at any one time is a global composite estimate, which is the appropriately weighted sum of all candidate tracks for a target. It is the retention of all the hypotheses and all the candidate tracks that makes optimal tracking impractical. Clearly, optimal tracking is a multiple frame data association approach with the number of frames in the data association equal to number of frames of data available. The so called "gated optimal" tracking is optimal tracking except that gates are used to eliminate unlikely track-observation pairs [3]. The gating process reduces processing complexity but since it is a trimming process, the results are sub-optimal.

The SSH tracker was designed for tracking a single target with false signals. The algorithm uses local combining to reduce the number of candidate tracks. Tracks are selected to be combined based on the which observations they use. The number of frames used in the data association processing is a design parameter.

Some target tracking approaches partition the processing into the three major functions of: track initiation (acquisition), track maintenance (extension or continuation), and track termination. The tracks are started in the track initiation processing and then continued in track maintenance processing until terminated by the track termination logic. The optimal and MHT approaches incorporate all three phases in the process of enumerating hypotheses and updating tracks. By comparison, the nearest neighbor algorithm, JPDA, SMPH, and SSH approaches are typically track maintenance approaches that must be augmented by separate track initiation and track termination processing.

3. Multiple Sensor Algorithm Architectures

There are many different ways that data from multiple sensor can be combined. The differences between various multiple sensor approaches may not be important for tracking with a sparse population of observations. With challenging conditions of a moderate to dense population of observations, the difference between the various tracking approaches can have a significant impact on both performance and the processing complexity. There is virtually an infinite number of possible algorithm architectures for multiple target tracking with multiple sensors. One view of the different types of algorithm architectures is summarized in this section.

Four generic types of algorithm architectures for track maintenance and for track initiation have been identified [3,10]. This classification of algorithm architectures is based primarily on how the association processing is performed over time and over the ensemble of sensors. These four types have since been adopted by the SDI Panels on Tracking, however, they have given some of these generic types different names [11]. The four types of track maintenance architectures are as follows:

Type I: Independent Sensor Architecture.
Type II: Hierarchical Sensor Architecture
Type III: Observation Fusion Architecture
Type IV: Centralized Architecture.

In the Independent Sensor Architecture, the tracks are processed for each sensor without use of the data from the other sensors. Frame-to-frame data association and filtering are performed without any sensor-to-sensor processing. Each user obtains tracks based on a single sensor. Note that each observation is subjected to only one association process but that single-sensor tracks need to be retained in track files for each sensor. Also, there is no improvement in the track quality due to the existence of multiple sensor data.

In the Hierarchical Sensor Architecture, tracks are first processed for each sensor without use of data from the other sensors. Single-sensor tracks are then fused using track-to-track association to form multiple-sensor tracks. Frame-to-frame association and filtering are followed by sensor-to-sensor processing. Note that each observation is subjected to two association processes and multiple-sensor tracks as well as single-sensor tracks for each sensor are retained in track files. Feedback of the multiple-sensor tracks to the single sensor track processing can be employed.

In the Observation Fusion Architecture, multiple sensor processing of the observations from all sensors is first employed. The processing of observations consists of associating observations from one frame of data from all sensors and computing an improved estimate of the position of each target. These estimated target positions are then used in frame-to-frame association and filtering. Sensor-to-sensor processing precedes frame-to-frame processing. Note that each observation is subjected to two association processes but only one set of multiple-sensor tracks need be retained in track files.

In the Centralized Architecture, observation-to-track association is followed by filtering with prior multiple-sensor tracks. Typically the data association processing uses the multiple-sensor tracks and one frame of data from a sensor; the tracks are updated and then a frame of data from another sensor along with the updated multiple-sensor tracks is processed. Note that each observation is subjected to only one association process and only one set of multiple-sensor tracks need be retained in track files.

The four track initiation architectures are conceptually the same as the track maintenance architectures summarized above [3,11].

A clear distinction should be made between the functional (logical) algorithm architecture and the physical distribution of the processing. With multiple platforms and on-board processing, there are many ways that each of the algorithm architectures can be physically distributed over the platforms and ground (or shipboard) stations. Also, there are many ways that each of the generic algorithm architectures can be implemented. Finally, the type of track initiation architecture need not be the same as the selected type of track maintenance.

4. Multiple Frame, Probabilistic Data Association

A multiple frame, probabilistic data association approach will be described for track maintenance using data from multiple sensors. A Type IV, Centralized Processing Architecture, has been chosen for this paper because it offers superior performance, especially with a dense population of observations. Also it seems to be conceptually easier to apply a multiple frame data association approach to the other algorithm architectures.

Before track maintenance can proceed, tracks must first be formed by the track initiation function. The track initiation process will typically use a number of frames of data to identify and form new tracks. Almost any one of the various track initiation approaches in the literature can be used to first form the new tracks, see for example [6,7].

To employ multiple frame data association with the Centralized Processing Architecture, an ordering scheme must first be established for the frames of data from all the sensors. All the frames of data can be interspersed by ordering them based on the time each frame or scan of data starts. If the frame times for some or all the sensors are simultaneous, then the ordering of the frames of data from those sensors for a given frame time can be arbitrary.

Whether the sensors are simultaneously synchronized or not, the frames of data from all the sensors are interspersed into a single sequence of frames for the data association and filtering processing. Note that each of these interspersed frames of data contains all the observation for a single frame (or scan) of data from a sensor. The sequence of interspersed frames contains a frame of data first from one sensor, then from another, then another, and so forth. These frames form a time ordered sequence or, in the case of simultaneous sensors, the time sequence is partially ordered.

With the Centralized Architecture, this intentional ordering of the frames of data is not necessary for single frame association approaches such as JPDA. With JPDA, it is fairly straight forward to do the data association for each frame of data as it becomes available independent of the frames of data from the other sensors. It is the updated tracks that employ and carry the information from the prior frames of data from all the sensors to the data association processing.

Even with the interspersed frames of data, it is possible to obtain late observations as input to the tracker. The delay can be caused by a longer communication lag from one sensor than from another. Also, scanning sensors can cause late observations. An observation for a target by the first scanning sensor can be taken later than the observation for the same target taken by another scanning sensor whose scan started later than the first sensor. For late observations, computing the hypothesis probabilities and updating the filter is fairly straight forward if there is no process noise (no potential maneuvers). The ideal computations can be very complex with process noise and late observations.

It is the interspersing of the frames of data from all the sensors that permits the application of multiple frame data association with the Centralized Architecture. Section 4.1 describes a probabilistic data association approach that employs multiple frames of data in the data association computations.

4.1. Data Association with Retrodicted Global Combining

Instead of using single frame data association for tracking with multiple sensors, multiple frame probabilistic data association can be used to improve performance. An algorithm, called Global Combining Data Association, Retrodicted (GCDA_R) or, more specifically, Global Combining Data Association, Retrodicted N Frames (GCDA_RN) [4] can be used for multiple sensor tracking. JPDA enthusiasts might prefer to call this approach Joint Probability Data Association, Retrodicted (JPDA_R) or, more specifically, Joint Probability Data Association, Retrodicted N Frames (JPDA_RN). In this approach the process of globally combining the multiple hypotheses uses probabilistic rules to compute composite tracks.

There are two types of composite tracks computed in this approach. For one type of composite track, the *current composite track*, the current candidate track data at any given time is used to compute the single best track for each apparent target for use by the user.

Typically, a composite track consists of the composite state estimate and its covariance matrix. To compute the composite track, the candidate probabilities are first computed for each candidate track. The candidate probability for a candidate track is computed by summing all the hypothesis probabilities for all the hypotheses that include that track. The results are then normalized. A composite state estimate for a track is then computed by multiplying the state vector for each candidate track for an apparent target by its candidate probability and summing the result. The covariance matrix is computed in a similar way [4].

The other composite track, the *retrodicted composite track*, the single best track N frames earlier for each apparent target is computed based on the candidate tracks computed at that time. The hypothesis probabilities used, however, are based on all the available data since that time. The hypothesis probabilities for that time point are retrodicted probabilities, i.e., computed base on subsequent data. The retrodicted composite tracks are used to generate subsequent candidate tracks and hypothesis probabilities.

The retrodicted hypothesis probabilities and retrodicted composite tracks are the result of computations for prior states and prior hypothesis probabilities based on data up to and including the current time. A retrodicted probability or decision is analogous to a smoothed estimate in filtering [4].

There are two phases to the algorithm. The first phase sets up and starts the process and then the second phase continues the process until all the tracks are terminated. The interspersed frames of data are input to the GCDA_RN algorithm. A summary of the steps of the algorithm follows, see the reference [4] for further details and alternatives.

1. Phase I -- Initiate Track Maintenance.

1-1. Phase I, Step 1. The algorithm starts with new tracks formed by the track initiation function. The track frame index, n_T, is set to zero; the index for the first subsequent frame of data, n_R, is set to one (this is also the index for the retrodict frame to be processed); and the index for the last frame in the first processing cycle, n_C, is set to $N+1$.

1-2. Phase I, Step 2. Processing of this step cannot be completed until frame n_C-1 data is available, i.e., N frames of data subsequent to the frames used to create the frame n_T tracks. Compute candidate tracks based on the frame n_T tracks and N subsequent frames of data. The method used is the same as would be used in gated optimal tracking. Gates are established for each candidate track. If there are more than one observation in a gate for a candidate track, the track is split. Splitting a track generates one candidate track for each of the observations in the gate plus one more for the hypothesis that all the observations in the gate are due to new source. The updated state vector and its covariance matrix for each track and the hypothesis probabilities are computed for the N frames.

1-3. Phase I, Step 3. If the user needs the best single track for each of the targets for each frame, then compute all the current composite tracks for each apparent target for each frame during Phase I, Step 1 processing. The current composite tracks are computed as outlined for composite tracks in Section 4.

1-4. Phase I, Step 4. This step cannot be

completed until frame n_C is available, i.e., N+1 frames of data subsequent to the frame used to create the frame n_T tracks. Gates for frame n_C are computed for all candidate tracks predicted forward from frame n_C-1. All the possible hypotheses are generated and their probabilities are computed for frame n_C. Then the current composite tracks for frame n_C are computed and provided to the user.

1-5. Phase I, Step 5. The retrodicted hypothesis probabilities are computed for all hypotheses for frame n_R. A retrodicted hypothesis probability in this case is the probability that a hypothesis for frame n_R is correct given data to frame n_C. These probabilities are computed as follows:

> For each frame n_R hypothesis, all subsequent tracks and hypotheses that it generated are traced to frame n_C and those hypotheses identified. The probabilities of the identified hypotheses are summed to form the retrodicted hypothesis probability for the frame n_R hypothesis.

The retrodicted hypothesis probabilities are used to compute the retrodicted composite tracks. These composite tracks are computed as described in Section 4 for composite tracks except that the retrodicted hypothesis probabilities are used in the computations. The computations for the retrodicted composite tracks use the tracks and hypotheses generated earlier for frame n_R.

A processing cycle has been completed; increment n_T, n_R and n_C by one.

Note that the retrodicted tracks (their state vector estimates and corresponding covariance matrices) serve in the next processing cycle as the tracks for frame n_T. They are used to generate subsequent candidate tracks and hypothesis probabilities in the next processing cycle.

2. Phase II -- Continue Track Maintenance:

Perform Phase I Steps 2, 4 and 5.

The above Phase II process is repeated, as new frames of data become available, until all tracks are terminated by the track termination logic. As individual composite tracks are terminated, they are then eliminated from the computations for the hypotheses. Also as new tracks are initiated by the track initiation processing function, they can be included in the above process using a modified form of the above Phase I processing [4]. An alternative is to generate the new tracks within the above processing. This alternative approach may not be practical unless N is large enough to discern a probable new track from a sequence of observations that are not mostly from one target. Note that the JPDA approach can be viewed as a special case of this approach. Specifically the JPDA algorithm is the same as the GCDA_R0, i.e., with N equal to zero.

4.2 Other Multiple Frame Data Association Approaches

Using the interspersed frames as input to a tracker, a MHT approach can also be used with the Type IV, Centralized Architecture. Other multiple frame data association approaches are also discussed in the reference [4].

5. References

1. Singer, R.A. and R.G. Sea, "New Results in Optimizing Surveillance System Tracking and Data Correlation Performance in Dense Multitarget Environments," *IEEE Trans. Auto. Control*, Vol. AC-18, No. 6, pp. 571-582, December 1973.

2. Drummond, O.E., Multiple-Object Estimation, UCLA Ph.D. Dissertation, 1975, Xerox University Microfilms No. 75-26,954.

3. Drummond, O.E., "Multiple Target Tracking Lecture Notes," UCLA 1985 and subsequent versions, Technology Training Corp., Torrance CA.

4. Drummond, O.E., "Multiple Target Tracking with Multiple Frame, Probabilistic Data Association," to appear in *Signal and Data Processing of Small Targets 1993*, *Proc. SPIE*, Vol. 1954, 1993.

5. Drummond, O.E. (Editor), "Introduction," *Signal and Data Processing of Small Targets 1992*, *Proc. SPIE*, Vol. 1698, 1992, p. xi.

6. Blackman, S.S., *Multiple Target Tracking With Radar Applications*, Artech House, Denham, Mass. 1986.

7. Bar-Shalom, Y. and T.E. Fortmann, *Tracking and Data Association*, Academic Press, San Diego, CA 1987.

8. Singer, R.A., R.G. Sea, and K. Housewright, "Derivation and Evaluation of Improved Tracking Filters for Use in Dense Multi-target Environments," *IEEE Trans. Information Theory*, Vol. IT-20, No.4, July 1974, pp. 423-432.

9. Reid, D.B., "An Algorithm for Tracking Multiple Targets," *IEEE Trans. Auto. Control*, AC-24, Dec. 1979, pp. 843-854.

10. Drummond, O.E. and S.S. Blackman, "Challenges of Developing Algorithms for Multiple Sensor, Multiple Target Tracking, *"Signal and Data Processing of Small Targets 1989, Proc. SPIE*, Vol. 1096, 1989, pp. 244-256.

11. Frenkel, G. and B.E. Fridling, "Survey of Strategic Defense Initiative Tracking Algorithms," IDA Paper P-2284, Institute of Defense Analyses, Alexandria, VA, November 1989.

Proceedings of the
American Control Conference
San Francisco, California • June 1993

A FREQUENCY DOMAIN DESIGN METHOD FOR PID CONTROLLERS

T. J. D. Barnes, L. Wang and W.R. Cluett

Department of Chemical Engineering
University of Toronto, Toronto, Canada M5S 1A4

Abstract

This paper will provide a frequency domain design method for PID controllers, which is based on a least-squares fit of the actual to the desired open-loop Nyquist plot. The algorithm is simple and achieves a unique minimum of the sum of the squared errors for a given desired response. Graphical measures will be introduced which will aid the designer in assessing whether the desired performance is achievable with a PID controller.

1 Introduction

Methods for tuning PID controllers have typically concentrated on determining desirable controller parameters using as little process information as possible. This has been done in order to keep the tuning procedures simple and has facilitated the development of autotuners. For example, the Ziegler-Nichols tuning procedure [6] involves process information at but a single point on the process frequency response. More recently, the trend has been to look beyond PID to model-based controller designs for improved performance. Much effort has beeen expended along the way to show that for certain simple classes of models, a controller with the PID structure is in fact produced from various model based designs. However, model approximations or model reductions and hence modelling error must be immediately introduced with higher order systems in order to still arrive at a PID structure. Despite this apparent limitation, many types of processes are still under PID control.

Our interest in this study is to move back into the frequency domain. Specifically, our objective is to study the direct design of PID controllers from frequency domain process information. The design method is based on the minimization of the sum of the squared errors between the desired and actual open-loop Nyquist plots. This work is very much in the spirit of other work [1,2] where frequency domain methods are also used for low order controller design without the restriction of an intermediate low order process model. Our particular interest here is to examine the performance capabilities and limitations of the PID controller using this design technique.

We will first identify the natural weighting function associated with the frequency domain minimization. We will then present some simple graphical measures, based on the desired performance and the process frequency response, which give a clear indication to the designer whether or not the desired performance is in fact achievable with a PID controller. If the desired performance cannot be attained, it will be shown that the designer can continue to use the graphical measures to determine how much the desired performance must be adjusted. Finally, we will present three examples to illustrate our results.

2 The Frequency Domain Design Method

This section introduces a frequency domain design method for PID controllers. The method attempts to match the actual open-loop Nyquist plot to the desired open-loop Nyquist plot by a suitable choice of controller parameters. This match is accomplished by means of a least-squares minimization.

2.1 The loss function and the algorithm

Assume that the process is described by its frequency response function $G(jw)$, where $0 \leq w < \infty$. We will select the feedback controller to have the structure

$$C(s) = \frac{c_2 s^2 + c_1 s + c_0}{s} \tag{1}$$

This controller is equivalent to a conventional PID controller with proportional gain $K_c = c_1$, integral time constant $\tau_I = \frac{c_1}{c_0}$ and derivative time constant $\tau_D = \frac{c_2}{c_1}$. A performance specification is made in the form of the desired closed-loop transfer function $G'_{cl}(jw)$. The objective here is to choose the parameters c_0, c_1 and c_2 such that the loss function

$$V = \sum_i |G'_{ol}(jw_i) - \frac{G(jw_i)}{jw_i}(c_2[jw_i]^2 + c_1[jw_i] + c_0)|^2 \tag{2}$$

is minimized, where $G'_{ol}(jw)$ is the Nyquist locus of the desired open-loop transfer function ($G'_{ol} = \frac{G'_{cl}}{1-G'_{cl}}$) and w_i ranges over both positive and negative frequencies. This becomes a linear least-squares problem by defining $\phi(jw_i) = [jw_iG(jw_i) \quad G(jw_i) \quad -j\frac{G(jw_i)}{w_i}]$ and $\theta^T = [c_2 \quad c_1 \quad c_0]$, yielding

$$V = \sum_i |G'_{ol}(jw_i) - \phi(jw_i)\theta|^2 \qquad (3)$$

The parameter vector θ which minimizes V can be found by applying the standard least-squares result [3]

$$\hat{\theta} = (\sum_i \phi(jw_i)^*\phi(jw_i))^{-1}(\sum_i \phi(jw_i)^* G'_{ol}(jw_i)) \qquad (4)$$

where A^* denotes the complex conjugate transpose of A. If we assume that $G'_{ol}(jw)$ and $G(jw)$ are symmetric, then the solution of $\hat{\theta}$ simplifies to

$$\begin{aligned}\hat{\theta} \;=\; & [\sum_i [Re(\phi(jw_i))^T * Re(\phi(jw_i)) \\ & + Im(\phi(jw_i))^T * Im(\phi(jw_i))]]^{-1} \\ \times\; & \sum_i [Re(\phi(jw_i))^T * Re(G'_{ol}(jw_i)) \\ & + Im(\phi(jw_i))^T * Im(G'_{ol}(jw_i))] \qquad (5)\end{aligned}$$

where w_i now ranges over only positive frequencies.

Remark:
The frequency domain design method for a PID controller is a special case of a more general algorithm [1]. However, with the controller structure in the PID form, the estimate for θ can be found by solving a linear least-squares problem which has an analytical solution. With a more general controller structure, the problem is nonlinear and requires a numerical solution.

2.2 The implicit weighting function

The loss function V in equation (3) can be rewritten in the form

$$V = \sum_i |W(jw_i)|^2|Y(jw_i) - [c_2[jw_i]^2 + c_1[jw_i] + c_0]|^2 \qquad (6)$$

where $W(jw_i) = \frac{G(jw_i)}{jw_i}$ and $Y(jw_i) = \frac{G'_{ol}(jw_i)jw_i}{G(jw_i)}$. $W(jw_i)$ is referred to as the implicit weighting function for this minimization problem. The effect of this weighting function is that it will tend to emphasize the frequency regions where $|W(jw_i)|^2$ is large and de-emphasize the frequency regions where $|W(jw_i)|^2$ is small. For stable processes with strictly proper transfer functions, $|W(jw_i)|$ is finite for $0 < w_i < \infty$, and decays to zero as w_i increases. The speed of the decay is dependent on the distribution of the process poles and zeros and the relative degree of the transfer function. For example, a first order system with gain $K = 1$ and time constant $\tau = 1$ will give $|W(jw_i)|^2$ in the following form

$$|W(jw)|^2 = \frac{1}{w^2(w^2+1)} \qquad (7)$$

which is illustrated in figure 1.

The shape of $|W(jw)|^2$ naturally determines the frequency range over which the minimization of V takes place. Here, we will designate this frequency region as $w_m \le w_i \le w_M$, where we will select w_m and w_M such that $|W(jw_m)|^2 \approx 10^{4-5}$ and $|W(jw_M)|^2 = 1$. We have found that this frequency region captures the significant dynamics without over-emphasizing the low frequency region.

2.3 Choice of desired closed-loop performance

From the loss function in (6), it can be seen that in order to guarantee a small error in the frequency domain fit, the structure of $Y(jw)$ needs to satisfy, for $w_m \le w \le w_M$ and some constants α_1, α_2, and β,

$$Re(Y(jw)) \approx \alpha_1 - \alpha_2 w^2 \qquad (8)$$

$$Im(Y(jw)) \approx \beta w \qquad (9)$$

The structure of $Y(jw)$ can be checked graphically by plotting the real part against w^2 and the imaginary part against w. If the desired performance is achievable with a PID controller structure, then both plots should be approximately linear over the frequency range (w_m, w_M).

3 Examples

Example 1: a second order system
There are a few process structures which yield an exact PID controller when using model-based design methods [4,5]. For example, with a second order process

$$G(jw) = \frac{K}{\tau^2(jw)^2 + 2\zeta\tau jw + 1} \qquad (10)$$

if we choose the desired closed-loop transfer function as

$$G'_{cl}(jw) = \frac{1}{\tau_{cl}jw + 1} \qquad (11)$$

this gives

$$G'_{ol}(jw) = \frac{1}{\tau_{cl}jw} \qquad (12)$$

and

$$Y(jw) = \frac{\tau^2(jw)^2 + 2\tau\zeta jw + 1}{K\tau_{cl}} \quad (13)$$

where the real and imaginary parts of $Y(jw)$ exactly satisfy equations (8) and (9). Therefore, using any three points on the frequency response of $G(jw)$, the algorithm will uniquely determine the PID parameters as $K_c = \frac{2\tau\zeta}{K\tau_{cl}}$, $\tau_I = 2\tau\zeta$, and $\tau_D = \frac{\tau}{2\zeta}$.

Example 2: a first order plus delay system
Consider that the process is described by

$$G(jw) = \frac{Ke^{-djw}}{\tau jw + 1} \quad (14)$$

and we will choose the desired closed-loop transfer function as

$$G'_{cl}(jw) = \frac{e^{-djw}}{\tau_{cl} jw + 1} \quad (15)$$

Note that it is standard practice to select the desired closed-loop transfer function to have the same delay as the process. Then

$$\begin{aligned} Y(jw) &= \frac{jw(\tau jw + 1)}{K(\tau_{cl} jw + 1 - e^{-djw})} \\ &= \frac{\tau jw + 1}{K(\tau_{cl} - j\frac{1-cosdw}{w} + \frac{sindw}{w})} \quad (16) \end{aligned}$$

By defining $Q(w) = (\tau_{cl} + \frac{sindw}{w})^2 + (\frac{1-cosdw}{w})^2 = \tau_{cl}^2 + 2\tau_{cl}\frac{sindw}{w} + 2\frac{1-cosdw}{w^2}$, we see that

$$\begin{aligned} Re(Y) &= \frac{1}{KQ}(\tau_{cl} + \frac{sindw}{w} \\ &\quad -\tau(1 - cosdw)) \quad (17) \\ Im(Y) &= \frac{1}{KQ}(\tau\tau_{cl} w + \tau sindw \\ &\quad +\frac{1 - cosdw}{w}) \quad (18) \end{aligned}$$

Figures 2 and 3 show the real and imaginary parts of $Y(jw)$ for $\frac{d}{\tau} = 0.2, 1$, and 3 with $K = 1$, $\tau = 5$, and the desired closed-loop time constant $\tau_{cl} = 3$. Both figures illustrate that for the smallest value of $\frac{d}{\tau}$, the real and imaginary parts of $Y(jw)$ satisfy equations (8) and (9), indicating that the PID controller structure will be able to achieve the desired response. However, as $\frac{d}{\tau}$ increases, the real and imaginary parts of $Y(jw)$ depart from linearity. This indicates that it will become more and more difficult to achieve the desired performance using the PID controller structure with increasing $\frac{d}{\tau}$.

To illustrate the effects of changing the desired closed-loop time constant τ_{cl} on $Y(jw)$, we will increase τ_{cl} to 10 and then to 15 while maintaining $\frac{d}{\tau} = 3$. Figures 4 and 5 compare the real and imaginary parts of $Y(jw)$ for the three different values of τ_{cl}. Both parts move towards linearity as τ_{cl} increases. This indicates that the desired performance is now achievable. However, it is interesting to note that the resulting controller approaches a PI structure as the slope of $Re(Y)$ tends to zero.

Example 3: a high order system
Consider a higher order system [2] described by

$$G(s) = \frac{1}{(s+1)^8} \quad (19)$$

We will choose the desired closed-loop transfer function to be

$$G'_{cl}(s) = \frac{e^{-ds}}{\tau_{cl}^2 s^2 + 2\zeta\tau_{cl} s + 1} \quad (20)$$

It is important to specify a time delay in the desired closed-loop performance for higher order systems in order to compensate for the phase shift of $G(jw)$. The time-delay $d = 2$ is selected to be equal to the 'apparent' delay in the system (19) and $\zeta = 0.7$ is chosen as the desirable damping factor. τ_{cl} is adjusted such that equations (8) and (9) are approximately satisfied.

For this example, with the above parameters,

$$Y(jw) = \frac{jw(jw+1)^8 e^{-2jw}}{\tau_{cl}^2[jw]^2 + 1.4\tau_{cl} jw + 1 - e^{-2jw}} \quad (21)$$

Figures 6 and 7 illustrate the variation of the real and imaginary parts of $Y(jw)$ for $\tau_{cl} = 1, 3$, and 5. Both figures indicate that as τ_{cl} increases, the real and imaginary parts converge to straight lines against w^2 and w, respectively. Based on these graphical results, we would choose τ_{cl} to be either 3 or 5 as we expect both to have actual responses which closely match the desired performances. We have proceeded with the design for all three values of τ_{cl}.

In figure 8, the desired closed-loop step responses are plotted. Figure 9 shows the actual closed-loop step responses achieved under PID control, with the controller parameters determined by the algorithm given by equation (5) applied over the frequency range (0.01, 1). As predicted from figures 6 and 7, the response for $\tau_{cl} = 1$ deviates considerably from the desired performance, while the actual responses for $\tau_{cl} = 3$ and 5 are both close to those desired.

4 Conclusions

This paper presents an algorithm for the design of PID controllers based on the process frequency response. Examples have been given to illustrate the effectiveness of the algorithm. The choice of the desired closed-loop performance has been studied subject to improving the match between the desired and actual open-loop Nyquist plots. Since the proposed algorithm is based on the open-loop Nyquist plot, the stability of the closed-loop system may be evaluated using the Nyquist stability criteria, and may also be extended to an assessment of robust stability in the presence of uncertainty in the process frequency response information [1].

References

[1] E. Goberdhansingh, L. Wang, and W.R. Cluett. Robust control system design using direct frequency response. *Proceedings of American Control Conference, Chicago*, 3026–3030, 1992.

[2] M. Lilja. A frequency domain method for low order controller design. *IFAC 11th Triennial World Congress, Tallinn*, 223–228, 1990.

[3] L. Ljung. *System Identification: Theory for the User.* Prentice-Hall, Englewood Cliffs, New Jersey, 1987.

[4] M. Morari and E. Zafiriou. *Robust Process Control.* Prentice-Hall, Englewood Cliffs, NJ, 1989.

[5] D. E. Seborg, T. F. Edgar, and D. A. Mellichamp. *Process Dynamics and Control.* John Wiley and Sons, New York, 1989.

[6] J. G. Ziegler and N. B. Nichols. Optimum settings for automatic controllers. *Transactions of the American Society of Mechanical Engineers*, Vol. 62:759–768, 1942.

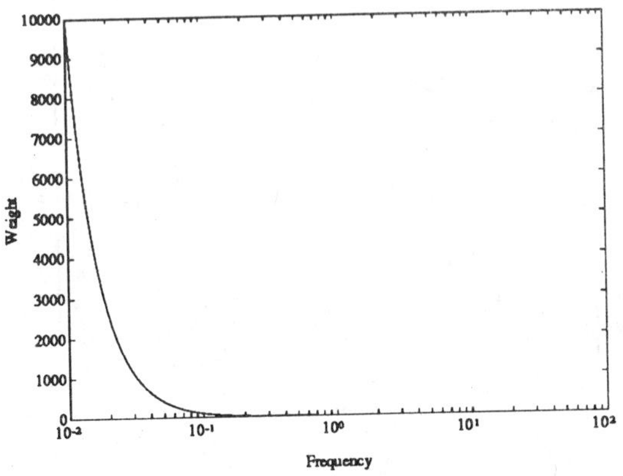

Figure 1: Implicit weighting function for a first order system

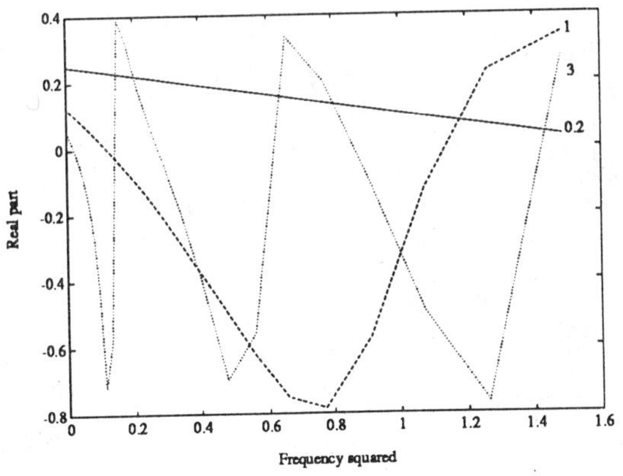

Figure 2: Effect of changing $\frac{d}{\tau}$ on $Re(Y)$

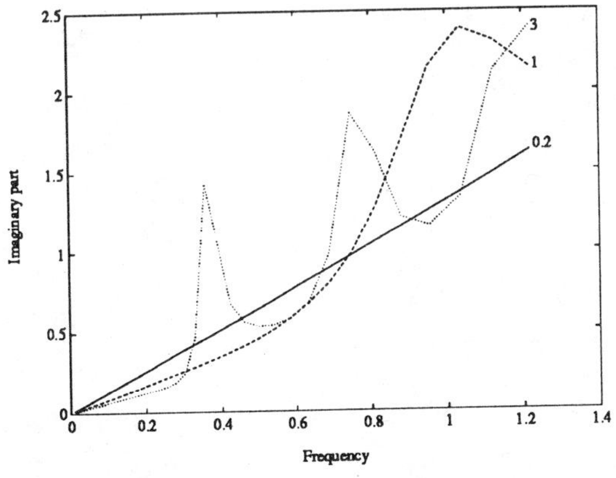

Figure 3: Effect of changing $\frac{d}{\tau}$ on $Im(Y)$

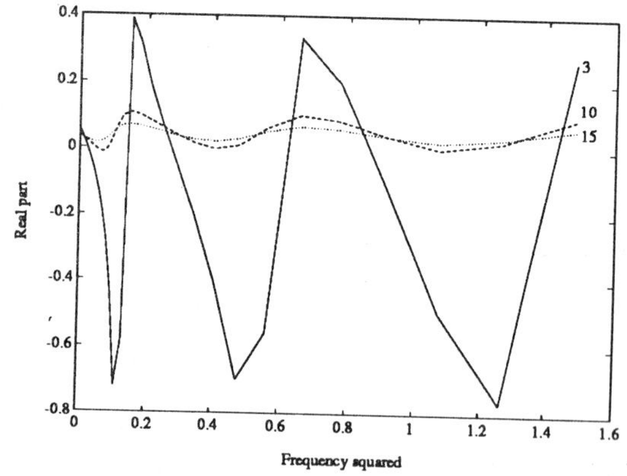

Figure 4: Effect of changing τ_{cl} on $Re(Y)$

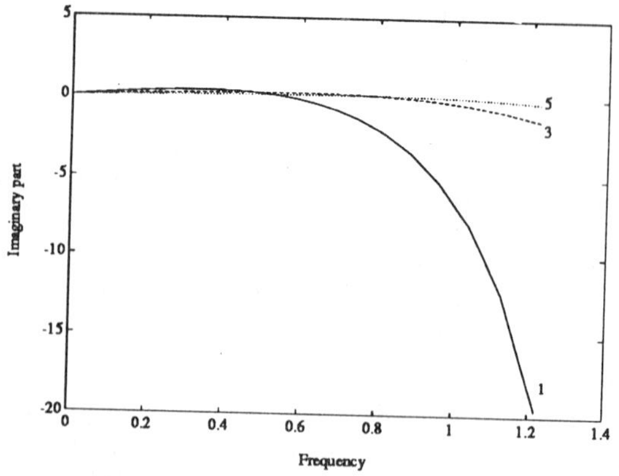

Figure 7: Effect of changing τ_{cl} on $Im(Y)$

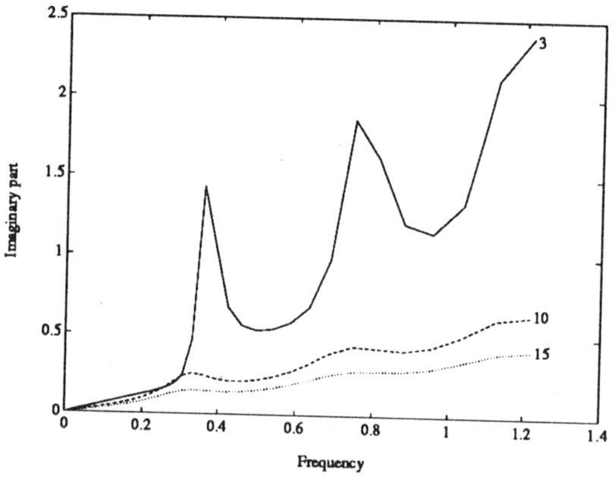

Figure 5: Effect of changing τ_{cl} on $Im(Y)$

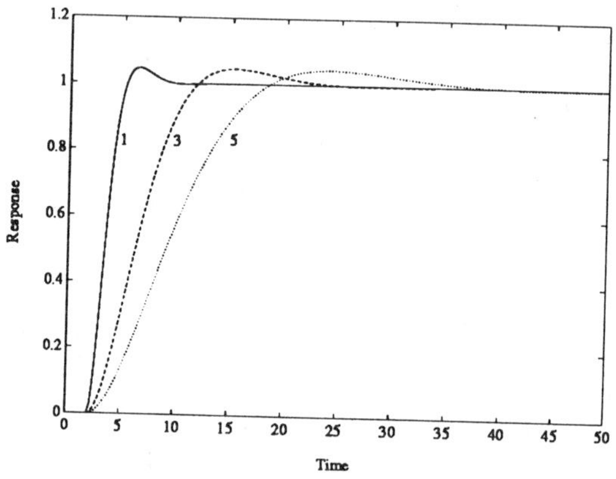

Figure 8: Desired performance for varying τ_{cl}

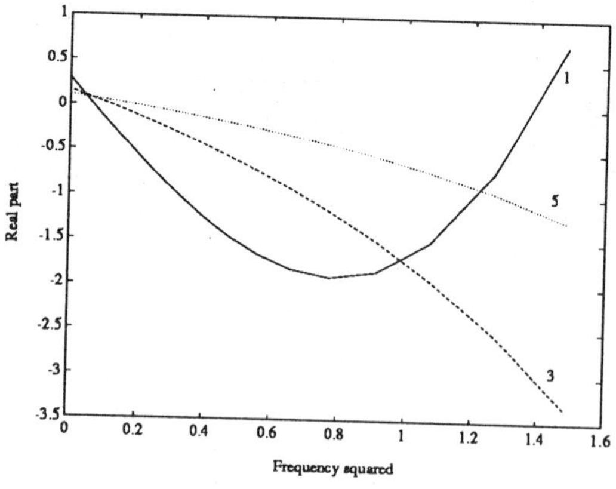

Figure 6: Effect of changing τ_{cl} on $Re(Y)$

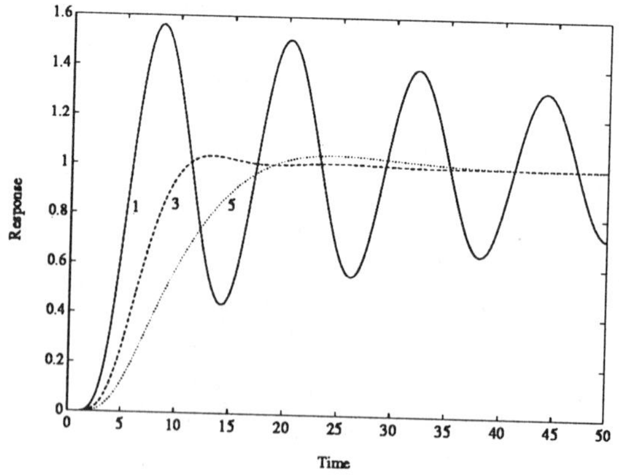

Figure 9: Actual performance for varying τ_{cl}

Proceedings of the
American Control Conference
San Francisco, California • June 1993

Experimental Design for Robust Process Control Using Schroeder-Phased Input Signals

Daniel E. Rivera* and Xiangqin Chen*
Department of Chemical, Bio and Materials Engineering
Arizona State University, Tempe, Arizona 85287-6006

and

David S. Bayard
Jet Propulsion Laboratory
California Institute of Technology
Pasadena, California 91109

Abstract

The use of Schroeder-phased, multisinusoid input signals for system identification in the process industries is described in this paper. We show that the Schroeder-phased input displays a number of significant properties which make it an attractive alternative to the PRBS input for identification in the presence of noise.

I. Introduction

Experimental testing represents the most time consuming step in system identification in the process industries. Because identification testing in industry is usually performed while the plant is in normal operating mode, it is of paramount importance that the input signal be designed to be informative while causing minimal disruption on operations.

In this paper we consider Schroeder-phased multisinusoid signals and frequency-response plant set estimation as described by Bayard [1] as an alternative to PRBS testing. The Schroeder-phased input design has the special property of placing input energy only at the discrete frequency points used in the computation. The usefulness of the Schroeder-phased input for robust process control follows from certain key properties of the error distributions established in [1]:

- *The error distributions are plant independent and statistically independent at each frequency grid point. Furthermore, the error probability distributions are exact and not asymptotic approximations.* Using these properties leads to a precise characterization of the plant set to a specified statistical confidence, e.g., $(1-\kappa)\cdot 100\%$.
- *The Discrete Fourier Transform (DFT) estimator is unbiased for any data length and hence does not require special frequency windowing functions.* The absence of windowing distortions may seem somewhat remarkable to researchers familiar with the usual "leakage effects" associated with using white noise or PRBS inputs.

*also affiliated with the Control Systems Engineering Laboratory, CIM Systems Research Center

In this paper we explore the potential benefits of the Schroeder-phased input signal for identifying process systems. Among these are:

1. This input is simple to generate - the corresponding collection of sinusoids can be added to a process under normal operations in a manner acceptable to plant personnel, just like the PRBS.
2. The frequency-response estimates and uncertainty bounds are derived for finite length data sets. This is crucial in process systems because of the long time constants that characterize chemical processes and the tendency of the literature to include only asymptotic results.
3. Unbiased estimation (without windowing) means less design variables to choose from in the estimation procedure. This leads to less decisions made by the process control engineer and a corresponding reduction in skill level associated with effective use of the technique.
4. Each period of the Schroeder-phased signal generates a natural time interval from which a corresponding frequency response estimate can be visualized and inspected by the control engineer. This can lead the engineer to make changes to the signal or continue implementing the existing signal in order to decrease the effects of noise. The evolution of the plant frequency response with time results in a natural monitoring technique that is appealing to engineering practice.

In this paper we derive simple-to-use guidelines for Schroeder-phased signal design and show how frequency responses and norm-bounded uncertainty descriptions that are obtained from Schroeder-phased generated data are useful for control-relevant identification and robust loopshaping.

II. Schroeder-Phased Signal Design

A Schroeder-phased signal is composed of a harmonically related sum of sinusoids,

$$u_s(k) = \lambda \sum_{i=1}^{n_s} \sqrt{2\alpha_i} \cos(\omega_i kT + \phi_i) \qquad (1)$$

where T is the sampling time, $\omega_i = 2\pi i/N_s T$, and $n_s \leq N_s/2$. The total power is normalized as $\sum_{i=1}^{n_s} \alpha_i = 1$ where the relative power in each component $\{\alpha_i > 0, i = 1, ..., n_s\}$ is user specified. In order to minimize peaking in the time domain the sinusoids are phased according to Schroeder [2] as,

$$\phi_i = 2\pi \sum_{j=1}^{i} j\alpha_j \qquad (2)$$

Choosing the phases to minimize peaking at the plant output is also possible; however, this requires some prior plant knowledge. λ is a scaling factor selected after generating the Schroeder-phased signal that insures that the time-domain magnitude does not exceed a deviation of $\pm u_{sat}$.

The Schroeder-phased signal has a discrete power spectrum with frequencies spaced $2\pi/N_s T$ intervals apart up to the Nyquist frequency $\frac{\pi}{T}$. Specifying N_s, the values of α_i, and T allows the engineer to tailor the frequency range to meet the particular excitation requirements for the identification problem at hand. In this paper we consider the situation where T is specified initially by the control system designer. We obtain guidelines for selecting the remaining parameters of the Schroeder-phased signal that are similar to guidelines for PRBS input design recently proposed by Rivera [3]. The goal is to generate a low-pass signal with power up to frequency ω_{n_s}; this is accomplished by specifying α_i as:

$$\alpha_i = \begin{cases} \frac{1}{n_s} & i = 1, \ldots, n_s \\ 0 & i = n_s + 1, \ldots, N_s/2 \end{cases} \qquad (3)$$

An *a priori* estimate of the dominant plant time constant τ_{dom} can be used as a basis for determining the high and low frequency ranges for the Schroeder-phased signal

$$\omega_* = \frac{1}{\beta \tau_{dom}} \leq \omega \leq \frac{\alpha}{\tau_{dom}} = \omega^* \qquad (4)$$

α is selected to insure that sufficiently high frequency content is available in the input signal, commensurate with how much faster the closed-loop response is expected to be relative to the open-loop response. For example, with $\alpha = 2$, the designer expects the closed-loop time constant to be one half that of the open-loop response (i.e. twice as fast) and this requires higher frequency content in the input. β, on the other hand, is specified to tailor how much low-frequency information will be present in the input signal. Choosing higher values of β results in lower frequency information: $\beta = 3$ will provide information down to a frequency roughly corresponding to the 95% settling time of process, $\beta = 4$ for the 98% settling time, and $\beta = 5$ for the 99% settling time. The relationship between (3) and (4) can be expressed as

$$\omega_* \geq \frac{2\pi}{N_s T} \qquad \omega^* \leq \frac{2\pi n_s}{N_s T} \qquad (5)$$

which yields the following guidelines for Schroeder signal parameter selection:

$$N_s \geq \frac{2\pi\beta\tau_{dom}}{T} \qquad n_s \geq \frac{N_s T \alpha}{2\pi\tau_{dom}} \qquad (6)$$

The selection of signal magnitude is dependent upon the length of the data set and the noise characteristics of the problem; this is discussed further in Section III. We illustrate the Schroeder-phased signal guidelines via an example:

<u>**Example 1.**</u> Consider the following first-order plant with delay

$$p(s) = \frac{e^{-s}}{s+1} \qquad (7)$$

sampled at $T = 0.3$ min. Using τ_{dom}=1.5 min and specifying $\alpha = 2$ (i.e., 2 times the open-loop bandwidth) and $\beta = 3$ (the 95% settling time) leads to (from (6)) a choice of $N_s = 96$ and $n_s = 7$, resulting in a total period length of 28.8 minutes.

We contrast this design with that of a PRBS signal using the guidelines established in [3]. Using the same values for α, β and τ_{dom} as before, we obtain a switching time of $T_{sw} = 2.1$ minutes and a sequence length $N = 16$, which results from using $n_r = 4$ shift registers in the PRBS generation algorithm. The total elapsed time for one PRBS period is 31.5 minutes, which is slightly longer than the corresponding Schroeder-phased period.

A comparison of the power spectrum for a Schroeder-phased signal with $u_{sat} = 1.75$ and a PRBS input with $u_{sat} = 1.0$ is shown in Figure 1. Both signals display the same bandwidth; however, only the Schroeder-phased input is truly low-pass. A time-domain comparison is shown in Figure 2. While the Schroeder-phased signal does involve a larger u_{sat} compared to a PRBS signal of equivalent average power, the Schroeder signal uses substantially lower move sizes, an important practical consideration in the process industries. Examining the corresponding "steady-state" output time series generated for each input signal from the plant (7), (Figure 3), one finds that both responses are qualitatively similar and show similar deviation from the nominal operating point.

III. Frequency Response and Uncertainty Estimation

For this discussion, it will be useful to make the following assumptions,

Assumption 1. The true plant is a single-input, single-output unknown exponentially stable linear time-invariant (LTI) transfer function assumed to have a sampled-data representation $p(z)$ in the forward shift operator z.

Assumption 2. The output disturbance $v(k)$ can be represented by $v(k) = Wd(k)$ where $d(k)$ is a normalized white Gaussian zero-mean noise sequence. W is a linear filter which be decomposed as $W(z) = \sigma\overline{W}(z)$ where $\sigma < \infty$ is a scalar (possibly unknown); and $\overline{W}(z)$ is a *known* stable and stably invertible transfer function.

Assumption 3. The system is driven by Schroeder-phased sinusoidal input (1) and allowed to reach steady-state before experimental data is taken.

In order to "whiten" the effect of the noise Schroeder-phased frequency response estimation, the time domain input u_s and output y_s will be inverse filtered by $\overline{W}$ to give filtered signals $\tilde{u}_s$ and $\tilde{y}_s$ as follows,

$$\overline{W}(z^{-1})\tilde{y}_s(k) = y_s(k); \quad \overline{W}(z^{-1})\tilde{u}_s(k) = u_s(k)$$

Since the frequencies in u_s are harmonically related, both the input $\tilde{u}_s$ and deterministic part of the output $\tilde{y}_s$ at steady-state will be periodic with period N_sT. Assume that m periods of filtered input/output data $\tilde{u}_s, \tilde{y}_s$ are collected at steady-state. Denote the output data from the ℓth period as,

$$\tilde{y}_s^{\ell}(k) = \tilde{y}_s(k + (\ell - 1)N_s)$$

for $k = 0, ..., N_s - 1$ and $\ell = 1, ..., m$.

Frequency domain estimates of the true plant p^* are constructed by taking DFT's on the filtered time-domain data

$$p^*(\omega_i) = \frac{\frac{1}{m}\sum_{\ell=1}^{m}\tilde{Y}_s^{\ell}(\omega_i)}{\tilde{U}_s(\omega_i)} \tag{8}$$

where,

$$\begin{aligned} \tilde{Y}_s^{\ell}(\omega_i) &= \frac{1}{N_s}\sum_{k=0}^{N_s-1}\tilde{y}_s^{\ell}(k)e^{-j\omega_i kT} \\ \tilde{U}_s(\omega_i) &= \frac{1}{N_s}\sum_{k=0}^{N_s-1}\tilde{u}_s(k)e^{-j\omega_i kT} \end{aligned}$$

It is emphasized that the DFT is evaluated precisely on the points of support of the Schroeder-phased input (1). The use of the radix-2 FFT algorithm to implement (8) requires using the full number of sinusoids ($n_s = N_s/2$) in the sum (1) and choosing N_s as some power of 2. A slower but still effective mixed-radix FFT algorithm can be used when these conditions are not satisfied. It should be clear that (8) should not be computed at frequencies where $\alpha_i = 0$.

It has been assumed that $W = \sigma\overline{W}$, where $\overline{W}$ is assumed known, and σ may be either known or unknown. If σ is unknown, it can be estimated as follows,

$$\hat{\sigma}^2 = \hat{\sigma}_1^2 + \hat{\sigma}_2^2 \tag{9}$$

where

$$\begin{aligned} \hat{\sigma}_1^2 &= \frac{2\sum_{\ell=1}^{m}\sum_{i=1}^{n_s}|\tilde{Y}_s^{\ell}(\omega_i) - \overline{Y}(\omega_i)|^2}{N_s(mN_s - 2n_s)} \\ \hat{\sigma}_2^2 &= \frac{\sum_{\ell=1}^{m}\left(|\tilde{Y}_s^{\ell}(0)|^2 + 2\sum_{i=n_s+1}^{N_s/2}|\tilde{Y}_s^{\ell}(\omega_i)|^2\right)}{N_s(mN_s - 2n_s)} \end{aligned}$$

$$\overline{Y}(\omega_i) = \frac{1}{m}\sum_{\ell=1}^{m}\tilde{Y}_s^{\ell}(\omega_i)$$

The usefulness of the noise variance estimator is that it leads to specifying a confidence region in the Nyquist diagram for the estimate $p^*(\omega_i)$. The analysis of this result is shown in [1]. The confidence region for the case of σ^2 estimated by $\hat{\sigma}^2$ is a perfect circle centered at $p^*(\omega_i) = \hat{b}_i + j\hat{a}_i$ of radius ϵ_i where

$$\epsilon_i^2 = \frac{\hat{\sigma}^2|\overline{W}(e^{-j\omega_i T})|^2 2F_{1-\kappa}(2, mN_s - 2n_s)}{\lambda^2\alpha_i mN_s} \tag{10}$$

$F_{1-\kappa}(2,\nu)$ is the 2-way Fisher statistic computed for a specified statistical confidence of $(1-\kappa)\cdot 100\%$. Noting that $F_{1-\kappa}(2,\nu)$ is bounded as ν becomes large (e.g., $F_{1-\kappa}(2,\nu) \leq 9$ for $1 - \kappa = .999$ and $\nu > 30$), it becomes clear that the uncertainty region increases with the noise-to-signal ratio $\hat{\sigma}^2\overline{W}/\lambda^2\alpha_i$ and decreases as the amount of measurement data mN_s increases. Thus (10) provides significant insight regarding the important practical issues of signal magnitude and test length in system identification. Noise in the data set can be overcome by either increasing signal power or lengthening the test duration. The decision to follow one approach over the other is dependent upon the circumstances being faced by the control engineer, such as operational restrictions, etc.

Under the conditions stated in Assumptions 1-3, the confidence region defined by (10) is exact. However, it is approximate if the conditions are violated, i.e., 1) the system has not reached steady-state before the data is taken, 2) the noise $v(k)$ is not Gaussian, or 3) inverse filtering by $\overline{W}$ is omitted. The effect of 1) is to create a bias in the estimate, and the previous expressions must be correspondingly modified. In contrast, it is noted in [1] that the effect of 2) and 3) are mild and may be violated in practice while maintaining reasonable results. The use of a Schroder-phased signal for frequency response and uncertainty estimation is illustrated with an example:

Example 2. We consider again the first-order dead-time plant model with a Schroeder-phased input signal as discussed in Example 1. We add white noise to the output signal such that the signal-to-noise ratio (defined by the ratio of standard deviations σ_y/σ) is 0.86. Figure 4 shows the evolution of the frequency response estimate and uncertainty regions ($\kappa = 0.95$) for four values of the input period m. Clearly, there is a marked improvement in the plant estimate and substantial reduction in the size of the uncertainty regions with increasing values of m.

Figure 4 demonstrates the potential value of the frequency response and uncertainty estimation procedure presented here as a "monitoring" technique for identification testing in process systems. Each period of the Schroeder signal can be collected and analyzed in real time, providing engineers the information necessary to make adjustments to the signal or improve the understanding of the system dynamics. The tie between this procedure and robust process control, particularly the computation of loopshaping bounds on the closed-loop transfer functions in real time, is shown in the next section.

IV. Application to Robust Loopshaping and Control-Relevant Parameter Estimation

The confidence regions defined by (10) can be expressed in terms of a norm-bounded multiplicative uncertainty as follows

$$|(p(e^{j\omega_i T}) - p^*(\omega_i))p^{*\,-1}(\omega_i)| \leq \bar{\ell}_m(\omega_i) = \epsilon_i/|p^*(\omega_i)| \quad (11)$$

In [4] we show how a robust performance test such as the μ performance measure

$$\mu^* = \sup_{\omega} |\eta^*(e^{j\omega T})\bar{\ell}_m(\omega)| + |\epsilon^*(e^{j\omega T})w_P(j\omega)| \quad (12)$$

can be incorporated into a procedure for determining control-relevant prefilters for parametric model estimation using prediction-error techniques [5]. w_P weights the sensitivity function $\epsilon = (1+pc)^{-1}$, which determines the controlled variable response. $\eta = pc(1+pc)^{-1}$ is the complementary sensitivity function; η^* and ϵ^* are the frequency responses of the closed-loop transfer functions based on the estimated frequency response p^*. Whenever $\mu^* < 1$, the following condition is satisfied for the closed-loop system

$$|\epsilon| \leq 1/|w_P| \quad \forall p \in \bar{\ell}_m \quad 0 \leq \omega \leq \pi/T$$

The paper by Braatz *et al.* [6] provides a procedure for determining necessary and sufficient condition bounds on the closed-loop transfer functions from knowledge of the process uncertainty and performance specifications on the closed-loop system (i.e., robust loopshaping). For a SISO system, sufficient bounds on η^* and ϵ^* are

$$|\eta^*| < \frac{1 - |w_P|}{|w_P| + \bar{\ell}_m} \qquad |\epsilon^*| < \frac{1 - \bar{\ell}_m}{|w_P| + \bar{\ell}_m} \quad (13)$$

The reader is referred to [6] for a description of upper and lower necessary bounds on these closed-loop transfer functions.

Using the frequency response and uncertainty estimation procedure shown in Section III, one realizes that the robust loopshaping bounds on η^* and ϵ^* can be computed in real-time, *during identification testing*. The decision to halt or modify an identification test can be determined on the basis of how these bounds evolve with increasing number of Schroeder signal periods m. We illustrate this with an example:

Example 3. Consider the plant and noise conditions described in Example 2. The amplitude ratio for the plant and uncertainty estimates for $m = 5$ are shown in Figure 5. The expression for w_p is

$$w_P = 0.5\left(\frac{0.85s + 1}{0.85s}\right) \quad (14)$$

(14) specifies a maximum closed-loop time constant of $\tau_{cl} = 2.25$ min and $\max_\omega |\epsilon| = 2.0$. Necessary and sufficient bounds on η^* and ϵ^* are shown in Figure 6, which are satisfied by the parametric model

$$\tilde{\eta}(z) = \frac{(1-0.8)^2 z^2}{(z-0.8)^2} \quad (15)$$

(15) can be incorporated directly into the statement of the control-relevant prefilter developed in [5]:

$$L(z) = \tilde{p}_e(z)\tilde{p}^{-1}(z)\tilde{\epsilon}(z)\tilde{\eta}(z)(r(z) - d(z)) \quad (16)$$

which then weights the estimation for a parametric transfer function model $\tilde{p}(z)$ and noise model $\tilde{p}_e(z)$. Additional discussion of this procedure is found in [4]. Further refinement of this methodology and its implementation using an industrial-scale testbed facility are areas of current research activity.

V. Acknowledgement

The support of Shell Development Company and the National Science Foundation (Grant No. CTS-9110528) is gratefully acknowledged.

References

[1] Bayard, D.S., "Statistical plant set estimation using Schroeder-phased multisinusoidal input design," *1992 American Control Conference*, Chicago, pgs. 2988-2995, also *J. Applied Mathematics and Computation*, forthcoming.

[2] Schroeder, M.R., *IEEE Trans. Information Theory*, **16**, 85, Jan. 1970.

[3] Rivera, D.E. "Monitoring Tools for PRBS Testing in System Identification," Paper 131d, *AIChE National Meeting*, Miami Beach, 1992.

[4] Rivera, D.E. "Towards an integrated methodology for the identification and design of robust low-order controllers," paper 154a *AIChE National Meeting*, Los Angeles, 1991.

[5] Rivera, D.E., J.F. Pollard, and C.E. García, *IEEE Trans. Autom. Cntrl.*, **37**, 964, 1992.

[6] Braatz, R.D., M. Morari, and J.H. Lee, "Necessary/Sufficient Loopshaping Bounds for Robust Performance," *AIChE National Meeting*, Los Angeles, 1991.

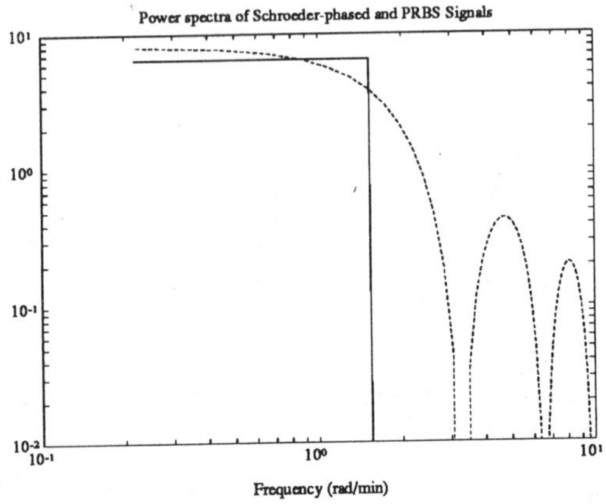

Figure 1: Power spectra comparison, Example 1. Solid: Schroeder-phased; Dashed: PRBS.

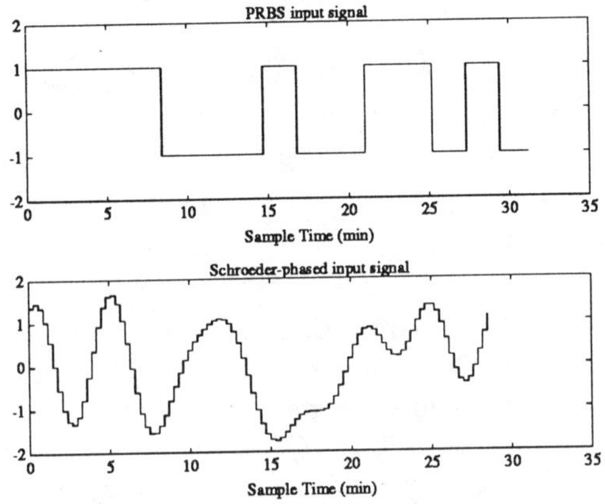

Figure 2: Comparison of PRBS and Schroeder input time series, Example 1.

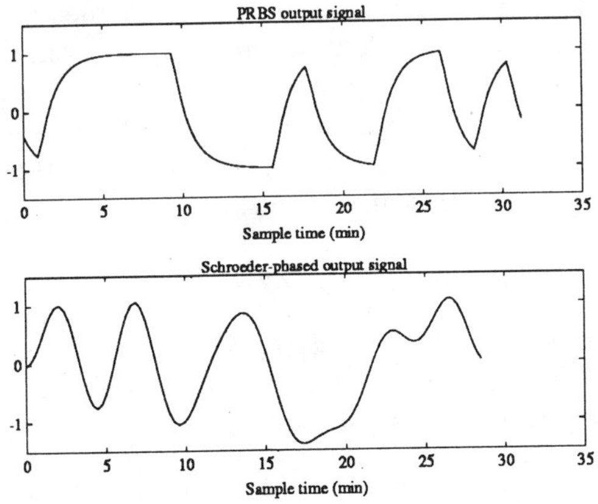

Figure 3: Comparison of output time series for first-order deadtime plant, Example 1.

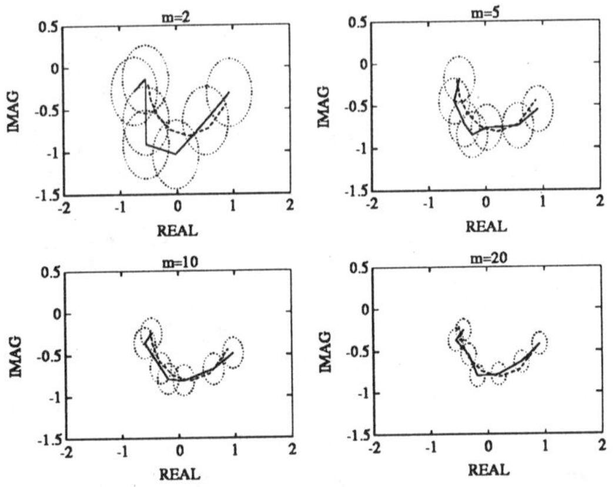

Figure 4: Nyquist plots and 95% confidence regions, Example 2. Solid line: p^*, dashed line: p.

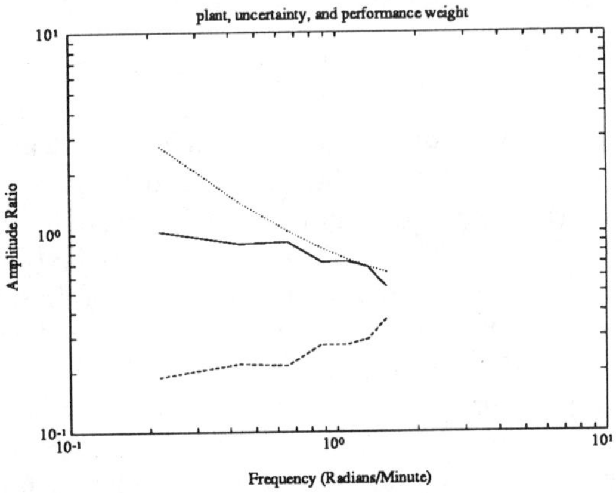

Figure 5: Amplitude ratios for plant and uncertainty estimates and weight function, Example 3. Solid: p^*, dashed: $\bar{\ell}_m$, dotted: w_p.

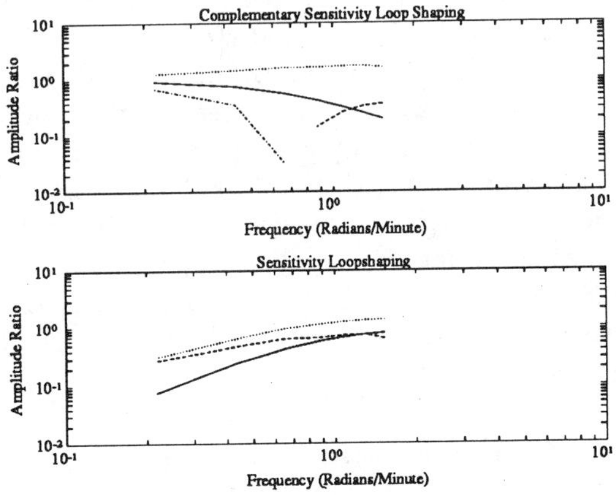

Figure 6: Robust complementary sensitivity and sensitivity loopshaping bounds, Example 3. Solid: $\tilde{\eta}$ and $\tilde{\epsilon}$, dotted: necessary upper bounds, dash-dot: necessary lower bounds, dashed: sufficient upper bounds.

Proceedings of the
American Control Conference
San Francisco, California • June 1993

Receding Horizon Recursive State Estimation

Kenneth R. Muske and James B. Rawlings
Department of Chemical Engineering, The University of Texas at Austin, Austin, TX 78712
Jay H. Lee
Department of Chemical Engineering, Auburn University, Auburn, AL 36849

Abstract

A discrete time, receding horizon, recursive state estimation scheme based on the batch state estimation least squares formulation is presented. It is shown that this procedure yields the same state estimate as the standard Kalman filter. Nominal stability of a constrained batch state estimation formulation is demonstrated and a constrained, receding horizon, recursive state estimation formulation is presented.

1. Introduction

Since the state is not directly measured in most applications, state estimates based on the output measurements are required to implement any state feedback controller, such as the linear quadratic regulator. The standard method to do state estimation for linear systems is the Kalman filter, which is an equivalent recursive solution to the least squares batch state estimation problem [1]. In this article, an equivalent receding horizon, recursive state estimation method is discussed. A quadratic program formulation for constrained batch state estimation is presented and shown to be stable. A quadratic program formulation for constrained, receding horizon, state estimation is also presented. The motivation for the addition of constraints to the state estimation problem is to improve the performance of the state estimator. The Kalman filter yields the optimal state estimate for a linear system with zero mean, uncorrelated, normally distributed state and measurement noise of a given covariance. Although process noise rarely follows these assumptions, they are used since the actual stochastic process is generally unknown. The constrained formulation is applied to prevent physically unrealistic state estimates due to spurious output measurements and to improve the robustness of the state estimator.

2. Batch State Estimation

The time invariant, discrete, dynamical system is

$$\begin{aligned} x_{k+1} &= Ax_k + w_k, \qquad k = 0,1,2,\ldots \qquad (1) \\ y_k &= Cx_k + v_k \end{aligned}$$

in which $x_k \in \Re^n$ is the state vector, $w_k \in \Re^n$ is a state noise vector, $y_k \in \Re^l$ is the measured output, and $v_k \in \Re^l$ is a measurement noise vector. In order to simplify this discussion, inputs are not considered.

Optimal batch state estimation is performed using the following least squares formulation [1]

$$\begin{aligned} \min \Phi_k &= (\hat{x}_{0|k} - \bar{x}_0)^T Q_0^{-1} (\hat{x}_{0|k} - \bar{x}_0) + \qquad (2) \\ & \sum_{j=0}^{k-1} \hat{w}_j^T Q^{-1} \hat{w}_j + \sum_{j=0}^{k} \hat{v}_j^T R^{-1} \hat{v}_j \end{aligned}$$

$$\text{Subject to:} \qquad \begin{aligned} \hat{x}_{j+1|k} &= A\hat{x}_{j|k} + \hat{w}_j \\ \hat{v}_j &= y_j - C\hat{x}_{j|k} \end{aligned}$$

in which R^{-1} is a symmetric positive definite penalty matrix on the output prediction error, Q^{-1} is a symmetric positive definite penalty matrix on the estimated state noise vectors, Q_0^{-1} is a symmetric positive definite penalty matrix on the initial state estimate error, and $\bar{x}_0$ is an *a priori* estimate of the state at time $k = 0$. This is a deterministic formulation that minimizes Φ_k based on the corresponding penalty matrices of $\hat{w}_j$ and $\hat{v}_j$. It can be shown that when w_j and v_j are independent, zero mean, normally distributed random variables with covariances Q and R, respectively, and $\bar{x}_0$ is an independent, normally distributed random variable with covariance Q_0, this formulation maximizes the conditional probability density function of the state estimates

$$p(\hat{x}_{0|k}, \ldots, \hat{x}_{k|k} \mid y_0, \ldots, y_k)$$

with respect to $\{\hat{x}_{0|k}, \ldots, \hat{x}_{k|k}\}$ [1].

The state estimate at time j given output measurements up to time k is

$$\hat{x}_{j|k} = A^j \bar{x}_0 + \sum_{i=0}^{k} A^{j-i} \hat{w}_{i-1} \qquad (3)$$

in which A^{j-i} is defined to be zero for all $j < i$ and $\hat{w}_{-1}$ is defined to be $\hat{x}_{0|k} - \bar{x}_0$. When $j \leq k$, this formula computes the optimal smoothed estimate of the past state value. When $j > k$, this formula computes the optimal prediction of the future state value. The series of estimated state noise vectors, $\hat{w}_j$, determined from the solution of the least squares formulation are

$$\begin{bmatrix} \hat{w}_{-1} \\ \vdots \\ \hat{w}_{k-1} \end{bmatrix} = (E_k + Q_k)^{-1} G_k \begin{bmatrix} y_0 - C\bar{x}_0 \\ \vdots \\ y_k - CA^k \bar{x}_0 \end{bmatrix}$$

The matrices E, F, and G are defined by the following recursions.

$$E_0 = F_0, \quad E_{j+1} = \begin{bmatrix} A_j^T E_j A_j + F_j & \tilde{A}_j^T F_0 \\ F_0 \tilde{A}_j & F_0 \end{bmatrix}$$

$$F_0 = C^T R^{-1} C, \quad F_{j+1} = \begin{bmatrix} F_j & \tilde{A}_j^T F_0 \\ F_0 \tilde{A}_j & F_0 \end{bmatrix}$$

$$G_0 = C^T R^{-1}, \quad G_{j+1} = \begin{bmatrix} G_j & \tilde{A}_j^T G_0 \\ 0 & G_0 \end{bmatrix}$$

The matrices A_j and Q_j are $n(j+1) \times n(j+1)$ square matrices with A and Q^{-1}, respectively, on the diagonal. The matrix $\tilde{A}_j$ is defined as $[A^{j+1}\ A^j\ \ldots\ A]$.

3. Receding Horizon State Estimation

The batch state estimation formulation uses all k output measurements to determine k state noise vectors and obtain the state estimate at time $k+1$. The number of decision variables in this approach becomes prohibitive as time progresses. In the standard Kalman filter formulation, the optimal state estimate at time $k+1$ is determined recursively from the optimal state estimate and output measurement at time k. In the receding horizon formulation, the optimal state estimate at time $k+1$ is determined recursively from the optimal state estimate at time $k-N$ and the most recent $N+1$ output measurements using the following least squares formulation.

$$\min \Psi_k^N = \hat{w}_{k-N-1|k}^T P_{k-N}^{-1} \hat{w}_{k-N-1|k} + \sum_{j=k-N}^{k-1} \hat{w}_{j|k}^T Q^{-1} \hat{w}_{j|k} + \sum_{j=k-N}^{k} \hat{v}_{j|k}^T R^{-1} \hat{v}_{j|k} \quad (4)$$

Subject to:

$$\hat{x}_{j+1|k} = A\hat{x}_{j|k} + \hat{w}_{j|k}$$
$$\hat{v}_{j|k} = y_j - C\hat{x}_{j|k}$$

The initial condition for the state vector at time $k-N$ is determined from the estimate computed N time intervals in the past.

$$\hat{x}_{k-N|k} = \hat{x}_{k-N|k-N-1} + \hat{w}_{k-N-1|k}$$

The state estimates for time $k \leq N$ are determined from the batch state estimation formulation in Eq. 2. The penalty matrix P_{k-N} is the filtering algebraic Riccati matrix in which $P_0 = Q_0$. Note that this is the covariance of the state estimate at time $k-N$ in the stochastic interpretation.

The estimate of the state vector at time $k+1$ given output measurements up to time k is computed as

$$\begin{aligned} \hat{x}_{k+1|k} &= A^{N+1}\hat{x}_{k-N|k-N-1} + L_{N|k} Y_{N|k} \quad (5) \\ L_{N|k} &= \tilde{A}_N (E_N + \tilde{Q}_N^{k-N})^{-1} G_N \\ Y_{N|k} &= \begin{bmatrix} y_{k-N} - C\hat{x}_{k-N|k-N-1} \\ \vdots \\ y_k - CA^N \hat{x}_{k-N|k-N-1} \end{bmatrix} \end{aligned}$$

in which the matrix $\tilde{Q}_N^{k-N}$ at time k is defined in the same manner as Q_N except that P_{k-N}^{-1} replaces Q_0^{-1} as the first matrix on the diagonal. This estimate will be shown to be the Kalman filter estimate after presenting the following relationship for P_k.

Lemma 1 *The filtering algebraic Riccati matrix, P_k, can be computed as follows for all $N \geq 0$ and all $k > N$.*

$$P_k = Q + \tilde{A}_N (E_N + \tilde{Q}_N^{k-N-1})^{-1} \tilde{A}_N^T$$

Proof: See the Appendix.

Theorem 1 *The state estimate $\hat{x}_{k+1|k}$ computed in Eq. 5 from the solution of the least squares problem in Eq. 4 is the Kalman filter state estimate at time k.*

Proof: The proof is by induction. For $N = 0$, the solution of the least squares formulation in Eq. 4 yields the following estimate for all $k \geq 0$.

$$\begin{aligned} \hat{x}_{k+1|k} &= A\hat{x}_{k|k-1} + L_k(y_k - C\hat{x}_{k|k-1}) \\ L_k &= A(C^T R^{-1} C + P_k^{-1})^{-1} C^T R^{-1} \end{aligned}$$

This is the Kalman filter state estimate for all $k \geq 0$ with $P_0 = Q_0$. The estimate at time k from the solution of the quadratic program in Eq. 4 for a horizon length of $M+1$ can be obtained by replacing N with $M+1$ in the expression in Eq. 5. Partitioning the matrices in this expression, performing the partitioned matrix inverse, and using the relation in Lemma 1 results in the following expression (See the Appendix).

$$\begin{aligned} \hat{x}_{k+1|k} = & A^{M+2}\hat{x}_{k-M-1|k-M-2} + \\ & (A - L_k C) L_{M|k-1} Y_{M|k-1} + \\ & L_k (y_k - CA^{M+1}\hat{x}_{k-M-1|k-M-2}) \end{aligned}$$

Assuming the expression in Eq. 5 is the Kalman filter result for a horizon of length M for all $k \geq M$, then the proceeding expression can be simplified as follows.

$$\hat{x}_{k+1|k} = A\hat{x}_{k|k-1} + L_k(y_k - C\hat{x}_{k|k-1})$$

This is the Kalman filter state estimate at time $k+1$ for all $k \geq M$ which proves the theorem.

Corollary 1 *The state estimate $\hat{x}_{k+1|k}$ computed in Eq. 5 from the solution of the least squares problem in Eq. 4 in which P_∞^{-1} is the first matrix on the diagonal of $\tilde{Q}_N$ for all time k is the steady-state Kalman filter state estimate at time k.*

Proof: The proof is by induction. For $N = 0$, the solution of the least squares problem in Eq. 4 yields the following estimate for all $k \geq 0$.

$$\begin{aligned} \hat{x}_{k+1|k} &= A\hat{x}_{k|k-1} + L_\infty(y_k - C\hat{x}_{k|k-1}) \\ L_\infty &= A(C^T R^{-1} C + P_\infty^{-1})^{-1} C^T R^{-1} \end{aligned}$$

This is the steady-state Kalman filter state estimate for all $k \geq 0$. The remainder of this proof proceeds in the same manner as the induction argument presented in Theorem 1 using the following relationship which is a result of Lemma 1.

$$P_\infty = Q + \tilde{A}_N(E_N + \tilde{Q}_N^\infty)^{-1}\tilde{A}_N^T, \qquad N \geq 0$$

4. Constrained Batch State Estimation

Estimated state noise and state constraints of the following form are considered in the constrained batch state estimation problem in which $d \in \Re^p$, $f \in \Re^q$, and $d_i, f_i > 0$.

$$\begin{aligned} D\hat{w}_j &\leq d, \qquad j = -1, 0, \ldots, k-1 \qquad (6) \\ F\hat{x}_{j|k} &\leq f, \qquad j = j_1, \ldots, k, \ldots, j_2 \qquad (7) \end{aligned}$$

This constraint formulation guarantees that $\hat{x}_{j|k} = 0$ is feasible. The estimated state noise constraints in Eq. 6 are applied on all of the state noise vectors. The estimated state constraints in Eq. 7 are applied on the smoothed past state estimates and the future state estimates from time $j_1 \geq 1$ to $k+j_2 \geq k+1$. The value of j_2 is chosen such that feasibility of the future state estimates in Eq. 3 up to time $k+j_2$ implies feasibility of these constraints on an infinite horizon. The value of j_1 is chosen as the smallest value that ensures feasibility of the estimated state constraints. The existence of finite values for j_1 and j_2 can be shown by the norm bounding argument presented in [2].

Stability of the constrained batch state estimation formulation for a non-zero initial reconstruction error is demonstrated in Theorems 2 and 3. This formulation is stable provided the reconstruction error of the estimate at time k converges to zero from an arbitrary non-zero initial condition with no state and measurement noise. Without noise, the reconstruction error is determined by the following dynamic equation.

$$\begin{aligned} \xi_{j|k} &= x_j - \hat{x}_{j|k} = A\xi_{j-1|k} - \hat{w}_{j-1} \\ \hat{v}_j &= C\xi_{j|k} \end{aligned}$$

The objective function in Eq. 2 is expressed in terms of the reconstruction error as

$$\min \Phi(k) = \hat{w}_{-1}^T Q_0^{-1} \hat{w}_{-1} + \qquad (8)$$

$$\sum_{j=0}^{k-1} \hat{w}_j^T Q^{-1} \hat{w}_j + \sum_{j=0}^{k} \xi_{j|k}^T C^T R^{-1} C \xi_{j|k}$$

For stable A, the following result applies.

Theorem 2 *For stable A, $\xi_{k|k} = 0$ is an asymptotically stable solution of the constrained batch state estimation quadratic program with objective function Eq. 8 and feasible constraints Eqs. 6 and 7 for all $\xi_0 \in \Re^n$.*

Proof: Feasibility of the constraints at time $k = 0$ can be guaranteed by the selection of j_1 in Eq. 7. This implies that the state noise sequence $\{\hat{w}_{-1}, 0, \ldots, 0\}$ is feasible at each time k since the state estimates computed at time $k > 0$ are the same as the future state estimates computed at time $k = 0$. The objective function value at time k with this state noise vector sequence is

$$\begin{aligned} \bar{\Phi}_k &= \hat{w}_{(-1)}^T Q_0^{-1} \hat{w}_{(-1)} + \xi_0^T \bar{R} \xi_0 \\ \bar{R} &= \sum_{j=0}^{k} A^{T^j} C^T R^{-1} C A^j \end{aligned}$$

Since optimization will be performed at each time k, the value of Φ_k can be no greater than $\bar{\Phi}_k$. Therefore Φ_k is bounded above by $\lim_{k\to\infty} \bar{\Phi}_k$, which can be determined from the previous expression with $\bar{R}$ the solution of the following discrete Lyapunov equation.

$$\bar{R} = A^T \bar{R} A + C^T R^{-1} C$$

Optimization at each time k also implies the following relationship since the first k values of $\hat{w}_j$ computed at time k will not necessarily be optimal at time $k-1$.

$$\Phi_k - \xi_{k|k}^T C^T R^{-1} C \xi_{k|k} - \hat{w}_{k-1} Q^{-1} \hat{w}_{k-1} \geq \Phi_{k-1}$$

Since Q and R are positive definite, the sequence $\{\Phi_k\}$ is monotonically nondecreasing and bounded above which implies that the sequence converges. Therefore $\hat{w}_{k-1}^T Q^{-1} \hat{w}_{k-1}$ converges to zero which implies $\hat{w}_{k-1}$ converges to zero. For stable A, this implies $\xi_{k|k}$ converges to zero.

If A is unstable, then (C, A) must be detectable for the reconstruction error to convergence to zero. The set of initial reconstruction errors is also restricted due to the state noise constraints in Eq. 6. The reconstruction error will converge to zero if and only if $\xi_0 \in \mathcal{V}^n$ in which $\mathcal{V}^n$ denotes the set of initial reconstruction errors for which there exists a state noise sequence $\{\hat{w}_j\}$ that zeros the unstable modes of ξ_0. In this case, the system is constrained detectable. Since the future estimates of the state vector computed by Eq. 3 are unbounded, the estimated state constraints in Eq. 7 are not considered for unstable A. The following result then applies for unstable A.

Theorem 3 *For unstable A with (C, A) detectable, $\xi_{k|k} = 0$ is an asymptotically stable solution of the constrained batch state estimation quadratic program with objective function Eq. 8 and feasible constraint Eq. 6 for all $\xi_0 \in \mathcal{V}^n$.*

Proof: Since $\xi_0 \in \mathcal{V}^n$, there exists a state noise sequence that zeros the unstable modes of ξ_0. Using this state noise sequence, the convergence of $\hat{w}_k$ and $\xi_{k|k}^T C^T R^{-1} C \xi_{k|k}$ to zero can be shown in the same manner as in Theorem 2. This implies that $\xi_{k|k}^T \mathcal{O}^T R_n \mathcal{O} \xi_{k|k}$ converges to zero in which $\mathcal{O}$ is the observability matrix and R_n is constructed in the same manner as Q_n with R^{-1}. Since (C, A) is detectable, the unstable modes are not in the null space of $\mathcal{O}$. Therefore, the unstable modes converge to zero. The convergence of the stable modes to zero follows from the convergence of $\hat{w}_k$ to zero.

5. Constrained Receding Horizon State Estimation

The constraints in Eqs. 6 and 7 can be applied to the receding horizon, recursive state estimation formulation in Eq. 4 resulting in the following constrained, receding horizon, recursive state estimation formulation [3].

$$\min \Psi_k^N = \hat{w}_{k-N-1|k}^T P_{k-N}^{-1} \hat{w}_{k-N-1|k} + \sum_{j=k-N}^{k-1} \hat{w}_{j|k}^T Q^{-1} \hat{w}_{j|k} + \sum_{j=k-N}^{k} \hat{v}_{j|k}^T R^{-1} \hat{v}_{j|k} \quad (9)$$

Subject to:

$$\hat{x}_{j+1|k} = A\hat{x}_{j|k} + \hat{w}_{j|k}$$
$$\hat{v}_{j|k} = y_j - C\hat{x}_{j|k}$$
$$D\hat{w}_{j|k} \le d, \; j = k-N-1, \ldots, k-1$$
$$F\hat{x}_{j|k} \le f, \; j = \max(j_1, k-N), \ldots, j_2$$

This formulation determines the constrained state estimates from time $k - N$ recursively from the most recent $N + 1$ output measurements as follows

$$\hat{x}_{k-N+j|k} = A^j \hat{x}_{k-N|k-N-1} + \sum_{i=0}^{N} A^{j-i} \hat{w}_{k-N-1+i|k}$$

in which A^{j-i} is defined to be zero for all $j < i$ and $\hat{w}_{k-N-1|k}$ is defined to be $\hat{x}_{k-N|k} - \hat{x}_{k-N|k-N-1}$. The stability properties of this formulation are currently under study.

6. Example

Consider the following SISO non-minimum phase plant.

$$A = \begin{bmatrix} 4/3 & -2/3 \\ 1 & 0 \end{bmatrix}, \quad C = \begin{bmatrix} -2/3 & 1 \end{bmatrix}$$

In this example, the output computed with the estimated states from the standard Kalman filter with covariance matrices

$$Q = I, \quad R = 1, \quad Q_0 = Q$$

is compared to the output computed with the estimated states from the constrained, receding horizon, recursive state estimation formulation of Eq. 9 with the following estimated state constraints.

$$-1 \le C\hat{x}_{j|k} \le 1$$

The initial state estimate, $\bar{x}_0$, is zero in both cases. At time $k = 1$, the output measurement changes from 0 to 10 and then returns to 0 for all time $k > 1$. There is no input or state noise in this example. The estimated outputs $\hat{y}_{k+1|k} = C\hat{x}_{k+1|k}$ computed with the estimated states from the standard Kalman filter and the constrained, receding horizon state estimator are shown in Figure 1. As shown in this figure, the dynamic response of each of the outputs is similar except that the deviation from the origin is reduced in the case of the receding horizon constrained estimator. The dynamic response of the constrained batch state estimator is essentially identical to that of the constrained receding horizon state estimator in this example and, therefore, is not included in Figure 1.

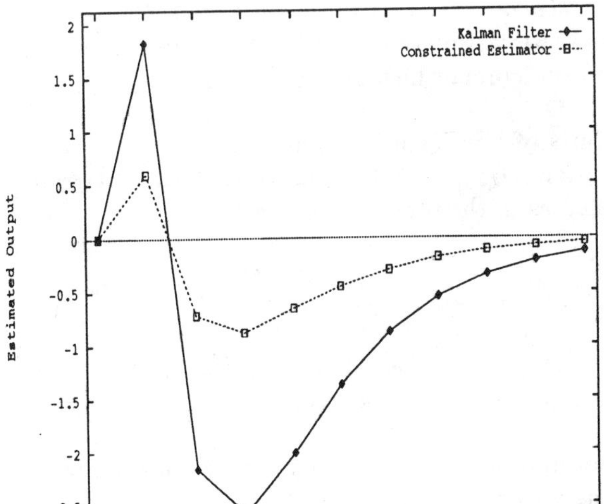

Figure 1: Comparison of the estimated output, $\hat{y}_{k+1|k}$, using the Kalman filter and the constrained receding horizon estimator.

Appendix

Proof of Lemma 1

The proof is by induction. For $N = 0$, the result is obtained from the matrix inversion lemma on the filtering algebraic Riccati matrix recursion equation for all $k \geq 1$. For $N > 0$, change the index k in the expression in Lemma 1 to $j + N$ and partition the expression as follows in which $\tilde{E}_0 = F_0 + Q^{-1}$.

$$
\begin{aligned}
P_{j+N} &= Q + \mathcal{A}_{N-1} \begin{bmatrix} \mathcal{E}_{N-1} & \mathcal{F}_{N-1} \\ \mathcal{F}_{N-1}^T & \tilde{E}_0 \end{bmatrix}^{-1} \mathcal{A}_{N-1}^T \\
\mathcal{A}_{N-1} &= \begin{bmatrix} A\tilde{A}_{N-1} & A \end{bmatrix}, \quad \mathcal{F}_{N-1} = \tilde{A}_{N-1}^T F_0 \\
\mathcal{E}_{N-1} &= A_{N-1}^T E_{N-1} A_{N-1} + F_{N-1} + \tilde{Q}_{N-1}^{j-1}
\end{aligned}
$$

Performing the partitioned matrix inversion and multiplying yields

$$
\begin{aligned}
P_{j+N} &= Q + A\left(\mathcal{W}_{N-1} + \tilde{E}_0^{-1}\right) A^T \\
\mathcal{W}_{N-1} &= \tilde{E}_0^{-1} Q^{-1} \tilde{A}_{N-1} W_{N-1}^{-1} \tilde{A}_{N-1}^T Q^{-1} \tilde{E}_0^{-1} \\
W_{N-1} &= E_{N-1} + \tilde{Q}_{N-1}^{j-1} + \tilde{A}_{N-1}^T \mathcal{Q} \tilde{A}_{N-1} \\
\mathcal{Q} &= Q^{-1} - Q^{-1} \tilde{E}_0^{-1} Q^{-1}
\end{aligned}
$$

This expression can be simplified by performing the matrix inversion lemma first with $\tilde{E}_0^{-1}$ and then with Q^{-1}. Assuming P_{j+N-1} is $Q + \tilde{A}_{N-1}(E_{N-1} + \tilde{Q}_{N-1}^{j-1})^{-1} \tilde{A}_{N-1}^T$ for all $j \geq 1$ results in

$$
P_{j+N} = Q + A\left(P_{j+N-1}^{-1} + C^T R^{-1} C\right)^{-1} A^T
$$

This recurrence can be shown to be the filtering algebraic Riccati matrix recursion by using the matrix inversion lemma which proves the lemma.

Details of the Proof of Theorem 1

Partition $L_{M+1|k}$ as follows in which $\tilde{E}_0$ and $\mathcal{A}_M$ are defined as in the proof of Lemma 1.

$$
\begin{aligned}
L_{M+1|k} &= \mathcal{A}_M \begin{bmatrix} \mathcal{E}_M & \mathcal{F}_M \\ \mathcal{F}_M^T & \tilde{E}_0 \end{bmatrix}^{-1} \begin{bmatrix} G_M & \mathcal{G}_M \\ 0 & G_0 \end{bmatrix} \\
\mathcal{F}_M &= \tilde{A}_M^T F_0, \quad \mathcal{G}_M = \tilde{A}_M^T G_0 \\
\mathcal{E}_M &= A_M^T E_M A_M + F_M + \tilde{Q}_M^{k-M-1}
\end{aligned}
$$

Performing the partitioned matrix inverse and multiplying yields

$$
L_{M+1|k} = A\left[\tilde{E}_0^{-1} Q^{-1} \tilde{A}_M W_M^{-1} G_M \quad (\mathcal{W}_M + \tilde{E}_0^{-1}) G_0\right]
$$

in which $\mathcal{W}_M$ and W_M are defined as in the Proof of Lemma 1. This expression can be simplified performing the same steps as in Lemma 1 to the following.

$$
L_{M+1|k} = \left[(A - L_k C)\tilde{A}_M (E_M + \tilde{Q}_M^{k-M-1})^{-1} G_M \quad L_k\right]
$$

Substituting $L_{M|k-1}$ for the expression in Eq. 5 and multiplying with the partitioned $Y_{M+1|k}$ yields the result in the proof of Theorem 1.

References

[1] Andrew H. Jazwinski. *Stochastic Proceses and Filtering Theory.* Academic Press, New York, 1970.

[2] James B. Rawlings and Kenneth R. Muske. The stability of constrained receding horizon control. Accepted for publication in *IEEE Transactions on Automatic Control*, July 1992.

[3] Kenneth R. Muske and James B. Rawlings. Model predictive control with linear models. *AIChE Journal*, 39(2):262–287, 1993.

Proceedings of the
American Control Conference
San Francisco, California • June 1993

On-line State and Parameter Estimation and Adaptive Optimization of a Continuous Bioreactor (Ethanol Fermentation) Using State Equations

R.Thatipamala, G.A.Hill and S.Rohani
Department of Chemical Engineering
University of Saskatchewan, Saskatoon, Canada S7N 0W0

Abstract

On-line optimization of bioprocesses is a difficult task due to lack of suitable on-line sensors, absence of accurate mathematical models, and complex non-linear dynamic behaviour. In the present investigation, an algorithm was developed for on-line state estimation and optimization of a continuous bioreactor (ethanol fermentation), using state equations. A number of case studies are presented which verify the performance of the algorithm.

1. Introduction

Bioprocesses are highly complex, non-linear, poorly defined, and time-dependent systems. The automatic control of these processes at their optimal states is of considerable interest since it can reduce operating costs, improve product quality and productivity. The following important characteristics hinder any realistic approach for on-line state estimation and subsequent optimal control of a given bioprocess: (a) lack of reliable on-line sensors for important state variables such as biomass, substrate, and product concentrations; (b) absence of good mathematical models which would take into account the numerous factors which influence the growth of microorganisms; and (c) strong non-linear dynamic behaviour with poorly identified time-varying parameters[1,2]. In the present investigation, state equations are used to estimate the unmeasured state variables and time-varying parameters and subsequent adaptive on-line optimization of a fermentation process. This article briefly describes the method and its implementation for optimization of ethanol productivity in a continuous bioreactor.

2. Algorithm

2.1 Process Model Equations

The process model equations for a continuous ethanol bioreactor are obtained in non-linear state space representation by using mass/component balances. Four important state variables: (i) biomass concentration (X), (ii) product concentration (P), (iii) substrate concentration (S), (iv) carbon dioxide evolution rate (q); and two critical time-varying parameters: (i) specific growth rate (μ_x), and (ii) instantaneous biomass yield ($Y_{x/s}$); are considered in formulating the following equations:

$$\frac{dX}{dt} = (\mu_x - D)\,X \qquad (1)$$

$$\frac{dS}{dt} = (S_{in} - S)\,D - \frac{\mu_x X}{Y_{x/s}} \qquad (2)$$

$$\frac{dP}{dt} = \frac{\mu_x X Y_{p/s}}{Y_{x/s}} - DP \qquad (3)$$

$$\frac{q}{V} = \frac{\mu_x X Y_{co_2/p}}{Y_{x/s}} + MX \qquad (4)$$

These are the four basic equations relating all important variables in the fermenter [volume, V is considered as constant]. The two time-varying parameters (μ_x and $Y_{x/s}$) are not expressed by any analytical function of state variables but are considered as general functions of the environment and estimated in real time. [Extensive batch and continuous experiments[3,4] have indicated that the parameters: $Y_{p/s}$, $Y_{co2/p}$, and M (in equations 3 and 4) are fairly constant under a wide range of operating conditions].

2.2 On-line State Estimation

Carbon dioxide evolution rate (q) is one of the most frequently measured variables for adaptive control and optimization applications of fermentation[5,6]. In addition, the authors have developed a successful method for on-line monitoring of a wide range of biomass concentrations using a spectrophotometer based on a new equation[4,7]: [$\log(T/T_0) = K \log(C/C_0)$]. As a result two of the state variables (X and q) are the measured variables in the present investigation. At every sampling instant, the important variables are estimated on-line based on the following logic:

a) X is estimated using on-line information from the spectrophotometer;
b) μ_x (the most important parameter) is estimated using a discrete form of equation 1 and on-line estimation of X;
c) P and $Y_{x/s}$ are estimated based on a discrete form of equations 3 and 4, using both X and q measurements;
d) S is estimated using a discrete form of equation 2.

In addition, other growth parameters are calculated from the estimations of the above time-varying parameters, using the following two correlations [Various inhibition models indicate that most effects of inhibition are expected to reflect in parameter μ_m; while continuous experiments indicate that $Y^{min}_{x/s}$ is another uncertain parameter[4].]:

$$\mu_x = \mu_m\left(1 - \frac{P}{P_m}\right)^n \qquad (5)$$

$$Y_{x/s} = \left(Y^{max}_{x/s} - Y^{min}_{x/s}\right)\left(1 - \frac{P}{P_m}\right)^n$$

$$+ Y^{min}_{x/s} \qquad (6)$$

In the above two correlations P_m, n, and $Y^{max}_{x/s}$ are considered to be known constants [Both P_m and n can be considered as characteristics of the yeast strain being used for fermentation and $Y^{max}_{x/s}$ was observed to be a constant in batch and continuous experiments].

2.3 Index of Performance and On-line Optimization

Ethanol is the most desirable product in this fermentation and the rate of production of ethanol per unit volume of reactor (or productivity, DP) can be considered the most significant factor in evaluating the performance of the continuous reactor. As a result **"D * P"** is considered as the Index of Performance (IP) in the present optimization studies:

$$IP = (D * P)_{steady\ state} \qquad (7)$$

Dilution rate is considered as the manipulated/input variable for optimizing the above index of performance/output variable (similar to previous research studies[5,8]). The manipulated variable is updated using the steepest descent technique based on the following equation:

$$D_{t+1} = D_t + \alpha \frac{d(DP)_{ss}}{dD}$$

$$\approx D_t + \alpha \frac{\Delta(DP)_{ss}}{\Delta D} \qquad (8)$$

where α is the optimization gain; and d(DP)ss/dD is the steady state process gain i.e. the net gain in Index of Performance (at steady state) for a given change in manipulated variable [based on the present environmental conditions in the bioreactor]. At every sampling instant the steady-state gain [i.e.$\Delta(DP)_{ss}/\Delta D$] is estimated by solving differential equations 1, 2, and 3 (along with equations 5 and 6) using a fourth-order Runge-Kutta method. The required change in manipulated variable to improve the productivity is determined using equation 8, based on the steady-state gain estimation. Thus, important state variables and critical time-varying parameters, and the steady state process gain are estimated on-line at every sampling instant using transient information from both of the sensors.

3.Materials and Methods

Microorganism: Saccharomyces cerevisiae, NRRL Y 132, was used in this study. It was provided by the US Department of Agriculture, Peoria, IL.

Fermentation Medium and Methods for Off-line Analysis: The composition of the medium and methods for off-line analysis of biomass, glucose, and ethanol concentrations were identical to the ones used in batch experimental studies. The details are given elsewhere[3].

Experimental set-up: Figure 1 shows a schematic diagram of the continuous stirred tank bioreactor, along with peripheral instruments configured for adaptive optimal control studies. A

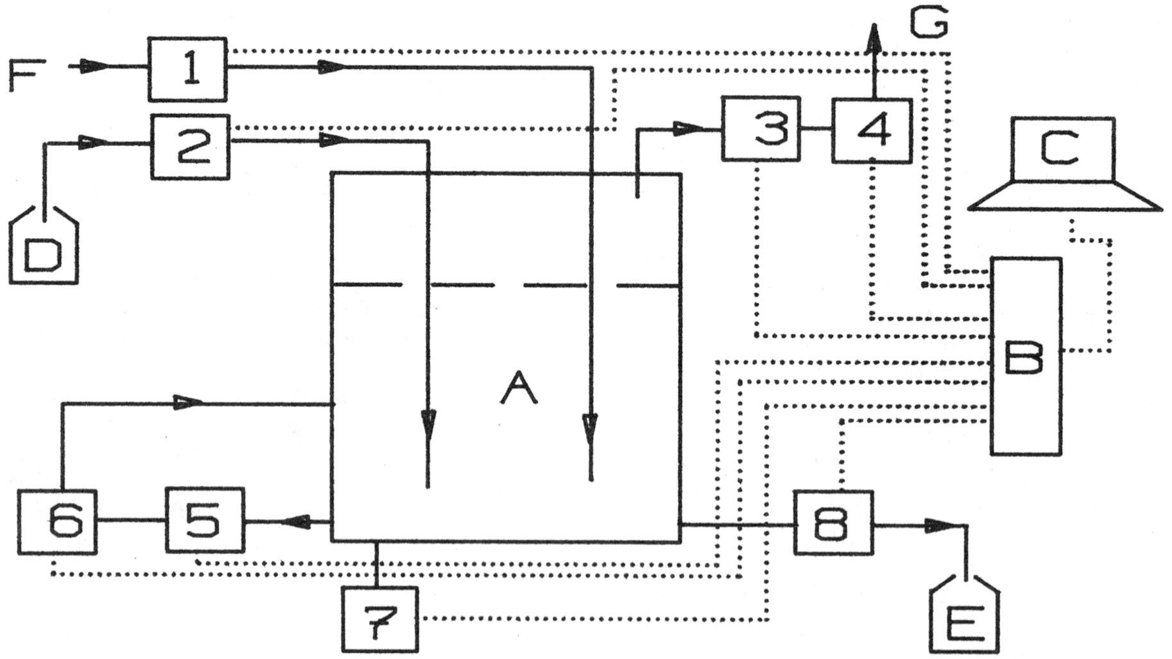

Figure 1. Schematic diagram of fermentation control system: (A) Fermenter; (B) Opto-board; (C) Computer; (D) Feed bottle; (E) Product bottle; (F) Filtered air supply; (G) Exhaust gases; (1) Inlet air flow meter; (2) Feed pump; (3) Outlet gas flow meter; (4) IR gas analyzer; (5) Recycle pump; (6) Spectrophotometer; (7) Pressure transducer; (8) Product pump.

New Brunswick Scientific model C30 Bioflo apparatus was used with a locally fabricated fermenter with a working volume of 450 mL (size 750 mL). The temperature of the fermenter was maintained at 30° C (within ±0.2°), by heating and cooling mechanisms. Two peristaltic pumps were used for pumping the inlet substrate stream and outlet product stream to and from the bioreactor (30 to 250 mL/h). A third peristaltic pump was used to recycle the fermentation broth through a modified flow-through sterilized cylindrical cuvette mounted on a simple Spectronic 21 spectrophotometer set at 600 nm. An Infrared Gas Analyzer was used to monitor CO_2 composition in the outlet gas stream. Two electronic gas flow meters were used to monitor inlet air and outlet gas flow rates. A Foxboro Differential Pressure Transmitter (823 DP) was used to estimate the volume in the fermenter. An OPTO-22 board was used for communicating between the process and the computer, an IBM PC 486/33 with software written in Turbo Pascal. A sampling time of 30 sec was used in all the experiments.

At every sampling instant on-line information is obtained from the spectrophotometer; infrared gas analyzer; outlet gas flow meter; inlet gas flow meter; and the pressure transducer.

Similarly at every sampling instant the output signals to the feed pump and product pump are updated based on input information and the "given criteria".

The product flow rate is manipulated to maintain a constant volume in the fermenter, whereas feed flow rate is manipulated for optimizing the productivity of the bioreactor.

Continuous Experiments: The concentration of glucose in the feed solution was 150 g/L in all experiments. The fermenter was inoculated with about 100 mL of inoculum. After waiting for 5 to 6 hours the continuous runs were started at a predetermined dilution rate. On-line monitoring was initiated a couple of hours before this stage. After reaching steady state, open loop or closed loop algorithms were initiated. Samples from the fermenter (for off-line analysis) were collected at appropriate intervals. Steady state was assumed to have been reached when the biomass concentration remained constant (within ±2%) for more than 5 hours.

Filtering of Noise from Biomass and q Measurements: A simple algorithm was developed using a moving average filter (past 10 samples) in combination with a noise-spike filter[9] to eliminate the noise from the input signal of the spectrophotometer. Similarly another moving average filter (past 10 samples) was used to eliminate the noise in q measurements.

4.Results and Discussion

4.1 Open-loop On-line State Estimation Studies:
A number of open-loop experiments were conducted to verify the performance of the algorithm for on-line state and parameter estimation in a continuous bioreactor. Figures 2 and 3 show the typical results of on-line critical parameter (μ_x and $Y_{x/s}$) estimation for a step increase in dilution rate. It is interesting to note that the dynamic on-line estimation is quite similar to the results from batch and continuous experiments[3] [results from continuous experiments are based on steady state information; whereas batch results indicate an average value from several dynamic measurements]. The estimation of biomass, product, and substrate concentrations was within ±5% of off-line measurements[3].

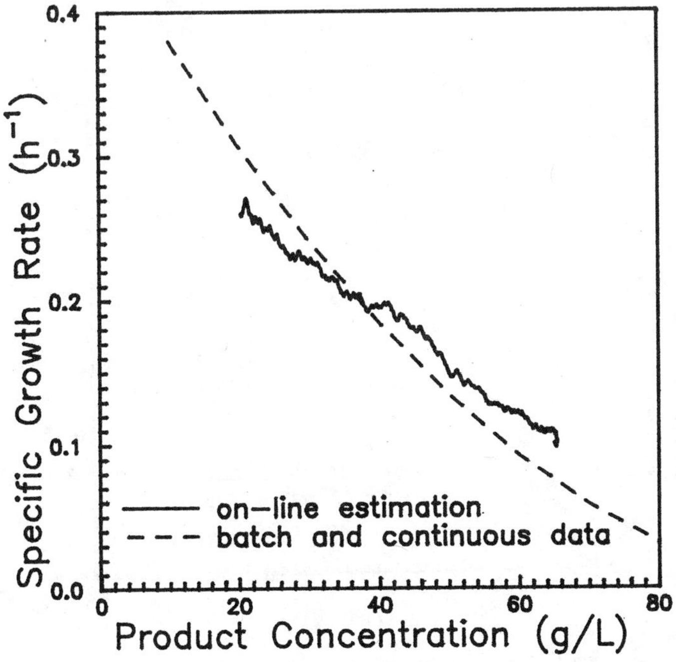

Figure 2. Open-loop studies: On-line estimation of specific growth rate (h^{-1}).

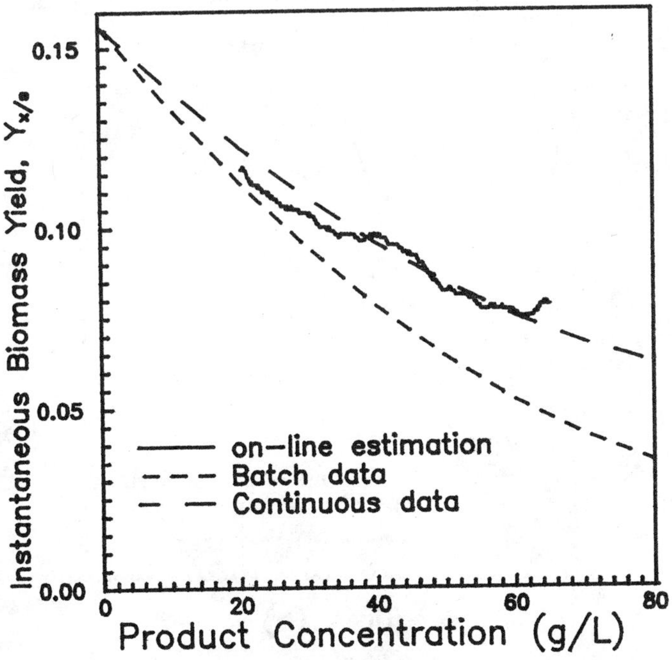

Figure 3. Open-loop studies: On-line estimation of instantaneous biomass yield.

4.2 Closed-loop On-line Optimization Studies:

Simulation studies were carried out, using kinetic information from batch and continuous experiments, before conducting closed-loop experiments. The results indicate that the optimum productivity is around 8.8 g/L/h with a corresponding dilution rate between 0.22 and 0.26 h^{-1}. A number of case studies were then investigated to verify the performance of the algorithm in reaching the optimum productivity. Typical results are presented in Figures 4, 5 and 6 and are described below:

Case-I: Closed-loop Optimization (starting D=0.3 h^{-1}): The experimental results from this case study are presented in Figure 4. The system reaches the "optimum productivity" of 9.0 g/L/h starting from a productivity of 5.0 g/L/h in a period of 15 hours. Besides the corresponding dilution rate, D_{opt} (=0.24) is close to the value predicted in simulation studies. From the results it can be observed that the manipulated variable is adjusted very smoothly, which can be considered as a desirable feature.

Case II: Response to a Change in Feed Composition- Adaptation to Ever Changing Environment: A Change in feed composition was introduced by replacing the original feed bottle with a nutrient deficient feed bottle, to evaluate the performance of the adaptive algorithm. As a result, the

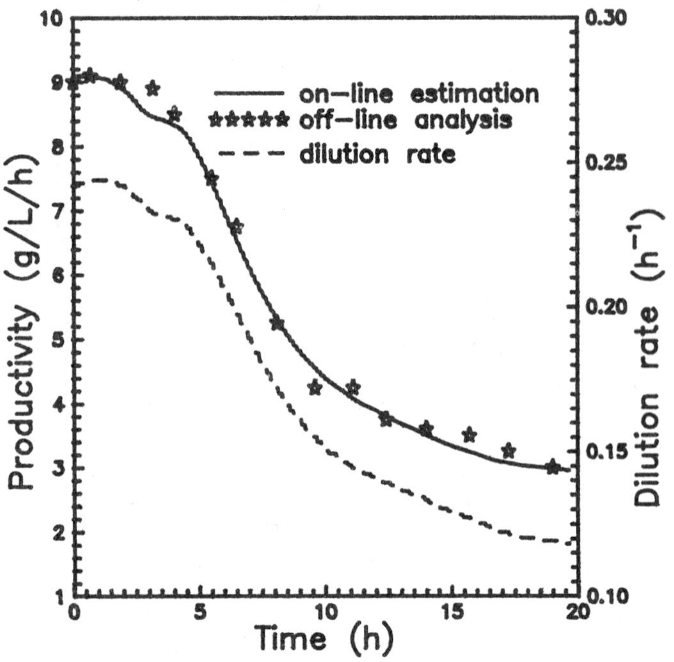

Figure 5. Case II: Response to a change in feed composition - Adaptation to ever changing environment.

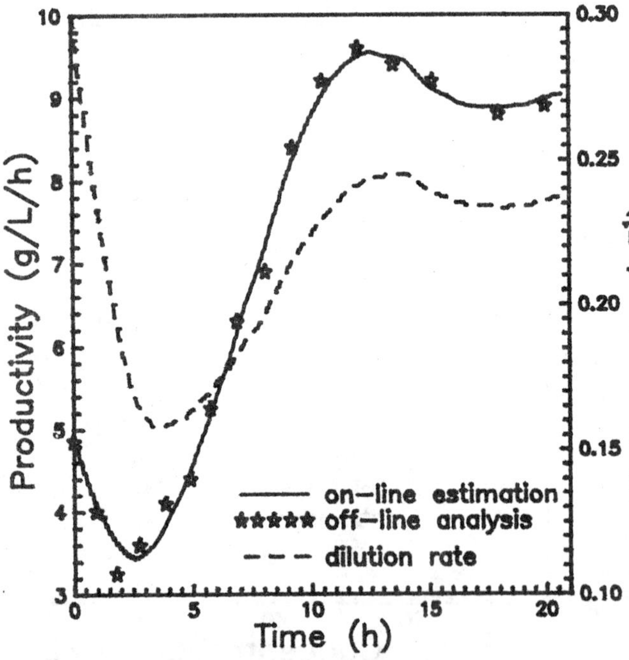

Figure 4. Closed-loop studies: Case I: Adaptive on-line optimization (starting dilution rate is 0.3 h^{-1}).

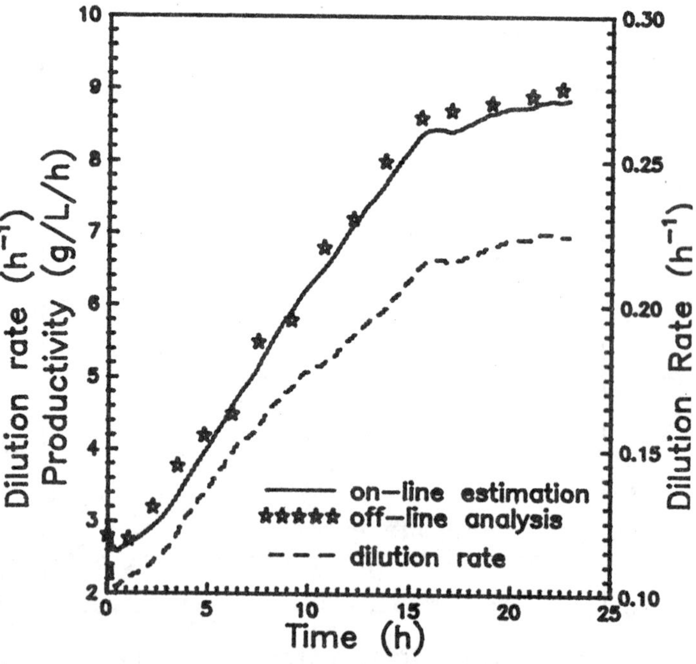

Figure 6. Case III: Regaining the optimum with the "original" feed solution.

concentration of the nutrients in the CSTBR was expected to decrease smoothly (exponential decay) creating an ever changing environment in the bioreactor. Simulation studies indicate that the optimum productivity reduces to 3.8 g/L/h with the new feed solution. The experimental results are plotted in Figure 5. From the response of the algorithm it can be observed that the algorithm senses the ever changing environment quite accurately, and adjusts the manipulated variable accordingly. The productivity smoothly shifts from 9.0 to 4.0 g/h/L in a period of 20 hours. It approaches the new optimum tangentially (similar to exponential decay!).

CASE III: Regaining the optimum with the original feed solution: Regaining the optimum after a disturbance can be considered as more crucial in optimization studies. It reflects the true robustness of the algorithm. To evaluate such a performance, the original feed bottle was restored by replacing the nutrient deficient feed bottle. The experimental results from this case study are presented in Figure 6. From the results it can be observed that the algorithm is quite successful in reaching the original optimum productivity during a period of 15 hours which is also the time taken for the build-up of nutrients in the CSTBR. These results indicate that the algorithm can sense the change in the environment of the bioreactor almost "instantaneously" for all practical purposes, and track the optimum accordingly.

CASE IV: Closed-loop Optimization: Starting D=0.1 h^{-1}: In this case study the system has reached the "optimum productivity" of 8.9 g/L/h starting from a productivity of 6.8 g/L/h in a period of 20 hours with a corresponding dilution rate of 0.24 h^{-1}. These results (Case I and IV) indicate that the algorithm is successful in reaching the optimum point from both ends of the operating conditions (starting either from a lower or from a higher dilution rate).

5.Conclusions

An algorithm is developed for on-line state estimation and optimization of a continuous bioreactor. A number of case studies were carried out to verify the performance of the algorithm. Experimental results indicate that the algorithm is successful:

i) in on-line estimation of unmeasurable state variables and time-varying parameters;
ii) in reaching the optimum productivity based on the given performance index;
iii) in tracking the optimum in an ever changing environment; and
iv) in regaining the optimum after an imposed disturbance, exhibiting desirable robustness.

Acknowledgement: The authors are grateful for the financial support of the Natural Sciences and Engineering Research Council of Canada (**NSERC**) and to the University of Saskatchewan for a graduate scholarship (to the first author).

Nomenclature

C	Concentration of absorbing species (g/L)
C_0	Concentration of reference solution (g/L)
D	Dilution rate (h^{-1})
K	Dimensionless constant in new equation
M	CO_2 evolution due to maintenance (g/gDW/h)
n	power of product inhibition in equation 5
P	ethanol concentration (g/L)
P_m	Maximum product concentration (g/L)
q	Carbon dioxide evolution rate (g/h)
S	Substrate concentration (g/L)
T	absolute transmittance
T_0	transmittance of reference solution
V	Volume of the fermenter (L)
X	Biomass concentration (gDW/L)
$Y_{x/s}$	Instantaneous biomass yield (gDW of biomass/g of substrate)
$Y^{max}_{x/s}$	Maximum instantaneous biomass yield (gDW of biomass/g of substrate)
$Y^{min}_{x/s}$	Minimum instantaneous biomass yield (gDW of biomass/g of substrate)
$Y_{p/s}$	Product yield (g of ethanol/g of substrate)
$Y_{co2/p}$	CO_2 evolution as related to product formation (g of CO_2/g of ethanol formed)
μ_x	Specific growth rate (h^{-1})
μ_m	Maximum specific growth rate (h^{-1})
α	Optimization gain

References

1. Wang,N.S. and G.Stephanopoulos. Biotechnol. Bioeng. Symp. # **14**: 635-656 (1984).
2. Dochain,D. and A.Pauss. Can.J.Chem.Eng., **66**, 626-631 (1988).
3. Thatipamala,R., Rohani,S. and G.A.Hill. Biotechnol. Bioeng. **40:** 289-297 (1992).
4. Thatipamala,R. Ph.D.Thesis (in preparation), University of Saskatchewan, Canada (1993).
5. Chang,Y.K. and H.C.Lim. Biotechnol. Bioeng. **34:** 577-591 (1989).
6. Leigh,J.R., Tampion,J. and M.H.Ng. "Progress in Industrial Microbiology: Vol. 25" (M.E.Bushell (Ed.)), Elsevier, Netherlands (1988).
7. Thatipamala,R., Rohani,S. and G.A.Hill. Biotechnol. Bioeng. **38:** 1007-1011 (1991).
8. Rolf,M.J. and H.C.Lim. Biotechnol. Bioeng. **27:** 1236-1245 (1985).
9. Seborg,D.E., Edgar,T.F., Mellichamp,D.A. "Process Dynamics and Control", John Wiley & Sons, Inc. New York (1989).

Proceedings of the
American Control Conference
San Francisco, California • June 1993

When is Nonlinear Dynamic Modeling Necessary?

Michael Nikolaou
Chemical Engineering Department
Texas A&M University
College Station, TX 77843-3122

INTERNET: m0n2431@venus.tamu.edu

Keywords: Nonlinear, inner product, norm, Hilbert, approximation.

ABSTRACT

The purpose of this paper is to propose an answer to the title's question, and examine the ramifications of the provided answer. Our proposition is to quantify the nonlinearity of a system by a carefully defined 2-norm, which results from a newly constructed inner product. We develop the pertinent theory which allows the easy computation of this norm for a broad class of nonlinear dynamic systems, through Monte Carlo calculations. Explicit formulae are provided for linear systems. In addition, the problem of best approximation of a nonlinear system by a linear or nonlinear model is put in perspective, and pathways to computationally convenient solutions are charted. Practical issues are elucidated through examples of chemical engineering relevance. Further elaboration will be included in forthcoming publications.

1. Introduction

A fundamental question of nonlinear systems research is:

"When is nonlinear dynamic modeling necessary?"

Although the formulation of this question is strikingly simple, a general answer is formidable. This paper is an attempt to put the above problem in perspective, and propose an answer. In particular, we address the following questions, common in most research on nonlinear dynamic systems (for reviews see Bequette, 1991 and Kravaris and Kantor, 1990):

- How nonlinear is a "nonlinear" dynamic system?
- When is *nonlinear* system modeling necessary?
- What nonlinear models can be used and how?
- Is a particular nonlinearity really a major bottleneck ?
- How does feedback alter a system's nonlinearity characteristics?

In this paper, we show that by properly constructing an appropriate nonlinearity measure, one can successfully quantify a dynamic system's nonlinearity in terms of an easily computable number. The data required for the computation of this number can be collected in a straightforward manner, through experiments and/or Monte Carlo computer simulation. The theoretical properties and applicability of this newly constructed nonlinearity quantifier extend far beyond the mere quantification of a nonlinearity, and the theory's full potential will be explored in a series of papers to follow. Some areas of applicability are explored in this paper, and the corresponding theoretical developments are presented. An Example of a chemical process is used to elucidate the theory developed in the paper, and substantiate its practicality.

2. Quantifying nonlinearities in dynamic systems

To develop a nonlinearity measure, we first provide a definition of nonlinear operators corresponding to dynamic nonlinear systems. For such a class of operators we construct an *inner product*, based on which we define a corresponding *2-norm*. We then address, in the above context, the problem of best approximation of a nonlinear operator by a linear or nonlinear operator.

Definition 1: A nonlinear operator P, corresponding to *nosteps* time-steps (with *nosteps* in $\mathbf{N} \cup \{\infty\}$), is defined as a continuous mapping from $\mathbf{R}^{nosteps}$ to $\mathbf{R}^{nosteps}$, such that the input sequence

$$u := [u_1, u_2, u_3, \ldots, u_{nosteps}]^T \quad (1)$$

is mapped to the output sequence

$$y := [y_2, y_3, \ldots, y_{nosteps+1}]^T = Pu := [(P\,u)_1, (P\,u)_2, \ldots, (P\,u)_{nosteps}]^T \quad (2)$$

Definition 2: The operator P: $\mathbf{R}^{nosteps} \to \mathbf{R}^{nosteps}$: $u \to P\,u$ is called unbiased if

$$u = \theta \Rightarrow P\,u = \theta \quad (3)$$

Remark 1: In the sequel we will consider unbiased operators everywhere. These operators may describe either continuous or batch processes. The reader is alerted to the fact that deviation variables should always be used. In the case of continuous processes the deviation is calculated with respect to input and output values at a nominal steady state, whereas for batch processes deviation variables are defined in terms of nominal input and output trajectories.

Definition 3: The null operator O, and the identity operator I are defined as

$$O\,u = \theta, \text{ for all } u \in \mathbf{R}^{nosteps} \quad (4)$$

and

$$I\,u = u, \text{ for all } u \in \mathbf{R}^{nosteps} \quad (5)$$

Postulate: If $P \neq O$, then

$$P\,u = \theta \Leftrightarrow u = \theta \quad (6)$$

Remark 2: If the left inverse of P exists (i.e $P^{-1}P = I$), then

$$P\,u = \theta \Rightarrow P^{-1}P\,u = P^{-1}\,\theta \Rightarrow u = \theta \quad (7)$$

Therefore, the existence of the left inverse of an unbiased nonlinear operator implies the above equivalence (6).

Theorem 1: The equation

$$\langle P; Q\rangle := \frac{1}{nosteps} \lim_{\substack{noinputs \to \infty \\ u^r \neq \theta}} \sum_{r=1}^{noinputs} \frac{\langle P\,u^r, Q\,u^r\rangle}{noinputs} \quad (8)$$

defines an inner product $\langle P; Q\rangle$ of the operators P: $\mathbf{R}^{nosteps} \to \mathbf{R}^{nosteps}$ and Q: $\mathbf{R}^{nosteps} \to \mathbf{R}^{nosteps}$, where u^r is a random vector in

$$U = [umin, umax] \times \ldots \times [umin, umax] \text{ in } (\mathbf{R} \cup \{\pm\infty\})^{nosteps}$$

with probability distribution

$$p(u_1^r)\, p(u_2^r) \ldots p(u_{nosteps}^r) > 0 \text{ on } U, \quad (9)$$

and $\langle P\,u^r, Q\,u^r\rangle$ is the standard inner product of the vectors $P\,u^r$ and $Q\,u^r$, defined as

$$\langle P\,u^r, Q\,u^r\rangle := \sum_{i=1}^{nosteps} \left[(P\,u^r)_i\,(Q\,u^r)_i\right] \geq 0 \quad (10)$$

Proof: See Nikolaou (1993a).

Remark 3: The probability distribution $p(u_1^r)\, p(u_2^r) \ldots p(u_{nosteps}^r)$ can be either uniform on [*umin, umax*], or any other continuous distribution that is nonzero everywhere on [*umin, umax*]. By selecting this distribution appropriately, the importance of input signals deviating far from steady state can be quantified.

Remark 4: Theorem 1 and its proof not only define an inner product of two nonlinear operators, but also suggest a method for its computation. For a given value of *nosteps*, $\langle P; Q\rangle$ can be computed as follows:

- *Initiation*: For a random vector $u^r \in \mathbf{R}^{nosteps}$ with entries identically distributed in [*umin, umax*], compute

$$S_1 = \frac{\langle P\,u^r, Q\,u^r\rangle}{nosteps} = \frac{1}{nosteps} \sum_{i=1}^{nosteps} \left[(P\,u^r)_i\,(Q\,u^r)_i\right] \quad (11)$$

- *Step* ***noinputs***: Consider additional random u^r in $\mathbf{R}^{nosteps}$ with entries identically distributed in [*umin, umax*], and compute the partial sums

$$S_{noinputs} = \frac{1}{nosteps} \sum_{r=1}^{noinputs} \frac{\langle P\,u^r, Q\,u^r\rangle}{noinputs} \quad (12)$$

- *Termination*: Stop when

$$\sigma\langle P; Q\rangle = \sqrt{\sum_{r=1}^{noinputs} \frac{\left[\frac{\langle P\,u^r, Q\,u^r\rangle}{nosteps} - S_{noinputs}\right]^2}{nosteps\,(nosteps-1)}} \quad (13)$$

is small enough.

By the strong law of large numbers (a standard result in statistics), the partial sums $S_{noinputs}$ are asymptotically normally distributed, and, by definition, tend to $\langle P; Q\rangle$ as $noinputs \to \infty$. For *noinputs* number of inputs u^r in $\mathbf{R}^{nosteps}$, $S_{noinputs}$ is the best estimate of $\langle P; Q\rangle$, with standard deviation $\sigma_{\langle P;Q\rangle}$.

The data required in the above procedure can be collected either after direct experimentation (provided the number of experiments is not prohibitively large), or through computer simulation, provided a computer model is available.

The above algorithm can naturally be executed in parallel, through independent calculation of each term

$$\frac{1}{nosteps} \sum_{r=1}^{noinputs} \langle P u^r, Q u^r \rangle$$

in $S_{noinputs}$. ♦

The inner product introduced in Theorem 1 can be used to define a norm for a nonlinear operator in a standard way:

Definition 4: Let P: $\mathbf{R}^{nosteps} \rightarrow \mathbf{R}^{nosteps}$ be a continuous, discrete-time, nonlinear operator. Then the 2-norm of P is defined as

$$\|P\| := \sqrt{\langle P; P \rangle} \qquad (14)$$

Remark 5: The 2-norm defined above can be contrasted to the induced norm of P over a set U, defined as

$$\|P\|_{ip} := \sup_{u \in U} \frac{\|P u\|_p}{\|u\|_p} \overset{\boxed{p=2}}{=} \sup_{u \in U} \frac{\sqrt{\langle P u, P u \rangle}}{\sqrt{\langle u, u \rangle}} \qquad (15)$$

where U is a subset of an l_p space of p-summable sequences $\{u_i\}$ (i.e. such that $\sum_i |u_i|^p < \infty$, $1 \le p \le \infty$), and $\|.\|_p$ its corresponding norm (Nikolaou and Manousiouthakis, 1989). The induced norm has the advantage that it can be used to generate bounds on the output of a nonlinear operator, through the inequality

$$\|P u\|_p \le \|P\|_{ip} \|u\|_p \quad \text{for all } u \in U \qquad (16)$$

However, the computation of the induced norm is quite tedious, compared to the computation of the 2-norm defined by eqn. (14), whose computation will be shown in the sequel to be easy. A common feature of both norms is the fact that both are defined over a *set* of possible inputs (e.g. bounded by *umin* and *umax*), instead of over an entire space (e.g. l_p). ♦

Theorem 1 and Definition 4 are the cornerstones of this work, since they establish the framework within which subsequent results are derived. The deep structure of the inner-product space defined above is the subject of rigorous mathematical analysis on Hilbert spaces, which extends beyond the scope of this paper. Some significant implications of the above development are presented next.

3. Best approximation of a nonlinear operator

The problem of optimally approximating a nonlinear operator P by another operator A can be formulated (Desoer and Wang, 1975) as

$$\min_A \|A - P\| \qquad (17)$$

where A is an operator belonging to a class of operators over which the approximation is to be performed. The norm used above can be any operator norm. We propose to use the 2-norm defined through eqn. (14). As we will show, this selection results in a particularly simple solution of problem (17). We will distinguish two cases, namely approximation of P by a linear operator L, and by a nonlinear operator N.

3.1 *Best approximation of a nonlinear operator P by a linear operator L*

If A is a linear operator L in problem (17) (i.e. $\min_L \|L - P\|$), it can be represented in a number of ways. For a linear moving-average model (i.e. $y_k = \sum_{i=1}^{nopastu} h_i u_{k-i}$) we have that

$$y := [y_2, y_3, \ldots, y_{nosteps+1}]^T = \left[\sum_{i=1}^{nopastu} h_i u_{2-i}, \ldots, \sum_{i=1}^{nopastu} h_i u_{nosteps+1-i} \right]^T =$$

$$= \sum_{i=1}^{nopastu} \left(h_i [u_{1-(i-1)}, \ldots, u_{nosteps-(i-1)}]^T \right) =$$

$$= \sum_{i=1}^{nopastu} \left(h_i (L_i u) \right) = \left(\sum_{i=1}^{nopastu} h_i L_i \right) u = L u$$

which means that L can be represented as

$$L = \sum_{i=1}^{nopastu} h_i L_i \qquad (18)$$

where L_i is a linear operator corresponding to a time-delay of i–1 time steps, i.e.

$$L_i [u_1, u_2, u_3, \ldots, u_{nosteps}]^T = [u_{1-(i-1)}, \ldots, u_{-1}, u_0, u_1, u_2, u_3, \ldots, u_{nosteps+1-i}]^T$$
$$= [\ 0 \ \ldots \ 0 \ \ u_1 \ \ u_2 \ \ldots \ u_{nosteps+1-i}\ ]^T$$
$$\begin{matrix} \downarrow & \ldots & \downarrow & \downarrow & \downarrow & \ldots & \downarrow \\ 1 & \ldots & i-1 & i & i+1 & \ldots & nosteps \end{matrix} \qquad (19) ♦$$

The family of operators $\{L_i\}_{i=1}^{nopastu}$ have several important properties, some of which are captured in the following results.

Theorem 2: The inner product of two operators from the basis set $\{L_i\}_{i=1}^{nopastu}$ is

$$\langle L_i; L_j \rangle = \begin{cases} \dfrac{nosteps - \max(i, j) + 1}{4\ nosteps} (umax + umin)^2 & \text{if } i \neq j \\[2ex] \|L_i\|^2 = \dfrac{nosteps - i + 1}{3\ nosteps} (umax^2 + umax\ umin + umin^2) & \text{if } i = j \end{cases} \qquad (20)$$

Proof: See Nikolaou (1993a).

Corollary 1: If the bounds *umin* and *umax* on the input u are symmetric about zero, i.e. *umin* = –*umax*, then the set $\{L_i\}_{i=1}^{nopastu}$ is orthogonal, i.e.

$$\langle L_i; L_j \rangle = \begin{cases} 0 & \text{if } i \neq j \\[1ex] \|L_i\|^2 = \dfrac{nosteps - i + 1}{3\ nosteps} umax^2 & \text{if } i = j \end{cases} \qquad (21)$$

Moreover, for any *umin*, *umax*, an orthonormal basis $\{\Gamma_i\}_{i=1}^{nopastu}$ can be constructed through Gram-Schmidt orthogonalization.

Proof: Substitution of *umin* by –*umax* into eqn. (20) yields eqn. (21). Gram-Schmidt orthogonalization is a standard procedure in functional analysis (Yosida, 1974). In the current context it becomes

$$Y_1 = L_1, \Gamma_1 = Y_1/\|Y_1\|; \; Y_{i+1} = L_{i+1} - \sum_{j=1}^{i} \langle L_{i+1}; \Gamma_j \rangle \Gamma_j, \; \Gamma_{j+1} = Y_{j+1}/\|Y_{j+1}\|$$

Corollary 2: The limit of $\langle L_i; L_j \rangle$ as *nosteps* → ∞ is well defined, as follows.

$$\lim_{nosteps \to \infty} \langle L_i; L_j \rangle = \begin{cases} \dfrac{(umax + umin)^2}{4} & \text{if } i \neq j < \infty \\[2ex] \|L_i\|^2 = \dfrac{umax^2 + umax\ umin + umin^2}{3} & \text{if } i = j < \infty \end{cases} \qquad (22)$$

Proof: Clear, after taking the limit *nosteps* → ∞ in eqn. (20).

Corollary 3: The 2-norm of any linear dynamic system is explicitly given by

$$\|L\|^2 = 2 \sum_{i=1}^{j-1} \sum_{j=2}^{\infty} \eta_i \eta_j \frac{nosteps - \max(i, j) + 1}{4\ nosteps} (umax + umin)^2 +$$

$$+ \sum_{i=1}^{\infty} \eta_i^2 \frac{nosteps - i + 1}{3\ nosteps} (umax^2 + umax\ umin + umin^2) \qquad (23)$$

where $\{\eta_i\}_{i=1}^{\infty}$ are the unit pulse response coefficients of that system.

Proof: Straightforward, from eqns. (18) and (20).

Remark 6: Equation (16) can be used to show that the stability of a nonlinear system with respect to its induced 2-norm $\|P\|_{i2} < \infty$ guarantees that the 2-norm defined by eqn. (14) is also finite. Indeed,

$$\|P\|^2 = \langle P; P \rangle = \frac{1}{nosteps} \lim_{\substack{noinputs \to \infty \\ u^r \neq 0}} \sum_{r=1}^{noinputs} \frac{\langle P u^r, P u^r \rangle}{noinputs} \overset{(16)}{\le}$$

$$\frac{1}{nosteps} \lim_{\substack{noinputs \to \infty \\ u^r \neq 0}} \sum_{r=1}^{noinputs} \frac{\|P\|_{i2}^2 \|u\|^2}{noinputs} = \|P\|_{i2}^2 \|L_1\|^2 < \infty \Rightarrow \frac{\|P\|}{\|P\|_{i2}} \le \|L_1\| \qquad (24)$$

It is also a standard result in functional analysis that if P belongs to a *finite* dimensional space, then the two norms $\|P\|$ and $\|P\|_{i2}$ are *equivalent*, i.e. there also exists a positive constant r_1 such that

$$0 < r_1 \le \frac{\|P\|}{\|P\|_{i2}} \le \|L_1\| := r_2 < \infty \qquad (25)$$

Through the above inequality the submultiplicativity of the induced 2-norm can be used to establish a similar property for the 2-norm as follows. For two operators P_1, P_2 we have

$$\|P_1 P_2\| \le r_2 \|P_1 P_2\|_{i2} \le r_2 \|P_1\|_{i2} \|P_2\|_{i2} \le \frac{r_2}{r_1^2} \|P_1\| \, \|P_2\|.$$

It should be reminded that if P is a linear system, then closed-form expressions exist for $\|P\|_{i2}$ (Desoer and Vidyasagar, 1975). ♦

Based on the above results, we can now state the solution of problem (17), when A is a linear operator L.

Theorem 3: The solution of problem (17) for A being a linear operator L represented by eqn. (18) is uniquely defined by the system of equations

$$\Phi h = \chi \tag{26}$$

where

$$\Phi = \begin{bmatrix} \langle L_1; L_1\rangle & \langle L_1; L_2\rangle & \cdot\cdot & \langle L_1; L_{nopastu}\rangle \\ \langle L_2; L_1\rangle & \langle L_2; L_2\rangle & \cdot\cdot & \langle L_2; L_{nopastu}\rangle \\ \cdot & \cdot & & \cdot \\ \langle L_{nopastu}; L_1\rangle & \langle L_{nopastu}; L_2\rangle & \cdot\cdot & \langle L_{nopastu}; L_{nopastu}\rangle \end{bmatrix}$$

$$h = [h_1 \ h_2 \ \ldots \ h_{nopastu}]^T$$

$$\chi = [\langle L_1; P\rangle \ \langle L_2; P\rangle \ \ldots \ \langle L_{nopastu}; P\rangle]^T$$

Proof: It is a standard application of the projection theorem in inner product spaces (Luenberger, 1969). See Nikolaou (1993a).

Remark 7: Equation (26) is reminiscent of the solution to the standard least squares minimization, i.e.

$$\min_{h_i} \sum_{k=1}^{\infty} \left(\sum_{i=1}^{nopastu} h_i u_{k-i} - y_k \right)^2$$

where $\{y_k\}_{k=1}^{\infty}$ is a given sequence. The difference of our approach is that the system has to start from steady state every *nosteps* time-steps. A similar distinction can also be made between this work and Manousiouthakis and Sourlas (1992).

Corollary 4: If the bounds *umin* and *umax* on the input u are symmetric about the zero steady state, i.e. $umin = -umax$, then the solution of problem (17), when A is a linear operator L, is

$$h_i = \frac{\langle L_i; P\rangle}{\langle L_i; L_i\rangle} = \frac{\langle L_i; P\rangle}{\|L_i\|^2} = \frac{\langle L_i; P\rangle}{\frac{nosteps - i + 1}{3 \ nosteps} umax^2}, \quad i = 1, \ldots, nopastu < nosteps \tag{27}$$

Proof: Equation (21) implies that the off-diagonal terms of the matrix Φ in eqn. (26) are zero, which immediately implies eqn. (27).

Corollary 5: If $umin = -umax$, the coefficients $\{h_i\}_{i=1}^{nopastu}$ satisfy *Bessel*'s inequality

$$\sum_{i=1}^{nopastu} \|L_i\|^2 |h_i|^2 \le \|P\|^2$$

the equality (known as *Parseval*'s equality) holding when $P = \sum_{i=1}^{nopastu} h_i L_i$. Consequently, if $\|P\|^2 < \infty$, then $\lim_{i \to \infty} |h_i| = 0$

Proof: See Nikolaou (1993a). ♦

The importance of Bessel's inequality is that the difference between the right and left-hand sides of the inequality, when $nopastu \to \infty$, is a measure of the nonlinearity of P. This will be demonstrated in the Example.

3.2 *Best approximation of an operator P by a nonlinear operator N*

This development is presented in detail in Nikolaou (1993b).

4. Example

The reaction

$$A \xrightarrow{k_1} B \xrightarrow{k_2} C$$

occurs in an isothermal continuous stirred-tank reactor (ICSTR), modelled by the dimensionless equations (Ray, 1981)

$$\frac{dx}{d\tau} = -x - Da_1 x^2 + 1 + u, \qquad \frac{dz}{d\tau} = Da_1 x^2 - z - Da_2 z^{1/2} + v \tag{28}$$

The input to this system is u and the output y is $(z - z_s)$ (v is kept at its zero steady state). Notation and parameter values are given in Table 1. Approximation of the derivatives in equations (28) by forward finite differences ($\delta\tau = 0.1$) defines the (discrete-time) nonlinear operator

$$P_{ICSTR}: [u_1, u_2, u_3, \ldots, u_{nosteps}]^T \to [y_2, y_3, \ldots, y_{nosteps+1}]^T$$

We apply our theory to examine the nonlinearity characteristics of the above system. For all Monte Carlo simulations the values $nosteps = 100$, $noinputs = 1000$ were chosen, resulting in two significant digits of accuracy, the next digit being uncertain. The code was written in FORTRAN 77. The subroutine RNUN from the IMSL (1989) library was used for random number generation. All calculations were performed in a Sun SparcStation 1®. Simulation run-times were too short (in the order of a few seconds) to warrant detailed recording.

Table 1. Parameters of ICSTR

C_A, C_B	Concentrations of species A and B in the ICSTR
C_{Af}, C_{Bf}	Concentrations of species A and B in the feed
C_{Aref}	Reference concentration of species A
F	Feed/effluent flowrate
V	Reaction volume
k_1, k_2	Reaction rate constants
u, v	$= \left(\frac{C_{Af}}{C_{Aref}} - 1, \frac{C_{Bf}}{C_{Aref}}\right)$; dimensionless inputs; $(\ge -1.0, \ge 0.0)$
x, z	$= \left(\frac{C_A}{C_{Aref}}, \frac{C_B}{C_{Aref}}\right)$; dimensionless system states
τ	$= \frac{tF}{V}$; dimensionless time
Da_1, Da_2	$= \left(\frac{k_1 C_{Aref} V}{F}, \frac{k_2 V}{F C_{Aref}^{1/2}}\right)$; Damkoehler numbers; (1.0, 2.0)
u_s, v_s	Steady state values of the inputs u, v; (0.0, 0.0)
x_s, z_s	Steady state values of x, z; (0.61803399, 0.030825002)

Application of equations (26) and (27) yields the results of Table 2 and Figures 1 to 3. It can be seen that for inputs u in the ranges [– 0.1, 0.1] or [– 1, 1] the coefficients h_i for the optimal linear approximations $L_{o,j}$ are virtually identical to those of the linearization of P_{ICSTR} around its steady state. This suggests that the nonlinearity of the operator P_{ICSTR} is almost negligible for these ranges of inputs. This conclusion is supported by the results of Table 3, where the 2-norms of P_{ICSTR}, $L_{o,1}$, $L_{o,2}$, and L_s in the intervals [– 0.1, 0.1] and [– 1, 1] are shown to be almost the same.

Table 2. Coefficients of optimal linear approximators $L_{o,j}$ and steady-state linearization L_s of P_{ICSTR}

Interval no. j	1	2	3	4	**Steady state**
[$umin_j$, $umax_j$]	[–0.1,0.1]	[–1, 1]	[–1, 5]	[–1, 10]	**linearization**
h_1	0.0000	0.0000	–0.0053	– 0.0088	0.0000
h_2	0.0124	0.0123	0.0202	0.0283	0.0124
h_3	0.0137	0.0136	0.0299	0.0407	0.0137
h_4	0.0120	0.0119	0.0312	0.0416	0.0120
h_5	0.0098	0.0098	0.0288	0.0381	0.0097
h_6	0.0076	0.0077	0.0244	0.0323	0.0077
h_7	0.0060	0.0060	0.0199	0.0268	0.0060
h_8	0.0047	0.0047	0.0156	0.0215	0.0047
h_9	0.0036	0.0037	0.0120	0.0172	0.0037
h_{10}	0.0028	0.0029	0.0089	0.0135	0.0028
h_{11}	0.0022	0.0022	0.0066	0.0105	0.0022
h_{12}	0.0017	0.0018	0.0047	0.0081	0.0017
h_{13}	0.0013	0.0014	0.0032	0.0062	0.0013
h_{14}	0.0011	0.0011	0.0021	0.0046	0.0010
h_{15}	0.0008	0.0009	0.0014	0.0037	0.0008
h_{16}	0.0006	0.0007	0.0008	0.0026	0.0006
h_{17}	0.0005	0.0005	0.0003	0.0019	0.0005
h_{18}	0.0003	0.0003	0.0000	0.0012	0.0004
h_{19}	0.0002	0.0002	– 0.0005	0.0005	0.0003
h_{20}	0.0002	0.0002	– 0.0006	0.0002	0.0002
$\sum_{i=1}^{nopastu} \|L_i\|^2 \|h_i\|^2$	2.33 E–6	2.33 E–4	NA‡	NA‡	2.33 E–6

‡ $\{L_i\}_{i=1}^{nopastu}$ are not orthogonal on these intervals. The sum of the squares for the coefficients of the orthonormal bases $\{\Gamma_i\}_{i=1}^{nopastu}$ should be examined.

Table 3. Norms of P_{ICSTR}, its steady-state linearization L_s, and optimal linear approximations $L_{o,j}$ over various input intervals j

j	$\|P_{ICSTR}\|^2$	$\|L_s\|^2$	$\|L_{o,1}\|^2$	$\|L_{o,2}\|^2$	$\|L_{o,3}\|^2$	$\|L_{o,4}\|^2$
1	***2.35 10⁻⁶***	$2.33\ 10^{-6}$	***2.33 10⁻⁶***	$2.30\ 10^{-6}$	$1.48\ 10^{-5}$	$2.74\ 10^{-5}$
2	***2.35 10⁻⁴***	$2.33\ 10^{-4}$	$2.33\ 10^{-4}$	***2.30 10⁻⁴***	$1.48\ 10^{-3}$	$2.74\ 10^{-3}$
3	***0.163***	$2.67\ 10^{-2}$	$2.67\ 10^{-2}$	$2.67\ 10^{-2}$	***0.166***	0.334
4	***1.68***	0.132	0.132	0.132	0.820	***1.65***

Table 4. Assessment of the error made in the approximation of P_{ICSTR} by linear operators over various input intervals

j	\F(‖L\L(s) − P_{ICSTR}‖,‖P_{ICSTR}‖)	$\frac{\|L_{o,1} - P_{ICSTR}\|}{\|P_{ICSTR}\|}$	$\frac{\|L_{o,2} - P_{ICSTR}\|}{\|P_{ICSTR}\|}$	$\frac{\|L_{o,3} - P_{ICSTR}\|}{\|P_{ICSTR}\|}$	$\frac{\|L_{o,4} - P_{ICSTR}\|}{\|P_{ICSTR}\|}$
3	0.60	0.60	0.60	***0.16***	0.48
4	0.72	0.72	0.72	0.31	***0.13***

Expanding the range of values for possible inputs u to the reactor dramatically increases the reactor's nonlinearity characteristics, as shown in Tables 2 through 4. Table 2 shows that the coefficients h_i change significantly for inputs in the intervals [− 1, 5] and [− 1, 10]. Table 3 shows that the 2-norms of P_{ICSTR} and L_s are very different for inputs in the ranges [− 1, 5] and [− 1, 10]. Table 3 also demonstrates that "reasonable" approximation of P_{ICSTR} by $L_{o,j}$ may be possible, if average approximation over the corresponding intervals [$umin_j$, $umax_j$] is considered (compare the numbers in bold-italics in Table 3). However, if the 2-norms of $L_{o,j}$ are considered over intervals different from the ones over which they are optimal approximators, then "large" discrepancies exist. Table 4 demonstrates that for the intervals [−1, 5] and [−1, 10] "average errors" of 16% and 13%, respectively, are expected. This dependence of approximation of P_{ICSTR} on [$umin_j$, $umax_j$] is another manifestation of its nonlinearity characteristics.

The relative linearity of P_{ICSTR} in the intervals [− 0.1, 0.1] and [− 1, 1] can also be verified by using Bessel's inequality. Comparison between $\sum_{i=1}^{nopastu} \|L_i\|^2 |h_i|^2$ (Table 2) and $\|P_{ICSTR}\|^2$ (Table 3) over the above two intervals shows that these quantities are close to each other. (In fact $\sum_{i=1}^{nopastu} \|L_i\|^2 |h_i|^2$ appears *greater* than $\|P_{ICSTR}\|^2$ (contrary to Bessel's inequality), since the third digit is uncertain.)

According to the results in Tables 3 and 4, linear operators approximating P_{ICSTR} for *small* inputs *on the average* underpredict outputs corresponding to *larger* inputs. This prediction is verified in Figs. 4 to 6. It is evident that if the step responses of the ICSTR were used to assess the ICSTR's nonlinearity, one might draw the conclusion that for inputs in the interval [-1, 1] the reactor is "nonlinear" (due to the significant difference between the square- and diamond-marked curves of Figure 5). This would be true *only if the probability distribution of values of the input u were an impulse around 1*. For practical purposes this may not be likely. Therefore the above conclusion about the reactor's nonlinearity should be considered in the appropriate context.

The next question that we pose for this reactor is "How are the nonlinearity characteristics of the reactor altered if a linear feedback controller is used?" To design the controller, we use the standard linear internal model control (IMC) methodology (Morari and Zafiriou, 1989), applied to L_s. Figure 7 shows the closed-loop system, corresponding to the nonlinear operator P_{CL}: $y^{SP} \to y$. It should be noted that a saturation block is added after the linear IMC controller C (= $Q[I-L_sQ]^{-1}$; $Q=L_s^{-1}F$), to enforce the natural hard constraint

$$u \geq -1$$

This necessitates that two sets of simulations be distinguished. One for which u is never allowed to reach its lower bound −1 (Table 1), and another, for which the above constraint can be active. This distinction is made in order to separate the reactor nonlinearity from the saturation block nonlinearity. Four different values of α (0.8, 0.7, 0.6, and 0.1) were used in the IMC filter

$$F(z) = \left(\frac{1-\alpha}{z-\alpha}\right)^2$$

Small α results in a closed loop that is close to linear, but prone to controller output saturation. Large α results in control action u that avoids its saturation bound −1 more easily, at the expense of closed-loop linearity. The results of the Monte Carlo simulations for y^{SP} in [0, $ySPmax$] are shown in Figure 8. Figure 8a verifies that nonlinearity increases as $ySPmax$ increases. Figure 8b explains how decreasing α tightens control, but increases the probability of process input saturation, thus yielding higher nonlinearity. Figure 8c quantifies a long known qualitative fact (Black, 1934; 1977): High forward gain increases the linearity of a feedback loop. Comparing, for example, the lines corresponding to α = 0.6 and α = 0.7, we notice that for $ySPmax \leq \sim 0.1$ tighter control (α = 0.6) indeed results in lower nonlinearity. However, as $ySPmax$ increases, the saturation block is saturated more frequently for α = 0.6, thus distorting linearity to a larger extent than for α = 0.7. Similar observations can be made for other values of α.

Figure 8 provides a quantitative answer to the question "How do constraints alter the linearity of a closed-loop system?". Coping with the dramatic difference in closed-loop nonlinearity resulting from controller output saturation explains the popularity of constrained model predictive control (Prett and García, 1988).

5. Discussion and conclusions

In this work we examined the problem of assessing nonlinearities of dynamic systems. The key to quantifying nonlinearities was the development of a nonlinear operator's 2-norm (Definition 4), based on a newly constructed inner product for nonlinear operators (Theorem 1). Well established results of regression theory were unified under the proposed framework (Remark 7), while several properties of the new nonlinearity measure were established, and computational procedures were proposed for the calculation of related quantities. The proposed framework, provides valuable insight into the approximation of a nonlinear operator by a linear or nonlinear one. Pertinent algorithms are simple, intuitively appealing, easy to code, and trivial to run on nowadays' computers. This was demonstrated through a number of simulations on a chemical processing system, for which

- nonlinearities were *quantified* for various ranges of process inputs;
- *optimal linear* models were developed;
- *feedback* effects on nonlinearities were quantified;
- the effects of *constraints* on closed-loop linearity were quantified.

At this point, we have explored only but a few of the repercussions of the theory proposed in this paper. A "laundry list" of items to investigate is given in Nikolaou (1993b).

6. Literature cited

Bakshi, B. N., and G. Stephanopoulos, "Wave-Net: A Multiresolution, Hierarchical Neural Network with Localized Learning", *AIChE J.*, **39**, 1, 57-81 (1993).

Bequette, B. W., "Nonlinear Control of Chemical Processes: A Review", *Ind. Eng. Chem. Res.*, **30**, 1391-1413 (1991).

Black, H. S., "Inventing the negative feedback amplifier",*IEEE Spectrum.*, 55-60, (Dec. 1977).

Black, H. S., "Stabilized feedback amplifiers",*Bell Syst. Tech. J.*, 1-18, (Jan. 1934).

Desoer, C. A., and M. Vidyasagar, *Feedback Systems: Input-Output Properties*, Academic Press, New York (1975).

Desoer, C. A., and Y.-T. Wang, "Foundations of Feedback Theory for Nonlinear Dynamical Systems", *IEEE Trans. Circ. Syst.*, vol. CAS-27, no. 2, 104-123 (1980).

IMSL, *User's Manual-IMSL Math/Library*, Version 1.1, Houston (1989).

Kravaris, C., and J. C. Kantor, "Geometric Methods for Nonlinear Process Control. 1. Background; 2. Controller Synthesis", *Ind. Eng. Chem. Res.*, **29**, 2295-2310; 2310-2323 (1990).

Luenberger, D. G., *Optimization by Vector Space Methods*, John Wiley and Sons (1969).

Manousiouthakis, V., and D. Sourlas, "Development of Linear Models for Nonlinear Systems", p. 125c, AIChE Annual Meeting, Miami (1992).

Morari, M. and E. Zafiriou, *Robust Process Control*, Prentice Hall (1989).

Nikolaou, M. and V. Manousiouthakis, "A Hybrid Approach to Nonlinear System Stability and Performance", *AIChE Journal*, **35**, 4, 559-572 (1989).

Nikolaou, M., "How Nonlinear is a 'Nonlinear' System? Old and New Results Under a Unifying Theory", *AIChE J.*, submitted (1993).

Nikolaou, M., "Neural Networks Modeling Nonlinear Dynamical Systems", *this Proceedings*, (1993).

Prett, D. M. and C. E. García, *Fundamental Process Control*, Butterworths, Stoneham MA (1988).

Ray, W. H., *Advanced Process Control*, McGraw-Hill (1981).

Yosida, K., *Functional Analysis*, Springer Verlag (1974).

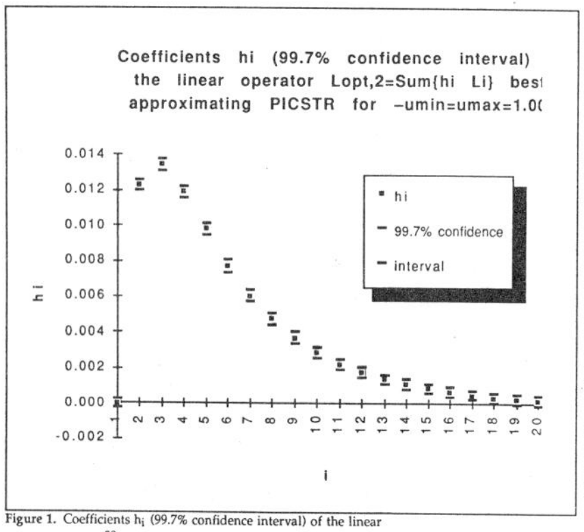

Figure 1. Coefficients h_i (99.7% confidence interval) of the linear operator $L_{opt,2} = \sum_{i=1}^{20} h_i L_i$, best approximating P_{ICSTR} for $-umin = umax = 1$.

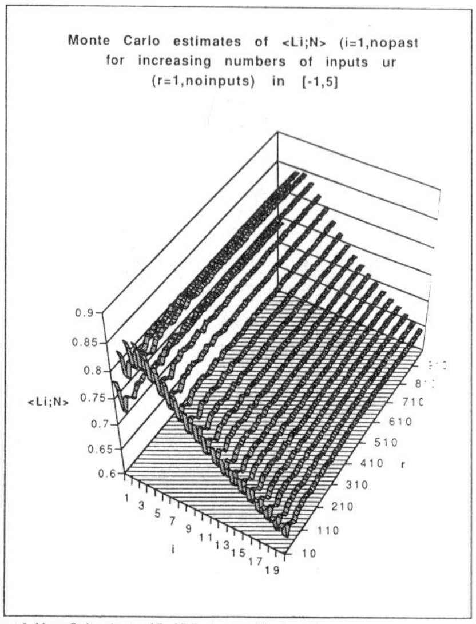

Figure 2. Monte Carlo estimates of $\langle L_i; N\rangle$ ($i = 1$, *nopastu*) for increasing numbers of inputs u^r ($r = 1$, *noinputs*) in [-1, 5]

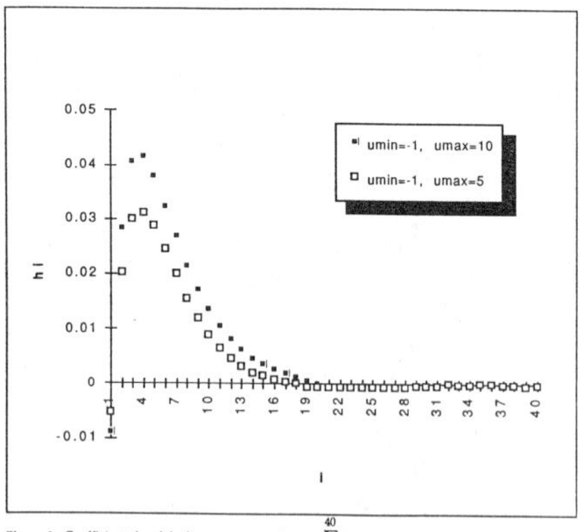

Figure 3. Coefficients h_i of the linear operators $L_{opt,j} = \sum_{i=1}^{40} h_i L_i$, ($j = 3, 4$) best approximating P_{ICSTR} for [*umin* ,*umax*] = [-1, 5], [-1, 10].

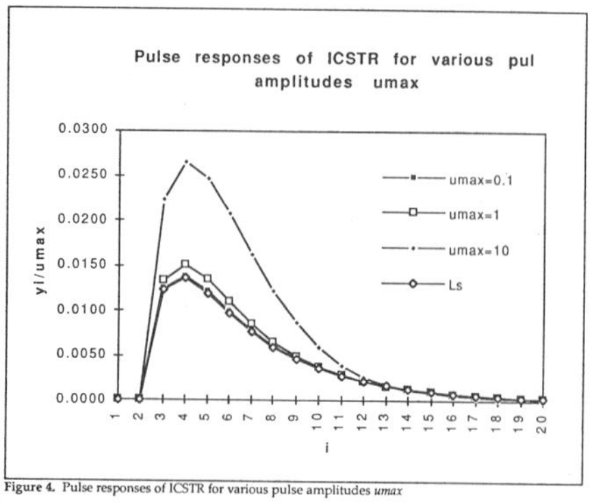

Figure 4. Pulse responses of ICSTR for various pulse amplitudes *umax*

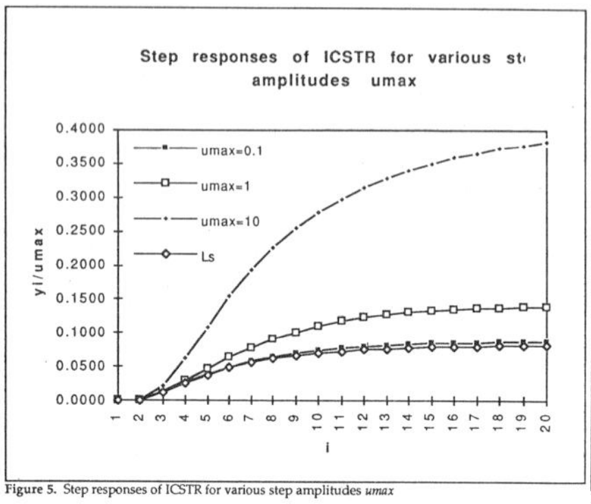

Figure 5. Step responses of ICSTR for various step amplitudes *umax*

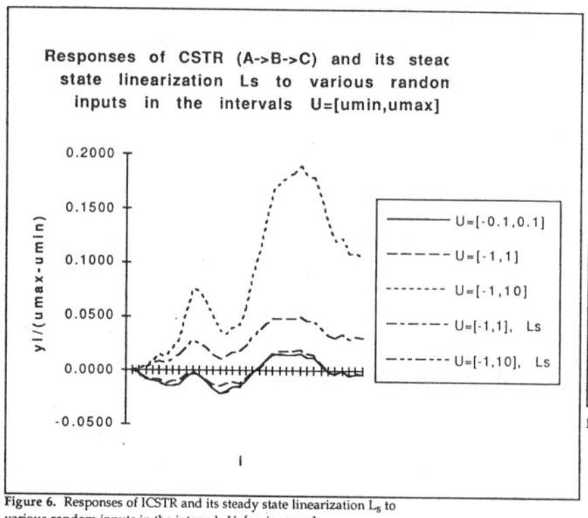

Figure 6. Responses of ICSTR and its steady state linearization L_s to various random inputs in the intervals U=[*umin*, *umax*].

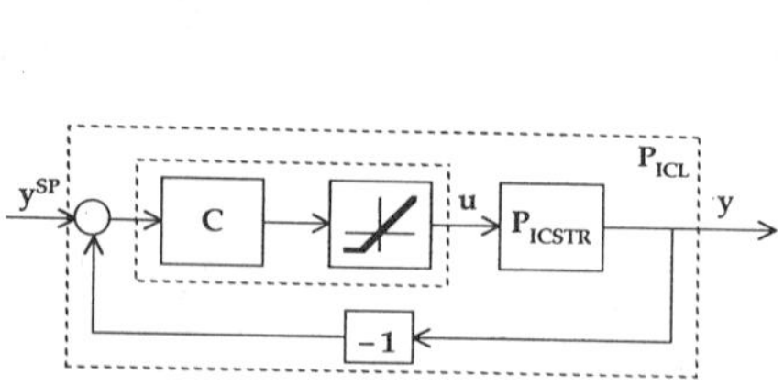

Figure 7. Feedback loop for ICSTR.

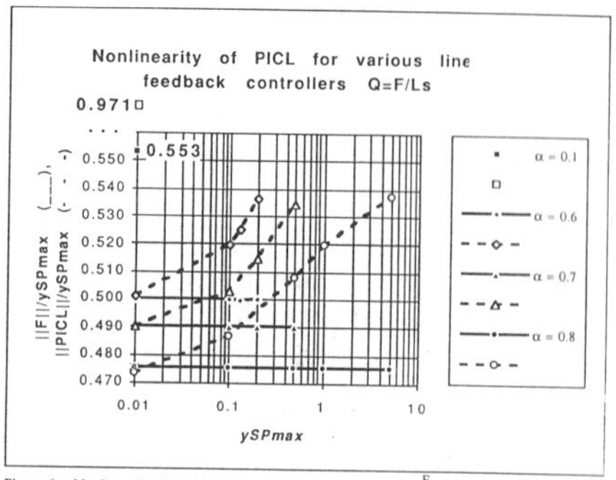

Figure 8a. Nonlinearity of P_{ICL} for various feedback controllers $Q = \frac{F}{L_s}$.

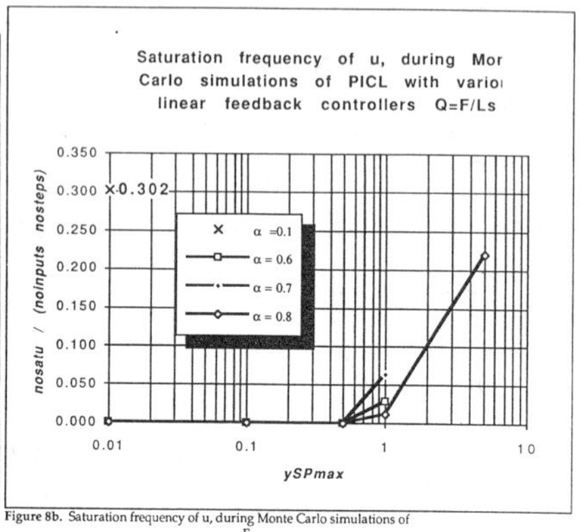

Figure 8b. Saturation frequency of u, during Monte Carlo simulations of P_{ICL} for various feedback controllers $Q = \frac{F}{L_s}$.

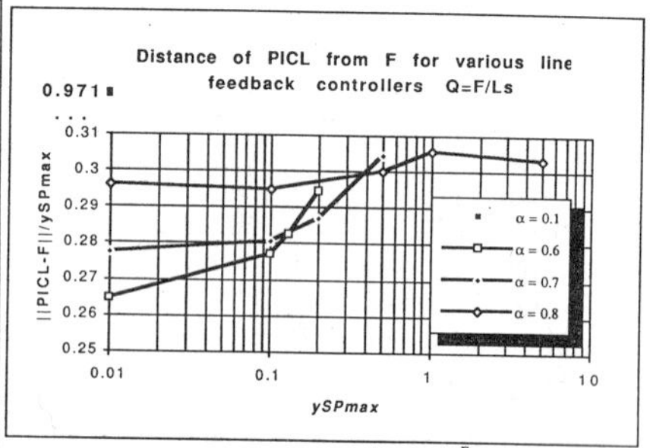

Figure 8c. Distance of P_{ICL} from F for various feedback controllers $Q = \frac{F}{L_s}$.

Proceedings of the
American Control Conference
San Francisco, California • June 1993

Kalman Filtering of 3-D Gyroscopic Measurements

Marcelo C. Algrain
Dept. of Electrical Engineering
University of Nebraska-Lincoln

Abstract

This paper presents a new Kalman filtering method to estimate 3-D angular motion based on noisy gyroscopic measurements. The estimation problem is nonlinear since the dynamics of 3-D angular motion are described by Euler's equations. Instead of using complex extended Kalman filtering techniques to solve this problem, a novel approach is developed where the nonlinear Euler's model is decomposed into two pseudo-linear models, making it possible to run two interlaced discrete-linear Kalman filters. This technique, IKF, takes advantage of the linear form's simplicity, computational efficiency and higher convergence speed, overcoming many drawbacks of conventional extended Kalman filtering techniques. The IKF effectiveness is evaluated through a computer simulation, which demonstrates that the new method yields excellent 3-D angular velocity estimates, very small mean-square-estimation errors, and about ten-to-one signal-to-noise ratio (SNR) improvement over angular velocity measurements obtained from 3 orthogonal gyroscopes, even under very low SNR conditions.

IKF Method for 3-D Angular Motion Estimation

The Kalman filter is a linear minimum-error-variance recursive estimation technique. Its ability to produce more accurate values of measured variables is attributed to the use of statistical information about the process that generated those variables, and statistical information about the noise in the measurements of those variables, in the computation of these estimates. Furthermore, the filter incorporates knowledge about the system itself through a model of its dynamic characteristics. The system dynamics for 3-D angular motion are described by Euler's equations of motion. Thus, the angular accelerations along the body's principal axes of inertia are given by:

$$\dot{W}_X = (I_{YY}-I_{ZZ})I_{XX}^{-1}\,(W_YW_Z) + I_{XX}^{-1}M_X \qquad (1.a)$$
$$\dot{W}_Y = (I_{ZZ}-I_{XX})I_{YY}^{-1}\,(W_XW_Z) + I_{YY}^{-1}M_Y \qquad (1.b)$$
$$\dot{W}_Z = (I_{XX}-I_{YY})I_{ZZ}^{-1}\,(W_XW_Y) + I_{ZZ}^{-1}M_Z \qquad (1.c)$$

where I_{XX}, I_{YY}, and I_{ZZ} are the principal moments of inertia about the roll, pitch, and yaw axes, respectively; M_X, M_Y, and M_Z are the torques applied to the roll, pitch, and yaw axes, respectively; W_X, W_Y, and W_Z are the body angular velocities along roll, pitch, and yaw axes, respectively.

Equations 1.a-c provide a set of nonlinear differential equations that completely defines the angular motion of a rigid-body in 3-D space. To use them as the system model for the discrete Kalman filter they need to be expressed as difference equations. This can be accomplished (for sufficiently small time intervals) by approximating an angular acceleration with the first forward difference between consecutive angular velocities, as follows:

$$\dot{W} \cong [W(n+1) - W(n)] \,/\, T \qquad (2)$$

where: $\dot{W}$ = angular acceleration
$W(n+1)$ = angular velocity at time index "n+1"
$W(n)$ = angular velocity at time index "n"
T = incremental time step

Substituting Equation 2 into Equations 1.a-c, and after some manipulations, the following state-space representation for the discrete-time progression of 3-D angular velocities is obtained:

$$X_W(n+1) = X_W(n) + A(n)X_A(n) + B(n)U_W(n) \qquad (3)$$

X_W = $[\,W_X\ W_Y\ W_Z\,]$
X_A = $[\,A_X\ A_Y\ A_Z\,] = [\,W_YW_Z \quad W_XW_Z \quad W_XW_Y\,]$
U_W = $[\,M_X\ M_Y\ M_Z\,]$

and the matrices A and B are defined as follows:

$$A(n) = \begin{bmatrix} T(I_{YY}-I_{ZZ})I_{XX}^{-1} & 0 & 0 \\ 0 & T(I_{ZZ}-I_{XX})I_{YY}^{-1} & 0 \\ 0 & 0 & T(I_{XX}-I_{YY})I_{ZZ}^{-1} \end{bmatrix}$$

$$B(n) = \begin{bmatrix} TI_{XX}^{-1} & 0 & 0 \\ 0 & TI_{YY}^{-1} & 0 \\ 0 & 0 & TI_{ZZ}^{-1} \end{bmatrix}$$

To complete Euler's equivalent linear model, a way must be devised to propagate the products of angular velocity components. The products were earlier defined in vector form:

$$X_A = [A_X\ A_Y\ A_Z] = [W_YW_Z \quad W_XW_Z \quad W_XW_Y] \qquad (4)$$

Differentiating each element in Equation 4 leads to the following relationships:

$$\dot{A}_X = W_Z\dot{W}_Y + W_Y\dot{W}_Z \qquad (5.a)$$
$$\dot{A}_Y = W_Z\dot{W}_X + W_X\dot{W}_Z \qquad (5.b)$$
$$\dot{A}_Z = W_Y\dot{W}_X + W_X\dot{W}_Y \qquad (5.c)$$

Using first difference approximations for continuous time derivatives in Equations 5.a-c (forward difference on the left, backward difference on the right side of the equations), leads to the following state-space representation for the progression in time of products of orthogonal angular velocity components:

$$X_A(n+1) = X_A(n) + F[X_W(n),\ X_W(n-1)] + U_A(n) \qquad (6)$$

where U_A is an error term which forces the equality. Then,

$$F[X_W(n),\ X_W(n-1)] = [F_X\ F_Y\ F_Z] \qquad (7)$$

$$F_X = [W_Y(n)-W_Y(n-1)]W_Z(n) + [W_Z(n)-W_Z(n-1)]W_Y(n)$$
$$F_Y = [W_X(n)-W_X(n-1)]W_Z(n) + [W_Z(n)-W_Z(n-1)]W_X(n)$$
$$F_Z = [W_X(n)-W_X(n-1)]W_Y(n) + [W_Y(n)-W_Y(n-1)]W_X(n)$$

Equation 6 gives a linear model for propagation of the state vector X_A. This model contains a nonlinear function of the state vector X_W, but it is linear in terms of the state vector X_A, thus complying with the linearity criteria for that state variable. This is the key consideration in developing a pseudo-linear Euler's equivalent model. Therefore, Equations 3 and 6 provide a discrete-time Euler's equivalent model that allows for estimating the 3-D angular velocities using two discrete-linear Kalman filters running simultaneously. The first filter estimates orthogonal angular velocity components; the second estimates their products (taken two at a time). The result is an optimal filtering technique that allows for robust, efficient, accurate estimation of 3-D angular jitter.

Compute Simulation Results

The performance of the IKF technique estimating the 3-D angular velocity of a body is evaluated in this section through a computer simulation example. The actual angular velocity is obtained by solving Euler's equations numerically. The integration algorithm used is a fourth-order Runge-Kutta. The simulation incremental time step is 0.01 seconds. The body is assumed to be a rigid-body having the following normalized principal moments of inertia: $I_{XX} = 1.00$ (roll axis), $I_{YY} = 0.75$

(pitch axis), and $I_{ZZ} = 0.50$ (yaw axis). The torque disturbances M_X, M_Y and M_Z (applied to each of the orthogonal axes) have Gaussian distribution with zero mean and variance of one. Also, to be able to visualize the time plots of the torque disturbances, and of the resulting angular velocities, the torque signal bandwidths are limited to 1 Hz. This is done for illustration purposes only, and it is not a limitation of the technique. The torque disturbances define the vector $U_W = [M_X\ M_Y\ M_Z]^T$ as a random forcing function applied to the body, causing a rotation at angular velocity $W = [W_X\ W_Y\ W_Z]^T$.

Figures 1.A, 2.A and 3.A show the IKF angular velocity estimates in the roll, pitch and yaw axes, respectively. For comparison, the actual velocity values W_X, W_Y and W_Z are shown as dotted lines. To generalize the estimation case, all variables are given in normalized form. The measured angular velocity components (obtained from 3 orthogonal gyroscopes) are shown in Figure 1.B, 2.B and 3.B, respectively. The noise components in each of these measurements also have Gaussian distribution, zero mean and variance of one (low signal-to-noise ratio condition).

Comparing the values of the actual 3-D angular velocity W, its estimate X_W and its measurement Z_W (see Figures 1, 2 and 3), it is clear that the IKF technique provides outstanding 3-D angular velocity estimates in spite of the very low signal-to-noise ratio conditions imposed. Furthermore, this was also found to be true for other cases where the distributions for torque disturbances and/or measurement noises are not Gaussian, and even for some deterministic cases.

In addition, the IKF estimates would not be seriously affected by uncertainties in the exact values of the moments of inertias, as long as the errors are not severe. This is important since the moments of inertia could change if the parameters within the body change due to various factors, such as fuel consumption, geometric changes, etc. If the significance of these factors becomes large, it may be necessary to correct the moments of inertia accordingly to preserve good estimation accuracy.

To further demonstrate the improvements IKF estimates offer over gyroscope measurements, the estimation Mean-Square-Errors (MSE) of the two are compared in Table I. In all cases, the MSE for the IKF is about one order of magnitude smaller than the MSE for the measurements. In addition, Table II provides the means of the angular velocity estimation error for each axis and for the measurement noises. These means are nearly zero, attesting to the unbiasedness of the IKF approach.

Table I: MSE of Velocity Estimates

Estimation Case	IKF	Measured
Roll Axis	0.0566	0.9779
Pitch Axis	0.0850	0.9096
Yaw Axis	0.1151	1.0993

Table II: Mean Velocity Estimation Errors

Estimation Case	IKF	Measured
Roll Axis	0.0252	-0.0165
Pitch Axis	0.1894	0.0079
Yaw Axis	-0.1069	0.0405

Summary and Conclusions

This paper presents a new Kalman filtering technique that reduces the MSE between 3-D actual angular velocity values and estimated ones by an order of magnitude (when compared to the MSE resulting from direct gyroscopic measurements), even under extremely low signal-to-noise ratio conditions. This is important since it could allow a relaxation on gyro noise specifications which would lead to substantial savings. The filtering problem is nonlinear in nature because the dynamics of 3-D angular motion are described by Euler's equations. This nonlinear set of differential equations state that the angular acceleration in one axis is proportional to the torque applied to that axis, and to the products of angular velocity components in the other two axes of rotation. Instead of using extended Kalman filtering techniques to solve this complex problem, a new approach is used where the nonlinear Euler's model is decomposed into two pseudo-linear models (primary and auxiliary). The first model describes the time progression of the states containing the linear terms, while the other characterizes the propagation of the auxiliary state vector containing the nonlinearities. This makes it possible to run two interlaced discrete-linear Kalman filters simultaneously. The new approach takes advantage of the simplicity, computational efficiency and higher convergence speed of the linear Kalman filter form, and it overcomes many of the drawbacks typical of conventional extended Kalman filtering techniques.

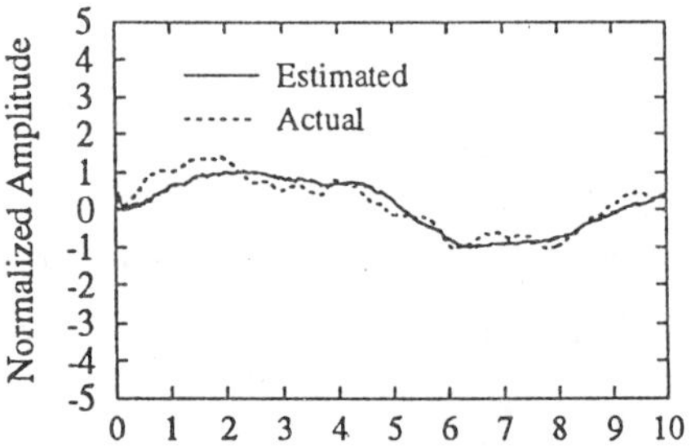

Fig. 1.A Actual and Estimated W_X

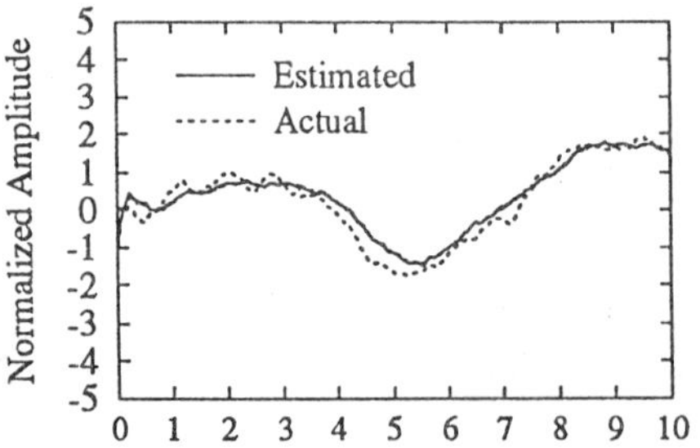

Fig. 2.A Actual and Estimated W_Y

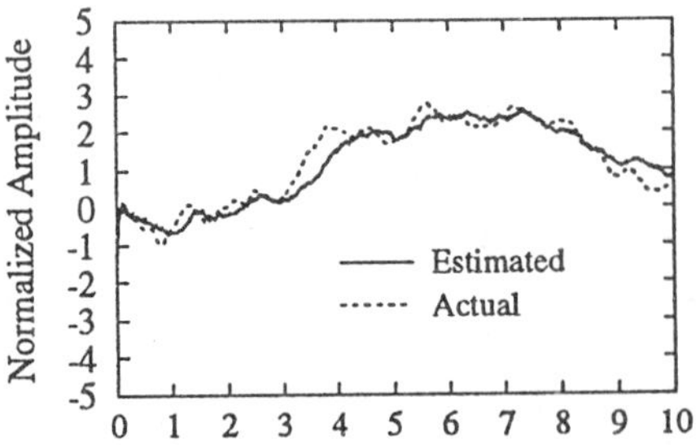

Fig. 3.A Actual and Estimated W_Z

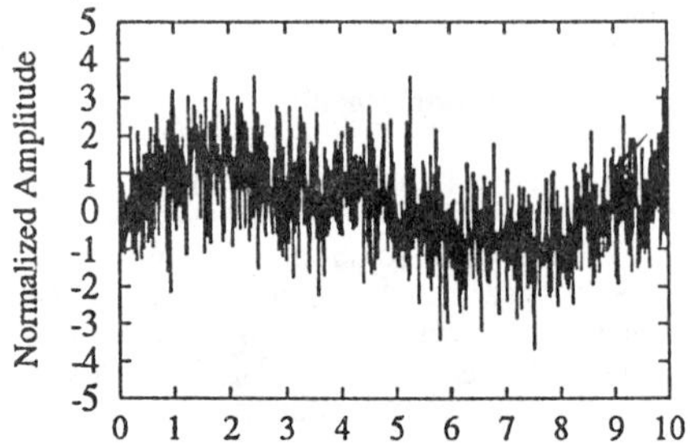

Fig. 1.B Roll Rate (W_X) Measurement

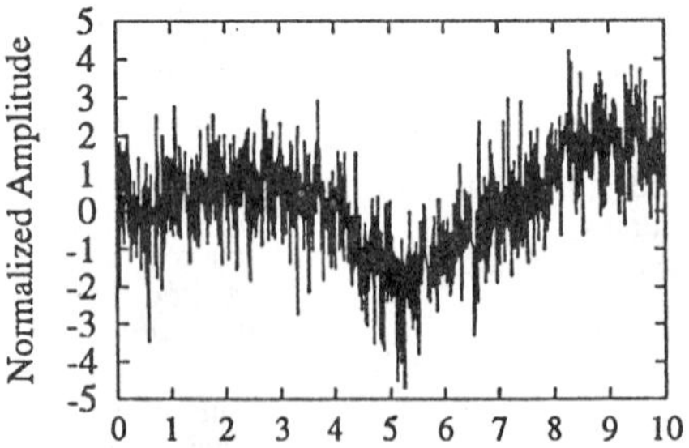

Fig. 2.B Pitch Rate (W_Y) Measurement

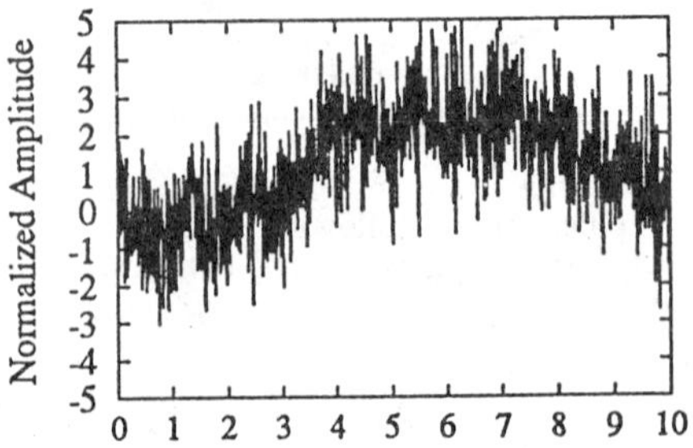

Fig. 3.B Yaw Rate (W_Z) Measurement

Proceedings of the
American Control Conference
San Francisco, California • June 1993

A Quantitative Performance Index for Model-Based Monitoring Systems

Kunsoo Huh (Assistant Professor)
Department of Mechanical Engineering
Hanyang University
Seoul, Korea

Jeffrey L. Stein (Associate Professor)
Department of Mechanical Engineering and Applied Mechanics
The University of Michigan
Ann Arbor, MI 48109-2125

ABSTRACT

Model-based Monitoring (MBM) systems based on state observer theory are attractive for machine monitoring because practical, inexpensive, and reliable sensors can be located remote to the signal(s) of interest. Then, a model of the machine plus an estimation algorithm convert the output of the remote sensors to signals representing the desired local behavior. While this type of monitoring system has shown much promise in the laboratory, it has not been widely accepted by industry because, in practice, these systems often have poor performance with respect to accuracy, bandwidth, reliability (false alarms), and robustness.

In this paper, the limitations of the deterministic state observer are investigated quantitatively from the machine monitoring viewpoint. The limitations in the transient and steady-state observer performance are quantified by the estimation error bounds, and from these error bounds performance indices are selected. Then, based on the relationships between the indices, a main index is determined in order to represent the overall observer performance. This index could form the basis for an observer design methodology that should improve the performance of model-based monitoring systems.

1. Introduction

Since the state observer theory was introduced for the deterministic case by Luenberger [22] and for the stochastic case by Kalman and Bucy [19], many Model-based Monitoring (MBM) systems based on deterministic/stochastic state observer approaches have been proposed for machine monitoring ([18], [23], [39], [29], etc.). These MBM systems use sensors that are easily installed (or are already present for control purposes) along with a model of the machine to provide an estimate of specific system variables.

Although these MBM systems have shown much promise in the laboratory, they have not been widely accepted in the industrial environment. In particular, MBM systems based on deterministic state observers are rarely adopted because the observers often produce large transient or steady-state errors which cause false alarms or even turn-off in monitoring systems ([15]). This is a result of conventional design techniques used to develop deterministic state observers. These techniques start from *a priori* selection of the desired observer poles based on the estimation speed specification (i.e., how fast the estimation error should go to zero). Generally, the observer specification can be met by assigning one or a couple of the observer poles. Then, the remaining poles are usually placed in an arbitrary manner close to those poles already assigned and the resulting observer can be very ill-conditioned. This means that transient and steady-state performance of the observer can become very sensitive to ill-conditioning factors such as unknown initial estimates, unknown changes in the monitored machine, and instrument or sensor errors. This inconsistent state observer performance is due to inadequate observer design methodologies which do not explicitly account for the factors affecting MBM performance with regard to the shape of the transient error and the steady-state bias error of the estimates. These factors include measurement bias and noise, model uncertainty, and unknown initial conditions. By not accounting for these factors an ill-conditioned observer can result. An ill-conditioned state observer is one that works well when the conditions are exactly as assumed (i.e., the remote sensors have no bias error, and the model of the system is perfect), but works poorly if they are not. A new observer design methodology is required to correct this inconsistency and to design a well-conditioned observer. What is missing, however, are quantitative indices that show *a priori* what the conditioning of a particular observer might be and that can be used to design well-conditioned observers.

The objective of this paper is to find performance indices for evaluating the effects of the factors that cause the deterministic state observer[1] to be ill-conditioned and to determine a main index by combining the indices so that an observer design methodology can be developed.

This study involves two steps. The first is to find the performance indices that represent the effects of the ill-conditioning factors on the state observer performance. This is accomplished using a sensitivity analysis, or maximum error analysis, to reveal how these factors affect transient and steady-state performance. More specifically, the analysis involves determining the upper bounds of the sensitivity or error relation, which are derived by utilizing matrix norm theory. Then these upper bounds are used to determine dominant indices which can be manipulated at the observer design stage. This determination is based on the premise that "small" upper bounds guarantee "small" relative errors.

The second step of this work is to determine a single main index, by combining the performance indices, in order to represent the overall performance of Model-based monitoring (MBM) systems. This step depends on the specific machine monitoring application. If one of the performance requirements considered in the first step is needed for a specific monitoring problem, only the corresponding index needs to be minimized and that index becomes the main index of the monitoring problem. However, for overall observer performance, it is shown that inequality relations exist between the performance indices, i.e. one of them dominates all the others. In this case, the dominant index becomes the main index of the MBM system.

This paper is organized as follows. Section 2 summarizes the literature regarding transient and steady-state observer performance. Section 3 investigates the effects on the transient performance due to two ill-conditioning factors: unknown initial estimates and round-off error. Section 4 investigates effects on the

[1] Note that the types of estimators available for model-based monitoring systems include: state observers, input observers, state and input observers, parameter estimators etc. The deterministic state observer (i.e., an observer that assumes that the systems quantities have no statistical properties) is the simplest to characterize and easiest to implement. Thus, this paper focuses on deterministic observers.

steady-state estimation accuracy due to another two ill-conditioning factors: plant perturbation and sensor bias error in measuring input and output. Section 5 gives an example of a mechanical dynamic system and illustrates the effects of the above ill-conditioning factors. Finally, Section 6 proposes the main index for the well-conditioned observer so that it can form the basis for the observer design methodology.

2. Background

The literature related to performance of state observers in the context of monitoring systems is surprisingly sparse. Traditionally, observer design has been defined in the context of control systems where the observer provides information (feedback) that the controller requires but that cannot be measured. While this role for the observer is similar to the role that observers play for machine tool monitoring, the performance required of the observer in these two circumstances is quite different. The main difference is that control systems are relatively insensitive to large but short acting errors in the measurements (or estimates of them). The actuator will usually temporarily saturate, or the control algorithm may smooth these spikes out due to its own filter-like characteristics. Monitoring systems, on the other hand, need a high bandwidth accurate estimate or at least a "close to" accurate estimate of the quantity even during transient periods. Because diagnostic systems are often designed to indicate faults based on the signal exceeding a threshold, large error spikes can cause false alarms. Finally, these error spikes cannot simply be filtered out because then the high frequency information in the estimate, which is often very important, is lost.

To be more specific, in the context of the control problem, the design techniques for observers have been concerned with a certain transient and steady-state error behavior. That is, the main goal is limited to driving the transient estimation error to as small a value (the steady-state error) as possible. This is done by placing the poles of the observer in a specific location to force the estimates to converge to the proper values within a predetermined amount of time. This is called an *a priori* pole placement technique in that the pole locations are chosen first and the observer is designed to accurately place the poles. In control literature, there has been a great deal of work done on this pole placement/stabilization problem in closed-loop control systems; such as eigenvalue sensitivity analysis ([40], [12] and [3]), robust pole-placement by eigenvalue/eigenvector assignment ([24], [1] and [33]), and optimal controller design including eigenvalue sensitivity ([31], [20], [27], [8], [32], [16], [5], [21], [4] and [7]). Traditionally, these results have been assumed to be equally useful for the transient error characterization of observer-based monitoring systems.

However, from a monitoring point of view, the main issue of transient observer performance is the shape of the transient estimation error. The transient error shape depends not only on the observer eigenvalues but also on the corresponding eigenvectors. Moreover, it is sensitive to the initial conditions chosen for the observer (which are always unknown) and to the round-off errors in implementing the observer. Fortunately, as unlike a closed-loop control system, the transient shape is not affected directly by model perturbations (i.e., the real plant being different from a model of the plant used to design the observer), unless the estimated states are feedback to the control system. There is essentially no control literature that deals with the transient shape issue as a function of these quite real problems for implementing machine tool monitoring systems based on observer theory.

The design of observers with respect to the steady-state accuracy is better developed in the literature than for transient shape performance, but it is still inadequate. The steady-state performance of the state observer is usually represented by the accuracy robustness. The estimated states of the observer are supposed to converge to the true values if the plant model is exact and the observer is stable ([22]). However, in practice, the parameters of the real system may change during operation, and sensors always have bias error and noise. The effects of these factors has been demonstrated by Stefani [34]. He showed that relatively small errors in the model may cause disproportionately large steady-state errors in state estimation.

To maintain steady-state estimation accuracy when the machine is perturbed, various methods have been developed. Battacharyya [2] studied the required conditions based on the structure of the model perturbation in order to preserve the accuracy. Furuta *et al* [10] derived the necessary and sufficient conditions for the existence of a zero sensitivity observer for a certain structure of the perturbed model. Stefani [35] introduced the minimum integrated estimation error bound using the redundancy in the measurement output. Galimidi and Barmish [11] developed a norm bound for the insensitive observer using a Lyapunov function based approach. From a canonical-form machine model, Shafai and Carrol [30] designed a Proportional/Integral observer to be less sensitive to parameter variations of the system. Djaferis [9] proposed a robust observer design method based on the transfer function representation of the observer dynamics. Haddad and Bernstein [14] designed a robust observer by minimizing a bound on the quadratic estimation errors. When there are a few time-varying parameters, Park and Stein [26] estimate the parameters and states simultaneously by transforming unknown parameters into unknown inputs.

Despite all of this work on steady-state estimation accuracy of observers, the basic problem still exists for practical machine tool monitoring problems. This is because all of the above approaches are based on the assumption that machine perturbations occur in a certain decomposed forms or are represented by specific structures. But that is almost never the case in machine monitoring problems. For example, the system matrix $\boldsymbol{A}$ may have many time-varying parameters and the perturbed part in the system matrix is usually too complicated to be modeled as suggested by these papers. Thus, none of these techniques can be easily applied for estimating the states to the desired steady-state accuracy for typical machine sensing problems.

3. Transient Performance Of State Observers

In this section, the transient performance of deterministic state observers is investigated with respect to two ill-conditioning factors: unknown initial estimates and round-off errors. The effects are expressed quantitatively to determine the indices. First, the effects of unknown initial estimates are studied concerning transient shape sensitivity and the maximum (integrated) transient error. Then effects of round-off error in designing and implementing the observer are examined with respect to observer eigenvalue sensitivity.

3-1 Effects of initial estimates on transient performance

3-1-1 Transient error shape sensitivity: The effect of the unknown initial estimates on the transient error shape is investigated to determine the dominant index that quantifies this effect. The transient error shape is largely dependent on the initial slope ($e(t)/dt\,|_{t=0}$) of the estimation error response. If the magnitude of initial error slope varies significantly due to unknown initial estimates, then the transient shape will also be very sensitive to the choice of the initial estimates. This means the transient shape will be inconsistent when implemented for machine monitoring.

The sensitivity of the initial error shape can be expressed with respect to the choice of the initial estimates, especially to the directionality of the initial estimates. The effect of the initial estimate directionality can be represented via estimation error equation, which can be derived from a linear machine model and the Luenberger observer ([22]). Suppose the following linear time-invariant state equation is the perfect plant (machine) model.

$$\dot{x}(t) = \boldsymbol{A}x(t) + \boldsymbol{B}u(t)$$
$$y(t) = \boldsymbol{C}x(t) \qquad (1)$$

where $x \in \mathbb{R}^n$, $y \in \mathbb{R}^q$, and $u \in \mathbb{R}^m$. Then, a full-order Luenberger observer can be built to estimate the unmeasurable states,

$$\dot{\hat{x}}(t) = \boldsymbol{A}\hat{x}(t) + \boldsymbol{B}u(t) + \boldsymbol{L}(y(t) - \boldsymbol{C}\hat{x}(t)) \qquad (2)$$

where $\hat{x} \in \mathbb{R}^n$ is the estimate of the state variables. From Eqs (1) and (2), the estimation error is expressed as;

$$e(t) = x(t) - \hat{x}(t)$$
$$\dot{e}(t) = (\boldsymbol{A} - \boldsymbol{LC}) \cdot e(t) = \boldsymbol{A_2} \cdot e(t) \qquad (3)$$

where $A_2 = A\text{-}LC$. If the plant model of Eq (1) is perfect and the (A,C) pair is observable (or less restrictively, detectable), Eq (3) means that the observer, Eq (2), will give asymptotic estimates of the states with zero steady-state error. To characterize the transient shape of the observer due to unknown initial estimate error $e(0)$ ($= x(0) - \hat{x}(0)$), the initial slope of the estimation error is considered as follows: The observer matrix A_2 in Eq (3) can be decomposed by using the Singular Value Decomposition (SVD) method;

$$A_2 = U_{A_2} \Sigma_{A_2} V_{A_2}^{H} \tag{4}$$

where U_{A2} and V_{A2} are left and right singular matrices, respectively, and defined as;

$$U_{A2} = [u_1\ u_2\ u_3\ \ldots\ u_n\ ]_{A2}$$
$$V_{A2} = [v_1\ v_2\ v_3\ \ldots\ v_n\ ]_{A2}$$
$$\Sigma_{A2} = Diag\ [\sigma_1, \sigma_2, \sigma_3, \ \ldots.. \ , \sigma_n]_{A2}\,.$$

Based on Eq (3) and Eq (4), the initial slope can be described as the following sum:

$$\dot{e}(t)\big|_{t=0} = A_2 \cdot e(0) = \sum_{k=1}^{n} \sigma_k u_k v_k^{H} \cdot e(0) \tag{5}$$

where u_k and v_k are columns of the left and right singular matrices, respectively. To consider the effect of directionality of the initial estimates, the initial estimate vector $e(0)$ is expressed as

$$e(0) = e_0\ \varepsilon(0)$$

where $e_0 = \|e(0)\|_2$ and $\varepsilon(0) = e(0)\ /\|e(0)\|_2$. If $\varepsilon(0)$ is the same as one of the columns of V_{A2}, for example, $\varepsilon(0) = v_i$, then $v_k^{H}e(0) = 0$ for k i, and the Eq (5) becomes

$$\dot{e}(t)\big|_{t=0} = \sigma_i e_0 \cdot u_i. \tag{6}$$

The above equation means that the initial slope of the estimation error signal is in the direction of u_i with magnitude $\sigma_i e_0$. Because $\sigma_1 > \sigma_2 > \cdots > \sigma_n$, the largest time derivative $\sigma_1 e_0$ occurs in the direction of u_1 if the initial error is in the direction of v_1, and the smallest time derivative $\sigma_n e_0$ occurs in the direction of u_n if the initial error is in the direction of v_n. Therefore, if the magnitude difference among the singular values is large, the initial error slope in Eq (6) becomes very sensitive to the direction of the initial estimates. With $\| u_i \|_2=1$, the magnitude sensitivity of the initial slope at the transient period depends on the singular values, and it is bounded as follows;

$$\sigma_n(A_2) \le \frac{\left\|\dot{e}(t)\big|_{t=0}\right\|_2}{e_0} \le \sigma_1(A_2) = \kappa_2(A_2)\cdot\sigma_n(A_2) \tag{7}$$

$$\text{where } \kappa_2(A_2) = \frac{\sigma_1(A_2)}{\sigma_n(A_2)}. \tag{8}$$

$\kappa_2(A_2)$ is called the condition number of the observer matrix $(A\text{-}LC)$ and is defined in terms of L_2 norm ([37]).

Eq (7) suggests that the condition number ($\kappa_2(A_2)$) of the observer matrix is the main index to describe the initial slope sensitivity to the direction of the initial estimates, and in turn, to represent the transient shape sensitivity due to unknown initial estimates. For example, if the state observer has a large value for the condition number, its transient shape becomes very sensitive to the choice of initial estimates, especially to the directionality of them. If the condition number of a state observer is close to one, the initial slope of the transient error will be consistent regardless of the choice of the initial estimates. If partial information about the initial state variables is available, careful choice of the initial estimates can reduce the transient error significantly. It is illustrated in an example in Section 5 that for ill-conditioned observers ($\kappa_2(A_2)$ >>1) the directionality of the initial estimates affects the transient shape more severely than the magnitude of the initial error.

3-1-2 Integrated Size of the Overall Transient Error: The effect of unknown initial estimates on the size of the transient error is investigated and a dominant index is determined to represent the effect. The size of the transient error is a very important issue for machine monitoring applications and can be represented by the maximum transient error or the integrated transient error. The maximum and the integrated transient errors are measured by a matrix norm (e.g. $\|\cdot\|_1$), and upper bounds for them are derived by using matrix norm properties. The error response is obtained from the observer eigensystem representation, and the matrix norm is applied to obtain the upper bound.

Suppose the observer matrix has distinct eigenvalues. Then the eigensystem can be expressed as

$$(A\text{-}LC)\,P = P\,M_o \tag{9}$$

where $M_o = Diag\ [\mu_1, \mu_2, \mu_3, \cdots, \mu_n]$: eigenvalues,
$P = [p_1, p_2, \cdots, p_n]$: normalized eigenvectors $\|p_i\|_2=1$.

From Eqs (3) and Eq (9), the error response is expressed as

$$\begin{aligned} e(t) &= \exp\{(A-LC)t\}\cdot e(0) \\ &= P\cdot\exp(M_o\cdot t)\cdot P^{-1}\cdot e(0) \end{aligned} \tag{10}$$

where $e(0)$ is the initial error at time t = 0. Applying L_1 matrix norm on the above equation and using matrix norm properties ([13]), an upper bound of the error norm can be calculated as follows:

$$\begin{aligned} \|e(t)\|_1 &= \left\|P\cdot\exp(M_o\cdot t)\cdot P^{-1}\cdot e(0)\right\|_1 \\ &\le \|P\|_1\cdot\left\|\exp(M_o\cdot t)\right\|_1\cdot\left\|P^{-1}\right\|_1\cdot\|e(0)\|_1 \\ &= \kappa_1(P)\cdot\max_j\left|e^{\mu_j t}\right|\cdot\|e(0)\|_1 \end{aligned} \tag{11}$$

$$\text{where } \kappa_1(P) = \|P\|_1\,\|P^{-1}\|_1. \tag{12}$$

$\kappa_1(P)$ is called the eigensystem condition number based on L_1 norm. The above equation shows that at any time t, the absolute sum of the transient error can be manipulated only by the condition number $\kappa_1(P)$, because the initial error is not known *a priori*. Note that the observer poles are assumed to have negative real parts.

To get the integrated norm of the estimation error, Eq (11) is integrated in time from zero to infinity. Because all the observer poles have negative real parts, the integrated norm of the absolute estimation error is finite and has the bound of

$$\begin{aligned} \int_{t=0}^{\infty}\|e(t)\|_1\,dt &\le \kappa_1(P)\cdot\int_{t=0}^{\infty}\max_j\left|e^{\mu_j t}\right|dt\cdot\|e(0)\|_1 \\ &= \kappa_1(P)\cdot\frac{1}{\min_j\left|\mathrm{Re}(\mu_j)\right|}\cdot\|e(0)\|_1. \end{aligned} \tag{13}$$

In the above upper bound, the condition number $\kappa_1(P)$ is the only manageable index which can be altered to control the size of the integrated transient error. On the right side of the Eq (13), the norm of the initial estimates cannot be manipulated because they are not known. In addition, the minimum real part of the observer poles is determined based approximately on the required convergence speed. However, the condition number $\kappa_1(P)$ depends on the structure and eigenvalues of the observer matrix $(A\text{-}LC)$ and, therefore, can be reduced at the observer design stage. It should be noted that a large value in the condition number does not necessarily mean large transient errors, but a small condition number assures a small transient estimation error.

3-2 Effect of round-off error on observer eigenvalues

The effect of round-off errors in the observer design is studied with respect to observer eigenvalue variation, and a dominant index is selected to represent the eigenvalue sensitivity. The round-off errors should not shift the dominant observer poles from the desired location because the convergence speed in the state estimation is primarily determined by the observer poles. In the observer design, round-off errors occur when selecting the observer gain and when implementing the observer matrix. This is expressed in the following two cases:

Case i: Observer gain matrix has round-off error of εE at observer design stage:

$$L \dashrightarrow L + \varepsilon E \tag{14}$$

where E contains elements such that $|e_{ij}| < 1$, $\varepsilon \ll 1$

Case ii: Observer matrix has round-off error of $\varepsilon \Delta o$ at implementation stage:

$(A - LC) \dashrightarrow (A - LC + \varepsilon \Delta o)$ where $\varepsilon \ll 1$ and $\|\Delta o\|_2 < n$.

In this section, only **Case i** is considered with regard to its effect on the observer eigensystem (Eq (9)). Study of **Case ii** is omitted because its effect will be the same as **Case i** except replacing Δo for EC. The sensitivity relation is derived between the dominant observer poles and the round-off errors. The analysis is largely based on previous results regarding the eigenvalue perturbation problem ([40] and [25]).

Suppose μ_1 is the closest observer eigenvalue to origin and p_l and q_l are the right and left eigenvector with $\|p_l\|_2 = \|q_l\|_2 = 1$ corresponding to μ_1, respectively. Then the round-off error of Eq (14) affects the dominant pole, μ_1, as

$$|\mu_1 - \mu_1'| = \varepsilon \cdot \frac{|q_l^T \cdot EC \cdot p_l|}{|q_l^T p_l|} \le \varepsilon \cdot \frac{\|EC\|_2}{|q_l^T p_l|}. \tag{15}$$

The derivation for Eq (15) is straightforward from Wilkinson [40], and only the result is given. The above analysis shows that the inverse of $|q_l^T p_l|$ of the observer matrix is the most important index representing the effect of the round-off error on the dominant observer poles. If the eigenvector matrix P can be chosen such that $|q_l^T p_l|=1$, small error in implementing the observer gain will induce at most the same error on the observer poles.

4. Steady-state Accuracy of the State observer

In this section, steady-state accuracy of the deterministic state observer is investigated with respect to two ill-conditioning factors: arbitrary plant perturbations and sensor measurement bias. The steady-state accuracy of the state observer is another very important requirement from the machine monitoring standpoint because extremely biased estimates would be interpreted as a fault condition. The effects of the ill-conditioning factors on the accuracy error are expressed mathematically to determine the dominant index for the steady-state observer performance. More specifically, the effects are measured by the magnitude of the relative estimation error, and an upper bound of the error is derived using matrix norm theory. The relative estimation error is defined as the ratio of the observer error based on a plant model with respect to true state values of the real plant.

Suppose the following equation represents a real plant.

$$\begin{aligned} \dot{x}(t) &= \underline{A}x(t) + Bu(t) \\ y(t) &= Cx(t) \end{aligned} \tag{16}$$

where $x \in \mathbb{R}^n$, $y \in \mathbb{R}^q$, and $u \in \mathbb{R}^m$. Let's assume that Eq (1) is a model of the above plant with some uncertainly in A matrix and is given again for convenience.

$$\begin{aligned} \dot{x}(t) &= Ax(t) + Bu(t) \\ y(t) &= Cx(t) \end{aligned} \tag{1}$$

where A is a system model for the plant $\underline{A}$ and assumed not to be accurate. If measurement sensors for input and output have static bias errors, the measurement vectors can be expressed as the following form. Measurement noise is not considered here.

$$\begin{aligned} u'(t) &= u(t) + \delta u \\ y'(t) &= y(t) + \delta y \end{aligned} \tag{17}$$

where δu and δy represent static bias in measuring the input and output, respectively. Based on a system model [Eq (1)] and measurement [Eq (17)], a full-order state observer can be built as

$$\begin{aligned} \dot{\hat{x}}(t) &= A\hat{x}(t) + Bu'(t) + L(y'(t) - C\hat{x}(t)) \\ &= (A - LC)\hat{x}(t) + Bu'(t) + Ly'(t) \end{aligned} \tag{18}$$

where $\hat{x} \in \mathbb{R}^n$ is the estimate of the state variables. The estimation error equation can be derived from Eqs (16) and (18) as follows:

$$\begin{aligned} &e(t)=x(t)-\hat{x}(t), \\ &\dot{e}(t)=(A-LC)\cdot e(t) -(A-\underline{A})x(t)+B(u(t)-u'(t))+L(y(t)-y'(t)) \\ &\quad =(A-LC)\cdot e(t) -\underbrace{\{(A-\underline{A})x(t)+B\cdot\delta u+L\cdot\delta y\}}_{(\phi)} \end{aligned} \tag{19}$$

The observer error equation with general error sources was well formulated by Powell [28]. If only the steady-state accuracy of the observer is considered ignoring time-derivative terms, steady-state solution of Eq (19) will be of the following form [assuming that (A-LC) is non-singular (i.e. observer poles are non-zero)]:

$$e_{ss} = A_2^{-1}\{(A - \underline{A}) \cdot x_{ss} + B \cdot \delta u + L \cdot \delta y\} \tag{20}$$

where $A_2 = A\text{-}LC$. By applying $\mathbf{L_2}$ norm ([37]) to the above equation, the upper bound for the quadratic sum of the accuracy error can be expressed as;

$$\begin{aligned} \|e_{ss}\|_2 &= \left\|(A - LC)^{-1}\{(A - \underline{A}) \cdot x_{ss} + B \cdot \delta u + L \cdot \delta y\}\right\|_2 \\ &\le \|A_2^{-1}\|_2 \cdot \|(A - \underline{A}) \cdot x_{ss} + B \cdot \delta u + L \cdot \delta y\|_2 \\ &\le \frac{\kappa_2(A_2)}{\|A_2\|_2}\left\{\|A - \underline{A}\|_2 \cdot \|x_{ss}\|_2 + \|B \cdot \delta u + L \cdot \delta y\|_2\right\} \end{aligned} \tag{21}$$

where $\kappa_2(A_2) = \| A_2 \|_2 \| A_2^{-1}\|_2$. Then the relative error with respect to the true states is

$$\frac{\|e_{ss}\|_2}{\|x_{ss}\|_2} \le \kappa_2(A_2)\left\{\frac{\|A - \underline{A}\|_2}{\|A_2\|_2} + \frac{\|B \cdot \delta u + L \cdot \delta y\|_2}{\|A_2\|_2\|x_{ss}\|_2}\right\} \tag{22}$$

or,

$$\frac{\|e_{ss}\|_2}{\|x_{ss}\|_2} \le \kappa_2(A_2) \cdot \underbrace{\left\{\frac{\|A - \underline{A}\|_2}{\|A_2\|_2} + \frac{\|B \cdot \delta u + L \cdot \delta y\|_2}{\|B \cdot u_{ss} + L \cdot y_{ss}\|_2}\right\}}_{(\rho)}. \tag{23}$$

If the perturbation vector (ϕ) in Eq (19) is assumed to be arbitrary in direction, the condition number of the observer matrix (A-LC) is the only part in the upper bound of Eq (21), that can be manipulated. The above relation shows that the relative estimation error will be small if the size of (ρ) in Eq (23) is small and the condition number $\kappa_2(A_2)$ is not too large. However, the converse is not true, as van der Sluis [38], Noble and Daniel [25], Chan and Foulser [6] etc. showed for conditioning of linear equations. A large condition number does not necessarily mean that the observer is always ill-conditioned. However, it is true that if the condition number is large, the observer is ill-conditioned for some perturbation vector.

Remark 1: Eq (20) shows that the estimation error depends not only on the size of the right-hand terms in the equation, but also on the orientation of the perturbation vector (ϕ) of Eq (19). Based on the SVD (Singular Value Decomposition) analysis as used in Section 3-1, it can be shown that the estimation error depends on the projection of the perturbation vector (ϕ) onto the right singular matrix of the inverse of A_2 (or left singular matrix of A_2). Thus, for example, a customized robust observer can be designed if the orientation of the perturbation vector is fixed and known *a priori*. But that is not always the case in reality. For example, sensor bias is usually specified as arbitrary in direction (e.g. ± 5%) and the system matrix A may have many time-varying parameters.

Remark 2: In the discrete-time domain, it will hardly be possible to guess the orientation of the perturbation vector because single parameter variation in a continuous model may affect every element of the resulting transition matrix in the discretized model.

Based on the study in Sections 3 and 4, the obtained indices to represent the state observer performance are summarized in Table 1, where $\kappa_2(A\text{-}LC)$, $\kappa_1(P)$ and $|q_l^T p_l|$ are the condition number of the observer matrix $(A\text{-}LC)$ in terms of L_2 norm, the condition number of the eigensystem P in terms of L_1 norm, and the inner product of right and left eigenvectors, respectively. The usefulness of these indices is illustrated with an example in the next section.

Table 1: Indices for the state observer performance

Performance Criteria	Upper bound	Performance Indices
Transient shape sensitivity to initial condition	Eq (7)	$\kappa_2(A\text{-}LC)$
Maximum and integrated transient error	Eqs (12) & (13)	$\kappa_1(P)$
Eigenvalue sensitivity to round-off error	Eq (15)	$\lvert q_l^T p_l \rvert$
Steady-state accuracy robustness to plant perturbation input/output measurement bias	Eq (23)	$\kappa_2(A\text{-}LC)$

5. Example Study

The effects of the ill-conditioning factors studied in the previous sections are illustrated in a mechanical servo drive example. Fig. 1 shows a model a servo mechanism. The model contains an armature controlled DC motor with winding resistance and inductance as well as motor armature inertia. The motor armature is connected to a set of gears that drive a compliant shaft supported by bearings at both ends. The load is assumed to be purely inertial. This is a common model of the basic subsystem of many machine tool feed-drive or spindle-drive systems. The objective is to design a state observer capable of estimating the load momentum (load inertia times speed) based on measurement of the motor voltage and speed.

Assuming that the servo drive system parameters are time-invariant, a 4th order linear state equation for the experimental set-up in our lab is derived. The parameter values of the system matrix are taken from Stein and Park [36], and the eigenvalues of the system matrix are calculated as { -28+j 2026, -28-j 2026, -142 and -384 }.

$$\dot{x}(t) = Ax(t) + Bu(t)$$
$$y(t) = Cx(t)$$

where

$$x=\begin{bmatrix} p_g \\ p_m \\ p_w \\ \theta \end{bmatrix},\quad A=\begin{bmatrix} -R_b/I_g & k/I_m & 0 & -n_g/C \\ -k/I_g & -R_i/I_m & 0 & 0 \\ 0 & 0 & -R_w/I_w & 1/C \\ n_g/I_g & 0 & -1/I_w & 0 \end{bmatrix},\quad B=\begin{bmatrix} 0 \\ 1 \\ 0 \\ 0 \end{bmatrix} \qquad (24)$$

$u(t)$ = V, $C = [\,1\ 0\ 0\ 0\,]$,

and, C : Compliance of the power train (1/6000 rad/Nm)
Ig : Motor inertia (including the gear inertia) (1/750 Kgm^2)
Im : Electrical inductance of the motor (1/1000 H)
Iw : Load inertia (1/600 Kgm^2)
k : Motor constant (0.25 Vsec/rad or Nm/A)
n_g : Gear reduction ratio (1/3)
Pg : Momentum of the armature and gears
Pm : Flux linkage
Pw : Momentum of the load

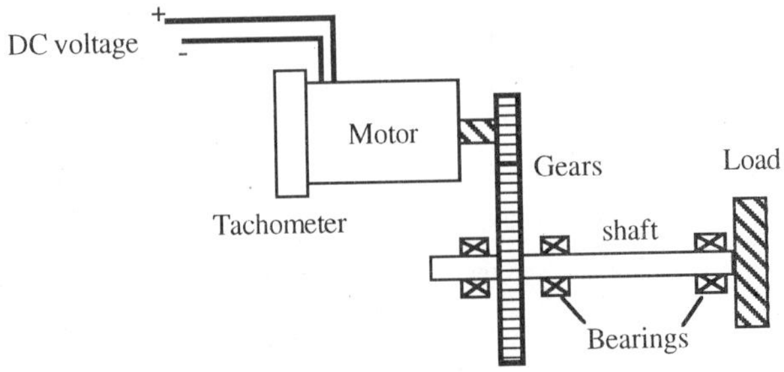

Fig. 1: DC servo drive system

Ri : Electrical resistance of the motor (0.5 Ω)
Rb : The damping coefficient of the bearing on the motor shaft (0.03 Nm sec/rad)
Rw : The damping coefficient of the bearing on the load shaft (0.1 Nm sec/rad)
θ : Angular displacement of the power train (rad)
V : Motor armature voltage (V=100 DC volt)

Suppose the required time constant for the state estimation is 0.025 sec. Then from *a priori* selection of the desired observer poles for this observable system, a state observer can be designed by a conventional pole-placement technique. The full-order deterministic state observer designed in this way becomes

Desired poles: Λ_o = Diag{ -40, -50, -60, -70 }

Designed gain: L = [-362.5 -146.49016 1130.09686 1965.97623]^T (25)

Designed eigenvalues: eig($A\text{-}LC$) = {-39.70, -51.01, -58.98, -70.31}

Estimation performance of the designed observer is demonstrated regarding the effects of the ill-conditioning factors proposed in this paper. Moreover, usefulness of the performance indices developed in this study is illustrated by comparing the values of the upper bounds with the actual errors. Performance indices of Table 1 have the following values for the designed observer:

$$\kappa_2(A\text{-}LC) = 4.89\ e{+}6,$$
$$\kappa_1(P) = 9.6\ e{+}6, \qquad (26)$$
$$|q_l^T p_l| = -\ 1.12\ e{-}6\ .$$

Transient shape sensitivity w.r.t. initial estimates (Section 3-1-1)

Using the observer gains of Eq (25), the full-order observer was built to compare the performance for two different sets of initial conditions.

Case 1: All initial conditions are zero except $e_1(0)$.
(because $x_1(0)$ is known (measured))

One of the estimation results is given in Fig. 2 for $\hat{x}_3(t)$, the estimate of the load momentum. It shows extremely large errors in the transient period, even though Euclidean norm of the initial error is small ($\|e(0)\|_2$ = 0.174). This transient error would cause the associated diagnostic system to generate a false alarm.

Case 2: Initial conditions are set based on the directionality analysis. According to the SVD method on the matrix $(A\text{-}LC)$, this observer turns out to be very ill-conditioned ($\kappa_2(A\text{-}LC)$ = 4.89 $e{+}6$). Hence its characteristics in the transient period is very sensitive to the directionality of initial conditions as shown in Eq (7). If the approximate initial values of the state variables can be guessed, the initial condition should be chosen so that the initial error is placed along the direction of v_4 (the fourth column of V_{A2}). For mechanical structures such as the above DC-servo drive, if motor speed is known, other states can be predicted from steady-state analysis. In this example, initial conditions of the observer are chosen roughly as follows: $\hat{x}_1(0)$ can be chosen perfectly to match the first element of v_4 because x_1 is measured. $\hat{x}_2(0)$ and $\hat{x}_3(0)$ can be determined approximately from $x_1(0)$, and $\hat{x}_4(0)$ is assigned to the same value of the fourth element of v_4 because x_4 is usually very small with a stiff shaft. The following is the chosen initial estimate:

$$\begin{bmatrix} \hat{x}_1(0) \\ \hat{x}_2(0) \\ \hat{x}_3(0) \\ \hat{x}_4(0) \end{bmatrix} = \begin{bmatrix} 0.731 \\ 0.022 \\ -0.775 \\ 0.053 \end{bmatrix}.$$

One of the estimation results is given in Fig. 3 for $\hat{x}_3(t)$, the estimate of the load momentum. It shows much better transient shape than Case 1, even though Euclidean norm of the initial error ($\|e(0)\|_2 = 1.067$) is larger than Case 1.

It should be noted that the purpose of this comparison is not to propose a guideline for the selection of initial estimates in the state observer, but instead, to demonstrate how the transient performance of an ill-conditioned state observer can be extremely sensitive to the choice of the initial estimates. In most cases the initial values of unmeasured state variables can not be guessed at all, and the above analysis can not help to choose initial conditions properly. However, this analysis illustrates that such a high sensitivity of the transient shape to the initial condition can be expected from a large value in the performance index, $\kappa_2(\boldsymbol{A}\text{-}\boldsymbol{LC})$. With a small value in the index, consistent shape of the transient error is guaranteed as shown in Eq (7).

Integrated Size of the Overall Transient Error (Section 3-1-2)

From the simulation results of this example, the maximum value, $\max_t \|e(t)\|_1$, and the integrated sum of the $\mathbf{L}_1$ norm of the transient estimation error are found, respectively. The upper bounds for these are also calculated by using Eqs (12) and (13) based on the performance indices in Eq (26). Compared to the actual values of 8.3 *e+2* and 70.7, Eqs (12) and (13) give upper bound values of 1.88 *e+5* and 4.18 *e+4*, respectively. These values are larger than the actual values as would be expected. However, a huge peak in the transient error of Fig. 3 is expected from a large value in the performance index and clearly this will cause a false alarm in monitoring systems.

Eigenvalue Sensitivity (Section 3-2)

Notice that even the 9-digit observer gains in Eq (25) do not give exact pole placement. The round-off error in choosing the observer gain is,

$$\varepsilon \boldsymbol{E} = 3\times10^{-6} \begin{bmatrix} 0.0003 \\ 1 \\ 0.4667 \\ 0.1333 \end{bmatrix} \qquad (27)$$

where $\varepsilon \boldsymbol{E}$ is defined in Section 3-2. The designed observer in Eq (25) show that the above round-off error induces the pole-placement error of 0.3 on the dominant observer pole. The upper bound value for the pole-placement error can be calculated from Eq (15) with the index of Eq (26).

$$|\mu_1 - \mu_1'| \leq 2.98$$

Even though the upper bound with the performance index, $|q_1^T p_1|$ in Eq (26) gives a conservative value, it clearly illustrates that large amplification in the pole-placement error due to a round-off error in observer gain can be expected from a large value in the performance index.

Accuracy Robustness (Section 4)

Steady-state accuracy robustness is considered with respect to three cases; plant perturbation, input and output measurement bias. Performance of the designed observer is simulated for each case to demonstrate the effects of the indices [Eq (23)] on the estimation accuracy.

Case a (Modeling error): Suppose the damping coefficient of the load bearing is reduced to a half of the initial value during operation (which is a very common phenomena). This perturbs only one element of the nominal model of Eq (24), and the size of the perturbation can be represented in terms of the $\mathbf{L}_2$ norm,

$$\|\underline{\boldsymbol{A}} - \boldsymbol{A}\|_2 = 30.$$

Based on the value of the performance index, $\kappa_2(\boldsymbol{A}\text{-}\boldsymbol{LC})$, in Eq (26) and the $\mathbf{L}_2$ norm size of the designed observer,

$$\|\boldsymbol{A}\text{-}\boldsymbol{LC}\|_2 = 6.44\ e{+}3,$$

the upper bound for the accuracy error is calculated from Eq (23) and compared with the actual simulation results in Table 2. For the perturbed plant, one of the estimation results from the observer of Eq (18) is given in Fig. 4 for $\hat{x}_3(t)$, the estimate of the load momentum. This shows that even though Eq (23) gives a conservative upper bound, it demonstrates the role of the condition number in accuracy robustness. As expected for the ill-conditioned ($\kappa_2(\boldsymbol{A}\text{-}\boldsymbol{LC}) >> 1$) observer, accuracy error induced by a small plant perturbation can be extremely large.

Case b (Input sensing error): Suppose the system matrix $\boldsymbol{A}$ is accurate ($\boldsymbol{A} = \underline{\boldsymbol{A}}$), but there is +2% bias error in input measurement. The size of the above sensing error can be represented in terms of the $\mathbf{L}_2$ norm,

$$\|\boldsymbol{B}\delta u\|_2 = 2.$$

Based on the value of the performance index in Eq (26) and the $\mathbf{L}_2$ norm size of the designed observer, the upper bound for the accuracy error is calculated from Eq (23) and compared with the actual simulation results in Table 2. Again, the calculated upper bound is conservative, but a large value in the condition number tells the possibility that large steady-state error can occur due to an input sensing error.

Case c (Output sensing error): Suppose the system matrix $\boldsymbol{A}$ is accurate ($\boldsymbol{A} = \underline{\boldsymbol{A}}$) but there is +2% bias error in output measurement. The size of the above sensing error can be represented in terms of $\mathbf{L}_2$ norm.

$$\|\boldsymbol{L}\delta y\|_2 = 20.4$$

Based on the value of the performance index in Eq (26) and the $\mathbf{L}_2$ norm size of the designed observer, the upper bound for the accuracy error is calculated from Eq (23) and compared with the actual simulation results in Table 2. Again, the calculated upper bound is conservative, but a large value in the condition number tells the possibility that large steady-state error can occur due to an output sensing error. ♦

In summary, the above results (Cases a, b and c) show that the upper bound of Eq (23) provides conservative bounds compared to the simulation results, but clearly demonstrate the effect of the large condition number $\kappa_2(\boldsymbol{A}\text{-}\boldsymbol{LC})$ on the steady-state accuracy error of the state observer.

Table 2: Comparison of the upper bounds and the actual simulated results.

Performance Evaluation	Upper bound	Actual value
Maximum transient error $\max_t \|e(t)\|_1$	$\leq$ 1.88 *e+5* [Eq(11)]	= 8.3 *e+2*
Integrated transient error $\int_0^\infty \|e(t)\|_1 dt$	$\leq$ 4.18 e+4 [Eq(13)]	= 70.7
Pole-placement error due to a round-off error of Eq (27): $\|\mu_1 - \mu_1'\|$	$\leq$ 2.98. [Eq (15)]	= 0.3
Steady-state accuracy error $\left(\frac{\|e_{ss}\|_2}{\|x_{ss}\|_2} \times 100\%\right)$ due to		
Case a: modeling error $\|\Delta A\|_2 = 30$	$\leq$ 2.28 *e+6* % [Eq (23)]	= 2.53 *e+5* %
Case b: input sensing error $\|\boldsymbol{B}\delta u\|_2 = 2$	$\leq$ 3.47 *e+5* % [Eq (23)]	= 1.51 *e+5* %
Case c: output sensing error $\|\boldsymbol{L}\delta y\|_2 = 20.4$	$\leq$ 1.55 *e+6* % [Eq (23)]	= 1.51 *e+5* %

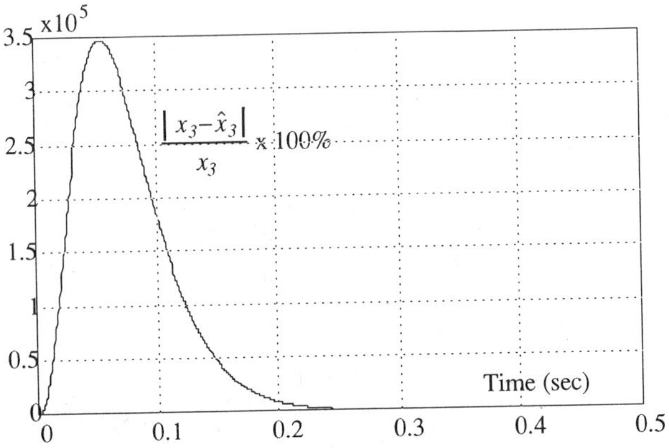

Fig. 2: Estimation error of $\hat{x}_3(t)$ from the conventional observer
Case 1: With zero initial condition
(True $x_3(t)$ at steady-state = 0.1672)

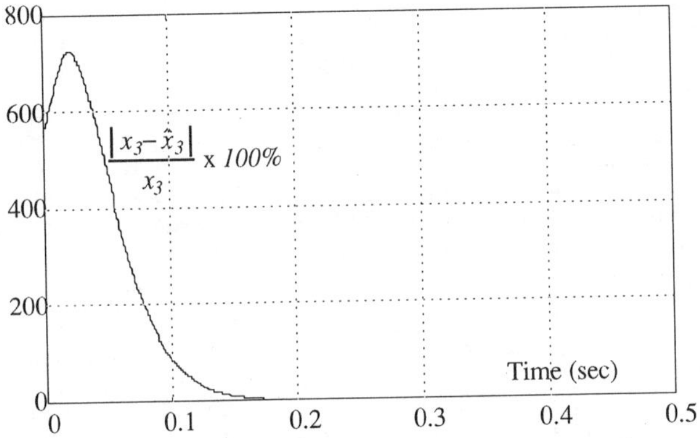

Fig. 3: Estimation error of $\hat{x}_3(t)$ from the conventional observer
Case 2: With the directionality analysis
(True $x_3(t)$ at steady-state = 0.1672)

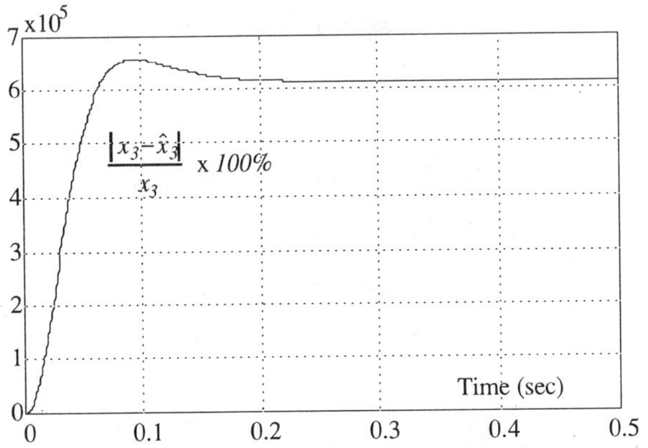

Fig. 4: Estimation error of $\hat{x}_3(t)$ from the conventional observer
Case a: With the plant perturbation ΔA
(True $x_3(t)$ at steady-state = 0.173)

6. A Main Index For The Well-Conditioned Observer

From the standpoint of observer-based monitoring performance, every upper bound or every index given in Table 1 should be minimized. An observer with the minimized indices is a well-conditioned observer in the sense that the effects of the ill-conditioning factors on the observer performance are guaranteed to be small.

In order to quantify the conditioning of the observer in a simpler way and to formulate a design procedure for the well-conditioned observer, a single index that represents all the indices needs to be determined. This is necessary because for a given observable pair $(\boldsymbol{A},\boldsymbol{C})$ and a fixed set of observer eigenvalues, it is not easy to select the observer gain $\boldsymbol{L}$ minimizing all the indices simultaneously. For example, in SISO systems, observer gains are determined uniquely based just on a set of desired observer poles. For MIMO systems, it is still impossible to minimize the indices together by a fixed gain selection of $\boldsymbol{L}$ because the gain values $\boldsymbol{L}$ minimizing each index usually do not coincide with each other. It would appear that the well-conditioned observer design is a trade-off problem between minimizing the indices. However, it turns out that there exists another index that dominates all the performance indices listed in Table 1. That is the condition number of the eigenvector matrix $\boldsymbol{P}$ in terms of the $\mathbf{L_2}$ norm definition. This condition number is given by

$$\kappa_2(\boldsymbol{P}) = \|\boldsymbol{P}\|_2 \, \|\boldsymbol{P}^{-1}\|_2 \qquad (28)$$

Based upon the following inequality relations between the above index and the performance indices of Table 1,

$$\kappa_1(\boldsymbol{P}) \le n \cdot \kappa_2(\boldsymbol{P}) \quad \text{: see Golob and Van Loan [13],}$$
$$|q_1^T p_1| \le \kappa_2(\boldsymbol{P}) \quad \text{: see Stewart [37],} \qquad (29)$$
$$\kappa_2(\boldsymbol{A}-\boldsymbol{LC}) \le \kappa_2(\boldsymbol{P})^2 \frac{|\mu_1|}{|\mu_n|} \quad \text{: see Appendix A,}$$

It can be concluded that the condition number $\kappa_2(\boldsymbol{P})$ of the observer matrix is the first index that should be minimized at the observer design stage and, therefore, it can be proposed as the main index for the overall well-conditioned observer. Once this index is minimized at the observer design stage, the ratio $(|\mu_1|/|\mu_n|)$ should be made small in order to obtain a small value in the performance index $\kappa_2(\boldsymbol{A_2})$. A design methodology to develop the well-conditioned observer by minimizing the main index is reported in a subsequent paper [17].

Remark 3: If one, or only some, of the performance criteria in Table 1 is required for a particular monitoring problem, only the corresponding index needs to be minimized in the observer design. Suppose an observer designer is only interested in the accuracy robustness of steady-state estimation for the monitoring problem. Then $\kappa_2(\boldsymbol{A}\text{-}\boldsymbol{LC})$ (condition number of the observer matrix) is the sole index to be minimized at the observer design stage.

7. Summary and Conclusion

Estimation performance of the ill-conditioned state observer is evaluated quantitatively regarding transient error shape, eigenvalue sensitivity to round-off errors, and accuracy robustness to plant perturbation and measurement bias. It is shown that conditioning of the state observer performance is characterized by three performance indices: (1) the condition number of the observer matrix $(\boldsymbol{A}\text{-}\boldsymbol{LC})$ in terms of $\mathbf{L_2}$ norm, (2) the condition number of the eigensystem $\boldsymbol{P}$ in terms of $\mathbf{L_1}$ norm, and (3) the inner product of right and left eigenvectors corresponding to the dominant observer poles. Then, for the overall observer performance, it is claimed that $\kappa_2(\boldsymbol{P})$ (condition number of the eigensystem $\boldsymbol{P}$ in terms of $\mathbf{L_2}$ norm) is the main index to be minimized for overall well-conditioned observer performance.

If observability ([22]) of a plant model is defined as the existence condition for the state observer, the minimum value in the main index $\kappa_2(\boldsymbol{P})$ can be stated as a quality condition of the state observer based on this study. Moreover, it is proposed that once a particular state observer is designed by some method, the quality of the observer should be checked by the main index before the observer is implemented.

8. References

[1] A.N. Jr. Andry, J.C. Chung and E.Y. Shapiro, "Modalized Observers," IEEE *Transactions on Automatic Control*, Vol. AC-29, No. 7, pp. 669-672, 1984,.

[2] S.P. Battacharyya, "The Structure of Robust Observers," IEEE *Transactions on Automatic Control*, Vol. 21, August, pp. 581-588, 1976.

[3] W.A. Berger, R.J. Perry and H.H. Sun, "Eigenvalue Sensitivity in Multivariable Systems," Proceedings, CH2767-2, pp. 433-436, 1989.
[4] S.P. Burrows and R.J. Patton, "Optimal Eigenstructure Assignment for Multiple Design Objectives," *American Control Conference*, Vol 2, pp. 1678-1683, 1990.
[5] R. Byers and S. Nash, "Approaches to Robust Pole Assignment," *International Journal of Control*, Vol. 49, No. 1, pp. 97-117, 1989.
[6] T.F. Chan and D.E. Foulser, "Effectively Well-Conditioned Linear Systems," SIAM *Journal on Scientific and Statistical Computing*, Vol. 9, No. 6, pp. 963-969, 1988.
[7] J. Changsheng, "New Method of Robust Pole Assignment by Output Feedback," *IEE Proceedings-D*, Vol. 138, No. 2, March, pp. 172-176, 1991.
[8] A. Dickman, "On the Robustness of Multivariable Linear Feedback System in State-Space Representation," IEEE *Transactions on Automatic Control*, Vol. AC-32, No. 5, pp. 407-410, 1987.
[9] T.E. Djaferis, "Robust Observers for Systems with Parameters," *Systems and Control Letters*, Vol. 7, pp. 385-394, 1986.
[10] K. Furuta, S. Hara and S. Mori, "A Class of Systems with the Same Observer," IEEE *Transactions on Automatic Control*, Vol. 21, August, pp. 572-576, 1976.
[11] A.R. Galimidi and B.R. Barmish, "Robustness of Luenberger Observers: Linear Systems Stabilized Via Nonlinear Control," *American Control Conference*, Vol 2, pp. 968-974, 1984.
[12] E.G. Gilbert, "Conditions for Minimizing the Norm Sensitivity of Characteristic Roots," IEEE *Transactions on Automatic Control*, Vol. 29, No. 7, pp. 658-661, 1984.
[13] G.H. Golob and C.F. Van Loan, *Matrix Computations*, 2nd Ed., The Johns Hopkins University Press, Baltimore and London, 1989.
[14] W.M. Haddad and D.S. Bernstein, "Robust, Reduced-Order, Nonstrictly Proper State Estimation Via the Optimal Projection Equations with Guaranteed Cost Bounds," IEEE *Transactions on Automatic Control*, Vol. 33, June, pp. 591-595, 1988.
[15] J. Handscombe, "Diagnostics Through the 80s And into the 90s," *Control Engineering*, Nov., pp. 124-132, 1990.
[16] A. Haraldsdottir, P.T. Kabamba and A.G. Ulsoy, "Sensitivity Reduction by State Derivative Feedback," *Trans. of ASME, Journal of Dynamic System, Measurement and Control*, Vol. 110, Mar., pp. 84-93, 1988.
[17] K. Huh and J.L. Stein, "Well-Conditioned Observer Design for Model-Based Monitoring Systems," *American Control Conference*, 1993.
[18] K. Janssen and P.M. Frank, "Component Failure Detection via State Estimation," IFAC 9th World Congress, Budapest, Hungary, Vol. 1, pp 2213-2218, 1984.
[19] R.E. Kalman and R.S. Bucy, "New results in Linear Filtering and Prediction Theory" *Journal of Basic Engineering*, Transactions of ASME Series D., Vol. 83, No. 3, pp. 95-108, 1961.
[20] J. Kautsky, N.K. Nichols and P. Van Dooren, "Robust Pole Assignment in Linear State Feedback," *International Journal of Control*, Vol. 41, No. 5, pp. 1129-1155, 1985.
[21] L.H. Keel and S.P. Bhattacharyya, "State-Space Design of Low-Order Stabilizers," IEEE *Transactions on Automatic Control*, Vol. AC-35, No. 2, pp. 182-186, 1990.
[22] D.G. Luenberger, "Observers for Multivariable systems," IEEE *Transactions on Automatic Control*, Vol. AC-11, pp. 190-197, 1966.
[23] W.C. Merrill, J.C. DeLaat and W.M. Bruton, "Advanced Detection, Isolation, and Accommodation of Sensor Failures-Real-Time Evaluation," *Journal of Guidance, Control and Dynamics*, Vol. 11, No. 6, pp. 517-526, 1988.
[24] B.C. Moore and G. Klein, "Engenvector Selection in the Linear Regulator Problem: Combining Modal and Optimal Control," *Proceedings of the IEEE Conference on Decision and Control*, pp. 214-215, 1976.
[25] B. Noble and J.W. Daniel, , *Applied Linear Algebra*, 2nd Ed., Prentice-Hall, Inc., Englewood Cliffs, 1977.
[26] Y. Park and J.L. Stein, "Closed Loop Simultaneous Input and State Observer", *International Journal of Control*, Vol. 48, No. 3, pp. 1121-36, 1988.
[27] P.HR. Petkov, N.D. Christov and M.M. Konstantinov, "A Computational Algorithm for Pole Assignment of Linear Multiinput Systems," IEEE *Transactions on Automatic Control*, Vol. AC-31, No. 11, pp. 1044-1047, 1986.
[28] J.D. Powell, "Mass Center Estimation in Spinning Drag-Free Satellites," *Journal of Spacecraft*, Vol. 9, No, 6, pp. 399-405, 1972.
[29] W.B. Ribbens and R.N. Riggins Jr., "Detection and Isolation of Plant Failures in Dynamic Systems," *American Control Conference*, pp. 1514-1521, 1991.
[30] B. Shafai and R.L. Carroll, "Design of Proportional-Integral Observer for Linear Time-Varying Multivariable Systems," Proceedings of 24th Conference of *Decision and Control*, Ft. Lauderdale, FL., Dec., pp. 597-599, 1985.
[31] R.E. Skelton and D.A. Wagie, "Minimal Root Sensitivity in Linear Systems," *Journal of Guidance*, Vol. 7, No. 5, pp. 570-574, 1984.
[32] K.M. Sobel, S.S. Banda and E.Y. Shapiro, "Robust Modalized Observer with Flight Control Application," Proceedings for the 27th Conference on *Decision and Control*, Austin, Texas, pp. 1018-1019, 1988.
[33] S.K. Spurgeon, "Pole Placement Extensions for Multivariable Systems - A Survey," *American Control Conference*, Vol. 2, pp. 1660-1665, 1990.
[34] R.T. Stefani, "Observer Steady-State Errors Induced by Errors in Realization," IEEE *Transactions on Automatic Control*, Vol. AC-21, April, pp. 280-282, 1976.
[35] R.T. Stefani, "Reducing the Sensitivity to Parameter Variations of a Minimum-order Reduced-order Observer," *International Journal of Control*, Vol. 35, No. 6 pp. 983-995, 1982.
[36] J.L. Stein and Y. Park, "Measurement Signal Selection and a Simultaneous State and Input Observer," *Journal of Dynamic Systems Measurement and Control* , Vol. 110, No. 2, pp. 151-159, June, 1988.
[37] G.W. Stewart, *Introduction to Matrix Computations*, Academic Press, New York and London, 1973.
[38] A. van der Sluis, "Stability of Solutions of Linear Algebraic Systems," *Numerische Mathematik*, Vol. 14, pp. 246-251, 1970.
[39] H. Waller and R. Schmidt, "The Application of State Observers in Structural Dynamics," *Mechanical Systems and Signal Processing*, Vol. 4, No. 3, pp. 195-213, 1990.
[40] J.H. Wilkinson, *The Algebraic Eigenvalue Problem*, Clarendon Press, Oxford, 1965.

Appendix-A (Relation between bounds of $\kappa_2(\boldsymbol{P})$ and $\kappa_2(\boldsymbol{A_2})$)

Using eigensystem representation [Eq (9)] of the observer matrix,

$$\begin{aligned}\kappa_2(A_2) &= \left\|A_2\right\|_2 \cdot \left\|A_2^{-1}\right\|_2 \\ &= \left\|PM_oP^{-1}\right\|_2 \left\|PM_o^{-1}P^{-1}\right\|_2 \\ &\leq \left\|P\right\|_2 \left\|M_o\right\|_2 \left\|P^{-1}\right\|_2 \left\|P\right\|_2 \left\|M_o^{-1}\right\|_2 \left\|P^{-1}\right\|_2 \\ &= \kappa_2(P)^2 \frac{|\mu_1|}{|\mu_n|}.\end{aligned}$$

Q.E.D.

Proceedings of the
American Control Conference
San Francisco, California • June 1993

High Order Filters for Estimation in Non-Gaussian Noise

Stelios C. A. Thomopoulos

Decision and Control Systems Laboratory
Dept. of Electrical and Computer Engineering
The Pennsylvania State University
University Park, PA 16802

Thomas W. Hilands

Applied Research Laboratory
The Pennsylvania State University
University Park, PA 16802

Abstract. In this paper high order vector filter equations are developed for estimation in non-Gaussian noise. The difference between the filters developed here and the standard Kalman filter is that the filter equation contains nonlinear functions of the innovations process. These filters are general in that the initial state covariance, the measurement noise covariance, and the process noise covariance can all have non-Gaussian distributions. Two filter structures are developed. The first filter is designed for systems with asymmetric probability densities. The second is designed for systems with symmetric probability densities. Experimental evaluation of these filters for estimation in non-Gaussian noise, formed from Gaussian sum distributions, shows that these filters perform much better than the standard Kalman filter, and close to the optimal Bayesian estimator.

1 Introduction

The new filters are referred to as high order filters (HOFs). For both of these filters it is assumed that the 5th and higher order moments of all densities are negligible. As such, these filters are approximations of the optimal minimum variance solution. However, it is shown through simulation experiments that these filters can approach the performance of the optimal minimum variance filter under certain conditions. The performance of the HOFs is compared to the standard Kalman filter, which uses only first and second moments, and to the optimal Bayesian estimator. The Gaussian sum distributions, † for which the optimal Bayesian estimator has been derived by Sorenson and Alspach [1], were used as the test-bed for comparison. The optimal Bayesian estimator of [1] requires the accurate knowledge of the *a priori* densities so that an approximation can be made using Gaussian sums. On the other hand, the HOFs require knowledge of only a finite number of moments of these densities. All techniques previously developed for non-Gaussian filtering are computationally intensive. The HOFs developed here share that characteristic. However, they are much less computationally intensive than the Gaussian sum filter.

† Gaussian sum distributions are non-Gaussian distributions that are expressed as a normalized weighted average of different Gaussian distributions (Gaussian mixture).

2 System Model

Consider the problem of estimating the n-dimensional vector $\mathbf{x}_k$ from K measurements of the m-dimensional vector $\mathbf{z}_k$. The linear plant and measurement equations have the form

$$\begin{aligned} \mathbf{x}_k &= \Phi_{k-1}\mathbf{x}_{k-1} + \mathbf{w}_{k-1} \\ \mathbf{z}_k &= H_k\mathbf{x}_k + \mathbf{v}_k \end{aligned} \tag{1}$$

where $\mathbf{w}_{k-1}$, $\mathbf{v}_k$ are mutually independent, white, zero-mean, possibly non-Gaussian random sequences. The uncertainty in the initial estimate $\hat{\mathbf{x}}_0$ may also have a non-Gaussian distribution and is independent from $\mathbf{w}_{k-1}$ and $\mathbf{v}_k$. It is also assumed that the 2nd through 4th moments of the distributions of $\hat{\mathbf{x}}_0$, $\mathbf{w}_{k-1}$ and $\mathbf{v}_k$ are known.

The Kronecker product operator $\otimes$ [2] is implemented in order to use 2-dimension matrix operations throughout this derivation.

In the development to follow the column stack operator is also used. If an $n \times n$ matrix A consists of columns $\mathbf{a}_1, \mathbf{a}_2, \cdots, \mathbf{a}_n$ then the column stack of A is defined by

$$\text{cst}(A) \equiv [\mathbf{a}_1^T \mathbf{a}_2^T \cdots \mathbf{a}_n^T]^T \tag{2}$$

$\text{cst}(A)$ is dimensioned $nn \times 1$. If the matrix $A = E[\mathbf{x}\mathbf{x}^T]$ then $\text{cst}(A) = E[\mathbf{x} \otimes \mathbf{x}]$, where $E[.]$ is the expectation operator.

The $2^{nd}, 3^{rd}$, and 4th moments of the random vector $\mathbf{w}_k$ are given as $E[\mathbf{w}_k \otimes \mathbf{w}_j^T] = Q_k^{(2)}\delta_{kj}$, $E[\mathbf{w}_k \otimes \mathbf{w}_j^T \otimes \mathbf{w}_l] = Q_k^{(3)}\delta_{kjl}$, and $E[\mathbf{w}_k \otimes \mathbf{w}_j^T \otimes \mathbf{w}_l \otimes \mathbf{w}_m^T] = Q_k^{(4)}\delta_{kjlm}$. Similarly, the $2^{nd}, 3^{rd}$, and 4th moments of the random vector $\mathbf{v}_k$ are given by $R_k^{(2)}\delta_{kj}$, $R_k^{(3)}\delta_{kjl}$, and $R_k^{(4)}\delta_{kjlm}$. The moments of the initial estimation error are given by $P_0^{(2)}$, $P_0^{(3)}$, and $P_0^{(4)}$.

Let the prediction error $\tilde{\mathbf{x}}_{k|k-1}$ and the filtered error $\tilde{\mathbf{x}}_{k|k}$ be defined as

$$\begin{aligned} \tilde{\mathbf{x}}_{k|k-1} &= \mathbf{x}_k - \hat{\mathbf{x}}_{k|k-1} \\ \tilde{\mathbf{x}}_{k|k} &= \mathbf{x}_k - \hat{\mathbf{x}}_{k|k} \end{aligned} \tag{3}$$

where the hat indicates expected value. The innovations vector is given by

$$\begin{aligned}\tilde{\mathbf{z}}_k &= \mathbf{z}_k - H_k \hat{\mathbf{x}}_{k|k-1} \\ &= H_k \tilde{\mathbf{x}}_{k|k-1} + \mathbf{v}_k\end{aligned} \tag{4}$$

It can be shown [3] that $E[(\mathbf{x}_k - \hat{\mathbf{x}}_{k|k-1})|\mathbf{z}_k]$ is a function of only $\tilde{\mathbf{z}}_k$ so that

$$E[(\mathbf{x}_k - \hat{\mathbf{x}}_{k|k-1})|\mathbf{z}_k] = \sum_{i=0}^{\infty} K_k^{(i)} \tilde{\mathbf{z}}_k^{\otimes i}$$

where the superscript $\otimes i$ denotes the ith kronecker product of the vector $\tilde{\mathbf{z}}_k$. $K_k^{(i)}$ denotes the ith order filter gain, which has dimension $n \times m^i$. It follows that

$$\hat{\mathbf{x}}_{k|k} = \hat{\mathbf{x}}_{k|k-1} + \sum_{i=1}^{\infty} K_k^{(i)} \tilde{\mathbf{z}}_k^{\otimes i}$$

Using (3) the expression for the filter error becomes

$$\tilde{\mathbf{x}}_{k|k} = \tilde{\mathbf{x}}_{k|k-1} - \sum_{i=1}^{\infty} K_k^{(i)} \tilde{\mathbf{z}}_k^{\otimes i}. \tag{5}$$

By setting $K_k^{(i)} = 0$, for $i > 1$, the standard linear Kalman filter results. In order to bound the equations for the derivation of the high order filters it is assumed that $\tilde{\mathbf{z}}_k^{\otimes i}$ is negligible for $i > I$. The truncated relation now becomes

$$\tilde{\mathbf{x}}_{k|k} = \tilde{\mathbf{x}}_{k|k-1} - \sum_{i=0}^{I} K_k^{(i)} \tilde{\mathbf{z}}_k^{\otimes i}. \tag{6}$$

Equation (6) forms the basis for the development of the HOFs.

3 Non-Gaussian Filtering for Asymmetrical Distributions

The non-Gaussian filter for asymmetrical distributions is derived by letting $I = 2$ in (6) and obtain the filter error

$$\tilde{\mathbf{x}}_{k|k} = \tilde{\mathbf{x}}_{k|k-1} - K_k^{(0)} - K_k^{(1)} \tilde{\mathbf{z}}_k - K_k^{(2)} \tilde{\mathbf{z}}_k^{\otimes 2} \tag{7}$$

It is required that $E[\tilde{\mathbf{x}}_{k|k-1}] = E[\mathbf{v}_k] = 0$, since the estimator must be unbiased, and using (4) in (7)

$$E[\tilde{\mathbf{x}}_{k|k-1}] = 0 = -K_k^{(0)} - K_k^{(2)} E[\tilde{\mathbf{z}}_k^{\otimes 2}] \tag{8}$$

where $E[\tilde{\mathbf{z}}_k^{\otimes 2}] = \text{cst}(H_k P_{k|k-1}^{(2)} H_k^T + R_k^{(2)})$. Substituting (8) into (7) yields

$$\tilde{\mathbf{x}}_{k|k} = \tilde{\mathbf{x}}_{k|k-1} - K_k^{(1)} \tilde{\mathbf{z}}_k - K_k^{(2)} \tilde{\zeta}_k \tag{9}$$

where $\tilde{\zeta}_k$ is defined for notational convenience as

$$\begin{aligned}\tilde{\zeta}_k &= (\tilde{\mathbf{z}}_k^{\otimes 2} - E[\tilde{\mathbf{z}}_k^{\otimes 2}]) \\ &= ((\tilde{\mathbf{z}}_k \otimes \tilde{\mathbf{z}}_k) - \text{cst}(H_k P_{k|k-1}^{(2)} H_k^T + R_k^{(2)}))\end{aligned} \tag{10}$$

with $E[\tilde{\zeta}_k] = 0$. The corresponding filter equation is

$$\hat{\mathbf{x}}_{k|k} = \hat{\mathbf{x}}_{k|k-1} + K_k^{(1)} \tilde{\mathbf{z}}_k + K_k^{(2)} \tilde{\zeta}_k \tag{11}$$

The formulas for the gains $K_k^{(1)}$ and $K_k^{(2)}$ result from the requirement for a minimum variance solution. Using (9) the equation for the variance of the *a posteriori* density becomes

$$\begin{aligned}P_{k|k}^{(2)} &= E[\tilde{\mathbf{x}}_{k|k} \tilde{\mathbf{x}}_{k|k}^T] \\ &= E[\tilde{\mathbf{x}}_{k|k-1} \tilde{\mathbf{x}}_{k|k-1}^T] - E[\tilde{\mathbf{x}}_{k|k-1} \tilde{\mathbf{z}}_k^T] K_k^{(1)\,T} \\ &\quad - E[\tilde{\mathbf{x}}_{k|k-1} \tilde{\zeta}_k^T] K_k^{(2)\,T} - K_k^{(1)} E[\tilde{\mathbf{z}}_k \tilde{\mathbf{x}}_{k|k-1}^T] \\ &\quad + K_k^{(1)} E[\tilde{\mathbf{z}}_k \tilde{\mathbf{z}}_k^T] K_k^{(1)\,T} + K_k^{(1)} E[\tilde{\mathbf{z}}_k \tilde{\zeta}_k^T] K_k^{(2)\,T} \\ &\quad - K_k^{(2)} E[\tilde{\zeta}_k \tilde{\mathbf{x}}_{k|k-1}^T] + K_k^{(2)} E[\tilde{\zeta}_k \tilde{\mathbf{z}}_k^T] K_k^{(1)\,T} \\ &\quad + K_k^{(2)} E[\tilde{\zeta}_k \tilde{\zeta}_k^T] K_k^{(2)\,T}.\end{aligned} \tag{12}$$

The gains are then determined from the matrix minimum principal [4] by evaluating

$$\frac{\partial \text{trace}\,\{P_{k|k}^{(2)}\}}{\partial K_k^{(1)}} = 0, \qquad \frac{\partial \text{trace}\,\{P_{k|k}^{(2)}\}}{\partial K_k^{(2)}} = 0. \tag{13}$$

Carrying out these operations on (12) yields

$$\begin{aligned}K_k^{(1)} &= (E[\tilde{\mathbf{x}}_{k|k-1} \tilde{\mathbf{z}}_k^T] - K_k^{(2)} E[\tilde{\zeta}_k \tilde{\mathbf{z}}_k^T]) E[\tilde{\mathbf{z}}_k \tilde{\mathbf{z}}_k^T]^{-1} \\ K_k^{(2)} &= (E[\tilde{\mathbf{x}}_{k|k-1} \tilde{\zeta}_k^T] - K_k^{(1)} E[\tilde{\mathbf{z}}_k \tilde{\zeta}_k^T]) E[\tilde{\zeta}_k \tilde{\zeta}_k^T]^{-1}.\end{aligned} \tag{14}$$

It is observed that $E[\tilde{\zeta}_k \tilde{\zeta}_k^T]$ is singular. This is a consequence of the fact that $\tilde{\zeta}_k$ contains repeated terms. For example, if the dimensionality M of the innovations vector $\tilde{\zeta}_k$ is 2, then the term $(\tilde{z}_k(1)\tilde{z}_k(2) - E[\tilde{z}_k(1)\tilde{z}_k(2)])$, where $\tilde{z}_k(j)$ is the jth of $\tilde{\mathbf{z}}_k$, appears twice in $\tilde{\zeta}_k$. The number of repeated terms is a function of the dimensionality M of the innovations vector. To avoid this singularity, define the collapsed vector $\tilde{\zeta}_{k_c}$ such that

$$\tilde{\zeta}_{k_c} \equiv T_M \tilde{\zeta}_k \tag{15}$$

where T_M is a matrix of 1's and 0's designed to eliminate redundant columns or rows from $\tilde{\zeta}_k$. For example if $M = 2$

$$T_M = \begin{bmatrix} 1 & 0 & 0 & 0 \\ 0 & 1 & 0 & 0 \\ 0 & 0 & 0 & 1 \end{bmatrix} \quad \text{or} \quad \begin{bmatrix} 1 & 0 & 0 & 0 \\ 0 & 0 & 1 & 0 \\ 0 & 0 & 0 & 1 \end{bmatrix} \tag{16}$$

Since $\tilde{\zeta}_{k_c}$ does not contain repeated terms, $[\tilde{\zeta}_{k_c} \tilde{\zeta}_{k_c}^T]$ is non-singular. Let $K_{k_c}^{(2)}$ denote the collapsed gain associated with replacing $\tilde{\zeta}_k$ with $\tilde{\zeta}_{k_c}$ in (14). Solving for $K_k^{(1)}$ and $K_{k_c}^{(2)}$ yields

$$\begin{aligned}K_k^{(1)} &= (E[\tilde{\mathbf{x}}_{k|k-1} \tilde{\mathbf{z}}_k^T] \\ &\quad - E[\tilde{\mathbf{x}}_{k|k-1} \tilde{\zeta}_{k_c}^T]\, E[\tilde{\zeta}_{k_c} \tilde{\zeta}_{k_c}^T]^{-1}\, E[\tilde{\zeta}_{k_c} \tilde{\mathbf{z}}_k^T]) \\ &\quad \times (E[\tilde{\mathbf{z}}_k \tilde{\mathbf{z}}_k^T] - E[\tilde{\mathbf{z}}_k \tilde{\zeta}_{k_c}^T]\, E[\tilde{\zeta}_{k_c} \tilde{\zeta}_{k_c}^T]^{-1}\, E[\tilde{\zeta}_{k_c} \tilde{\mathbf{z}}_k^T])^{-1} \\ K_{k_c}^{(2)} &= (E[\tilde{\mathbf{x}}_{k|k-1} \tilde{\zeta}_{k_c}^T] \\ &\quad - E[\tilde{\mathbf{x}}_{k|k-1} \tilde{\mathbf{z}}_k^T]\, E[\tilde{\mathbf{z}}_k \tilde{\mathbf{z}}_k^T]^{-1}\, E[\tilde{\mathbf{z}}_k \tilde{\zeta}_{k_c}^T]) \\ &\quad \times (E[\tilde{\zeta}_{k_c} \tilde{\zeta}_{k_c}^T] - E[\tilde{\zeta}_{k_c} \tilde{\mathbf{z}}_k^T] E[\tilde{\mathbf{z}}_k \tilde{\mathbf{z}}_k^T]^{-1}\, E[\tilde{\mathbf{z}}_k \tilde{\zeta}_{k_c}^T])^{-1}.\end{aligned} \tag{17}$$

Equation (11) requires that

$$K_k^{(2)} \tilde{\zeta}_k = K_{k_c}^{(2)} \tilde{\zeta}_{k_c} \tag{18}$$

Using (15) in (18), $K_k^{(2)}$ is then obtained from

$$K_k^{(2)} = K_{k_c}^{(2)} T_M \tag{19}$$

It can easily be shown that if all 3rd moments are zero then $K_k^{(2)} = 0$ and $K_k^{(1)}$ reduces to the gain for the standard Kalman filter.

Using the state model (1) the prediction equation becomes

$$\hat{\mathbf{x}}_{k|k-1} = \Phi_{k-1}\hat{\mathbf{x}}_{k-1|k-1}. \tag{20}$$

The corresponding prediction error from (3) is given by

$$\tilde{\mathbf{x}}_{k|k-1} = \Phi_{k-1}\tilde{\mathbf{x}}_{k-1|k-1} + \mathbf{w}_{k-1}. \tag{21}$$

The prediction moments are then be evaluated as

$$\begin{aligned} P_{k|k-1}^{(2)} &= E[\tilde{\mathbf{x}}_{k|k-1}\tilde{\mathbf{x}}_{k|k-1}^T] \\ P_{k|k-1}^{(3)} &= E[(\tilde{\mathbf{x}}_{k|k-1}^{\otimes 2})\tilde{\mathbf{x}}_{k|k-1}^T] \\ P_{k|k-1}^{(4)} &= E[(\tilde{\mathbf{x}}_{k|k-1}^{\otimes 2})(\tilde{\mathbf{x}}_{k|k-1}^{\otimes 2})^T] \end{aligned} \tag{22}$$

These expressions are expanded in [5]. Similarly, the moments of the filter error can be evaluated using equation (9). The filter moments become

$$\begin{aligned} P_{k|k}^{(2)} &= E[\tilde{\mathbf{x}}_{k|k}\tilde{\mathbf{x}}_{k|k}^T] \\ P_{k|k}^{(3)} &= E[(\tilde{\mathbf{x}}_{k|k}^{\otimes 2})\tilde{\mathbf{x}}_{k|k}^T] \\ P_{k|k}^{(4)} &= E[(\tilde{\mathbf{x}}_{k|k}^{\otimes 2})(\tilde{\mathbf{x}}_{k|k}^{\otimes 2})^T] \end{aligned} \tag{23}$$

It is observed that the equation for the nth filter error moment requires the availability of prediction and measurement error moments of order $2n$. This is a consequence of the fact that the filter error given by (9) is a second order function of the innovations. Since only the prediction order moments up to 4th order are propagated, the equations for the 3rd and 4th order filter moments are truncated so that they contain only 3rd and 4th order functions of the prediction and measurement error moments. An alternative would be to completely expand the 3rd and 4th order filter moments in terms of all $2n$ prediction and measurement error moments and approximate the higher moments using suitable functions of the 2nd through 4th moments.

4 Non-Gaussian Filtering for Symmetrical Distributions

The derivation for the non-Gaussian filter for symmetrical distributions follows the same general procedure as in the previous section. If the errors are assumed to have only even moments, then it can be shown that $K_k^{(i)} = 0$ for $i = 0, 2, 4, \cdots$ [5]. The truncated non-Gaussian filter for symmetrical distributions is obtained by letting $I = 3$ in equation (6) and obtain the filter error

$$\tilde{\mathbf{x}}_{k|k} = \tilde{\mathbf{x}}_{k|k-1} - K_k^{(1)}\tilde{\mathbf{z}}_k - K_k^{(3)}(\tilde{\mathbf{z}}_k^{\otimes 3}). \tag{24}$$

with corresponding filter equation

$$\hat{\mathbf{x}}_{k|k} = \hat{\mathbf{x}}_{k|k-1} + K_k^{(1)}\tilde{\mathbf{z}}_k + K_k^{(3)}\,\tilde{\mathbf{z}}_k^{\otimes 3}. \tag{25}$$

The estimator is required to be unbiased. By definition all odd moments of the innovations are zero. Since $E[\tilde{\mathbf{x}}_{k|k-1}] = 0$, the expected value of the estimation error given in (24) is zero. For notational convenience let

$$\tilde{\alpha}_k = \tilde{\mathbf{z}}_k^{\otimes 3} \tag{26}$$

with $E[\tilde{\alpha}_k] = 0$.

The formulas for the gains $K_k^{(1)}$ and $K_k^{(3)}$ result from the requirement for a minimum variance solution. The variance of the a *posteriori* density function is given by

$$\begin{aligned} P_{k|k}^{(2)} &= E[\tilde{\mathbf{x}}_{k|k}\tilde{\mathbf{x}}_{k|k}^T] \\ &= E[\tilde{\mathbf{x}}_{k|k-1}\tilde{\mathbf{x}}_{k|k-1}^T] - E[\tilde{\mathbf{x}}_{k|k-1}\tilde{\mathbf{z}}_k^T]K_k^{(1)\,T} \\ &\quad - E[\tilde{\mathbf{x}}_{k|k-1}\tilde{\alpha}_k^T]K_k^{(3)\,T} - K_k^{(1)}E[\tilde{\mathbf{z}}_k\tilde{\mathbf{x}}_{k|k-1}^T] \\ &\quad + K_k^{(1)}E[\tilde{\mathbf{z}}_k\tilde{\mathbf{z}}_k^T]K_k^{(1)\,T} + K_k^{(1)}E[\tilde{\mathbf{z}}_k\tilde{\alpha}_k^T]K_k^{(3)\,T} \\ &\quad - K_k^{(3)}E[\tilde{\alpha}_k\tilde{\mathbf{x}}_{k|k-1}^T] + K_k^{(3)}E[\tilde{\alpha}_k\tilde{\mathbf{z}}_k^T]K_k^{(1)\,T} \\ &\quad + K_k^{(3)}E[\tilde{\alpha}_k\tilde{\alpha}_k^T]K_k^{(3)\,T}. \end{aligned} \tag{27}$$

From the matrix minimum principal [4]

$$\frac{\partial \text{trace}\,\{P_{k|k}^{(2)}\}}{\partial K_k^{(1)}} = 0, \quad \frac{\partial \text{trace}\,\{P_{k|k}^{(2)}\}}{\partial K_k^{(3)}} = 0. \tag{28}$$

Carrying out these operations on (27)

$$\begin{aligned} K_k^{(1)} &= (E[\tilde{\mathbf{x}}_{k|k-1}\tilde{\mathbf{z}}_k^T] - K_k^{(3)}E[\tilde{\alpha}_k\tilde{\mathbf{z}}_k^T]) \times E[\tilde{\mathbf{z}}_k\tilde{\mathbf{z}}_k^T]^{-1} \\ K_k^{(3)} &= (E[\tilde{\mathbf{x}}_{k|k-1}\tilde{\alpha}_k^T] - K_k^{(1)}E[\tilde{\mathbf{z}}_k\tilde{\alpha}_k^T]) \times E[\tilde{\alpha}_k\tilde{\alpha}_k^T]^{-1}. \end{aligned} \tag{29}$$

Similar to the $E[\zeta_k\zeta_k^T]$ for the asymmetric filter, it is observed that $E[\tilde{\alpha}_k\tilde{\alpha}_k^T]$ is singular. A collapsed vector $\tilde{\alpha}_{k_c}$ is defined such that

$$\tilde{\alpha}_{k_c} \equiv U_M\tilde{\alpha}_k \tag{30}$$

where U_M is a matrix of 1's and 0's designed to extract only one of each term from $\tilde{\alpha}_k$. Since $\tilde{\alpha}_{k_c}$ does not contain repeated terms, $[\tilde{\alpha}_{k_c}\tilde{\alpha}_{k_c}^T]$ is nonsingular. Let $K_{k_c}^{(3)}$ denote the collapsed gain associated with replacing $\tilde{\alpha}_k$ with $\tilde{\alpha}_{k_c}$ in (29). Solving (28) for $K_k^{(1)}$ and $K_{k_c}^{(3)}$ yields

$$\begin{aligned} K_k^{(1)} &= (E[\tilde{\mathbf{x}}_{k|k-1}\tilde{\mathbf{z}}_k^T] \\ &\quad - E[\tilde{\mathbf{x}}_{k|k-1}\tilde{\alpha}_{k_c}^T]\,E[\tilde{\alpha}_{k_c}\tilde{\alpha}_{k_c}^T]^{-1}\,E[\tilde{\alpha}_{k_c}\tilde{\mathbf{z}}_k^T]) \\ &\quad \times (E[\tilde{\mathbf{z}}_k\tilde{\mathbf{z}}_k^T] - E[\tilde{\mathbf{z}}_k\tilde{\alpha}_{k_c}^T]\,E[\tilde{\alpha}_{k_c}\tilde{\alpha}_{k_c}^T]^{-1}\,E[\tilde{\alpha}_{k_c}\tilde{\mathbf{z}}_k^T])^{-1} \\ K_{k_c}^{(3)} &= (E[\tilde{\mathbf{x}}_{k|k-1}\tilde{\alpha}_{k_c}^T] \\ &\quad - E[\tilde{\mathbf{x}}_{k|k-1}\tilde{\mathbf{z}}_k^T]\,E[\tilde{\mathbf{z}}_k\tilde{\mathbf{z}}_k^T]^{-1}\,E[\tilde{\mathbf{z}}_k\tilde{\alpha}_{k_c}^T]) \\ &\quad \times (E[\tilde{\alpha}_{k_c}\tilde{\alpha}_{k_c}^T] - E[\tilde{\alpha}_{k_c}\tilde{\mathbf{z}}_k^T]E[\tilde{\mathbf{z}}_k\tilde{\mathbf{z}}_k^T]^{-1}\,E[\tilde{\mathbf{z}}_k\tilde{\alpha}_{k_c}^T])^{-1}. \end{aligned} \tag{31}$$

Equation (25) requires that

$$K_k^{(3)}\tilde{\alpha}_k = K_{k_c}^{(3)}\tilde{\alpha}_{k_c} \tag{32}$$

Using (30) in (32), $K_k^{(3)}$ is then obtained from

$$K_k^{(3)} = K_{k_c}^{(3)}\,U_M. \tag{33}$$

The 2nd and 4th prediction moments are generated from the prediction errors. These moments are expressed as

$$\begin{aligned} P_{k|k-1}^{(2)} &= E[\tilde{\mathbf{x}}_{k|k-1}\tilde{\mathbf{x}}_{k|k-1}^T] \\ P_{k|k-1}^{(4)} &= E[(\tilde{\mathbf{x}}_{k|k-1}^{\otimes 2})(\tilde{\mathbf{x}}_{k|k-1}^{\otimes 2})^T] \end{aligned} \tag{34}$$

Similarly, using equation (24) the moments of the filter error can be evaluated. The 2nd, and 4th moments of the filter error are obtained from

$$P^{(2)}_{k|k} = E[\tilde{\mathbf{x}}_{k|k}\tilde{\mathbf{x}}^T_{k|k}]$$
$$P^{(4)}_{k|k} = E[(\tilde{\mathbf{x}}^{\otimes 2}_{k|k})(\tilde{\mathbf{x}}^{\otimes 2}_{k|k})^T] \quad (35)$$

Equation (24) dictates that the filter variance should include 6th order functions of the prediction and measurement error moments. These higher order terms are not included in the filter variance expression, just as all 5th and higher order terms are disregarded in the development of the asymmetrical filter. By doing so it is implicitly assumed that the contributions from these higher order terms are negligible. As noted previously, if these terms were included in the derivation of the filter moments it would necessitate some approximation procedure for these high order prediction and measurement moments, since only 2nd and 4th order prediction moments are propagated. Similarly the 4th order filter moment requires the availability of 6th, 8th, 10th, and 12th order prediction and measurement error moments. Again the 4th order expansion is truncated to include only 4th order functions of the prediction and measurement errors.

5 Experimental Evaluation of the Non-Gaussian Filters

A scalar model is used to evaluate the performance of the filters. The plant and measurement equations for this model have the form

$$x_k = 0.5x_{k-1} + w_{k-1}$$
$$z_k = x_k + v_k \quad (36)$$

where w_k and v_k are mutually independent, zero mean possibly non-Gaussian random processes, and the initial estimation error for x_0 may also be non-Gaussian. The non-Gaussian distributions are modeled as the sum of two Gaussian distributions with unit variance. In general the non-Gaussian distribution for a random variable y is given by

$$p(y) = \sum_{i=1}^{I} \epsilon_i N(\mu_i, 1) \quad (37)$$

where $\sum_{i=1}^{I} \epsilon_i = 1$. For the special case of two distributions ($I = 2$) the parameter D is defined as the separation between the means of the distributions. In this case for $p(y)$ to have zero mean $\mu_1 = -\epsilon_2 * D$, and $\mu_2 = \epsilon_1 * D$. If $\epsilon_1 = \epsilon_2$, $p(y)$ is symmetric. If $D = 0$, $p(y)$ is Gaussian.

5.1 Asymmetrical Filter Results

An asymmetrical distribution with $\epsilon_1 = 0.2$, $\epsilon_2 = 0.8$, and $I = 2$ in equation (37). The system represented by equations (36) is used to evaluate the different filters for various combinations of non-Gaussian process noise v_k, measurement noise w_k, and initial estimation error $\tilde{x}_0$. The three noise models are given in Table 1 below.

Table 1. Noise Models for Non-Gaussian Filter Evaluation

Model	v_k	w_k	$\tilde{x}_0$
1	$\sum^I \epsilon_i N(\mu_i, 1)$	$N(0,1)$	$N(\hat{x}_0, 1)$
2	$N(0,1)$	$\sum^I \epsilon_i N(\mu_i, 1)$	$N(\hat{x}_0, 1)$
3	$N(0,1)$	$N(0,1)$	$\sum^I \epsilon_i N(\mu_i + \hat{x}_0, 1)$

A Monte-Carlo analysis was performed to determine the sample variance of the estimation error. The separation between the distributions for the non-Gaussian noise for these experiments was $D = 10$. The number of samples for each simulation run was $K = 10$. The estimation error and filter error variance resulting from one run are shown in Figure 1. Fifty separate simulation runs of the system were made for each model. The estimation error was accumulated over the last five samples of each run resulting in a total of 250 samples of the estimation error. The sample variances of the filter error $\hat{P}^{(2)}_{k|k}$ and the prediction error $\hat{P}^{(2)}_{k|k-1}$ are presented in Table 2 for every estimator for each model.

Table 2. Sample Variances for the Asymmetrical Filter - $D = 10$

Filter Type	Model 1		Model 2		Model 3	
	$\hat{P}^{(2)}_{k\|k}$	$\hat{P}^{(2)}_{k\|k-1}$	$\hat{P}^{(2)}_{k\|k}$	$\hat{P}^{(2)}_{k\|k-1}$	$\hat{P}^{(2)}_{k\|k}$	$\hat{P}^{(2)}_{k\|k-1}$
Kalman	1.25	1.35	0.983	18.4	0.575	1.20
HOF	0.952	1.29	0.828	18.5	0.575	1.20
Gaus Sum	0.575	1.20	0.575	18.5	0.575	1.20

The Monte Carlo results show that in relation to the Kalman filter the HOF performs very well in asymmetrical non-Gaussian noise.

5.2 Symmetrical Filter Results

A symmetrical non-Gaussian distribution is created with parameter values $\epsilon_1 = 0.5$, $\epsilon_2 = 0.5$, and $I = 2$ in equation (37). The system represented by equation (36) was evaluated for various combinations of non-Gaussian process noise v_k, measurement noise w_k, and initial estimation error $\tilde{x}_0$ as expressed in Table 1.

The Monte Carlo results for 250 samples are given in Table 3. This table shows that the symmetrical HOF performs better than the standard Kalman filter, but not quite as good as the optimal Gaussian sum filter.

Table 3. Sample Variances for the Symmetrical Filter - $D = 10$

Filter Type	Model 1		Model 2		Model 3	
	$\hat{P}^{(2)}_{k\|k}$	$\hat{P}^{(2)}_{k\|k-1}$	$\hat{P}^{(2)}_{k\|k}$	$\hat{P}^{(2)}_{k\|k-1}$	$\hat{P}^{(2)}_{k\|k}$	$\hat{P}^{(2)}_{k\|k-1}$
Kalman	1.33	1.35	0.947	25.7	0.575	1.20
HOF	1.22	1.32	0.908	25.7	0.575	1.20
Gaus Sum	0.575	1.20	0.575	25.6	0.575	1.20

Several other non-Gaussian distributions, including other Gaussian sum combinations, uniform, Rayleigh, and log-normal distributions are used to evaluate the HOFs in [5]. The estimation error and filter error variance resulting from one simulation run for the model in (37) with Gaussian initial estimation error and process noise ($p_0 = q_k = 1$), and uniform measurement noise ($r_k = 8.3$) are given in Figure 2. In this case the HOF performs significantly better than the standard Kalman Filter. For all non-Gaussian distributions considered in [5] the HOFs outperformed the standard Kalman filter. In addition, an edgeworth expansion is used in [5] to estimate 5th and higher order moments of the noise for the prediction and filter moments in the HOF. The use of these expansions resulted in very little performance improvement over the truncated HOFs.

6 Conclusion

Two approximate methods for filtering have been presented for estimation in the presence of asymmetric and symmetric distributions of non-Gaussian noise. Simulation studies have shown that the HOFs can perform very well in non-Gaussian noise. For non-Gaussian distributions made up of known Gaussian sums, the non-Gaussian filters presented here give a reasonable compromise between the optimal but very computationally intensive Gaussian sum filter, and the suboptimal but easily implemented standard Kalman filter. In addition, when only the moments of the distributions are known and a Gaussian sum filter cannot be used, the non-Gaussian filters offer a means to obtain improved performance over the standard Kalman filter.

References

1 H. W. Sorenson and D. L. Alspach, "Recursive Bayesian Estimation Using Gaussian Sums," *Automatica*, vol. 7, pp. 465–479, 1971.

2 W. J. Vetter, "Matrix Calculus Operations and Taylor Expansions," *SIAM Review*, vol. 15, no. 2, pp. 352–369, April, 1973.

3 T. S. Rao and M. Yar, "Linear and Non-Linear Filters for Linear, but not Gaussian Processes," *Int. J. Control*, vol. 39, no. 1, pp. 235–246, 1984.

4 D. F. Liang and G. S. Christensen, "New estimation Algorithms for Discrete Nonlinear Systems and Observations with Multiple Time Delays," *Int. Journal of Cont.*, vol. 23, no. 5, pp. 613–625, 1976.

5 T. W. Hilands, "High Order Nonlinear Estimation with Signal Processing Applications," *Ph. D. Thesis*, The Pennsylvania State University, 1992.

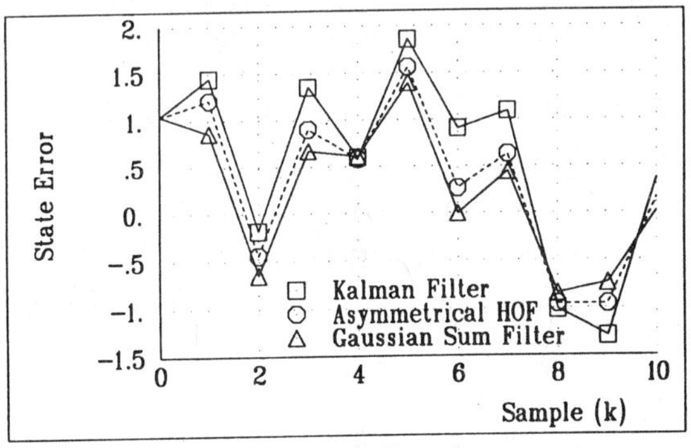

(a) Estimation Error $\tilde{x}_{k|k}$

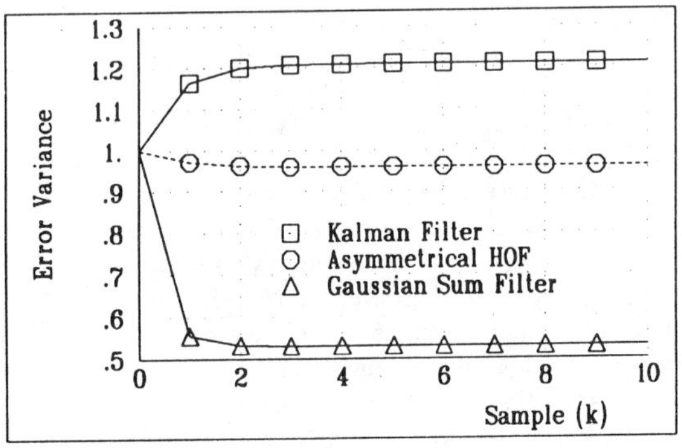

(b) Error Variance $P_{k|k}$

Figure 1 Typical Asymmetrical Filter Results, Model 1, $D = 10$, Bimodal Measurement Noise

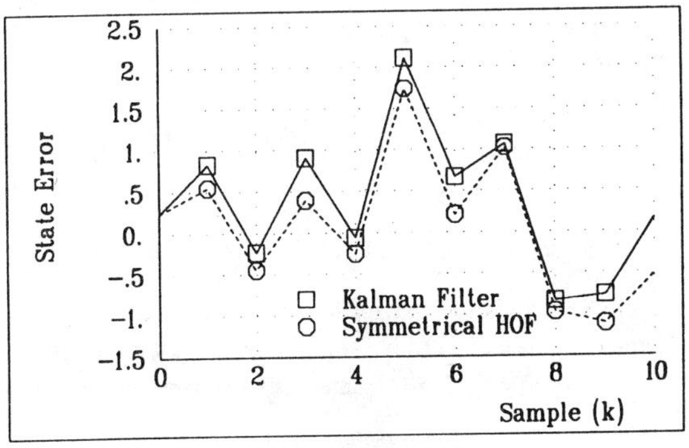

(a) Estimation Error $\tilde{x}_{k|k}$

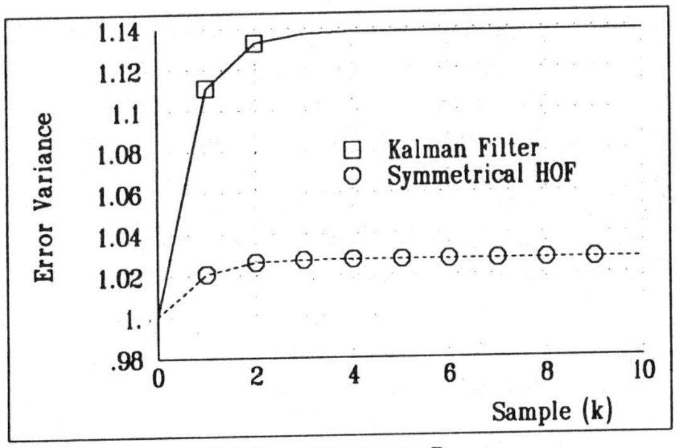

(b) Error Variance $P_{k|k}$

Figure 2 Typical Symmetrical Filter Results, Model 1, Uniform Measurement Noise

Proceedings of the
American Control Conference
San Francisco, California • June 1993

An Improved Autoregressive Spectral Estimation Method Using the Kalman Filter System Identification Technique

Chung-Wen Chen* Gordon Lee**
North Carolina State University, Raleigh, NC 27695-7921

Jer-Nan Juang+
NASA Langley Research Center, Hampton, VA 23665-5225

Abstract

This paper presents an improved multichannel autoregressive spectral estimation method by smoothing the autoregressive (AR) model obtained by the least-squares technique. The smoothing is based on the relationship between a state-space model and an AR model of a stochastic signal. The method starts with the classical least-squares estimation of an AR model of the signal, and then uses the Kalman filter system identification method to obtain a state-space model and the corresponding Kalman filter gain. The model and filter gain are in turn used to reconstruct a smoothed AR model, which is used to produce an improved spectral estimation. A numerical example is included to illustrate the feasibility of the method.

1. Introduction

Power spectral estimation methods can be classified into two categories:[1] non-parametric and parametric. Non-parametric approaches do not assume a model for the signal, and can be further divided into the correlogram (indirect) and the periodogram (direct) methods. The correlogram method estimates the autocorrelation sequence first and then Fourier transforms it to obtain the power spectral density (PSD)[2]; the periodogram method uses the Fast Fourier Transform (FFT) directly on the data and obtains a smoothed PSD through averaging over data segments and windowing[3,4]. On the other hand, parametric methods model the signal using time-series structures such as the autoregressive (AR) model, the moving average (MA) model, and the mixed autoregressive moving average (ARMA) model. Hence, the PSD is a function of the model parameters. The model parameters are estimated by fitting the data to an assumed model, optimized according to some error criterion. Using the FFT, some non-parametric methods may have the merit of faster calculation; however, in general, non-parametric methods require longer data records than parametric methods do in order to achieve good results.

Among the parameteric methods, the autoregressive (AR) spectral estimation has received the most attention of all the time-series models[1]. The main reasons are that the estimation of an AR model from data is a linear problem which can be solved easily, and the AR spectra tend to have sharp peaks which implies higher resolution[1]. On the contrary, estimation based on MA and ARMA models are difficult non-linear problems which requires complicated and computationally intensive non-linear estimation techniques. To identify an AR model, the least-squares (LS) estimation is the most commonly used method. If the signal can be properly modeled by an AR model, the AR parameters estimated by the LS method will converge when the number of data goes to infinity. The convergence rate depends on the noise level. For a short data record, however, the estimated AR parameters might still be significantly different from the true values.

Recently some new methods of identifying a state-space model from data have been developed in the fields of system identification and state estimation.[5-8] These methods greatly exploit the relation between state-space models and difference models of linear systems. Through the method of Kalman filter system identification[5,6] (which is classically used to solve the problem of state estimation for systems with unknown model and unknown noise statistics), a method to smooth out the AR model obtained by the LS can be developed. The smoothed AR model provides a more accurate spectral estimation of the signal. Since spectral estimation is of interest for its own sake, this paper introduces an application of the newly developed system identification methods to the field of spectral estimation.

2. Multichannel Autoregressive Spectral Estimation

An autoregressive model that represents many stochastic processes encountered in practice is

$$y(k)+a_1y(k-1)+\cdots+a_qy(k-q)=\varepsilon(k) \tag{1}$$

or in short,

$$\sum_{i=0}^{q}a_iy(k-i)=\varepsilon(k), \qquad (a_0=I_p) \tag{2}$$

where $y(i)\in R^{p\times 1}$ is the measured signal vector at time index i, and $\varepsilon(i)\in R^{p\times 1}$ is an inaccessible white noise sequence. The matrix coefficients a_i $(i=1,\cdots,q)$ are the AR parameters. If all the AR parameters and the covariance of the white sequence $\{\varepsilon(k)\}$ are known, the power spectrum of $y(k)$ can be computed by letting $z=e^{j\omega}$ in the following equation:[1]

$$S_{yy}(z)=\left(\sum_{i=0}^{q}a_iz^{-i}\right)^{-1}\Phi_{\varepsilon\varepsilon}\left(\sum_{i=0}^{q}a_iz^{i}\right)^{-T}=A^{-1}(z)\Phi_{\varepsilon\varepsilon}A^{-T}\left(z^{-1}\right) \tag{3}$$

so that

$$S_{yy}(\omega)=G(\omega)\Phi_{\varepsilon\varepsilon}G^*(\omega), \qquad \left(G(\omega)=A^{-1}(e^{-j\omega})\right) \tag{4}$$

where $G^*(\omega)$ is the transpose conjugate of $G(\omega)$; $\Phi_{\varepsilon\varepsilon}$ is the auto-covariance of $\{\varepsilon(k)\}$. In practice, the AR parameters can be estimated using the least-squares method. Writing Eq. (1) as

$$y(k)=\theta\phi(k)+\varepsilon(k), \tag{5}$$

where $\theta=[a_1, \cdots, a_q]$, and

---

* Research Associate, Mars Mission Research Center, Member AIAA.

** Professor, Mars Mission Research Center, Member AIAA.

\+ Principal Scientist, Spacecraft Dynamics Branch, Fellow AIAA.

$$\phi^T(k-1) = \left[y^T(k-1), \quad \cdots, \quad y^T(k-q)\right], \tag{6}$$

and stacking up data to form

$$\Phi_k = \begin{bmatrix} \phi^T(1) \\ \vdots \\ \phi^T(k-1) \end{bmatrix}, \qquad Y_k = \begin{bmatrix} y^T(2) \\ \vdots \\ y^T(k) \end{bmatrix}, \tag{7}$$

the least-squares solution of θ is

$$\hat{\theta}_k = \left(\Phi_k^T \Phi_k\right)^{-1} \Phi_k^T Y_k \tag{8}$$

The subscript k indicates the number of data used.

The covariance of $\varepsilon(k)$ can be estimated by calculating the sample covariance of $\hat{\varepsilon}(k)$, where

$$\hat{\varepsilon}(i) = y(i) - \hat{\theta}_k \phi(i), \qquad (i = 1, 2, \cdots, k). \tag{9}$$

That is,

$$\hat{\Phi}_{\varepsilon\varepsilon} = \frac{1}{k} \sum_{i=1}^{k} \hat{\varepsilon}(i) \hat{\varepsilon}^T(i). \tag{10}$$

3. The Kalman Filter System Identification Method

The same stochastic process (1) can also be represented by a state-space model:

$$\begin{aligned} x(k+1) &= Ax(k) + w(k), \\ y(k) &= Cx(k) + v(k) \end{aligned} \tag{11}$$

where $x(k) \in R^{n\times 1}$ is the state vector, $y(k) \in R^{p\times 1}$ is the output vector, $w(k)$ and $v(k)$ are process and measurement noises, respectively; and A and C are the state-space parameters. It is assumed that both noises are white and uncorrelated. For this system, there exists a Kalman filter which can provide the optimal state estimation, given output measurements.[10] If the state-space parameters and the noise covariances of both process and measurement noises are known, the Kalman filter can be calculated and, therefore, is known; otherwise it exists but is unknown. However, even if the Kalman filter is unknown, the filter formulation provides a relationship between input-output data, which in turn provides a relationship between the state-space parameters and the AR parameters. Based upon this relationship, the state-space parameters and the corresponding Kalman filter gain can be identified from data.

The steady-state Kalman filter can be written in the form of the innovation model:[10]

$$\hat{x}(k) = A\hat{x}(k-1) + AKe(k-1) \tag{12}$$

$$y(k) = C\hat{x}(k) + e(k) \tag{13}$$

where $\hat{x}(k)$ is the *a priori* state estimate (the estimated state made before taking the current data into consideration), the residual $e(k)$ is the difference between the real measurement, $y(k)$, and the predicted measurement, $\hat{y}(k) = C\hat{x}(k)$, and K is the optimal steady-state Kalman filter gain. Substituting $e(k)$ in Eq. (12) according to Eq. (13), one obtains

$$\hat{x}(k) = \bar{A}\hat{x}(k-1) + AKy(k-1)$$

where

$$\bar{A} = A(I_n - KC). \tag{14}$$

Note that $\bar{A}$ is the filter system matrix. Substituting Eq. (14) repeatedly into Eq. (13) one can derive the difference equation :

$$\begin{aligned} &y(k) - CAKy(k-1) - C\bar{A}AKy(k-2) - \cdots \\ &- C\bar{A}^{r-1}AKy(k-r) - C\bar{A}^r AK\hat{x}(k-r) = e(k) \end{aligned} \tag{15}$$

Because the Kalman filter is stable in general, for a sufficiently large r, the last term on the left side of Eq. (15) is negligibly small and can be dropped from the equation; therefore, Eq. (15) becomes

$$y(k) - \sum_{i=1}^{r} C\bar{A}^{i-1}AKy(k-i) = e(k). \tag{16}$$

Comparing Eq. (16) with Eqs. (1) and (2), one can see that $a_i = C\bar{A}^{i-1}AK$, $\varepsilon(k) = e(k)$, and $q = r$. Through this derivation, the AR parameters are now explicitly represented in terms of the state-space parameters and the Kalman gain. We called the matrix sequence $\{CAK, \; C\bar{A}AK, C\bar{A}^2AK, \cdots\}$ the *stochastic filter Markov parameters* because the sequence has a Markov-parameter form ($\{CB, CAB, CA^2B \; \cdots\}$) with the system matrix belonging to the filter ($\bar{A}$ instead of A), and the input matrix AK (instead of B) contains stochastic information K.

From the stochastic filter Markov parameters one can calculate another set of Markov-type parameters $\{CAK, CA^2K, CA^3K, \cdots\}$, which is called the *stochastic system Markov parameters* because the system matrix A belongs to the original system and the input matrix is AK. The calculation follows the following equation,[6,9] where $b_i = CA^{i-1}AK$:

$$b_j = a_j + \sum_{i=1}^{j-1} a_{j-i} b_i \tag{17}$$

The relation in Eq. (17) can be more easily understood through z-domain representations. The z-domain expression of Eq. (16) is:

$$A(z)Y(z) = E(z) \tag{18}$$

where

$$A(z) = I_p - \sum_{i=1}^{q} C\bar{A}^{i-1}AKz^{-i},$$

$$Z(y(k)) = Y(z), \quad Z(\varepsilon(k)) = E(z).$$

On the other hand, introducing Eq. (12) into Eq. (13) repeatedly, one has

$$y(k) = e(k) + CAKe(k-1) + \cdots = e(k) + \sum_{i=1}^{\infty} CA^{i-1}AKe(k-i) \tag{19}$$

which has a z-domain expression

$$Y(z) = B(z)E(z), \qquad B(z) = I_p + \sum_{i=1}^{\infty} CA^{i-1}AKz^{-i}. \tag{20}$$

Comparing Eqs. (18) and (20), one concludes that $A^{-1}(z) = B(z)$, or $A(z)B(z) = I_p$. That is,

$$\left(I_p - \sum_{i=1}^{q} C\bar{A}^{i-1}AKz^{-i}\right)\left(I_p + \sum_{i=1}^{\infty} CA^{i-1}AKz^{-i}\right) = I_p. \tag{21}$$

Note that the multiplication of two polynomials is the convolution of their coefficients; thus, Eq. (17) can be derived.

Using the Eigensystem Realization Algorithm (ERA)[11] one can decompose the system stochastic Markov parameters $\{CAK, CA^2K, CA^3K, \cdots\}$ into a set of state-space parameters A, C along with the Kalman filter gain K. The ERA determines the dimension of the system by analyzing the magnitude of the singular values of a data matrix called the general Hankel matrix; the small singular values are attributed to noise sources and are truncated. The realized model is not unique, or is unique only under a similarity transformation; however, the stochastic system

Markov parameters are unique. For more details about the ERA, readers are referred to Ref. [11].

4. A Smoothed Spectral Estimation

The LS estimation of an AR model implicitly assumes that all the parameters are independent because one actually optimizes each parameter independently. Therefore, the resultant AR parameter sequences could be jagged if the data record is not long enough and the order of the AR model is large. This will degrade the quality of the spectral estimation.

Using the Kalman filter system identification method, one obtains A, C, and K from the LS estimated AR model, which can be in turn used to reconstructed the AR parameters according to Eq. (16). The reconstructed AR parameter sequences are smoother and thus yields a better spectral estimation. The process of using the Kalman filter system identification method to obtain an improved autoregressive spectral estimation is depicted in Fig. 1, compared with the traditional non-smoothed method.

After obtaining a smoothed AR model, one should calculate the new residual (prediction error) and its covariance according to Eqs. (9) and (10). The spectrum then can be obtained using Eq. (4).

Remark 1: Equation (16) provides a criterion for selecting the order of the AR model for the LS process. It is known that the residual of an optimal Kalman filter is white; therefore, the order of the AR model selected for performing the least-squares must be large enough to produce a white prediction error sequence. The order of the reconstructed AR model can be determined by checking the magnitude of the reconstructed stochastic filter Markov parameters. The infinite sequence is truncated at a point where the higher order terms are negligibly small.

Remark 2: The order (dimension) of the system is determined through the ERA by observing the magnitude of the singular values of the general Hankel matrix[11]. The sorted singular value sequence is truncated, retaining comparatively larger values; the number of the retaining singular values is the order of the system. If the order chosen is as large as the AR model before smoothing, then the ERA can match the system stochastic Markov parameters *too* well and there will be no smoothing effect. Usually the order of the system is smaller than the order of the AR model. This can be seen from Eq. (16); only when the filter gain K makes the filter system matrix $\bar{A}$ deadbeat will the AR mode have the same order as the system (in the single-input single-output case). This is seldom the case. From this point of view, the smoothing is actually done through the ERA by providing a reduced-order system model.

Remark 3: In order to validate the reconstructed AR model, one can check the whiteness of the residual, re-calculated using the smoothed AR model. If the model is reasonably good, the new residual should be close to a white sequence.

5. Numerical Example

Consider a signal sequence $\{y(k)\}$ which is generated by a system described by Eq. (11) with the following state-space parameters:

$$A = diag\left(\begin{bmatrix} 0.9856 & 0.1628 \\ -0.1628 & 0.9856 \end{bmatrix}, \begin{bmatrix} 0.8976 & 0.4305 \\ -0.4305 & 0.8976 \end{bmatrix}, \begin{bmatrix} 0.8127 & 0.5690 \\ -0.5690 & 0.8127 \end{bmatrix}\right)$$

$$C = \begin{bmatrix} 1.5119 & 0.0000 & 2.0000 & 0.0000 & 1.5119 & 0.0000 \\ 1.3093 & 0.0000 & 0.0000 & 0.0000 & -1.3093 & 0.0000 \end{bmatrix}.$$

The input is a Gaussian white noise $\{w(k)\}$ with covariance $Q = I_6$; the output is contaminated by another Gaussian white noise $\{v(k)\}$ with covariance

$$R = \begin{bmatrix} 107.3356 & 0.1545 \\ 0.1545 & 36.8147 \end{bmatrix}.$$

Using the above information, the optimal steady-state Kalman filter gain and in turn the theoretical AR model can be calculated. Through Eq. (3) the theoretical spectrum of $\{y(k)\}$ can also be computed.

Now, suppose 1000 pieces of data for $\{y(k)\}$ are available. Assuming an AR model with an order of 20 (denoted by AR(20)), the least-squares estimation of the parameter sequences is shown in Fig. 2 (dash-dot lines) compared with the theoretical values (solid lines). The estimated curves are jagged because the number of data is not large enough. Using the Kalman filter system identification method described above, the reconstructed AR parameter sequences are also shown in Fig. 2 (dash lines) for comparison. It can be seen that the reconstructed curves are smoother and closer to the theoretical curves.

Figure 3 shows the estimated spectral density function (dashed lines) calculated directly using the AR model obtained by the LS; the theoretical PSD is included for comparison. Similarly, Fig. 4 shows the estimated spectral density (dashed lines) calculated using the reconstructed AR model. It can be seen that the spectral estimation has been greatly improved. For comparison, Fig. 5 shows the estimated spectral density (dashed lines) obtained by a non-parametric approach – the Welch method. This method divides the data into several segments of 200 samples each, applies an FFT along with the Hanning window on each segment separately, and then averages the results. The resulting curves are jagged, which is typical for this method.

6. Conclusion

An improved AR spectral estimation method has been developed. The method obtains a smoothed AR model through identifying a stochastic state-space model. The relation between the AR model and the state-space model are derived through the perspective of the Kalman filter. The method is useful especially when the order required for the AR model is large and the data record is comparatively short.

References

1. Marple, Jr., S. Lawrence, *Digital Spectral Analysis with Applications,* Prentice-Hall Inc. Englewood Cliffs, New Jersey., 1987, pp. 130-273.
2. Blackman, R. B. and Tukey, J. W., *The Measurement of Power Spectra from the Point of View of Communication Engineering,* Dover Publication, Inc., New York, 1958; also appeared in the January 1958 and March 1958 Bell Syst. Tech. Journal.
3. Welch, P. D., "The Use of Fast Fourier Transform for the Estimation of Power Spectrum: A Method Based on Time Averaging over Short Modified Periodograms," *IEEE Trans. Audio Electroacoust.*, Vol. AU-15, June 1967, pp. 70-73.
4. Oppenheim, A. V. and Schafer, R., *Digital Signal Processing,* Prentice-Hall Inc. Englewood Cliffs, New Jersey., 1975, pp. 532-562.
5. Chen, C.-W., Huang, J.-K., Phan, M., and Juang, J.-N., "Integrated System Identification and State Estimation for Control of Large Flexible Space Structures," Paper No. 90-

3740-CP, *Proceedings of the AIAA Guidance, Navigation, and Control Conference*, Portland, Oregon, August 1990.

6. Chen, C.-W., *Integrated System Identification and Adaptive State Estimation for Control of Flexible Space Structures*, Ph.D. Dissertation, Old Dominion University, Norfolk, Virginia, August 1991.

7. Phan, M., Horta, L.G., Juang, J.-N., and Longman, R.W., "Linear System Identification Via an Asymptotically Stable Observer," Paper No. AIAA-91-2734, *Proceedings of the AIAA Guidance, Navigation, and Control Conference*, New Orleans, Louisianas, August 1991.

8. Juang, J.-N., Phan, M., Horta, L.G., and Longman, R.W., "Identification of Observer/Kalman Filter Markov Parameters: Theory and Experiment," Paper No. AIAA-91-2735, *Proceedings of the AIAA Guidance, Navigation, and Control Conference*, New Orleans, Louisianas, August 1991.

9. Juang, J.-N., Chen, C. W., and Phan, M., "Identification of an Observer from Test Data with a Known Discrete Model" *in preparation for NASA Technical Memo.*

10. Goodwin, G. C., and Sin, K. S., *Adaptive Filtering, Prediction and Control,* Prentice-Hall, Inc., Englewood Cliff, New Jersey, 1984, pp. 250.

11. Juang, J.-N., and Pappa, R. S., " An Eigensystem Realization Algorithm for Modal Parameter Identification and Model Reduction," *Journal of Guidance, Control, and Dynamics*, Vol. 8, Sept.-Oct. 1985, pp. 620-627.

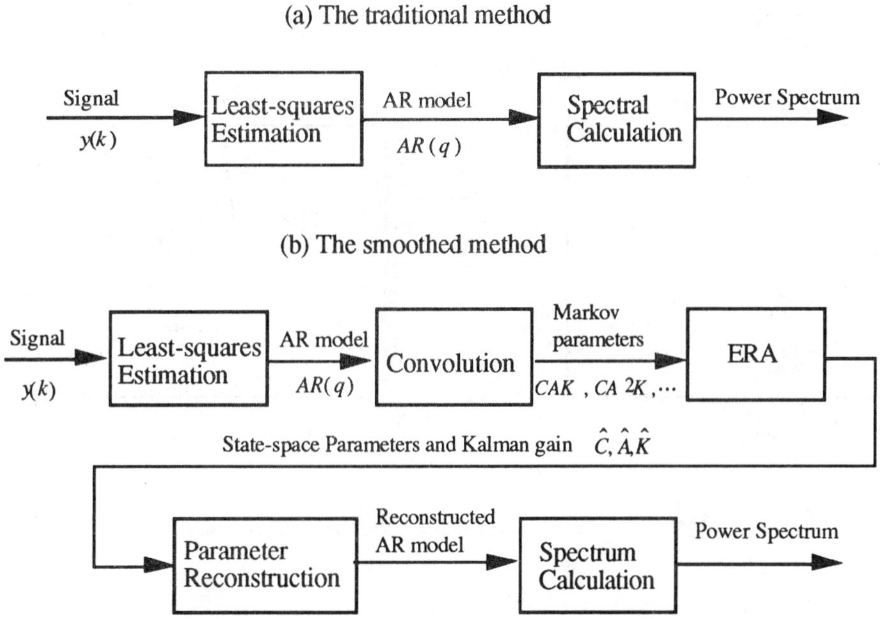

Fig. 1. Procedures of the traditional and the smoothed AR spectral estimation.

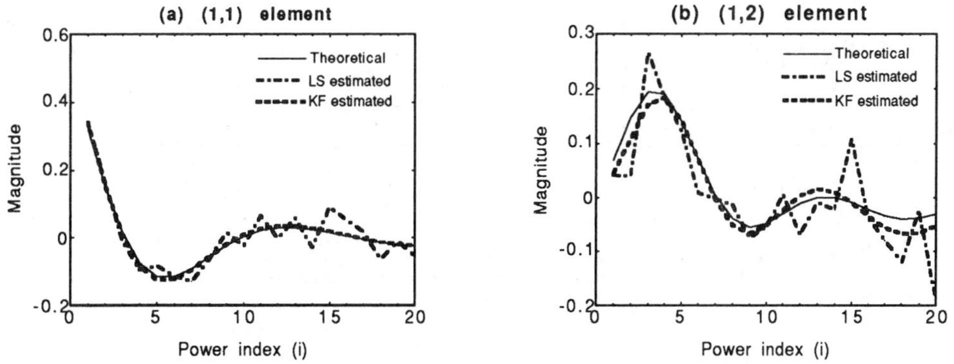

Fig. 2. Comparison of the estimated, reconstructed and true filter stochastic Markov parameters.

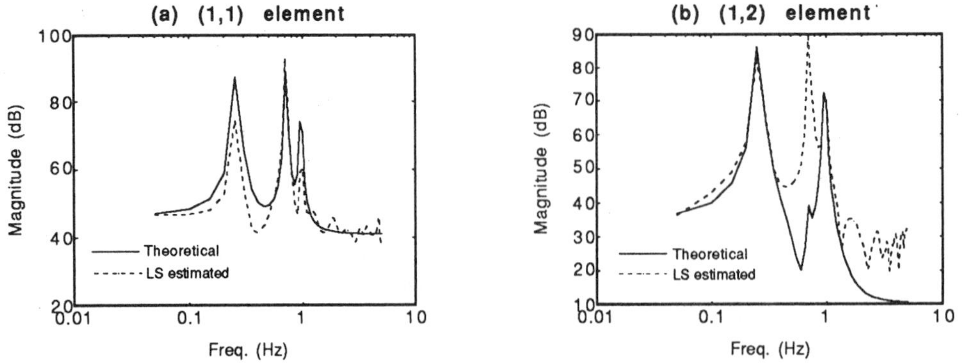

Fig. 3. Power spectrum estimated by the traditional least-squares method.

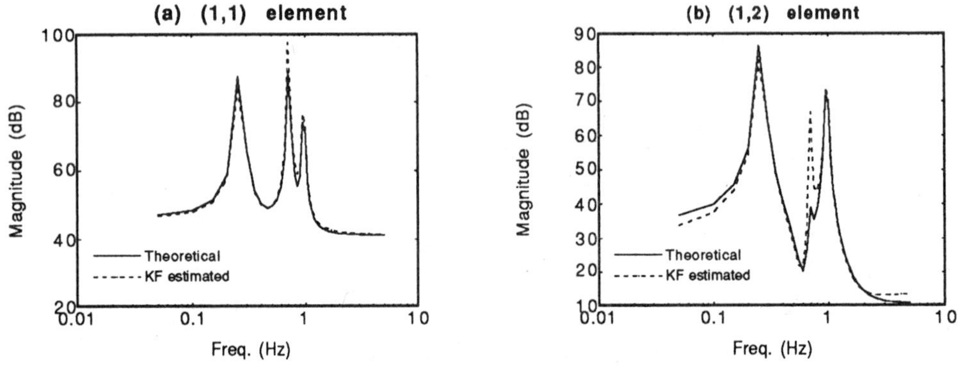

Fig. 4. Power spectrum estimated by the Kalman filter method.

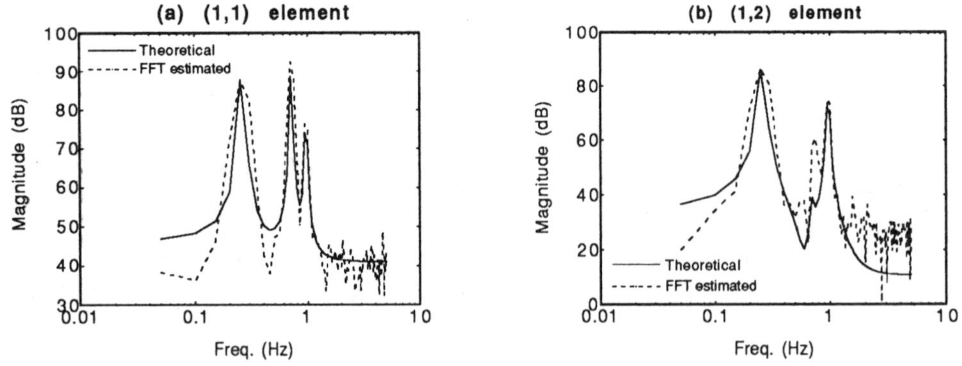

Fig. 5. Power spectrum estimated by the Welch method.

Proceedings of the
American Control Conference
San Francisco, California • June 1993

A Design Approach for a GPS User Segment for Aerospace Vehicles

John J. Dougherty, Hossny El-Sherief, Daniel J. Simon, and Gary A. Whitmer

TRW Systems Integration Group
San Bernardino, California 92402

Abstract

As new applications for the use of the Global Positioning System (GPS) on aerospace vehicles emerge, more attention is being paid to the design of the user segment, which comprises the hardware and software employed by the user to obtain navigation information from GPS. The complexity of the design of the user segment, as well as the performance demanded of the components (such as the antenna), depends on user requirements such as total navigation accuracy. Other factors, for instance the expected satellite/vehicle geometry or the accuracy of an accompanying inertial navigation system, can also affect the user segment design. The interaction between these effects, the user requirements, and the user segment design is studied. Design curves are developed which allow quick trade studies to be performed.

I. Introduction

GPS is a satellite navigation system developed and maintained by the United States Department of Defense [1]. Because of the versatility provided by the global availability and the passive nature of the user segment, GPS is being used in a wide range of aerospace applications. Among these are on-board navigators and trajectory references for range safety and for testing inertial navigation systems.

GPS user segment designs can be broadly classified into two categories: receiver- and translator-based designs. A GPS receiver processes GPS signals to estimate its own position and velocity. This information can be used directly, or can be combined with other navigation estimates (from an inertial navigation system, for instance) to get a best-estimate of the vehicle position and velocity. A GPS receiver must compensate for known measurement errors in real time [2]. A GPS translator, on the other hand, is a relatively simple device whose function is to frequency shift ("translate") the GPS signals from one frequency band to another, such as a telemetry band. The translated signal is then retransmitted to a ground receiving station, where it is time-tagged and processed or recorded for later processing.

Oftentimes an application will require the use of a receiver-based user segment. For instance, using GPS for on-board navigation usually demands a receiver. On the other hand, when using a GPS user segment as a navigation reference for testing inertial navigation systems, a translator-based segment offers several advantages, including low cost, weight, and power consumption and high reliability. Furthermore, ground post-processing of the signals allows for the use of highly accurate satellite orbital information not available in real-time and highly detailed corrections.

This paper considers the performance factors which affect the design of a GPS user segment. Although the results apply to various other applications, GPS used as a navigation reference for testing inertial navigation systems is considered as a specific example [3].

II. User Requirements and the GPS User Segment

A. Contributors To System Performance

The ability to meet application-specific performance requirements depends on the design of the GPS user segment as well as other factors relating to the system performance. This relationship is illustrated in Figure 1. Each box represents either a measure of performance or a factor affecting performance; boxes higher in the figure depend on boxes connected to them from below.

At the top of the figure is the user's requirement on the performance of the whole system. For GPS/inertial navigation system hybrids, the user's requirement would typically be on the total navigation accuracy [4]. For an autonomous GPS navigation system, the user requirement would be on the GPS navigation accuracy. For the case of GPS used as a trajectory reference for flight testing inertial navigation systems, the user requirement would be on measures such as estimation uncertainties.

The three-dimensional measurement accuracy of the GPS user segment can be determined independently of other components in the user's system, as illustrated in the second level of Figure 1. It depends on the satellite geometry [5], the vehicle flight path, and the one-dimensional GPS measurement accuracy. The measurement accuracy depends on the receiver or translator design, the antenna design, the accuracy of the satellite ephemeris data, relativity and atmospheric effects, and fixed characteristics of GPS. The data used in this study are based on the literature [6][7] and flight test experience.

Receivers and translators can be designed to process the L_1 (1575.42 MHz) or L_2 (1227.60 MHz) signals or both. Processing two frequencies allows for better ionospheric refraction corrections. In addition, receivers and translators can be designed to process one or both of the GPS codes. The GPS L_1 signal is quadrature modulated by two pseudorandom codes, a 1.023 Mbit/s coarse acquisition (C/A) code and a 10.23 Mbit/s precision (P) code [2]. The type of code used determines the range precision which can be achieved.

The design and calibration of the antenna affects the accuracy of the phase-derived delta range measurement. The antenna phase induces a delta range error through three mechanisms: error in the phase calibration, vehicle attitude error coupled with the antenna phase slope, and ionospheric refraction correction error. The accuracy of the phase center calibration also affects the calculation of vehicle reference point to phase center lever arm, effectively introducing measurement errors.

The GPS satellite ephemerides are obtained either in real time from the GPS navigation message [8] or from satellite tracking data spanning a period of several days both before and after the time of interest.

Two different data correction schemes are considered. The coarser correction scheme adjusts the GPS measurements for satellite clock phase and frequency, drift in the translator carrier frequency, and changes in the signal path length due to ionospheric and tropospheric refraction. A coarse correction for relativistic effects is also built into the GPS clock frequency. A finer approach does the coarse corrections plus precise corrections for general and special relativistic effects due to the vehicle motion and higher accuracy tropospheric refraction corrections based on weather data.

B. GPS Error Model

The various contributors to GPS measurement errors were modeled and then simulated to assess their impact on the user segment performance. Although this model applies to a translator-based user segment, it can be used for receivers by taking the receive time and location to be coincident with the translation time and location.

The GPS range measurement is modeled as

$$\begin{aligned} R^i(t_k) = {} & r^i(t_k) + \underline{S}^i(t_k^*)^T C_{RH}{}^i(t_k^{**}) \underline{X}_P{}^i \\ & + (t_k^{**} - t_o) \underline{S}^i(t_k^*)^T C_{RH}{}^i(t_k^{**}) \underline{X}_V{}^i \\ & + (t_k^{**} - t_o) X_{CF}{}^i + c/10^9 X_{CP}{}^i + B^i(t_k) X_{TSF}{}^i(t_k) \\ & + X_{RAI}{}^i(t_k) + \underline{S}^i(t_k^*)^T C_{RB}(t_k^*) \underline{X}_{LA} + v_R{}^i(t_k) \end{aligned}$$

where

R^i is the measured range from the ith satellite to the vehicle to the ground;

r^i is the true range;

t_k is the ground receive time;

t_k^* is the vehicle translation time;

t_k^{**} is the satellite transmission time;

t_o is the reference time;

$\underline{S}^i$ is the unit vector from the vehicle to the ith satellite;

$C_{RH}{}^i$ is the direction cosine matrix from the HLC frame for the ith satellite to the reference frame;

C_{RB} is the direction cosine matrix from the vehicle body frame to the reference frame;

c is the speed of light;

B^i is the tropospheric refraction correction for the ith satellite;

$\underline{X}_P{}^i$, $\underline{X}_V{}^i$, $X_{CF}{}^i$, $X_{CP}{}^i$, $X_{TSF}{}^i$, and $X_{RAI}{}^i$ are per-satellite GPS errors;

$\underline{X}_{LA}$ are global GPS errors;

$v_R{}^i$ is the range measurement noise for the ith satellite.

The GPS delta range measurement is modeled as follows:

$$\begin{aligned} D^i(t_k) = {} & d^i(t_k) \\ & + [\underline{S}^i(t_k^*)^T C_{RH}{}^i(t_k^{**}) - \underline{S}^i(t_{k-1}^*)^T C_{RH}{}^i(t_{k-1}^{**})] \underline{X}_P{}^i \\ & + [(t_k^{**} - t_o) \underline{S}^i(t_k^*)^T C_{RH}{}^i(t_k^{**}) \\ & \quad - (t_{k-1}^{**} - t_o) \underline{S}^i(t_{k-1}^*)^T C_{RH}{}^i(t_{k-1}^{**})] \underline{X}_V{}^i \\ & + (t_k^{**} - t_{k-1}^{**}) X_{CF}{}^i \\ & + B^i(t_k) X_{TSF}{}^i(t_k) - B^i(t_{k-1}) X_{TSF}{}^i(t_{k-1}) \\ & + X_{DRI}{}^i(t_k) - X_{DRI}{}^i(t_{k-1}) + X_{DRA}{}^i(t_k) - X_{DRA}{}^i(t_{k-1}) \\ & + [\underline{S}^i(t_k^*)^T C_{RB}(t_k^*) - \underline{S}^i(t_{k-1}^*)^T C_{RB}(t_{k-1}^*)] \underline{X}_{LA} \\ & + X_{GR}{}^i(t_k) + X_{SR}{}^i(t_k) + v_{AC}{}^i(t_k) - v_{AC}{}^i(t_{k-1}) \end{aligned}$$

where

$D^i(t_k)$ is the measured delta range from the ith satellite to the vehicle to the ground over the interval $(t_{k-1},t_k]$;

$d^i(t_k)$ is the true delta range;

$X_{DRI}{}^i$ and $X_{DRA}{}^i$ are per-satellite GPS errors;

X_{GR}^i and X_{SR}^i are residual general and special relativity effects;

$v_{AC}^i(t_k) - v_{AC}^i(t_{k-1})$ is the one-step anticorrelated delta range measurement noise for the ith satellite; $v_{AC}^i(t_k)$ is white and Gaussian.

The GPS errors X_n^i and X_n (where n=TSF, LA, etc.) are assumed to be constants, random constants, or random variables from a first-order Gauss-Markov process.

C. Flight Testing Inertial Navigation Systems

To estimate inertial navigation system (INS) errors the INS telemetry is processed with the GPS measurement data to generate observations that are functions of the INS errors and the GPS errors. Specifically, the corrected GPS range and delta range are differenced with the equivalent quantities as indicated by the INS under test. These INS-indicated ranges and delta ranges are determined by using integrated accelerometer data and the satellite ephemerides. The GPS minus INS-indicated ranges and delta ranges are used as the observations for a Kalman filter. The Kalman filter state vector contains an element for each modeled INS and GPS error.

III. GPS User Segment Performance Measures

A. General Performance Measures

The performance of a GPS user segment, including its ability to achieve user objectives, can be quantified using various measures. Measures of the ability to meet user requirements are application-specific. On the other hand, measures of performance at lower levels in the system design can be defined without reference to the specific application.

The GPS three-dimensional measurement accuracy can be quantified by a six by six position/velocity error covariance matrix. Here, position and velocity measurements are assumed to be independent, and therefore this accuracy can be expressed instead as two smaller matrices, each three by three. These GPS position and velocity error covariance matrices P_{POS} and P_{VEL} are calculated by propagating the GPS error variances into position/velocity space.

Because P_{POS} and P_{VEL} are matrices and therefore rather unwieldy, a scalar representation of measurement accuracy derived from them, known as the spherical error probable (SEP), is used instead. The SEP is defined as the 50th percentile probability radius. One SEP each can be calculated from the position and velocity covariance matrices; smaller SEPs indicate better GPS performance.

The GPS one-dimensional measurement accuracy can be expressed as two (scalar) standard deviations, one each for range and delta range. These one-dimensional accuracies are calculated by propagating GPS error variances into range and delta range space. Smaller numbers represent better performance.

The GPS satellite geometry is usually quantified by the Geometric Dilution of Precision. Because the completion of the GPS constellation will mean uniformly good geometry, this study did not vary the assumed satellite geometry; a full constellation was used in the simulations.

B. Performance Measures for INS Flight Testing

Several different measures can be used to quantify the ability to estimate INS errors given the GPS data. One important measure is the total estimation uncertainty. This information is produced by the filter in the form of a large covariance matrix, a square matrix with a side dimension equal to that of the filter state. Because the uncertainty in this form is very unwieldy, a preferable measure is a circular error probable (CEP) based on it. This scalar is produced by propagating the state space error covariance matrix into impact space and then calculating a 50th percentile radius.

IV. GPS User Segment Design Analysis

An analysis of a GPS user segment was performed to determine the effects on performance of the design parameters described in Section II; the results of the analysis are presented in this section. These results can be used to determine the basic design parameters for a GPS user segment needed to achieve a desired performance.

Four fundamental design parameters were varied in the analysis: the code type (C/A or P), the number of frequencies (single or dual), the measurement correction scheme (coarse or fine), and the antenna phase calibration error standard deviation (from 20 to 80 degrees in ten degree increments). Four user segment configurations, representing various combinations of code type, frequency usage, and measurement correction scheme, were studied. Furthermore, the antenna phase calibration error was varied for one of the configurations. Figures 2 through 6 show the results of the analysis.

The one-dimensional results (Figures 2 and 4) do not depend on either the vehicle motion or the specific user application, other than the assumption that conditions permit the user segment to produce useful measurements. The three-dimensional results (Figures 3, 5, and 6) depend on the relative motion between the vehicle and the GPS satellites. The analysis considered a missile on a 4000 mile trajectory and nominal satellite coverage. Figure 6 is for the specific case of GPS as a trajectory reference for evaluating inertial navigation system errors.

Figures 2 and 3 contain the one- and three-dimensional position accuracies for the four configurations. Figures 4 and 5 present the one-dimensional range rate accuracies and the three-dimensional velocity accuracies. The largest effects on GPS measurement accuracy are the code type, which establishes the range resolution, and whether a second frequency is used for ionospheric corrections. Range rate measurements with coarse corrections also contain large residual refraction errors during the first 100 seconds of flight, within the troposphere. As seen in Figure 5, the antenna phase calibration error also has a significant effect on range rate for the dual frequency configurations; otherwise, its contribution gets swamped by the ionospheric refraction error. Note that the antenna phase error does not affect the range measurement (see Section II.B).

Figure 6 shows the effects of the user segment configuration on the ability to estimate the total INS navigation error. Refraction errors (ionospheric for the L_1 only configuration, tropospheric for the coarse correction case) are seen to degrade the ability to estimate the total error due to the INS. On the other hand, the antenna phase error is important only if the measurements are derived from dual frequency P code using fine corrections.

V. Summary

The performance required of a GPS user segment depends on the application-dependent objectives. The performance is achieved by appropriate design of the measurement calculation scheme, the antenna, and the receiver or translator. Performance measures can be defined at various levels; each level takes into account various components of the overall application. The top level measures presented here are peculiar to the specific application of GPS as a navigation reference for testing INSs, but the other measures are not. Therefore, the one- and three-dimensional accuracy data presented here can be used to design GPS user segments for a wide variety of applications.

The results of this study indicate that the ability to track P code on two different frequencies is the most critical aspect of GPS user segment design. In addition, the extra effort required to perform fine data corrections, especially tropospheric refraction corrections, results in a significant improvement in GPS accuracy. Antenna phase calibration is critical only if dual frequency tracking is used.

References

1) Spilker, J. J., Jr., "GPS Signal Structure and Performance Characteristics," Global Positioning System Papers, Vol. I, The Institute of Navigation, Washington, D.C., 1980, pp. 29-54.

2) Kao, M. H., and Eller, D. H., "Multiconfiguration Kalman Filter Design for High-Performance GPS Navigation," IEEE Transactions on Automatic Control, Vol. AC-28, 1983, pp. 304-314.

3) Dougherty, J. J., El-Sherief, H., and Hohman, D. S., "The Use of GPS for Evaluating Inertial Measurement Unit Errors," submitted for review.

4) Simon, D. and El-Sherief, H., "A Fault Tolerant Optimal Interpolative Net", IEEE International Conference on Neural Networks, 1993.

5) Simon, D. and El-Sherief, H., "Design of Global Positioning System Receivers for Integrated Inertial Navigation Systems", IEEE Conference on Decision and Control, submitted for review.

6) "NAVSTAR GPS User Equipment" (Public Release Version), U.S. Air Force Space Systems Division, NAVSTAR-GPS Joint Program Office, Los Angeles, CA, February 1991.

7) Janiczek, P. and Gilbert, S. (eds.), Global Positioning System Papers, Vol. I-III, The Institute of Navigation, Washington, D.C., 1980.

8) Van Dierendonck, A. J., et al., "The GPS Navigation Message," Global Positioning System Papers, Vol. I, The Institute of Navigation, Washington, D.C., 1980, pp. 55-73.

9) McAllister, D. F. and Wilcox, J. C., "Digital Computer Program for Generalized Inertial Guidance System Error Analysis, Version II, Modification 1," TRW Systems Group, 10 March 1969.

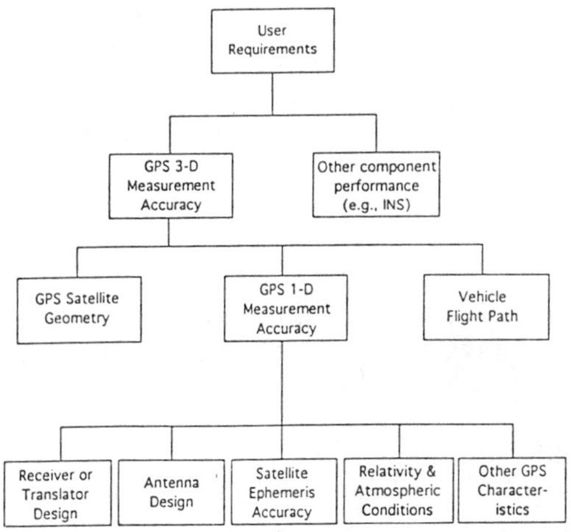

Figure 1 - User Segment Design

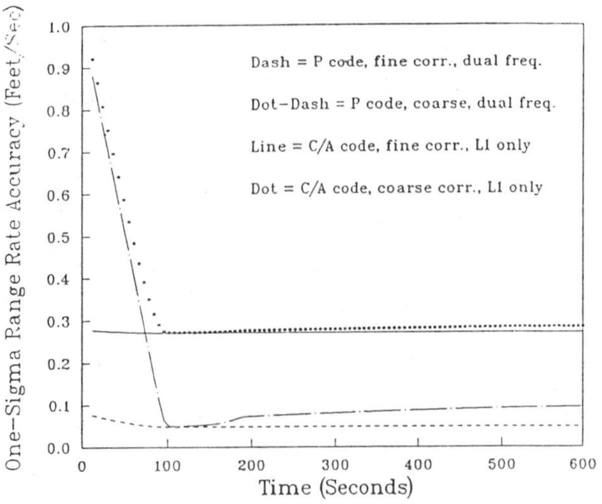

Figure 4 - GPS Range Rate Measurement Accuracy

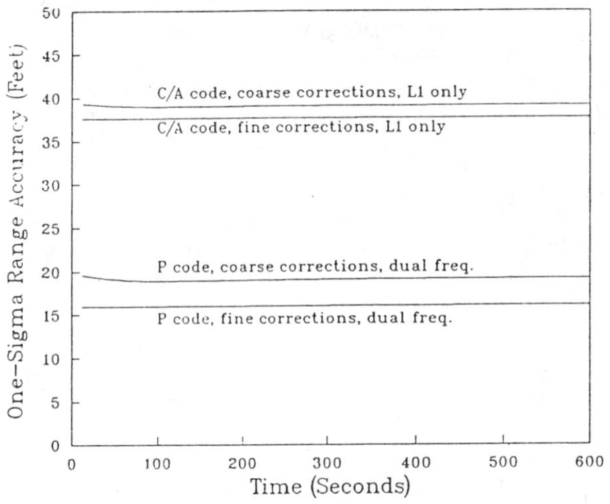

Figure 2 - GPS Range Measurement Accuracy

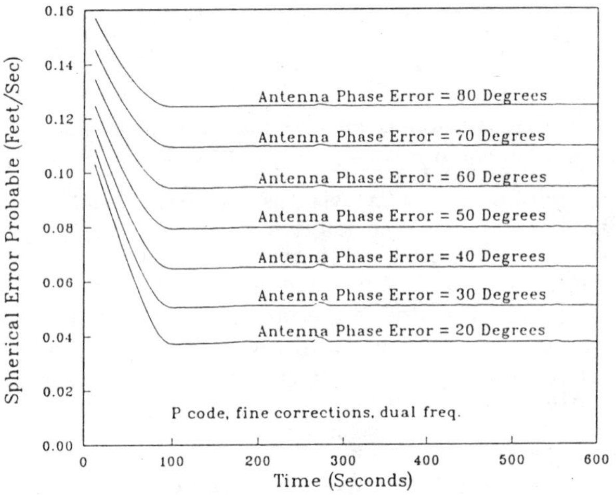

Figure 5 - GPS Velocity Spherical Error Probable

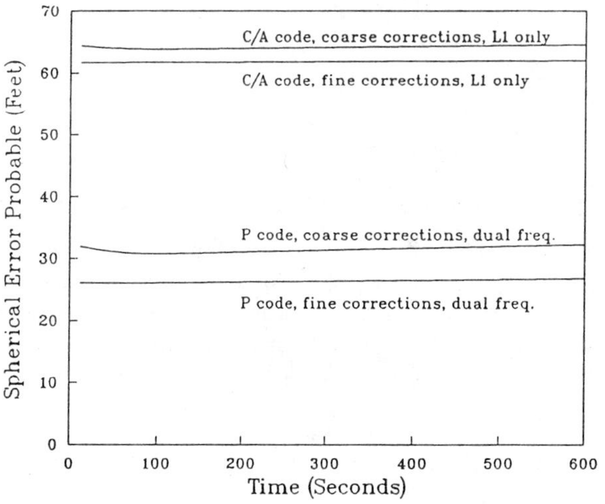

Figure 3 - GPS Position Spherical Error Probable

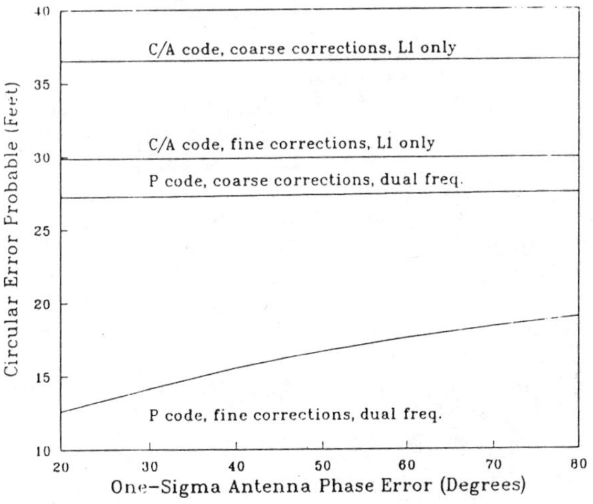

Figure 6 - Total INS Estimation Error

Proceedings of the
American Control Conference
San Francisco, California • June 1993

Optimal ℓ^∞ to ℓ^∞ Estimation

Petros Voulgaris

University of Illinois, Urbana, IL 61801
Coordinated Science Laboratory

ABSTRACT

In this paper we consider the problem of finding a filter that minimizes the worst case magnitude (ℓ^∞) of the estimation error in the case of linear time invariant systems subjected to unknown but magnitude bounded (ℓ^∞) inputs. These inputs consist of process and observation noise, as well as initial conditions; also, the optimization problem is considered over an infinite time horizon. Taking a model matching approach, suboptimal solutions are presented which stem from the resulting ℓ^∞-induced norm minimization problem.

1. INTRODUCTION

Worst case estimation is an alternative approach to stochastic estimation when statistical information about the uncertainty is not available. The subject of worst case estimation for linear systems has been treated by several researchers and is often related to the advances in robust control. As an example, we is refer to [1,11] and references therein where, the subject of worst case estimation is treated in the presence of energy (ℓ^2 or $\mathcal{L}^2$) bounded input uncertainty with the objective to minimize the worst case energy of the estimation error. Also, the case where the noise is magnitude bounded and the objective is to minimize the worst case magnitude of the error, is treated in [2,9,14,10] and references therein. In particular, in [2] Euclidean norms for the magnitude are considered and the authors present a recursive algorithm (not necessarily optimal) with similar structure to Kalman filters. In [9,14] optimal algorithms are presented for pointwise estimation problems where the uncertainty is magnitude (ℓ^∞) bounded. More specifically, these algorithms are obtained by solving finite dimensional linear programs; also, time varying bounds on the magnitude of the noise can be handled. However, these algorithms are not recursive and cannot be easily implemented when the ammount of data is large, and in particular, for infinite horizon problems.

In this paper we consider the infinite horizon optimal filtering problem in discrete-time, linear-time-invariant systems (LTI), stable or unstable, when the sources of uncertainty are ℓ^∞-bounded process and observation noise together with uknown (but bounded) initial conditions. We set up the problem as a model matching problem [7] over ℓ^∞-bounded operators. In the case where the initial condition is known, the resulting problem is a model matching problem involving time invariant operators. Hence, a recursive suboptimal (arbitrarily close to optimal) estimator can be produced by solving a standard ℓ^1-optimization [3]. In the case where the initial condition is not known the resulting model matching problem is time varying. Yet, these time varying operators have a specific structure that is being exploited. A suboptimal solution consists of utilizing the suboptimal known-inital-condition (KIC) estimator after some *apriori* computable time index N which depends on the KIC solution, while up to time N the solution of $N+1$ finite dimensional linear programs is required to construct the suboptimal estimates. This time index N, represents the time that takes the suboptimal KIC filter to make the error that is due only to initial conditions very small. Solving the $N+1$ linear programs ammounts to finding the optimal pointwise estimator for the time interval $0-N$ and is therefore equivalent with the approach in [9,14]. Also, conditions are given under which the suboptimal KIC filter is also suboptimal in the presence of unknown initial conditions; this, of course, would be the case whenever the initial condition is relatively small so that it does not affect the worst case estimation error.

The paper is organized as follows: in the next section the problem is defined in terms of ℓ^∞ norms. In Section 3 the problem is put to a model matching form, and the solution follows for stable systems in subsection 3.1 where we separate the unknown initial condition case from the known (KIC); in subsection 3.2 the case of unstable systems is treated by appropriatelly transforming the problem to the stable case. Finally, we conclude in Section 4.

In the paper the following notation and terminology is utilized: $x(i)$, $A(i,j)$ represent the ith and the ijth element respectively of the real vector x and the real matrix A. Also, $A(i,.)$ represents the ith row of A, $|x|_\infty \stackrel{\text{def}}{=} \max_i |x(i)|$, $|A|_\infty \stackrel{\text{def}}{=} \max_i \sum_j |A(i,j)|$. If $y = \{y_0, y_1, \ldots\}$ represents a sequence of real matrices y_i, then its λ-transform is $y(\lambda) \stackrel{\text{def}}{=} \sum_{i=0}^\infty \lambda^i y_i$. Furthermore, $\ell^1 \stackrel{\text{def}}{=} \{y : \|y\|_{\ell^1} \stackrel{\text{def}}{=} \sup_i |(y_i \ldots y_0)|_\infty < \infty\}$; in the case where y_i's are vectors we define $\ell^\infty \stackrel{\text{def}}{=} \{y : \|y\|_{\ell^\infty} \stackrel{\text{def}}{=} \sup_i |y_i|_\infty < \infty\}$, $\ell_e^\infty \stackrel{\text{def}}{=} \{y : P_k y \in \ell^\infty \ \forall k = 0, 1, \ldots\}$ where P_k is the truncation operator defined as $P_k y = \{y_0, \ldots, y_k, 0, 0, \ldots\}$. An operator T on ℓ_e^∞ is called causal if $P_k T = T P_k$, $k = 0, 1, \ldots$; T is stable if it is a bounded operator on ℓ^∞. The space of all linear causal bounded operators T on ℓ^∞ is denoted by $\mathcal{L}_{TV}$. If $T \in \mathcal{L}_{TV}$ it can represented with the following lower triangular matrix $T = \begin{pmatrix} t_{00} & 0 & \cdots \\ t_{10} & t_{11} & \cdots \\ \vdots & \vdots & \ddots \end{pmatrix}$ and $\|T\|_{\mathcal{L}_{TV}} = \sup_i |T(i,.)|_\infty$. $\mathcal{L}_{TI}$ is the subspace of $\mathcal{L}_{TV}$ which contains all causal time invariant ℓ^∞-bounded operators (i.e. Toeplitz matrices). Also, $\mathcal{L}_{TI}$ is isometrically isomorphic to ℓ^1 i.e., $\mathcal{L}_{TI} \simeq \ell^1$.

2. PROBLEM DEFINITION

Consider the following linear, time invariant, finite dimensional system

$$\begin{aligned} x_{k+1} &= Ax_k + Bw_k \\ z_k &= C_1 x_k \\ y_k &= Cx_k + \zeta_k \end{aligned} \tag{1}$$

where w, ζ are process and measurement noise respectively with $\left\| \begin{pmatrix} w \\ \zeta \end{pmatrix} \right\|_{\ell^\infty} \leq 1$, z is an output to be estimated, and y is the measurment signal. Also, associated to the above system, there is an unknown initial condition x_0 which can be arbitrary as long as $|x_0|_\infty \leq 1$. The problem of interest is as follows (OBJ):

Based on the measurments y, construct a linear causal estimator Q of the output z i.e., $\hat{z} = Qy$ such that the following worst case error is minimized: $J \stackrel{\text{def}}{=} \sup_{w,\,\zeta,\,x_0} \|z - \hat{z}\|_{\ell^\infty}$. Note that there is no loss of generallity in assuming that the uncertainty bounds are all equal to 1. In the case where the norm bounds on w, ζ, x_0 are different than 1, we can always normalize the bounds by appropriate scaling. Next, we transform the problem to an estimation problem where the initial condition is equal to zero. This is done by considering the time varying system

$$\begin{aligned} \bar{x}_{k+1} &= A\bar{x}_k + Bw_k + L_k d_k \\ z_k &= C_1 \bar{x}_k + D_{1k} d_k \\ y_k &= C\bar{x}_k + \zeta_k + D_k d_k \\ \bar{x}_0 &= 0 \end{aligned} \tag{2}$$

where $L_k = \begin{cases} A, & k = 0 \\ 0, & k > 0 \end{cases}$, $D_{1k} = \begin{cases} C_1, & k = 0 \\ 0, & k > 0 \end{cases}$, $D_k = \begin{cases} C, & k = 0 \\ 0, & k > 0 \end{cases}$, w, ζ are as before, d is a disturbance with $\|d\|_{\ell^\infty} \leq 1$, and the system has initial condition $\bar{x}_0 = 0$. Letting $\tilde{w} \stackrel{\text{def}}{=} \begin{pmatrix} w \\ d \\ \zeta \end{pmatrix}$ the following lemma can be easily verified:

Lemma 2.1 *The estimation problem (OBJ) is equivalent to finding a linear causal map Q for the system of Equation 2 such that the criterion $\sup_{\tilde{w}} \|z - \hat{z}\|_{\ell^\infty}$ is minimized with $\hat{z} = Qy$, $\|\tilde{w}\|_{\ell^\infty} \leq 1$ and $\bar{x}_0 = 0$.*

3. PROBLEM SOLUTION

Pertaining to the system of Equation 2 let H, V represent the maps $H = (H_{zw}\ H_{zd}\ H_{z\zeta}) : \tilde{w} \rightarrow z$, $V = (V_{yw}\ V_{yd}\ V_{y\zeta}) : \tilde{w} \rightarrow y$ Note H_{zw}, $H_{z\zeta}$, V_{yw}, $V_{y\zeta}$ are time invariant with λ-transforms $H_{zw}(\lambda) = C_1((1/\lambda)I - A)^{-1}B$, $H_{z\zeta}(\lambda) = 0$, $V_{yw}(\lambda) = C((1/\lambda)I - A)^{-1}B$, $V_{y\zeta}(\lambda) = I$. The map $\tilde{w} \rightarrow z - \hat{z}$ is given as $T \stackrel{\text{def}}{=} H - QV$. Lemma 2.1 states that we are seeking for Q to minimize the ℓ^∞ induced norm of the map T i.e., to minimize $\|T\|_{\mathcal{L}_{TV}} = \|H - QV\|_{\mathcal{L}_{TV}}$. Clearly, since the map $\zeta \rightarrow z - \hat{z}$ is equal to $-Q$ then Q should be a stable operator in $\mathcal{L}_{TV}$ so that the cost J is bounded. To make our point clearer we consider first the case where the system in Equation 1 is stable i.e., the eigenvalues of A have magnitude strictly less than 1.

Stable Systems

Note, that since we assumed that the system is stable then H, $V \in \mathcal{L}_{TV}$. In addition, H_{zw}, $H_{z\zeta}$, V_{yw}, $V_{y\zeta}$ are in $\mathcal{L}_{TI}$. First we consider the case of known initial conditions for the system of Equation 1.

Known initial condition: Without loss of generality, since the system is linear, we may assume that $x_0 = 0$ which ammounts to setting $d = 0$ in system of Equation 2. In this case the estimation problem transforms to a model maching problem involving time invariant systems

$$\mu_0 \stackrel{\text{def}}{=} \inf_{Q \in \mathcal{L}_{TV}} \|(H_{zw}\ 0) - Q(V_{yw}\ I)\|_{\mathcal{L}_{TV}} \tag{3}$$

In [13] it was shown that, for the above minimization, time varying Q offers no advantage over time invariant. As a matter of fact, for this type of problems even nonlinear Q does not perform better than LTI Q [4]. The problem of finding the optimal Q in $\mathcal{L}_{TI}$ is a ℓ^1-optimization problem. The reader is referred to [3,5,8,6] in order to see how solutions can be obtained using linear programming methods. More specifically, this problem has a "2-block" structure which implies that the optimization problem is, in general, an infinite dimensional linear programming problem. Approximate, finite dimensional, linear programming methods of solution are established in [3,5,8,6]. Using these methods one can obtain recursive Q's that achieve performance within any predefined distance from optimal.

Certain properties of the optimal solution to the above problem that provide intuition are presented in the propositions that follow.

Proposition 3.1 *Let $\|V_{yw}\|_{\ell^1} \leq 1$. Then, $\mu_0 = \|H_{zw}\|_{\ell^1}$ and hence, $\overline{Q}_0 = 0$ is an optimal filter.*

The above proposition has an interesting interpretation: recall that the map from the measurement noise ζ to the measurment signal y has norm $\|I\|_{\ell^1} = 1$; the interpretation therefore is that if the "signal to noise ratio" given by $\|V_{yw}\|_{\ell^1} / \|I\|$ is less than 1 then the best estimate is 0. Clearly, such cases are not interesting for estimation since any useful information is severely corrupted by measurment noise.

The next proposition gives a sufficient condition for the problem to have in fact a 1-block structure.

Proposition 3.2 *Let $V_{yw}(\lambda) = \lambda V_o(\lambda)$ where V_o has a left inverse V_{ol} in $\mathcal{L}_{TI}$ with $\|V_{ol}\|_{\ell^1} \leq 1$. Then, the optimal Q of Equation 3 is also optimal for the problem $\mu_{01} = \inf_{Q\in\ell^1} \|H_{zw} - QV_{yw}\|_{\ell^1}$.*

The above proposotion shows that under the stated conditions, the optimal KIC estimator is obtained by ignoring the measurement noise and minimizing the effect only of the process noise. In this case the solution is dominated by the 1-block structure. Note also that in this case $\|V_{yw}\|_{\ell^1} = \|V_o\|_{\ell^1} \geq \|V_{ol}\|_{\ell^1}^{-1} \geq 1$. However, the condition $\|V_{yw}\| \geq 1$ alone (i.e., "signal to noise" ratio ≥ 1) is not in general sufficient for a 1-block structure dominance. Next, we treat the more difficult case of unknown initial conditions.

Unknown initial condition: In the case where the initial condition is unknown but bounded as $|x_0|_\infty \leq 1$ the operators H and V are time varying and can be identified with the following lower triangular matrix representation $H = \begin{pmatrix} h_{00} & 0 \\ h & H_0 \end{pmatrix}$, $V = \begin{pmatrix} v_{00} & 0 \\ v & V_0 \end{pmatrix}$ where $h_{00} = (0 \;\; C_1 \;\; 0)$, $v_{00} = (0 \;\; C \;\; I)$, $h = (h(i,.))_{i=0}^\infty$, $v = (v(i,.))_{i=0}^\infty$ are the $\infty \times 1$ block matrices given as $h(i,.) = (C_1A^iB \;\; C_1A^{i+1} \;\; 0)$, $v(i,.) = (CA^iB \;\; CA^{i+1} \;\; 0)$, and H_0, V_0 are the time invariant operators with the Toeplitz representation $H_0 = \begin{pmatrix} h_0 & 0 & \cdots \\ h_1 & h_0 & \cdots \\ \vdots & \vdots & \ddots \end{pmatrix}$, $V_0 = \begin{pmatrix} v_0 & 0 & \cdots \\ v_1 & v_0 & \cdots \\ \vdots & \vdots & \ddots \end{pmatrix}$ with

$$h_0 = (0 \;\; 0 \;\; 0),\; h_i = (C_1A^{i-1}B \;\; 0 \;\; 0),\;\; i \geq 1$$
$$v_0 = (0 \;\; 0 \;\; I),\; v_i = (CA^{i-1}B \;\; 0 \;\; 0),\;\; i \geq 1$$

Identifying the estimator $Q \in \mathcal{L}_{TV}$ as a $\infty \times \infty$ lower triangular matrix we can partition it as $Q = \begin{pmatrix} q_{00} & 0 \\ q & Q_0 \end{pmatrix}$ where $q = (q(i,.))_{i=0}^\infty$ is a block $\infty \times 1$ matrix and Q_0 is a block $\infty \times \infty$ lower triangular matrix. We note that Q_0 is not necessarily a time invariant operator i.e., Toeplitz. The resulting map T is represented as

$$T = \begin{pmatrix} t_{00} & 0 \\ t & T_0 \end{pmatrix} = \begin{pmatrix} h_{00} - q_{00}v_{00} & 0 \\ h - qv_{00} - Q_0v & H_0 - Q_0V_0 \end{pmatrix}.$$

Note that H_0, V_0 are equal to $(H_{zw} \; 0 \; 0)$, $(H_{yw} \; 0 \; I)$ respectively which are in turn identical to $(H_{zw} \; 0)$, $(H_{yw} \; I)$ that we considered in the known initial condition case. Hence, $\mu_0 = \inf_{Q_0\in\mathcal{L}_{TV}} \|H_0 - Q_0V_0\|_{\mathcal{L}_{TV}}$.

Let now $\mu \stackrel{\text{def}}{=} \inf_{Q\in\mathcal{L}_{TV}} \|H - QV\|_{\mathcal{L}_{TV}}$, and define the "pointwise cost" $\nu_i \stackrel{\text{def}}{=} \inf_{Q(i,.)} |T(i,.)|_\infty$. This implies $\nu_0 = \inf_{q_{00}} |t_{00}|_\infty = \inf_{q_{00}} |h_{00} - q_{00}v_{00}|_\infty$ and for $i \geq 0$ $\nu_{i+1} = \inf_{q(i,.),Q_0(i,.)} |(h(i,.) - q(i,.)v_{00} - Q_0(i,.)v \;\; H_0(i,.) - Q_0(i,.)V_0)|_\infty$. Observe that because of the definition of the $|\bullet|_\infty$ matrix norm, the computation of ν_i as well as of the corresponding optimizer $\hat{Q}(i,.)$ is a finite dimensional linear programming problem. The variables to be specified are the elements of the (block) row $\hat{Q}(i,.)$ i.e., the elements in $\hat{Q}(i,j)$, $j = 0,\ldots,i$ since $\hat{Q}(i,j) = 0$, $j > i$. Clearly, the optimal $\hat{Q}(i,.)$ should have bounded elements for, otherwise, the cost is infinite; hence ν_i can be achieved. The optimal cost ν_i is in fact the optimal (smallest) worst case error $|z_i - \hat{z}_i|_\infty$ that one can obtain based on the measurements $y_0, y_1, \ldots, y_i$. In particular, the optimal pointwise estimate will be given by $\hat{z}_i = \sum_{j=0}^i \hat{Q}(i,j)y_j$. Our model matching approach for the pointwise optimal estimate is in essence equivalent with the approach of [9,14] where a general set membership uncertainty framework is utilized. Next, we present a lemma that demonstrates a basic relation of the optimal infinite horizon cost μ with μ_0 and ν_i's :

Lemma 3.1 *Given any integer $N = 0,1,\ldots$ the following holds $\mu \geq \max(\nu_0, \nu_1, \ldots, \nu_N, \mu_0)$.*

Therefore, if one can find a Q and a N such that $\|T\|_{\mathcal{L}_{TV}} \leq \max(\nu_0, \nu_1, \ldots, \nu_N, \mu_0) + \epsilon$ for some given $\epsilon > 0$, then, Q is a ϵ-suboptimal solution. In the sequel we demonstrate how we can achieve this. To this end, let $\epsilon > 0$ and let $\overline{Q}_0$ be a time invariant operator in $\mathcal{L}_{TI}$ that satisfies $\left\|H_0 - \overline{Q}_0V_0\right\|_{\mathcal{L}_{TV}} \leq \mu_0 + \epsilon/2$. As we already mentioned in the known initial condition case, this is always possible. Let $\overline{Q}_0$ and $\overline{T}_0 \stackrel{\text{def}}{=} H_0 - \overline{Q}_0V_0$ have the Toeplitz representations $\overline{Q}_0 = \begin{pmatrix} \overline{q}_0 & 0 & \cdots \\ \overline{q}_1 & \overline{q}_0 & \cdots \\ \vdots & \vdots & \ddots \end{pmatrix}$, $\overline{T}_0 = \begin{pmatrix} \overline{t}_0 & 0 & \cdots \\ \overline{t}_1 & \overline{t}_0 & \cdots \\ \vdots & \vdots & \ddots \end{pmatrix}$. Also, define the following sequences in ℓ^1 $h_{zd} = \{C_1, C_1A, C_1A^2 \ldots\}$, $v_{yd} = \{C, CA, CA^2, \ldots\}$, $\phi = h_{zd} - \overline{Q}_0v_{yd}$. Since $\phi \in \ell^1$ there exists a computable integer N such that $|\phi_i|_\infty < \epsilon/2 \;\; \forall i > N$. Let now $\hat{q}_{00}$, $\hat{q}(i,.)$, $\hat{Q}_0(i,.)$ be such that $\nu_0 = |h_{00} - \hat{q}_{00}v_{00}|_\infty$, and for $i = 0,\ldots,N-1$

$$\nu_{i+1} = |(h(i,.) - \hat{q}(i,.)v_{00} - \hat{Q}_0(i,.)v \;\; H_0(i,.) - \hat{Q}_0(i,.)V_0)|_\infty \tag{4}$$

As already mentioned, the computation of $\hat{q}_{00}$, $\hat{q}(i,.)$, $\hat{Q}_0(i,.)$ can be performed by solving the $N+1$ independent finite dimensional linear programs of Equation 4. The following theorem gives a ϵ-suboptimal estimator

Theorem 3.1 *The estimator $\overline{Q} = \begin{pmatrix} q_{00} & 0 \\ q & Q_0 \end{pmatrix}$ with $q_{00} = \hat{q}_{00}$, $q(i,.) = \begin{cases} \hat{q}(i,.), & 0 \leq i < N \\ \overline{q}_{i+1}, & i \geq N \end{cases}$, $Q_0(i,.) = \begin{cases} \hat{Q}(i,.), & 0 \leq i < N \\ \overline{Q}_0(i,.), & i \geq N \end{cases}$, achieves $\left\|H - \overline{Q}V\right\|_{\mathcal{L}_{TV}} \leq \mu + \epsilon$.*

Note that for time $k \geq N+1$ the estimator of Theorem 3.1 coincides with the ϵ-suboptimal estimator $\overline{Q}_0$ that corresponds to the known initial condition problem i.e., $(\overline{Q}y)(k) = (\overline{Q}_0y)(k)$, $k \geq N+1$. Hence the meaning of the above theorem is that the known initial condition estimator will provide ϵ-suboptimal estimates after the precomputable time index N. This time N ammounts to the time that takes the known initial condition estimator $\overline{Q}_0$ to drive the estimation error that is due only to initial conditions within a small bound $\epsilon/2$. For the time period 0 to N, the (sub)optimal estimates can be obtained by solving $N+1$ linear programs; these estimates correspond to obtaining the optimal pointwise esimates. Once time N is passed, optimal pointwise estimation does not improve on the infinite time cost J. An interesting question is the following: under what condition does the estimator $\overline{Q}_0$ provide as good performance as $\overline{Q}$? Clearly, that will be the case whenever the initial condition uncertainty is small enough. In particular, for $\overline{Q}_0$ to be as good as $\overline{Q}$ it is sufficient that $|(H-\overline{Q}_0V)(i,.)|_\infty \leq \mu_0+\epsilon,\ i=0,1,\ldots,N$ which means that $\mu_0 \leq \mu \leq \mu_0+\epsilon$. Hence, we have the following

Corollary 3.1 *The known initial condition estimator $\overline{Q}_0$ is ϵ-suboptimal if $|(\overline{T}_0(i,.)\ \ \phi_i)|_\infty \leq \mu_0+\epsilon,\ i=0,1,\ldots,N$.*

In the case where the above condition is violated one can find by how much the initial condition uncertainty has to be reduced so that $\overline{Q}_0$ yields ϵ-suboptimal performance. To do this, let $a_m = \max\{a \in (0,1) : |(\overline{T}_0(i,.)\ a\phi_i)|_\infty \leq \mu_0+\epsilon,\ i=0,1,\ldots,N\}$. Then, $\overline{Q}_0$ is ϵ-suboptimal whenever $|x_0|_\infty \leq a_m$, and $\left\|\begin{pmatrix} w \\ \zeta \end{pmatrix}\right\|_{\ell^\infty} \leq 1$.

Discussion: In the previous sections we presented how suboptimal estimators can be constructed. Although the construction of a suboptimal reqursive KIC estimator is easy, the construction in the case of unknown initial conditions is more involved. In particular, one has to solve the $N+1$ linear programs of Equation 4 in order to obtain the optimal filter for the time $0-N$, and then "switch" to the KIC estimator. The time index N is computed from the knowledge of the KIC filter by requiring that the sequence ϕ satisfies $|\phi_i|_\infty < \epsilon/2\ \forall i > N$. In what follows we comment upon the size of N and relate it to the solution of the KIC case, when the latter results to a finite impulse response (FIR) map $\overline{T}_0$ from the input $\begin{pmatrix} w \\ \zeta \end{pmatrix}$ to the estimation error $z-\hat{z}$. First we have the following existence lemma

Lemma 3.2 *If (A,C) is an observable pair, then, given any $\epsilon > 0$, there exists a suboptimal map $\overline{T}_0 : \begin{pmatrix} w \\ \zeta \end{pmatrix} \rightarrow z-\hat{z}$ of the form $\overline{T}_0(\lambda) = \overline{t}_0 + \overline{t}_1\lambda + \ldots + \overline{t}_n\lambda^n$ such that $\left\|\overline{T}_0\right\|_{\ell^1} \leq \mu_0+\epsilon$ for some n.*

Such a solution can be obtained with the methods in [3,5,8]. This of course implies that the suboptimal $\overline{Q}_0$ has also finite impulse response. The support n of the suboptimal solution will in general depend on the degree of desired accuracy: the larger n is allowed, the closer to the optimal value μ_0 the filter performance assumes. This is not to say however, that the optimal solution should necessarily have infinite support. Let now $\overline{Q}_0(\lambda) = \sum_{i=0}^{n} \overline{q}_i\lambda^i$ and let n_0 be the number of eigenvalues of A at the origin (if any). The following lemma characterizes a bound on the index N.

Lemma 3.3 *If (A,B) is a reachable pair, then $\phi_i = 0$ for $i > n_0+n-1$.*

In view of the above, one can always take $N = n_0 + n - 1$. Also, in the case where suboptimal solutions are FIR, the support of ϕ does not depend on the bound on the size $|x_0|_\infty$ of the initial condition uncertainty. More specificaly, if take $N = n_0+n-1$ suggested in Lemma 3.3 then $\phi_i = 0,\ i > N$ no matter what the bound on the initial condition uncertainty may be; i.e., the index N will be the same for any initial condition uncertainty. This is to say that the (sub)optimal filter $\overline{Q}$ produces the same estimates as the KIC filter $\overline{Q}_0$ for time larger than N no matter what the initial conditions are. Note however, that the estimates of $\overline{Q}$ for time $0-N$ depend on the size of the initial condition uncertainty. Finally, we should also stress, that the index N does not represent the time that takes the initial condition response of the system to become arbitrarily small but rather, it represents the time that takes the KIC filter to bring the error due to initial condition to a small level. Hence, even in systems with very "slow" eigenvalues the resulting N need not necessarily be large as the following example indicates:

Example 3.1 Consider the system $x_{k+1} = \begin{pmatrix} 0 & -.9 \\ 1 & 0 \end{pmatrix} x_k + \begin{pmatrix} 1 \\ 0 \end{pmatrix} w_k,\ z_k = (1\ \ 0)x_k,\ y_k = (.5\ \ 1)x_k + \zeta_k$ where w, ζ are process and observation noise respectively with $|w_k| \leq 1$ and $|\zeta_k| \leq 1$ for $k = 0,1,2,\ldots$. The eigenvalues of the A-matrix are located at $\pm.9487\jmath$. For the known initial condition case we obtain (within 10^{-8} of the optimal) $\overline{Q}_0(\lambda) = .3673 - .7347\lambda$, $\overline{T}_0(\lambda) = (.8163\lambda\ \ .3673 - .7347\lambda)$, and $\mu_0 = 1.9183$. For the index N we have that $\phi_i = 0,\ i > 0$ and hence, we can take $N = 0$; this means that if initial condition uncertainty is allowed, there is only 1 linear program to be solved in order to compute the suboptimal estimator.

Unstable Systems
In the case of unstable systems i.e., when the eigenvalues of A are not in the open unit disk, the problem can be transformed using coprime factorization to a model matching problem involving only stable systems. Moreover, the resulting problem has the same structure as in the stable system case. This is done in the sequel. First, we make the following assumption

Assumption 3.1 *The pair (A,C) is detectable.*

Due to the above assumption there is an estimator Q_1 such that the resulting error $z-\hat{z}$ is bounded. Such a Q_1 can be taken any observer of the form: $\hat{x}_{k+1} = A\hat{x}_k - K(y_k - C\hat{x}_k)$, $\hat{z}_k = C_1\hat{x}_k$, $\hat{x}_0 = 0$ where K is any matrix such that $A_K = A+KC$ is a stable matrix. Now, we can parametrize Q as $Q = Q_1+Q_2$ where Q_2 is any system in $\mathcal{L}_{TV}$. If we define $\tilde{H} \stackrel{\text{def}}{=} H - Q_1V$ then $\tilde{H} \in \mathcal{L}_{TV}$. A state space description of $\tilde{H}$ is $\tilde{H} = (A_K, (B\ \ L_k+KD_k\ \ K), C_1, (0\ \ D_{1k}\ \ 0))$, $k = 0,1,\ldots$

Then, the filtering problems becomes $\mu = \inf_{Q_2 \in \mathcal{L}_{TV}} \left\| \tilde{H} - Q_2 V \right\|_{\mathcal{L}_{TV}}$ Note that $V = (V_{yw}\ V_{yd}\ V_{y\zeta}) = (V_{yw}\ V_{yd}\ I)$ is unstable; let G represent the map $\begin{pmatrix} w \\ d \end{pmatrix} \to y$ i.e., $G = (V_{yw}\ V_{yd})$ and consider a coprime factorization $G = \tilde{M}^{-1}\tilde{N}$. A set of (left)coprime factors can be obtained from the following state space description [7, 12]: $\tilde{M} = (A_K, K, C, I)$, $\tilde{N} = (A_K, (B_K)_k, C, (D_K)_k)$, $k = 0, 1, \ldots$ where $(B_K)_k = (B \quad L_k + KD_k)$, $(D_K)_k = (0 \quad D_k)$, $k = 0, 1, \ldots$. Note that $\tilde{M} \in \mathcal{L}_{TI}$ whereas $\tilde{N} \in \mathcal{L}_{TV}$. The following lemma can now be derived

Lemma 3.4 *The estimation error $z - \hat{z}$ is bounded iff $Q_2 = \tilde{Q}\tilde{M}$, where $\tilde{Q}$ is any stable operator in $\mathcal{L}_{TV}$.*

In view of the above, if $\tilde{V} = (\tilde{N}\ \tilde{M})$ then $\tilde{V}$ is in $\mathcal{L}_{TV}$ with state space representation $\tilde{V} = (A_K, (B\ L_k + KD_k\ K), C, (0\ D_k\ I))$, $k = 0, 1, \ldots$ Moreover, the estimation problem transforms to $\inf_{\tilde{Q} \in \mathcal{L}_{TV}} \left\| \tilde{H} - \tilde{Q}\tilde{V} \right\|_{\mathcal{L}_{TV}}$ where $\tilde{H}$, $\tilde{V}$ are stable maps in $\mathcal{L}_{TV}$. From the state space desctiptions of $\tilde{H}$, $\tilde{V}$ it is clear that $\tilde{H}$, $\tilde{V}$ are of the same form as in the stable system case: the new A-matrix is A_K and the new B-matrix is $(B \quad L_k + KD_k \quad K)$ whereas the rest remain the same. In terms of input-output matrix representations they are of the form $\tilde{H} = \begin{pmatrix} \tilde{h}_{00} & 0 \\ \tilde{h} & \tilde{H}_0 \end{pmatrix}$, $\tilde{V} = \begin{pmatrix} \tilde{v}_{00} & 0 \\ \tilde{v} & \tilde{V}_0 \end{pmatrix}$ where $\tilde{h}$, $\tilde{v}$ are $\infty \times 1$ block matrices the rows of which decay exponentially fast (as the largest eigenvalue of $A + KC$) and $\tilde{H}_0$, $\tilde{V}_0$ are time invariant operators in $\mathcal{L}_{TI}$. In particular, $\tilde{H}_0$ and $\tilde{V}_0$ are given as $\tilde{H}_0 = (A_K, (B\ 0\ K), C_1, (0\ 0\ 0))$, $\tilde{V}_0 = (A_K, (B\ 0\ K), C, (0\ 0\ I))$ Also, note that $\tilde{V}_0 = (\tilde{N}_0\ 0\ \tilde{M}_0)$ where $\tilde{M}_0$ and $\tilde{N}_0$ are the left coprime factors of V_{yw} given by $\tilde{M}_0 = \tilde{M}$, $\tilde{N}_0 = (A_K, B, C, 0)$. From the above discussion, it follows that the problem is exactly as in the case of stable systems and a ϵ-suboptimal $\overline{\tilde{Q}}$ can be obtained similarly. The suboptimal estimator in this case is given as $\overline{Q} = Q_1 + \overline{\tilde{Q}}\tilde{M}$. Finally note that in the known initial condition case, one has to solve the following ℓ^1 optimization $\mu_0 = \inf_{\tilde{Q}_0 \in \mathcal{L}_{TI}} \left\| \tilde{H}_0 - \tilde{Q}_0 \tilde{V}_0 \right\|_{\mathcal{L}_{TI}}$ Once a suboptimal $\overline{\tilde{Q}}_0$ is obtained the corresponding suboptimal filter is given as $\overline{Q}_0 = Q_1 + \overline{\tilde{Q}}_0 \tilde{M}_0$.

4. CONCLUSIONS

In this paper we presented how suboptimal, infinite-horizon estimators can be constructed utilizing a model matching approach over ℓ^∞ bounded operators. In the known initial condition (KIC) case the problem is simply a ℓ^1-optimization. In the unknown initial condition case, optimal pointwise estimation can be used until a precomputable time index after which, the KIC recursive estimator can be utilized.

5. REFERENCES

[1] T. Basar, "Optimum performance levels for minimax filters, predictors and smoothers," *Syst. Contr. Lett.*, vol. 16, 1991, pp. 309-318.

[2] D.P. Bertsekas and I.B. Rhodes, "Recursive state estimation for set membership description of uncertainty," *IEEE Trans. A-C*, Vol AC-16, 1971, pp. 117-124.

[3] M.A. Dahleh and J.B. Pearson. "Optimal rejection of persistent disturbances, robust stability and mixed sensitivity minimization," *IEEE Trans. Automat. Contr.*, Vol AC-33, pp. 722-731, August 1988.

[4] M.A. Dahleh and J.S. Shamma, "Rejection of persistent bounded disturbances: Nonlinear controllers", *Syst. Contr. Lett.*, vol. 18, 1992, pp. 245-253.

[5] M.A. Dahleh. "BIBO stability robustness in the presence of coprime factor perturbations," *IEEE Trans. A-C*, Vol AC-37, no 3, 1992.

[6] I. Diaz-Bobillo and M.A. Dahleh, "Minimization of the maximum Peak-to-Peak Gain: The general multiblock problem," to appear IEEE trans A-C.

[7] B.A. Francis. *A Course in H_∞ Control Theory*, Springer-Verlag, 1987.

[8] J.S. McDonald and J.B. Pearson, "ℓ^1-Optimal control of multivariable systems with output norm onstraints," *Automatica*, Vol 27, 1991, pp. 317-329.

[9] M. Milanese and R. Tempo, "Optimal algorithms theory for robust estimation and prediction," *IEEE Trans. A-C*, Vol AC-30, 1985, pp. 730-738.

[10] M. Milanese and A. Vicino, "Optimal estimation for dynamic systems with set membership uncertainty: an overview," *Automatica*, Vol 27, 1991, pp. 997-1011.

[11] K.M. Nagpal and P.P. Khargonekar, "Filtering and smoothing in an H^∞ setting," *IEEE Trans. A-C*, Vol AC-36, no 2, 1991, pp. 152-166.

[12] R. Ravi, P.P. Khargonekar, K.D. Minto and C.N. Nett. "Controller parametrization for time-varying multirate plants" *IEEE Trans on Automatic Control*, AC-35, no. 11, pp. 1259-1262, November 1990.

[13] J.S. Shamma and M.A. Dahleh, Time varying vs. time invariant compensation for rejection of persistent bounded disturbances and robust stability, *IEEE Trans. A-C*, Vol AC-36, July 1991, pp. 838-847.

[14] R. Tempo, "Robust estimation and filtering in the presence of bounded noise," *IEEE Trans. A-C*, Vol AC-33, no 9, 1988, pp. 864-867.

Proceedings of the
American Control Conference
San Francisco, California • June 1993

A Disturbance Accommodating Estimator for Bilinear Systems

Mehrdad Saif
saif@cs.sfu.ca
School of Engineering Science
Simon Fraser University
Burnaby, BC V5A 1S6
CANADA

Abstract

In this article, an approach for designing a reduced order estimator for a class of nonlinear systems driven by external completely unknown and time varying disturbances is presented. The estimator's error dynamics in this case is completely independent of the input. Necessary and sufficient conditions for existence of the estimator along with numerical examples are presented.

I. Introduction

A special class of nonlinear systems in which the control appears as both additive and multiplicative terms is commonly referred to as bilinear systems. There are a number of motivation in studying this class of nonlinear systems. First, they closely resemble linear systems for which a well developed theory exists, and even offer certain advantages to linear systems-for instance controllability wise. Secondly, bilinear systems arise in variety of physical situations, and many practical processes are of this type. Nuclear reactors, field controlled d.c. motors, HVAC systems, heat exchangers, and many biomedical processes such as the immune system, among variety of other systems are known to be described by bilinear system of differential equations (see [1,2] and references cited).

Just as in linear system theory, the problem of estimating the state of a bilinear system is an important problem for designing controllers for such systems. However, the estimation problem for bilinear systems has not been studied as extensively as that of linear systems. Hara and Furuta [4], presented one of the earlier results on the design of minimum and full order state and linear function of state estimators for bilinear systems. Later, Derese and Noldus [5], presented some additional results on the necessary and sufficient conditions for existence of bilinear estimator proposed by [4]. Williamson [3], presented a design approach for single output systems. In [6,7] Lyapunov based approach for designing bilinear estimators was proposed. As opposed to the approach of [4], the error dynamics in the approach of [6,7] is dependent on the input to the system. However, the estimators proposed by [6,7] are applicable to a broader class of bilinear system than that of [4].

The objective of this paper is to provide an approach for designing reduced order bilinear estimators for bilinear systems that are driven by unknown disturbances. Such unknown disturbances can arise in the dynamical equation of the bilinear system due to system parameter uncertainties, actuator failures, plant disturbances, etc. The problem of estimating the state of a linear system driven by unknown disturbances have been addressed by a number of authors (see [8,9] and references cited). It is felt that the approach presented there for designing such estimators, referred to as unknown input observer (UIO) for linear systems, is particularly attractive due to its simplicity in the design and computation. As well, the design of estimators for descriptor systems driven by unknown disturbances has also been the subject of investigation by several authors (e.g. [10,11]). To our knowledge, only [12] considers the design of estimator for bilinear systems driven by disturbances. However, in [12] it is assumed that the disturbances satisfy a certain homogeneous differential equation. That is, the disturbances are modeled by the output of a known unforced linear system. In such a case, the disturbance model can simply be augmented with that of the plant, resulting in a higher dimensional disturbance free bilinear system for which the approach of [4] was used for estimating the unavailable state variables. In the present paper, we make no a priori assumption whatsoever with regard to the unknown disturbances.

II. Preliminaries

Consider a time invariant bilinear system with no uncontrollable state described in state space formulation

$$\dot{\tilde{\mathbf{x}}} = \tilde{\mathbf{A}}^o\tilde{\mathbf{x}} + \sum_{i=1}^{q}\tilde{\mathbf{A}}^i u_i\tilde{\mathbf{x}} + \tilde{\mathbf{B}}\mathbf{u} + \tilde{\mathbf{D}}\mathbf{v} \qquad (1-a)$$

$$\mathbf{y} = \tilde{\mathbf{C}}\tilde{\mathbf{x}} = [\mathbf{0} \quad \mathbf{I}]\tilde{\mathbf{x}} \qquad (1-b)$$

where $\tilde{\mathbf{x}} \in \Re^n, \mathbf{u} \in \Re^q, \mathbf{v} \in \Re^m, \mathbf{y} \in \Re^p$ are the state, control, unknown disturbance (input), and output, respectively. Note that in (1-b) a special form for the observation matrix $\tilde{\mathbf{C}}$ is assumed. This is not a restriction, since as long as $\tilde{\mathbf{C}}$ is of full rank there exist a similarity transformation that can bring the output equation in that desired form [13]. Also, in the remainder of this paper it is assumed that the disturbance distribution matrix, $\tilde{\mathbf{D}}$, is of full rank. Note that if this is not the case, then $\tilde{\mathbf{D}}$ can be written as product of two full rank matrices, and upon redefining the disturbance input, we can end up with a new disturbance distribution matrix which would be of full rank.

The system in (1) can be written in the following partitioned form

$$\dot{\tilde{\mathbf{x}}} = \begin{bmatrix}\dot{\tilde{\mathbf{x}}}_1\\ \dot{\tilde{\mathbf{x}}}_2\end{bmatrix} = \begin{bmatrix}\tilde{\mathbf{A}}^o_{11} & \tilde{\mathbf{A}}^o_{12}\\ \tilde{\mathbf{A}}^o_{21} & \tilde{\mathbf{A}}^o_{22}\end{bmatrix}\begin{bmatrix}\tilde{\mathbf{x}}_1\\ \tilde{\mathbf{x}}_2\end{bmatrix} + \sum_{i=1}^{q}\begin{bmatrix}\tilde{\mathbf{A}}^i_{11} & \tilde{\mathbf{A}}^i_{12}\\ \tilde{\mathbf{A}}^i_{21} & \tilde{\mathbf{A}}^i_{22}\end{bmatrix}u_i\begin{bmatrix}\tilde{\mathbf{x}}_1\\ \tilde{\mathbf{x}}_2\end{bmatrix} + \begin{bmatrix}\tilde{\mathbf{B}}_1\\ \tilde{\mathbf{B}}_2\end{bmatrix}\mathbf{u} + \begin{bmatrix}\tilde{\mathbf{D}}_1\\ \tilde{\mathbf{D}}_2\end{bmatrix}\mathbf{v} \qquad (2-a)$$

$$\mathbf{y} = \tilde{\mathbf{C}}\tilde{\mathbf{x}} = [\mathbf{0} \quad \mathbf{I}]\tilde{\mathbf{x}} \qquad (2-b)$$

where
$\tilde{\mathbf{A}}^o_{11} \in \Re^{(n-p)x(n-p)}, \tilde{\mathbf{A}}^o_{12} \in \Re^{(n-p)xp}, \tilde{\mathbf{A}}^o_{21} \in \Re^{px(n-p)}$, and $\tilde{\mathbf{A}}^o_{22} \in \Re^{pxp}$ and the remaining matrices are appropriately dimensioned. Similar to [4], we state the following Definition.

Definition-The Bilinear Canonical Form (BICAF) of the bilinear system in (1) and (2) is described as

$$\dot{\mathbf{x}}=\begin{bmatrix}\dot{\mathbf{x}}_1\\ \dot{\mathbf{x}}_2\end{bmatrix}=\begin{bmatrix}\mathbf{A}^o_{11} & \mathbf{A}^o_{12}\\ \mathbf{A}^o_{21} & \mathbf{A}^o_{22}\end{bmatrix}\begin{bmatrix}\mathbf{x}_1\\ \mathbf{x}_2\end{bmatrix}+\sum_{i=1}^{q}\begin{bmatrix}\mathbf{0} & \mathbf{A}^i_{12}\\ \mathbf{A}^i_{21} & \mathbf{A}^i_{22}\end{bmatrix}u_i\begin{bmatrix}\mathbf{x}_1\\ \mathbf{x}_2\end{bmatrix}+\begin{bmatrix}\mathbf{B}_1\\ \mathbf{B}_2\end{bmatrix}\mathbf{u}+\begin{bmatrix}\mathbf{0}\\ \mathbf{D}_2\end{bmatrix}\mathbf{v} \quad (3-a)$$

$$\mathbf{y}=\mathbf{C}\mathbf{x}=[\mathbf{0}\quad \mathbf{I}]\mathbf{x} \quad (3-b)$$

Theorem 1 - The Bilinear system described in (1) and (2) can be transformed into BICAF using the similarity transformation matrix $\mathbf{P}_1$, where $\mathbf{x}=\mathbf{P}_1\tilde{\mathbf{x}}$, given by

$$\mathbf{P}_1=\begin{bmatrix}\mathbf{I}_{(n-p)x(n-p)} & \mathbf{E}\\ \mathbf{0} & \mathbf{I}_{pxp}\end{bmatrix} \quad (4)$$

if and only if

$$\rho(\mathbf{CT})=\rho(\mathbf{T}_2)=\rho(\mathbf{T})=r\leq \min(p,m+q(n-p)) \quad (5)$$

where $\rho(.)$ denotes rank of the matrix argument, and

$$\mathbf{T}=\begin{bmatrix}\mathbf{T}_1\\ \mathbf{T}_2\end{bmatrix} \quad (6)$$

$$\mathbf{T}_1=[\tilde{\mathbf{A}}^1_{11}\quad \tilde{\mathbf{A}}^2_{11}\quad \ldots\ldots\quad \tilde{\mathbf{A}}^q_{11}\quad \tilde{\mathbf{D}}_1]$$

$$\mathbf{T}_2=[\tilde{\mathbf{A}}^1_{21}\quad \tilde{\mathbf{A}}^2_{21}\quad \ldots\ldots\quad \tilde{\mathbf{A}}^q_{21}\quad \tilde{\mathbf{D}}_2]$$

Proof: The above can be proved by simply noticing that given $\mathbf{x}=\mathbf{P}_1\tilde{\mathbf{x}}$, then

$$\mathbf{A}^i=\mathbf{P}_1\tilde{\mathbf{A}}^i\mathbf{P}_1^{-1}=\begin{bmatrix}\tilde{\mathbf{A}}^i_{11}+\mathbf{E}\tilde{\mathbf{A}}^i_{21} & \tilde{\mathbf{A}}^i_{12}+\mathbf{E}\mathbf{A}^i_{21}-\tilde{\mathbf{A}}^i_{11}\mathbf{E}-\mathbf{E}\tilde{\mathbf{A}}^i_{21}\mathbf{E}\\ \tilde{\mathbf{A}}^i_{21} & \tilde{\mathbf{A}}^i_{22}-\tilde{\mathbf{A}}^i_{21}\mathbf{E}\end{bmatrix}$$

As well

$$\mathbf{D}=\mathbf{P}_1\tilde{\mathbf{D}}=\begin{bmatrix}\tilde{\mathbf{D}}_1+\mathbf{E}\tilde{\mathbf{D}}_2\\ \tilde{\mathbf{D}}_2\end{bmatrix}$$

Thus, we require

$$\tilde{\mathbf{A}}^i_{11}+\mathbf{E}\tilde{\mathbf{A}}^i_{21}=\mathbf{0} \qquad \forall i=1,2,\ldots,q$$

$$\tilde{\mathbf{D}}_1+\mathbf{E}\tilde{\mathbf{D}}_2=\mathbf{0}$$

Given $\mathbf{T}$ as in (6), the above can be written as

$$\mathbf{E}\mathbf{T}_2=-\mathbf{T}_1 \quad (7)$$

Clearly, a solution to (7) will exist if and only if $\rho(\mathbf{T}_2)=\rho(\mathbf{T})$, and given the structure of the observation matrix $\tilde{\mathbf{C}}$ in (1), condition (5) is readily obtained. Note also that due to the structure of the transformation operator $\mathbf{P}_1$ and the fact that $\mathbf{C}=\tilde{\mathbf{C}}\mathbf{P}_1^{-1}$, the desired form of the $\tilde{\mathbf{C}}$ is not altered under this transformation, i.e., $\mathbf{C}=\tilde{\mathbf{C}}$.

III. Bilinear Estimator

The objective is to design an estimator of the form

$$\dot{\mathbf{w}}=\mathbf{G}_1\mathbf{w}+\mathbf{G}_2\mathbf{y}+\mathbf{G}_3\mathbf{u}+\sum_{i=1}^{q}\mathbf{G}^i_4u_i\mathbf{y} \quad (8)$$

where

$$\hat{\mathbf{x}}=\mathbf{N}_1\mathbf{w}+\mathbf{N}_2\mathbf{y} \quad (9)$$

so that $\|\tilde{\mathbf{x}}(t)-\hat{\mathbf{x}}(t)\|\to 0$ as $t\to\infty$, independently of the input.

Theorem 2 - A necessary condition for existence of the bilinear estimator described above is that $p\geq m$.

Proof: Assume that an asymptotically estimator of the form (8) exist. In such a case the error dynamics would be of the form

$$\dot{\mathbf{e}}=\mathbf{Q}\mathbf{e} \quad (10)$$

where

$$\mathbf{e}=\tilde{\mathbf{x}}-\hat{\mathbf{x}}$$

and $\mathbf{Q}$ is a matrix with all of its eigenvalues in the left hand plane. Now using (2) and (8-10), we obtain the following conditions which have to be satisfied

$$\mathbf{J}\tilde{\mathbf{A}}^o-\mathbf{Q}\mathbf{J}-\mathbf{N}_1\mathbf{G}_2\tilde{\mathbf{C}}=\mathbf{0}$$

$$\mathbf{J}\tilde{\mathbf{B}}-\mathbf{N}_1\mathbf{G}_3=\mathbf{0}$$

$$\mathbf{J}\tilde{\mathbf{A}}^i-\mathbf{N}_1\mathbf{G}^i_4\tilde{\mathbf{C}}=\mathbf{0} \qquad \forall i=1,2,\ldots,q$$

$$\mathbf{Q}\mathbf{N}_1-\mathbf{N}_1\mathbf{G}_1=\mathbf{0}$$

$$\mathbf{J}\tilde{\mathbf{D}}=\mathbf{0}$$

$$\text{where}\quad \tilde{\mathbf{D}}=\begin{bmatrix}\tilde{\mathbf{D}}_1\\ \tilde{\mathbf{D}}_2\end{bmatrix},\quad \text{and}\quad \mathbf{J}=(\mathbf{I}-\mathbf{N}_2\tilde{\mathbf{C}})$$

The last equation in the above implies that

$$\mathbf{N}_2\tilde{\mathbf{D}}_2=\tilde{\mathbf{D}}$$

Clearly, for $\mathbf{N}_2$ to exist, $\rho(\tilde{\mathbf{D}}_2)=\rho(\tilde{\mathbf{D}})=$ m has to be satisfied. Moreover, by Sylvester's Inequality Theorem, this would imply that $p\geq m$.

Before we state the main result for the bilinear estimator design, assume that $p>m$ and consider the following new partition of the system in BICAF

$$\dot{\mathbf{x}}=\begin{bmatrix}\dot{\mathbf{x}}_1\\ \dot{\mathbf{y}}_1\\ \dot{\mathbf{y}}_2\end{bmatrix}=\begin{bmatrix}\mathbf{A}^o_1\\ \mathbf{A}^o_2\\ \mathbf{A}^o_3\end{bmatrix}\begin{bmatrix}\mathbf{x}_1\\ \mathbf{y}_1\\ \mathbf{y}_2\end{bmatrix}+\sum_{i=1}^{q}\begin{bmatrix}\mathbf{A}^i_1\\ \mathbf{A}^i_2\\ \mathbf{A}^i_3\end{bmatrix}u_i\begin{bmatrix}\mathbf{x}_1\\ \mathbf{y}_1\\ \mathbf{y}_2\end{bmatrix}+\begin{bmatrix}\mathbf{B}_1\\ \mathbf{B}_2\\ \mathbf{B}_3\end{bmatrix}\mathbf{u}+\begin{bmatrix}\mathbf{0}\\ \mathbf{D}_{21}\\ \mathbf{D}_{22}\end{bmatrix}\mathbf{v} \quad (11-a)$$

$$\begin{bmatrix}\mathbf{y}_1\\ \mathbf{y}_2\end{bmatrix}=\begin{bmatrix}\mathbf{0} & \mathbf{I}_{(p-m)x(p-m)} & \mathbf{0}\\ \mathbf{0} & \mathbf{0} & \mathbf{I}_{mxm}\end{bmatrix}\begin{bmatrix}\mathbf{x}_1\\ \mathbf{x}_2\\ \mathbf{x}_3\end{bmatrix} \quad (11-b)$$

where without loss of generality we have assumed that $\mathbf{D}_{22}$ is of full rank. Now, premultiply (11-a) by matrix $\mathbf{P}_2$ given by

$$\mathbf{P}_2=\begin{bmatrix}\mathbf{I} & \mathbf{0} & \mathbf{0}\\ \mathbf{0} & \mathbf{I} & -\mathbf{D}_{21}\mathbf{D}_{22}^{-1}\\ \mathbf{0} & \mathbf{0} & \mathbf{I}\end{bmatrix}$$

to get

$$\begin{bmatrix}\dot{\mathbf{x}}_1\\ \dot{\mathbf{y}}_1-\mathbf{D}_{21}\mathbf{D}_{22}^{-1}\dot{\mathbf{y}}_2\\ \dot{\mathbf{y}}_2\end{bmatrix}=\begin{bmatrix}\mathbf{A}^o_1\\ \mathbf{A}^o_2-\mathbf{D}_{21}\mathbf{D}_{22}^{-1}\mathbf{A}^o_3\\ \mathbf{A}^o_3\end{bmatrix}\begin{bmatrix}\mathbf{x}_1\\ \mathbf{y}_1\\ \mathbf{y}_2\end{bmatrix}+\sum_{i=1}^{q}\begin{bmatrix}\mathbf{A}^i_1\\ \mathbf{A}^i_2-\mathbf{D}_{21}\mathbf{D}_{22}^{-1}\mathbf{A}^i_3\\ \mathbf{A}^i_3\end{bmatrix}u_i\begin{bmatrix}\mathbf{x}_1\\ \mathbf{y}_1\\ \mathbf{y}_2\end{bmatrix}+$$

$$\begin{bmatrix}\mathbf{B}_1\\ \mathbf{B}_2-\mathbf{D}_{21}\mathbf{D}_{22}^{-1}\mathbf{B}_3\\ \mathbf{B}_3\end{bmatrix}\mathbf{u}+\begin{bmatrix}\mathbf{0}\\ \mathbf{0}\\ \mathbf{D}_{22}\end{bmatrix}\mathbf{v} \quad (12)$$

Upon defining

$$\bar{\mathbf{A}}_1^i = \mathbf{A}_1^i \quad \forall i = 0,1,2,\ldots,q \quad \text{and} \quad \bar{\mathbf{B}}_1 = \mathbf{B}_1 \tag{13}$$

$$\bar{\mathbf{A}}_2^i = \mathbf{A}_2^i - \mathbf{D}_{21}\mathbf{D}_{22}^{-1}\mathbf{A}_3^i \quad \forall i = 0,1,2,\ldots,q \quad \text{and} \quad \bar{\mathbf{B}}_2 = \mathbf{B}_2 - \mathbf{D}_{21}\mathbf{D}_{22}^{-1}\mathbf{B}_3 \tag{14}$$

$$\bar{\mathbf{A}}_j^i = \begin{bmatrix} \bar{\mathbf{A}}_{j1}^i & \bar{\mathbf{A}}_{j2}^i & \bar{\mathbf{A}}_{j3}^i \end{bmatrix} \quad j = 1,2 \quad \text{and} \quad \forall i = 0,1,2,\ldots,q \tag{15}$$

$$\bar{\mathbf{u}} = \bar{\mathbf{A}}_{12}^o \mathbf{y}_1 + \bar{\mathbf{A}}_{13}^o \mathbf{y}_2 + \sum_{i=1}^{q}\left(\bar{\mathbf{A}}_{12}^i u_i \mathbf{y}_1 + \bar{\mathbf{A}}_{13}^i u_i \mathbf{y}_2\right) + \bar{\mathbf{B}}_1 \mathbf{u} \tag{16}$$

$$\mathbf{z} = \dot{\mathbf{y}}_1 - \mathbf{D}_{21}\mathbf{D}_{22}^{-1}\dot{\mathbf{y}}_2 - \bar{\mathbf{A}}_{22}^o \mathbf{y}_1 - \bar{\mathbf{A}}_{23}^o \mathbf{y}_2 - \sum_{i=1}^{q}\left(\bar{\mathbf{A}}_{22}^i u_i \mathbf{y}_1 + \bar{\mathbf{A}}_{23}^i u_i \mathbf{y}_2\right) - \bar{\mathbf{B}}_2 \mathbf{u} \tag{17}$$

and using (12), the above definitions and keeping in mind that the $\bar{\mathbf{A}}_{11}^i = 0 \quad \forall i$, we get the following dynamical system

$$\dot{\mathbf{x}}_1 = \bar{\mathbf{A}}_{11}^o \mathbf{x}_1 + \bar{\mathbf{u}} \tag{18-a}$$

$$\mathbf{z} = \bar{\mathbf{A}}_{21}^o \mathbf{x}_1 + \sum_{i=1}^{q} \bar{\mathbf{A}}_{21}^i u_i \mathbf{x}_1 \tag{18-b}$$

Note now that the system in (18-a) does not involve any nonlinearities and is driven by completely known signal $\bar{\mathbf{u}}$. Thus, we can define an estimator of the following form for the system in (18)

$$\dot{\hat{\mathbf{x}}}_1 = \bar{\mathbf{A}}_{11}^o \hat{\mathbf{x}}_1 + \bar{\mathbf{u}} + \mathbf{M}\left(\mathbf{z} - \bar{\mathbf{A}}_{21}^o \hat{\mathbf{x}}_1 - \sum_{i=1}^{q} \bar{\mathbf{A}}_{21}^i u_i \hat{\mathbf{x}}_1\right)$$

where $\mathbf{M}$ is the estimator's gain. Inserting (16) and (17) into the above we get

$$\dot{\hat{\mathbf{x}}}_1 = \left(\bar{\mathbf{A}}_{11}^o - \mathbf{M}\bar{\mathbf{A}}_{21}^o\right)\hat{\mathbf{x}}_1 - \sum_{i=1}^{q} \mathbf{M}\bar{\mathbf{A}}_{21}^i u_i \hat{\mathbf{x}}_1 + \mathbf{M}(\dot{\mathbf{y}}_1 - \mathbf{D}_{21}\mathbf{D}_{22}^{-1}\dot{\mathbf{y}}_2) + \left[\left(\bar{\mathbf{A}}_{12}^o - \mathbf{M}\bar{\mathbf{A}}_{22}^o\right) + \sum_{i=1}^{q}\left(\bar{\mathbf{A}}_{12}^i u_i - \mathbf{M}\bar{\mathbf{A}}_{22}^i u_i\right)\right]\mathbf{y}_1 +$$
$$\left[\left(\bar{\mathbf{A}}_{13}^o - \mathbf{M}\bar{\mathbf{A}}_{23}^o\right) + \sum_{i=1}^{q}\left(\bar{\mathbf{A}}_{13}^i u_i - \mathbf{M}\bar{\mathbf{A}}_{23}^i u_i\right)\right]\mathbf{y}_2 + (\bar{\mathbf{B}}_1 - \mathbf{M}\bar{\mathbf{B}}_2)\mathbf{u} \tag{19}$$

Eliminating the terms involving the derivatives of the outputs in the above by defining

$$\mathbf{w} = \hat{\mathbf{x}}_1 - \mathbf{M}(\mathbf{y}_1 - \mathbf{D}_{21}\mathbf{D}_{22}^{-1}\mathbf{y}_2)$$

and selecting $\mathbf{M}$ such that

$$\mathbf{M}\bar{\mathbf{A}}_{21}^i = \mathbf{0} \qquad \forall \quad i = 1,2,\ldots,q \tag{20}$$

will result in (8) and (9) where

$$\mathbf{G}_1 = \left(\bar{\mathbf{A}}_{11}^o - \mathbf{M}\bar{\mathbf{A}}_{21}^o\right) \tag{21}$$

$$\mathbf{G}_2 = [\mathbf{F} \qquad \mathbf{H}] \tag{22}$$

$$\mathbf{G}_3 = (\bar{\mathbf{B}}_1 - \mathbf{M}\bar{\mathbf{B}}_2) \tag{23}$$

$$\mathbf{G}_4^i = \left[\left(\bar{\mathbf{A}}_{12}^i - \mathbf{M}\bar{\mathbf{A}}_{22}^i\right) \quad \left(\bar{\mathbf{A}}_{13}^i - \mathbf{M}\bar{\mathbf{A}}_{23}^i\right)\right] \quad \forall i = 1,2,\ldots,q \tag{24}$$

$$\mathbf{F} = \left(\bar{\mathbf{A}}_{12}^o - \mathbf{M}\bar{\mathbf{A}}_{22}^o\right) + \mathbf{G}_1\mathbf{M} \tag{25}$$

$$\mathbf{H} = \left(\bar{\mathbf{A}}_{13}^o - \mathbf{M}\bar{\mathbf{A}}_{23}^o\right) - \mathbf{G}_1\mathbf{M}\mathbf{D}_{21}\mathbf{D}_{22}^{-1} \tag{26}$$

$$\mathbf{N} = [\mathbf{M} \qquad -\mathbf{M}\mathbf{D}_{21}\mathbf{D}_{22}^{-1}] \tag{27}$$

$$\mathbf{N}_1 = \begin{bmatrix} \mathbf{I} \\ \mathbf{0} \end{bmatrix} \qquad \mathbf{N}_2 = \begin{bmatrix} \mathbf{N} \\ \mathbf{I} \end{bmatrix} \tag{28}$$

Defining the estimation error of the reduced order estimator as

$$\mathbf{e}_1 = \mathbf{x}_1 - \hat{\mathbf{x}}_1 \tag{29}$$

and using (8),(12-18),and (20-29), it is easy to show that the error dynamics of the estimator is governed by

$$\dot{\mathbf{e}}_1 = \mathbf{G}_1\mathbf{e}_1 \tag{30}$$

Thus, in order to achieve asymptotic convergence of the estimation error, the estimator's gain $\mathbf{M}$ has to belong to the set $\aleph$ given by

$$\aleph = \left\{ \mathbf{M}:\mathbf{M}\bar{\mathbf{A}}_{21}^i = \mathbf{0} \quad \forall i = 1,2,\ldots,q \quad \text{and} \quad \Re e\left(\Lambda\left(\bar{\mathbf{A}}_{11}^o - \mathbf{M}\bar{\mathbf{A}}_{21}^o\right)\right) < 0 \right\}$$

The procedure to select the appropriate estimator gain is similar to that proposed in [4]. Consider writing $\mathbf{M}$ as

$$\mathbf{M} = \mathbf{M}_1\mathbf{M}_2 \tag{31}$$

where $\mathbf{M}_2 \in \Re^{o\times(p-m)}$ and o is the nullity of Ω defined by

$$\Omega = \begin{bmatrix} \bar{\mathbf{A}}_{21}^1 & \bar{\mathbf{A}}_{21}^2 & \ldots & \bar{\mathbf{A}}_{21}^q \end{bmatrix}$$

Thus, $\mathbf{M}_2^T$ is a matrix whose columns are the basis vectors for the null space of Ω^T. Next $\mathbf{M}_1$ is selected such that all the eigenvalues of $(\bar{\mathbf{A}}_{11}^o - \mathbf{M}_1\mathbf{M}_2\bar{\mathbf{A}}_{21}^o)$have desired eigenspectrum. Of course, such $\mathbf{M}_1$ will exists if and only if the pair $\{\bar{\mathbf{A}}_{11}^o, \mathbf{M}_2\bar{\mathbf{A}}_{21}^o\}$ is completely observable [13].

To summarize the results we shall state the following Theorem.

Theorem 3 - A reduced order estimator of the type (8) for the bilinear system in (1) exists if and only if
a) The transformation to BICAF exists, and
b) The set $\aleph$ is not an empty set.
Furthermore the eigenspectrum of the estimator can be arbitrarily assigned if and only if
c) p>m, and
d) The pair $\{\bar{\mathbf{A}}_{11}^o, \mathbf{M}_2\bar{\mathbf{A}}_{21}^o\}$ is completely observable.

With regard to condition (c) in the above, we shall state the following:
Theorem 4 - The eigenspectrum of the estimator can not be arbitrarily placed if p=m. However, an asymptotically stable estimator with fixed rate of convergence may exist.

The above can easily be verified by considering the BICAF in (3), definition (29), and the estimator given by (8), with

$$\hat{\mathbf{x}}_1 = \mathbf{w} + \mathbf{N}\mathbf{y} \tag{32}$$

Now if an asymptotically stable estimator exist, then we must have

$$\dot{\mathbf{e}}_1 = \mathbf{Q}_1\mathbf{e}_1$$

where $\mathbf{Q}_1$ is a matrix with all of its eigenvalues in the left hand plane. Using the above and the previous equations, it is easy to arrive at the following

$$\mathbf{Q}_1 = \mathbf{A}_{11}^o - \mathbf{N}\mathbf{A}_{21}^o$$

$$\mathbf{G}_1 = \mathbf{Q}_1$$

$$\mathbf{G}_2 = \mathbf{B}_1 - \mathbf{N}\mathbf{B}_2$$

$$\mathbf{G}_3 = \mathbf{A}_{12}^o - \mathbf{N}\mathbf{A}_{22}^o + \mathbf{Q}_1\mathbf{N}$$

$$\mathbf{G}_4^i = \mathbf{A}_{12}^i - \mathbf{N}\mathbf{A}_{22}^i \qquad \forall \quad i = 1,2,\ldots,q$$

$$\mathbf{N}\mathbf{A}_{21}^i = \mathbf{0} \qquad \forall \quad i = 1,2,\ldots,q$$

$$\mathbf{N}\mathbf{D}_2 = \mathbf{0}$$

Now, recall that $\mathbf{D}_2$ is a pxp full rank matrix. As a result, the last equation will then imply that the estimator's gain $\mathbf{N}$ is zero. Thus,

$$\dot{\mathbf{w}} = \mathbf{A}^o_{11}\mathbf{w} + \mathbf{B}_1 u + \mathbf{A}^o_{12}\mathbf{y} + \sum_{i=1}^{q} \mathbf{A}^i_{12} u_i \mathbf{y} \tag{33}$$

Clearly, the structure of the estimator is completely fixed by the system's parameters, and it would be asymptotically stable if and only if all the eigenvalues of $\mathbf{A}^o_{11}$ are in the left hand plane.

IV. Illustrative Examples

Example 1 - Consider the following bilinear system

$$\dot{\tilde{\mathbf{x}}} = \begin{bmatrix} -1 & -2 & 0 & 3 \\ 2 & 0 & -1 & 1 \\ 0 & 2 & -3 & 1 \\ 0 & -1 & 1 & 0 \end{bmatrix}\tilde{\mathbf{x}} + \begin{bmatrix} -1 & -0.5 & -1 & 0 \\ 1 & 0 & -0.5 & -1 \\ 0 & -1 & 0 & -0.5 \\ -1 & 0 & 0 & 0 \end{bmatrix} u\tilde{\mathbf{x}} + \begin{bmatrix} 1 \\ 0 \\ -1 \\ 1 \end{bmatrix} u + \begin{bmatrix} 1 \\ -1 \\ 0 \\ 1 \end{bmatrix} v$$

$$\mathbf{y} = \begin{bmatrix} 0 & 1 & 0 & 0 \\ 0 & 0 & 1 & 0 \\ 0 & 0 & 0 & 1 \end{bmatrix}\tilde{\mathbf{x}}$$

It is desired to design an estimator capable of estimating the first state variable of this system. The following similarity transformation was obtained using the results of Section II:

$$\mathbf{P}_1 = \begin{bmatrix} 1 & 1 & 0 & 0 \\ 0 & 1 & 0 & 0 \\ 0 & 0 & 1 & 0 \\ 0 & 0 & 0 & 1 \end{bmatrix}$$

Using the above, the following BICAF representation of the system was obtained

$$\dot{\mathbf{x}} = \begin{bmatrix} 1 & -3 & -1 & 4 \\ 2 & -2 & -1 & 1 \\ 0 & 2 & -3 & 1 \\ 0 & -1 & 1 & 0 \end{bmatrix}\mathbf{x} + \begin{bmatrix} 0 & -0.5 & -1.5 & -1 \\ 1 & -1 & -0.5 & -1 \\ 0 & -1 & 0 & -0.5 \\ -1 & 1 & 0 & 0 \end{bmatrix} u\mathbf{x} + \begin{bmatrix} 1 \\ 0 \\ -1 \\ 1 \end{bmatrix} u + \begin{bmatrix} 0 \\ -1 \\ 0 \\ 1 \end{bmatrix} v$$

$$\mathbf{y} = \begin{bmatrix} 0 & 1 & 0 & 0 \\ 0 & 0 & 1 & 0 \\ 0 & 0 & 0 & 1 \end{bmatrix}\mathbf{x}$$

Next, a first order bilinear estimator with its pole at -10 was designed using equations (8,9,19-25). The resulting estimator is given by

$$\dot{\mathrm{w}} = -10\mathrm{w} + [-41.5 \quad -1.0 \quad -56.5]\mathbf{y} - 4.5\mathrm{u} + [-0.5 \quad 1.25 \quad 4.5]\mathrm{u}\mathbf{y}$$

$$\hat{\mathbf{x}} = \begin{bmatrix} 1 \\ 0 \\ 0 \\ 0 \end{bmatrix}\mathrm{w} + \begin{bmatrix} 5.5 & 0 & 5.5 \\ 1 & 0 & 0 \\ 0 & 1 & 0 \\ 0 & 0 & 1 \end{bmatrix}\mathbf{y}$$

The performance of the estimator for the following set of conditions

$$\mathrm{v} = 1 + \sin(2\pi t)$$

$$\mathrm{u} = 1$$

$$\mathbf{x}(0) = [1 \quad 0 \quad 0 \quad 0]^T$$

is illustrated in Figure 1, where the solid line is the $\mathbf{x}_1$ and the dotted line is the estimator's estimate ($\hat{\mathbf{x}}_1$).

Figure 1 - Actual and estimated trajectories

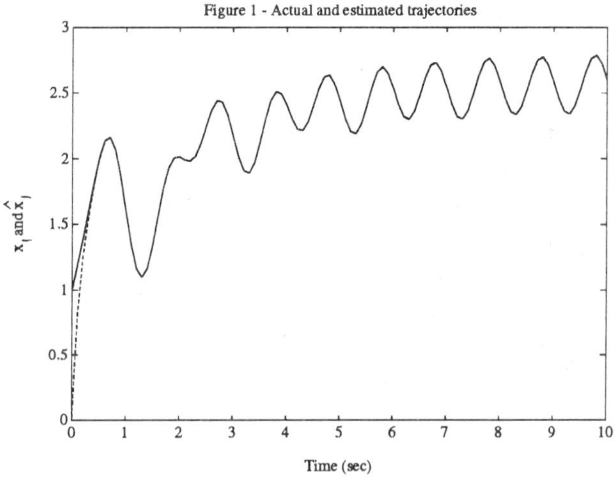

Example 2 - Consider the following MIMO bilinear system

$$\dot{\tilde{\mathbf{x}}} = \begin{bmatrix} -6 & 0 & 4 & 0 \\ 0 & -1 & 0 & 1 \\ -4 & 1 & 0 & 0 \\ 0 & 0 & -1 & -3 \end{bmatrix}\tilde{\mathbf{x}} + \sum_{i=1}^{2} \begin{bmatrix} 0 & 0 & 0 & 0 \\ 0 & 0 & 0 & 0 \\ 0 & 0 & 1 & 0 \\ 0 & 0 & 0 & 0 \end{bmatrix} u_i\tilde{\mathbf{x}} + \begin{bmatrix} 1 & 0 \\ 0 & 0 \\ 0 & 1 \\ 1 & -1 \end{bmatrix}\mathbf{u} + \begin{bmatrix} 1 & 0 \\ 0 & 0 \\ 1 & 0 \\ 0 & 1 \end{bmatrix}\mathbf{v}$$

$$\mathbf{y} = \begin{bmatrix} 0 & 0 & 1 & 0 \\ 0 & 0 & 0 & 1 \end{bmatrix}\tilde{\mathbf{x}}$$

The following transformation matrix will bring the system into BICAF

$$\mathbf{P}_1 = \begin{bmatrix} 1 & 0 & -1 & 0 \\ 0 & 1 & 0 & 0 \\ 0 & 0 & 1 & 0 \\ 0 & 0 & 0 & 1 \end{bmatrix}$$

where

$$\dot{\mathbf{x}} = \begin{bmatrix} -2 & -1 & 2 & 0 \\ 0 & -1 & 0 & 1 \\ -4 & 1 & 4 & 0 \\ 0 & 0 & -1 & -3 \end{bmatrix}\mathbf{x} + \sum_{i=1}^{2} \begin{bmatrix} 0 & 0 & -1 & 0 \\ 0 & 0 & 0 & 0 \\ 0 & 0 & 1 & 0 \\ 0 & 0 & 0 & 0 \end{bmatrix} u_i\mathbf{x} + \begin{bmatrix} 1 & -1 \\ 0 & 0 \\ 0 & 1 \\ 1 & -1 \end{bmatrix}\mathbf{u} + \begin{bmatrix} 0 & 0 \\ 0 & 0 \\ 1 & 0 \\ 0 & 1 \end{bmatrix}\mathbf{v}$$

$$\mathbf{y} = \begin{bmatrix} 0 & 0 & 1 & 0 \\ 0 & 0 & 0 & 1 \end{bmatrix}\mathbf{x}$$

Note that here the number of disturbance inputs are equal to that of the outputs. Thus, it is not possible to design an estimator with arbitrary rate of convergence. However, it can easily be verified that a second order estimator with fixed poles located at {-2,-1} exists for this system and is given by (33)

$$\dot{\mathbf{w}} = \begin{bmatrix} -2 & -1 \\ 0 & -1 \end{bmatrix}\mathbf{w} + \begin{bmatrix} 2 & 0 \\ 0 & 1 \end{bmatrix}\mathbf{y} + \sum_{i=1}^{2} \begin{bmatrix} -1 & 0 \\ 0 & 0 \end{bmatrix} u_i\mathbf{y} + \begin{bmatrix} 1 & -1 \\ 0 & 0 \end{bmatrix}\mathbf{u}$$

The following set of conditions were considered for the purpose of the simulation

$$u_1 = 1 + \sin(t)$$

$$u_2 = -2$$

$$v_1 = 1 + 2\sin(2\pi t)$$

$$v_2 = 4\cos(2\pi t) \quad \text{and}$$

$$x(0) = [1 \quad 2 \quad 0 \quad 0]^T$$

Figures 2, and 3 illustrate the performance of the estimator.

Figure 2 - Actual and estimated trajectories

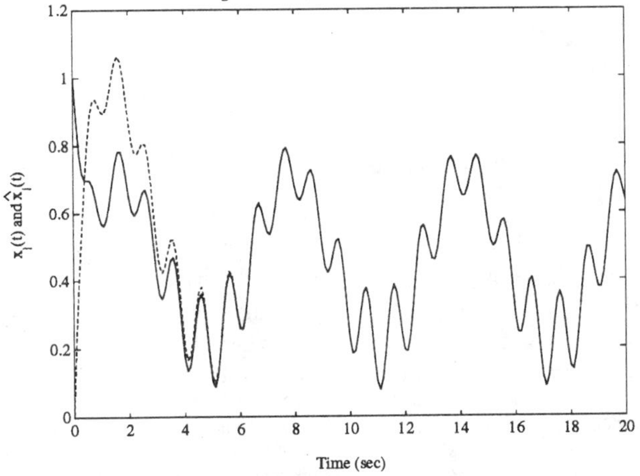

Figure 3 - Actual and estimated trajectories

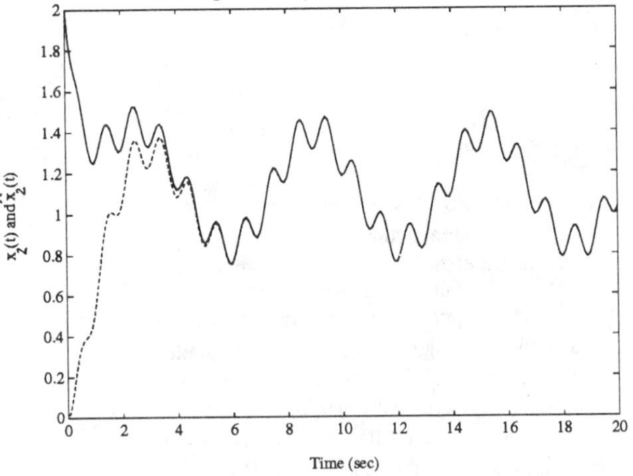

It should be mentioned once again that in this case it is not possible to achieve faster rate of convergence for the estimator.

V. Conclusions

A simple approach for designing reduced order estimators for bilinear systems driven by completely unknown disturbances was introduced in this paper. Necessary and sufficient conditions for existence of such an estimator was given. The appealing feature of the estimation scheme is that the estimation error dynamics is completely independent of the input to the nonlinear system. On the other hand, due to this fact, certain restrictive conditions have to be satisfied (see Theorem 3 and Theorem 4) in order for an asymptotically stable estimator with arbitrary rate of convergence to exist. Numerical examples illustrate that when these aforementioned conditions are satisfied, the proposed approach provides a powerful and simple means for estimating the state of a bilinear system, accommodating time varying completely unknown disturbances at the same time.

Acknowledgement

This work was supported by Natural Sciences and Engineering Research Council (NSERC) of Canada, and the President's Research Grant from SFU.

References

[1] R.R. Mohler, *Nonlinear Systems: Applications to Bilinear Systems*, Vol. II, **Prentice Hall**, NJ, 1991.

[2] C. Bruni, G. DiPillo, and G. Koch, *Bilinear Systems: An Appealing Class of "Nearly Linear" Systems in Theory and Applications*, **IEEE Trans. Aut. Control**, Vol. AC-19, pp. 334-348, 1974.

[3] D. Williamson, *Observation of Bilinear Systems with Applications to Biological Control*, **Automatica**, Vol. 13, pp. 243-254, 1977.

[4] S. Hara, and K. Furuta, *Minimal Order State Observers for Bilinear Systems*, **Int. J. Control**, Vol. 24, No. 5, pp.705-718, 1976.

[5] I.A. Derese, and E.J. Noldus, *Existence of Bilinear State Observers for Bilinear Systems*, **IEEE Trans. Aut. Control**, Vol. AC-26, No. 2, pp. 590-592, 1981.

[6] Y. Funahashi, *Stable State Estimator for Bilinear Systems*, **Int. J. Control**, Vol. 29, No. 2, pp. 181-188, 1979.

[7] I.A. Derese, P. Stevens, and E.J. Noldus, *Observers for Bilinear Systems with Bounded Input*, **Int. J. Syst. Sci.**, Vol. 10, No. 6, pp. 649-668, 1979.

[8] Y. Guan, and M. Saif, *A Novel Approach to the Design of Unknown Input Observers*, **IEEE Trans. Aut. Control**, Vol. 36, No. 5, pp. 632-635, 1991.

[9] M. Saif, and Y. Guan, *Decentralized State Estimation in Large-scale Interconnected Dynamical Systems*, **Automatica**, Vol. 28, No. 1, pp. 215-219, 1992.

[10] C.W. Yang, and H.L. Tan, *Observer Design for Singular Systems with Unknown Inputs*, **Int. J. Cont.**, Vol. 49, No. 6, pp. 1937-1946, 1989.

[11] P.N. Paraskevopoulos, F.N. Koumboulis, K.G. Tzierakis, and G.E. Panagiotakis, *Observer Design for Generalized State Space Systems with Unknown Inputs*, **Systems & Control Letters**, Vol. 18, pp. 309-321, 1992.

[12] Y.Q. Ying, M. Rao, and Y.X. Sun, *State-Disturbance Composite Observer for Bilinear Systems*, **Proceedings of the 1990 American Control Conference,** pp. 1917-1921. Also, *Bilinear State-Disturbance Composite Observer and Its Applications*, **Int. J. Syst. Sci.**, Vol. 22, No. 12, pp. 2489-2498, 1991.

[13] C.T. Chen, *Linear Systems Theory and Design*, **HRW Publishing**, NY, 1984.

Proceedings of the
American Control Conference
San Francisco, California • June 1993

IMPROVING THE ROBUSTNESS OF STATIONARY KALMAN FILTER VIA PARAMETRIC DESIGN

Steve Daley# and Hong Wang*

#Engineering Research Centre, GEC-Alsthom, Leicester, U.K.
*Department of Paper Science, UMIST, Manchester, U.K.

Abstract

This paper presents a novel design approach for a robust sub-optimal Kalman filter using parametric eigenstructure placement. Initially, a system without model uncertainty is considered, and a condition for the parametrically designed filter to be optimal is obtained. It is shown, under this condition, that there is a subset of the parametrically designed gain matrices which will also lead to a Kalman filter. For the system with structured model uncertainty, a performance functional index is constructed in which the penalty terms to both the sensitivity and the non-optimality of the filter are included. A parametrically designed gain matrix is then evaluated via standard minimisation and the so-obtained filter is shown to be sub-optimal and more robust than Kalman filter.

Preliminaries

Consider the following system without model uncertainties

$$dx(t) = Ax(t)dt + Bu(t)dt + d\omega(t) \quad (1)$$

$$dy(t) = Cx(t)dt + d\eta(t) \quad (2)$$

where $x(t) \in R^n$ is the state vector, $u(t) \in R^m$ is the control input and $y(t) \in R^p$ is the output vector. $\omega(t)$ and $\eta(t)$ are independent Brownian motion processes with

$$\mathrm{E}\{d\omega(t)d\omega^T(t)\} = Qdt \quad (3)$$

$$\mathrm{E}\{d\eta(t)d\eta^T(t)\} = Rdt \quad (4)$$

and $Q = Q^T \geq 0$ $R = R^T > 0$ are constant matrices. A, B and C are known parameter matrices with proper dimensions. It is well known, [1], that the minimum variance state estimation vector $\hat{x}(t)$ will satisfy the following equations

$$d\hat{x}(t) = A\hat{x}(t)dt + Bu(t)dt + K_{opt}(t)(dy(t) - C\hat{x}(t)dt) \quad (5)$$

$$\frac{dP(t)}{dt} = AP(t) + PA^T + Q - P(t)C^TR^{-1}CP(t) \quad (6)$$

$$K_{opt}(t) = P(t)C^TR^{-1} \quad (7)$$

Since all the parameter matrices of the system (1) are constant, the following stationary estimates can be obtained.

$$d\hat{x}(t) = A\hat{x}(t)dt + Bu(t)dt + K_{opt}(dy(t) - C\hat{x}(t)dt) \quad (8)$$

$$0 = AP + PA^T + Q - PC^TR^{-1}CP \quad (9)$$

$$K_{opt} = PC^TR^{-1} \quad (10)$$

In the rest of the paper, only the above stationary estimation will be considered. Define the estimation error as

$$\tilde{x}(t) = x(t) - \hat{x}(t) \quad (11)$$

then, it can be obtained that

$$d\tilde{x}(t) = (A - K_{opt}C)\tilde{x}(t)dt - K_{opt}d\eta(t) + d\omega(t) \quad (12)$$

where all the eigenvalues of $A - K_{opt}C$ lie inside the left hand complex plane. Denote $\Lambda = \{\lambda_1, \lambda_2, \ldots, \lambda_n\}$ as the set of eigenvalues of the matrix $A_c = A - K_{opt}C$. It is assumed that all these eigenvalues are distinct real values and are different from the eigenvalues of matrix A, as theoretically no difficult will arise in dealing with the case when there are common poles between them, [2]-[3]. Based on this assumption and from the parametric design viewpoint, the same eigenvalue assignment can also be achieved by the following gain

$$K = W^{-1}F \quad (13)$$

$$F = (f_1^T \ f_2^T \ . \ . \ . \ f_n^T)^T \quad (14)$$

$$W = (w_1^T \ w_2^T \ . \ . \ . \ w_n^T)^T = V^{-1} \quad (15)$$

$$w_i = f_iC(A - \lambda_iI)^{-1} \quad (16)$$

where $f_i(i = 1, 2, \ldots, n)$ are arbitrary parameter row vectors, $V = (v_1, v_2, \ldots, v_n)$ and v_i is eigenvector. Compared with K_{opt}, it can be seen that the parametric design will give a set of gain matrices. Moreover, with the proper choice of the parameter row vectors f_i, additional properties can be achieved, such as reducing the sensitivity of the eigenvalues of A_c to parameter variations, [2]. Therefore, a gain matrix K could be found which can not only assign the eigenvalues of matrix A_c to the set Λ, but also leads to a more robust filter which is insensitive to the parameter variations in matrix A, B and C. This forms the original purpose of this paper. As can be seen in the sequel, a systematic design procedure is obtained with which the users can easily reach a good balance between optimality and robustness of the resulting filter.

Optimality condition

Since the gain matrix $K = W^{-1}F$ will also assign the poles of the matrix A_c to desired locations, it is natural to consider the problem of selecting the arbitrary raws f_i such that the resulting gain will lead to the following minimum variance estimation

$$d\hat{x}(t) = A\hat{x}(t)dt + Bu(t)dt + K(dy(t) - C\hat{x}(t)) \quad (17)$$

This means that the equality $K = K_{opt}$ holds. The re-arrangement of this equality yields

$$f_i(R - C(A - \lambda_iI)^{-1}PC^T) = 0 \quad (18)$$

It can be seen that the null space of $(R - C(A - \lambda_iI)^{-1}PC^T)^T$ is not empty, therefore, the following theorem can be obtained

Theorem. 1 The state estimates (17) with parametric gain matrix $K = W^{-1}F$ is minimum variance estimates if and only if the arbitrary parametric vectors f_i $(i = 1, 2, \ldots, n)$ are chosen such that the equality

$$f_i(R - C(A - \lambda_i I)^{-1}PC^T) = 0 \quad (19)$$

holds and the resulting matrix W is invertible.

To simplify the notation of the next section, denote $\Sigma_i = R - C(A - \lambda_i I)^{-1}PC^T$.

Robust redesign

The presence of structured model uncertainties will now be considered since in practical systems modelling errors widely exist. In this case, the system equation becomes

$$dx(t) = (A + \Delta A(t))x(t)dt + (B + \Delta B(t))u(t)dt + d\omega(t) \quad (20)$$

$$dy(t) = (C + \Delta C(t))x(t)dt + d\eta(t) \quad (21)$$

where $\Delta A(t)$, $\Delta B(t)$ and $\Delta C(t)$ are structured model uncertainties of the form

$$\Delta A(t) = \sum_{i=1}^{l} M_i \varepsilon_i(t); \Delta B(t) = \sum_{i=1}^{l} N_i \varepsilon_i(t); \Delta C(t) = \sum_{i=1}^{l} L_i \varepsilon_i(t)$$

where matrices M_i, N_i and $L_i (i = 1,2,\ldots,l)$ are known whereas $\varepsilon_i(t)\ (i = 1,2,\ldots,l)$ are unknowns of possibly large values. The estimation error becomes

$$d\tilde{x}(t) = (A_c + \Delta A_c(t))\tilde{x}(t)dt + \Delta A_c(t)\hat{x}(t)dt + $$
$$+\Delta B(t)u(t)dt - Kd\eta(t) + d\omega(t) \quad (22)$$
$$\Delta A_c(t) = \Delta A(t) - K\Delta C(t) \quad (23)$$

In the presence of the structured model uncertainties, both the Kalman filter (5)-(7) and the parametrically designed filter using the gain matrix in (13) are no longer optimal in the sense that the estimation are not minimum variance and unbiased, in some cases they will even lead to an divergent estimator. Therefore, it is natural that modifications should be made to improve the performance of the estimation. For this work, the following improvements will be considered:

1) Enhance the robustness of the estimation with respect to the structured model uncertainties ΔA, ΔB and ΔC;

2) Ensure that the estimation is as good as possible, i.e., sub-minimize the variance of the estimation error.

To improve robustness, the sensitivity of the eigenvalues of A_c with respect to the model uncertainties needs to be minimized. Denote the sensitivity of the ith eigenvalue λ_i with respect to the variations of ε_j as

$$d\lambda_{ij} = \frac{\partial \lambda_i}{\partial \varepsilon_j} \quad (i = 1,2,\ldots,n; j = 1,2,\ldots,l) \quad (24)$$

and the sensitivities of w_i, v_i and A_c with respect to the variations of ε_j as

$$dw_{ij} = \frac{\partial w_i}{\partial \varepsilon_j}; dv_{ij} = \frac{\partial v_i}{\partial \varepsilon_j} \quad (25)$$

$$dA_{c_j} = \frac{\partial A_c}{\partial \varepsilon_j}; d\lambda_{ij} = w_i dA_{c_j} v_i \quad (26)$$

then

$$dA_{c_j} = M_j - W^{-1}FL_j \quad (27)$$

$$d\lambda_{ij} = f_i C(A - \lambda_i I)^{-1}(M_j - W^{-1}FL_j)v_i \quad (28)$$

It is therefore essential that the arbitrarily selected parameter vectors $f_i (i = 1,2,\ldots,n)$ should be chosen such that the objective function

$$J_1 = \sum_{i,j=1}^{n,l} \beta_{ij}^2 (d\lambda_{ij})^2 \quad (29)$$

is as small as possible, where β_{ij}^2 are weights.

To optimize the estimation, the resulting matrix $K = W^{-1}F$ should be as close as possible to the Kalman filter gain. Using the optimality condition in the previous section, the arbitrary parameter vectors $f_i (i = 1,2,\ldots,n)$ should be chosen such that

$$J_2 = \sum_{i=1}^{n} \eta_i^2 \| f_i \Sigma_i \| \quad (30)$$

is made as small as possible, where $\eta_i^2 (i = 1,2,\ldots,n)$ are weights.

Moreover, since the magnitude of the estimation error response depends on $v_i w_i$, to have a desirable estimation performance it is apparent that the variations of $v_i w_i$ with respect to the structured model uncertainties be as small as possible. Therefore, the objective function

$$J_3 = \sum_{i,j=1}^{n,l} \gamma_{ij}^2 \| d(v_i w_i)_{ij} \| = \sum_{i,j=1}^{n,l} \gamma_{ij}^2 \| (dv_{ij}) w_i + v_i (dw_{ij}) \| \quad (31)$$

should also be considered, where $\gamma_{ij}^2 (i = 1,2,\ldots,n; j = 1,2,\ldots,l)$ are weights. Combining (29), (30) and (31), the performance function

$$J_r = J_1 + J_2 + J_3 =$$
$$\sum_{i,j=1}^{n,l} \beta_{ij}^2 (d\lambda_{ij})^2 + \sum_{i=1}^{n} \eta_i^2 \| \Sigma_i f_i \| + \sum_{i,j=1}^{n,l} \gamma_{ij}^2 \| d(v_i w_i)_{ij} \| \quad (32)$$

can be obtained and the arbitrary parameters f_i should be chosen so that J_r is minimized .

Concluding remarks

Using the optimality condition under which the parametrically designed gain matrix will lead to a Kalman filter, a new performance function can be obtained. This performance function takes into account both robustness and dynamic performance of the resulting filter. A suboptimal filter gain matrix can be obtained via minimisation and is shown to result in a filter of higher robustness than Kalman filter. Therefore, a good balance between the dynamic performance and the robustness of the filter can be made.

Acknowledgements: The authors would like to thank Dr T J Owens for many valuable discussions on parametric design, and Dr J F Marsh for his great help during the authors' stay at Brunel University. This work was partly performed under ESPRIT 2255, TOMPUSS project.

References

[1] J. C.Doyle, "Guaranteed margins for LQG regulators", *IEEE Trans. Automat. Contr.*, vol. **AC-23**, pp. 756-757, 1978.

[2] T.J.Owens and J.O'Reilly, "Parametric state feedback control with response insensitivity,", *Int. J. Contr.*, vol.**45**, pp. 791-809, 1987.

[3] T.J.Owens and J.O'Reilly, "Parametric state-feedback control for arbitrary eigenvalue assignment with minimum sensitivity," *IEE Proceedings, Pt.D*, vol.**136**, pp.307-314.

IMPROVING THE ROBUSTNESS OF STATIONARY KALMAN FILTER VIA PARAMETRIC DESIGN

Steve Daley# and Hong Wang*

#Engineering Research Centre, GEC-Alsthom, Leicester, U.K.
*Department of Paper Science, UMIST, Manchester, U.K.

Abstract

This paper presents a novel design approach for a robust sub-optimal Kalman filter using parametric eigenstructure placement. Initially, a system without model uncertainty is considered, and a condition for the parametrically designed filter to be optimal is obtained. It is shown, under this condition, that there is a subset of the parametrically designed gain matrices which will also lead to a Kalman filter. For the system with structured model uncertainty, a performance functional index is constructed in which the penalty terms to both the sensitivity and the non-optimality of the filter are included. A parametrically designed gain matrix is then evaluated via standard minimisation and the so-obtained filter is shown to be sub-optimal and more robust than Kalman filter.

Preliminaries

Consider the following system without model uncertainties

$$dx(t) = Ax(t)dt + Bu(t)dt + d\omega(t) \qquad (1)$$

$$dy(t) = Cx(t)dt + d\eta(t) \qquad (2)$$

where $x(t) \in R^n$ is the state vector, $u(t) \in R^m$ is the control input and $y(t) \in R^p$ is the output vector. $\omega(t)$ and $\eta(t)$ are independent Brownian motion processes with

$$\mathrm{E}\{d\omega(t)d\omega^T(t)\} = Qdt \qquad (3)$$

$$\mathrm{E}\{d\eta(t)d\eta^T(t)\} = Rdt \qquad (4)$$

and $Q = Q^T \geq 0$ $R = R^T > 0$ are constant matrices. A, B and C are known parameter matrices with proper dimensions. It is well known, [1], that the minimum variance state estimation vector $\hat{x}(t)$ will satisfy the following equations

$$d\hat{x}(t) = A\hat{x}(t)dt + Bu(t)dt + K_{opt}(t)(dy(t) - C\hat{x}(t)dt) \qquad (5)$$

$$\frac{dP(t)}{dt} = AP(t) + PA^T + Q - P(t)C^TR^{-1}CP(t) \qquad (6)$$

$$K_{opt}(t) = P(t)C^TR^{-1} \qquad (7)$$

Since all the parameter matrices of the system (1) are constant, the following stationary estimates can be obtained.

$$d\hat{x}(t) = A\hat{x}(t)dt + Bu(t)dt + K_{opt}(dy(t) - C\hat{x}(t)dt) \qquad (8)$$

$$0 = AP + PA^T + Q - PC^TR^{-1}CP \qquad (9)$$

$$K_{opt} = PC^TR^{-1} \qquad (10)$$

In the rest of the paper, only the above stationary estimation will be considered. Define the estimation error as

$$\tilde{x}(t) = x(t) - \hat{x}(t) \qquad (11)$$

then, it can be obtained that

$$d\tilde{x}(t) = (A - K_{opt}C)\tilde{x}(t)dt - K_{opt}d\eta(t) + d\omega(t) \qquad (12)$$

where all the eigenvalues of $A - K_{opt}C$ lie inside the left hand complex plane. Denote $\Lambda = \{\lambda_1, \lambda_2, \ldots, \lambda_n\}$ as the set of eigenvalues of the matrix $A_c = A - K_{opt}C$. It is assumed that all these eigenvalues are distinct real values and are different from the eigenvalues of matrix A, as theoretically no difficult will arise in dealing with the case when there are common poles between them, [2]-[3]. Based on this assumption and from the parametric design viewpoint, the same eigenvalue assignment can also be achieved by the following gain

$$K = W^{-1}F \qquad (13)$$

$$F = (f_1^T \ f_2^T \ \ . \ . \ . \ \ f_n^T)^T \qquad (14)$$

$$W = (w_1^T \ w_2^T \ \ . \ . \ . \ \ w_n^T)^T = V^{-1} \qquad (15)$$

$$w_i = f_iC(A - \lambda_iI)^{-1} \qquad (16)$$

where $f_i (i = 1, 2, \ldots, n)$ are arbitrary parameter row vectors, $V = (v_1, v_2, \ldots, v_n)$ and v_i is eigenvector. Compared with K_{opt}, it can be seen that the parametric design will give a set of gain matrices. Moreover, with the proper choice of the parameter row vectors f_i, additional properties can be achieved, such as reducing the sensitivity of the eigenvalues of A_c to parameter variations, [2]. Therefore, a gain matrix K could be found which can not only assign the eigenvalues of matrix A_c to the set Λ, but also leads to a more robust filter which is insensitive to the parameter variations in matrix A, B and C. This forms the original purpose of this paper. As can be seen in the sequel, a systematic design procedure is obtained with which the users can easily reach a good balance between optimality and robustness of the resulting filter.

Optimality condition

Since the gain matrix $K = W^{-1}F$ will also assign the poles of the matrix A_c to desired locations, it is natural to consider the problem of selecting the arbitrary raws f_i such that the resulting gain will lead to the following minimum variance estimation

$$d\hat{x}(t) = A\hat{x}(t)dt + Bu(t)dt + K(dy(t) - C\hat{x}(t)) \qquad (17)$$

This means that the equality $K = K_{opt}$ holds. The re-arrangement of this equality yields

$$f_i(R - C(A - \lambda_iI)^{-1}PC^T) = 0 \qquad (18)$$

It can be seen that the null space of $(R - C(A - \lambda_iI)^{-1}PC^T)^T$ is not empty, therefore, the following theorem can be obtained

<u>Theorem. 1</u> The state estimates (17) with parametric gain matrix $K = W^{-1}F$ is minimum variance estimates if and only if the arbitrary parametric vectors f_i $(i = 1, 2, \ldots, n)$ are chosen such that the equality

$$f_i(R - C(A - \lambda_i I)^{-1}PC^T) = 0 \quad (19)$$

holds and the resulting matrix W is invertible.

To simplify the notation of the next section, denote $\Sigma_i = R - C(A - \lambda_i I)^{-1}PC^T$.

Robust redesign

The presence of structured model uncertainties will now be considered since in practical systems modelling errors widely exist. In this case, the system equation becomes

$$dx(t) = (A + \Delta A(t))x(t)dt + (B + \Delta B(t))u(t)dt + d\omega(t) \quad (20)$$

$$dy(t) = (C + \Delta C(t))x(t)dt + d\eta(t) \quad (21)$$

where $\Delta A(t)$, $\Delta B(t)$ and $\Delta C(t)$ are structured model uncertainties of the form

$$\Delta A(t) = \sum_{i=1}^{l} M_i \varepsilon_i(t); \Delta B(t) = \sum_{i=1}^{l} N_i \varepsilon_i(t); \Delta C(t) = \sum_{i=1}^{l} L_i \varepsilon_i(t)$$

where matrices M_i, N_i and $L_i (i = 1,2,\ldots,l)$ are known whereas $\varepsilon_i(t)$ $(i = 1,2,\ldots,l)$ are unknowns of possibly large values. The estimation error becomes

$$d\tilde{x}(t) = (A_c + \Delta A_c(t))\tilde{x}(t)dt + \Delta A_c(t)\hat{x}(t)dt + $$
$$+ \Delta B(t)u(t)dt - Kd\eta(t) + d\omega(t) \quad (22)$$

$$\Delta A_c(t) = \Delta A(t) - K\Delta C(t) \quad (23)$$

In the presence of the structured model uncertainties, both the Kalman filter (5)-(7) and the parametrically designed filter using the gain matrix in (13) are no longer optimal in the sense that the estimation are not minimum variance and unbiased, in some cases they will even lead to an divergent estimator. Therefore, it is natural that modifications should be made to improve the performance of the estimation. For this work, the following improvements will be considered:

1) Enhance the robustness of the estimation with respect to the structured model uncertainties ΔA, ΔB and ΔC;

2) Ensure that the estimation is as good as possible, i.e., sub-minimize the variance of the estimation error.

To improve robustness, the sensitivity of the eigenvalues of A_c with respect to the model uncertainties needs to be minimized. Denote the sensitivity of the ith eigenvalue λ_i with respect to the variations of ε_j as

$$d\lambda_{ij} = \frac{\partial \lambda_i}{\partial \varepsilon_j} \quad (i = 1,2,\ldots,n; j = 1,2,\ldots,l) \quad (24)$$

and the sensitivities of w_i, v_i and A_c with respect to the variations of ε_j as

$$dw_{ij} = \frac{\partial w_i}{\partial \varepsilon_j}; dv_{ij} = \frac{\partial v_i}{\partial \varepsilon_j} \quad (25)$$

$$dA_{c_j} = \frac{\partial A_c}{\partial \varepsilon_j}; d\lambda_{ij} = w_i dA_{c_j} v_i \quad (26)$$

then

$$dA_{c_j} = M_j - W^{-1}FL_j \quad (27)$$

$$d\lambda_{ij} = f_i C(A - \lambda_i I)^{-1}(M_j - W^{-1}FL_j)v_i \quad (28)$$

It is therefore essential that the arbitrarily selected parameter vectors $f_i(i = 1,2,\ldots,n)$ should be chosen such that the objective function

$$J_1 = \sum_{i,j=1}^{n,l} \beta_{ij}^2 (d\lambda_{ij})^2 \quad (29)$$

is as small as possible, where β_{ij}^2 are weights.

To optimize the estimation, the resulting matrix $K = W^{-1}F$ should be as close as possible to the Kalman filter gain. Using the optimality condition in the previous section, the arbitrary parameter vectors $f_i(i = 1,2,\ldots,n)$ should be chosen such that

$$J_2 = \sum_{i=1}^{n} \eta_i^2 \| f_i \Sigma \| \quad (30)$$

is made as small as possible, where $\eta_i^2 (i = 1,2,\ldots,n)$ are weights.

Moreover, since the magnitude of the estimation error response depends on $v_i w_i$, to have a desirable estimation performance it is apparent that the variations of $v_i w_i$ with respect to the structured model uncertainties be as small as possible. Therefore, the objective function

$$J_3 = \sum_{i,j=1}^{n,l} \gamma_{ij}^2 \| d(v_i w_i)_{ij} \| = \sum_{i,j=1}^{n,l} \gamma_{ij}^2 \| (dv_{ij})w_i + v_i(dw_{ij}) \| \quad (31)$$

should also be considered, where $\gamma_{ij}^2 (i = 1,2,\ldots,n; j = 1,2,\ldots,l)$ are weights. Combining (29), (30) and (31), the performance function

$$J_r = J_1 + J_2 + J_3 =$$
$$\sum_{i,j=1}^{n,l} \beta_{ij}^2 (d\lambda_{ij})^2 + \sum_{i=1}^{n} \eta_i^2 \| \Sigma_i f_i \| + \sum_{i,j=1}^{n,l} \gamma_{ij}^2 \| d(v_i w_i)_{ij} \| \quad (32)$$

can be obtained and the arbitrary parameters f_i should be chosen so that J_r is minimized .

Concluding remarks

Using the optimality condition under which the parametrically designed gain matrix will lead to a Kalman filter, a new performance function can be obtained. This performance function takes into account both robustness and dynamic performance of the resulting filter. A suboptimal filter gain matrix can be obtained via minimisation and is shown to result in a filter of higher robustness than Kalman filter. Therefore, a good balance between the dynamic performance and the robustness of the filter can be made.

Acknowledgements: The authors would like to thank Dr T J Owens for many valuable discussions on parametric design, and Dr J F Marsh for his great help during the authors' stay at Brunel University. This work was partly performed under ESPRIT 2255, TOMPUSS project.

References

[1] J. C.Doyle, "Guaranteed margins for LQG regulators", *IEEE Trans. Automat. Contr.*, vol. **AC-23**, pp. 756-757, 1978.

[2] T.J.Owens and J.O'Reilly, "Parametric state feedback control with response insensitivity,", *Int. J. Contr.*, vol.**45**,pp. 791-809, 1987.

[3] T.J.Owens and J.O'Reilly, "Parametric state-feedback control for arbitrary eigenvalue assignment with minimum sensitivity," *IEE Proceedings, Pt.D*, vol.**136**,pp.307-314.

Proceedings of the
American Control Conference
San Francisco, California • June 1993

Output Feedback Variable Structure Control Design Using Dynamic Compensation for Linear Systems

Riad El-Khazali
Mu'tah University
Mu'tah - Al - Karak
JORDAN

R. A. DeCarlo
School of Electrical Engineering
Purdue University
West Lafayette, IN 47907

Abstract: This paper develops an output feedback variable structure controller using dynamic compensation for linear state models when the Davidson-Kimura condition is not satisfied. In general, the need to use extra dynamics follows from the relative dimensions and the structural properties of the system. The method of equivalent control is used to describe an "augmented reduced order system" in the sliding mode. Due to the reduction of order of the system in the sliding mode, the order of the compensator depends on the dimension of the reduced order system. A switched controller guaranteeing asymptotic stability to the switching surface is given. All points are illustrated by a simple example.

1. Introduction

The problem of using output feedback in variable structure systems (VSS) has been successfully investigated for linear systems [8, 9, 12]. The switching surface design process and the controller specification for the case $n \leq m+r-1$ were investigated in [7,8,9,12]. Here it was shown that under certain controllability and observability assumptions and certain dimensional and rank condition, one can select a switching surface matrix so that the system in the sliding mode has prescribed eigenvalues [7,8]. A control strategy guaranteeing asymptotic stability to the switching surface was also detailed.

In this paper we wish to consider the same problem for the case $n > m + r - 1$. The problem solution requires implementing extra dynamics in the form of a dynamic compensator. The compensator parameters are determined during the switching surface design procedure [9].

The paper is organized as follows: section 2 introduces the problem statement and general background. Section 3 discusses the switching surface and the dynamic compensator design. The control design is summarized in section 4. A numerical example and conclusions are given in sections 5 and 6, respectively.

2. General Background and Problem Statement

Consider the usual linear time-invariant system

$$\begin{aligned} \dot{x}(t) &= A\,x(t) + B\,u(t) \\ y(t) &= C\,x(t) \end{aligned} \tag{1}$$

where $x \in R^n$, $y \in R^r$, $u \in R^m$ are the state, output, and input vectors respectively. A, B and C are constant matrices of proper dimensions, rank[B] = m, and rank[C] = r.

Assumption 1. The triple (C, A, B) is complete, $n > m + r - 1$, and $r > m$.

The case when $n \leq m + r - 1$ and $r > m$ is discussed in [8,9,12] where sufficient conditions are given for the complete assignability of the eigenvalues of the reduced order system of (1) in the sliding mode. The completeness of the triple (C, A, B) is necessary for pole placement using output feedback [4]. Unfortunately, the observability of the pair (C, A) doesn't guarantee the observability of the reduced order pair nor of the "augmented reduced order system" [7, 8, 9,12] Further observability conditions are needed.

In this paper, the assumption $n > m + r - 1$ will require the presence of a dynamic compensator, i.e., additional dynamics, inputs, and outputs, to achieve sufficient control over the closed-loop pole locations for the system in the sliding mode. [5,9]

Assumption 2: The dynamic compensator has the form

$$\begin{aligned} \dot{z}_q(t) &= -u_c(t) \\ u_c(t) &= W\,y(t) + H\,z_q(t) \end{aligned} \tag{2}$$

where u_c is the compensator control vector and $z_q \in R^q$ is the state of the compensator which has order q.

The constant matrices $W \in R^{q\times r}$ and $H \in R^{q\times q}$ are determined during the switching surface design process. The control vector, $u(y,z_q)$, of the system (1) has components $u_i(y,z_q)$ given by

$$u_i(y,z_q) = \begin{cases} u_i^+(y,z_q) & \text{when} \quad \sigma(y,z_q) > 0 \\ u_i^-(y,z_q) & \text{when} \quad \sigma(y,z_q) < 0 \end{cases} \tag{3}$$

where the switching surface, $\sigma(y,z_q) = 0$, is defined as

$$\sigma(y,z_q) = [S \mid S_q]\begin{bmatrix} y \\ z_q \end{bmatrix} = [0] \tag{4}$$

where $S \in R^{m\times r}$ and $S_q \in R^{m\times q}$ are parameter matrices to be designed.

The switching surface and the dynamic compensator should be chosen to stabilize the system in the sliding mode or to achieve some form of tracking or regulation. The control $u(y,z_q)$ is chosen to drive the augmented output vector, $(y^t,z_q^t)^t$ to the switching surface. This process will be accomplished according to the following two phases.

First Phase: Given system (1) and a symmetric set of n-m+q complex numbers $\Lambda_{n-m+q} = \{\lambda_1, ..., \lambda_{n-m+q}\}$, find real maps S, S_q, W, and H such that in the sliding mode, the n-m+q eigenvalues of the augmented reduced order system (equation (12) below) are precisely those of the set Λ_{n-m+q}.

The first phase of design process anticipates a reduction of order of an augmented system composed of the original system (1) and the dynamic compensator (2). The reduced order system will have dimension n-m+q.

Second Phase: Determine a switched control of the form (3) such that the system's output trajectory is globally attractive (stable) to the sliding surface (4) or to the origin from any point in the augmented output space.

3. Switching Surface Design

The combined system and dynamic compensator is called the augmented system and is given by

$$\begin{aligned} \dot{x}_a(t) &= A_a\,x_a(t) + B_a\,u_a(t) \\ y_a(t) &= C_a\,x_a(t) \end{aligned} \tag{5a}$$

with augmented switching surface

$$\sigma(y_a) = S_a\,y_a(t) = [0] \tag{5b}$$

where $x_a = [x^t \;\; z_q^t]^t \in R^{n+q}$, $y_a = [y^t \;\; z_q^t]^t \in R^{r+q}$, $u_a = [u^t \;\; u_c^t]^t \in R^{m+q}$, and $S_a = [S \;\; S_q]$. The matrices A_a, B_a, and C_a are defined in the obvious way.

Writing the augmented system in the regular form [3] simplifies the switching surface design process. Then, the method of the equivalent control [1] may be used to define the reduced order structure of the system restricted to the switching surface. However, the usual method of evaluating the equivalent control cannot be used, i.e., one cannot simply differentiate $\sigma(y_a)$ and solve for $u_a \in R^{m+q}$. This is because the reduced order system would then be independent of the compensator dynamics. It is essential to reject only the m variables that correspond to the control vector of the original plant, u. To do this it is convenient to write the augmented system (5) in the regular form defined as:

$$\begin{bmatrix} \dot z_1 \\ \dot z_q \\ \dot z_2 \end{bmatrix} = \begin{bmatrix} A_{11} & 0 & A_{12} \\ 0 & 0 & 0 \\ A_{21} & 0 & A_{22} \end{bmatrix} \begin{bmatrix} z_1 \\ z_q \\ z_2 \end{bmatrix} + \begin{bmatrix} 0 & 0 \\ I_q & 0 \\ 0 & B_2 \end{bmatrix} \begin{bmatrix} u_q \\ u \end{bmatrix}$$

$$\begin{bmatrix} y \\ z_q \end{bmatrix} = \begin{bmatrix} C_1 & 0 & C_2 \\ 0 & I_q & 0 \end{bmatrix} \begin{bmatrix} z_1 \\ z_q \\ z_2 \end{bmatrix} \tag{6}$$

where I_q is an identity matrix of dimension q, $z_1 \in R^{n-m}$, $z_2 \in R^m$, $A_{11}, A_{12}, A_{21}, A_{22}, B_2, C_1$, and C_2 are real matrices of appropriate dimensions. The switching surface in the regular form is given by

$$\sigma(z_1,z_q,z_2) = [S \mid S_q] \begin{bmatrix} C_1 & 0 & C_2 \\ 0 & I_q & 0 \end{bmatrix} \begin{bmatrix} z_1 \\ z_q \\ z_2 \end{bmatrix} = [0] \tag{7}$$

Augmented Reduced Order System (AROS)

To compute the AROS, assume that the system state vector is initially on the switching surface and remains there, i.e., there exists a sliding mode on $\sigma(z_1,z_q,z_2) = 0$ in which case $\dot\sigma(z_1,z_q,z_2) = 0$. Solving (7) for z_2 yields

$$z_2 = -(SC_2)^{-1} [SC_1 \mid S_q] \begin{bmatrix} z_1 \\ z_q \end{bmatrix} \equiv - [KC_1 \mid (SC_2)^{-1} S_q] \begin{bmatrix} z_1 \\ z_q \end{bmatrix} \tag{8}$$

where $K \equiv (SC_2)^{-1}S$. Well posedness, i.e., existence and uniqueness of the equivalent control [1,2], requires the following assumption.

Assumption 3. Assume that $CB = C_2 B_2$ has full rank. [8,9,12]

The control vector of the compensator in the sliding mode takes the form

$$u_c = [W(I_r - C_2K) C_1 \mid (H - WC_2(SC_2)^{-1} S_q)] \begin{bmatrix} z_1 \\ z_q \end{bmatrix} \tag{9}$$

Here, switching surface design reduces to finding W, H, and $K = (SC_2)^{-1}S$ which implicitly defines a full row rank matrix, S. As discussed in [8], K must satisfy $KC_2 = I_m$ implying that K must lie in the set

$$\mathbf{K_1} = \{K : K = C_2^{-L} + \Gamma M^t ; M^t C_2 = [0]\} \tag{10}$$

where C_2^{-L} is any left universe of C_2 and where $\Gamma \in R^{mx(r-m)}$ is a free parameter matrix to be determined.

Since $W \in R^{qxr}$ is also a free parameter matrix, the presence of the projector, $P = (I_r - C_2 K)$, in equation (9) limits the available feedback because it projects out all free parameters in W that belong to the row space of the left annihilator of P. Since $PC_2 = [0]$, then $I_m[P^t] \subset I_m[M]$ which leads to the following result.

Lemma 1 [9]. Let $K \in R^{mxr}$, $KC_2 = I_m$, u_q be defined by (9), and let $P = (I_r - C_2K)$, then there exist matrices $W_1 \in R^{qx(r-m)}$, and $H_1 = H$, such that u_c reduces to

$$u_c = W_1 \hat C_1 z_1 + H_1 z_q \tag{11}$$

where $\hat C_1 \equiv M^t C_1$.

Remark 1: From lemma 1 it can be assumed, without loss of generality, that $WC_2 = [0]$. If so equation (9) reduces to (11) as expected.

Now substituting from (11) and (10) into (6) yields the AROS dynamics in the sliding mode, i.e.,

$$\begin{bmatrix} \dot z_1 \\ \dot z_q \end{bmatrix} = \begin{bmatrix} (\hat A_{11} - A_{12}\Gamma \hat C_1 & -A_{12}S_q \\ -W_1\hat C_1 & -H_1 \end{bmatrix} \begin{bmatrix} z_1 \\ z_q \end{bmatrix} \tag{12}$$

where $\hat A_{11} \equiv (A_{11} - A_{12}C_2^{-L}C_1)$, $\hat C_1 \equiv M^tC_1$, $M^tC_2 = [0]$, $W_1 \in R^{qx(r-m)}$, $\Gamma \in R^{mx(r-m)}$, $S_q \in R^{mxq}$, and $H_1 \in R^{qxq}$. Equation (12) can be rewritten as

$$\dot{\tilde z}_1 = (\tilde A_{11} - \tilde A_{12} \tilde K \tilde C_1)\tilde z_1 \tag{13}$$

where $\tilde z_1 \equiv [z_1^t \mid z_q^t]^t$, $\tilde A \equiv \begin{bmatrix} \hat A_{11} & 0 \\ 0 & 0 \end{bmatrix}$, $\tilde A_{12} \equiv \begin{bmatrix} \tilde A_{12} & 0 \\ 0 & I_q \end{bmatrix}$,

$\tilde K \equiv \begin{bmatrix} \Gamma & S_q \\ W_1 & H_1 \end{bmatrix}$, and $\tilde C_1 \equiv \begin{bmatrix} C_1 & 0 \\ 0 & I_q \end{bmatrix}$.

Switching Surface Design Algorithm

Observe that the AROS given by equation (13) exhibits an output feedback structure. The theory of output feedback [5, 6] is then used to evaluate the output feedback matrix, $\tilde K$. The order of the compensator may be found from

$$q = \frac{(n\text{-}m) - r_{A_{12}}(r\text{-}m)}{r_{A_{12}} + (r\text{-}m) - 1} \geq 0 ; \qquad r > m \tag{14}$$

where $r_{A_{12}} \equiv \text{rank}\,[A_{12}]$.

Clearly, the controllability and observability of the AROS is necessary to relocate the poles in the sliding mode [4]. The controllability of the pair $(\tilde A_{11}, \tilde A_{12})$ is guaranteed since (A,B) is controllable. However, the observability of $(\hat C_1, \hat A_{11})$ is somewhat different. As discussed in [7, 8, 9,12] the observability of the original pair, (C,A), does not guarantee the observability of the pair (C_1, A_{11}) nor the observability of the pair $(\hat C_1, \hat A_{11})$. The implication is that one must check the observability of the pair $(\hat C_1, \hat A_{11})$. If the pair $(\hat C_1, \hat A_{11})$ is observable, then the pair $(\hat C_1, \hat A_{11})$ is also observable. Therefore, the following assumption becomes necessary.

Assumption 4. The pair $(\hat C_1, \hat A_{11})$ is observable.

Lemma 2 [5]. Consider the AROS given by (13). Let the triple $(\tilde C_1,\tilde A_{11},\tilde A_{12})$ be complete and $\Lambda_{n-m+q} = \{\lambda_1,\ldots,\lambda_{n-m+q}\}$ be a symmetric set of n-m+q complex numbers, then there exists a real matrix, $\tilde K \in R^{(m+q)x(r-m+q)}$ such that $\sigma(\tilde A_{11}) = \Lambda_{n-m+q}$, or at least within an arbitrary small neighborhood of Λ_{n-m+q}.

With this lemma, the switching surface design problem using a dynamic compensator may be summarized as follows:

1. Construct the AROS as in (13).
2. Determine the order of the compensator from equation (14).
3. Solve for $\tilde K$ using any existing output feedback algorithm such as [11].
4. If step 3 fails, increase the dimension of the compensator, q, by one and find $\tilde K$. Repeat as necessary.
5. Evaluate the submatrices, Γ, W_1, H, and S_q from

$$\tilde K = \begin{bmatrix} \Gamma & S_q \\ W_1 & H_1 \end{bmatrix}$$

6. Finally specify the switching surface map and the gains of the compensator using the equalities:
   i) $S = C_2^{-L} + \Gamma M^t$
   ii) $W = W_1 M^t$
   iii) $H = H_1$
   iv) $S_q = S_q$.

4. Controller Design

The second phase of the problem is to determine a switched control which drives the system's augmented output trajectory to the switching manifold given in equation 4. In the subsequent discussion, we assume that the linear system satisfies n > m+r-1, r > m, the triples (C, A, B), and $(\widehat{C}_1, \widehat{A}_{11}, A_{12})$ are complete, and rank[CB] = m. With such structural properties, the augmented linear system described by equation (13) is stabilizable using dynamic output feedback [5]. Consider the augmented system given by (6) and suppose that a proper switching surface matrix, S_a, and a dynamic compensator is selected such that $\sigma(\widetilde{A}_{11} - \widetilde{A}_{12}\widetilde{K}\widetilde{C}_1) = \Lambda_{n-m+q}$. The control design is simplified if one views the augmented system in a new coordinate frame called the normal form [13]. In obtaining the normal form, it is helpful to write the fully determined augmented system (equations (6), (11), and (12)) as

$$\begin{bmatrix} \dot{z}_{1a} \\ z_{2a} \end{bmatrix} = \begin{bmatrix} A_{11a} & A_{12a} \\ A_{21a} & A_{22a} \end{bmatrix} \begin{bmatrix} z_{1a} \\ z_{2a} \end{bmatrix} + \begin{bmatrix} 0 \\ B_2 \end{bmatrix} u \tag{15}$$

$$y_a = [C_{1a} \mid C_{2a}] \begin{bmatrix} z_{1a} \\ z_{2a} \end{bmatrix}$$

with switching surface

$$\sigma(z_{1a}, z_{2a}) = [S \mid S_q]\,[C_{1a} \mid C_{2a}] \begin{bmatrix} z_{1a} \\ z_{2a} \end{bmatrix} = [0] \tag{16}$$

where $z_{1a} = [z_1^t \;\; z_q^t]^t \in R^{n-m+q}$, $z_{2a} = z_2 \in R^m$, $A_{21a} = [A_{21} \;\; 0]$,

$$A_{22a} = [A_{22}],\; A_{11a} \equiv \begin{bmatrix} A_{11} & 0 \\ -WC_1 & -H_1 \end{bmatrix},\; A_{12a} \equiv \begin{bmatrix} A_{12} \\ 0 \end{bmatrix},\; C_{2a} \equiv \begin{bmatrix} C_2 \\ \\ 0 \end{bmatrix}, \text{ and}$$

$$D_{1a} \equiv \begin{bmatrix} C_1 & 0 \\ \\ 0 & I_q \end{bmatrix}.$$ Recall that the matrices W and H_1 are known from the first phase of design.

To transform (15) into the normal form [13], consider the state transformation

$$\begin{bmatrix} q_a \\ \sigma \end{bmatrix} = T_n \begin{bmatrix} z_{1a} \\ z_{2a} \end{bmatrix} \quad T_n = \begin{bmatrix} I_{n-m+q} & 0 \\ S_a C_{1a} & S_a C_{2a} \end{bmatrix} \tag{17}$$

The augmented system in the normal form is given by

$$\begin{bmatrix} \dot{q}_a \\ \dot{\sigma} \end{bmatrix} = \begin{bmatrix} A_{11_n} & A_{12_n} \\ A_{21_n} & A_{22_n} \end{bmatrix} \begin{bmatrix} q_a \\ \sigma \end{bmatrix} + \begin{bmatrix} 0 \\ S_a C_{2a} B_2 \end{bmatrix} u \tag{18}$$

where $A_{11n} = [A_{22a} - A_{12a}(S_aC_{2a})^{-1}S_aC_{1a}$, $A_{12n} = A_{12a}(S_aC_{2a})^{-1}$, $A_{21n} = [S_aC_{1a}A_{11a} + S_aC_{2a}A_{21a} - (S_aC_{1a}A_{12a} + S_aC_{2a}A_{22a})(S_aC_{2a})^{-1} S_aC_{1a}]$, and $A_{22n} \equiv [S_aC_{1a}A_{12a} + S_aC_{2a}A_{22a}]\,(S_aC_{2a})^{-1}$. The switching surface in normal form is

$$\sigma = [0 \mid I_m] \begin{bmatrix} q_a \\ \sigma \end{bmatrix} = [0] \tag{19}$$

Remark 2: From the definition of A_{11n}, and from equations (12), and (13), it follows that $\sigma(A_{11n}) = \sigma(\widetilde{A}_{11} - \widetilde{A}_{12}\widetilde{K}\widetilde{C}_1) = \Lambda_{n-m+q}$ which is chosen to have elements in the open left half complex plane. Hence, A_{11n} is a stability matrix.

Before discussing the design procedure, let us introduce some necessary definitions. For i, j = 1,2 let $p_{ijn} \equiv \|A_{ijn}\|$ denote the spectral norm of A_{ijn}, i.e., $\|A_{ijn}\| = \max\{\|A_{ijn}\, x\| : \|x\| = 1\}$. Define also $\lambda_{min} \equiv \min\{|\lambda_1|,...,|\lambda_{n-m+q}|\}$ where $\lambda_i \in \Lambda_{n-m+q}$.

Controller Design

The control design in variable structure output-feedback control (VSOFC) requires the convergence of the augmented system's output trajectory to the switching surface, and ultimately, to the origin, thus a switched control must be used to drive the system's trajectory to the switching surface, at least asymptotically.

Let us propose the following output feedback control [9]

$$u = -(SC_2B_2)^{-1} \begin{cases} F_0 y_a + \dfrac{\rho_{21}\rho_{12n}\sigma_{max}}{\lambda_{min}\sigma_{min}}\,\sigma + \alpha \operatorname{sgn} \sigma & \text{if } \|\sigma\| > \epsilon \\ F_0 y_a + \dfrac{l_{21}\rho_{12n}\sigma_{max}}{\lambda \;\; \sigma}\,\sigma + \dfrac{\alpha}{\epsilon}\,\sigma & \text{if } \|\sigma\| < \epsilon \end{cases} \tag{20}$$

where $l_{21} \equiv \|L_{21}\|$, a > 0, sgn σ = [sgn σ_1,...,sgn σ_m], i.e., sgn σ is the usual signum function, and where

$$F_0 \equiv (S_aC_{1a}A_{12a} + S_aC_{2a}A_{22a})\, C_{2a}^{-L} \tag{21}$$

and

$$L_{21} \equiv S_aC_{1a}(A_{11a} - A_{12a}C_{2a}^{-L}C_{1a}) + S_aC_{2a}(A_{21a} - A_{22a}C_{2a}^{-L}C_{1a}) \tag{22}$$

In addition define σ_{max}, and σ_{min} as the maximum and the minimum singular values of U, respectively, where $U \in R^{(n-m+q)x(n-m+q)}$ is a nonsingular matrix that diagonalizes A_{11n}, i.e.

$$U^{-1} A_{11n} U = D \tag{23}$$

where $D = \text{diag}(\lambda_1,...,\lambda_{n-m+q})$.

To show the viability of the control given by (20), the justification proceeds more easily if one diagonalizes the matrix A_{11n}. This is easily done by introducing the following nonsingular transformation

$$\begin{bmatrix} q_n \\ \sigma \end{bmatrix} = \begin{bmatrix} U^{-1} & 0 \\ 0 & I_m \end{bmatrix} \begin{bmatrix} q_a \\ \sigma \end{bmatrix} \tag{24}$$

The system model in the new coordinate takes the form

$$\begin{bmatrix} \dot{q}_n \\ \dot{\sigma} \end{bmatrix} = \begin{bmatrix} D & U^{-1}A_{12n} \\ A_{21n}U & A_{22n} \end{bmatrix} \begin{bmatrix} q_n \\ \sigma \end{bmatrix} + \begin{bmatrix} 0 \\ SCB \end{bmatrix} u \tag{25}$$

$$y_a = \left[(I_{r+q} - C_{2a}(S_aC_{2a})^{-1}S_a)C_{1a}U \mid C_{2a}(S_aC_{2a})^{-1}\right] \begin{bmatrix} q_n \\ \sigma \end{bmatrix} \tag{26}$$

with switching surface given in equation (19).From (21) and (26), it follows that

$$F_0 y_a = [(S_aC_{1a}A_{12a} + S_aC_{2a}A_{22a})\, C_{2a}^{-L}C_{1a} - (S_aC_{1a}A_{12a} + S_aC_{2a}A_{22a})\,(S_aC_{2a})^{-1}C_{2a}^{-L}C_{1a}]\, Uq_n + A_{22n}\sigma$$

From the definition of A_{21n}, (equation (18)), and (22) yields

$$F_0 y_a = (A_{21_n} - L_{21})\, Uq_n + A_{22_n}\sigma \tag{27}$$

This expression is helpful in proving the following result.

Theorem 1. The system described by (25) is globally asymptotically stable with the control given by (20).

Proof. Consider the following candidate Lyapunov function

$$V = \frac{\sigma_{max}\, l_{21}}{\lambda_{min}} \|q_n\| + \|\sigma\| \tag{28}$$

Differentiating (28) and substituting from (20), (25), and (27) with $\|q_n\| \neq 0$, and $\|\sigma\| > \epsilon$ yields

$$\dot{V} = \frac{\sigma_{max}\, l_{21}}{\lambda_{min}} \frac{q_n^t \dot{q}_n}{\|q_n\|} + \frac{\sigma^t \dot{\sigma}}{\|\sigma\|}$$

Substituting for $\dot{q}_n$ and $\dot{\sigma}$ produces

$$\dot{V} = \frac{\sigma_{max}\, l_{21}}{\lambda_{min}} \frac{q_n^t}{\|q_n\|} (Dq_n + U^{-1} A_{12_n}\sigma) + \frac{\sigma^t}{\|\sigma\|}\left(L_{21} q_n - \frac{l_{21}\sigma_{max}\rho_{12_n}}{\lambda_{min}\sigma_{min}} \sigma - \alpha \operatorname{sgn} \sigma \right)$$

Since $q_n^t D q_n \leq -\lambda_{min} \|q_n\|^2$, $q_n^t U^{-1} A_{12_n}\sigma \leq \frac{\rho_{12n}}{\sigma_{min}} \|q_n\|\, \|\sigma\|$, $\sigma^t L_{21} q_n \leq l_{21} \|\sigma\|\, \|q_n\|$, and since $\frac{\sigma^t \operatorname{sgn} \sigma}{\|\sigma\|} > 1$, the result follows.

The same argument applies when $\|\sigma\| < \epsilon$. This completes the proof.

5. Numerical Example

Consider a linear system given by (1) in the regular form where

$$A = \begin{bmatrix} -0.0108 & -33.93 & -0.1305 & 0.1057 & 3.5223 \\ 0 & 0 & -0.108 & 0 & 0 \\ -0.0153 & 207.35 & -0.1846 & 0.1495 & 4.9828 \\ 0 & 0 & 0 & 0 & 33.3333 \\ -78 & 0 & 0 & -0.6 & -99 \end{bmatrix}, \quad B = \begin{bmatrix} 0 \\ 0 \\ 0 \\ 0 \\ 78 \end{bmatrix}$$

$$C = \begin{bmatrix} 1 & 0 & 0 & 0 & 0 \\ 0 & 1 & 0 & 0 & 0 \\ 1 & 0 & 0 & 1 & 33.33 \end{bmatrix}$$

Part 1. The order of the compensator may be determined from (14). Since n = 5, $r_{A12} = 1$, r = 3, and m = 1, equation (14) yields a 1st-order dynamic compensator. From Lemma 1 and Remark 1 the dynamic compensator takes the form

$$\dot{z}_q = -h_1 z_q - [\omega_1\ \omega_2\ 0] \begin{bmatrix} y_1 \\ y_2 \\ y_3 \end{bmatrix}$$

Part 2: The switching surface is given by

$$\sigma(y, z_q) = \left[C_2^{-L} + \Gamma M^t \mid S_q \right] \begin{bmatrix} y \\ z_q \end{bmatrix} = [0]$$

where $\Gamma = [\gamma_1, \gamma_2]$, $S_q = [s_{q_1}]$, C_2^{-L} is any left inverse of C_2, and

$$M^t = \begin{bmatrix} 1 & 0 & 0 \\ 0 & 1 & 0 \end{bmatrix}.$$

Part 3: The AROS of equation (12) yields

$$\begin{bmatrix} \dot{z}_1 \\ \dot{z}_2 \\ \dot{z}_3 \\ \dot{z}_4 \\ \dot{z}_q \end{bmatrix} = \begin{bmatrix} -0.1165 & -33.93 & -0.1305 & 0 & 0 \\ 0 & 0 & -0.108 & 0 & 0 \\ -0.1648 & 207.35 & -0.1846 & 0 & 0 \\ -1.0 & 0 & 0 & -1 & 0 \\ 0 & 0 & 0 & 0 & 0 \end{bmatrix} \begin{bmatrix} z_1 \\ z_2 \\ z_3 \\ z_4 \\ z_q \end{bmatrix} - \begin{bmatrix} 3.5223 & 0 \\ 0 & 0 \\ 4.9828 & 0 \\ 33.33 & 0 \\ 0 & 1 \end{bmatrix} \begin{bmatrix} \gamma_1 & \gamma_2 & s_{q_1} \\ w_1 & w_2 & h_1 \end{bmatrix} \begin{bmatrix} 1\,0\,0\,0\,0 \\ 0\,1\,0\,0\,0 \\ 0\,0\,0\,0\,1 \end{bmatrix} \quad (29)$$

Suppose one desires to place the eigenvalues of (29) at $\lambda_1 = -15$, $\lambda_2 = -15$, $\lambda_3 = -8$, $\lambda_4 = -5$, and $\lambda_5 = -1$, then an acceptable output feedback matrix, $\tilde{K}$, is given by

$$\tilde{K} = \begin{bmatrix} \gamma_1 & \gamma_2 & s_{q_1} \\ w_1 & w_2 & h_1 \end{bmatrix} = \begin{bmatrix} 8.4922 & -508.43 & -0.06586 \\ -69.984 & 5155.0 & 7.7865 \end{bmatrix}$$

Notice that $\tilde{K}$ is chosen in such a way that yields a reasonable spectral norm of the matrix L_{21} defined by (22).

Part 4: The switching surface matrix and the dynamic compensator matrices are, respectively, given by W = [-69.984 5155 0.0], H = 7.7865, and

$$S_a = [\, S \mid S_q] = [\, 8.4922 \quad -508.43 \quad 0.03 \quad -0.06586]$$

Part 5. Controller design.

The procedure to evaluate the controller is summarized as follows:

(1) Hence the switching surface and the dynamic compensator are selected, the first step of the controller design is to rewrite the augmented system given by (6) as

$$\begin{bmatrix} \dot{z}_1 \\ \dot{z}_q \\ \dot{z}_2 \end{bmatrix} = \begin{bmatrix} \hat{A}_{11} & 0 & A_{12} \\ -WC_1 & -H_1 & 0 \\ A_{21} & 0 & A_{22} \end{bmatrix} \begin{bmatrix} z_1 \\ z_q \\ z_2 \end{bmatrix} + \begin{bmatrix} 0 \\ 0 \\ B_2 \end{bmatrix} u$$

(2) The system is next transformed into the normal form. The augmented system submatrices, A_{11n}, A_{12n}, A_{21n}, A_{22n}, and C_n in the normal form are, respectively, given by

$$A_{11_n} = \begin{bmatrix} -30.029 & 1756.9 & -0.1307 & 0 & 0.232 \\ 0 & 0 & -0.10799 & 0 & 0 \\ -42.48 & 2740.8 & -0.18457 & 0 & 0.32819 \\ -284.07 & 16948 & 0 & -1 & 2.1955 \\ 69.984 & -5155 & 0 & 0 & -7.7865 \end{bmatrix}$$

$$A_{12_n} = \begin{bmatrix} 3.5223 \\ 0 \\ 4.9828 \\ 33.33 \\ 0 \end{bmatrix}, \quad A_{21_n} = [496.66, -34513, 53.794; 2.34, -3.96]$$

$A_{22n} = -67.982$, and

$$C_n = \begin{bmatrix} 1 & 0 & 0 & 0 & 0 & 0 \\ 0 & 1 & 0 & 0 & 0 & 0 \\ -283.07 & 16948 & 0 & 0 & 2.1955 & 33.33 \\ 0 & 0 & 0 & 0 & 0 & 1 \end{bmatrix}$$

Observe that A_{11n} is a stability matrix and represents the matrix of the AROS in the sliding mode, i.e., a simple test yields $\sigma(A_{11n}) = \{-15, -10, -8, -5, -1\}$.

(3) The control vector given by (20) is used without a boundary layer and yields

$$u = -\frac{1}{78} \begin{cases} F_0 y_a + 4000\,\sigma + 2.0 \operatorname{sgn} \sigma & \text{if } \|\sigma\| > 0 \\ 0 & \text{if } \|\sigma\| = 0 \end{cases}$$

where $l_{2_1} = \|L_{21}\| = 299.38$, $\rho_{12_n} = \|A_{12_n}\| = 33.887$, $\lambda_{min} = 1$, $F_0 = [0 \ \ 0 \ \ -2.0395 \ \ 0 \ \ 0]$, and $L_{21} = [-64.487,\ -282.19,\ 53.794,\ 2.34,\ 54.214]$

6. Conclusion

A new variable structure output feedback control technique using dynamic compensation is introduced for linear time-invariant systems. Problems arise when the Kimura-Davison condition is not satisfied necessitating the implementation of extra dynamics in the form of a dynamic compensator. The switching surface design of this paper includes in its details a simple procedure to evaluate the matrices of the compensator.

The controller used is of two parts; a linear and a switched parts. The gain of the switched part is small which reduces the effect of chattering in the sliding mode. Moreover the gain selection of the linear part is straightforward.

REFERENCES

[1] V. I. Utkin, Sliding Mode and Their Application in Variable Structure Systems, MIR Publishers, Moscow, 1978.

[2] R. A. DeCarlo, S. H. Żak, and G. P. Mathews, "Variable Structure Control of Nonlinear Multivariable Systems: A tutorial," IEEE Proc. , Vol. 76, pp. 212-232, March 1988.

[3] A. G. Lukyanov and V. I. Utkin, "Methods of Reducing Equations of Dynamic Systems to Regular Form," Automat. Remote Control No. 4, pp. 5-13, 1981.

[4] W. M. Wonham, Linear Multivariable Control: A Geometric Approach, Third Edition, Springer-Verlag, New York, 1979.

[5] H. Kimura, "A Further Result on the Problem of Pole Assignment by Output Feedback," IEEE Trans. Automat. Control, Vol. 22, No. 3, pp. 458-463, 1977.

[6] E. J. Davison and S. H. Wang, "On Pole Assignment in Linear Multivariable Systems Using Output Feedback," IEEE Trans. Automat. Control, pp. 516-518, 1975.

[7] R. El-Khazali and R. A. DeCarlo, "Variable Structure Output Feedback Control: Switching Surface Design," Proceeding of the Twenty-Ninth Annual Allerton Conference on Communication, Control, and Computing, Monticello, Ill., Sept. 1991.

[8] ________, "Variable Structure Output Feedback Control," ACC, pp. 871-875, Chicago, Ill., 1992.

[9] Riad El-Khazali, "Variable Structure Output Feedback Control with Application to a Chemical Process and a Power System," Ph.D. Thesis, Purdue University, August 1992.

[10] O. M. E. El-Ghezawi, A. S. Zinober, and S. A. Billings, "Analysis and Design of Variable Structure Systems Using a Geometric Approach," Int. J. Control, Vol. 38, No. 6, pp. 1121-1134, 1983.

[11] P. Misra and R. Patel, "Numerical Algorithms for Eigenvalue Assignment by Constant and Dynamic Output-Feedback," IEEE Trans. Automat. Contr., Vol. AC-34, No. 6, pp. 579-587, June 1989.

[12] R. El-Khazali and R. A. DeCarlo, "Output Feedback Variable Structure Control Design," accepted for publication in Automatica.

[13] K. K. D. Young, P. V. Kokotovic, and V. I. Utkin, "A singular perturbation analysis of high-gain feedback systems," IEEE Trans. Aut. Control, Vol. AC-22, No. 2, pp. 931-938, 1977.

Proceedings of the
American Control Conference
San Francisco, California • June 1993

Variable Structure Discrete Time Position Control

Richard Paden, Graduate Student
Masayoshi Tomizuka, Professor
Department of Mechanical Engineering
University of California at Berkeley, Berkeley, CA 94720

Abstract

A robust, nonlinear controller is proposed for point to point positioning of a single degree of freedom system. This controller is developed for discrete time implementation and is based upon the discrete time input to state relations of a second order positioning system with bounded parametric uncertainties.

The controller's robustness properties are derived from a variable structure control law that is adapted from continuous time sliding mode control to discrete time. The sliding surface is chosen to be parabolic in order to produce fast convergence to the desired position and to minimize the effect of stiction with a high velocity approach to the position setpoint.

To establish the effectiveness of the proposed control scheme, it is implemented on a single axis direct drive robot. Simulations are also conducted for comparison purposes.

1. Introduction

Fast, accurate position control is a crucial element in many automated processes. The effect of Coulomb friction, often termed as stiction, can make highly accurate positioning considerably more difficult. Moreover, parametric modelling uncertainties can greatly degrade the performance of certain control schemes. Sliding mode control has been proposed for robust position control [2]. Due to limitations in sensor and actuator bandwidth, this approach is often impractical, since it may require very fast input switching. To overcome this problem, the use of a boundary layer around the sliding surface has been proposed to allow the input bandwidth to be limited [3]. This approach is not easily adapted for discrete implementation and in many applications, digital implementation is highly desirable. An algorithm for robust nonlinear position control based on a discrete time sliding control concept has been proposed [1]. This approach featured a parabolic sliding surface and assumed bounded parametric uncertainties in the system model. A parabolic sliding surface is desirable in motion control because it globally limits the acceleration required for the state to stay on the sliding surface, whereas remaining on a linear sliding surface requires an input that is proportional to the magnitude of the state and is therefore very large when large errors exist. Furthermore, a parabolic sliding surface can lead to nearly time optimal responses assuming the input magnitude is strictly bounded.

In the paper last mentioned, [1], a nonlinear feedback control law was synthesized based upon a discrete time equivalent of the continous time model and its assumed parameter bounds. The controller was designed to drive the system near to the parabolic sliding surface, thereby achieving fast position control and mitigating the effect of stiction by approaching the desired position at a high velocity.

This paper proposes a similar approach, with some notable differences. A set of control laws are synthesized based on a chosen sliding surface and the discrete time relations derived from the system model. As in the work previously mentioned, this surface is chosen to be parabolic for good robustness with respect to stiction effects and short positioning times. However, this parabolic surface is generalized to allow a constant slope term to be added for enhanced stability and reduced noise sensitivity properties. Additionally, the method of approximating the parabolic sliding surface with a linear surface based on the state at each sampling instant has been replaced with a method that considers the sliding surface exactly. Another noteworthy difference is that the free response is characterized by explicit discrete time relations, rather than norm based relations. Finally, the control laws are designed to restrict sign changes in the velocity, which will assure stability under certain conditions.

This paper begins by introducing the type of system for which position control is to be considered. Next a method is established for deriving the control law structures for various state conditions. A section is then devoted to design rules for some of the control parameters. Finally, experimental and simulation results are presented and discussed.

2. System Description

A positioning system is assumed to be described by the following second order model:

$$\dot{\mathbf{x}}(t) = \mathbf{A}\mathbf{x}(t) + \mathbf{B}u(t) \tag{1}$$

$$\mathbf{A} = \begin{bmatrix} 0 & 1 \\ 0 & a \end{bmatrix} \qquad \mathbf{B} = \begin{bmatrix} 0 \\ b \end{bmatrix}$$

The system parameters a and b are assumed to be uncertain but bounded in the following manner:

$$a_{min} \leq a \leq a_{max} \qquad b_{min} \leq b \leq b_{max} \tag{2}$$

Since the controller to be proposed for this system is to be implemented in discrete time, it is necessary to consider a discretization of the system. The parameters a and b are assumed to be constant between each sampling period. By defining $\mathbf{x} = [x\ v]^T$,where x and v denote the position and velocity, respectively, the following discrete time relations are easily derived:

$$x_{k+1} = x_k + C_1 v_k + C_2 b\, u_k \tag{3}$$

$$v_{k+1} = e^{aT} v_k + C_1 b\, u_k \quad (4)$$

where the sampling period is T and the constants C_1 and C_2 are given by:

$$C_1 = \frac{e^{aT} - 1}{a} \quad (5)$$

$$C_2 = \frac{e^{aT} - aT - 1}{a^2} \quad (6)$$

Some analysis of these quantities leads to the following relations:

$$0 < C_1(a_{min}) \equiv C_{1min} \le C_1 \le C_{1max} \equiv C_1(a_{max}) \quad (7)$$

$$0 < C_2(a_{min}) \equiv C_{2min} \le C_1 \le C_{2max} \equiv C_2(a_{max}) \quad (8)$$

The maximal and minimal values of C_1 and C_2 will be essential in the controller development.

3. Controller Formulation

A sliding function is proposed in the following form:

$$s = x + \lambda_1 v + \lambda_2 sgn(v) v^2 \quad (9)$$

where λ_1 and λ_2 are positive constants. A graphical representation is given in Fig. 1. Since a discrete time controller is proposed, it is not possible to force the system state to reach and remain on the surface defined by $s = 0$. Instead, acceptable performance may be obtained by directing the system state near to this surface.

Substituting the discrete time Eqs. (3) and (4) into Eq. (9), an expression for the value of the sliding function at the next sampling instant may obtained in terms of the current system state and the input applied at a sampling instant k may be obtained.

$$\begin{aligned} s_{k+1} = {} & [x_k + (C_1 + \lambda_1 e^{aT}) v_k + \lambda_2 sgn(v_{k+1}) e^{2aT} v_k^2] \\ & + [C_2 + \lambda_1 C_1 + 2\lambda_2 sgn(v_{k+1}) C_1 e^{aT} v_k] b u_k \\ & + [\lambda_2 sgn(v_{k+1}) C_1^2] b^2 u_k^2 \end{aligned}$$

This expression may be rewritten as

$$s_{k+1} = K_0 + K_1 b u_k + K_2 b^2 u_k^2 \quad (10)$$

by the transparent definitions of the functions K_0, K_1, and K_2 which are seen to depend on the parameters a, b, $sgn(v_{k+1})$, and the system state.

A control law for the state space region where $x_k < 0$ and $v_k > 0$ will be developed based on the following requirements:

$$v_{k+1} > 0 \quad (11)$$

$$s_{k+1} \le 0 \quad (12)$$

where the former requirement supersedes the latter in the case of conflict. In general it may not be possible to satisfy both requirements simultaneously, but sufficient conditions for the compatibility of these requirements will be given later in the paper.

Control laws can be developed based on these requirements, but because of the uncertain system parameters a and b, this control law must have several different structures for different state space regions. In the proposed formulation, the control law has eight separate structures. The controller will be developed in the left half plane of the state space (i.e $x \le 0$), and the control law will be deduced in the right half plane by transparent symmetry.

For the afformentioned region, requirement (11) implies:

$$u_k > -\frac{e^{a_{min}T} v_k}{C_{1min} b_{max}} \equiv -m v_k \equiv U_A \quad (13)$$

Notice that by imposing this requirement, it is assured that $sgn(v_{k+1}) = 1$. It is evident that if $K_0 > 0$ then requirement (12) can only be assured to be satisfied by choosing a negative u_k. Since the constants, $K_i (i = 0, 1, 2)$ are uncertain, it becomes necessary to consider their extreme values. In this case, their maxima may evaluated simply by taking $a = a_{max}$, i.e.:

$$K_0 \le K_0(a = a_{max}) \equiv K_{0,max} \quad (14)$$

$$K_1 \le K_1(a = a_{max}) \equiv K_{1,max} \quad (15)$$

$$K_2 \le K_2(a = a_{max}) \equiv K_{2,max} \quad (16)$$

If $K_{0,max} \ge 0$, requirement (12) implies:

$$u_k \le \frac{-K_{1,max} + R_{max}}{2K_{2,max} b_{min}} \equiv U_{max,1} \quad (17)$$

$$R_{max}^2 \equiv K_{1,max}^2 - 4K_{0,max} K_{2,max} \quad (18)$$

It is possible that R_{max}^2 may be negative for certain states where $s_k > 0$; in this case $U_{max,1}$ may be taken equal to U_A. This will generally not occur in the normal operating range of the system.

If $K_{0,max} < 0$, requirement (12) may be met for some $u_k > 0$. Specifically, it is required that:

$$u_k \le \frac{-K_{1,max} + R_{max}}{2K_{2,max} b_{max}} \equiv U_{max,2} \quad (19)$$

If $v_k < 0$, requirement (11) becomes problematic, so it will be relaxed. Hence it becomes difficult to assume a sign for v_{k+1} and it becomes difficult to find a strict upper bound for u_k. A sufficient condition on u_k in order to meet requirement (12) in this region may be stated with the aid of the following definition:

$$U_{max,v=0} \equiv U_{max,2}(x_k, v_k = 0) \quad (20)$$

Note that the preceding relation defines a maximum input for a certain negative x_k and a zero velocity. The requirement (12) will be met by:

$$u_k \le -m v_k + U_{max,v=0} \equiv U_{max,3} \quad (21)$$

where m is defined implicitly in Eq. (13).

Figure 2 shows the left half plane of the state space divided into four regions. A maximum input, $U_{max,i}$ has been defined for the regions designated 1,2 and 3. The fourth region corresponds to where requirement (11) superesedes (12), and the maximum input is defined by Eq. (13). The figure shows an intersection of the surfaces $K_{0,max} = 0$ and $s = 0$. This occurs if and only if $a_{max} < 0$.

It is worth noting that $U_{max}(x_k, v_k)$ has been defined in such a way that it is continuous in the left half plane. The variable structure only causes some discontinuous gradients at the boundary lines, but not in the state to input mapping itself. It is possible to take $u_k(x_k, v_k) = U_{max}(x_k, v_k)$, but it may be more practical to use a lesser input in regions 2 and 3 of Fig. (2). One approach is to find a minimum input in these regions which satisfies:

$$U_{min}(x_k, v_k) \le U_{max}(v_k, v_k) \quad (22)$$

In region 2, a second requirement is imposed, superseded by the above in the event of conflict. The requirement is:

$$s_{k+1} \ge s_k \quad (23)$$

This method is favored by the authors, but there are many alternatives. The minimum inputs in regions 1,3, and 4 will be taken as:

$$U_{min,1} = U_{max,1} \quad (24)$$

$$U_{min,3} = 0 \quad (25)$$

$$U_{min,4} = U_A \quad (26)$$

In region 2, determining U_{min} is slightly more complicated. The specific rule depends upon the sign of the following quantity:

$$N \equiv K_0(a = a_{min}) - s_k \equiv K_{0,min} - s_k \quad (27)$$

In terms of $K_{0,min}$ and $K_{2,min}$ which are simply evaluated by taking $a = a_{min}$, the minimum input in region 2 when $N \geq 0$ may be stated in the following manner:

$$U_{min,2} = \frac{K_{1,min} - \sqrt{K_{1,min}^2 + 4NK_{2,min}}}{2K_{2,min}b_{max}} \quad (28)$$

If $N < 0$, the corresponding relation is:

$$U_{min,2} = \frac{K_{1,min} - \sqrt{K_{1,min}^2 + 4NK_{2,min}}}{2K_{2,min}b_{min}} \quad (29)$$

The input can be taken as a weighted average of the minimum and maximum values given for that particular region, i.e :

$$u_{k,i} = (1-\gamma)U_{max,i} + \gamma U_{min,i} \quad (30)$$

Where the constant γ is between 0 and 1. Choosing γ near 0 produces a very aggressive control law. In the presence of significant unmodeled dynamics, such as the dynamics typically associated with electric motors, choosing γ to be reasonably large will mitigate the excitement of these unmodeled dynamics by effectively requiring less rapid input changes near the sliding surface.

The control law in the right half plane of the state space is a simple transformation of the left half plane control law.

$$u_{k,RHP}(x_k, v_k) = -u_{k,LHP}(-x_k, -v_k) \quad (31)$$

where $u_{k,RHP}$ and $u_{k,LHP}$ denote the state to input mapping in their respective half planes. This concludes the controller formulation.

4. Sliding Surface Design

Consider a region in the left half plane where $v_k > 0$ and $s_k < 0$, referring to figure 2. Define this as region A. This region contains part of region 2, will usually contain part of region 3, and could contain part of region 4. In region 2, a positive input may be chosen to meet requirement (12), so that requirement (11) may be easily satisfied simultaneously. In region 1, a negative input may be chosen that satisfies both requirements (11) and (12) simultaneously, but in region 4 requirement (12) must be relaxed in order meet (11). If region A does not contain any part of region 4, then requirements (11) and (12) will be compatible throughout it. A sufficient condition for assuring this is that $\lambda_1 > \lambda_{1min}$, where:

$$\lambda_{1min} \equiv \frac{C_{1min}C_{1max}b_{max} - C_{2max}e^{a_{min}T}b_{min}}{C_{1min}(1 - e^{a_{max}T})b_{max} + C_{1max}e^{a_{min}T}b_{min}} \quad (32)$$

where C_{1max} and C_{2max} are defined by equations (7) and (8), and

$$C_{1min} = C_1(a = a_{min}) \quad (33)$$

$$C_{2min} = C_2(a = a_{min}) \quad (34)$$

This amounts to a upper bound on the slope of the sliding surface near the origin. In general, a positive λ_1 may always be chosen to meet this requirement if $a_{max} \leq 0$,which amounts to a passivity assumption and is quite reasonable.

If both requirements (11) and (12) are satisfied, it is easily seen from the form of the discrete time transition equations (3) and (4) that a state in region A will still be in region A at the next sampling instant, and it is reasonably obvious that it will not leave the upper quadrant of the left half plane during that interval. This leads to a straight forward demonstration of the asymptotic stabilty of this system under the state feedback control law previously developed. While setting λ_1 high will insure stablity, Eq. (32) is not a necessary condition for stablity, and it may be more effective to set $\lambda_1 < \lambda_{1min}$ and allow the possibility of some overshoot in exchange for a faster approach to the origin. Evaluating λ_{1min} is a good starting point for setting λ_1 ,however. Assuming $a_{max} < 0$, some analysis of the sliding surface defined by (9) leads to the conclusion that the least upper bound on the magnitude of the acceleration needed to meet requirement (12) in region A is given by:

$$|\dot{V}_{max}| = \frac{1}{2\lambda_2} \quad (35)$$

If a linear sliding surface were used, the input bound would be proportional to the magnitude of the state, whereas this bound does not depend on the state. This is the key motivation for using a parabolic sliding surface. Designating U_{sat} as a nominal upper bound on the magnitude of the input, a sensible design rule may be stated as:

$$\lambda_2 = \frac{1}{2b_{min}U_{sat}} \quad (36)$$

This will guard against overshooting $S = 0$ due to actuator saturation.

In the controller formulation stiction is not considered explicitly. Generally, the high velocity approach to the origin and the high sensitivity of the control law proposed to the position state will tend to lead to relatively low steady state errors due to stiction. If a stiction effect is considered to be added as a disturbance term in Eq. (2), and the magnitude of the stiction effect is assumed to be upper bounded by a constant H, an upper bound on the steady state error can be determined. In order for a steady state error to exist, it is necessary for the stiction effect to be larger than the input effect at that position state, i.e. :

$$H \geq bu_k(x_k, v_k = 0) \quad (37)$$

In the left half plane of the state space, the input at zero velocity may be expressed as:

$$\frac{u_k(x_k \leq 0, v_k = 0)}{1-\gamma} = \frac{-(C_{2max} + \lambda_1 C_{1max}) + R_0}{2\lambda_2 C_{1max}^2 b_{max}} \quad (38)$$

$$R_0 = \sqrt{(C_{2max} + \lambda_1 C_{1max})^2 - 4\lambda_2 C_{1max}x_k} \quad (39)$$

Near $x_k = 0$ the above expression may be well approximated by:

$$u_k(x_k \leq 0, x_k = 0) = \frac{(1-\gamma)x_k}{b_{max}(C_{2max} + \lambda_1 C_{1max})} \quad (40)$$

Using this approximation and Eq. (37), an acceptably accurate upper bound on the steady state error, e_{ss}, can be given.

$$|e_{ss}| \leq H \frac{b_{max}}{b(1-\gamma)}(C_{2max} + \lambda_1 C_{1max}) \quad (41)$$

If it is assumed that $aT << 1$, then a further approximation yields:

$$|e_{ss}| \leq H \frac{b_{max}}{b(1-\gamma)} T(\lambda_1 + \frac{1}{2}T) \quad (42)$$

The preceeding expression shows that the steady state error bound depends strongly on the sampling period, T, chosen. It is also noteworthy that the linear slope parameter λ_1 is a crucial factor in this expression. If a small λ_1 is chosen, steady state errors will be restricted to a very small range. This is part of the motivation for using a sliding surface with a quadratic form. Evaluating Eq. (42) can give a good indication as to whether acceptable positioning accuracy can be attained from a given set of system and controller parameters.

5. Simulation and Experimental Results

The proposed controller is implemented on a system consisting of a 14 inch NSK direct drive motor connected to a single axis robot arm. Simulations are also conducted using a model of this system. This model is the same as given by Eq. (2), except for the addition of a driver dynamics model and the effect of stiction. The appropriate values for the parameters a and b in Eq. (2) have been determined in the following manner:

$$a = damping\ constant\ / system\ inertia \quad (43)$$

$$b = torque\ constant\ / system\ inertia \quad (44)$$

The dynamics of the driver have found to be well approximated by the following linear filter:

$$\frac{1}{\tau_1 s + 1} \frac{1}{\tau_2 s + 1} \quad (45)$$

$$\tau_1 = 7msec \quad \tau_2 = 0.16msec \quad (46)$$

The controller has been formulated without considering these dynamics and they will have some effect on the closed loop system performance.

Varying the load of the robot arm creates an effective variation in the system parameters a and b. For the loading conditions used, the minimum and maximum values of these parameters are found as:

$$b_{min} = 13.22 \quad b_{max} = 47.0 \quad a_{min} = -1.69 \quad a_{max} = -0.47 \quad (47)$$

Since this controller does not depend on accurate system identification, the following nominal values are taken for input calculations and simulation :

$$b_{min} = 13 \quad b_{max} = 47 \quad a_{min} = -1.7 \quad a_{max} = -0.4 \quad (48)$$

A sampling time of 5 milliseconds was chosen to represent a meaningful period for which the input was fixed, but not so long as to preclude high performance. The bound λ_{1min} evaluates to 0.0151 by Eq. (32). To allow a faster response, λ_1 is chosen lower than this, at 0.01. This will allow the possibility of overshooting the desired position, but this is taken to be acceptable. The other sliding surface parameter is chosen as $\lambda_2 = 0.01$. The coefficient γ is chosen at 0.5 based upon a compromise between performance and excitation of the driver dynamics.

In simulation, a stiction effect of 1.5 Nm was chosen to roughly correspond to the actual system. An input magnitude limit of 10 was imposed to correspond to the voltage input limitation of the NSK motor. Results of simulations with a low and high inertial load are given in Figs. 3 and 4. These figures show the state trajectory of the system from its initial state to its final state, with an expanded view of the final approach shown the upper right corner. The effect of the driver dynamics is noticeable in these simulations, particularly in the case of the simulation with the light load. This is acceptable in this case, but unmodeled dynamics could present considerable difficulty.

Experiments conducted with a 14 inch NSK direct drive motor (Model No.RS1410) yielded results given in Figs. 5 and 6. These plots correspond precisely with those shown for the simulations in Figs. 3 and 4. Figure 5 corresponds to a light inertial load and Fig. 6 corresponds to a heavy inertial load. The position signal was obtained from an encoder and the velocity was estimated by backwards differencing, resulting in significant noise. The time required for the position to settle within 0.001 radians of the desired position was 0.375 seconds with the light load and 0.310 seconds with the heavy load. The magnitudes of the final position errors were less than 0.0006 radians in both cases.

6. Conclusion

A robust variable structure discrete time position controller was formulated and presented. This controller is based upon a sliding surface concept and the explicit discrete time relations corresponding to a second order system with two uncertain parameters. Guidelines for selecting the free controller parameters are also given.

Results obtained in simulation and experiment confirm the effectiveness of this controller in obtaining positioning that is both accurate despite the presence of stiction and quite fast. These properties are also seen to be insensitive to large changes in the system parameters that are within the predetermined bounds.

Acknowledgement

This work was supported in part by MICRO (Microelectronics Innovation and Computer Research Oppurtunities), (No. 91-158). This material is based upon work supported under a National Science Foundation Graduate Fellowship. Any opinions, findings, conclusions, or recommendations expressed are those of the authors and do not reflect the views of the National Science Foundation.

References

[1] Jabbari, A. and Tomizuka, M. (1990), "Robust Nonlinear Control of Positioning Systems with Stiction," American Control Conference, vol. 2, pp. 1097-1102.

[2] Slotine, J.J.E., and Sastry, S.S. (1983), "Tracking Control of Nonlinear Systems Using Sliding Surface with Application to Robot Manipulators," Int. J. Control, 1983, vol. 38, NO. 2, pp. 465-492.

[3] Slotine, J.J.E., and Li, W., "Applied Nonlinear Control," Prentice-Hall, Englewood Cliffs, N.J., 1991.

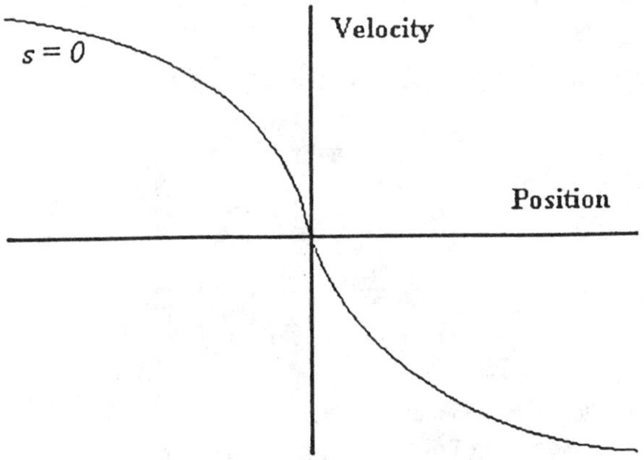

Figure 1. Sliding Surface Definition

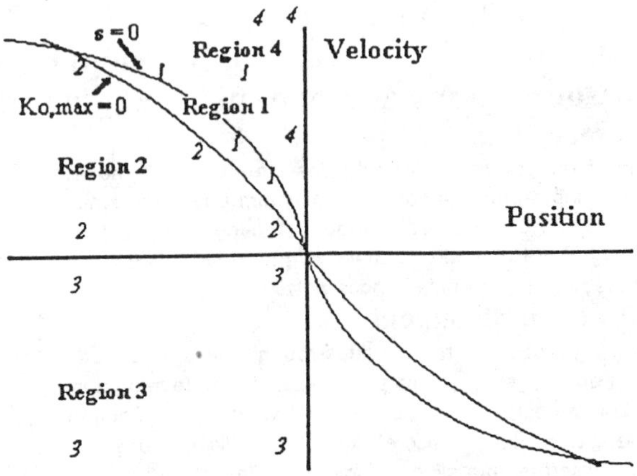

Figure 2. Regions Defined in Left Half Plane

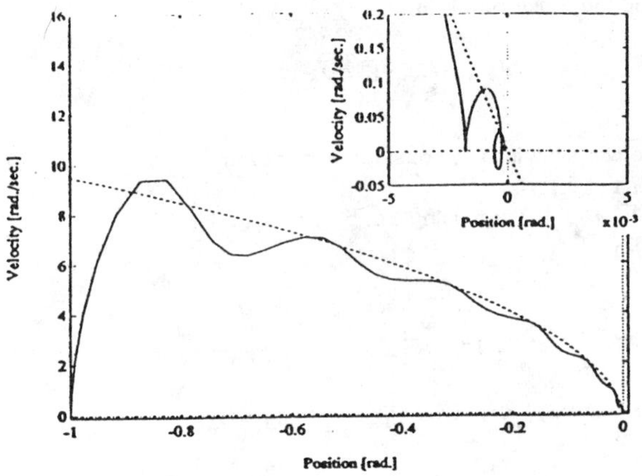

Figure 3. Simulation Result with Low Inertia.

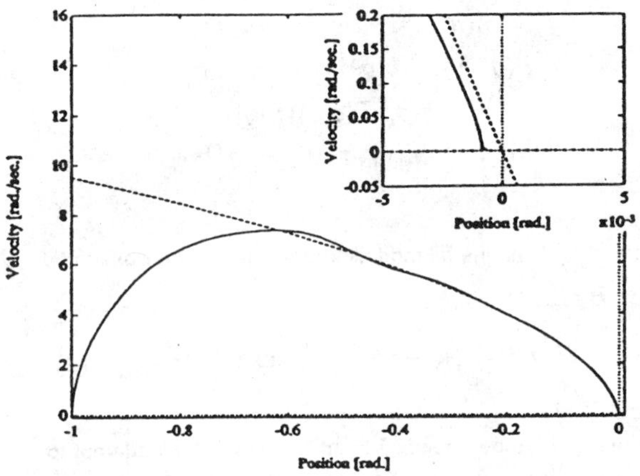

Figure 4. Simulation Result with High Inertia.

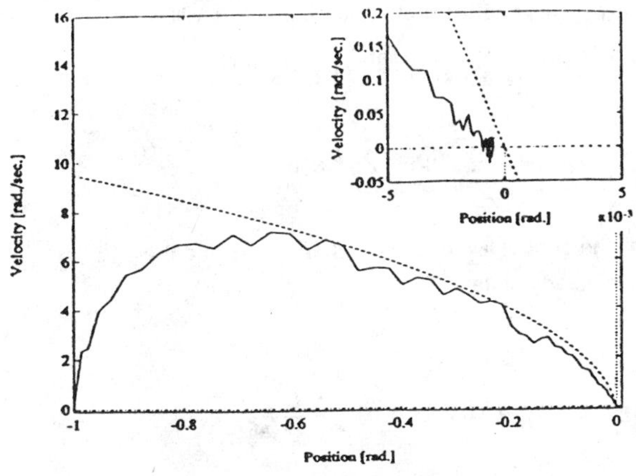

Figure 5. Experimental Result with Low Inertia.

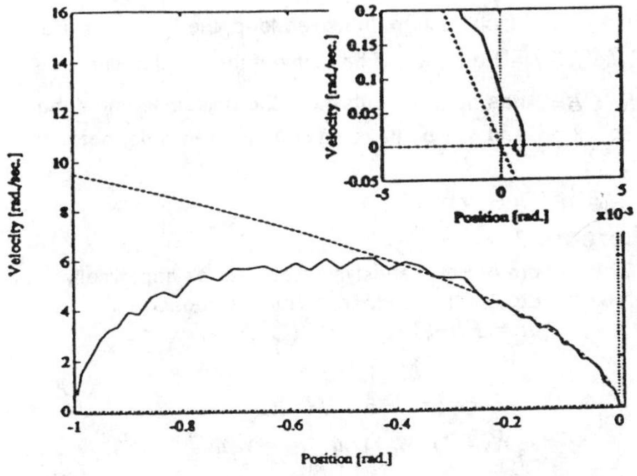

Figure 6. Experimental Result with High Inertia.

Proceedings of the
American Control Conference
San Francisco, California • June 1993

Discrete Time Sliding Mode Control Via Input-Output Models

J. K. Pieper and K. R. Goheen
Department of Mechanical Engineering, Carleton University, Ottawa, Ont.

Abstract

The developed controller achieves a quasi-sliding mode in discrete input-output model non-minimum phase dynamic systems and exhibits performance robustness in that convergence to the sliding mode is guaranteed despite bounded plant parameter uncertainty.

1. Problem Statement

Sliding mode control provides robustness to bounded model uncertainty [1]. This paper attempts to develop a single-input-single-output controller, based on input-output models, to achieve a discrete time quasi-sliding mode. Other discrete time slidng mode controllers have been developed [3] but all have used state space models. This work is based on [2] with the original inclusion of non-minimum phase plants and parameter uncertainty.

The sampled-data single-input plant to be controlled is assumed exactly modelled by

$$\begin{aligned} A(q^{-1})y_k &= q^{-d}B(q^{-1})u_k + p_k \\ A(q^{-1}) &= 1 + a_1 q^{-1} + \dots + a_n q^{-n} \\ B(q^{-1}) &= b_0 + b_1 q^{-1} + \dots + b_n q^{-n},\ b_0 \neq 0 \\ p_k &= \Gamma(q^{-1})y_k \\ \Gamma(q^{-1}) &= \gamma_0 + \gamma_1 q^{-1} + \dots + \gamma_n q^{-n} + \dots \end{aligned} \tag{1}$$

where p_k contains all modelling error. It is further assumed that $H = E\Gamma$ and

$$H(q^{-1}) = h_0 + \dots + h_j q^{-j} + \dots\ ,\quad \max_i |h_i| \le \gamma_{\max} \tag{2}$$

where E is to be specified later. The control will attempt to induce a sliding mode defined as

$$\begin{aligned} s_k &= C(q^{-1})y_k - q^{-d}R(q^{-1})u_k = 0 \\ C(q^{-1}) &= c_0 \dots + c_n q^{-n},\quad R(q^{-1}) = r_0 \dots + r_n q^{-n} \end{aligned} \tag{3}$$

in the closed loop system. In closed loop, the dynamics are $(AR-CB)y_k=0$ and so will be stable if the Diophantine $AR-CB=0$ has no roots outside of the unit circle and if the pairs (A,B) and (C,R) have no common unstable roots.

2. Main Result

Thereom 1

The system of Eq. 1 satisfying Eq. 2 will asymptotically behave as Eq. 3 if the feedback control is chosen as

$$\begin{aligned} u_k &= (EB + (1-q^{-d})R)^{-1}(C - F + W)y_k \\ C &= AE + q^{-d}F \\ L &= C - F,\quad M = EB \\ W(q^{-1}) &= w_0 + w_1 q^{-1} + \dots + w_n q^{-n} \end{aligned} \tag{4}$$

$$w_i = \begin{cases} -\phi\, sign(s_k y_{k-i}) & |s_k| > \dfrac{\phi + \gamma_{\max}}{2} \displaystyle\sum_{j=0}^{n-1} |y_{k-j}| \\ 0 & otherwise \end{cases}$$

$$\gamma_{\max} < \phi < \frac{2}{n}\left(\sum_{i=0}^{n} |c_i| - \sum_{i=0}^{n} |r_i| \sum_{i=0}^{n} |l_i| \left(\sum_{i=0}^{n} |m_i| \right)^{-1} \right) - \gamma_{\max}$$

Proof of the theorem is found in two steps.

Step 1: No Modelling Error. $\gamma_{\max}=0$. Substituting the control of Eq. 4 into Eq. 1 where $p_k=0$ gives

$$\begin{aligned} Ay_{k+d} &= B(EB - (1-q^{-d})R)^{-1}(C - F + W)y_k \\ \rightarrow\ Cy_{k+d} - Ru_k - Cy_k + Ru_{k-d} &= Wy_k \end{aligned}$$

Now using the definition of Eq. 3,

$$\Delta s_{k+d} = s_{k+d} - s_k = Wy_k. \tag{5}$$

There are two situations to consider. First assume $|s_k| > \frac{\phi}{2}\sum_{j=0}^{n-1} |y_{k-j}|$. Then using Eq. 5,

$$\begin{aligned} s_k \Delta s_{k+d} &\le -\frac{\phi^2}{2}\left(\sum_{i=0}^{n-1} |y_{k-i}| \right)^2 \\ \rightarrow\ s_k \Delta s_{k+d} &\le -\frac{1}{2}(\Delta s_{k+d})^2\ \rightarrow\ s_{k+d}^2 \le s_k^2. \end{aligned}$$

The second possible scenario is that $|s_k| < \frac{\phi}{2}\sum_{j=0}^{n-1} |y_{k-j}|$. In this case $W=0$ and from Eq. 5, $\Delta s_{k+d}=0$ and $s_k = s_{ss} = constant$, and the input and output data will asymptotically decay to $y_k = y_{ss}$ and $u_k = u_{ss}$ and

$$s_{ss} y_{ss} = \sum_{i=1}^{n} c_i y_{ss}^2 + \sum_{i=1}^{n} u_{ss} y_{ss}. \tag{6}$$

Now recall the control law of Eq. 4 when $W=0$ and the system is in steady state

$$u_k = u_{ss} = (EB)^{-1}(C-F)y_{ss} = \frac{L}{M} y_{ss}.$$

Substituting this information back into Eq. 6 gives,

$$|s_{ss}| \geq \left(\left|\sum_{i=1}^{n} c_i\right| - \left|\sum_{i=1}^{n} r_i\right| \left|\sum_{i=1}^{n} l_i\right| \left|\sum_{i=1}^{n} m_i\right|^{-1} \right) |y_{ss}|$$

as long as $|y_{ss}|>0$. But, by assumption, $|s_k|<\frac{\phi}{2}n|y_{ss}|$. Now if ϕ is chosen according to the bounds of Theorem 1, there results a contradiction implying that s_k will not remain steady but will either approach the sliding surface or move to where the switching gain is active and stability is guaranteed. Note that a sufficient condition for a suitable ϕ to exist is that

$$\left|\sum_{i=1}^{n} c_i\right| > \left|\sum_{i=1}^{n} f_i\right| \left(1 - \left|\sum_{i=1}^{n} e_i\right| \left|\sum_{i=1}^{n} b_i\right| \left|\sum_{i=1}^{n} r_i\right|^{-1} \right)^{-1}.$$

Step 2: Minimum Phase Plant. $R=0$. The loop dynamics of Eq. 1 with control Eq. 4 can be written,

$$(AE+q^{-d})y_{k+d}=Cy_k+Wy_k+Ep_{k+d}.$$

Thus using Eqs. 3 and 5,

$$\Delta s_{k+d}=s_{k+d}-s_k=Wy_k+ETy_{k+d}$$

$$\Rightarrow \quad s_k\Delta s_{k+d}\leq -|s_k|\left(\sum_{i=0}^{n} \phi|y_{k-i}|+\gamma_{\max}|y_{k-i}|\right).$$

Now, first assume that $|s_k|>\frac{1}{2}(\phi+\gamma_{\max})\sum_{i=0}^{n-1}|y_{k-i}|$ and that $\phi>\gamma_{\max}$, then

$$s_k\Delta s_{k+d}\leq -\frac{(\phi+\gamma_{\max})^2}{2}\sum_{j=0}^{n}|y_{k-j}|\sum_{i=0}^{n}|y_{k-i}|.$$

But $\Delta s_{k+d}=Wy_k+Hy_{k+d}$, therefore $s_k\Delta s_{k+d}\leq -\frac{1}{2}(\Delta s_{k+d})^2$. Now consider that the sliding function value, s_k, is at the limit of the region of attraction, that is $|s_k|=\frac{1}{2}(\phi+\gamma_{\max})\sum_{i=0}^{n}|y_{k-i}|$ and that the system is in steady state with $s_k=s_{ss}$ and $y_k=y_{ss}$ so that $|s_{ss}|=\frac{\phi+\gamma_{\max}}{2}n|y_{ss}|$. The steady value of the sliding function can be expressed $|s_{ss}|=|\sum_{i=1}^{n}c_i|\,|y_{ss}|$. Equating these expressions and rearranging gives

$$\phi\leq\frac{2}{n}\left|\sum_{i=1}^{n}c_i\right|-\gamma_{\max}.$$

Values of ϕ at or larger than this quantity will cause s_k to increase while values of ϕ that strictly observe the limit will cause the system to drift within the sliding region.

Non-minimum phase and uncertain systems satisfy Theorem 1 as a linear superposition of Steps 1 and 2 with stability formally unchanged.

3. Example: Non-Minimum phase plant

Consider the plant

$$y_k=1.1y_{k-1}+u_{k-1}+1.2u_{k-2}+p_1y_{k-1}$$

where $p_1\in[-0.5,0.5]$. Choosing $R=1$ satisfies the Diophantine and the control is computed as

$$u_k=-0.1u_{k-1}+0.5w_0y_k-0.05y_{k-1}$$

$$w_0=\begin{cases}-\phi sign(s_ky_k) & |s_k|>\frac{\phi+\gamma_{\max}}{2}|y_k| \\ 0 & otherwise\end{cases}.$$

Using $y_0=y_1=1$, $u_0=0$ and $\phi=0.5$ the simulated result is shown in Fig. 1. As p_1 is increased to $p_1\in[-1,1]$ without altering the controller it is seen from Fig. 1 that stability is maintained despite large modelling error.

References

[1] DeCarlo R.A., S. Zak and G. Matthews, 1988. "Variable Structure Control of Nonlinear Multivariable Systems: A Tutorial". Proceedings of the IEEE. Vol. 76, no. 3, pages 212-232.

[2] Furuta K., 1991. "VSS-Type Self-Tuning Control", Proceedings of the IECON '91, Kobe, Japan.

[3] Pieper J.K. 1992. Discrete Time Sliding Mode Control. Ph.D. Thesis, Queen's University Department of Mechanical Engineering.

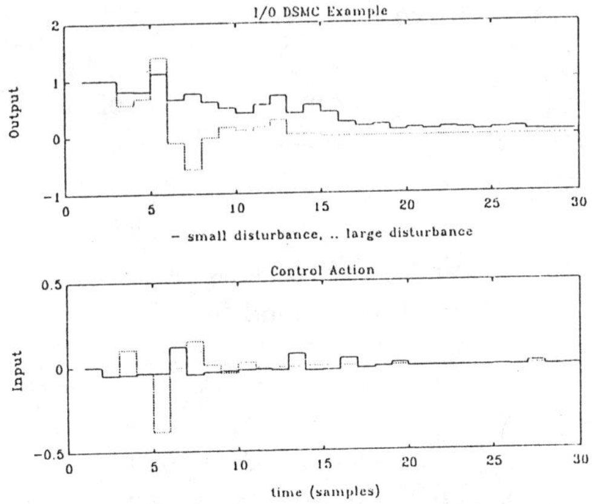

Figure 1. Unstable non-minimum phase plant under discrete sliding control with small and large uncertainty.

Proceedings of the
American Control Conference
San Francisco, California • June 1993

Discrete-Time Sliding-Mode in Stochastic Systems

Sergey Drakunov, Wu-Chung Su, Ümit Özgüner

Department of Electrical Engineering
The Ohio State University
2015 Neil Avenue
Columbus, OH 43210

Abstract

In this paper, we study the discrete-time sliding mode control for continuous-time linear systems with stationary stochastic disturbances. We study both cases of disturbances with bounded and unbounded power spectra. In the first case, the disturbance is assumed to satisfy an Ito type stochastic differential equation. The optimal filtering problem is solved to minimize the deviation from the sliding manifold in the mean square sense. Since the system under control is continuous with a sampled controller, the corresponding filtering problem is of mixed continuous-discrete type. Its solution provides optimal estimates as conditional expectation of the discrete-time disturbances, given the σ-algebra generated by the continuous-time random process.

I. Introduction

The robustness properties of sliding-mode control algorithms are due to the high frequency switching of the control variables. However, theoretically desirable high frequency switching is often not permitted due to physical constraints. Even if such switchings were possible, it is likely that unmodeled high frequency modes will be excited, which in turn deteriorates the performance.

In case of discrete-time controllers the upper bound of the switching frequency is limited by the value T^{-1}, where T is the sampling time and the discontinuous control law leads to chattering in the boundary layer of the sliding manifold $\mathcal{S} = \{x : S(x) = 0\}$. Even without disturbances, the size of this boundary layer is of order $O(T)$. The possible solution of the problem is in using the discrete-time sliding mode concept [5], where the main idea is to decrease control amplitude when the system state reaches the vicinity of $\mathcal{S}$ so that at discrete time instants the state vector belongs to the manifold. Between these instants the state vector is allowed to deviate from $\mathcal{S}$. It may be shown that this reduces the boundary layer to the size of order $O(T^2)$.

The main difficulty in implementation of discrete-time sliding-mode control algorithms is the necessity of having information about the system for calculating the equivalent control u_{eq}, which drives the state to the manifold in the boundary layer of $\mathcal{S}$ in one step. If neglected, the external disturbances and possible parameter variations cause overshoot, and even for bounded excitations result in a boundary layer of order $O(T)$.

To minimize overshoot, one may use disturbance prediction during the sample intervals. For disturbances with sufficient smoothness, prediction based on Taylor series can be used. In a companion work we have shown that this promotes the boundary layer to $O(T^2)$ accuracy [6]. In many cases, this is sufficient for practical needs. Further increase of accuracy is limited by the fact that the well known matching condition [3] needed for invariancy in the continuous-time system is generally not valid for the sampled version.

In this paper, we study the discrete-time sliding mode control for continuous-time linear systems with stochastic disturbances. The disturbance is assumed to satisfy an Ito type stochastic differential equation. The optimal filtering problem is solved to minimize the deviation from the sliding manifold in the mean squared sense. Since the system under control is continuous-time with a sampling controller, the corresponding filtering problem is of mixed continuous-discrete type. Its solution provides optimal estimates as conditional expectation of the discrete-time disturbances given, the σ-algebra generated by the continuous-time random process.

It will be shown that the use of optimal disturbance estimates for calculating equivalent control provides accuracy of order $O(T^{\frac{1}{2}})$ in the mean squre sense for noise with unlimited bandwidth and of order $O(T^2)$

for finite bandwidth.

II. Discrete-time sliding-modes

Consider the linear time-invariant system:

$$\dot{x} = Ax + Bu + Df, \qquad (1)$$

where $x \in R^n$, $y \in R^m$, $f \in R^l$ and A, B, D are constant matrices of appropriate dimensions. The use of a sliding-mode control law for stabilizing (1) allows one to achieve complete disturbance rejection if the matching condition

$$rank[B, D] = rank[B] \qquad (2)$$

is satisfied[3].

The sliding-mode control design assumes that for bounded components of the control variable

$$|u_i| \leq M_i \qquad (3)$$

the control law is the following:

$$u_i = -M_i sgn(s_i), \qquad (4)$$

where $S = col(s_1, s_2, \ldots, s_m)$ specifies switching function of the form :

$$S = Cx. \qquad (5)$$

The matrix C is chosen in such a way that the sliding-mode occurs on the manifold $\mathcal{S} = \{x|Cx = 0\}$ and the system (1) constrained on $\mathcal{S}$ is asymptotically stable.

The use of digital controllers for implementing this type of control requires some modification of the control law (4) since its direct use leads to chattering in the boundary layer of the sliding manifold. This substantially deteriorates the closed loop system performance.

The discretization of a continuous system (1) by a sample/hold element at the instants $t_k = kT$ results in a discrete-time system

$$\mathrm{x}_{k+1} = \Phi \mathrm{x}_k + \Gamma \mathrm{u}_k + \mathrm{d}_k, \qquad (6)$$

where $x_k = x(t_k), \Phi = e^{AT}$, $\Gamma = \int_0^T e^{A\lambda} d\lambda B$, $d_k = \int_0^T e^{A\lambda} Df((k+1)T - \lambda) d\lambda$, $u(t) = u_k$ for $t_k < t \leq t_{k+1}$. The sampling process will generally result in two problems in control design. First of all, the control range space in the kth sampling period T shrinks from $(L^2_{[t_k,t_{k+1}]})^m$ to R^m, where m is the number of control inputs. Complete rejection of intersample disturbances will thus be impossible. Secondly, the lumped effect of the disturbance d_k will cover the whole state space R^n, which is generally outside the span of the control matrix Γ and can not be compensated in one sampling period.

These problems are inherent limitations of sampled controllers, however, they can be alleviated by using the discrete-time sliding-mode control concept [4], [5], which assumes introduction of a boundary layer around the sliding set. The size of the boundary layer is defined by the restrictions on the control (3). If in the boundary layer of the sliding manifold, the control is picked such that $S_k = S(t_k) = 0$, then the order of the deviation is $O(T^2)$ and not $O(T)$ in spite of deviations between sampling. As a result the amplitude of chattering is reduced.

If the disturbance can be measured, the control law in the boundary layer which forces the system state to remain on the sliding manifold at the discrete-time instants is

$$u_k^{eq} = -(C\Gamma)^{-1} C\Phi x_k - (C\Gamma)^{-1} d_k. \qquad (7)$$

This control law assumes that the future values of the disturbance f in (1) are known since d_k depends on the values of f after the decision on u_k should be made. In practice, of course, this is rarely the case. Therefore, in order to reduce the deviation from the manifold the prediction of d_k is needed.

Deterministic disturbance prediction was considered in [6]. Assuming sufficient smoothness of f it was shown that the approximation guarantees the $O(T^2)$ boundary layer. In the present paper, we study the stochastic case.

III. Stochastic Disturbance Models

To minimize the effects caused by disturbances on the boundary layer of the sliding manifold we consider the control law

$$u_k^{eq} = -(C\Gamma)^{-1} C\Phi x_k - (C\Gamma)^{-1} \hat{d}_k, \qquad (8)$$

where $\hat{d}_k$ is the estimate of d_k given the measurement of the continuous-time system (1) state on the interval preceding the time instant t_k and is optimized in the mean-square sense.

The disturbances under consideration are stationary random processes with finite second moments.

If the power spectrum $S_f(\omega)$ of the noise f has compact support (is zero outside some interval Ω) then by using the sampling theorem [1] the signal $f(t)$ can be expressed in terms of its sampled values $f(nT)$.

$$f(t) = \sum_{-\infty}^{\infty} f(nT) \frac{\sin \Omega(t - nT)}{\Omega(t - nT)}, \quad T = \frac{\pi}{\Omega} \qquad (9)$$

where T is the sampling period and Ω is the bandwidth of its power spectrum. Although (9) is not realizable due to its noncausality, it reveals an important fact: the autocorrelation function need not necessarily be known for estimating a band-limited process. We shall show later that there does exist a realizable incomplete model for such disturbances which enables prediction with arbitrarily small error if sufficiently large number of past samples are available.

The other type of disturbances we study are those with rational $S_f(\omega)$. In this case an accurate formulation of the problem involves the system description in the form of Ito [7] stochastic differential equations:

$$dx = Axdt + Budt + (D\xi dt + Rdw_1) \tag{10}$$

$$d\xi = W\xi dt + Qdw_2, \tag{11}$$

where $w_1(t)$, $w_2(t)$ are independent standard Wiener processes. Here $D\xi$ represents the colored part of the noise and the formal expression $R\frac{dw_1}{dt}$ the white part.

We apply the following assumptions:

Assumption 1. W has asymptotically stable eigenvalues;

Assumption 2. $rank R = n$;

Assumption 3. The processes $Rw_1(t)$ and $Qw_2(t)$ are uncorrelated;

IV. Unlimited Bandwidth Case

Consider the discrete-time version of (10)

$$x_{k+1} = \Phi x_k + \Gamma u_k + \eta_k + v_k, \tag{12}$$

where

$$\eta_k = \int_{t_k}^{t_{k+1}} e^{W(t_{k+1}-\lambda)} D\xi(\lambda)d\lambda, \tag{13}$$

is the colored part of the disturbance and

$$v_k = \int_{t_k}^{t_{k+1}} e^{W(t_{k+1}-\lambda)} Rdw_1(\lambda) \tag{14}$$

is discrete-time white noise.

The discretization of (11) leads to the equation

$$\xi_{k+1} = \Psi\xi_k + q_k. \tag{15}$$

Let $S_k = S(t_k)$, then from (12)

$$S_{k+1} = C\Phi x_k + C\Gamma u_k + C(\eta_k + v_k). \tag{16}$$

Applying the control law

$$u_k^{eq} = -(C\Gamma)^{-1}C\Phi x_k - (C\Gamma)^{-1}C\hat{\eta}_k, \tag{17}$$

we obtain

$$S_{k+1} = C(\eta_k + v_k - \hat{\eta}_k). \tag{18}$$

To minimize $E\|S_{k+1}\|^2$ given the observation of $x(t)$ up to the instant t_k the estimate $\hat{\eta}_k$ should be picked to be a conditional expectation

$$\hat{\eta}_k = E(\eta_k|\mathcal{F}_{t_k}), \tag{19}$$

where we denote as $\mathcal{F}_t$ a σ-algebra generated by the process $x(t)$

$$\mathcal{F}_t = \sigma\{x(\tau)|0 \le \tau \le t\}. \tag{20}$$

Such choice of u_k^{eq} means that in the closed loop system discrete-time sliding mode [5] occurs on the manifold

$$E(S_{k+1}|\mathcal{F}_{t_k}) = 0. \tag{21}$$

Since $w(t)$ is a martingale [7], taking a conditional expectation of both sides of (13), given the σ-algebra $\mathcal{F}_{t_k}$ and using (11), we have

$$\hat{\eta}_k = \int_{t_k}^{t_{k+1}} e^{W(t_{k+1}-\lambda)} Dd\lambda\hat{\xi}(t_k) = \Xi\hat{\xi}(t_k), \tag{22}$$

where the matrix Ξ is of the form

$$\Xi = \int_0^T e^{W\lambda} Dd\lambda, \tag{23}$$

and $\hat{\xi}$ is a conditional expectation:

$$\hat{\xi}(t) = E(\xi(t)|\mathcal{F}_t). \tag{24}$$

Therefore, from (22) it follows that in order to obtain the values of $\hat{\eta}_k$ we need a filter to calculate $\hat{\xi}(t_k)$. The following theorem provides the form of such a filter.

Theorem 1 *If assumptions 1-3 hold, the optimal estimate of $\xi(t_k)$ is*

$$\hat{\xi}(t_k) = z_k + Lx_k, \tag{25}$$

where z_k satisfies

$$z_k = \Lambda z_{k-1} + \zeta_{k-1} + \Pi u_{k-1} \tag{26}$$

with Λ, Π and ζ_k defined by:

$$\begin{aligned} \Lambda &= e^{HT}, \\ \Pi &= \int_0^T e^{H\lambda}d\lambda M, \\ \zeta_{k-1} &= \int_{t_{k-1}}^{t_k} e^{H(t_k-\lambda)}Nx(\lambda)d\lambda, \end{aligned} \tag{27}$$

where the matrices H, N, M, L are

$$\begin{aligned} H &= W - LD, \\ N &= -LA + WL - LDL, \\ M &= -LB, \\ L &= (R^TR)^{-1}DP \end{aligned} \tag{28}$$

and P is the positive definite solution of the algebraic matrix Ricatti equation

$$PW^T + WP - PD^T(RR^T)^{-1}DP + QQ^T = 0. \tag{29}$$

Proof. From (10), (11) and using Assumptions 1-4 it follows [7] that $\hat{\xi}(t)$ satisfies the equation of the stationary Kalman filter:

$$d\hat{\xi} = W\hat{\xi}dt + L(D\xi dt + Rdw_1 - D\hat{\xi}dt), \qquad (30)$$

where the matrix L is defined in (28) and P is the positive definite solution of the algebraic matrix Ricatti equation (29).

Substituting $(D\xi dt + Rdw_1)$ from the right hand side of (10) into (30) we obtain:

$$d\hat{\xi} = W\hat{\xi}dt + L(dx - Axdt - Budt - D\hat{\xi}dt). \quad (31)$$

An important point here is that by introducing a new variable $z = \hat{\xi} - Lx$ we can rewrite this equation as an ordinary differential equation without stochastic differentials:

$$\dot{z} = Hz + Nx + Mu, \qquad (32)$$

where matrices H,N and M are defined as (28).

The discrete-time version of (32) results in a discrete-time filter

$$z_k = \Lambda z_{k-1} + \zeta_{k-1} + \Pi u_{k-1} \qquad (33)$$

with Λ, Π, and ζ defined in (27). Then the optimal estimate of $\xi(t_k)$ is

$$\hat{\xi}(t_k) = z_k + Lx_k. \qquad \text{Q.E.D} \qquad (34)$$

Substituting the estimate (34) into the equation (22) we obtain an optimal $\hat{\eta}_k$ as:

$$\hat{\eta}_k = \Xi(z_k + Lx_k). \qquad (35)$$

The filter (33), (34) together with (22) provides a way to calculate the conditional expectation of η_k given the information from the continuous-time process $x(t)$. This is a substantially more accurate estimate compared to the one obtained from only discrete-time samples $x(t_k)$. This estimate can be calculated by a digital controller with an additional sampler providing the values of ζ_k.

The quantity $\eta_k + v_k - \hat{\eta}_k$ from the right hand side of (18) is a discrete-time white noise process with variance of order $O(T)$. It means that the mean square deviation of S_{k+1} from zero is of order $O(T^{\frac{1}{2}})$.

V. Band-limited Random disturbances

If the disturbance $f(t)$ in (1) is a random process which is wide sense stationary (WSS) with finite power and finite bandwidth; i.e.,

$$S_f(\omega) = 0, \quad for\ |\omega| > \Omega, \qquad (36)$$

then the prediction error of d_k can be arbitrarily small in the mean square sense.

Now the goal is to find a real sequence $\{a_i\}$ to predict d_k, by

$$\tilde{d}_k = \sum_{i=1}^{k} a_i d_{k-i} \qquad (37)$$

such that

$$E\{|d_k - \tilde{d}_k|^2\} \longrightarrow 0 \quad as \quad k \rightarrow \infty$$

The disturbance d_k can be evaluated by feeding $f(t)$ into a linear, time-invariant system as

$$\dot{d}(t) = Ad(t) + Df(t), \quad d(0) = 0. \qquad (38)$$

Solving (38), we have $d(t) = \int_0^t e^{A\lambda}Df(t-\lambda)d\lambda$ with $t \geq 0$. It should be noted that the matrix A must be stable for the process $d(t)$ to be well defined. If the original open loop system is not, a stablizing preliminary state feedback in continuous time should be applied beforehand. Also note that $d_k \neq d(kT)$ but

$$d((k+1)T) = d_k + e^{AT}d_{k-1} + \cdots + e^{kAT}d_0 \qquad (39)$$

It is observed that $d((k+1)T)$ is a function of d_i, $i = 0, 1, ..., k$. If we can predict $d((k+1)T)$ at $t = kT$, then d_k is found immediately since all the past values of d_i are available. Equation (38) also implies that $d(t)$ is a random process generated by feeding $f(t)$ into the system $H(s)$, where

$$H(s) = (sI - A)^{-1}D \qquad (40)$$

Note that $d(t)$ is not stationary because the initial value is assigned, however, it approaches to WSS asymptotically with power spectrum $S_d(\omega) = H(\omega)S_f(\omega)H^*(\omega)$, which is both finite power and band-limited as $f(t)$ is. In other words, $d(t)$ can still be treated as WSS for a sufficiently long time span. We shall use a theorem by Papoulis [1] to predict a band-limited random precess by using its past sampled values:

If $S_d(\omega) = 0$ for $|\omega| > \Omega$ and $T < \frac{\pi}{\Omega}$, then given an arbitrary positive number ϵ, we can find a set of coefficients a_i such that

$$E\{|d(t) - \sum_{i=1}^{\infty} a_i d(t - iT)|^2\} < \epsilon.$$

In practice, a finite sequence of length p is sufficient for any ϵ. Therefore,

$$\tilde{d}(t) = \sum_{i=1}^{p} a_i d(t - iT) \qquad (41)$$

To find a_i's is equivalent to constructing a causal filter

$$\rho(\omega) = \sum_{i=1}^{p} a_i e^{-jT\omega i} \quad (42)$$

such that $\rho(\omega) \simeq 1$ for $|\omega| < \Omega$ as $p \to \infty$. One can make use of the Fejer-Riesz theorem [2] to solve for the real coefficients a_i's. It has also been pointed out in [1] that if $T < \frac{\pi}{3\Omega}$ then $a_i = (-1)^{i-1} C_i^p$ will be a legitimate choice.

To apply (41) to the prediction of $d(t)$, we assume that $pT < t$ since $d(t)$ is not defined for negative time. In other words, the controller should collect sufficient past samples for the prediction to be accurate enough.

Theorem 2 *If the continuous time matching condition holds and $f(t)$ has autocorrelation function $R_f(\tau)$ with $\ddot{R}_f(0)$ bounded, then the discrete time sliding manifold can be reached with $O(T^2)$ accuracy.*

Proof. Since (2) holds, there exists a matrix Λ with appropriate dimensions such that

$$D = B\Theta$$

Let $u_k = v_k + g_k$. Choose $g_k = -\Theta f(kT)$ to compensate d_k and $v_k = -(C\Gamma)^{-1} C\Phi x_k$ to approach the sliding surface, then

$$\begin{aligned} s_{k+1} &= -C\Gamma\Theta f(kT) + Cd_k \\ &= C\int_0^T e^{A\lambda} B\Theta(f((k+1)T-\lambda) - f(kT))d\lambda \end{aligned}$$

$$E[|s_{k+1}|^2] = Tr\{E[s_{k+1}s_{k+1}^*]\}$$
$$= Tr\{C\int_0^T\int_0^T e^{A\lambda_1} B\Theta G(\lambda_1,\lambda_2)\Theta^* B^* e^{A^*\lambda_2} d\lambda_1 d\lambda_2 C^*\}$$

where $G(\lambda_1,\lambda_2) = R_f(\lambda_2-\lambda_1) - R_f(T-\lambda_1) - R_f(T-\lambda_2) + R_f(0)$

Since $\ddot{R}_f(0)$ is bounded, $G(\lambda_1,\lambda_2) = O(T^2)$ and $E[|s_{k+1}|] = O(T^2)$. Q.E.D.

The disturbance compensation term $-\Theta f(kT)$ is not necessarily optimal among all possible choices of g_k. In fact, if d_k is known exactly, the optimal solution in the mean square sense is $g_k = -(\Gamma^T\Gamma)^{-1}\Gamma^T d_k$. Now that we are able to predict d_k with arbitrary accuracy, the control law (8) will yield to $E[|s_{k+1}|] \leq O(T^2)$.

VI. Conclusions

The theory of sliding mode is derived from a continuous time concept where a discontinuous high-speed switching control is employed to steer the states towards and maintain them on a predesigned manifold, or switching surface, in which the desired system performance can be achieved. When applying a continuous time concept to discrete time design or a digital controller in an analog system, it is inevitable that one encounters some inherent constraints such as sampling rate, nonideal sliding mode, limited accuracy, and so on. In this paper, we have shown that discrete time sliding mode can be reached with $O(T^2)$ error for band-limited disturbances with smooth autocorrelation functions and $O(T^{\frac{1}{2}})$ for disturbances with unlimited bandwidth in the mean square sense. As mentioned before, the control signal space is generally not sufficient to cover the whole disturbance space in discrete time.

The errors essentially come from either the inexactness of the disturbance prediction processes or the limitation of the control rank space due to the sample/hold. In spite of these, the resultant system performance is still superior to the discrete implementation of continuous time sliding mode controller design, which suffers from chattering in the control variable and overshooting the sliding surface. Another advantage of the proposed method is that the prediction process is executed on-line without the need of estimating an upper bound for the disturbance.

Acknowledgement

This research reported in this paper was supported by AFOSR, Grant No. F49620-92-J-0460.

Reference

[1] A. Papoulis, "A note on the predictability of band-limited processes," *Proceedings of the IEEE*, vol. 13, no. 8, pp. 1332-1333, August 1985.

[2] A. Papoulis, *Signal analysis.* New York:McGraw-Hill, 1977.

[3] B. Drazenovic, "The invariance condition in variable structure systems," *Automatica*, vol. 5, pp. 287-295, 1969.

[4] V.I. Utkin and S.V. Drakunov, "On discrete-time sliding modes," Preprints of IFAC Workshop on Nonlinear Control, Capri, Italy, 1989.

[5] S.V. Drakunov and V.I. Utkin, "Sliding Mode Control in Dynamic Systems", *International Journal of Control*, v. 55, Nb. 4, pp. 1029-1037, 1992.

[6] Wu-Chung Su, S. Drakunov and U. Ozguner, "Sliding mode control in discrete time linear systems", to appear in Proceedings IFAC Congress, 1993.

[7] R.Bucy and P. Josef, "Filtering for Stochastic Processes with Applications to Guidance", Chelsea Pub Co., New York, N. Y., 1987.

Proceedings of the
American Control Conference
San Francisco, California • June 1993

BANG BANG CONTROL OF AN OVERHEAD CARTESIAN CRANE

DeSantis, R.M., Krau, S.,

Génie Electrique et Genie Informatique
Ecole Polytechnique de Montréal

Abstract

A motion controller for a 3-D Cartesian crane is designed under the constraint that the control action belong to a discrete set of assigned values. The design procedure rests upon a two step approach. First, one determines a constraint-free motion controller satisfying the required specifications. In a second step, this controller is replaced with an equivalent controller satisfying the discrete constraint. The first step is implemented by adopting a heuristic 3-D ext ension of a wellproven 2-D controller; the second, by applying recent sliding mode results.

1. Introduction

The operation of an overhead crane entails the motion control of the girder, the trolley, and the hoisting apparatus so that the suspended load move along a pre-specified path. Among the techniques succesfully explored to automatize this operation, one finds open and closed loop optimal control [Ri.1, Sa.1, Ka.1], pole placement and LQG linear state feedback [Hu.1], fuzzy controllers [Ya.1], etc..

Most of these controllers are designed by assuming that the voltage applied to the crane motors be arbitrarily selectable within a certain continuous range of values. Practical considerations, on the other hand, make it convenient or necessary that crane motors be energized with only a discrete number of voltage levels. It becomes then of interest to explore the modalities by which the proposed "continuous" controllers might be replaced with a "discrete" controller which, though constrained by a finite number of output levels, does, nevertheless, produce an action equivalent to that of the original controller.

The usual approach to implement this replacement, is to simply insert in cascade with the continuous controller a pulse width modulator. In addition to the cost of the extra equipement involved, a disadvantage of such a solution, however, is that a small delay is generated which may have a destabilizing influence on the feedback system.

The application of recent sliding mode controllers [De.1, De.2] offers an alternative approach. As it has been shown in a preliminary study [De.3], these controllers do not require, at least in principle, a special equipment, nor do they necessarily introduce an additional delay. Moreover, they may also offer the potential to lead to an overall feedback system dynamics which is less sensitive to parameter variation and external perturbation.

The development in [De.3] was confined to a 2-D travel motion of the crane's load (that is: a motion contained in a vertical plane with either the trolley or the girder blocked). In what follows we will consider the more realistic case where the trolley and the girder move concurrently, causing a 3-D motion of the load. In contrast to the well familiar 2-D motion, a 3-D motion implies a dynamics of the load which is intrinsically nonlinear and intercoupled. The Lyapunov linearization, which is routinely applied in the 2-D case, is no longer applicable; a key hypothesis of the basic result in [De.2], which plays an essential role in the 2-D case [De.3], is no longer satisfied.

2. The Mathematical Problem

Let a nonlinear time-varying dynamical plant be described by the differential equation

$$\dot{x}(t) = f_0(x,t) + B_0(x,t)(u(t) + p(t))$$

$$x(0) = x_0. \tag{1}$$

where $x(t) \in R^n$ represents the plant state, $u(t) \in R^m$ is the control, $p(t) \in R^m$ represents the influence of parameter and external perturbations; $f_0(x,t)$ and $B_0(x,t)$ are appropriately dimensioned real valued vector and matrix functions.

The problem that we consider is to design a (discrete) control satisfying the following two constraints: a) the feedback system dynamics must conform to some given specifications; b) the components of the control action, $u(t)$, are constrained to belong to an assigned discrete set, $u_i(t) \in U_i := \{u_{i1}, \ldots, u_{iN}\}$, $i = 1 \ldots m$.

In a number of applications (such as in the motion control of an overhead crane), various techniques have been made available which succesfully lead to a control law satisfying the first constraint. One way to solve the problem is therefore to first develop one such a (continuous) control law, $u_D(x,t)$, and to then replace it with a control, $u(x,t)$, satisfying the second constraint and capable of producing the same state trajectory as $u_D(x,t)$.

The developments in [De.2, De.3] suggest this latter step to be developed by adopting a sliding mode controller obtained from the continuous controller by means of the following procedure. Using the notation

$$\sigma(t) := B_0(x,t)B_0^+(x,t)S(t) \tag{2}$$

where $B_0^+(x,t)$ denotes the pseudo-inverse of $B_0(x,t)$, and

$$S(t) := \int_0^t \{\dot{x}(t) - f_0(x,t) - B_0(x,t)u_D(x,t)\}dt, \tag{3}$$

the discrete controller is selected so as to provide an output such that

$$u_i^*(t) \in U_i,\ i= 1, \ldots, m \tag{4}$$

and

$$SGN\{u_i^*(t)-u_{Di}(x,t)+p_i(t)\}:=-SGN\{[B_0\sigma(t)]_i\} \tag{5}$$

The key property of such a controller is formalized by the following result (a variation of theorem 1 in [De.2]).

Lemma 1. If $B_0(x,t)$ is of a full rank then: the dynamics of (1) submitted to a discrete control (2-5) is described by

$$\dot{x}(t) = f_0(x,t) + B_0(x,t)u_D(x,t) \tag{6}$$

Remark 1. Under nominal operating conditions, the discrete controller considered by Lemma 1 generates a state trajectory identical to that of the continuous controller (nominal trajectory). Under perturbed conditions, the state trajectory generated by the discrete controller remains identical to the nominal trajectory provided that parameter variations and external perturbations may be represented in terms of an input equivalent perturbation.

Remark 2. Lemma 1 gives little information about the behavior of the system in the presence of parameter variations and external perturbations which are not representable as in (1). This is in contrast to theorem 1 in [De.2] where use was made of the additional hypothesis that $B_0(x,t)B_0^+(x,t)$ is a constant matrix. This hypothesis allows a more complete robustness characterization of the dynamics of the plant with respect to a more general class of perturbations. As it will be shown in the next section, however, such an hypothesis is not applicable in the case of an overhead crane operating in 3-D space. Hence the availability of a somewhat more restrictive result and the openness of the question as to the behavior of the discrete controller under perturbed conditions of a general kind. In what follows, such a question will be investigated on the basis of simulation experiments.

3. The Overhead Crane Model

Assuming a suspension cable with a constant length, the kinematic configuration of a Cartesian crane can be represented in terms of the parameters x_1 x_2 x_3 x_4 where (see figure 1):

x_1 gives the position of the girder with respect to the inertial frame;

x_2 gives the position of the trolley with respect to the girder;

x_3 is the angle between the z axis of the inertial frame and the z axis of the load frame;

x_4 is the angle between the z_x plane of the inertial frame and the vertical plane containing the z axis of the load frame.

The state of the crane can be represented, in turn, in terms of a vector $x \epsilon R^9$,

$$x' := [x_1\ x_2\ x_3\ x_4\ x_5\ x_6\ x_7\ x_8\ x_9]' \tag{7}$$

where: x_1 x_2 x_3 x_4 are as defined above, x_5 is the torsional twist of the cable, and

$$x_6 := \dot{x}_1,\ x_7 := \dot{x}_2,\ x_8 = \dot{x}_3,\ x_9 := \dot{x}_4. \tag{8}$$

The control can be represented by a 2 dimensional vector $u \epsilon R^2$, $u:=[u_1,u_2]'$, where: u_1 is the propulsion force developed by the girder motor, and u_2 is the force developed by the trolley motor.

Using the notations in table 1, and taking into account the non-holonomic constraint

$$\dot{x}_5 = x_9 \cos x_3, \tag{9}$$

the dynamics of the crane may be modelled in terms of the following differential equation (adapted from [Ka.1])

$$\dot{x} = f(x) + B(x)u \tag{10}$$

where: $x \epsilon R^9$, $u \epsilon R^2$, and matrix functions f(x) and B(x) are described by

$$f(x) := \begin{bmatrix} F_1 \\ \\ F_2 \end{bmatrix} \qquad B(x) := \begin{bmatrix} 0 \\ \\ B_2 \end{bmatrix} \tag{11}$$

with

$$F_1' := [f_1\ f_2\ f_3\ f_4\ f_5]'$$

$$F_2' := [f_6\ f_7\ f_8\ f_9]'$$

$$[f_1\ f_2\ f_3\ f_4\ f_5]' := [x_6\ x_7\ x_8\ x_9\ x_9\cos(x_3)]'$$

$$F_2 := M^{-1}\tilde{F}_2 \qquad \tilde{F}_2' := [\tilde{f}_6\ \tilde{f}_7\ \tilde{f}_8\ \tilde{f}_9]'$$

$$\tilde{f}_6 := c\sin x_3 \cos x_4 (x_8^2+x_9^2) - 2c\cos x_3 \cos x_4 x_8 x_9;$$

$$\tilde{f}_7 := c\sin x_3 \cos x_4 (x_8^2+x_9^2) + 2c\sin x_4 \cos x_3 x_8 x_9;$$

$$\tilde{f}_8 := -e\sin x_3 \cos x_4 x_8^2 - g\sin x_3;$$

$$\tilde{f}_9 := -p\cos x_3 x_5 - h\sin x_3 \cos x_3 x_8 x_9; \tag{12}$$

$$B_2 := M^{-1} \begin{bmatrix} 1 & 0 \\ 0 & 1 \\ & \\ 0 & 0 \\ 0 & 0 \end{bmatrix} \tag{13}$$

where $M:=[m_{ij}]$ with

$m_{11}=a \quad m_{12}=0 \quad m_{13}=c\cos x_3 \sin x_4 \quad m_{14}= c\sin x_3 \cos x_4$

$m_{21}=0 \quad m_{22}=b \quad m_{23}=c\cos x_3 \cos x_4 \quad m_{24}=-c\sin x_3 \sin x_4$

$m_{31}=c\cos x_3 \sin x_4 \quad m_{32}=c\cos x_3 \cos x_4 \quad m_{33}=d \quad m_{34}=0$

$m_{41}=c\sin x_3 \cos x_4 \quad m_{42}=-c\sin x_3 \sin x_4 \quad m_{43}=0$

$$m_{44}=ml^2 \sin x_3{}^2+I_a \cos x_3{}^2+I_t \sin x_3{}^2 \qquad (14)$$

To be noted that, to simplify notations, the inertia matrix of the load has been assumed to be diagonal and given by

$$J:= \begin{matrix} I_t & 0 & 0 \\ 0 & I_t & 0 \\ 0 & 0 & I_a \end{matrix}$$

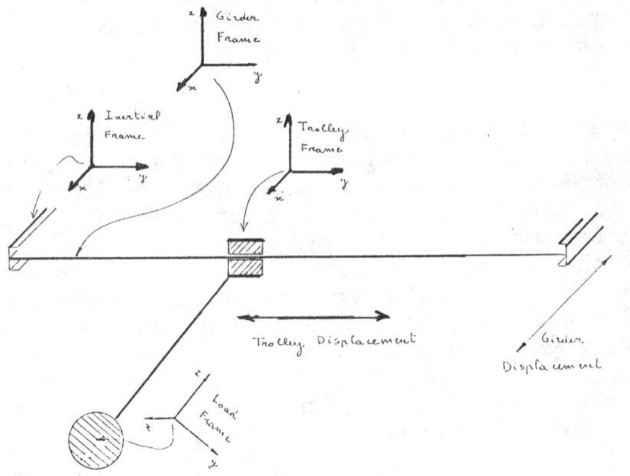

Figure 1: 3-D Euclidean Overhead Crane

m_{gi}:=mass of the girder;

m_{tr}:=mass of the trolley;

m_{lo}:=mass of the load;

l:=length of the cable;

g_0:=gravitational acceleration;

I_a:=inertia of the load with respect to the z axis;

I_t:=load inertia with respect to the x axis (and y axis);

p:=twist compliance of the suspended cable;

$a:=m_{gi}+m_{tr}+m_{lo}$;	$b:=m_{gi}+m_{tr}$;
$c:=m_{gi}l$;	$d:=m_{gi}l^2+I_t$;
$e:=I_a-I_t-m_{gi}l^2$;	$g:=m_{gi}g_0 l$;
$h:=2m_{gi}l^2+2(I_t-I_a)$;	

Table 1: List of Symbols

4. Design of the Motion Controller

In line with the procedure discussed in sections 1 and 2, we first develop a (continuous) motion controller satisfying the dynamic specifications. As it is of a common practice in similar studies, this controller is selected as a state feedback of the family

$$[u_{D1}\ u_{D2}]:= u_D:= -K[x - x_D] \qquad (15)$$

where x_D represents the desired (equilibrium) state, and K is an appropriate (usually state dependent) gain matrix.

Letting

$$x_D:=[x_{D1}\ x_{D2}\quad 0\ 0\ 0\ 0\ 0\ 0]', \qquad (16)$$

where $(x_{D1}\ x_{D2})$ denotes the desired position of the trolley with respect to the fixed frame, a heuristic extension of the approach in [Hu.1, De.3] suggests that a suitable state feedback controller is given by

$$u_{D1}=-K_A[x_1-x_{D1}\ \ x_3\sin(x_4)\ \ \dot{x}_1\ \ \dot{x}_3\sin(x_4)] \qquad (17)$$

$$u_{D2}=-K_B[x_2-x_{D2}\ \ x_3\cos(x_4)\ \ \dot{x}_2\ \ \dot{x}_3\cos(x_4)] \qquad (18)$$

where K_A, (K_B), is a constant matrix computed so as to stabilize the crane under the hypothesis that the trolley (the girder) is blocked and that the crane motion is confined to a vertical plane [De.3, Hu.1, Kr.1].

Adopting the physical parameters in table 2, and imposing these constrained motions to be characterized by the eigenvalues $p_1 = p_2 = p_3 = p_4 = -1$ (for the vertical motion with the trolley blocked), and $p_1 = p_2 = p_3 = p_4 = -1.5$ (for the vertical motion with the girder blocked), one obtains

$$K_A=[-3920\quad -15660\quad 237470\quad 28300]$$

$$K_B=[-2478\quad -6608\quad -9940\quad -24063] \qquad (19)$$

Next, we consider the implementation of the continuous controller (17-19) by means of a discrete controller. The entries of this latter controller will be required to satisfy the constraint

$$u_i^* \in U_i:=\{\pm u_{ij}\},\ i=1,2,\ j=1,2, \qquad (20)$$

with

$$U_1 =\{\ 0, +- 250,\ +- 600\ +- 2500,\ +- 4500\}$$

$$U_2 =\{\ 0,\ +- 950,\ +- 1500,\ +- 3500\}. \qquad (21)$$

Following lemma 1, a suitable discrete controller may be obtained by selecting $u_i(t) \in U_i$ so that

$$SGN\{u_i^*(t)-u_{Di}(x,t)+p_i(t)\}:=-SGN\{[B_0'\sigma(t)]_i\} \qquad (22)$$

where $B_0(x)$ is given by (11, 13, 14) and $\sigma(t)$ is obtained by combining (2, 3) with (11-14, and 17-19). Observe that

$$S(t):= \begin{bmatrix} S_1 \\ S_2 \end{bmatrix} \qquad (23)$$

with $S_1=0$, and

$$S_2(t):=q-\int_0^t \{F_{02}(x) + B_{02}(x)u_D(x)\}dt,$$

where

$$\dot{q}:=[x_5\ x_6\ x_7\ x_8\ x_9]', \qquad (24)$$

and $F_{02}(x)$, $B_{02}(x)$ are the nominal values of $F_2(x)$, $B_2(x)$.

It follows that condition (5) becomes

$$SGN\{u_i^*(t)-u_{Di}(x,t)+\max\{|p_i(t)|\}\}:= SIGN\{[B_{02}'(x)B_{02}(x)B_{02}^+(x)S_2(t)]_i\}$$

This condition is met by selecting $u_i^*(t)$ as given by

$$ui*(t)= -M(t)_i SIGN\{[B_{02}'(x)B_{02}(x)B_{02}^+(x)S_2(t)]_i\}$$

with $M(t)_i$ the smallest element in $\{u_{ij}\}$ such that

$$M(t)_i > |u_{Di}(x,t)| + \max|p_i(t)|, \qquad (25)$$

where we take $\max|p_i(t)|= 100$.

mass of the girder:	5000 Kg
mass of the trolley:	4200 Kg
mass of the load:	600 Kg
length of the cable:	8 m
gravitational acceleration:	9 m/sec^2
inertia of the load with respect to z axis:	.1 Kg m^2
inertia of the load with respect to x axis:	.01 Kg m^2
load inertia to y axis:	.01 Kg m^2
cable compliance coefficient:	.1 N*m/rad

Table 2: Nominal Parameter Values

5. Simulation Experiments

The comparative behavior of the discrete controller and of its continuous counterpart have been investigated by simulations. These simulations have been carried out by considering the the following **Basic Test Procedure:** the crane's dynamic model is defined by (10-14), with crane nominal parameters as in table 2.

The continuous controller is described by (17, 18) with K_A, K_B as in (19). The discrete controller is described by (23, 25). The two controllers are both required to implement a transfer of the crane from an initial state [0 0 0 0 0 0 0 0 0]' to a final state [1 1 0 0 0 0 0 0 0]'.

Test N.1: STEP RESPONSE UNDER NOMINAL OPERATING CONDITIONS

Objective: To illustrate comparative behavior under nominal operating conditions.

Modalities: As stipulated in the basic test procedure under nominal operating conditions (absence of perturbation, system parameters correspond to their expected values).

Results and Discussion: As predicted by Lemma 1, the results of this test have confirmed that under nominal operating conditions the output behavior of the continuous controller and of its discrete counterpart are identical.

Test N.2: THE INFLUENCE OF A BIGGER THAN EXPECTED LOAD MASS

Objective: To illustrate comparative behavior under the presence of a bigger than expected load mass.

Modalities: Identical to those of experiment N.1 with the exception that the load mass is now assumed to be equal to 7000 Kg rather than have the nominal value of 5000 Kg.

Results and Discussion: The presence of a bigger than expected load mass causes perturbations which may not be represented in terms of the vector p(t) considered by Lemma 1. Thus a theoretical result allowing us to predict its influence is not available. The simulation results that we have obtained indicate, nevertheless, that the dynamics of the continuous and the discrete controllers remain essentially equivalent. They also indicate a dynamic behavior only slightly different from the nominal one. The robustness to this type of perturbation appears to be quite acceptable in both the discrete and the continuous controller.

Test N.3: INFLUENCE OF AN EXTERNAL PERTURBATION

Objective: To illustrate comparative behavior under the application of a sinusoidal perturbation to the trolley.

Modalities: Identical to those in test N.1 with the exception that now a sinusoidal perturbation force is applied to the trolley. The frequency of this perturbation is .2 hertz; the amplitude 100 N.

Results and Discussion: In this case one has $p(t)= 100B_0 \sin(.4\pi t)$. From Lemma 1 one expects this perturbation to have an influence over the dynamics of the continuous controller, and no influence over the dynamics of the discrete controller. Simulation results have confirmed this expectation. From the perspective of this test, the sensitivity performance of the discrete controller is superior to that of the continuous controller it attempts to emulate.

Test N.4: INFLUENCE OF A DELAY IN THE LOOP

Objective: To analyze sensitivity to the presence of a delay in the feedback loop.

Modalities: Identical to those of experiment N.1 with the exception that a delay of 1 msec is now introduced in the application of the control action.

Results and Discussion: The available theoretical results are not applicable in the presence of a delay. It is therefore once again difficult to predict the outcome of this experiment prior to its implementation. The simulation results that we have obtained, suggestnevertheless that while the dynamic behavior produced by both the continuous and the discrete controller is influenced by this perturbation, this influence is somewhat more damaging in the case of the latter controller. This, in turn, suggests that, in implementing the continuous controller by means of a discrete action, a particular attention has to be taken so as to minimize such a delay.

Conclusions

The design of a motion controller for an over-head Cartesian crane in 3-D space, under the constraint that the control action belong to a set with a finite number of values, may be carried out by following a two step approach: first design a constraint-free (continuous) controller satisfying the required motion specifications; second, replace this continuous controller with an equivalent discrete controller satisfying the finite number of values constraint.

In implementing this approach three types of difficulties have to be confronted: the solutions proposed by the literature to carry out the first step appear to be either excessively complex (as for instance in [Ka.1]), or only applicable to the 2-D case (as in [Ri.1, Hu.1, De.3]); the presence of nonlinear intercouplings in the 3-D model prevents a Lyapunov type linearization of the plant model and hence the adoption of results based on such a linearization (as it was the case in [De.3]); finally, the 3-D model does not satisfy the hypotheses underlying the procedure proposed in [De.2] (notably: the matrix $B_0(x,t)B_0^+(x,t)$ fails to be time-invariant).

An effective way to overcome the first difficulty is to obtain a 3-D controller by the combination of two 2-D controllers of the type proposed in [Hu.1, De.3]. The input to these controllers is represented by the projection of the load motion over the vertical planes associated with the girder's and with the trolley's motion. The second and third difficulties may be overcome by modifying the main result in [De.2] so as to make it applicable to the problem under consideration (Lemma 1).

In agreement with theoretical predictions, simulation results confirm the validity of this approach. In particular, they show that under nominal operating conditions the dynamics generated by the ensuing discrete controller is identical to that of the continuous controller. This remains the case under the presence of input equivalent parameter and external perturbations (such as friction forces acting on the girder or the trolley).

The available theory, however, does not allow one to predict the influence of perturbations such as those related to an only approximate knowledge of the crane physical parameters (such as mass load, girder and trolley mass, cable length, etc..). Nevertheless, the simulation results do suggest, however, that even in this case the dynamics of the discrete controller compares favorably with that associated with the continuous controller.

On the other hand, not all the simulation results, are in favor of the discrete controller. In particular, the performance of the discrete controller appears to be problematic in the presence of a delay in the control loop. In addition to this, one has to expect that the high frequency switching produced by the discrete controller may not be entirely compatible with the physical capabilities of the crane motors.

References

De.1, DeCarlo, R.A., Zak, S.H., Matthews, G.P., Variable Structure Control of Nonlinear Multivariable Systems: A Tutorial, **Proceedings of the IEEE**, Vol 76, N.3, 1988.

De.2, DeSantis, R.M., The Implementation of a Continuous Controller Via a Discrete Valued Controller, **ASME Journal of Dynamic Systems Measurement and Control,** Vol 115, Sept 1992, pp.400-406.

De.3, DeSantis, R.M., Locatelli, A., Bartoletti, P., Pareti, F., Sia, V. On the Sliding Mode Control of an Overhead Crane, **Proc 1990 Canadian Conference on Electrical and Computer Engineering,** pp. 26.3.1-26.3.5.

Ka.1, Kamal A.F. Moustafa, A.M. Ebeid, Nonlinear Modeling and Control of an Overhead Crane Load Sway, **Journal of Dynamic Systems Measurement and Control**, Trans ASME, Vol. 10, September 1988.

Kr.1, Krau, S., Discrete Implementation of the Continuous Control of an Overhead Crane in 3-D Space, (M.Sc.A. Thesis, Ecole Polytechnique de Montreal, Fall 1991).

Hu.1, Hurteau, R., DeSantis, R.M., Microprocessor Based Adaptive Control of a Crane System, **22nd IEEE Decision and Control Conference**, San Antonio, Texas, Dec 1983.

Ri.1, Ridout, A.J., Anti-Swing Control of the Overhead Crane Using Linear FeedBack, **Journal IEEE Australia**, Vol. 9, N.1/2, pp. 17-26.

Sa.1, Sakawa Y., Shindo Y., Optimal Control of Container Cranes", **Automatica**, Vol. 18, N.3, pp. 257-266, Pergamon Press, England, 1982.

Ya.1, Yasonobu S., Hasegawa T., Evaluation of an Automatic Container Crane Operation System Based on Predictive Fuzzy Control, **Control Theory and Advanced Technology**, Vol. 2, N.3, pp. 419-432, Mita Press, 1986.

Acknowledgement

This work originated during a stay by the first author with the Control Group of the Politecnico di Milano. Thanks are due to professors Arturo Locatelli and Sergio Bittanti, and to their students Bartoletti, Pareti and Sia for helpful interaction.

Proceedings of the
American Control Conference
San Francisco, California • June 1993

THE VARIABLE STRUCTURE CONTROL FOR A CLASS OF NONLINEAR MULTIVARIABLE SYSTEMS WITH DELAYS

LIU YONGQING and YUAN FUSHUN

DEPARTMENT OF AUTOMATION, SOUTH CHINA UNIVERSITY OF TECHNOLOGY, GUANGZHOU, 510641, P.R.CHINA

Abstract

In this paper, a new robust control approach-variable structure control for a class of multiinput nonlinear systems with time-delays is proposed. And the result of unconditional stabilization of closed-loop control system is obtained. The variable structure control approach proposed in this paper has the following advantages. Firstly,with this method the whole design task is decomposed into two phases of design for two isolated lower order subsystems, and is greatly reduced. Secondly, the system has invariance in the presence of parameter uncertainties external disturbanceafter the sliding motion occurs. The result of the paper is also suit to the invariant linear systems with time-delays. In the last place, to support the conclusion of the paper a numeral simulation example is given.

Key words: Nonlinear multivariable system with time-delays; Variable structure control.

1. Introduction

With the fast development of the sciences and technology a great number of nonlinear time delay systems have or will come out. In fact, there are always various phenomenons of pure time delay in every physical systems especially in electronic, mechanical, biological, metallurgical, and chemical systems. Even in the system controlled by computers there still exists the time delay. The reason is that it too takes some time for computers to complete the numeral computations. This time delay is a result of inherent delay in the components of the system. Moreover,in sometimes a time delay is deliberately introduced into a system for control purposes. The mathematical formula of a time delay system results in a system of delay-different equations.

Variable structure control is a technique which was developed primarily by the Union researchers in the last two decades. The main advantages of this approach lie in : firstly, the considered system can be decomposed into two isolated lower order subsystems and its control design is reduced; secondly, after the sliding motion occurs the system possesses desirable insensitivity properties to parameter uncertainties and external disturbances. It is because of above advantages of the variable structure control techniquethat it has been extensively applied in the linear and nonlinear systems without any time delay[1].

However about the time delay system, the theory of variable structure control begins to be developed almost just now. At present the result of variable structure control about the time delay system dose not come out except the references[2-4]. In this paper the variable structure control for a class of multiinput nonlinear systems with time delays is studied. And the result of unconditional stabilization of closed-loop control system is obtained. In the last place to support the conclusion of the paper a numeral simulation example is given.

* This work was supported by The Foundation of Chinese National Natural Sciences.

2. Formulation of the Problem

In this paper, consider the following multivariable nonlinear system with time delay only in the state variables:

$$\dot{X}(t)=\sum_{i=0}^{p} A_i(t;\ X(t-\tau_0),\ \dots,\ X(t-\tau_p))X(t-\tau_i)+B_0u \qquad (2.\ 1)$$

$$X(t)=\phi(t),\ -\tau\le t\le 0=\tau_0\le\tau_1\le\cdots\le\tau_p=\tau$$

where $X(t)\epsilon R^n$ is the state vector ; $u\epsilon R^m$ is the input control vector; $B_0\epsilon R^{n\times m}$ is control matrix; $A_i\epsilon R^{n\times n}$ is coefficient matrix(i=1, ..., p); m, n and p are all certain positive integers.

The following assumptions are made:

(1). The matrix B_0 includes only constant elements and is of full rank;

(2). $(A_0(t;\ X(t-\tau_0),\ \dots,\ X(t-\tau_p)),\ B_0)$ is a pair of controllable matrices in large[5];

(3). Rank $(A_i,\ B_0)$=Rank (B_0), and $A_i=B_0\times D_i$ where $D_i\epsilon R^{m\times n}$; i=1, ..., p;

(4). A_0 is input linearizable. Specifically, let $A_0=A_{ONC}+A_{OC}$ where A_{OC} contains only constants and A_{ONC} contains nonlinear time varying terms. For A_0 to be input linearizable each column of A_{ONC}

must be in the image of B_0[6].

(5). For each fixed feedback structure the system (2. 1) is Lipschits.

Then the system (2. 1) can be rewritten as the following form:

$$\dot{X}(t)=A_0X(t)+B_0[u+\sum_{i=1}^{p} D_iX(t-\tau_i)] \quad (2.\ 2)$$

and we have the following theorem:

Theorem 2. 1 If the system (2. 1) satisfies the assumptions (1) and (2), then there is an invertible invariant linear state transformation as follows:

$$Y(t)=TX(t) \quad (2.\ 3)$$

where

(1). $TB_0=(0 \mid B^T)^T$, and $B\varepsilon R^{m\times m}$ is an invertible matrix;

(2). (A^{11}, A^{12}) is a pair of invariant and controllable matrices where

$$TA_0T^{-1}=\begin{pmatrix} A^{11} & A^{12} \\ A^{21} & A^{22} \end{pmatrix}$$

Proof: Because B_0 is of full rank in column, we can assume that B as an invertible matrix and do not lose generality, where

$$B_0=(B^{*T} \mid B^T)^T,\ \det(B)\neq 0$$

Then so long as we take the linear transformation matrix T as the following:

$$T=\begin{pmatrix} I_{n-m} & -B^*B^{-1} \\ 0 & I_m \end{pmatrix}$$

the following equality is obviously correct:

$$TB_0=(0 \mid B^T)^T$$

If T is taken as follows:

$$T=\begin{pmatrix} I_{n-m} & -B^*B^T \\ 0 & B^{-1} \end{pmatrix}$$

we can obtain the simpler result as the following:

$$TB_0=(0 \mid I_m)^T$$

Up to now result (1) has been proved[7] .

About result (2), we know that linear transformation and state feedback can not change controllability of the system. From this point and with the theory of controllable matrix the result (2) can be proved.

From this theorem (2. 2) can be again expressed as the following form:

$$\begin{cases} \dot{Y}_1(t)=A^{11}Y_1(t)+A^{12}Y_2(t) & (2.\ 4) \\ \dot{Y}_2(t)=A^{21}Y_1(t)+A^{22}Y_2(t)+B[u+\sum_{i=1}^{p} D_iT^{-1}Y(t-\tau_i)] & (2.\ 5) \end{cases}$$

where $Y_1\varepsilon R^{n-m}$; $Y_2\varepsilon R^m$; and all coefficient matrices have corresponding dimensions. From here we shall develop our discussion to face the system (2. 4)-(2. 5).

3. Main Results

Let the switching function have the following linear form:

$$S=C_1Y_1(t)+C_2Y_2(t) \quad (3.\ 1)$$

Then the corresponding switching surface equation is as the following:

$$S=C_1Y_1(t)+C_2Y_2(t)=0 \quad (3.\ 2)$$

where $S\varepsilon R^m$; $C_1\varepsilon R^{m\times(n-m)}$; $C_2\varepsilon R^{m\times m}$. Our first important task is to select properly the switching matrix $(C_1 \mid C_2)$ which makes the sliding equation approximately stable.

In the first place we can take the matrix C_2 as a arbitrary m×m invertible matrix. For simplicity of the calculation behind, the matrix C_2 is taken as the following:

$$C_2=B^{-1} \quad (3.\ 3)$$

According to the equality (3. 2), on the switching surface the following equation is always correct:

$$Y_2(t)=-C_2^{-1}C_1Y_1(t)=-BC_1Y_1(t) \quad (3.\ 4)$$

Substituting (3. 4) into (2. 4) we can obtain the dynamic equation of the sliding motion as following:

$$\dot{Y}_1(t)=(A^{11}-A^{12}BC_1)Y_1(t) \quad (3.\ 5)$$

From theorem 2. 1 it is known that (A^{11}, A^{12}) is controllable. And matrix B is invertible. So we can properly select the matrix C_1 to ensure the sliding mode approximately stable.

Next we come to design the variable structure control law to make the approaching condition $S^T\cdot\dot{S}<0$ satisfied. In other words, the trajectory of the system from any point of state pace can go into the switching surface (3. 2).

For the above purpose we can easily obtain the following formula:

$$\dot{S}|_{(2.\ 4)(2.\ 5)}=C_1\dot{Y}_1(t)+C_2\dot{Y}_2(t)=(C_1A^{11}+B^{-1}A^{21})Y_1(t)+$$
$$+(C_1A^{12}+B^{-1}A^{22})Y_2(t)+u+\sum_{i=1}^{p} D_iT^{-1}Y(t-\tau_i)$$

Therefore so long as the variable structure control law u is taken as the following:

$$u=-(C_1A^{11}+B^{-1}A^{21})Y_1(t)-(C_1A^{12}+B^{-1}A^{22})Y_2(t)-$$
$$-\sum_{i=1}^{p} D_iT^{-1}Y(t-\tau_i)-kS-\varepsilon\cdot \mathrm{sign}(S)$$

where k and ε are all positive numbers, then the following formula is obviously correct:

$$S^T\cdot\dot{S}=-kS^TS-\varepsilon S^T\mathrm{sign}(S)<0$$

That is, the approaching condition of the sliding mode is satisfied and the going course has certain approaching rate ε>0. Hence it is assured that the trajectory from any point can begin sliding motion in finite time.

The above result is obviously suite to the invariant linear time delay system with constant coefficient matrices $A_i (i=1, \ldots, p)$ from the presses of above proof.

4. Algorism

To sum up we have the following algorism of variable structure control.

(1). Examine whether or not the considered system satisfies the assumed conditions;

(2). Construct the invertible linear state transformation $Y(t)=TX(t)$. And obtain (2. 4)-(2. 5);

(3). Take $C_2=B^{-1}$ in the equation of the switching surface (3. 2);

(4). Establish the dynamic equation of the sliding mode (3. 5) from(2. 4) and the switching surface equation (3. 2);

(5). Select the matrix C_1 using the technique of pole location and optimization in order to make matrix $A^{11}-A^{12}BC_1$ approximately stable or have certain spectrum;

(6). Determine the variable structure control law from (3. 6).

5. Numeral simulation example

Consider the following nonlinear time delay system:

$$\dot{X}(t)=A_0X(t)+A_1X(t-\tau_1)+A_2X(t-\tau_2)+B_0u \qquad (5.\ 1)$$

where

$$A_0=\begin{pmatrix} 0 & 2 & -1 \\ 3 & 0 & 1 \\ 0 & 0 & 2 \end{pmatrix} \qquad B_0=\begin{pmatrix} 1 & 0 \\ 2 & 1 \\ 0 & 2 \end{pmatrix}$$

$$A_1=\begin{pmatrix} x_1(t-\tau_1) & 0 & 3 \\ 2x_1(t-\tau_1)+1 & 2x_2(t) & 6+(x_3(t))^2 \\ 2 & 4x_2(t) & 2(x_3(t))^2 \end{pmatrix} \qquad A_2=\begin{pmatrix} 0 & 1 & -1 \\ 1 & 4 & 1 \\ 2 & 4 & 6 \end{pmatrix}$$

According to the algorism of the above section, we study the simulation example as following:

(1). By examination we know that the all assumed conditions are satisfied in system (5. 1). And where

$$D_1=\begin{pmatrix} x_1(t-\tau_1) & 0 & 3 \\ 1 & 2x_2(t) & (x_3(t))^2 \end{pmatrix} \qquad D_2=\begin{pmatrix} 0 & 1 & -1 \\ 1 & 2 & 3 \end{pmatrix}$$

(2). Resolving the matrix equation $TB_0=(0 \ \vdots\ I)^T$ we obtain transformation matrix T and T^{-1} as the following:

$$T=\begin{pmatrix} -2 & 1 & -0.5 \\ 1 & 0 & 0 \\ 0 & 0 & 0.5 \end{pmatrix} \qquad T^{-1}=\begin{pmatrix} 0 & 1 & 0 \\ 1 & 2 & 0.5 \\ 0 & 0 & 0 \end{pmatrix}$$

By calculation we can get:

$$TA_0T^{-1}=\begin{pmatrix} -4 & -5 & 0 \\ 2 & 4 & -1 \\ 0 & 0 & 2 \end{pmatrix},\ A^{11}=-4,\ A^{12}=(-5 \quad 0\ )_{1\times 2}$$

$$A^{21}=\begin{pmatrix} 2 \\ 0 \end{pmatrix} \qquad A^{22}=\begin{pmatrix} 4 & -1 \\ 0 & 2 \end{pmatrix}$$

(3). Let $C_2=\mathrm{diag}(1,\ 1)$ and $C_1=(0 \quad 1)^T$. Therefore $A^{11}-A^{12}C_1=-4$;

The switching function is given by:

$$S=(C_1 \ \vdots\ I_{2\times 2})Y(t)=\begin{pmatrix} 0 & 1 & 0 \\ 1 & 0 & 0 \end{pmatrix}(y_1(t) \quad y_2(t) \quad y_3(t))^T$$

and the equation of the sliding mode is described by the following:

$$\dot{y}_1(t)=(A^{11}-A^{12}C_1)y_1(t)$$

that is

$$\dot{y}_1(t)=-4y_1(t)$$

(4). From (3. 6) take the variable structure control law as following:

$$u=-(C_1A^{11}+A^{21})y_1(t)-(C_1A^{12}+A^{22})y_2(t)-D_1T^{-1}Y(t-\tau_1)-$$
$$-D_2T^{-1}Y(t-\tau_2)-4S-0.3\mathrm{sign}(S)$$

(6). Now we simulate the following system of equations:

$$\begin{cases} \dot{Y}_1(t)=A^{11}Y_1(t)+A^{12}Y_2(t) \\ \dot{Y}_2(t)=-C_1(A^{11}Y_1(t)+A^{12}Y_2(t))-4S-0.3\mathrm{sign}(S) \end{cases} \quad \text{if } S\neq 0$$

$$\begin{cases} \dot{y}_1(t)=(A^{11}-A^{12}C_1)y_1(t) \\ Y_2(t)=-C_1y_1(t) \end{cases} \quad \text{if } S\equiv 0$$

$$X(t)=T^{-1}Y(t)$$

that is, let $s_1=y_2(t)$ and $s_2=y_1(t)+y_3(t)$. Then the closed-loop system is given by

$$\begin{cases} \dot{y}_1(t)=-4y_1(t)-5y_2(t) \\ \dot{y}_2(t)=-4s_1-0.3\mathrm{sign}(s_1) \\ \dot{y}_3(t)=4y_1(t)+5y_2(t)-4s_2-0.3\mathrm{sign}(s_2) \end{cases} \quad \text{if } (s_1)^2+(s_2)^2\neq 0$$

$$\begin{cases} \dot{y}_1(t)=-4y_1(t) \\ y_2(t)=0 \\ y_3(t)=-y_1(t) \end{cases} \quad \text{if } s_1=s_2\equiv 0$$

$$\begin{cases} x_1(t)=y_2(t) \\ x_2(t)=y_1(t)+2y_2(t)+0.5y_3(t) \\ x_3(t)=2y_3(t) \end{cases}$$

$$\begin{cases} y_1(0)=0.5 \\ y_2(0)=0.2 \\ y_3(0)=-0.3 \end{cases}$$

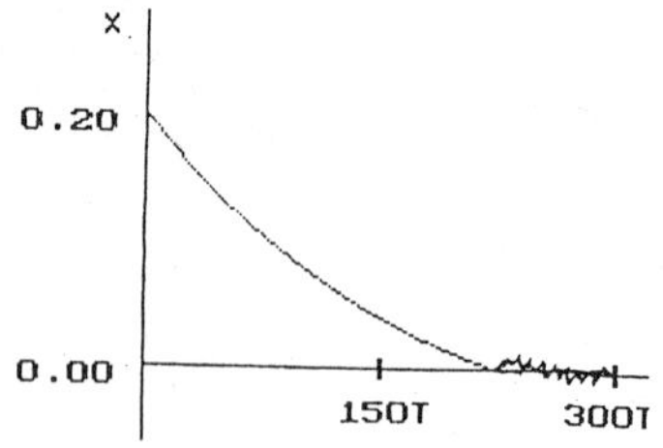

Fig.1 State $x_1(t)$ T=0.003s

Then all the state curves $x_1(t)$, $x_2(t)$ and $x_3(t)$ are shown in figures 1-3. They are all obviously convergent to t axis.

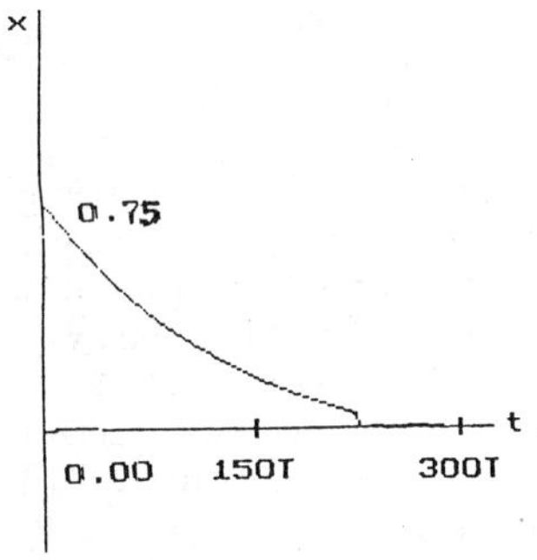

Fig.2 State $x_2(t)$ T=0.003s

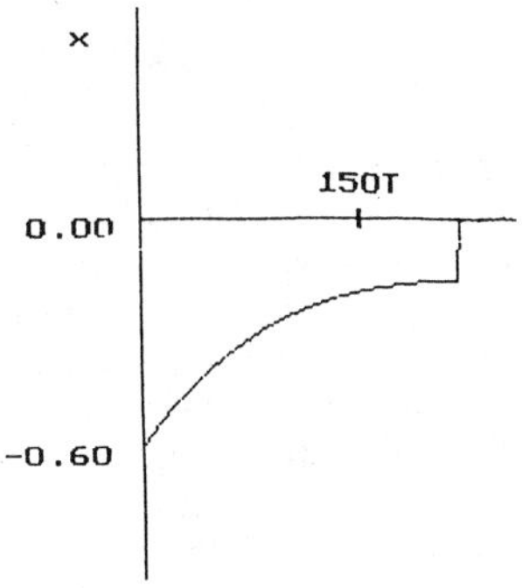

Fig.3 State $x_3(t)$ T=0.003s

6. Conclusion

The problem of effectively controlling for multivariable nonlinear time delay system has been a difficulty problem because of its infinite dimension. And the variable structure control has many advantages such as simplicity in design, easily realization, and robustness to varying of internal parameter and external disturbance. Therefore it provides a comparatively practical way to study the time delay control system. In this paper the variable structure control for a class of nonlinear time delay systems is studied under certain conditions. The result of unconditional stability of closed-loop is obtained. The result is obviously correct for linear invariant time delay system. At last, to support the conclusion of the paper a numeral simulation example is given.

References

1. W.B.Gao, Introduction to the variable structure control, The publishing house of science and technology of China, Beijing, China, 1990(in chinese);
2. E.M.Jafarov, Analysis and synthesis of multidimensional SVS with delays in sliding modes, Preprints of 11-th IFAC world congress, Tallinn, Vol.6, p44-49, 1991;
3 F.S.Yuan and Y.Q.Liu, On the variable structure control of n-dimension invariant systems with single time-delay and multiinput,AMSE, Advances in modelling & simulation, Vol.31, No.3, p57-64, 1992;
4. Y.M.Hu and Q.J.Zhou, Variable structure control of control systems with delay, Journal of automation, Vol.19, No.5, 1991(in chinese);
5. R.Sommer, Control design for mulitivariable nonlinear time-delay systems, Int.J. Control, Vol.31, No.5, p883-891;
6. G.P.Matthews and R.A.DeCarlo, Decentralized variable structure control for class of nonlinear multiinput multioutput nonlinear systems, Proc. 24th Annual IEEE Conf. on Decision and Control, Fort Lauderdale, Florude, 1985, p1719-1724;
7. B.Drazennonic, The invariance condition in variable structure system, Automatica, 1969, Vol.5, p287-295.

Proceedings of the
American Control Conference
San Francisco, California • June 1993

VSS-Type Self-Tuning Control -β Equivalent Control Approach-

Katsuhisa Furuta*

Abstract: This paper is concerned with the discrete-time variable structure control and its application to self-tuning control. The proposed variable structure control is designed by using the pulse transfer function. In the first, the variable structure control for the deterministic discrete-time system is proposed based on the generalized minimum variance control. In the next, the proposed method is extended so that self-tuning control is realized for the plant with uncertain parameters by identifying the control law on-line. The simulation study shows the effectiveness of the proposed algorithm.

1 Introduction

The self-tuning control is effective to the control of the process with uncertain parameters [1]. But while parameter identification is not completed, the self-tuning control gives undesirable slugging responses. The sliding mode control based on the variable structure systems is robust to small parameter uncertainty for the continuous time plant. When uncertainty is larger than one taken account in the design, the sliding mode does not exist and the undesirable response yields [2,3]. Slotine [4] solved this problem by combining the variable structure and adaptive control. This approach can treat the model following problem[5,6], but it requires the all state variables without using observers, since the plant model is not accurate.

The implementation of the control by the computer requires discretization and brings undesirable responses like chattering. Milosavljevic [7] proposed a continuous control using discrete-time measurement and gave a necessary condition of the discrete sliding mode. Sarpturk and others [8] considered a sufficient condition of the discrete-time sliding mode and gave the discontinuous control at the sliding surface like a continuous sliding control. Drakunov and Utkin [9] proposed a different sliding mode approach, where the existence of the sliding surface was proved by the contraction mapping. The author [10] gave a design method of a discrete sliding mode control based on the proposed sufficient condition. The sliding mode is generalized to a sliding sector and the control designed does not yield chattering of the response. All those methods require state variables and have the problem how to determine the sliding surface and to observe state variables especially in the case that the plant parameters are uncertain. The author also applied the variable structure control to the self-tuning of the plant described by a transfer function [12]. But the design parameters are not enough to improve the response. Chan [11] has proposed to modify [10] by introducing one design parameter for the discrete-time sliding mode control of a linear system represented by the state space.

This paper presents a discrete-time VSS method for a system described by the transfer function employing a design parameter β extending [12]. Both cases that parameters are known and unknown are considered. In these cases, the discrete-time VSS control is designed based on the generalized minimum variance. For the plant with uncertain parameters, this paper considers self-tuning control for a system represented by the transfer function. First is the VSS control based on the generalized minimum variance control for the known parameter model. The second method is the discrete time adaptive control based on VSS, which achieves the simultaneous stabilization and parameter identification, which globally stabilizes the output but parameters do not necessarily converge.

The organization of the paper is as follows. Section 2 gives a discrete-time VSS controller design using the generalized minimum variance control for a known plant. Section 3 gives the VSS-type self-tuning control with simultaneous identification and VSS control. Simulations of examples are shown in Session 4.

*Tokyo Institute of Technology, 2-12-1, Oh-Okayama Meguro-ku Tokyo 152 Japan. Fax +81-3-3720-5269

2 Generalized Minimum Variance Control Using VSS

This paper considers a single input and output system. The following discrete relation represents the controlled plant with input u_k and output y_k,

$$A(q^{-1})y_k = q^{-d}B(q^{-1})u_k \tag{1}$$

where $A(q^{-1})$ and $B(q^{-1})$ have not common factors and q denotes the time shift operator defined by

$$q^{-t}y_k = y_{k-t}$$

and $A(q^{-1})$ and $B(q^{-1})$ are assumed known and representing

$$\begin{aligned} A(q^{-1}) &= 1 + a_1q^{-1} + a_2q^{-2} + \cdots + a_nq^{-n} \\ B(q^{-1}) &= b_0 + b_1q^{-1} + b_2q^{-2} + \cdots + b_mq^{-m} \quad (b_0 \neq 0) \end{aligned}$$

In the next, we define the polynomial

$$C(q^{-1}) = 1 + c_1q^{-1} + c_2q^{-2} + \cdots + c_nq^{-n}$$

so that $C(q^{-1})$ is a Schur polynomial. The objective of the control in this chapter is to minimize the generalized variance of the controlled variables s_{s+d}, that is, in the deterministic case, to give the control input satisfying

$$s_{k+d} = C(q^{-1})[y_{k+d} - r_{k+d}] + Q(q^{-1})u_k = 0 \tag{2}$$

where r_k is the reference, and the error will be defined as

$$e_k = y_k - r_k$$

$C(q)$ and $Q(q^{-1})$ are determined so that the error vanishes if the above (2) is kept satisfied. In the case $Q(^{-1}) = 0$, $C(q^{-1})$ is easily designed just by assigning the all zeros in the unit disk. In the first, the generalized minimum variance control without using VSS will be discussed. The equation (2) is rewritten as

$$\begin{aligned} s_{k+d} &= (E(q^{-1})B(q^{-1}) + Q(q^{-1}))u_k + F(q^{-1})y_k - C(q^{-1})r_{k+d} \\ &= G(q^{-1})u_k + F(q^{-1})y_k - C(q^{-1})r_{k+d} \end{aligned} \tag{3}$$

where $E(q^{-1})$ and $F(q^{-1})$ are polynomials determined to satisfy

$$C(q^{-1}) = A(q^{-1})E(q^{-1}) + q^{-d}F(q^{-1}) \quad (4)$$

and $G(q^{-1})$ is defined as

$$G(q^{-1}) = E(q^{-1})B(q^{-1}) + Q(q^{-1}) \quad (5)$$

The control input to make $s_{k+d} = 0$ is, therefore, given by

$$u_k = -G(q^{-1})^{-1}[F(q^{-1})y_k - C(q^{-1})r_{k+d}] \quad (6)$$

This paper considers to use the variable structure control in addition to the above conventional minimum variance control so that the output satisfies $s = 0$. $C(q^{-1})$ and $Q(q^{-1})$ are chosen to make the control system stable satisfying following lemma[1].

[Lemma] The necessary and sufficient condition that the output making $s_{k+d} = 0$ stable is that all zeros of

$$A(q^{-1})Q(q^{-1}) + B(q^{-1})C(q^{-1}) = 0 \quad (7)$$

are inside the unit disk and (Q, C), (A, C), (B, Q) have not common zeros outside of the unit disk.

Instead of (6) the following input is considered to be used,

$$u_k = -G(q^{-1})^{-1}[F(q^{-1})y_k - C(q^{-1})r_{k+d} - \beta s_k - v_k] \quad (8)$$

where

$$0 < \beta \leq 1$$

Substituting (8) into (1), the following relation is derived.

$$s_{k+d} = v_k + \beta s_k \quad (9)$$

The auxiliary control input v is chosen as the state feedback with the variable coefficients.

$$v_k = h_0 e_k + h_1 e_{k-1} + \cdots + h_{n-1} e_{k-n+1} \quad (10)$$

This paper defines that the control input with $v = 0$ is the β equivalent control and provides $s_{k+d} = \beta s_k$. This paper extends the results of [10] defining the equivalent control of a discrete-time system with $\beta = 1$. A similar parameter was introduced by Chan [11] for the sliding mode control of a state space system. This paper uses the parameter for the VSC of a linear system represented by a transfer function.

The control law given as follows gives stable system.

[Theorem 1] For the plant (1), if the coefficients of the feedback control law are chosen

$$h_i = \begin{cases} h & s_k e_{k-i} < -\delta_i \\ 0 & | s_k e_{k-i} | \leq \delta_i \quad (i = 0, 1, \cdots, n-1) \\ -h & s_k e_{k-i} > \delta_i \end{cases} \quad (11)$$

then the control system becomes stable, where

$$\delta_i = \eta \sum_{j=0}^{n-1} | e_{k-i} || e_{k-j} | h \quad (12)$$

and

$$\eta \geq \frac{\alpha}{2(\alpha\beta - \alpha + 1)} \quad (13)$$

and it is assumed that $\alpha \geq 1$.

Proof) Substituting (10) into (8) the input of the system u_k is written as

$$u_k = -\frac{1}{G(q^{-1})}\{F(q^{-1})y_k - \beta s_k - C(q^{-1})r_{k+d} - \sum_{i=0}^{n-1} h_i e_{k-i}\} \quad (14)$$

Using (1) and (2), the following relation yields

$$s_{k+d} = \beta s_k + \sum_{i=0}^{n-1} h_i e_{k-i} \quad (15)$$

Defining

$$\Delta s_{k+d} \stackrel{d}{=} s_{k+d} - s_k = \sum_{i=0}^{n-1} h_i e_{k-i} - (1-\beta)s_k \quad (16)$$

The stability is firstly proved in the case $| s_k e_{k-i} | > \delta_i$, which will be said the outside of the sector, for some i. For the choice of the feedback coefficients for the auxiliary control input as (11), the following relation exists.

$$\begin{aligned} s_k \Delta s_{k+d} &= s_k \sum_{i=0}^{n-1} h_i e_{k-i} - (1-\beta)s_k^2 \\ &< -\sum_{i=0}^{n-1} \delta_i | h_i | - (1-\beta)s_k^2 \\ &\leq -\eta(\sum_{i=0}^{n-1} | h_i || e_{k-i} |)^2 - (1-\beta)s_k^2 \\ &\leq -\frac{\alpha}{2}(\Delta s_{k+d})^2 \end{aligned} \quad (17)$$

since

$$\begin{aligned} \Delta s_{k+d}^2 &\leq (\sum_{i=0}^{n-1} | h_i || e_{k-i} |)^2 - 2(1-\beta)(\sum_{i=0}^{n-1} h_i e_{k-i} s_k) + (1-\beta)^2 s_k^2 \\ &\leq (2(1-\beta)\eta + 1)(\sum_{i=0}^{n-1} | h_i || e_{k-i} |)^2 + (1-\beta)^2 s_k^2 \\ &\leq \frac{2}{\alpha}\{\eta(\sum_{i=0}^{n-1} | h_i || e_{k-i} |)^2 + (1-\beta)s_k^2\} \end{aligned}$$

On the other hand, $s_{k+d}^2 - s_k^2 = 2\Delta s_{k+d} \cdot s_k + (\Delta s_{k+d})^2$. (17) tells that

$$s_{k+d}^2 + (\alpha - 1)(\Delta s_{k+d})^2 < s_k^2 \quad (18)$$

This concludes that the s_k decreases outside of the sector and $\Delta s_{k+d} \longrightarrow 0$ as $k \longrightarrow \infty$ (17) yields either that

$$\lim_{k \to \infty} e_k = 0 \quad (19)$$

if the error state is kept outside of the sector or it will be inside the sector.

In the next, it is considered the inside of the sector that $| s_k e_{k-i} | \leq \delta_i$ are satisfied for all i. This is the case that it is controlled so that $s_k = 0$ by the fact

$$s_{k+d} = \beta s_k$$

On the surface $s_k = 0$, from the Lemma , the control law making $s_k = 0$ will decrease e_k and the error state kept to stay inside the sector gives $\lim_{k \to \infty} e_k = 0$. Therefore the closed loop system becomes stable.

The sufficient condition for the existence of the sector is given from (10) as

$$0 \leq h < \eta^{-1} \max_{0 \leq j \leq n} \{|c|_j\} \quad (20)$$

where $c_0 = 1$.

3 VSS-Type Self-Tuning Control

In the previous sections, the plant parameters $A(q^{-1})$, $B(q^{-1})$ are assumed to be known. In the practical situation, however, the plant parameters are not known exactly. In such situation, the self-tuning control with simultaneous plant control and parameters identification should be achieved. There exist explicit and implicit algorithm in the self-tuning control. In the former, plant parameters are identified first, based on which the control law is determined. Implicit one, on the other hand, identifies the control law directly. In this section the implicit algorithm will be given, and the former can be similarly realized [13]. The plant considered in this section is assumed a single input system represented by (1). The given plant is considered to have the known delay d in the control action. Parameters $\{a_i, b_i\}$ of $A(q^{-1})$ and $B(q^{-1})$ are, however, assumed unknown except b_0 ($\neq 0$). In this section the control algorithm is determined based on the generalized minimum variance control. The different control laws and parameters identifications are employed inside and outside of the sector. The sector is defined by

$$\mathcal{S}_k = \{s_k| \mid s_k \mid\leq \left(\frac{(1-\beta)d + \sqrt{(1-\beta)^2d^2 + 2d^2\gamma}}{\gamma}\right)(|\phi_k|)\} \tag{21}$$

where

$$\gamma = \frac{2}{\alpha}(1-\beta) - (1-\beta)^2$$

$$|\phi_k| = \sum_{j=0}^{n-1}|y_{k-j}| + \sum_{j=1}^{m+d-1}|u_{k-j}|$$

The proposed design method is the improved version of [12] in the sense that the sector is smaller. In the outside of the sector, control and parameter identification are done simultaneously based on the Lyapunov function. The polynomial s_k is defined by (2). When parameters $A(q^{-1})$, $B(q^{-1})$ are known,s_k is given by (3).

When $A(q^{-1})$ and $B(q^{-1})$ are unknown, $G(q^{-1})$ and $F(q^{-1})$ can not be obtained exactly. In this case the control input u_k is determined by using the estimate of $G(q^{-1})$ and $F(q^{-1})$, denoted by $\hat{G}(q^{-1})$ and $\hat{F}(q^{-1})$, as follows:

For the outside of the sector:

$$\begin{aligned} u_k &= -\hat{G}_k(q^{-1})^{-1}\Big[\hat{F}_k(q^{-1})y_k - \beta s_k - C(q^{-1})r_{k+d} \\ &\quad -\sum_{j=0}^{n-1}h_je_{k-j} - \sum_{j=1}^{m+d-1}w_ju_{k-j} - \sum_{j=0}^{n-1}t_jr_{k-j}\Big] \end{aligned} \tag{22}$$

where $\{h_j\}$, $\{w_j\}$ and $\{t_j\}$ are nonlinear bang-bang type functions depending on the state outside of the sector and take values out of h, 0, $-h$. Since b_0 is assumed known, g_0 can be given and let the estimate of $G(q^{-1})$ and $F(q^{-1})$ be

$$\hat{\theta}_k = \hat{\theta}_{k-d} + \Gamma^{-1}\phi_k s_k \quad (\Gamma > 0) \tag{23}$$

θ, ϕ are defined as

$$\begin{aligned} \theta &= [f_0, f_1, \cdots, f_{n-1}, g_1, \cdots, g_{m+d-1}]^T \\ \phi &= [y_k, y_{k-1}, \cdots, u_{k-1}, \cdots, u_{k-m-d+1}]^T \end{aligned}$$

For the inside of the sector;

$$u_k = -\hat{G}_k(q^{-1})^{-1}\left[\hat{F}_k(q^{-1})y_k - C(q^{-1})r_{k+d}\right] \tag{24}$$

where error defined by

$$\begin{aligned} &\{ A(q^{-1})\hat{G}_k(q^{-1}) + q^{-d}B(q^{-1})\hat{F}_k(q^{-1})\}e_k \\ &= \{B(q^{-1})C(q^{-1}) - A(q^{-1})\hat{G}_k(q^{-1}) - q^{-d}B(q^{-1})\hat{F}_k(q^{-1})\}r_k \end{aligned}$$

equivalently

$$\begin{aligned} &\{ A(q^{-1})Q(q^{-1}) + B(q^{-1})C(q^{-1}) \\ &\quad +\hat{E}(q^{-1})(A(q^{-1})\hat{B}(q^{-1}) - \hat{A}(q^{-1})B(q^{-1}))\}e_k \\ &= -\{A(q^{-1})Q(q^{-1})+\hat{E}(q^{-1})(A(q^{-1})\hat{B}(q^{-1})-\hat{A}(q^{-1})B(q^{-1}))\}r_k \end{aligned}$$

is assumed always decreasing its norm in the sector. The above condition tells that the gain of the estimated model is equal to that of the plant, $Q(1) = 0$ and

$$A(q^{-1})Q(q^{-1}) + B(q^{-1})C(q^{-1})$$

is at least Schur polynomial.

The following main theorem yields for stabilizing the closed loop system.

[Theorem 2]The control system, which is employed for the outside of the sector $\mathcal{S}_k$ where control and the simultaneous parameter estimation by (22) and (23) respectively, brings either the system into the sector or vanishing the error. The coefficients of (22) $\{h_i\}$, $\{w_i\}$ and $\{t_i\}$ are given by the following relations:

$$h_i = \begin{cases} h & s_ke_{k-i} < -\delta_i \\ 0 & |s_ke_{k-i}| \leq \delta_i \quad (i = 0, 1, 2, \cdots, n-1) \\ -h & s_ke_{k-i} > \delta_i \end{cases} \tag{25}$$

$$w_i = \begin{cases} h & s_ku_{k-i} < -\sigma_i \\ 0 & |s_ku_{k-i}| \leq \sigma_i \quad (i = 1, 2, 3, \cdots, m+d-1) \\ -h & s_ku_{k-i} > \sigma_i \end{cases} \tag{26}$$

$$t_i = \begin{cases} h & s_kr_{k-i} < -\gamma_i \\ 0 & |s_kr_{k-i}| \leq \gamma_i \quad (i = 0, 1, 2, \cdots, n-1) \\ -h & s_kr_{k-i} > \gamma_i \end{cases} \tag{27}$$

where

$$\begin{aligned} \delta_i &= \eta_a|e_{k-i}|\left(\sum_{j=0}^{n-1}|e_{k-j}| + \sum_{j=1}^{m+d-1}|u_{k-j}| + \sum_{j=0}^{n-1}|r_{k-j}|\right)h \\ &\quad (i = 0, 1, \cdots, n-1) \end{aligned} \tag{28}$$

$$\begin{aligned} \sigma_i &= \eta_a|u_{k-i}|\left(\sum_{j=0}^{n-1}|e_{k-j}| + \sum_{j=1}^{m+d-1}|u_{k-j}| + \sum_{j=0}^{n-1}|r_{k-j}|\right)h \\ &\quad (i = 0, 1, \cdots, m+d-1) \end{aligned} \tag{29}$$

$$\begin{aligned} \gamma_i &= \eta_a|r_{k-i}|\left(\sum_{j=0}^{n-1}|e_{k-j}| + \sum_{j=1}^{m+d-1}|u_{k-j}| + \sum_{j=0}^{n-1}|r_{k-j}|\right)h \\ &\quad (i = 0, 1, \cdots, n-1) \end{aligned} \tag{30}$$

where

$$\eta \geq \frac{\alpha}{1 - \alpha + \alpha\beta}$$

The d is the upper bound of the uncertainty of the parameters defined by

$$\max_i|\theta_i - \hat{\theta}_{ki}| < d$$

where $\hat{\theta}_{ki}$ denote the i-th element of $\hat{\theta}_k$ and $\alpha > 1$. The following Lyapunov function

$$V_k = \frac{1}{2}s_k^2 + \frac{1}{2}\tilde{\theta}_{k-d}^T\Gamma\tilde{\theta}_{k-d} \tag{31}$$

decreases outside of the sector.

By using the control (24) inside the sector the stability of the closed system is assured.

Proof) In this proof the outside of the sector is considered. In the proof the convergence of the state to the region will be proved. In the outside of the sector, the difference of the Lyapunov function is given by

$$\begin{aligned}\Delta V_{k+d} &= V_{k+d} - V_k \\ &= \frac{1}{2}(s_k + \Delta s_{k+d})^2 - \frac{1}{2}s_k^2 + \frac{1}{2}\tilde{\theta}_k^T \Gamma \tilde{\theta}_k \\ &\quad -\frac{1}{2}\tilde{\theta}_{k-d}^T \Gamma \tilde{\theta}_{k-d} \end{aligned} \tag{32}$$

Using the relation of $\tilde{\theta}_k$, and substituting (22) to (3)

$$\tilde{\theta}_k = \theta - \hat{\theta}_k \tag{33}$$

$$\begin{aligned} s_{k+d} &= \hat{G}_k(q^{-1})u_k + \hat{F}_k(q-1)y_k + \tilde{\theta}_k^T \phi_k - C(q^{-1})r_{k+d} \\ &= \beta s_k + \sum_{j=0}^{n-1} h_j e_{k-j} + \sum_{j=0}^{m+d-1} w_j u_{k-j} + \sum_{j=0}^{n-1} t_j r_{k-j} + \tilde{\theta}_k^T \phi_k \end{aligned} \tag{34}$$

Substituting these relations to (32), the following relation is derived.

$$\begin{aligned} \Delta V_{k+d} &= s_k \Delta s_{k+d} + \frac{1}{2}(\Delta s_{k+d})^2 - \tilde{\theta}_k^T \phi_k s_k - \frac{1}{2}\phi_k^T \Gamma^{-1} \phi_k s_k^2 \\ &= s_k \left(\sum_{j=0}^{n-1} h_j e_{k-j} + \sum_{j=1}^{m+d-1} w_j u_{k-j} + \sum_{j=0}^{n-1} t_j r_{k-j} - (1-\beta)s_k \right) \\ &\quad + \frac{1}{2}(\Delta s_{k+d})^2 - \frac{1}{2}\phi_k^T \Gamma^{-1} \phi_k s_k^2 \end{aligned} \tag{35}$$

On the other hand the following relation exists from (34).

$$\begin{aligned} & s_k \left(\sum_{j=0}^{n-1} h_j e_{k-j} + \sum_{j=1}^{m+d-1} w_j u_{k-j} + \sum_{j=0}^{n-1} t_j r_{k-j} - (1-\beta)s_k \right) \\ \le & -\sum_{j=0}^{n-1} |h_j|\delta_j - \sum_{j=1}^{m+d-1} |w_j|\sigma_j - \sum_{j=0}^{n-1} |t_j|\gamma_j - (1-\beta)s_k^2 \\ \le & -\frac{\alpha}{2}(\Delta s_{k+d})^2 \end{aligned}$$

where the i-th component of $\tilde{\theta}_k$, $\tilde{\theta}_{ki}$, satisfies

$$|\tilde{\theta}_{ki}| < d.$$

and

$$\begin{aligned} & (\Delta s_{k+d})^2 \\ &= \left\{ -(1-\beta)s_k + \sum_{j=0}^{n-1} h_j e_{k-j} + \sum_{j=0}^{m+d-1} w_j u_{k-j} + \sum_{j=0}^{n-1} t_j r_{k-j} + \tilde{\theta}_k^T \phi_k \right\}^2 \\ &\le (1-\beta)^2 s_k^2 - 2(1-\beta)s_k \Theta_1(k) \\ &\quad + 2(1-\beta)d|s_k| \mid \phi_k \mid + 2\Theta_2(k)^2 + 2d^2(\mid \phi_k \mid)^2 \\ &\le \{(1-\beta)^2 s_k^2 + 2(1-\beta)ds_k \mid \phi_k \mid + 2d^2(\mid \phi_k \mid)^2\} \\ &\quad + \{2(1-\beta)\Theta_3(k) + 2\Theta_2(k))^2\} \\ &\le \frac{2}{\alpha}\left\{(1-\beta)s_k^2 + \Theta_3(k)\right\} \end{aligned}$$

where

$$\Theta_1(k) = \sum_{j=0}^{n-1} h_j e_{k-j} + \sum_{j=0}^{m+d-1} w_j u_{k-j} + \sum_{j=0}^{n-1} t_j r_{k-j}$$

$$\Theta_2(k) = \sum_{j=0}^{n-1} \mid h_j \mid\mid e_{k-j} \mid + \sum_{j=0}^{m+d-1} \mid w_j \mid\mid u_{k-j} \mid + \sum_{j=0}^{n-1} \mid t_j \mid\mid r_{k-j} \mid$$

$$\Theta_3(k) = \sum_{j=0}^{n-1} |h_j|\delta_j + \sum_{j=1}^{m+d-1} |w_j|\sigma_j + \sum_{j=0}^{n-1} |t_j|\gamma_j$$

The following relation is derived.

$$\Delta V_{k+d} < -\frac{1}{2}\phi_k^T \Gamma^{-1} \phi_k s_k^2 - \frac{\alpha - 1}{2}(\Delta s_{k+d})^2 \tag{36}$$

This relation tells that $\Delta s_{k+d} \longrightarrow 0$ as $(k \longrightarrow \infty)$ outside of the sector. Similar to the proof of [**Theorem 1**] this shows that the error vanishes or the state is brought into the inside of the sector. This gives the proof for the outside of the sector.

Since in the inside of the sector, the control law (24)which is assumed sable is taken. So the closed loop system is stable.

The theorem provides the adaptive control system design using the variable structure system. A sufficient condition of the existence of the sector is given by (20) similar to Section 2.

4 Examples

This section studies the proposed algorithm by the simulation. The plant considered is a non-minimum phase system represented by

$$y_{k+1} + a_1 y_k + a_2 y_{k-1} = b_0 u_k + b_1 u_{k-1}$$

where $a_1 = -1.3$, $a_2 = 0.42$, $b_0 = 1$, $b_1 = -0.3$. The polynomial $C(q^{-1})$ is chosen as

$$C(q^{-1}) = 1 + q^{-1} + 0.25q^{-2}$$

The parameters are assumed $\hat{a}_1 = -1$, $\hat{a}_2 = 0.5$, $\hat{b}_0 = 1$, $\hat{b}_1 = -0.35$.

The $Q(q^{-1})$ is chosen as

$$Q(q^{-1}) = (1 - q^{-1})Q_0$$

Q_0 is chosen as 0.1. $\hat{E}(q^{-1})$ and $\hat{F}(q^{-1})$ are chosen as $\hat{E}(q^{-1}) = 1 - q^{-1}$, $\hat{F}(q^{-1}) = 3 - 1.25q^{-1} + 0.5q^{-2}$. The responses to the step reference are shown in Fig.1, 2, 3 for the generalized minimum variance control, VSS control with $h = 0.5, \alpha = 1.4, \beta = 0.7$, and VSS type self-tuning control with $h = 0.01, \alpha = 1.0, \beta = 0.8$ and $\Gamma = 40I$. The most appropriate parameters are chosen for the corresponding methods. s_k and v_k for the last two cases are shown in Fig.4 and 5. The figures show that the VSS type control improves the response remarkably.

5 Conclusion

This paper, in the first, presents a discrete-type VSS control for a known plant based on the generalized minimum variance control. The control law proposed has the different feedback coefficients of the past output characterized by the sector instead of the sliding surface. In the second the VSS control system for unknown parameter plant is considered. The simultaneous control and parameters' estimation are done by using VSS control where control law contains switching feedback coefficients of not only past output but also past input. The latter gives the globally stable self-tuning system and shows its effectiveness through simulations.

The author appreciates the simulations done by Mr. Yaodong Pan who is a research student of Tokyo Institute of Technology on leave from Changsha Institute of technology, and the comments given by Dr. Ulf Holmberg of JSPS visiting fellow at Tokyo Institute of Technology.

References

[1] K.J.Astrom and B.Wittenmark, *Adaptive Control*, Addison-Wesley Publishing Co. (1989)

[2] V.I.Utkin, "Variable Structure System with Sliding Mode:A Survey, " *IEEE Transaction on Automatic Control*, AC-22, No.2,212-222 (1964)

[3] R.A.DeCarlo, S.H.Zak, G.P.Matthews,"Variable Structure Control of Nonlinear Multivariable Systems: A Tutorial", *Proceeding of the IEEE*, Vol. 76, No.3, pp. 212-232, (1988)

[4] J.J.E,Slotine and W.Li,*Applied Nonlinear Control* , Prentice Hall(1991)

[5] T-P.Leung, Q-J. Zhou, C-Y. Su, "An Adaptive Variable Structure Model Following Control Design for Robot Manipulators" , *IEEE Transactions of Automatic Control*, Vol. 36, No. 3, pp. 347-353, (1991)

[6] A.A.Bahnasawi, S. Z. Eid, M.S.Mahmoud, "Adaptive model-following control based on variable structure systems", *Int. J. Sys. Sci.*, Vol.22, No.2, pp 333-349, (1991)

[7] C.Milosavljevic, "General Conditions for the Existence of a Quasiliding Mode on the Switching Hyperplane in Discrete Variable Structure Systems", *Automation and Remote Control*, pp.307-314,(1985)

[8] S.Z.Sarpurk, Y.Istefanopulos, O. Kaynak,"On the Stability of Discrete- Time Sliding Mode Control Systems", *IEEE Transactions on Automatic Control*, Vol.32, No.10, 930-932, (1987)

[9] S.V.Drakunov, V.I.Utkin, "On Discrete-Time Sliding Mode", *IFAC Symposium on Nonlinear Control System Design*, pp. 484-489, (1989)

[10] K.Furuta,"Sliding mode control of a discrete system",*System & Control Letters*, Vol. 14, 145-152, (1990)

[11] C.Y.Chan,"Servo-Systems with Discrete-Variable Structure Control," *System & Control Letters*, Vol.17, 321-325, (1991)

[12] K.Furuta, "VSS-Type Self-Tuning Control", *IEEE Transactions on Industrial Electronics*, Vol. , No.2, (1993)

[13] K.Furuta,"VSS-Type Self-Tuning Control,"*Proceedings of IEEE IECON'91 Kobe* , 2085-2089, (1991)

[14] K.Furuta,K.Kosuge,K.Kobayashi,"VSS-Type Self-Tuning Control of Direct Drive Motor",*Proceedings of IECON'89*, (1989)

[15] K.S.Narendra, Y-H. Lin,"Stable Discrete Adaptive Control", *IEEE Transaction on Aut. Control*,Vol.25, No.3, 456-461, (1980)

[16] G.C.Goodwin,P.J.Ramadge,P.E.Caines,"Discrete-Time Multivariable Adaptive Control", *IEEE Transaction on Aut. Control*, Vol.25, No.3, 449-461, (1980)

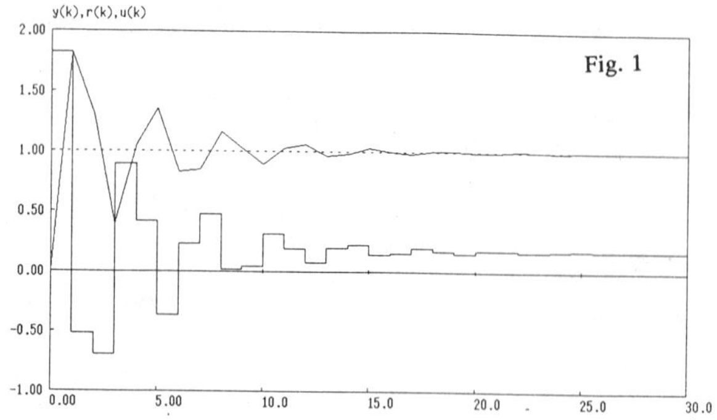

Fig. 1

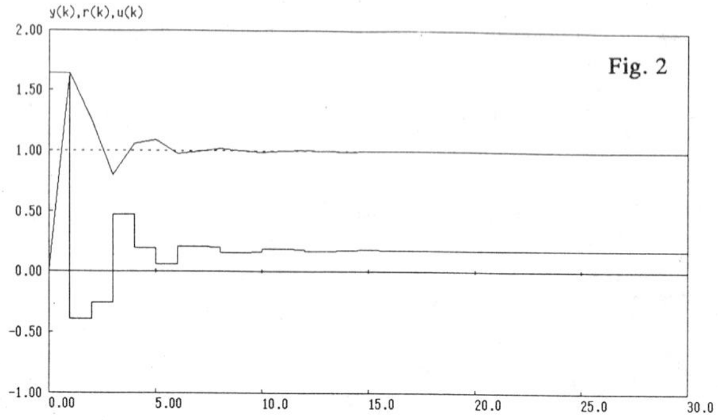

Fig. 2

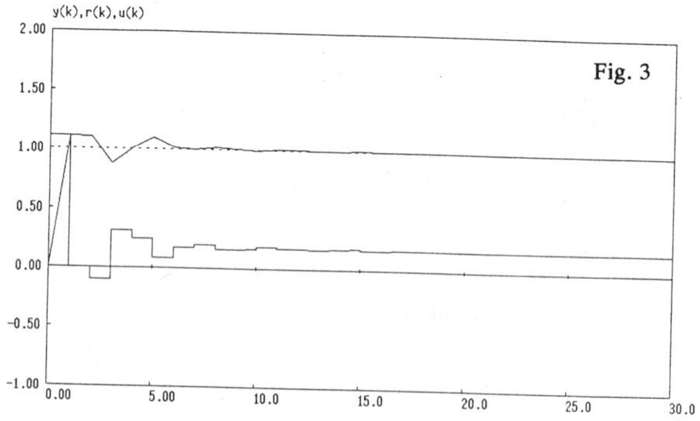

Fig. 3

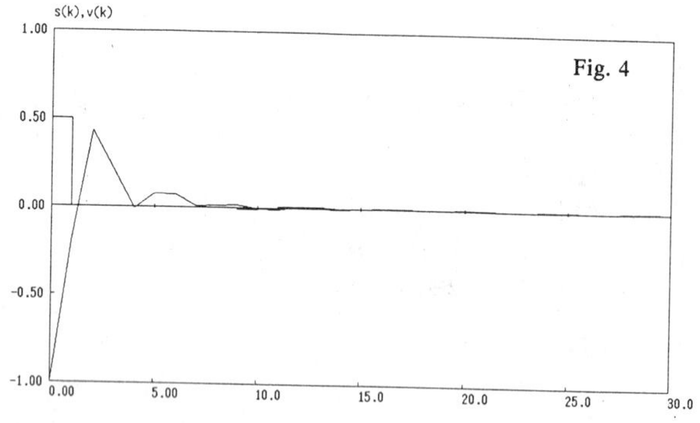

Fig. 4

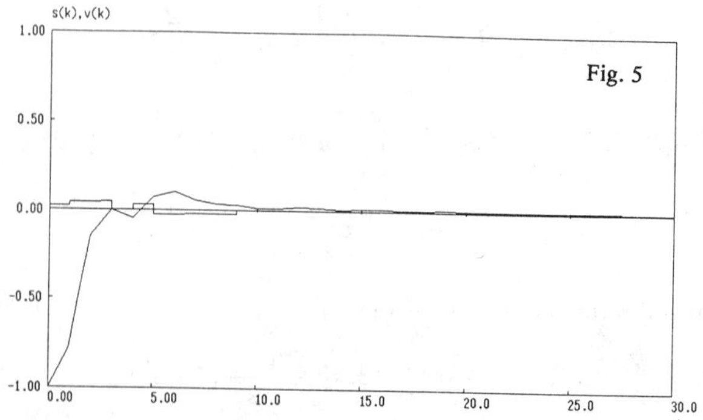

Fig. 5

Proceedings of the
American Control Conference
San Francisco, California • June 1993

An Adaptive Variable Structure Control for a Class of Nonlinear Time-Varying Systems

Chiang-Ju Chien[1] *and Li-Chen Fu*[1,2]

[1]Department of Electrical Engineering
[2]Department of Computer Science and Information Engineering
National Taiwan University, Taipei, Taiwan, Republic of China

Abstract

Motivated by the recent advance in adaptive output feedback control of affine nonlinear systems [8-10], an adaptive variable structure controller is proposed in this paper for solving the model reference adaptive control of nonlinear time-varying systems. Asymptotic output tracking performance can be achieved for relative degree one case. When the relative degree of the nonlinear system is greater than one, a systematic design procedure is given under a modified sector-type condition so that the closed-loop stability and the tracking performance are achieved similar to that in relative degree one case.

1. Introduction

In the researches of adaptive control for affine nonlinear systems, it usually assumes that the unknown parameters enter linearly into some known nonlinear vector fields. Based on the differential geometric approach [1-2], the adaptive version of state-feedback control for such kind of nonlinear systems have been developed in [3-6]. However, besides a number of constraints on the nonlinear systems, the above researches will require a common assumption that the state measurement is available. Recently, in order to relax such assumption, a more challenging problem has been proposed in the field of adaptive output-feedback control [7-10].

In this paper, we develop a new approach, which is different from those in [8-10], to solve the adaptive output-feedback control problem for a class of nonlinear time-varying systems using a variable structure method. Using this new adaptation scheme, we release the standard requirement of the upper bounds on some unknown parameters which are frequently observed in the field of robust linear MRAC. For this class of nonlinear time-varying systems with relative degree one, the asymptotic output tracking performance can be achieved. Under suitable conditions for the control parameters, the tracking performance and the transient behavior of output error will in general be better than the conventional adaptive version for this class of nonlinear systems. For relative degree greater one, more restrictions are needed so that a systematic adaptive variable structure controller can be derived to achieve the closed-loop stability and tracking performance, which is similar to that in relative degree one case.

2. Problem Formulation

We consider an affine nonlinear system of the form :

$$\dot{x} = f(x) + \sum_{i=1}^{m} \psi_i^*(t) f_i(x) + g(x)u, \; y = h(x) \tag{1}$$

where $\psi_1^*(t), \ldots, \psi_m^*(t)$ are bounded unknown time-varying parameters, $x \in R^n$ is the state vector, $u \in R$ is the control input, $y \in R$ is the control output; $f, g, f_i, i = 1, \ldots, m$ are smooth vector fields with $f(0) = 0, g(0) \neq 0$ and h is a smooth function with $h(0) = 0, \forall x \in R^n$. The following is the most relevant condition on the nonlinear system described above throughout this paper.

• **Assumption I** : The nonlinear system described in (1) can be transformed into the following output-feedback form :

$$\dot{z} = Az + P(y)\Psi^*(t) + b\delta(y)u, \quad y = c^\top z \tag{2}$$

where

$$A = \begin{bmatrix} -a_1 & 1 & 0 & \cdots & 0 \\ \vdots & & & \ddots & \vdots \\ -a_n & 0 & 0 & \cdots & 0 \end{bmatrix}, \; b = \begin{bmatrix} b_1 \\ \vdots \\ b_n \end{bmatrix},$$

$$\begin{aligned} c^\top &= [1 \;\; 0 \;\; \cdots \;\; 0] \\ P(y) &= [p_0(y), p_1(y), \ldots, p_m(y)] \in R^{n\times(m+1)}, \\ \Psi^*(t) &= [1, \psi_1^*(t), \ldots, \psi_m^*(t)]^\top \in R^{m+1} \end{aligned}$$

In particular, (c, A) is an observable pair, $a_j, b_j, j = 1, \ldots, n$ are unknown constants, $\delta(y) \neq 0, \forall y \in R$ is a known nonlinear function and $p_i(y) \in R^n, i = 0, \ldots, m$ are some known nonlinear vectors. Furthermore, $\delta(y)$ and $P(y)$ are uniformly bounded if y is uniformly bounded. Note that the sufficient and necessary condition for the the existence of the transformation can be found in [8-10]. □

In order to suit the controller design purpose here, another condition on the system in (1) is needed to guarantee the feasibility of applying output feedback and variable structure control. The followings are the investigations of the condition and the resulting effect.

• **Assumption II** : The nonlinear system (1) has known relative degree ρ, i.e. $L_g L_f^i h = 0, i = 0, \ldots, \rho - 2$, $\forall x \in R^n$, $L_g L_f^{\rho-1} h \neq 0$, for some $x \in R^n$ and b in (2) is Hurwitz. □

• **Assumption III** : When $\rho = 1$, the sign of b_1 is assumed to be known and without loss of generality, we assume $b_1 > 0$. □

• **Assumption IV** : When $\rho \geq 2$, b_ρ is assumed to be known and without loss of generality, we assume $b_\rho = 1$. Furthermore, $P(y)$ is assumed to satisfy the modified sector type condition $|P(y)| \leq \kappa \|(y)_t\|_\infty + \kappa$, where κ denotes some unknown positive constant. □

Remark 2.1 : It is noted that the transfer function

$$G(s) \;=\; c^\top (sI - A)^{-1} b \;=\; \frac{b_\rho s^{n-\rho} + \cdots + b_n}{s^n + a_1 s^{n-1} + \cdots + a_n} \tag{3}$$

is a minimum-phase system with relative degree ρ according to Assumptiom II, and that Assumption III, IV guarantee some knowledge of the high frequency gain for $G(s)$. □

For the nonlinear system described in (1), the control objective is to design the input $u(t)$ such that the output $y(t)$ tracks the output $y_m(t) = M(s)[r_m](t)$, where $M(s)$ is a stable system with relative degree ρ and $r_m(t)$ is a uniformly bounded reference input. First, from the point of view of frequency-domain representation, (2) can be described as

$$y \;=\; G(s)\Big[\delta(y)u + \sum_{j=\rho}^{n} \frac{s^{n-j}}{b_\rho s^{n-\rho} + \cdots + b_n} (P(y)\Psi^*(t))_j\Big] \tag{4}$$

where $G(s)$ is defined as in (3) and $(P(y)\Psi^*(t))_j$ denotes the j-th element of $P(y)\Psi^*(t)$. It should be noted that $\frac{s^{n-j}}{b_\rho s^{n-\rho}+\cdots+b_n}, j = \rho, \ldots, n$ are stable proper or stable strictly proper transfer functions. Now define $y = G(s)[v]$, then, from the traditional model reference control strategy, it can be easily shown that there exists $\Theta^* = [\theta_1^*, \cdots, \theta_{2n}^*]^\top \in R^{2n}$ and $\theta_{2n}^* > 0$ such that if $v = \Theta^{*\top}[\frac{a(s)}{n(s)}[v], \frac{a(s)}{n(s)}[y], y, r_m]^\top$ with $a(s) = [1, s, \ldots, s^{n-2}]^\top$ and $n(s)$ being a monic Hurwitz polynomial of degree $n - 1$, then the closed loop transfer function from r_m to y equals $M(s)$. In fact, one can readily find that u satisfies

$$\delta(y)u = \Theta^{*\top} w + \sum_{j=\rho}^{n} \Delta_j(s)\Big[(P(y)\Psi^*(t))_j\Big] \tag{5}$$

where $w = [\frac{a(s)}{n(s)}[\delta(y)u], \frac{a(s)}{n(s)}[y], y, r_m]^\top$ and $\Delta_j(s) = (\frac{\theta_1^* + \cdots + \theta_{n-1}^* s^{n-2}}{n(s)} - 1)\frac{s^{n-j}}{b_\rho s^{n-\rho}+\cdots+b_n}$ being proper stable or strictly proper stable. Note that (5) is usually referred as the matching condition used for the derivation of error model and hence, the controller design later.

3. Adaptive VS Controller For Nonlinear Plants

When the nonlinear system (1) is relative degree one satisfying Assumption I,II,III, the adaptive variable structure controller is now designed as

$$u(t) = \frac{-sgn(e_o)}{\delta(y)}(\beta_1(t)|w(t)| + \beta_2(t)m(t)) \quad (6)$$

where $\beta_i(t)$ is the control parameter updated by

$$\begin{aligned} \dot{\beta}_1(t) &= \gamma_1|e_o(t)||w(t)| \\ \dot{\beta}_2(t) &= \gamma_2|e_o(t)|m(t) \end{aligned} \quad (7)$$

with $\beta_i(0) > 0, \gamma_i > 0$, and $m(t)$ being defined as the bounding function $m(t) = \sup_{t \geq \tau} |P(y(\tau))|$

The adaptive variable structure control scheme for the nonlinear system (1) with relative degree $\rho > 1$ which satisfies Assumption I, II, IV is designed systematically as follows:

- **Systematic Design Procedure**

(1) Choose an operator $L_1(s) = \ell_1(s) \cdots \ell_{\rho-1}(s) = (s+\alpha_1)\cdots(s+\alpha_{\rho-1})$ such that $M(s)L_1(s)$ is SPR.

(2) Define augmented signal and auxiliary errors

$$\begin{aligned} y_a(t) &= M(s)L_1(s)\Big[-v_1 + \frac{1}{L_1(s)}[\delta(y)u]\Big](t) \\ e_{a1}(t) &= e_o(t) - y_a(t) \\ e_{ai}(t) &= -[v_{i-1}]_{av} + \frac{1}{\ell_{i-1}(s)}[\delta(y)u](t), \; i = 2, \ldots, \rho \end{aligned} \quad (8)$$

where $[v_i]_{av}$ is the average control of v_i which is given as $[v_i]_{av} = \frac{1}{F(\tau s)}[v_i] = \frac{1}{(\tau s+1)^2}[v_i]$ with τ being small enough.

(3) Design the u, v_i, and m as follows:

$$v_i(t) = -sgn(e_{ai}(t))(\beta_{i1}(t)|\xi_i(t)| + \beta_{i2}(t)m(t) + \beta_{i3}(t)) \quad (9)$$

with $i = 1, \ldots, \rho, \delta(y)u(t) = v_\rho(t)$ and

$$\begin{aligned} \xi_1(t) &= \frac{1}{\ell_1(s)} \cdots \frac{1}{\ell_{\rho-1}(s)}[w] = \frac{1}{L_1(s)}[w] \\ \xi_i(t) &= \frac{1}{F(\tau s)}\ell_{i-1}(s)[\xi_{i-1}](t), \; i = 2 \ldots \rho \\ m(t) &= \|(y)_t\|_\infty \end{aligned}$$

(4) Finally, the adaptation laws are given as follows :

$$\begin{aligned} \dot{\beta}_{i1}(t) &= \gamma_{i1}|e_{ai}(t)||\xi_i(t)| \\ \dot{\beta}_{i2}(t) &= \gamma_{i2}|e_{ai}(t)|m(t) \\ \dot{\beta}_{i3}(t) &= \gamma_{i3}|e_{ai}(t)| \end{aligned} \quad (10)$$

with $\beta_{i1}(0) > 0, \beta_{i2}(0) > 0, \beta_{i3}(0) > 0$ and $\gamma_{ij} > 0$.

4. Global Stability and Tracking Performance

Theorem 4.1 : Consider the nonlinear system (1) satisfying Assumption I - III, with relative degree $\rho = 1$. If the controller is designed as in (6) and the parameter update law is chosen as in (7), then the tracking error e_o will converge to zero asymptotically while all signals inside the closed loop system remain uniformly bounded. □

Proof : see [11]

Theorem 4.2 : Consider the nonlinear system (1) with relative degree ρ satisfies Assumption I,II,IV. If the controller is designed as in (8) (9) and parameter update law is chosen as in (10), then there exists $\tau^* > 0$ such that for all $\tau \in (0, \tau^*)$, the following facts will hold,

(1) all signals inside the closed-loop system remain uniformly bounded,

(2) the auxiliary errors $e_{ai}, i = 1, \ldots, \rho$, converge to zero asymptotically,

(3) the tracking error e_o will converge to a residual set asymptotically whose size is a class K function of the design parameter τ. □

Proof : see [11]

Remark 4.1 : Since the right hand side of the adaptation law is always positive, the control parameters will increase unless the tracking error can converge to zero exactly. However, in practice the tracking error can not converge to zero due to some possible existence of noise or disturbance. Hence, a modification of adaptation law is needed in the practical implementation of this adaptive variable structure controller. A choice of the modification can be found as follows (relative degree one case, for example) :

$$\begin{aligned} \dot{\beta}_1(t) &= \gamma_1|e_o(t)||w(t)| - \sigma\beta_1(t) \\ \dot{\beta}_2(t) &= \gamma_2|e_o(t)|m(t) - \sigma\beta_2(t) \end{aligned}$$

for some constant $\sigma > 0$. □

5. Conclusion

Under some suitable coordinate free geometric condition, an affine nonlinear system can be transformed, via a state transformation, into a so-called output-feedback form. An adaptive variable structure controller is then proposed in this paper to solve the nonlinear model reference control problem. It is shown that the asymptotic output tracking performance can be achieved for relative degree one case. When the relative degree is greater than one, we use a modified sector type conditions on the nonlinearity and derive a systematic design procedure so that the closed-loop stability and the tracking performance are achieved similar to that in relative degree one case. Ongoing research is to relax the restrictions on the nonlinearity $P(y)$ for the general case.

Reference

[1] A. Isidori, *Nonlinear Control Systems,* 2nd ed., Berlin, Spring-Verlag, 1989.

[2] H. Nijmeijer and A. van der Schaft, *Nonlinear Dynamical Control Systems,* Berlin, Spring-Verlag, 1990.

[3] D. Taylor, P.V. Kokotovic, R. Marino and I. Kanellakopoulos, "Adaptive regulation of nonlinear systems with unmodeled dynamics," *IEEE Trans. Automat. Contr.*, Vol. 34, No. 4, pp. 405-412, 1989.

[4] I. Kanellakopoulos, P.V. Kokotovic and R. Marino, "An extended direct scheme for robust adaptive nonlinear control," *Automatica*, Vol. 27, No. 2, pp. 247-255, 1991.

[5] I. Kanellakopoulos, P.V. Kokotovic and A.S. Morse, "Systematic design of adaptive controllers for feedback linearizable systems," *IEEE Trans. Automat. Contr.*, Vol. 36, No. 11, pp. 1241-1253, 1991.

[6] S.S. Sastry and A. Isidori, "Adaptive control of linearizable systems," *IEEE Trans. Automat. Contr.*, Vol. 34, No. 11, pp. 1123-1131, 1989.

[7] I. Kanellakopoulos, P.V. Kokotovic and R.H. Middleton, "Indirect adaptive output-feedback control of a class of nonlinear systems," *Proc. IEEE 29th Conf. Decision Contr.*, pp. 2714-2719, 1990.

[8] I. Kanellakopoulos, P.V. Kokotovic and A.S. Morse, "Adaptive output - feedback control of a class of nonlinear systems," *Proc. IEEE 30th Conf. Decision Contr.*, pp. 1082-1087, 1991.

[9] R. Marino and P. Tomei, "Global adaptive output-feedback control of nonlinear systems," *Proc. IEEE 30th Conf. Decision Contr.*, pp. 1077-1081, 1991.

[10] R. Marino and P. Tomei, "Observer-based adaptive stabilization for a class of non-linear systems," *Automatica*, Vol. 28 No. 4, pp. 787-793, 1992.

[11] C.J. Chien and L.C. Fu, "An adaptive variable structure control for a class of nonlinear time-varying systems," *Technique Report*, National Taiwan University, R.O.C., 1993.

Proceedings of the
American Control Conference
San Francisco, California • June 1993

Experimental Results of a Learning Controller Applied to Tip Tracking of a Flexible Beam

W. Cheng J.T.Wen D.Hughes
The Department of Electrical, Computer and Systems Engineering
Rensselaer Polytechnic Institute
Troy, NY 12180-3590, USA

Abstract

This paper presents the experimental results of a learning controller applied to the tip trajectory tracking of a flexible beam. The overall controller consists of a feedback portion to ensure closed loop stability and a feedforward portion obtained via off–line learning to improve the tracking performance. Neither the model information nor the states of the flexible beam are required for the feedforward learning. Experimental results have verified that the tracking performance of the tip position is satisfied while maintaining the boundedness of the internal states.

Key words: Learning control, Flexible beam, Output tracking, Trajectory tracking, Feedforward learning.

1 Introduction

Effective control of flexible structures is needed in applications including slewing of articulated members in a spacecraft, large flexible manipulators, and precision positioning of a disk drive arm. Due to the flexible nature of such systems, the dimension of the state space is typically very high (theoretically infinite) as compared with the number of actuators and sensors. As a result, this class of problems is recognized to be very challenging.

A class of feedforward plus feedback control strategy has recently been proposed [1, 2]. However, the feedforward is highly model dependent; the required model information is usually difficult to obtain accurately. Some adaptive controllers have been proposed to identify the parameter information on–line, but these controllers can only adapt to the uncertainty in the payload and the adaptation laws are complicated [3, 4].

Iteratively learning controllers have been proposed in recent years as another means to avoid the requirement of the model information. Most current approaches for the learning controllers can only applied to the tracking control of rigid arms since they require all states of the plant [5, 6, 7, 8, 9]. In [10, 11], a learning controller that only requires the measurable outputs of the plant is proposed, but the plant is required to be strictly positive real (SPR).

In this paper, we address the problem of tracking an output of a flexible structure which is not necessarily SPR with respect to the input, and the states are not directly measurable. As explained above, the existing literature on learning control is not directly applicable. By using a simple idea of probing the system with basis signals, we have developed a scheme to find a feedforward for output trajectory tracking. We have successfully applied this method to the tip trajectory tracking of a flexible beam in our laboratory. The goal of this paper is to briefly summarize the basic algorithm (a full discussion, including extensions to the time–varying and nonlinear cases can be found in [12]) and present the experimental results.

The rest of the paper is organized into the following sections: Section 2 states the output tracking problem. Section 3 summarizes our approach for mutli–input/multi–output linear systems. Section 4 gives the experimental results for a flexible beam in our laboratory. Performance of the learning controller is compared with a model based inverse dynamics type controllers [2] and the feedback controller alone. Input torque peaking and a method to reduce this effect are also addressed.

2 Problem Statement

Considering a linear time invariant system:

$$\begin{aligned} \dot{x} &= Ax + Bu \\ y &= Cx \end{aligned} \qquad (1)$$

where $A \in R^{n\times n}$, $B \in R^{n\times p}$ and $C \in R^{\ell\times n}$. Since we only consider feedforward control (feedback stabilization loop is already closed), we assume A is Hurwitz.

The objective is to find $u \in \mathcal{U}$, $\mathcal{U}$ is a subspace of $L_2([0,T];\mathbf{R}^p)$ such that $\|y - y_d\|$ is minimized ($\|\cdot\|$ is the $L_2([0,T];\mathbf{R}^\ell$ norm) for a given y_d that is continuous in $[0,T]$.

For our experimental work, we consider a single flexible beam. The hub of the beam is driven by a control torque about the vertical axis and the tip is free. The output of interest is the tip position.

The modal truncated model of the flexible beam is of the following form:

$$\ddot{q} + D\dot{q} + \Omega^2 q = \hat{b}\tau \tag{2}$$

where q is the mode amplitude, D is a positive semidefinite damping matrix, τ is the control torque at the hub, Ω^2 is a diagonal matrix consisting of the square of the resonant angular frequencies, and the input matrix $\hat{b}$ is

$$\hat{b} = \frac{1}{\rho}[\Psi_0'(0), \Psi_1'(0), \ldots]^T$$

where Ψ_i's are the mode shapes. Consider a control law of the following form:

$$\tau = \tau_{fb} + u$$

where τ_{fb} is a feedback control that asymptotically stabilizes the origin and u is the feedforward control which we will select based on the output trajectory tracking criterion. A particularly simple τ_{fb} that can be used is the proportional–derivative (PD) feedback of the hub position (we have used this choice in all our experiments). More sophisticated feedback control (such as the one in [13]) can also be used without affecting the subsequent argument. Define the state as $x = [q^T, \dot{q}^T]^T$ and select the output of interest as the tip position of the beam, the closed loop system (including the hub PD feedback) is of the form (1) with

$$A = \begin{bmatrix} 0 & I \\ -\Omega^2 - K_p\hat{b}\hat{b}^T & -D - K_v\hat{b}\hat{b}^T \end{bmatrix}$$

$$B = \begin{bmatrix} 0 \\ \hat{b} \end{bmatrix} \quad C = \begin{bmatrix} c & 0 \end{bmatrix}$$

where $c = \begin{bmatrix} \Psi_0(L) & \Psi_1(L) & \ldots \end{bmatrix}$, and K_p and K_v are the hub PD feedback gains. As stated before, it can be shown that A is Hurwitz for any $K_p > 0, K_v > 0$ [2].

3 Feedforward Learning Control

We shall choose u_i as a linear combination of selected basis functions $\{H_j\}_{j=1}^m$, $H_j \in L_2([0,T];\mathbf{R}^p)$. In other words,

$$\mathcal{U}_i = \text{span}\{H_j : j = 1, \ldots, m\} \quad \mathcal{U} = \mathcal{U}_i \times \mathcal{U}_i \times \ldots \times \mathcal{U}_i \tag{3}$$

and each u_i can be represented as

$$u_i(t) = \sum_{j=1}^{m} W_{ij} H_j(t) \tag{4}$$

where W_{ij}, $i = 1, \ldots, p$, $j = 1, \ldots, m$ are constant scalar weights. The objective is now to find a set of these weights W_{ij} so that a norm of the output tracking error is minimized in some sense.

By substituting (4) into (1) and using linearity, we have

$$y = \sum_{i=1}^{p}\sum_{j=1}^{m} W_{ij}\eta_{ij}$$

where η_{ij}'s are the output trajectories corresponding to the jth basis function H_j feeding into the ith input channel (with all other input channels set to zero):

Now the original output tracking problem can be posed as a least square problem:

> Find W_{ij}, $i = 1, \ldots, p$, $j = 1, \ldots, m$, to minimize
>
> $$J_1 = \int_0^T (e^T(t)Q(t)e(t) + u^T(t)R(t)u(t))\, dt$$
>
> where $Q(t)$, $R(t)$ are positive semidefinite weighting matrices.

$e = y - y_d = \sum_{i=1}^{p}\sum_{j=1}^{m} W_{ij}\eta_{ij} - y_d$ is the tracking error. The selection of $Q(t)$ and $R(t)$ critically affects the type of feedforward control obtained. For the flexible beam experiment, the torque to beam tip transfer function is non–minimum–phase. If $Q(t)$ is chosen to be the identity matrix for all $t \in [0,T]$, $u(t)$ tends to exhibit peaking. This is a consequence of the inversion of a non–minimum–phase system [1]. As explained in [2], there are two solutions to this problem: non–causal input as in [1] or asymptotic output tracking rather than exact output tracking. Our best results are obtained when $Q(t)$ for some initial period is set small, and $R(t)$ is set to zero except for the end of the period $[0,T]$ where a small penalty is used to avoid large torque at the end.

In summary, the proposed off–line learning strategy is the follows:

1. Stabilize the plant by a feedback of the measurable outputs so that the desired disturbance and robustness properties are obtained
2. Excite the closed loop system (1) at the ith input with the chosen basis functions $H_j(t)$ while holding other inputs zero and obtain the corresponding outputs of interest η_{ij}.
3. Compute the weight vector W_d by the least square method

4. The learned control feedforward is $u_i(t) = \sum_{j=1}^{m} W_{ij} H_j(t)$, where W_{ij} is obtained the step 3.

4 Experimental Results

The flexible beam testbed in the Control Laboratory for Mechanical Structure (CLaMS) in Rensselaer Polytechnic Institute is used to conduct experiments for the learning control described above. The beam is driven by a DC motor at one end about a vertical axis, and the other end is free. The motor is energized by a power amplifier which is controlled by a single voltage signal. The hub angle is measured by a resolver. Four strain gauges are mounted on the beam, located at $[.0065m, .2715m, .366m, .579m]$ away from the hub. The beam strains at these locations are converted to voltage signals by strain gauges. The realtime computer is a networked set of four Inmos Transputer micro-processors which are connected to a PC-486 host for software development and user interface. These Transputers also connect to a VME signal bus on which resides the digital to analog (D/A) and analog to digital (A/D) circuit cards providing the motor drive (computer output) and sensor (computer input) signal interfaces. The control analysis and design on performed on a SUN Sparcstation using MATLAB. The controller parameters are saved in a MATLAB file which are then read in by the real time computer. The sensory data are also saved in a MATLAB file after each experiment. We currently do not have capability to directly measure the beam tip position. For the experimentation, we have used the five available outputs and a 4-mode observer to reconstruct an approximate tip position.

Hub PD feedback are used as the feedback components in the controller. The feedback gains of the hub position and hub velocity are: $K_p = 2.2378$ (NM/Rad) and $K_v = 1.1651$ (NM/Rad/sec).

A minimal jerk trajectory and sinusoids of two different frequencies are chosen as the desired trajectories. The duration of each desired trajectory is 6 seconds.

Two different types of basis functions are used:
Fourier Basis: 25 basis functions with a constant function C_m, and $A_m \sin(nt)$, $A_m \cos(nt)$, $n = 1, \ldots, 12$, where $A_m = B_m = C_m 1000$d/a units.
Square Waves: 25 basis functions with a constant function and 12 square wave signals with frequencies $\frac{n}{2\pi}$, $n = 1, \ldots, 12$, and another 12 square waves shifted by 90°. The peak amplitudes of all signals are 1000 d/a units.

The performance of the learning controller is quite good with either Fourier and square wave basis functions. The results are shown in Fig. 1–2. The Fourier basis appears to provide a better tracking performance. The selection of the basis functions remains to be fully explored. The non–minimum–phase nature of the input/output transfer function is evident in the initial undershooting of the tip output. A small amount of residue oscillation can be seen in the signal, this is due to the selection of the PD feedback controller which does not suppress higher frequency vibration effectively. From the strain gauge plots (not shown), it can be seen that internal states are bounded. This is expected since a stabilizing feedback loop with hub PD feedback is used.

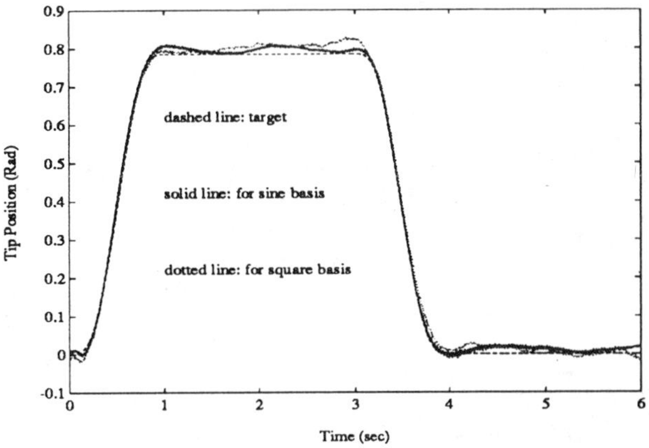

Figure 1: Tip Position Tracking for a Minimum Jerk Trajectory

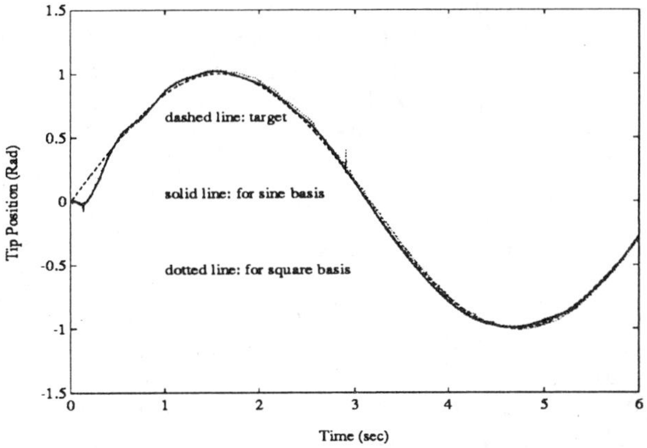

Figure 2: Tip Position Tracking for A Sinusoid

For a fast trajectory, excessive control effort may be required causing the actuator to saturate (see Fig. 6).

This can be avoided by performing a constrained least square instead of the standard least square in solving for the feedforward. Fig. 3 compares the feedforward torque for the constrained versus the constrained cases (for tracking the sinusoid in Fig. 6). As expected, the peak torque in the constrained case is reduced, but at a reduced tracking performance.

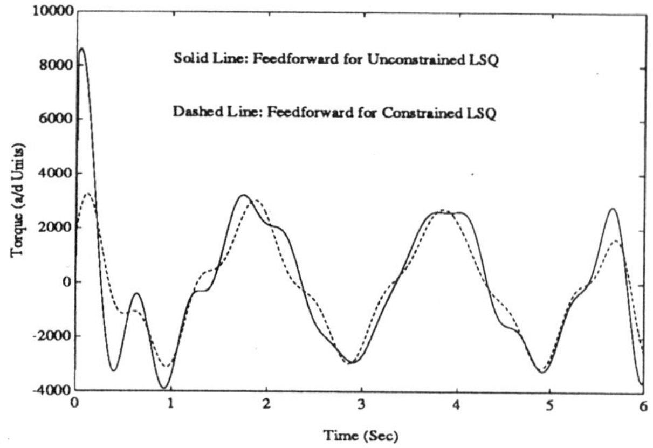

Figure 3: Feedforward Torque for Constrained and Unconstrained Least Square Methods

When Q is chosen to be identity and R is zero in the least square problem, the output tracking error is minimized. However, due to the non-minimum-phase nature of the system, the input exhibits peaking at the end of the period. This peaking is considerably reduced when the weighting $Q(t)$ is reduced to $1/100$ for $t \in [0, .16]$. If the torque is further penalized through $R(t) = .0001$, $t \in [5.84, 6]$, the torque level is further reduced; see Fig. 4. The output trajectory tracking is only minimally affected with these modifications. In both of the modified cases, the tracking errors increased by about 1° (for a 45° step) at the beginning and the end of the 6sec period.

The tracking performance of the learning controller is compared with the baseline PD controller and an inverse dynamics based controller (based on the identified model). The results are shown in Fig. 5–6. The initial glitch in the trajectory corresponding to the learning control is due to the saturation of strain gauge and the subsequent effect in the observer that generates the tip position. From these results, it is seen that model based feedforward has better tracking performance than the PD controller alone, but by far the best performance is with the learning controller.

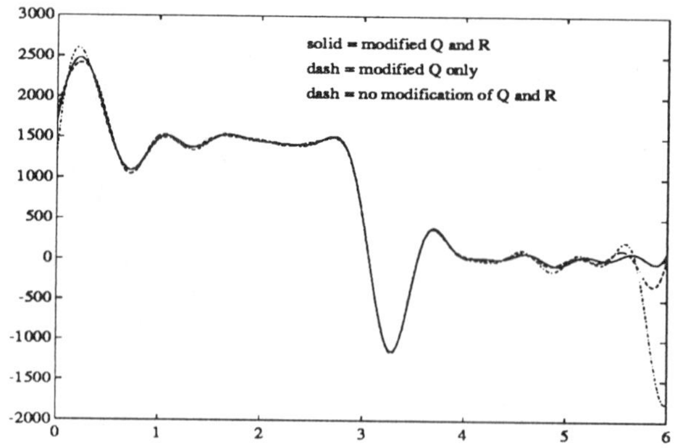

Figure 4: Feedforward Torque Comparison for Different Weightings

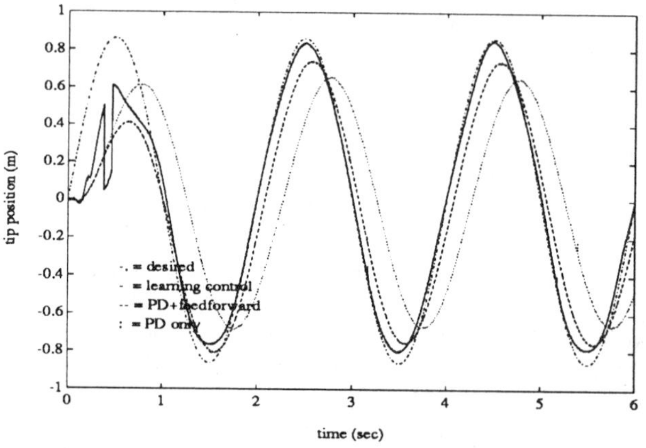

Figure 5: Tip Tracking Comparison for a Sinusoid: $f = \frac{1}{2}$Hz

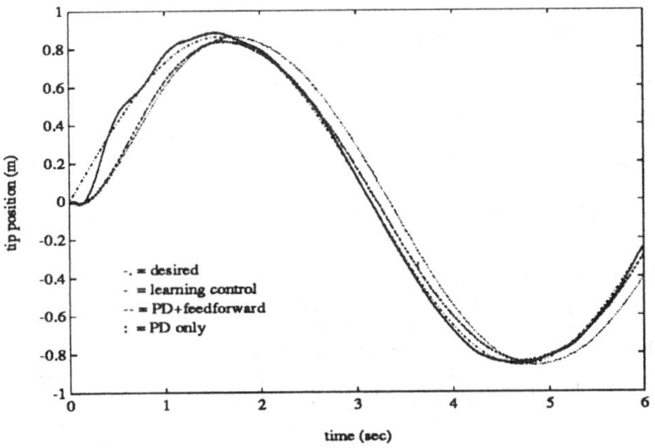

Figure 6: Tip Tracking Comparison for a Sinusoid with $f = \frac{1}{6.28}$Hz

5 Conclusion and Future Work

In this paper, we have presented experimental results of an off-line learning controller for the tracking of a flexible beam. The results show that the proposed learning controller is feasible and good tracking performance is achieved. Our future work will focus on disturbance rejection and parameter adaptation.

Acknowledgment

This work was supported in part by the National Science Foundation under Grant No.MSS-9113633 and Army Research Office under grant DAALO3-92-G-012.

References

[1] B. Paden, B. Riedle, and E. Bayo. Exponentially stable tracking control for multi-joint flexible-link manipulators. In *Proc. 1990 American Control Conference*, pages 680–684, San Diego, CA, June 1990.

[2] L. Lanari and J.T. Wen. A family of asymptotic stable control laws for flexible robots based on a passivity approach. CIRSSE Report 85, Rensselaer Polytechnic Institute, February 1991.

[3] S.Yurkovich, A.P.Tzes, I.Lee, and K.L.Hillsley. Control and system identification of a two-link flexible manipulator. In *Proc. 29th IEEE Conf. Decision and Control*, pages 1626–1641, 1990.

[4] C. H. Meng and J. S. Chen. Dynamic modeling and payload-adaptive control of a flexible manipulator. In *Proc. 1988 IEEE Robotics and Automation Conference*, 1988.

[5] S.Kawamura, F. Miyazaki, and S. Arimoto. Realization of robot motion based on a learning method. *IEEE Transaction on Systems, Man, and Cybernetics*, 18:126–134, 1988.

[6] T. Kuc and K. Nam. CMAC based iterative learning control of robot manipulators. In *Proc. 28th IEEE Conf. Decision and Control*, pages 2613–2618, Tampa, FL, December 1989.

[7] W.Messner, R.Horowitz, W.W.Kao, and M.Boals. A new adatpive learnig rule. Ramp 89-10/esrc 89-12, April 1989.

[8] D.M.Dawson, Z.Qo, and J.F.Dorsey. On the learning control of a robot manipulator. In *Proc. 28th IEEE Conf. Decision and Control*, pages 2632–2634, 1989.

[9] Z.Qu, J.Dorsey, D.M.Dawson, and R.W.Johnson. A new learning control scheme for robots. In *Proc. 1991 IEEE Robotics and Automation Conference*, pages 1463–1468, 1991.

[10] S.Arimoto, S.Kawamura, F.Miyazaki, and Tamaki. Learning control theory for dnamical systems. In *Proc. 25th IEEE Conf. Decision and Control*, pages 1375–1378, 1985.

[11] S.Arimoto, T.Naniwa, and H.Suzuki. Selective learning with a forgetting factor for robotic motion control. In *Proc. 1991 IEEE Robotics and Automation Conference*, pages 728–733, 1991.

[12] W. Cheng and J. Wen. A class of learning controllers with application to the tracking control of a flexible beam. In *1993 IEEE Robotics and Automation Conference*, Altana, GE, 1993.

[13] D. Hughes and J.T. Wen. An observer based passive controller design for flexible structures. In *Proc. 1993 IEEE Robotics and Automation Conference*, Atlanta, GA, May 1993.

Proceedings of the
American Control Conference
San Francisco, California • June 1993

A Robust Power absorbing H^∞ Controller Design For Flexible Structures

H. Bouguerra* and B. C. Chang*
Department of Mechanical Engineering and Mechanics
Drexel University
Philadelphia, PA 19104

Abstract

An H^∞ mixed sensitivity problem is formulated for the control of uncertain large flexible structures. The plant model is based on the driving point mobility (inverse of the mechanical impedance) for the structure at the junction where the collocated dual actuators and sensors meet the structure. One way to obtain an expression for the point mobility for the structure is by analyzing the wave mode dynamics along its structural members. In the presence of bounded power propagating disturbances we seek a stabilizing controller to minimize their effect in an H^∞ optimal sense. Specifically, we show the minimization of the power of the reflected and transmitted waves at the control junction is equivalent to the minimization of the H^∞-norm of the weighted system sensitivity function together with a weighted output complementary sensitivity function. A weighted constraint on the control input is added in order to yield a robustly stable closed-loop system in the face of additive plant uncertainties. The obtained controller is verified to absorb power from the structure and hence adds overall damping to it.

Modeling

The control of the inherently weakly damped structures is of major importance in today's design of large flexible space structures. The usual complex structure will be considered to consist of a network of structural members. The structural dynamics of the network will be dominated by the dynamics of the individual members and the junctions between them. Thus accurate member models is essential and will be a prerequisite to any good network description. The individual members (often one-dimensional and slender) will act as wave guides to propagating disturbances. If we consider the disturbances as waves injecting power (energy) into the structure then the control objective would be to dissipate as much as possible of the total power flow into the structure. Specifically, and in order to minimize the effects of the incoming waves we will make use of the transfer mobility [3] of the structure by applying forces proportional to velocities at the control junctions. It is at these junctions where one hopes to get the most out of any control policy.

The propagating waves through the structural member shown in Figure 1 may be generated by disturbances acting on the member itself or they may be reflected and transmitted at discontinuities along the member.

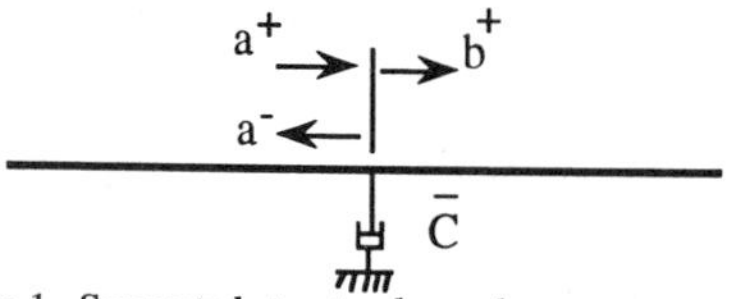

Figure 1. Supported structural member as a waveguide.

In the absence of external forces and supports the displacement of the structural member modeled as an Euler-Bernoulli beam [1, 2] can be characterized by

$$w(x) = A_r e^{-ikx} + A_l e^{ikx} + A_r^n e^{-kx} + A_l^n e^{kx} \tag{1}$$

where the time dependence of the form $exp(-i\omega t)$ has been dropped for brevity and the wave number k as a function of frequency ω can be obtained from $k^4-\omega^2\rho A/EI=0$, where ρ, A, E and I are the physical parameters of the member. The constants A_r and A_l can be interpreted as the amplitudes of the right (positive)-going and left (negative)-going propagating waves, respectively. Similarly, the two near field components A_r^n and A_l^n represent the amplitudes of the right- and left-going attenuating waves which decay exponentially with respect to the spatial coordinate x.

It is convenient to reconsider Eqn. (1) and denote by $\boldsymbol{a}^+=[A_r \;\; A_r^n]^T$ and $\boldsymbol{a}^-=[A_l \;\; A_l^n]^T$ the two vectors representing positive and negative-going wave mode amplitudes, respectively. The beam displacement, slope, bending moment and shear force can now be found from

$$\begin{bmatrix} w \\ \frac{1}{k}\frac{\partial w}{\partial x} \end{bmatrix} = \begin{bmatrix} 1 & 1 \\ -i & -1 \end{bmatrix}\mathbf{a}^+ + \begin{bmatrix} 1 & 1 \\ i & 1 \end{bmatrix}\mathbf{a}^- \tag{2}$$

$$\begin{bmatrix} M/EIk^2 \\ V/EIk^3 \end{bmatrix} = \begin{bmatrix} 1 & -1 \\ -i & 1 \end{bmatrix}\mathbf{a}^+ + \begin{bmatrix} 1 & -1 \\ i & -1 \end{bmatrix}\mathbf{a}^- \tag{3}$$

A crude attempt to try to suppress the vibrations of the beam by power (energy) dissipation would be to place a simple dashpot support at some point along the beam, say $x=0$. When discontinuities occur at some point along the beam, as shown in Figure 1 incoming waves from the left of the discontinuity represented by the positive-going wave mode amplitudes $\boldsymbol{a}^+$ will give rise to reflected waves $\boldsymbol{a}^-$ together with transmitted ones $\boldsymbol{b}^+$ to the right of the discontinuity. The relations between these waves can be expressed in the form $\boldsymbol{a}^- = R\,\boldsymbol{a}^+$ and $\boldsymbol{b}^+ = T\,\boldsymbol{a}^+$ where R and T are the reflection and transmission matrices, respectively. To insure the continuity condition of the beam at the location of the support the appropriate expressions for the displacements and the slopes of the beam to the left and to the right of the discontinuity must match. Furthermore, the support exerts a force proportional to the coefficient of damping $\overline{C}$ and the velocity of the beam at that point. Thus for equilibrium, the bending moments on both sides of the discontinuity at hand are the same whereas a shear force balance on both sides of the discontinuity requires $i\omega\overline{C}w = V^+ - V^-$. The reflection and transmission matrices can now be solved for to yield

$$R = \frac{C}{4+(1-i)C}\begin{bmatrix} -1 & -1 \\ i & i \end{bmatrix}, \qquad T = I + \frac{C}{4+(1-i)C}\begin{bmatrix} -1 & -1 \\ i & i \end{bmatrix} \tag{4}$$

where $C = \omega\overline{C}/EIk^3$ is the new dimensionless damping factor. The coefficient multiplying $\overline{C}$ in this expression is known as the mobility of the structure and will be denoted by $P(i\omega)$. It is easy to derive expressions, i.e. transfer functions, relating the input (generalized forces) to the output (generalized velocities) whose product is power. These expressions are known as transfer admittances or driving point mobilities (inverse of the mechanical impedance) in the case of collocated actuators and sensors. The analysis of wave dynamics in the structure is not the only way to obtain accurate estimates of these transfer admittances. The modal analysis approach based on finite element methods can also be used provided that the structure is lightly damped which is the case in most applications. Still yet another way to compute the dereverberated mobility of a structure is through the use of the cepstrum of the impulse response [3]. The cepstrum is the inverse Fourier transform of the log of the complex spectrum.

By means of the analytical continuation through the entire complex plane, the driving point mobility for the beam being considered can be verified to be $P(s) = 1/\sqrt{s}$. This expression is irrational and can be approximated by a rational transfer function consisting of a set of stable alternating poles and zeros. For this example a set of five poles and five zeros that are logarithmically equally spaced along the negative real axis of the complex plane is used. With this approximation the magnitude is within $2dB$ of the actual magnitude over a frequency range of six decades and the phase is within five degrees of the actual phase over the same frequency range. The actual transfer function rolls off at high frequencies but the approximating transfer function of equal number of poles and zeros tend to a constant at high frequencies. This constant is attenuated at high frequencies by a low-pass filter.

In many cases we consider the incident waves to consist of the propagating waves only because of the attenuating nature of the near fields. The latters have negligible effect when the disturbances occur far enough from the control junction. The power carried in a propagating wave is proportional to the square of its amplitude. Thus the power reflected and transmitted per unit incident power is $|R_{11}|^2+|T_{11}|^2$ which of course equals unity if the support at the control junction dissipates no energy. It is obvious that the minimization of the reflected and transmitted power should result in an increase in the power dissipated at the control junction.

If we now reconsider Figure 1 and suppose the dashpot shown there exhibits a damping coefficient that is a function of frequency. This is of course equivalent to replacing $\overline{C}$ with a compensator, say $K(s)$ at the control junction. Moreover, by making use of the mobility $P(s)$ of the structure the propagating reflected and transmitted wave relations from Eqn (4) become

$$R_{11} = \frac{1}{4}\frac{P(i\omega)K(i\omega)}{1-\frac{-1+i}{4}P(i\omega)K(i\omega)}, \qquad T_{11} = 1+\frac{1}{4}\frac{P(i\omega)K(i\omega)}{1-\frac{-1+i}{4}P(i\omega)K(i\omega)} \tag{5}$$

The expression for R_{11} is of the form $PK(I-PK)^{-1}$ which is known as the output complementary sensitivity function in a H^∞ disturbance rejection problem. By keeping the H^∞-norm of the complementary sensitivity as small as possible it can be verified that the magnitude of the transfer function for R_{11} is also small. Hence we expect smaller amount of the total incident power would be reflected from the control junction. We also

* This work was supported in part by AFOSR under Contract F33615-C-3600 and in part by NASA Langley Research Center under Grant NAG-1-1102.

would expect that whatever quantity of the injected power is not absorbed by the controller would be transmitted past the junction. The H^∞ disturbance rejection problem is usually posed as a mixed sensitivity problem in order to address the disturbance effects on the output error response. This is usually achieved by including the sensitivity function which is of the form $(I-PK)^{-1}$ in the H^∞ minimization problem. It turns out in the numerical example to be considered later that the inclusion of the sensitivity function results in a considerable increase in the power absorbed by the controller. This should not be a surprise given the expression for T_{11}, above and its close relation to the sensitivity function.

H^∞minimization

Suppose the incident propagating waves are the result of additive disturbances at the plant output then the measured plant output is related to the control input and the disturbance via $y=P(s)u+d$, where $P(s)$ denotes the driving point mobility for the structure, $d(s)$ represents the bonded power disturbance and $u(s)$ is the control action. Introducing the control law $u=K(s)y$ we have the disturbance rejection problem of Figure 2 below

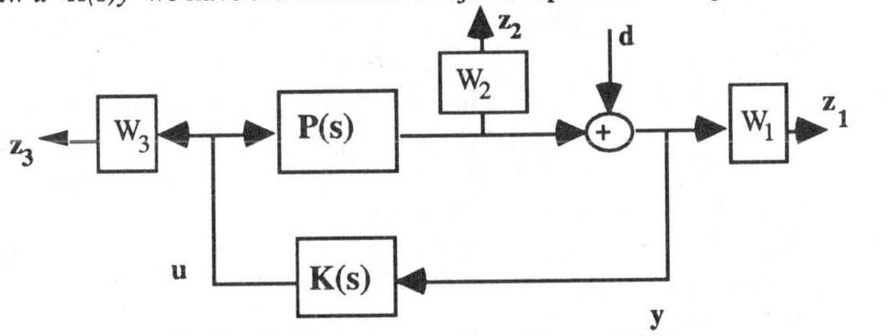

Figure 2. Disturbance attenuation problem.

The controlled variables are chosen such that with the weights $W_i(s)=1$ the system sensitivity function is represented by the transfer function from the disturbance $d(s)$ to the output variable z_1. Similarly the output complementary sensitivity function is the transfer relation between the disturbance and the output variable z_2 . Since it was established that these relations are intimately related to the reflection and transmission coefficients mentioned earlier, we now formally pose the problem of minimizing the power of the reflected and transmitted waves as a H^∞ minimization problem:

Let $T_{dz}(\omega)$ denote the Fourier transform of the impulse response of the input-output system relating the power signal disturbance $d(s)$ to the controlled output signal $z(s)$, then the following is true [5]:

$$\|T_{dz}\|_\infty = \sup_{\omega \in \mathbf{R}} \bar{\sigma}[T_{dz}(\omega)] = \sup_{pow(d)\le 1} pow(z) \qquad (6)$$

where $\bar{\sigma}$ denotes the maximum singular value of the transfer function $T_{dz}(\omega)$ and $pow(d)$ is the square root of the average power of the signal $d(t)$ over all time. Eqn. (6) is basically saying that if the exogenous input signal $d(t)$ is not known a priori but is of bounded power then the square root of the average power of the output signal of the system is at most equal to the H^∞-norm of the system impulse response $T_{dz}(\omega)$. Thus, if $T_{dz}(\omega)$ represents the transfer function of the closed-loop system, then in order to minimize the effects of disturbances by minimizing the power of the output signals (the reflected and transmitted wave modes at the control junction) then one of the design objective would be to include a stabilizing controller within the transfer function $T_{dz}(\omega)$ such that its H^∞-norm is minimized. It is well known that any design of a control law for the purpose of disturbance rejection (power absorption in this case) must incorporate a constraint on the control input in order to address the robust stability of the closed-loop system in the face of plant uncertainties [6]. These objectives are often competing and the realization of one can only be achieved on the expense of the other. The standard H^∞ problem [4] can now be posed as a mixed sensitivity problem where a proper stabilizing controller $K(s)$ for the generalized plant below is sought in order to minimize the H^∞-norm of the closed-loop transfer function matrix $T_{dz}(s)$.

$$\begin{bmatrix} z \\ y \end{bmatrix} = \left[\begin{array}{c|c} W_1 & W_1P \\ 0 & W_2P \\ 0 & W_3 \\ \hline I & P \end{array}\right] \begin{bmatrix} d \\ u \end{bmatrix}, \qquad T_{dz}(s) = \begin{bmatrix} W_1(I-PK)^{-1} \\ W_2PK(I-PK)^{-1} \\ W_3K(I-PK)^{-1} \end{bmatrix} \qquad (7)$$

The W_i's are weights to be chosen by the designer appropriate to the plant and design objectives being considered. Usually, W_1 is a low frequency filter indicating that the disturbances introduced at the plant output are low frequency signals. On the other hand W_2 and W_3 can be assumed to be a high frequency filter to include unmodeled dynamics and to insure a constraint on the magnitude of the control input.

Power absorption analysis

In the formulation proposed by MacMartin et. al. [3], an attempt was made to design an optimal H^∞ control that would directly minimize the net power flow into the structure, that is the power due to external disturbance plus the power dissipated by the controller. This formulation results in the necessity to model the disturbances in a prespecified manner which is unrealistic for most practical examples. The controller derived this way will certainly dissipate power optimally if the disturbances happen to enter in the way they were specified to do. Otherwise there are no guarantees on the controller performance in the case of errors in the disturbance modeling.

In order to verify the performance of the H^∞ controller computed via our approach, namely its ability to absorb power, we derive an expression for the power absorbed by the controller. In the absence of disturbances and since $P(s)$ is a mobility, the instantaneous power flow into the structure due to the controller is the product of the control input $u(s)$ and the output $y(s)$. The usual time domain expression for the power as a time integral of the instantaneous power flow averaged over all time can be transformed to an equivalent expression in the frequency domain by applying Parseval's theorem to obtain

$$P_{avg} = \frac{1}{2\pi}\int_0^\infty \left[S_{uy}(\omega) + S_{yu}(\omega)\right] d\omega \qquad (8)$$

where $S_{uy}(\omega)$ is the cross-power spectral density which is simply the Fourier transform of the cross-correlation function between the two signals $u(t)$ and $y(t)$. The integrand in Eqn. (8), namely, $\boldsymbol{P(\omega)=S_{uy}(\omega)+S_{yu}(\omega)}$ can be considered to represent the power being absorbed by the controller at each frequency ω. Using the following input-output relations:

$$u = K(I-PK)^{-1}d = Hd, \qquad y = (I-PK)^{-1}d = (I+PH)d. \qquad (9)$$

for u and y in terms of the new variable H , the power absorbed by the controller at each frequency becomes

$$\mathbf{P}(\omega) = \left[H^\sim(I+PH) + (I+PH)^\sim H\right]S_{dd} \qquad (10)$$

where $H^\sim$ stands for $H(-\omega)$. The quantity within the brackets in Eqn. (10) represents the fraction of the power absorbed by the controller relative to the power of the external disturbances. This fraction, plotted in Fig. 3 below, is always negative which indicates that energy is being dissipated and hence resulting in an increase in the overall damping of the structure.

In Fig. 4 the maximum singular value at each frequency of the control complementary sensitivity function (curve b) is plotted together with the inverse of the maximum singular value of the plant uncertainties (curve a). The latter is computed from the difference between the approximating transfer function of stable poles and zeros and the exact dereverberated mobility for the structure. As expected and since the design included a constraint on the control complementary sensitivity function higher tolerances on the additive plant uncertainties are allowed at higher frequencies. This means that the closed-loop system is robustly stable in the face of plant perturbations occurring at high frequencies which may be a result of unmodeled dynamics.

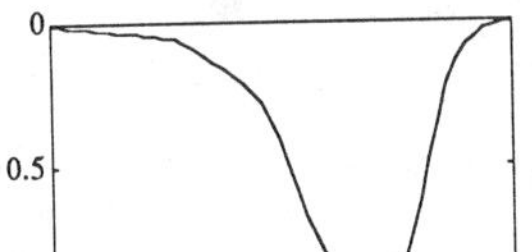

Figure 3. Power absorbed per unit power input vs. frequency

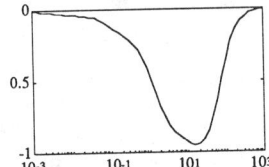

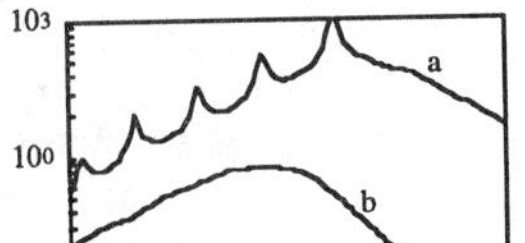

Figure 4. σ-plots: a) additive plant uncertainties b)control complementary sensitivity function

References

[1] B. R. Mace, " Wave Reflection and Transmission in Beams, " Journal of Sound and Vibration (1984) **97**(2), 237-246.

[2] B. R. Mace, "Active Control of Flexural Vibrations, " Journal of Sound and Vibration (1987) **114**(2), 253-270.

[3] D. G. MacMartin and S. R. Hall, "Control of Uncertain Structures Using An H∞ Power Flow Approach to Control "Journal of Guidance, Control, and Dynamics **14**(3)May' 91

[4] K. Glover and J. C. Doyle," State-Space formulae for all stabilizing controllers that satisfy an H^∞-norm bound and relations to risk sensitivity, " System & Control Letters **11**(1988), 167-172

[5] J. C. Doyle, B. A. Francis, and A. R. Tannenbaum, Feedback Control Theory. Macmillan Publishing Co., N. Y.

[6] J. C. Doyle and G. Stein, " Multivariable feedback design: Concepts for a classical/modern synthesis," IEEE Trans. Aut. Cont., vol. AC-**26**, 4-16, Feb.'81

Proceedings of the
American Control Conference
San Francisco, California • June 1993

Decentralized Interaction Control for Flexible Structures

Philip G. Good
Dale A. Lawrence

Department of Aerospace Engineering Sciences
University of Colorado, Boulder, CO 80309

Abstract

A control scheme for bringing flexible structures into interaction is developed using an auxiliary interaction control which augments a simple nominal interaction controller. Two types of auxiliary interaction control are theoretically investigated to improve the stability of the interaction, one using open loop modal (OLM) information, the other closed loop modal (CLM) information. The implementation of the nominal interaction control with each method of auxiliary interaction control is investigated on a computer model designed to simulate a simple space station to space shuttle 'docking' maneuver.

Introduction

If two or more controlled substructures are brought together to interact it is likely that stability or performance problems will result, as was demonstrated in [1]. Local Interaction Control (LIC) is a method for bringing two such substructures together in a stable, low order, low cost manner.

The LIC controls the actuation between two interacting substructures and has uses in space construction scenarios such as: the interaction between the Space Station and a space vehicle or a payload, the interaction of a space platform and flexible space module during construction, and stabilization of two modules during joining.

Centralized approaches for dealing with interacting substructures include LQG, H-infinity, and multi-variable Nyquist array methods [2, 3], which involve eliminating the original controllers and designing a new controller for the combined systems. A decentralized way [4] to deal with the structural interaction problem is to design the original controllers to be robust enough to handle changes in the plant which will occur when another structure comes into contact with it.

Local Interaction Control is a decentralized interaction controller which consists of a nominal interaction controller designed for interaction performance and an auxiliary interaction controller which addresses any interaction instabilities. The approach uses only sensors and actuators local to the interaction location and does not share any current sensor or actuator information with the original substructure controllers.

The main focus of this paper is on the auxiliary interaction control schemes, of which two methods are examined. One, which uses information about the open loop modes (OLM), is based on the concept of the residual mode filter (RMF) [5]. The other, which uses information about the closed loop modes (CLM), is based on the idea of a disturbance accommodating controller (DAC) [6].

1. Nominal Behavior

Let the two *Lyapunov stable* [7] substructures be combined in the open loop state space system below

$$\dot{\mathbf{x}}_o = \mathbf{A}_o\mathbf{x}_o + \mathbf{B}_o\mathbf{u} \qquad \mathbf{y} = \mathbf{C}_o\mathbf{x}_o \tag{1}$$

Let the control input $\mathbf{u}$ be defined by

$$\mathbf{u} \equiv \mathbf{u}_D + \bar{\mathbf{u}}_D \tag{2}$$

where $\mathbf{u}_D \equiv -\mathbf{G}_D\mathbf{y}$ is the nominal interaction control, and $\bar{\mathbf{u}}_D$ is the auxiliary interaction control. With only nominal interaction control the closed loop minimum system is

$$\dot{\mathbf{x}}_o = (\mathbf{A}_o - \mathbf{B}_o\mathbf{G}_D\mathbf{C}_o)\mathbf{x}_o \tag{3}$$

If (3) is stable then the nominal interaction control can be viewed as adequate and no further control is necessary. However, if (3) is unstable then a stabilization method must be developed, leading to the need for the auxiliary interaction control.

The development of the auxiliary interaction control begins by placing the open loop minimum system (1) into *Jordan form* [7] with the decomposition matrix $\mathbf{X}$ and arbitrarily placing the Jordan blocks along the diagonal [8]. Let one such ordering of the system be partitioned into state vectors $\mathbf{x}_s$ and $\mathbf{x}_u$, so that

$$\mathbf{X}^{-1}\mathbf{A}_o\mathbf{X} = \begin{bmatrix} \mathbf{A}_s & 0 \\ 0 & \mathbf{A}_u \end{bmatrix} \tag{4}$$

The open loop state space system can then be represented in its partitioned states by

$$\begin{aligned} \dot{\mathbf{x}} &= \begin{Bmatrix} \dot{\mathbf{x}}_s \\ \dot{\mathbf{x}}_u \end{Bmatrix} = \begin{bmatrix} \mathbf{A}_s & 0 \\ 0 & \mathbf{A}_u \end{bmatrix} \begin{Bmatrix} \mathbf{x}_s \\ \mathbf{x}_u \end{Bmatrix} + \begin{bmatrix} \mathbf{B}_s \\ \mathbf{B}_u \end{bmatrix}\mathbf{u} \\ &= \mathbf{A}\mathbf{x} + \mathbf{B}\mathbf{u} \\ \mathbf{y} &= \begin{bmatrix} \mathbf{C}_s & \mathbf{C}_u \end{bmatrix} \begin{Bmatrix} \mathbf{x}_s \\ \mathbf{x}_u \end{Bmatrix} \\ &= \mathbf{C}\mathbf{x} \end{aligned} \tag{5}$$

The partitioned system of (5) with nominal interaction control can be expressed in its unstable closed loop form by

$$\begin{aligned} \dot{\mathbf{x}} &= \mathbf{A} - \mathbf{B}\mathbf{G}_D\mathbf{C}\mathbf{x} \\ &= \left[\begin{array}{c|c} \mathbf{A}_s - \mathbf{B}_s\mathbf{G}_D\mathbf{C}_s & -\mathbf{B}_s\mathbf{G}_D\mathbf{C}_u \\ \hline -\mathbf{B}_u\mathbf{G}_D\mathbf{C}_s & \mathbf{A}_u - \mathbf{B}_u\mathbf{G}_D\mathbf{C}_u \end{array}\right] \begin{Bmatrix} \mathbf{x}_s \\ \mathbf{x}_u \end{Bmatrix} \end{aligned} \tag{6}$$

Let the partitioning from (5) into states $\mathbf{x}_s$ and $\mathbf{x}_u$ be such that the left upper block of (6), $(\mathbf{A}_s - \mathbf{B}_s\mathbf{G}_D\mathbf{C}_s)$, is stable. If this block is not stable then repartition with a new ordering of the columns of $\mathbf{X}$ to produce new partitioned states, $\mathbf{x}_s$ and $\mathbf{x}_u$, so that $(\mathbf{A}_s - \mathbf{B}_s\mathbf{G}_D\mathbf{C}_s)$ is stable. This can be done by systematically eliminating states from the open loop system until the closed loop is stable, or by using an algorithmic approach [9].

Once the nominal interaction control has been applied and the system has been partitioned as in (5), the auxiliary interaction control methods can be developed to stabilize the system.

2. OLM Auxiliary Interaction Control

The open loop mode (OLM) auxiliary interaction control method uses the open loop modes which are driven unstable by the nominal interaction control, then filters these modes out of the input to the controller. The OLM method is based on the residual mode filter (RMF), which has been used in the structural control field primarily for eliminating unstable spillover modes. The theory behind the development of the RMF can be found in [5], while results of its application can be found in [10, 11]. The following is an adaptation of the RMF for use in the interaction of two separate substructures.

The OLM auxiliary interaction controller is defined in terms of the partitioned $\mathbf{x}_u$ states, as seen below

$$\begin{aligned} \dot{\hat{\mathbf{x}}}_u &= \mathbf{A}_u\hat{\mathbf{x}}_u + \mathbf{B}_u\mathbf{u} \\ \hat{\mathbf{y}}_u &= \mathbf{C}_u\hat{\mathbf{x}}_u \\ \overline{\mathbf{u}}_D &\equiv \mathbf{G}_D\hat{\mathbf{y}}_u \end{aligned} \tag{7}$$

where $\mathbf{A}_u$, $\mathbf{B}_u$, and $\mathbf{C}_u$ are defined in (4, 5).

Lemma 1:
Given that the original, non-interacting substructures of (1) were stable, and that the systems were partitioned in (4) so that $(\mathbf{A}_s - \mathbf{B}_s\mathbf{G}_D\mathbf{C}_s)$ is stable, then with $\mathbf{u} \equiv \mathbf{u}_D + \overline{\mathbf{u}}_D$, where $\mathbf{u}_D = -\mathbf{G}_D\mathbf{y}$ is the nominal interaction control and $\overline{\mathbf{u}}_D$ is defined in (7), the interacting substructures are stable.

Proof:
Defining the filter error $\mathbf{e}_u$ by $\mathbf{e}_u \equiv \hat{\mathbf{x}}_u - \mathbf{x}_u$, the closed loop state equations become

$$\begin{Bmatrix} \dot{\mathbf{e}}_u \\ \dot{\mathbf{x}}_s \\ \dot{\mathbf{x}}_u \end{Bmatrix} = \begin{bmatrix} \mathbf{A}_u & 0 & 0 \\ -\mathbf{B}_s\mathbf{G}_D\mathbf{C}_u & \mathbf{A}_s - \mathbf{B}_s\mathbf{G}_D\mathbf{C}_s & 0 \\ \mathbf{B}_u\mathbf{G}_D\mathbf{C}_s & -\mathbf{B}_u\mathbf{G}_D\mathbf{C}_s & \mathbf{A}_u \end{bmatrix} \begin{Bmatrix} \mathbf{e}_u \\ \mathbf{x}_s \\ \mathbf{x}_u \end{Bmatrix} \tag{8}$$

Given that the original non-interacting systems are stable, the open loop partition $\mathbf{A}_u$ is stable. Because $(\mathbf{A}_s - \mathbf{B}_s\mathbf{G}_D\mathbf{C}_s)$ and the block diagonals of (8) are stable, then due to *triangular partitioning* [12], the system of (8) is stable. Similarity transformations can then be used to show that the interacting substructures of (1) with nominal interaction control and OLM auxiliary interaction control are stable. Δ

The implementation of the nominal interaction control and OLM auxiliary interaction control can be seen in Figure 1.

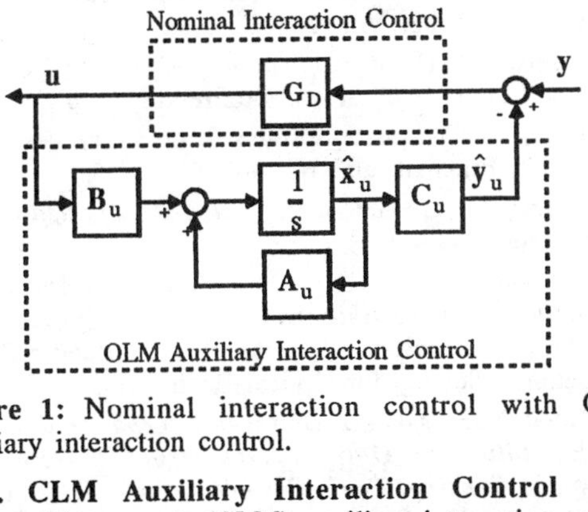

Figure 1: Nominal interaction control with OLM auxiliary interaction control.

3. CLM Auxiliary Interaction Control

The closed loop mode (CLM) auxiliary interaction control will be developed based on the disturbance accommodating control (DAC) scheme. The DAC has been used in the past to eliminate the effects of a known disturbance input on a system. The theory and use of the DAC can be found in [6, 13, 14]. The following is an adaptation of the DAC for use in the interaction of two separate structures.

The development begins with a *Jordan decomposition* on the closed loop system of (6) with the decomposition matrix $\mathbf{\Phi}_T$, so that

$$\mathbf{A}_T \equiv \mathbf{\Phi}_T^{-1}(\mathbf{A} - \mathbf{B}\mathbf{G}_D\mathbf{C})\mathbf{\Phi}_T \tag{9}$$

Partition $\mathbf{x}_T$ into states $\mathbf{x}_{Ts}$ and $\mathbf{x}_{Tu}$ so that

$$\begin{aligned} \dot{\mathbf{x}}_T &= \mathbf{A}_T\mathbf{x}_T + \mathbf{B}_T\mathbf{u} \\ &= \begin{bmatrix} \mathbf{A}_{Ts} & 0 \\ 0 & \mathbf{A}_{Tu} \end{bmatrix} \begin{Bmatrix} \mathbf{x}_{Ts} \\ \mathbf{x}_{Tu} \end{Bmatrix} + \begin{bmatrix} \mathbf{B}_{Ts} \\ \mathbf{B}_{Tu} \end{bmatrix}\mathbf{u} \\ \mathbf{y} &= \mathbf{C}_T\mathbf{x}_T \\ &= \begin{bmatrix} \mathbf{C}_{Ts} & \mathbf{C}_{Tu} \end{bmatrix} \begin{Bmatrix} \mathbf{x}_{Ts} \\ \mathbf{x}_{Tu} \end{Bmatrix} \end{aligned} \tag{10}$$

Let the columns of $\mathbf{\Phi}_T$ be arranged so that all of the unstable eigenvalues of $(\mathbf{A} - \mathbf{B}\mathbf{G}_D\mathbf{C})$ are contained in the Jordan blocks of $\mathbf{A}_{Tu}$. Introduce the new output, $\mathbf{y}^E \equiv \mathbf{C}_T^E\mathbf{x}_T$, to be used as input for an estimator of the unstable modes. The CLM controller is then defined by

$$\begin{aligned} \dot{\hat{\mathbf{x}}}_{Tu} &= \mathbf{A}_{Tu}\hat{\mathbf{x}}_{Tu} + \mathbf{B}_{Tu}\mathbf{u} + \mathbf{K}_T\left(\mathbf{y}^E - \hat{\mathbf{y}}_u^E\right) \\ \hat{\mathbf{y}}_u &= \mathbf{C}_{Tu}\hat{\mathbf{x}}_{Tu} \\ \hat{\mathbf{y}}_u^E &= \mathbf{C}_{Tu}^E\hat{\mathbf{x}}_{Tu} \\ \overline{\mathbf{u}}_D &= \mathbf{G}_D\hat{\mathbf{y}}_u \end{aligned} \tag{11}$$

The CLM estimator gain matrix, $\mathbf{K}_T$, is chosen so that $\left(\mathbf{A}_{Tu} - \mathbf{K}_T\mathbf{C}_{Tu}^E\right)$ is stable. By defining the estimator error as $\mathbf{e}_T \equiv \hat{\mathbf{x}}_{Tu} - \mathbf{x}_{Tu}$ and by partitioning the inverse of the decomposition matrix so that

$$\mathbf{\Phi}_T^{-1} = \begin{bmatrix} \overline{\phi}_{ss} & \overline{\phi}_{su} \\ \overline{\phi}_{us} & \overline{\phi}_{uu} \end{bmatrix} \tag{12}$$

the closed loop system with nominal interaction control and CLM auxiliary interaction control can be expressed as

$$\begin{Bmatrix} \dot{\mathbf{x}}_s \\ \dot{\mathbf{e}}_T \\ \dot{\mathbf{x}}_u \end{Bmatrix} = \left[\mathbf{A}_{Ko} + \Delta\mathbf{A}_K\right] \begin{Bmatrix} \mathbf{x}_s \\ \mathbf{e}_T \\ \mathbf{x}_u \end{Bmatrix} \tag{13}$$

where $\mathbf{A}_{Ko}$ and $\Delta\mathbf{A}_K$ are defined below

$$\begin{aligned} \mathbf{A}_{Ko} &\equiv \left[\begin{array}{cc|c} \mathbf{A}_s - \mathbf{B}_s\mathbf{G}_D\mathbf{C}_s & \mathbf{B}_s\mathbf{G}_D\mathbf{C}_{Tu} & 0 \\ \mathbf{K}_T\mathbf{C}_{Ts}^E\overline{\phi}_{ss} & \mathbf{A}_{Tu} - \mathbf{K}_T\mathbf{C}_{Tu}^E & 0 \\ \hline -\mathbf{B}_u\mathbf{G}_D\left(\mathbf{C}_s - \mathbf{C}_{Tu}\overline{\phi}_{us}\right) & \mathbf{B}_u\mathbf{G}_D\mathbf{C}_{Tu} & \mathbf{A}_u \end{array}\right] \\ \Delta\mathbf{A}_K &\equiv \begin{bmatrix} \mathbf{B}_s\mathbf{G}_D\mathbf{C}_{Tu}\overline{\phi}_{us} & 0 & -\mathbf{B}_s\mathbf{G}_D\left(\mathbf{C}_u - \mathbf{C}_{Tu}\overline{\phi}_{uu}\right) \\ 0 & 0 & \mathbf{K}_T\mathbf{C}_{Tu}^E\overline{\phi}_{su} \\ 0 & 0 & -\mathbf{B}_u\mathbf{G}_D\left(\mathbf{C}_u - \mathbf{C}_{Tu}\overline{\phi}_{uu}\right) \end{bmatrix} \end{aligned} \tag{14}$$

If the upper left partition of $\mathbf{A}_{Ko}$ is stable, then because $\mathbf{A}_u$ was defined as stable, by triangular partitioning $\mathbf{A}_{Ko}$ is stable. From perturbation results [15] $(\mathbf{A}_{Ko} + \Delta\mathbf{A}_K)$ is stable if

$$\left\|\Delta\mathbf{A}_K\right\| < \underline{\sigma}(\mathbf{A}_o) \tag{15}$$

where $\underline{\sigma}(\mathbf{A}_o)$ is the minimum singular value of $\mathbf{A}_O$. This proves the following lemma.

Lemma 2:
Let the original, non-interacting structures of (1) be stable, and let the partitioning in (5) be such that $(\mathbf{A}_s - \mathbf{B}_s\mathbf{G}_D\mathbf{C}_s)$ is stable. Let $\mathbf{u} \equiv \mathbf{u}_D + \overline{\mathbf{u}}_D$, where $\mathbf{u}_D$ is the nominal interaction control and $\overline{\mathbf{u}}_D$ is the CLM auxiliary control defined in (11). Given a stable upper left partition of $\mathbf{A}_{Ko}$ in (14) and the inequality of (15), the interacting systems are stable. Δ

The closed loop system with nominal interaction control and CLM auxiliary control are shown in block diagram form in Figure 2 below.

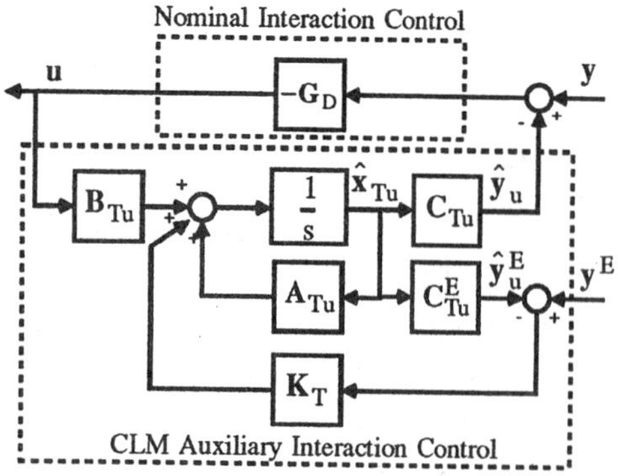

Figure 2: The nominal interaction control with the stabilizing CLM auxiliary interaction control.

4. Simulation Results

The local interaction control methods were implemented on a computer model of two interacting substructures, as seen in Figure 3, representative of a linear docking or berthing operation between the Space Station and the Space Shuttle.

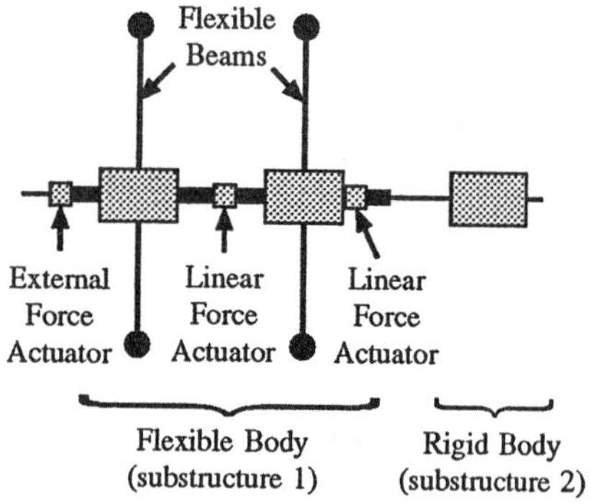

Figure 3: Model of a flexible substructure interacting with a rigid substructure confined to linear motion.

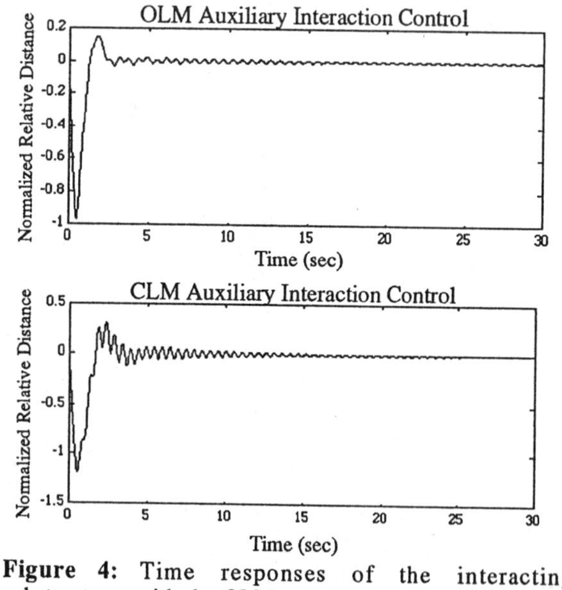

Figure 4: Time responses of the interacting substructures with the OLM and CLM auxiliary interaction control methods.

An inertial position controller was implemented on the flexible body and a nominal interaction controller was implemented to maintain a safe relative distance between the two substructures during interaction. When the substructures were brought into interaction there was an instability, requiring an auxiliary interaction control.

Both the OLM and CLM auxiliary interaction controllers were implemented on the unstable closed loop system, resulting in stable systems, as seen in the time responses of Figure 4. The slowly decaying mode does not hurt the interaction performance, but represents the substructure modes which pass through the controller. The OLM method was found to satisfy the performance objective of maintaining a normalized relative interaction distance below one, while the CLM method exceeded the performance limit slightly. The CLM auxiliary interaction controller was found to stabilize the system, however the inequality of (15) was not found to hold.

Conclusions

This paper has presented a method for bringing separate structures into interaction without the need for modifying original controllers or the need for updating original controllers during the interaction. The OLM method has been seen to have the advantage of stability given an accurate knowledge of the open loop modes but has shown possible large amounts of computation in discovering the OLM modes. The CLM approach has an advantage in that only one eigenvalue analysis needs to be done to determine CLM modes but the stability inequality has been found to possibly be conservative.

References

1. Wie, B., A. Hu, and R. Singh, Journal of Guidance, Control, and Dynamics, 1990. Vol. 13(6): p. 993.

2. Doyle, J.C. and G. Stein, IEEE Transactions on Automatic Control, 1981, February. Vol. AC-26(1).

3. MacFarlane, A.G.J. and I. Postlethwaite, Int. J. of Control, 1977. Vol. 25(1): p. 81-127.

4. Michel, A.N., SIAM Journal of Control, 1974. Vol. 12(3): p. 554-579.

5. Balas, M.J., Journal of Mathematical Analysis and Applications, 1988. Vol. 133(2).

6. Johnson, C.D., in *Control and Dynamic Systems,* C.T. Leondes, Editor. 1976, Academic Press: N.Y. p. 387-490.

7. Chen, C.T., *Linear Systems Theory and Design.* 1984, N.Y.: Holt, Rinehart, and Winston.

8. Strang, G., *Linear Algebra and its Applications.* 1976, N.Y.: Academic Press.

9. Gooyabadi, A.A. and M.J. Balas. in *International Symposium and Exhibition on Optical Engineering and Photonics in Aerospace Sensing.* 1992. Orlando: Spie - The International Society for Optical Engineering.

10. Good, P.G. and M.J. Balas. in *International Symposium and Exhibition on Optical Engineering and Photonics in Aerospace Sensing.* 1992. Orlando: Spie - The International Society for Optical Engineering.

11. Davidson, R.A., Phd., University of Colorado, Boulder (1990).

12. Golub, G.H. and C.F. VanLoan, *Matrix Computations.* 2nd ed. 1989, Baltimore: Johns Hopkins University Press.

13. Balas, M.J., Journal of Interdisciplinary Modeling and Simulation, 1980. Vol. (January).

14. Wonham, W.M., *Linear Multivariable Control: a Geometric Approach.* 2nd ed. 1979, New York: Springer-Verlag.

15. Maybeck, P.S., *Stochastic Models, Estimation, and Control.* Mathematics in Science and Engineering, ed. R. Bellman. Vol. 3. 1982, New York: Academic Press.

Proceedings of the
American Control Conference
San Francisco, California • June 1993

Broadband Structural Control using Statistical Energy Analysis Concepts

Douglas G. MacMartin
Institute for Aerospace Research
National Research Council of Canada

Steven R. Hall
Space Engineering Research Center
Dept. of Aeronautics and Astronautics
Massachusetts Institute of Technology.

Abstract

An approach is described for designing broadband controllers for flexible structures with collocated sensors and actuators. The Statistical Energy Analysis assumptions of equipartition and incoherence, together with conservation of energy, are used to express the average value of a global $\mathcal{H}_2$ performance metric in terms of the power dissipation of the compensator. This power dissipation can be represented using a dereverberated model; an experimentally determined local structural model that ignores the effect of the reverberant field. Minimizing the resulting cost yields controllers with good performance which are guaranteed to be stabilizing. The approach is demonstrated experimentally on the M.I.T. Space Engineering Research Center interferometer testbed. This approach achieved a performance reduction that was approximately 30% greater than the constant gain "rate feedback" approach.

1 Introduction

Active control of lightly damped, modally dense structures is difficult due to the parametric uncertainty that is inherent in any model of such a structure. The first few modes of the structure can usually be modelled with sufficient accuracy for many state space control design techniques. However, it may be necessary to have some control authority over many more modes of the structure. This might be due to stringent performance requirements, a need to control relatively high frequency modes that couple into audible acoustic modes, or a requirement to add active damping to structural modes in the roll-off region of a high authority controller.

A multiple level approach to the structural control design process has been suggested [1]. For the low frequency region where a good model is available, a High Authority Controller (HAC) can be designed, using non-collocated, MIMO feedback loops. The HAC can be augmented with a higher bandwidth Low Authority Control (LAC) loop, which provides damping, and therefore robustness in the roll-off region of the HAC. The LAC also provides a direct performance benefit by reducing the peak magnitude of the transfer function, reduces the sensitivity of the model to uncertainty, and increases confidence in model reduction. The LAC must operate in a frequency region in which modal uncertainty is significant, and therefore must take advantage of the positivity between collocated and dual sensors and actuators in order to guarantee robustness. (Duality implies that the product of the sensed and actuated variable is proportional to the power flow into the structure, as in force and collocated velocity.)

Because of the number of modes in the bandwidth of these problems, and the uncertainty in their frequencies and mode shapes, it may be useful to model only some statistical aspects of the response, rather than attempting to model the detailed modal behaviour of the structures. One field of research that uses a stochastic approach to the modelling of flexible structures is Statistical Energy Analysis (SEA) [2,3]. In order to estimate the structural response using minimal information, SEA makes use of conservation of energy, incoherence, and equipartition. Incoherence requires that different modal amplitudes are uncorrelated, and equipartition requires that modes closely spaced in frequency have similar energy. These properties have been shown to hold for the average over uncertainty of the state space covariance [4]. SEA also makes use of an average, or dereverberated input mobility to make power flow predictions for uncertain structures.

Supported by Sandia National Laboratory under contract 69-4391 and by the M.I.T. Space Engineering Research Center under NASA grant NAGW-1335.

Presented at the 1993 American Control Conference, San Francisco, CA.

Previous research with a dereverberated model [5] and with related wave-based models [6] has shown that an impedance matching control design approach can yield greater damping than the rate feedback typically used for the LAC. Both $\mathcal{H}_2$ [6] and $\mathcal{H}_\infty$ [5] optimizations of the power flow have been used for control design using local models. The $\mathcal{H}_2$ approach does not guarantee closed-loop stability when implemented on the actual structure. The $\mathcal{H}_\infty$ approach [5] fixes this problem, but does not minimize the actual global $\mathcal{H}_2$ cost. The difficulty with both approaches is that they do not incorporate sufficient information about the structure into the control design process.

The structural modelling principles used in this paper are motivated by SEA. An experimentally determined dereverberated model is used to describe the local structural properties at a collocated and dual actuator/sensor pair. The equipartition and incoherence assumptions allow the expected value of the desired global quadratic cost to be expressed as a mixed $\mathcal{H}_2/\mathcal{H}_\infty$ cost functional of the local structural power flow properties. An $\mathcal{H}_\infty$ constraint similar to that in [5] guarantees that the optimal compensators will be positive real, and hence stabilizing for any uncertainty in the structure. The compensator that minimizes this cost can be obtained from a numerical optimization.

2 Local Modelling

Because the purpose of the LAC is to add damping in a frequency region in which the structural modes are uncertain, a detailed modal model is inappropriate. Furthermore, for sufficiently high uncertainty, the phase of any noncollocated transfer function is completely unknown. There is, however, some phase information in the transfer function between collocated and dual actuators and sensors. In order to develop an appropriate model for such a transfer function, consider an arbitrary structure as shown in Figure 1, from [5]. Incoming disturbances w_i propagate towards the actuator/sensor location, and are partially dissipated, and partially reflected back into the structure as outgoing disturbances w_o. In order to maximize dissipation, only the "local" structural dynamics that describe the relationship between the inputs u and w_i and the outputs y and w_o must be known. The details of how w_o propagates throughout the structure and returns as another incoming disturbance w_i are uncertain, and must be ignored.

The local structural dynamics can be modelled using the dereverberation approach from SEA [5]. The structural response due to the actuator can be divided into a *direct field* that is due to the local dynamics, and a *reverberant field* that is created by reflections from other parts of the structure. The dereverberated model includes only the effects of the direct field, and not the response created by reflections. Given the experimentally measured (reverberant) transfer function $G_{\exp}(s)$

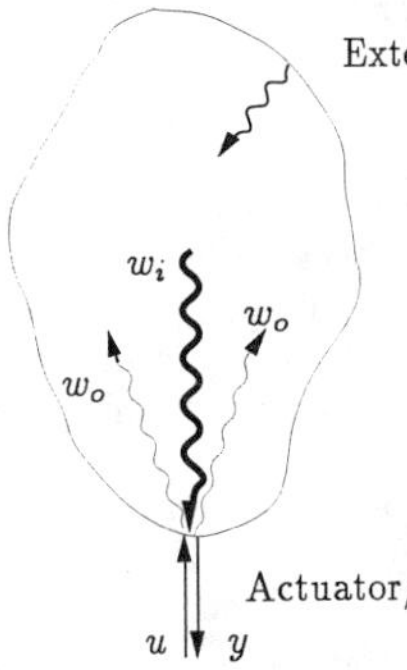

Figure 1: Arbitrary structure

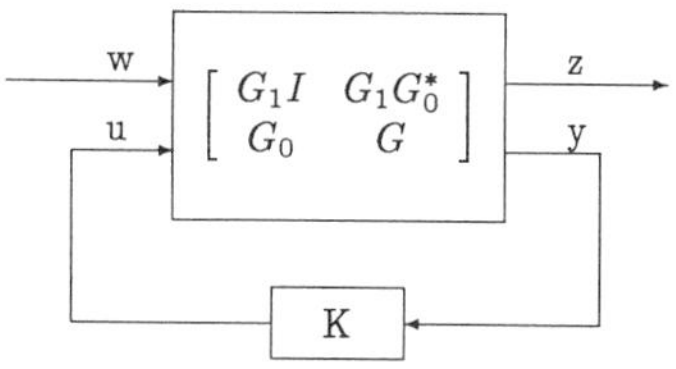

Figure 2: Power flow model.

between collocated and dual actuators and sensors, the dereverberated transfer function $G(s)$ can be obtained by taking an average of the logarithmic magnitude of the reverberant transfer function [3]. That is, $G(s)$ minimizes a cost functional of the form

$$J = \int_0^\infty (\log |G_{\text{exp}}| - \log |G|)^2 \, \mathrm{d}(\log \omega) \tag{1}$$

Since complex poles are associated with oscillation, or reverberation, the dereverberated transfer function can be described using only real poles and zeroes. Fitting the log magnitude of $G_{\text{exp}}(s)$ with $G(s)$ constrained to be of this form gives the desired transfer function. The gradients can be computed analytically, and the minimization performed using a quasi-Newton optimization. The number of poles used to describe the dereverberated transfer function can be increased until there is no significant decrease in the cost J. Usually, only a few poles are required. A typical comparison of the dereverberated and measured transfer functions is shown in Figure 6.

Given the dereverberated mobility $G(s)$ at the control input location, the compensator that dissipates the most power, frequency by frequency, can be shown [5] to be the impedance matching control law

$$u = \frac{1}{G^T(-s)} y \tag{2}$$

This compensator is non-causal (or unstable) unless $G(s)$ is a constant, and a stable, causal approximation must be found. The cost functional derived in the next section implicitly describes the relative importance of matching the magnitude and phase of the non-causal impedance match, and the relative importance of different frequency regions.

Note that this impedance matching solution is only appropriate if the dereverberated transfer function is used, rather than the full reverberant transfer function. The impedance match of the reverberant transfer function makes the structure *less* damped, so that more power is added to the structure by the disturbance, and hence more power is available to be dissipated. The reason for this is that the correct performance metric is not the just the power input to the structure from the control, but the total power input from both the control and the external disturbances. The reverberant impedance match dissipates more power than the dereverberated match, but may actually increase the *total* power input by increasing the power added by the disturbance [7]. However, if the structure is sufficiently uncertain, then on average, the control force will be uncorrelated with the motion at the disturbance location. The disturbance input power can then be ignored when determining the optimal control law. For this case, the control force will also be uncorrelated with the reverberant field at the control location, and hence only the dereverberated transfer function should be used.

Once the dereverberated driving point mobility G for the system has been obtained, the power properties of the driving point can be represented in state space for control design, as in [5]. Find G_0 stable and minimum phase and G_1 inner (or all-pass) such that $G_0 G_0^* = G + G^*$ and $G_1 G_0^*$ is stable. The resulting control problem can now be formulated as a standard two-input two-output problem, as shown in Figure 2. The inputs are the control u and the disturbance w, normalized so that $w^* w$ is the incoming power. The outputs are the sensor signal y and a cost variable z, defined so that $z^* z$ is the power reflected back into the structure as a function of frequency. This figure describes the two-input, two-output actuator/sensor location in Figure 1; w and z here correspond to the incoming and outgoing waves w_i and w_o.

The transfer function from w to z is given by the lower linear fractional transformation (LFT)

$$H(s) \triangleq \frac{z(s)}{w(s)} = G_1 I + G_1 G_0^* K (I - GK)^{-1} G_0 \tag{3}$$

Due to the normalization of the disturbance power w, $H^* H$ is the fraction of the incoming power reflected back into the structure from the control system, and $(I - H^* H)$ is the fraction dissipated by the controller. The transfer function H is the generalization of the reflection coefficient in a wave model to an arbitrary structure. In open loop, $H = I$ and $I - H^* H = 0$. The impedance matching control law in Eq'n (2) dissipates the maximum power possible, and yields $H = 0$ and $I - H^* H = I$.

3 Performance Metric

The local structural properties are described by the dereverberated mobility. The average value of a global $\mathcal{H}_2$ performance metric can be described in terms of this information by taking advantage of the properties of parametrically uncertain systems. In particular, the average covariance satisfies the SEA assumptions of equipartition and incoherence [4], as well as conservation of energy. From a wave perspective, equipartition and incoherence imply a "diffuse" field [2]; the waves coming from all directions are uncorrelated, and have equal intensities.

The global $\mathcal{H}_2$ cost can be written as the rms amplitude of a vector $z(t)$ that depends on the deflections and velocities of the structure. Using the modal incoherence assumption, the average mean-square value of z over both the uncertainty and the noise can be expressed as a sum over the average modal energies [2, p. 119]. For a modally dense structure, this sum can be approximated by an integral of the form

$$J = \left\langle z^T z \right\rangle \simeq \int_{-\infty}^{\infty} C(\omega) E(\omega) \, \mathrm{d}\omega \tag{4}$$

The function $E(\omega)$ is the average energy in the structure per unit bandwidth, and $C(\omega)$ describes the contribution of energy to the cost at each frequency. The approximation in Eq'n (4) is valid above the Schroeder cutoff frequency [8], where the modal spacing is equal to the half power bandwidth of each mode. With modal frequency uncertainty, the average system has a smoother transfer function, and hence a lower Schroeder cutoff frequency. For the limiting case that yields the dereverberated mobility as the average transfer function, Eq'n (4) holds at all frequencies.

The structural energy $E(\omega)$ can be related to the power dissipated by the controller, $\Pi_{\text{diss}}(\omega)$. Assuming a diffuse field, the power flowing towards the actuator is proportional to the total energy in the structure [2]. Using the results of Section 2 yields

$$\Pi_{\text{diss}}(\omega) = (I - H(j\omega)^* H(j\omega)) E(\omega) \tag{5}$$

The unknown Π_{diss} in this equation can be determined from conservation of energy:

$$\omega \eta E + \Pi_{\text{diss}} = \Pi_{\text{in}} \tag{6}$$

This equation is fundamental to SEA. The first term on the left hand side is the power dissipation within the structure, which is proportional to the average structural energy E. The loss factor η is often poorly known, but is sufficiently small for many applications that it can be neglected.

The power input from external disturbance sources $\Pi_{\text{in}}(\omega)$ can be estimated or measured reasonably well for most systems. If the disturbances are specified by the power spectral density $V(\omega)$ of a force input, then the power input can be determined by using the dereverberated mobility at the disturbance source, denoted G_d:

$$\Pi_{\text{in}} = (G_d + G_d^*) V \tag{7}$$

Eq'ns (5) and (6) can be solved for the structural energy

$$E(\omega) = \frac{\Pi_{\text{in}}(\omega)}{(\gamma^2 I - H^* H)} \tag{8}$$

where $\gamma = \sqrt{1 + \omega\eta}$. Eq'n (8) is valid provided that $\|H\|_\infty < \gamma$, so that the required inverse exists. Otherwise, the power added by the control exceeds that dissipated by the damping, and the cost is infinite. The

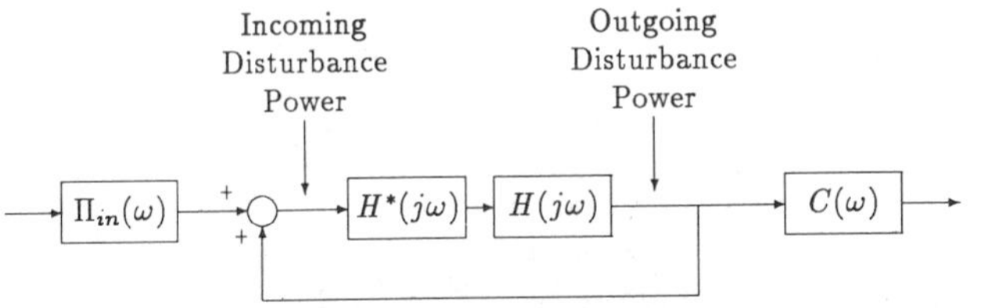

Figure 3: Block diagram representation of cost for $\gamma = 1$.

reflection coefficient H is a function of frequency, and is not indicated as such for brevity. The damping parameter γ is approximately unity for lightly damped systems, and is also, in general, a function of frequency.

From Eq'ns (4) and (8), the total cost is

$$J = \int_{-\infty}^{\infty} \frac{1}{\gamma^2} \frac{C(\omega)\Pi_{\text{in}}(\omega)}{(I - \gamma^{-2} H^* H)}\, d\omega \qquad (9)$$

The maximum possible power is dissipated by a non-causal compensator, which yields $H = 0$, and a closed loop cost of

$$J_{\min} = \int_{-\infty}^{\infty} \frac{1}{\gamma^2} C(\omega)\Pi_{\text{in}}(\omega)\, d\omega \qquad (10)$$

This expression provides an alternate approach for obtaining the weighting functions. Rather than separately computing the effect of the disturbance on the structural energy (given by $\Pi_{\text{in}}(\omega)$), and the effect of the energy on the cost (given by $C(\omega)$), the product of the weightings can be computed directly from the transfer function between the disturbance and the performance. The integrand of Eq'n (10) is the minimum achievable quadratic performance at each frequency, obtained if the structure is critically damped. The weighting function $W(j\omega)$ satisfying $W(j\omega)^* W(j\omega) = \gamma^{-2} C(\omega)\Pi_{in}(\omega)$ can therefore be computed from the experimentally measured open-loop transfer function from disturbance to performance using the same algorithm as the computation of the dereverberated transfer function.

Subtracting the minimum achievable cost in Eq'n (10) from the total cost does not change the minimization problem, but yields a better conditioned optimization problem, and elucidates certain features of the cost. Therefore, redefine the cost to be

$$J = \int_{-\infty}^{\infty} C(\omega)\Pi_{\text{in}}(\omega) \frac{\gamma^{-2} H^* H}{I - \gamma^{-2} H^* H}\, d\omega \qquad (11)$$

The compensator that minimizes this cost also minimizes the average (with respect to uncertainty) of the global $\mathcal{H}_2$ performance metric. The knowledge that the structure approximately conserves energy is preserved.

This cost can be compared with those of previous optimal impedance matching approaches. Given the spectrum Φ_{dd} of the incoming waves, the $\mathcal{H}_2$ cost of Miller *et al.* [6] is

$$J_{\mathcal{H}_2} = \int_{-\infty}^{\infty} \text{tr}\left\{\Phi_{dd}(\omega) H^* H\right\} d\omega \qquad (12)$$

The unweighted $\mathcal{H}_\infty$ cost of MacMartin and Hall [5] is $J_{\mathcal{H}_\infty} = \|H\|_\infty$.

The integrand of the cost in Eq'n (11) can be represented in block diagram form as shown in Figure 3. The $\mathcal{H}_2$ minimization of power flow in Eq'n (12) is equivalent to the block diagram without the feedback loop. This feedback accounts for the fact that any energy imparted to the structure at some frequency will return to the actuator location eventually. The disturbance power that reaches the actuator is the sum of the external disturbance power, and the power in the outgoing disturbances.

With reference to Figure 1, this result corresponds to ignoring the details of how the outgoing disturbance w_o propagates and returns as another incoming disturbance w_i, but retaining the fact that it does return. The phase of the returning disturbance is unknown, but for light damping, the energy is the same as that in w_o. All of the uncertainty in the structure has therefore been represented in terms of a single uncertainty with unit magnitude and unknown phase, which leads to an $\mathcal{H}_2/\mathcal{H}_\infty$ interpretation of the cost in Eq'n (11). As shown in [9], this cost functional is strongly related to the $\mathcal{H}_2/\mathcal{H}_\infty$ approach

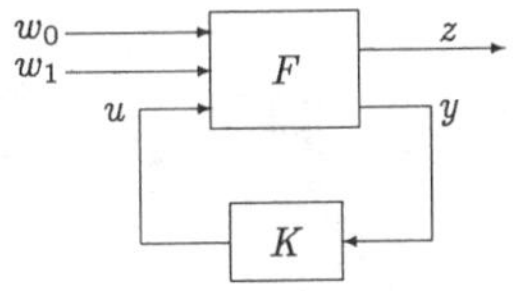

Figure 4: Feedback System

taken in [10], and can be interpreted as a Stackelberg non-zero sum dynamic differential game. With unity weightings, the cost can also be interpreted as the average $\mathcal{H}_2$ cost of a system with uncertainty of known magnitude but unknown phase [7].

Both $\Pi_{\text{in}}(\omega)$ and $C(\omega)$ in Eq'n (11) are purely real functions of frequency, and can thus be factored as $\Pi_{\text{in}}(\omega) = \Pi_+^* \Pi_+$ and $C(\omega) = C_+^* C_+$, where $\Pi_+(j\omega)$ and $C_+(j\omega)$ are both stable. Define $H_0 = \sqrt{2\pi}\gamma^{-2} C_+ H \Pi_+$, $H_1 = H$, and $\hat{H}(s) = [H_0(s)\ H_1(s)]$. Then the combined $\mathcal{H}_2/\mathcal{H}_\infty$ cost functional considered here can be defined as

$$L(\hat{H}, \gamma) \triangleq \frac{1}{2\pi} \int_{-\infty}^{\infty} \text{tr}\left\{(I - \gamma^{-2} H_1 H_1^*)^{-1} H_0 H_0^*\right\} d\omega \qquad (13)$$

Further properties on this cost functional can be found in [9].

4 Optimization of Performance

The compensator that minimizes $L(\hat{H}, \gamma)$ will guarantee that $\|H_1\|_\infty < \gamma$, so that between the controller and the internal dissipation, power is dissipated at all frequencies, and thus the closed loop system is stable. A numerical optimization approach for obtaining the optimal compensator has been used, since there is no known closed-form solution. This approach is based on a state space evaluation of the cost, and the derivatives of this cost with respect to the parameters of a fixed-order compensator.

Given the state space representation of the compensator and the dereverberated mobility, the state space representation of H can be obtained from the LFT in Eq'n (3). The state space representation of $\hat{H}(s) = [C_+ H \Pi_+\ H]$ can be obtained from those of H and the weightings $C(\omega)$ and $\Pi_{\text{in}}(\omega)$. The cost can then be evaluated based on the following theorem from [7,9]. Consider a state space representation for $\hat{H} = [H_0\ H_1]$:

$$\hat{H}(s) = C(sI - A)^{-1} [B_0\ B_1] + [0\ D] \qquad (14)$$

and define $Z = (I - \gamma^{-2} D D^T)^{-1}$, $W = (I - \gamma^{-2} D^T D)^{-1}$, and $\bar{A} = A + \gamma^{-2} B_1 D^T Z C$. If a non-zero term D_0 were included in Eq'n (14), then $H_0 \notin \mathcal{H}_2$ and hence $L(\hat{H}, \gamma)$ would not exist.

Theorem 1 *Let $\hat{H} = [H_0\ H_1]$ be given by Eq'n (14), Z, W and $\bar{A}$ given as above, $\gamma \in \mathbb{R}$, and $\|H_1\|_\infty < \gamma$. Then $L(\hat{H}, \gamma) = \text{tr}\left\{C^T Z C Q\right\}$ where Y, Q satisfy $(\bar{A} + Y C^T Z C)$ stable and*

$$\bar{A} Y + Y \bar{A}^T + Y C^T Z C Y + \gamma^{-2} B_1 W B_1^T = 0 \qquad (15)$$

$$(\bar{A} + Y C^T Z C) Q + Q(\bar{A} + Y C^T Z C)^T + B_0 B_0^T = 0 \qquad (16)$$

Proof: See [7,11]. □

The compensator K of a given fixed order that minimizes this cost can be found using numerical optimization. The system can be described by the block diagram in Figure 4. The inputs to the plant F are the disturbances corresponding to H_0 and H_1, and the control u, and the outputs are the performance, and the sensed output y.

The necessary conditions that an optimal compensator must satisfy can be obtained by appending the constraint equations (15) and (16) to the cost using matrix Lagrange multipliers X and P, and differentiating the augmented cost with respect to X, Y, P, Q, and the free parameters of the compensator system matrix. Making the appropriate definitions in comparing the state space representation of the closed loop system $\hat{H}_{cl}$ and Eq'n (14), Y satisfies the Riccati equation (15), Q satisfies the Lyapunov equation (16), P satisfies the dual Lyapunov equation

$$P(\bar{A} + Y C^T Z C) + (\bar{A} + Y C^T Z C)^T P + C^T Z C = 0 \qquad (17)$$

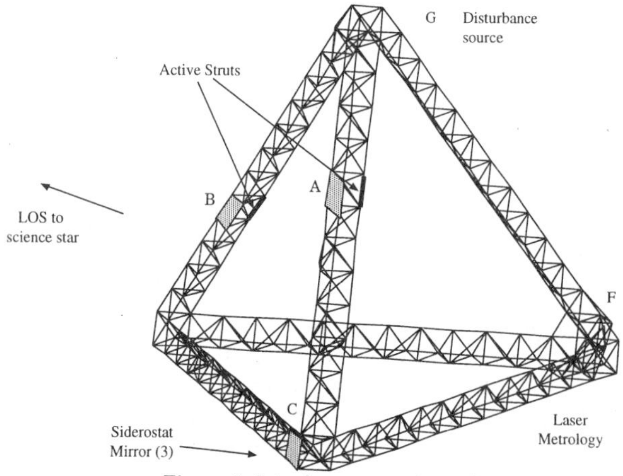

Figure 5: Interferometer schematic

and X satisfies

$$X(\bar{A}+YC^TZC)+(\bar{A}+YC^TZC)^TX+PQC^TZC+C^TZCQP=0 \quad (18)$$

The gradients of the augmented cost with respect to the compensator parameters can also be computed [7, 11] and used as the basis of a quasi-Newton numerical optimization. Any positive real compensator is guaranteed to stabilize the structure and hence satisfy the $\mathcal{H}_\infty$-norm constraint. However, since the optimization problem is non-convex, local minima are likely to exist, and thus an initial guess which is close to the expected optimum is desirable. In practice, the $\mathcal{H}_\infty$ impedance matching solutions of [5] result in excellent convergence behaviour. It appears likely that for this problem, the optimal compensator with no constraint on the compensator state dimension does not have finite order. In practise, the compensator order can be increased until there is no significant decrease in the cost.

5 Experimental Demonstration

The approach described in the previous sections was demonstrated on the multi-point alignment testbed in the Space Engineering Research Center laboratory at M.I.T. This testbed and the associated research program are intended to evaluate the benefits of the application of controlled structures technology to a space-based astronomical interferometer requiring large baselines and precision alignment. A detailed description of the testbed, its scientific motivation, performance metric, disturbances, sensors, and actuators can be found in [12]. The following section gives a brief synopsis of the relevant details.

5.1 Interferometer Testbed Description

The interferometer testbed consists of six 3.5 meter long triangular truss legs, which form a tetrahedron, as shown schematically in Figure 5 (from [12].) Three mock siderostats, labeled A, B, and C, are located on three legs of the truss. Light from the science star would be collected by these siderostats and combined at the vertex labeled F, out of the plane of the three siderostats. A laser is mounted at this vertex in order to provide an optical measurement of the pathlengths between this vertex and each of the three siderostat locations. The difference between any two of these pathlengths will be denoted A–B, B–C, and C–A.

The full-scale interferometer determines information about the science star by measuring the phase difference between the light waves from different siderostats. On the testbed, the performance goal is to maintain each of the three possible differential pathlength (DPL) measurements to below 50 nm rms displacement between 10 and 500 Hz. The disturbance environment is created by three piezoelectric disturbance sources mounted at the vertex labeled G in Figure 5. The force spectrum for these actuators is flat at low frequencies, with a two-pole roll-off at 70 Hz. The contribution to the open-loop DPL in different frequency regimes is shown in Figure 10. On average, for the three different differential pathlengths, over 85% of the mean-square displacement occurs above 80 Hz. The current finite element model of the structure does not accurately predict the modal frequencies or mode shapes above 80 Hz. Thus any active control for this frequency region must either be based on a measurement model, or use an approach that does not rely on precise knowledge of the modal frequencies.

Because a low authority controller relies on phase stabilization, the compensator must remain positive real at frequencies much higher than that at which performance is desired. Thus, without a very high sample rate, the time delay of a digital computer is unacceptable. The LAC is instead implemented using analog circuits. Active strut actuators were used, which can replace any single strut on the interferometer truss, giving the control designer a great deal of flexibility in placement. Each active strut contains a pre-loaded piezoceramic stack and a load cell. Two active struts were sufficient to demonstrate the effectiveness of the control design techniques, although more would be necessary to demonstrate substantial performance improvements. The two low authority control laws can be designed and implemented independently.

Since the goal of the LAC is to add active damping, the active approach can also be compared with a passive damping approach. A high loss factor viscous "D-strut" was used [13], which can be interchanged with any strut on the structure. Each strut has a stiffness comparable to the dynamic stiffness of the structure at 50 Hz, and a peak loss factor between $\eta = 1$ and $\eta = 1.5$ which occurs between 55 and 70 Hz. These struts are designed to add significant damping in a frequency range that is relatively narrow compared to the damping provided by a viscoelastic treatment. This frequency distribution for the damping is consistent with the goals of low authority control. The damping requirements of the LAC are broadband relative to those of a HAC, in the sense that authority is desired over a large number of modes. However, the requirements on the LAC are often narrowband relative to the damping provided by constant gain (or rate) feedback.

5.2 Control Design

In order to get sufficient control authority over those modes that strongly influence the performance metric, the active struts were placed close to two of the siderostat plates, denoted A and B in Figure 5. Placement schemes based on maximum residue locations of the finite element model are inconsistent with the assumptions of poor modal information that require low authority control, since much of the benefit of LAC is provided in a frequency region above that in which the finite element model is valid. Using engineering intuition, therefore, is essential. Placing the struts in the truss longerons opposite the siderostat plates A and B gives significant authority over the motion of these plates.

The load cell in the active strut can be considered to be collocated with the actuator, since the frequency at which non-collocation becomes important is much higher than required. However, for impedance matching control, the actuated and sensed variable should also be dual, in the sense that their product should be the power flow into the structure. In the interferometer testbed, the active strut is significantly stiffer than the dynamic stiffness of the rest of the structure in the frequency range of interest, and therefore commands displacement. Since the actuator commands displacement, it also effectively commands the extension rate of the strut. The dual variable to extension rate is force, and thus the impedance matching solution requires that the extension rate and force be related through a compensator. Equivalently, the transfer function between the extension and the integral of force can be constrained.

In order to design impedance matching compensators between the integral of force and the stack voltage, the dereverberated driving point transfer function must be identified. As noted in Section 2, this transfer function can be determined by averaging the log magnitude of the experimental transfer function. For both of the active strut transfer functions, three poles were adequate to describe the dereverberated transfer function in the frequency range of interest. The fitted and measured transfer functions are plotted for the active strut at plate B in Figure 6. The measured transfer functions at A and B are positive real up to 622 Hz, and are within 10° of positivity up to 1500 Hz, where the dynamics of the actuator and sensor, or the non-collocation becomes important. The plotted transfer function also assumes perfect integration. In reality, the low frequency roll-off of the integrator determines a low frequency limit to positivity as well. The load cell integrator used had a corner frequency of $\omega_i = 11.25$ Hz and a damping of $\zeta_i = .7071$.

Once the dereverberated transfer function has been identified, various compensators can be designed. The compensator that dissipates

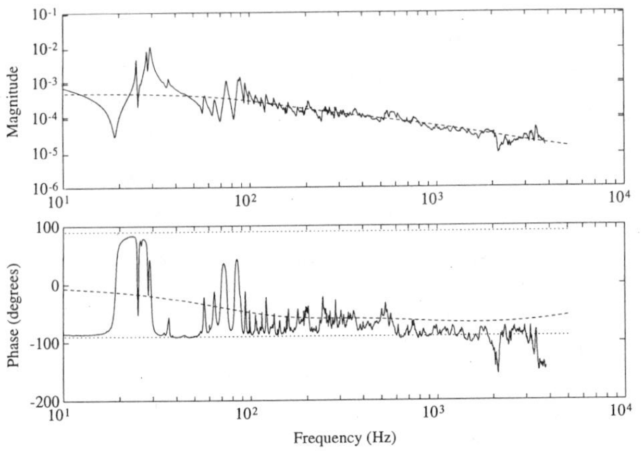

Figure 6: Measured (solid) and dereverberated (dashed) transfer function between active strut voltage and integrated force near plate B. (In Volts/Volt.)

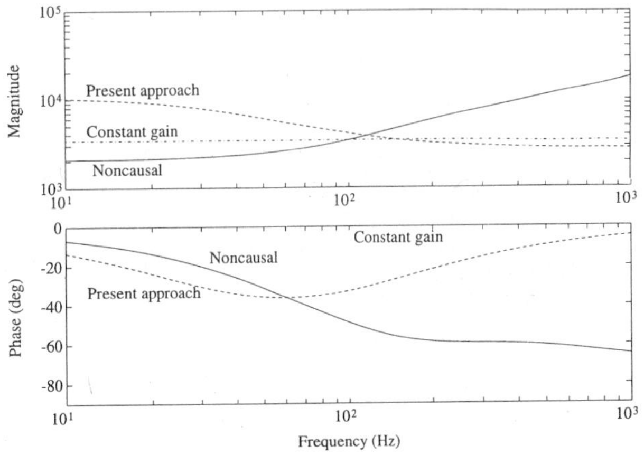

Figure 8: Compensators for active strut at plate B. Non-causal optimum (solid), constant gain solution (dash-dot), and present approach (dashed).

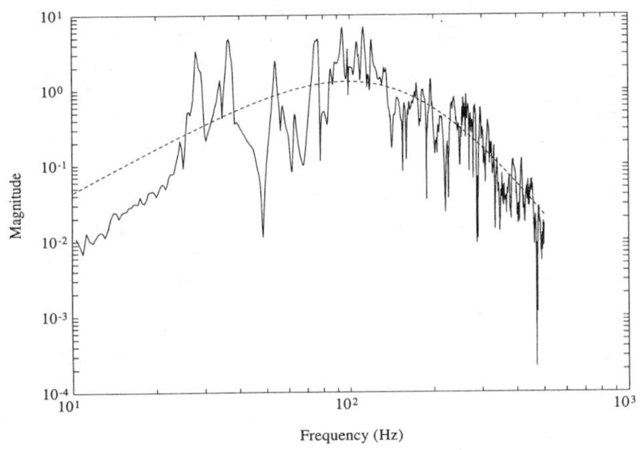

Figure 7: Weighting function used in control design (dashed), and transfer function from disturbance to pathlength BF (solid).

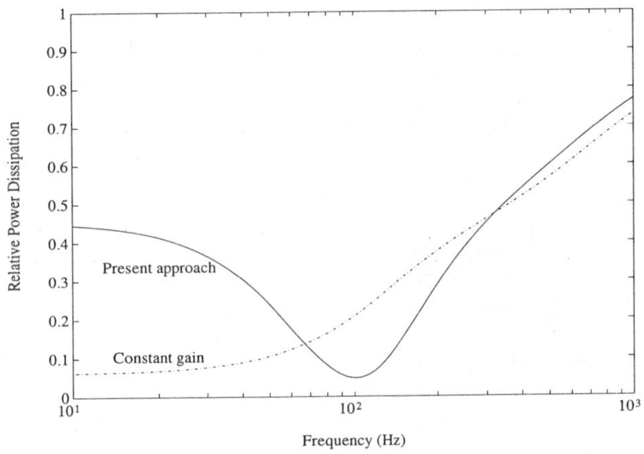

Figure 9: Relative power dissipation for compensators at plate B. Constant gain solution (dash-dot), and present approach (solid).

the maximum power from a structure is the impedance match given by Eq'n (2). Since both dereverberated transfer functions are frequency dependent, this optimization yields a non-causal transfer function, which cannot be implemented, and must be approximated.

The simplest approximation that can be made is to constrain the compensator to be a constant gain. The optimal gain at a given frequency ω_0 is the magnitude of the non-causal solution at that frequency, so

$$K_C = \frac{1}{|G(j\omega_0)|} \tag{19}$$

This is the "rate feedback" solution. The constant gain solution only corresponds to feedback of rate for a force actuator. For any other actuator, constant gain impedance matching generalizes the concept of rate feedback.

Now consider the design of compensators using the technique developed herein. The frequency distribution of the active damping requirements are dictated by the disturbance input power and the performance, as described in Section 3. The product $C(\omega)\Pi_{in}(\omega)$ can be determined from the experimentally measured transfer function from disturbance to performance. The resulting seven pole weighting function $W(j\omega)$ obtained by fitting the transfer function between the disturbance and the absolute pathlength BF with real poles and zeroes is shown in Figure 7, along with the measured transfer function. The filter that shapes the spectrum of the disturbance is included in the transfer function. The pathlength BF was chosen because the primary influence on the performance due to the active strut at plate B will be through minimizing this absolute pathlength. The central frequency ω_0 in the constant gain feedback, Eq'n (19), was chosen to be 100 Hz, where the weighting function is a maximum.

For both strut locations, the optimal compensators corresponding to the chosen weighting required only a single pole-zero pair. Increasing the compensator order further did not appreciably change the cost. The resulting compensators are shown in Figure 8 for the strut at siderostat plate B. Those for the active strut at plate A are similar. Greater damping is obtained by the frequency dependent compensators by more closely matching both the magnitude and phase of the non-causal optimum at the centre frequency of the weighting function. The closed-loop power reflection coefficient H for each of the compensators is plotted in Figure 9. A value of unity indicates that all of the incoming power is being reflected (no dissipation), while a value of zero indicates the complete dissipation attained by the non-causal impedance match at that frequency. While the constant gain compensator was chosen to maximize dissipation at 100 Hz, it achieves its best damping at lower frequencies due to the fact that the experimentally determined dereverberated impedance is almost constant at low frequencies, and thus any constant gain feedback has the correct phase in this frequency region.

5.3 Results

The performance is composed of the rms differential pathlength error for the three different combinations of pathlengths. This data is shown in Table 1 for several different cases. For pathlength B–C, Figure 10 shows the corresponding relative improvement over the baseline performance for each of several frequency regions.

The baseline testbed configuration has no active or passive damping

	rms DPL in nm			% Change		
	A–B	B–C	C–A	A–B	B–C	C–A
Baseline truss	495	417	602	0	0	0
With active struts	492	424	594	−0.7	1.8	−1.2
With D-struts	469	403	564	−5.4	−3.3	−6.2
Constant Gain	443	378	557	−10.5	−9.4	−7.4
Present approach	444	355	549	−10.4	−14.9	−8.8

Table 1: Achieved performance, and relative change with respect to baseline, for 10–500 Hz

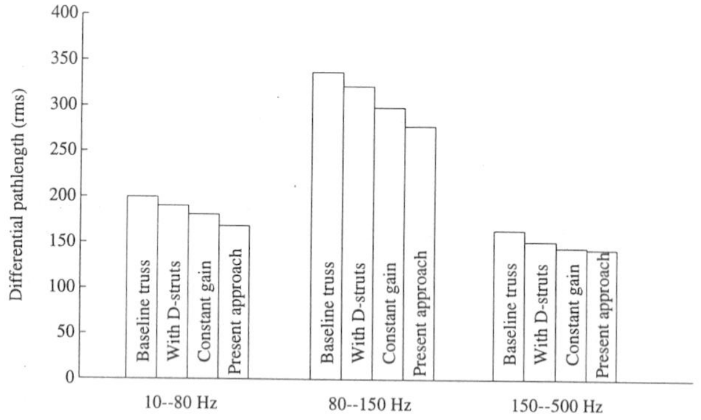

Figure 10: Differential pathlength error B–C, for baseline, with two D-struts, with constant gain feedback, and using the present approach. (rms in nm).

struts in place. Adding the active struts to the structure with no control results in a change in the performance metric due to the different stiffness and damping characteristics of the active strut as compared to a nominal strut. The performance with each active strut replaced by a D-strut is included to illustrate the possible improvement in damping achieved per strut by an active technique over a passive technique. Active control using the optimization approach of this paper yields about a 30% increase in the performance achieved per strut over the constant gain solution.

As predicted by the power flow analysis in Figure 9, the approach of this paper achieves greater damping in the frequency region around 100 Hz than the constant gain feedback. Also note that in this experiment, only 2 of the 641 struts in the structure were actively damped. The purpose of the experiment was not to demonstrate the performance achievable by LAC, but rather to compare alternative LAC techniques. A larger number of active struts would be required to achieve substantial performance improvements.

The data presented above gives the improvement in performance obtained by using low authority control alone. However, another benefit of implementing a low authority controller is that it adds damping in the roll-off region of a high authority control loop. As a result, higher performance HAC controllers can be implemented. Therefore, the performance improvement that can be attributed to low authority control also includes the difference between the achievable performance of a high authority controller before and after implementation of the LAC.

Note that if broadband damping is required, a passive damping scheme might incur a smaller weight penalty than an active approach. However, most applications will have relatively narrowband requirements on the added damping. This is the case for the performance specifications of the interferometer problem, or for the requirement of adding damping in the roll-off region of a high authority controller. In these cases, an active approach has advantages over passive damping augmentation. This is due to the greater peak damping capability of an active approach, together with its flexibility in tuning the target frequency, and the potential elimination of any weight penalty by using the same hardware as the HAC.

6 Conclusions

A structural modelling approach based on the modelling principles of Statistical Energy Analysis can be used to represent the average value of a global mean-square performance metric in terms of only local structural information. The local information is given by the experimentally determined dereverberated transfer function. The approach yields a mixed $\mathcal{H}_2/\mathcal{H}_\infty$ optimization problem, which can be solved numerically. The resulting optimal compensators guarantee closed loop stability.

The approach was demonstrated experimentally on a complex laboratory structure, and approximately 30% better performance reduction was obtained over the usual "rate feedback," or constant gain approach. The active approach achieved greater performance reduction than a passive approach due to a higher peak damping capability, and the ability to tune the controller to target the most important frequency region.

Acknowledgements

The comments and suggestions of Dr. Dennis Bernstein, Dr. Andreas von Flotow, and Dr. David Miller are much appreciated, as is the assistance of Dina Pery and the rest of the SERC interferometer team.

References

[1] Aubrun, J.-N., "Theory of the Control of Structures by Low-Authority Controllers," *AIAA J. of Guid. and Control*, Vol. 3, Sept–Oct 1980, pp. 444–451.

[2] Hodges, C. H. and Woodhouse, J., "Theories of Noise and Vibration Transmission in Complex Structures," *Reports on Progress in Physics*, Vol. 49, 1986, pp. 107–170.

[3] Lyon, R., *Statistical Energy Analysis of Dynamical Systems: Theory and Applications*, Cambridge MA: The MIT Press, 1975.

[4] Hall, S. R., MacMartin, D. G., and Bernstein, D. S., "Covariance Averaging in the Analysis of Uncertain Systems," To appear, *IEEE Trans. Auto. Control*, 1993.

[5] MacMartin, D. G. and Hall, S. R., "Control of Uncertain Structures using an $\mathcal{H}_\infty$ Power Flow Approach," *AIAA J. of Guid., Control, and Dyn.*, Vol. 14, May–June 1991, pp. 521–530.

[6] Miller, D. W., Hall, S. R., and von Flotow, A. H., "Optimal Control of Power Flow at Structural Junctions," *J. of Sound and Vibration*, Vol. 140, No. 3, 1990, pp. 475–497.

[7] MacMartin, D. G., *A Stochastic Approach to Broadband Control of Parametrically Uncertain Structures*, Ph.D. thesis, Dept. of Aero. and Astro., M.I.T., Cambridge, MA, June 1992.

[8] Nelson, P. A., Curtis, A. R. D., Elliot, S. J., and Bullmore, A. J., "The Active Minimization of Harmonic Enclosed Sound Fields, Part I: Theory," *J. of Sound and Vibration*, Vol. 117, No. 1, 1987, pp. 1–13.

[9] MacMartin, D. G., Hall, S. R., and Mustafa, D., "On a Cost Functional for $\mathcal{H}_2/\mathcal{H}_\infty$ Minimization," *Proc., IEEE Conf. on Decision and Control*, Honolulu, HI, Dec. 1990, pp. 1010–1012.

[10] Zhou, K., Doyle, J., Glover, K., and Bodenheimer, B., "Mixed $\mathcal{H}_2$ and $\mathcal{H}_\infty$ Control," *Proc., Am. Control Conf.*, San Diego, CA, May 1990, pp. 2502–2507.

[11] MacMartin, D. G. and Hall, S. R., "Broadband Control of Flexible Structures using Statistical Energy Analysis Concepts," Submitted to *AIAA J. of Guid., Control and Dyn.*, 1993.

[12] Blackwood, G. H., Jacques, R. N., and Miller, D. W., "The MIT Multipoint Alignment Testbed: Technology Development for Optical Interferometry," *Proc., SPIE Conf. on Active and Adaptive Optical Systems*, San Diego, CA, July 1991.

[13] Anderson, E. H., Blackwood, G. H., and How, J. P., "Passive Damping in the MIT SERC Controlled Structures Testbed," *Proc., International Symposium on Active Materials and Adaptive Structures*, Alexandria, VA, Nov. 1991.

Proceedings of the
American Control Conference
San Francisco, California • June 1993

Balanced LQG Compensator for Flexible Structures

Wodek Gawronski

Jet Propulsion Laboratory, California Institute of Technology, Pasadena, CA 91109

Abstract

The analysis of open-loop balanced flexible structures has been extended for closed-loop structures. LQG compensator gains (i.e., the gains of a controller and of an estimator) are obtained from the solutions of the controller Riccati equation (CARE) and the estimator Riccati equation (FARE). For the balanced compensator the solutions of CARE and FARE are equal and diagonal. Thus, a balanced LQG compensator puts the same effort into control and estimation of the system. An approximate balanced LQG compensator for flexible structures is determined in this paper. Its properties allow one to obtain a reduced-order compensator, which preserves the stability and performance of the full-order compensator. The performance of an LQG compensator depends on the weights of the quadratic performance index and on the variance of the estimator noise. The relationships between weights/variances and characteristic values of the system as well as between weights/variances and plant/estimator pole location are derived in this paper. Thus the weights can be determined in advance to meet the requirements of a closed-loop system.

1. Introduction

Control issues for flexible structures have gained increasing attention, especially in space applications. The growing interest reflects recent efforts to maintain high precision positioning of ever lighter and more flexible structures. This paper contributes to this effort by developing a balanced LQG compensator for flexible structures. There have been many investigations into analysis and design of LQG compensators, and a good insight into the variety of approaches can be obtained from Kwakernaak and Sivan (1972), Maciejowski (1989), Anderson and Moore (1990), and Furuta and Sano (1988). The LQG design procedures yield an optimal compensator. However, an optimal solution is not necessarily a reasonable one, since it is dependent on the weights of the quadratic performance index and on the variance of the estimator noise. Thus, the index weight and filter covariance need to be pre-determined in order to obtain a reasonable performance. The relationships between weights/variances and characteristic values of the system, as well as between weights/variances and plant/estimator pole location, are derived in this paper, making possible the design of an optimal compensator that satisfies the requirements.

The controller and estimator gains of an LQG compensator are obtained from the solutions of the controller Riccati equation (CARE) and the estimator Riccati equation (FARE). In the approach presented, the equal and diagonal solution of CARE and FARE is sought. The equal and diagonal solution of CARE and FARE is the balanced LQG solution, and its diagonal entries are the characteristic values of the system (Jonckheere and Silverman, 1983). Jonckheere and Silverman show for a specific case that the balanced LQG solution exists. In this paper the transformation to the balanced LQG representation is derived for the general case. It is also shown that flexible structures in a Moore balanced representation (Moore, 1981; Gawronski and Juang, 1990; Gawronski and Williams, 1991) are approximately LQG balanced. In the LQG balanced representation a balanced performance is obtained for a controller and an estimator. Thus the action of a highly efficient controller is not deteriorated by poor estimator accuracy, nor on the other hand is it overdetermined by an overperforming estimator.

The LQG balanced representation is used for compensator reduction. The pole mobility index characterizes the importance of the closed-loop component of the compensator. The states with small mobility index are truncated, leaving a closed-loop system with a stable reduced compensator.

2. LQG Compensator

In this paper a flexible structure is defined as a controllable and observable linear system with distinct complex conjugate pairs of poles (N poles, N is even), and with small and negative real parts of the poles. In other words, it is a linear system with vibrational properties. In the Moore balanced coordinates it consists of $n=N/2$ components (Gawronski and Juang, 1990; Gawronski and Williams, 1991, and each component consists of two states.

Let (A,B,C) be a state-space triple of a flexible structure. Its controllability and observability grammians W_c and W_o are positive-definite and satisfy the Lyapunov equations

$$AW_c+W_cA^T+BB^T=0, \qquad A^TW_o+W_oA+CC^T=0 \tag{1}$$

The system representation is balanced in the sense of Moore (c.f., Moore, 1981) if its controllability and observability grammians are diagonal and equal

$$W_c=W_o=\Gamma^2, \quad \Gamma=diag(\gamma_1,\dots,\gamma_N), \quad i=1,\dots,N \tag{2}$$

where $\gamma_i>0$ is the ith Hankel singular value of the system.

Consider a flexible structure with an LQG compensator as in Fig.1. The noises v and w are uncorrelated, where v is the process noise with intensity V, and w is measurement noise with intensity W

$$V=E(vv^T), \ W=E(ww^T), \ E(vw^T)=0, \ E(v)=0, \ E(w)=0 \tag{3}$$

where $E(.)$ is an expectation operator. It is assumed that $W=I$ without loss of generality. The task is to determine the controller gain (K_p) and estimator gain (K_e) such that the performance index J

$$J^2=E\left(\int_0^\infty (x^TQx+u^TRu)dt\right) \tag{4}$$

is minimal, where R is a positive definite input weight matrix, and Q a positive semi-definite state weight matrix. It is assumed $R=I$ without loss of generality.

The minimum of J is obtained for the feedback $u=-K_px$, where the gain matrix

$$K_p=B^TS, \tag{5}$$

is obtained from the solution S of the controller Riccati equation (CARE) (Kwakernaak and Sivan, 1972)

$$A^TS+SA-SBB^TS+Q=0 \tag{6}$$

The optimal estimator gain is given by

$$K_e=PC^T, \tag{7}$$

where P is the solution of the estimator Riccati equation (FARE)

$$AP+PA^T-PC^TCP+V=0. \tag{8}$$

3. Balanced LQG Compensator

The balancing of CARE and FARE equations is considered. Jonckheere and Silverman (1983), and Opdenacker and Jonckheere (1985) have shown that a balanced solution for CARE and FARE equations exists in case of $Q=C^TC$ and $V=BB^T$. Namely, there exists a diagonal positive definite $M=diag(\mu_i)$, $i=1,...,n$, $\mu_i>0$, such that

$$S=P=M \tag{9}$$

A state-space representation with the condition (9) satisfied is called an LQG balanced representation, and μ_i, $i=1,...,n$ are the characteristic values of (A,B,C).

Consider the transformation T of the state x such that $x=T\bar{x}$, then $\bar{A}=T^{-1}AT$, $\bar{B}=T^{-1}B$, $\bar{C}=CT$; in the new coordinates

$$\bar{S}_c=T^TS_cT, \quad \bar{Q}_c=T^TQ_cT, \quad \bar{S}_f=T^{-1}S_fT^{-T}, \quad \bar{Q}_f=T^{-1}Q_fT^{-T} \tag{10}$$

The solution of CARE and FARE is LQG balanced if

$$S_c=S_f=M, \; M=diag(\mu_1,\mu_2,...,\mu_n), \; \mu_1\geq\mu_2\geq...\geq\mu_n>0 \tag{11}$$

There exists a transformation T, such that CARE and FARE are balanced.

Result 1. The transformation T to the LQG balanced representation is obtained as follows. Decompose S_c and S_f

$$S_c=P_c^TP_c, \quad S_f=P_fP_f^T \tag{12}$$

and form a matrix H

$$H=P_cP_f \tag{13}$$

Find the singular value decomposition of H

$$H=VMU^T \tag{14}$$

then

$$T=P_fUM^{-1/2}=P_c^{-1}VM^{1/2}, \quad T^{-1}=M^{-1/2}V^TP_c=M^{1/2}U^TP_f^{-1} \tag{15}$$

The introduction of the above transformation T to (10) shows that (11) is satisfied.

Now consider weighting matrices of special form, and the corresponding balanced solution.

Result 2. For a fully controllable system, and the weights Q_c and Q_f as follows

$$Q_c=W_c^{-1}B(I+R_c^{-1})B^TW_c^{-1}, \quad Q_f=W_o^{-1}C^T(I+R_f^{-1})CW_o^{-1} \tag{16}$$

one obtains CARE and FARE solutions as follows

$$S_c=W_c^{-1}, \quad S_f=W_o^{-1} \tag{17}$$

Proof. Introduction of Eqs.(16) and (17) to CARE gives

$$A^TS_c+S_cA+S_cBB^TS_c=0 \tag{18}$$

which is the Lyapunov equation (1) for $S_c=W_c^{-1}$. Similar proof can be shown for the FARE solution. □

The weights as in Eq.(16) are for collocated sensors and actuators, and penalize each open-loop balanced state reciprocally to its degree of controllability and observability, trying to make each state of plant and estimator equally influenced by the feedback.

Corollary 1. In the Moore balanced representation $W_c=W_o=\Gamma^2$, thus for weights Q_c, Q_f as in Eq.(16) one obtains an LQG balanced system, with $M=\Gamma^{-2}$.

The matrix Π

$$\Pi=\Gamma_o^2\Gamma_c^{-2}=diag(\pi_i)=diag(\gamma_{oi}^2/\gamma_{ci}^2) \tag{19}$$

is the ratio of open- and closed-loop Hankel singular values, or the ratio of open- and closed-loop state variances excited by the white noise input. Thus Π represents the closed-loop performance. For weights as in Result 2, and a system in the Moore balanced coordinates one obtains

Corollary 2. In the Moore balanced representation, for weights as in (16)

$$\Pi=3I \tag{20}$$

Proof. The Lyapunov equation for the closed-loop controllability grammian W_c is as follows

$$(A-BB^TS_c)W_c+W_c(A^T-S_cBB^T)+BB^T=0 \tag{21a}$$

According to (17) $S_c=\Gamma_o^{-2}$, and introducing $W_c=\Gamma_o^2/3$ to (21a), one obtains

$$A\Gamma_o^2+\Gamma_o^2A^T+BB^T=0 \tag{21b}$$

which shows that $W_c=\Gamma_o^2/3$ is a solution of (21a), and consequently that $\Pi=3I$. □

Result 3. For a fully controllable system, and the weights Q_c and Q_f as follows

$$Q_c=C^TC+W_oBR_c^{-1}B^TW_o, \quad Q_f=BB^T+W_cC^TR_f^{-1}CW_c \tag{22}$$

one obtains CARE and FARE solutions as follows

$$S_c=W_o, \quad S_f=W_c \tag{23}$$

Proof. By introduction of (22) to CARE and FARE equations.

Corollary 3. In the Moore balanced representation $W_c=W_o=\Gamma^2$, thus for weights Q_c, Q_f as in Eq.(22) one obtains an LQG balanced system, with $M=\Gamma^2$.

Define $C_o^T=[C^T \; W_oBR_c^{-1/2}]$, $B_o=[B \; W_cC^TR_f^{-1/2}]$, then the LQG closed-loop system is interpreted as a system with unitary weights and with the auxiliary inputs and outputs as defined by matrices B_o, C_o. For collocated sensors and actuators, and for $R_c=R_f=I$, one obtains $C_o^T=B_o=[I \; W_c]B=[I \; W_o]C^T$ and $Q_c=Q_o$.

4. Approximately Balanced LQG Compensator

In the following sections an approximate equality between two variables is used in the following sense. Two variables x and y are approximately equal ($x\cong y$) if $x=y+\varepsilon$, and $\|\varepsilon\|/\|y\|\ll 1$.

It will be shown that for flexible structures the balanced representation (in the Moore sense) produces diagonally dominant solutions of CARE and FARE, and in the case of $Q=V$ it produces approximate LQG balanced solutions S and P, such that $S\cong P\cong M$. In order to prove it, assume a diagonal weight matrix Q

$$Q=diag(q_iI_2), \qquad i=1,...,n. \tag{24}$$

then the following is true.

Result 4a. There exist $q_i\leq q_{oi}$, where $q_{oi}>0$, $i=1,...,n$, such that $S\cong diag(s_iI_2)$ is the solution of (6), where

$$s_i\cong(\beta_{pi}-1)/2\gamma_i^2, \quad \beta_{pi}^2=1+2q_i\gamma_i^2/\zeta_i\omega_i \tag{25}$$

Proof is presented in the Appendix.

A similar result is obtained for the FARE equation, namely, for a diagonal V

$$V=diag(v_i I_2), \qquad i=1,\dots,n. \tag{26}$$

the following is true:

Result 4b. There exist $v_i \leq v_{oi}$ where $v_{oi}>0$, $i=1,\dots,n$, such that $P \cong diag(p_i I_2)$ is the solution of (8), where

$$p_i \cong (\beta_{ei}-1)/2\gamma_i^2, \quad \beta_{ei}^2=1+2v_i\gamma_i^2/\zeta_i\omega_i \tag{27}$$

Proof is similar to Result 2a.

If the i-th diagonal entry of P and the respective entry of S are equal, say to μ_i, i.e.,

$$p_i=s_i=\mu_i \tag{28}$$

the i-th component is LQG balanced. Additionally, if S and P are equal, as in Eq.(9), where $M=diag(\mu_i)$, $i=1,\dots,n$, the system is LQG balanced. If S, P, M are diagonally dominant, i.e., $v_i+\varepsilon_{vi} \cong s_i+\varepsilon_{si} \cong \mu_i$, with ε_{vi} and ε_{si} small ($|\varepsilon_{vi}/v_i| \ll 1$, $|\varepsilon_{si}/s_i| \ll 1$), then the system is approximately LQG balanced.

From Eqs. (25) and (27) it follows that for $Q=diag(q_i)=V=diag(v_i)$, the system is approximately LQG balanced. Indeed, the balanced CARE/FARE solution is

$$S \cong P \cong M=diag(\mu_i), \quad \mu_i=(\beta_i-1)/2\gamma_i^2, \quad \beta_i^2=1+2q_i\gamma_i^2/\zeta_i\omega_i \tag{29}$$

Next it is shown that the weight Q

$$Q=diag(0,0,\dots,q_i I_2,\dots 0,0), \qquad q_i \leq q_{oi} \tag{30a}$$

shifts the i-th pair of complex poles of the flexible structure, and leaves the remaining pairs of poles almost unchanged. Only the real part of the pair of poles is changed (just moving the pole apart from the imaginary axis and stabilizing the system), and the imaginary part of the poles remains unchanged.

Result 5a. For the weight Q as in Eq.(30a) and $q_i \leq q_{oi}$, the closed-loop pair of flexible poles $(\lambda_{cri}, \pm j\lambda_{cii})$ relates to the open-loop poles $(\lambda_{ori}, \pm j\lambda_{oii})$ as follows

$$(\lambda_{cri}, \pm j\lambda_{cii}) \cong (\beta_{pi}\lambda_{ori}, \pm j\lambda_{oii}), \qquad i=1,\dots,n \tag{31a}$$

where β_{pi} is defined in Eq.(25). For proof see the Appendix.

The real parts of the poles are shifted by β_{pi}, while the imaginary part remains unchanged. The above proposition has additional interpretations. Note that the real part of the open-loop pole is $\lambda_{oi}=-\zeta_i\omega_i$ and that the real part of the closed-loop pole is $\lambda_{ci}=-\zeta_{ci}\omega_i$; note also that the height of the open-loop resonant peak is $\alpha_{oi}=\kappa/2\zeta_i\omega_i$, where κ is a constant, and the closed-loop resonant peak is $\alpha_{ci}=\kappa/2\zeta_{ci}\omega_i$. From (31a) one obtains $\beta_{pi}=\lambda_{cri}/\lambda_{ori}$, hence it is not difficult to see that

$$\beta_{pi}=\zeta_{ci}/\zeta_i=\alpha_{oi}/\alpha_{ci} \tag{32}$$

i.e., that β_{pi} is a ratio of closed- and open-loop damping factors, or that it is a ratio of open- and closed-loop resonant peaks. Therefore, if a suppression of the i-th resonant peak by the factor β_{pi} is required, the appropriate weight q_i is determined from Eq.(25)

$$q_i=0.5(\beta_{pi}^2-1)\zeta_i\omega_i\gamma_i^{-2} \tag{32}$$

Note the relatively large β_{pi} even for small q_i, i.e., a significant pole shift to the left. Also, β_{pi} increases with the increase of γ_i, and decreases with the increase of $\zeta_i\omega_i$, i.e., there is a significant pole shift for highly observable and controllable states with small damping. In terms of the transfer function profile, the weight q_i suppresses the resonant peak at frequency ω_i while leaving the natural frequency unchanged. Due to weak coupling between the states, the assignment of one pair of states does not significantly impact other states. Thus the weight assignment can be done for each pair of states separately.

The estimator poles are shifted in a similar manner. Denote

$$V=diag(0,0,\dots,v_i I_2,\dots 0,0), \quad v_i \leq v_{oi}, \tag{30b}$$

then the following is true:

Result 5b. For the weight V as in Eq.(30b) and $v_i \leq v_{oi}$, the estimator pair of poles $(\lambda_{eri}, \pm j\lambda_{eii})$ relates to the open-loop poles $(\lambda_{ori}, \pm j\lambda_{oii})$ as follows

$$(\lambda_{eri}, \pm j\lambda_{eii}) \cong (\beta_{ei}\lambda_{ori}, \pm j\lambda_{oii}), \qquad i=1,\dots,n \tag{31b}$$

where β_{ei} is defined in Eq.(27). Proof is similar to Result 2a.

The limiting values q_{oi} and v_{oi} in Results 2a and 2b are determined. Their values are rather fuzzy numbers. Despite their fuzziness they are not difficult to determine anyway. There are several symptoms that q_i is approaching q_{oi}, or that v_i is approaching v_{oi}. In the controller case, q_{oi} is the weight for which the i-th pair of complex poles of the plant departs from the horizontal trajectory in the root-locus plane, or it is the weight for which the i-th resonant peak of the plant transfer function disappears (the peak is flattened). And in the estimator case, v_{oi} is the covariance for which the i-th pair of complex poles of the estimator departs from the horizontal trajectory in the root-locus plane, or it is a covariance for which the i-th resonant peak of the estimator transfer function disappears.

5. Reduced-Order Compensator

From an implementation point of view it is crucial to obtain a compensator of the smallest possible order that preserves the stability and performance of the full-order compensator. Although the size of a plant determines the size of a compensator, in order to assure the quality of the closed-loop system, the plant model is not reduced excessively in advance. Therefore, the compensator reduction is a part of compensator design. The balanced LQG design procedure provides this opportunity.

In order to successfully perform the compensator reduction, an index of the importance of each compensator component is introduced. In the open-loop case Hankel singular values serve as reduction indices. In the closed-loop case the characteristic values were used as reduction indices by Jonckheere and Silverman (1983). They are not a good choice, however, since they do not properly reflect the effectiveness of the compensator.

The proposed effectiveness of the closed-loop system is evaluated by the degree of damping of flexible motion of the structure. The damping, on the other hand, depends on the pole mobility to the right-hand side of the complex plane. Therefore, if a particular pair of poles is easily moved (i.e., when small weight is required to move the poles), the respective states are easy to control and to estimate. On the contrary, if a particular pair of poles is difficult to move (i.e., even a large weight insignificantly moves the poles), the respective states are difficult to control and to estimate. In the latter case the action of the compensator is irrelevant, and the states which are difficult to control and estimate can be reduced; this demonstrates that pole mobility is a good indicator of the importance of a particular compensator state.

Consider an LQG balanced system, and denote the pole mobility index σ_i as a product of the a square of Hankel singular value and the characteristic value of a system

$$\sigma_i=\gamma_i^2\mu_i \tag{34a}$$

This combines the system observability and controllability properties of the open-loop system with the compensator performance. The larger the Hankel singular value of the component, the larger the corresponding pole mobility index (c.f. Fig.2b). Also, the more heavily weighted the component, the larger its pole mobility index (see Fig.2a). In order to show that σ_i is connected with the pole mobility, note from Eqs.(29) and (34a) that

$$\sigma_i=0.5(\beta_i-1) \tag{35}$$

For $\beta_i=1$ the i-th pole is stationary, and σ_i is equal to zero; for a shifted pole one obtains $\beta_i>1$ and $\sigma_i>0$. The matrix Σ of pole mobility indices is defined

$$\Sigma=diag(\sigma_1, \sigma_2, \ldots, \sigma_{n-1}, \sigma_n) \tag{34b}$$

and from Eq.(34a) one obtains

$$\Sigma=\Gamma^2 M \tag{34c}$$

In the following, a reduction technique is discussed. Assume Σ in Eq.(34b) has a descending order, i.e., $\sigma_i\geq 0$, $\sigma_{i+1}\leq\sigma_i$, $i=1,\ldots,n$, and divide it as follows

$$\Sigma=diag(\Sigma_r, \Sigma_t) \tag{36}$$

where Σ_r consists of first k entries of Σ, and Σ_t the remaining ones. If the entries of Σ_t are small in comparison with the entries of Σ_r, the compensator is reduced by truncating its last n-k states. Note that the value of σ_i depends on weight q_i, and if for a given weight the resonant peak is too large to be accepted (or a pair of poles too close to the imaginary axis) the weighting of this particular component should be increased to damp this particular component. The growth of weight increases the value of σ_i, which can save this particular component from reduction.

In order to investigate stability and performance of the reduced-order compensator, consider the closed-loop system as in Fig.1. Denoting the state $x_o=[x^T\ \varepsilon^T]^T$, where $\varepsilon=x-\hat{x}$, one obtains the closed-loop equations

$$\dot{x}_o=A_o x_o+B_o u+B_v v+B_w w, \qquad y=C_o x_o \tag{37a}$$

where

$$A_o=\begin{bmatrix} A-BK_p & BK_p \\ 0 & A-K_eC \end{bmatrix},\ B_o=\begin{bmatrix} B \\ 0 \end{bmatrix},\ B_v=\begin{bmatrix} B \\ B \end{bmatrix},\ B_w=\begin{bmatrix} 0 \\ -K_e \end{bmatrix}, \tag{37b}$$

$$C_o=[C\ -C] \tag{37c}$$

Let the matrices A, B, C be partitioned conformably to Σ in Eq.(36)

$$A\cong\begin{bmatrix} A_r & 0 \\ 0 & A_t \end{bmatrix},\quad B=\begin{bmatrix} B_r \\ B_t \end{bmatrix},\quad C=[C_r\ C_t] \tag{38}$$

then the reduced compensator representation is (A_r,B_r,C_r). The compensator gains are divided similarly

$$K_p=[K_{pr}\ K_{pt}],\quad K_e^T=[K_{er}^T\ K_{et}^T] \tag{39}$$

and the resulting reduced closed-loop system is as follows

$$A_{or}=\begin{bmatrix} A-BK_p & BK_p \\ 0 & A_r-K_{er}C_r \end{bmatrix},\ B_{or}=\begin{bmatrix} B \\ 0 \end{bmatrix},\ B_{vr}=\begin{bmatrix} B \\ B_r \end{bmatrix},\ B_{wr}=\begin{bmatrix} 0 \\ -K_{er} \end{bmatrix}, \tag{40a}$$

$$C_{or}=[C\ -C_r] \tag{40b}$$

Although (A_r,B_r,C_r) is stable, the stability of the closed-loop system with reduced compensator (A_{or},B_{or},C_{or}) is neither obvious nor guaranteed. But one can determine when to expect a stable closed-loop system with the reduced-order compensator. In order to discuss this question, introduce (38) and (39) to (37b) to obtain

$$A_o=\begin{bmatrix} A_r-B_rK_{pr} & -B_rK_{pt} & B_rK_{pr} & B_rK_{pt} \\ -B_tK_{pr} & A_t-B_tK_{pt} & B_tK_{pr} & B_tK_{pt} \\ 0 & 0 & A_r-K_{er}C_r & -K_{er}C_t \\ 0 & 0 & -K_{et}C_r & A_t-K_{et}C_t \end{bmatrix} \tag{41}$$

Consider now the term B_tK_p

$$B_tK_p=B_tB^TS=[B_tB_r^TS_r\ \ B_tB_t^TS_t]\cong[0\ \ diag(2\zeta_i\omega_i\sigma_i)] \tag{42}$$

where $B_tB_t^T\cong diag(2\zeta_i\omega_i\mu_i)$, $i=1,\ldots,q$ is used. Eq.(42) shows that for small σ_i one obtains small B_tK_p, and in consequence small B_tK_{pr} and B_tK_{pt}. In a similar way it can be shown that K_eC_t is small. Therefore, for small σ_i the closed-loop matrix as in Eq.(41) is as follows

$$A_o\cong\begin{bmatrix} A_r-B_rK_{pr} & -B_rK_{pt} & B_rK_{pr} & B_rK_{pt} \\ 0 & A_t & 0 & 0 \\ 0 & 0 & A_r-K_{er}C_r & 0 \\ 0 & 0 & -K_{et}C_r & A_t \end{bmatrix} \tag{43}$$

which shows that the poles of a truncated system have not been changed significantly, and that the poles of the retained subsystem are not influenced by the truncated part (negligible spillover). The system with the reduced compensator is stable. Of course, since Eq.(43) represents an approximation of A_o, the above statement is not an unconditional truth, but depends on the mobility indices. If the reduced-order compensator is obtained by reducing states with small σ_i, the reduced-order compensator *is expected* to be stable. That is, although it is not guaranteed, there is a well-founded expectation to obtain a stable reduced-order compensator.

In addition to the stability evaluation, the pole mobility indices give a good estimate of the performance of the reduced-order compensator. Namely, by truncating states with small pole mobility indices the system performance will not be deteriorated significantly. As evidence, note that for A_o as in Eq.(41) the estimation error is

$$\dot{\varepsilon}_r=(A_r-K_{er}C_r)\varepsilon_r-K_{er}C_t\varepsilon_t,\quad \dot{\varepsilon}_t=-K_{et}C_r\varepsilon_r+(A_t-K_{et}C_t)\varepsilon_t \tag{44a}$$

and from Eq.(43) the error of the reduced-order compensator is determined

$$\dot{\varepsilon}_{rr}=(A_r-K_{er}C_r)\varepsilon_{rr},\qquad \dot{\varepsilon}_{tt}=-K_{et}C_r\varepsilon_{rr}+A_t\varepsilon_{tr} \tag{44b}$$

It was already shown that $K_{er}C_t\cong 0$, and $K_{et}C_t\cong 0$ for small σ_i, thus $\varepsilon_r\cong\varepsilon_{rr}$ and $\varepsilon_{tt}\cong\varepsilon_t$, i.e., the estimation errors and truncation errors of the full-order and the reduced-order compensators are almost the same. Similar properties can be shown for the controller performance. The performance of full- and reduced-order compensators is compared later in the application section.

As an alternative measure of performance of the closed-loop system, consider an index π_i

$$\pi_i=\gamma_{oi}^2/\gamma_{ci}^2 \tag{45a}$$

It is a ratio of the open-loop Hankel singular value to the closed-loop Hankel singular value, and can be also interpreted as a ratio of variances of open-loop (σ_{oi}^2) and closed-loop (σ_{ci}^2) states excited by the white-noise input

$$\pi_i=\sigma_{oi}^2/\sigma_{ci}^2 \tag{45b}$$

Obviously, if the *i-th* closed-loop variance is small in comparison to the *i-th* open-loop variance, the controller action at the *i-th* state is considered important, thus the state is not deleted. If the closed-loop variances are about the same as the open-loop variances, the controller action is considered marginal, and the state can be deleted without loss of performance. In order to determine π_i in a closed form the closed-loop Lyapunov equation is considered

$$(A-BB^TS)\Gamma_c^2+\Gamma_c^2(A-BB^TS)^T+BB^T=0 \quad (46a)$$

or, for the *i-th* pair of variables

$$(A_i-B_iB_i^Ts_i)\gamma_{ci}^2+\gamma_{ci}^2(A_i-B_iB_i^Ts_i)^T+B_iB_i^T\cong 0 \quad (46b)$$

Introducing Eq.(A.3) from Appendix gives

$$\gamma_{ci}^2+2\gamma_{ci}^2\gamma_{oi}^2s_i-\gamma_{oi}^2\cong 0 \quad (47)$$

or,

$$\pi_i=\gamma_{oi}^2/\gamma_{ci}^2\cong 1+2s_i\gamma_{oi}^2=\beta_i \quad (48)$$

thus the ratio of closed- and open-loop response to white noise is equal to the pole shift. Another useful interpretation follows from Eq.(47)

$$\sigma_i=0.5(\gamma_{oi}^2-\gamma_{ci}^2)/\gamma_{ci}^2 \quad (49)$$

i.e. the pole mobility index is proportional to relative change to white noise response of the open- and closed-loop systems.

6. Applications

A simple 3-degree-of-freedom system is considered as in Fig.3, with masses $m_1=m_2=m_3=1$, stiffness $k_1=10, k_2=3, k_3=4$, and a damping matrix $D=0.004K+0.001M$, where K, M are stiffness and mass matrices, respectively. The input force is applied to the mass m_3; the output is the rate of the same mass, and the poles of the open-loop system are $\lambda_{o1,o2}=-0.0024\pm j0.9851$, $\lambda_{o3,o4}=-0.0175\pm j2.9197$, and $\lambda_{o5,o6}=-0.0295\pm j3.8084$. The weight matrix Q and the covariance matrix V are chosen as follows: $Q=V=diag(0.4, 0.4, 2, 2, 6, 6)$. The nonzero entries of Q and V shift the poles to the right, so that the peaks in the closed-loop transfer function are flattened as in Fig.4. The matrix V is chosen to be equal to Q to obtain a balanced LQG compensator. For these matrices the solution S of CARE and the solution P of FARE are equal and diagonally dominant,

$$S=P\cong M=diag(1.3288, 1.3261, 4.3161, 4.1301, 25.2817, 24.0490),$$

and the corresponding gains are sign-symmetric (Jonckheere and Silverman, 1983)

$$k_p=[0.0039,\ 0.8893,\ 0.2978,\ -1.9291,\ 2.1378,\ -2.1636]$$

$$k_e^T=[-0.0039,\ 0.8893,\ -0.2978,\ -1.9291,\ -2.1378,\ -2.1636]$$

The Hankel matrix of the plant is

$$\Gamma=diag(7.9776,\ 7.9776,\ 2.2337,\ 2.3336,\ 0.4893, 0.4890)$$

thus the matrix Σ is obtained

$$\Sigma\cong diag(84.5658,\ 84.3920,\ 21.5332,\ 20.6058,\ 6.0453,\ 5.7586)$$

Poles of the open-loop plant, closed-loop systems and estimator are shown in Fig.5. The closed-loop poles and estimator poles were shifted horizontally with respect to the open-loop poles, in agreement with the Results 2a and 2b. For the chosen weights the projected (from Eq.(32)) and actual shifts are 137 vs 146 for the first pair of poles, 33 vs 34 for the second pair of poles, and 8.5 vs 10 for the third pair of poles. Moreover, since the compensator is balanced, the poles of the closed-loop system and the estimator overlap. The closed-loop impulse response in Fig.6 (solid line), shows good vibration damping properties, which is also confirmed by the closed-loop transfer function, Fig.4 (dashed line). The compensator is reduced from six to four state variables. The truncated states are related to the smallest diagonal entries $(5.7586,\ 6.0453)$ of Σ. The impulse response of the full and reduced-order compensator are compared in Fig.6, showing good coincidence. However, if the two states corresponding to the medium values of Σ $(20.6058,\ 21.5332)$ are deleted, the performance of the reduced-order compensator is significantly deteriorated, and if the states corresponding to the largest entries of Σ are reduced, the compensator is unstable.

Next, the application of the LQG compensator to the truss structure from Fig.7 is investigated. For this structure $l_1=70$ in., $l_2=100$ in., each truss has a cross-section area of 2 in.^{2}, elastic modulus of 10^6 lb/in.^{2}, and mass density of 2 lb sec^2/in.^{2}. Vertical control forces are applied at nodes *na1* and *na2*, and the output rates are measured in the vertical direction at nodes *no1* and *no2*. The system has 26 states (13 balanced components), two inputs, and two outputs. The weight (Q) and covariance (V) matrices are assumed equal and diagonal, $Q=V=diag(q_1,q_1,q_2,q_3,\ldots,q_{13},q_{13})$, where $q_1=200$, $q_2=400$, $q_3=1000$, $q_4=2000$, $q_5=10000$, $q_6=20000$, $q_7=\ldots=q_{13}=200$. The CARE and FARE solutions are diagonally dominant, so that the resulting matrix Σ is diagonally dominant. The plots of diagonal entries of Σ are plotted in Fig.8. Poles of the open-loop structure as well the closed-loop system and the estimator are shown in Fig.9. For the balanced compensator the poles of the closed-loop system and the estimator overlap. The open-loop transfer functions are shown in Fig.10 (solid line) and the closed-loop transfer functions of the plant and estimator overlap in Fig.10 (dashed line), and show that the oscillatory motion of the structure is damped out. The compensator is reduced by truncating the 14 states, which correspond to the small pole mobility indices $\sigma_i<0.5$. The resulting reduced-order compensator has 12 states. The impulse responses of the full and reduced-order compensator are compared in Fig.11, showing good coincidence.

7. Conclusions

The properties of Moore balanced representation of flexible structures have been extended for the closed-loop systems. A balanced LQG compensator is obtained that pays the same attention to controlling and to estimating the system. The properties of the balanced LQG system are used to obtain a reduced-order compensator that preserves the stability and performance of the full-order compensator, as illustrated with the LQG balanced control of a truss structure. Since LQG balancing and Moore open-loop balancing coincide for flexible structures, the open-loop reduction (based on Moore balancing) and the LQG reduction form a unified approach to system reduction, useful due to its simplicity.

Acknowledgment

This research was performed at the Jet Propulsion Laboratory, California Institute of Technology, under a contract with the National Aeronautics and Space Administration.

References

Anderson, B.D.O., and Moore, J.B.: *Optimal Control*, Prentice Hall, Englewood Cliffs, 1990.

Furuta, K., Sano, A., and Atherton, D.: *State Variable Methods in Automatic Control*, Wiley, Chichester, 1988.

Gawronski, W.: "Sequential Design of a Linear Quadratic Controller for the Deep Space Network Antennas," *AIAA Guidance, Navigation, and Control Conf.*, Hilton Head, 1992.

Gawronski, W., and Juang, J.-N., "Model Reduction for Flexible Structures," in: *Control and Dynamics Systems*, ed. C.T. Leondes, vol.36, pp.143-222, Academic Press, New York, 1990.

Gawronski, W., and Mellstrom, J.A.: "Modeling and Simulations of the DSS 13 Antenna Control System," *TDA Progress Report*, 42-106, Jet Propulsion Laboratory, California Institute of Technology, August 1991.

Gawronski, W., and Williams, T.: "Model Reduction for Flexible Space Structures," *Journal of Guidance, Control, and Dynamics*, vol.14, No.1, Jan. 1991, pp.68-76.

Jonckheere, E.A., and Silverman, L.M.: "A New Set of Invariants for Linear Systems - Application to Reduced Order Compensator Design," *IEEE Trans. autom. Control*, Vol. AC-28, No 10, 1983.

Kwakernaak, H., and Sivan, R.: *Linear Optimal Control Systems*, Wiley-Interscience, New York, 1972.

Maciejowski, J.M.: *Multivariable Feedback Design*, Addison-Wesley, Wokingham, 1989.

Moore, B.C., "Principal Component Analysis in Linear Systems, Controllability, Observability and Model Reduction," *IEEE Trans. autom. Control*, vol.26, No.1, Jan. 1981.

Opdenacker, P., and Jonckheere, E.A.: "LQG Balancing and Reduced LQG Compensation of Symmetric Passive Systems," *Int. J. Control*, vol.41, no.1, pp.73-109, 1985.

Appendix. Proofs

Proof of Result 4a. For a flexible system with n components (or $N=2n$ states), the balanced grammian has the following form (see Gawronski and Juang, 1990; Gawronski and Williams, 1991)

$$\Gamma \cong diag(\gamma_1,\gamma_1,\gamma_2,\gamma_2,\ldots,\gamma_n,\gamma_n), \qquad \text{(A.1)}$$

and the matrix A is almost block-diagonal, with dominant 2×2 blocks on the main diagonal

$$A \cong diag(A_i), \quad A_i = \begin{bmatrix} -\zeta_i\omega_i & -\omega_i \\ \omega_i & -\zeta_i\omega_i \end{bmatrix}, \quad i=1,\ldots,n \qquad \text{(A.2)}$$

where ω_i is the i-th natural frequency, and ζ_i is the i-th modal damping. Introducing Eqs.(A.1) and (A.2) to (1) gives

$$\gamma_i^2(A_i+A_i^T) \cong -B_iB_i^T \cong -C_i^TC_i. \qquad \text{(A.3)}$$

Due to diagonally dominant matrix A for a flexible structure in balanced representation, and for Q as in Eq.(24), there exist $q_i \leq q_{oi}$, $i=1,\ldots,n$, such that the solution S of the Riccati equation (6) is also diagonally dominant with 2×2 blocks S_i on the main diagonal

$$S_i \cong s_iI_2, \quad s_i>0, \quad i=1,\ldots,n. \qquad \text{(A.4)}$$

Thus, equation (6) turns into a set of the following equations

$$s_i(A_i+A_i^T)-s_i^2B_iB_i^T+q_iI_2=0, \qquad i=1,\ldots,n. \qquad \text{(A.5)}$$

For a balanced system $B_iB_i^T \cong -\gamma_i^2(A_i+A_i^T)$, see Eq.(A.3), and $A_i+A_i^T=-2\zeta_i\omega_iI_2$, see Eq.(A.2). Therefore Eq.(A.5) is now

$$s_i^2+s_i/\gamma_i^2-0.5q_i/\zeta_i\omega_i\gamma_i^2=0, \quad i=1,\ldots,n. \qquad \text{(A.6)}$$

There are two solutions of Eq.(A.6), but for a stable system and for $q_i=0$ it is required that $s_i=0$, therefore (25) is the unique solution of Eq.(A.6).

Proof of Result 5a. For small q_i the matrix A of the closed-loop system is diagonally dominant $A_o \cong diag(A_{oi})$, $i=1,\ldots,n$, and $A_{oi}=A_i-B_iB_i^Ts_i$. Introducing Eq.(A.3) one obtains

$$A_{oi} \cong A_i+2s_i\gamma_i^2(A_i+A_i^T), \qquad \text{(A.7)}$$

and introducing A_i as in Eq.(A.2) to Eq.(A.7) one obtains

$$A_{oi} = \begin{bmatrix} -\beta_{pi}\zeta_i\omega_i & -\omega_i \\ \omega_i & -\beta_{pi}\zeta_i\omega_i \end{bmatrix}, \qquad \text{(A.8)}$$

with β_{pi} as in Eq.(25).

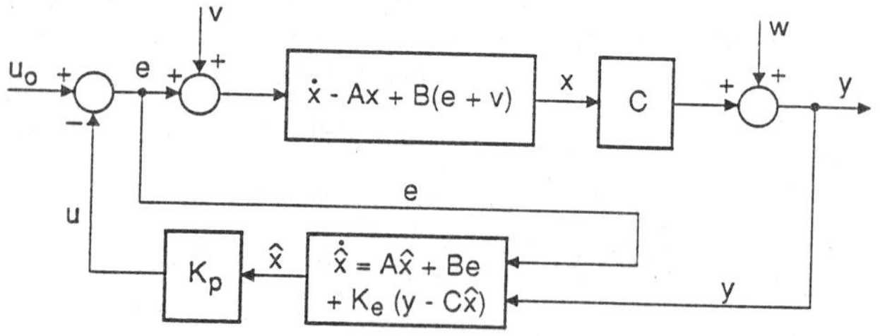

Fig.1. Block diagram of flex. structure with LQG compensator.

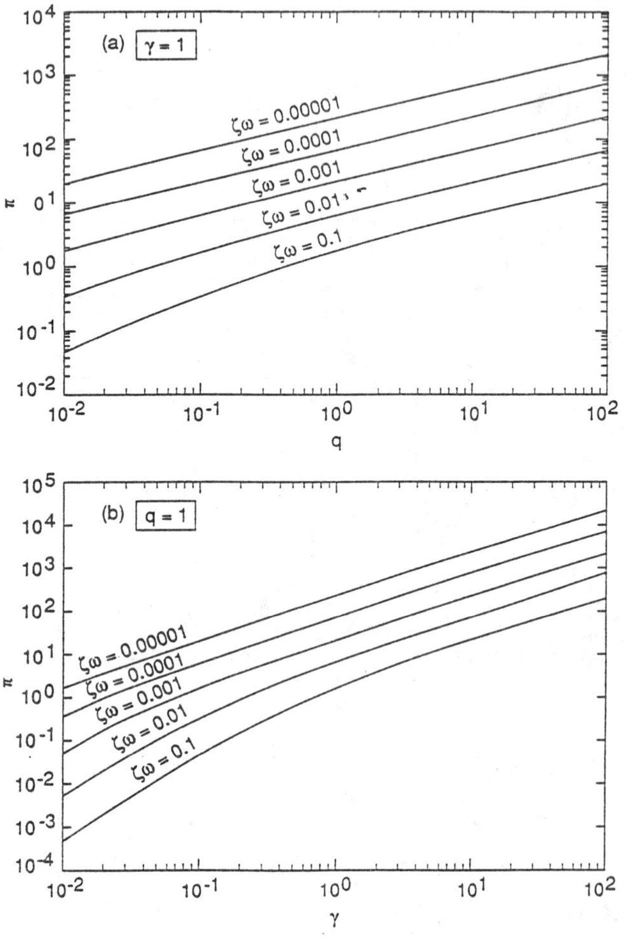

Fig.2. Pole mobility index vs. weight.

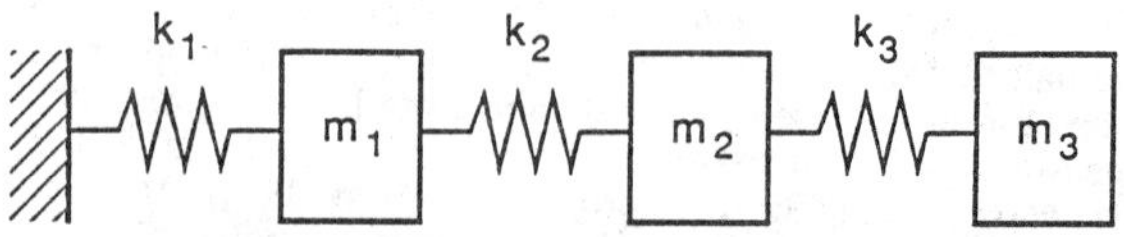

Fig.3. Simple flexible system.

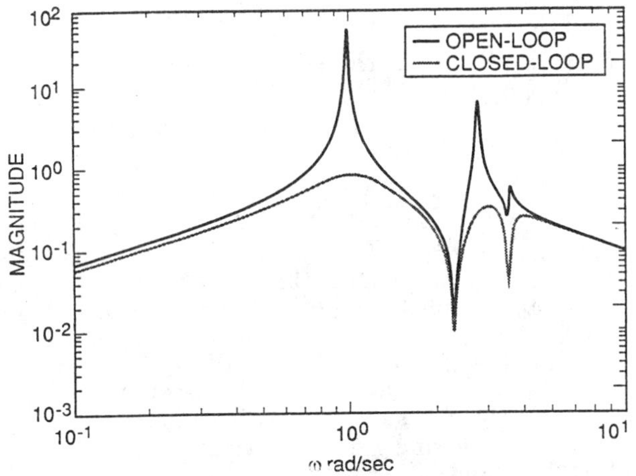

Fig.4. Transfer functions of simple flexible system.

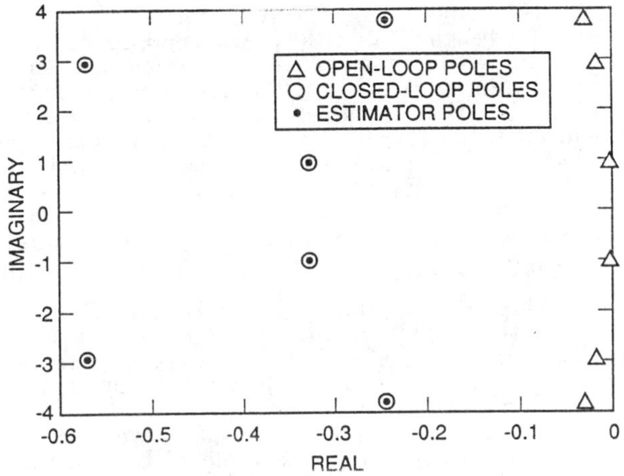

Fig.5. Poles of simple flexible system, and estimator.

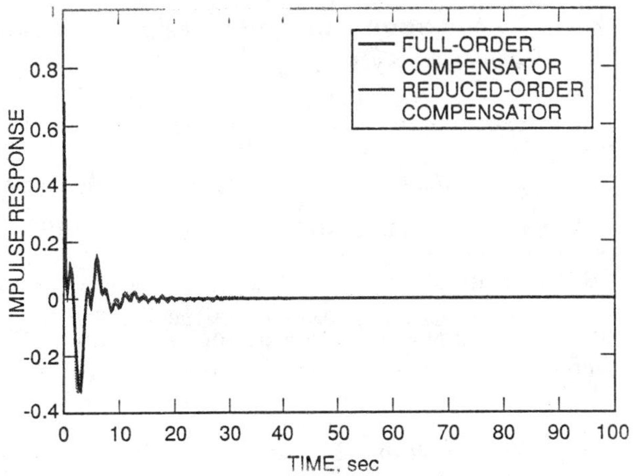

Fig.6. Impulse responses of full and reduced compensator.

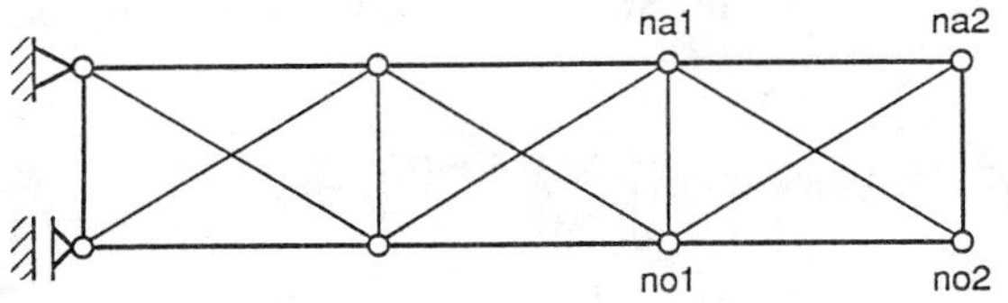

Fig.7. Truss structure.

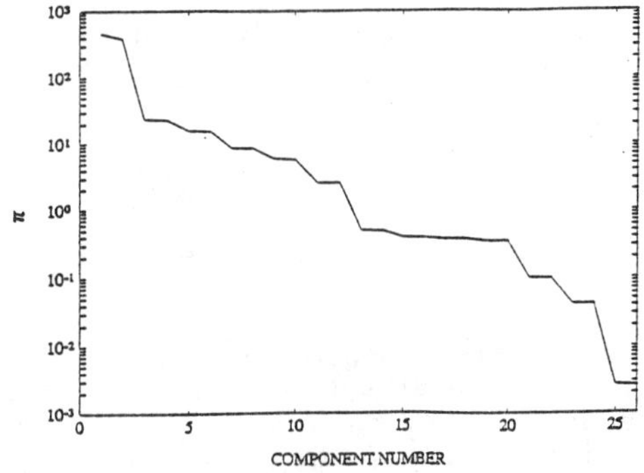

Fig.8. Pole mobility indices for truss structure.

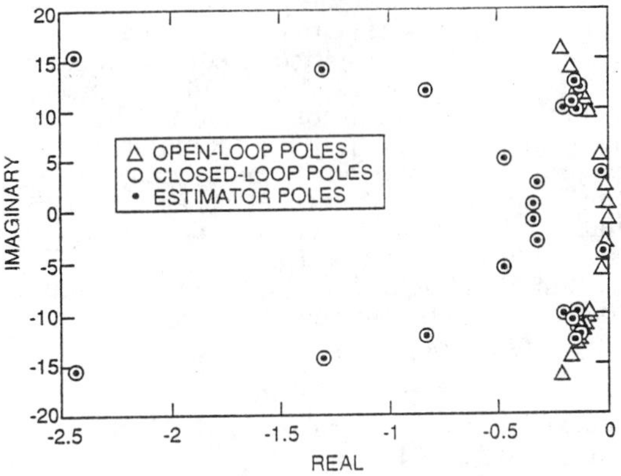

Fig.9. Poles of truss structure, and estimator.

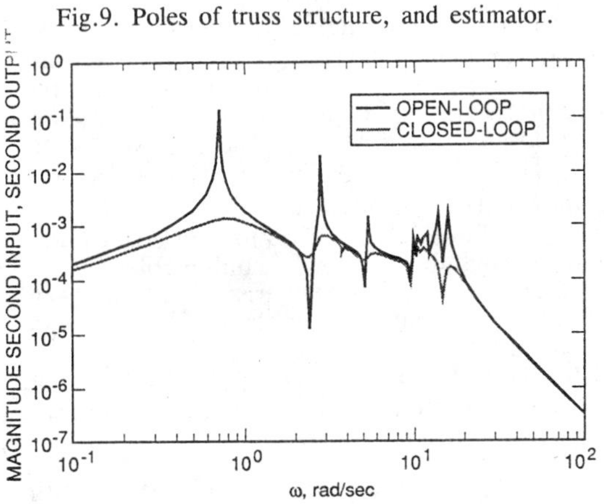

Fig.10. Transfer functions of truss structure.

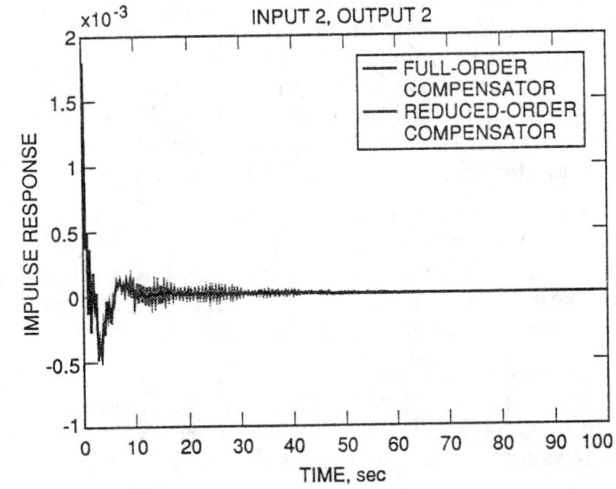

Fig.11. Impulse responses of full and reduced compensator

Proceedings of the
American Control Conference
San Francisco, California • June 1993

A Homotopy Algorithm for Maximum Entropy Design

Emmanuel G. Collins, Jr., Larry D. Davis, Stephen Richter
Harris Corporation, Government Aerospace Systems Division
Melbourne, Florida 32902

Abstract

Maximum entropy design is a generalization of LQG that was developed to enable the synthesis of robust control laws for flexible structures. The method was developed by Hyland and motivated by insights gained from Statistical Energy Analysis. Maximum entropy design has been used successfully in control design for ground-based structural testbeds and certain benchmark problems. The maximum entropy design equations consist of two Riccati equations coupled to two Lyapunov equations. When the uncertainty is zero the equations decouple and the Riccati equations become the standard LQG regulator and estimator equations. A previous homotopy algorithm to solve the coupled equations relies on an iterative scheme that exhibits slow convergence properties as the uncertainty level is increased. This paper develops a new homotopy algorithm that does not suffer from this defect and in fact has quadratic convergence rates along the homotopy curve.

1. Introduction

The linear-quadratic-gaussian (LQG) compensator has been developed to facilitate the design of control laws for complex, multi-input multi-output (MIMO) systems such as flexible structures. However, it is well known that an LQG compensator can yield a closed-loop system with arbitrarily poor robustness properties. This deficiency has led to generalizations of LQG that allow the design of robust controllers, e.g. [1-6]. One such generalization of LQG is the maximum entropy control design approach [2-4] originated by Hyland. Maximum entropy control design was developed specifically to enable robust control law design for flexible structures. The approach was motivated by insights from Statistical Energy Analysis and has proven to be an effective tool in the design of robust control laws for ground-based flexible structure testbeds [7,8] and for certain benchmark problems [9,10].

The rigorous theoretical foundation for maximum entropy design is not yet complete. However, in Ref. 11 it is shown that for an open loop system, a Lyapunov function based on the maximum entropy constraint equation predicts unconditional stability for changes in the undamped natural frequency. The results of Ref. 11 also provide evidence that the theoretical foundation of maximum entropy analysis and design may be related to recent robustness results based on parameter-dependent Lyapunov functions [12].

The computation of full-order maximum entropy controllers requires the solution of a set of equations consisting of two Riccati equations coupled to two Lyapunov equations. If the uncertainty is assumed to be zero, these equations decouple and the Riccati equations become the standard LQG Riccati equations. A homotopy algorithm for solving these equations is described in [13]. This algorithm is based on first solving an LQG problem and gradually increasing the uncertainty level until the desired degree of robustness is achieved. Unfortunately, the algorithm of [13] relies on an iterative scheme that tends to have increasingly poor convergence properties as the uncertainty level is increased.

The contribution of this paper is the development of a new homotopy algorithm for full-order maximum entropy design. Unlike the previous approach, this algorithm has quadratic convergence rates along the homotopy curve. The algorithm has been implemented in MATLAB and is illustrated using a control problem for the ACES testbed at NASA Marshall Space Flight Center in Huntsville, Alabama. A useful feature of maximum entropy design, seen in the example, is that it often produces controllers that are effectively reduced-order controllers. Other features of maximum entropy controllers are described in [7,8].

The paper is organized as follows. Section 2 develops the maximum entropy design equations. Section 3 gives a brief synopsis of homotopy methods. Next, Section 4 discusses a new homotopy algorithm for maximum entropy control design. Section 5 illustrates the algorithm using a 17th order model of one of the transfer functions of the ACES structure at NASA Marshall Space Flight Center. Finally, Section 6 discusses the conclusions.

2. The Maximum Entropy Design Equations

Consider the system

$$\dot{x}(t) = Ax(t) + Bu(t) + w_1(t) \qquad (2.1a)$$

$$y(t) = Cx(t) + Du(t) + w_2(t) \qquad (2.1b)$$

where $x \in \mathrm{IR}^{n_x}, u \in \mathrm{IR}^{n_u}, y \in \mathrm{IR}^{n_y}, w_1 \in \mathrm{IR}^{n_x}$ is white disturbance noise with intensity $V_1 \geq 0, w_2 \in \mathrm{IR}^{n_y}$ is white observation noise with intensity $V_2 > 0$, and w_1 and w_2 have cross correlation $V_{12} \in \mathrm{IR}^{n_x \times n_y}$. It is assumed that (A, B) is stabilizable and (A, C) is detectable. Also, the matrix A is assumed to be of the form

$$A = \text{ block-diag}\{A^{(1)}, A^{(2)}\} \qquad (2.2)$$

where $A^{(1)}$ represents the nominal dynamics of the uncertain modes and is in real normal form; for example,

$$A^{(1)} = \text{block-diag}\left\{\begin{bmatrix} -\nu_1 & \omega_1 \\ -\omega_1 & -\nu_1 \end{bmatrix}, -\nu_2, \begin{bmatrix} -\nu_3 & \omega_3 \\ -\omega_3 & -\nu_3 \end{bmatrix}\right\}. \qquad (2.3)$$

We also assume that the only the modes with complex eigenvalues (corresponding to the 2 × 2 blocks

Supported by SANDIA National Laboratories under contract 54-7609 and the Air Force Office of Scientific Research under contract F49620-91-0019.

$\begin{bmatrix} -\nu_j & \omega_j \\ -\omega_j & -\nu_j \end{bmatrix}$) are uncertain and that the uncertainty patterns $A_i \in \mathbb{R}^{n_x \times n_x}$ are of the form

$$A_i = \text{block-diag}\{0,\ldots,0,\begin{bmatrix} 0 & 1 \\ -1 & 0 \end{bmatrix},0,\ldots,0\}. \tag{2.4}$$

Notice that the A_i correspond to errors in the undamped natural frequencies.

The *maximum entropy control design problem* is stated as follows. Find a full-order dynamic compensator (i.e., a compensator of order n_x),

$$\dot{x}_c(t) = A_c x_c(t) + B_c y(t), \quad u(t) = -C_c x_c(t) \tag{2.5}$$

which stabilizes $\tilde{A}_s$, defined below, and minimizes the cost-functional

$$J(A_c, B_c, C_c) = \text{tr}\tilde{Q}\tilde{R} \tag{2.6}$$

where $\tilde{Q}$ satisfies

$$0 = \tilde{A}_s\tilde{Q} + \tilde{Q}\tilde{A}_s^{\text{T}} + \tilde{V} \tag{2.7}$$

and

$$\tilde{A}_s = \tilde{A} + \frac{1}{2}\sum_{i=1}^{n_\alpha} \alpha_i^2 \tilde{A}_i^2 \tag{2.8}$$

$$\tilde{A}_i = \text{block-diag}\{A_i, 0_{n_x}\} \tag{2.9}$$

$$\tilde{A} = \begin{bmatrix} A & -BC_c \\ B_cC & A_c - B_cDC_c \end{bmatrix} \tag{2.10}$$

$$\tilde{R} = \begin{bmatrix} R_1 & R_{12}C_c \\ C_c^{\text{T}}R_{12}^{\text{T}} & C_c^{\text{T}}R_2C_c \end{bmatrix}. \tag{2.11}$$

Notice that if no uncertainty is assumed (i.e., $\alpha_i \triangleq 0$), then the maximum entropy control design problem becomes the standard LQG problem. The solution to the maximum entropy problem is characterized by the following theorem.

Theorem 2.1.[2-4]. Suppose (A_c, B_c, C_c) solves the maximum entropy control design problem. Then, there exist nonnegative-definite matrices $P, Q, \hat{P}$, and $\hat{Q}$ such that A_c, B_c, and C_c are given by

$$A_c = A_s - BR_2^{-1}P_a - Q_aV_2^{-1}C + Q_aV_2^{-1}DR_2^{-1}P_a \tag{2.12}$$

$$B_c = Q_aV_2^{-1}, \quad C_c = R_2^{-1}P_a \tag{2.13, 14}$$

where

$$A_s = A + \sum_{i=1}^{n_\alpha} \alpha_i^2 A_i^2. \tag{2.15}$$

$$P_a = B^{\text{T}}P + R_{12}^{\text{T}}, \quad Q_a = QC^{\text{T}} + V_{12} \tag{2.16}$$

and the following conditions are satified:

$$0 = A_s^{\text{T}}P + PA_s + R_1 - P_a^{\text{T}}R_2^{-1}P_a + \sum_{i=1}^{n_\alpha}\alpha_i^2 A_i^{\text{T}}(P + \hat{P})A_i \tag{2.17}$$

$$0 = A_sQ + QA_s^{\text{T}} + V_1 - Q_aV_2^{-1}Q_a^{\text{T}} + \sum_{i=1}^{n_\alpha}\alpha_i^2 A_i(Q + \hat{Q})A_i^{\text{T}} \tag{2.18}$$

$$0 = (A_s - Q_aV_2^{-1}C)^{\text{T}}\hat{P} + \hat{P}(A_s - Q_aV_2^{-1}C) + P_a^{\text{T}}R_2^{-1}P_a \tag{2.19}$$

$$0 = (A_s - BR_2^{-1}P_a)\hat{Q} + \hat{Q}(A_s - BR_2^{-1}P_a)^{\text{T}} + Q_aV_2^{-1}Q_a^{\text{T}}. \tag{2.20}$$

Remark 2.2. If no uncertainty is assumed, (i.e., $\alpha_i \triangleq 0$), then (2.17)–(2.20) decouple, (2.17) and (2.18) become the standard LQG regulator and estimator Riccati equations, and (A_c, B_c, C_c) defined by (2.12)–(2.14) is an LQG compensator.

3. Homotopy Methods for the Solution of Nonlinear Algebraic Equations

In the next section, we present a homotopy algorithm for solving the maximum entropy design equations (2.17)–(2.20). A "homotopy" is a continuous deformation of one function into another. Over the past several years, homotopy or continuation methods (whose mathematical basis is algebraic topology and differential topology) have received significant attention in the mathematics literature and have been applied successfully to several important problems (see e.g. [14]). Recently, the engineering literature has also begun to recognize the utility of these methods for engineering applications (see e.g. [15]). The purpose of this section is to provide a very brief description of homotopy methods for finding the solutions of nonlinear algebraic equations. The reader is referred to [14,15] for additional details.

The basic problem is as follows. Given set Θ and Φ contained in $\mathbb{R}^n$ and a mapping $F : \Theta \rightarrow \Phi$, find solutions to

$$F(\theta) = 0. \tag{3.1}$$

Homotopy methods embed the problem (3.1) in a larger problem. In particular let $H : \Theta \times [0,1] \rightarrow \mathbb{R}^n$ be such that:

$$H(\theta, 1) = F(\theta) \tag{3.2}$$

and certain continuity conditions are satisfied [15]. A homotopy algorithm then constructs a procedure to compute the actual curve σ such that the initial solution $\theta(0)$ is transformed to a desired solution $\theta(1)$ satisfying

$$0 = H(\theta(1), 1) = F(\theta(1)). \tag{3.3}$$

Differentiating $H(\theta(\lambda), \lambda) = 0$ with respect to λ yields *Davidenko's differential equation*

$$\frac{\partial H}{\partial \theta}\frac{d\theta}{d\lambda} + \frac{\partial H}{\partial \lambda} = 0. \tag{3.4}$$

Together with $\theta(0) = \theta_0$, (3.4) defines an initial value problem which by numerical integration from 0 to 1 yields the desired solution $\theta(1)$. Some numerical integration schemes are described in [15].

4. A Homotopy Algorithm for Full-Order Maximum Entropy Control Design

This section discusses a novel homotopy algorithm that can be used to design full-order maximum entropy controllers. The algorithm is based on explicitly solving the four coupled maximum entropy design equations given in (2.17)–(2.20) and is given in detail in [19].

4.1 The Homotopy Map

To define the homotopy map we assume that the plant matrices (A, B, C, D), the cost weighting matrices (R_1, R_2, R_{12}), the disturbance matrices (V_1, V_2, V_{12}) and the vector of uncertainty weights $(\alpha \in \mathbb{R}^{n_\alpha})$ are functions of the homotopy parameter $\lambda \in [0, 1]$. In particular, the following is assumed.

$$\begin{bmatrix} A(\lambda) & B(\lambda) \\ C(\lambda) & D(\lambda) \end{bmatrix} = \begin{bmatrix} A_0 & B_0 \\ C_0 & D_0 \end{bmatrix} + \lambda\left(\begin{bmatrix} A_f & B_f \\ C_f & D_f \end{bmatrix} - \begin{bmatrix} A_0 & B_0 \\ C_0 & D_0 \end{bmatrix}\right). \tag{4.1}$$

$$\begin{bmatrix} R_1(\lambda) & R_{12}(\lambda) \\ R_{12}^{\mathrm{T}}(\lambda) & R_2(\lambda) \end{bmatrix} = L_R(\lambda) L_R^{\mathrm{T}}(\lambda) \tag{4.2}$$

where

$$L_R(\lambda) = L_{R,0} + \lambda(L_{R,f} - L_{R,0}) \tag{4.3}$$

and $L_{R,0}$ and $L_{R,f}$ satisfy

$$L_{R,0} L_{R,0}^{\mathrm{T}} = \begin{bmatrix} R_{1,0} & R_{12,0} \\ R_{12,0}^{\mathrm{T}} & R_{2,0} \end{bmatrix} \tag{4.4}$$

$$L_{R,f} L_{R,f}^{\mathrm{T}} = \begin{bmatrix} R_{1,f} & R_{12,f} \\ R_{12,f}^{\mathrm{T}} & R_{2,f} \end{bmatrix}. \tag{4.5}$$

$$\begin{bmatrix} V_1(\lambda) & V_{12}(\lambda) \\ V_{12}^{\mathrm{T}}(\lambda) & V_2^{\mathrm{T}}(\lambda) \end{bmatrix} = L_V(\lambda) L_V^{\mathrm{T}}(\lambda) \tag{4.6}$$

where $L_V(\lambda)$ is defined analogously to $L_R(\lambda)$.

The homotopy is defined by the equations

$$0 = A_s(\lambda)^{\mathrm{T}} P(\lambda) + P(\lambda) A_s(\lambda) + R_1(\lambda) - P_a(\lambda)^{\mathrm{T}} R_2(\lambda)^{-1} P_a(\lambda) + \sum_{i=1}^{n_\alpha} \alpha_i^2(\lambda) A_i^{\mathrm{T}} P(\lambda) A_i + \sum_{i=1}^{n_\alpha} \alpha_i^2(\lambda) A_i^{\mathrm{T}} \hat{P}(\lambda) A_i \tag{4.7}$$

$$0 = A_s(\lambda) Q(\lambda) + Q(\lambda) A_s(\lambda)^{\mathrm{T}} + V_1(\lambda) - Q_a(\lambda) V_2^{-1}(\lambda) Q_a(\lambda)^{\mathrm{T}} + \sum_{i=1}^{n_\alpha} \alpha_i^2(\lambda) A_i Q(\lambda) A_i^{\mathrm{T}} + \sum_{i=1}^{n_\alpha} \alpha_i^2(\lambda) A_i \hat{Q}(\lambda) A_i^{\mathrm{T}} \tag{4.8}$$

$$0 = [A_s(\lambda) - Q_a(\lambda) V_2^{-1}(\lambda) C(\lambda)]^{\mathrm{T}} \hat{P}(\lambda) + \hat{P}(\lambda)[(A_s(\lambda) - Q_a(\lambda) V_2^{-1}(\lambda) C(\lambda))] + P_a(\lambda)^{\mathrm{T}} R_2^{-1}(\lambda) P_a(\lambda) \tag{4.9}$$

$$0 = [A_s(\lambda) - B(\lambda) R_2^{-1}(\lambda) P_a(\lambda)] \hat{Q}(\lambda) + \hat{Q}(\lambda)[A_s(\lambda) - B(\lambda) R_2^{1}(\lambda) P_a(\lambda)]^{\mathrm{T}} + Q_a(\lambda) V_2^{-1}(\lambda) Q_a(\lambda)^{\mathrm{T}} \tag{4.10}$$

where

$$A_s(\lambda) \triangleq A(\lambda) + \frac{1}{2} \sum_{i=1}^{n_\alpha} \alpha_i^2(\lambda) A_i^2 \tag{4.11}$$

$$P_a(\lambda) \triangleq B(\lambda)^{\mathrm{T}} P(\lambda) + R_{12}(\lambda)^{\mathrm{T}} \tag{4.12}$$

$$Q_a(\lambda) \triangleq Q(\lambda) C(\lambda)^{\mathrm{T}} + V_{12}(\lambda). \tag{4.13}$$

4.2 The Derivative and Correction Equations

The homotopy algorithm of [19] uses a predictor/corrector numerical integration scheme. The predictor steps requires derivatives $(\dot{P}(\lambda), \dot{Q}(\lambda), \dot{\hat{P}}(\lambda), \dot{\hat{Q}}(\lambda))$, where $\dot{M} \triangleq dM/d\lambda$, while the correction step is based on using Newton corrections, denoted here as $(\Delta P, \Delta Q, \Delta\hat{P}, \Delta\hat{Q})$. The matrix equations that can be used to solve for the derivatives are of the form

$$0 = A_P^{\mathrm{T}} \dot{P} + \dot{P} A_P + R + \sum_{i=1}^{n_\alpha} \alpha_i^2 A_i^{\mathrm{T}} \dot{P} A_i + \sum_{i=1}^{n_\alpha} \alpha_i^2 A_i^{\mathrm{T}} \dot{\hat{P}} A_i \tag{4.18}$$

$$0 = A_Q \dot{Q} + \dot{Q} A_Q^{\mathrm{T}} + V + \sum_{i=1}^{n_\alpha} \alpha_i^2 A_i \dot{Q} A_i^{\mathrm{T}} + \sum_{i=1}^{n_\alpha} \alpha_i^2 A_i \dot{\hat{Q}} A_i^{\mathrm{T}} \tag{4.19}$$

$$0 = A_Q^{\mathrm{T}} \dot{\hat{P}} + \dot{\hat{P}} A_Q + \hat{R} + G_C \dot{Q} \hat{F} + \hat{F} \dot{Q} G_C + H_P^{\mathrm{T}} \dot{P} K_P + K_P^{\mathrm{T}} \dot{P} H_P \tag{4.20}$$

$$0 = A_P \dot{\hat{Q}} + \dot{\hat{Q}} A_P^{\mathrm{T}} + \hat{V} + G_B \dot{P} \hat{E} + \hat{E} \dot{P} G_B + H_Q \dot{Q} K_Q^{\mathrm{T}} + K_Q \dot{Q} H_Q^{\mathrm{T}}. \tag{4.21}$$

The correction equations are *identical* in form. These coupled modified Lyapunov equations can be solved efficiently using the technique described in [16].

5. An Illustration of Maximum Entropy Design Using the ACES Structure

This section illustrates the design of a maximum entropy controller for a 17th order model of one of the single-input, single-output (SISO) transfer functions of the Active Control Technique Evaluation for Spacecraft (ACES) structure at NASA Marshall Space Flight Center [17]. The actuator and sensor are respectively a torque actuator and a collocated rate gyro. The model, which was constructed from test data using the Eigensystem Realization Algorithm [18], includes the actuator and sensor dynamics. A first order all-pass filter was appended to the model to approximate the computational delay associated with digital implementation.

The Bode plots of the open loop plant are illustrated in Figure 5.1. The basic control objective is to provide damping to the lower frequency modes of the structure (i.e., the modes less than 3 Hz) as measured by the rate gyro. Each of the 8 flexible modes is considered uncertain. (Note that there are two modes at

2.4 Hz, one of which is virtually unobservable.) Maximum entropy design is used to add uncertainty to each of the modes to increase the design robustness. The uncertainty vector $\alpha \in \mathbb{R}^8$ is given by

$$\alpha = \beta * \alpha_0 \tag{5.1}$$

where each element of $\alpha_0 \in \mathbb{R}^8$ has unity value, reflecting equal uncertainty in each of the flexible modes and β is a scale factor chosen to represent the level of uncertainty.

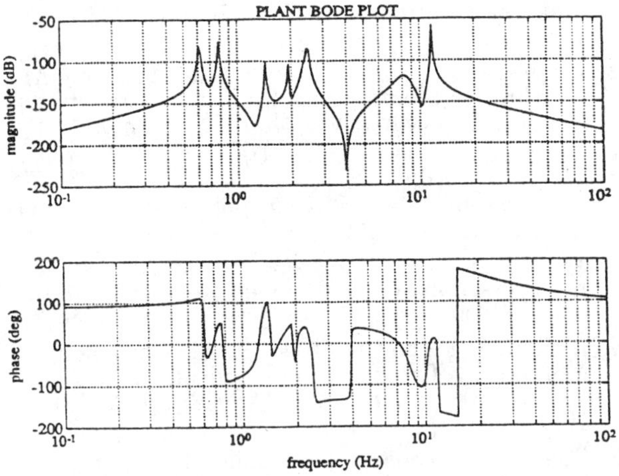

Figure 5.1 Bode Plot of SISO ACES Transfer Function.

For this example, the MATLAB implementation of the maximum entropy homotopy algorithm was run on a 486, 33 MHz PC. Table 5.1 shows some of the run time statistics of the program. The highest uncertainty design, corresponding to $\beta = 5$ was obtained in approximately one hour. Notice that the number of flops and the run time are essentially linear with respect to the log of the scale factor β. This general trend has also been observed in other design examples.

Figures 5.2 and 5.3 compare respectively the magnitude and phase of the initial LQG controller and the maximum entropy controllers corresponding to $\beta = 1$ and $\beta = 5$. Notice that the $\beta = 5$ controller has a very smooth frequency response and is positive real over a very large frequency band. Although this controller has noticeably lower gain in the performance region (i.e., less than 3 Hz) the loop transfer function still has magnitude between 15 and 40 dB at each of the modes in this region. Hence, the maximum entropy controller provides significant damping to the structure.

The smoothness of the maximum entropy controller indicates that it's effective order is much less than 17. Using balanced controller reduction [20], a 4th order compensator was obtained whose input-outpt map was nearly identical to the 17th order compensator. The ability to produce what are essentially reduced-order controllers is an important practical feature of maximum entropy design. Another interesting feature of maximum entropy design is that it will sometimes widen and deepen controller notches in order to robustly gain stabilize certain modes. This property is illustrated in [7,8].

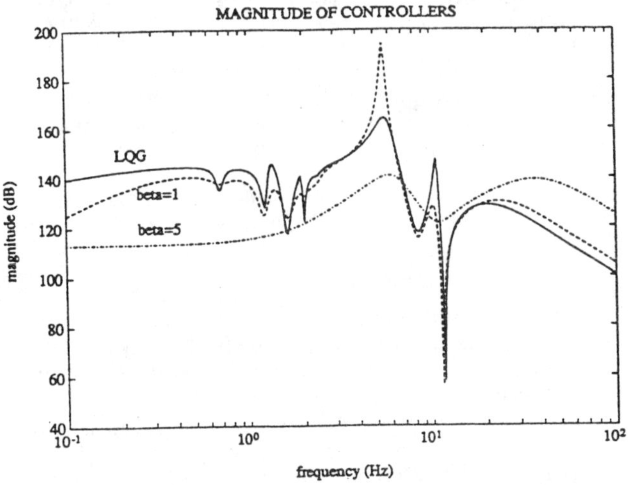

Figure 5.2 Magnitude Frequency Response of LQG and Maximum Entropy Controllers.

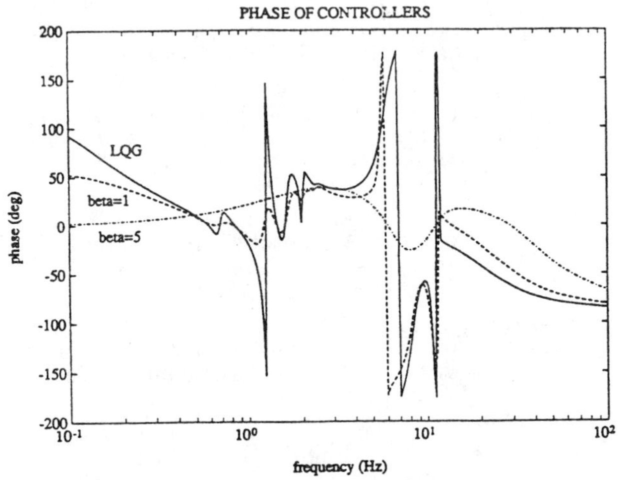

Figure 5.3 Phase Frequency Response of LQG and Maximum Entropy Controllers.

Initial beta	Final beta	Megaflops	RealTime (sec.)	Predictions & Corrections
0	.01	1246.25	1027.27	43
0.1	.1	1061.41	884.80	36
.1	1	1061.49	889.84	36
1	5	1083.25	995.87	41

Table 5.1. Run-Time Statistics of the Maximum Entropy Homotopy Algorithm.

6. Conclusions

This paper has presented a new homotopy algorithm for maximum entropy control design. The algorithm relies on solving four coupled Lyapunov equations at each prediction step or correction iteration. Efficient solution of these equations makes the algorithm feasible for large scale systems. The current solution procedure is based on diagonalizing the coefficient matrices A_p and A_q of the Lyapunov equations. This is usually possible. However, it is possible that this diagonalization will be intractable for some points along the homotopy path. In this case, one could randomly perturb the system matrices so that diagonalization is possible. The perturbation is then removed at the end of the homotopy curve. This type of random perturbation is commonly used in "probability one homotopies" [14]. An alternative is to embed a numerical conditioning test in the program to determine whether the coefficient matrices are truly diagonalizable. If they are not, then one can solve the coupled Lyapunov equations using a non-diagonal alternative such as the Schur decomposition.

References

1. Stein, G. and Athans, M., "The LQG/LTR Procedure for Multivariable Feedback Control Design," *IEEE Transactions on Automatic Control*, Vol. AC-32, February 1987, pp. 105-114.
2. Hyland, D. C., "Maximum Entropy Stochastic Approach to Controller Design for Uncertain Structural Systems," *Proceedings of the American Control Conference*, pp. 680-688, Arlington, VA, June 1982.
3. Bernstein, D. S., and Hyland, D. C., "The Optimal Projection/Maximum Entropy Approach to Designing Low-Order, Robust Controllers for Flexible Structures," *Proceedings of the IEEE Conference on Decision and Control*, pp. 745-752, Fort Lauderdale, FL, December 1985.
4. Bernstein, D. S., and Hyland, D. C., "The Optimal Projection Approach to Robust, Fixed-Structure Control Design" *Mechanics and Control of Large Flexible Structures*, pp. 237-293, J. L. Junkins, Ed., AIAA, 1990.
5. Tahk, M., and Speyer, J., "Modeling of Parameter Variations and Asymptotic LQG Synthesis," *IEEE Transactions on Automatic Control*, Vol. AC-32, September 1987, pp. 793-801.
6. Bernstein, D. S., "Robust Stability and Performance Analysis Via Fixed-Order Dynamic Compensation with Guaranteed Cost Bounds," *Mathematics of Control, Signals, and Systems,* Vol. 3, 1990, pp. 239–271.
7. Collins, E. G., Jr., Phillips, D. J., and Hyland, D. C., "Robust Decentralized Control Laws for the ACES Structure," *Control Systems Magazine*, Vol. 11, April 1991, pp. 62-70.
8. Collins, E. G., Jr., King, J. A., Phillips, D. J., and Hyland, D.C., "High Performance, Accelerometer-Based Control of the Mini-MAST Structure," *AIAA J. Guidance Control and Dynamics*, Vol. 15, July 1992, pp. 885-892.
9. Cheung, M-F, and Yurkovich, S., "On the Robustness of MEOP Design Versus Asymptotic LQG Synthesis," *IEEE Transactions on Automatic Control*, Vol. 33, November 1988, pp. 1061-1065.
10. Collins, E. G., Jr., King, J. A., and Bernstein, D. S., "Application of Maximum Entropy/ Optimal Projection Design Synthesis to a Benchmark Problem," *AIAA J. Guidance Control and Dynamics*, to appear.
11. Bernstein, D. S., Haddad, W. M., Hyland, D. C., and Tyan, F., "A Maximum Entropy-Type Lyapunov Function for Robust Stability and Performance Analysis," *Systems and Control Letters*, to appear.
12. Haddad, W.M., and Bernstein, D.S., "Parameter-Dependent Lyapunov Functions, Constant Real Parameter Uncertainty, and the Popov Criterion in Robust Analysis and Synthesis: Part 1, Part 2," *Proceedings of the IEEE Conference on Decision and Control*, pp. 2274-2279, pp. 2618–2623, Brighton, U.K., December 1991.
13. Collins, E. G., and Richter, S., "A Homotopy Algorithm for Synthesizing Robust Controllers for Flexible Structures Via the Maximum Entropy Design Equations," *Third Air Force/NASA Symposium on Recent Advances in Multidisciplinary Analysis and Optimization*, pp. 1449-1454, San Diego, Ca, May 1990.
14. Watson, L. T., "Numerical Linear Algebra Aspects of Globally Convergent Homotopy Methods," *SIAM Rev.*, Vol. 28, pp. 529–545, 1986.
15. Richter, S. L., and DeCarlo, R. A.,"Continuation Methods: Theory and Applications," *IEEE Trans. Circ. Syst.*, Vol. CAS–30, pp. 347–352, 1983.
16. Richter, S., Davis, L. D., Collins, E. G., Jr., "Efficient Computation of the Solutions to Modified Lyapunov Equations," *SIAM Journal of Matrix Analysis and Applications,* to appear.
17. Irwin, R. D., Jones, V. L., Rice, S. A., Seltzer, S. M., and Tollison, D. J., *Active Control Technique Evaluation for Spacecraft (ACES),* Final Report to Flight Dynamics Lab of Wright Aeronautical Labs, Report No., AFWAL-TR-88-3038, June 1988.
18. Juang, J. N., and Pappa, R. S., "Effects of Noise on Modal Parameters Identified by the Eigensystem Realization Algorithm," *J. Guid. Contr. Dyn.*, Vol. 9, pp. 294–303, 1986.
19. Collins, E. G., Jr., Davis, L. D., and Richter, S., "A Homotopy Algorithm for Maximum Entropy Design," *J. Guid. Contr. Dyn.*, submitted.
20. Yousuf, A. and Skelton, R. E., "A Note on Balanced Controller Reduction," *IEEE Trans. Autom. Contr.*, Vol. 29, pp. 254–257, 1984.

Proceedings of the
American Control Conference
San Francisco, California • June 1993

Maximum Entropy Controller Synthesis for Colocated and Noncolocated Systems

Jonathan H. Friedman* and Dennis S. Bernstein†

The University of Michigan
Ann Arbor, MI 48109

1 Introduction

Maximum Entropy controller synthesis was developed specifically for the robust control of flexible structures. The foundation of the approach was laid in a series of technical reports and conference papers [1-4] while subsequent investigations of the method illustrated its robustness and performance properties [5-10]. These studies culminated in the experimental application of the technique to structural control testbeds [11].

Although the original rationale for the Maximum Entropy approach was based upon stochastic arguments, recent research has sought to develop a deterministic Lyapunov function framework [12-14]. A complete theoretical framework for the Maximum Entropy method is, however, not yet available. The goal of this paper, therefore, is to facilitate the development of such a framework by providing well-documented numerical examples that illustrate the characteristics of the method. We feel that such illustrative examples are of value to researchers seeking to understand the method and the promising experimental results already obtained by using it [11].

The examples we consider in this paper were chosen to contrast the properties of Maximum Entropy controllers in two key cases, namely, colocation and noncolocation. Our results confirm and extend observations that have been made previously, namely, that Maximum Entropy controllers employ positive real phase stabilization in the colocated case and wider and deeper notch gain stabilization in the noncolocated case. By carefully documenting such features we hope to better understand the nature of the approach while facilitating comparison with alternative techniques for controlling flexible structures.

To obtain Maximum Entropy controllers, we used a standard quasi-Newton technique in conjunction with the appropriate cost gradient expressions. This technique was applied to $\mathcal{H}_2$ / $\mathcal{H}_\infty$ synthesis [15,16] but has not been previously used for Maximum Entropy synthesis. Prior numerical techniques for computing Maximum Entropy controllers include iterative algorithms [2] as well as homotopy methods [10,17]. These techniques directly solve the coupled Riccati and Lyapunov equations that characterize the Maximum Entropy controllers.

2 Maximum Entropy Controller Synthesis

Consider the structural model

$$\dot{x} = Ax + Bu + D_1 w, \tag{1}$$
$$y = Cx + D_2 w, \tag{2}$$

*Graduate Student, Department of Aerospace Engineering
†Associate Professor, Department of Aerospace Engineering

with feedback controller

$$\dot{x}_c = A_c x_c + B_c y, \tag{3}$$
$$u = C_c x_c, \tag{4}$$

performance variables

$$z = E_1 x + E_2 u, \tag{5}$$

and performance measure

$$J(A_c, B_c, C_c) = \lim_{t\to\infty} \mathbb{E}\left\{\frac{1}{t}\int_0^t z^T(s)z(s)ds\right\}, \tag{6}$$

where $x \in \mathbb{R}^n$, $u \in \mathbb{R}^m$, $y \in \mathbb{R}^\ell$, $w \in \mathbb{R}^d$, $z \in \mathbb{R}^q$, and $x_c \in \mathbb{R}^{n_c}$. The disturbance w is a standard white noise signal and $\mathbb{E}$ denotes expectation. The matrix A is assumed to be in real normal coordinates, that is,

$$A = \begin{bmatrix} \begin{bmatrix} -\eta_1 & \omega_{d1} \\ -\omega_{d1} & -\eta_1 \end{bmatrix} & 0 & \cdots & 0 \\ 0 & \ddots & & \vdots \\ \vdots & & \ddots & 0 \\ 0 & \cdots & 0 & \begin{bmatrix} -\eta_r & \omega_{dr} \\ -\omega_{dr} & -\eta_r \end{bmatrix} \end{bmatrix}, \tag{7}$$

so that $n = 2r$. Note that η_i and ω_{di} represent the decay rate and damped natural frequency of the ith mode, respectively. Thus, if ζ_i and ω_{ni} denote the damping ratio and natural frequency, respectively, of the ith mode, where $0 \le \zeta_i \le 1$, then $\eta_i = \zeta_i\omega_{ni}$ and $\omega_{di} = \omega_{ni}\sqrt{1-\zeta_i^2}$. Following standard LQG or $\mathcal{H}_2$ theory, the performance $J(A_c, B_c, C_c)$ is given by

$$J(A_c, B_c, C_c) = \operatorname{tr}\, \tilde{Q}\tilde{E}^T\tilde{E}, \tag{8}$$

where $\tilde{Q}$ satisfies

$$0 = \tilde{A}\tilde{Q} + \tilde{Q}\tilde{A}^T + \tilde{D}\tilde{D}^T \tag{9}$$

and where $\tilde{A}$, $\tilde{D}$, and $\tilde{E}$ are defined by

$$\tilde{A} \triangleq \begin{bmatrix} A & BC_c \\ B_cC & A_c \end{bmatrix}, \quad \tilde{D} \triangleq \begin{bmatrix} D_1 \\ B_cD_2 \end{bmatrix}, \quad \tilde{E}^T \triangleq \begin{bmatrix} E_1 \\ E_2C_c \end{bmatrix}. \tag{10}$$

Maximum Entropy controller synthesis addresses the case in which the damped natural frequencies are uncertain. In this case (1) is replaced by

$$\dot{x} = \left(A + \sum_{i=1}^{r}\sigma_i A_i\right) + Bu + D_1 w, \tag{11}$$

δ_2	Stable?	Minimum Phase?	Positive Real?	$\mathcal{H}_2$ Nominal State Cost	$\mathcal{H}_2$ Nominal Control Cost	Stability Boundary	
0 (LQG)	No	Yes	No	13.8522	1.9189	1.4318	1.4655
0.3	Yes	Yes	No	14.2884	1.7801	1.1533	10^{15}
10	Yes	Yes	Yes	15.2425	1.7937	-10^{15}	10^{14}
1000	Yes	Yes	Yes	15.1942	1.8463	-10^{13}	10^{14}

Table 1: Compensator Comparison – Colocated Case

where σ_i is an uncertain parameter representing uncertainty in ω_{di} and A_i is the matrix

$$A_i \triangleq \begin{bmatrix} 0 & \cdots & & \cdots & 0 \\ & \ddots & & & \\ \vdots & & \begin{bmatrix} 0 & 1 \\ -1 & 0 \end{bmatrix} & & \vdots \\ & & & \ddots & \\ 0 & & \cdots & & 0 \end{bmatrix} \tag{12}$$

with nonzero elements corresponding to the ith mode. Now, in place of (9) we utilize

$$0 = \tilde{A}\tilde{Q}+\tilde{Q}\tilde{A}^T+\sum_{i=1}^{r}\delta_i^2\left[\frac{1}{2}\tilde{A}_i^2\tilde{Q}+\tilde{A}_i\tilde{Q}\tilde{A}_i^T+\frac{1}{2}\tilde{Q}\tilde{A}_i^{2T}\right]+\tilde{D}\tilde{D}^T, \tag{13}$$

where $\tilde{A}_i \triangleq \begin{bmatrix} A_i & 0 \\ 0 & 0 \end{bmatrix}$ and δ_i is a measure of the magnitude of the uncertainty σ_i.

To minimize $J(A_c, B_c, C_c)$ given by (8) where $\tilde{Q}$ satisfies (13), we define a Lagrangian function

$$\mathcal{L}(A_c, B_c, C_c, \tilde{Q}) \triangleq \text{tr}\ \tilde{Q}\tilde{E}^T\tilde{E} + \text{tr}\ \tilde{P}\Big(\tilde{A}\tilde{Q}+\tilde{Q}\tilde{A}^T \tag{14}$$

$$+\sum_{i=1}^{r}\delta_i^2\left[\frac{1}{2}\tilde{A}_i^2\tilde{Q}+\tilde{A}_i\tilde{Q}\tilde{A}_i^T+\frac{1}{2}\tilde{Q}\tilde{A}_i^{2T}\right]+\tilde{D}\tilde{D}^T\Big),$$

where $\tilde{P}$ is a nonzero Lagrange multiplier. Now by partitioning $\tilde{Q}$ and $\tilde{P}$ as

$$\tilde{Q} = \begin{bmatrix} Q_1 & Q_{12} \\ Q_{12}^T & Q_2 \end{bmatrix}, \quad \tilde{P} = \begin{bmatrix} P_1 & P_{12} \\ P_{12}^T & P_2 \end{bmatrix},$$

and assuming for simplicity that $E_1^TE_2 = 0$ and $D_1D_2^T = 0$, it can be shown that $\tilde{P}$ satisfies

$$0 = \tilde{A}^T\tilde{P}+\tilde{P}\tilde{A}+\sum_{i=1}^{r}\delta_i^2\left[\frac{1}{2}\tilde{A}_i^{2T}\tilde{P}+\tilde{A}_i^T\tilde{P}\tilde{A}_i+\frac{1}{2}\tilde{P}\tilde{A}_i^2\right]+\tilde{E}^T\tilde{E}, \tag{15}$$

and the cost gradients are given by

$$\frac{\partial J(A_c,B_c,C_c)}{\partial A_c} = 2\left(Q_{12}^TP_{12}+Q_2P_2\right), \tag{16}$$

$$\frac{\partial J(A_c,B_c,C_c)}{\partial B_c} = 2C\left(Q_1P_{12}+Q_{12}P_2\right) + 2D_2D_2^TB_c^TP_2, \tag{17}$$

$$\frac{\partial J(A_c,B_c,C_c)}{\partial C_c} = 2\left(Q_{12}^TP_1+Q_2P_{12}^T\right)B + 2Q_2C_c^TE_2^TE_2. \tag{18}$$

The expressions (16)-(18) follow from the fact that the cost gradients are equal to the gradients of the Lagrangian [16].

To perform the optimization, we used the MATLAB subroutine *fminu*, which implements the BFGS quasi-Newton algorithm. The search algorithm was modified to ensure closed-loop stability within the line search subroutine. As in the $\mathcal{H}_2$ / $\mathcal{H}_\infty$ synthesis [15,16] and the homotopy methods [10,17] we initialized the optimization routine with the standard LQG solution. In addition to the optimization routine we used the algorithm developed in [18] for solving (13) and (15).

3 Illustrative Example: Colocated Case

The first example is a two-mass system with a colocated sensor/actuator pair as shown in Figure 1, where the measured output y_c is the velocity of mass M_1. The dynamics of the system are given by

$$M_1\ddot{q}_1 + C_1\dot{q}_1 + K_1q_1 = u + C_2(\dot{q}_2-\dot{q}_1) + K_2(q_2-q_1), \tag{19}$$

$$M_2\ddot{q}_2 + C_2(\dot{q}_2-\dot{q}_1) + K_2(q_2-q_1) = 0, \tag{20}$$

$$y_c = \dot{q}_1 \tag{21}$$

with the parameter values given in Figure 1. Letting $x_1 = q_1$, $x_2 = \dot{q}_1$, $x_3 = q_2$, and $x_4 = \dot{q}_2$, the plant can be described by Equations (1) and (2), where

$$A = \begin{bmatrix} 0 & 1 & 0 & 0 \\ -\frac{(K_1+K_2)}{M_1} & -\frac{(C_1+C_2)}{M_1} & \frac{K_2}{M_1} & \frac{C_2}{M_1} \\ 0 & 0 & 0 & 1 \\ \frac{K_2}{M_2} & \frac{C_2}{M_2} & -\frac{K_2}{M_2} & -\frac{C_2}{M_2} \end{bmatrix}, \tag{22}$$

$$B^T = \begin{bmatrix} 0 & \frac{1}{M_1} & 0 & 0 \end{bmatrix}, \quad C = \begin{bmatrix} 0 & 1 & 0 & 0 \end{bmatrix}, \tag{23}$$

$D_2 = \begin{bmatrix} 0 & 1 \end{bmatrix}$. Then by means of a coordinate transformation we place A in real normal coordinates as in (7), so that A, B, and C become

$$A = \begin{bmatrix} -0.0002 & 0.2208 & 0 & 0 \\ -0.2208 & -0.0002 & 0 & 0 \\ 0 & 0 & -0.0103 & 1.4322 \\ 0 & 0 & -1.4322 & -0.0103 \end{bmatrix}, \tag{24}$$

$$B = \begin{bmatrix} -0.1439 \\ 0.2168 \\ -0.0426 \\ 1.1892 \end{bmatrix}, C^T = \begin{bmatrix} -0.0545 \\ 0.0819 \\ -0.0352 \\ 0.8181 \end{bmatrix}, \tag{25}$$

and D_2 is unchanged from (23). The performance criterion was chosen so that LQG synthesis would place a notch at the second mode. This is accomplished when

$$D_1 = \begin{bmatrix} 0 & 0 \\ 1 & 0 \\ 0 & 0 \\ 0 & 0 \end{bmatrix}, \quad E_1 = \begin{bmatrix} 1 & 0 & 0 & 0 \\ 0 & 0 & 0 & 0 \end{bmatrix}, \quad E_2 = \begin{bmatrix} 0 \\ 1 \end{bmatrix}. \tag{26}$$

This matrix E_1 weights the amplitude of the first mode but does not penalize the amplitude or velocity of the

δ_2	Stable?	Minimum Phase?	Positive Real?	$\mathcal{H}_2$ Nominal State Cost	$\mathcal{H}_2$ Nominal Control Cost	Stability Boundary	
0 (LQG)	Yes	Yes	Yes	772.9009	11.0468	1.4245	1.4341
0.2	Yes	Yes	No	776.1827	10.4267	1.3242	1.4887
0.5	Yes	No	No	786.9195	8.5317	1.1482	1.7400
1.0	Yes	No	No	816.7371	5.4372	1.0300	10^{16}

Table 2: Compensator Comparison – Noncolocated Case

second mode. In practice this performance criterion reflects the situation in which the closed-loop performance depends primarily upon the lower frequency modes, while the higher frequency modes are highly uncertain.

Note that in (25) the nominal damped natural frequencies and damping ratios are $\omega_{d1} = 0.2208$, $\omega_{d2} = 1.4322$, $\zeta_1 = 0.0011$, and $\zeta_2 = 0.0072$, and that the plant is positive real (as seen in Figure 2). Since we are concerned with the closed-loop consequences of uncertainty in the second damped natural frequency, one potential solution would be to apply a positive real compensator to guarantee closed-loop stability [19]. In Table 1 and Figure 3 we compare the standard LQG design to three Maximum Entropy designs, where the only parameter that is varied is δ_2, which is a measure of the magnitude of the uncertainty δ_2 in the second damped natural frequency. The Maximum Entropy controller, with a small measure of uncertainty δ_2, first adjusts the phase so that the controller is stable, then continues to alter the phase as δ_2 increases, yielding positive real controllers as δ_2 becomes large. Note that this change in phase increases the phase margin at the second mode, as seen in Figure 4. The increase in robustness obtained by increasing δ_2 was also assessed by determining the range of values of σ_2 for which the closed-loop system remains stable. This range of values, which increases with δ_2, is given by the last column of Table 1 and is illustrated by the performance/robustness tradeoff curves shown in Figure 5.

It is important to stress that, although the use of positive real controllers in the colocated case is standard practice to achieve robustness [19], the Maximum Entropy method is the only technique we know of that yields such controllers as a direct consequence of uncertainty.

4 Illustrative Example: Noncolocated Case

In the second example we examine the same two–mass system as in Section 3. However, in this example the sensor/actuator pair is noncolocated, so that in place of (21) the measured output is

$$y_{\mathrm{nc}} = \dot{q}_2, \tag{27}$$

the velocity of mass M_2, as seen in Figure 1. For this case the matrix C in (23) is replaced by

$$C = \begin{bmatrix} 0 & 0 & 0 & 1 \end{bmatrix}, \tag{28}$$

so that after the coordinate transformation the matrix C in (25) becomes

$$C = \begin{bmatrix} -0.1063 & 0.1597 & 0.0018 & -0.0419 \end{bmatrix}. \tag{29}$$

Also the matrix E_1 in (26) is increased by a factor of 10, so that

$$E_1 = \begin{bmatrix} 10 & 0 & 0 & 0 \\ 0 & 0 & 0 & 0 \end{bmatrix}. \tag{30}$$

This increase was used to enhance the notching characteristics of the LQG compensator and to better demonstrate the properties of the Maximum Entropy controllers. As will be seen, this increase also led to the use of lower values of δ_2 to achieve levels of robustification comparable to these obtained in the colocated case.

Since the plant is not positive real, the Maximum Entropy method can no longer guarantee closed-loop stability by adjusting the phase of the compensator. Instead, the method robustifies the LQG design by widening and deepening the notch at the second mode. In addition, it can be seen that the center notch frequency moves to the right, which makes the stability region asymmetric for larger δ_2. On the other hand, we found that the notch can be centered at the nominal damped natural frequency by decreasing the nominal design frequency. However, experience shows that this approach also does not necessarily lead to a symmetric stability region. We suspect that the notch center frequency moves to the right to avoid possible overlap with the lower modal frequency. For these designs the performance/robustness tradeoff curves are shown in Figure 5 and the stability boundaries are given in Table 2.

Despite the fact that phase no longer appears to be the principal means of robustification, the Maximum Entropy synthesis method does adjust the phase of the compensator in the noncolocated case. In particular, as δ_2 increases, the compensator transitions from minimum phase to nonminimum phase, as seen in Figure 3. This change in phase increases the phase margin near the second mode (see Figure 4) as in the colocated case. The potential advantages of employing a nonminimum phase notch filter for a noncolocated system with multiple crossover frequencies (such as a structure) are discussed in [20] and [21].

5 Conclusions

The purpose of this paper was to contrast the robustness of Maximum Entropy controllers in the colocated and noncolocated cases, and to demonstrate a new computational technique for Maximum Entropy controller synthesis. Based upon these examples, we can conclude that Maximum Entropy controllers tend toward phase stabilization in the colocated case and employ robustified notch filters in the noncolocated case to achieve the robustness properties shown in Figure 5. The starting point for these designs was LQG theory, which, in this case, yielded rather sensitive controllers. There exist, of course, alternative methods for robustifying LQG designs, such as loop shaping, frequency weighting, and $\mathcal{H}_\infty$ Theory. A comparison of these techniques with Maximum Entropy controllers remains a topic for future investigation.

Acknowledgments

We wish to thank Emmanuel Collins of Harris Corporation for providing a computer program for implementing the algorithm given in Ref. 18, James King of Harris Corporation for several helpful suggestions, and James Freudenberg for helpful comments. This research was funded in part by the Air Force Office of Scientific Research under grant F49620-92-J-0127 and a National Science Foundation Graduate Fellowship.

References

[1] D.C. Hyland. Optimal regulation of structural systems with uncertain parameters. Technical Report TR-551, MIT, Lincoln Laboratory, February 1981. DDC#ADA-099111/7.

[2] D.C. Hyland and A.N. Madiwale. A stochastic design approach for full-order compensation of structural systems with uncertain parameters. In *Proceedings of the AIAA Guidance and Control Conference*, pages 324–332, Albuquerque, NM, August 1981.

[3] D.C. Hyland. Maximum Entropy stochastic approach to controller design for uncertain structural systems. In *Proceedings of the American Control Conference*, pages 680–688, Arlington, VA, June 1982.

[4] D.C. Hyland. Minimum information stochastic modeling of linear systems with a class of parameter uncertainties. In *Proceedings of the AIAA Guidance and Control Conference*, pages 620–627, Arlington, VA, June 1982.

[5] D.S. Bernstein and S.W. Greeley. Robust controller synthesis using the Maximum Entropy design equations. *IEEE Transactions on Automatic Control*, AC-13:362–364, 1986.

[6] A. Gruzen. Robust reduced order control of flexible structures. Report CSDL-T-900, C.S. Draper Laboratory, April 1986.

[7] A. Gruzen and W.E. Vander Velde. Robust reduced order control of flexible structures using the Optimal Projection/Maimum Entropy design methodology. In *Proceedings of the AIAA Guidance and Control Conference*, Williamsburg, VA, Aug. 1986.

[8] M. Cheung and S. Yurkovich. On the robustness of MEOP design versus asymptotic LQG synthesis. *IEEE Transactions on Automatic Control*, Vol. 33:1061–1065, 1988.

[9] D.S. Bernstein and D.C. Hyland. Optimal projection approach to robust fixed-structure control design. In J.L. Junkins, editor, *Mechanics and Control of Flexible Structures*, volume 129 of *Progress in Astronautics and Aeronautics*, chapter 10, pages 237–293. American Institute of Aeronautics and Astronautics, Inc., Washington, D.C., 1990.

[10] E.G. Collins, Jr., J.A. King, and D.S. Bernstein. Robust control design for the benchmark problem using the Maximum Entropy approach. In *Proceedings of the American Control Conference*, pages 1935–1936, Boston, MA, June 1991.

[11] E.G. Collins,Jr., D.J. Phillips, and D.C. Hyland. Robust decentralized control laws for the ACES structure. *IEEE Control Systems Magazine*, pages 62–70, April 1991.

[12] W.M. Haddad and D.S. Bernstein. Parameter-dependent Lyapunov functions, constant real parameter uncertainty, and the Popov criterion in robust analysis and synthesis. In *Proceedings of IEEE Conference on Decision and Control*, Brighton, U.K., Dec. 1991. Part I, pages 2274–2279, Part II, pages 2632–2633.

[13] D.S. Bernstein, W.M. Haddad, D.C. Hyland, and F. Tyan. Maximum Entropy-type Lyapunov functions for robust stability and performance analysis. In *Proceedings of the American Control Conference*, pages 2639–2643, Chicago, IL, June 1992.

[14] S.R. Hall, D.G. MacMartin, and D.S. Bernstein. Covariance averaging in the analysis of uncertain systems. In *Proceedings of IEEE Conference on Decision and Control*, pages 1842–1849, Tucson, AZ, Dec. 1992.

[15] D.R. Seinfeld, W.M. Haddad, D.S. Bernstein, and C.N. Nett. H_2/H_∞ controller synthesis: Illustrative numerical results via quasi-newton methods. In *Proceedings of the American Control Conference*, pages 1155–1156, Boston, MA, June 1991.

[16] D.R. Seinfeld. H_2/H_∞ Optimal Controller Synthesis via Quasi-Newton Methods. Master's thesis, Florida Institute of Technology, 1991.

[17] E.G. Collins, Jr., L.D. Davis, and S. Richter. A homotopy algorithm for Maximum Entropy design Lyapunov equations. *AIAA Journal of Guidance, Control, and Dynamics*. in preparation.

[18] S. Richter, L.D. Davis, and E.G. Collins, Jr. Efficient computation of the solutions to modified Lyapunov equations. *SIAM Journal Matrix Analysis and Applications*. to appear.

[19] S.M. Joshi. *Control of Large Flexible Space Structures*, volume 131 of *Lecture Notes in Control and Information Sciences*. Springer–Verlag, 1989.

[20] B. Wie and K.W. Byun. New generalized structural filtering concept for active vibration control synthesis. *AIAA Journal of Guidance, Control, and Dynamics*, 12(3):147–154, July-Aug. 1989.

[21] J. Doyle, B. Francis, and A. Tannenbaum. *Feedback Control Theory*. Macmillan Publishing Company, New York, NY, 1992.

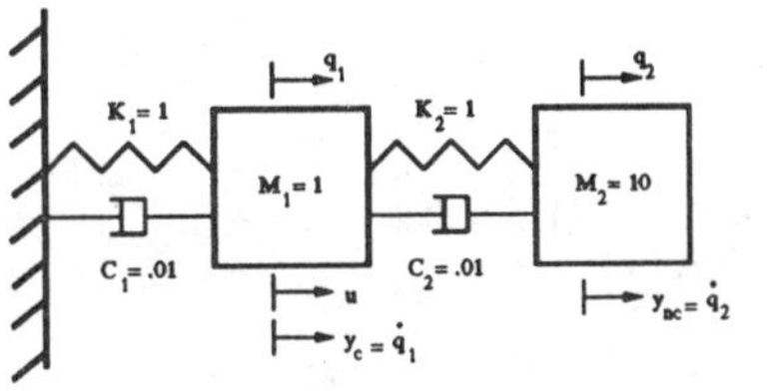

Figure 1: Two – Mass System

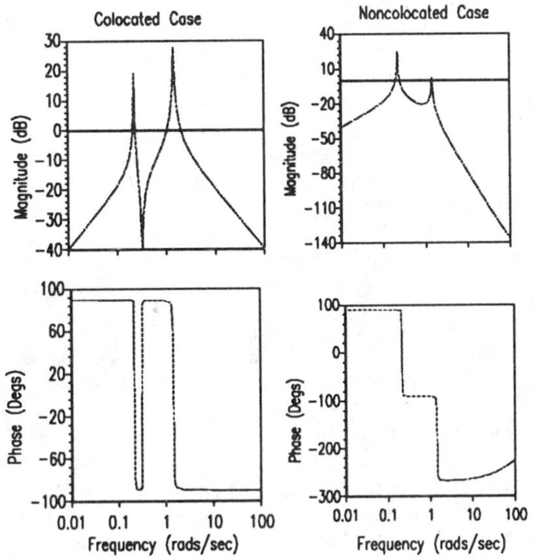

Figure 2: Plant Transfer Functions

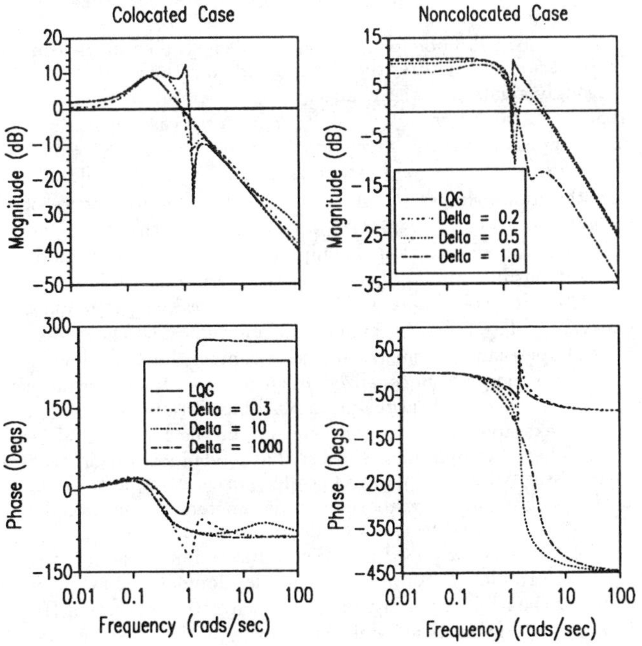

Figure 3: Compensator Transfer Functions

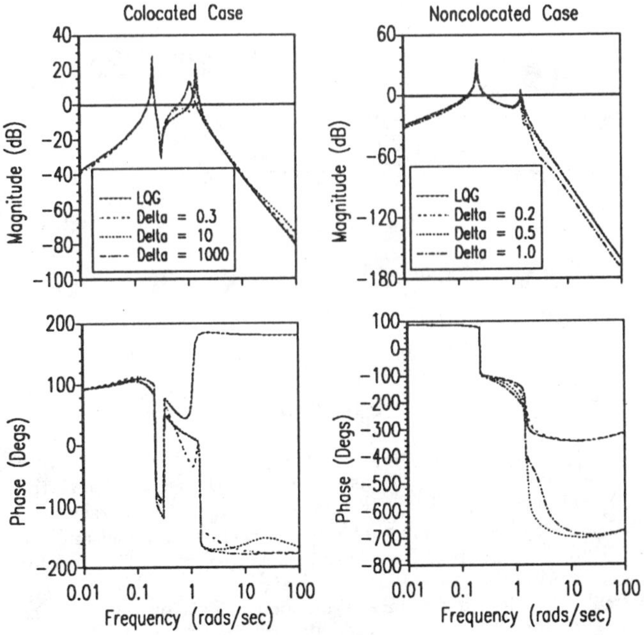

Figure 4: Loop Gain Transfer Functions

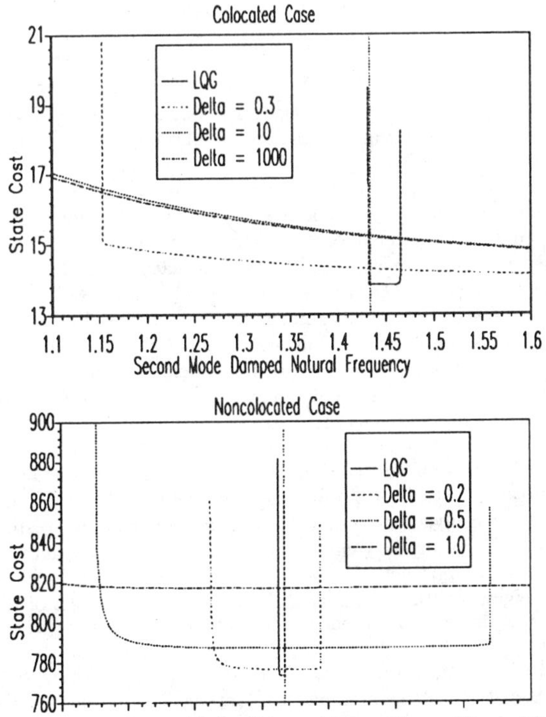

Figure 5: $\mathcal{H}_2$ State Cost for the perturbed system.

Proceedings of the
American Control Conference
San Francisco, California • June 1993

ACTIVE VIBRATION CONTROL USING EIGENVECTOR ASSIGNMENT FOR MODE LOCALIZATION

Byung-Keun Song and Suhada Jayasuriya
Department of Mechanical Engineering
Texas A&M University
College Station, TX 77843-3123

ABSTRACT

In this paper we propose an algorithm for eigenstructure assignment in which the assignment of eigenvectors play the key role while the eigenvalue placement plays a secondary role. Eigenvectors are closely related to classical mode shapes and the specification of special mode shapes can be effectively used for distributing the vibrational energy of flexible structures. In particular by choosing a linearly independent set of mode shapes so that the relative magnitude at a certain prespecified coordinate is small, that coordinate may be somewhat isolated from excessive vibrational energy. This localization of vibrational energy by choosing mode shapes is similar to the phenomenon of normal mode localization in so called periodic structures. Two examples illustrate the various notions presented in the paper.

I. INTRODUCTION

It is well known that the closed-loop eigenvalues of a controllable system can be arbitrarily assigned by linear state feedback [1]. When the system is single-input single-output (SISO) the state feedback gains are unique but when the system is multiple-input the state feedback gains are not unique, i.e., the closed loop system cannot be uniquely determined by only assigning closed-loop eigenvalues. Therefore some added freedom is available in MIMO systems for prescribing some eigenvectors chosen from an admissible class in addition to placing the closed loop poles at prescribed locations. Moore [2] first proposed a design scheme based on the assignment of distinct closed-loop eigenvalues and the corresponding eigenvectors chosen from an admissible eigenvectors set for MIMO systems. Klein and Moore [3] then extended it to include non-distinct closed-loop eigenvalues and generalized eigenvectors. Porter and D'azzo [4, 5] also gave a method and an algorithm for assignnig the closed-loop eigenstructure of multivariable linear systems. Cunningham [6] proposed practical procedures for selecting closed loop eigenvalues and eigenvectors that achieve a desired transient response behavior. Fahmy [7] generalized and extended the eigenvalue-assignment approach of Brogan [8, 9] to include the entire closed-loop eigenstructure of linear multivariable systems. All of these methods have been based on the standard state-space description of plant dynamics.

In this paper, on the other hand, we consider the problem of eigenstructure assignment in plants which are naturally described by a set of simultaneous second order differential equations. Any system that exhibits an oscillatory behavior belongs to this class of plants. So in particular, this system description is useful in cases where structural vibrations are important. Developed is an effective algorithm for the eigenstructure assignment of this class of systems. With the proposed algorithm the mode shapes of the system can be prespecified so that vibrational energy is distributed in a predetermined manner. This, in contrast to the standard pole placement philosophy, emphasizes the need for altering the eigenvectors (or more precisely the mode shapes) as the key to redistributing vibrational energy. Of course within this framework it is also possible to assign a number of eigenvalues when the system has more than one input.

The influence of eigenvectors in distributing vibrational energy has been amply demonstrated by the phenomenon of mode localization. Normal mode localization is a manifestation of disorder in what are normally periodic structures. The dynamics of perfectly periodic systems are known to have special characteristics, notably frequency bands that alternately pass and stop travelling waves with the natural frequencies of the structure lying within the passbands. Moreover, the normal mode shapes of periodic structures are themselves periodic. Hodges [10] demonstrated with simple examples that when the periodicity is disturbed that it can have some amazing consequences. Disruption in the periodicity leads to attenuation of waves in all frequency bands irrespective of any dissipation in the system. Equivalently, each normal mode whose amplitude is periodic along the length of a perfectly periodic structure has its amplitude spatially localized in the disordered counterpart. This localized behavior of the mode shapes, or equivalently the attenuation of all travelling waves, means that energy injected into one end of a disordered periodic structure is not able to propagate arbitrarily far, but is confined to the region near the input (Shaw et al. [11]).

While normal mode localization has been studied in the context of periodic structures the fact remains that the phenomenon is strongly related to the changes brought about in the mode shapes. In fact it is not difficult to imagine cases where the mode shapes of a particular system would have a relatively small amplitude at one location in all of its modes. As an example consider the mode shapes $[1\ 0.1]^T$, $[1\ -0.1]^T$ in a two degree of freedom vibratory system. Here the amplitude at the second coordinate is forced to be small compared to the first. Such mode shapes if feasible would indicate that the vibrations can be localized at the first coordinate with the second coordinate remaining relatively isolated. In the paper we show that such choices for mode shapes can be realized by active control thereby allowing vibrational energy to be localized at specific coordinates or more precisely to isolate vibrations from reaching certain coordinates.

Two examples illustrate the efficacy of the proposed algorithm. These examples also suggest that mode localization need not necessarily be restricted to so called periodic systems. We in fact show that large pertubations in parameters in non-periodic systems can be used to effect mode localization.

The paper is organized as follows. In section II we give the problem formulation followed by the development of an algorithm for the arbitrary assignment of eigenvectors in section III. In section IV given is an illustrative example followed by conclusions in section V.

II. STATEMENT OF THE PROBLEM

Many physical systems can be described by a set of second order linear ordinary differential equations (ODEs). Consider an n-DOF system governed by n linear second order ODEs

$$\ddot{\mathbf{z}}(t) + \hat{\mathbf{C}}\dot{\mathbf{z}}(t) + \hat{\mathbf{K}}\mathbf{z}(t) = \mathbf{u}(t) \quad (1)$$

where $\mathbf{z}(t) \in \mathbf{R}^n$ is a vector of generalized coordinates, $\mathbf{u}(t) \in R^n$ is a forcing vector, and $\hat{\mathbf{C}}$, and $\hat{\mathbf{K}}$ are $n \times n$ real matrices. System (1) can be represented in the state space form

$$\dot{\mathbf{x}}(t) = \mathbf{A}\mathbf{x}(t) + \mathbf{B}\mathbf{u}(t) \quad (2)$$

where

$$\mathbf{x} = \begin{bmatrix} \mathbf{z} \\ \dot{\mathbf{z}} \end{bmatrix}, \quad \mathbf{A} = \begin{bmatrix} \Theta_{n\times n} & \mathbf{I}_{n\times n} \\ -\hat{\mathbf{K}}_{n\times n} & -\hat{\mathbf{C}}_{n\times n} \end{bmatrix}, \quad \mathbf{B} = \begin{bmatrix} \Theta_{n\times n} \\ \mathbf{I}_{n\times n} \end{bmatrix}.$$

Since the output of the above system is $\mathbf{z}(t)$ we get

$$\mathbf{y}(t) = \mathbf{C}\mathbf{x}(t) \quad (3)$$

where $\mathbf{C} = [\ \mathbf{I}_{n\times n} \quad \Theta_{n\times n}\ ]$.

It is well known that the eigenvalues of the closed loop system can be arbitrarily placed while the associated eigenvectors may be chosen from a set of admissible eigenvectors if the open loop system is completely controllable. However, the output response of a system depends on both the eigenvalues and the associated eigenvectors. Consequently, in this study we concentrate on the arbitrary assignment of eigenvectors and eigenvalues using state feedback control

$$\mathbf{u}(t) = \mathbf{K}\mathbf{x}(t) = \begin{bmatrix} \mathbf{K}_1 & \mathbf{K}_2 \end{bmatrix} \begin{bmatrix} \mathbf{z} \\ \dot{\mathbf{z}} \end{bmatrix}.$$

From (2) and the above equation, the closed-loop equations become

$$\dot{\mathbf{x}}(t) = \mathbf{A}_{cl}\,\mathbf{x}(t) \quad (4)$$

where

$$\mathbf{A}_{cl} = \mathbf{A} + \mathbf{B}\mathbf{K} = \begin{bmatrix} \Theta_{n\times n} & \mathbf{I}_{n\times n} \\ (-\hat{\mathbf{K}} + \mathbf{K}_1)_{n\times n} & (-\hat{\mathbf{C}} + \mathbf{K}_2)_{n\times n} \end{bmatrix}.$$

Now the problem is to choose the feedback gain matrix $\mathbf{K}$ so that the closed loop system has a set of $2n$ (including repeated ones) desired eigenvalues $\{\lambda_i\}$ and associated eigenvectors $\{\mathbf{X}_i\}$.

Let us consider the generalized eigen-problem

$$(\mathbf{A}_{cl} - \lambda_i \mathbf{I})\,\mathbf{X}_i^{(l,j)} = \mathbf{X}_i^{(l-1,j)} \quad (5)$$

where

$$i = 1, 2, \cdots, p\,;\ j = 1, 2, \cdots, k_i\,;\ l = 1, 2, \cdots, m_{ji} \quad (6)$$

Without loss of generality, here we assume that the closed-loop system matrix $\mathbf{A}_{cl}$ has p distinct eigenvalues λ_i with geometric multiplicity (i.e., the number of Jordan blocks) k_i and algebraic multiplicity

$$m_i = \sum_{j=1}^{k_i} m_{ji} \quad \text{for} \quad i = 1, 2, \cdots, p \quad (7)$$

with

$$2n = \sum_{i=1}^{p} m_i \quad (8)$$

associated vectors $\mathbf{X}_i^{(l,j)}$ which are linearly independent. The vectors $\mathbf{X}_i^{(1,j)}$ $(j = 1, 2, \cdots, k_i)$ are the k_i eigenvectors associated with the eigenvalue λ_i, while the rest of the vectors in each of the k_i strings of vectors are generalized eigenvectors associated with the eigenvalue λ_i [4]. The entire set of $2n$ linearly independent vectors associated with the eigen-spectrum $\{\lambda_1, \lambda_2, \cdots, \lambda_p\}$ serves as a basis for the 2n-dimensional state space.

III. MODE SHAPES AND EIGENVALUES ASSIGNMENT

By substituting $\mathbf{A}_{cl}$ and $\mathbf{X}_i$ into (5), we obtain the equation

$$\begin{bmatrix} -\lambda_i \mathbf{I} & \mathbf{I} \\ -\hat{\mathbf{K}} + \mathbf{K}_1 & -\hat{\mathbf{C}} + \mathbf{K}_2 - \lambda_i \mathbf{I} \end{bmatrix} \begin{bmatrix} \mathbf{Z}_i^{(l,j)} \\ \dot{\mathbf{Z}}_i^{(l,j)} \end{bmatrix} = \begin{bmatrix} \mathbf{Z}_i^{(l-1,j)} \\ \dot{\mathbf{Z}}_i^{(l-1,j)} \end{bmatrix} \quad (9)$$

where the subscripts i, j, l are the same as in (6).

Now, we have the following easy proposition.

Proposition :

(i) System (2) is controllable and observable, and

(ii) both the eigenvalues and the associated mode shapes of its closed loop system ($\mathbf{A}_{cl}$) given in (4) can be arbitrarily assigned with a unique state feedback $\mathbf{u} = \mathbf{K}\mathbf{x}$ so long as the mode shape vectors form a linearly independent set.

Proof : Omitted.

Remark : In conventional pole placement, the emphasis is usually placed only on arbitrary assignability of eigenvalues whereas the above proposition deals with the assignability of both the eigenvalues and the mode shapes. In vibration studies the upper half of the eigenvector, $\mathbf{Z}_i$, is referred to as a 'mode shape'.

Next, we will explicitly solve the matrix equation for the state feedback gain matrix, $\mathbf{K}$, in terms of the eigenvalues, λ_i, and the associated mode-shape vectors, $\mathbf{Z}_i^{(l,j)}$.

This is done by first obtaining $\dot{\mathbf{Z}}_i^{(l,j)}$ using (??) and then constructing the $2n$ eigenvectors $\mathbf{X}_i^{(l,j)}$, which in turn is used to obtain the $2n$ vectors defined by

$$\mathbf{W}_i^{(l,j)} \triangleq \begin{bmatrix} \hat{\mathbf{K}} & \hat{\mathbf{C}} - \lambda_i \mathbf{I} \end{bmatrix} \mathbf{X}_i^{(l,j)} - \dot{\mathbf{Z}}_i^{(l-1,j)}. \quad (10)$$

Now, we have the useful identity

$$\mathbf{W}_i^{(l,j)} = \begin{bmatrix} \mathbf{K}_1 & \mathbf{K}_2 \end{bmatrix} \mathbf{X}_i^{(l,j)} = \mathbf{K}\mathbf{X}_i^{(l,j)} \quad (11)$$

which can be easily proven by substituting (11) into (12). Next, construct the two matrices defined by

$$\mathbf{X} \triangleq \begin{bmatrix} \mathbf{X}_1^{(1,1)} & \cdots & \mathbf{X}_p^{(m_{k_p p}, k_p)} \end{bmatrix} \quad (12)$$

and

$$\mathbf{W} \triangleq \begin{bmatrix} \mathbf{W}_1^{(1,1)} & \cdots & \mathbf{W}_p^{(m_{k_p p}, k_p)} \end{bmatrix} \quad (13)$$

with the predetermined $2n$ vectors $\mathbf{W}_i^{(l,j)}$ and $\mathbf{X}_i^{(i,j)}$, respectively. From (11), (12) and (13), we obtain a matrix equation

$$\mathbf{W} = \mathbf{K}\mathbf{X}\,. \quad (14)$$

Note that $\mathbf{X}$ is invertible since the eigenvectors are linearly independent.

Finally, obtain the state feedback matrix $\mathbf{K}$ in terms of $\mathbf{X}$ and $\mathbf{W}$ from (14) as

$$\mathbf{K} = \mathbf{W}\mathbf{X}^{-1} \quad (15)$$

Note that we can also obtain $\mathbf{K}_{(n\times 2n)}$ directly by just solving $2n^2$ algebraic equations from (11) without having to introduce $\mathbf{W}_i$.

Now, consider the case where the closed loop system has distinct eigenvalues. In this case the superscripts l, j are not needed because for this case $k_i = m_{ji} = 1$, $p = 2n$. Hence the eigenproblem (5) can be replaced by

$$(\mathbf{A}_{cl} - \lambda_i \mathbf{I})\mathbf{X}_i = 0 \quad \text{for} \quad i = 1, 2, \cdots, 2n\,. \quad (16)$$

The rest of the equations should also be changed appropriately.

This is done by disregarding the terms with the superscript $(l-1, j)$ and deleting the superscript (l, j). Also in this case, we can arbitrarily assign the $2n$ mode shape vectors as long as they are linearly independent. As will be seen later this is an important consideration for the mode localization application.

IV. AN EXAMPLE

In this section we study the dynamics of an oscillatory two degree of freedom system that can be thought of as a model of a flexible structure. In particular, we wish to address the question of distributing the vibrational energy so that at a chosen coordinate the relative displacement is kept small irrespective of the type of disturbance signals appearing at the two coordinates. Our strategy is to localize the vibrational energy away from the coordinate to be isolated. This is done by choosing two mode shapes in which the relative displacement of the coordinate to be isolated is small. We also introduce some viscous damping to eliminate excessive oscillations at resonant frequencies. Once the desired mode shapes and frequencies are chosen we use the development of the previous section to determine the feedback gain matrix.

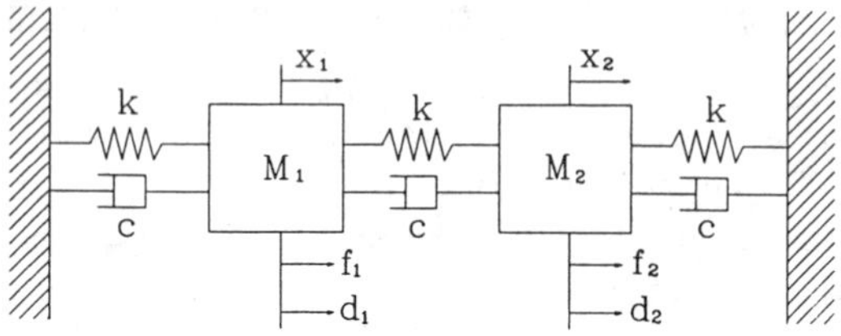

Figure 1. Two degree-of-freedom mechanical system.

Consider the two degree-of-freedom mechanical system shown in Fig. 1. The equations of motion for the system can be described in the state-space form as

$$\begin{aligned} \dot{\mathbf{x}}(t) &= \mathbf{A}\,\mathbf{x}(t) + \mathbf{B}\,\mathbf{f}(t) + \mathbf{E}\,\mathbf{d}(t) \\ \mathbf{y}(t) &= \mathbf{C}\,\mathbf{x}(t) \end{aligned} \tag{17}$$

where

$$\mathbf{A} = \begin{bmatrix} 0 & 0 & 1 & 0 \\ 0 & 0 & 0 & 1 \\ -2k/m_1 & k/m_1 & -2c/m_1 & c/m_1 \\ k/m_2 & -2k/m_2 & c/m_2 & -2c/m_2 \end{bmatrix},$$

$$\mathbf{B} = \mathbf{E} = \begin{bmatrix} 0 & 0 \\ 0 & 0 \\ 1/m_1 & 0 \\ 0 & 1/m_2 \end{bmatrix}, \quad \mathbf{C} = \begin{bmatrix} 1 & 0 & 0 & 0 \\ 0 & 1 & 0 & 0 \end{bmatrix}$$

with the state vector $\mathbf{x} = [\ x_1 \ \ x_2 \ \ \dot{x}_1 \ \ \dot{x}_2\ ]^T$, the control vector $\mathbf{f} = [\ f_1 \ \ f_2\ ]^T$ and the disturbance vector $\mathbf{d} = [\ d_1 \ \ d_2\ ]^T$.

The contol objective is to isolate the motion of m_2 from that of m_1 through mode localization. Without loss of generality, set $m_1 = m_2 = k = 1$, $c = 0$ to simplify computation, so that the system matrices become

$$\mathbf{A} = \begin{bmatrix} 0 & 0 & 1 & 0 \\ 0 & 0 & 0 & 1 \\ -2 & 1 & 0 & 0 \\ 1 & -2 & 0 & 0 \end{bmatrix}, \quad \mathbf{B} = \mathbf{E} = \begin{bmatrix} 0 & 0 \\ 0 & 0 \\ 1 & 0 \\ 0 & 1 \end{bmatrix}, \tag{18}$$

$$\mathbf{C} = \begin{bmatrix} 1 & 0 & 0 & 0 \\ 0 & 1 & 0 & 0 \end{bmatrix}.$$

It is easy to see that the open-loop system has eigenvalues, $\lambda_{1,2} = \pm 1i$ and $\lambda_{3,4} = \pm 1.73i$ with the associated mode shapes

$$\begin{bmatrix} X_1 \\ X_2 \end{bmatrix}^1 = \begin{bmatrix} X_1 \\ X_2 \end{bmatrix}^2 = \begin{bmatrix} 1 \\ 1 \end{bmatrix} \text{ and } \begin{bmatrix} X_1 \\ X_2 \end{bmatrix}^3 = \begin{bmatrix} X_1 \\ X_2 \end{bmatrix}^4 = \begin{bmatrix} 1 \\ -1 \end{bmatrix}.$$

Suppose that mass 2 amplitude of oscillation is required to be much less (say, about -20 db) compared to mass 1. To achieve the required performance, let us utilize the state feedback control law,

$$\begin{bmatrix} f_1(t) \\ f_2(t) \end{bmatrix} = \mathbf{K}\mathbf{x}(t) \tag{19}$$

where $\mathbf{K} \in \mathbf{R}^{2\times 4}$ is the feedback matrix to be determined, and $\mathbf{x}(t) \in \mathbf{R}^4$ is the state vector.

Let us first assign distinct self conjugate eigenvalues to provide a damping ratio $\zeta = .707$ while keeping the damped natural frequencies unchanged from the original undamped natural frequencies, by choosing:

$$\lambda_{1,2} = -1 \pm 1i \text{ and } \lambda_{3,4} = -1.73 \pm 1.73i\,,$$

and let us confine most of the vibrational energy to be absorbed by mass 1, by localizing the associated mode shapes as follows:

$$\begin{bmatrix} X_1 \\ X_2 \end{bmatrix}^1 = \begin{bmatrix} X_1 \\ X_2 \end{bmatrix}^2 = \begin{bmatrix} 1 \\ .1 \end{bmatrix} \text{ and } \begin{bmatrix} X_1 \\ X_2 \end{bmatrix}^3 = \begin{bmatrix} X_1 \\ X_2 \end{bmatrix}^4 = \begin{bmatrix} 1 \\ -.1 \end{bmatrix}.$$

Here, we deliberately chose coordinate 2 displacement to be 10 % of coordinate one displacement. The frequencies although were arbitrarily set can in general be chosen to satisfy additional design requirements.

With the upper half of the eigenvectors specified by the mode shapes the entries of the lower half of the four eigenvectors can be determined by (10), thus completing the entire set of eigenvectors:

$$\mathbf{X}^i = \begin{bmatrix} X_1 \\ X_2 \\ \lambda_i X_1 \\ \lambda_i X_2 \end{bmatrix}^i \tag{20}$$

Now from (11), we can obtain one set of 2 independent equations for each $i = 1, 2, 3, 4$. However, for a self-conjugate pair of eigenvalues the associated two sets of equations are dependent. Consequently, a total of 4 (2 for each $i = 1, 3$) independent complex algebraic equations are obtained as follows:

$$\begin{bmatrix} K_{11}-2 & K_{12}+1 & K_{13}-\lambda_i & K_{14} \\ K_{21}+1 & K_{22}-2 & K_{23} & K_{24}-\lambda_i \end{bmatrix} \mathbf{X}^i = \mathbf{\Theta}\,,\ i = 1,\, 3 \tag{21}$$

By separating the 4 complex algebraic equations into real and imaginary parts, we get 8 independent real algebraic equations with 8 unknown elements of the state feedback matrix $\mathbf{K}$. And the state feeback matrix $\mathbf{K}$ is obtained from the equations as follows:

$$\mathbf{K} = \begin{bmatrix} -2 & 19 & -2.734 & 7.341 \\ -.8 & -2 & .0734 & -2.734 \end{bmatrix} \tag{22}$$

With this $\mathbf{K}$ the resulting closed loop system matrix $\mathbf{A}_{cl}$ becomes

$$\mathbf{A}_{cl} = \begin{bmatrix} 0 & 0 & 1 & 0 \\ 0 & 0 & 0 & 1 \\ -4 & 20 & -2.734 & 7.341 \\ .2 & -4 & .0734 & -2.734 \end{bmatrix}. \tag{23}$$

Note that the elements of $\mathbf{A}_{cl}$ appear substantially perturbed from the open loop entries of $\mathbf{A}$ given in (20). This fact is interesting since it shows that we have achieved mode localization with a matrix structure that is far removed from symmetry. This shows that one does not need a so called periodic structure and small perturbations to exhibit the phenomenon of mode localization.

The resulting closed loop system was simulated with a number of disturbance inputs to ascertain its performance. Figure 2 shows the Bode plots of the closed loop system due to disturbance d_1 and Fig. 3 shows that due to d_2. These depict the

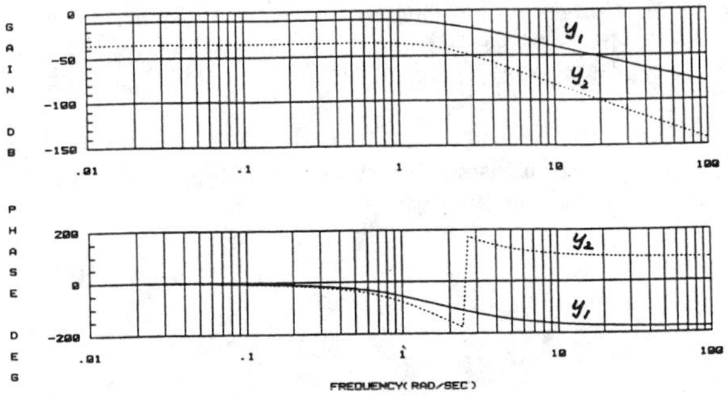

Figure 2. Bode plots of y_1/d_1 and y_2/d_1 for example 1.

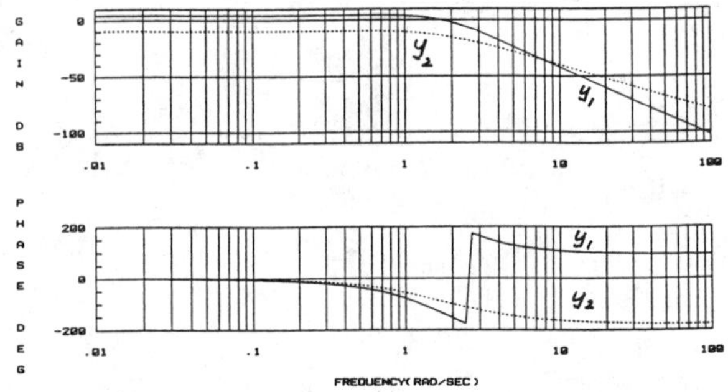

Figure 3. Bode plots of y_1/d_2 and y_2/d_2 for example 1.

kind of attenuation or amplification to be expected from various sinusoidal disturbances. From Fig. 2 it is clear that the output y_2 is attenuated more than y_1 and is about 25 *db* lower when the disturbance is d_1 or is at the first mass.

When only the disturbance d_2 is present, the amplitude of y_2 is about 13*db* lower than that of y_1 up to a disturbance frequency of 1 rad/sec and thereafter the slope of the y_1 gain is steeper than that of y_2 gain making the difference in gains smaller with increasing frequencies, being equal at 8 rad/sec, and then again increasing as the frequency increases beyond 8 rad/sec. As can be seen from Fig. 3 the displacement of mass 2 can be attenuated for all frequencies within the bandwidth.

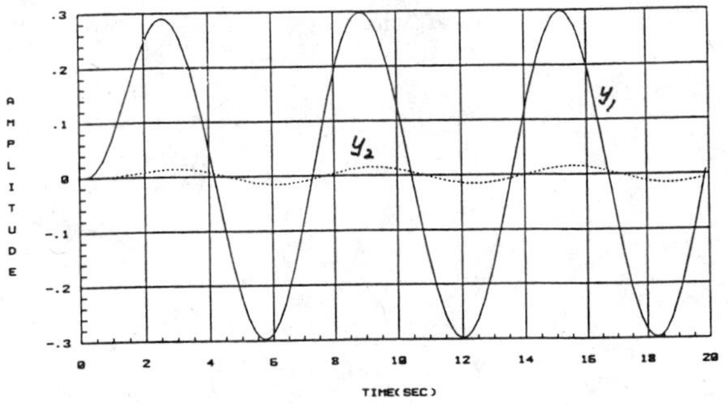

Figure 4. y_1 and y_2 vs t of example 1 for $d_1(t) = \sin t$.

Shown in Figs. 4-9 are time responses that result from various disturbance inputs. We see in all of them except for $d_2 = \sin 10t$ that the output y_2 is relatively well isolated from the disturbance. The steady state responses of y_2 and y_1 due to the disturbance $d_2 = \sin 10t$ are comparable. But even in this case, it is interesting to note that, during the initial transient phase the maximum displacement of y_1 is much larger than y_2 as is evident from Fig. 7. This however is not surprising and was expected from Fig. 3.

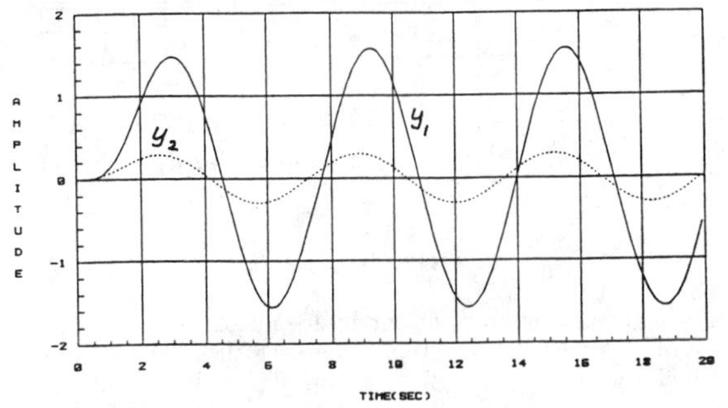

Figure 5. y_1 and y_2 vs t of example 1 for $d_2(t) = \sin t$.

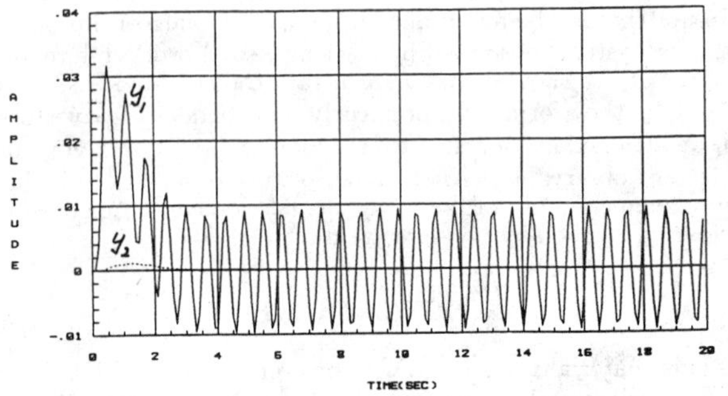

Figure 6. y_1 and y_2 vs t of example 1 for $d_1(t) = \sin(10t)$.

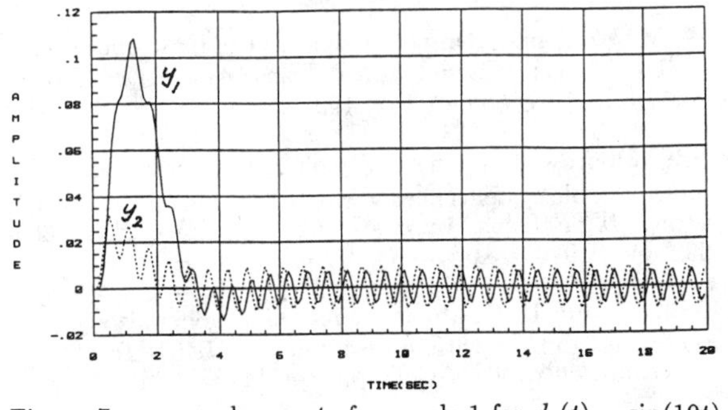

Figure 7. y_1 and y_2 vs t of example 1 for $d_2(t) = \sin(10t)$.

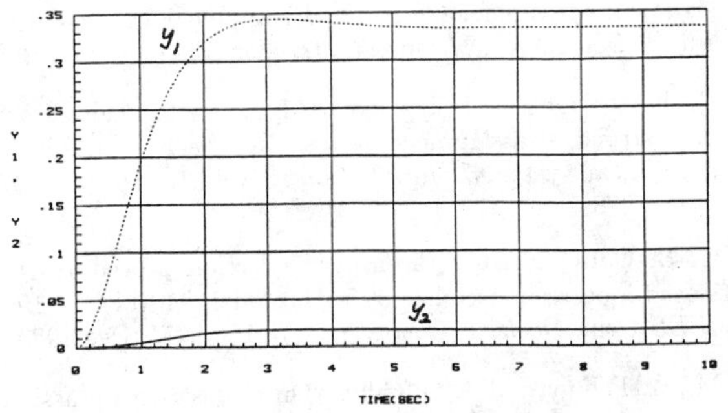

Figure 8. y_1 and y_2 vs t of example 1 for $d_1(t) = 1(t)$.

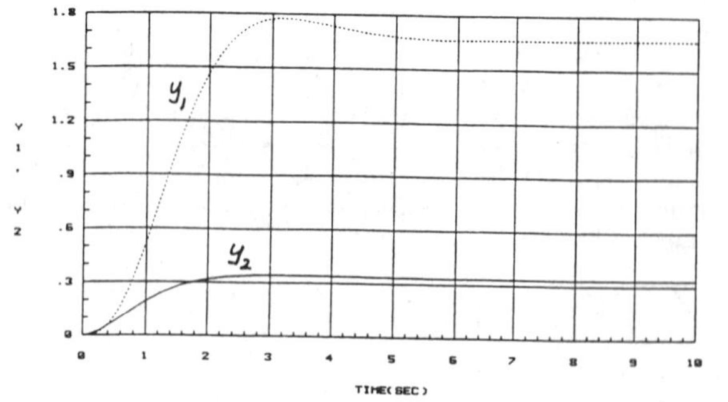

Figure 9. y_1 and y_2 vs t of example 1 for $d_2(t) = 1(t)$.

V. CONCLUSION

It has been shown that mode localization is an effective means of disturbance isolation whenever the disturbances are not precisely known. It can be accomplished by modifying the system with state feedback so that the mode shapes take on a special structure. In particular mode shapes are chosen in such a way that the relative magnitude of the coordinate to be isolated is small. Once the mode shapes are prespecified the required gain matrix may be determined using a special algorithm developed for systems described by a set of second order differential equations. We showed that an arbitrary choice of mode shapes, so long as they form a set of linearly independent eigenvectors, can be attained as long as the open loop system is both controllable and observable. Another interesting observation is that the phenomenon of normal mode localization can occur even in systems described by non-circular matrices.

ACKNOWLEDGMENT

This material is based in part on work supported by Texas Advanced Research Program under Grant No: 999903-069.

REFERENCES

[1] W. M. Wonham , "On pole assignment in multi-input, controllable linear system," *IEEE Trans. Automatic. Contr.*, vol. AC-12, pp.660-665, Dec. 1967.

[2] B. C. Moore, "On the flexibility offered by state feedback in multivariable systems beyond closed loop eigenvalue assignment," *IEEE Trans. Automatic. Contr.*, vol. AC-21, pp.689-692, Oct. 1976.

[3] G. Klein and B. C. Moore, "Eigenvalue-generalized eigenvector assignment with state feedback," *IEEE Trans. Automatic. Contr.*, vol. AC-22, pp. 140-141, Feb. 1977.

[4] B. Porter and J. J. D'Azzo, "Closed-loop eigenstructure assignment by state feedback in multivariable linear systems," *Int. J. Contr.*, vol. 27, pp.487-492, Mar. 1978.

[5] B. Porter and J. J. D'Azzo, "Algirithm for closed-loop eigenstructure assignment by state feedback in multivariable linear systems," *Int. J. Contr.*, vol. 27, pp. 943-947, June 1978.

[6] T. B. Cunningham, "Eigenspace selection procedures for closed loop response shaping with modal control," in *19th IEEE Conf. Decision Contr.*, pp. 178-186, NM. Dec 1980.

[7] M. M. Fahmy and J. O'Reilly, "On eigenstructure assignment in linear multivariable Systems," *IEEE Trans. Automatic. Contr.*, vol. AC-27, no. 3, June 1982.

[8] W. L. Brogan, *Modern Control Theory*, Prentice-Hall, Inc., Englewood Cliffs, New Jersey, 1985

[9] W. L. Brogan, "Applilcations of a determinant identity to pole-placement and observer problems," *IEEE Trand. Automat. Contr.*, vol. AC-19, pp. 612-624, Oct. 1974.

[10] C. H. Hodges, "Confinement of vibration by structural irregularity," *Journal of Sound and Vibration*, vol. 82, no.3, pp. 411-424, 1982.

[11] J. Shaw, S. Jayasuriya, and M. Rabins, "Normal mode localizations of a disordered structure," Report, Texas A&M University, June 1990.

Proceedings of the
American Control Conference
San Francisco, California • June 1993

On Relative Degrees and Zero Dynamics from System Configuration

S.-T. Wu and K. Youcef-Toumi

Department of Mechanical Engineering
Massachusetts Institute of Technology

Abstract

Relative degrees and zero dynamics are intrinsic system properties associated with a given input-output pair. In the design of output tracking controllers, the relative degree and the stability of the zero dynamics of the control plant are usually assumed to be known in advance, and are determined by analyzing the system dynamic equations. With the help of bond graphs and through physical reasoning, a set of rules are proposed in this paper to determine the relative degree and the stability of the zero dynamics for a class of systems independent of the system dynamic equations. The rules establish a connection between these system properties and the physical structures, and are useful guidelines on the adjustment of relative degrees and zero dynamics for the purpose of control design.

1 Introduction

One of the major objectives of feedback control is to cope with uncertainties of various kinds. While a good controller should be able to guarantee satisfactory performance in the presence of system uncertainties and external disturbances, there are some properties of the control plant that must be acquired in advance before the design of a control algorithm can be undertaken. In the design of tracking controllers such as adaptive control (e.g., [1, 2, 3]) , sliding control (e.g., [3]), time delay control [4, 5, 6], and global feedback linearization [7], two of the most common *a priori* system properties are: relative degrees of the control plant and the stability of its zero dynamics. In single-input/single-output linear systems, the relative degree is the excess of poles over zeros in the system transfer function. Relative degrees determine the structure, order, and complexity of the controller. Zero dynamics are defined to be the internal dynamics of a system when the input is chosen in such a way that the output is identically zero; for linear systems the zero dynamics are characterized by the zeros of the transfer functions. The stability of zero dynamics is closely related to the boundedness of the control actions in performing output tracking. A system is called *minimum-phase* if its zero dynamics are stable and *non-minimum-phase* if the zero dynamics are unstable. Zero dynamics are an intrinsic system property and are not changed by feedback control action.

This paper investigates the issues of relative degrees and zeros/zero dynamics by reasoning on the system physical configurations rather than analyzing the mathematical equations. The objectives are to gain insight into the physical aspects of zero dynamics and relative degrees and to develop efficient guidelines on the identification and adjustment of these system properties for the purpose of control design.

The relationship between relative degrees and bond graph models was addressed in [8], where the relative degree is determined by a "table-look-up" approach for a limited class of systems based on the relations of the transfer functions and the corresponding bond graph models. Developed from the time-domain interpretation of relative degrees, the rule presented in the paper is much simpler and is applicable to a large class of systems.

The relations between the system zeros and the system mechanical structure was investigated in [9], which provided a physical interpretation for the transfer function zeros of control systems with mechanical flexibilities. The work in [9] was a frequency-domain observation, while this paper takes a time-domain approach on a broader class of systems and specifically describes the relations between the zeros/zero dynamics and the physical structure.

2 Determination of Relative Degree from Physical Configurations

In this section a simple rule of identifying the relative degree between an input-output pair for a class of systems will be presented. The rule is derived from the observations of bond graph models [11, 12]. The mathematical justifications are presented in [10].

The system under consideration in this paper consists of 1-port elements, C's (generalized capacitance), I's (generalized inertance or inductance), R's (generalized resistance) and 2-port passive transducers, TF's (ideal transformers), GY's (ideal gyrators), and energy sources, S_e (effort source such as force and voltage source) or S_f (flow source such as velocity and current source).

2.1 Rule for Identifying Relative Degrees

Definition 1:
path: A series of effort and flow variables connecting one specified variable to another in a bond graph model according to the causal implication is called a path between the two specified variables. (Illustrated below.)

It is noted that the concept of path is similar to the concept of "causal path" which was used in [13] to construct signal flow graphs from bond graphs, and in [14] to determine the "index of nilpotency".

Definition 2:
shortest path: Among the alternative paths connecting two variables, the one that yields the minimum number of *independent* energy storage elements less *dependent* energy storage elements on the path is called the shortest path connecting the two variables.

As an illustration, Fig. 1 shows two alternative paths connecting the flow variable f_6 and the input variable e_{in}. For path 1, f_6 is connected to e_6 because the former is *dictated* by the latter, i.e. e_6 is the input variable to the I element while f_6 is the corresponding output variable, as the causal stroke implies. (e_6 is called the *causal variable* of f_6.) In turn e_6 is connected to e_3 since the causal stroke implies that e_6 is dictated by e_3. Similarly, e_3 is connected to e_5 because e_5, together with e_4, dictates e_3, and so forth. Path 2 follows a different route by way of e_4 which is also a causal variable of e_3. In this case path 2 is the shortest path connecting f_6 and e_{in}, since there are two independent energy storage elements on Path 2 compared to 3 on Path 1. Note that there are only two paths connecting f_6 and e_{in} in this example. A route that encircles the same element more than once is not considered a legitimate path.

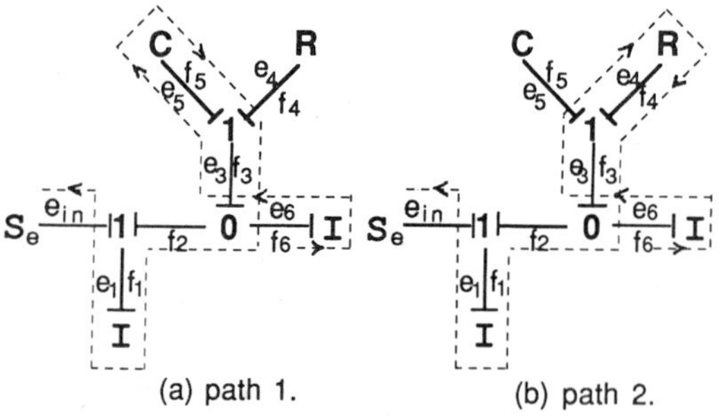

Figure 1: Two alternative paths from the output f_6 to the input e_{in}.

With the definition of path and shortest path, the rule of determining relative degrees can now be stated.

Rule 1: The relative degree between a given output variable and an input variable is the *excess of independent energy storage elements over dependent energy storage elements on the shortest path* from the output variable to the input in the bond graph model.

For examples, the relative degree between f_6 and e_{in} in Fig. 1 is 2 since there are two independent energy storage elements on the shortest path (path 2) from f_6 to e_{in}. And in Fig. 2, (which is similar to one shown in [15],) the relative degree between f_1 and f_{in} is 0 since there is one independent energy storage element I_1 *and* one dependent energy storage element I_2 on the shortest path from f_1 to f_{in}.

With the rule, one can readily determine the relative degree for *any* input-output pair in the bond graph model. Moreover, for a given variable which is a linear combination of some flow/effort variables in the bond graph model, the relative degree associated with the given variable is in general the same as that associated with the constituent flow/effort variable which yields the *lowest* relative degree.

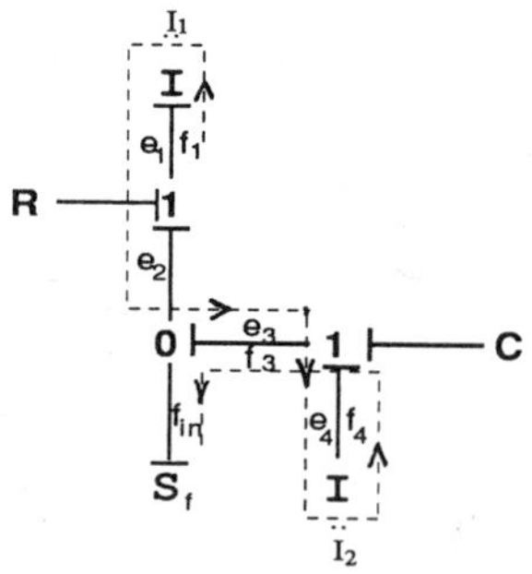

Figure 2: A system with a dependent energy storage element.

There is an exception to the rule if in the bond graph model there exist more than one *shortest* paths. For example, if there are two paths having the same number of independent energy storage elements less the number of dependent energy storage elements, and this same number, denoted by r', is the least among other alternative paths, then it is *possible* to have the relative degree *larger* than r', *provided that the parameters of the elements are forced to satisfy a specific algebraic constraint* [10].

2.2 Examples

In this section some physical examples are given to illustrate the rule stated in the previous section and to show how relative degrees are related to the system physical structure.

Example 1: A Lumped-parameter Mechanical System.

Figure 3 shows a mass-spring connected system and the corresponding bond graph model. Given the force F as the input variable, the relative degrees will be determined when different output variables are selected.

To find the relative degree in the conventional way, the system dynamic equations have to be derived first. The output variable is

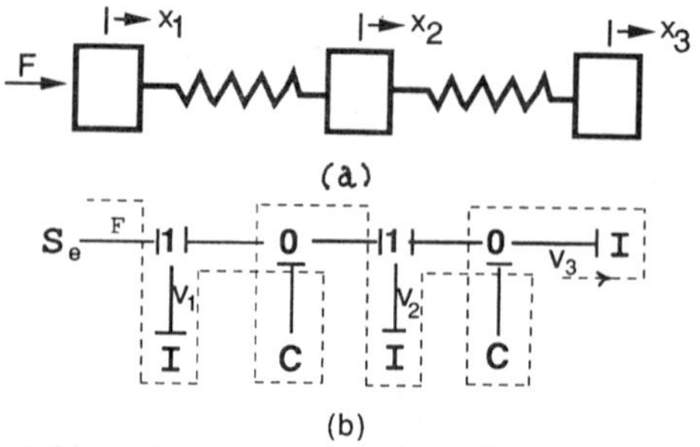

Figure 3: A lumped-parameter mechanical system: (a)schematic; (b)bond graph model.

then differentiated with respect to time repeatedly until an explicit relationship between the input and output variable is generated. Instead of using the system equations and the differentiation procedure, Rule 1 is now applied to determine the relative degrees by examining the bond graph in Fig. 3. Following the path indicated by the dashed line in Fig. 3, it is seen that there is one independent energy storage element on the shortest path from v_1 to the input F, and hence the relative degree between v_1 and F is 1. Since v_1 is the first time derivative of x_1, it follows that the relative degree between x_1 and F is 2. Note that there is a unique path from each power variable to the input, and thus the path is the shortest.

Similarly, there are 3 independent energy storage elements on the shortest path from v_2 to F, the relative degree is 3 between v_2 and F and therefore is 4 between x_2 and F. For the case of taking x_3 as the output variable, there are 5 independent energy storage elements between v_3 and F; as a result the relative degree is 5 between v_3 and F, and is 6 between x_3 and F.

Besides the efficiency in determining the relative degree between a pair of input-output variables for a given physical structure, the rule also makes it easy to visualize how the relative degree changes as the physical structure is adjusted. Suppose there is some dissipative effect present in the system of Fig. 3, and dampers are added between the masses as shown in Fig. 4. By inspecting the bond graph of Fig. 5a, it can be easily figured out that the relative degree for the input-output pair of (F, v_2) becomes 2 since now the generalized capacitor C is off the shortest path from v_2 to F, and there are only 2 independent energy storage elements on the path. The relative degree is reduced by one due to the presence of the damper between the two masses. Note that from the equivalent bond graph of Fig. 5b the same number of independent energy storage elements is obtained on the shortest path from v_2 to F.

It is also seen that the relative degree for (F, v_3) is reduced to 3 by the inclusion of the two dampers in the model.

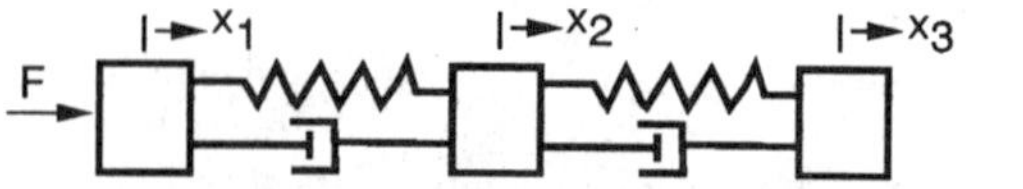

Figure 4: A mass-spring-damper system

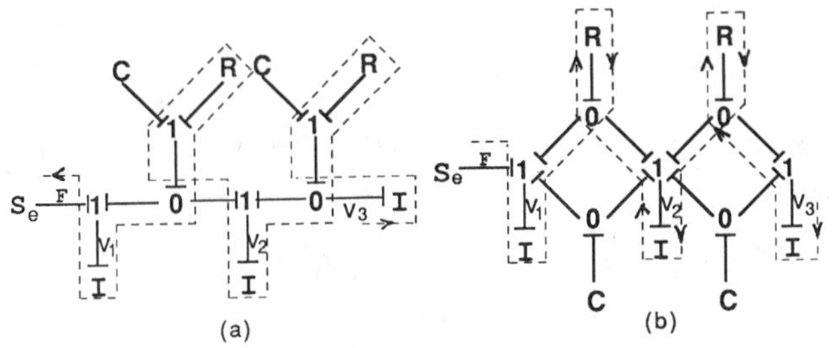

Figure 5: Two equivalent bond graphs for the mass-spring-damper system.

Example 2: A Distributed Parameter System

Fig. 6 shows a uniform flexible bar which is undergoing longitudinal motion. For the purpose of analysis, the continuous system is usually discretized into a finite dimensional model. Two different approximation methods are to be discussed here.

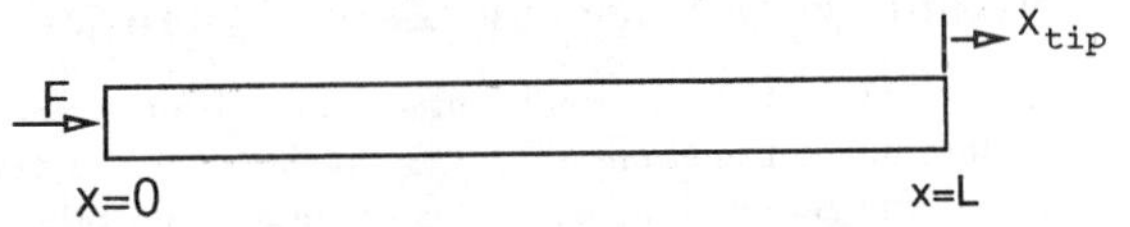

Figure 6: A uniform bar in longitudinal motion.

The first approximation is a lumped parameter model which is composed of finite elements of mass and spring connected in series, as shown in Fig. 7. The second approximation is by modal decomposition where a finite number of natural modes of vibration are used to approximate the system, as shown in Fig. 8. The derivation of a similar bond graph for a fixed-end bar can be found in [12]. Note that in Fig. 8, q_i is the coordinate describing the displacement of the *i'th* natural mode in free-end-vibration. The coordinate q_0 describes the rigid-body motion. The tip velocity is a linear combination of the flow variables $\dot{q}_0 \cdots \dot{q}_n$.

It will be shown that the two different models yield very different relative degrees between the control input and the displacement at the tip..

The relative degree associated with the control input F and the tip displacement is now determined. For the lumped model approximation of Fig. 7, counting the number of independent energy storage elements on the shortest path from v_{tip} to F, we find that the relative degree is $2n-1$ between v_{tip} and F, n being the number of mass elements taken, and is therefore $2n$ between x_{tip} and F.

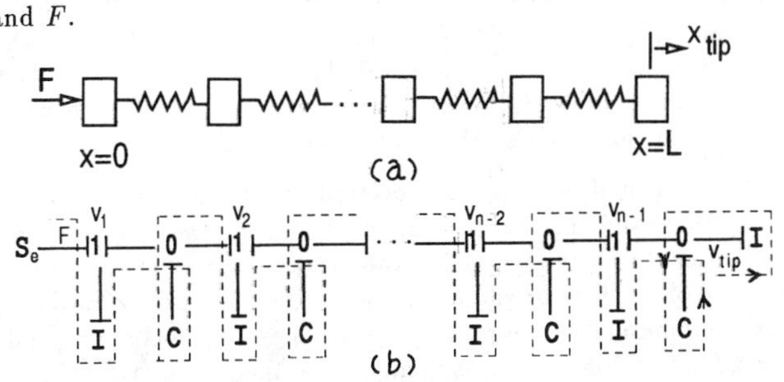

Figure 7: Serially-connected-element model of the uniform bar:(a)schematic; (b)bond graph.

The relative degree from the modal approximation, on the other hand, yields a relative degree of 2, no matter how many modes are taken. This is easily seen from Fig. 8, where there is one independent energy storage element on the shortest path from each $\dot{q}_i$ to F and hence the relative degree between each $\dot{q}_i$ and F is 1. Since the tip velocity is a linear combination of $\dot{q}_i$, the relative degree is 1 between the tip velocity and the input, and is therefore 2 between the tip displacement and the input.

The two different models also imply fundamentally different zero dynamics, to be discussed later.

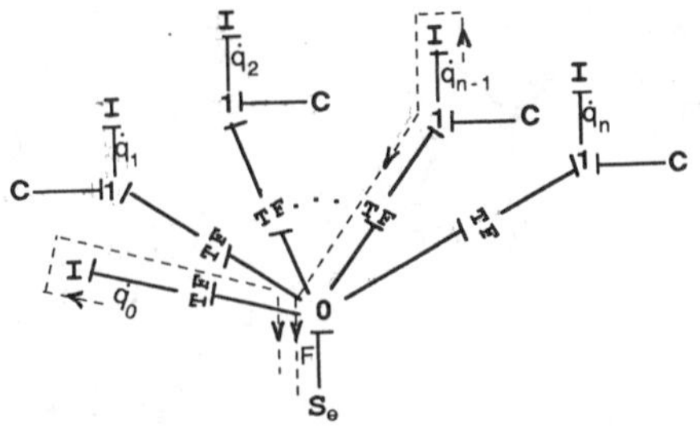

Figure 8: Finite-mode model of the uniform bar.

3 Stability of Zero Dynamics

The zero dynamics of a system associated with an input-output pair are defined to be the internal dynamics of the system when the input is chosen in such a way that the output variable is kept identically zero. For single-input/single-output systems, the zero dynamics are fully characterized by the zeros in the forward transfer functions, i.e., the zeros are the eigenvalues of the zero dynamics. The stability of the zero dynamics is closely related to the boundedness of the control action in output tracking control. It is known that perfect output tracking is impossible with bounded control action for non-minimum phase linear systems, i.e., systems with right-half-plane zeros.

In this section, the zero dynamics for a class of passive systems will be analyzed with the help of bond graph without deriving the system dynamic equations explicitly. In particular, we will discuss the stability of the zero dynamics and how the zero dynamics are affected by the elements in the bond graph model. For rigorousness the systems are assumed to be linear. However the results may be applied to a class of nonlinear systems since the reasoning procedure is independent of the detailed mathematical equations.

3.1 Systems with Stable Zero Dynamics

Consider the system of Fig. 9, where there is a single power line connecting the input source and the output variable, f_2. Note that a *power line* is a serial connection of bonds, **0**, and **1** junctions and is different from *path* that is defined in the previous section.

From the definition of zero dynamics, its stability is determined by the internal dynamics when the output, f_2, is *identically* 0. To find the characteristics of the zero dynamics, let's examine the behavior of the system when the system is arbitrarily perturbed from the equilibrium state and the output variable, f_2, is kept zero all the time.

The system model is reproduced in Fig. 10, where the dashed lines indicate a "relaxed" bond, i.e. a bond with both of its associated flow and effort variables being identically zero. In Fig. 10.a, the bond associated with f_2 is relaxed since f_2 is kept identically

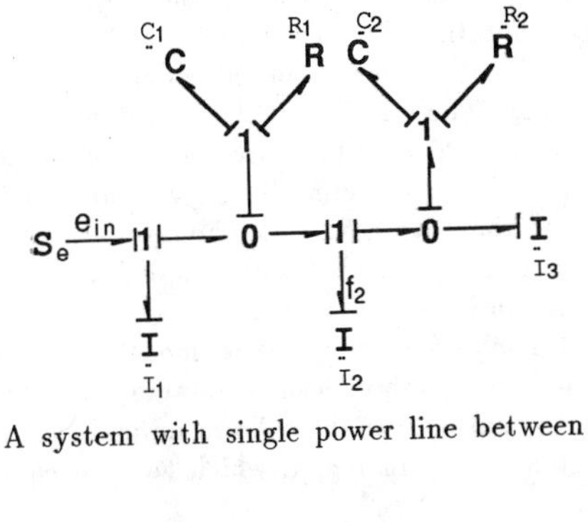

Figure 9: A system with single power line between input and output.

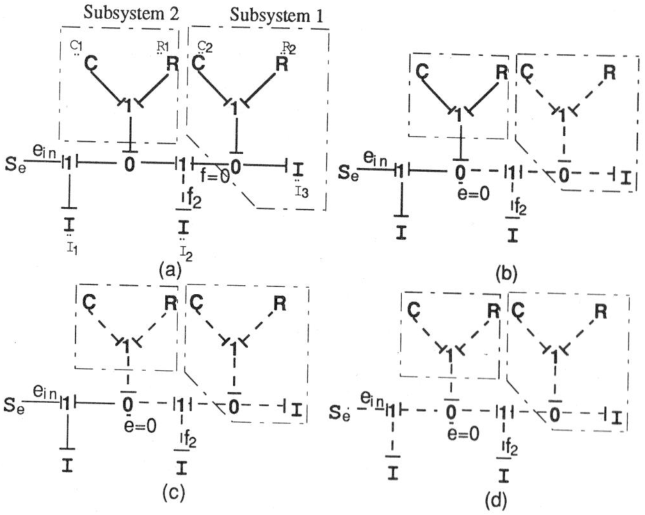

Figure 10: History of energy decay.

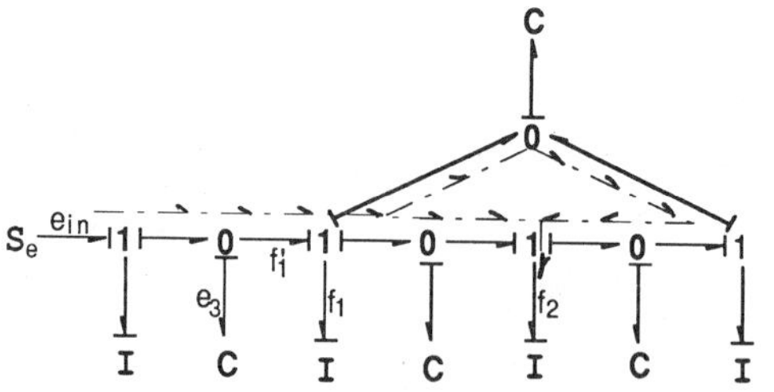

Figure 11: A system with multiple power lines.

zero by definition.

Since the power flow into Subsystem 1 (Fig. 10a) is identically zero because f_2 is identically zero, *the subsystem is isolated from other parts of the system in terms of energy transfer*. Because Subsystem 1 is constituted by a set of passive elements with a dissipative one in it, the energy it possesses decays over time and the bonds in the subsystem are relaxed eventually, as shown in Fig. 10b.

Bond 1 is relaxed as soon as the Subsystem 1 is relaxed, due to the constraint imposed by the **1** junction. As soon as bond 1 is relaxed, Subsystem 2 is isolated from the other parts of the system because the power flowing into the subsystem vanishes. It follows that Subsystem 2 dissipates out its energy asymptotically (Fig. 10c) due to the presence of the resistance R_1. The zero dynamics are therefore asymptotically stable. moreover, the energy dissipates at a rate determined exclusively by the elements in the subsystem. As soon as Subsystem 2 is relaxed, the remaining bonds relax (Fig. 10d) from the causal implication.

Note that the above arguments are independent of the detailed structures of the subsystems, as long as they are constituted by passive elements. The example is thus representative of a class of systems with a single effort or flow source. The stability of the zero dynamics for such a system is summarized in the following rule.

Rule 2: *For a system with a flow or effort variable as the output variable, the zero dynamics are stable or marginally stable if there is a single power line connecting the input source and the output variable. Moreover, each subsystem off this single power line (such as Subsystem 1 and Subsystem 2 of Fig. 10) independently determines a set of zeros.*

An example of the bond graph models with more than one power lines connecting the input variable and the output variable is shown in Fig. 11. Suppose in this system f_2 is taken as the output variable. The stability of the zero dynamics may not be determined by Rule 2, since there are double power lines (indicated by the dashed lines) connecting the input source and f_2. If e_3 or f_1 is taken as the output variable, however, the zero dynamics *are* stable according to Rule 2 since there is a single power line connecting the input source to f_1 or e_3.

Rule 2 also holds for systems whose models can be simplified to an equivalent bond graph with single power line between the input source and the output variable. An example is the mass-spring-damper system shown in Fig. 4, which has two equivalent bond graph models as shown in Fig. 5. The system is minimum-phase with *any* flow or effort variable as the output variable according to Rule 2, since in the equivalent bond graph model (Fig. 5b), given any power variable there is a single power line connecting the input source to the given variable.

3.2 Systems with Unstable Zero Dynamics

In the previous subsection the sufficient conditions for systems to be minimum-phase has been given. It will be shown in this subsection that the zero dynamics of a system may go unstable if Rule 2 is not satisfied.

The system under consideration is the same one as in Fig. 6, a uniform bar in longitudinal motion. As mentioned earlier, there are two alternative approaches to modeling the system: One is a serially-connected-element model of Fig. 7; another is a finite-mode model of Fig. 8. Besides the difference in relative degree between the two models as shown earlier, they also possess different characteristics in the stability of zero dynamics.

For the serially-connected-element model of Fig. 7, since the relative degree is equal to the system order when the tip motion is taken as the output, there are no zero dynamics for such a model. Moreover, according to Rule 2 the zero dynamics for this model with any flow or effort variable in the bond graph as the output variable are stable or marginally stable. In other words, the system has a stable or marginally stable zero dynamics taking the displacement at any point on the bar as the output variable. (The zero dynamics are strictly stable if structural damping of the bar is taken into account.)

The finite-natural-mode model of Fig. 8, on the other hand, can be shown to be non-minimum phase if the input and the output are located at opposite ends of the bar. That is, for this model there are right-half-plane zeros in the transfer function between the input force and the displacement at the end of the bar. (The fact of unstable zero dynamics associated with noncolocated flexible manipulator has been established in [16].)

The right-half-plane zeros associated with the finite-mode model imply that the bond graph of this model must have a different pattern from that of Fig. 7. Since the output variable in this case is not one of the flow or effort variable in the bond graph but a linear combination of the flow variables $\dot{q}_0, \cdots, \dot{q}_n$, auxiliary bonds are added to Fig. 8.a to explicitly show the output variable v_{tip} (Fig. 12). Notice that the bond associated with the output variable is in dashed line since the output variable is identically zero as far as the zero dynamics are concerned.

It is seen that there are multiple power lines connecting the input and the output variable in the bond graph model of Fig. 12. Unlike the system of Fig. 4 with the bond graph model in Fig. 5, the multiple power lines can not be reduced to a single one, due to the transformers (TF's) whose moduli are not identical and are not of the same sign. This example shows that a bond graph model with multiple power lines between the output and the input variable may be unstable.

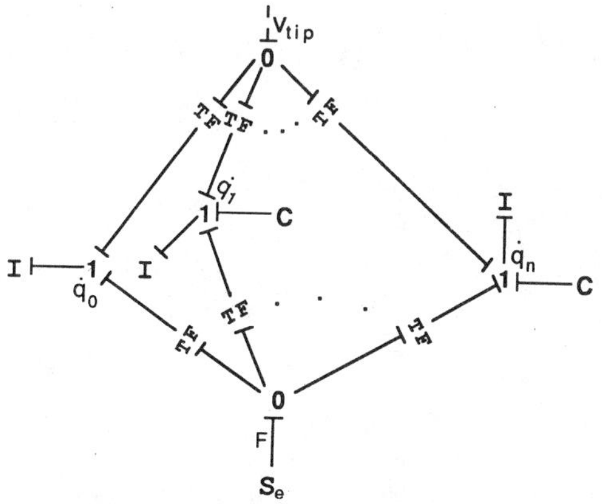

Figure 12: Finite-mode model with auxiliary bonds for the output variable.

3.3 Invariant Elements

The zeros of a system are independent of the parameters of some elements. These elements are called *invariant elements* which are defined below in bond graphs.

Definition *Invariant elements* : Given an input-output pair in the bond graph model, the common I, C or R elements which appear on *each* path from the output variable to the input variable are called the invariant elements.

For example, in Fig. 9, where f_2 is taken as the output variable, there are two alternative paths from the output to the input. It is seen that the elements I_1 and I_2 are the common elements on both paths and therefore are the invariant elements associated with the given input-output pair, while the other elements, C_1, R_1, C_2, R_2, and I_3 are non-invariant elements.

Rule 3: *Given an input-output pair, the zeros of a linear system are independent of the parameters of the invariant elements.*

Take the example of Fig. 10. The energy of Subsystem 1 decays at a rate independent of the elements in the other parts of the system; once Subsystem 1 is relaxed, Subsystem 2 is isolated from the rest of the system, as explained in Section 3.1, and its energy in turn decays at a speed determined only by the elements in the subsystem. In other words, the energy decaying rates for the zero dynamics are dictated by the elements in Subsystem 1 and Subsystem 2, which are composed of *non*-invariant elements.

4 Conclusions

The relative degrees and zero dynamics were investigated in this paper from an approach independent of the system dynamic equations. Relative degrees were shown to be readily recognizable for a class of SISO systems once the bond graph models are constructed. It implies that the relative degree of a system is determined by how the elements interact with each other but is in general independent of the parameters of the elements or the detailed constitutive law of each element.

The approach in the research of zero dynamics is by physical reasoning on the system structure rather than analyzing the dynamic equations. The rules presented in the paper not only give a qualitative description of whether a system is minimum phase, but also help separate the modes of the zero dynamics. For linear systems, each mode of the zero dynamics independently determine a set of zeros.

The rules lend insight into the physical implications of relative degrees and zeros/zero dynamics. They may serve as effective guidelines on modifying these system properties through the adjustment of the structures and parameters of the control plant or by the choice of an appropriate input-output pair.

References

[1] Narendra, K. S. and Annaswammy, A. M., *Stable Adaptive Systems*, Prentice Hall, 1989.

[2] Sastry, S. S. and Bodson, M., *Adaptive Control -Stability, Convergence, and Robustness*, Prentice Hall, 1989.

[3] Slotine, J.-J. E. and Li, W., *Applied Nonlinear Control*, Prentice-Hall, 1991.

[4] Youcef-Toumi, K. and Ito, O., "Controller Design for Systems with Unknown Dynamics", *ASME Journal of Dynamic Systems, Measurement, and Control*, March 1990, pp. 133-142.

[5] Hsia, T. C. and Gao, L. S., "Robot Manipulator Control Using Decentralized Linear Time-Invariant Time-Delay Controllers", *Proceedings of IEEE international Conference on Robotics and Automation*, 1990, pp. 2070-2075.

[6] Youcef-Toumi, K. and Wu, S.-T., "Input/Output Linearization using Time Delay Control", *ASME Journal of Dynamic Systems Measurement and Control*, March, 1992, pp. 10-19.

[7] Isidori, A., *Nonlinear Control Systems: An Introduction*, Lecture Notes in Control and Information Sciences, 2nd Edition, Springer-Verlag, 1989.

[8] Redfield, R. C. and Krishnan, S., "A Procedure to Obtain Frequency Domain Input-Output Relations Directly from Bond Graphs", ASME Winter Annual Meeting, 1990.

[9] Miu, D. K., "Physical Interpretation of Transfer Function Zeros for Simple Control Systems With Mechanical Flexibilities," *ASME Journal of Dynamic Systems, Measurement, and Control*, Vol. 113, pp. 419–424, September 1991.

[10] Wu, S.-T., "Input/Oupput Linearization of Uncertain Systems with Time Delay Control," Ph.D. Thesis, Department of Mechanical Engineering, Massachusetts Institute of Technology, February 1993.

[11] Paynter, H. M., *Analysis and Design of Engineering Systems*, M.I.T. Press, 1961.

[12] Karnopp, D. C., Margolis, D. L., and Rosenberg, R.C., *System dynamics -A Unified Approach*, John Wiley & Sons, 2nd edition, 1990.

[13] F. T. Brown, "Direct Application of the Loop Rule to Bond Graphs", the ASME Journal of Dynamic Systems, Measurement and Control, Vol.21, No.3, pp.253–261, 1972.

[14] Van Dijk J and Breedveld, P. C., "Simulation of System Models Containing Zero-order Causal Paths I, Classification of Zero-order Paths," *Journal of Franklin Institute*, Vol 328, No 5/6, pp 959-979,1991.

[15] Margolis, D. L. and Baker, D., " The Fulcrum Isolator: A Low Power, Nonlinear, Vibration Control Component", *ASME Journal of Dynamic Systems, Measuremen,t and Control*, March, 1992, pp. 148-154..

[16] Cannon, R. H. and Schmitz, E., "Initial Experiment on the End-Point Control of a Flexible One-Link Robot," *Int. J. of Robotics Research*, Vol.3.3, 1984.

Proceedings of the
American Control Conference
San Francisco, California • June 1993

On Fixed Order Controllers for Delay Systems: Discrete Time Case[1]

Hitay Özbay and *Thaddeus E. Peery*
Department of Electrical Engineering
The Ohio State University
Columbus, OH 43210

Abstract

In this short paper we present our preliminary results on the problem of finding fixed order stabilizing controllers for SISO discrete time finite dimensional plants. We assume that the controller has a computational time delay which increases with its dimension. This time delay is appended to the plant, and a fixed order stabilizing controller is investigated for the modified plant. We obtain necessary and sufficient conditions on the structure of fixed order controllers stabilizing a given plant with a time delay depending on the order of the controller.

1 Introduction and Problem Formulation

In this short paper we study the problem of finding fixed order stabilizing controllers for SISO discrete time finite dimensional plants with delays. The motivation for this problem comes from the fact that many *optimal* control schemes (e.g. H^∞, H^2) lead to an optimal controller whose dimension is at least of the same order as the dimension of the plant. Therefore, if the order of the plant is large (and/or the weights are of large order) then the optimal controller has a large order. In general, practical implementation of such a large dimensional controller is difficult. Because in this case large memory is required in the controller in order to realize its "states" in an analog or digital computer. In a controller, the memory size is limited because of physical restrictions. Moreover, as the complexity of computations increases, the computation time also increases. This introduces a *time delay* in the control action, and further limits the closed loop performance.

Usually, this time delay is a monotone increasing function of the controller dimension. Hence the controller transfer function is (for continuous time systems) $C(s) = C_n(s)e^{-h_n s}$ where $C_n(s)$ is an n-th order rational function and h_n is a positive number increasing with n (typically $h_n \to \infty$, as $n \to \infty$). This means that the finite dimensional part of the controller, i.e. $C_n(s)$, must be a controller for the *modified plant* $P_h(s) = e^{-h_n s}P(s)$ where $P(s)$ is the original plant. For meaningful cost functions (e.g. in LQG/LTR [4] and H^∞ control, [2]) the optimal performance level for P_h is worse than the optimal performance level for P, if $h_n > 0$.

Let $\gamma(C_n, P_h)$ denote the performance level (e.g H^∞ or H^2 cost) for the closed loop system (C_n, P_h); and define

$$\gamma_n := \inf_{C_n} \gamma(C_n, P_h)$$

where the infimum is taken over all $n-$th order controllers C_n stabilizing P_h. Intuitively, $\gamma_0 > \gamma_1$, provided h_1 is close to $h_0 \approx 0$. This means that we can improve the performance by increasing the controller order, if the time delay in the first order controller is sufficiently small. On the other hand, for some N one expects that $\gamma_N < \gamma_{N+1}$ if h_{N+1} is "considerably larger" than h_N. Therefore, if h_n increases slowly for small n's and then increases fast enough, the function γ_n will have a minimum. In order to be able to compute the unique optimal controller one must make sure that γ_n is a convex function of n.

[1]This work was supported by the National Science Foundation under grant No. MSS-9203418.

More importantly, one must be able to compute γ_n for a given plant P and a delay function h_n, for every $n \geq 0$. A fixed order controller minimizing an H^2 type of performance cost, for an infinite dimensional P_h can be obtained from the optimal projection equations of [1]. In order to solve control problems involving other types of performance measures (e.g. H^∞) it seems necessary to characterize the set of all nth order controllers stabilizing $e^{-h_n s}P(s)$. However, this is a rather difficult problem. Partly because time delays for continuous time systems cause infinite dimensionality. We will leave the continuous time case to a future work, and now discuss the discrete time version of this problem. Let $P(z)$ be a finite dimensional plant and $C(z) = z^{h_n}C_n(z)$ be the controller, where z^{h_n} represents a time delay of h_n unit; then we want to find a parametrization of all nth order controllers $C_n(z)$ stabilizing $z^{h_n}P(z)$.

2 Discrete time systems with delays proportional to the dimension of the controller

In order to illustrate what kind of mathematical issues are involved in the solution of the above problem we now look at the following special case where $h_n = n$, i.e. nth order controller leads to an n step delay. So, the controller is in the form $C(z) = z^n C_n(z)$ where $C_n(z)$ is an nth order rational causal transfer function. Moreover, we assume that the plant is causal and already stable, with

$$P(z) = \frac{N(z)}{D(z)}$$

where $N(z)$ and $D(z)$ are coprime polynomials. We will further assume that both $N(z)$ and $D(z)$ have degree m.

Remark 1: The controller $C(z) = z^n C_n(z)$ stabilizes the closed loop system with the plant $P(z)$ if and only if $C_n(z)$ stabilizes the modified plant $z^n P(z)$. To see this note that the characteristic equation for the closed loop system is

$$1 + P(z)C(z) = 1 + P(z)z^n C_n(z) = 0,$$

Since $P(z)$ is stable and causal it cannot have a pole at the origin. That is there is no unstable pole zero cancellation in the product $P(z)C(z) = z^n P(z)C_n(z)$. Therefore, we can see $C_n(z)$ as the controller for the modified plant $z^n P(z)$. □

We now present our main result which can be seen as a characterization of all nth order controllers $C_n(z)$ stabilizing the modified plant $z^n P(z)$. In what follows we will be denoting the poles of $P(z)$ (i.e. the zeros of $D(z)$) by $p_1, \ldots, p_m$.

Lemma: There exists an nth order controller $C_n(z)$ stabilizing the closed loop system $(C_n(z), z^n P(z))$ if and only if there exists a polynomial $Q_d(z)$ of degree less or equal to $n+m$, satisfying
(i) $Q_d(z_i) = 0$ implies $|z_i| > 1$, i.e. Q_d is a stable polynomial, and
(ii) $Q_d(p_i) = p_i^n N(p_i)$ for all $i = 1, \ldots, m$.

Proof: Since $z^n P(z)$ is stable, $C_n(z)$ stabilizes the closed loop system with plant $z^n P(z)$ if and only if it is in the form

$$C_n(z) = \frac{Q(z)}{1 - z^n P(z) Q(z)} \qquad Q \in \mathbb{R}H^\infty.$$

The fact that $C_n(z)$ is an nth order rational function poses extra restrictions on the free parameter $Q(z)$. Let us write Q as a ratio of two coprime polynomials (of unknown orders for the moment)

$$Q(z) = \frac{Q_n(z)}{Q_d(z)}.$$

Then, we have

$$C_n(z) = \frac{D(z)Q_n(z)}{D(z)Q_d(z) - z^n N(z) Q_n(z)}.$$

Define

$$C_{num}(z) = D(z)Q_n(z) \quad \text{and} \quad C_{den}(z) = C_{num}(z)/C(z).$$

Note that the ratio of polynomials $\frac{C_{num}(z)}{C_{den}(z)}$ has to be an nth order rational function. But since

$$C_{den}(z) = D(z)Q_d(z) - z^n N(z) Q_n(z)$$

its order is

$$ord(C_{den}(z)) \geq n + m + ord(Q_n(z)).$$

So, in the ratio $\frac{C_{num}(z)}{C_{den}(z)}$ there have to be cancellations of at least m terms. Let p_i's be the zeros of $D(z)$, and z_i's are the zeros of $Q_n(z)$. Note that $C_{num}(z)$ becomes zero only at either p_i's or z_i's. Consider both cases now:

$$C_{den}(p_i) = -p_i^n N(p_i) Q_n(p_i) \quad \text{and} \quad C_{den}(z_i) = D(z_i) Q_d(z_i).$$

At least m of these (i.e. $C_{den}(p_i)$'s and $C_{den}(z_i)$'s) must be zero. Suppose for some i we have $C_{den}(p_i) = 0$, then we must have $Q_n(p_i) = 0$ since $p_i \neq 0$ and $N(p_i) \neq 0$, but this means that for this particular i we have $z_i = p_i$. Conversely, suppose for some i we have $C_{den}(z_i) = 0$, then we must have $D(z_i) = 0$ since $Q_d(z_i) \neq 0$, but this means that for this particular i we have $p_i = z_i$. Thus we conclude that $Q_n(z)$ and $D(z)$ can only differ by a constant, i.e. we must have

$$Q_n(z) = Q_o D(z) \tag{1}$$

where Q_o is a constant.

If we use the relationship (1) in $C_n(z)$ we get

$$C_n(z) = \frac{D(z)}{Q_d(z)/Q_o - z^n N(z)}.$$

Since Q_o is a constant we can absorb it into the coefficients of $Q_d(z)$, in other words we can choose $Q_o = 1$ without loss of generality. We now have $C_n(z) = D(z)/C'_{den}(z)$ where

$$C'_{den}(z) = Q_d(z) - z^n N(z).$$

Note that

$$ord(C'_{den}(z)) \geq n + m.$$

Therefore, we still need m more cancellations. However, $D(z)$ is exactly mth order, with zeros p_i's, $i = 1, \ldots, m$. Thus, we must have

$$Q_d(p_i) - p_i^n N(p_i) = 0\ , \quad \text{for all } i = 1, \ldots, m. \tag{2}$$

Since the order of $C_n(z)$ cannot exceed n, the free polynomial $Q_d(z)$ has to be of order less than or equal to $(n+m)$, and it has to satisfy the interpolation conditions given by (2), i.e. conditions (ii) of the Lemma. Finally, since $Q = Q_n/Q_d$ has to be stable, the free polynomial Q_d cannot have zeros inside the closed unit disc, i.e. it has to satisfy the first condition of Lemma. □

Remark 2: The above lemma characterizes the set of all nth order controllers stabilizing the closed loop system with the plant $z^n P(z)$. Since $Q_d(z)$ can be $(n+m)$th order, we have an $(n+1)$ dimensional freedom in choosing Q_d when m interpolation conditions are taken into account. That is the set of all nth order compensators stabilizing the modified plant $z^n P(z)$ lies in an $n+1$ dimensional subset of $\mathbb{R}^{(n+m+1)}$. Note that after the cancellations imposed by (2), the nth order controller $C_n(z)$ becomes an all-pole type compensator. However, we must remind the reader that the overall controller for the actual plant $P(z)$ has n zeros (all of them at the origin). If the delay in the controller is not precisely equal to its order (say the delay is p units when the controller order is $n > p$), then we have extra freedom in choosing some of the zeros of the controller ($n - p$ of them to be exact). □

3 Conclusions

The effects of time delays caused by the controller dimension, are studied in this short paper. We have obtained a characterization of all nth order controllers stabilizing the "modified plant" $z^n P(z)$ where $P(z)$ is the actual discrete time plant which is assumed to be causal, stable and finite dimensional with the same number of poles and zeros. This characterization involves finding a stable polynomial, whose degree has a known upper bound, satisfying certain interpolation conditions. In case of side conditions such as robust stability, or H^∞ type performance requirement, this polynomial is also required to satisfy a uniform inequality type constraint, see [3].

Acknowledgements: We would like to thank Professor Ümit Özgüner for helpfull discussions on the problem formulation.

References

[1] Bernstein, D. S. and D. C. Hyland, "The optimal projection equations for fixed order dynamic compensation of infinite dimensional systems, *SIAM J. Control and Optimization* **24** (1986), pp. 122–151.

[2] Foias, C, A. Tannenbaum, G. Zames, "Some explicit formulae for the singular values of a certain Hankel operators with factorizable symbol," *SIAM J. Math. Analysis* **19** (1988), pp. 1081–1091.

[3] Özbay, H. and T. E. Peery, "On fixed order stabilizing controllers for discrete time systems with delays," Control Research Laboratory Technical Report No. 1061-W92-R, Department of Electrical Engineering, The Ohio State University, Winter 1992.

[4] Stein, G and M. Athans, "The LQG/LTR procedure for multivariable feedback control design," *IEEE Transactions on Automatic Control* **32** (1987), pp. 105–114.

Proceedings of the
American Control Conference
San Francisco, California • June 1993

AN OBSERVER DESIGN FOR TIME-DELAY CONTROL AND ITS APPLICATION TO DC SERVO MOTOR

Pyung H. Chang, Jeong W. Lee

Department of Precision Engineering & Mechatronics
Korea Advanced Institute of Science and Technology
373-1 Kusung-dong Taejon, Korea

Abstract

Recently the Time Delay Control (TDC) method has been proposed as a promising technique in the robust control area, where the plants have nonlinear dynamics with parameter variations and substantial disturbances are present. TDC method, however, requires the measurements of all the state variables, together with their derivatives. This requirement imposes a severe limitation on the applications to most real systems.

In order to solve this measurement problem, we proposed an observer design method that can stably reconstruct the state variables and their derivatives. Then, for a simulation study, the controller/observer based on our design method has been applied to a nonlinear plant, the result of which confirmed that the controller/observer performs satisfactorily as predicted. Finally we made experimentations on a DC servo motor that is subject to substantial amount of inertia variations and external disturbances. The results showed that the controller/observer performs quite robustly under those variations and disturbances, and is much less sensitive to sensor noise than the controller using numerical differentiations.

1 Introduction

The main purpose of using robust control method is to assure control performances (such as accuracy, stability, speed, etc) in the presence of significant plant uncertainties. The plant uncertainties, in general, include external disturbances, unpredictable parameter variations, and unmodeled plant nonlinear dynamics.

So far, several approaches for robust control have been proposed and a considerable progress has been made in this area[3]. One of the popular techniques for robust control is LQG/LTR technique[1,7]. LQG/LTR technique achieves robustness results through frequency domain analysis. But, it may require excessively high gain. (An approximate LTR method, which alleviates this difficulty, is given in [7].)

H^{∞} - related theory is another approach for robust control. A number of mathematical results have appeared, which expedite the computation of optimal sensitivity solution for H^{∞} norms[5,8]. However the computation of H^{∞} optimization is difficult and the problem of effective simultaneous robust performance and robust stabilization is still an area for further research.

Adaptive or self tuning control may be considered another candidate for robust control [2]. In this approach, feedback gain is updated by using the recursive parameter estimation so that the plant output may follow the desired response. This approach works well for the plant with slowly varying parameters, but not so well for the plant with large uncertainties[2]. In addition, this approach requires a large amount of real-time computation.

Sliding Mode Control is another powerful approach. Instead of using high loop gain or tuning gains by parameter estimation, this control method, by including the off-line estimation of plant uncertainties in the control input, explicitly *cancels* the plant uncertainties. Consequently, this technique shows quite robust responses in the presence of bounded parameter variations and external disturbances. However, as the amount of uncertainties increases, it reveals the chattering problem due to the switching control input, which may also excite unmodeled high frequency dynamics[11]. The chattering problem, by the way, has been greatly reduced by the use of a thin layer, called boundary layer, along the switching surface[10].

Recently, Time Delay Control(TDC) has been noted as an excellent robust nonlinear control algorithm[13]. TDC uses the time-delayed informations (the value of the control inputs and derivatives of state variables at the previous time step) to estimate both the plant dynamics (nominal part) and the uncertainties — parameter variation, external disturbance, and unmodeled dynamics. These informations are, then, used to cancel the nominal nonlinear dynamics and the uncertainties. Thus TDC does not require any real-time computation of nonlinear dynamics nor uses the parameter estimations. As the result, TDC shows quite robust responses, adaptively canceling the uncertainties; yet computationally much more efficient than the aforementioned methods. These merits have been clearly demonstrated in the successful applications of TDC to a robot[6,15] and a magnetic bearing [14].

In order to apply TDC to a plant, we need to be able to measure all of the state variables and their derivatives. Unfortunately, this is not always the case in practice. In many plants, even state variables are not available, not to mention their derivatives. Even when all the state variables are measurable, we need additional sensors or differentiators for their derivatives at the cost of further disadvantages: The use of derivative sensors makes the overall system more complex and expensive; the use of differentiators more sensitive to measurement noise. So, the measurability requirement presents a serious limitation on the implementations of TDC to real plants. In order to solve this problem, we propose an observer design method, specifically for TDC, that can stably reconstruct state variables and their derivatives.

In the following section, control problem is defined and TDC algorithm is reviewed. In section 3, we present an observer design method for TDC is presented. In section 4, effectiveness of proposed observer and sensitivity to sensor noise is evaluated through simulations. In section 5 we present the results of experimentations on a DC servo motor that is subject to substantial inertia variation and external disturbances. Finally in section 6, the results are summarized and conclusions are presented.

2 Review of Time Delay Control Law

For the sake of completeness, we briefly review TDC algorithm. The nonlinear plant in question is described as follows:

$$\dot{\mathbf{x}} = \mathbf{f}(\mathbf{x},t) + \mathbf{B}(\mathbf{x},t)\mathbf{u} + \mathbf{d}(t)$$
$$\mathbf{y} = \mathbf{C}\mathbf{x} \quad (1)$$

where $\mathbf{x} \in \Re^n$ is state vector, $\mathbf{u} \in \Re^r$ is control input, $\mathbf{y} \in \Re^m$ the plant output, $\mathbf{f}(\mathbf{x},t)$ represents plant dynamics, which is unknown, $\mathbf{d}(t)$ is unknown disturbance, $\mathbf{B}(\mathbf{x},t)$ is control distribution matrix, the ranges (instead of exact values) of which are known, and $\mathbf{C}$ is output distribution matrix. Note by the way that Equation (1) covers a broad range of nonlinear dynamic plants.

Rearranging Equation (1) into two terms — known part and unknown part — leads to

$$\dot{\mathbf{x}} = \hat{\mathbf{f}}(\mathbf{x},t) + \hat{\mathbf{B}}\mathbf{u}$$
$$\mathbf{y} = \mathbf{C}\mathbf{x} \quad (2)$$

where $\hat{\mathbf{B}}$ is a constant matrix representing the known range of $\mathbf{B}(\mathbf{x},t)$, and $\hat{\mathbf{f}}(\mathbf{x},t)$ the *unknown* parts including uncertainties in the plant and disturbances, which are expressed as

$$\hat{\mathbf{f}}(\mathbf{x},t) = \mathbf{f}(\mathbf{x},t) + (\mathbf{B}(\mathbf{x},t) - \hat{\mathbf{B}})\mathbf{u} + \mathbf{d}(t) \quad (3)$$

Regarding to the determination of $\hat{\mathbf{B}}$, one will find more detailed discussions in Hsia[6] and Youcef-Toumi[16].

Desired performance is specified with the response of a linear time invariant reference model as

$$\dot{\mathbf{x}}_m = \mathbf{A}_m\mathbf{x}_m + \mathbf{B}_m\mathbf{r} \quad (4)$$

where $\mathbf{x}_m \in \Re^n$ is state vector of the reference model, $\mathbf{A}_m$ is system matrix, $\mathbf{B}_m$ is command distribution matrix, and $\mathbf{r} \in \Re^r$ command vector. Then the control objective is to make the state of the plant track the response of the reference model (4). If the error is defined as $\mathbf{e} = \mathbf{x}_m - \mathbf{x}$, then error dynamics becomes from (3) and (4) as

$$\dot{\mathbf{e}} = \mathbf{A}_m\mathbf{e} + [-\hat{\mathbf{f}}(\mathbf{x},t) + \mathbf{A}_m\mathbf{x} + \mathbf{B}_m\mathbf{r} - \hat{\mathbf{B}}\mathbf{u}] \quad (5)$$

If we can find a control $\mathbf{u}$ such that

$$-\hat{\mathbf{f}}(\mathbf{x},t) + \mathbf{A}_m\mathbf{x} + \mathbf{B}_m\mathbf{r} - \hat{\mathbf{B}}\mathbf{u} = \mathbf{K}\mathbf{e} \quad (6)$$

where $\mathbf{K} \in \Re^{n\times n}$ is an error feedback gain matrix, then error dynamics becomes

$$\dot{\mathbf{e}} = (\mathbf{A}_m + \mathbf{K})\mathbf{e} \quad (7)$$

showing that the error vanishes as time goes on.

Equation (7), however, is not always satisfied if the number of controls is smaller than the number of the states, in which case a least square approximate solution is used to determine the control $\mathbf{u}$ as

$$\mathbf{u} = \hat{\mathbf{B}}^+[-\hat{\mathbf{f}}(\mathbf{x},t) + \mathbf{A}_m\mathbf{x} + \mathbf{B}_m\mathbf{r} - \mathbf{K}\mathbf{e}] \quad (8)$$

where $\hat{\mathbf{B}}^+$ is a pseudo-inverse of $\hat{\mathbf{B}}$. Incidentally, Equation (8) is used as the basic algorithm of TDC. The error dynamics in this case is obtained, by substituting Equation (8) into Equation (2), as the following:

$$\dot{\mathbf{e}} = (\mathbf{A}_m+\mathbf{K})\mathbf{e}+(\mathbf{I}-\hat{\mathbf{B}}\hat{\mathbf{B}}^+)[-\hat{\mathbf{f}}(\mathbf{x},t)+\mathbf{A}_m\mathbf{x}+\mathbf{B}_m\mathbf{r}-\mathbf{K}\mathbf{e}] \quad (9)$$

This equation obviously satisfies Equation (7), resulting in the same error dynamics, if

$$(\mathbf{I} - \hat{\mathbf{B}}\hat{\mathbf{B}}^+)[-\hat{\mathbf{f}}(\mathbf{x},t) + \mathbf{A}_m\mathbf{x} + \mathbf{B}_m\mathbf{r} - \mathbf{K}\mathbf{e}] = \mathbf{0} \quad (10)$$

The conditions for which Equation (10) is always satisfied are discussed in Youcef-Toumi[13]. Especially, it is noticeable that this equation is always satisfied when the phase variables are used as state variables.

When implementing the algorithm in (8), we must be able to estimate $\hat{\mathbf{f}}(\mathbf{x},t)$, the total effect of plant uncertainties. The estimation can be made by using Equation (2), together with the fact that when $\hat{\mathbf{f}}(\mathbf{x},t)$ and $\mathbf{x}$ are continuous functions with sufficiently small L, then the magnitude of $\hat{\mathbf{f}}(\mathbf{x},t)$ is very close to that of $\hat{\mathbf{f}}(\mathbf{x},t-L)$. That is

$$\hat{\mathbf{f}}(\mathbf{x},t) \cong \hat{\mathbf{f}}(\mathbf{x},t-L) \quad (11)$$

By combining Equation (11) and Equation (2), the effect of plant uncertainties can be estimated by

$$\hat{\mathbf{f}}(\mathbf{x},t) = \dot{\mathbf{x}} - \hat{\mathbf{B}}\mathbf{u}$$
$$\cong \dot{\mathbf{x}}(t-L) - \hat{\mathbf{B}}\mathbf{u}(t-L) \quad (12)$$

Substituting this into Equation (8) leads to the following TDC control law:

$$\mathbf{u} = \hat{\mathbf{B}}^+[-\dot{\mathbf{x}}(t-L)+\hat{\mathbf{B}}\mathbf{u}(t-L)+\mathbf{A}_m\mathbf{x}+\mathbf{B}_m\mathbf{r}-\mathbf{K}\mathbf{e}] \quad (13)$$

3 Observer design

As clearly shown in (13), the TDC control law requires the estimation of states and their derivatives. In practice, this requirement sets nontrivial limitations on the application of TDC to real plants. As a solution to this problem, we propose an observer design specifically for TDC controller.

3.1 Derivation of observer equation

In case that there are no uncertainties in the plant, perhaps a Luenberger type observer would suffice [9]. In the presence of substantial uncertainties in the plant, however, observer design become more complex, since we need to estimate the uncertainties in addition to states. Thus the structure of observer is nonlinear and the stability of observer is not easily analyzed [12].

Nevertheless, the observer design for TDC becomes especially simple when we make use of the fact that TDC enables the plant dynamics to immediately follow the reference model. More specifically, it is the reference model (linear and certain), instead of the plant model (nonlinear and uncertain), that is used to reconstruct the states.

Thus in the unknown system expressed in (2), the states are reconstructed by using the following linear observer:

$$\dot{\mathbf{z}} = \mathbf{A}_m\mathbf{z} + \mathbf{B}_m\mathbf{r} + \mathbf{F}\mathbf{C}(\bar{\mathbf{y}} - \mathbf{y})$$
$$= \mathbf{A}_m\mathbf{z} + \mathbf{B}_m\mathbf{r} + \mathbf{F}\mathbf{C}(\mathbf{z} - \mathbf{x}) \quad (14)$$

where $\mathbf{z} \in \Re^n$ is an observer state vector, $\mathbf{F}$ is an $(n \times m)$ constant observer gain matrix, and $\bar{\mathbf{y}} \in \Re^m$ is an observer output vector.

When this observer (together with TDC) is connected to the plant, the control input $\mathbf{u}$ is obtained by using the reconstructed states $\mathbf{z}$, in place of the feedback states $\mathbf{x}$. In addition, the uncertainties at time t are estimated with the reconstructed state $\mathbf{z}$ at $t-L$. Thus, the control input $\mathbf{u}$ and time delay estimation are determined as

$$\mathbf{u} = \mathbf{B}^+[-\hat{\mathbf{f}}(\mathbf{z},t) + \mathbf{A}_m\mathbf{z} + \mathbf{B}_m\mathbf{r} - \mathbf{K}(\mathbf{x}_m - \mathbf{z})] \quad (15)$$

$$\hat{\mathbf{f}}(\mathbf{z},t) \cong \dot{\mathbf{z}}(t-L) - \hat{\mathbf{B}}\mathbf{u}(t-L) \quad (16)$$

The overall system can be illustrated with the block diagram in Figure 1.

3.2 Overall stability of observer and controller

As to the stability of resulting system consisting of the plant, TDC, and the proposed observer, the following theorem will be presented as a sufficient condition for the stability of overall system. Thus if the proposed observer is designed so that the observer gains and time delay L

meet this condition, then the resulting system is made stable.

Theorem *The overall system under continuous TDC with $L > 0$ is internally stable, if $\hat{\mathbf{f}}(\mathbf{x}, t)$ is a continuous function of time and the eigenvalues λ of the following characteristic equation (17) lie in the open Left-Half-Plane.*

$$\det\{(\lambda\mathbf{I} - \mathbf{A}_e) - \hat{\mathbf{B}}\hat{\mathbf{B}}^{+}(e^{-L\lambda}\lambda\mathbf{I} - \mathbf{A}_e) \\ -\hat{\mathbf{B}}\hat{\mathbf{B}}^{+}(e^{-L\lambda}\lambda\mathbf{I} - \mathbf{A}_e)(\lambda\mathbf{I} - \mathbf{A}_o)^{-1}\mathbf{FC}\} = 0 \quad (17)$$

where

$$\mathbf{A}_e = (\mathbf{A}_m + \mathbf{K}) \quad , \quad \mathbf{A}_o = (\mathbf{A}_m + \mathbf{FC}) \quad (18)$$

This proof of this theorem, based on the results of Youcef-Toumi[17], will be presented in another article in the near future.

4 Simulation

To demonstrate the effectiveness of the proposed observer, the observer design is carried out for following second-order system.

$$\dot{\mathbf{x}} = \begin{bmatrix} 0 & 1 \\ \alpha & \beta \end{bmatrix} \mathbf{x} + \begin{bmatrix} 0 \\ b \end{bmatrix} u \\ y = [1 \ \ 0]\mathbf{x} \quad (19)$$

where

$$\alpha \equiv 2 \times x_2 \times \sin x_1 / (\frac{2}{3} + \cos x_1)$$
$$\beta \equiv \cos x_1 / (\frac{2}{3} + \cos x_1)$$
$$b \equiv 1/(\frac{2}{3} + \cos x_1)$$

where x_1 and x_2 represent states of plant. In this example, we assume α and β completely unknown, whereas the range of b is known. The reference model was selected as a second order system described by

$$\dot{\mathbf{x}}_m = \begin{bmatrix} 0 & 1 \\ -\omega_n^2 & -2\zeta\omega_n \end{bmatrix} \mathbf{x}_m + \begin{bmatrix} 0 \\ \omega_n^2 \end{bmatrix} r \quad (20)$$

with a natural frequency ω_n and dampling ratio ζ of $10 rad/sec$ and 1, respectively. The input command r was chosen to be 1. By considering observer gain matrix as $\mathbf{F} = [F_1 \ \ F_2]^T$, the proposed observer can be designed as

$$\dot{\mathbf{z}} = \begin{bmatrix} 0 & 1 \\ -\omega_n^2 & -2\zeta\omega_n \end{bmatrix} \mathbf{z} + \begin{bmatrix} 0 \\ \omega_n^2 \end{bmatrix} \mathbf{r} + \mathbf{F}(y - \bar{y}) \quad (21)$$

From (19),(20) and (13), TDC control law becomes:

$$\mathbf{u}(t) = \mathbf{u}(t-L) + \frac{1}{\hat{b}}[-\dot{x}_2(t-L) - \omega_n^2 x_1 - 2\zeta\omega_n x_2 + \omega_n^2 r] \quad (22)$$

where $\hat{b}$ is the nominal value of b, which is set 1.5.

As shown in (22), we need to estimate the state x_2 and state derivative $\dot{x}_2(t-L)$, which are the states that the observer is supposed to reconstruct. Without the observer, the state derivative, $\dot{x}_2(t-L)$, would have to be estimated by using numerical differentiation, which amplifies measurement noise to a large extent.

The performance of the observer was verified in two respects: first, whether it can satisfactorily reconstruct the states and their derivatives; second, how the use of the observer effects overall system performance as compared to the use of numerical differentiation. To this end, the proposed observer with the gain matrix of $\mathbf{F} = [230 \ \ 7600]^T$ was chosen with time delay of $L = 0.01$ second. This choices are based on the use of stability analysis in the previous section.

Accordingly, in the first simulation we checked how well the proposed observer can reconstruct states and their derivatives. As shown in Figure 2, the proposed observer reconstructed states and their derivatives very well indeed, with the plant satisfactorily following the desired model.

In the second simulation, a certain amount of sensor noise was applied to the closed-loop system, and noise corrupted response was obtained for the two cases: when the numerical differentiation was used; and when the proposed observer was used. For sensor noise, zero-mean Gaussian noise with standard deviations of $\sigma = 0.002$, 0.02 (0.2% and 2% of the magnitude of the command signal) were applied. As predicted, the responses in Figure 3 show that state derivatives estimated by numerical differentiation are extremely sensitive to sensor noise. When using the proposed observer, however, the reconstructed states and their derivatives are not so sensitive to sensor noise, with plant response closely following the desired model.

From these simulation results, we see that proposed observer can effectively reconstruct states and their derivatives, and at the same time is quite insensitive to sensor noise as compared to numerical differentiation — thus its use is justified.

5 Experiment

In order to assure the validity of the proposed observer in a real system, a DC servo motor system was selected to make experiments. The experimental setup is shown in Figure 4. The following three points have been examined:

- the robustness of the observer (with TDC controller) in the presence of parameter variations,
- the performance under external disturbance, and
- the sensitivity to sensor noise.

On the first two points, we tried to check if the proposed observer with TDC preserves the performances that TDC with numerical differentiator has shown [16]. For the purpose of comparison, PD controller was also used to the plant. On the third point, the focus is on the effectiveness of the use of observer as compared to the case with TDC alone. Thus, TDC with the proposed observer was compared with TDC with numerical differentiator.

The dynamics of DC servo motor is characterized by a second-order equation:

$$\mathbf{M}\ddot{\theta} + \mathbf{B}\dot{\theta} + \mathbf{D}(\theta, \dot{\theta}, t) = \tau \quad (23)$$

where θ is the motor shaft rotating angle, $\mathbf{M}$ is the effective moment of inertia of motor, $\mathbf{B}$ is the effective viscous friction coefficient, $\mathbf{D}(\theta, \dot{\theta}, t)$ is an unknown dynamics including internal nonlinearities and external disturbance, and τ is the input torque to the motor.

Defining the following second order system as the reference model,

$$\frac{d}{dt}\begin{bmatrix} \theta \\ \dot{\theta} \end{bmatrix} = \begin{bmatrix} 0 & 1 \\ -\omega_n^2 & -2\zeta\omega_n \end{bmatrix} \begin{bmatrix} \theta \\ \dot{\theta} \end{bmatrix} + \begin{bmatrix} 0 \\ \omega_n^2 \end{bmatrix} r \quad (24)$$

we have the following control law:

$$\tau(t) = \tau(t-L) + \hat{\mathbf{M}}[-\ddot{\theta}(t-L) + \omega_n^2(r - \theta) - 2\zeta\omega_n\dot{\theta}] \quad (25)$$

where $\ddot{\theta}$, $\dot{\theta}$ are determined by the following observer:

$$\dot{\mathbf{z}} = \begin{bmatrix} 0 & 1 \\ -\omega_n^2 & -2\zeta\omega_n \end{bmatrix} \mathbf{z} + \begin{bmatrix} 0 \\ \omega_n^2 \end{bmatrix} \mathbf{r} + \mathbf{f}(\mathbf{y} - \bar{\mathbf{y}}) \quad (26)$$

In the first experiment no external disturbance and parameter variation were applied to motor system, As shown in Figure 5, both control system followed desired response well.

In the second experiment, we tested robustness of the control systems to parameter variations by increasing the value of $\hat{M}$ to $0.1kg-cm^2$ (1.7 times to the nominal value) and $0.7kg-cm^2$ (12 times to the nominal value). This range of variation can be observed in the joint motors of a robot with small amount of gear reduction, when the end effector loads (or unloads) payloads.

As shown in (a) and (b) of Figure 6, the system with TDC (and the proposed observer) is hardly affected by the wide range of parameter variations, whereas the PD control system shows larger overshoot as the value of $\hat{M}$ increases owing to the change of closed-loop pole location.

In the third experiment, robustness to external disturbance was tested, where, as external disturbance, springs were attached to the load. More specifically, we used each of two spring disturbances: (1) a soft spring disturbance of $-K(0.5-\sin\theta)$ with $K=1.2kgf-cm$, which amounts to about 30% of motor stall torque; (2) a hard spring disturbance of $-K\sin\theta$ with $K=1.8kgf-cm$, which amounts to about 45 % of stall torque. To these soft and hard spring disturbances, their responses are shown in Figure 7. As shown in Figure 7(b), regardless of the magnitude of spring disturbances, the responses of TDC control system are almost identical to the desired response, demonstrating its ability to cancel external disturbance. To the contrast, PD control system, as shown in Figure 7(a), has steady state errors, which increase as the magnitude of spring disturbances increase. To reduce the steady state error we added some integral action to the controller (thus PID controller), which resulted in much better responses. It was, however, almost impossible to find an integral gain that guarantees stability when there are some parameter variations. Thus the case with PID was not included.

In order to see effectiveness of proposed observer, we have compared the response using observer with response using numerical differentiation. As shown in (a), (b), and (c) of Figure 8 we see that the observer works well and the states and their derivative reconstructed by observer are less noisy compared to those by numerical differentiation.

6 Conclusion

In this paper we proposed observer design method for TDC, and analyzed overall stability of observer and controller. It was shown that the proposed observer reconstruct states and their derivatives very well in the presence of plant uncertainties, while preserving the performance of TDC alone. Thus the TDC algorithm can be expanded to the unknown system where all states and their derivatives are not measurable. In addition, since the proposed observer does not need accurate mathematical model of plant uncertainties or nonlinear dynamics, its structure is very simple and easy to implement.

Effectiveness of proposed observer was evaluated through simulation and experiment. Through simulation for a second order unknown plant, it was demonstrated that the proposed observer reconstructed states and their derivatives very well and the good control performance of TDC was not degraded by observer. It was also demonstrated that the control system using observer is less sensitive to sensor noise than control system using numerical differentiation. The simulation results have been also confirmed by experiment. It was demonstrated that control system designed is very robust to external disturbance and motor inertia variation. It turned out that the proposed observer worked well and overall system of observer and controller was less sensitive to sensor noise.

References

[1] Athan, M, "A Tutorials on the LQG/LTR Method," Proc. of American Control Conference, pp. 1289-1296, Jun. 1986.

[2] Craig, J. J. and et al, "Adaptive Control of Mechanical Manipulator," Proc. of IEEE Int'l. Conf. on Robotics and Automation, pp.7-10, Apr. 1986.

[3] Dorato, P, "A historical Review of Robust Control ," IEEE Control System Magazine, vol. CSM-7, no. 2, pp. 44-47, Aprl. 1987.

[4] Doyle, J. C. and Stein, G, "Multivariable Feedback Design : Concepts for a classical/modern synthesis," IEEE Trans. on Automatic Control, vol AC-26, no. 2, pp. 4-16, Feb. 1981.

[5] Francis, B. A. and et al, "H^∞ -Optimal Feedback Controller for Linear Multivariable Systems," IEEE Trans. on Automatic Control, vol. AC-29, pp. 888-900, Oct. 1984.

[6] Hsia, T. C. and Gao, L. S, "Robot Manipulator Control Using Decentralized Time- invariant Time-Delayed Controller," Proc. of IEEE Int'l Conf. on Robotics and Automation, pp. 2070-2075, 1990.

[7] Kazerooni, K. and Houpt, P. K, " On Loop Transfer Recovery," Int'l. Journal of Control, vol. 43, pp. 981-996, Mar. 1986.

[8] Kimura, H, "Robust Stabilization for a Class of Transfer Functions," IEEE Trans. on Automatic Control, vol. AC-29, pp. 788-793, Sep. 1984.

[9] Luenberger, Y. Y, IEEE Trans. on Automatic Control, 11, 190, 1966.

[10] Slotine, J. J. and Sastry, S. S, "Tracking Control of Nonlinear Systems Using Sliding Surface with Application to Robot Manipulators," Int'l Journal of Control, vol. 38-2, pp. 465-492, 1983.

[11] Utkin, V. I. "Equations of Sliding Mode in Discontinuous Systems," Automation and Remote Control 1(II), 1972.

[12] Wladyslaw Mielczarski "Observing the State of a Synchronous generator Part I," Int'l Journal of Control, vol. 45, no. 3, pp. 987-1000, 1987.

[13] Youcef-Toumi, K. and Ito, O, "Controller Design for Systems with Unknown Dynamics," ASME Journal of Dynamic Systems Measurement and Control, vol. 112, no. 1, pp. 133-142, Mar. 1990.

[14] Youcef-Toumi, K. and Reddy, S, "Stability Analysis Of TDC with Application to High Speed Bearing," ASME Winter Annual meeting, 1990.

[15] Youcef-Toumi, K. and Shortlidge, C. C. "Control of Robot Manipulator Using Time Delay," Proc. of IEEE Int'l Conf. on Robotics and Automation, pp. 2391-2395, 1991.

[16] Youcef-Toumi, K. and Wu, S. T, "Input/Output Linearization Using Time Delay Control," Proc. of American Control Conference, pp. 1601-1606, 1991.

[17] Youcef-Toumi, K. and Reddy, S, "Analysis of Linear Time Invarient Systems with Time Delay," Proc. of American Control Conference, pp. 1940-1944, 1992.

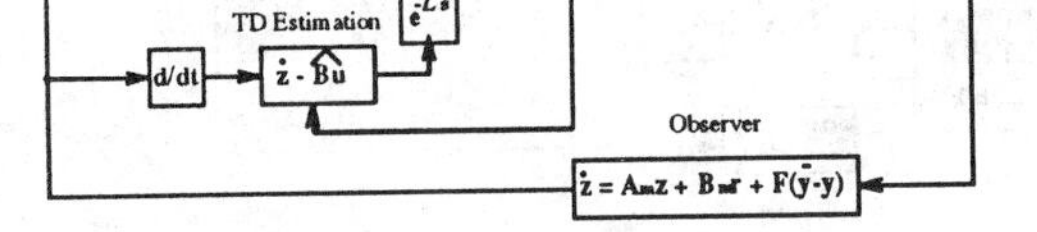

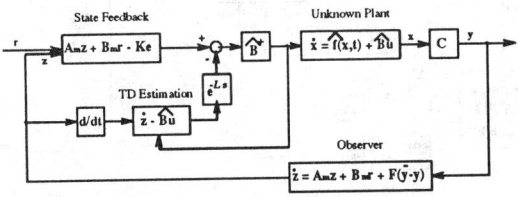

Figure 1: Block diagram of TDC system with proposed observer

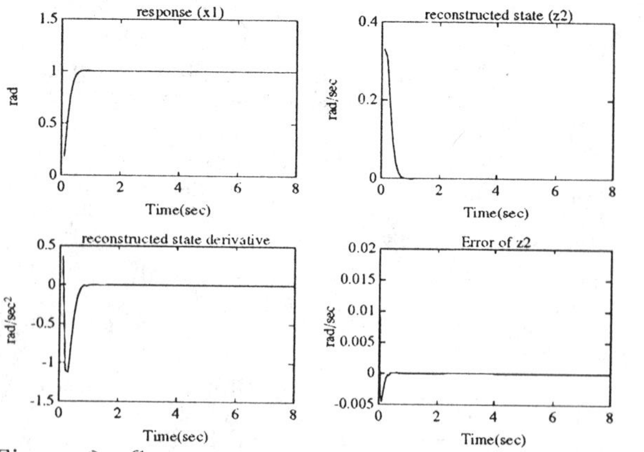

Figure 2: Step response of reconstructed states of TDC with observer, with no sensor noise.

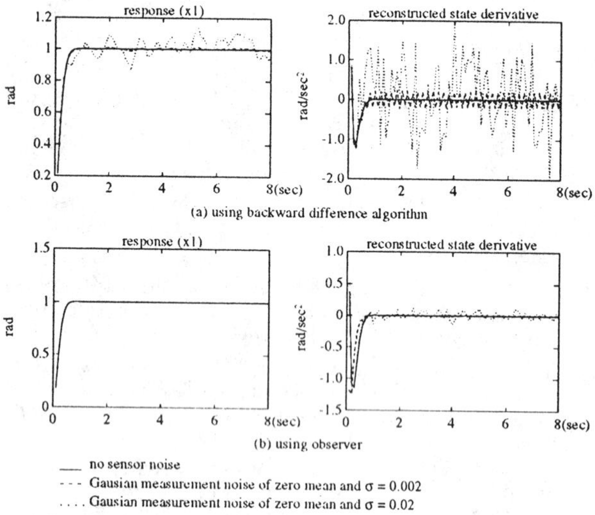

Figure 3: Noise corrupted step response with Gaussian measurement noise.

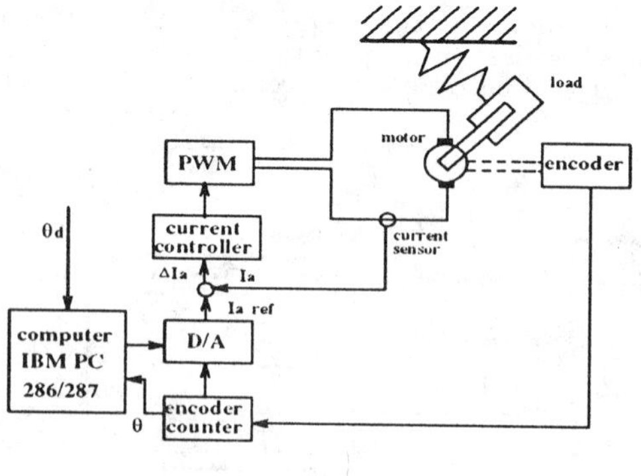

Figure 4: Experimental set-up of DC servo motor control system.

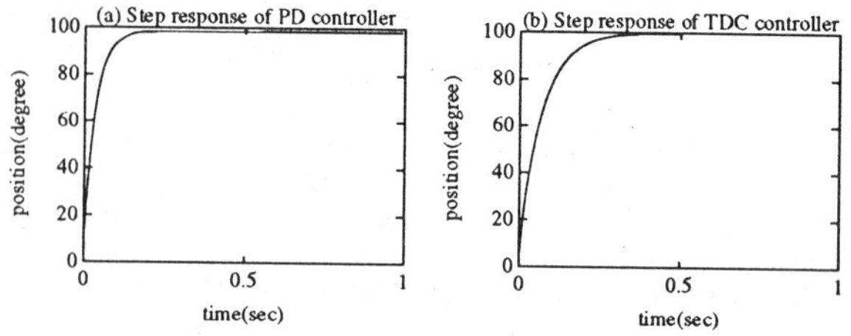

Figure 5: Experimental results without uncertainty for PD and TDC control system.

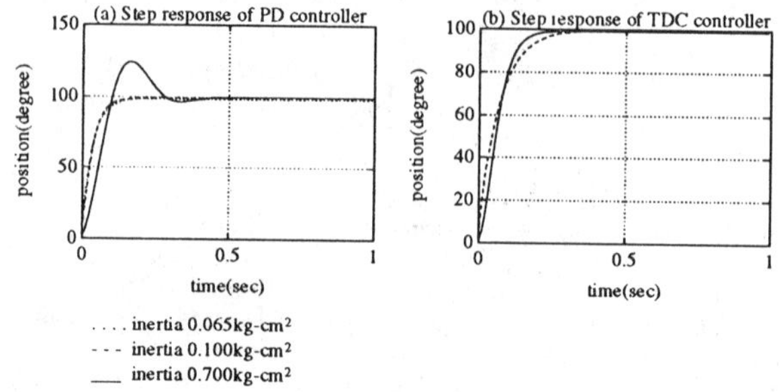

Figure 6: Experimental results with inertia variations: (a) PD control case; (b) TDC control case

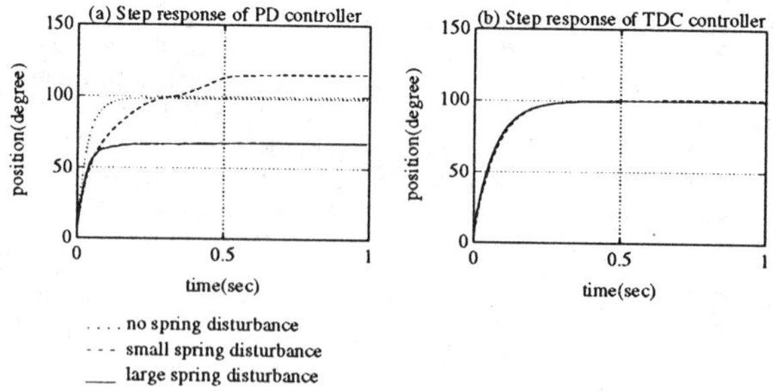

Figure 7: Experimental results with external spring disturbance: (a) PD control case; (b) TDC control case.

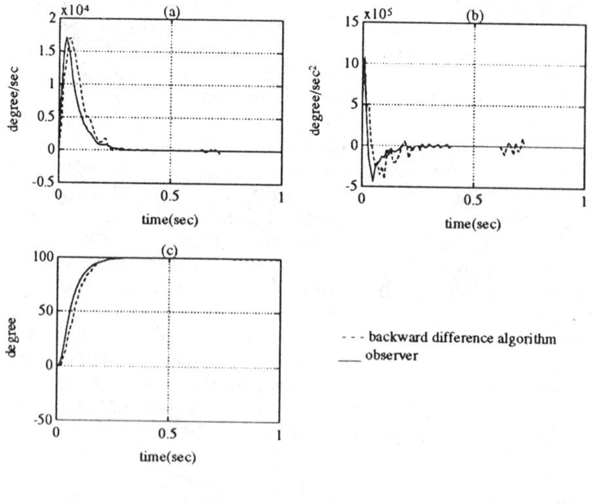

Figure 8: Experimental results when numerical differentiator and the proposed observer are compared.

Proceedings of the
American Control Conference
San Francisco, California • June 1993

On the Robust Stability of Interval Coefficients Neutral Type Linear Constant Control Systems with Multi-groups Multi-delays (1)*

Liu Yongqing†

Department of Automation, South China University of Technology,

Guangzhou, 510641, P.R.China

Gao Cunchen

Department of Mathematics, Yantai Teachers College,

Yantai, Shandong, 264000, P.R.China

Abstract

In this paper, we give out the result for the asymptotic stability of the closed-loop system of the deterministic coefficients linear constant control systems without time-delays

$$\dot{x}_i(t)=\sum_{j=1}^{n} a_{ij}x_j(t)+\sum_{r=1}^{m} b_{ir}u_r(t),\quad i=1,\dots,n$$

imply the robust asymptotic stability of the closed-loop system of the interval coefficients neutral type linear constant control systems with multi-group multi-delays

$$\dot{x}_i(t)=\sum_{j=1}^{n}\bar{a}_{1ij}^{(0)}x_j(t)+\sum_{r=1}^{N_1}\sum_{j=1}^{n}\bar{a}_{1ij}^{(r)}\left[x_j(t-\tau_{1ij}^{(r)})-x_j(t)\right]$$
$$+\sum_{l=1}^{N_2}\sum_{j=1}^{n}\bar{a}_{2ij}^{(l)}\left[\dot{x}_j(t-\tau_{2ij}^{(l)})-\dot{x}_j(t)\right]+\sum_{r=1}^{m}\bar{b}_{1ir}u_r(t),$$
$$i=1,\dots,n.$$

At the same time, we give out the estimate formulae of the interval length limitations and time delay limitation.

1. Putting Forward Questions

Signal and information transmission in control system is always with time delay, and we need to study multilevel hierarchy multi-loops negative feedback control system in practice. On the stabilization problem of the multi-group multi-delays neutral type linear or nonlinear continuous control systems had been studied by Liu Yongqing and Gao Cunchen [1]. In many practice problem, the exact model of a considered system may be unknown or the coefficient matrices of the equation which represent the system can not be obtained precisely. Therefore, researching and solving these problems in the theory and practice is very important. In 1989, 1991, Liu Yongqing etc had studied the robust stabilization and suboptimal control of interval coefficient neutral type linear large scale control system with time delay [2] [3]. In this paper, we discuss the robust stability of the interval coefficients neutral type linear constant control systems with multi-group multi-delays.

* The Priject Was Supported by the Science Fund of the Chinese Natural Sciences.

† The author is a *IEEE*'s member.

2. Robust Stabilization Problem of Interval Coefficients Neutral Type Linear Constant Control Systems with Multi-group Multi-delays

We consider interval coefficients neutral type linear constant control system with multi-group multi-delays

$$\dot{X}(t)=\bar{A}_1^{(0)}X(t)+\sum_{r=1}^{N_1}\bar{A}_1^{(r)}X(t-\tau_1^{(r)})+\sum_{l=1}^{N_2}\bar{A}_2^{(l)}\dot{X}(t-\tau_2^{(l)})+\bar{B}_1U(t),\qquad(2.1)$$

where time-delays $\tau_1^{(r)}=\tau_{1ij}^{(r)}>0$ and $\tau_2^{(l)}=\tau_{2ij}^{(l)}>0$ $(r=1,\dots,N_1,\ l=1,\dots,N_2;i,j=1,\dots,n)$ are constants or functions of variable t. $\tau_1^{(r)}$ and $\tau_2^{(l)}$ are only a kinds of expression of vector form. And vectors $X(t)=(x_1(t),\dots,x_n(t))^T$, $U(t)=(u_1(t),\dots,u_m(t))^T$, and constant matrices $\bar{A}_1^{(r)}$, $\bar{A}_2^{(l)}$ $(r=0,1,\dots,N_1,\ l=1,\dots,N_2)$, and $\bar{B}_1$ are not known precisely but them satisfy

$$\bar{P}_1^{(r)}\le\bar{A}_1^{(r)}\le\bar{Q}_1^{(r)}\quad \bar{P}_2^{(l)}\le\bar{A}_2^{(l)}\le\bar{Q}_2^{(l)}\qquad \bar{P}_3\le\bar{B}_1\le\bar{Q}_3,\qquad(2.2)$$
$$(r=0,1,\dots,N_1;\ l=1,\dots,N_2)$$

where $\bar{P}_1^{(r)}$, $\bar{Q}_1^{(r)}$, $\bar{P}_2^{(l)}$, $\bar{Q}_2^{(l)}$, $\bar{P}_3$, $\bar{Q}_3$ $(r=0,1,\dots,N_1,\ l=1,\dots,N_2)$, are the matrices of the lower and upper bounds of the interval coefficients respectively. Let

$$G=\{\bar{A}_1^{(r)},\ \bar{A}_2^{(l)},\ \bar{B}_1;\ \bar{P}_1^{(r)}\le\bar{A}_1^{(r)}\le\bar{Q}_1^{(r)},\ \bar{P}_2^{(l)}\le\bar{A}_2^{(l)}\le\bar{Q}_2^{(l)},$$
$$\bar{P}_3\le\bar{B}_1\le\bar{Q}_3,\quad r=0,1,\dots,N_1,\quad l=1,\dots,N_2\}$$

denote the set of all constant matrix group which satisfy (2.2). If we only know the matrices $\bar{P}_1^{(r)}$, $\bar{Q}_1^{(r)}$, $\bar{P}_2^{(l)}$, $\bar{Q}_2^{(l)}$, $\bar{P}_3$, $\bar{Q}_3$, $(r=0,1,\dots,N_1,\ l=1,\dots,N_2)$, but do not know the matrices $\bar{A}_1^{(r)}$ $\bar{A}_2^{(l)}$, $\bar{B}_1$, $(r=0,1,\dots,N_1,\ l=1,\dots,N_2)$ then the matrix group

$\{\bar{A}_1^{(r)}, \bar{A}_2^{(l)}, \bar{B}_1;\ r=0,1,\dots,N_1,\ l=1,\dots,N_2\}\in G$ is called interval matrix group. For every interval matrix group $\{\bar{A}_1^{(r)}, \bar{A}_2^{(l)}, \bar{B}_1\}\in G$, if the neutral type linear constant control system with multi-group multi-delays (2.1) can be stabilized, then the system (2.1) is called to be robust stabilization in the set G.

For all $\{\bar{A}_1^{(r)}, \bar{A}_2^{(l)}, \bar{B}_1\}\in G$, let $\bar{A}_1^{(r)}=\left(\bar{a}_{1ij}^{(r)}\right)_{n\times n}$, $\bar{A}_2^{(l)}=\left(\bar{a}_{2ij}^{(l)}\right)_{n\times n}$, $\bar{B}_1=\left(\bar{b}_{1if}\right)_{n\times m}$ $(m\le n)$, $(r=0,1,\dots,N_1;\ l=1,\dots,N_2)$,

then $\bar{p}_{1ij}^{(r)}\le\bar{a}_{1ij}^{(r)}\le\bar{q}_{1ij}^{(r)},\ \bar{p}_{2ij}^{(l)}\le\bar{a}_{2ij}^{(l)}\le\bar{q}_{2ij}^{(l)},\ \bar{p}_{3if}\le\bar{b}_{1if}\le\bar{q}_{3if}$ (2.3)

$$r=0,1,\dots,N_1,\quad l=1,\dots,N_2,$$

where $\bar{P}_1^{(r)}=(\bar{p}_{1ij}^{(r)})_{n\times n}$, $\bar{Q}_1^{(r)}=(\bar{q}_{1ij}^{(r)})_{n\times n}$, $\bar{P}_2^{(l)}=(\bar{p}_{2ij}^{(l)})_{n\times n}$, $\bar{Q}_2^{(l)}=(\bar{q}_{2ij}^{(l)})_{n\times n}$, $\bar{P}_3=(\bar{p}_{3if})_{n\times m}$, $\bar{Q}_3=(\bar{q}_{3if})_{n\times m}$. $(r=0,1,\dots,N_1)$, $(l=1,\dots,N_2)$. If $I-\sum_{l=1}^{N_2}\bar{A}_2^{(l)}$ is non-singular, then (2.1) can be rewritten into

$$\dot{X}(t)=A_1^{(0)}X(t)+B_1U(t)+\sum_{r=1}^{N_1}A_1^{(r)}\left[X(t-\tau_1^{(r)})-X(t)\right]+\sum_{l=1}^{N_2}A_2^{(l)}\left[\dot{X}(t-\tau_2^{(l)})-\dot{X}(t)\right] \quad (2.4)$$

where I is an identity matrix; $A_1^{(0)}=\left(a_{1ij}^{(0)}\right)_{n\times n}=\left(I-\sum_{l=1}^{N_2}\bar{A}_2^{(l)}\right)^{-1}\sum_{r=0}^{N_1}\bar{A}_1^{(r)}$, $B_1=(b_{1if})_{n\times m}=\left(I-\sum_{l=1}^{N_2}\bar{A}_2^{(l)}\right)^{-1}\bar{B}_1$, $A_1^{(r)}=\left(a_{1ij}^{(r)}\right)_{n\times n}=\left(I-\sum_{l=1}^{N_2}\bar{A}_2^{(l)}\right)^{-1}\bar{A}_1^{(r)}$, $A_2^{(l)}=\left(a_{2ij}^{(l)}\right)_{n\times n}=\left(I-\sum_{l=1}^{N_2}\bar{A}_2^{(l)}\right)^{-1}\bar{A}_2^{(l)}$ $(r=1,\dots,N_1,\ l=1,\dots,N_2)$. Since $P_1^{(0)}\le A_1^{(0)}\le Q_1^{(0)}$, $P_3\le B_1\le Q_3$, where $P_1^{(0)}=\left(I-\sum_{l=1}^{N_2}\bar{A}_{2*}^{(l)}\right)^{-1}\sum_{r=0}^{N_1}\bar{P}_1^{(r)}$, $Q_1^{(0)}=\left(I-\sum_{l=1}^{N_2}\bar{A}_2^{*(l)}\right)^{-1}\sum_{r=0}^{N_1}\bar{Q}_1^{(r)}$, $\bar{A}_{2*}^{(l)}=\left(\bar{a}_{2*ij}^{(l)}\right)_{n\times n}$, $\bar{A}_2^{*(l)}=\left(\bar{a}_{2ij}^{*(l)}\right)_{n\times n}$, $\bar{a}_{2*ij}^{(l)}=\frac{1}{2}\left[\left(\bar{a}_{2ijM}^{(l)}+\bar{a}_{2ijm}^{(l)}\right)-\left(\bar{a}_{2ijM}^{(l)}-\bar{a}_{2ijm}^{(l)}\right)\mathrm{sgn}\cdot\sum_{r=0}^{N_1}\bar{p}_{1ij}^{(r)}\right]$, $\bar{a}_{2ij}^{*(l)}=\frac{1}{2}\left[\left(\bar{a}_{2ijM}^{(l)}+\bar{a}_{2ijm}^{(l)}\right)+\left(\bar{a}_{2ijM}^{(l)}-\bar{a}_{2ijm}^{(l)}\right)\mathrm{sgn}\sum_{r=0}^{N_1}\bar{q}_{1ij}^{(r)}\right]$, $\bar{a}_{2ijM}^{(l)}=\max\{|\bar{p}_{2ij}^{(l)}|,|\bar{q}_{2ij}^{(l)}|\}$, $\bar{a}_{2ijm}^{(l)}=\min\{|\bar{p}_{2ij}^{(l)}|,|\bar{q}_{2ij}^{(l)}|\}$, $P_3=(p_{3if})_{n\times m}=\left(I-\sum_{l=1}^{N_2}\bar{A}_{2\Delta}^{(l)}\right)^{-1}\bar{P}_3$, $Q_3=(q_{3if})_{n\times m}=\left(I-\sum_{l=1}^{N_2}\bar{A}_2^{\Delta(l)}\right)^{-1}\bar{Q}_3$, $\bar{a}_{2\Delta ij}^{(l)}=\frac{1}{2}\left[\left(\bar{a}_{2ijM}^{(l)}+\bar{a}_{2ijm}^{(l)}\right)-\left(\bar{a}_{2ijM}^{(l)}-\bar{a}_{2ijm}^{(l)}\right)\mathrm{sgn}\,\bar{p}_{3ij}\right]$, $a_{2ij}^{\Delta(l)}=\frac{1}{2}\left[\left(\bar{a}_{2ijM}^{(l)}+\bar{a}_{2ijm}^{(l)}\right)+\left(\bar{a}_{2ijM}^{(l)}-\bar{a}_{2ijm}^{(l)}\right)\mathrm{sgn}\,\bar{q}_{3ij}\right]$, we have

$$\begin{cases}-\frac{1}{2}\left(Q_1^{(0)}-P_1^{(0)}\right)\le A_1^{(0)}-\frac{1}{2}\left(P_1^{(0)}+Q_1^{(0)}\right)\le\frac{1}{2}\left(Q_1^{(0)}-P_1^{(0)}\right)\\ -\frac{1}{2}\left(Q_3-P_3\right)\le B_1-\frac{1}{2}\left(P_3+Q_3\right)\le\frac{1}{2}\left(Q_3-P_3\right),\end{cases} \quad (2.5)$$

or

$$\begin{cases}-\frac{1}{2}\left(q_{1ij}^{(0)}-p_{1ij}^{(0)}\right)\le d_{1ij}\le\frac{1}{2}\left(q_{1ij}^{(0)}-p_{1ij}^{(0)}\right) & i,j=1,\dots,n;\\ -\frac{1}{2}\left(q_{3if}-p_{3if}\right)\le d_{3if}\le\frac{1}{2}\left(q_{3if}-p_{3if}\right), & f=1,\dots,m,\end{cases} \quad (2.6)$$

where $D_1=(d_{1ij})_{n\times n}=A_1^{(0)}-\frac{1}{2}\left(P_1^{(0)}+Q_1^{(0)}\right)$, $D_3=(d_{3if})_{n\times m}=B_1-\frac{1}{2}(P_3+Q_3)$.

Rewriting (2.4) into the following form:

$$\dot{X}(t)=\sum_{r=0}^{N_1}\frac{1}{2}\left(P_1^{(r)}+Q_1^{(r)}\right)X(t)+\frac{1}{2}(P_3+Q_3)U(t)+\sum_{r=0}^{N_1}\left[A_1^{(r)}-\frac{1}{2}\left(P_1^{(r)}+Q_1^{(r)}\right)\right]X(t)+\left[B_1-\frac{1}{2}(P_3+Q_3)\right]U(t)+\sum_{r=1}^{N_1}A_1^{(r)}\left[X(t-\tau_1^{(r)})-X(t)\right]+\sum_{l=1}^{N_2}A_2^{(l)}\left[\dot{X}(t-\tau_2^{(l)})-\dot{X}(t)\right]=AX(t)+BU(t)+(A_1-A)X(t)+(B_1-B)U(t)+\sum_{r=1}^{N_1}A_1^{(r)}\left[X(t-\tau_1^{(r)})-X(t)\right]+\sum_{l=1}^{N_2}A_2^{(l)}\left[\dot{X}(t-\tau_2^{(l)})-\dot{X}(t)\right], \quad (2.7)$$

the deterministic coefficients linear constant control system is that

$$\dot{X}(t)=AX(t)+BU(t) \quad (2.8)$$

where $A=(a_{ij})_{n\times n}$, $B=(b_{if})_{n\times m}$, $A_1=(a_{1ij})_{n\times n}$ are constant matrices, and

$$\begin{cases}a_{ij}=\sum_{r=0}^{N_1}\frac{1}{2}\left(p_{1ij}^{(0)}+q_{1ij}^{(0)}\right),\quad b_{if}=\frac{1}{2}\left(p_{3if}+q_{3if}\right),\\ a_{1ij}=\sum_{r=0}^{N_1}a_{1ij}^{(r)},\quad i,j=1,\dots,n;\ f=1,\dots,m.\end{cases} \quad (2.9)$$

Assume that the matrix pair $(A:B)$ is controllable, for linear constant control system (2.8), we can find the optimal control law

$$U(t)=-KX(t) \quad (2.10)$$

which minimize of the plant of the quadratic form for system (2.8)

$$J=\int_{t_0}^{+\infty}\left[X^T(t)QX(t)+U^T(t)RU(t)\right]dt \quad (2.11)$$

such that the zero solution is asymptotically stable for the closed-loop system of (2.8)

$$\dot{X}(t)=(A-BK)X(t), \quad (2.12)$$

where

$$K=R^{-1}B^TP=(k_{fj})_{m\times n}, \quad (2.13)$$

and P is the only one symmetric positive definite solution of Riccati matrix algebraic equation

$$A^TP+PA-PBR^{-1}B^TP+Q=0, \quad (2.14)$$

where R and Q are $m\times m$ and $n\times n$ symmetric positive definite constant matrices which are given, respectively. We choose

$$V(X(t))=X^T(t)PX(t) \quad (2.15)$$

as the Lyapunov function of closed-loop system (2.8), then there are constants $\beta_1>0$, $\beta_2>0$ such that

$$\beta_1X^T(t)X(t)\le V(X(t))\le\beta_2X^T(t)X(t). \quad (2.16)$$

Due to $Q+PBR^{-1}B^TP$ is a symmetric positive definite matrix, we have

$$\dot{V}(X(t))_{(2.8)}=-X^T(t)(Q+PBR^{-1}B^TP)X(t)\le-\alpha_1X^T(t)X(t)<0, \quad (2.17)$$

where $\alpha_1 = \lambda_{min}(Q+PBR^{-1}B^T P)$ is a positive constant. Let

$$\begin{cases} \max\limits_{1\le i,j\le n} \{|\bar{p}_{1ij}^{(r)}|,\ |\bar{q}_{1ij}^{(r)}|;\ r=0,1,\dots,N_1\} = \bar{a}_1; \\ \max\limits_{1\le i,j\le n} \{|\bar{p}_{2ij}^{(l)}|,\ |\bar{q}_{2ij}^{(l)}|;\ l=1,\dots,N_2\} = \bar{a}_1'; \\ \max\limits_{1\le i\le n,\ 1\le r\le m} \{|\bar{p}_{3ir}|, |\bar{q}_{3ir}|\} = \bar{b}_1; \\ \max\limits_{1\le i,j\le n} \{|p_{1ij}^{(r)}|,\ |q_{1ij}^{(r)}|;\ r=0,1,\dots,N_1\} = a_1; \\ \max\limits_{1\le i,j\le n} \{|p_{2ij}^{(l)}|,\ |q_{2ij}^{(l)}|;\ l=1,\dots,N_2\} = a_1'; \\ \max\limits_{1\le i,j\le n} \{|p_{ij}|\} = p_1; \quad \max\limits_{1\le r\le m,\ 1\le j\le n} \{|k_{rj}|\} = k_1. \end{cases} \tag{2.18}$$

Now, we make the control law (2.10) substitute (2.7) or (2.1) we obtain a closed-loop system of (2.7)

$$\dot{X}(t) = (A-BK)X(t) + (A_1 - A - B_1 K + BK)X(t) + \sum_{r=1}^{N_1} \bar{A}_1^{(r)} [X(t-\tau_1^{(r)}) - X(t)]$$
$$+ \sum_{l=1}^{N_2} \bar{A}_2^{(l)} [\dot{X}(t-\tau_2^{(l)}) - \dot{X}(t)]. \tag{2.19}$$

From the system (2.19), we give out the following *Lemma*.

Lemma 1[6] Assume that $nN_2\bar{a}_1' < 1$, and $X(t)$ is a solution of (2.19) or (2.1), and $\|X(t)\| < \delta$, $\|\dot{X}(t)\| < \delta$, $\|\ddot{X}(t)\|$ is bounded when $t_0 - \tau \le t \le t_0$. If $\|X(t)\| \le N$ $(t_0 - \tau \le t \le t_1,\ t_0 < t_1)$, then

$$\|\dot{X}(t)\| \le h_1 N, \quad \|\ddot{X}(t)\| \le H_1 N, \tag{2.20}$$

where

$$h_1 = n(\bar{d}_1 + N_1 \bar{a}_1)/(1 - nN_2\bar{a}_1') \quad \bar{d}_1 = \max_{1\le i,j\le n} \left\{ |\bar{a}_{1ij}^{(0)} - \sum_{r=1}^{m} \bar{b}_{1ir} k_{rj}| \right\}$$
$$H_1 = h_1^2 \tag{2.21}$$
$$\tau = \max\left\{ \tau_{1ij}^{(r)},\ \tau_{2ij}^{(l)};\ i,j=1,\dots,n;\ r=1,\dots,N_1;\ l=1,\dots,N_2 \right\}, \tag{2.22}$$

N is a constant or function of variable t.

From (2.10), we have

$$|u_r(t)| \le \sum_{j=1}^{n} |k_{rj}||x_j(t)| \le k_1 \sum_{j=1}^{n} |x_j(t)|, \quad r=1,\dots,m. \tag{2.23}$$

Lemma 2[2] Assume that the conditions of *Lemma* 1 are satisfied, then there are $t_j', t_j'' \in [t-\tau, t]$, such that the following inequalities to be hold:

$$|x_j(t-\tau_{1ij}^{(r)}) - x_j(t)| \le \tau \sum_{i=1}^{n} \left[(\bar{a}_1 + \bar{b}_1 k_1 m)|x_i(t_j')| + \bar{a}_1 \sum_{r=1}^{N_1} |x_i(t_j' - \tau_{1ji}^{(r)})| \right.$$
$$\left. + \bar{a}_1' h_1 \sum_{l=1}^{N_2} |x_i(t_j' - \tau_{2ji}^{(l)})| \right], \tag{2.24}$$

$$|\dot{x}_j(t-\tau_{2ij}^{(l)}) - \dot{x}_j(t)| \le \tau H_1 \sum_{i=1}^{n} |x_i(t_j'')|, \quad i,j=1,\dots,n. \tag{2.25}$$

where $t-\tau_{1ij}^{(r)} \le t_j' \le t$, $t-\tau_{2ij}^{(l)} \le t_j'' \le t$. Defining

$$\mathfrak{B} = \left\{ X; X\in R^n, V(X(t)) \le 4V(x_1(t),\dots,x_n(t)) \right\}. \tag{2.26}$$

Lemma 3[7] If $P_j = (x_1(t_j - \tau_{j1}),\dots,x_n(t_j - \tau_{jn})) \in \mathfrak{B}$, then

$$\sum_{i=1}^{n} x_i^2(t_j - \tau_{ji}) \le \beta_{11} \sum_{i=1}^{n} x_i^2(t), \qquad \sum_{i=1}^{n} x_i^2(t_j) \le \beta_{11} \sum_{i=1}^{n} x_i^2(t), \tag{2.27, 2.28}$$

where $\beta_{11} = 4\beta_2/\beta_1$ is a positive constant.

Theorem 1 Suppose that the conditions of *Lemma* 1 are satisfied, and the matrix pair $(A:B)$ is controllable, then there exist constants $\Delta_i > 0 (i=1,2,3)$ such that the asymptotic stability of the closed-loop system of the deterministic coefficients linear constant control system (2.8) imply the robust asymptotic stability of the closed-loop system of the interval coefficients neutral type linear constant control system with multi-group multi-delays (2.4) or (2.1) when

$$a_{pq} < \Delta_1,\ b_{pq} < \Delta_2,\ 0 \le \tau < \Delta_3, \tag{2.29}$$

where

$$\begin{cases} \Delta_1 = \alpha_1 [6p_1 n^2 (N_1 + 1)]^{-1},\ \Delta_2 = \alpha_1 (6p_1 n^2 k_1 m)^{-1}, \\ \Delta_3 = \alpha_1 \left\{ p_1 n^3 [N_1 a_1 (\bar{a}_1 + \bar{b}_1 k_1 m + N_1 \bar{a}_1 + N_2 \bar{a}_1' h_1) + N_2 a_1' H_1](1 + \beta_{11}) \right\}^{-1} \end{cases} \tag{2.30}$$

and

$$\begin{cases} a_{pq} = \max\limits_{1\le i,j\le n} \left\{ \frac{1}{2} |q_{1ij}^{(r)} - p_{1ij}^{(r)}|;\quad r=1,\dots,N_1 \right\}, \\ b_{pq} = \max\limits_{1\le i\le n,\ 1\le r\le m} \left\{ \frac{1}{2} |q_{3ir} - p_{3ir}| \right\}. \end{cases} \tag{2.31}$$

Proof: Under the conditions of *Theorem* 1, we can choose the optimal negative feedback vector function (2.10) which minimize the plant (2.11) with respect to quadratic form, that is, the zero solution of closed-loop system (2.12) is asymptotically stable. Rewriting control system (2.7) in scalar form

$$\dot{x}_i(t) = \sum_{j=1}^{n} a_{ij} x_j(t) + \sum_{r=1}^{m} b_{ir} u_r(t) + \sum_{j=1}^{n} (a_{1ij} - a_{ij}) x_j(t) + \sum_{r=1}^{m} (b_{1ir} -$$
$$b_{ir}) u_r(t) + \sum_{r=1}^{N_1} \sum_{j=1}^{n} a_{1ij}^{(r)} \left[x_j(t - \tau_{1ij}^{(r)}) - x_j(t) \right] + \sum_{l=1}^{N_2} \sum_{j=1}^{n} a_{2ij}^{(l)} \left[\dot{x}_j(t - \tau_{2ij}^{(l)}) - \right.$$
$$\left. \dot{x}_j(t) \right], \qquad i=1,\dots,n. \tag{2.32}$$

From two sum-sign terms at the head of (2.32) is the right side of the linear constant control system without time delay (2.8), while six sum-sign terms at the back of (2.32) is the perturbed term of control system (2.7) with the multi-group multidelays. Therefore, taking (2.10) as the suboptimal negative feedback vector function of control system (2.7) or (2.1), taking (2.15) as the positive definite symmetric Lyapunov function of control system (2.7) or (2.1). Calculating the derivative $\dot{V}(X(t))$ along the trajectory of (2.7), we have

$$\dot{V}_{(2.7)} = \sum_{i=1}^{n} \frac{\partial V}{\partial x_i} \dot{x}_i(t)|_{(2.7)} = \dot{V}_{(2.8)} + \sum_{i=1}^{n} \frac{\partial V}{\partial x_i} \left\{ \sum_{j=1}^{n} (a_{1ij} - a_{ij}) x_j(t) + \right.$$
$$\sum_{r=1}^{m} (b_{1ir} - b_{ir}) u_r(t) + \sum_{r=1}^{N_1} \sum_{i=1}^{n} a_{1ij}^{(r)} \left[x_j(t - \tau_{1ij}^{(r)}) - x_j(t) \right] + \sum_{l=1}^{N_2} \sum_{j=1}^{n} a_{2ij}^{(l)}$$
$$\left. \cdot \left[\dot{x}_j(t - \tau_{2ij}^{(l)}) - \dot{x}_j(t) \right] \right\} \le \dot{V}_{(2.8)} + 2p_1 \sum_{i,h=1}^{n} |x_h(t)| \left[a_{pq}(N_1 + 1) \sum_{j=1}^{n} |x_j(t)| \right.$$
$$+ b_{pq} \sum_{r=1}^{m} |u_r(t)| + a_1 \sum_{r=1}^{N_1} \sum_{j=1}^{n} |x_j(t - \tau_{1ij}^{(r)}) - x_j(t)| + a_1 \sum_{l=1}^{N_2} \sum_{j=1}^{n} |\dot{x}_j(t - \tau_{2ij}^{(l)}) -$$

$$\dot{x}_j(t)|\Big]. \tag{2.33}$$

From *Lemma* 2 and (2.23), putting (2.24) and (2.25) into (2.33), we have

$$\dot V_{(2.7)} \le \dot V_{(2.8)} + 2p_1 n \sum_{h=1}^{n} |x_h(t)| \sum_{j=1}^{n} \Big\{ a_{pq}(N_1+1)|x_j(t)| + b_{pq}k_1 m|x_j(t)| + \tau a_1 \sum_{r=1}^{N_1}\sum_{i=1}^{n}\Big[(\bar a_1+\bar b_1 k_1 m)|x_i(t_j')| + \bar a_1 \sum_{r=1}^{N_1}|x_i(t_j'-\tau_{1ji}^{(r)})| + \bar a_1' h_1 \sum_{l=1}^{N_2}|x_i(t_j'-\tau_{2ji}^{(l)})|\Big] + N_2 \tau a_1' H_1 |x_i(t_j'')| \Big\} \le \dot V_{(2.8)} + p_1 n \sum_{j,h=1}^{n}[a_{pq}(N_1+1)+b_{pq}k_1 m]\cdot [x_h^2(t)+x_j^2(t)] + \tau p_1 n \sum_{i,j,h=1}^{n}\Big\{N_1 a_1(\bar a_1+\bar b_1 k_1 m)[x_h^2(t)+x_i^2(t_j')] + N_1 a_1 \bar a_1 \cdot \sum_{r=1}^{N_1}[x_h^2(t)+x_i^2(t_j'-\tau_{1ji}^{(r)})] + N_1 a_1 \bar a_1' h_1 \sum_{l=1}^{N_2}[x_h^2(t)+x_i^2(t_j'-\tau_{2ji}^{(l)})] + N_2 a_1' H_1 \cdot [x_h^2(t)+x_i^2(t_j'')]\Big\}. \tag{2.34}$$

$$P_j = (x_1(t_j'-\tau_{1j1}^{(r)}),\dots,x_n(t_j'-\tau_{1jn}^{(r)})) \in \mathscr{B} \qquad (r=1,\dots,N_1),$$

$$Q_j = (x_1(t_j'-\tau_{2j1}^{(l)}),\dots,x_n(t_j'-\tau_{2jn}^{(l)})) \in \mathscr{B} \qquad (l=1,\dots,N_2), \quad j=1,\dots,n,$$

then we substitute correspondent terms of (2.34) with (2.27) and (2.28), and imply

$$\dot V_{(2.7)} \le \dot V_{(2.8)} + 2p_1 n^2 [a_{pq}(N_1+1)+b_{pq}k_1 m] \sum_{j=1}^{n} x_j^2(t) + \tau p_1 n^3 \Big[N_1 a_1(\bar a_1 + \bar b_1 k_1 m)(1+\beta_{11}) \sum_{i=1}^{n} x_i^2(t) + N_1^2 a_1 \bar a_1 (1+\beta_{11}) \sum_{i=1}^{n} x_i^2(t) + N_1 N_2 a_1 \bar a_1' h_1 (1+\beta_{11}) \sum_{i=1}^{n} x_i^2(t) + N_2 a_1' H_1 (1+\beta_{11}) \sum_{i=1}^{n} x_i^2(t)\Big] \le -\alpha_1 \sum_{i=1}^{n} x_i^2(t) + \Big\{2p_1 n^2 [a_{pq}(N_1+1) + b_{pq}k_1 m] + \tau p_1 n^3 [N_1 a_1(\bar a_1 + \bar b_1 k_1 m + N_1 \bar a_1 + N_2 \bar a_1' h_1) + N_2 a_1' H_1](1+\beta_{11})\Big\} \cdot \sum_{i=1}^{n} x_i^2(t). \tag{2.35}$$

From (2.29), when $a_{pq} < \Delta_1$, $b_{pq} < \Delta_2$, $0 \le \tau \le \Delta_1$, we have

$$\dot V_{(2.7)} < 0. \tag{2.36}$$

The proof of Theorem 1 is completed.

3. Discussion

For the multi-group multi-delays interval coefficients neutral type linear control system which has the time delays with its control vector function

$$\dot X(t) = \bar A_1^{(0)} X(t) + \sum_{r=1}^{N_1} \bar A_1^{(r)} X(t-\tau_1^{(r)}) + \sum_{l=1}^{N_2} \bar A_2^{(l)} \dot X(t-\tau_2^{(l)}) + \bar B_1 U(t) + \sum_{s=1}^{N_3} \bar B_1^{(s)} U(t-\tau_3^{(s)}) \tag{3.1}$$

by the above equivalence method of robust stabilization, we can obtain similarly result of *Theorem* 1.

For the multi-group multi-delays interval coefficients neutral type linear time-variating control system with multi-group multi-delays

$$\dot X(t) = \bar A_1^{(0)}(t) X(t) + \sum_{r=1}^{N_1} \bar A_1^{(r)}(t) X(t-\tau_1^{(r)}) + \sum_{l=1}^{N_2} \bar A_2^{(l)}(t) \dot X(t-\tau_2^{(l)}) + \bar B_1(t) U(t) + \sum_{s=1}^{N_3} \bar B_1^{(s)}(t) U(t-\tau_3^{(s)}) \tag{3.2}$$

by the above equivalence method of robust stabilization, we can obtain similarly result of *Theorem* 1.

References

[1] Liu Yongqing, and Gao Cunchen, "On stabilization for the multi-groups and the multi-delays neutral type linear control system (1); (2); (3); (4) International Hefei (China) Conference of Modeling, Simulation & Control, Oct. 6-8, 1992.

[2] Liu Yongqing, and Xie Shengli, "On the robustness stability of interval neutral type control systems with time delays (1)," International Conference on Systems Science 10, Sept. 19-22, 1989, Wroclaw, Poland.

[3] Liu Yongqing, and Xie Shengli, "On the decomposition problem for unconditional robust stability of large scale interval neutral type control systems with time-delays (1) IFAC Symposium Large Scale Systems 89 Theory and Application, Berlin, German Democratic, Aug. 29-31, 1989.

[4] Liu Yongqing, and Gao Shuchun, Robust stabilization problem of interval coefficients linear control systems with multi-group time-delays (1); (2)," Proceedings International AMSE Conference "Signals, Data & Systems," New Delhi (India), Dec. 9-11, 1991.

[5] Qin Yuanxun, Liu Yongqing, and Wang Lian, "On the equivalence problem of differential equation and differential difference equation in the theory of stability *Acta Mathematica Sinica*, Vol.9:3, 333-359, 1959.

[6] Li Senlin, "The fundamental theory of stability for differential difference equations (including neutral type)," *Science Bulletin* (China), 23:2, 88-93, 1978.

Proceedings of the
American Control Conference
San Francisco, California • June 1993

ON SOME STRUCTURES OF STABILIZING CONTROL LAWS FOR LINEAR AND TIME-INVARIANT SYSTEMS WITH BOUNDED POINT DELAYS AND UNMEASURABLE STATE

M. de la Sen

Departamento de Electricidad y Electrónica
Facultad de Ciencias
Universidad del País Vasco
Leioa (Bizkaia)-Aptdo. 644 de Bilbao
SPAIN

Abstract

This note considers the output-feedback stabilization by linear dynamic controllers of (open-loop) stabilizable and detectable time-invariant plants involving a finite set of bounded internal point delays. Two controllers involving, respectively, point and distributed delays are studied as well as their extension to the use of a feedback signal consisting of convolutions of the system output and controller state with an appropriately chosen linearly independent set of functions. It is concluded that an increase in the order of the controller dynamics can be used as an alternative stabilization technique to the use of delays in the controller.

1. INTRODUCTION

In (open-loop) stabilizable free-delay continuous systems, a usual problem is to elucidate the minimum order of a stabilizing controller since, in some situations, it is not possible to achieve closed-loop stabilization through the use of static output feedback gains [1-3] . This problem takes special relevance in adaptive control since the minimum order of the stabilizing controller is a necessary "a priori" knowledge for adaptive stabilization [2-3] . In these papers, an augmented system was used under plant stabilizability/detectability assumptions. Its stabilization through a static output-feedback linear controller was proved to be equivalent to the stabilization of the original system using a dynamic controller of sufficiently large order with both controllers being parametrically related to each other. In this note, the presence of bounded internal (i.e., in the state) point delays is considered and closed-loop stabilization is investigated under plant stabilizability and detectability assumptions,[5-7] of the current (i.e., that involving plant delays) and free-delay systems by using an augmented system. Two classes of stabilizing output-feedback controllers are obtained. The first one implies the use of a number of point delays while the second one has a unique distributed delay but, in general, higher order dynamics. A simple generalization is then given which consists of the use of feedback signals being the convolution of the output of the augmented system (or, equivalently, the output and state of the original plant and controller) with a finite set of linearly independent functions. Such functions are selected under rather weak assumptions including its realizability and analyticity on the instability region. A key observed fact is that higher orders in the controller dynamics can be used to preserve the stabilization properties as an alternative to the use of controller delays. The main new approach in this paper is that the structures of the stabilizing control laws are investigated through their ability to generate full generic ranks in the rank equations characterized the closed-loop stabilization by considering extended systems including the controllers.

2. FORMULATION

Plant and First Controller

Consider the LTI-system

$$S:\ \dot{x}(t)= A\,x(t)+\sum_{i=1}^{p} A_i\,x(t-h_i)+ B\,u(t) \qquad (1.a)$$

$$y(t)= C\,x(t) \qquad (1.b)$$

for all $t\geq 0$ where the state $x(.)\in \mathbb{R}^n$, the input $u(.)\in \mathbb{R}^m$, the output $y(.)\in \mathbb{R}^r$; and the $h_{(.)}$ are positive known delays with $h_{i+1}> h_i$ $(i= 1,2,...,p-1)$, some nonnegative integer p (p = 0 is related to the delay-free plant. All matrices in eqns. (1) are known, constant and of appropriate orders. Since the linear stabilizing output-feedback controller for S in the absence of delays is, in general dynamic [2-3] , the following controller structure is proposed.

$$G_1:\ \dot{z}(t)= F\,z(t)+ G\,y(t)+ z_0(t) \qquad (2.a)$$

$$u(t)= H\, z(t)+K\, y(t)+u_0(t) \quad (2.b)$$

$$z_0(t)= \sum_{i=1}^{q} (F_i\, z(t-h_i')+G_i\, y(t-h_i')) \quad (2.c)$$

$$u_0(t)= \sum_{i=1}^{q} (H_i\, z(t-h_i')+K_i\, y(t-h_i')) \quad (2.d)$$

for $t \geq 0$ where $z \in \mathbb{R}^{\ell}$ and the $h'_{(\cdot)}$ are the controller delays with $h'_{i+1} > h'_i > 0$ $(i= 1,2,\dots,q-1)$, some nonnegative integer q (if $q= 0$, the time-delayed contributions are deleted in (2)). All the matrices in (2) have orders compatible with the corresponding vectors. $x(\cdot)$ and $z(\cdot)$ in (1)-(2) are initialized with arbitrary continuous functions $\varphi: [-h_p, 0] \to \mathbb{R}^n$, $\varphi_z: [-h_q', 0] \to \mathbb{R}^{\ell}$ with $x(0)= \varphi(0)= x_0$ and $z(0)= \varphi_z(0)= z_0$, respectively, $u(t)= 0$ for $t<0$. From the standard existence and unicity Picard-Lindëloff theorem ([4], [8]), unique solutions $x(\cdot)$ and $z(\cdot)$ exist on $[-h_p, \infty)$ and $[-h_q', \infty)$, respectively, subjected to the above initializations. It will be then seen that different $z_0(\cdot)$ and $u_0(\cdot)$ signals than (2.c)-(2.d), involving typically higher-order dynamics, can be used to achieve stabilization.

Augmented System

The overall system (1)-(2) can be equivalently described by the following augmented plant and controller

$$\tilde{S}_{\ell}: \dot{\tilde{x}}(t)=\tilde{A}\,\tilde{x}(t)+\sum_{i=1}^{p} \tilde{A}_i\, \tilde{x}(t-h_i)+\tilde{B}\,\tilde{u}(t) \quad (3.a)$$

$$\tilde{y}(t)=\tilde{C}\,\tilde{x}(t) \quad (3.b)$$

$$\tilde{C}_{\ell}: \tilde{u}(t)=\tilde{K}\,\tilde{y}(t)+\sum_{j=1}^{q} \tilde{K}_j\, \tilde{y}(t-h_j') \quad (3.c)$$

where $\tilde{x}= [x^T \mid z^T]^T$, $\tilde{u}= [u^T \mid \dot{z}^T]^T$, $\tilde{y}= [y^T \mid z^T]^T$ are of dimensions $(n+\ell)$, $(m+\ell)$ and $(r+\ell)$, respectively, and

$$\left.\begin{array}{l} \tilde{A}_i= \mathrm{Diag}(A_i \mid 0);\ \tilde{B}=\mathrm{Diag}(B \mid I);\ \tilde{C}=\mathrm{Diag}(C \mid I) \\ \tilde{K} = \left[\begin{array}{c|c} K & H \\ \hline G & F \end{array}\right] ;\quad \tilde{K}_j = \left[\begin{array}{c|c} K_j & H_j \\ \hline G_j & F_j \end{array}\right] \end{array}\right\} (3.d)$$

$i= 1,2,\dots,p$; $j= 1,2,\dots,q$, and I is the ℓ-identity matrix. The initial conditions are $\tilde{\varphi}(\tau)= [\varphi^T(\tau) \mid \varphi_z^T(\tau)]^T$. The augmented system eqns. (3) is an extension in the presence of delays in (1)-(2) of that given in [2-3].

Stabilization of $\tilde{S}_{\ell}$ with a controller $\tilde{C}_{\ell}$

The concepts of stabilizability and detectability are directly extendable to delayed systems [5-7] from the undelayed case,[1]. In particular, the concept of γ-detectability is equivalent to spectral observability of all the modes corresponding to eigenvalues with real parts within $[-\gamma, \infty)$. It is also equivalent to infinite-time observability of such eigenvalues, [5], in the sense that there is no eigensolution $x(t)= \exp(\lambda t)\, x(0)$ generating $y \equiv 0$ on $[0,\infty)$ with $\mathrm{Re}\,\lambda \geq -\gamma$ for $x(0) \neq 0$. Note that a γ-stabilizable/detectable (γSD) system has all its uncontrollable and unobservable open-loop modes within the stability domain $\bar{\mathbb{C}}_{\gamma}$ (i.e., the complementary of $\mathbb{C}_{\gamma}$ in $\mathbb{C}$) where $\mathbb{C}_{\gamma} \triangleq \{z \in \mathbb{C}: \mathrm{Re}\ z \in [-\gamma, \infty)\}$, $\gamma \geq 0$. However, contrarily to the free-delay case, [1] , stabilizability/detectability has not been proved to guarantee closed-loop stabilization with a linear dynamic controller C_{ℓ} . These assumptions are now introduced to obtain results about closed-loop stabilization.

Assumption 1. System S is (open-loop) γSD; i.e., $\mathrm{rank}\,[sI-\mathcal{A}(s) \mid B] = \mathrm{rank}\,[sI-\mathcal{A}^T(s) \mid C^T] = n$ for all $s \in \mathbb{C}_{\gamma}$, where

$\mathcal{A}(s)= A + \sum_{i=1}^{p} e^{-h_i s} A_i$ and "s" denotes the Laplace transform variable. ■

Assumption 2. The delay-free particular S , namely $A_{(\cdot)}= 0$, $h_{(\cdot)}= 0$ in (1.a), is (open-loop) γSD; i.e.,
$\mathrm{rank}\,[sI-A \mid B] = \mathrm{rank}\,[sI-A^T \mid C^T]=n$, $\forall s \in \mathbb{C}_{\gamma}$. ■

From the matrix block structures of $\tilde{A}$, $\tilde{A}_{(\cdot)}$, $\tilde{B}$ and $\tilde{C}$, eqns. (3.d), Assumptions 1-2 imply that both the current and delay-free systems are (open-loop) γ-stabilizable (i.e., their closed-loop poles can be placed within $\bar{\mathbb{C}}_{\gamma}$) iff, respectively, the current and free-delay augmented systems $\tilde{S}_{\ell}$ are (open-loop) γ-stabilizable for all integer $\ell \geq 0$. In [2-3], the following result is proved for free-delay systems.

Lemma 1. Assume that $h_{(\cdot)}= 0$. If Assumption 2 holds then the free-delay $\tilde{S}_{\ell}$ is γSD for all integer $\ell \geq 0$, i.e.,
$\mathrm{rank}\,[sI-\tilde{A} \mid \tilde{B}]= \mathrm{rank}\,[sI-\tilde{A}^T \mid \tilde{C}^T]= n+\ell$ for all $s \in \mathbb{C}_{\ell}$. Furthermore, there exists a nonnegative integer ℓ_0 such that $\tilde{S}_{\ell}$ is γ-stabilizable with a static controller $\tilde{C}_{\ell}$ for all integer $\ell \geq \ell_0$ (i.e., $\mathrm{rank}\,[sI-\tilde{A}-\tilde{B}\tilde{K}\tilde{C}] = n+\ell$, some $\tilde{K} \in \mathbb{R}^{(m+\ell)\times(r+\ell)}$) or, equivalently, S is γ-stabilizable with a dynamic controller C_{ℓ} for all $\ell \geq \ell_0$. ■

According to Lemma 1, the dynamic stabilizing controller C_{ℓ} is required to have a minimum order ℓ_0 . The next technical lemma will be then applied for stabilization of S under a wide class of controller structures than (2) and (3). The concept of generic rank of the set of matrices $\{M_{\gamma} : \gamma \in \mathcal{M}\}$ for some index set $\mathcal{M}$ being defined as
$\mathrm{g.r.}\,[M_{\gamma}: \mathcal{M}\,] = \max\,\{\mathrm{rank}\, M_{\gamma} : \gamma \in \mathcal{M}\}$ (See [9-10]).

Lemma 2. Under Assumption 1, the following propositions hold.
(i) There exists a (in general nonunique, multiform and nonnecessarily continuous) matrix function $X : \mathbb{C}_{\gamma} \to \mathbb{R}^{(m+\ell)\times(r+\ell)}$ such that

$$\mathrm{g.r.}\ [sI-\tilde{\mathcal{A}}(s)-\tilde{B}X(s)\tilde{C}] = n+\ell,\ \forall s \in \mathbb{C}_{\gamma}, \text{all integer } \ell \geq 0,\quad X(s) \in \mathbb{R}^{(m+\ell)\times(r+\ell)} \quad (4.a)$$

and a matrix function $X_1: \mathbb{C}_{\gamma} \to \mathbb{R}^{m\times(r+\ell)}$ such that

$$\mathrm{g.r.}\ [sI-\tilde{\mathcal{A}}(s)-\tilde{B}X_1(s)\tilde{C}]=n,\ \forall s \in \mathbb{C}_{\gamma}, \text{all integer } \ell \geq 0,\quad X_1(s) \in \mathbb{R}^{m\times(r+\ell)} \quad (4.b)$$

(ii) If rank $[s_1 I-\tilde{A}(s_1)-\tilde{B}X_{s_1}\tilde{C}] = n+\ell$ for some $s_1 \in \mathbb{C}_\gamma$, then there is an open neighborhood of center s_1 in $\mathbb{C}_\gamma$ of radius $r>0$ ($\beta(s_1,r) \cap \mathbb{C}_\gamma$) such that

$$\text{rank}\,[sI-\tilde{A}(s)-\tilde{B}X_{s_1}\tilde{C}]= n+\ell, \forall s \in \beta(s_1,r)\cap \mathbb{C}_\gamma \quad (5)$$

This result also holds for generic ranks with X_{s_1} taking values in $\mathbb{R}^{(m+\ell)\times(r+\ell)}$

(iii) If, furthermore, Assumption 2 holds and $X(s)$ in (4.a) has a finite limit $\lim_{s\to\infty} X(s)= \tilde{K}\in\mathbb{R}^{(m+\ell)\times(r+\ell)}$, which γ-stabilizes the free-delay $\tilde{S}_\ell$ (for all integer $\ell \geq \ell_0$, some existing $\ell_0 \geq 0$ from Lemma 1), then there exist finite sets $s^*(N)$ of N distinct points in $\mathbb{C}_\gamma$, with $N \geq N_0$ (some integer $N_0 \geq 1$), and of real matrices $\Lambda[s^*(N)]$ defined by

$$s^*(N)= \{s_i \in \mathbb{C}_\gamma : s_i \neq s_j \text{ if } i \neq j \text{ ; } i= 1,2,\dots,N\}$$
$$\Lambda[s^*(N)] = \{X_{s_i}\in\mathbb{R}^{(m+\ell)\times(r+\ell)} : s_i \in s^*(N); i=1,2,\dots,N\} \quad (6)$$

such that

$$\text{rank}\,[s_i I - \tilde{A}(s_i) - \tilde{B}X_{s_i}\tilde{C}] = \underset{X\in\Lambda}{\text{g.r.}}\,[sI-\tilde{A}(s) - \tilde{B}X\tilde{C}] = n+\ell \quad (7.a)$$

$$\text{rank}\,[s_i I - A(s_i) - BX_{1s_i}\tilde{C}] = \underset{X_1\in\Lambda_1}{\text{g.r.}}\,[sI-A(s) - BX_1\tilde{C}] = n \quad (7.b)$$

for all $s \in \mathbb{C}_\gamma$, all $s_i \in s^*(N)$, $X_{s_i} \in \Lambda[s^*(N)]$; $i= 1,2,\dots N$ and block matrix partitions $X_{s_{(\cdot)}} = [X^T_{1s_{(\cdot)}} \mid X^T_{2s_{(\cdot)}}]$ with $X_{s_{(\cdot)}} \in \Lambda$, $X_{1s_{(\cdot)}} \in \Lambda_1 \subset \mathbb{R}^{m\times(r+\ell)}$. The triples $(N, s^*(N), \Lambda[s^*(N)])$ for each $N \geq N_0$ are nonunique. ∎

Remark 1. Lemma 2 (iii) establishes that if the free-delay $\tilde{S}_\ell$ is γ-stabilized with the static control law $\tilde{u}(t)= \tilde{K}\tilde{y}(t)$ for all $\ell \geq \ell_0$, then the generic ranks of Lemma 2 (i) are full if they are full for a finite set of points of $\mathbb{C}_\gamma$ and associated $X_{(\cdot)}$-matrices. These points satisfy Lemma 2 (ii) and are appropriately distributed so that the overall $\mathbb{C}_\gamma$ is covered by the union of the respective open neighborhoods. Lemma 2 (iii) will be then essential in the proofs of the closed-loop γ-stabilizability properties of C_ℓ, $\tilde{C}_\ell$, eqns. (2)-(3), and other subsequently studied controllers.

Assumptions 1-2 can be substituted by more restrictive conditions concerning open-loop controllability and observability ([5], [8]). Under these conditions, Lemmas 1-2 as well as the subsequent stability results still hold. The essential feature used in the proof of Lemma 2 is the existence of triples $(N, s^*(N), \Lambda[s^*(N)])$ which simultaneously satisfy Lemma (i) and Lemma (iii) in the sense that $X(s_i)$ [Lemma 2 (i)] = X_{s_i} [Lemma 2 (iii)] for $i= 1,2,\dots,N$. The next stability result is based on the fact that there exist some of these triples such that Lemma 2 (iii) (and thus Lemma 2 (i) is guaranteed and furthermore, the system of equations

$$\Delta X_{s_i} = X_{s_i} - \tilde{K} = \sum_{j=1}^{q} \tilde{K}_j e^{-hs_j} \quad (i= 1,2,\dots,N)$$

has a compatible solution $\tilde{K}_{(\cdot)}$ for some $\tilde{K}$ fulfilling Lemma 1 and some integer $q \geq N$. Matrices $\tilde{K}$, $\tilde{K}_{(\cdot)}$ lead to a γ-stabilizing controller $\tilde{C}_\ell$ for $\tilde{S}_\ell$.

Theorem 1. If Assumption 1-2 hold, then for all integers $\ell \geq \ell_0$ and $q \geq N$, where $\ell_0 \geq 0$ exists from Lemma 1, and $N \geq N_0$ (N_0 exists from Lemma 2 (iii) to be determined), there exist (in general) non-unique controllers C_ℓ and $\tilde{C}_\ell$ which γ-stabilize S and $\tilde{S}_\ell$, respectively, for any set of delays h_i' satisfying $h_{i+1}' > h_i' > 0$; $i= 1,2,\dots,q$.

Outline of proof: The proof is addressed by taking Laplace transforms in (3) with zero initial conditions to yield $\tilde{u}(s) = X(s)\tilde{y}(s)$ with $X(s)= \tilde{K} + \sum_{i=1}^{q} \tilde{K}_i e^{-h_i s}$ with $q \geq N$. A set of matrices $(\tilde{K}, \tilde{K}_{(\cdot)})$ is then calculated from a discrete set of matrices $X_{s(\cdot)}$ satisfying Lemma 2 (iii) for a $\tilde{K}$ that γ-stabilizes $\tilde{S}_\ell$ according to Lemma 1. Then Lemma 2 (iii) is used to guarantee full generic ranks in Lemma 2 (i) for the $(m+\ell)\times(r+\ell)$-matrix $X(s)$ fulfilling

$$M(N, q)\,\tilde{K}^* = [\Delta X^T_{s_1} \mid \Delta X^T_{s_2} \mid \dots \mid \Delta X^T_{s_N}]^T \quad (8)$$

with $\Delta X_{s_k} = X_{s_k} - \tilde{K}$ at points $s_k \in s^*(N)$ with $X \in \Lambda$ which has a solution $\tilde{K}^* = [\tilde{K}_1^T \mid \dots \mid \tilde{K}_q^T]^T$ if and only if

$$\text{rank}\,[M(N, q)] = \text{rank}\,[M(N, q) \mid \Delta X^*] = N_1 \leq N.$$ ∎

Remark 2. Note that the centres of the neighborhoods referred to in Lemma 2 (iii) and Theorem 1 can be chosen with a wide freedom since if Lemma 2 (iii) holds for some N and R (defining Π_R), it holds for all $N' > N$ and R by defining new triples $(N', s^*(N'), \Lambda[s^*(N')])$ with eqns. (6). This fact was crucial in the proof of the ending part of Theorem 1. Another essential argument in that proof, namely, the requirement of existence of triples jointly satisfying Lemma 2 (iii) and (8) is seen to be a very weak constraint. ∎

Second Controller

The fact that Lemma 2 is not directly related to the structures of C_ℓ and $\tilde{C}_\ell$ can be used to design different structures of controllers. $\tilde{C}_\ell$ is modified as follows:

$$\tilde{C}_\ell' : \tilde{u}(t)= \tilde{K}\tilde{y}(t) + \int_0^h \sum_{i=1}^{q} \tilde{K}_i e^{\lambda_i \theta} \tilde{y}(t-\theta)\, d\theta \quad (9)$$

and C_ℓ is correspondingly changed into C_ℓ' with $\ell \geq \ell_0$ (ℓ_0 existing from Lemma 1). Taking Laplace transforms in (9) with zero initial conditions, one gets

$$\tilde{u}(s)= [\tilde{K} + \sum_{i=1}^{q} \int_0^h \tilde{K}_i e^{(\lambda_i - s)\theta}\, d\theta]\,\tilde{y}(s) \quad (10.a)$$

$$= [\tilde{K} + \sum_{i=1}^{q} \frac{\tilde{K}_i}{s-\lambda_i} (1-e^{(\lambda_i - s)h})] \tilde{y}(s) \qquad (10.b)$$

According to (9), eqn. (8) can be rewritten as

$$\tilde{u}(t) = \tilde{K} \tilde{y}(t) + \sum_{i=1}^{q} v_i(t) \qquad (11)$$

Also, comparing eqns. (3) and (2) and eqn. (3.c) with (9), it follows that the control law associated with C'_ℓ is given by (2.a)-(2.b) together with

$$z_0(t) = \sum_{i=1}^{q} \int_0^h e^{\lambda_i \theta} (F_i\, z(t-\theta) + G_i\, y(t-\theta)) d\theta$$

$$= \sum_{i=1}^{q} \int_0^t e^{\lambda_i t} [F_i\, z(t-\theta) - e^{\lambda_i h} z(t-\theta-h))$$

$$+ G_i(y(t-\theta) - e^{\lambda_i h} y(t-\theta-h))]\, d\theta \qquad (12.a)$$

$$u_0(t) = \sum_{i=1}^{q} \int_0^h e^{\lambda_i \theta} (H_i\, z(t-\theta) + K_i\, y(t-\theta))\, d\theta$$

$$= \sum_{i=1}^{q} \int_0^t e^{\lambda_i t} [H_i\, z(t-\theta) - e^{\lambda_i h} z(t-\theta-h))$$

$$+ K_i(y(t-\theta) - e^{\lambda_i h} y(t-\theta-h))]\, d\theta \qquad (19.b)$$

Remark 3. Note from (10) that the control law (9) can be described by the augmented controller of state $\tilde{z} = [\tilde{x}^T, v_1, v_2, \ldots, v_q]^T$ so that $\tilde{S}_\ell$ and S are controlled, respectively, by dynamic controllers $\tilde{C}'_\ell$ and C'_ℓ of respective orders q and $(q+\ell)$. However, $\tilde{C}_\ell$ is static. Another difference is that $\tilde{C}'_\ell$ has a unique distributed delay while lying within a particular class of stabilizing controllers described in [6] for plants with distributed delays. Now, $d\,k(\theta) = \sum_{i=1}^{q} \tilde{K}_i\, e^{\lambda_i \theta}$ and $k(\theta)$ is a finite measure of bounded variation within $[0, h]$. It is then proved that C'_ℓ and $\tilde{C}'_\ell$ can be γ-stabilizing for S and $\tilde{S}_\ell$ so that controller delays can be substituted by higher order dynamics subject to weak conditions while preserving the closed-loop stabilization. ∎

The next technical result is then used.

Lemma 3. The following propositions hold. (i) Let $G \triangleq \{g_i : = \mathcal{D}_0 \subset \mathbb{R} \times \mathbb{R} \to \mathbb{R}\ ;\ i = 1,2,\ldots,p\}$ be a set of nonnecessarily continuous scalar real functions defined on $\mathcal{D}_0$ and being linearly independent (free system) on some subset $\mathcal{D} \subset \mathcal{D}_0$. Then, there exists a set of p distinct points $x_i \in \mathcal{D}'$ $(i = 1,2,\ldots,p)$ such that

$$\text{Det}\,(g_i(x_k)) = \begin{vmatrix} g_1(x_1) & g_2(x_1) \ldots g_p(x_1) \\ g_1(x_2) & g_2(x_2) \ldots g_p(x_2) \\ \vdots & \vdots \qquad \vdots \\ g_1(x_p) & g_2(x_p) \ldots g_p(x_p) \end{vmatrix} \neq 0 \qquad (13)$$

$i, k = 1, 2, \ldots, p$

with $\mathcal{D}'$ being any arbitrary subset of $\mathcal{D}$ of nonzero measure ($\mathcal{D}_0, \mathcal{D}$ and $\mathcal{D}'$ can be open or closed). (ii) Let $\mathcal{B} \triangleq \{\mathcal{B}_1, \mathcal{B}_2, \ldots, \mathcal{B}_p\}$ a set of distinct vector basis of the euclidean space $\mathbb{R}^p$ with $\mathcal{B}_k \triangleq \{e_i^k \in \mathbb{R}^p ;\ i = 1,2,\ldots,p\}$; $k = 1,2,\ldots,p$. Thus, there exists a set of vectors $\mathcal{B}^* \triangleq \{e'_i \in \mathbb{R}^p : e'_i = e_k^i \in \mathcal{B}_i$ for all i and some k belonging to $\{1,2,\ldots,p\}\}$ which is a basis of $\mathbb{R}^p$. (iii) Consider $\mathcal{D}' \triangleq \bigcup_{i=1}^{p} (\mathcal{D}'_i)$ in proposition (i) with the $\mathcal{D}'_{(.)}$ being pairwise disjoint sets. Thus, (13), and then prop. (i), can be guaranteed for a set of p points $x_i \in (\mathcal{D}'_i \cap \mathcal{D})$; $i = 1,2,\ldots,p$.

The next stability result follows from Lemmas 2-3.

Theorem 2. Theorem 1 holds, under the same assumptions, for controllers C'_ℓ and $\tilde{C}'_\ell$ for all real constant delay $h > 0$ and infinitely many choices of $\lambda_i \in \mathbb{C}_\gamma$ (i.e., the γ-stabilization domain) with $\lambda_i \neq \lambda_j$, $i \neq j$; $i, j = 1,2,\ldots,q$ ($q \geq N \geq N_0$, N_0 existing from Lemma 2). ∎

The proof is addressed similarly to that of Theorem 1.

General Convolution Controller

Controllers $\tilde{C}_\ell$ and $\tilde{C}'_\ell$ are generalized to the next convolution controller

$$\tilde{u}(t) = \tilde{K} \tilde{y}(t) + \sum_{i=1}^{q} \tilde{K}_i\, f_i(t) * \tilde{y}(t) \qquad (14.a)$$

$$\Rightarrow \tilde{u}(s) = \chi(s) \tilde{y}(s) = [\tilde{K} + \sum_{i=1}^{q} \tilde{K}_i\, f_i(s)]\, \tilde{y}(s) \qquad (14.b)$$

for any integers $\ell \geq \ell_0$ (ℓ_0 existing from Lemma 1), $q \geq N \geq N_0$ (N_0 defined in Lemma 2 (iii)) where $\tilde{K}$ γ-stabilizes $\tilde{S}_\ell$ and $f_{(.)}(s)$ are assumed to exist. Laplace transforms are taken for zero initial conditions and $*$ denotes the convolution integral. Note from (14.b) that this controller involves higher order dynamics with respect to $\tilde{C}'_\ell$. The two above presented controllers are a particularization of eqns. (14). In particular $f_i(t) = \delta(t - h'_i)$, $f_i(s) = e^{-h'_i s}$ for $\tilde{C}_\ell$ and $f_i(t) = e^{\lambda_i t} [1 - e^{\lambda_i h} \delta(t-h)]$, $f_i(s) = (1 - e^{(\lambda_i - s)h})/(s - \lambda_i)$ for $\tilde{C}'_\ell$. Note that the corresponding controller for S involves both output and controller state convolutions with the set $\{f_{(.)}\}$. (1) The set $F \triangleq \{\text{Re}\, f_i : = \mathbb{C}_\gamma \to \mathbb{R}\ ;\ i = 1,2,\ldots,q\}$ is a set of physically realizable and Laplace transformable functions being linearly independent on $\mathbb{C}_\gamma$. (2) The Laplace transform $f_i(s)$ is analytic on $\mathbb{C}_\gamma$ for $i = 1,2,\ldots,q$. (3) The algebraic system of real equations (8), being obtained from a triple $(N, s^*(N), \Lambda[s^*(N)])$, which satisfies Lemma 2 (iii), and with $M_i(N, q) = [\text{Re}\, f_1(s_i), \text{Re}\, f_2(s_i), \ldots, \text{Re}\, f_q(s_i)]$ $(i = 1,2,\ldots,N)$ has a compatible solution $\tilde{K}^*$ (it suffices to choose $q \geq N$ and to guarantee $M(N, q)$ to be full row rank under Lemma 3 (iii)).

Note that realizability of $f_{(.)}$ is required for realizability of (14.b). To find triples $(N, s^*(N), \Lambda[s^*(N)])$ fulfilling the above requirements is always possible since there are infinitely many triples satisfying Lemma 2 (iii) for all $N \geq N_0$ and infinitely many triples leading to a solvable algebraic system (8) for $q \geq N$.

3. CONCLUSIONS

This note has focused the problem of stabilization of a linear and time-invariant stabilizable/detectable system subject to point delays under two output-feedback stabilizing controller structures. It has been shown that the controller delays can be chosen freely independently of those of the plant. The first class of controllers has to satisfy constraints of minimum order in its dynamics and of minimum number of delays. The second one only involves a distributed delay at the expense of an increase in the order of the controller dynamics. A more general controller which involves convolutions of the controller state and output with a set of linearly independent functions can be used for closed-loop stabilization purposes. This generalization corroborates the above conclusion about a trade-off between the number of the controller delays and the order of its dynamics.

ACKNOWLEDGMENTS

The author is very grateful to DGICYT by its partial support of this work through Project PS90-0095.

REFERENCES

[1] T. Kailath, "Linear Systems", Englewood Cliffs, N.I.: Prentice-Hall, Inc., 1980.

[2] D.E. Miller and E.J. Davison, "An adaptive controller which provides Lyapunov stability", IEEE Trans. Automat. Control, Vol. AC-34, No. 6, pp. 599-609, June 1989.

[3] B. Martensson, "The order of any stabilizing regulator is sufficient a priori information for adaptive stabilization", Syst. Contr. Letters, pp. 87-91, July 1985.

[4] T.A. Burton, "Stability and periodic solutions of ordinary and functional differential equations", New York: Academic Press, 1985.

[5] E.B. Lee and A.W. Olbrot, "Observability and related structural results for linear hereditary systems", Int. J. of Control, Vol. 34, No. 6, pp. 1061-1078, 1981.

[6] A.W. Olbrot, "Stabilizability, detectability and spectrum assignment for linear autonomous systems with general time delays", IEEE Trans. Automat. Control, Vol. AC-23 , pp. 887-890, 1978.

[7] G. Tadmor, "Trajectory stabilizing controls in hereditary linear systems", SIAM J. Control and Optimization, Vol. 26, No. 1, pp. 138-154, Jan. 1988.

[8] M. de la Sen, "Fundamental properties of linear control systems with after-effect. Part I: The continuous case", Mathematical and Computer Modelling", Vol. 10, No. 7, pp. 473-489, 1988; "Ibid. Extensions including the discrete case", Ibid., pp. 491-502, 1988, Vol. 10, No. 7, pp. 491-502

[9] X.K. Xie, "A new matrix identity in control theory", in Proc. 24th IEEE Conf. Decision and Control, Vol. 1, pp. 539-541, 1986.

[10] X.K. Xie and Y. Yang, "Frequency domain characterization of decentralized fixed modes", IEEE Trans. Autom. Control, Vol. AC-31, No. 10, pp. 952-955, Oct. 1986.

[11] J.M. Ortega, "Numerical Analysis", New York: Academic Press, 1972.

[12] T.M. Apostol, "Mathematical Analysis", Reading, MA: Addison-Wesley Publishing Company, 1980.

[13] S. MacLane and G. Birkhooff, "Algèbre. Structures fondamentales", Vol. I, París: Gauthier-Villars, 1970.

[14] E.K. Blum, "Numerical Analysis and Computation Theory and Practice", Reading, MA: Addison-Wesley, 1972.

Proceedings of the
American Control Conference
San Francisco, California • June 1993

APPROXIMATE DISTURBANCE DECOUPLING FOR A CLASS OF NONLINEAR TIME DELAY SYSTEMS

M Velasco[1], Ja. Alvarez, R. Castro
Centro de Investigación y de Estudios Avanzados del IPN
Departamento de Ingeniería Eléctrica
Sección de Control Automático
Apartado Postal 14-740, 07000 México D.F.
e-mail:doct_aut@cinvesmx.bitnet

Abstract

In the present paper we deal with the approximate disturbance decoupling problem with measurement (DDPM) for a class of nonlinear systems with a simple time delay at the input. The analysis is based on a standard singularly perturbed form free of delay which is an approximation of the original system.

Keywords. Nonlinear systems, input delay, singular perturbations, disturbance decoupling.

1. Introduction

In general a dynamic system with time delay is a system in which there exists a delay of time between the application of a signal, usually the input or control signal, and the result of this action. This class of systems frequently appears in the field of process control due to the fact that one can always find time delays associated with electronic devices, mechanical components, etc. Mathematically, a system with delay can be described by means of a set of delay differential equations [1].
In this work we consider the disturbance decoupling problem for a class of nonlinear systems with a simple time delay at the input. Our approach consists in using an approximate model of the original system, which has the structure of a singularly perturbed system without delay. Thus, we can approximately solve the problem for the original system by using the singular perturbation theory [4] together with some already known results from the geometric nonlinear control literature [9]. This work is based in a similar approach followed independently by Sannuti [2] and Inuoe et al. [3] for linear systems. In the first section of the paper we briefly recall the disturbance decoupling problem for a class of nonlinear systems without delay by considering some results given in [9] and motivate the use of an approximate model. In section 3, we study the disturbance decoupling problem with measurement associated to the approximate model. Finally, we apply the developed methodology to an academic example and show some simulation results.

2. Description of the problem and the approximate model

The disturbance decoupling problem (DDP) has been extensively studied in the control literature and some solutions to the problem have been proposed in the case of linear and nonlinear systems free of delay; see, for instance [5], [6] for the linear case, and [7] for the nonlinear case.

A noncausal control law. We will consider a class of nonlinear delay systems given by

$$\dot{x}(t)=f(x(t))+g(x(t))u(t-\tau)+p(x(t))w \tag{1a}$$

$$y(t)=h(x), \tag{1b}$$

where the state vector $x \in \mathbb{X} \subset \mathbb{R}^n$, an open subset in $\mathbb{R}^n$, and the input $u(t)$ and the output $y(t) \in \mathbb{R}^m$. f, p, h and the m columns $g_1,..,g_m$, of the matrix g are smooth vector fields on $\mathbb{X}$. $w(t) \in \mathbb{R}$ is the disturbance signal, and τ is a real positive number considered as the time delay associated to the input signal.
In order to establish the difference between a system of the form (1) with a system free of delay, we will briefly recall the DDPM for the latter case. Consider a nonlinear system which has the same structure of (1) with $\tau \equiv 0$, we then have the following definition of the DDPM.

Definition 1 [9]. The Disturbance Decoupling Problem with Measurement. *Consider a system of the form (1) with $\tau \equiv 0$. Find, if possible, a regular static state feedback of the form*

$$u(t)=\alpha(x(t))+\beta(x(t))\upsilon(t)+\gamma(x)w(t) \tag{2}$$

defined in a neighborhood $\mathbb{U}$ of x^o, with $\upsilon(t)$ a new input, that makes the output independent of the disturbance $w(t)$ for all $t \geq 0$. ■

We also have the following result.

Proposition 1 [9]. *Suppose that the system (1) with $\tau \equiv 0$ has a well defined (vector) relative degree $\rho=col[\rho_1\ \rho_2 \cdots \rho_m]$ with respect to u at a point x^o. Then, the DDPM can be solved in a neighborhood $\mathbb{U}$ of x^o by means of a regular static state feedback of the form (2) if and only if*

$$L_pL_f^i h_j(x)=0,\ \forall\ x \in \mathbb{U} \text{ and } \forall\ 0 \leq i \leq \rho_j-2,\ 1 \leq j \leq m. \tag{3}$$

In this case a solution is given by

$$u(t)=-A^{-1}(x)[B(x)-\upsilon(t)+Q(x)w(t)], \tag{4}$$

where the entries a_{ij} of the mxm decoupling matrix $A(x)$ and the elements of the mx1 vectors $B(x)$, b_i, and $Q(x)$, q_i, are given by

$$a_{ij}=L_{g_j}L_f^{\rho_i-1}h_i(x),\quad b_i=L_f^{\rho_i}h_i(x),\quad q_i=L_pL_f^{\rho_i-1}h_i(x),\quad 1 \leq i,j \leq m.$$

with $\upsilon(t)$ a new mx1 input vector. ■

If we additionally assume that system (1) with $\tau \equiv 0$ has a well defined relative degree σ with respect to w in x^o, condition (3) can be written as

$$\rho_i \leq \sigma, \quad 0 \leq i \leq m. \tag{5}$$

Coming back to the original delay system ($\tau \neq 0$), we can define a vector relative degree in a similar way that for the case $\tau=0$.

Definition 2. *The nonlinear delay system (1) is said to have a (vector) relative degree $\rho=col[\rho_1 \cdots \rho_m]$ with respect to the input $u(t-\tau)$ at a point x^o if*

(i) $L_{g_j}L_f^k h_i(x)=0$, *for all* $1 \leq i,j \leq m$, *for all* $k<\rho_i-1$ *and for all* x *in a neighborhood of* x^o.

(ii) The decoupling matrix $A(x)$, *is not singular at* x^o. ■

[1] First autor's work supported by CONACyT, México.

It is important to notice that the relative degree associated to the disturbance w(t) of system (1) coincides with the one of the nondelay system, this is σ. Then, if $\rho_i \leq \sigma$, a solution to the DDPM associated with a system of the form (1) is given by

$$u(t-\tau)=-A^{-1}(x(t))[B(x(t))-\omega(t)+Q(x(t))w(t)]$$

which is equivalent to write

$$u(t)=-A^{-1}(x(t+\tau))[B(x(t+\tau))-\omega(t+\tau)+Q(x(t+\tau))w(t+\tau)]. \qquad (6)$$

However this solution requires future values of the states and, therefore, it is not possible to implement it directly. For this reason, we will consider now an equivalent approximation of system (1) which is free of delay. This approximation is a new augmented system in the so-called standard singular perturbation form which will be described in what follows.

In order to minimize the notation we will sometimes use the condensed form

$$L_g L_f^k h_i(x)=[L_{g_1} L_f^k h_i(x) \quad L_{g_2} L_f^k h_i(x) \ldots L_{g_m} L_f^k h_i(x)]. \qquad (7)$$

The approximate model. Consider again system (1). We want to transform it into a new singularly perturbed system which is free of delay. This approach was proposed independently by Sannuti [2] and Inoue et al. [3] for linear systems. The methodology consists in the segmentation of the delay τ into k subintervals of time, this is $\tau=k\varepsilon$, where ε is a real positive number, and setting

$$\begin{aligned} z_1(t)&=u(t-\varepsilon)\\ z_2(t)&=u(t-2\varepsilon)\\ &\vdots\\ z_k(t)&=u(t-k\varepsilon)=u(t-\tau), \end{aligned} \qquad (8)$$

where

$$z_i=[z_{i1},z_{i2},..,z_{im}]^T=[u_1(t-i\varepsilon),u_2(t-i\varepsilon),..,u_m(t-i\varepsilon)]^T, \quad 1\leq i\leq k,$$

and $u=[u_1,..,u_m]^T$. Taking the approximate time derivative of the first expression in equation (8) we have that

$$\dot z_1(t)=\dot u(t-\varepsilon)\cong(u(t)-u(t-\varepsilon))/\varepsilon=(u(t)-z_1(t))/\varepsilon.$$

In the same way we get

$$\begin{aligned} \varepsilon\dot z_1(t)&\cong u(t)-z_1(t)\\ \varepsilon\dot z_2(t)&\cong z_1(t)-z_2(t)\\ &\vdots\\ \varepsilon\dot z_k(t)&\cong z_{k-1}(t)-z_k(t). \end{aligned} \qquad (9)$$

Let z be a vector of dimension mk, $z=[z_1^T......z_k^T]^T$. Then, equation (9) can be written as

$$\varepsilon\dot z(t)=A_o z(t)+B_o u(t) \qquad (10a)$$

where

$$A_o=\begin{bmatrix} -I & 0 & .. & .. & .. & 0\\ I & -I & 0 & .. & .. & 0\\ 0 & I & -I & 0 & .. & 0\\ . & & . & & & .\\ . & & & . & & 0\\ 0 & .. & .. & .. & I & -I \end{bmatrix}, \quad B_o=\begin{bmatrix} I\\ 0\\ .\\ .\\ .\\ 0 \end{bmatrix} \qquad (10b)$$

with the matrices $A_o \in \mathbb{R}^{mkXmk}$, $B_o \in \mathbb{R}^{mkXm}$ and $I \in \mathbb{R}^{mXm}$. Therefore, the nonlinear delay system (1) can be approximated by an augmented system described by

$$\begin{aligned} \dot x(t)&=f(x(t))+g(x(t))z_k+p(x(t))w(t)\\ \varepsilon\dot z(t)&=A_o z(t)+B_o u(t)\\ y(t)&=h(x), \end{aligned} \qquad (11)$$

which is in the standard singular perturbation form. Thus, we can apply the singular perturbation techniques [4] to this augmented system free of delay in order to solve the DDPM in an approximate way.

3. The approximate disturbance decoupling problem

In this section we will analyze the approximate disturbance decoupling problem associated with system (1) based on its singular perturbation approximation (11). This approximation can also be written as

$$\dot{\hat x}=\hat f(\hat x)+\hat g(\hat x)u(t)+\hat p(\hat x)w(t), \qquad (12a)$$

$$y=\hat h(\hat x), \qquad (12b)$$

where

$$\hat x=\begin{bmatrix} x\\ z \end{bmatrix}, \quad \hat f=\begin{bmatrix} f(x)+g(x)z_k\\ A_o z/\varepsilon \end{bmatrix}, \quad \hat g=\begin{bmatrix} 0\\ B_o/\varepsilon \end{bmatrix}, \quad \hat p=\begin{bmatrix} p(x)\\ 0 \end{bmatrix}, \quad \hat h(\hat x)=h(x).$$

From this last representation we can get, after some computations, the functions

$$L_{\hat f}^i \hat h_j(\hat x)=L_f^i h_j(x):=\zeta_i^j(x) \text{ for all } 1\leq i\leq \rho_j-1, \text{ and } 1\leq j\leq m,$$

$$L_{\hat f}^{\rho_j+r} \hat h_j(\hat x):=\zeta_{\rho_j+r}^j(x,z_{k-r},z_{k-r+1},..,z_k), \text{ for all } 0\leq r\leq k-1 \text{ and } 1\leq j\leq m.$$

Thus, we can see that if system (1) has a vector relative degree $\rho=\mathrm{col}[\rho_1...\rho_m]$ at x^o with respect to the input $u(t-\tau)$, then

$$L_{\hat g} L_{\hat f}^i \hat h_j(\hat x)=0, \quad 0\leq i\leq \rho_j+k-2, \quad 1\leq j\leq m, \quad \forall\ x\in \mathbb{U} \text{ and all } z, \text{ and}$$

$$L_{\hat g} L_{\hat f}^{\rho_j+k-1} \hat h_j(\hat x)\neq 0 \text{ at } x=x^o \text{ and all } z.$$

Also if system (1) has a relative degree σ at x^o with respect to the disturbance w(t), we have that

$$L_{\hat p} L_{\hat f}^i \hat h_j(\hat x)=0, \quad 0\leq i\leq \sigma-2, \quad 1\leq j\leq m, \quad \forall\ x\in \mathbb{U} \text{ and all } z, \text{ and}$$

$$L_{\hat p} L_{\hat f}^{\sigma-1} \hat h_j(\hat x)\neq 0 \text{ at } x=x^o \text{ and all } z, \text{ for some } 1\leq j\leq m.$$

Then, if we denote the vector relative degree associated to the input u(t) of system (12) at x^o and all z, as

$$\rho_a=\mathrm{col}[\rho_{a1}..\rho_{am}],$$

we find that

$$\rho_{ai}=\rho_i+k, \quad 1\leq i\leq m.$$

This coincides with what we intuitively expect since the vector relative degree can be thought as representing the number of output derivatives necessary before the input appears, and the approximate model (12) "moves" the input k derivatives further away from the output as compared to the nondelay system.

Also, if the relative degree associated to the disturbance w of (12) at x^o and all z, is denoted by σ_a we see that $\sigma_a=\sigma$. Therefore, for the new system (12), we can not assure that the necessary and sufficient condition for the solution of the DDPM,

$$\rho_{ai}\leq\sigma_a, \quad 0\leq i\leq m,$$

can be always satisfied. So that, we consider again the system (12) in the standard singular perturbation form, this is

$$\dot x=\tilde f(x,z,w) \qquad (13a)$$

$$\varepsilon\dot z=\tilde g(z,u) \qquad (13b)$$

$$y=h(x), \qquad (13c)$$

where

$$\tilde f=f(x)+g(x)z_k+p(x)w(t),$$

$$\tilde g=A_o z+B_o u(t)$$

From system (13), which is of dimension n+mk, we can obtain a reduced model of dimension n using the concept of slow manifold [4]. For doing so, we define an invariant manifold $\mathbb{M}_\varepsilon=\phi$, parameterized by ε as

$$z(t)=\phi(t,\varepsilon)$$

and such that

$$\begin{bmatrix} x(t_o) \\ z(t_o) \end{bmatrix} \in \mathbb{M}_\varepsilon \Rightarrow \begin{bmatrix} x(t) \\ z(t) \end{bmatrix} \in \mathbb{M}_\varepsilon, \ \forall\ t \geq t_o.$$

The dynamics of the complete system restricted to $\mathbb{M}_\varepsilon$, is described by

$$\dot{x}(t)=\tilde{f}(x,\phi(t,\varepsilon),w)=f(x)+g(x)D\phi(t,\varepsilon)+p(x)w \tag{14a}$$

$$z_k(t)=D\phi(t,\varepsilon)=\phi_k(t,\varepsilon), \qquad D=[0\ I], \tag{14b}$$

where $D \in \mathbb{R}^{mXmk}$ and $I \in \mathbb{R}^{mXm}$. Then, the reduced slow system is now characterized in terms of the function $\phi(t,\varepsilon)$. Now, we will try to find an explicit expression for $\phi(t,\varepsilon)$. Taking the time derivative of $z(t)=\phi(t,\varepsilon)$ and multiplying it by ε we get

$$\varepsilon\frac{d\phi(t,\varepsilon)}{dt}=\tilde{g}(\phi(t,\varepsilon),u(t)) \tag{15}$$

that is known in the literature as the *manifold condition* [4]. In our case, equation (15) takes the form

$$\varepsilon\frac{d\phi(t,\varepsilon)}{dt}=A_o\phi(t,\varepsilon)+bu(t). \tag{16}$$

If there exists a solution of the above partial differential equation in terms of ϕ, the slow reduced system is defined by equation (14). However, it is not possible, in general, to find an explicit solution of equation (15) or, equivalently, (16). Thus, it is common in the literature of singular perturbation theory to try to find an approximate solution for ϕ.

Zero order approximation.
For the simplest approximation we consider $\varepsilon=0$. Then, from the manifold condition (16) we have that

$$z(t)=\phi(t)=-A_o^{-1}B_ou(t)$$

and from equation (10b) we get

$$\phi(t)=\begin{bmatrix} I \\ \vdots \\ I \end{bmatrix}u(t).$$

Thus

$$z_k(t)=D\phi(t)=-DA_o^{-1}B_ou(t)=u(t).$$

Therefore using the last equation we obtain the approximate reduced slow system

$$\dot{x}(t)=f(x(t))+g(x(t))u(t)+p(x)w(t) \tag{17}$$

$$y(t)=h(x(t)).$$

Also the following standard assumption from the singular perturbation theory has to be satisfied in order to assure the stability of the fast subsystem (13b).

Assumption 1 [4]. *The eigenvalues of $\partial\tilde{g}/\partial z$, evaluated at each z, for $\varepsilon=0$, have real part smaller than a fixed negative number, i.e.*

$$\mathrm{Re}\lambda\{\frac{\partial\tilde{g}}{\partial z}\} \leq -c < 0, \quad \blacksquare$$

In our case this condition results as

$$\mathrm{Re}\lambda(A_o) \leq -c < 0,$$

which is always satisfied since $\lambda_i(A_o)=-1,\ \forall\ 1\leq i\leq n$.
We can see that for the approximate slow system (17), the vector relative degree ρ with respect to u(t) and the relative degree σ with respect to w(t) are now equal to the one corresponding to the original system (1) with $\tau=0$. Therefore, for the slow system (17), the DDPM is solvable if and only if $\rho_i\leq\sigma$, i=1,..,m, and an approximate solution to this problem for system (11), or equivalently (12), is given by

$$u(t)=-A^{-1}(x)[B(x)-\omega(t)+Q(x)w(t)] \tag{18}$$

where the elements of the new input vector $\omega(t)$ can be chosen in order to achieve additional performances, like e.g. asymptotic zero output regulation. If this is the case, each $\omega_i(t)$, i=1,..,m, may be given as

$$\omega_i(t)=-\sum_{j=0}^{\rho_i-1} a_{ij}y_i^{(j)}(t).$$

with a_{ij} being real constant coefficients selected in such way that the polynomials

$$s^{\rho_i}+a_{i\rho_i-1}s^{\rho_i-1}+\ldots+a_{i0}=0$$

are Hurwitz.

An improved approximation.
Since the approximation already described will be appropriate only in the case that τ is very small, we will now consider a better one based in a power series expansion of the function $\phi(t,\varepsilon)$ and the control u(t) around $\varepsilon=0$, namely

$$\phi(t,\varepsilon)=\phi_o(t)+\varepsilon\phi_1(t)+O(\varepsilon^2), \quad u(t)=u_o(t)+\varepsilon u_1(t)+O(\varepsilon^2).$$

Substituting the last expression in the manifold condition we will have

$$\varepsilon\frac{d(\phi_o+\varepsilon\phi_1)}{dt}+O(\varepsilon^2)=A_o(\phi_o+\varepsilon\phi_1)+B_o(u_o+\varepsilon u_1)+O(\varepsilon^2).$$

Taking terms of order zero in the last expression we have

$$0=A_o\phi_o+B_ou_o.$$

A solution to this equation is chosen as

$$\phi_o(t)=-A_o^{-1}B_ou_o(t),$$

where the control $u_o(t)$ is given by equation (18) and represents the solution of order zero ($\varepsilon=0$) to the DDPM for the approximated system (17).
Considering now the terms of order one in the manifold condition we get

$$\frac{d\phi_o(t)}{dt}=A_o\phi_1+B_ou_1,$$

and a solution for ϕ_1 is selected as

$$\phi_1(t)=A_o^{-1}[\frac{d\phi_o(t)}{dt}-B_ou_1(t)]=-A_o^{-2}B_o\frac{du_o(t)}{dt}-A_o^{-1}B_ou_1(t).$$

The exact slow subsystem (13a) can now be approximated up to $O(\varepsilon^2)$ by setting $\phi=\phi_o+\varepsilon\phi_1$, by the "corrected slow subsystem",

$$\dot{x}(t)=\bar{f}(x,\varepsilon)+\bar{g}(x)u_1+p(x)w \tag{19a}$$

$$y=h(x), \tag{19b}$$

where

$$\bar{f}(x,\varepsilon):=f(x)+g(x)D[-A_o^{-1}B_ou_o(t)-\varepsilon A_o^{-2}B_o\frac{du_o(t)}{dt}]$$

$$\bar{g}(x):=-\varepsilon g(x)DA_o^{-1}B_o.$$

Notice in particular that the vector relative degree of system (19) with respect to $u_1(t)$ is equal to the vector relative degree of system (1) with respect to $u(t-\tau)$ defined at x^o, i.e. $\rho=\mathrm{col}[\rho_1..\rho_m]$. Thus

$$L_{\bar{f}}^k h_i(x,\varepsilon)=L_f^k h_i(x)+L_g L_f^{k-1}h_i(x)D[-A_o^{-1}B_ou_o(t)-\varepsilon A_o^{-2}B_o\frac{du_o(t)}{dt}]$$

$$=L_f^k h_i(x), \text{ for } 1\leq k\leq\rho_i-1.$$

Let us set the state space coordinate transformation

$$(\nu,\eta)=\mathrm{col}(\nu_1^T,..,\nu_m^T,\eta)$$

defined in a neighborhood $\mathbb{U}$ of x^o, by

$$\nu_i=\begin{bmatrix} \nu_{i,1} \\ \nu_{i,2} \\ \vdots \\ \nu_{i,\rho_i} \end{bmatrix}=\begin{bmatrix} h_i(x) \\ L_{\bar{f}}h_i(x,\varepsilon) \\ \vdots \\ L_{\bar{f}}^{\rho_i-1}h_i(x,\varepsilon) \end{bmatrix}, \text{ for } 1\leq i\leq m, \quad \eta=\begin{bmatrix} \eta_1 \\ \eta_2 \\ \vdots \\ \eta_{n-\alpha} \end{bmatrix}=\begin{bmatrix} \pi_{\alpha+1}(x) \\ \pi_{\alpha+2}(x) \\ \vdots \\ \pi_n(x) \end{bmatrix} \tag{20}$$

with $\alpha=\rho_1+..+\rho_m$ and $\pi_{\alpha+1}(x),..,\pi_n(x)$ arbitrary smooth functions defined on $\mathbb{U}$ [9].
In this new coordinates system (19) becomes

$$\begin{aligned}&\dot{\nu}_{1,1}=\nu_{1,2}(x,\varepsilon)+d_{1,1}(x,\varepsilon)w\\&\dot{\nu}_{1,2}=\nu_{1,3}(x,\varepsilon)+d_{1,2}(x,\varepsilon)w\\&\quad\vdots\\&\nu_{1,\rho_1}=\gamma_{1,\rho_1}(x,\varepsilon)+C_{1,\rho_1}(x,\varepsilon)u_1+d_{1,\rho_1}(x,\varepsilon)w\\&y_i=[1\ 0..0]\nu_i\end{aligned}\tag{21a}$$

for $1\le i\le m$, where

$$\gamma_{1,\rho_1}(x,\varepsilon)=L_{\bar f}^{\rho_1}h_i(x,\varepsilon),\quad C_{1,\rho_1}(x,\varepsilon)=L_{\bar g}L_{\bar f}^{\rho_1-1}h_i(x,\varepsilon),$$

$$d_{1,k}(x,\varepsilon)=L_pL_{\bar f}^{k-1}h_i(x,\varepsilon),\quad 1\le k\le\rho_1.$$

As far as the remaining set of equations is concerned, we can not expect any special form for the corresponding equations. If the distribution spanned by the vector fields $\bar{g}_1(x),..,\bar{g}_m(x)$ is not involutive (which is the most general case), we can only write generically, with a vector notation,

$$\dot{\eta}=q_1(\nu,\eta,\varepsilon)+q_2(\nu,\eta)u_1+q_3(\nu,\eta)w\tag{21b}$$

where

$$q_1(\nu,\eta,\varepsilon)=\begin{bmatrix}L_{\bar f}\pi_{\alpha+1}(x,\varepsilon)\\\vdots\\L_{\bar f}\pi_n(x,\varepsilon)\end{bmatrix},\quad q_2(\nu,\eta)=\begin{bmatrix}L_{\bar g}\pi_{\alpha+1}(x)\\\vdots\\L_{\bar g}\pi_n(x)\end{bmatrix},\quad q_3(\nu,\eta)=\begin{bmatrix}L_p\pi_{\alpha+1}(x)\\\vdots\\L_p\pi_n(x)\end{bmatrix}.$$

We then can state the following result.

Lemma 1. *Assume that system (1) has a vector relative degree $\rho=[\rho_1...\rho_m]$ with respect to the input $u(t-\tau)$ and a relative degree σ with respect to the disturbance $w(t)$, both at x^o. Then, there exists a causal first order approximate solution to the DDPM associated to system (1) if and only if*

$$\rho_1\le\sigma,\ \textit{for}\ 1\le i\le m.\tag{22}$$

Proof. Sufficiency. If condition (22) holds, system (19) takes the form

$$\begin{aligned}&\dot{\nu}_{1,1}=\nu_{1,2}\\&\dot{\nu}_{1,2}=\nu_{1,3}\\&\quad\vdots\\&\nu_{1,\rho_1}=\gamma_{1,\rho_1}(x,\varepsilon)+C_{1,\rho_1}(x,\varepsilon)u_1+d_{1,\rho_1}(x,\varepsilon)w\\&y_i=[1\ 0..0]\nu_i,\ \text{for}\ 1\le i\le m,\\&\dot{\eta}=q_1(\nu,\eta,\varepsilon)+q_2(\nu,\eta)u_1+q_3(\nu,\eta)w,\end{aligned}$$

which, from an input-output point of view, can be written as

$$y_1^{(k)}(t)=L_f^kh_i(x)\ \text{for}\ 1\le k\le\rho_1-1,$$

$$y_1^{(\rho_1)}(t)=L_f^{\rho_1}h_i(x)+L_gL_f^{\rho_1-1}h_i(x)u_o+\varepsilon L_gL_f^{\rho_1-1}h_i(x)D\phi_1+$$
$$+L_pL_f^{\rho_1-1}h_i(x)w,$$

for $1\le i\le m$. In a more compact setting

$$\begin{bmatrix}y_1^{(\rho_1)}(t)\\\vdots\\y_m^{(\rho_m)}(t)\end{bmatrix}=B(x)+A(x)u_o(t)+\varepsilon A(x)D\phi_1(t)+Q(x)w(t).$$

when substituting $u_o(t)$, from (18), and $\phi_1(t)$ in the last equation we get

$$\begin{bmatrix}y_1^{(\rho_1)}(t)\\\vdots\\y_m^{(\rho_m)}(t)\end{bmatrix}=\vartheta(t)-\varepsilon A(x)D[A_o^{-2}B_o\frac{du_o(t)}{dt}+A_o^{-1}B_ou_1(t)].$$

Then, by choosing

$$u_1(t)=DA_o^{-2}B_o\frac{du_o(t)}{dt}$$

we have

$$\begin{bmatrix}y_1^{(\rho_1)}(t)\\\vdots\\y_m^{(\rho_m)}(t)\end{bmatrix}=\vartheta(t).$$

which corresponds to a set of systems whose input-output behavior is identical to that of a set of linear systems having transfer functions

$$H_i(s)=\frac{1}{s^{\rho_1}}\ \text{for}\ 1\le i\le m,$$

and which are decoupled from the disturbance w(t).
The proof of necessity is straightforward. ■

From the proof of Lemma 1 the causal control law which solves the DDPM for the corrected subsystem (19) can be written as

$$u(t)=u_o(t)+\varepsilon u_1(t)$$

$$=u_o(t)+\varepsilon DA_o^{-2}B_o[\frac{\partial u_o}{\partial x}(f(x)+g(x)u_o+p(x)w)+\frac{\partial u_o}{\partial w}\dot{w}+\frac{\partial u_o}{\partial\vartheta}\dot{\vartheta}]\tag{24}$$

with $u_o(t)$ given by equation (18).
From equation (24) we can also see that u(t) will depend, in general, on the disturbance w(t), even if $\rho_1<\sigma$. This fact represents a great difference with respect to the nondelay case.

4. Example

Consider the nonlinear delay system of the form (1) with

$$f(x)=\begin{bmatrix}x_2\\x_3(x_2+1)\\-(x_3-1)-(x_2+1)^2(x_1+1)\end{bmatrix},\quad g(x)=\begin{bmatrix}0\\1\\0\end{bmatrix},\quad p(x)=\begin{bmatrix}0\\0\\1\end{bmatrix},\quad h(x)=x_1.\tag{25}$$

From system (25) we can see that

$$f(x^o)=f(0)=0,\quad h(x^o)=h(0)=0.$$

Computing the relative degrees ρ and σ we obtain

$$\rho=2\ \text{y}\ \sigma=3.$$

Therefore the disturbance decoupling condition $\rho\le\sigma$ is fulfilled. The approximated augmented system free of delay is given by

$$\dot{x}(t)=\begin{bmatrix}x_2\\x_3(x_2+1)+z_k\\-(x_3-1)-(x_2+1)^2(x_1+1)\end{bmatrix}+\begin{bmatrix}0\\0\\1\end{bmatrix}w(t),\tag{26}$$

$$z(t)=A_oz+B_ou(t),$$

$$y(t)=x_1,$$

where k=3 and the matrices A_o y B_o are given by equation (10b). Considering the first approximation (case ε=0) we have that $z_k(t)=u_o(t)$, therefore, from equation (18), we have that

$$u_o(t)=-[L_gL_fh(x)]^{-1}\{L_f^2h(x)-\vartheta(t)+L_pL_fh(x)\},\quad\vartheta(t)=-a_oy(t)-a_1\dot{y}(t)$$

where

$$L_gL_fh(x)=1,\quad L_f^2h(x)=x_3(x_2+1)\ \text{and}\ L_pL_fh(x)=0$$

and a_0, a_1 are chosen so that $s^2+a_1s+a_0=0$ is Hurwitz. Thus

$$\begin{aligned}u_o(t)&=-x_3(x_2+1)-a_oy(t)-a_1\dot{y}(t)\\&=-x_3(x_2+1)-a_ox_1-a_1x_2.\end{aligned}\tag{27}$$

From equation (23) we have that

$$u_1(t)=DA_o^{-2}B_o[\frac{\partial u_o}{\partial x}(f(x)+g(x)u_o+p(x)w(t))+\frac{\partial u_o}{\partial w}\dot{w}+\frac{\partial u_o}{\partial\vartheta}\dot{\vartheta}]$$

$$=k\left[-a_0\ \ -(x_3+a_1)\ \ -(x_2+1)\right]\begin{bmatrix} x_2 \\ -a_0x_1-a_1x_2 \\ -(x_3-1)-(x_2+1)^2(x_1+1)+w(t)\end{bmatrix}$$

$$=k\{-a_0x_2+(x_3+a_1)(a_0x_1+a_1x_2)+$$

$$+(x_2+1)[(x_3-1)+(x_2+1)^2(x_1+1)-w(t)]\}$$

Finally, we obtain the following control which solves the DDPM for the first order approximate system, this is

$$u(t)=u_0(t)+\varepsilon u_1(t)$$

$$=-x_3(x_2+1)-a_0x_1-a_1x_2+k\varepsilon\{-a_0x_2+(x_3+a_1)(a_0x_1+a_1x_2)+$$

$$+(x_2+1)[(x_3-1)+(x_2+1)^2(x_1+1)-w(t)]\}. \quad (28)$$

In figures 1 to 3 we show the respective simulations for the two orders of approximation. In Figure 1, we can see the effects of the disturbance at the output signal when using feedback (27) and (28), figures 2 and 3 show the state x1 and x2, respectively. In all the simulations we have set

$$w(t)=0.3Cos(3t),\ t\geq 0,\quad \tau=0.2,\quad k=3,\quad a_0=2,\quad a_1=3.$$

It is easy to see that the control law (28) improve the results obtained with the feedback control law (27). This is in accordance with our expectancies because of the better approximation used.

5. Conclusions

In this work we have presented necessary and sufficient conditions for the solvability of the approximate disturbance decoupling problem with measurement associated with a class of nonlinear delay systems. The principal advantage of this approach is that we can avoid the prediction of future values of the states. The order of decoupling of the disturbance will be a function of the delay τ and the order of approximation considered in the control signal. In general, we will need measurement of the disturbance.

On the other hand, the stability of the overall closed loop system will depend directly on the value of the delay. Some results have been obtained in relation to this issue for linear systems [10]. In the case of nonlinear systems it would be worthwhile to study this problem as a future research subject.

Acknowledgment. The authors would like to acknowledge the third reviewer for many useful suggestions.

References

[1] J. Hale. *Theory of Functional Differential Equations.* Springer-Verlag, New York, 1977.

[2] P. Sannuti. *Near Optimum design of time-lag systems by singular perturbations method.* Pre-print of the 11-th. JACC, paper No. 20-A, 1970.

[3] K. Inoue, H. Akashi, K. Ogino, Y. Sawaragi. *Sensitivity approaches to Optimizations of Linear Systems with time Delays.* Automatica, vol 7, 671-679, 1971.

[4] P. Kokotovic, H. Khalil, J. O'Reilly. *Singular Perturbations in Control: Analysis and Design.* Academic Press, N.Y., 1986.

[5] W. M. Wonham and S. Morse. *Decoupling and pole assignment in linear multivariable systems: A geometric approach.* SIAM J. Control, vol. 8, 1970.

[6] P. L. Falb and W. A. Wolovich. *Decoupling in the design and synthesis of multivariable control systems.* IEEE Trans. on Automat. Contr. AC-12, 1967.

[7] A. Isidori, A. J. Krener, C. Gorri-giorgi and S. Monaco. *Nonlinear Decoupling via Feedback: A Differential Geometric Approach.* IEEE Trans. on Autom. Control, AC-26, No. 2, 1981.

[8] K. Khorasani. *Robust stabilization of nonlinear systems with unmodelled dynamics.* Int. J. Control, vol 50, No. 3, 827-844, 1989.

[9] A. Isidori, *Nonlinear Control Systems.* 2nd. ed. Springer Verlag, 1989.

[10] Górecki H., Fuksa S., Grabowski P. and Korytowski A. *Analysis and Synthesis of time Delay Systems.* John Wiley & Sons, 1989.

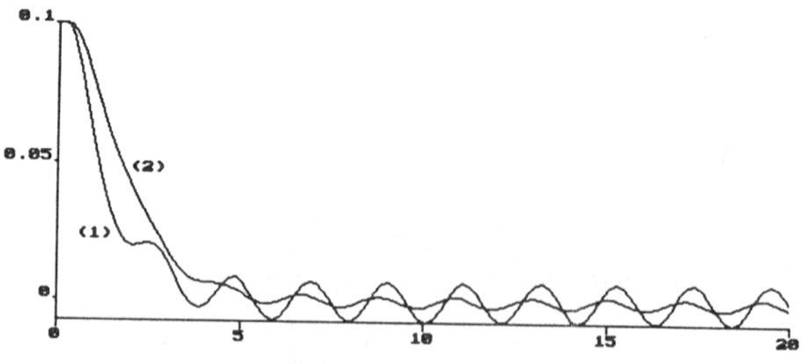

Figure 1. Output x1 of the original system (25) with the feedback control law (27) (curve 1) and (28) (curve 2).

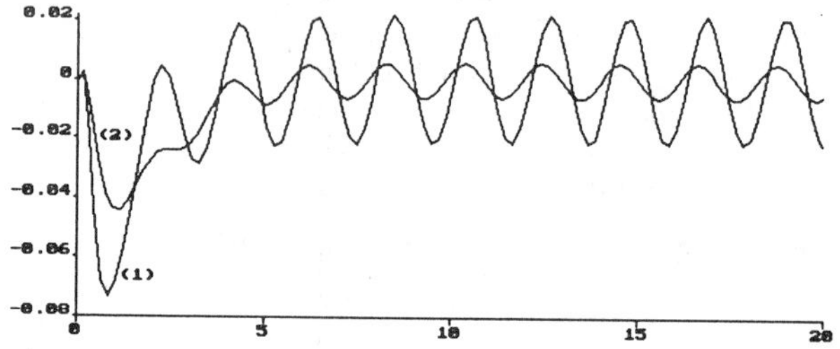

Figure 2. State x2 for the closed loop system (25)-(27) (curve 1) and (25)-(28) (curve 2).

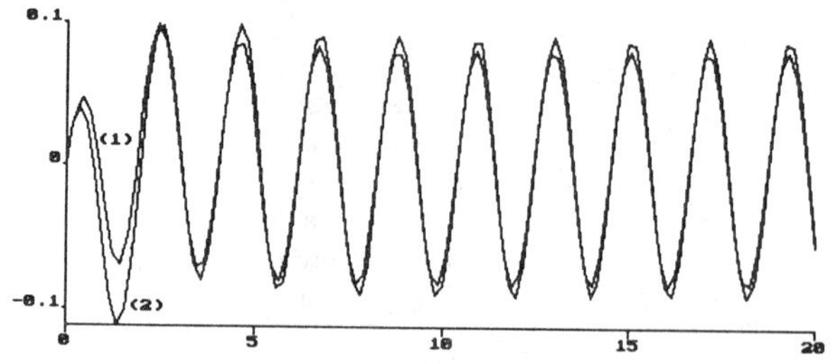

Figure 3. State x3 for the closed loop system (25)-(27) (curve 1) and (25)-(28) (curve 2).

Proceedings of the
American Control Conference
San Francisco, California • June 1993

STABILIZATION OF DISCRETE BILINEAR SYSTEMS WITH TIME DELAYED FEEDBACK

Xueshan Yang and Yury Stepanenko
Department of Mechanical Engineering
University of Victoria
Victoria, B.C. V8W 3P6

Abstract

In this paper we present new existence theorems of stabilization and a controller design procedure for time-varying discrete bilinear systems. Unlike other publications on stabilization of bilinear systems we consider the output feedback with time delays, and the control law from a broader class of functions. The main theorems basically state that under broad conditions, the zero state of the systems can be made asymptotically stable by the output feedback. The controller design procedure is simple and effective as it is illustrated by the simulation results.

I. Introduction

Bilinear systems are an important subclass of nonlinear systems, and numerous real world dynamical plants can be presented by models with a bilinear structure. Bilinear systems and control have been summarized by Mohler [1]. Some new results on stability of bilinear systems with feedback can be found in [2] - [8], and some notable results of stabilization for bilinear systems have been investigated in [9] - [16]. Most papers consider continuous time bilinear systems. Little studies stabilizing bilinear systems for time-varying discrete case, although [10] consider stabilization of bilinear systems for time-invariant discrete systems, and [11] studies time-varying continuous bilinear systems.

Most publications on stabilization of bilinear systems focus on the design of a specific controller which can be used to stabilize a bilinear system. Little has been written regarding the analysis of the stabilizing problem for bilinear discrete systems by a nonlinear feedback control law from a large class of functions. The feedback function in most literature is considered from the classes of linear, Lipschitz, and quadratic functions. In addition, the control is considered as the functions of output at the present time only. Delay is a common factor in many engineering and physical systems [17]. Paper [7] gives stability criteria for time-varying discrete bilinear systems with time delayed feedback, but it does not consider the stabilization problems.

In this paper, we study time varying discrete bilinear systems with time delayed feedback. The feedback is considered from a larger class (comparable functions class). We analyze this stabilization problem and present a new procedure for controller design.

The structure of the paper is the follows. We present the concepts of comparable functions and comparable systems in Section II, and show that bilinear systems belong to the comparable system class. The main results on stabilizing bilinear systems are given in Section III. We give some stability criteria for time-varying discrete bilinear systems, and build the existence theorems, which state that under some broad conditions bilinear systems can be stabilized by an output feedback from the class of comparable functions. Following these stabilizing theorems, a new procedure for the design of stabilizing controllers is given. An example of the controller design for a bilinear discrete motor control system shows the design procedure to be effective and easily applicable in practice.

Notations and Definitions

Let R^n denote the real n-dimensional vector space. The norm of a vector $x \in R^n$ is denoted by $\|x\| \triangleq (x^T x)^{1/2}$. A norm of matrix A is defined by $\|A\| \triangleq \left(\sum_{i,j} |a_{ij}|^2\right)^{1/2}$. $\lambda(A)$ and $\lambda_{\max}(B)$ denote the eigenvalues of A, and maximal eigenvalues of B respectively, where B is a real symmetric matrix. Z^+ denotes the set of non-negative integers, that is $Z^+ \triangleq \{0, 1, 2, \cdots\}$. $F_A \triangleq \sup_{t \in Z^+} \|A(t)\|$, and A^- denotes the generalized inverse matrix of A. If $A \triangleq (a_{ij})_{n\times m}$, then $\vec{A} \triangleq \left[a_{11}, \cdots, a_{1n}; a_{21}, \cdots, a_{2n}; \cdots; a_{m1}, \cdots, a_{mn}\right]$ is called straighten up by line. $\Re(A) \triangleq \{Ax : x \in R^n\}$ denotes the linear space generated by the column vectors of A, and $\otimes$ denotes the Kronecker product.

CF – comparable function or comparable functions in one variable, see Definition 1
CF-2 – comparable functions in two variables, see Definition 1
SCF-r – simple comparable functions in r variables, see Definition 1.

A nonlinear system with time delayed feedback can be described by

$$x(t+1) = g(x(t), u(t), t), \quad g(0,0,t) = 0, \quad \forall\ t \geq t_0, \tag{1}$$

$$y(t) = h(x(t), t), \tag{2}$$

$$u(t) = f(y(t), y(t-1), \cdots, y(t-r+1)), \tag{3}$$

where x, y, u are appropriate dimensional vectors, and g, h, f are nonlinear functions.

Definition 1 (Comparable Function):

The general definition for r variable can be found [18]. For simplicity, we give the particular case.

The particular case : If there exist real numbers $\alpha_j \geq 0$, $q_j > 0$, $j = 1, \cdots, r$; $r \geq 1$. Also, there exists at least an i, $1 \leq i \leq r$ such that $\alpha_i > 0$, and the following inequality holds for all $t \in Z^+$, such as

$$\|\phi(x_1(t), x_2(t), \cdots, x_r(t), t)\| \leq \alpha_1 \|x_1(t)\|^{q_1} + \alpha_2 \|x_2(t)\|^{q_2} + \cdots + \alpha_l \|x_r(t)\|^{q_r}, \tag{4}$$

then the nonlinear function $\phi(x_1(t), x_2(t), \cdots, x_r(t), t)$ is called a simple comparable function in r variables (**SCF-r**).

In most cases, the definitions of comparable functions in their special cases of $r = 1$, $r = 2$ are more important.

1) One variable case:

If there exist $k_1 > 0$ and $k_j \geq 0$; integer $v \geq 2$; $j = 2, \cdots, v$; and $0 < q_1 < \cdots < q_v$, such that a nonlinear function $\phi(x(t), t)$ satisfies the following condition:

$$\|\phi(x(t), t)\| \leq k_1 \|x(t)\|^{q_1} + \cdots + k_v \|x(t)\|^{q_v},$$

for all $t \in Z^+$, then this function ϕ is called a comparable function (**CF**), and the class of comparable function is called the CF class.

2) Two variable cases:

If there exist non-negative real number $l_j, j = 1, \cdots, m$; $d_j, j = 1, \cdots, n$; and e_{ij} $(i = 1, \cdots, l, j = 1, \cdots, k)$, with $l_1 d_1 \neq 0$ (or $e_{11} \neq 0$), such that nonlinear function $\phi(x_1(t), x_2(t), t)$ satisfies the following condition

$$\|\phi(x_1(t), x_2(t), t)\| \leq \sum_{j=1}^{m} l_j \|x_1(t)\|^{z_j} + \sum_{j=1}^{n} d_j \|x_2(t)\|^{f_j} + \sum_{i=1}^{l} \sum_{j=1}^{k} e_{ij} \|x_1(t)\|^{s_i} \|x_2(t)\|^{r_j}, \quad (5)$$

holds for all $t \in Z^+$, then the nonlinear function $\phi(x(t), u(t), t)$ is called the comparable function in two variables (**CF-2**). Here, $0 < z_1 < z_2 \cdots < z_m$; $0 < f_1 < f_2 \cdots < f_n$; $0 < s_1 < s_2 \cdots < s_l$; and $0 < r_1 < r_2 \cdots < r_k$.

Remark 1: Definition 1 is also valid for time invariant functions such as $\phi(x_1(t), x_2(t), \cdots, x_r(t))$ $r \geq 1$.

Definition 2 (Comparable Systems):

If there exist $b_1 > 0$; $b_j \geq 0$, $j = 2, \cdots, m$; integer $l \geq 2$; and $0 < q_1 < q_2 < \cdots < q_l$, such that the nonlinear system (1) – (3) satisfies the following condition:

$$\|x(t+1)\| \leq b_1 \|x^*(t)\|^{q_1} + \cdots + b_l \|x^*(t)\|^{q_l}, \quad (6)$$

for all $t \in Z^+$, then system (1) – (3) is called a comparable system. Here, $\|x(t)\| \leq \|x^*(t)\|$, $x^*(t)$ is any measurable function with $x^*(0) = x(0)$.

II. Comparable Systems

In this paper, we assume that the feedback function f is in the CF class. The following properties of CF are useful for the stability analysis.

Lemma 1: The following functions ϕ with $\phi(0) = 0$ are in the CF class:

1) the linear functions,
2) the functions in the Lipschitz class,
3) the quadratic functions,
4) the functions with arbitrary order bounded derivatives,
5) the polynomial functions,
6) the bilinear functions.

Proof : See [19].

Remark 2: This Lemma 1 shows that the CF class is a large class and most functions we use are in this CF class.

The time varying discrete bilinear systems can be described as follows:

$$x(t+1) = A(t)x(t) + \sum_{i=1}^{m} B_i(t)x(t)u_i(t) + C(t)u(t), \quad (7)$$

$$y(t) = H(t)x(t), \quad (8)$$

$$u(t) = f(y(t), y(t-1), \cdots, y(t-r+1)), \quad r \geq 1 \quad (9)$$

where $x \in R^n$, $y \in R^p$, $p \leq n$, $u \in R^m$. $A(t)$, $B_i(t)$ $(i = 1, \cdots, m)$ are $n \times n$ matrices, $C(t)$ is an $n \times m$ matrix, $H(t)$ is an $p \times n$ matrix, $f : R^p \to R^m$ is CF. Here, we assume that $C(t)$, $H(t)$ are bounded by F_C, F_H respectively; and $u(t) = \{u_1(t), u_2(t), \cdots, u_m\}^T$.

In the following, we show that bilinear systems are comparable systems.

Lemma 2: Suppose f is in the SCF-r class, then, this bilinear system (7) – (9), is a comparable system satisfying (6).

Proof: Since f is the SCF-r satisfying (4), then there exist real numbers $a_j \geq 0$, $l_j > 0, j = 1, \cdots, r$; and there exists at least an i, $0 \leq i \leq r$ such that $a_i > 0$, and the following inequality

$$\begin{aligned}\|u(t)\| &= \|f(y(t), \cdots, y(t-r+1))\| \\ &\leq a_1 \|y(t)\|^{l_1} + a_2 \|y(t-1)\|^{l_2} + \cdots + a_r \|y(t-r+1)\|^{l_r} \\ &= \alpha_1 \|x(t)\|^{l_1} + \alpha_2 \|x(t-1)\|^{l_2} + \cdots \\ &\quad + \alpha_r \|x(t-r+1)\|^{l_r}, \quad (10)\end{aligned}$$

holds for all $t \in Z^+$, where $\alpha_1 \triangleq a_1 F_H^{l_1}, \cdots, \alpha_r \triangleq a_r F_H^{l_r}$; and there exists at least an i, $1 \leq i \leq r$ such that $\alpha_i = a_i F_H^{l_i} > 0$.

Taking the norm for both sides of (7), and assuming $A(t)$, $B_i(t)$ are bounded by F_A, F_{B_i} respectively, then,

$$\|x(t+1)\| \leq F_A \|x(t)\| + \sum_{i-1}^{m} F_{B_i} \|x(t)\| \|u_i(t)\| + F_C \|u(t)\|. \quad (11)$$

Let

$$\|x^*(t)\| \triangleq \max_{t-r+1 \leq j \leq t} \|x(j)\| \quad \text{if} \quad t \geq r, \quad (12)$$

and

$$\|x^*(t)\| \triangleq \max_{0 \leq j \leq t} \|x(j)\| \quad \text{if} \quad t < r. \quad (13)$$

It is obvious, for all $t \in Z^+$,

$$\|x(t)\| \leq \|x^*(t)\|. \quad (14)$$

Substituting (10) into (11), noticing (12) – (14), and reordering the left side of the obtaining inequality by increasing powers of $q_j, j = 1, \cdots, l$, we obtain

$$\|x(t+1)\| \leq b_1 \|x^*(t)\|^{q_1} + \cdots + b_l \|x^*(t)\|^{q_l},$$

for all $t \in Z^+$, with $0 < q_1 < \cdots < q_l$, and $b_1 > 0$. Thus, (6) is held, and the result is directly forward by Definition 2.

Remark 3: The condition that $A(t)$, $B_i(t)$ are bounded by F_A, F_{B_i} respectively can be released, see proof of Theorem 1 in Section III.

Lemma 3: For any nonlinear comparable systems satisfying (6), if $q_1 \geq 1$ and $b_1 < 1$, then the zero state of system (1) – (3) is uniformly asymptotically stable.

Proof: (see [19])

Remark 4: Lemma 2 and Lemma 3 show that if the feedback function is in the CF class, then the bilinear systems are comparable systems. Therefore, the stability of the bilinear systems is only dependent on the coefficient of the lowest power.

III. Stabilization Analysis for Discrete Bilinear Systems

In this section we establish the existence theorems for stabilizing bilinear systems, and give a new approach for the design of stabilizing controllers.

Without loss generality, we assume $t_0 = 0$ in the following. Let

$$\lambda_{1a} \triangleq \sup_{t \geq 0} \lambda_{\max}[A^T(t)A(t)], \quad (15)$$

$$\lambda_2 \triangleq \sup_{t \geq 0} \max_{1 \leq i,j \leq m} \{\max |\lambda[B_i^T(t)B_j(t)]|\},$$

$$\lambda_3 \triangleq \sup_{t\geq 0} \max_{1\leq i\leq m} \{\max |\lambda[B_i^T(t)A(t) + A^T(t)B_i(t)]|\}.$$

Assume that $u(t)$ is CF satisfying

$$\|u(t)\| \leq k_1\|y(t-j_1)\|^{q_1} + \cdots + k_r\|y(t-j_r)\|^{q_r}, \quad (16)$$

where $1 < q_1 < \cdots < q_r$; $j_1, \cdots, j_r$ is any available integer with $0 \leq j_1, \cdots, j_r \leq r$; $k_j, j = 2, \cdots, r$ is any non-negative number and $k_1 > 0$.

Theorem 1: For the bilinear system (7), (8), f is CF defined by (16), thus:

1) When $q_1 > 1$ and $1 < q_1 < \cdots < q_r$, if $\lambda_{1a} < 1$, then the zero state of the bilinear closed loop system is uniformly asymptotically stable.

2) When $q_1 = 1$ and $1 = q_1 < \cdots < q_r$, if $\lambda_{1a}^{1/2} + k_1 F_H F_C < 1$ then the zero state of the bilinear closed loop system is uniformly asymptotically stable.

3) When $q_1 = \cdots = q_r = 1$, if $\lambda_{1a}^{1/2} + r^{1/2} k F_H F_C < 1$ then the zero state of the bilinear closed loop system is uniformly asymptotically stable, where $k = (k_1^2 + \cdots + k_r^2)^{1/2}$.

Proof:

1) Without loss generality in the proof, we can use $\|u(t)\| \leq k_1\|y(t-j_1)\|^{q_1}$ instead of (16), because the local stability of bilinear systems is only dependent on the coefficient of lowest power by Lemma 3.

Let $z(t+1) = A(t)x(t) + \sum_{i=1}^m B_i(t)x(t)u_i(t)$. By [5] then

$$z^T(t+1)z(t+1) \leq \lambda_{1a}\|x(t)\|^2 + \sum_{i=1}^m \lambda_3\|x(t)\|^2|u_i(t)| + \sum_i \sum_j \|x(t)\|^2|u_i(t)||u_j(t)|.$$

By Hölder's inequality, we have

$$\sum_{i=1}^m |u_i(t)| \leq \sqrt{m}\|u(t)\| \leq \sqrt{m} k_1 F_H^{q_1}\|x(t-j_1)\|^{q_1},$$

$$\begin{aligned}\sum_{i=1}^m \sum_{j=1}^m |u_i(t)||u_j(t)| &\leq m\left(\sum_{i=1}^m u_i^2(t)\right)^{1/2}\left(\sum_{j=1}^m u_j^2(t)\right)^{1/2} \\ &= m\|u(t)\|^2 \\ &\leq m k_1^2 F_H^{2q_1}\|x(t-j_1)\|^{2q_1}.\end{aligned}$$

So,

$$\|z(t+1)\|^2 \leq \lambda_{1a}\|x(t)\|^2 + \lambda_3 m^{1/2} k_1 F_H^{q_1}\|x(t)\|^2\|x(t-j_1)\|^{q_1} + \lambda_2 m {k_1}^2 F_H^{2q_1}\|x(t)\|^2\|x(t-j_1)\|^{2q_1}.$$

Hence,

$$\|z(t+1)\| \leq \lambda_{1a}^{1/2}\|x^*(t)\| + \left\{\lambda_3 m^{1/2} k_1 F_H^{q_1}\right\}^{1/2}\|x^*(t)\|^{1+q_1/2} + (\lambda_2 m)^{1/2} k_1 F_H^{q_1}\|x^*(t)\|^{1+q_1},$$

where $x^*(t)$ is defined by (12), (13). So,

$$\begin{aligned}\|x(t+1)\| &\leq \|z(t+1)\| + F_C\|u(t)\| \\ &\leq \|z(t+1)\| + k_1 F_H^{q_1} F_C\|x(t-j_1)\|^{q_1} \\ &\leq \lambda_{1a}^{1/2}\|x^*(t)\| + k_1 F_H^{q_1} F_C\|x^*(t)\|^{q_1} + \left\{\lambda_3 m^{1/2} k_1 F_H^{q_1}\right\}^{1/2} \\ &\bullet \|x^*(t)\|^{1+q_1/2} + (\lambda_2 m)^{1/2} k_1 F_H^{q_1}\|x^*(t)\|^{1+q_1}. \quad (17)\end{aligned}$$

Since $q_1 > 1$ and $\lambda_{1a} < 1$, then the zero state of system (8), (9), (16) is uniformly asymptotically stable by Lemma 3.

2) In fact, from (17), notice $q_1 = 1$, then (17) can be rewritten as:

$$\begin{aligned}\|x(t+1)\| &\leq \|z(t+1)\| + k_1 F_H F_C\|x(t-j_1)\| \\ &\leq \lambda_{1a}^{1/2}\|x^*(t)\| + k_1 F_H F_C\|x^*(t)\| \\ &+ \left\{\lambda_3 m^{1/2} k_1 F_H\right\}^{1/2}\|x^*(t)\|^{3/2} \\ &+ (\lambda_2 m)^{1/2} k_1 F_H\|x^*(t)\|^2.\end{aligned}$$

By Lemma 3, the zero state of system (8), (9), (16) is uniformly asymptotically stable provided $\lambda_{1a}^{1/2} + k_1 F_H F_C < 1$.

3) (see [7]).

Remark 5: This theorem demonstrates the way to set a controller to guarantee that the closed loop bilinear system is stable. For example, if set $u(t)$ satisfies (16) with a linear part $q_1 = 1$, then one can set $0 < k_1 < \frac{1-\lambda_{1a}^{1/2}}{F_H F_C}$, to ensure the local stability (see case 2). If set $q_1 = \cdots = q_r$, then one can set $0 < k < \frac{1-\lambda_{1a}^{1/2}}{r^{1/2} F_H F_C}$, $k = (k_1^2 + \cdots + k_r^2)^{1/2}$ to ensure the local stability (see case 3).

Theorem 1 shows that if $\lambda_{1a} < 1$ $q_1 > 1$ the zero state of system (8), (9), (16) is uniformly asymptotically stable. Now, we consider the case of $\lambda_{1a} \geq 1$. In this case, we want to find a feedback law to stabilize the bilinear systems.

Theorem 2: For bilinear system (7) – (8), there exists a feedback function f belonging to the class of comparable functions with linear part $S(t)x(t)$, such that the zero state of the bilinear closed loop system is uniformly asymptotically stable, provided $S(t)$ satisfies

$$\lambda_1 \triangleq \sup_t \lambda_{\max}\left[\Big(A(t) + C(t)S(t)H(t)\Big)^T \Big(A(t) + C(t)S(t)H(t)\Big)\right] < 1,$$

where $S(t)$ is an $m \times p$ matrix bounded by F_S.

Proof: Let

$$\begin{aligned}u(t) &= f(y(t), \cdots, y(t-r+1)) \\ &= S(t)y(t) + f_1(y(t), \cdots, y(t-r+1)), \quad (19)\end{aligned}$$

where f_1 is a CF with the lowest power larger than 1. It is obvious that u(t) is in the CF class with a linear part $S(t)x(t)$

In the following we are going to prove that provided $S(t)$ satisfies $\lambda_1 < 1$, then the zero state of system (7), (8), (19) is uniformly asymptotically stable.

Let

$$P(t) \triangleq A(t) + C(t)S(t)H(t),$$

then

$$\lambda_1 = \sup_t \lambda_{\max}[P(t)^T P(t)].$$

Thus,

$$x(t+1) = P(t)x(t) + \sum_{i=1}^m B_i(t)x(t)u_i(t) + C(t)f(y(t), \cdots, y(t-r+1)).$$

Let $z(t+1) \triangleq P(t)x(t) + \sum_{i=1}^m B_i(t)x(t)u_i(t)$, then

$$z^T(t+1)z(t+1) \leq \lambda_1\|x(t)\|^2 + \sum_{i=1}^m \lambda_3\|x(t)\|^2|u_i(t)| + \sum_i \sum_j \lambda_2\|x(t)\|^2|u_i(t)||u_j(t)|.$$

By Hölder's inequality, we have

$$\sum_{i=1}^{m} |u_i(t)| \le \sqrt{m}\Big[F_S F_H \|x(t)\| + \|f_1(y(t),\cdots,y(t-r+1))\|\Big].$$

$$\sum_{i=1}^{m}\sum_{j=1}^{m} |u_i(t)||u_j(t)| \le m\Big(\sum_{i=1}^{m} u_i^2(t)\Big)^{1/2}\Big(\sum_{j=1}^{m} u_j^2(t)\Big)^{1/2} \le m\Big[F_S F_H\|x(t)\| + \|f_1(y(t),\cdots,y(t-r+1))\|\Big]^2.$$

Hence,

$$\|z(t+1)\| \le {\lambda_1}^{1/2}\|x(t)\| + \Big[\lambda_3 m^{1/2} F_S F_H\Big]^{1/2}\|x(t)\|^{3/2} + \Big[\lambda_3 m^{1/2}\|f_1(y(t),\cdots,y(t-r+1)\ \|\Big]^{1/2}\|x(t)\| + (\lambda_2 m)^{1/2}\|x(t)\|\Big[F_S F_H\|x(t)\| + \|f_1(y(t),\cdots,y(t-r+1)\|\Big]^2.$$

So,

$$\begin{aligned}\|x(t+1)\| &\le \|z(t+1)\| + F_C\|f_1(y(t),\cdots,y(t-r+1))\| \\ &\le {\lambda_1}^{1/2}\|x(t)\| + \Big[\lambda_3 m^{1/2}F_S F_H\Big]^{1/2}\|x(t)\|^{3/2} \\ &+ \Big[\lambda_3 m^{1/2}\|f_1(y(t),\cdots,y(t-r+1))\|\Big]^{1/2}\|x(t)\| \\ &+ (\lambda_2 m)^{1/2}\|x(t)\|\Big[F_S F_H\|x(t)\| + \|f_1(y(t),\cdots,y(t-r+1))\|\Big] \\ &+ F_C\|f_1(y(t),\cdots,y(t-r+1))\|.\end{aligned}$$

From the assumption of f_1 in (19), we know that the lowest power of f_1 is larger than 1. Directly apply Lemma 3, if $\lambda_1 < 1$ then the zero state of system (7), (8), (19) is uniformly asymptotically stable. We have completed this proof.

The important thing is to find an $S(t)$ to ensure $\lambda_1 < 1$. The following criteria are easily applied.

Theorem 3: For bilinear system (7) - (8), a given matrix P is defined by following (21), if one of the three conditions holds, then there is an S such that $A(t)+C(t)S(t)H(t) = P(t)$ and the zero state of closed loop bilinear system (7) - (8) is uniformly asymptotically stable.

1) rank $(C(t)\otimes H^T(t))$ = rank $\Big(C(t)\otimes H^T(t)\vdots\vec{A}_1(t)\Big)$

2) $\vec{A}_1(t) \in \Re\Big(C(t)\otimes H^T(t)\Big)$

3) $C(t)C^-(t)A_1(t)H^-(t)H(t) = A_1(t)$,

where

$$A_1(t) \triangleq P(t) - A(t), \tag{20}$$

and

$$P(t) = \begin{pmatrix} p_{11}(t) & 0 & \dots & 0 \\ 0 & p_{22}(t) & \dots & 0 \\ \vdots & \vdots & \vdots & \vdots \\ 0 & 0 & \dots & p_{nn}(t)\end{pmatrix}, \tag{21}$$

where $|p_{jj}(t)| < 1$, for all $j = 1,\cdots,n$.

Proof: Since

$$P(t) = A(t) + C(t)S(t)H(t). \tag{22}$$

from Theorem 2, we know that if $\lambda_1 < 1$ then the zero state of system (7), (8), (19) is uniformly asymptotically stable. From the construction of $P(t)$ (see (21)), one can ensure $\lambda_1 < 1$. The problem is whether a solution of $S(t)$ exists satisfying the matrix equation (22). Then we can set $u(t)$ the same as (19).

By (20), (22),

$$\begin{aligned} C(t)S(t)H(t) &= A_1(t) \\ \Leftrightarrow \overrightarrow{C(t)S(t)H(t)} &= \vec{A}_1(t) \\ \Leftrightarrow \Big(C(t)\otimes H^T(t)\Big)\vec{S}(t) &= \vec{A}_1(t).\end{aligned}$$

By linear algebra theorems, we know that either 1) or 2) is the sufficient and necessary condition of existing solutions to the above linear equations.

Then, the general solution of $S(t)$ is

$$\begin{aligned} S(t) = &\ C^-(t)A_1(t)H^-(t) + Z(t) \\ &- C^-(t)C(t)Z(t)H(t)H^-(t),\end{aligned}$$

where $Z(t)$ is arbitrary $m \times p$ matrix, and $C^{-1}(t), H^-(t)$ are arbitrary generalized inverse matrices of $C(t)$ and $H(t)$ respectively. We have completed the proof of 1) and 2).

For 3), since $C(t)C^-(t)A_1(t)H^-(t)H(t) = A_1(t)$, then $S(t) = C^-(t)A_1(t)H^-(t)$ is a solution of matrix equation (22). Then we can set $u(t)$ the same as in (19).

A special case of 3) is also useful.

The special case of 3) : If $m = p = n$, and C and H are full rank, then there exists a unique solution of (22) for $S(t)$ such as:

$$S(t) = C^{-1}(t)A_1(t)H^{-1}(t), \tag{23}$$

for all $t \in Z^+$. Then there exists a feedback function f (see (19)), and the zero state of system (7), (8), (19) is uniformly asymptotically stable.

Remark 6: There are many ways to set $p_{ij}(t)$ of (21). If necessary, one can choose other ways to set $P(t)$, provided $\sup_t \lambda_{\max}[P^T(t)P(t)] < 1$.

The approach for the design of stabilizing controllers

Step 1 For given bilinear systems (7), (8), check the eigenvalues of $A(t)^T A(t)$, if $\lambda_{1a} \ge 1$ proceed to next step.

Step 2 Check the ranks and dimensions of $C(t)$ and $H(t)$. If $m = p = n$, and $C(t)$, $H(t)$ are full ranks, one can use (23) to obtain the solution of $S(t)$. Alternatively, to obtain $S(t)$ without the inverse matrices see Step 4.

Step 3 If it is not in the case of Step 2, check the parameters of (7), (8) combining with the conditions of Theorem 3. Once they satisfy one of the conditions, then proceed to Step 4. Alternatively, try to adjust $p_{ij}(t)$ of (21), provided $\sup_t \lambda_{\max}[P^T(t)P(t)] < 1$. Then check Theorem 3 again. If one of the conditions of Theorem 3 is now satisfied, then proceed to Step 4.

Step 4 Let $S(t) = \{s_{ij}(t)\}_{m\times p}$ and set $P(t)$. Solve the following set of equations for $s_{ij}(t)$ such as: $C(t)S(t)H(t) = P(t) - A(t)$. In many cases, using the equations of the matrix component is an easier way of obtaining $S(t)$ than directly using the matrix equation. Then proceed to Step 5.

Step 5 Set $u(t) = S(t)y(t) + f_1(y(t),\cdots,y(t-r+1))$, as in (19), where f_1 is a comparable function with lowest power larger than 1, or $f_1 \equiv 0$. For example, we can set $u(t) = S(t)y(t) + H(t)\widetilde{y(t)}$, where $\widetilde{y(t)} = [y_1^2(t-l),\cdots,y_p^2(t-l)]^T$, where l is arbitrary available integer with $1 \le l \le r$.

Example 1: A discrete simplified model of motor control systems is as follows:

$$x_1(t+1) = x_1(t) + a_1x_2(t) + b_1x_1(t)u_1(t) + c_1u_1(t), \quad (24)$$
$$x_2(t+1) = x_2(t) + a_2x_2(t) + c_2u_2(t). \quad (25)$$

Equations (24) and (25) can be represented by

$$x(t+1) = Ax(t) + B_1x(t)u_1(t) + Cu(t), \quad (26)$$

where $x(t) = [x_1(t), x_2(t)]^T$, $u(t) = [u_1(t), u_2(t)]^T$, and

$$A = \begin{bmatrix} 1 & a_1 \\ 0 & 1+a_2 \end{bmatrix}, \quad B_1 = \begin{bmatrix} b_1 & 0 \\ 0 & 0 \end{bmatrix}, \quad C = \begin{bmatrix} c_1 & 0 \\ 0 & c_2 \end{bmatrix}.$$

Here consider a specific case. Suppose

$$a_1 = 300, \ a_2 = -10, \ b_1 = 30, \ c_1 = 1, \ c_2 = 2,$$

we have $\lambda_{1A} = 1$, *and* $\lambda_{2A} = -9$. It is easy to see that the corresponding linear system, $B_1 = 0$, is unstable.

Set

$$S = \begin{bmatrix} s_{11} & s_{12} \\ s_{21} & s_{22} \end{bmatrix}, \quad P = \begin{bmatrix} p_{11} & 0 \\ 0 & p_{22} \end{bmatrix}, \quad (27)$$

$$P \triangleq A + CS = \begin{bmatrix} 1+c_1s_{11} & a_1+c_1s_{12} \\ c_2s_{21} & 1+a_2+c_2s_{22} \end{bmatrix}.$$

Choose $s_{11}, s_{12}, s_{21}, s_{22}$ such as

$$|1+c_1s_{11}| = |p_{11}| < 1,$$

$$a_1 + c_1s_{12} = 0,$$

$$c_2s_{21} = 0,$$

$$|1+a_2+c_2s_{22}| = |p_{22}| < 1.$$

Thus we get $s_{12} = -a_1/c_1$, $s_{21} = 0$, and

$$s_{11} \in (-2/c_1, \ 0), \quad \text{if} \quad c_1 > 0$$

or $s_{11} \in (0, \ -2/c_1)$, if $c_1 < 0$,

$$s_{22} \in [(-2-a_2)/c_2, \ -a_2/c_2], \quad \text{if} \quad c_2 > 0$$

or $[-a_2/c_2, \ (-2-a_2)/c_2]$, if $c_2 < 0$, In this specific case, $s_{11} \in (-2, \ 0)$, $s_{12} = -300$, $s_{21} = 0$, $s_{22} \in (4, \ 5)$.

Two types of feedback controllers, are to be studied:

Type 1: Set

$$u(t) = Sx(t). \quad (28)$$

then, $\lambda_1 \triangleq \lambda_{\max}[P^TP] = 0.64 < 1$, the zero state of this system (26), (28) is uniformly asymptotically stable.

Type 2: $u(t) = Sx(t) + G\widetilde{x(t)}$, where S is same as in Type 1, and

$$G = \begin{bmatrix} g_{11} & g_{12} \\ g_{21} & g_{22} \end{bmatrix} \quad \text{and} \quad \widetilde{x(t)} = [x_1^2(t-1), x_2^2(t-1)]^T. \quad (29)$$

Thus, the feedback control is

$$u(t) = Sx(t) + G\widetilde{x(t)}. \quad (30)$$

Using Theorem 2, the system (26), (30) is uniformly asymptotically stable since $\lambda_1 < 1$. Here, $s_{11} = 0.5, s_{12} = -100, s_{21} = 0, s_{22} = 4.1$, and $g_{11} = 100, g_{12} = 0, g_{21} = 0, g_{22} = 200$, $\lambda_1 = 0.64$, the zero state of this feedback system is uniformly asymptotically stable.

VI. Acknowledgements

The authors acknowledge the support of the Natural Science and Engineering Research Council of Canada, the Institute for Robotic and Intelligent Systems (IRIS) and Precarn Associates Inc.

References

[1] R.R. Mohler, "Nonlinear systems," vol.2, "Application to bilinear control," Prentice-Hall, New Jersey, 1990.

[2] L.K. Chen, Xueshan Yang and R.R. Mohler, "Stability analysis of bilinear systems," IEEE Trans. Autom. Control, vol. 36, 11, 1310-1315, 1991.

[3] C. Gounaridis-Minaidis, and N. Kalouptsidis, "Stability of discrete-time bilinear systems with constant inputs," Int. J. Control, vol. 43, pp 663-669, 1986.

[4] Xueshan Yang, L. K. Chen and R. M. Burton, "Stability of discrete bilinear systems with output feedback," Int. J. Contr., vol. 52, 135-158, 1989.

[5] Xueshan Yang, "Stability of discrete bilinear systems," Ph.D. Dissertation, Dept. of Electrical Engineering, Oregon State University, Corvallis, 1989.

[6] Xueshan Yang and George Miminis, "The stability of discrete deterministic and stochastic nonlinear systems," Journal of Mathematical Analysis and Applications, vol. 3 of 3, 2682-2687, 1992.

[7] Xueshan Yang and Lung-Kee Chen, "Stability of discrete bilinear systems with time delayed feedback functions," IEEE Trans. Automat. Contr., vol. 38, 1, 158-163, 1993.

[8] R. R. Mohler, Xueshan Yang and L. K. Chen, "A general methodology for bilinear system stability with output feedback," Proc. of 11th IFAC World Congress on Automatic Control, 6, 102-105.

[9] M. Slemrod, Stabilization of bilinear control systems with applications to nonconservative problems in elasticity, SIAM J. Control and Optimization, 16, 131 - 141, 1978.

[10] T. Ionescu and R. V. Monopoli, "On the stabilization of bilinear systems via hyperstability," IEEE Trans. Automat. Contr., vol. AC-20, pp. 280-284, 1975.

[11] R. Longchamp, "Stable feedback control of bilinear systems," IEEE Trans. Automat. Contr., vol. AC-25, pp. 37-45, 1980.

[12] J. P. Quinn, "Stabilization of bilinear systems by quadratic feedback controls," Journal of Mathematical, Analysis and Application, vol. 75, pp. 66-80, 1980.

[13] P. O. Gutman, "Stabilizing controllers for bilinear systems," IEEE Trans. Automat. Contr., vol. AC-26, pp. 917-922, 1981.

[14] E. P. Ryan and N. J. Buckingham, "On asymptotically stabilizing feedback control of bilinear systems," IEEE Trans. Automat. Contr., vol. AC-28, pp. 863-864, 1983.

[15] F. Asamoah and M. Jamshidi, "Stabilization of a class of singularly perturbed bilinear systems," Int. J. Control, 46, 1589-1594, 1987.

[16] R. Genesiom and A. Tesi, "The output stabilization of SISO bilinear systems," IEEE Trans. Automat. Contr., vol. AC-33, pp. 950-955, 1988.

[17] J. L. Marshall, "Control of time-delay systems," IEE Control Engineering Series 10, Peter Peregrinus LTD, 1979.

[18] Xueshan Yang and Yury Stepanenko, "On stability of a class of Discrete Nonlinear systems, " Proc. of 31st IEEE Conference on Decision and Control, vol. 4 of 4, 3446-3451, 1992.

[19] Xueshan Yang and Yury Stepanenko, "A stability criterion for discrete nonlinear systems with time delayed feedback,' IEEE Trans. Automat. Contr, to appear, 1993.

Author Index

An alphabetical index to all volumes by authors' and coauthors' surnames.
Session code and page number are shown. 'W' sessions may be found in volume 1, 'T' in volume 2, and 'F' in volume 3
'×' indicates that no manuscript was received. Session chairs and organizers ('org.') are included in this index.